GEORGIA *continued*

GAU	Atlanta University, Atlanta.
GAuA	Augusta College, Augusta.
GColuC	Columbus College, Columbus.
GCuA	Andrews College, Cuthbert.
GDC	Columbia Theological Seminary, Decatur.
GDS	Agnes Scott College, Decatur.
GDecA*	Agnes Scott College, Decatur.
GDecCT*	Columbia Theological Seminary, Decatur.
GDoS	South Georgia College, Douglas.
GEU	Emory University, Atlanta.
GHi	Georgia Historical Society, Savannah.
GMM	Mercer University, Macon.
GMW	Wesleyan College, Macon.
GMiW	Woman's College of Georgia, Milledgeville.
GMilvC*	Woman's College of Georgia, Milledgeville.
GOgU	Oglethorpe University, Oglethorpe University.
GSDe*	University of Georgia, DeRenne Library.
GU	University of Georgia, Athens.
GU-De	— DeRenne Georgia Library.
GU-Ex	— Georgia State College of Business Administration Library, Atlanta.

HAWAII

HU	University of Hawaii, Honolulu.
HU-EWC	Center for Cultural and Technical Interchange between East and West, Honolulu.

ILLINOIS

I	Illinois State Library, Springfield.
IC	Chicago Public Library.
ICA	Art Institute of Chicago, Chicago.
ICF	Chicago Natural History Museum, Chicago.
ICF-A	— Edward E. Ayer Ornithological Library.
ICHi	Chicago Historical Society, Chicago.
ICIP	Institute for Psychoanalysis, Chicago.
ICJ	John Crerar Library, Chicago.
ICMILC*	Center for Research Libraries, Chicago.
ICMcC	McCormick Theological Seminary, Chicago.
ICN	Newberry Library, Chicago.
ICRL	Center for Research Libraries, Chicago.
ICU	University of Chicago, Chicago.
ICarbS	Southern Illinois University, Carbondale.
IEG	Garrett Theological Seminary, Evanston.
IEN	Northwestern University, Evanston.
IEdS	Southern Illinois University, Edwardsville.
IGK	Knox College, Galesburg.
IHi	Illinois State Historical Library, Springfield.
ILS	St. Procopius College, Lisle.
IMunS	Saint Mary of the Lake Seminary, Mundelein.
INS	Illinois State University, Normal.
IRA	Augustana College Library, Rock Island.
IRivfR	Rosary College, River Forest.
IU	University of Illinois, Urbana.
IU-M	— Medical Sciences Library, Chicago.
IU-U	— Chicago Undergraduate Division, Chicago.

IOWA

IaAS	Iowa State University of Science and Technology, Ames.
IaDL	Luther College, Decorah.
IaDuC	Loras College, Dubuque.
IaDuU	University of Dubuque, Dubuque.
IaDuU-S	— Theological Seminary Library.
IaDuW	Wartburg Theological Seminary, Dubuque.
IaU	University of Iowa, Iowa City.

IDAHO

IdB	Boise Public Library.
IdPI	Idaho State University, Pocatello.
IdPS*	Idaho State University, Pocatello.
IdU	University of Idaho, Moscow.

INDIANA

In	Indiana State Library, Indianapolis.
InAndC	Anderson College, Anderson.
InCollS*	St. Joseph's College, Rensselaer.
InGo	Goshen College Biblical Seminary Library, Goshen.
InHi	Indiana Historical Society, Indianapolis.
InIB	Butler University, Indianapolis.

INDIANA *continued*

InLP	Purdue University, Lafayette.
InNd	University of Notre Dame, Notre Dame.
InOlH*	St. Leonard College Library, Dayton, Ohio.
InRE	Earlham College, Richmond.
InRenS	St. Joseph's College, Rensselaer.
InStme	St. Meinrad's College & Seminary, St. Meinrad.
InU	Indiana University, Bloomington.

KANSAS

K	Kansas State Library, Topeka.
KAS	St. Benedict's College, Atchison.
KAStB*	St. Benedict's College, Atchison.
KHi	Kansas State Historical Society, Topeka.
KKcB	Central Baptist Theological Seminary, Kansas City.
KMK	Kansas State University, Manhattan.
KStMC*	St. Louis University, School of Divinity Library, St. Louis, Mo.
KU	University of Kansas, Lawrence.
KU-M	— Medical Center Library, Kansas City.
KWiU	Wichita State University, Wichita.

KENTUCKY

Ky-LE	Library Extension Division, Frankfort.
KyBgW	Western Kentucky State College, Bowling Green
KyHi	Kentucky Historical Society, Frankfort.
KyLo	Louisville Free Public Library.
KyLoS	Southern Baptist Theological Seminary, Louisville.
KyLoU	University of Louisville, Louisville.
KyLx	Lexington Public Library.
KyLxCB	Lexington Theological Seminary, Lexington. (Formerly College of the Bible)
KyLxT	Transylvania College, Lexington.
KyMoreT	Morehead State College, Morehead.
KyU	University of Kentucky, Lexington.
KyWA	Asbury College Library, Wilmore.
KyWAT	Asbury Theological Seminary, Wilmore.

LOUISIANA

L	Louisiana State Library, Baton Rouge.
L-M	Louisiana State Museum Library, New Orleans.
LCA	Not a library symbol.
LCS	Not a library symbol.
LHi	Louisiana History Society, New Orleans.
LNHT	Tulane University Library, New Orleans.
LNT-MA	Tulane University, Latin American Library, New Orleans.
LU	Louisiana State University, Baton Rouge.
LU-M	— Medical Center Library, New Orleans.
LU-NO	— Louisiana State University in New Orleans.

MASSACHUSETTS

M	Massachusetts State Library, Boston.
MA	Amherst College, Amherst.
MB	Boston Public Library.
MBAt	Boston Athenaeum, Boston.
MBBC*	Boston College, Chestnut Hill.
MBCo	Countway Library of Medicine. (Harvard-Boston Medical Libraries)
MBH	Massachusetts Horticultural Society, Boston.
MBHo*	Massachusetts Horticultural Society, Boston.
MBM*	Countway Library of Medicine (Harvard-Boston Medical Libraries).
MBMu	Museum of Fine Arts, Boston.
MBU	Boston University.
MBdAF	U.S. Air Force Cambridge Research Center, Bedford.
MBrZ	Zion Research Library, Brookline.
MBrigStJ*	St. John's Seminary, Brighton.
MBtS	St. John's Seminary Library, Brighton.
MCM	Massachusetts Institute of Technology, Cambridge.
MCR	Radcliffe College, Cambridge.
MCSA	Smithsonian Institution, Astrophysical Observatory, Cambridge.
MChB	Boston College, Chestnut Hill.
MH	Harvard University, Cambridge.
MH-A	— Arnold Arboretum.
MH-AH	— Andover-Harvard Theological Library.
MH-BA	— Graduate School of Business Administration Library.
MH-FA	— Fine Arts Library. (Formerly Fogg Art Museum)
MH-G	— Gray Herbarium Library.
MH-HY	— Harvard-Yenching Institute. (Chinese-Japanese Library)

MASSACHUSETTS *continued*

MH-L	— Law School Library.
MH-P	— Peabody Museum Library.
MH-PR	— Physics Research Library.
MHi	Massachusetts Historical Society, Boston.
MMeT	Tufts University, Medford.
MNF	Forbes Library, Northampton.
MNS	Smith College, Northampton.
MNoeS	Stonehill College Library, North Easton.
MNtcA	Andover Newton Theological School, Newton Center.
MSaE	Essex Institute, Salem.
MShM	Mount Holyoke College, South Hadley.
MU	University of Massachusetts, Amherst.
MWA	American Antiquarian Society, Worcester.
MWAC	Assumption College, Worcester.
MWC	Clark University, Worcester.
MWH	College of the Holy Cross, Worcester.
MWalB	Brandeis University, Waltham.
MWelC	Wellesley College, Wellesley.
MWhB	Marine Biological Laboratory, Woods Hole.
MWiW	Williams College, Williamstown.
MWiW-C	— Chapin Library.

MARYLAND

MdAN	U.S. Naval Academy, Annapolis.
MdBE	Enoch Pratt Free Library, Baltimore.
MdBG	Goucher College, Baltimore.
MdBJ	Johns Hopkins University, Baltimore.
MdBJ-G	— John Work Garrett Library.
MdBP	Peabody Institute, Baltimore.
MdBWA	Walters Art Gallery, Baltimore.
MdU	University of Maryland, College Park.
MdW	Woodstock College, Woodstock.

MAINE

MeB	Bowdoin College, Brunswick.
MeBa	Bangor Public Library.
MeU	University of Maine, Orono.
MeWC	Colby College, Waterville.
MeWaC*	Colby College, Waterville.

MICHIGAN

Mi	Michigan State Library, Lansing.
MiAC	Alma College, Alma.
MiD	Detroit Public Library.
MiD-B	— Burton Historical Collection.
MiDA	Detroit Institute of Arts, Detroit.
MiDU	University of Detroit, Detroit.
MiDW	Wayne State University, Detroit.
MiEM	Michigan State University, East Lansing.
MiEalC*	Michigan State University, East Lansing.
MiGr	Grand Rapids Public Library.
MiH*	Michigan College of Mining and Technology, Houghton.
MiHM	Michigan College of Mining and Technology, Houghton.
MiU	University of Michigan, Ann Arbor.
MiU-C	— William L. Clements Library.

MINNESOTA

MnCS	St. John's University, Collegeville.
MnH*	Minnesota Historical Society, St. Paul.
MnHi	Minnesota Historical Society, St. Paul.
MnRM	Mayo Clinic and Foundation Library, Rochester.
MnSJ	James Jerome Hill Reference Library, St. Paul.
MnSSC	College of St. Catherine, St. Paul.
MnU	University of Minnesota, Minneapolis.

MISSOURI

MoHi	Missouri State Historical Society, Columbia
MoK	Kansas City Public Library.
MoKL	Linda Hall Library, Kansas City
MoKU	University of Missouri at Kansas City, Kansas City.
MoS	St. Louis Public Library.
MoSB	Missouri Botanical Garden, St. Louis.
MoSC*	Concordia Seminary Library, St. Louis.
MoSCS	Concordia Seminary Library, St. Louis.
MoSM	Mercantile Library Association, St. Louis.
MoSU	St. Louis University, St. Louis.
MoSU-D	— School of Divinity Library, St. Louis.
MoSW	Washington University, St. Louis.
MoU	University of Missouri, Columbia.

The National Union Catalog

Pre-1956 Imprints

The National Union Catalog

Pre-1956 Imprints

A cumulative author list representing Library of Congress printed cards and titles reported by other American libraries. Compiled and edited with the cooperation of the Library of Congress and the National Union Catalog Subcommittee of the Resources Committee of the Resources and Technical Services Division, American Library Association

Volume 336

LISZT, FRANZ (TARANTELLE) -
LIVON, JEAN

Mansell 1974

Mansell Information/Publishing Limited
3 Bloomsbury Place, London WC1

The American Library Association
50 East Huron Street, Chicago, Illinois 60611

The paper on which this catalog has been printed is supplied by P. F. Bingham Limited and has been specially manufactured by the Guard Bridge Paper Company Limited of Fife, Scotland. Based on requirements established by the late William J. Barrow for a permanent/durable book paper it is laboratory certified to meet or exceed the following values:

Substance 89 gsm
pH cold extract 9·4
Fold endurance (MIT ½kg. tension) 1200
Tear resistance (Elmendorf) 73 (or 67 × 3)
Opacity 90·3%

Library of Congress Card Number: 67–30001
ISBN: 0 7201 0415 7

Printed by Balding & Mansell Limited, London and Wisbech, England
Bound by Bemrose & Sons Limited, Derby, England

American Library Association

Resources and Technical Services Division

RESOURCES COMMITTEE

SUBCOMMITTEE ON THE NATIONAL UNION CATALOG

Chairman GORDON R. WILLIAMS
Director CENTER FOR RESEARCH LIBRARIES
5721 Cottage Grove Avenue, Chicago, Illinois 60637

Members

DOUGLAS W. BRYANT *University Librarian*
Widener Library, Harvard University
Cambridge, Massachusetts 02138

VERNER W. CLAPP 1901-1972 *formerly*
Consultant Council on Library Resources, Inc.

JOHN W. CRONIN *formerly*
Director Processing Department
Library of Congress
2129 32nd Place, S.E.
Washington, D.C. 20020

CHARLES W. DAVID *formerly*
Director of Library Development
Marine Historical Association
854 Radnor Road
St. Davids, Pennsylvania 19087

WILLIAM S. DIX *University Librarian*
Princeton University
Princeton, New Jersey 08540

RALPH E. ELLSWORTH *formerly*
Director University of Colorado Libraries
Boulder, Colorado 80302

HERMAN H. FUSSLER *Professor*
Graduate Library School
University of Chicago
Chicago, Illinois 60637

WARREN J. HAAS *Vice President*
for Libraries and Information Services
Columbia University
New York City, New York 10027

RUTHERFORD D. ROGERS *University Librarian*
Yale University
New Haven, Connecticut 06520

GEORGE A. SCHWEGMANN, JR. *formerly*
Chief Union Catalog Division
3534 Porter Street, N.W.
Washington, D.C. 20016

FREDERICK H. WAGMAN *Director*
University of Michigan Libraries
Ann Arbor, Michigan 48104

WILLIAM J. WELSH *Director*
Processing Department
Library of Congress
Washington, D.C. 20540

Publisher's Note

Because of the large number of sources from which the information in the National Union Catalog has been collected over a long period of time an understanding of its scope and an acquaintance with its methods is necessary for the best use to be made of it. Users are therefore earnestly advised to make themselves familiar with the introductory matter in Volume 1. This fully defines the scope of the Catalog and sets out the basis on which the material reported to the National Union Catalog has been edited for publication in book form.

National Union Catalog Designation

Each main entry in the Catalog has been ascribed a unique identifying designation. This alphanumeric combination appears uniformly after the last line of the entry itself and consists of:

1 The letter N, signifying National Union Catalog.
2 The initial letter under which the entry is filed.
3 A number representing the position of the entry within the sequence under its initial letter.

This National Union Catalog designator is sufficient both to identify any main entry in the Catalog and to establish its position within the sequence of volumes. It is, however, recommended that when referring to titles by the National Union Catalog designation a checking element, such as the key word or initials of the title, be added.

Reported Locations

Alphabetic symbols which represent libraries in the United States and Canada follow the National Union Catalog designation. These groups of letters signify which libraries have reported holding copies of the work. The first library so represented usually is the one that provided the catalog information.

Printed on the end sheets of each volume is a list of most frequently used symbols, each followed by the full name of the library. *List of Symbols*, containing a comprehensive list of symbols used, is published as a separate volume with the Catalog. The Library of Congress has also issued *Symbols Used in the National Union Catalog of the Library of Congress*. In cases where a symbol is not identified in these lists the National Union Catalog Division of the Library of Congress will, on enquiry, attempt to identify the library concerned.

Other Developments

Under the terms of their agreement with the American Library Association, the publishers have undertaken to apply, as far as is practicable, new developments in library science and techniques which may have the effect of further enhancing the value of the Catalog. To this end, the publishers will be pleased to receive suggestions and enquiries relating to technical and production aspects of the Catalog and will be glad to consider proposals calculated to improve its utility and amenity. Mansell Information/Publishing Limited will be pleased also to advise libraries on possible applications of the methods and techniques developed for this and similar projects to their own requirements.

J.C.
London, *August 1968*

VOLUME 336

Liszt, Franz, 1811-1886.
Tarantelle aus Venezia e Napoli. Für Orchester bearbeitet von Karl Müller-Berghaus. Partitur.
Mainz. Schott. [188-?] 51 pp. F°.

April 8, 1902.
E3579 — T.r. — Mueller-Berghaus, Carl, ed. — Orchestra. Music.

NL 0406169 MB

M3 .3 .L77C88 Case Liszt, Franz, 1811-1886, arr.
Cui, César, 1835-1918.
[Tarantella, orchestra, op. 12; arr.]
FOR OTHER EDITIONS SEE MAIN ENTRY
Tarentelle. Pour piano par Franz Liszt. Paris, Durand & Schœnewerk [1886] Pl. no. D. S. 3570.

Liszt, Franz, 1811-1886.
Tarantelle di bravura, d'après la tarantelle de la Muette de Portici d'Auber. Pour piano. Par Fr[anz] Liszt. Hambourg, A.Cranz. [n.d.] Pl.no.P[ietro] Mechetti 4161.
23p. 35cm.
1. Tarentellas (Piano) 2. Auber, Daniel François Esprit, 1782-1871. La muette de Portici. Tarentelle.

NL 0406171 IaU

Liszt, Franz, 1811-1886.
Tarantelle di bravura, d'après la tarantelle de La muette de Portici d'Auber, pour piano ... par Fr. Liszt, Leipzig, A. Cranz [n.d.]
23 p. 35cm.

NL 0406172 OU

qM786.41 L69t Liszt, Franz, 1811-1886.
Tarantelle di bravura d'après la Tarantelle de la muette de Portici d'Auber. Pour piano. Vienne, P. Mechetti [18--] Pl. no. P.M.No. 4161.
[23]p. 34cm.
1. Piano music. I. Title.

NL 0406173 IU MB NcD ICN

MM 785.32 L699t Liszt, Franz, 1811-1886.
[Tasso]
Tasso, lamento e trionfo; symphonische Dichtung No. 2 für grosses Orchester. London, E. Eulenburg; New York, Edition Eulenburg [n.d.] Pl. no. E.E. 3648.
miniature score (92 p.) 19cm. (Edition Eulenburg, no. 448)
1.Symphonic poems - Scores. I.T.

NL 0406174 MiDW OrU KU INS WaU OrU NSyU CoU NjR CLU CaBVaU

W.C.L. M785.1 L774TA Liszt, Franz, 1811-1886
[Symphonische Dichtungen Nr. 2. Tasso]
Tasso: Lamento e trionfo. Leipzig, New York, Breitkopf & Härtel [n.d.] Pl. no. Part. B. 47.
score (79 p.) 27 cm. (Partitur-Bibliothek, Gruppe I)
Caption title.
Symphonic poem.
1. Symphonic poems. Scores. I. Title. II. Title: Tasso.

NL 0406175 NcD MiU

Liszt, Franz, 1811-1886.
...Tasso, lamento e trionfo... Leipzig, Breitkopf & Härtel [1856]
79 p. 25½ cm.
Imperfect: p.79 mutilated.
At head of title: Symphonische dichtungen für grosses orchester.

NL 0406176 NjP MB

VM 215 L 77t LISZT, FRANZ, 1811-1886.
[Tasso, lamento e trionfo. Symphonische Dichtung no.2, arr.] Tasso, lamento e trionfo. [Symphonische Dichtung] Nr.2, für 2 Klaviere 4 Händen. (Partitur) Leipzig, Breitkopf & Härtel[188-?]
score(35p.) 33cm. (his Symphonische Dichtungen für 2 Klaviere zu 4 Händen. Nr.2)
Cover title.
Breitkopf & Härtel's Klavier-Bibliothek.
Preface in German and French.
Plate no.: 9314.

NL 0406177 ICN

MM 785.1 L774T Liszt, Franz, 1811-1886.
(Tasso)
Tasso, lamento e trionfo. Leipzig, Breitkopf & Hartel (19--) Pl.no.26540.
xip.,miniature score(88p.) 19cm.
1. Symphonic poems I. Title.

NL 0406178 NBC

M1002 .L77T3 19- Liszt, Franz, 1811-1886.
[Tasso]
Tasso, lamento e trionfo. Symphonische Dichtung Nr. 2 für grosses Orchester. Leipzig, E. Eulenburg [19--] Pl. no. 26540.
xi p. miniature score. (88 p.) 19cm. (Eulenburg's kleine Orchester-Partitur-Ausgabe. Symphonien Nr. 48)
1. Symphonic poems. 2. Orchestral music—Scores. I. Title.

NL 0406179 ViU OOxM NcU RPB ViU MiU CtY

VM 35 L 77t LISZT, FRANZ, 1811-1886.
...Tasso, lamento e trionfo... Leipzig, Breitkopf[1904?]
23p. (his Symphonische dichtungen für pianoforte zu zwei händen. nr.2)
On cover: Edition Breitkopf. nr.2442.
"Bearbeitung von Th. Forchhammer."
Plate no.: E.B. 2442.

NL 0406180 ICN

-VM 1002 L 77t LISZT, FRANZ, 1811-1886.
...Tasso, lamento e trionfo. Symphonische dichtung no.2 für grosses orchester... Leipzig, Eulenburg[1911]
92p. (Eulenburg's kleine partitur-ausgabe. Symphonien. no.48)
Full score in miniature.
Plate no.: E.E. 3648.

NL 0406181 ICN NNUN

LISZT,F[ranz],1811-1886.
Tasso; lamento e trionfo. [Symphonische dichtung,nr.2. Pianoforte. Arrang. von Th. Forchhamer.] Leipzig,etc.,Breitkopf & Härtel [1904].
4°. pp.(2),23.
(Breitkopf & Härtel's Klavier-bibliothek.)
Cover serves as title-page.

NL 0406182 MH RPB

Liszt, Franz, 1811-1886.
... Tasso, lamento e trionfo ... [symphonische dichtung, nr. 2] Leipzig, [ca 1918] cover-title, 88 p. 34 cm. (Breitkopf und Härtels partitur-bibliothek, nr. 2174)
Orchestral score.

NL 0406183 RPB

sM1002 .L77T2 Liszt, Franz, 1811-1886.
[Tasso]
Tasso: lamento e trionfo. Symphonische Dichtung. Wien, Wiener Philharmonischer Verlag [193-]
miniature score (88 p.) (Philharmonia Partituren, No.79)
1. Symphonic poems. I. Title.

NL 0406184 ICU DCU CSt MeB NBuG LU CLU MB MtU OrP

Liszt, Franz, 1811-1886.
[Technische Studien, piano]
Technische Studien, für Pianoforte. Unter Redaktion von A. Winterberger. Technical studies, for the pianoforte, with a digest thereof by A. Winterberger. Leipzig, J. Schuberth [1886] Pl. no. 6250-
12 v. 34 cm. (Edition Schuberth, no. 2611-22)
First ed.
L. C. set incomplete: v. 2-12 wanting.
1. Piano—Studies and exercises. I. Title.
M3.3.L77T4 76-207771

NL 0406185 DLC IU

f MT 225 .L77 Liszt, Franz, 1811-1886.
Technische Studien für Pianoforte. Unter Redaction von A. Winterberger. Leipzig, J. Schuberth [1886]
12 v. in 3.
Xerox copy.
1. Piano--Instruction and study. 2. Piano--Studies and exercises. I. Title.

NL 0406186 ICU

Film 12211 Liszt, Franz, 1811-1886.
[Technische Studien, piano]
Technische Studien für Pianoforte. Unter Redaktion von A.Winterberger. Leipzig, J.Schuberth [1887-1888]
12v.in 3.
Vol.1 imperfect: title page wanting; title supplied from vol.2.
Microfilm (negative) Urbana, Univ. of Illinois Library, 1969. 1 reel.

NL 0406187 IaU

Liszt, Franz, 1811-1886.
[Technische Studien, piano]
Technische Studien, für Pianoforte; in 2 Bänden bearb. und hrsg. von Martin Krause. Technical studies for the pianoforte; arr. and edited in 2 v. by Martin Krause. Leipzig, J. Schuberth, 1901.
2 v. in 1. 34 cm. (Edition Schuberth, Nr. 7321-7322)
CONTENTS.—v. 1. Die Tonleiterformen und ihre Vorbereitungen.—v. 2. Die Akkordformen.
1. Piano—Studies and exercises. I. Title.
MT225.L775 2-8453 rev*

NL 0406188 DLC OrP

Music Film 58 Liszt, Franz, 1811-1886.
Technische Studien für Pianoforte. Technical studies for pianoforte. Bearb. und hrsg. von Martin Krause. [Leipzig, J. Schuberth, 1901]
Ed. Schuberth, Nr. 7321-7322.
Microfilm copy (negative) made in 1965 by the Library of Congress Photoduplication Service.
Collation of the original: 2v.

NL 0406189 IEN

VOLUME 336

Liszt, Franz, 1811-1886.
[Rhapsodies hongroises, piano. Selections]

Ten Hungarian rhapsodies; edited by August Spanuth and John Orth. Boston, O. Ditson Co. [c1904]
152 p. port. 32 cm. (The Musicians library [8])
Contents.—No. 2, C♯ minor-F♯ major.—No. 6, D♭ major-B♭ major.—No. 8, F♯ minor-F♯ major.—No. 9, Carnaval de Pesth.—No. 10, D major.—No. 11, A minor-F♯ major.—No. 12, C♯ minor-D♭ major.—No. 13, A minor-A major.—No. 14, F minor-F major.—No. 15, Rákóczy marsch.
1. Piano music. I. Title: Hungarian rhapsodies. (Series: The Musicians library)
M1.M9L4 4-30153 rev*

00xM CaBVa
NL 0406190 DLC NN CU NN ViU IU ICU PSt CtY MeB

Liszt, Franz, 1811-1886.
Liszts Testament. Aus dem Französischen ins Deutsche übertragen und herausgegeben von Friedrich Schnapp. Weimar: H. Böhlaus, 1931. 31 p. front. (facsim.) 25cm. (Franz-Liszt-Bund, Weimar. Gabe für die Mitglieder. Nr. 2.)

1. No subject. I. Schnapp, Friedrich, editor.
Juilliard Foundation Fund.
N. Y. P. L. February 28, 1933

NL 0406191 NN

Liszt, Franz, 1811-1886.
Thematisches verzeichniss der werke, bearbeitungen und transcriptionen von F. Liszt. Neue vervollständigte ausg. Leipzig, Breitkopf & Härtel [n. d.]
iv, 162 p. 26cm.
Publisher's number: 14373.
Title of earlier edition, 1855, reads: Thematisches verzeichniss der werke von F. Liszt. Von dem autor verfasst.

Library of Congress ML134.L7A3 8-12989

NL 0406192 DLC MtBC WU ICU ICN NB PP OkU NN OO

Liszt, F[ranz] 1811-1886.
Thematisches verzeichniss der werke von F. Liszt. Von dem autor verfasst. Leipzig, Breitkopf & Härtel, 1855.
2 p. l., 97 p. 26cm.
Engr. t.-p.
"Literarische werke": p. 95.
"Anhang. Schriften über Franz Liszt": p. 95. "Portraits, etc.": p. 96-97.

Library of Congress ML134.L77 5-22928

NL 0406193 DLC IaU MB

Liszt, Franz, 1811-1886.
...The thirteenth psalm set to music for tenor solo, chorus, and orchestra, by Franz Liszt. The English adaptation by the Rev. Dr. Troutbeck... London: Novello, Ewer and Co. [1888.] Publ. pl. no. 8014. 49 p. 4°.
Vocal score. English words.
At head of title: Novello's original octavo edition.
Caption-title reads: Lord, how long wilt thou forget me? (Psalm xiii).

Krehbiel Collection.
1. Psalms. 2. Choruses, with orchestra.—Vocal score. 3. Troutbeck, John, 1832-99. 4. Title: Lord, how long wilt thou forget me?
N. Y. P. L. June 16, 1924

NL 0406194 NN CaBVa IEN NcD

Liszt, Franz, 1811-1886.
Thirty songs by Franz Liszt, edited by Carl Armbruster ... Boston, Oliver Ditson company; New York, C. H. Ditson & co.; [etc., etc., 1911]
xiv p., 2 l., 144 p. port. 32cm. (The musicians library)
Edition for high voice.

Library of Congress M1.M9L41H 11-29245
———— Edition for low voice. M1.M9L41L
Copyright A 297912 [a33b1] 784.3

NN CU OU MeB NIC PSt OrP Or CaBVa
NL 0406195 DLC CtY MeB NcU FTaSU CLSU OO OCl MB

Liszt, Franz, 1811-1886. No. 26 in **M.203.15
Thou art like unto a flower. [Arranged for male voices by L. Schehlmann.]
Boston. Schmidt. [1894.] (3) pp. L. 8°.

April 8, 1902.
E3579 — T.r. — Part songs. — Schehlmann, Louis, ed.

NL 0406196 MB

M38
.S
.S
Liszt, Franz, 1811-1886, arr.

Schubert, Franz Peter, 1797-1828.
[Du bist die Ruh; arr.]
Thou art the rest. Du bist die Ruh. Transcribed by Franz Liszt. Rev. and fingered by Wm. Scharfenberg. [New York] G. Schirmer, c1882.

M25
L77E83
D1
Liszt, Franz, 1811-1886.
[Études de concert, piano]
Three concert studies; edited by Edward Dannreuther. London, Augener [c1898] Pl. no. 11263.
39 p. 31cm. (Augener's edition, 8222)
Contents.- A♭ major.- F minor.- D♭ major.

1. Piano music. I. Title: Concert studies.

NL 0406198 CSt MdBP

[Liszt, Franz] 1811-1886.
[Toccata, piano]
Toccata. [18—]
[8] p. 17 x 26 cm.
Holograph, in ink.
From the collection of the Baroness Olga de Meyendorff.

1. Piano music.
ML96.L58 M 59-77

NL 0406199 DLC

M
1010
.L77T7
Liszt, Franz, 1811-1886
[Totentanz]
Totentanz (Danse macabre) Paraphrase über "Dies irae" für Piano und Orchester. Edited from the original and the Complete edition and with foreword by Max Alberti. London, E. Eulenburg; New York, Eulenburg Miniature Scores [n.d.] Pl. no. E. E. 6137.
miniature score (78 p.) (Edition Eulenburg no. 722)
1. Piano with orchestra - Scores. I. Title. II. Title: Danse macabre.

NSyU UU OrU
NL 0406200 INS CoU MH NBC FTaSU MiDW OrU CU-I MsSM

Liszt, Franz, 1811-1886.
[Totentanz; arr.]
"Todten Tanz" für Pianoforte allein.
[1864?] [7] p.

Microfilm of holograph in the Library of Congress. Imperfect: pages [5-7] wanting on microfilm. TOSCANINI MEMORIAL ARCHIVES.

1. Music - Manuscripts - Facsimiles. (TITLE)

NL 0406201 NN

Liszt, Franz, 1811-1886.
[Totentanz]
Todtentanz (Danse macabre) Paraphrase über Dies Irae, für Piano und Orchester. Leipzig, C. F. W. Siegel [1865] Pl. no. 2814.
score (68 p.) 33 cm.
First ed.
1. Piano with orchestra—Scores. 2. Dies irae (Music) I. Title. II. Title: Danse macabre.
M3.3.L77T55 a 64-49514/M
———— Copy 2. Reissued from original plates. M1010.L77T7 1865

NL 0406202 DLC IU

Liszt, Franz, 1811-1886.
[Totentanz; arr.]
Todtentanz; Paraphrase über Dies Irae, für Piano und Orchester. Arrangement für zwei Pianoforte. Leipzig, C. F. W. Siegel [1865] Pl. no. 2816.
2 scores (41 p. each) 34 cm.
First ed.
1. Piano with orchestra—2-piano scores. 2. Dies irae (Music) I. Title.
M3.3.L77T55 64-45671/M

NL 0406203 DLC NN

Liszt, Franz, 1811-1886.
[Totentanz; arr.]
Todtentanz (Danse macabre) Paraphrase über Dies irae, für Piano und Orchester. Arrangement für Pianoforte allein. Leipzig, C. F. W. Siegel [1865] Pl. no. 2815.
31 p. 33 cm.
First ed.
1. Piano music, Arranged. 2. Dies irae (Music) I. Title. II. Title: Danse macabre.
M3.3.L77T55 b 64-49515/M
———— Copy 2. Reissued from original plates. M37.L

NL 0406204 DLC

Liszt, Franz, 1811-1886.
... Totentanz (Danse macabre) Paraphrase über: "Dies irae" für Piano und Orchester von Franz Liszt. Neue, nach eignen Angaben des Komponisten revidierte Ausgabe, herausgegeben von Alexander Siloti ... Leipzig, E. Eulenburg [18--]
18 cm. (Eulenburg's kleine Orchester-Partitur-Ausgabe. Konzerte No. 22)

NL 0406205 CtY

Liszt, Franz, 1811-1886. **M.403.96
Todtentanz. (Danse macabre.) Paraphrase über „Dies irae," für Piano und Orchester. Partitur.
Leipzig. Siegel. [1888.] (3), 68 pp. F°.

April 11, 1902.
E3573 — T.r. — Pianoforte. Music. Pianoforte and orchestra.

NL 0406206 MB

M1010
L77T7k
Liszt, Franz, 1811-1886.
[Totentanz]
Totentanz; paraphrase über "Dies irae" für Pianoforte und Orchester. Danse macabre. Dance of death. Haláltánc. New York, E.F. Kalmus [19--?]
48 p. 32cm.

1. Piano with orchestra. I. Title. II. Title:Danse macabre. III.Title:Dance of death. IV.Title:Haláltánc.

NL 0406207 CSt

q786.4
L69t
Liszt, Franz.
Totentanz (Danse macabre) Paraphrase über "Dies irae" für piano und orchester. Neue, nach eigenen angaben des komponisten rev. ausg. hrsg. von A. Siloti. Leipzig, C. F. W. Siegels musikalienhandlung [1911]
45p.

NL 0406208 IU

M1010
L5
T6
1911
Liszt, Franz, 1811-1886
[Totentanz. Piano & orchestra]
... Totentanz (Danse macabre) ... neue, nach eignen angaben des komponisten rev. ausgabe, hrsg. von Alexander Siloti ... Leipzig, E. Eulenburg [1911]
miniature score. (88p.) 19cm. (Eulenburg's kleine orchester-partitur-ausgabe, konzerte, no. 22.
Publisher's plate no.: 15474.

NL 0406209 RPB ICU NcU ICN OCl

VOLUME 336

M215
.L5T6 Liszt, Franz, 1811-1886.
[Todtentanz; arr.]
Totentanz, for piano and orchestra; two-piano score. [Ed. by] Sauer. New York, Paragon Music Publishers [1946]
score (34 p.) 31cm. (Paragon music library, v. 5)
Publisher's pl. no.: P L 5.

1. Piano with orchestra—2-piano scores. I. Sauer, Emil G. C., 1862- ed. II. Title.

NL 0406210 MB CoU

Liszt, Franz, 1811-1886, arr.
Transcriptions sur les operas de Richard Wagner
see under Wagner, Richard, 1813-1886.

VAULT FOLIO
M3.3
.L77
S6 Liszt, Franz, 1811-1886.
₍Sonetti del Petrarca₎
Tre sonetti di Petrarca, per il pianoforte. Milano, G. Ricordi ₍1846₎ Pl. no. 18846-18848.
3v. in 1. 33cm.

First edition of 1st version, published by Haslinger, Ricordi, and Latte, 1846. Cf. Grove, 5th edition.
Bound in following order: no.2, no.3, no.1.

NL 0406212 NcU

M
784.3
L774so
Seh Liszt, Franz, 1811-1886.
₍Sonetti del Petrarca₎
Tre sonetti del Petrarca per voce con accompagnamento di pianoforte. Deutsche Uebersetzung von P. Cornelius. Mayence ₍i.e. Mainz₎ B. Schott ₍1883?₎ Pl. no. 23558.
score (15p.)

Contents.- Sonetto XXXIX (47)- Sonetto XC (104)- Sonetto CV (123)
Number 104 for baritone, 47 and 123 for baritone or mezzo-soprano.

NL 0406213 FTaSU

M25
L77R4
no.13
T5 Liszt, Franz, 1811-1886.
₍Rhapsodies hongroises, piano. No. 13₎
13ieme ₍i.e. Treizieme₎ rhapsodie hongrois pour piano. Revue et doigtee par O. Thumer. London, Augener ₍189-?₎ Pl. no. 12165.
14 p. 31cm. (Augener's edition, 8219G)

1. Piano music. I. Title: Rhapsodie hongroise.

NL 0406214 CSt

Liszt, Franz, 1811-1886.
₍Rhapsodie hongroise, piano, no. 13₎

13ᵐᵉ ₍i. e. Treizième₎ rapsodie hongroise. ₍Édition de travail par₎ Alfred Cortot. Paris, New York, Salabert ₍1949₎
16 p. 32 cm. (Édition de travail des œuvres de Liszt)
"Édition nationale de musique classique, no. 5467."
Duration: 7 minutes.

1. Piano music—Instructive editions. I. Cortot, Alfred, 1877–

MT247.L56C6174 50-27203

NL 0406215 DLC ViU

M
1620
L77T7++ Liszt, Franz, 1811-1886.
₍Songs. Selections₎
30 ₍i.e. Trente₎ mélodies, pour chant et piano. Textes français et allemand. Version française de Gustave Samazeuilh. ₍Paris₎ Durand ₍1923₎
130 p. 31cm. (Édition classique A. Durand & fils, no 12137)

1. Songs with piano.

NL 0406216 NIC IaU

M
1554
L77
T8 Liszt, Franz, 1811-1886.
Trinkspruch, für Männerchor. ₍Leipzig, Steingräber-Verlag₎ 1929.
score (8 p.) 24cm.

"Beilage der "Zeitschrift für Musik" zu dem Aufsatz: Seb. Röckl, Ein unbekanntes Männerquartett von Franz Liszt, im Juni-Heft 1929."

NL 0406217 NIC

₍**Liszt, Franz**₎ 1811-1886.
₍Tristesse₎

Tristesse (Alfred de Musset) 1872.
₍3₎ p. 27 x 35 cm.
Holograph, in ink.
At end: 28 Mai 72. Weimar.
For voice and piano.
Published: Leipzig, Kahnt, 1879.
From the collection of the Baroness Olga de Meyendorff.

1. Songs (Medium voice) with piano. I. Title.

ML96.L58 M 59-76

NL 0406218 DLC

Liszt, Franz, 1811-1886, arr.
Trockne Blumen
see under Schubert, Franz Peter, 1797-1828.

LISZT, FRANZ, 1811-1886.
[ÉTUDES DE CONCERT]
Trois caprices poétiques pour piano [par] Fr. Liszt. Nouvelle éd. revue par I. Philipp. Paris, Costallat [1906?] Pl.no.15383 bis R. 35cm.

CONTENTS.—Lamento.—La leggierezza.—Un sospiro.

1. Piano.

NL 0406220 NN

Liszt, Franz, 1811-1886.
₍Études de concert, piano₎

Trois caprices poétiques. ₍Édition de travail par₎ Alfred Cortot. Paris, New York, Salabert ₍1950₎
38 p. 32 cm. (Édition de travail des œuvres de Liszt)
"Édition nationale de musique classique, no. 5427."
CONTENTS.—Il lamento.—La leggierezza.—Un sospiro.

1. Piano music—Instructive editions. I. Cortot, Alfred, 1877– ed. II. Title: Caprices poétiques.

MT247.L56C582 50-37110

NL 0406221 DLC ViU

Liszt, Franz, 1811-1886.
₍Caprices-valses, piano₎

3 ₍i. e. Trois₎ caprices-valses pour le piano. Vienne, C. Haslinger ₍186-?₎ Pl. no. C.H. 11,501–
v. 33 cm.
CONTENTS.—1. Valse de bravoure.

1. Waltzes (Piano) I. Title: Caprices-valses.

M32.L 64-57579/M

NL 0406222 DLC

q786.47
L69t Liszt, Franz, 1811-1886.
... Trois etudes de concert; As dur (Lamento) F moll (Allegrezza) Des dur (Sosprio) für klavier zu 2 händen. Neuausg. von Max Pauer. Braunschweig, H. Litolff, n.d.
29p. (Collection Litolff ₍no.2597₎)

NL 0406223 IU CaBVa OrP OU

Liszt, Franz, 1811-1886
₍Études de concert, piano₎
Trois études de concert. New revision by Ignaz Friedman. Wien, Universal-Edition ₍n.d.₎
33 p. 30½cm.

Publisher's plate no.: U.E. 5847, 5981, 5940.
Contents.- Il lamento.- La leggiereaaz.- Un sospiro.

NL 0406224 IdU OrP CSt

Liszt, Franz, 1811–1886.
3 études de concert pour piano . . . par F. Liszt . . . Leipsic: F. Kistner ₍ca. 1850₎. Publ. pl. nos. 1653, 1655. v. f°.

no. 1, 3 bound with his: Grandes études de Paganini. Leipzig ₍ca. 1850₎. f°.

1. Piano.—Studies.

1916.

NL 0406225 NN IaU CU

M25
.L57
U5 Liszt, Franz, 1811-1886.
₍Ungarische Nationalmelodien, piano₎
3 ₍i.e. Trois₎ mélodies hongroises. Paris, E. Gérard ₍n.d.₎ Pl. no. C.M. 5276.
9p. 34cm.

NL 0406226 NcU

VAULT FOLIO
M3.3
.L77
U49 Liszt, Franz, 1811-1886.
₍Ungarische Nationalmelodien, piano₎
3 ₍i.e. Trois₎ mélodies hongroises. Paris, B. Latte ₍ca. 1840₎ Pl. no. B.L. 3403.
9p. 34cm.

First edition.

NL 0406227 NcU

Liszt, Franz, 1811–1886.
₍Works, organ. Selections₎

Trois œuvres pour orgue; rev., annotées et doigtées par Marcel Dupré. Paris, S. Bornemann, ©1941.
1 p. l., 90 p. 17 x 35 cm.
CONTENTS.—Fantaisie and fugue on the choral: Ad nos, ad salutarem undam.—Prelude and fugue on: B. A. C. H.—Variations on: Weinen, Klagen, Sorgen, Zagen.

1. Canons, fugues, etc. (Organ) 2. Variations (Organ) I. Dupré, Marcel, 1886– ed.

M7.L75D8 51-53416

NL 0406228 DLC OO NcD FTaSU CU-S IEN NN NcU ICU

Liszt, Franz, 1811-1886.
₍Paraphrases de concert₎

Trois paraphrases de concert, de Verdi. Pour piano par François Liszt. Leipzig, New York, J. Schuberth ₍1860₎ Pl. no. 2573–
v. 34 cm.
First ed.
CONTENTS.—no. 1. Trovatore.—no. 2. Ernani.—

1. Piano music, Arranged. 2. Operas—Excerpts, Arranged. I. Verdi, Giuseppe, 1813-1901. Rigoletto. II. Title: Paraphrases de concert.

M3.3.L77P2 64-46168/M

NL 0406229 DLC NcU

VOLUME 336

Liszt, Franz, 1811–1886.
 ⌜Valses oubliées⌝
 . . . Trois valses oubliées. (Vergessene Walzer) Pour piano . . . no. Berlin, E. Bote & G. Bock ⌜190-?⌝ Pl.no. 12599, 12910–12911. v. in port. 34cm.
 Reissue of the 1881–84 edition.

 1. Piano. 2. Waltzes (Piano).
N. Y. P. L.

NL 0406230 NN

LISZT, FRANZ, 1811-1886.
 [RHAPSODIE HONGROISE, PIANO, NO. 12]
 3. série des rhapsodies hongroises pour le piano par F. Liszt: no. 12. Berlin, Schlesinger (R. Lienau) [186-?] Pl. no. S. 4089. 17 p. 34cm.
 Microfilm.

1. Piano. I. [Title] Troisième.

NL 0406231 NN

M25 Liszt, Franz, 1811-1886.
L77R4 ⌜Rhapsodies hongroises, piano. No. 3-4⌝
no.3-4 3ieme & 4ieme ⌜i.e. Troisieme et quatrieme rhapsodies hongroises pour piano. Revues et
T5 doigtées par O. Thümer. London, Augener ⌜189-?⌝ Pl. no. 11591-11592.
 13 p. 31cm. (Augener's edition, 8219c)

 1. Piano music. I. Title: Rhapsodies hongroises.

NL 0406232 CSt

Liszt, Franz, 1811-1886.
 Trovatore von Verdi. Konzert-paraphrase für pianoforte von Franz Liszt ... Leipzig, C. F. Peters [n. d.]
 17 p. 31 cm. in cover 36 cm. (Edition Peters no. 2554)

NL 0406233 CU

Liszt, Franz, 1811-1886, arr.
 Tscherkessen-Marsch
 see under Glinka, Mikhail Ivanovich, 1804-1857. [supplement]

M25 Liszt, Franz, 1811-1886.
L56E82 [Etudes, piano (1838)]
 Twelve etudes, opus 1. Piano solo. Edited by H. Vetter. London, Novello [c1906]
 37 p. 31cm. (Novello edition)

 1. Piano music.

NL 0406235 CoU

M25 **Liszt, Franz, 1811-1886.**
L77B8 ⌜Works, piano. Selections⌝
 Twelve grand studies. St. Louis, Kunkel Bros. ⌜1894⌝
 2v. 32cm. (Kunkel's royal edition)

 At head of title: Liszt-Bülow.
 Contents.- v.1. Prelude. Whisperings of autumn. With the tide. Restlessness. Murmurings in the forest. Greetings of love.

NL 0406236 IaU

Liszt, Franz, 1811–1886.
 ⌜Songs. Selections⌝
 Twelve songs. The English translations by Theo. Baker. With a critical note by Richard Aldrich. For high voice. New York, G. Schirmer, ©1902.
 2 v. in 1. 31 cm. (Mastersongs by great composers)
 Schirmer's library of musical classics, v. 642, 644.
 CONTENTS.—v. 1. Mignon's Lied (Song of Mignon) Es war ein König in Thule (There was a king in Thule) Es muss ein Wunderbares sein (It must be wonderful withal) Freudvoll und leidvoll (Joyful and woeful) Die Schlüsselblume (The primrose) In Liebeslust (Love's delight)—v. 2. Die Loreley (Loreley) Du bist wie eine Blume (Ah, sweet as any flower) Oh quand je dors (O, while I sleep) S'il est un charmant gazon (If there be a charming lawn) Kling leise, mein Lied (Breathe lightly, my lay) Die drei Zigeuner (The three gypsies)

 1. Songs (High voice) with piano.

 M1620.L77S3 3–7580 rev*

NL 0406238 DLC OOxM IU OCl NN INS CtY MB

M Liszt, Franz, 1811-1886.
1620 ⌜Songs. Selections⌝
L77 Twelve songs for voice and piano; with a
S32 critical note by Richard Aldrich; the English translations by Theodore Baker. New York, G. Schirmer ⌜n.d.⌝ Pl.no.39661.
 61 p. (Schirmer's library of musical classics)
 For high voice.
 CONTENTS.--Mignon's lied--Es war ein König in Thule--Es muss ein Wunderbares sein--Freudvoll und Leidvoll--Die Schlusselblumen--In Liebeslust--Die Lorely--Du bist wie eine Blume--Oh Quand je dors--S'il est un charmant gazon--Kling'leise,mein Lied--Die drei Zigeuner.
 1. Songs (High voi with piano.

NL 0406239 NSyU IU

Liszt, Franz, 1811–1886.
 ⌜Songs. Selections⌝
 Twelve songs. The English translations by Theo. Baker. With a critical note by Richard Aldrich. For low voice. New York, G. Schirmer, ©1902.
 2 v. 31 cm. (Mastersongs by great composers)
 Schirmer's library of musical classics, v. 643, 645.
 CONTENTS.—v. 1. Mignon's Lied (Song of Mignon) Es war ein König in Thule (There was a king in Thule) Es muss ein Wunderbares sein (It must be wonderful withal) Freudvoll und leidvoll (Joyful and woeful) Die Schlüsselblume (The primrose) In Liebeslust (Love's delight)—v. 2. Die Loreley (Loreley) Du bist wie eine Blume (Ah, sweet as any flower) Oh! quand je dors (O, while I sleep) S'il est un charmant gazon (If there be a charming lawn) Kling' leise, mein Lied (Breathe lightly, my lay) Die drei Zigeuner (The three gypsies)

 1. Songs (Low voice) with piano.

 M1620.L77S32 M 60–35

NL 0406241 DLC OrP CLSU

M Liszt, Franz, 1811-1886.
1620 [Songs. Selections.]
.5 Twelve Songs for Voice and Piano.
.L699B3 With a Critical note by Richard Aldrich. The English Translations by Theodore Baker. For Low Voice. New York, G. Schirmer, c1942. Pl.no. 39660.
 61 p. 30 cm. (Schirmer's Library of Musical Classics, Vol. 1613)
 German words, with English translation.

 1. Songs (Low voice) with piano.

NL 0406242 OKentU IU NcD OrU MtU

Liszt, Franz, 1811-1886, arr.
 Twenty-four songs
 see under Schubert, Franz Peter, 1797-1828.

Liszt, Franz, 1811–1886.
 ⌜Works, piano. Selections⌝
 Twenty original piano compositions; edited by August Spanuth. Boston, O. Ditson Co. ⌜©1903⌝
 xiii, 147 p. port. 32 cm. (The Musicians library)

 1. Piano music. (Series: The Musicians library (Boston))

 M22.L77S54 3–10707 rev*

 WaSp CaBVaU CaBVa OrSaW
NL 0406244 DLC OrP OkU NIC CU NN MB PSt CtY OrP

Liszt, Franz, 1811–1886.
 ⌜Works, piano. Selections⌝
 Twenty piano transcriptions; edited by August Spanuth. Boston, O. Ditson Co. ⌜©1903⌝
 xiv, 156 p. port. 32 cm. (The Musicians library. ⌜5⌝)

 1. Piano music. (Series: The Musicians library (Boston))

 M1.M9L43 4–30152 rev*

 OkU
NL 0406245 DLC PSt N NIC CU NN OCl OO OClCC MdBP

M **Liszt, Franz, 1811-1886.**
1620 **[Songs. Selections]**
L69tw **Twenty songs with piano accompaniment. The English version by Francis Hueffer. London, Novello, Ewer and Co. [188-?] Pl. no. 6697.**
 76 p. (Albums of German song)
 English words.

 1. Songs with piano. I. Hueffer, Francis.

NL 0406246 CLU OO NBuG NN CaBVaU

M
22 Liszt, Franz, 1811-1886.
.L77E8 ⌜Etudes, piano (1863)⌝
 Two concert etudes; edited and fingered by Rafael Joseffy: 1. Waldesrauschen (Forest murmurs) 2. Gnomenreigen (Dance of the gnomes). Two legends; edited and fingered by Louis Oesterle: 1. St. Francois d'Assisse. La prédication auxoiseaux (St. Francis of Assisi. The bird-sermon) 2. St. Francoise de Paule marchant sur les flotes (St. Francis of Paul walking on the waves). New York, G. Schirmer ⌜1909⌝
 48p. 31cm. (Schirmer's library of musical classics, v. 1753)

1. Piano music. I. Liszt, Franz, 1811-1886. Legendes. II. Title: Concert etudes. III. Title: Legends.

NL 0406248 LLafS

 Liszt, Franz, 1811-1886.
M25 ⌜Études, piano (1863)⌝
L77E8 Two concert etudes. Edited and fingered by Rafael Joseffy. For the piano. New York, G. Schirmer ⌜c1909⌝ Pl.no.42608.
 18 p. 30cm. (Schirmer's library of musical classics, vol.1753)
 Contents.-1. Waldesrauschen (Forest murmurs). 2.Gnomenreigen (Dance of the Gnomes)
 With composer's Legendes.

 1.Piano music. I.Joseffy, Rafael, 1852-1915, ed.

NL 0406249 CSt

⌜Liszt, Franz⌝ 1811–1886.
 ⌜Two unidentified fragments of piano compositions. 186-?⌝
 ⌜2⌝ p. 18 x 27 cm.
 Holograph, in ink.
 From the collection of the Baroness Olga de Meyendorff.
 CONTENTS.—Schlüss Takte.—Rühig.

 1. Piano music.

 ML96.L58 M 59–82

NL 0406250 DLC

VOLUME 336

M25
L77E8
Liszt, Franz, 1811-1886.
[Légendes]
Two legends. Edited and fingered by Louis Oesterle. For the piano. New York, G. Schirmer [c1899] Pl.no.42608.
p.19-48. 30cm. (Schirmer's library of musical classics, vol.1753)
Contents.-1. St.François d'Assise. La prédication aux oiseaux (St.Francis of Assisi. The bird-sermon).-2. St.François de Paule marchant sur les flots. (St.Francis of Paul walking on the waves)
With composer's Études, piano (1863).
1.Piano music. I.Oesterle, Louis, ed

NL 0406251 CSt

M25
.L57
M46
Liszt, Franz, 1811-1886.
[Mélodies russes. Chanson bohémienne]
Ty ne povierish kak ty mila. Air bohémien, transcrit par Fr. Liszt. St. Petersbourg [18--] Pl. no. 2980.
13p. 34cm. (Edition Bernard)
Russian title transliterated.

NL 0406252 NcU

Liszt, Franz, 1811-1886.
Ueber allen Gipfeln ist Ruh! Solo Männer-Quartett mit Begleitung von 2 Hörnern. Licht, mehr Licht! Männerchorgesang, mit 2 Trompeten & 3 Posaunen. Göthe-Feier-Weimar componirt von Franz Liszt... Hamburg, New York [etc.] Schuberth & co. [18--]
14 p. (music) 26.5 cm.
[Liszt. Männerchor]

NL 0406253 CtY

Liszt, Franz, 1811-1886.
Ungarische fantasie für pianoforte u. orchester, von Franz Liszt. Arrangement des orchesters (Zweites pianoforte) von Hans von Bülow ... v. 1 Leipzig, C. F. Peter [n. d.]
1 v. 32 cm. (Edition Peters no. 1187a)
Contents.- v. [1] Piano solo.

NL 0406254 CU MH

M
1011
L77F21++
Liszt, Franz, 1811-1886.
[Fantasie über ungarische Volksmelodien, piano & orchestra; arr.]
Ungarische Fantasie für Pianoforte u. Orchester. Arrangement des Orchesters (zweites Pianoforte) von Hans von Bülow. Leipzig, G. Heinze [18--?] Pl. no. G.914 H.
39 p. 31cm.
1. Piano with orchestra--2 piano scores. I. Title.

NL 0406255 NIC MH OCl

Liszt, Franz, 1811-1886.
Ungarische Fantasie. (Fantaisie hongroise.) Piano solo. [Leipzig: C. F. Peters, 188-?] Publ. pl. no. 6959. 23 p. f°.
Cover-title.
At head of cover-title: Edition Peters. no. 1187a. Liszt.
t.-p. reads: Ungarische Fantasie für Pianoforte u. Orchester...
Arranged for piano solo.

1. Piano.—Fantasias. 2. Concertos.—Piano and orchestra.
N. Y. P. L. February 1, 1918.

NL 0406256 NN

M
786.4
L774f
Ku
Liszt, Franz, 1811-1886.
[Fantasie über ungarische Volksmelodien, piano & orchestra; arr.]
Ungarische Fantasie als Concertstück für Piano allein bearbeitet. St. Louis, Mo., Kunkel [c1888] Pl. no. 1007.
score (19p.)
1. Piano with orchestra - Piano scores.

NL 0406257 FTaSU

M3
.3
.L77D45
b
Case
Liszt, Franz, 1811-1886, arr.
Schubert, Franz Peter, 1797-1828.
[Divertissement à la hongroise, piano, 4 hands, D. 818, G minor; arr.]
Ungarische Melodien. Aus dem ungarischen Divertissement zu 4 Händen, op. 54, zweihändig auf eine neue leichtere Art gesetzt von Franz Liszt. Wien, A. Diabelli [1846] Pl. no. 8353-8355.

ML96
.L58
Case
Liszt, Franz, 1811-1886, arr.
Schubert, Franz Peter, 1797-1828.
[Divertissement à la hongroise, piano, 4 hands, D. 818, G minor. Marcia; arr.]
Ungarische Melodien, cah. 2. Aus dem ungarischen Divertissement zu 4 Händen, op. 54, zu 2 Händen gesetzt von Fr. Liszt. Vienne, A. Diabelli [1846] Pl. no. 8354.

Liszt, Franz, 1811-1886.
[Rhapsodie hongroise, piano, no. 16; arr.]
Ungarische Rhapsodie, von F. Liszt. 4 händige Ausg. [1882]
14 p. 33 cm.
Holograph, in ink.
At end: F. Liszt, Mars 82.
Arr. for piano, 4 hands.
Published: Budapest, Táborszky & Parsch, 1882.
From the collection of Richard Burmeister.
1. Piano music (4 hands), Arranged. I. Title.
ML96.L58 M 59-807

NL 0406260 DLC

Liszt, Franz, 1811-1886.
Ungarische rhapsodie (no. 1 in F) Parts. Leipzig, New York, J. Schuberth & co., n. d.
35 cm.
Publ. no. 5295.
Namely:
2 violin 1; 2 violin 2; 2 viola; 2 violoncello; 2 double-bass; 1 flute 1; 1 flute 2; 1 piccolo; 1 oboe 1; 1 oboe 2; 1 clarinet 1; 1 clarinet 2; 1 bassoon 1; 1 bassoon 2; 1 bassoon 3; 1 horn 1; 1 horn 2; 1 horn 3; 1 horn 3; 1 horn 4; 1 trumpet 1; 1 trumpet 2; 1 trumpet 3; 1 tenor trombone 1; 1 tenor trombone 2; 1 bass trombone; 1 ophicleide; 1 triangle and cymbals; 1 harp.

NL 0406262 CU

Liszt, Franz, 1811-1886.
Ungarische rhapsodie (no. 1 in F) für grosses orchester bearbeitet vom componisten und F. Doppler Leipzig, J. Schuberth & co., n. d.
62 p. 31 cm.
Publ. no. 5224.
Orchestral score.

NL 0406263 CU

WM
1060
L 77u2
D 69
LISZT, FRANZ, 1811-1886.
Ungarische rhapsodie (no.2, in D moll u. G dur)[-von] Franz Liszt. Bearbeitung von F.Doppler. [Leipzig,B.Senff,n.d.]
52p. (his Ungarische rhapsodien für grosses orchester)
Caption title.
Full score.
Plate nos.: 2451, 5238.

NL 0406264 ICN

Liszt, Franz, 1811-1886.
Ungarische rhapsodie (no. 3 in D dur) fur grosses orchester bearbeitet vom componisten und F. Doppler. Leipzig, etc., J. Schuberth & co., n. d.
36 p. 28 cm.
Publ. no. 5237
Orchestral score.

NL 0406265 CU

Liszt, Franz, 1811-1886.
Ungarische rhapsodie (no. 4 in D moll u. G. dur) Leipzig, etc., J. Schuberth & co., n. d.
52 p. 27 cm.
Publ. no. 5238.

NL 0406266 CU MCM

LISZT,Franz,1811-1886.
Ungarische rhapsodie. No.4.in D mol u G dur. Für das pianoforte zu vier handen. Leipzig,etc.,J.Schuberth & Co.,1878?
4°. pp.23.
Cover serves as title-page.

NL 0406267 MH

Liszt, Franz, 1811-1886.
Ungarische rhapsodie (no. 5 in E moll) für grosses orchester bearbeitet vom componisten und F. Doppler. Leipzig, etc., J. Schuberth & co., n. d.
24 p. 28 cm.
Publ. no. 5239.
Orchestral score.

NL 0406268 CU MCM

Liszt, Franz, 1811-1886.
Ungarische rhapsodie (no. 6, Pesther carneval) für grosses orchester bearbeitet vom componisten und F. Doppler. Leipzig, etc., J. Schuberth & co., n. d.
74 p. 28 cm.
Publ. no. 5240.
Orchestral score.

NL 0406269 CU MCM

M25
L77R4
no.6
1927
Liszt, Franz, 1811-1886.
[Rhapsodie hongroise, piano, no. 6]
Ungarische Rhapsodie; Nr. 6. Hrsg. von Moriz Rosenthal. Berlin, Ullstein [c1927]
12 p. 31cm. (Tonmeister Ausgabe, 299)
1.Piano music. I.Title. II.Title: Rhapsodie hongroise.

NL 0406270 CSt

VOLUME 336

LISZT, FRANZ, 1811-1886.
[RHAPSODIE HONGROISE, PIANO, NO. 12]
Ungarische Rhapsodie Nr. 12. Neu-Ausg. von Eugen D'Albert. Mainz, B. Schott's Söhne [c1906] 15 p. 34cm. (Edition Schott. No. 06428 1/2)

1. Piano. I. D'Albert, Eugen, 1864-1932, ed.

NL 0406271 NN

LISZT, FRANZ, 1811-1886.
[RHAPSODIE HONGROISE, PIANO, NO. 13]
Ungarische Rhapsodie No. 13. Neu-Ausg. von Eugen d'Albert. Mainz, B. Schott's Söhne [c1906] 11 p. 34cm. (Edition Schott. 06430)

1. Piano. I. D'Albert, Eugen, 1864-1932, ed.

NL 0406272 NN

LISZT, FRANZ, 1811-1886.
[RHAPSODIE HONGROISE, PIANO, NO. 14]
Ungarische Rhapsodie No. 14. Neu-Ausg. von Eugen D'Albert. Mainz, B. Schott's Söhne [1906?] 16 p. 34cm. (Edition Schott. No. 06431 1/2)

"Einzel-Ausg."

1. Piano. I. D'Albert, Eugen, 1864-1932, ed.

NL 0406273 NN

Liszt, Franz, 1811-1886.
[Rhapsodie hongroise, piano, no. 19; arr.]
Ungarische Rhapsodie Nr. 19. Rhapsodie hongroise nr. 19. Hungarian rhapsody nr. 19. Für Pianoforte zu zwei Händen. Zum Konzertgebrauch frei bearb. von Ferruccio Busoni. Leipzig, Breitkopf & Härtel [1920]
15 p. 31 cm. (Edition Breitkopf, Nr. 4959)

1. Piano music, Arranged. I. Busoni, Ferruccio Benvenuto, 1866-1924, arr.
M39.L 49-30651*

NL 0406274 DLC

Liszt, Franz, 1811-1886.
Ungarische rhapsodien no. 1-5, frei bearbeitet für das pianoforte zu vier händen vom componisten. Schuberth, n. d.

NL 0406275 OrP

Liszt, Franz, 1811-1886.
Ungarische rhapsodien (Rhapsodies hongroises) für klavier zu 2 händen. Neuausgabe von Max Pauer. Braunschweig, Litolff, n. d.
2 v. (Collection Litolff, no. 2590, 2591)
v. 1. No. 1-9. v. 2. No. 10-15 and Rhapsodie espagnole

NL 0406276 CaBVa

M786.4
L774rh.3 Liszt, Franz, 1811-1886.
[Rhapsodies hongroises, piano]
Ungarische Rhapsodien. [Bearbeitung von] Eugen d'Albert. Mainz, B.Schott's Söhne [19--]
2v. 33cm. (His Klavier-Werke, Bd.1-2)

I. Albert, Eugen d', 1864-1932. II.Title.

NL 0406277 IEN

Liszt, Franz, 1811-1886.
[Rhapsodies hongroises, piano. Selections; arr.]
Ungarische Rhapsodien, für grosses Orchester. Bearb. vom Componisten und F. Doppler. Leipzig, J. Schuberth [1875] Pl. no. 5224, 5236, 5237-5240.
score (6 v. in 1) 27 cm.
First ed.
CONTENTS.—No. 1 (i. e. 14)—No. 2 (i. e. 12)—No. 3 (i. e. 6)—No. 4 (i. e. 2)—No. 5.—No. 6 (i. e. 9)
1. Orchestral music, Arranged—Scores. I. Doppler, Franz, arr. II. Title.
M3.3.L77R693 68-39154/M

NL 0406278 DLC MB

VM
1060
L 77u2 LISZT, FRANZ, 1811-1886.
[Ungarische rhapsodie no.2, D minor] Franz Liszt's ungarische rhapsodien für grosses orchester, bearbeitet vom componisten und F.Doppler... No.2 in D moll u. G dur... Partitur... Leipzig,Schuberth[1911]
60p.

"Pour grand orchestre par Jul. H.Matthey."
Plate no.: 6675a (1911)

NL 0406279 ICN

M28
.L57
U5 Liszt, Franz, 1811-1886.
[Ungarischer Sturm-Marsch, piano]
Ungarischer Sturm-Marsch, für das Pianoforte. Neue Bearb. Berlin, Schlesinger, 1876.
19p. 34cm.

NL 0406280 NcU

VM
1046
L 77u LISZT, FRANZ, 1811-1886.
Ungarischer Sturmmarsch. Neue Bearbeitung. [Leipzig?Schlesinger?1876?]
score(50p.) 27cm.

Title-page and p.1-4 wanting.
Caption title.
Plate no.: S.2983.
See Grove, Dictionary of music and musicians, p.308, no.610.

NL 0406281 ICN MB

LISZT, Franz, 1811-1886. No. 5 in **M.212.10
"Ungarn's Gott." Gedicht von Alexander Petöfi, componirt für Bary-ton-Stimme und Chor (ad libitum) mit Clavier-Begleitung von Franz Liszt. Budapest. Táborszky & Parsch. [188-?] 9 pp. F°.
The words are in Hungarian and German.

NL 0406282 MB

Liszt, Franz, 1811-1886.
[Die Vätergruft; arr.]
Die Vätergruft (Uhland) The last of his clan. Leipzig, C. F. Kahnt Nachfolger [189-?] Pl. no. 4298a.
score (19 p.) 27 cm. (*His* Lieder mit Orchester)
For bass and orchestra; acc. originally for piano.
German, French, and English words.

1. Songs (Low voice) with orchestra—Scores. I. Title. II. Title: The last of his clan.
M1617.L78V3 64-59465/M

NL 0406283 DLC

Liszt, Franz, 1811-1886.
[Valse oubliée, piano, no. 1, F♯ major]
Valse. 1881.
[11] p. 26 cm.
Holograph, in ink.
On page [1]: F. Liszt. 23 Juillet 81.
Published: Berlin, Bote & Bock, 1881.
From the collection of the Baroness Olga de Meyendorff.

1. Waltzes (Piano)
ML96.L58 M 59-78

NL 0406284 DLC

Liszt, Franz, 1811-1886.
[Valse oubliée, piano, no. 1, F-sharp major]
Valse. 1881. 11 p.

Microfilm of holograph in the Library of Congress. TOSCANINI MEMORIAL ARCHIVES.

1. Music - Manuscripts - Facsimiles.

NL 0406285 NN

VAULT
FOLIO
M3.3
.L77
V3 Liszt, Franz, 1811-1886.
[Valse à capriccio sur deux motifs de Lucia et Parisina, piano]
Valse à capriccio sur deux motifs de Lucia e [sic] Parisina, pour le piano, par F. Liszt. Vienna, T. Haslinger [184?] Pl. no. T.H.8720.
23p. 33cm.
First edition.

NL 0406286 NcU

Liszt, Franz, 1811-1886.
[Valse de concert, piano]
Valse de concert. Transcription pour piano d'après la Suite en forme de valse de J. de Végh, par Fr. Liszt. Budapest, Harmonia [18—] Pl. no. H. 108.
28 p. 34 cm.

1. Waltzes (Piano) I. Végh von Verëb, Johann, 1845-1918. Suite en forme de valse. II. Title.
M32.L 64-45670/M

NL 0406287 DLC NN

LISZT,F[ranz],1811-1886.
Valse de concert sur deux motifs de Lucia et Parisina. 2e ed.entierement revue et corrigée par l'auteur. Vienne,C.Haslinger qm. Tobie,etc.,etc.,[18-].
4°. pp.19. (3 caprices-valses pour le piano,3.)

NL 0406288 MH

M3
.3
.L77F43
Case Liszt, Franz, 1811-1886, arr.
Gounod, Charles François, 1818-1893.
[Faust. Waltz; arr.]
Valse de l'opéra Faust. Pour le piano par Franz Liszt. Berlin, Bote & Bock [1861] Pl. no. 5529.

(MUS)
M32
.8
.L56M4 Liszt, Franz, 1811-1886.
Valse de Méphisto. Episode du "Faust" de Lenau, pour piano à 2 mains. Révision par C. Saint-Saëns. Paris, Durand [c1917]
27 p. 31 cm. (Edition classique A. Durand & fils, No. 9463)

Originally for orchestra.

1. Waltzes (Piano) I. Title. II. Title: La danse dans l'auberge du village.

NL 0406290 ViU

qM786.41 Liszt, Franz, 1811-1886.
L69vi [Valse impromptu, piano]
Valse impromptu. Original-Ausg. Leipzig, J. Schuberth [n.d.] Pl. no. 1659.
15p. 34cm.

1. Waltzes (Piano)

NL 0406291 IU

VOLUME 336

Liszt, Franz, 1811-1886.
Valse-impromptu. Rev. and fingered by Wm. Scharfenberg. [New York] G. Schirmer, c1883.
30 cm. (His Original works and transcriptions for the piano)

NL 0406292 CtY OU

786.45M Liszt, Franz, 1811-1886.
L 699 V ⌊Valse impromptu, piano⌋
Valse-impromptu. Rev. and fingered by William Scharfenberg. ⌊New York⌋ G. Schirmer, °1883.
15 p. 34cm.
Caption title.

NL 0406293 OO WaT

M32 Liszt, Franz, 1811-1886.
L77V22 ⌊Valse impromptu, piano⌋
P4 Valse impromptu; pour piano. Edition originale. Leipzig, C.F.Peters ⌊1891?⌋ Pl. no. 7526.
15 p. 31cm. (Edition Peters, 2555)

1.Piano music. I.Title.

NL 0406294 CSt

Liszt, Franz, 1811-1886.
Valse impromptu. [For pianoforte.]
(In The Century Library of Music. Vol. 12, Music, pp. 902-914. New York. 1901.)

F8321 — Waltzes. — T.r. — Pianoforte. Music.

NL 0406295 MB

M39 Liszt, Franz, 1811-1886.
L58 ⌊Réminiscences de Robert le Diable. Valse infernal⌋
R44 Valse infernale de Robert le Diable. ⌊Based on Robert le Diable, by Giacomo Meyerbeer⌋ Paris, Imp. Buttner-Thierry ⌊18--⌋ Pl. no. 3394.
score (22 p.)

1. Piano music. I. Meyerbeer, Giacomo, 1791-1864. Robert le Diable.

NL 0406296 WaU

Liszt, Franz, 1811-1886.
Valse mélancholique, composée pour le piano par F. Liszt ... Paris, M. Schlesinger [etc., etc., 18--]
1 p.l., 2-7 p. (music) 30.5 cm. [Liszt. Pianoforte compositions and transcriptions. v. 1]

NL 0406297 CtY

Liszt, Franz, 1811-1886.
⌊Valse mélancolique, piano⌋
Valse mélancolique, composée pour le piano. Vienne, T. Haslinger ⌊1840⌋ Pl. no. T. H. 8195.
7 p. 31 cm.
First ed. of 1st version.

1. Waltzes (Piano) I. Title.

M3.3.L77V3 64-59960/M

NL 0406298 DLC

M781.5 Liszt, Franz, 1811-1886.
L774vaL1 [Valse oubliée, piano, no.1, F♯ maj.]
Valse oubliée for piano. London, Schott [n.d.]
7p. 31cm. (Edition Schott no.07042)

● 1.Waltzes (Piano).

NL 0406299 CLSU CSt FTaSU

786.45M Liszt, Franz, 1811-1886.
L 699 Va ⌊Valse oubliée, piano, no.1, F sharp major⌋
no.1 Valse oubliée (Vergessener Walzer) Ed. and fingered by A.R. Parsons. ⌊New York⌋ G. Schirmer, °1883.
9 p. 32cm.
Caption title.

NL 0406300 OO

M32 Liszt, Franz, 1811-1886.
L77V27 ⌊Valse oubliée, piano, no. 1, F♯ major⌋
no.1 Valse oubliée; no. 1, freely rev. by
1921 Rudolph Ganz. New York, Composer's Music ⌊c1921⌋ Pl. no. C.M.C.330.
12 p. 31cm. (Concert programs of Rudolph Ganz, series 1, no. 6)

1.Waltzes (Piano) I.Title.

NL 0406301 CSt

M
786.4 Liszt, Franz, 1811-1886.
L774vl ⌊Valse oubliée, piano, no. 1, F♯ major⌋
S Valse oubliée. Edited by Carl Deis. New York, G. Schirmer, c1938. Pl. no. 37719.
score (9p.) (Franz Liszt original works for the piano)
Caption title.

1. Waltzes (Piano) I. Deis, Carl, ed.

NL 0406302 FTaSU WaT CtY

Liszt, Franz, 1811-1886.
⌊Valse oubliée, piano, no. 1, F♯ major; arr.⌋
Valse oubliée, arr. by Colin Taylor. London, New York, Oxford University Press ⌊1948⌋
2 scores (12 p. each) 31 cm. (The Two-piano series)
Cover title.

1. Waltzes (2 pianos) I. Title.

M215.L 48-21065 rev*

NL 0406303 DLC

Liszt, Franz, 1811-1886.
⌊Soirées de Vienne. No. 6⌋
Varianten zu dem 6ten Heft (A moll und A dur) der Soirées de Vienne. Cadenz—Don Juan Fantasia. ⌊1869?⌋
leaf. 26 cm.
Holograph, in ink.
Liszt's additions, corrections, and emendations to 2 piano pieces.
At bottom of recto: Mit der Bitte die Varianten zu dem Schubert'schen Walzer (Bach-Händel betiteit) der liebenswürdigsten Excellency Frau Baronin Marie von Schleinitz mitzutheilen. F. Liszt.

I. Liszt, Franz, 1811-1886. Reminiscences de Don Juan. II. Title: Soirées de Vienne.

ML96.L58 M 59-831

NL 0406304 DLC

Liszt, Franz, 1811-1886.
⌊Variationen über das Motiv von Bach, piano⌋
Variationen über das Motiv von Bach (Basso continuo des ersten Satzes seiner Cantate Weinen, Klagen, Sorgen, Zagen und des Crucifixus der H-moll-Messe) Für das Pianoforte. Berlin, Schlesinger'schen Buch & Musikhandlung ⌊1875⌋ Pl. no. S. 6930.
19 p. 34 cm.

1. Variations (Piano) I. Bach, Johann Sebastian, 1685-1750. Weinen, Klagen, Sorgen, Zagen. Weinen, Klagen, Sorgen, Zagen. II. Title.

M27.L 64-57580/M

NL 0406305 DLC CLSU

Liszt, Franz, 1811-1886.
[Variationen über das Motiv von Bach, piano.]
Variationen über das Motiv von Bach (Basso continuo des ersten Satzes seiner Cantate Weinen, Klagen, Sorgen, Zagen und des Crucifixus der H-moll-Messe) Für das Pianoforte. Berlin, Schlesinger'schen Buch & Musikhandlung [1875] Pl. no. S. 6930. 19 p. 34 cm.

Microfilm. New York, New York Public

Library, 1972.

1. Variations (Piano) (1) Bach, Johann Sebastian, 1685-1750. Weinen, Klagen, Sorgen, Zagen. Weinen, Klagen, Sorgen, Zagen. (2) TITLE: Weinen, Klagen, Sorgen, Zagen. (TITLE)

NL 0406307 NN

---

sVM LISZT, FRANZ, 1811-1886.
27 ...Variationen über das motiv von Bach...basso
L 77v continuo des ersten satzes der Kantate nr. 12 "Weinen, klagen, sorgen, zagen" und des "Crucifixus" aus der H-moll-messe. Herausgegeben von Moriz Rosenthal... Berlin, Ullstein ⌊c1927⌋
20p. 31cm. (Tonmeister ausgabe nr. 317)

Piano solo.
Plate no.: T.A. nr. 317.

NL 0406308 ICN

Liszt, Franz, 1811-1886.
Variationen über den Basso continuo des ersten Satzes der Cantate: "Weinen, Klagen, Angst, und Noth sind des Christen Thränenbrod" und des Crucifixus der H-moll-Messe von Sebastian Bach, für Orgel, Harmonium, oder Pedal-Flügel gesetzt von Dr. Franz Liszt. Erfurt: G. W. Körner ⌊186-?⌋. Publ. pl. no. 267. 17 p. ob. 8°.

Dedication at head of title.

1. Organ.—Variation. 2. Bach, Johann Sebastian, 1685-1750.
N. Y. P. L. November 14, 1917.

NL 0406309 NN MB

Liszt, Franz, 1811-86 (2)
Variationen über das Motiv von Bach
Variationen über Weinen, Klagen, Sorgen, Zagen. [Piano solo] Rédigés par I. Friedman. Wien, Universal-Edition [19 -]
Score (17 p.) (His Oeuvres pour piano)
Universal-Edition, 5902

NL 0406310 MH OO CtY OrP

---

qM786.8 Liszt, Franz, 1811-1886.
L69v ⌊Variations, Weinen, Klagen, Sorgen, Zagen;
1942 arr.⌋
Variations on the basso continuo of the first part of the cantata "Weinen, Klagen" and of the Crucifixus of the B minor mass by Johann Sebastian Bach. By Franz Liszt. Arr. and ed. for organ ⌊by⌋ Joseph Bonnet. New York, J. Fischer ⌊c1942⌋
21p. 32cm. (Fischer edition no.7872)

NL 0406311 IU LU NcU OrP

VOLUME 336

Liszt, Franz, 1811-1886.
[Variationen über das Motiv von Bach, piano]

Variations on the theme by Bach: [music] basso continuo of the first movement of his cantata Weinen, Klagen, and of the Crucifixus of the B minor mass. Edited by Isidor Philipp. [New York] G. Schirmer, °1946.
23 p. 30 cm.
Caption title.
1. Variations (Piano) I. Bach, Johann Sebastian, 1685-1750. Weinen, Klagen, Sorgen, Zagen. Weinen, Klagen, Sorgen, Zagen. II. Philipp, Isidore Edmond, 1863-1958, ed. III. Title.
M27.L 48-19232 rev*/M

NL 0406312 DLC ICU

Liszt, Franz, 1811-1886.
[Variationen über das Motiv von Bach, piano]

Variations sur le thème de Bach: Pleurer, gémir ... Weinen, Klagen ... [Éd. par] Alfred Cortot. Paris, New York, Salabert [1949]
28 p. 32 cm. (Édition de travail des œuvres de Liszt)
Édition nationale de musique classique, no. 5431.
1. Piano music—Instructive editions. 2. Variations (Piano) I. Bach, Johann Sebastian, 1685-1750. Weinen, Klagen, Sorgen, Zagen. Weinen, Klagen, Sorgen, Zagen. II. Cortot, Alfred, 1877-1962, ed. III. Title.
MT247.L56C63 49-54093 rev*/M

NL 0406313 DLC ViU NN

Liszt, Franz, 1811-1886.
[Années de pèlerinage, 2. année, suppl. Venezia e Napoli]

Venezia e Napoli; gondoliera, canzone e tarantella pour piano. Supplément aux Années de pèlerinage, 2. volume: Italie. Mayence, B. Schott's Söhne [18- Pl. no. 16500.
items. 32-35 cm.
Reissued from original plates.
1. Piano music. I. Title.
M25.L 64-50603/M

NL 0406314 DLC NcU NN ICN

LISZT, FRANZ, 1811-1886.
[ANNÉES DE PÈLERINAGE, 2. ANNÉE, SUPPL. VENEZIA E NAPOLI]
Venezia e Napoli: gondoliera, canzone e tarantella pour pianoforte par F. Liszt. Revised by Carlyle Petersilea. Boston, White, Smith [c1885]
Pl. no. 6108. 1 no. 36cm.

[No.] 1.

1. Piano. I. Title.

NL 0406315 NN

M24
.L77A51 Liszt, Franz, 1811-1886.
1909 [Années de pèlerinage. 2. Année, suppl. Venezia e Napoli]
"Venezia e Napoli" (Supplément à l'Italie); for pianoforte, ed. and rev. by Rafael Joseffy. New York, G. Schirmer, °1909.
31 p. 31cm. (Schirmer's library, vol. 917)
At head of title: Années de pèlerinage
I. Title. II. Title: Venezia e Napoli.

NL 0406316 ViU

786.43M Liszt, Franz, 1811-1886.
L 699 A [Années de pèlerinage. 2.année(Supplément)]
2.année
suppl. D
Venezia e Napoli. Révision par S. Riéra. A. Durand [°1919]
31 p. 31cm. (Edition classique A. Durand & Fils, no. 9776)
At head of title: Années de pèlerinage. Italie Supplément.
Contents.--Gondoliera.--Canzone.--Tarentelle.

NL 0406317 OO

Liszt, Franz, 1811-1886.
[Années de pèlerinage. 2. année, suppl. Venezia e Napoli]

Venezia e Napoli. [Édition de travail par] Alfred Cortot. Paris, New York, Salabert [1949]
36 p. 32 cm. (Édition de travail des oeuvres de Liszt)
"Édition nationale de musique-classique, no. 5472."
For piano.
Duration: 14 minutes, 40 seconds.
CONTENTS.—Gondoliera.—Canzone.—Tarantella.
1. Piano music—Instructive editions. I. Cortot, Alfred, 1877- II. Title.
MT247.L56C56 50-32982

NL 0406318 DLC

Liszt, Franz, 1811-1886.
[Années de pèlerinage, 2. année, suppl. Venezia e Napoli. Gondoliera]

Venezia: Gondoliera. Rev., fingered and edited with an illustrative pref. by A. R. Parsons. [New York] G. Schirmer, °1882.
9 p. 35 cm. (Morceaux brillants pour le piano-forte, no. 23)
1. Piano music. I. Title. II. Title: Gondoliera.
M25.L 64-49505/M

NL 0406319 DLC

Liszt, Franz, 1811-1886.
Venezia e Napoli. Gondoliera. Revised and fingered by Louis Oesterle. New York, E. Schuberth & co. [c1892]
8 p. 36 cm. (Select pianoforte compositions. 5th series)
Caption title.

NL 0406320 CU

LISZT, FRANZ, 1811-1886.
[ANNÉES DE PELERINAGE, 2. ANNÉE, SUPPL. VENEZIA E NAPOLI. TARANTELLA]
Venezia e Napoli, III: Tarantella [von] F. Liszt. Neue, sorgfältig durchgeschene Ausg. von K. Klindworth. Mainz, B. Schott's Söhne, c1912. 19 p. 34cm.

Caption title.

1.Tarantellas (Piano)

NL 0406321 NN

LISZT, FRANZ, 1811-1886.
[ANNÉES DE PÈLERINAGE. 2. ANNÉE, SUPPL. VENEZIA E NAPOLI. TARANTELLA. ARR. FOR ORCHESTRA]
Venezia e Napoli: Tarantella [di] F. Liszt... [1930?] score (36 p.) 36cm.

Arranger's holograph, in pencil, with corrections in ink.

On t. p., in another hand: By Mitya Stillman.
On p. [1]: 1915-1916-Dec. 24, 1930.
Arranged for orchestra by Stillman. Originally for piano.
Imperfect: t. p. mutilated.
1. Autographs (Music)-- Stillman, M. I. Stillman, Mitya, 1893-1936, arr. II. Title.

NL 0406323 NN

Liszt, Franz, 1811-1886.
[Tarantelle di bravura d'après la tarantelle de La muette de Portici]

Veränderungen in der Tarantelle aus der Stumer von Portici. 1869.
[4] p. 26 cm.
Holograph, in ink.
Liszt's corrections for his piano piece.
At end: Fräulein Sophia Menter in freundlichster Ergebenheit ... September 69. F. Liszt.
I. Title: Tarantelle aus der Stumer von Portici.
ML96.L58 M 59-817

NL 0406324 DLC

Liszt, Franz, 1811-1886.
Vereins-Lied . . . für Männerchor.
Leipzig. Kahnt. [186-?] 15 pp. L. 8°.

April 11, 1902.
E3573 — T.r. — Part songs.

NL 0406325 MB

Liszt, Franz, 1811-1886.
[Romance oubliée, piano]

Vergessene Romanze (Romance oubliée) [1880]
[3] p. 17 x 26 cm.
Holograph, in ink.
Published: Hanover, Simon, 1881.
From the collection of the Baroness Olga de Meyendorff.
1. Piano music. I. Title. II. Title: Romance oubliée.
ML96.L58 M 59-79

NL 0406326 DLC

Liszt, Franz, 1811-1886.
[Valse oubliée, piano, no. 1, F♯ major; arr.]

Vergessener Walzer. Für Violoncell und Klavier übertragen von Ferruccio Busoni. Leipzig, New York, Breitkopf & Härtel [°1917]
score (9 p.) and part. 32 cm. (Edition Breitkopf, Nr. 4952)
For violoncello and piano.
1. Waltzes (Violoncello and piano) I. Busoni, Ferruccio Benvenuto, 1866-1924, arr. II. Title.
M236.L M 53-859

NL 0406327 DLC OrP

M2072.7
.L5V5 Liszt, Franz, 1811-1886.
[Via crucis. German & Latin]
Via crucis, for mixed chorus and soli with organ or piano accompaniment. New York, E. F. Kalmus [n. d.]
score (46 p.) 31cm. (Kalmus piano series)

1. Choruses, Sacred (Mixed voices, 4 pts.) with organ. I. Title.

NL 0406328 AAP ICU

MUSIC
M780.52 Liszt, Franz, 1811-1886.
L774v [Via Crucis der Kreuzweg. Organ-vocal score. Latin and German]
Via Crucis; der Kreuzweg; die 14 Stationen des Kreuzweges, für gemischten Chor und Soli, mit Begleitung der Orgel oder des Klaviers. Leipzig, Breitkopf & Härtel [c1936]
score (46p.) 33cm. (Breitkopf & Härtels Partitur-Bibliothek, Nr.1966)
For chorus (SATB) solo voices, and organ or piano acc.

NL 0406329 CLSU NjP

Liszt, Franz, 1811-1886.
31 Vier grosse original-beitraege.
L8068 4°
[In Lebert, S. and Stark, L. Grosse theoretisch-praktische klavierschule. Stuttgart, 1869. v. 4. p. 162-195]

NL 0406330 DLC

VOLUME 336

Liszt, Franz, 1811–1886.
⌊Kleine Klavierstücke, piano⌋

Vier kleine Klavierstücke. ⌊1865–76⌋
4 items. 10–36 cm.
Holographs, in ink.
Title from the composer's Musikalische Werke (Leipzig, Breitkopf & Härtel 1928)
At end of item 1: Janvier 65; item 2: Fevrier 65; item 3: pour le 22 Juillet, 73. F. Liszt; item 4: 28 Juillet, 76. F. Liszt.
From the collection of the Baroness Olga de Meyendorff.
First and 3d items: 36 cm.; 2d, 16 x 27 cm.; 4th, 19 x 28 cm.
1. Piano music. I. Title: Kleine Klavierstücke.

ML96.L58 M 59–65

NL 0406331 DLC

Liszt, Franz, 1811-1886, arr
Vier Lieder von Franz Schubert
see under Schubert, Franz Peter, 1797-1829.

Liszt, Franz, 1811–1886.
⌊Die Legende von der heiligen Elisabeth. Selections; arr.⌋

Vier Stücke aus der Legende der heiligen Elisabeth, für das Pianoforte zu vier Händen von Franz Liszt. Leipzig, C. F. Kahnt ⌊1869⌋ Pl. no. -1943.
v. 29 cm.
First ed. of Liszt's arrangement for piano, 4 hands.
Originally for orchestra.
CONTENTS.— —no. 2. Marsch der Kreuzritter.—no. 3. Der Sturm.—no. 4. Interludium.
1. Piano music (4 hands), Arranged. 2. Oratorios—Excerpts, Arranged. I. Title: Legende der heiligen Elisabeth.

M3.3.L77L45 b 64–46924/M

NL 0406333 DLC

VM 2021 K 96g LISZT, FRANZ, 1811-1886.
Vierstimmige männergesänge... Cöln, Eck & comp. ⌊18--⌋
31p. and 4 pt. 28cm. (with Kunz, Konrad Max. Grabgesang... ⌊18--⌋)

Full score with piano accompaniment and separate voice parts.
German words.
Contents.—Wir sind nicht mumien.—Das düstre meer umrauscht.—Unter allen wipfeln ist ruh.—Gottes ist der ori- ent.

NL 0406334 ICN

Liszt, Franz, 1811–1886. No. 11-14 in **M.203.8
Vierstimmige Männergesänge. No. 1–4.
Mainz. Schott. [184–?] 4 parts in 1 v. L. 8°.
Contents. — 1. Rheinweinlied. 2. Studentenlied. 3, 4. Reiterlied, 1te, 2te Version.

April 11, 1902.
E3685 — Part songs.

NL 0406335 MB NN CtY IaU

LISZT, FRANZ, 1811-1886.

Vierstimmige Männergesänge, nos. 1 & 4. Mainz, B. Schott's Söhne [18--] score (2 v.)

Microfilm (master negative)

NL 0406336 NN IaU

M 786.4 L774g4 Br Liszt, Franz, 1811–1886.
⌊Grandes études de Paganini, piano. Étude no. 4⌋
Die vierte Etüde aus der Sammlung Grandes études de Paganini transcrites pour le piano. In ihren drei Bearb. neu hrsg. und mit einem Vorwort versehen von Eduard Reuss. Leipzig, New York, Breitkopf & Härtel ⌊pref. 1895⌋ Pl. no. 20986.
score (21p.)

1. Piano music. I. Paganini, Nicolò. 1782–1840.

NL 0406337 FTaSU

⌊**Liszt, Franz**⌋ 1811–1886.
⌊Valse oubliée, piano, no. 4⌋

Vierter vergessener Walzer (Quatrième valse oubliée) ⌊1883?⌋
⌊12⌋ p. 35 cm.
Holograph, in ink.
Published: Bryn Mawr, Pa., T. Presser, 1954.

1. Waltzes (Piano) I. Title: Vergessener Walzer. II. Title: Valse oubliée.

ML96.L58 M 59–795

NL 0406338 DLC

Liszt, Franz, 1811-1886.
[Le vieux vagabond]
Le vieux vagabond. [1848?] [4] p. 24 x 32 cm.

Holograph sketch in ink. Pages bound in order of [1, 2, 4, 3] First line: Dans ce fossé cessons de vivre. First published: Leipzig, Breitkopf und Härtel, 1918. Searle no. 304; Raabe 565; Walker 308; Albrecht llll. Werke series VII, no. 1. Song for

baritone and piano. Words in French by P. Béranger.

1. Music - Manuscripts. (TITLE)

NL 0406340 NN

Liszt, Franz, 1811–1886.
⌊Grandes études, piano⌋

Vingt-quatre grandes études, pour le piano, par F. Liszt. Paris, M. Schlesinger ⌊1839– Pl. no. M. S. 2756–
v. 35 cm.
First ed.
Only 12 études were published.

1. Piano music.

M3.3.L77G73 64–45637/M

NL 0406341 DLC

Liszt, Franz, 1811–1886.
⌊Grandes études, piano⌋

24 ⌊i. e. Vingt-quatre⌋ grandes études, pour le piano. Vienne, T. Haslinger ⌊1839⌋ Pl. no. T. H. 7745–7746.
2 v. 34 cm.
First ed.
Only 12 études were published.

1. Piano music.

M3.3.L77G73 a 64–50650/M

NL 0406342 DLC

Liszt, Franz, 1811–1886.

Vive Henri IV. ⌊187–?⌋
⌊7⌋ p. 18 x 27 cm.
Holograph, in ink.
At end: F. Liszt.
For piano.
From the collection of the Baroness Olga de Meyendorff.

1. Piano music. 2. Folk-songs, French (Instrumental settings) I. Title.

ML96.L58 M 59–60

NL 0406343 DLC

Liszt, Franz, 1811–1886. No. 1 in **M.407.19
Die Vogelpredigt des heiligen Franz von Assisi. Legende . . . für Orchester bearbeitet von Felix Mottl. Partitur.
= Budapest. Rózsavölgyi & Comp. [189–?] 37 pp. 8°.

G6981 — T.r. — Orchestra. Music. — Mottl, Felix, ed.

NL 0406344 MB

Liszt, Franz, 1811–86 (2)

Vom Fels zum Meer; deutscher Sieges-Marsch. Berlin, Schlesinger [186- ?]

Miniature score (23 p.)
For orchestra

NL 0406345 MH MB CtY

VAULT FOLIO M3.3 .L77 V6 Liszt, Franz, 1811-1886.
⌊Vom Fels zum Meer; arr.⌋
Vom Fels zum Meer! Deutscher Sieges-Marsch. Arrangement für Piano zu zwei Händen vom Componisten. Berlin, Schlesinger; New York, B. Westermann ⌊1865⌋ Pl. no. S. 5282 A.
15p. 35cm.

First edition.
For piano; originally for orchestra.

NL 0406346 NcU

Liszt, Franz, 1811–1886. No. 1 in **M.342.15
Von der Wiege bis zum Grabe. Symphonische Dichtung. Partitur.
Berlin. Bote & Bock. [187–?] 29 pp. F°.

April 11, 1902.
E3573 — T.r. — Symphonic poems.

NL 0406347 MB

Liszt, Franz, 1811-1886.
[Von der Wiege bis zum Grabe]
...Von der Wiege bis zum Grabe; symphonische Dichtung nach einer Zeichnung von Michael Zichy componirt von Franz Liszt. Du berceau jusqu'à la tombe... Berlin, E. Bote & G. Bock [etc., etc.,1883] Pl.no. 12812. 29cm.

Score: orchestra.

First edition.
Contents.—Die Wiege.—Der Kampf um's Dasein.—Zum Grabe: Die Wiege des zukünftigen Lebens.

1. Symphonic poems. I. Zichy, Mihály, 1827-1906. II. Title.

NL 0406349 NN

Liszt, Franz, 1811-1886.
Wagner-Liszt album
see under Wagner, Richard, 1813-1883.

M786.47 L77ln Music lib. **Liszt, Franz, 1811-1886.**
Waldesrauschen (Forest murmers) for piano solo. New York, E. F. Kalmus ⌊n.d.⌋
10p. port. (on cover) 32cm. (Kalmus Piano Series)

Cover title.
Concert etude.

I. Title. II. Title: Forest murmers.

NL 0406351 NcU

VOLUME 336

Liszt, Franz, 1811-1886.
M25 [Etudes, piano (1863) Waldesrauschen]
L77E8 Waldesrauschen (Rustling woods - Dans les
no.1 bois) London, Duff, Stewart, c1894.
1894 9 p. 36cm. (Celebrated piano solos, concert pieces, no. 1)

1.Piano music. I.Title: Waldesrauschen. II.Title: Rustling woods. III.Title: Dans les bois.

NL 0406352 CSt

Liszt, Franz, 1811-1886. 8050a.235.19
Waldesrauschen. [For pianoforte.]
(In The Century Library of Music. Vol. 19, Music, pp. 1536-1548. New York. 1902.)

F8330 — T.r. — Pianoforte. Music.

NL 0406353 MB

M
786.4 Liszt, Franz
L69W Waldesrauschen (Forest murmurs); revision, phrasing and fingering by Hans T. Seifert. Carl Fischer, c1905.
11 p.

NL 0406354 WaT FTaSU

Liszt, Frazn, 1811-1886, arr.
Walzer aus der Oper Margarete
see under Gounod, Charles Francois, 1818-1893.

Liszt, Franz, 1811-1886, arr.

M38
.5
.S Schubert, Franz Peter, 1797-1828. OTHER EDITIONS E MAIN ENTRY
[Der Wanderer, D. 493; arr.]

Der Wanderer; Lied, für das Piano-Forte übertragen von Fr. Liszt. Wien, A. Diabelli [18—] Pl. no. D. et C. no. 6541.

---

q785.2 Liszt, Franz, 1811-1886.
L69w Was man auf dem berge hört; symphonische dichtung no.1. What one hears on the mountains; symphonic poem no.1. A qu'on entend sur la montagne; poème symphonique no.1 ... [Leipzig, Breitkopf & Härtel, 18--?]
146p. (On cover: Breitkopf & Härtels partitur-bibliothek)
Caption title.
Full score.
Plate no.: Part.B. 2173.

1. Symphonies. I. Title.

NL 0406357 IU NBC

Liszt, Franz, 1811-1886, arr.
Wedding march
see under Mendelssohn-Barthddy, Felix, 1809-1847.

Liszt, Franz, 1811-1886.
[Weihnachtsbaum; arr.]

Weihnachtsbaum; 12 Clavierstücke (zumeist leichter Spielart) Berlin, A. Fürstner; New York, G. Schirmer, °1882.
3 v. 34 cm.
First ed. of Liszt arrangement for piano, 4 hands; originally for piano.
CONTENTS.—Psallite.—O heilige Nacht!—Die Hirten an der Krippe.—Adeste fideles.—Scherzoso.—Carillon.—Schlummerlied.—Altes provençalisches Weihnachtslied.—Abendglocken.—Ehemals!—Ungarisch.—Polnisch.
1. Piano music (4 hands), Arranged. 2. Christmas music. I. Title.

M3.3.L77W42 65-53168 rev/M

NL 0406359 DLC NcU MH

---

qM786.43 Liszt, Franz, 1811-1886.
L774w [Weihnachtsbaum. Selections]

Weihnachtsbaum. Christmas tree. Arbre de Noël. Pianoforte. [London, Hinrichsen Edition, Ltd., 1953]
score (2v.) [Hinrichsen ed. no. 88a-b]

Contents.-I. An old Christmas Carol.- II. Scherzoso.

1. Piano music 2. Christmas music. I. Title.

NL 0406360 ICarbS OrP OCl NSyU MB NIC WaU

M
785.7585 Liszt, Franz, 1811-1886.
L774w [Weihnachtslied; arr.]
Spr Weihnachtslied, old Provencial Christmas carol. Arr. by Albert Seay [for] woodwind quintet. Old Greenwich, Conn., Jack Spratt, c1952.
score ([2]p.) and 5 parts.

For flute, oboe, clarinet, horn, bassoon.

1. Wind quintets (Bassoon, clarinet, flute, horn, oboe), Arranged. 2. Christmas music.

NL 0406361 FTaSU

Liszt, Franz, 1811-1886.
Weimar's Volkslied. Zur Carl-August-Feier
Music (September 1857) gedichtet von Peter Cornelius,
L58 componirt von Franz Liszt. Für Männerchor mit
w858 Orchester ...
Weimar, Verlag und Eigenthum von T.F.A.Kühn [1858]
Publ.no.36. 25pp. 34cm.
Lithographed t.-p.; music printed from the plates
First sung on September 3, 1857, at the laying of the corner-stone of the Carl-August-Denkmal at Weimar.
This is the original edition.

NL 0406362 CtY

Film Liszt, Franz, 1811-1886.
12982

Weimar's Volkslied. Gedichtet von Peter Cornelius. Weimar, T.F.A.Kühn [1857?]
13p.

For voice and piano; also published in 5 other versions, including male chorus and winds. Cf. Grove.
Microfilm (negative) Washington, D.C., Library of Congress, 1969. 1 reel.
On reel with the composer's Gruss.

Leipzig [1885] - Gaudeamus igitur. Leipzig [1871] - Vierstimmige Männergesänge. Mainz [1843] - Festgesang. Leipzig [1887] - An die Künstler. Weimar, 1854. - An die Künstler. Leipzig [1856]

1. Songs (Medium voice) with piano. I. Title.

NL 0406364 IaU

Liszt, Franz, 1811-1886. 8057.151
Weimar's folk-song. [Part song, T. T. B. B.]
(In Boylston Club Collection . . . Pp. 88-93. Boston. 1875.)

F8025 — T.r. — Part songs.

NL 0406365 MB

Liszt, Franz, 1811-1886.
[Weinen, Klagen, Sorgen, Zagen]

Weinen, Klagen, Sorgen, Zagen; Praeludium nach Joh. Seb. Bach, für das Pianoforte. Berlin, Schlesinger'schen Buch-und Musikhandlung [1863] Pl. no. S. 4325.
5 p. 34 cm.
First ed.?

1. Piano music. I. Bach, Johann Sebastian, 1685-1750. Weinen, Klagen, Sorgen, Zagen. Weinen, Klagen, Sorgen, Zagen. II. Title.

M3.3.L77W44 64-59479/M

NL 0406366 DLC NN

Liszt, Franz, 1811-1886.
[Complete works for piano]
Werke; für klavier zu 2 händen, von Franz Liszt. Herausgegeben von Emil von Sauer. Leipzig, C. F. Peters [c1917-
12 v.
Contents.- v. 1-2. Ungarische Rhapsodien.- v. 3-4. Etüden.- v. 5-6. Original - Kompositionen.- v. 7-8. Bearbeitungen aus Opern.- v. 9. Lieder - Bearbeitungen.- v. 10. Bearbeitungen.- v. 11. Konzerte und andere Werke mit Orchester.- v. 12. Supplement.

1. Piano music. I. Sauer, Emil, arr. II. Title.

NL 0406368 MsSM OrP CLSU IEN OCl MtU

Mus
M
22 Liszt, Franz, 1811-1886.
.L77 [Works, piano]
Pe Werke für Klavier zu 2 Händen. Hrsg. von Emil von Sauer. London, New York, C. F. Peters [c1945-
v.

Contents.- Bd.1. Ungarische Rhapsodien, Nr. 1-8.- Bd.2. Ungarische Rhapsodien, Nr. 9-16.- Bd.3. Études d'exécution transcendante.- Bd.4. Paganini-Etüden. Drei Konzert-Etüden. Waldesrauschen. Gnomenreigen.- Bd.5. Polonaise I, C moll. Polonaise II, E dur. Ballade I. Ballade II. Mephisto-Walzer I. Valse-Impromptu. Première valse oubliée. Grand galop chromatique Consolations. Deux légendes.- Bd.6. Liebesträume Harmonies poétiques et religieuses. Berceuse. Années de pèlerinage. Venezia e Napoli. Sonate, B minor.- Bd.7. Arrangements from Wagner's operas: Rienzi, Tannhäuser, Lohengrin, Der fliegende Holländer, Tristan und Isolde, Die Meistersinger von Nürnberg, Der Ring des Nibelungen, Parsifal.- Bd.8. Arrangements from operas and other works: Mozart, Don Juan; Gounod, Faust; Verdi, Rigoletto & Trovatore; Bellini, Norma; Auber, Stumme von Portici; Mendelssohn, Sommernachtstraum; Donizetti, Lucia; Rossini, Stabat Mater.- Bd.9. Lieder arrangements from: Schubert, Schumann, Beethoven, Chopin, Lassen, Liszt, Mendelssohn.- Bd.10. Soirées de Vienne, Valse-Caprices

Continued in next column

VOLUME 336

Continued from preceding column

d'après Schubert. Sechs Präludien und Fugen für Orgel von J.S. Bach. Variationen über den Basso continuo der Kantate Weinen, Klagen etc. von J.S. Bach. Orgel-Phantasie und Fuge in G moll von J.S. Bach. Soirées musicales de Rossini (Nr.2,9). Bd.11. Konzert, Eb major, Konzert, A major. Danse macabre (Totentanz). Phantasie über ungarische Volksmelodien. Schubert: Phantasie op.15. Weber: Polonaise brillante op.72. Bd.12. Arrangements: Wagner, Tannhäuser-Ouvertüre; Meyerbeer, Die Schlittschauhläufer; Liszt, Gretchen; Schubert, Op.40 (nos. 5,3), Op.121 (no.1); Originalwerke: Liszt, Scherzo und Marsch, Phantasie und Fuge über das Thema BACH.-

NL 0406373 FTaSU KU IEN OO

Liszt, Franz, 1811–1886.
[Works, piano]

Werke für Klavier zu 2 Händen; hrsg. von Emil von Sauer. Leipzig, C. F. Peters [1949– Pl. no. 9683–
v. 31 cm. (Edition Peters, Nr. 3600a
Includes thematic indexes.
CONTENTS.—Bd. 1–2. Rhapsodien.

1. Piano music. 2. Liszt, Franz—Thematic catalogs. I. Sauer, Emil Georg Konrad, Ritter von Aichried, 1862–1942, ed.

M22.L77S34 52—39775

NL 0406374 DLC OU GEU KU AAP MB NBC CSt MiU OOxM TU FTaSU CoU WaU NSyU OrP TxU

ML96 L58 Case

Liszt, Franz, 1811-1886, arr.

[Schumann, Robert Alexander] 1810–1856.
[Myrthen. Widmung; arr.]

Widmung. [186-?]

LISZT, FRANZ, 1811-1886.
[SOIRÉES DE VIENNE. No. 6]
Wiener Abende nach Fr. Schubert; Walzer-Caprices, Nr. 6. [Hrsg. von Eugen d'Albert] Berlin, E. Bote & G. Bock [c1917] 15 p. 34cm. (Liszt-d'Albert Ausgabe. Nr. 49)
Microfilm.
At head of title: Ausgabe Eugen d'Albert.
For piano.

1. Waltzes (Piano). I. Schubert, Franz, 1797-1828. II. Title.

NL 0406376 NN

M3 .3 .L77W55 Case

Liszt, Franz, 1811-1886, arr.

Schubert, Franz Peter, 1797–1828.
[Die Winterreise; arr.]

Winterreise. Wien, T. Haslinger [1839] Pl. no. T. H. 7765–7774.

MUSIC m780.3 L774m

Liszt, Franz, 1811-1886.
[Es muss ein Wunderbares sein]
A wondrous rapture must it be (Es muss ein Wunderbares sein.) Philadelphia, Oliver Ditson [c1911]
score (3p.) 31cm. (Songs of Franz Liszt)
For voice (High in Eb) and piano. Words in English and German.
Found (in the Musicians library) Thirty songs by Franz Liszt. Edited by Carl Armbruster.

1.Songs (High voice) with piano.
1.Title.

NL 0406378 CLSU

M1619 S69 v.648

Liszt, Franz, 1811-1886.
[Es muss ein Wunderbares sein, acc. piano]
A wondrous thing 't must be indeed. (Es muss ein Wunderbares sein) [Text by O. von Redwitz. New York] G.Schirmer, c1876. Pl.no.1773.
3 p. 35cm. (The most favorite songs by Franz Liszt, no.8)
Caption title.
English and German text.
No. 3 in a vol.lettered: Songs, v.648.

1.Title. II.Title: A wondrous thing 't must be indeed.

NL 0406379 CSt ViU

Liszt, Franz, 1811-1886. 4049a.422
Die Zigeuner und ihre Musik in Ungarn. Deutsch bearbeitet von Peter Cornelius.
Mainz. Schott. [1861.] (3), 259, (1) pp. 18½ cm., in 8s.

L5943 — Gypsies. F.a. Music. — Hungary. F.a. Music. — Cornelius, Carl August Peter, tr., 1824-1874.

NL 0406380 MB OCH OCl

Liszt, Franz, 1811–1886.
Die Zigeuner und ihre Musik in Ungarn. Deutsch bearb. von Peter Cornelius. Pesth, G. Heckenast, 1861.
259 p. 19 cm.

1. Gipsies. 2. Folk music, Gipsy—Hist. & crit. 3. Folk music, Hungarian—Hist. & crit. I. Title.

ML410.L7A185 8–12990*

NL 0406381 DLC NN OCl OCH MdBP NIC

Liszt, Franz, 1811-1886
Die zigeuner und ihre musik in Ungarn; in das deutsche übertragen von L. Ramann. xii,396p. Leipzig, Breitkopf und Härtel, 1883. (His Gesammelte schriften, hrsg. von L. Ramann, v.6)

NL 0406382 OCl KAS IU MH OCH

Liszt, Franz, 1811-1886. Mus 737.1.201
Zur säcular-feier Beethovens; cantate, gedichtet von Adolf Stern. Componirt für chor, soli, und orchester. Instrumental-einleitung. Leipzig, C. F. Kahnt, [187-].
l. 8°. pp. 55.

NL 0406383 MH ICN

Liszt, Franz, 1811–1886.
Zur Säcular-Feier Beethovens. Cantate gedichtet von Adolf Stern, componirt für Chor, Soli und Orchester von Franz Liszt. Zum erstenmal aufgeführt bei der Tonkünstler Versammlung in Weimar am 29. Mai 1870... Leipzig: C. F. Kahnt [1870]. 59 p. 4°.
Vocal score. German words.
Cover-title: Beethoven-Cantate...

BEETHOVEN ASSOCIATION FUND.
1. Cantatas. 2. Beethoven, Ludwig van. 3. Stern, Adolf Ernst, 1835-1907.
N. Y. P. L. October 10, 1923.

NL 0406384 NN MB

Liszt, Franz, 1811-1886.
Zur Säcular-Feier Beethovens. Cantate. Gedichtet von Adolf Stern, componirt für Chor, Soli und Orchester von Franz Liszt. Partitur.
— Leipzig. Kahnt. [1870.] 184 pp. 26½ cm. **M.435.66
Same. [Klavierauszug.] 59 pp. No. 1 in **M.194.21

L7890 — Double main card. — Liszt, Franz. (M1) — Stern, Adolf Ernst, 1835-1907. (M2) — Cantatas. (1) — Beethoven, Ludwig van. (1)

NL 0406385 MB

M1621 L57A6

Liszt, Franz, 1811-1886.
[Songs. Selections]
20 [i.e. Zwanzig] ausgewählte Lieder, für eine Singstimme mit Klavierbegleitung. Revidiert von Eugen d'Albert. Leipzig, C.F.Kahnt Nachfolger [1908]
2v.in 1. 27cm.

"In die Collection Litolff aufgenommen."
Texts in German, French and English.
Bound with: Cornelius, Peter. Brautlieder. Leipzig, n.d.- Schiegg, Anton, ed. Das erste Liedstudium. München, 1921.- Koschat, Thomas. Songs. Selections. Leipzig, n.d.

1. Songs (Medium voice) with piano. I. Albert Eugen d', 1864-1932, ed.

NL 0406387 IaU

Liszt, Franz, 1811–1886.
[Études, piano (1863)]

Zwei Concertetüden für die grosse Clavierschule von Lebert u. Stark. Berlin, T. Trautwein; New York, G. Schirmer, °1871.
2 v. 34 cm.
L. C. set incomplete: v. 1 wanting.
CONTENTS.—1. Waldesrauschen. 2. Gnomenreigen.

1. Piano music. I. Title: Concertetüden für die grosse Clavierschule von Lebert u. Stark.

M25.L 64–59750/M

NL 0406388 DLC NcU

Liszt, Franz, 1811–1886.
Zwei Episoden aus Lenau's Faust. N°. 1. Der nächtliche Zug. N°. 2. Der Tanz in der Dorfschenke (Mephisto Walzer). Für grosses Orchester, von Franz Liszt... Partitur... Leipzig: J. Schuberth & C°. [1865–66.] Publ. pl. no. 4004, 4005. 2 v. in 1. f°.
Full score.
With this is bound: H. Berlioz, Grande ouverture de Waverley. Op. 1. Paris [183–?].

BOEKELMAN COLLECTION.
1. Orchestra (Full).—Overtures. 2. Lenau, Nicolaus, pseud. of N. F. Niembsch, Edler von Strehlenau, 1802–50.
N. Y. P. L. October 7, 1918.

NL 0406389 NN MH MB

Liszt, Franz, 1811–1886.
...Zwei Etuden, von Franz v. Liszt... [Berlin: M. Bahn, ca. 1870]. Publ. pl. no. 24. 2 v. in 1. f°.
Caption-title. t.-p. reads: Études et pièces de concert de maitres célèbres pour piano... no. 9–10...
Contents: 1. Waldesrauschen. 2. Gnomenreigen.

1. Piano. 2. Title: Waldesrauschen. 3. Title: Gnomenreigen.
N. Y. P. L. July 1, 1927

NL 0406390 NN

M 1010 L77A2

Liszt, Franz, 1811-1886.
[Concertos, piano]

Zwei Konzerte für Pianoforte. Leipzig, E. Eulenburg [19--?] Pl. nos. E.E.3814, 3265.
miniature score (2 v. in 1) port. 19cm. (Eulenburgs kleine Partitur-Ausgabe)

Contents.--[1] Konzert No.1, Es dur.--[2] Zweites Konzert, A dur.

1. Concertos (Piano)--Scores.

NL 0406391 NIC OCU

VOLUME 336

Liszt, Franz, 1811–1886.
...Zwei Konzertetüden. [Von] Franz Liszt, hrsg. von Eugen d'Albert. Berlin: E. Bote & G. Bock, cop. 1917. Publ. pl. nos. B. & B. 18556–18557. 2 v. in 1. f°.

Caption-title. t.-p. reads: Ausgabe Eugen d'Albert. Franz Liszt. Ausgewählte Klavierwerke... No. 9–10.
Contents: 1. Waldesrauschen. 2. Gnomenreigen.

1. Piano. 2. D'Albert, Eugen, 1864– , editor.
N. Y. P. L. September 18, 1924

NL 0406392 NN

M
786.43
L699l
Liszt, Franz, 1811-1886.
[Légendes, piano]
Zwei Legenden. Neurevision von Ignaz Friedman. Wien, Universal-Edition [n.d.] Pl. no. U.E. 5875, 5984, 5939.
25 p. 30cm. (His Klavierwerke)

Contents.- Des hl. Franziskus von Assisi Vogelpredigt.- Der hl. Franziskus von Paula über die Wogen schreitend.
1. Piano music. I. T: Légendes.

NL 0406393 MiDW

Liszt, Franz, 1811–1886.
[Christus. Hirtengesang an der Krippe]
Zwei Orchestersätze aus dem Oratorium Christus. Leipzig, New York, J. Schurberth [1872– Pl. no. 4934–
v. 32 cm.
First ed.
CONTENTS.—no. 1. Hirtenspiel.

1. Oratorios—Excerpts—Scores. 2. Orchestral music—Scores.
M3.3.L77C5 64-46922/M

NL 0406394 DLC

Liszt, Franz, 1811–1886.
[Christus. Hirtengesang an der Krippe; arr.]
Zwei Orchestersätze aus dem Oratorium Christus. Clavierauszug zu 4 Händen v. Componisten. Leipzig, New York, J. Schuberth [1873– Pl. no. 5066–
v. 32 cm.
First ed.
Arr. for piano, 4 hands.
CONTENTS.—no. 1. Hirtenspiel.

1. Piano music (4 hands), Arranged. 2. Oratorios—Excerpts, Arranged.
M3.3.L77C5 a 64-46923/M

NL 0406395 DLC

Liszt, Franz, 1811–1886.
[Christus. Hirtengesang an der Krippe]
Zwei Orchestersätzer aus dem Oratorium Christus. Leipzig, C. F. Kahnt Nachfolger [190–] Pl. no. 4934.
score (2 v.) 34 cm.
L. C. set incomplete: v. 1 wanting.
Reissued from Schuberth plates.
CONTENTS.—No. 1. Histenspiel.—No. 2. Marsch: Die heiligen drei Könige.
1. Oratorios—Excerpts—Scores. 2. Orchestral music—Scores. I. Liszt, Franz, 1811-1886. Christus. Die heiligen drei Könige.
M2004.L55C54 65-77564/M

NL 0406396 DLC

M3
.3
.L77 I 25
Case
Liszt, Franz, 1811-1886, arr.
Wagner, Richard, 1813–1883.
[Tannhäuser. Einzug der Gäste; arr.]
Zwei Stücke aus R. Wagner's Tannhäuser und Lohengrin. Für das Pianoforte von Franz Liszt. Leipzig, Breitkopf & Härtel [1853] Pl. no. 8706–8707.

Liszt, Franz, 1811–1886.
Zwei Vortragsstücke (Introitus — Trauerode) für die Orgel, komponiert von Franz Liszt. Hrsg. von A. W. Gottschalg... Leipzig: C. F. W. Siegel [ca. 1890]. Publ. pl. no. 9196. 8 p. ob. 8°.

1. Organ. 2. Gottschalg, Alexander Wilhelm, 1827–1908, editor.
N. Y. P. L. April 17, 1918

NL 0406398 NN

Liszt, Franz, 1811-1886.
[Elegy, violin & piano, no. 2]
2te. Elegie an L. Ramann. [1877?] score ([6] l.) 33 x 24 cm.

Holograph in ink with additional marks in red ink and colored pencils. Includes two drafts both preceding and following the final version. Caption title appears l. [1] and l. [2] Dedicated to Lina Ramann. First published: Leipzig, C. F. Kahnt, 1878.

Searle no. 131; Raabe 472; Walker 354.

1. Music - Manuscripts. 2. Violin and piano music.

NL 0406400 NN

---

q785
L69z
Liszt, Franz, 1811-1886.
Zweite polonaise für grosses orchester bearb. von Carl Müller-Berghaus. Leipzig, Bartholf Senff, n.d.
71p.

Partitur.

NL 0406401 IU MB

Liszt, Franz, 1811–1886.
[Polonaise, piano, no. 2, E major; arr.]
Zweite Polonaise. Für Militärmusik bearb. von C. Hellmann. Leipzig, B. Senff, °1899.
score (46 p.) 34 cm.
For band.

1. Band music, Arranged—Scores. 2. Polonaises (Band)
M1258.L 79-274528

NL 0406402 DLC

VM
1060
L 77u2
M 94
LISZT, FRANZ, 1811-1886.
[Ungarische rhapsodie no.2, D minor]
Zweite ungarische rhapsodie, componiert von Franz Liszt. Für grosses orchester, bearbeitet von Karl Müller-Berghaus. Berlin, N. Simrock g.m.b.h. [n.d.]
61p.

Full score.
Plate no.: 21102.

NL 0406403 ICN

---

*
M1
.S444
v.41,
42
no.15
Liszt, Franz, 1811-1886.
[Rhapsodie hongroise, piano, no. 2; arr.]

Zweite Ungarische Rhapsodie für Violine, mit Begleitung des Pianoforte zum Concert-vortrag bearb. von Hans Sitt. Arrangement für 2 Pianoforte zu 8 Händen. Leipzig, Bartholf Senff [18—] Pl. no. 1524.
21, 21 p. 34cm. [Sheet music collection v. 41, 42, no. 15]
Corresponding parts in the two volumes.
1. Piano music (2 pianos, 8 hands), Arranged. I. Title: Ungarische Rhapsodie.

NL 0406404 ViU

Liszt, Franz, 1811–1886.
Zweite ungarische Rhapsodie, componirt von Franz Liszt. Für grosses Orchester bearbeitet von Karl Müller-Berghaus. Leipzig: B. Senff [1878]. Publ. pl. no. 1102. 64 p. 4°.

Arranged for full orchestra.
Full score.

ARTHUR MEES COLLECTION.
1. Orchestra (Full).—Misc. 2. Mueller-Berghaus, Karl, 1829–1907, editor.
N. Y. P. L. June 16, 1924

NL 0406405 NN MB

Liszt, Franz, 1811–1886.
[Rhapsodie hongroise, piano, no. 2. Arr. for violin & piano]
Zweite ungarische Rhapsodie. Für Violine mit Begleitung des Pianoforte zum Concertvortrag bearbeitet von Hans Sitt... Erleichterte Ausgabe für Violine mit Pianoforte... Leipzig, B. Senff [1880] Pl.no. 1513. 1 v. 35cm.
Score (19 p.) and violin part.

1. Violin and piano—Arr. I. Sitt, Hans, 1850–1922, arr.

NL 0406406 NN OU

Liszt, Franz, 1811–1886.
Zweite ungarische Rhapsodie, componirt von Franz Liszt. Für Violine mit Begleitung des Pianoforte zum Concertvortrag, bearbeitet von Hans Sitt... Arrangement für Pianoforte zu 4 Händen, Violine und Violoncell... Leipzig: B. Senff [ca. 1881]. Publ. pl. no. 1639. 3 parts in 1 v. f°.

Arranged for piano, 4 hands, violin and violoncello.
Piano, 4 hands, and violin and violoncello parts.

BOEKELMAN COLLECTION.
1. Piano, 3 hands, etc., with various instruments. 2. Sitt, Hans, 1850– .
N. Y. P. L. May 20, 1919.

NL 0406407 NN MB

M785
L69r2
191-
Liszt, Franz, 1811-1886.
[Rhapsodies hongroises, piano. No.2, arr.]
Zweite Ungarische Rhapsodie. Für grosses orchester bearb. von Karl Müller-Berghaus. Berlin, N. Simrock; sole agents for the U.S.A.: T. B. Harms Co., New York [191-?] Pl. no. 21102.
miniature score(64p.) 27cm.

Originally for piano.

NL 0406408 IU NIC

LISZT, FRANZ, 1811-1886.
[RHAPSODIE HONGROISE, PIANO, NO. 2. ARR. FOR 2 PIANOS]
II. Ungarische Rhapsodie. Second Hungarian rhapsody. 2 Pianoforte zu 8 Händen. [Arr.] Richard Kleinmichel. [Rev. Oscar Seyfferth] Leipzig, N. Simrock [192-?] Pl. no. 21524. 2 parts. 31cm. (Elite Edition. No. 823 (S.))

Title also in French.
1. Piano (2 pianos)--Arr. I. Kleinmichel, Richard, 1846-1901, arr. i [Title] Zweites.

NL 0406409 NN

Liszt, Franz, 1811–1886.
[Mephisto-Walzer, no. 2, orchestra; arr.]
2ter [i. e. Zweiter] Mephisto Walzer. Berlin, A. Fürstner; New York, G. Schirmer [°1881]
29 p. 34 cm.
First ed. of the composer's piano arrangement.

1. Waltzes (Piano) I. Title: Mephisto Walzer.
M3.3.L77M52 64-46166/M

NL 0406410 DLC CtY

VOLUME 336

Liszt, Franz, 1811-1886
Mephisto Walzer, piano, no.2.
2ter Mephisto Walzer, componirt von Franz Liszt. Edited and revised by A. R. Parsons. [Berlin, Adolph Fürstner, 1881]
3-29p. 34cm., in case 37cm.
Caption title.
Proofs (engraved) with Liszt's ms. revisions & corrections throughout.
Plate no.: F.2178.

At foot of p.3: Copyright by G. Schirmer. 1881 Stich und Druck der Roder'schen Officin in Leipzig. Eigenthum von Adolph Fürstner Berlin.

NL 0406412 MH

Liszt, Franz, 1811-1886. Mus 737.1.187
2er Mephisto walzer. Orchester partitur. Berlin, A. Fürstner, etc. etc. cop. 1881.
l. 8°. pp. 88.

NL 0406413 MH MB

Liszt, Franz, 1811-1886.
2tes Concert [A-dur] Pianoforte und Orchester ... von F. Liszt... London: Schott & Co. [1863.] Publ. pl. no. 16617. Solo 37 p. f°.
Arranged for piano solo.

Concertos.—Piano and orchestra. 2. Piano.
N. Y. P. L.
HUNEKER COLLECTION. November 9, 1921

NL 0406414 NN IEN

Liszt, Franz, 1811-1886.
2tes Concert; Pianoforte und Orchester ... von F. Liszt. Mainz: B. Schott's Söhne [1863]. Publ. pl. no. 16617. 1 p.l., 84 p. f°.
Full score.

1. Concertos.—Piano and orchestra.
N. Y. P. L.
JULIAN EDWARDS COLL. May 1, 1916.

NL 0406415 NN OrP CtY MB MH CU

VAULT FOLIO M3.3 .L77 C62
Liszt, Franz, 1811-1886.
[Concerto, piano, no.2, A major; arr.]
2 tes [i.e. Zweites] concert [für] Pianoforte und Orchester von F. Liszt. Mainz, B. Schott's Söhnes [1863] Pl. no. 16617.
55p. 32cm.
First edition.

NL 0406416 NcU

7785.6 L69c2 1906
Liszt Franz, 1811-1886.
[Concerto, piano, no.2, A maj.]
... Zweites konzert (A dur) für pianoforte mit orchester ... Leipzig, E. Eulenburg [1906]
108p. (Eulenburg's kleine partitur-ausgabe. Konzerte. no.20)
Miniature score.
Plate no.: E.E.3265.

1. Concerto. 2. Pianoforte music.

NL 0406417 IU ICN CtY OrP

Liszt, Franz, 1811-86 (2)
Songs. Selections. Arr.
42 Lieder von L. van Beethoven [et al.] für das Pianoforte übertragen. Leipzig, Breitkopf & Härtel [187-]
Score (123 p.) (Volksausgabe Breitkopf & Härtel, 366)

NL 0406418 MH PP

Liszt, Franz, 1811–1886, *arr.*
42 lieder von Ludwig van Beethoven, Robert Franz, Felix Mendelssohn Bartholdy, Robert und Clara Schumann, für das pianoforte übertragen von Franz Liszt. Leipzig, Breitkopf & Härtel [1876]
1 p. l., 123 p. 31 x 23½ᶜᵐ.
Publisher's plate no.: V. A. 366.
For piano solo, with the words; originally for solo voice with piano accompaniment.
1. Piano music, Arranged.
45-34717
Library of Congress M38.5.L

NL 0406419 DLC MB NN OO CtY

M38 .5 .S
Liszt, Franz, 1811-1886, arr.
Schubert, Franz Peter, 1797-1828.
[Songs. Selections; arr.]
12 [i. e. Zwölf] Lieder, für das Pianoforte übertragen von Franz Liszt. Hamburg, A. Cranz [1880?]

M 786.4 L774a Kah
Liszt, Franz, 1811-1886.
[Works, piano. Selections]
12 [i.e. Zwölf] Klavierstücke. Neue revidierte Ausgabe von Eugen d'Albert. Leipzig, C. F. Kahnt Nachfolger, c1908. Pl. no. 5479.
score (81p.)
Contents - Die Loreley. Ave Maria. Zweite Elegie. Ave maris stella. Vor der Schlacht. Nicht gezagt. Es rufet Gott uns mahnend. Un soir dans la montagne, aus Trois morceaux suisses. Pastorale, aus Der entfesselte Prometheus. Einleitung, aus Die Legende von der heiligen Elisabeth. Marsch der Kreuzritter, aus Die Legende von der heiligen Elisabeth. Hirtengesang an der Krippe, aus dem Oratorium, Christus
1. Piano music. 2. Piano music, Arranged.

NL 0406421 FTaSU

M 1002 L77A2
Liszt, Franz, 1811-1886.
[Symphonic poems. Selections]
Zwölf symphonische Dichtungen. Leipzig, E. Eulenburg [19--?]
miniature score (3 v.) port. 19cm. (Eulenburg's kleine Orchester-Partitur-Ausgabe)
Contents.--Bd.1. Ce qu'on entend sur la montagne. Tasso, lamento e trionfo. Les Préludes. Orpheus.--Bd.2. Prometheus. Mazeppa Festklänge. Heldenklage. Bd.3. Hungaria. Hamlet. Hunnenschlacht. Die Ideale.
1. Symphonic poems--Scores.

NL 0406423 NIC OU IaU NcU

Liszt, Franz, 1811-1886.
Zur Schiller-Feier
see his Künstler-Festzug.

Liszt, Franz Eduard von
see Liszt, Franz von, 1851-1919.

4K 4960
Liszt, Franz von, 1851-1919.
Bedingte Verurteilung und bedingte Begnadigung. [Berlin, O. Liebman, 1908]
91 p.

NL 0406426 DLC-P4 MH-L

Liszt, Franz von, 1851–1919.
O Brazil na legislação penal comparada (direito criminal dos estados extra-europeus) do professor dr. Franz von Liszt, collaboração e traducção pelos professores drs. João Vieira de Araujo ... e Clovis Bevilaqua ... Rio de Janeiro, Imprensa nacional, 1911.
xv, 68 p., 1 l. 25ᶜᵐ.
Contains bibliographies.
Contents.—1. ptie. Les Brésil dans la législation pénale comparée (droit criminel des États extra-européens) de mr. le prof. dr. Franz von Liszt.—2. ptie. O Brazil na legislação penal comparada (direito criminal dos estados extra-europeus) do professor dr. Franz von Liszt, traducção do dr. Clovis Bevilaqua.
1. Comparative law. 2. Criminal law—Brazil. I. Vieira de Araujo, João, 1844– ed. and tr. II. Bevilaqua, Clovis, 1859– joint ed. and tr. III. Title.
25—24640

NL 0406427 DLC DPU

Liszt, Franz von, 1851–
Die deliktsobligationen im system des Bürgerlichen gesetzbuchs. Kritische und dogmatische randbemerkungen, von dr. Franz v. Liszt ... Berlin, J. Guttentag, 1898.
vi, [2], 114 p. 23½ᶜᵐ. (*Added t.-p.:* Das recht des Bürgerlichen gesetzbuchs in einzeldarstellungen. VIII)
12-4120

NL 0406428 DLC

Liszt, Franz von, 1851–1919.
Derecho internacional público, por el Dr. Franz von Liszt ... Obra revisada por el Dr. Max Fleischmann ... Versión de la 12. ed. alemana por el Dr. Domingo Miral ... Barcelona, G. Gili, 1929.
4 p. l., 712 p. 25½ᶜᵐ.
1. International law and relations. I. Fleischmann, Max, 1872– ed. II. Miral y López, Domingo, tr. III. Title.
30-6992
Library of Congress JX3445.V48
Copyright A—Foreign 5598

NL 0406429 DLC UU

LISZT, [Franz] von, 1851-1919.
Die deterministischen gegner der zweckstrafe Berlin, n.d.
46 p.

NL 0406430 MH-L

Liszt, Franz von, 1851–1919.
Das deutsche reichs-pressrecht, unter berücksichtigung der literatur und der rechtsprechung, insbesondere des Berliner Obertribunals und des Reichsgerichtes, systematisch dargestellt von dr. Franz Eduard von Liszt ... Berlin und Leipzig, J. Guttentag, 1880.
xvi p., 1 l., 236 p. 17ᶜᵐ. (*Added t.-p.:* Lehrbücher des deutschen reichsrechtes. VIII)
1. Press law—Germany. 2. Law reports, digests, etc.—Germany. I. Title.
34-34082

NL 0406431 DLC MH

LISZT, Franz von, 1851-1919.
Das deutsche reichsstrafrecht auf grund des reichsstrafgesetzbuchs und der übrigen strafrechtlichen reichsgesetze... systematisch dargestellt. Berlin, Leipzig, 1881.
"Lehrbücher des deutschen reichsrechtes, VII"

NL 0406432 MH-L

VOLUME 336

Liszt, Franz von, 1851- ed.

Deutsche strafrechts-zeitung. Zentralorgan für das gesamte strafrecht, strafprozessrecht und die verwandten gebiete in wissenschaft und praxis des in- und auslandes ... 1.- jahrg.; apr. 1914-
Berlin, O. Liebmann, 1914-

Liszt, Franz von, 1851-1919.
Le droit international; exposé systématique par Franz von Liszt ... traduction française d'après la 9e édition allemande (1913) par Gilbert Gidel ... avec le concours de Léon Alcindor ... avant-propos de James Brown Scott. Paris, A. Pédone, 1927.
xii, 400 p. 25cm. (Half-title: Publications de la Dotation Carnegie pour la paix internationale. Division de droit international, Washington)
Cover dated: 1928.
1. International law and relations. I. Gidel, Gilbert Charles, 1880- tr. II. Alcindor, Léon, joint tr.
29-1657
Library of Congress JX3445.V43

NL 0406434 DLC OU ODW OCU MiU OOxM OC1W OO ICU NN NjP ViU NjR TU NcU MtU WaU OrPR

Liszt, Fránz von, 1851-

Das englische gesicht; England in kultur, wirtschaft und geschichte, von M. Frischeisen-Köhler [u. a.] ... Berlin [etc.] Ullstein & co., 1915.

Liszt, Franz von, 1851-1919.
Die falsche Aussage vor Gericht oder öffentlicher Behörde nach deutschen und österreichischem Recht. Graz, Leuschner & Lubensky, 1877.
xvii, 254 p. 21 cm.
"Abgekürzt angeführte Literatur": p. [xi]-xvii.
1. Perjury—Germany. 2. Perjury—Austria.
48-35528*

NL 0406436 DLC MH CtY-L

Liszt, Franz, 1851-1919.
Festschrift. Franz von Liszt, zum 60. Geburtstage ...
see under title

4K 1244 Liszt, Franz von, 1851-1919.
Die Gefängnisarbeit. Vortrag gehalten am 26. Juli 1900. Berlin, J. Guttentag, 1900.
20 p.
(Sammlung gemeinverständlicher Vorträge)

NL 0406438 DLC-P4

Liszt, Franz von, 1851- joint author.

Kahl, Wilhelm, 1849-
Gegenentwurf zum Vorentwurf eines deutschen strafgesetzbuchs, aufgestellt von ... W. Kahl ... F. v. Liszt ... K. v. Lilienthal ... J. Goldschmidt ... Berlin, J. Guttentag, g. m. b. h., 1911.

Liszt, Franz von, 1851-1919.
Der Gesetzentwurf über das Verfahren gegen Jugendliche. (In: Centralverband des Deutschen Bank- und Bankiergewerbes. E. V. Festgabe zum 60. Geburtstage des Herrn Geheimen Justizrats Professor Dr. Riesser. Berlin, 1913. 8°. p. 114-135.)
1. Criminals (Juvenile).—Jurisprudence, Germany.
N. Y. P. L. August 6, 1914.

NL 0406440 NN

Liszt, Franz von, 1851-1919.
Die grenzgebiete zwischen privatrecht und strafrecht. Kriminalistische bedenken gegen den Entwurf eines Bürgerlichen gesetzbuches für das Deutsche reich. Von dr. Franz von Liszt ... Berlin und Leipzig, Verlag von J. Guttentag (D. Collin) 1889.
3 p. l., 46 p. 23cm. (Added t.-p.: Beiträge zur erläuterung und beurtheilung des Entwurfes eines Bürgerlichen gesetzbuches für das Deutsche reich ... 5. hft.

NL 0406441 MiU-L NcD MH

Liszt, Franz von, 1851-1919.
Lipmann, Otto, 1880-
Grundriss der psychologie für juristen, von Otto Lipmann, mit einem vorwort von Franz von Liszt. 2. veränderte und verm. aufl. Leipzig, J. A. Barth, 1914.

Liszt, Franz von, 1851-1919.

Melczer, Karl.
... Grundzüge des völkerrechtes, unter berücksichtigung der friedensverträge für studienzwecke zusammengestellt nach v. Liszt und Strisower, von dr. Karl Melczer. Wien-Leipzig, C. W. Stern, 1922.

Liszt, Franz von, 1851-1919.
Der italienische Strafgesetzentwurf von 1887 (Entwurf Zanardelli) I. Buch. Allgemeiner Teil, kritisch besprochen Freiburg i. B., Mohr, 1888.
x, 49 p. 22 cm. (Abhandlungen des Kriminalistischen Seminars zu Marburg, 1. Bd., 1. Heft)
1. Criminal law—Italy. I. Title. (Series: Berlin. Universität. Kriminalistisches Institut. Abhandlungen, 1. Bd., 1. Heft)
60-58048

NL 0406444 DLC MiU-L MH

Liszt, Franz von, 1851-1919.
Der italienische Strafgesetzentwurf von 1887 (Entwurf Zanardelli). I. Buch. Allgemeiner Theil kritisch besprochen von Dr. Franz von Liszt... (In: Berlin. Univ. Kriminalistisches Institut. Abhandl. Freiburg i. B., 1889. Bd. [1.] p. 1-49. 8°.)
1. Criminal law—Italy, 1887.
N. Y. P. L. March 29, 1927

NL 0406445 NN MH

Liszt, Franz von, 1851-1919
... A jövö büntetöjoga. Irta Dr Liszt Ferencz ... Budapest, Franklin-Társulat könyvnyomdája, 1892.
52 p. 21½cm. (Magyar jogászegyleti értekezések, 76. VIII. köt. 5. füz.)
"Felolvastatott a Magyar jogászegylet és a Nemzetközi büntetöügyi egyesület Magyarországi osztályának 1892. április 4-én a Budapesti kir. törvényszék eskűdtszéki termében tartott együttes ülésén."
German translation: p. [26]-52.

NL 0406447 MH-L

Liszt, Franz von, 1851-1919.
Lässt das Zwangserziehungs-Gesetz Verbesserungen wünschenswerth erscheinen?
[n. p., 1887?]
24 p. 21.5 cm.
Caption title.

NL 0406448 MH-L

Liszt, Franz von, 1851-1919, ed.
Internationale kriminalistische vereinigung.
La legislación penal comparada, publicada por acuerdo de la Unión internacional de derecho penal, con el concurso de eminentes penalistas, por el doctor Franz von Liszt ... Tomo I: El derecho criminal de los estados europeos, traducido de la edición francesa por d. Adolfo Posada ... Madrid, Administración de la Revista de medicina y cirugía prácticas; [etc., etc.] 1896.

Law

Liszt, Franz von, 1851-1919, ed.
Internationale Kriminalistische Vereinigung.
La législation pénale comparée. 1er v. Le droit criminel des états européens [édité par Franz von Liszt] Berlin, O. Liebmann, 1894.

LISZT, Franz von, 1851-
Lehrbuch des deutschen strafrechts. 3te auf. Berlin und Leipzig, 1888.

NL 0406451 MH-L

Liszt, Franz von, 1851-1919.
Lehrbuch des deutschen strafrechts. Von dr. Franz von Liszt ... 4. durchgearb. aufl. Berlin, J. Guttentag, 1891.
xxiv, 696 p. 22cm.
Includes bibliographies.
1. Criminal law—Germany. I. Title.
40-18970

NL 0406452 DLC

4K Ger. 1971 Liszt, Franz von, 1851-1919.
Lehrbuch des deutschen Strafrechts. 5. durchgearb. Aufl. Berlin, J. Guttentag, 1892.
xxv, 710 p.

NL 0406453 DLC-P4 NN

Liszt, Franz von, 1851-1919.
Lehrbuch des deutschen Strafrechts. 7. durchgearb. Aufl. Berlin, J. Guttentag, 1896.
xxv, 694 p. 23 cm.
Includes bibliographies.
1. Criminal law—Germany. I. Title.
70-228763

NL 0406454 DLC

4K Ger. 2314 Liszt, Franz von, 1851-1919.
Lehrbuch des deutschen Strafrechts. 9. durchgearb. Aufl. Berlin, J. Guttentag, 1899.
719 p.

NL 0406455 DLC-P4

Liszt, Franz von, 1851-1919.
Lehrbuch des deutschen strafrechts. Von dr. Franz von Liszt ... 10. durchgearbeitete aufl. Berlin, J. Guttentag, 1900.
xxvi, 678 p. 22cm.
Includes bibliographies.
1. Criminal law—Germany. I. Title.
40-18971

NL 0406456 DLC MH CtY

VOLUME 336

Liszt, Franz von, 1851–1919.
Lehrbuch des deutschen strafrechts. Von dr. Franz v. Liszt ... 12. und 13. völlig durchgearbeitete aufl. Berlin, J. Guttentag, 1903.
xxvi, 689, [1] p. 22½cm.
Bibliography: p. [xxiv]–xxvi.

1. Criminal law—Germany. I. Title.

5-13056

NL 0406457 DLC

4K Ger 1108
Liszt, Franz von, 1851-1919
Lehrbuch des deutschen Strafrechts. 14. und 15., völlig durchgearbeitete Aufl. Berlin, J. Guttentag, 1905.
694 p.

NL 0406458 DLC-P4 CU

Liszt, Franz von, 1851–1919.
Lehrbuch des deutschen strafrechts. Von dr. Franz v. Liszt ... 16. und 17., völlig durchgearbeitete aufl. (26.–30. tausend.) Berlin, J. Guttentag, 1908.
xxiv, 689, [1] p. 22cm.
"Literatur" at the beginning of each section.

1. Criminal law—Germany.

41-34759

NL 0406459 DLC MH

Liszt, Franz von, 1851–
Lehrbuch des deutschen strafrechts. Von dr. Franz v. Liszt ... 18., völlig durchgearb. aufl. (30.–32. tausend.) Berlin, J. Guttentag, 1911.
xxvii, 708 p. 23½cm.
Contains bibliographies.

11-29911

Library of Congress

NL 0406460 DLC

4K Ger 1288
Liszt, Franz von, 1851-1919.
Lehrbuch des deutschen Strafrechts. 20., völlig durchgearb. Aufl. Berlin, J. Guttentag, 1914.
714 p.

NL 0406461 DLC-P4 MH-L NcD-L

Liszt, Franz von, 1851–1919.
Lehrbuch des deutschen strafrechts. Von dr. Franz Liszt ... 21. und 22. völlig durchgearb. aufl. (37.–40. tausend). Berlin und Leipzig, Vereinigung wissenschaftlicher verleger W. de Gruyter & co., 1919.
xxvi, 698 p. 22½cm.
Each paragraph has bibliography.
"Abkürzungen": p. [xxiii]–xxvi.

I. Title.

20-20406

NL 0406462 DLC CtY

4K Ger. 1300
Liszt, Franz von, 1851-1919.
Lehrbuch des deutschen Strafrechts. 23. Aufl. nach dem Tode des Verfassers besorgt von Eberhard Schmidt. Berlin, Vereinigung wissenschaftlicher Verleger, 1921.
732 p.

NL 0406463 DLC-P4 MiU-L

Liszt, Franz von, 1851–1919.
Lehrbuch des deutschen strafrechts, von dr. Franz v. Liszt ... 25. vollkommen durchgearbeitete und zum teil umgestaltete aufl. (46.–48. tausend) besorgt von dr. Eberhard Schmidt ... Mit einem bildnis Franz von Liszts. Berlin und Leipzig, W. de Gruyter & co., 1927.
xxxiv, 976 p. front. (port.) 23cm.
Contains bibliographies.

1. Criminal law—Germany. I. Schmidt, Eberhard, 1891– ed. II. Title.

28-25891

NL 0406464 DLC IU CtY OU

Liszt, Franz von, 1851–1919.
Lehrbuch des deutschen strafrechts, von dr. Franz v. Liszt .. 26., völlig neubearb. aufl. (49.–51. tausend) von dr. Eberhard Schmidt ... Berlin und Leipzig, W. de Gruyter & co., 1932–
v. 22½cm.
"Abkürzungen" (bibliography): v. 1, p. [xvi]–xx. "Literatur" at beginning of most of the chapters.
CONTENTS.—1. bd. Einleitung und allgemeiner teil.

1. Criminal law—Germany. I. Schmidt, Eberhard, 1891– ed.

42-44127

NL 0406465 DLC NBuU-L

Liszt, Franz von, 1851–
Lehrbuch des österreichischen pressrechts, von dr. Franz von Liszt ... Leipzig, Breitkopf und Härtel, 1878.
xx, 400 p. 23cm.

11-31246

NL 0406466 DLC

LISZT, Franz von, 1851-1919.
Meineid und falsches zeugniss: eine straf-rechtsgeschichtliche studie. Wien, 1876.

NL 0406467 MH-L

Liszt, Franz von, 1851-1919.
Ett mellaneuropeiskt statsförbund såsom den tyska utrikespolitikens närmaste mal ... Stockholm [1914]
54 p. 20.5 cm.
(Mellan krig och fred, 2)
A translation of his "Ein mitteleuropäischer Staatenverband als nächstes Ziel der deutschen auswärtigen Politik."

NL 0406468 CtY

Law

Liszt, Franz von, 1851–1919.
Международное право въ систематическомъ изложеніи. Подъ ред. В. Э. Грабаря перевелъ со 2., совершенно перер. изд. М. Мебель. Съ дополненіями редактора и Очеркомъ частнаго международнаго права, сост. А. А. Пиленко. Юрьевъ, Изд. М. А. Полянской, 1902.
xvi, 404, lxiv p. 24 cm.
"Литература международнаго права": p. 32–36.

1. International law. I. Grabar', Vladimir Èmmanuilovich, 1865– ed. II. Mebel', M. A., tr. III. Pilenko, Aleksandr Aleksandrovich, 1873– Mezhdunarodnoe chastnoe pravo.
Title transliterated: Mezhdunarodnoe pravo.

49-55862

NL 0406469 DLC

Liszt, Franz von, 1851–1919.
Международное право въ систематическомъ изложеніи. Переводъ съ 5. нѣмецкаго изд. подъ ред. В. Э. Грабаря. 2. русское изд., совершенно перер. Съ дополненіями редактора и Очеркомъ частнаго международнаго права, составленнымъ Б. Э. Нольде. Юрьевъ, Тип. К. Маттисена, 1909.
xx, 581, clxxxiv p. 23 cm.
"Приложенія" (documents, including treaties): p. [i]–clxix at end.
Includes bibliographies.

1. International law. I. Nol'de, Boris Èmmanuilovich, baron, 1876–1948. Ocherk chastnogo mezhdunarodnogo prava. II. Russia. Treaties, etc. III. Title.
Title transliterated: Mezhdunarodnoe pravo v sistematicheskom izlozhenii.

JX3445.V4 1909 52-58274

NL 0406470 DLC

Law

Liszt, Franz von, 1851–1919.
Международное право въ систематическомъ изложеніи. Пер. съ 6. нѣмецкаго изд. подъ ред. В. Э. Грабаря. 3. русское изд., совершенно перер. Съ доп. редактора и Очеркомъ частнаго международнаго права, сост. Б. Э. Нольде. Юрьевъ, Тип. К. Маттисена, 1912.
xx, 574, clxxxiv p. 23 cm.
"Литература международнаго права": p. 52–58.
"Переводъ сдѣланъ ... М. А. Мебелемъ": p. viii.
1. International law. I. Grabar', Vladimir Èmmanuilovich, 1865– ed. II. Mebel', M. A., tr. III. Nol'de, Boris Èmmanuilovich, baron, 1876–1948. Ocherk mezhdunarodnago chastnago prava.
Title transliterated: Mezhdunarodnoe pravo.

49-55864*

NL 0406471 DLC

Law

Liszt, Franz von, 1851–1919.
Международное право въ систематическомъ изложеніи. Переводъ съ 6. нѣмецкаго изд., подъ ред. и съ доп. В. Э. Грабаря. 4. русское изд., испр. и доп. Юрьевъ, Тип. К. Маттисена, 1917.
xvi, 472, clxxxiv p. 26 cm.
Bibliographical footnotes.

1. International law. I. Title.
Title transliterated: Mezhdunarodnoe pravo v sistematicheskom izlozhenii.

59-55415

NL 0406472 DLC

Law

Liszt, Franz von, 1851–1919.
Международное право въ систематическомъ изложеніи. Пер. съ 6. нѣмецкаго изд. подъ ред. В. Э. Грабаря. 4. русское изд., совершенно перер. Съ дополненіями редактора и Очеркомъ частнаго международнаго права, сост. Б. Э. Нольде. Рига, Изд. Д. Гликсмана, 1923.
xx, clxxxiv, 574 p. 24 cm.
"Литература международнаго права": p. 52–58.
"Переводъ сдѣланъ ... М. А. Мебелемъ." — p. viii (1st group)
1. International law. I. Grabar', Vladimir Èmmanuilovich, 1865– ed. II. Mebel', M. A., tr. III. Nol'de, Boris Èmmanuilovich, baron, 1876–1948. Ocherk mezhdunarodnago chastnago prava.
Title transliterated: Mezhdunarodnoe pravo.

49-55863

NL 0406473 DLC

LISZT, Fr[anz], 1851-1919.
...Mezinárodní právo v systematickém podání. Dle čtvrtého vydání přeložil J. Elgart. Praha, 1906.

NL 0406474 MH-L

Liszt, Franz von, 1851–1919.
Ein mitteleuropäischer staatenverband als nächstes ziel der deutschen auswärtigen politik, von prof. dr. Franz von Liszt ... Leipzig, S. Hirzel, 1914.
3 p. l., 3–45, [1] p. 22 cm. (*On cover:* Zwischen krieg und frieden. 2)

1. Germany—For. rel. 2. Europe—Politics—1871–1918.

DD117.L67 15-7290

NL 0406475 DLC NN NjP OU MiU

Liszt, Franz von, 1851-.
Prison labor; a lecture by F. von Liszt, July 26, 1900. Translated by A. B. Salant, with notes. [New York?, 1900.] 19 p. 8°.
Title from cover.
—— —— A second copy.

1. Prison labor. 2. Salant, Aaron B., translator.
N. Y. P. L. May 13, 1913.

NL 0406476 NN DL NjP MH

VOLUME 336

Liszt, Franz von, 1851-1919.
Das Problem der Kriminalität der Juden, von Franz v. Liszt ... Giessen: A. Töpelmann, 1907. 11 p. 8°.

Excerpt: Festschrift der juristischen Fakultät der Universität Giessen zur dritten Jahrhundertfeier der Alma Mater Ludoviciana.

SCHIFF COLLECTION.
448275A. 1. Criminology—Stat.—Jews. 2. Criminology—Stat.—Germany.
N. Y. P. L. March 17, 1930

NL 0406477 NN MH-L DLC-P4

Liszt, Franz von, 1851-1919.
... Rechtsgut und Handlungsbegriff im Bindingschen Handbuche. Ein kritischer Beitrag zur juristischen Methodenlehre. Von Professor v. Liszt. [Berlin, 1886?]
[663] -698 p. 21 cm.
Caption title.
At head of title: 1.
"Zeitschrift f. d. ges. Strafrechtsw. VI."

NL 0406478 MH-L

---

223 Liszt, Franz von, 1851-1919
20.8.4 Rechtsgutachten in Sachen der Niederfüllbacher Stiftung, von ... F.v. Liszt ... ₍München, Duncker und Humblot, 1917₎
₍125₎-153 p. 23½cm.
Caption title.
"Sonderabdruck aus Niemeyers Zeitschrift für internationales Recht" v.27.
With author's autograph.

NL 0406479 MH-L

LISZT, Franz [Eduard] von, 1851-
Die reform des juristischen studiums in Preussen. Berlin, 1886.
56 p.
Rektoratsrede - Marburg.

NL 0406480 MH-L CtY

Liszt, Franz von, 1851- joint ed.
Aschrott, Paul Felix, 1856-
Die reform des Reichsstrafgesetzbuch. Kritische besprechung des vorentwurfs zu einem strafgesetzbuch für das Deutsche Reich unter vergleichender berücksichtigung des österreichischen und schweizerischen vorentwurfs. Unter mitwirkung von professor dr. L. v. Bar ... ₍u. a.₎ hrsg. von dr. P. F. Aschrott ... und dr. Franz von Liszt ... Berlin, J. Guttentag, g. m. b. h., 1910.

Liszt, Franz von, 1851-
Die reform des strafverfahrens. Von dr. Franz v. Liszt ... Berlin, J. Guttentag, g. m. b. h., 1906.
56 p. 23½cm.
"Die nachstehenden aufsätze sind zuerst in der "Nation" (nummer 14, 16, 18, 20, 22, 24 des xxv. jahrgangs) erschienen."—Vormerkung.

11-29963

Library of Congress

NL 0406482 DLC

LISZT, Franz von, 1851-
Sind gleiche grundsätze des internationalen strafrechts für die europäischen staaten anzustreben und eventuell welche? Gutachten im auftrage der ständigen deputation des deutschen juristentages. Berlin, Leipzig, 1882.
34 p.

NL 0406483 MH-L

Liszt, Franz von, 1851-1919
Die strafbaren handlungen gegen ausländische staaten in den Strafgesetzentwürfen der gegenwart. Von dr. Franz v. Liszt ... (In Berlin. Universität. Juristische fakultät. Festschrift ... für Ferdinand von Martitz. Berlin, 1911. p. ₍437₎-467)

NL 0406484 NNC

Liszt, Franz von, 1851-1919, ed.
FOR OTHER EDITIONS SEE MAIN ENTRY
Germany. *Laws, statutes, etc.*
... Strafgesetzbuch für das Deutsche reich. Textausg. mit anmerkungen und sachregister. 24. aufl. bearb. von dr. Franz v. Liszt und dr. Ernst Delaquis ... Berlin, J. Guttentag, 1914.

Liszt, Franz von, 1851-1919, ed.
Germany. *Laws, statutes, etc.*
... Strafgesetzbuch mit erläuterungen und nebengesetzen, früher von dr. Franz v. Liszt † und dr. Ernst Delaquis. 33. aufl. von dr. Eduard Kohlrausch ... Berlin und Leipzig, W. de Gruyter & co., 1937.

Law Liszt, Franz von, 1851-1919.
Internationale kriminalistische vereinigung.
Die strafgesetzgebung der gegenwart in rechtsvergleichender darstellung. Hrsg. von der Internationalen kriminalistischen vereinigung ... Berlin, O. Liebmann, 1894-99.

Liszt, Franz von, 1851-1919. *6212.85
Strafrecht und Strafprozessrecht.
(In Systematische Rechtswissenschaft. Pp. 195-206. Berlin. 1906.)
Literatur, p. 286.

G6387 — Criminal law.

NL 0406488 MB

HV7407 Liszt, Franz von, 1851-
.L77 Strafrechtliche aufsätze und vorträge. Von dr. Franz v. Liszt ... Berlin, J. Guttentag, g. m. b. h., 1905.
2 v. in 1. 23cm.

NL 0406489 ICU MiU-L DLC-P4 CtY MH

Liszt, Franz von, 1851-1919.
Strafrechtsfälle zum akademischen gebrauch. 3te auf., herausgegeben von Franz von Liszt. Jena, 1884.

NL 0406490 MH-L

4K Liszt, Franz von, 1851-1919.
Ger Strafrechtsfälle zum akademischen
1145 Gebrauch. 5., völlig umgearbeitete und verm. Aufl. Jena, G. Fischer, 1895.
viii, 109 p.

NL 0406491 DLC-P4 MH

Liszt, Franz von, 1851-
Strafrechtsfälle zum akademischen gebrauch. Von dr. Franz v. Liszt ... 7. durchgesehene aufl. Jena, G. Fischer, 1902.
viii, 122 p. 22½cm.

1. Criminal law.

NL 0406492 ICU MH-L

Liszt, Franz von, 1851-1919.
Strafrechtsfälle zum akademischen gebrauch. 9. durchgesehene aufl. Jena, Fischer, 1909.
viii, 123 p.

NL 0406493 NNC

LISZT, Franz von, 1851-1919.
Strafrechtsfälle zum akademischen gebrauch. 10te auf. Jena, 1911.
131 p.

NL 0406494 MH-L DLC-P4

Liszt, Franz von, 1851-1919.
Strafrechtsfälle zum akademischen Gebrauch 11. Aufl. Jena, 1913.

NL 0406495 MH-L

Liszt, Franz von, 1851-1919.
Franz v. Liszt's Strafrechtsfälle zum akademischen gebrauch. 12. durchgearb. aufl., hrsg. von dr. Ernst Heinrich Rosenfeld ... Jena, G. Fischer, 1920.
x, 147, ₍1₎ p. 23cm.
Based on Adolf Dochow's Strafrechtsfälle. *cf.* Vorwort zur zwölften auflage.

1. Criminal law—Germany—Cases. I. Rosenfeld, Ernst Heinrich, 1869- ed. II. Dochow, Adolf, 1844-1881. Strafrechtsfälle.

44-18556

NL 0406496 DLC ICU

Liszt, Franz von, 1851-1919.
Franz v. Liszt's Strafrechtsfälle zum akademischen gebrauch. 13. völlig durchgearb. aufl., hrsg. von dr. Ernst Heinrich Rosenfeld ... Jena, G. Fischer, 1922.
x, 134 p. 22½cm.
Based on Adolf Dochow's Strafrechtsfälle.

1. Law — Study and teaching. ₍1. Study of law₎ 2. Criminal law—Cases. I. Rosenfeld, Ernst Heinrich, 1869- ed. II. Dochow, Adolf, 1844-1881. Strafrechtsfälle. III. Title: Strafrechtsfälle.

24-15446

Library of Congress

NL 0406497 DLC

Liszt, Franz von, 1851-1919.
... Tötung und Lebensgefährdung (§§ 211-217, 222 RStrGB.) Bearb. von Professor Dr. Franz v. Liszt ... ₍Berlin, Otto Liebmann, 1905₎
158 p. 26½cm.
Caption title.
At head of title: Verbrechen und Vergehen wider das Leben. (Abschn. 16 des II. Teiles des RStrGB.) 1.

On cover: Sonderabdruck aus der Vergleichenden Darstellung des deutschen und ausländischen Strafrechts ... hrsg. ... von ... Dr. Karl Birkmeyer, Dr. Fritz van Calker, Dr. Reinhard Frank ... ₍u.a.₎
Contains bibliographies.
Author's autograph on p. ₍1₎

NL 0406499 MH-L

VOLUME 336

Liszt, Franz von, 1851-1919.
... Traité de droit pénal allemand, par dr. Franz von Liszt ... Traduit sur la 17e ed. allemande (1908) avec l'autorisation de l'auteur et de l'éditeur par René Lobstein ... Avec une préface de E. Garçon ... Paris, Giard & Brière, 1911-1913.
2v. 23 cm. (At top of t.p.: Bibliothèque internationale de droit privé et de droit criminel ...)

NL 0406500 CtY-L

Liszt, Franz von, 1851–1919.
... Tratado de derecho penal, traducido de la 18.ª ed. alemana y adicionado con la historia del derecho penal en España por Quintiliano Saldaña ... 2. ed. Madrid, Editorial Reus (s. a.) 1926–29.
3 v. diagrs. 23cm. (*Half-title:* Biblioteca jurídica de autores españoles y extranjeros. vol. XI, XXVI, XXVII)
Vols. 2–3: Traducido de la 20.ª ed. alemana por Luis Jiménez de Asúa ... y adicionado con el derecho penal español por Quintiliano Saldaña ...
Contains bibliographies.
1. Criminal law—Germany. 2. Criminal law—Spain. 3. Criminal law—Spain—Hist. I. Saldaña y García Rubio, Quintiliano, 1878– ed. and tr. II. Jiménez de Asúa, Luis, 1889– tr. III. Title.
32–1580

NL 0406501 DLC OU

LISZT, Franz von, 1851?-
Das verbrechen als sozialpathologische erscheinung. Dresden, 1899-

NL 0406502 MH

Liszt, Franz von, 1851-1919.
Verbrechen und Vergehen wider das Leben
see under title

Liszt, Franz von, 1851–1919.
Das völkerrecht, systematisch dargestellt von dr. Franz v. Liszt ... Berlin, O. Haering, 1898.
xv, (1), 254 p. 22cm.
Includes bibliographies.
1. International law and relations. I. Title.
38–6874
Library of Congress JX3445.V4 1898
341

NL 0406504 DLC IU MH

Liszt, Franz von, 1851–
Das völkerrecht, systematisch dargestellt von Dr. Franz v. Liszt ... 2. durchaus umgearbeitete aufl. Berlin, O. Haering, 1902.
xiii, (1), 412 p. 23½cm.
"Die litteratur des völkerrechts": p. 31–33.
CONTENTS.—Einleitung.—I. buch. Die rechtssubjekte und ihre allgemeine rechtsstellung.—II. buch. Der völkerrechtliche verkehr der staaten im allgemeinen.—III. buch. Die völkerrechtliche regelung und friedliche verwaltung gemeinsamer interessen.—IV. buch. Die staatenstreitigkeiten und deren austragung.
Library of Congress 2–14735

NL 0406505 DLC NjP NcD ICJ

Liszt, Franz von, 1851–1919.
Das völkerrecht, systematisch dargestellt von dr. Franz von Liszt ... 3. durchgearb. aufl. Berlin, O. Häring, 1904.
xii, 466, (2) p. 23cm.
1. International law and relations. I. Title.
Library of Congress JX3445.V4 1904 5–7463

NL 0406506 DLC NcD

Liszt, Franz von, 1851–
Das völkerrecht, systematisch dargestellt von dr. Franz von Liszt ... 4. durchgearb. aufl. Berlin, O. Häring, 1906.
xii, (2), 482 p. 23cm.
1. International law and relations. I. Title.
6–21413
Library of Congress JX3445.V4 1906

NL 0406507 DLC GU-L MH

Liszt, Franz von, 1851–
Das völkerrecht, systematisch dargestellt von dr. Franz von Liszt ... 5. durchgearb. aufl. Berlin, O. Häring, 1907.
xii, (2), 510 p. 23½cm.
1. International law and relations. I. Title.
Library of Congress JX3445.V4 1907 8–26210

NL 0406508 DLC

Liszt, Franz von, 1851–
Das völkerrecht, systematisch dargestellt von dr. Franz von Liszt ... 6. umgearb. aufl. Berlin, O. Häring, 1910.
xii, 564 p. 23½cm.
"Die literatur des völkerrechts": p. 40–43.
1. International law and relations.
10–22976
Library of Congress JX3445.V4 1910

NL 0406509 DLC MiU NcD

LISZT, Franz, ritter von, 1851-
Das völkerrecht systematisch dargestellt. 7e aufl. unveränderter abdruck der sechsten auflage. Berlin, O. Häring, 1911.

NL 0406510 MH

Liszt, Franz von, 1851– 341.02 Q902
97095 Das Völkerrecht systematisch dargestellt von Dr. Franz von Liszt, ... Achte Auflage. (Unveränderter Abdruck der 6. und 7. Auflage.) Berlin, O. Häring, 1912.
xii, 564 p. 23cm.
"Die Literatur des Völkerrechts," p. 40–43.

NL 0406511 ICJ

Liszt, Franz von, 1851–1919.
Das völkerrecht, systematisch dargestellt von dr. Fran von Liszt ... 9. umgearb. aufl. Berlin, O. Häring, 1913.
xii, 565 p. 23 cm.
"Die literatur des völkerrechts": p. 42–45.
CONTENTS.—Einleitung.—I. buch. Die rechtssubjekte des völkerrechtlichen staatenverbandes.—II. buch. Der völkerrechtliche verkehr innerhalb des staatenverbandes.—III. buch. Die interessengemeinschaft des völkerrechtlichen staatenverbandes.—IV. buch. Die staatenstreitigkeiten und deren austragung.—Anhang.
1. International law.
JX3445.V4 1913 13—13375

NL 0406512 DLC WaU-L NcD MiU

Liszt, Franz von, 1851– 3613.81
Das Völkerrecht systematisch dargestellt. 10., umgearbeitete Auflage.
— Berlin. Springer. 1915. xii, 560 pp. [Encyklopaedie der Rechtswissenschaft.] 23 cm., in 8s.
K6283 — S.r. — Law. Law of nature and of nations.

NL 0406513 MB NN ViU-L NjP DNW ICJ DLC-P4

JX3445 .V4 1918
Liszt, Franz von, 1851–1919.
Das völkerrecht, systematisch dargestellt von dr. Franz von Liszt ... 11. umgearb. aufl. Berlin, J. Springer, 1918.
xiii, 561, (1) p. 24cm.
"Die literatur des völkerrechts": p. 39–41.
CONTENTS.—Einleitung.—I. buch. Die rechtssubjekte des völkerrechtlichen stattenverbandes.—II. buch. Der völkerrechtliche verkehr innerhalb des staatenverbandes.—III. buch. Die interessengemeinschaft des völkerrechtlichen staatenverbandes.—IV. buch. Die erledigung der staatenstreitigkeiten.—Anhang.
1. International law (and relations) I. Title.
A 19—1389
Carnegie endow. int. peace. Library
for Library of Congress

NL 0406514 NNCE WaU NNC CtY PU-L DLC

Liszt, Franz von, 1851–1919.
Das völkerrecht, systematisch dargestellt von dr. Franz von Liszt ... 11., umgearb. aufl., unveränderter neudruck. Berlin, J. Springer, 1920.
xiii, 561, (1) p. 23½cm.
"Die literatur des völkerrechts": p. 39–41.
1. International law and relations.
Library of Congress JX3445.V4 1920 20–20582

NL 0406515 DLC OClW

Liszt, Franz von, 1851–1919.
Das völkerrecht, systematisch dargestellt von Franz von Liszt. 12. aufl. bearb. von dr. Max Fleischmann ... Berlin, J. Springer, 1925.
xviii, (2), 764 p. front. (port.) 23½cm.
1. International law and relations. I. Fleischmann, Max, 1872– II. Title.
26–1066
Library of Congress JX3445.V4 1925

NL 0406516 DLC WaU-L KMK IU NcD MiU OU OO OOxM CtY ViU-L ODW

LISZT, Franz v[on], 1851-
Vom staatenverband zur völkergemeinschaft; ein beitrag zur neuorientierung der staatenpolitik und des völkerrechts. München, Leipzig, n.d.
77 p.
"Fehler und forderungen, schriftenfolge zur neugestaltung deutscher politik," 2.

NL 0406517 MH-L NjP

Liszt, Franz von, 1851–1919.
Vom staatenverband zur völkergemeinschaft; ein beitrag zur neuorientierung der staatenpolitik und des völkerrechts, von professor dr. Franz v. Liszt ... München und Berlin, G. Müller (1917)
79, (1) p. 19½cm. (*Half-title:* Fehler und forderungen ... hft. 2)
1. International organization. 2. World politics.
30–8731
Library of Congress JC362.L5

NL 0406518 DLC InU

H 787.17.49(10)
Liszt, Franz von, 1851-1919.
Von der Nibelungentreue; Rede am 18.Nov. 1914. Hrsg. von der Zentralstelle für Volkswohlfahrt und dem Verein für Volkstümliche Kurse von Berliner Hochschullehrern. Berlin, Heymann, 1914.
26 p. (Deutsche Reden in schwerer Zeit, 10)

NL 0406519 MH OU

VOLUME 336

Liszt, Franz von, 1851-1919.
Das wesen des völkerrechtlichen staatenverbandes und der internationale prisenhof, von Franz v. Liszt. (In Berlin. Universität. Juristische fakultät. Festgabe ... für Otto Gierke. Breslau, 1910. v. 3, p. ₍19₎-44)

1. International law. 2. Prize courts.

NL 0406520 NNC MH

Liszt, Franz von, 1851- ed.
Zeitschrift für die gesamte strafrechtswissenschaf
see under title

Liszt, Franz von, 1851–1919.
... Der zweckgedanke im strafrecht. Frankfurt am Main, V. Klostermann ₍1943₎
42, ₍1₎ p. 22½cm. (*On cover:* Deutsches rechtsdenken, lesestücke für rechtswahrer bei der Wehrmacht ... Hft. 6)
"Diese akademische antrittsrede, bekannt geworden unter dem namen 'Marburger programm,' erschien als universitätsschrift 1883 in Marburg. Sie wurde wieder abgedruckt in der 'Zeitschrift für die gesamte strafrechtswissenschaft' III, 1 ff. und nochmals in der sammlung 'Franz von Liszts Strafrechtliche aufsätze und vorträge,' bd. 1 (1905) s. 126–179 ... Im folgenden geben wir den text, gekürzt um die rein polemischen teile."—p. ₍2₎
"Schrifttum": p. 42.
1. Criminal law—Addresses, essays, lectures. 2. Punishment—Addresses, essays, lectures.
46–42827

NL 0406522 DLC

Liszt, Franz von, 1851–1919.
Der Zweckgedanke im Strafrecht. ₍2. Aufl.₎ Frankfurt am Main, V. Klostermann ₍1948₎
44 p. 21 cm. (Deutsches Rechtsdenken, hrsg. von Erik Wolf. Heft 11)
"Diese akademische Antrittsrede, bekannt geworden unter dem Namen 'Marburger Programm,' erschien als Universitätsschrift 1883 in Marburg. Sie wurde wieder abgedruckt in der 'Zeitschrift für die gesamte Strafrechtswissenschaft' III, 1 ff. und nochmals in der Sammlung 'Franz von Liszts Strafrechtliche Aufsätzte und Vorträge,' Bd. 1 (1905) S. 126–179 ... Im Folgenden geben wir den Text, gekürzt um die rein polemischen teile."
1. Criminal law—Addresses, essays, lectures. 2. Punishment—Addresses, essays, lectures. I. Title. (Series)
48–26356*

NL 0406523 DLC CtY-M

Liszt, Rudolph G.
The last word in make-up (make-up encyclopedia) by Dr. Rudolph G. Liszt; illustrated by the author. ₍New York₎ Contemporary play publications ₍1938₎
112 p. front., plates, ports. 20½cm.

1. Make-up, Theatrical. I. Title. II. Title: Make-up encyclopedia.
39–27141
Library of Congress PN2068.L5
——— Copy 2. ₍8₎ 792

OClJC OCl OLak OClCC
NL 0406524 DLC Or WaT OrU TU FTaSU WaU OEac OClh

Liszt, Rudolph G.
The last word in make-up, by Dr. Rudolph G. Liszt, illustrated by the author, 45 unretouched photographs, 80 illustrations by the author. New York city, Dramatists play service ₍1942₎
xviii p., 1 l., 107 p. incl. tables. front., plates, ports. 19½cm.
A new edition, completely rewritten. *cf.* Author's pref.

1. Make-up, Theatrical. I. Title.
42–17623
Library of Congress PN2068.L5 1942
792

OLak OCl OU
NL 0406525 DLC WaS OrPR WaSpG CoU WaWW NN NcGU

Liszt, Rudolph G
The last word in make-up; illus. by the author. ₍Rev. ed., completely rewritten₎ New York, Dramatists Play Service ₍1949₎
xviii, 111 p. illus., ports. 20 cm.

1. Make-up, Theatrical. I. Title.
PN2068.L5 1949 792 49–48129*

NL 0406526 DLC NIC CoU ViU OClU

780.92 Liszt. Roma, Tipografia A. Befani, 1886.
L699Li 23 p.
Article signed: G. M. A.
"Estratto dal periodico La Rassegna italiana del 15 Settembre 1886."

1. Liszt, Franz, 1811-1886. I. A., G. M. II. G. M. A.

NL 0406527 WaU

ML 410 LISZT. Paris, La revue musicale, 1928.
.L7 L7 127 p. illus. (La revue musicale, numéro special, May, 1928)
Cover title.

1. Liszt, Franz, 1811-1886.

NL 0406528 InU ICU

Liszt Ferenc Zeneművészeti Főiskola, *Budapest*
see
Budapest. Zeneművészeti Főiskola.

Liszt-museum, Weimar
see
Weimar. Liszt-museum.

M3
L77L5
Liszt Society, London.

Liszt, Franz, 1811–1886.
₍Works₎
Liszt Society publications. London, Schott ₍19
Pl. no. S. & Co. ltd.

PH 3194 LISZTI, LÁSZLÓ, gróf, 1628?-1663
.L77 Munkái. ₍Pest, 1852₎
1852 312 p. (Újabb Nemzeti Könyvtár, 2. fol.)

NL 0406532 InU

PH
3194
.158
A1
1891
Liszti, László, gróf, 1628?-1663.
Listi László munkái. Életrajzzal bevezette Komáromy András. 3. kiad. Budapest, Franklin-Társulat, 1891.
591 p. 15 cm. (Olcsó könyvtár; II. sorozat, 761-766)
On spine: 77 köt.
Bibliographical footnotes.

NL 0406533 NNC

Lisztner, A. Scharp, pseud.
see Hathaway, Richard L

Liszynski, Josephus 1821-
Consideratio bilis physiologica et pathologica. Berolini, typ. Schnitzerianis, 1863.
30 p., 1 l. 8°.

NL 0406535 DNLM

Lit, Dr. pseud.
see Becker, Henry J.

Lit, Alfred, 1914–
The magnitude of the Pulfrich stereophenomenon as a function of binocular differences of intensity at various levels of illumination. ₍n. p., 1949₎
159–181 p. diagrs. 23 cm.
Thesis—Columbia University.
Reprinted from the American journal of psychology, v. 62, 1949.
Vita.
Bibliographical footnotes.

1. Space-perception. I. Title: Pulfrich stereophenomenon.
QP491.L5 A 53–6268
Columbia Univ. for Library of Congress Libraries ₍4₎†

NL 0406537 NNC DLC

₍Lit, Beckie₎
ס'מוז קומען! ביי בלומע באבע ₍pseud.₎ ארויסגעגעבען
דורך מערי סארקין. ניו־יארק, 1944 ₍New York₎
128 p. 16½cm.
Text corrected in manuscript.

I. Title. *Title transliterated:* S'muz kumen.
45–21059
Library of Congress PJ5129.L5S6

NL 0406538 DLC

Lit, J.G. de
see Lint, Jan Gérard de, 1867-

Lit, *Mrs.* Janice Shane (Reed)-, 1885- L610.7139 20 v.12
.... Storage, handling, and sale of food in Philadelphia, [by] Janice S. Reed Lit, ... Philadelphia, Published by the Henry Phipps Institute, 1916.
55 p. incl. plans, tables. plates. 25½cm. (*In* Twelfth report of the Henry Phipps Institute for the study, treatment, and prevention of tuberculosis.)
Some plates have illustrations on both sides.
Part of a study of food conditions in Philadelphia, conducted by the Henry Phipps Institute.

NL 0406540 ICJ

512.83 Lit, R R
L71b2 Beginselen van de leer der determinanten, met voorbeelden en toepassingen. 2.druk. Amsterdam, 1913.
40p.

NL 0406541 IU

Le lit de camp; scènes de la vie militaire, par l'auteur de La prima donna et la garçon Boucher
see under [Burat de Gurgy, Edmond] 1810-1840.

VOLUME 336

Lit. J. H. U. v. 1-2; spring 1946-Apr. 1947. [Baltimore]
2 v. in 1. 23 cm. irregular.
Title varies: spring 1946- JHU lit.
"Literary magazine of the Johns Hopkins University."
No more published?
L. C. set incomplete: v. 2, no. 1 wanting.

I. Johns Hopkins University. II. Title: JHU lit.

LH1.J7L5 52-37761

NL 0406543 DLC MdBE MdBJ

Lit méchanique pour les malades. [exécuté par le sieur Garat.] [Paris]: De l'imprimerie d'Andre' - Charles Cailleau, ... [1772]

NL 0406544 NNNAM

Lita, *pseud.*
... Med skjell på halen. Oslo, H. Aschehoug & co., 1929.
154 p. 20½cm.

I. Title.

Library of Congress PT8950.L66M4 1929 30-6272

NL 0406545 DLC

Lita, *pseud.*
Min knapphullsblomst, av Lita. 5. tusen. Oslo, H. Aschehoug & co., 1931.
136 p. 21cm.

I. Title.

Library of Congress PT8950.L66M5 1931 32-3171
Copyright A—Foreign 14884
839.8236

NL 0406546 DLC

Lita, Ricardo Palanca y
see Palanca y Lita, Ricardo, d. 1885.

Litaba tsa lilemo. Morija, Sesuto Book Depot, 1931.
80 p. 19 cm.

1. Lesotho—History—Chronology.

DT787.L58 72-203025

NL 0406548 DLC

Litai, Hayim
see his later name
Lazar, Hayim.

Litais de Gaux, ________, joint author.

Bescherelle, Louis Nicolas, 1802-1883.
Grammaire nationale; ou, Grammaire de Voltaire, de Racine, de Bossuet, de Fénelon, de J.-J. Rousseau, de Buffon, de Bernardin de Saint-Pierre, de Chateaubriand, de Casimir Delavigne et de tous les écrivains les plus distingués de la France; renfermant plus de cent mille exemples, qui servent à fonder les règles, et forment comme une espèce de panorama où se déroule notre langue telle que la nation l'a faite, telle qu'elle doit la parler; ouvrage éminemment classique, destiné à dévoiler le mécanisme et le génie de la langue française, par m. Bescherelle aîné ... et mm. Bescherelle jeune et Litais de Gaux. 13. éd., précédée d'une introduction, par m. Philarète Chasles ... Paris, Garnier frères, 1867.

Litais de Gaux, ——. 4681.3
Théorie du verbe et traité des participes.
(In Verlac. Dictionnaire synoptique de tous les verbes de la langue française . . . Pp. 1-198. Paris. 1865.)

G774 — Verbs. French. — Participles. French. — France. Lang. Gram.

NL 0406552 MB

Litaize, André.
... Pourquoi les drapeaux de Staline ne flottent pas sur nos Pyrénées; le témoignage d'un pèlerin de Saint-Jacques. Épinal (Vosges) Éditions du "Foyer vosgien," 1941.
3 p. l., [5]-245, [1] p. incl. plates, maps (1 double) 20½ cm.
Bibliographical foot-notes.

1. Spain—Hist.—Civil war, 1936-1939.—2. Spain—Hist.—Civil war, 1936-1939—Personal narratives. I. Title.

A 47-5514

Harvard univ. Library
for Library of Congress

NL 0406553 MH CLU CSt-H MnU

Litaize, Gaston. Cortège.

M702
.07

Orgue et cuivres. Paris, Éditions musicales de la Schola cantorum et de la Procure générale de musique [1951?]

M7
O7
v.9

Litaize, Gaston
[Cortège]
Cortège pour orgue, 3 trompettes et 3 trombones [par] Gaston Litaize. Sonata da chiesa per la Pasqua pour orgue et trompette [par] Henri Gagnebin. Paris, c1951.
score (38 p.) and 3 parts. 33cm. (Orgue et liturgie, 9: Orgue et cuivres)

Parts laid in (for Litaize's Cortège: 1 trumpets 1-3, 1 trombones 1-3. - (for Gagnebin's Sonata): 1 trumpet.

I. Gagnebin, Henri, 1886- Sonata da chiesa, trumpet & organ.

NL 0406555 CU NN

M
785.666
L775c
EMSC

Litaize, Gaston.
[Cortège, organ & brasses]
Cortège, pour trois trompettes, trois trombones et orgue. Paris, Éditions Musicales de la Schola Cantorum [n.d.] Pl. no. 0.009L.
score (24p.) and 2 parts. (Orgue et Liturgie, 9)

Bound with: Sonata da chiesa, per la Pasqua, organ & trumpet, by Henri Gagnebin.

1. Organ with band - Scores and parts. I. Ser.

NL 0406556 FTaSU

Litaize, Gaston.
[Pièces, organ]

Douze pièces pour grand orgue, par Gaston Litaize ... Paris, A. Leduc [1939]
2 v. 34 x 27cm.
Publisher's plate nos.: A. L. 19,712, A. L. 19,732.

1. Organ music.

Library of Congress M11.L 46-33359

NL 0406557 OrSaW NcU DLC OO FTaSU MH NSyU IaU IU KEmT WaU

M14
.3
.L57M5

Litaize, Gaston.

Messe basse pour tous les temps. Paris, Éditions musicales de la Schola cantorum et de la Procure générale de musique [195-?] Pl. no. S.6707P.
25 p. 32 cm. (Orgue et liturgie, 42)
For organ.

1. Organ masses. I. Title. (Series)

M14.3.L57M5 78-270132

NL 0406558 DLC MdBP FTaSU MH

Mus
M
250
L5R4
Ld

Litaize, Gaston.

Récitatif et thème varié, pour clarinette et piano. Paris, A. Leduc [c1946] Pl. no. A.L. 21171.
score (16p.) and 1 part.
Cover title:

For clarinet and piano.

1. Clarinet and piano music. 2. Variations (Clarinet and piano) I. Title.

NL 0406559 FTaSU

Litaize, Gaston.
[Préludes liturgiques]

24 [i. e. Vingt-quatre] préludes liturgiques, pour orgue sans pédale. Paris, Éditions musicales de la Schola Cantorum et de la Procure générale de musique, °1953-[55]
3 v. 32 cm. (L'organiste liturgique, 1, 4, 9)

1. Organ music. I. Title: Préludes liturgiques. (Series)

M14.3.L57P7 79-272708
[M17] [M11]

NL 0406560 DLC MH

852.6
L775c

Litala, Ignazio de.
Un can lecca la cenere e l'altro la farina; proverbio. Le vecchie portano chi le porta? proverbio. Milano, C. Barbini, 1876.
112p. 14cm. (His Teatro, v. 1)

Galleria teatrale.

I. Title. II. Title: Le vecchie portano chi le porta?

NL 0406561 IEN

Litala, Luigi de.
El contrato de trabajo. 2. ed., italiana totalmente corr. Traducción de Santiago Sentis Melendo. Buenos Aires, López & Etchegoyen, 1946.
590 p. 23 cm.

1. Labor contract—Italy.

48-26354*‡

NL 0406562 DLC

Litala, Luigi de.
... Il contratto di lavoro. Torino, Unione tipografico-editrice Torinese, 1929.
3 p.l., 420 p. 23.5 cm.

NL 0406563 CtY

4HD
1126

Litala, Luigi de
Il contratto di lavoro. 2. edizione interamente riv. Torino, Unione tipografico-editrice torinese, 1931.
496 p.

NL 0406564 DLC-P4 NN

Litala, Luigi de.
... Il contratto di lavoro. 3. ed. riveduta e notevolmente ampliata. Torino, Unione tipografico-editrice torinese, 1937.
2 p. l., 627 p. 23½cm.
Bibliographical foot-notes.

1. Labor contract—Italy. I. Title.

Library of Congress HD7811.I 8L5 1937 45-29098
331.11

NL 0406565 DLC CtY

VOLUME 336

Litala, Luigi de.
Il contratto di lavoro. 4. ed. riv. e ampliata. Torino, Unione tip.-editrice torinese, 1949.
642 p. 25 cm.
Bibliography: p. [626]-627.

1. Labor contract—Italy.

50-38552

NL 0406566 DLC NNC

Litala, Luigi de.
... Il contratto di servizio domestico e il contratto di portierato. Roma, U. S. I. L. A., società anonima editrice, 1933.
1 p. l., [5]-133 p. 22½cm.
"Bibliografia": p. [9]

1. Labor contract—Italy. 2. Servants—Italy. 3. Janitors. I. Title.

35-32955

Library of Congress [2] 331.18472

NL 0406567 DLC

Litala, Luigi de.
Derecho procesal del trabajo. Traducción de Santiago Sentís Melendo. Adiciones de derecho argentino por Diego Lamas. Buenos Aires, Bosch [1949]
3 v. 24 cm. (Colección Ciencia del proceso, 4-6)
Bibliography: v. 3, p. [371]-392.
Contents.—v. 1. Introducción. Nociones generales. Las controversias colectivas.—v. 2. Las controversias individuales del trabajo.—v. 3. Las controversias individuales del trabajo (continuación) Las controversias en materia de seguros sociales.

1. Labor courts—Italy. 2. Labor courts—Argentine Republic. I. Title. (Series)

50-3018 rev

NL 0406568 DLC CtY-L

Litala, Luigi de.
... Diritto delle assicurazioni sociali e norme complementari. Torino, Unione tipografico-editrice torinese, 1934.
3 p. l., [3]-549 p. 23½cm.
Includes bibliographies.

1. Insurance, State and compulsory—Italy.

45-29097

Library of Congress HD7183.L5

331.2544

NL 0406569 DLC CtY

Litala, Luigi de.
Diritto delle assicurazioni sociali. 3. ed. riv. e ampliata. [Torino] Unione tipografico-editrice torinese [1951]
662 p. 25 cm.

1. Insurance, Social—Italy.

52-26090 ‡

NL 0406570 DLC IU NcD

LITALA, Luigi de.
Diritto penale del lavoro e della pubblica economia con una introduzione al diritto del lavoro. Torino, Unione tipografico-editrice torinese, 1939.
8°.

NL 0406571 MH-L

Litala, Luigi de.
... Diritto processuale del lavoro. Torino, Unione tipografico-editrice torinese, 1936.
2 p. l., 532 p. 24cm.
"Bibliografia": p. [501]-515.

1. Labor courts—Italy.

39-8423

NL 0406572 DLC DLC-P4 MiU-L NSyU

Litala, Luigi de.
... Diritto processuale del lavoro. 2. ed. riv. Torino, Unione tipografico-editrice torinese, 1938.
2 p. l., 554 p. 24cm.
"Bibliografia": p. [523]-537.

1. Labor courts—Italy. I. Title.

41-16872

NL 0406573 DLC

Litala, Luigi de.
La responsabilità civile derivante dall'infortunio. Milano, Giuffrè, 1952.
[501]-519 p. 24 cm. (I Quaderni de la Rivista italiana di previdenza sociale, 8)

1. Employers' liability—Italy. 2. Torts—Italy. I. Title.

55-31455 ‡

NL 0406574 DLC

LITALA Y CASTELVI, Joseph de, 1627-1701.
Cima del monte Parnaso español con las tres musas castellanas, Caliope, Urania y Euterpe, etc. En Caller, por Onofrio Martin, 1672.

sm.4°.
Contains autograph of Diego de Messa y Avendano.

NL 0406575 MH NNH

Λιτανεία, hoc est supplicatio ad Deum Opti[mum] Max[imum] pro Germania, habita in celebri quadam Germaniae urbe, in die cinerum. [n. p., ca. 1520]
[7] l. 20 cm.
Caption title.
Published also in pt. 2 (p. 500-511) of J. E. Kapp's Kleine Nachlese einiger ... zur Erlauterung der Reformations-Geschichte Urkunden. Leipzig, 1727-33.

1. Catholic Church—Doctrinal and controversial works—Protestant authors.
Title transliterated: Litaneia.

BR303.L5 50-41887

NL 0406576 DLC MH

Litaniae ad usum patrum Societatis Jesu provinciae mexicanae. Angelopoli, Typographia Regalis Divi Ignatij Collegij, 1765.
1 p.l., 45 p. 4to

Bound in paper wrappers.

NL 0406577 InU

Litaniae Lauretanae

See

Catholic church, Liturgy and ritual. Litany of Loreto.

Litaniae omnium Sanctorum
see Catholic Church. Liturgy and ritual. Litany of the Saints.

M2154 .2 L573 Case X

Litaniae Septem Deiparae Virgini musice decantandae.
Antverpiae, Excudebat Petrus Phalesius, 1598.
56 l.

Principally for 4 voices, unacc.
Proof impression of the publishing house and press of Phalesius.
Contains seven different musical versions of the Litany of the Blessed Virgin, and one version of the Litany of the Holy Name and of the Magnificat.
With autograph of C. P. Serrure.

NL 0406580 CU-B

Litaniae Solemnes seu laudes in die Paschae
see under Catholic Church. Liturgy and ritual.

Litanie de' pellegrinilombardi. [Napoli, 1848.
f°. Broadside.
Repr.: La Patria, 1848.
In: BWL p.v. 1, no. 126.

NL 0406582 NN

---

*FC6 M456m 2321

La litanie dv cardinal Mazarin: où sont contenues[!] tous les eloges de ce grand prelat. A Paris.M. DC. LII.
7p. 24cm., in case 28cm.
Title vignette.
Moreau 2321.
A satire.
In folder; in case labeled: Mazarinades.

NL 0406583 MH

La litanie du soleil
see
Litany of the sun.

De Litanie van Onze Lieve Vrouw, geteekend door Alfred Ost, getoonzet door Arthur Meulemans; tekst van L. Uten, s. J. Tielt, J. Lannoo [1944]
[145] p. incl. illus. (1 col.) 36½ cm.
"Huldealbum aan kunstschilder Alfred Ost en toondichter Arthur Meulemans bij hun zestigste verjaring, 1884-1944."
"De Litanie van Onze Lieve Vrouw, getoonzet door Arthur Meulemans voor gemengd koor en orgel; facsimile van het handschrift van den toondichter": p. [105]-[145]
The score, for mixed chorus and organ, has caption: Litaniae lauretanae.

1. Choruses, Sacred (Mixed voices, 8 pts.) with organ. 2. Litanies (Music) I. Catholic church. Liturgy and ritual. Litany of Loreto. II. Ost, Alfred, 1884- illus. III. Meulemans, Arthur, 1884- IV. Uten, L.

M2012.L583 A F 48-160

Rochester. Univ. Libr.
for Library of Congress [2]†

NL 0406585 NRU NN DLC

Litanies at Baptism
see under Moravian Church. Liturgy and ritual.

Les litanies de la divinité de N. S. Jésus-Christ jusqu'à sa naissance, avec les quinze principales prophéties qui l'ont annoncée, par Rustique [pseud.] Paris. Impr. de Pillet fils aîné, 1864.
23 p. 18cm. (*Binder's title:* Réfutations de la Vie de Jésus. [v. 13, no. 5])

1. Messiah—Prophecies. I. Rustique, pseud.

34-25642

Library of Congress BT301.R42R4 vol. 13, no. 5

(232.9) 232.12

NL 0406587 DLC

VOLUME 336

Litanies de la rose
see under [Gourmont, Remy de] 1858-1915.

Litanies de la Ste. Vierge. [A une voix, S. ou T. Accomp. d'orgue.] Paris. [Heugel. [186-?] 5 pp. [Petite maitrise. Année 1. No. 17.] F°.

April 11, 1902.
E3573 — S.r. — Church music. Anthems, &c.

NL 0406589 MB

Les Litanies de la Sainte Vierge. Pieuses lectures pour tous les jours du mois de Marie. Lille, Desclée, de Bouwer et Cie, 1900.
21 p. 12°.

NL 0406590 NN

Litanies des aristocrates. n. p. [1790.]
14 p.

NL 0406591 NN

---

*FC6 M456m 2322
Les litanies dv temps.
[Paris,1650]
16p. 22cm.,in case 28cm.
Moreau 2322.
Colophon: A Paris,Chez François Noël,ruë Saint Iacques, aux Colomnes d'Hercule.
In folder; in case labeled: Mazarinades.

NL 0406592 MH WU

Litanies du Tiers-état. [Paris, 1789?]
15 p.
No. 24 of a volume of pamphlets

NL 0406593 NjP MB

French Rev. DC 141 F87+ v.566
Litanies du Tiers Etat. [n.p., 1789]
8 p. 19cm.
Bound with: Aux âmes chrétiennes.
Same text as: Litanies du Tiers Etat du royaume de France adressées au Roi.

NL 0406594 NIC NjP

French Rev. DC 141 F87+ v.566
Litanies du Tiers-Etat. [n.p., 1789]
12 p. 21cm.

NL 0406595 NIC

Litanies du Tiers-état. n. p. [1791?]
11 p.
No. 13 of a volume of pamphlets.

NL 0406596 NjP

DC 141 F87+ v.481
Litanies du Tiers-Etat du royaume de France, adressées au Roi...le premier jour de l'an 1789. Paris, Impr. royale, 1789.
14 p. 19 cm.
Includes: Le Gloria in excelsis du peuple, 4 p.
1. France--History--Revolution--Claims. 2. France--History--Revolution--Anecdotes. 3. France. Etats Généraux. Tiers Etat.

NL 0406597 NIC

Litanies of prayer and praise
see under [Hughson, Shirley Carter] 1867-1949, ed.

LITANTE, JUDITH.
Hazards of learning to sing. [n.p.] 1942. [8] p. 23cm.
1. Singing--Instruction, 1901- 2. Singing--Study and teaching.

NL 0406599 NN

The Litany ... College Misericordia.
Dallas, Pa. [c19
v. illus. (incl. ports.) plates (part col.) 27½cm.
I. Misericordia college, Dallas, Pa.
CA 30-921 Unrev'd
Library of Congress LD7251.D245

NL 0406600 DLC

The Litany and Suffrages from the Book of common prayer, with the music from the Sarum processional. Organ accompaniment by Francis Burgess ... [London] Pub. for the Plainsong & mediæval music society, 1904.
1 p. l., [2]-6, [4] p. 28cm.
I. Church of England. Book of common prayer. Litany. II. Catholic church. Liturgy and ritual. Processional. Salisbury. III. Burgess, Francis. IV. Plainsong and mediæval music society, London.
Library of Congress M2.P6 7-18242

NL 0406601 DLC MB MH CU

The Litany appendix...
see under [Pollock, Thomas Benson] 1836-1896.

---

*EB65 A100 681l3
A litany for the fast.
[London, ca.1681]
broadside. 30x19.5cm.
In verse.

NL 0406603 PU MH

A litany for time of war: and A penitential... Words & music... Cambridge: W. Heffer & Sons, Ltd. [1914.] 2 l. 8°.
A litany for time of war: God of pity, God of love; words by A. C. Yorke, music by Rev. J. Hipwell. A penitential: O God, to whom all hearts are plain; words by A. C. Yorke...composer unknown.
1. Hymns.
N. Y. P. L. September 7, 1915.

NL 0406604 NN

Litany for use in time of war.
London, 1914.

NL 0406605 NjP

---

*EB65 A100 682l9
A litany from Geneva, in answer to that from St. Omers.
London,Printed for the use of all true Blue Brimighams,1682.
broadside. 19x29cm.
In verse.
Ms. date at end: 10 June 1682.

NL 0406606 MH NjP IU

Film 1027
A litany from Geneva in answer to that from St. Somers. London, Printed for the use of all true Brimighams, 1682.
Microfilm copy (negative) Original in the Harvard University Library. 1961.
Filmed with Good news in bad times. 1683.
Collation of the original as determined from the film: 1 l. (broadside)
Wing. Short-title catalogue no. L 2535.

NL 0406607 OU

Litany of Loreto
see
Catholic church. *Liturgy and ritual. Litany of Loreto.*

Litany of Re
see
Litany of the sun.

Litany of the Blessed Virgin
see Catholic Church. Liturgy and ritual. Litany of Loreto.

---

*pEB65 A100 679l2
The litany. Of the D[uke]. of B[uckingham].
[London,1679?]
broadside. 36.5x29cm.
In verse.
This copy is printed on thin paper, with an urn watermark.
*pEB65 A100 679l2a
Another copy. 35x27.5cm.
This copy is printed on thick paper, with watermark: FT/GGGVT.

NL 0406611 MH DFo TxU CtY

The Litany of the life of Jesus. For Sunday School or general devotion. Albany, S.R. Gray, 1869.
33 p. 12°.

NL 0406612 NN

BL 2450 R2L77+ 1875
Litany of the sun.
La litanie du soleil; inscriptions recueillies dans les tombeaux des rois à Thèbes; traduites et commentées par E. Naville. Leipzig, W. Engelmann, 1875.
iv, 130 p. and atlas (49 plates) 31cm.
1. Ra (Egyptian deity) I. Naville, Édouard, 1844-1926, ed. & tr.

NL 0406613 NIC OCl RPB

VOLUME 336

Litany of the sun.
The myth of Ra (the supreme sun-god of Egypt) with copious citations from the solar and pantheistic litanies, by W. R. Cooper... [2],52p. London, Hardwicke & Bogue; [etc.,etc.] 1877.

"A paper read before the Victoria institute, or Philosophical society of Great Britain, to which is added the discussion thereon."

NL 0406614 OCl

Litany of the sun.
Traduction comparée des hymnes au soleil composant le XVe chapitre du rituel funéraire égyptien par Eugene Lefebure. Paris, A. Franck, 1868.
126 p.
Contains also the Egyptian text.

NL 0406615 OCl

The litany, set to the chant of the Sarum Processional. London, Oxford University Press, 1935.
16 p. 22 cm.
"This music presents in quaver notation a transcription by the late Rev. Dr. G.H. Palmer from the plainsong of the Sarum Processional."

NL 0406616 NcD

Litaraturny muzeĭ I͡Akuba Kolasa, *Minsk*
see
Akademii͡a navuk BSSR, *Minsk. Litaraturny muzeĭ I͡Akuba Kolasa.*

Litaraturny muzeĭ I͡Anki Kupaly, *Minsk*
see
Akademii͡a navuk BSSR, *Minsk. Litaraturny muzeĭ I͡Anki Kupaly.*

Litarczek (Georg Carl) [1888-]. *Ueber den Einfluss von Körpergrösse und Gewicht, Blutdruck und Alter auf das Orthodiagramm des Herzens. 82pp. 8°. Berlin, E Ebering, 1915.

NL 0406619 DNLM CtY

[Litardière, René de]
Contribution à l'étude de la flore de la Corse. [Bastia: C. Piaggi, 1921.] p. [187-]242. 4°. (Soc. des sciences historiques et naturelles de la Corse.)

Caption-title.
On cover: Bulletin. no. 437-440.
Signed: R. de Litardière.

1. Botany, Corsica. 2. Société des sciences historiques et naturelles de la Corse.
N. Y. P. L. August 10, 1923.

NL 0406620 NN

Botany Library
QK418 .L57
fasc.1

Litardière, René de.
Contributions à l'étude de la flore du Grand atlas, par R. de Litardière et R. Maire. Rabat, l'Institut scientifique chérifien; Paris, Émile Larose, 1924-
v. illus. (Société des sciences naturelles du Maroc./ Mémoires, t.4, no.1)

1. Botany - Morocco - Atlas Mts. I. Title. (Series)

NL 0406621 NcU MnU ICF NNBG MH-A

581.9459 L71c

Litardière, René de.
Contributions à l'étude phytosociologique de la Corse; le massif du Renoso, par R. de Litardière et G. Malcuit. Paris, P. Lechevalier, 1926.
143p. illus., plates(1 fold.) 24cm.

"Liste des travaux floristiques relatifs à des plantes du massif du Renoso": p.5-8.

1. Botany--Corsica. I. Malcuit, G., joint author.

NL 0406622 IU

Bot. lib. QK1 .A573 t.2 no.2

Litardière, René de.
Études sociologiques sur les pelouses xérophiles calcaires du domaine atlantique français. [Caen, Pub. par René Viguier, 1928]
47p. (Archives de botanique, t.2, no.2)

1. Botany - France. I. Title.

NL 0406623 NcU

Bot. lib. QK1 .A573 t.3 no.4

Litardière, René de.
Les hêtraies de l'Incudine, par R. de Litardière et G. Malcuit. [Caen, Pub. par René Viguier, 1929]
11p. plates. (Archives de botanique, t.3, no.4)
At head of title: Contributions à l'étude phytosociologique de la Corse.
1. Botany - Corsica. 2. Beech. I. Malcuit, G joint author. II. Title. III. Title: Contributions à l'étude phytosociologique de la Corse.

NL 0406624 NcU

Bot. lib. QK1 .A573 t.2 no.4

Litardière, René de.
Les montagnes de la Corse orientale entre le Golo et le Tavignano. [Caen, Pub. par René Viguier, 1928]
184p. plates. (Archives de botanique, t.2, no.4)

At head of title: Contributions a l'étude phytosociologique de la Corse.

1. Botany - Corsica. I. Title. II. Title: Contributions a l'étude phytosociologique de la Corse.

NL 0406625 NcU

Bot. lib. QK1 .A573 t.2 no.1, etc.

Litardière, Réne de.
Nouvelles contributions a l'étude de la flore de la Corse. [Caen, Pub. par René Viguier, 1928-
v. (Archives de botanique, t.2, no.1, etc.)

1. Botany - Corsica. 1. Title.

NL 0406626 NcU

Bot. lib. QK1 A573 t.4 no.4

Litardière, René de.
Les pozzines du massif de l'Incudine. [Caen, 1930]
18p. plates. (Archives de botanique, t.4, no.4)

At head of title: Contributions à l'étude phytosociologique de la Corse.

1. Botany - Corsica. I. Title. II. Title: Contributions à l'étude phytosociologique de la Corse.

NL 0406627 NcU

576.3323 L775R

Litardière, René de.
Recherches sur l'élément chromosomique dans la caryocinèse somatique des Filicinées ... [Lierre, Joseph Van In & Cie.; Louvain, A. Uystpruyst, 1921]
[255]-473 p. 9 plates (8 fold.) 29 cm.

"Extrait de la Revue 'La Cellule', t. XXXI, 2d fascicule."
"Errata" slip tipped to title page.
Bibliography: p. [429]-441.

1. Karyokinesis. 2. Chromosomes. 3. Ferns. Anatomy.

NL 0406629 NcD MH CtY

Litardière, René de.
—— Voyage botanique en Corse, juillet-août, 1908. [Le Mans. 1909.] l. 8°.
Bulletin de l'Académie internationale de géographie botanique, 1909, xviii, 37-212.

NL 0406630 MH-A

Litardo, E González
see
González Litardo, E.

Litaud, René.
... Sur un cas de neuro-fibromatose localisée ... Paris, 1922.
40 p. illus. 23.5 cm.
Thèse - Univ. de Paris.

NL 0406632 CtY DNLM

Litaudon (Achille-Paul-Henry). *Diagnostic précoce de la paralysie générale et son traitement. 63 pp. 8°. Paris, 1917. No. 46.

NL 0406633 DNLM CtY

1513 .2525 .591

Litaudon, M
Histoire du canton de Chevagnes. Moulins, Les impr. réunies, 1950-52
2 v.in 1. illus.,map. 23 cm

1. CHEVAGNES, FRANCE - HIST.

NL 0406634 NjP MH CU

Litaudon, M
Moulins en 1460. Dessins inédits de Robert Génermont. Moulins, Crépin-Leblond, 1947.

182 p. illus., ports., maps (part fold.) 23 cm. (Curiosités bourbonnaises, 2. sér., 44)

1. Moulins, France—Descr.

DC801.M85L5 52-23747

NL 0406635 DLC MH NN

Litauen und seine Deutschen
see under Landsmannschaft der Litauendeutschen im Bundesgebiet.

Das LITAUEN-BUCH; eine auslese aus der Zeitung der 10. Armee. Zeitung der 10. Armee, 1918.

195 p. illus., plates (incl. ports., maps, facsims.)

NL 0406637 CaBVaU

VOLUME 336

Law Litauer, Jan Jakób, ed. 1871–

Poland. *Laws, statutes, etc.*
Kodeks postępowania cywilnego; tekst kodeksu i przepisów wprowadzających z orzecznictwem Sądu Najwyższego oraz przepisy uzupełniające i związkowe, oprac. Jan Jakub Litauer [i] Witold Święcicki. [Warszawa] Czytelnik, 1947.

Law Litauer, Jan Jakób, 1871–

Poland. *Laws, statutes, etc.*
Kodeks postępowania niespornego. Księga 1, część ogólna, oraz przepisy szczegółowe jednolitego postępowania niespornego z objaśnieniami w oprac. Jana Jakóba Litauera. Łódź, Prawo, 194

Litauer, Jan Jakób, ed. 1871–

Poland (1918–) *Laws, statutes, etc.*
... Komentarz do procedury cywilnej: postępowanie sporne, postępowanie zabezpieczające, przepisy wprowadzające Kodeks postępowania cywilnego. Warszawa, Wydaw. "Bibljoteka prawnicza", 1933.

LITAUER, Jan Jakób, 1871-
Materjaly do dziejow sadownictwa okupacyjnego w Polsce. 1795-1796. Warszawa, 1916.

NL 0406641 MH-L

Litauer, Jan Jakób, ed. 1871–

Torosiewicz, Dawid, *d.* 1849.
Myśli o powołaniu obrońców sądowych, w krótkości zebrane przez Dawida Torosiewicza ... W Warszawie, Druk. S. Orgelbranda synów, 1822–1917.

Litauer, Jan Jakób, 1871–
O terminach i trybie podawania skarg w sprawach administracyjnych Królestwa polskiego, przez Jana Jakóba Litauera ... Warszawa, Skład główny w księg. Gebethnera i Wolffa, 1897.
2 p. l., iii, 47 p. 19½cm.

1. Administrative courts—Poland. 2. Civil procedure—Poland. I. Title: Skargi w sprawach administracyjnych.

41-35700

NL 0406643 DLC

Litauer, Jan Jakób, ed. 1871–

Poland (1918–) *Laws, statutes, etc.*
... Polska procedura cywilna; projekty uchwalone przez Komisję kodyfikacyjną: Kodeks postępowania cywilnego, ustawa o wprowadzeniu Kodeksu, ustawa o kosztach sądowych. Uzasadnienie ogólne i tekst projektów; przypisami, uwagami i skorowidzem opatrzył Jan Jakób Litauer ... Warszawa, "Bibljoteka prawnicza", 1930.

Law Litauer, Jan Jakób, 1871– ed.

Poland. *Laws, statutes, etc.*
Prawo cywilne, obowiązujące na obszarze b. Kongresowego Królestwa Polskiego; z dodaniem tekstu francuskiego, ustaw uzupełniających i związkowych oraz orzecznictwa kasacyjnego. Pod red. Jana Jakóba Litauera. Warszawa, F. Hoesick, 1929.

Litauer, Jan Jakób, 1871-
Rzut oka na polskie projekty ustawodawcze norm miedzynarodowego i miedzydzielnicowego prawa prywatnego. Warszawa, 1925.
30 p. (Wydawnictwo czasopisma prawiczego "Palestra.")
(An analysis of the Polish project of the codification of private international and interprovincial law.)

NL 0406646 MH-L

Litauer, Jan Jakób, 1871-
...Uwagi nad projektem ustawy autorskiej/referenta Prof. Zolla. [Kraków: Nakładem Komisji kodyfikacyjnej Rzeczypospolitej Polskiej, 1920?] 32 p. 8°.

Caption-title.
At head of title: Komisja kodyfikacyjna Rzeczpospolitej polskiej. Sekcja prawa cywilnego. J. J. Litauer.

1. Copyright—Poland. 2. Poland. Komisja kodyfikacyjna. Wydział cywilny.
N. Y. P. L. October 10, 1925

NL 0406647 NN

Litauer, Jan Jakób, 1871–
Wyrok zaoczny w polskiej procedurze cywilnej. Warszawa, 1935.
21 p. 24 cm.
Cover title.
"Odbitka z 'Polskiego procesu cywilnego.'"

1. Judgments by default—Poland. I. Title.

57-45650

NL 0406648 DLC

Litauer, Marjan, 1907-
... Les purpuras aigus hémorragiques avec syndrome agranulocytaire au cours du traitement antisyphilitique ... Paris [1932]
Thèse - Univ. de Paris.
"Bibliographie": p. 62-68.

NL 0406649 CtY

Litauer, Stefan.
Chiny w walce o wyzwolenie. Warszawa, Wydawnictwo "Przegladu politycznego", 1927.
32 p. Folded map.
Presentation copy with author's autograph.

NL 0406650 MH

4DK Pol.-280 Litauer, Stefan.
Soumrak polského Londýna. [Z polského originálu Zmierzch "Londynu" prelozil Helena Teigová. V Praze] Práce, 1947.
65 p.

NL 0406651 DLC-P4

Litauer, Stefan.
Zmierzch "Londynu." Warszawa, Czytelnik [1945]
53 p. 22 cm. (Biblioteka społeczno-polityczna, nr. 12)

1. Poland—Hist.—1918-1945. I. Title.

DK440.L48 59-42970

NL 0406652 DLC MiD MH NN

Litauische Akademie der Wissenschaften, *Vilna*
see
Lietuvos TSR Mokslų akademija, *Vilna.*

Litauische Armeezeitung
see Armeezeitung Scholtz.

Litauische litterarische gesellschaft, Tilsit.

Bartsch, Christian, 1832–1891, *ed. and tr.*
Dainu balsai. Melodieen litauischer volkslieder, gesammelt und mit textübersetzung, anmerkungen und einleitung im auftrage der Litauischen litterarischen gesellschaft hrsg. von Christian Bartsch ... Heidelberg, C. Winter, 1886–89.

Litauische litterarische Gesellschaft, Tilsit.
Giesmiu balsai. Litauische Kirchen-Gesänge
see under Hoffheinz, W ed.

Litauische literarische gesellschaft, *Tilsit.*
Mitteilungen der Litauischen literarischen gesellschaft. 1.–6. bd. (hft. 1–31) 1880–1912. Heidelberg, C. Winters universitätsbuchhandlung, 1883–1912.
6 v. illus., plates (part col.) maps, plans. 23cm. irregular.
Vol. 6 (no. 31) has special t.-p.: Beiträge zur litauischen dialektologie, von dr. Alexander Doritsch. 1911.
Contents to v. 2–6 (no. 7–31) may be found in J. Müller's Die wissenschaftlichen vereine und gesellschaften Deutschlands, 1917, p. 1178–1185.
Includes music.
No more published.
Incomplete: v. 1, no. 1, 1880, wanting.
1. Lithuanian literature — Societies. 2. Lithuanian language — Dialects. 3. Music—Lithuania.

6-24718 Revised
Library of Congress PG8503.L7
[r32b2] 891.92062

NL 0406657 DLC OClU IU OU NjP NN NBuC MiU CtY MH

Litauische litterarische gesellschaft, Tilsit. Bibliothek
... Katalog der Bibliothek. Tilsit, Gedruckt bei O. v. Mauderode, 1892.
1 p. l., 38 p. 23cm.

1. Lithuanian literature—Bibl.

8-14387
Library of Congress Z2514.L4T5

NL 0406658 DLC MiU

Litauische und lettische drucke des 16. jahrhunderts hrsg. von Adalbert Bezzenberger ... Göttingen, R. Peppmüller [etc.] 1874–84.
4 v. 23½cm.
Contents.—I. [hft.] Der litauische katechismus vom jahre 1547.—[II. hft.] Der lettische katechismus vom jahre 1586. Das litauische taufformular vom jahre 1559. Anhang: Das (angeblich altpreussische) lettische Vaterunser des Simon Grunau.—III. hft. Bartholomäus Willent's litauische uebersetzung des Luther'schen Enchiridions und der Episteln und Evangelien ... hrsg. von Fritz Bechtel.—IV. hft. Szyrwid's Punkty kazań (Punktay Sakimu) vom jahre 1629 ... hrsg. von Richard Garbe.
I. Bezzenberger, Adalbert, 1851–1922, ed. II. Bechtel, Friedrich, 1855–1924, ed. III. Garbe, Richard, 1857–1927, ed.

5—31972
Library of Congress PG8002.L4

NL 0406659 DLC NcU CtY NN MdBJ MiU ICU CU PBm PU MiU MH OClW

Litauische Universität, *Kaunas*
see Kaunas. Universitetas.

Litauischer Bibliographiedienst
See
Lietuvių bibliografinė tarnyba, Memmingen, Germany.

VOLUME 336

Літаври. ч. 1–
квіт. 1947–
Зальцбург, Нові дні.
no. in v. 20 cm. monthly.
Organ of Spilka ukraïns'kykh naukovtsiv, literatoriv i mystsiv u Avstriï.

1. Ukrainians in Austria—Period. 2. Ukrainian literature in foreign countries—Period. I. Spilka ukraïns'kykh naukovtsiv, literatoriv i mystsiv u Avstriï. *Title transliterated: Litavry.*

DB34.U5S633 54-35164

NL 0406662 DLC CoU PPiU

Litawski, Jerzy.
Bezpośrednie ustawodawstwo ludowe. Kraków, Księg. L. Frommera, 1932.
121 p. 24 cm.
Thèse—Uniwersytet Jagielloński, Krakow.
Added t.-p. in French.
Errata leaf inserted.
"Literatura": p. [117]-121.

1. Referendum. 2. Referendum—Poland. I. Title.

JF491.L5 48-31042*

NL 0406663 DLC

Litawski, Odo Joseph, 1910–
Glimpses of Indian architecture. Foreword by Sir Samuel Runganadhan. With 31 illus. Frankfurt on Main, O. Lembeck, 1947.
62 p. illus., map. 25 cm.

1. Architecture—India. I. Title.

NA1501.L5 720.954 48-19365*

NL 0406664 DLC CtY

Litch, Josiah. 7459a.145
An address to the clergy, on the near approach of the glorious, everlasting kingdom of God on earth . . .
= Boston. Dow & Jackson. 1840. 88 pp. 12°.
A later edition entitled, "An address to the public," etc., is on shelf-number 7488.10.

F4794 — Millennium.

NL 0406665 MB

BT
890
L57

Litch, Josiah.
An address to the public, and especially the clergy, on the near approach of the glorious, everlasting Kingdom of God on earth ... By J. Litch. Boston, Joshua V. Himes, 1842.
132 p. 17 cm.
With this is bound the author's Judaism overthrown. Boston, 1843, and Refutation of "Dowling's reply to Miller." Boston, 1842; Bliss, Sylvester. An exposition of the twenty-fourth of Matthew. Boston, 1843; Bliss, Sylvester. Inconsistencies of Colver's literal fulfilment of Daniel's prophecy. Boston, 1843; Bliss, Sylvester. The chronology of the Bible. New York, 1843; Bliss, Sylvester. Review of Rev. O. R. Daggett's sermon. Boston, 1842; Bliss, Sylvester. Exposition of Zechariah XIV. Boston, 1843; Bliss, Sylvester. Paraphrase of Daniel XI and XII. Boston, 1844; Bliss, Sylvester. Reasons of our hope. Boston, 1843; A Paraphrase of Matthew 24th and 25th. Boston, 1843.

1. Millennium. I. Title.

NL 0406668 NRCR CLamB ICN MB

Litch, Josiah.
Christ yet to come: a review of Dr. I. P. Warren's "Parousia of Christ." By Rev. Josiah Litch ... with an introduction by Rev. A. J. Gordon ... Boston, American millennial association, 1880.
xii, [13]-192 p. 19½cm.

1. Second advent. 2. Warren, Israel Perkins, 1814-1892. The parousia. I. American millennial association. II. Title.

37-15031

Library of Congress BT885.W32

232.6

NL 0406669 DLC OrU PPLT OO

Litch, Josiah.
A complete harmony of Daniel and the Apocalypse, by Rev. J. Litch... Philadelphia: Claxton, Remsen & Haffelfinger, 1873. 300 p. 12°.

363312A. 1. Bible. O. T.: Daniel. 2. Bible. N. T.: Revelation.
N. Y. P. L. September 11, 1928

NL 0406670 NN PPLT OO DLC

Litch, Josiah.
Dialogue on the nature of man, his state in death, and the final doom of the wicked, by Rev. Josiah Litch... Philadelphia: J. Litch[, 185–?]. 54 p. 16°.

1. Future life and future state.
N. Y. P. L. November 15, 1928

NL 0406671 NN

Litch, Josiah.
A dissertation on the chronology of prophecy. By Josiah Litch. [Boston: Joshua V. Himes, 1842]
18 p. illus. 22cm.
Caption title.
Bound with, as issued: General Conference of Christians Expecting the Advent of the Lord Jesus Christ. The first report. Boston, 1842.

1. Prophecies. I. Title.

NL 0406672 MiU-C

Litch, Josiah.
Dissertation on the fall of the Ottoman Empire ... Delivered ... June, 1841.
p. 8°. [Second Advent Tracts, No. 11]

NL 0406673 CtY

Litch, Josiah.
A dissertation on the second advent. By Josiah Litch. [Boston: Joshua V. Himes, 1842]
16 p. 22cm.
Caption title.
Bound with, as issued: General Conference of Christians Expecting the Advent of the Lord Jesus Christ. The first report. Boston, 1842.

1. Second Advent. I. Title.

NL 0406674 MiU-C

Litch, Josiah, and M. Grant.
The doctrine of everlasting punishment: a discussion of the question "Do the Scriptures teach the doctrine of the eternal conscious suffering of the wicked?", between Dr. J. Litch...and Eld. Miles Grant...on the evenings of November 9, 10, 11, and 12, A. D. 1858, at the Music Hall, in Boston. Phonographically reported by Jas. M. W. Yerrinton... Boston: Damrell & Moore, 1859. 135 p. 12°.

1. Future punishment. 2. Grant, Miles.
N. Y. P. L. November 16, 1928

NL 0406675 NN MH

Sem
236.082
Se2a
v.5

Litch, Josiah.
Judaism overthrown: or, The kingdom restored to the true Israel; with the Scripture evidence of the epoch of the kingdom in 1843. Boston, Joshua V. Himes, 1843.
38 p. (Second advent library)
Bound with his: An address to the public.
1. Kingdom of God. I. Title. II. Series.

NL 0406676 CLamB PPL ICN NRCR

Litch, Josiah.
Fitch, Charles, 1804-1843.
Letter to Rev. J. Litch, on the second coming of Christ, with the sentiments of Cotton Mather on the same subject, approved by Thomas Prince ... By Charles Fitch ... Boston, J. V. Himes, 1841.

Litch, Josiah.
Messiah's throne and millennial glory, by Josiah Litch... Philadelphia: The author, 1855. viii, 316 p. 12°.

363983A. 1. Millennium.
N. Y. P. L. October 18, 1928

NL 0406678 NN MH-AH

Litch, Josiah.
.... The pre-millennial advent vindicated: being a review of Rev. Dr. David Brown's Post -millennial advent of christ, by Rev, J. Litch,...Boston:American Millennial Association, YA27125
301p. 17cm.

NL 0406679 DLC PPL NN ICRL IU

Litch, Josiah.
Prophetic expositions; or, A connected view of the testimony of the prophets concerning the kingdom of God and the time of its establishment. By Josiah Litch ... Boston, J. V. Himes, 1842.
v. 17cm.

1. Bible. Prophecies. 2. Kingdom of God. I. Title.

Printed by the Wesleyan University Library, 1936

NL 0406680 CtW ICN MWA NN ICN NNUT MH CtY

C
614
.8
v.7

LITCH, JOSIAH.
Refutation of "Dowling's reply to Miller," on the second coming of Christ in 1843... With a preface, by Joshua V.Himes. Boston,Himes, 1842.
90p. [Second advent library. v.7, no.1]

NL 0406681 ICN CLamB MiU-C KyU NRCR

Litch, Josiah.
Restitution; Christ's kingdom on earth; the return of Israel, with their political emancipation . Bost.,1848.

NL 0406682 Nh CtW

LITCH,Josiah.
[Three pamphlets,dated 1842 and 1843,in volume lettered:-Second Advent library,5.]

NL 0406683 MH-AH

VOLUME 336

Litch, Samuel, 1779-1860.
An astronomical and geografical catechism, for the use of common scools [!] and private persons. By Samuel Litch ... Jaffrey, N. H. Printed by Salmon Wilder, 1814.
vi, [7]-118 p. 12½cm.
"Compiled from different authors, (a considerable part from Mr. Bingham)"—p. v.

1. Geography—Text-books—1800-1870. I. Bingham, Caleb, 1757-1817.
Library of Congress G125.L77 5-42722 Revised

NL 0406684 DLC CSt MH PHi CSmH

Litch, Samuel, 1779-1860, comp.
A concise treatise of rhetoric; extracted from the writings of Dr. Blair, Ushor, &c. for the use of common schools and private persons. By Samuel Litch ... Jaffrey [N. H.] Printed by Salmon Wilder, 1813.
114 p. 12 1/2 cm. 1/2 sheep.

1. English language—Rhetoric.

NL 0406685 CSmH MiU MH

76
L175c
Litch, Samuel, 1779-1860, comp.
A concise treatise of retoric; extracted from the writings of Dr. Blair, Usher, &c. for the use of common schools and private persons. Jaffrey [N.H.] Salmon Wilder, 1813.
119, [1]p. 13cm.
Includes poetry.

NL 0406686 RPB

Litch, Wilbur Fisk, 1840-1912.
...Address. (Pennsylvania college of dental surgery, 1880)
Pamph.

NL 0406687 PPWD

Litch, Wilbur Fisk, 1840- ed.
The American system of dentistry. In treatises by various authors. Ed. by Wilbur F. Litch ... Philadelphia, Lea brothers & co., 1886-1887.
3 v. illus., plates. 25cm.
CONTENTS.—I. Regional and comparative dental anatomy, dental histology, and dental pathology.—II. Operative and prosthetic dentistry.—III. Anæsthesia and anæsthetics. Physiology and digestion, voice and speech. Associate dental and oral pathology. Oral surgery. Eruption of the teeth. Materia medica and therapeutics. Metallurgy. Jurisprudence.
1. Dentistry.
Library of Congress RK51.L77 7-7052

NL 0406688 DLC OC1W-H DNLM WaU FU-HC PPC PPWD OO MiU OC1W ICJ MB

Litch, Wilbur Fisk, 1840-1912.
Anaesthesia and anaesthetics. [Philadelphia, Lea Brothers & Co., 1887]
p.19-216. illus. 24cm.
Caption title.
Extract from The American system of dentistry ... Ed. by Wilbur F. Litch. v.3, p.19-216, 1887.

NL 0406689 IEN-D PPC MB

Litch, William B.
Autopsy, by William B. Litch ... [Oregon, Ill., "Independent" book and job print, 1884]
cover-title, [16] p. 17½cm.
In verse.

I. Title.
Library of Congress PS2248.L27 35-36884
Copyright 1884: 6714 811.49

NL 0406690 DLC

374.24
L71
Litchen, Ruth E
How to use group discussion. Washington, 1952.
7p. 28cm. (National Council for the Social Studies. How to do it series, no.6)
Caption title.
Bibliography: p.7.

1. Discussion. I. Title. II. Series.

NL 0406691 OrU

LB1045
.N38
no.6
1955
Litchen, Ruth E
How to use group discussion. rev. ed. Washington, National Council for the Social Studies, 1955.
7 p. 28cm. (National Council for the Social Studies. How to do it series no. 6)
Bibliography: p. 7.
1. Forums (Discussion and debate. I. Ser.

NL 0406692 ViU NRU

Litcher, Henry Leonard.
The universal link; an exposition of the cosmic forces and their relation to the plant and animal kingdoms, by Henry Leonard Litcher, A. O. C. [San Jose, Calif., The Primordial publishing association, °1934-
v. diagrs. 24cm.

I. Title.
Library of Congress Q173.L75 35-974
———— Copy 2.
Copyright A 77867 [2] 500

NL 0406693 DLC

Litchfield, Beals Ensign, 1823-
Autobiography of Beals E. Litchfield; or, Forty years intercourse with the denizens of the spirit world and inspirational poems by the same author. Ellicottville, N. Y., B. E. Litchfield, 1893.
xv, [17]-486 p. front. (port.) 22cm.

1. Spiritualism.
Library of Congress BF1283.L5A3 32-35954 920.9

NL 0406694 DLC TxU CaOLU

Litchfield, Beals Ensign, 1823-
Leaflets of thought gathered from the tree of life. Containing some of the experience of a spirit who has been in spirit life fifty-seven years. Presented to humanity through the mediumship of B. E. Litchfield... New York: The Law and trade prtg. co., 1890. xvi, 287 p. 2 ports. (incl. front.) 18½cm.

17016B. 1. Spiritualism—Communications.
N. Y. P. L. March 26, 1940

NL 0406695 NN

Litchfield, Dorothy Hale, 1902- ed.
Classified list of 4800 serials currently received in the libraries of the University of Pennsylvania and of Bryn Mawr, Haverford, and Swarthmore colleges, edited by Dorothy Hale Litchfield ... for the Board of graduate education and research. Philadelphia, University of Pennsylvania press, 1936.
ix, 411 p. 23½ cm.
Bibliography: p. xxxvii-lvii.
1. Periodicals—Bibl.—Union lists. 2. Libraries—Pennsylvania. I. Pennsylvania. University. Board of graduate education and research. II. Pennsylvania. University. Library. III. Bryn Mawr college. Library. IV. Haverford college. Library. V. Swarthmore college, Swarthmore, Pa. Library. VI. Title.
Library of Congress Z6945.L778 36-21309
[a50q1] 016.05

NL 0406696 DLC NcRS PBm PV PP MiU OC1CC OCU OU ODW OO OC1 OC1W IdU CoU NN WaWW WaS OrU OrCS MtU

Litchfield, Dorothy Hale, 1902-
Microfilm reading machines ... by D. H. Litchfield and M. A. Bennett. New York [The authors] 1943.
4 pts. in 1 v. 24½cm.
Cover-title.
"Reprints of a series of articles in Special libraries, vol. 34, 1943."
Includes "References."

1. Reading machines. I. Bennett, Mary Angela, 1906- joint author. II. Title.
Columbia univ. Libraries for Library of Congress [4] A 44-406

NL 0406697 NNC NcRS CU PSt PU

---

ar X
1832
Litchfield, Edward H plaintiff.
Litchfield vs. Sisson and Liston. [v.p., 1901-02]
61, v. 299 p. maps. 27cm.
Binder's title.
Contains the argument by the counsel for the defendents before the N. Y. Supreme Court, Franklin Co., and the case on appeal before the N. Y. Supreme Court, Appellate Division, 3d Dept.
I. Sisson, George W defendent. II. Liston, James, defendent.

NL 0406698 NIC

Litchfield, Edward Harold, 1914-
Another chapter in Michigan civil service reform ... [n.p., 1941?]
[1], 76-82 p. 25 cm.
Reprinted from the American political science review, vol. XXXV, no. 1, February, 1941.
(In his Collected writings, v. 1.)

NL 0406699 RPB

Litchfield, Edward Harold, 1914-
[Collected writings]
v. 31 cm.
Reprints and articles from magazines.

NL 0406700 RPB

Litchfield, Edward Harold, 1914- ed.
Governing postwar Germany, by Edward H. Litchfield and associates: Arnold Brecht [and others] Ithaca, N. Y., Cornell University Press [1953]
xvii, 661 p. illus. 25 cm.
Bibliographical footnotes.

1. Germany—Pol. & govt.—1945- I. Title.
JN3971.A58L5 354.43 53-12380

NL 0406701 DLC MB TxU OOxM OC1 OO ODW OC1W NcD NN TU NIC ViU NcC PPT PU OCU PV OU PPL PSt MiU OrP OrC CaBVaU ScU ICU OrU OrPR WaS WaT CaBVa IdPI Or

---

Litchfield, Edward Harold, 1914-
The "open back door" - a case study ... [n.p., 1941?]
cover-title, 6 p. 23 cm.
Reprinted from National municipal review, vol. XXX, no. 2, February 1941.
(In his Collected writings, v. 1.)

NL 0406702 RPB

VOLUME 336

JF 1338 A2 L78 Litchfield,Edward Harold,1914-
Public service training. ₍n.p., 1943₎
₍8₎ l. 29 cm.
Cover title.

1.Public administration--Study and teaching. I.Title.

NL 0406703 MiU

Litchfield, Edward Harold, 1914- joint author.

Benson, George Charles Sumner, 1908–
... The State administrative board in Michigan; a study of central administrative controls by a plural executive, by George C. S. Benson ... with the collaboration of Edward H. Litchfield ... Ann Arbor, University of Michigan press, 1938.

Wason JQ770 L77 Litchfield, Edward Harold, 1914-
Training for administration in Indonesia, by Edward H. Litchfield and Alan C. Rankin. Ithaca, N. Y., School of Business and Public Administration, Cornell University, 1954.
iii,47 p. tables. 22cm.

1. Public administration--Study and teaching. 2. Indonesia--Pol. & govt. I. Rankin, Alan C joint author. II. Cornell University. Graduate School of Business and Public Adminis tration. III. Title.

NL 0406705 NIC

Litchfield, Edward Harold, 1914–
... Voting behavior in a metropolitan area, by Edward H. Litchfield ... Ann Arbor, University of Michigan press, 1941.
vii, 98 p. incl. tables. fold. map, diagrs. (part fold.) 23 cm. (University of Michigan. ₍Bureau of government₎ Michigan governmental studies, no. 7)
Thesis (PH. D.)—University of Michigan, 1940.
Thesis note in preface.
"This study of voting behavior in the city of Detroit ... covers five elections during the years 1930 to 1938, including two presidential elections."—Pref.
1. Voting. 2. Elections—Detroit. I. Title.
41—52812
Library of Congress JS847.A3L55
₍a49e½₎ 324.77434

PPT RPB WaTC OrU
NL 0406706 DLC DAU MoU N MiU FMU OCl ViU ODW PSt

[Litchfield, Edward Harold] 1914-
When the Republicans win. III. Pipe-line government in Michigan. Article in the New Republic, vol. 103, no. 9, August 26, 1940.
p. 270-272. 31 cm. (In his Collected writings, v. 1.)

NL 0406707 RPB

018.2 L776e Litchfield, Edward Hubert.
The Edward Hubert Litchfield library of standard sets, art reference and other books. The second and final part. Public auction sale, December 11... December 12... New York, Parke-Bernet Galleries, inc, 1951.
87p. 24cm.

"Sale no. 1297"
763 titles
1.Art - Catalogs. 2.Bibliography - Rare books. I. Parke-Bernet Galleries, inc., New York. II. Title.

NL 0406708 CLSU

Pamphlet F New York 71 Litchfield, Edwin C.
Motives to effort in America. An address before the Young Men's Association for mutual improvement in the village of West Troy, delivered February 13, 1840. Troy, N.Y., N. Tuttle, book and job printer, 1840.
31 p. 20cm.

NL 0406709 NIC

LITCHFIELD, ELECTUS D , firm, New York.
Some examples of the work of Electus D. Litchfield, architect. [New York, Architectural catalog co.] 1930. 1 v. of plates. 34cm.

I. Architectural catalog company, inc., New York.

NL 0406710 NN

Litchfield, Electus Darwin, 1872–
An architectural monograph on Portsmouth, N. H., an early American metropolis, with text by Electus D. Litchfield; prepared for publication by Russell F. Whitehead ... ₍Saint Paul, White pine bureau₎ 1921.
16 p. illus. 29cm. (*On cover:* The white pine series of architectural monographs. vol. VII, no. 1)

1. Architecture, Domestic—Portsmouth, N. H. 2. Architecture, Colonial. I. Whitehead, Russell Fenimore, 1884– II. Title.
21-6874
Library of Congress NA7238.P6L5
——— Copy 2. NA1.W6 vol. VII, no. 1

OC1MA MB
NL 0406711 DLC WaS OrU FU NcD MsU MeB ViU MiU MU

Litchfield, Electus Darwin, 1872-
Electus Litchfield collection
see under [Columbia university. Libraries Avery architectural library. Electus Litchfield collection]

Litchfield, Esther.
Sands of Scituate, by Esther Litchfield. Boston, Mass., The Stratford company ₍©1933₎
2 p. l., iii, 63 p. 19½cm.
Poems.

I. Title.
33-15890
Library of Congress PS3523.I 78S3 1933
Copyright A 63273 ₍2₎ 811.5

NL 0406713 DLC

Litchfield, Francis.
Three years' results of the Farthinghoe clothing society, with a few remarks on the policy of encouraging provident habits among the working classes ... Northampton, Printed by J.Freeman ₍etc., etc.₎ 1832.
22 p. 21.5 cm.

NL 0406714 MH-BA NN

Litchfield, Frederick, 1850-1930.
Antiques, genuine and spurious; an art expert's recollections and cautions, by Frederick Litchfield ... London, G. Bell and sons, ltd., 1921.
xiii p., 1 l., 277 p. col. front., plates, port. 24cm.
CONTENTS.—Introductory.—Porcelain.—Furniture.—Enamels.—Bronzes.—Recollections and some stories.—Reference to museums and private collections.

1. Art objects—Collectors and collecting. 2. Forgery of works of art. I. Title.
21—10782
Library of Congress NK1125.L5

OC1 NN MB
NL 0406715 DLC ICJ WaS OrP ICRL OClh ICJ PP CtY

Litchfield, Frederick, 1850-1930.
Antiques, genuine and spurious; an art expert's recollections and cautions, by Frederick Litchfield ... London, G. Bell and sons, ltd., 1924.
xiii p., 1 l., 277 p. col. front., plates, port. 24cm.
"Cheaper reissue May 1924."
CONTENTS. — Introductory. — Porcelain. — Furniture. — Enamels. — Bronzes.—Recollections and some stories.—Reference to museums and private collections.

NL 0406716 ViU

Litchfield, Frederick, 1850-1930.
... The collection of old Worcester porcelain ..
see under Drane, Robert, 1833-1914.

Litchfield, Frederick, 1850- ed.

Chaffers, William, 1811-1892.
Collectors' handbook of marks & monographs on pottery & porcelain. Ed. by Frederick Lichfield ₍!₎ assisted by R. L. Hobson and Justus Brinkman. ₍New ed.₎ Los Angeles, Borden Pub. Co., 1947.

Litchfield, Frederick, 1850-1930.
How to collect old furniture, by Frederick Litchfield ... ₍3d impression₎ London, G. Bell and sons, 1904.
xiv, 169, ₍1₎ p. front., illus., plates, facsim. 21½cm.

1. Furniture. 2. Collectors and collecting. I. Title.
Library of Congress NK2240.L7 5—11697

CU ICJ MB CaBVa CaBVaU ICJ
NL 0406719 DLC WaU MiGr PU PP OClSA OCl OCIMA CtY

Litchfield, Frederick, 1850-1930.
How to collect old furniture, by Frederick Litchfield ... London, G. Bell and sons, 1906.
xiv, 169, ₍1₎ p. front., illus., plates, facsim. 21½cm.
"Fourth impression, May, 1906."

NL 0406720 ViU NN

Litchfield, Frederick, 1850-1930.
How to collect old furniture. London: G. Bell and Sons, Ltd., 1920. 169 p. illus., pl. 8°.

NL 0406721 NN CtY

Litchfield, Frederick, 1850-1930.
Illustrated history of furniture: from the earliest to the present time. London. Truslove & Shirley. 1892. xvi, 280 pp. Illus. Plates. L. 8°.
*4101.58

G7328 — Furniture. Hist.

NL 0406722 MB PPD PPL MiU

Film 2597 Litchfield, Frederick, 1850-
Illustrated history of furniture, from the earliest to the present time. With numerous illus. 2d ed. London, Truslove & Shirley, 1892.
xviii, 282 p. illus., plans.

Microfilm (negative). ₍Columbus, Ohio State University Libraries, Photoduplication Services, 1970₎ 1 reel. 35 mm.
1. Furniture - History. I. Title.

NL 0406723 OU KMK MiGr MdBP MiD

VOLUME 336

Litchfield, Frederick, 1850-

NK2270 L55 Illustrated history of furniture: from the earliest to the present time. By Frederick Litchfield ... Boston, Estes & Lauriat, 1893.

280 p. front., illus., plates, plans. 28 1/2 cm. Brown cloth.
"This work is limited to an edition of two hundred copies for America. This copy is no. 26"
"List of the names of some artists and manufacturers of past times ..." p. [251]-262.
Errata on p. [268]

1. Furniture— History.

NL 0406724 CSmH MdBWA MWA MH

NK 2270 L77 1893 Litchfield, Frederick, 1850-
Illustrated history of furniture, from the earliest to the present time. 3d ed. London, Truslove and Hanson, 1893.
xx, 280 p. illus. 29 cm.

First edition published in 1892.
"List of the names of some artists and manufacturers of past times": p. ⌐251⌐-262.

1. Furniture - History. I. Title.

NL 0406725 OU MeB NcRS DDO ViU PP PU

NK 2270 L77 1899 Litchfield, Frederick, 1850-
Illustrated history of furniture, from the earliest to the present time. 4th ed. London, Truslove, Hanson & Comba, 1899.
xx, 272 p. col. front., illus., plans. 26cm.

First ed. published in 1892.
1. Furniture--History. I. Title.

NL 0406726 NIC CaBVaU PPPM ICN OU OC1W

NK 2270 .L7 1903 Litchfield, Frederick, 1850-
Illustrated history of furniture, from the earliest to the present time, by Frederick Litchfield. ⌐5th ed.⌐ London, Truslove and Hanson ltd. New York, J. Lane, 1903.
xviii, 272p. col. front., illus.
First edition published in 1892.

1. Furniture--Hist. I. Title.

NL 0406727 INS CtY CU TU MB

Litchfield, Frederick, 1850-1930.
Illustrated history of furniture, from the earliest to the present time, containing over three hundred and fifty illustrations of representative examples of the different periods, by Frederick Litchfield ... 6th ed., rev. and considerably enl. London, Truslove and Hanson ltd., 1907.
xxii, 358 p. col. front., illus., plans. 26½cm.
"List of the names of some artists and manufacturers of past times ...": p. ⌐332⌐-345.
First edition published in 1892.
1. Furniture—Hist.

Library of Congress NK2270.L7 9—29395

NN ICJ ViU NjR OC1MA CaBVaU
NL 0406728 DLC MtU WaS MnU-A TU PP OC1 ODW OOxM

NK2270 L5 1922 Litchfield, Frederick, 1850-
Illustrated history of furniture, from the earliest to the present time, containing 400 illus. of representative examples of the different periods. [2d American ed. uniform with the rev. and enl. 7th British ed.] Boston, Medici Society of America [1922]
xviii, 459 p. col. front., illus., plates.

1. Furniture - Hist.

NL 0406729 CU ICU CtY ViU

Litchfield, Frederick, 1850-
Illustrated history of furniture, from the earliest to the present time, containing four hundred illustrations of representative examples of the different periods, by Frederick Litchfield ... 7th ed., rev. and considerably enl. London, Truslove and Hanson, ltd. ⌐1922⌐
xviii, 459 p. col. front., illus., pl. 28 cm.
First edition published in 1892.
"List of the names of some artists and manufacturers of past times ...": p. ⌐429⌐-443.
1. Furniture—Hist.

NK2270.L7 1922 23—8912

PPPM NN NcU MiGr OC1 OOxM IdU WaS
NL 0406730 DLC NcD PP OC1h NcU MiU KU TU OU MB

Litchfield, Frederick, 1850- ed.

Chaffers, William, 1811-1892.
Marks & monograms on European and oriental pottery and porcelain. Ed. by Frederick Lichfield ⌐!⌐ assisted by R. L. Hobson ⌐and⌐ Justus Brinkman. 14th rev. ed. Los Angeles, Borden Pub. Co., 1946.

Litchfield, Frederick, 1850- ed.

Chaffers, William, 1811-1892.
The new collector's hand-book of marks and monograms on pottery & porcelain of the renaissance and modern periods, with upwards of 5000 marks, by William Chaffers; chiefly selected from his larger work entitled "Marks and monograms on pottery and porcelain". A new ed. (1914) rev. and considerably augm. by Frederick Litchfield ... London, Reeves and Turner, 1914.

Litchfield, Frederick, 1850-
Pottery and porcelain; a guide to collectors. London, Bickers, 1879.
vi, 215 p. illus. 20cm.

1. Pottery—Hist. 2. Pottery—Marks. 3. Pottery—Collectors and collecting. I. Title.

NL 0406733 MB

Litchfield, Frederick, 1850-
Pottery and porcelain: a guide to collectors. By Frederick Litchfield ... 2d ed. London, Bickers & son, 1880.
xv, 211 p. incl. front., illus., plates, port. 20 cm.

1. Pottery—Hist. 2. Porcelain—Hist. 3. Pottery—Collectors and collecting. 4. Porcelain—Collectors and collecting.

Library of Congress NK4230.L7 1880 34—24530
⌐a49b½⌐ 738

NL 0406734 DLC

NK 4230 L776 1884 Litchfield, Frederick, 1850-1930.
Pottery and porcelain: a guide to collectors. 3d. ed., rev. and augmented. London, Bickers, 1884.
216p. illus. 20cm.

1. Pottery - Hist. 2. Porcelain - Hist. 3. Pottery - Collectors and collecting. 4. Porcelain - Collectors and collecting. 5. Pottery - Marks.

NL 0406735 MU DDO

Litchfield, Frederick, 1850-
Pottery and porcelain; a guide to collectors, by Frederick Litchfield ... Containing 150 illustrations of specimens of various factories, 7 coloured plates, and marks and monograms of all the important markers. London and New York, Truslove, Hanson & Comba, ltd., 1900.
xv, 362 p. col. front., illus., plates (part col.) 26cm.
First edition published in 1879.

1. Pottery—Hist. 2. Pottery—Marks. 3. Pottery—Collectors and collecting.

Library of Congress NK4230.L7 1900 1—12550

PPL OC1MA
NL 0406736 DLC MB OU MiU ICJ MB CSmH WaU ODW PPPM

NK 4230 L776 1905 Litchfield, Frederick, 1850-1930.
Pottery and porcelain; a guide to collectors. New ed. rev. & enl. New York, J. Lane, 1905.
399p. illus. 26cm.

1. Pottery - Hist. 2. Porcelain - Hist. 3. Pottery - Collectors and collecting. 4. Porcelain - Collectors and collecting. 5. Pottery - Marks. I. Title.

NL 0406737 MU ICJ

Litchfield, Frederick, 1850-
Pottery & porcelain; a guide to collectors, by Frederick Litchfield... Containing nearly two hundred illustrations of specimens of various factories, nine coloured plates, and marks and monograms of all the important makers. New edition, revised and considerably augmented. London: Truslove & Hanson, Ltd., 1912. xvi, 510 p., 46 pl. (9 col'd). illus. 4°.
Bibliography, p. 486-487.

1. Pottery.—Handbooks. 2. Pottery. —Marks and monograms.
N. Y. P. L. December 10, 1914.

NL 0406738 NN MdBWA CU OC1 PP

Litchfield, Frederick, 1850-
Pottery and porcelain; a guide to collectors, by Frederick Litchfield ... 4th ed., new, completely rev. and improved, containing seventy-two full-page plates—eight of them in colour—also numerious illustrations in the text, including the marks and monograms of all the important makers. New York, The Macmillan company, 1925.
xv, 464 p. illus. 72 pl. (part col.; incl. col. front.) 25½ cm.
Printed in Great Britain.
"First edition published in 1879."
Bibliography: p. 435-436.
1. Pottery—Hist. 2. Porcelain—Hist. 3. Pottery—Collectors and collecting. 4. Porcelain—Collectors and collecting. 5. Pottery—Marks.

NK4230.L7 1925 26-26145

CaBViPA Or WaS
OC1MA OC1 OLak OC1L WaE OrP NcD WaT IdU CaBVaU
NL 0406739 DLC PPL OO MB NjNbS OC1W NN PPT PP

Litchfield Frederick, 1850-
Pottery and porcelain: a guide to collectors. 6th ed. Revised by Frank Tilley, containing the marks and monograms of the important factories. New York, M. Barrows [1950?]

356 p. illus.

1. Pottery - Hist. 2. Pottery - Marks. 3. Pottery - Collectors and collecting.

NL 0406740 WaTC IdB

Litchfield, Frederick, 1850-
Pottery and porcelain, a guide to collectors. 5th ed., enl. and completely rev. by Frank Tilley. Containing the marks and monograms of the important factories. New York, M. Barrows ⌐1951⌐
xii, 356 p. illus. (part col.) 26 cm.
Bibliography: p. 331-334.

1. Pottery—Hist. 2. Porcelain—Hist. 3. Pottery—Collectors and collecting. 4. Porcelain — Collectors and collecting. 5. Pottery — Marks.

NK4230.L7 1951 738 51-14172

WaT OOxM
NL 0406741 DLC NN Vi CU MB PSt CaBViPA Or Wa WaS

Litchfield, Frederick, 1850-1930.
Pottery and porcelain; a guide to collectors. 6th ed. rev. by Frank Tilley. Containing the marks and monograms of the important factories. London, A. and C. Black ⌐1953⌐
xii, 356 p. illus. (part col.) 26 cm.
Bibliography: p. 331-334.

1. Pottery—Hist. 2. Porcelain—Hist. 3. Pottery—Collectors and collecting. 4. Porcelain — Collectors and collecting. 5. Pottery — Marks.

NK4230.L7 1953 738 53—2226

NL 0406742 DLC TU MB MnU-A MH OrU MiU CSt AAP OrCS

VOLUME 336

Litchfield, George A. Which is the best form of life insurance? 1. Natural-premium system. 6 pp. (*N. Am. Rev.* v. 156, 1893, p. 594.)

NL 0406743 MdBP

Litchfield, Gertrude.
Les enfants; a book of verse in French-Canadian dialect [by] Gertrude Litchfield. Boston, R. G. Badger, 1911.
61 p. 19½cm. $1.25

11-749

NL 0406744 DLC MiU NN MB

Litchfield, Grace Denio, 1849-
As a man sows, and other stories, by Grace Denio Litchfield ... New York, London, G. P. Putnam's sons, 1926.
vii, 388 p. 19½cm.
CONTENTS.—As a man sows.—The question.—Tangle-town.—"Hearts are dust, hearts' loves remain."—A desecrated memory.—An erring Saint John.—Two sides of a triangle.—The little brown bungalow.—The day of deliverance.—Peace and the sword.—One result.—When the Brownes came back.—The old Springfield rifle.
I. Title.
Library of Congress PZ3.L71As 26-11634

NL 0406745 DLC

Litchfield, Grace Denio, 1849-
Baldur the beautiful. n.p., n.d.
62 l. 21 cm.

NL 0406746 RPB

Litchfield, Grace Denio, 1849-
Baldur the Beautiful, by Grace Denio Litchfield ... New York and London, G. P. Putnam's sons, 1910.
ix, 73 p. 17½cm. $1.00

11-545

NL 0406747 DLC FU PU PP OU OO NIC

Litchfield, Grace Denio, 1849-
The burning question, by Grace Denio Litchfield ... New York and London, G. P. Putnam's sons, 1913.
vi p., 1 l., 307 p. 19cm. $1.25
I. Title.
Library of Congress PZ3.L71B 13-3071

NL 0406748 DLC OCl

Litchfield, Grace Denio, 1849-
Collected poems [by] Grace Denio Litchfield. New York and London, G. P. Putnam's sons, 1913.
ix, 341 p. 19½cm. $1.75

Library of Congress PS2249.L2 1913 13-24129

NL 0406749 DLC WaS NcD OO OClW MiU NN MB

Litchfield, Grace Denio, 1849-
Collected poems [by] Grace Denio Litchfield. New York and London, G. P. Putnam's sons, 1922.
x, 413 p. 19cm. $1.75

Library of Congress PS2248.L3 1922 22-23319

NL 0406750 DLC

Litchfield, Grace Denio, 1849-
Criss-Cross, by Grace Denio Litchfield ... New York & London, G. P. Putnam's sons, 1885.
iv, 256 p. 17½cm.

Library of Congress PZ3.L71C 7-19002†

NL 0406751 DLC NN NcD MdBP OU MiU MB CU PPL

M-film
810.8
Am35
336-3

Litchfield, Grace Denio, 1849-
Criss-cross. New York, G. P. Putnam's Sons, 1885.
iv, 256 p.

Microfilm (positive) Ann Arbor, Mich., University Microfilms, 1977. 3d title of 13. 35 mm. (American fiction series, reel 336.3)

NL 0406752 KEmT

Litchfield, Grace Denio, 1849-
A hard-won victory, by Grace Denio Litchfield ... New York and London, G. P. Putnam's sons, 1888.
1 p. l., 384 p. 17½cm.

I. Title.
Library of Congress PZ3.L71H 7-19001

NL 0406753 DLC CU PPL NcD MiU MB

M-film
810.8
Am35
336-4

Litchfield, Grace Denio, 1849-
A hard-won victory. New York, G. P. Putnam's Sons, 1888.
384 p.

Microfilm (positive) Ann Arbor, Mich., University Microfilms, 1977. 4th title of 13. 35 mm. (American fiction series, reel 336.4)

NL 0406754 KEmT

Litchfield, Grace Denio, 1849-
In the crucible [a novel] by Grace Denio Litchfield ... New York [etc.] G. P. Putnam's sons, 1897.
iv p., 1 l., 344 p. 20cm. (The Hudson library. no. 18)

I. Title.
Library of Congress PZ3.L71 I 7-19000

NL 0406755 DLC WaS NcD CU NcU CtY OCl NN

Litchfield, Grace Denio, 1849-
In the hospital, by Grace Denio Litchfield. New York and London, G. P. Putnam's sons, 1885.
2 p. l., 14 p. 17cm.
Verse.

I. Title.
Library of Congress PS2248.L3 I 5 28-4764

NL 0406756 DLC MB CtY

Litchfield, Grace Denio, 1849-
The knight of the Black Forest, by Grace Denio Litchfield ... New York & London, G. P. Putnam's sons, 1885.
1 p. l., 169 p. front., plates. 17½cm.

I. Title.
Library of Congress PZ3.L71K 7-18999

NL 0406757 DLC NcD KEmT PPL CU MiU MB

Litchfield, Grace Denio, 1849-
The knight of the Black Forest, by Grace Denio Litchfield ... New York & London, G. P. Putnam's sons, 1894.
1 p. l., 169 p. front., plates. 17½cm.

NL 0406758 ViU

PS
2248
.L3D619

Litchfield, Grace Denio, 1849-
Läkaren; en dikt. Fritt från engelskan, efter Grace D. Litchfield, i originalets versmått, af Oscar Alf. Fliesburg. [Minneapolis, Tryckt hos Olson, Sjöstrand & Co., 1898]
15 p. 18 cm.

On cover: From The doctor's window.

NL 0406759 MnHi

Litchfield, Grace Denio, 1849-
The letter D, by Grace Denio Litchfield ... New York, Dodd, Mead and company, 1904.
4 p. l., 322 p. 19½cm.

I. Title.
Library of Congress PZ3.L71L 4-25682

NL 0406760 DLC CLSU OClW OCl

PZ7
.L711
Li

Litchfield, Grace Denio, 1849-
Little he and she, by Grace Denio Litchfield ... illustrations by Louis Meynelle. Boston, D. Lothrop company [©1890]
3 p. l., 11-175 p. front., illus., plates. 21cm.

NL 0406761 MB

Litchfield, Grace Denio, 1849-
Little Venice, and other stories, by Grace Denio Litchfield ... New York and London, G. P. Putnam's sons, 1890.
3 p. l., 298 p. front. 17½cm.
CONTENTS.—Little Venice. — Selina's singular marriage. — Myrtle.—One chapter.—An American flirtation.—La Rochefoucauld's saying.—Hilary's husband.—The price I paid for a set of Ruskin.

I. Title.
Library of Congress PZ3.L71Li 7-18998

NL 0406762 DLC NcD CU PPL OClW OCl ViU MB

Litchfield, Grace Denio, 1849-
Mimosa leaves [poems] by Grace Denio Litchfield; illustrated by Helen & Margaret Armstrong. New York, G. P. Putnam's sons, 1895.
ix p., 1 l., 112 p. illus. 17½cm.
Title within ornamental border.
Many of the poems have appeared in various magazines. *cf.* p. v.

I. Title.
Library of Congress PS2248.L3M5 12-36175

NL 0406763 DLC ViU PP NjP NBuG

VOLUME 336

Litchfield, Grace Denio, 1849-
The moving finger writes, by Grace Denio Litchfield ... New York & London, G. P. Putnam's sons, 1900.
iv p., 1 l., 265 p. 20cm.

I. Title.

Library of Congress PZ3.L71M 1-29076 rev.

NL 0406764 DLC WaS NcD CU PPL ViU NN MB

Litchfield, Grace Denio, 1849-
Narcissus, and other poems, by Grace Denio Litchfield ... New York and London, G. P. Putnam's sons, 1908.
2 p. l., iii-v, 60 p. 17½cm.
Largely reprinted from the Century magazine, the Bookman and the Independent.

8-12552

NL 0406765 DLC FU PU ViU NN MB

Litchfield, Grace Denio, 1849-
The nun of Kent; a drama in five acts, by Grace Denio Litchfield ... New York and London, G. P. Putnam's sons, 1911.
3 p. l., 125 p. 17½cm. $1.00

11-29629

NL 0406766 DLC ViU MdBP PU PHC PP NN MB

Litchfield, Grace Denio, 1849-
Only an incident, by Grace Denio Litchfield. New York [etc.] G. P. Putnam's sons, 1883.
2 p. l., iii, 226 p. 17½cm.

I. Title.

Library of Congress PZ3.L71O 7—18997

NL 0406767 DLC NcD CU PPGi PPL MB

M-film
810.8
Am35
336-5

Litchfield, Grace Denio, 1849-
Only an incident, New York, G. P. Putnam's Sons [c1883]
iii, 226 p.

Microfilm (positive) Ann Arbor, Mich., University Microfilms, 1977. 5th title of 13. 35 mm. (American fiction series, reel 336.5)

NL 0406768 KEmT

Litchfield, Grace Denio, 1849-
The song of the sirens, by Grace Denio Litchfield. New York and London, G. P. Putnam's sons, 1917.
2 p. l., 99 p. 17½cm. $1.00
Alternate pages blank.

I. Title.

Library of Congress PS2248.L3S6 17-11825

NL 0406769 DLC FU PU OC1W ViU

Litchfield, Grace Denio, 1849-
The supreme gift, by Grace Denio Litchfield ... with a frontispiece by Alice Barber Stephens. Boston, Little, Brown, and company, 1908.
2 p. l., 300 p., 1 l. col. front. 20cm.

I. Title.

Library of Congress PZ3.L71Su 8-9529

NL 0406770 DLC PPL NN

Litchfield, Grace Denio, 1849-
The top of the ladder. Plate.
(In Greene, Sarah P. McL. Peter-Patrick and other boys. Pp. 104-121. Boston. [1887.]) 23.84

NL 0406771 MB

Litchfield, Grace Denio, 1849-
Vita; a drama [by] Grace Denio Litchfield. Boston, R. G. Badger, 1904.
3 p. l., 5-56 p. 20cm.

I. Title.

Library of Congress PS2248.L3V5 4-9941

NL 0406772 DLC OrU WaU WU OrU NcD NN

Litchfield, H Elizabeth

Life's web, and other poems ... Bath, Me. [R. W. Stearns print] 1892.
1p.l., [5]-15, [1]p. 17cm.

Imperfect copy: pp.7-10 wanting.

NL 0406773 RPB

Litchfield, Harold Spencer, 1893-
Song to Bruno [by] Harold S. Litchfield '20. In, Brown university - Commencement 1923. Presentation of the bronze Bruno for Brown ... [Providence, 1923] 17 cm. p. [2]

NL 0406774 RPB

Litchfield, Harry Robert, 1898-
Care of the infant and child; a book for mothers and nurses, by Harry R. Litchfield ... and Leon H. Dembo ... Baltimore, Waverly press, inc., 1930.
xi, 138 p. illus. 20½cm.

1. Infants—Care and hygiene. 2. Children—Care and hygiene. I. Dembo, Leon Haskins, 1895- joint author. II. Title.

31-34381 Revised

Library of Congress RJ61.L65
[r45d2] 649.1

NL 0406775 DLC KEmT DNLM ICJ OC1

WB
5
qL776c
1953

LITCHFIELD, Harry Robert, 1898-
Collected reprints of published manuscripts, by H. R. Litchfield and co-authors. [Brooklyn, 1953]
1 v. (various pagings) illus.
1. Medicine - Collected works

NL 0406776 DNLM

Litchfield, Harry Robert, 1898-
A pediatric manual for mothers; questions and answers on the care and feeding of infants and children [by] Harry R. Litchfield and Leon H. Dembo. New York, Grune & Stratton, 1951.
269 p. 19 cm.

1. Infants—Care and hygiene. 2. Children—Care and hygiene. I. Title.
RJ61.L66 618.92 51-6199 ‡

NL 0406777 TU DLC OrCS WaS MB OC1W-H ICU LU ICJ DNLM

RJ45
.L58

Litchfield, Harry Robert, 1898- ed.
Pediatric progress, therapeutics of infancy and childhood, edited by Harry R. Litchfield and Leon H. Dembo. Philadelphia, F.A. Davis Co., 1948-
v. illus. (part col.) 26 cm.

Includes bibliographies.
Supplement to Therapeutics of infancy and childhood.

NL 0406778 TU ICU DNLM OC1W PPSKF

Litchfield, Harry Robert, 1898- *ed.*
Therapeutics of infancy and childhood, edited by Harry R. Litchfield ... and Leon H. Dembo ... 117 contributors ... Philadelphia, F. A. Davis company, 1942.
4 v. illus., col. plates, map, tables, diagrs. 25½cm.
"References" at end of some of the chapters.
RJ45.L5 1942
—— —— Desk index. Philadelphia, F. A. Davis company [1943]
1 p. l., 203 p. 25½cm.
1. Infants—Diseases. 2. Children—Diseases. I. Dembo, Leon Haskins, 1895- joint ed. II. Title.

42-17682 Revised 2

Library of Congress RJ45.L5 1942 Desk index
[r46g2] 618.9

NL 0406779 DLC ICJ ICRL PPC

Litchfield, Harry Robert, 1898- *ed.*
Therapeutics of infancy and childhood, edited by Harry R. Litchfield ... and Leon H. Dembo ... 117 contributors ... Philadelphia, F. A. Davis company, 1943.
4 v. illus., col. plates, maps, tables, diagrs. 25½cm.
Paged continuously.
"References" at end of some of the chapters.
RJ45.L5 1943
—— —— Desk index. Philadelphia, F. A. Davis company [1943]
1 p. l., 204 p. 25½cm.
1. Infants—Diseases. 2. Children—Diseases. I. Dembo, Leon Haskins, 1895- joint ed. II. Title.

43-14929 Revised

Library of Congress RJ45.L5 1943 Index
[r45e2] 618.92

NL 0406780 DLC NcU-H

Litchfield, Harry Robert, 1898- *ed.*
Therapeutics of infancy and childhood, edited by Harry R. Litchfield ... and Leon H. Dembo ... 119 contributors ... 2d rev. ed. Philadelphia, F. A. Davis company, 1945.
4 v. illus., col. plates, map, tables, diagrs. 25½ cm.
Paged continuously.
"References" at end of some of the chapters.
RJ45.L5 1945
—— —— Desk index. 2d rev. ed. Philadelphia, F. A. Davis company, 1945.
123 p. 25½ cm.
1. Infants—Diseases. 2. Children—Diseases. I. Dembo, Leon Haskins, 1895- joint ed. II. Title.

U. S. Army Medical Libr. for Library of Congress RJ45.L5 1945 Index S G 45—300
[a50d1]† 618.92

NL 0406781 DNLM OC1W-H OU ICJ DLC

Litchfield, Harry Robert, 1898- *ed.*
Therapeutics of infancy and childhood, ed. by Harry R. Litchfield and Leon H. Dembo. 3d ed. Philadelphia, F. A. Davis Co., 1947.
4 v. (3829 p.) illus. (part col.) 26 cm.
Includes bibliographies.
RJ45.L5 1947
—— —— Desk index. 3d ed. Philadelphia, F. A. Davis Co., 1947.
148 p. 26 cm.
RJ45.L5 1947a

Continued in next column

VOLUME 336

Continued from preceding column

——— Pediatric progress. Philadelphia, F. A. Davis Co., 1948–
v. illus. (part col.) 26 cm.
Includes bibliographies.

1. Infants—Diseases. 2. Children—Diseases. I. Dembo, Leon Haskins, 1895– joint ed. II. Title.
RJ45.L5 1947b 618.92 Med 47-609 rev*
U. S. Army Medical Libr. for Library of Congress [WS366qL776t 1947] [r48m3†

NL 0406783 DLC DNLM OrU-M CaBVaU MsSM ICJ FU-HC PPT-M

Litchfield, *Mrs.* Henrietta Emma (Darwin) 1843– ed.
Emma Darwin, a century of family letters, 1792–1896, ed. by her daughter Henrietta Litchfield ... London, J. Murray, 1915.
2 v. fronts., plates, ports., geneal. tables. 22½cm.
Vol. 2 contains letters of Charles Robert Darwin.

1. Darwin, Mrs. Emma (Wedgwood) 1808–1896. 2. Darwin, Charles Robert, 1809–1882. 3. Darwin family.
15—15708
Library of Congress CT788.

NL 0406784 DLC ViU CU NIC PPL PU PBm OCl OO OClW MiU CtY NN ICJ MB ICN TU OrPR WaS CaBVaU

Litchfield, Henrietta Emma (Darwin) 1843– ed.
Emma Darwin, a century of family letters, 1792–1896, edited by her daughter Henrietta Litchfield ... New York, D. Appleton and company, 1915.
2 v. fronts., plates, ports., geneal. tables. 22½cm.
"Printed in England."

1. Darwin, Emma (Wedgwood) 1808–1896. 2. Darwin, Charles Robert, 1809–1882. 3. Darwin family.
26—26970
Library of Congress CT788.D25L5 1915 a

NL 0406785 DLC Or NN CSmH MH PP CaBVaU

Litchfield, Henrietta Emma (Darwin) 1843– ,ed

Emma Darwin, wife of Charles Darwin; a century of family letters. Privately printed. Cambridge, Univ. Press, 1904.
2 v. ports. 22cm.
"A biographical sketch of an infant", by Charles Darwin, pp. [285]–294, detached from Mind, a Quarterly Review, no.7, July 1877, bound in vol. 1 preceding title-page. Inscribed by author October 3, 1877 (in copy 1 only).
1. Darwin, Emma (Wedgwood) 1808–1896. 2. Darwin, Charles Robert, 1809–1882. 3. Darwin family. I. Darwin, Charles Robert, 1809–1882. A biographical sketch of an infant.

NL 0406786 ViU MH

[Litchfield, Mrs. Henrietta Emma (Darwin) 1843–
Richard Buckley Litchfield; a memoir written for his friends by his wife. Cambridge, [Eng.], Printed privately at the University Press, 1910.
Poet.
"It is also, incidentally, a history by the foundation and early years of the Working Men's College."

NL 0406787 MH

Litchfield, Henry Percy.
The Franco-German war of 1870. By Henry Percy Litchfield. Gracehill, Brooklyn, L. I., 1872.
2 p. l., 125 p. 17cm.

1. Franco-German war, 1870–1871.
Nov. 30, 99–127
Library of Congress DC291.L77 Copyright

NL 0406788 DLC

Litchfield, Henry Wheatland.
Ancient landmarks of Pembroke, by Henry Wheatland Litchfield ... Pembroke, G. E. Lewis, 1909.
188 p. front., plates, ports. 22½cm. $2.00

1. Pembroke, Mass.—Hist.
10-31021
Library of Congress F74.P41L7

NL 0406789 DLC MWA NN

F74
P4L5
Litchfield, Harry Wheatland, comp.
Annual officers of the town of Pembroke, 1712–1900. Compiled from the records by Harry W. Litchfield. [Pembroke, Mass.?] 1902–1903.
[106]p. 21½cm.
Manuscript copy.

NL 0406790 NBuG

Litchfield, Henry Wheatland.
The Attic alphabet in Thucydides: a note on Thucydides 8, 9². (Harvard University. Harvard studies in classical philology. Boston, 1912. 8°. v. 23, p. 129-154.)

1. Thucydides.
N. Y. P. L. September 23, 1912.

NL 0406791 NN OO MB

Litchfield, Henry Wheatland. *4957.15.24
Cicero's judgment on Lucretius.
(In Harvard studies in classical philology. Vol. 24, pp. 147–160. Cambridge. 1913.)

K1103 — Cicero, Marcus Tullius. — Lucretius Carus, Titus.

NL 0406792 MB OO

Litchfield, Henry Wheatland.
The First church in Pembroke 1708–1908, by H. W. Litchfield ... Pembroke [Mass.] Printed for the Parish by G. E. Lewis, 1908.
3 p. l., [2] p. front. 18½cm.

1. Pembroke, Mass. First church.
9-16255
Library of Congress F74.P37L7

NL 0406793 DLC MH-AH NN

Litchfield, Henry Wheatland. *Reserve Coll.377.55
[Mass. statutes on homosexual acts.]
= *Multigraphed manuscript.* [Cambridge. 192–?] 18 ff. 27½ cm.
The author's name appears only on page 18.

N3147 — Sexual perversion.—Massachusetts. Acts and laws. Sexual perversion.

NL 0406794 MB

Litchfield, Henry Wheatland. *4957.15.25
National *exempla virtutis* in Roman literature.
(In Harvard studies in classical philology. Vol. 25, pp. 1–71. Cambridge. 1914.)

K4174 — Latin literature. Hist. — Heroes. — Ethics.

NL 0406795 MB OO

LITCHFIELD, Henry Wheatland.
Quibus virtutum vitiorumque moralium exemplis ex suorum annalibus sumptis scriptores Latini antiqui usi sint quaeritur. Transl.and publ.as "National exempla virtutis in Roman literature," Harv.Stud.Class.Philol., 1914,25: 1-71.

Official copy of the thesis presented for a doctor's degree at Harvard University.

NL 0406796 MH

Litchfield, Isaac W., ed.
Science conspectus. v. 1–6; Dec. 1910–1916. **Boston, Mass.,** The Society of arts of the Massachusetts institute of technology, 1910–16.

Litchfield, J F B
Catalogue of [his] small ... collection of Coins and Tokens ..., To be sold at auction ... N.Y., on Sept. 13, 1880... Philad., 1880.
20 p. 8°. (Priced) [In Coin Catalogues, 1880]

NL 0406798 CtY

Litchfield, Mrs. J. S.
Far-north memories; being the account of ten years spent on the diamond-drills, and of things that happened in those days, by J. S. Litchfield. Australia: Angus & Robertson, Ltd., 1930. 212 p. front., plates. 12°.
Plates printed on both sides.

534465A. 1. Australia, North—Descr. and trav. 2. Australian tribes—North Australia. I. Title.
N. Y. P. L. July 13, 1931

NL 0406799 NN MH

[Litchfield, John]
Catalogue of a general library and theatrical collection of a gentleman who has devoted much of his attention to dramatic literature. [Sold at auction by Messrs. Robins, 19 May & following days, 1829.] [London, 1829]
27p.

NL 0406800 MH

Litchfield, John, – No. 2 in **T.96.228.2
The dramatic character of Mr. Parsons.
(In Bellamy, Thomas. The life of William Parsons. Pp. 51-59. London. 1795.)

J359 — Parsons, William. 1736–1795.

NL 0406801 MB

Litchfield, John.

Bellamy, Thomas, 1745–1800.
The life of Mr. William Parsons, comedian. Written by Thomas Bellamy. To which are added his dramatic character, by John Litchfield, esq., and a letter of intelligence, from Charles Dibdin, esq. London, Printed for the author, 1795.

VOLUME 336

[Litchfield, John, attributed author]
[Remarks on Mr. Colman's preface [to The iron chest] ... Also a summary comparison of the play of The iron chest with the novel of Caleb Williams ... Originally written for, and inserted in, the Monthly mirror; and now re-published (by permission of the proprietors), with alterations and additions. By a gentleman of the Middle-Temple.
London:Sold by Miller,Bond-street;Cawthorne, Strand;Symonds,Pater-noster-row;Crosby,Stationers' court; Martin and Bain.Fleet-street; and Vernor and Hood,Birchin-lane.[1796] <Price one shilling.>
8°. iv,31p. 22.5cm.
Advertisement dated: September 1, 1796.

NL 0406804 MH MB CtY CSmH

Litchfield, John Charles.
An attempt to establish a new system of medical education with a view to suppress ignorance, and preserve the respectability and utility of the medical character. London, S. Highley, 1827.
35p.(+1p.advertisements) 22cm.
"Addressed to parents and guardians, the rising generation of medical students, and to the pro- fession in general".

NL 0406805 KU-M

Litchfield, L L
Anniversary, 1866-1946. [Portage, Wis., Goodman Print., 1946]
[13] p. illus., ports. 23cm.
Cover title.
Contents: History of Briggsville Methodist Church 1866-1946- History of Moundville Methodist Church 1849-1946- History of Trinity Congregational Church, 1890-1946.
Includes mem- bership lists.

NL 0406806 WHi

Litchfield, Lawrence.
Bauxite, parts I & II, by Lawrence Litchfield, jr., vice-president, the Republic mining and manufacturing co. ... [1941]
13 p. illus., diagr. 29½cm.
"Reprinted from Chemical industries, February and March 1941."
1. Bauxite.

NL 0406807 NNC

Litchfield, *Mrs.* Marion Randall
see
Randall, Marion.

Litchfield, Mary Elizabeth, 1854- ed.
Spenser, Edmund, 1552?-1599.
Britomart, selections from Spenser's Faery queene, books III, IV, and V; ed. with introduction and notes by Mary E. Litchfield ... Boston, New York [etc.] Ginn & company [°1906]

Litchfield, Mary Elizabeth, 1854- ed.
Irving, Washington, 1783-1859.
Irving's Sketch book; complete ed., edited with introduction and notes by Mary E. Litchfield. Boston, Ginn & company, 1901.

Litchfield, Mary Elizabeth, 1854-
The nine worlds; stories from Norse mythology, by Mary E. Litchfield. Boston and London, Ginn & company, 1890.
vi p., 1 l., 163 p. front., pl., diagrs. 18½cm.
"References": p. 162-163.
I. Title.
12—36206

IU
NL 0406811 DLC WaS Or NcRS ViU NIC OCl PPFr NN MB

Litchfield, Mary Elizabeth, 1854-
(The) nine worlds; stories from Norse mythology. Bost. Ginn. , 1894.
164 p.

NL 0406812 OCl

Litchfield, Mary Elizabeth, 1854-
The nine worlds; stories from Norse mythology, by Mary E. Litchfield. Boston and London, Ginn & company, 1895.
vi p., 1 l., 163 p. front., pl., diagrs. 18 1/2cm.
"References": p. 162-163.

NL 0406813 MB

Litchfield, Mary E[lizabeth], 1854-
The nine worlds; stories from Norse mythology. Boston: Ginn & Co., 1897. vi(i), 163 p., 2 pl. illus. 12°.
References, p. 162-163.
Odin seeks wisdom from Mimir. The binding of the wolf. The judgment hall of the dead. Baldur and Loki. Baldur's dreams. The mistletoe. Loki makes trouble between the artists and the gods. How Thiassi captured Loki. Thiassi carries off Iduna. The gods grow old. Loki brings back Iduna. Thor and Thrym. Thor and Skrymir. Thor's journey to get the kettle for Ægir. Frey climbs into Odin's high seat. Frey's love for Gerd. Skirnir's journey to win Gerd for Frey. The death of Baldur. Baldur's funeral. Hermod's journey in search of Baldur. Logi at Ægir's feast. The capture of Loki. The twilight of the gods.
1. Mythology. 2. Title.
N. Y. P. L. September 21, 1912.

NL 0406814 NN PP PU

Litchfield, Mary Elizabeth, 1854-
The nine worlds; stories from Norse mythology by Mary E. Litchfield. Boston and London, Ginn & company, 1899.
vi p., 1 l., 163 p. front., pl., diagrs. 19cm.
"References": p. 162-163.

NL 0406815 MB PBa MH

Litchfield, Mary Elizabeth, 1854- ed.
Selections from five English poets; ed. with introduction and notes by Mary E. Litchfield. Boston, Ginn & company, 1901.
vii, 104 p. 19cm.
CONTENTS.—I. Dryden. A song for St. Cecilia's day.—II. Gray. Elegy written in a country churchyard.—III. Goldsmith. The traveller. The deserted village.—IV. Burns. The cotter's Saturday night.—V. Coleridge. The ancient mariner.
1. English poetry (Collections)
Library of Congress PR1175.L48 1-19805

NL 0406816 DLC OCl OO OClJC

Litchfield, Mary Elizabeth, 1854- ed.
Selections from five English poets; ed. with introduction and notes by Mary E. Litchfield. Boston, Ginn & company, 1902.
vii, 104 p. 19 cm.
CONTENTS.—I. Dryden. A song for St. Cecilia's day.—II. Gray Elegy written in a country churchyard.—III. Goldsmith. The traveller. The deserted village.—IV. Burns. The cotter's Saturday night.—V. Coleridge. The ancient mariner.

NL 0406817 ViU

Litchfield, Mary Elizabeth, 1854-
[Addison, Joseph] 1672-1719.
The Sir Roger de Coverley papers, from the Spectator: ed., with introduction and notes, by Mary E. Litchfield ... Boston, U. S. A., Ginn & company, 1899.

Litchfield, Mary Elizabeth, 1854- ed.
Spenser, Edmund, 1552?-1599.
Spenser's Britomart; from books III, IV, and V of the Faery queene, edited, with introduction and notes by Mary E. Litchfield. Boston and London, Ginn & company, 1896.

[Litchfield, Norma MacLeod]
... How to teach paper-folding and cutting: a practical manual-training aid, by MacLeod [pseud.] Lebanon, O., March brothers, 1892.
94 p. illus., diagrs. 21cm. (Manual-training series, no. 2)
1. Paper work.
Library of Congress LB1542.L5 CA 9—4018 Unrev'd

NL 0406820 DLC

[Litchfield, Norma MacLeod]
Lessons on common minerals, by McLeod [pseud.] New York, Teachers publishing company, 1891.
iv, [5]-65 p. 22cm.
1. Mineralogy—Study and teaching.
Library of Congress QE366.L77 13-22076

NL 0406821 DLC NN

[Litchfield, Norma MacLeod]
Talks about common things. By MacLeod [pseud.] ... New York, Teachers publishing company, 1891.
v, [7]-103, [1] p. 23cm.
1. Object-teaching. I. Title.
Library of Congress LB1519.L5 15-6627

NL 0406822 DLC ViU

Litchfield, Norman.
A history of Christ Church, Quaker Farms in Oxford, Connecticut. Quaker Farms, 1954.
200 p. illus. 23 cm.
1. Oxford, Conn. Christ Church, Quaker Farms.
BX5980.O85C5 283.746 54-4289 ‡

NL 0406823 DLC NN NcD

Litchfield, P.C.
Guide lines to the penny black: a detailed description of each one of the 2880 stamps and the plates from which it was printed. London, Robson Lowe, Ltd., 1949.
224 p. illus.
1. Postage-stamps—Gt. Brit.
I. Title: Penny black.

NL 0406824 CaOTP

VOLUME 336

*AC8 Litchfield, Paul, 1752?-1827.
L7115 A sermon, preached before the Massachusetts missionary society, at their annual meeting,
805s in Boston, May 28, 1805. By Paul Litchfield ... Salem [Mass.]:Printed by Joshua Cushing.1805.

24p. 24.5cm.
Original gray-blue wrappers preserved; bound in cloth.

NL 0406825 MH InU RPB ICN

Litchfield, Paul Weeks, 1875-

America is ready for a new rubber policy. [Akron, Ohio, Goodyear Tire and Rubber Co., 1947]
[4] p. illus. 28cm. (Notes on America's rubber industry, new ser., no. 8)

1. Rubber industry and trade—U. S. I. Title. II. Ser.

NL 0406826 ViU

Litchfield, Paul Weeks, 1875-
Autumn leaves; reflections of an industrial lieutenant, by P. W. Litchfield, with a foreword by Dr. Jerome C. Hunsaker. ... Illustrations by Rockwell Kent. [Cleveland, The Corday & Gross co., 1945]
3 p. l., 13-125 p. col. front., col. illus., mounted port., diagrs. 23½cm.

1. Conduct of life. 2. Business. 3. Success. I. Kent, Rockwell, 1882- illus. II. Title.

45-5797

Library of Congress BJ1611.L73

174

NL 0406827 DLC MiD TxU ICU CoU NcRS PPULC ViU OCl OCU OU OClCC OClW AAP OrU WaE OrCS

Litchfield, Paul Weeks, 1875-
Current trends in industry; toward social security—toward decentralization—toward New England; an address by P. W. Litchfield, president, the Goodyear tire & rubber co. [Akron? O., 1937?]
1 p. l., 11 p. 18½cm.
"The ... address was given ... November 20, 1936 ... in Boston, Mass., before the New England conference."

1. New England—Indus. I. Title.

43-27682

Library of Congress HC107.A11L5

NL 0406828 DLC DSI DL Or

TS1870
.G4
new ser.
no.14
1951

Litchfield, Paul Weeks, 1875-

The free world looks to America for synthetic rubber. [Akron, Ohio, Goodyear Tire and Rubber Co., 1951]
[4] p. illus. 28cm. ([Goodyear Tire and Rubber Company] Notes on America's rubber industry. new ser., no. 14)

1. Rubber, Artificial. I. Ser.

NL 0406829 ViU

Litchfield, Paul Weeks, 1875-

From swords to plowshares. [Akron, Ohio, Goodyear Tire and Rubber Co., 1947]
[4] p. illus. 28cm. (Notes on America's rubber industry, new ser., no. 7)

1. Rubber industry and trade—U. S. I. Title. II. Ser.

NL 0406830 ViU

Litchfield, Paul Weeks, 1875-

Guayule, asset or liability? [Akron, O., Goodyear Tire & Rubber Co., 1945]
[4] p. illus. 28cm. (Notes on America's rubber industry. new ser. no. 4)

1. Rubber, Artificial. I. Title. II. Ser.

NL 0406831 ViU

Litchfield, Paul Weeks, 1875-
History's lesson to air power, by P. W. Litchfield ... [Akron? O., 1944?]
[20] p. col. illus. 20½cm.

1. Aeronautics, Military. I. Title.

45-5025

Library of Congress UG630.L53

623.74

NL 0406832 DLC OrU MH NN

Litchfield, Paul Weeks, 1875-
The industrial republic; a study in industrial economics, by Paul W. Litchfield ... Akron, O. [The Superior printing company] 1919.
73 p., 1 l. 18cm.

1. Labor representation in regulation of industry. 2. Labor and laboring classes. I. Title.

19-14923

Library of Congress HD46.L5

NL 0406833 DLC Or OKentU KEmT OU OClWHi OCl

Litchfield, Paul Weeks, 1875-
The industrial republic; a study in industrial economics, by Paul W. Litchfield ... Boston and New York, Houghton Mifflin company, 1920.
3 p. l., 95, [1] p. 17½cm. $1.00

1. Employees' representation in management. 2. Labor and laboring classes. I. Title.

Library of Congress HD5650.L6 1920

20-10139

NL 0406834 DLC MtBC NcRS CU MoU PSt WaS PU OClW ODW ICJ MB NN

Litchfield, Paul Weeks, 1875-
The industrial republic; reflections of an industrial lieutenant [by] P. W. Litchfield; illustrations by Fred Ludekens. [Cleveland, The Corday & Gross co., 1946]
6 p. l., iii, [2], 201 p. illus., diagrs. 23½ cm.
"First printing, September 1946."
CONTENTS.—The industrial republic [reprint of the author's 1919 ed.]—Industry under the industrial assembly.—Industry under national unions.—A democratic solution.—In conclusion.

1. Industrial relations—U. S. 2. Personnel management. 3. Goodyear tire and rubber company, Akron, O. I. Title.

HD8072.L57 331 46-20784

NL 0406835 DLC ICRL DSI ViU NBuU AU NcD TxU PPD PPCuP PP MB ICJ CU WaS WaTC WaSpG

Litchfield, Paul Weeks, 1875-
Industrial voyage; my life as an industrial lieutenant. Illus. by Richard Bartlett. [1st ed.] Garden City, N. Y., Doubleday, 1954.
347 p. illus. 22 cm.

1. Goodyear Tire and Rubber Company, Akron, Ohio. I. Title.

HD9161.U54G65 926.78 54-10455 ‡

NL 0406836 DLC NN MB TU PP PPD OClW OCl OOxM TxU PPT OU PU ScCleU OrU OKentU MsSM WaTC Or WaT WaS WaE CaBViPA CaBVaU OrCS OrP

Litchfield, Paul Weeks, 1875-
... A labor relations program, by P. W. Litchfield. [1937]
1 p. l., 19 numb. l. 27½cm.

At head of title: United States chamber of commerce, Annual meeting, April 28, 1937.
Reproduced from typo-written copy.

1. Arbitration, Industrial. I. Title.

NL 0406837 NNC

TS1870
.G4
new ser.
no.16
1952

Litchfield, Paul Weeks, 1875-

A living stockpile for national security. [Akron? Ohio, Goodyear Tire and Rubber Co., 1952]
[4] p. illus. 28cm. ([Goodyear Tire and Rubber Company] Notes on America's rubber industry. New ser., no. 16)

1. Tires, Rubber. I. Title. II. Ser.

NL 0406838 ViU

TS1870
.G4
new ser.
no.13
1951

Litchfield, Paul Weeks, 1875-

Looking ahead to 1960. [Akron, Ohio, Goodyear Tire and Rubber Co., 1951]
[4] p. illus. 28cm. ([Goodyear Tire and Rubber Company] Notes on America's rubber industry, new ser., no. 13)

1. Rubber industry and trade. I. Ser.

NL 0406839 ViU

TS1870
.G4
new ser.
no.17
1952

Litchfield, Paul Weeks, 1875-

Modern farm miracle, 1932-1952. [Akron? Ohio, Goodyear Tire and Rubber Co., 1952]
[4] p. diagr. 28cm. ([Goodyear Tire and Rubber Company] Notes on America's rubber industry. New ser., no. 17)

1. Tires, Rubber. I. Title. II. Ser.

NL 0406840 ViU

Litchfield, Paul Weeks, 1875-

... A national policy for rubber, by P.W. Litchfield ... [Akron, O., 1946]
[4] p. 1 illus. 28cm. ([Goodyear tire and rubber company] Notes on America's rubber industry. new series, no.5)
Dated February 1946.

1. Rubber industry and trade. I. Title. II. Ser.

NL 0406841 ViU

Litchfield, Paul Weeks, 1875-
The president talks to the men; a group of radio addresses by P. W. Litchfield, president, the Goodyear tire & rubber company. [Akron, O., Goodyear tire & rubber co., inc., °1935]
cover-title, 184 p. illus. (incl. ports.) 23cm.
"This book is a revise of the original of the same title, with several chapters added."—Editor's note.

1. Goodyear tire & rubber company, Akron, O. I. Title.

37-38019

Library of Congress TS1885.U6L5 1935

——— Copy 2.

Copyright A 112235

678.06

NL 0406842 DLC OCl IU

Litchfield, Paul Weeks, 1875-
Remarks of Mr. P. W. Litchfield, president of the Goodyear tire & rubber co., at the annual meeting of stockholders held March 29, 1937... [Akron, O., 1937] 7 l. 20cm.

1. Goodyear tire and rubber company, Akron, O.
N. Y. P. L. June 30, 1947

NL 0406843 NN

VOLUME 336

Litchfield, Paul Weeks, 1875-
A report for 1941 to Goodyear employees, "soldiers of the production line," by P. W. Litchfield, chairman of the Board, the Goodyear tire & rubber company. [Akron? O., 1941?]
[36] p. illus. (incl. ports.) 28 x 21½cm.
Caption title.

1. Goodyear tire & rubber company, Akron, O.
Library of Congress TS1885.U6L516 43-3915
678

NL 0406844 DLC OClWHi

Litchfield, Paul Weeks, 1875-
The republic of business,...
Akron, O., 1920
HD6650
.L65

NL 0406845 DLC

Litchfield, Paul Weeks, 1875-
Rubber; problem child among our basic commodities. [Akron? Ohio, 1949]
[4] p. illus. 28 cm. (Goodyear Tire and Rubber Co. Notes on America's rubber industry. new ser., no. 11)
1. Rubber - U.S. I. Ser.

NL 0406846 ViU

Litchfield, Paul Weeks, 1875-
The rubber situation today; acute, dangerous and expensive, but there is a quick remedy right at hand. [Akron? Ohio, 1950]
[4] p. illus. 28 cm. (Goodyear Tire and Rubber co. Notes on America's rubber industry. new ser., no. 12)
1. Rubber - U.S. I. Ser.

NL 0406847 ViU

Litchfield, Paul Weeks, 1875-
Rubber's return to the western hemisphere; how the substance on which much of the American way of life is based is being brought back to the land from whence it came so that the danger of shortage constantly hanging over our heads, may be partially removed ... [Akron, Ohio] The Goodyear tire & rubber co. [1941]
[4] p. illus., map.
Caption title.

NL 0406848 MH-BA WaU PPD

Litchfield, Paul Weeks, 1875-
Some Wingfoot Clan editorials, [by] Paul W. Litchfield. [Akron, O.: The Superior Prtg. Co., 1919?] 123 p. 12°.
Reprinted from the house organ: Wingfoot Clan, of the Goodyear Tire & Rubber Company, 1912-1919.

527052A. 1. India rubber—Companies —U. S.
N. Y. P. L. May 27, 1931

NL 0406849 NN OClWHi

Litchfield, Paul Weeks, 1875-
Story of the airship. [Goodyear tire and rubber co., [c1926]
16 p.

NL 0406850 NcU OO WaS IaAS

Litchfield, Paul Weeks, 1875-
Thirty years of Goodyear, 1898-1928.
A statement tothe stockholders of the Goodyear tire & rubber co., n.p. 1928.
14 p.

NL 0406851 OO OClWHi

Litchfield, Paul Weeks, 1875-
Why? Why has America no rigid airships? A study of the characteristics of large ocean-crossing rigid airships, leading up to the question, Why does not America use all three, the dirigible, the airplane and the steamship, to provide this country with the best possible transportation system? By P. W. Litchfield and Hugh Allen. [Cleveland, Corday & Gross co., 1945]
143 p. incl. col. front., illus. (part col.; incl. ports., map) diagrs. 23½cm.
Bibliography: p. 143.

1. Air-ships. 2. Aeronautics, Commercial—U. S. I. Allen, Hugh, 1882- joint author. II. Title. III. Title: Why has America no rigid airships?
Library of Congress TL651.L55 46-720
6 0.13325

NL 0406852 DLC AU WaSpG WaTC NN WaS NcD NIC IU NN WaE GU

[Litchfield, Richard Buckley] d. 1903.
The beginnings of the Working men's college.
[London, Hudson & co., 1902]
cover-title, [3]-12 p. 22 cm.
Signed: R.B. Litchfield.
1. London. Working men's college.
I. Title.

NL 0406853 CU

Litchfield, Richard Buckley, *d.* 1903.
Tom Wedgwood, the first photographer; an account of his life, his discovery and his friendship with Samuel Taylor Coleridge, including the letters of Coleridge to the Wedgwoods and an examination of accounts of alleged earlier photographic discoveries; by R. B. Litchfield ... London, Duckworth and co., 1903.
xvi p., 1 l., 271 p. incl. geneal tab. front., pl., port., facsim. 23cm.

1. Wedgwood, Thomas, 1771-1805. 2. Coleridge, Samuel Taylor, 1772-1834.
3-11325

NL 0406854 DLC TU NIC TxU ScU CU PU-S NcD OU OO NjP ICJ NN MB

LITCHFIELD, Roland.
The modern inquisition in a Baptist Church: or, An unvarnished statement, showing the grounds on which he was excluded from, and the manner in which he has since been treated by the First Baptist Church in Cambridgeport; J.W. Parker, Pastor. Camb., Mass., 1854.
pp.46.

NL 0406855 MH DLC

738
L711m
Litchfield, Samuel, firm, London.
Marks & monograms on old china. [London, 1876?]
56 (i.e. 58)p. incl. 22 plates. fold. plate. 14 x 22cm.
Imperfect: all preceding p.9 wanting. Title from cover.
Letterpress on verso of each numbered plate.
1. Porcelain - Marks.

NL 0406856 TxU

Litchfield, Sarah.
Hello, Alaska, by Sarah Litchfield, illustrated by Kurt Wiese. Chicago, Ill., A. Whitman & company, 1945.
31, [1] p. illus. (part col.) 24 x 19cm.
Map on lining-papers.

1. Alaska—Descr. & trav. I. Wiese, Kurt, 1887- illus. II. Title.
45-1296
Library of Congress F909.L768
917.98

NL 0406857 DLC OrAshS MdBP IU WaS WaSp PP

Litchfield, T. S., *publisher.* No. 47 in *Cab.81.20.1
Gen. Putnam's duel with the British officer. [Engraving.]
— [Boston?] 1851. 12⅞ × 16.5 inches.

D4875 — Putnam, Israel, 1718-1790.

NL 0406858 MB

W823
L776c
Litchfield, Thomas.
The coldstreams and the musqueteers.
A novel. London, T. C. Newby, 1856.
3 v. 19 cm.
According to dealer's slip tipped in, this is a 1st edition.

NL 0406859 NcU

Litchfield, Vida, *comp.*
The old cider mill, and other gems; poems of yesterday, selected and arranged by Vida Litchfield. Chicago, Charles C. Thompson co. [1913]
2 p. l., 7-46 p. 21½cm. [Heart throb series of gift booklets, selected and arranged by Vida Litchfield, II] $0.35

I. Title.
Library of Congress PS586.L55 13-19471

NL 0406860 DLC

Litchfield, Vida, *comp.*
A pair of red lips, and other poems for maids and men, selected and arranged by Vida Litchfield. Chicago, Charles C. Thompson co. [1913]
2 p. l., 7-46 p. 21½cm. [Heart throb series of gift booklets selected and arranged by Vida Litchfield, I] $0.35

1. Love poetry. I. Title.
Library of Congress PN6110.L6L4 13-16916

NL 0406861 DLC

634.9
F11f
No.54
Litchfield, Wickliffe.
Forest statistics for Union County, Oregon, by Wickliffe Litchfield. 1937.
11p.

NL 0406862 WaWW

[Litchfield, Wilford Jacob] *comp.*
The Litchfield family in America.
[Southbridge, Mass., W. J. Litchfield]
v. 25cm.

1. Litchfield family (Lawrence Litchfield, d. 1649 or 1650)
CA 9-3909 Unrev'd
Library of Congress CS71.L776 1901-1906

NL 0406863 DLC Nh MH MB NNC OCl

VOLUME 336

E
7 [LITCHFIELD, WILFORD JACOB] comp.
.L 715 The Litchfield family in America. [Southbridge,Mass., W.J. Litchfield] 1901-1906.
5v. illus. 24cm.

Xerox copy.

NL 0406864 ICN

974.43 Litchfield, Wilford Jacob.
S726 Shuttleville, Southbridge, Mass. and the Litchfield Shuttle Company. Read at meeting of Society, Feb. 26, 1906. ⌊Southbridge, Mass., 1906⌋
⌊75⌋-90 p. 22 cm. (Quinabaug Historical Society, Southbridge, Mass. Leaflets, v. 2, nos. 10-11)

1. Southbridge, Mass. H 1. Massachusetts. Southbridge. 2. Litchfield Shuttle Company, Southbridge, Mass. I. Title. Series.

NL 0406865 N

Litchfield (William Frederick) [1869-1922]. Diphtheria in practice. 96 pp. 8°. London, Baillière, Tindall & Cox, 1908.

NL 0406866 DNLM ICJ

Litchfield, Conn.
0v31 Annual reports of the town ...
L6a Litchfield,
$20\frac{1}{2}$-$23\frac{1}{2}$cm.

Title varies: -1942/43, Reports of the selectmen and treasurer ... with slight variation of subtitle; 1943/44- , Annual reports of the town ...
Town incorporated, May, 1719.

NL 0406867 CtY

Litchfield, *Conn.*
Litchfield centennial celebration, July 4th, A. D. 1876. Historical address by G. C. Woodruff. Hartford, The press of the Case, Lockwood & Brainard co., 1876.
44 p. 22½cm.

1. Litchfield, Conn.—Hist. 2. Fourth of July celebrations. I. Woodruff, George Catlin, 1805-1885.

Rc-3252 Revised
Library of Congress F104.L7L7

NL 0406868 DLC MiU-C

Litchfield, Conn.

Litchfield County, *Conn.*
Litchfield County centennial celebration, held at Litchfield, Conn., 13th and 14th of August, 1851. Hartford, E. Hunt, 1851.

Litchfield, Conn. Board of education
School report of the town of Litchfield
1888/89 91/92 93/94; 1909/10 13/14-14/15. 17/18; 20/21 23/24
Litchfield, 1881-1924.
11 v. 22 cm.

NL 0406870 DHEW NNU-W

Litchfield, Conn. Charters.
Charter and by-laws of the Village of Litchfield, from its incorporation and organization in 1818 to 1862; together with a list of the public buildings, dwelling houses, offices, stores, shops, &c., therein, in April 1862. Litchfield: Enquirer Job Prtg. Off., 1862. 28 p. 8°.

1. Municipal charters and ordinances. U. S.: Conn.: Litchfield.
N. Y. P. L. January 25, 1915.

NL 0406871 NN IU

MF59.6 Litchfield, Conn. First Congregational Church.
L711h A history of the First Congregational Church in Litchfield, Connecticut, on its one hundred and twenty-sixth anniversary and the twenty-fifth anniversary of its restoration, September 11th 1955. ⌊Litchfield? Conn.⌋ 1955.
42 p. illus. 23 cm.

Cover title.
"The Christian value of an anniversary,

sermon delivered at the morning services September 11, 1955 ⌊by⌋ Robert L. Edwards minister": p. 2-5.
Bibliography: p. 22-25.

NL 0406873 CtY-D

Litchfield, Conn. First national bank.
The First national bank of Litchfield...the town's oldest business. Litchfield [n.d.] 12 l. illus., map. 23cm.

1. Banks and banking—U.S.—Conn.—Litchfield. 2. Litchfield, Conn.—Banks.

NL 0406874 NN

Litchfield, Conn. Historical Society
see
Litchfield Historical Society.

Litchfield, Conn. Law School
see Litchfield Law School, Litchfield.

Litchfield, Conn. Litchfield County medical association
see Litchfield County medical association, Litchfield, Conn.

Litchfield, Conn. Litchfield historical society
see
Litchfield historical society.

Litchfield, Conn. Litchfield school
see
Litchfield school, Litchfield, Conn.

Litchfield, Ill. Board of education.
Report 1896/97.
Litchfield, Ill., 1897-
1 v. 22 cm.

Contains Course of study and Rules and regulations.

NL 0406880 DHEW

Litchfield, Ill. Charters.
The charter; with synopsis of other statutues, revised ordinances, and statistics, pertaining to Litchfield, Illinois. Published by authority of the city council. Revised by B.S. Hood, city clerk, March, 1877. Litchfield, Coolidge & Martin, 1877.
196p. 17½cm.

NL 0406881 IHi

Litchfield, Ill. Charters.
The charter; with synopsis of other statutes, revised ordinances and statistics pertaining to Litchfield, Illinois. Revised by J. W. Rose. Litchfield, 1884. 168 p. lea. 8°.

1. Municipal charters and ordinances. U. S.: Ill.: Litchfield. 2. Rose, John W., ed.
N. Y. P. L. January 12, 1915.

NL 0406882 NN NcD

Rare Litchfield, Ill. Committee on Finance.
Book Fiscal statement and other statistics of
Room the City of Litchfield. Litchfield, Ill.
HJ
9013 v. (chiefly tables.) 28 cm.
L5a In slip-case.
Report year irregular.

NL 0406883 IEdS

Rare Litchfield, Ill. Ordinances, etc.
Book [City Code, Litchfield, Illinois. Litch-
Room field? Ill., 1866]
KFI
1631.5 102 p. 28 cm.
A84 Title supplied.
1866 In slip-case.
Title page wanting.

NL 0406884 IEdS NcD

Litchfield, *Me.*
Annual report of the municipal officers of the town ...
Augusta, Me.
v. tables. 23cm.
Report year irregular.

CA 34-1573 Unrev'd
Library of Congress JS13.L734 352.07416

NL 0406885 DLC

Litchfield, *Me.*
History of Litchfield and an account of its centennial celebration, 1895. Augusta, Kennebec journal print, 1897.
548 p. plates, ports. 23½cm.

1. Litchfield, Me.—Hist. 2. Litchfield, Me.—Geneal. I. Title.

Library of Congress F29.L7L7 1-1785

NL 0406886 DLC ICN NN MeB MB PHi Nh

Litchfield, Me. Litchfield Academy
see
Litchfield Academy, *Litchfield, Me.*

VOLUME 336

*JS997 .L77A15 1943 Litchfield, Minn. Charters.
Charter of the city of Litchfield; Minnesota. Home rule charter adopted Monday, June 28, 1943 by order of the city council of the city of Litchfield, 1943. [Litchfield, Minn., 1943]
41 p. 23cm.

NL 0406888 MnHi

---

943 Luth.724 L776f L776j LITCHFIELD, Minn. First Lutheran Church.
Jubilee album and history of First Lutheran Church, Litchfield, Minnesota. 1873-1923. Rock Island, Ill., Augustana Book Concern, 1923.
63p. illus. 22.5cm.

NL 0406889 MH-AH

Litchfield(N.H.)
Annual reports of the officers and committees for the year ending Feb. 15,1876- v.p.1902.

NL 0406890 Nh

Litchfield(N.H.) Free public library.
Catalogue of the books in the Free public library, Litchfield(N.H.),established,1892. Hollis,1901.

NL 0406891 Nh

TX715 .A566 Litchfield Academy, Litchfield, Me.

Anderson, Addie Earle, comp.
The Litchfield Academy cook book; a book of tested recipes given by pupils and friends of Litchfield Academy. Reunion ed. Richmond, Me., W. F. Dunham, printer, 1926.

Litchfield Advertiser
see Litchfield Monitor.

NK2265 .L5 19- Litchfield and Company.
Furniture and interiors of the 16th, 17th & 18th centuries. [London, New York, 19—]
56 p. (chiefly illus.) 32cm.

1. Furniture—Catalogs. 2. Decoration and ornament, Architectural. I. Title.

NL 0406894 ViU NBuG

Litchfield Centennial.
The centennial history of Litchfield, Illinois; one hundred years. [Litchfield, °1953]
208 p. illus. 29 cm.

1. Litchfield, Ill. I. Title.

F549.L74L5 54-34107 ‡

NL 0406895 DLC IHi NN IEdS

---

370 L71r Litchfield Conference on Education, 1955.
A report of the Litchfield Conference on Education, April 20, 1955. A regional meeting preliminary to the White House Conference, November, 1955, following the Statler Conference. November 30-December 1, 1954, held at Litchfield High School. Litchfield, Conn. [c1955?]
15p. illus., ports. 23cm.

1. Education--Congresses.

NL 0406896 IU

Litchfield County, Conn.
Litchfield County centennial celebration, held at Litchfield, Conn., 13th and 14th of August, 1851. Hartford, E. Hunt, 1851.
iv p., 1 l., [7]-212 p. front. 22½cm.
"Address ... on the occasion of the centennial celebration, 1851. By Judge Church": p. [21]-69. "The age of homespun. A discourse ... 1851. By Horace Bushnell": p. [105]-130.

1. Litchfield Co., Conn.—Hist. I. Church, Samuel, 1785-1854. II. Bushnell, Horace, 1802-1876. III. Litchfield, Conn. IV. Title.

Rc—3207

Library of Congress F102.L6L6

NL 0406897 FMU NcD NIC AU ICN NN MB NNPM PPPrHi NjP DLC CtHT-W OFH Wa MU Nh RPB MWA CtY TU

Litchfield County, Conn. North Consociation.
Address, etc., of the Consociation, as a Charitable Society, for educating Indigent, Pious Young Men, for the Gospel Ministry. Hartf'd., 1816.
8 p. 8°. [In College Pamphlets, v. 1362]

NL 0406898 CtY

Litchfield Co., Conn. North consociation.
Annual report of the registrar of the Litchfield North Assoc. and consociation. for the year 1866. Hartford, Case, Lockwood and company, 1867.
13 [1] p.

NL 0406899 OClWHi

Litchfield Co., Conn. North consociation.
Historical sketch; statistics and rules, of the North association and Consociation of Litchfield County. Hartford, Press of Case, Tiffany and company, 1852.
44 p. 22½cm.

1. Litchfield Co., Conn. South consociation.

22-20232

Library of Congress BX7108.L5A5

NL 0406900 DLC MWA CtY Nh

Case C 756 634 Litchfield Co., Conn. North consociation.
On the ordination of deacons. [Litchfield, Printed by T.Collier,1797]
11p.

Caption title.
A committee was appointed to publish the substance of certain manuscripts which had been read before the association.

NL 0406901 ICN MWA

Litchfield County, Conn. North consociation.
Proceedings of the north and south consociations of Litchfield County, Ct., in convention at Litchfield, July 7 and 8, 1852, to commemorate the centennial anniversary of their primitive organization. Hartford, Case, Tiffany & co., 1852.
154 p. 8°.
Title-page wanting.

1—3467

NL 0406902 DLC MH-AH MWA NBuG ICN NN

Litchfield County, Conn. South Consociation
see Congregational Churches in Connecticut. South Consociation of Litchfield County.

Litchfield County Association.
The one hundred and fiftieth anniversary of the Litchfield County association ... Litchfield, Conn., October 29, 1902. Litchfield, Conn. The Litchfield Enquirer press. 1903.
12,23,16,14 p.

NL 0406904 OClWHi

Litchfield County Choral Union,
[Concert programmes, reports, etc.] no. 1-48 (June 6, 1900-June 9, 1921). Winsted, 1900-21. 48 v. in 3. facsim., port. 8°.
Conductors: 1900-21, Richmond D. Paine and Arthur Mees. no. 1-6, held at Winsted; no. 7-date, at Norfolk.
Binder's title: Arthur Mees programs. no. 13-15.

1. Musical festivals. 2. Choral societies. 3. Programmes. 4. Paine, Richmond Peck, 1858- 5. Mees, Arthur, 1850-1923.
N. Y. P. L. June 17, 1924

NL 0406905 NN

Litchfield County choral union.
Litchfield County choral union, 1900-1912. Founded to honor the memory of Robbins Battell. Comp. by J. H. Vaill, secretary. Norfolk, Conn., Litchfield County university club, 1912.
2 v. front. (v. 1) plates, ports., facsim. 20½cm.
"These two volumes form part of a series published under the auspices of the Litchfield County university club."—Note, v. 1, p. [i]

1. Choral societies—Connecticut. 2. Concerts—Programs. 3. Battell, Robbins, 1819-1895. I. Vaill, Joseph H. II. Litchfield County university club.

16-7616

Library of Congress ML1511.8.L5V2

NL 0406906 DLC MiD NIC OU PPL PPCI NN MB MH MiU

ML28 .N7L5 Litchfield county choral union.
[Program of the] meeting and concert of the Litchfield county choral union. At the music shed, Norfolk, Connecticut ...
[n.p., 1
v. 23cm.

Cover-title.

1. Choral societies—Connecticut. 2. Concerts--Programs.

NL 0406907 DLC

Litchfield County Foreign Mission Society
see Foreign Mission Society of Litchfield County, Conn.

Litchfield County Historical and Antiquarian Society
see
Litchfield Historical Society.

Litchfield County hospital of Winchester, *Winsted, Conn.*
Report.
Winsted, Conn. [19
v. front., plates. 22cm.
Report year ends Sept. 30 since 1904.
Report for 1903/04 covers twenty months, from Feb. 1, 1903 to Oct. 1, 1904.

CA 8—535 Unrev'd

Library of Congress RA982.W6L7

NL 0406910 DLC NNC DNLM Or

VOLUME 336

Litchfield county medical association.
Fee table for professional services, adopted by the Litchfield county medical association, at its annual meeting, April 13th, 1871. [Litchfield, Conn., 1871]
sheet. 35½ x 22cm.

1. Physicians—Fees.
44-15663
Library of Congress R728.L77

NL 0406911 DLC

Litchfield County Monitor
see Litchfield Monitor.

Litchfield County University Club.
A brief historical sketch with list of members 1896-1903
see under Carter, Howard Williston, 1855-

Litchfield County University Club. *4439.252
Constitution and by-laws . . .
= [Canaan. Pease.] 1904. 17 pp. 12°.

NL 0406914 MB

Litchfield county university club.
Constitution of the Litchfield county university club. Adopted at the fourth annualmeeting, June 15, 1900. [Canaan, Conn., 1900?]
15 [1] p. 18 x 13.5 cm.

NL 0406915 CtY

Litchfield county university club.
Vaill, Dudley Landon.
The county regiment; a sketch of the Second regiment of Connecticut volunteer heavy artillery, originally the Nineteenth volunteer infantry, in the civil war, by Dudley Landon Vaill. [Winsted? Conn.] Litchfield county university club, 1908.

Litchfield County university club.
Litchfield County choral union.
Litchfield County choral union, 1900–1912. Founded to honor the memory of Robbins Battell. Comp. by J. H. Vaill, secretary. Norfolk, Conn., Litchfield County university club, 1912.

Litchfield County university club.
Phelps, Charles Shepherd.
Rural life in Litchfield County, by Charles Shepherd Phelps. Norfolk, Conn., Pub. under the auspices of the Litchfield County university club, 1917.

Litchfield County University Club.
Three addresses delivered at the sixth annual banquet of the Litchfield County university club. Norfolk, Connecticut, June 13, 1902. [New York, Priv. print.] 1902.
41 p. 23.5 cm.
Contents: Brief reminiscences of some Litchfield County men, by G. M. Woodruff. - A neglected element in education, by N. M. Calhoun. - "Behold the fowls of the air", by H. K. Job.

NL 0406919 CtY MWA MB OClWHi ICN

The Litchfield family in America
see under [Litchfield, Wilford Jacob] comp.

Litchfield Hills Federation.
The lure of the Litchfield hills... [Winsted, Conn.:] The Litchfield Hills Federation[, 1929]. 38 p. illus. (incl. ports.) f°.
Includes advertising matter.

1. Litchfield County, Conn.
N. Y. P. L. December 10, 1930

NL 0406921 NN

Litchfield Historical and Antiquarian Society
see
Litchfield Historical Society.

Litchfield historical society,
The bi-centennial celebration of the settlement of Litchfield, Connecticut, August 1–4, 1920. Comp. for the Litchfield historical society by Alain C. White. Litchfield, Conn., Enquirer print, 1920.
xv, 147 p. incl. front. plates. 23½cm.

1. Litchfield, Conn.—Hist. I. White, Alain Campbell, 1880– comp. II. Title.
21-19663
Library of Congress F104.L7L74

NL 0406923 DLC NIC CU CtW MB CtY NN

Litchfield Historical Society.
Catalogue. Edited by Mary B. Brewster. Litchfield, Conn., 1930.
xiii, 159 p. 24 cm.

I. Brewster, Mary B., 1889– ed.
F104.L7L7418 60-57194

NL 0406924 DLC NN

Litchfield historical society.
Catalogue of books, papers and manuscripts of the Litchfield historical society ... Noyes memorial building, Litchfield, Conn. [Litchfield, 1906]
2 p. l., 3–115 p. 24 cm.
August 1st, 1906: Fiftieth anniversary of the founding of the society.

1. Litchfield, Conn.—Bibl.
Z881.L776 14-21310 rev

NL 0406925 DLC MWA

Litchfield historical society.
Catalogue of the Litchfield historical society ... Noyes memorial building, Litchfield, Conn., June 1, 1905. [New York, The Brewer press, 1905]
106 p. 22½ cm.
Several pages blank.

F104.L7L742 14-20028 rev

NL 0406926 DLC

Litchfield Historical Society.
Catalogue of the... society... [Officers, members, etc., with list of exhibits.] June 1, 1905. [New York: Brewer Press, 1905.] 67 p. 8°.

1. Societies (National and patriotic), U. S.: Conn.: Litchfield. 2. Litchfield, Conn.—History.
N. Y. P. L. January 8, 1914.

NL 0406927 NN

Litchfield historical society.
Constitution and by-laws of the Litchfield historical society. Litchfield, Conn., 1904.
cover title, [10] p., 1 l. 17.5 cm.

NL 0406928 CtY

Litchfield historical society.
Constitution and by-laws of the Litchfield historical society. Litchfield, Conn., 1914.
cover-title, 10 p., 1 l. 17½ cm.

F104.L7L743 18-8753 rev

NL 0406929 DLC IU

Litchfield historical society,
White, Alain Campbell, 1880– *comp.*
The history of the town of Litchfield, Connecticut, 1720–1920. Comp. for the Litchfield historical society by Alain C. White. Litchfield, Conn., Enquirer print., 1920.

Litchfield historical society.
List of members ... corrected to January 10, 1914. [Litchfield, 1914]
8 p. 22½ cm.

F104.L7L75 18-8936 rev

NL 0406931 DLC

Litchfield historical society,
Litchfield's legacy [by] the young antiquarian
see under title

Litchfield historical society.
Presentation of the Reeve law school building to the Litchfield historical society at Litchfield, Conn. August 22d, 1911. Litchfield, Conn., The Litchfield enquirer press, 1911.
3 p. l., [9]–36 p. plates, ports. 22½ cm.

1. Litchfield law school, Litchfield, Conn.
F104.L7L77 13-16541 rev

NL 0406933 DLC PU-L NN NjP CtY MH-L

Litchfield historical society,
Z232 .C7F5
[**Fisher, Samuel Herbert**] 1867– *comp.*
The publications of Thomas Collier, printer, 1784–1808. Litchfield, The Litchfield historical society, 1933.

VOLUME 336

Litchfield Historical Society.
Reports of officers and committees presented at the annual meeting. 1909–
[Litchfield, Conn.]
v. in 24 cm.
Reports for 1919-20 issued in combined form.
Title varies.

F104.L7L78 13-16540 rev*‡

NL 0406935 DLC MB MWA

Litchfield historical society.
Semi-centennial of the Litchfield historical and antiquarian society; addresses at the opening of the new building and the presentation by the Mary Floyd Tallmadge chapter, Daughters of the American revolution, of a window in memory of the revolutionary soldiers of Litchfield County. July 5, 1908. Litchfield [The Tuttle, Morehouse & Taylor company, 1908]
iv, 59, [1] p. 2 pl. (incl. front.) 20½ cm.
1. Litchfield Co., Conn.—Hist.—Societies, etc. 2. Litchfield Co., Conn.—Hist.—Revolution.

F104.L7L785 14-20027 rev

NL 0406936 DLC IU NN

1115 **Litchfield historical society.**
.33 Some historic sites of Litchfield, Connecticut.
.591 [Litchfield, Conn.] 1933[1954]
12 p. illus. 24 cm.

1. Litchfield, Conn. - Hist. 2. Litchfield, Conn. - Descr. I. Title.

NL 0406937 NjP NNC NN CtY

Litchfield law school, Litchfield, Conn.
P96 Catalogue of the Law school at Litchfield
L71d Connecticut. Hartford, Press of Case, Tiffany
849 and company, 1849.
24p. 21½cm.

NL 0406938 CtY CtY-L CtHT-W

Litchfield law school, Litchfield, Conn.
P96 Catalogue of the Litchfield law school, from
L71d 1798 to 1827 inclusive. Published by the
828 students. Litchfield, Conn. Printed by S.S. Smith, 1828.
v, [1]-27p. 21cm.

NL 0406939 CtY PPAmP DLC-P4 CtY MB MH-L CSmH CtWT-W

Litchfield law school, Litchfield, Conn.
Catalogue, 1784-1833. Litchfield, 1900.

NL 0406940 Nh

Litchfield law school, Litchfield, Conn.
P96 ... The Litchfield law school. [Litchfield,
L71d Conn., Press of "The Litchfield enquirer", 1900]
900 cover-title, 27p. plates, ports. 22½cm.
"Reprint of 1900."
Issued under the direction of George M. Woodruff and Archibald M. Howe.

NL 0406941 CtY MH-L MiU-L

Litchfield law school, Litchfield, Conn.

Sampson, J P C.
An oration, delivered before the members of the Law institution, at Litchfield, on the Fourth of July, 1818. By J. P. C. Sampson ... New-York: Printed by E. Conrad, Frankfort-street. 1818.

The Litchfield Law School, Litchfield, Connecticut; a brief historical sketch.
[Litchfield, 1952?]
[3] p. illus.

NL 0406943 NNC-L

The Litchfield law school, 1775-1833.

[Fisher, Samuel Herbert] 1867–
... The Litchfield law school, 1775-1833. [New Haven; Published for the Tercentenary commission by the Yale university press, 1933.

Beinecke Library Folio AN7 L665 L665
Litchfield monitor. v.1-
Dec.21, 1784-
Litchfield [Printed by Thomas Collier, etc.]
25½-44cm. weekly.

Printer varies.
Some numbers printed on gray paper.
Publication suspended June 8-Nov.17, 1789.
Editor: Thomas Collier and others.
Title varies: Dec.21, 1784-March 1785, The Weekly monitor and American advertiser; April? 1785-Nov.28, 1786, The Weekly monitor; Dec.5, 1786-June 4, 1787, The Weekly monitor. And Litchfield town and county recorder; June 11-Dec.31, 1787, The Weekly monitor; Jan.7-June 16, 1788, Colliers (Litchfield) weekly monitor; June 23, 1788-April 20, 1789, The Weekly monitor; April 27-June 8, 1789, Weekly monitor. And the Litchfield advertiser; Nov. 17, 1789-Dec.4, 1790, Weekly monitor; Dec.11, 1790-Jan.3, 1791, Litchfield-County monitor; Jan. 10, 1791-Jan.4, 1792, Litchfield monitor; Jan. 11, 1792-Aug.20, 1794, The Monitor; Aug.27, 1794-June 3, 1795, Litchfield monitor; June 10, 1795-May 11, 1796, Litchfield monitor, and agricultural register; May 18, 1796-Feb.21, 1798, Weekly monitor; Feb.28, 1798-Feb. 26, 1800, The Monitor; March 5-Dec.10, 1800, The Farmer's monitor; Jan.21, 1801-June 8, 1803, The Monitor.
Ceased publication with July 29, 1807?

NL 0406947 CtY

Case
A The **Litchfield Monitor.**
6 v.13, no.707 (Feb.27,1799)
.5 v.13, no.751 (Jan.1,1800)
Litchfield[Conn.]1799-1800. F5.

Weekly.
Photostat copy (negative)

NL 0406948 ICN

Litchfield North Consociation
see Litchfield County, Conn. North Consociation.

Litchfield north west conference of Congregational churches.
The Annual survey, 1897. The proceedings and annual survey of the Litchfield north west conference of Congregational churches, for the year ending with the annual meeting, at East Canaan, Conn. Oct. 28, 1897. [Falls Village, F. E. Egleston, 1897.
11, [1] p.

NL 0406950 OClWHi

Litchfield Relief Society. Report of the committee, for the years 1882; 1883. 4°. *Litchfield*, 1883-4.

NL 0406951 DNLM

Litchfield school, *Litchfield, Conn.*
The hungry steam shovel & other stories by ten young authors of the Litchfield school for young boys; with illustrations by the authors and a preface by Charles Hanson Towne. Windham, Conn., Hawthorn house, 1935.
36 p. col. illus. 15½cm.
"First edition: limited to 500 copies."

1. Children as authors. I. Towne, Charles Hanson, 1877– II. Title.

Library of Congress PS647.S4L5 36-18
——— Copy 2.
Copyright A 83709 813.50822

NL 0406952 DLC PSC MH

Litchfield school for young boys, Litchfield, Conn.
see
Litchfield school, Litchfield, Conn.

Litchfield South Consociation
see Congregational Churches in Connecticut. South Consociation of Litchfield County.

The Litchfield squabble. An humourous poetical narration ...
see under Plain-Truth, Peter, pseud.

Litchfield Town and County recorder
see Litchfield Monitor.

Litchfield's legacy [by] the young antiquarian. [Litchfield, Conn.] Litchfield historical society, 1950.
24 p. 23 cm.
"The chapters in this book were first published in The Litchfield Enquirer."
In ms. on t.p.: Herbert L. Crapo.
1. Litchfield, Conn.--Hist.--Museums and Collections. I. Carpo, Herbert L. II. The young antiquarian. III. Litchfield historical society, Litchfield, Conn.

NL 0406957 NN WHi

Litchford, Henry E.
Raleigh, N.C. [1891]
see under Heck, George C.

VOLUME 336

Litchman, Charles H 1849-1902, ed.
Official history of the Improved Order of Red Men
see under Lindsay, George W., 1826-1902.

Litchman, Harold B., joint author.
Richards, Robert Hallowell, 1844–
Mining engineering notes, to accompany lectures of the first term, third year. v. 1– ⌐By⌐ Robert H. Richards assisted by Frederick W. Horton, Harold B. Litchman, Charles B. Hollis, Waldron T. ⌐1⌐ Schumacher. ⌐New York⌐ 1904–

Litchman, Mark M.
Papers by Mark M. Litchman, collected from various periodicals. 1927-32.
various paging.

NL 0406961 WaU-L

⌐Litchtveld, Lou⌐ 1903–
Afdaling in de vulkaan; roman ⌐door⌐ Albert Helman ⌐pseud.⌐ Amsterdam, Amsterdamsche Boek- en Courantmij., 1949.
356 p. 21 cm.

I. Title.

A 49-7707*

Harvard Univ. Library for Library of Congress ⌐1⌐

NL 0406962 MH

[Litchtveld, Lou, 1903-]
Waarom niet. [By] Albert Helman [pseud.] Rotterdam, Nijgh & Van Ditmar, 1933

NL 0406963 MH

Lite, Henry
see
Lyte, Henry, 1529?-1607

Lite, Joseph C
S&5gf 491 8 ... The role of aeration in the hatching of fertilized eggs of rotifers ... Philadelphia, Pa. ⌐1925⌐
Pamphlet
(Studies from the Zoölogical laboratory, the University of Nebraska, no.149)
By Joseph C. Lite and David Day Whitney.
"Reprinted from the Journal of experimental zoölogy, vol.43, no.1, November, 1925".
"Literature cited": p.9.

NL 0406965 CtY

ליטע; רעדאגירט פון מענדל סודארסקי, אוריה קאצענעלנבאגן ⌐און⌐ י. קיסין. ארויסגעגעבן פון "קולטור־געזעלשאפט פון ליטווישע ייִדן." ⌐New York, 1951–
v. illus., ports. 29 cm.
Added t. p.: Lite (Lithuania) Edited by Mendel Sudarsky, Uriah Katzenelenbogen ⌐and⌐ J. Kissin.

1. Jews in Lithuania—Hist. I. Jewish-Lithuanian Cultural Society "Lite," New York.
Title transliterated: Lite.

DS135.L5L5 52-46010

NL 0406966 DLC ViU UU

335.8 L71 Lite rays.
Bazen, N.D., Oliver-Mercer Electric Cooperative, inc.

1. Rural electrification. North Dakota. 2. Electrical cooperative associations, Rural. I. Oliver-Mercer Electric Cooperative, inc.

NL 0406967 DNAL

---

(594) St ser.E nr.2 Liteanu, Emil
Geologia ţinutului de câmpie din basinul inferior al Argeşului şi a teraselor Dunarii. II. Procese morfogenetice holocene în basinul inferior al Argeşului. Bucureşti, 1953.
99 p. illus.,2 col.maps. 24 cm. (Republica Populară Română. Comitetul Geologic de Cercetare şi Explorare a Bogăţiilor Subsolului. Studii technice şi economice. Seria E. Hidrogeologie, nr.2)
Includes bibliographies.

1.Rumania - Geology - Arges River Basin. 2.Geology, Stratigraphic - Quaternary. I.Title. II.Title: Procese morfogenetice holocene în basinul inferior al Argeşului.

NL 0406969 DI-GS

Case F 39 .326 1587Li LITEARCHIE contre les percitieux esprits, libelles, calomnies & apologies naguieres faictes par aucuns heretiques... Pour la conuersion des deuoyez restitution de l'Estat, et assopissement de ces troubles. Reueüe & corrigé par les docteurs. ⌐n.p.⌐1587.
42 ℓ. 17cm.

Bibl. nat. Cat. de l'histoire de France, v.1, p.313, no.339.

NL 0406970 ICN WU

Litegato, Giacomo
Hd31 10 L'Adige sconsolato, idilio. Per la partenza da Lendenara dell' illustrissimo Signor Girolamo Briani ... Di Giacomo Litegato ... Venetia,Appresso Gio:Batt:Ciotti,1613.
24p. 13cm.
Title within engraved border.
[Bound with Macedonio,M. Scielta delle poesie ... Venetia,1615]

NL 0406971 CtY

Litehiser, Robert Reid, 1893- joint author.
Woods, Kenneth Brady, 1905–
... Soil mechanics applied to highway engineering in Ohio, by K. B. Woods ... and R. R. Litehiser ... Columbus, College of engineering, the Ohio state university ⌐1938⌐

Литейное дело (*transliterated:* Liteĭnoe delo)
see
Литейное производство (*transliterated:* Liteĭnoe proizvodstvo)

TS200 .L56
Литейное производство. 1930–
⌐Москва⌐ Машгиз.
v. illus. 30 cm.
Monthly, 1930–Aug. 1953; bimonthly, Sept. 1953–
Publication suspended July 1941?–
Issues for 1930–41 called v. 1–11.
Organ of Vsesoiuznoe nauchnoe inzhenerno-tekhnicheskoe obshchestvo liteĭshchikov.
Title varies: 1930– Литейное дело.

1. Founding—Period. I. Vsesoiuznoe nauchnoe inzhenerno-tekhnicheskoe obshchestvo liteĭshchikov.
Title transliterated: Liteĭnoe proizvodstvo.

TS200.L56 49-44824 rev*

NL 0406974 DLC ICJ MdBJ

Liteĭnoe proizvodstvo.
Gusseisen mit Kugelgraphit ⌐von einem⌐ Autorenkollektiv. Berlin, Verlag Technik, 1953.
107 p. illus. 21 cm. (Schriftenreihe des Verlages Technik, Bd. 102)
Beiheft Nr. 121 zur Zeitschrift "Metallurgie und Giessereitechnik." Translation of 12 articles published in 1951 and 1952.

1. Cast-iron. 2. Graphite. I. Title.

TN710.L515 59-54037 ‡

NL 0406975 DLC

A Litel Treatise ageynste the mutterynge of some papistis in corners. Londini In Aedibvs Tho. Bertheleti. ... M.D.XXXIIII. ... [1534]
sm. 8vo 3/4 blue morocco

NL 0406976 CSmH

FILM A litel treatise ageynste the mutterynge of some papistis in corners. Londini in aedibvs Tho.Bertheleti. An.M.D.XXXIIII ...
Film reproduction,position 3.
University microfilms no.2737 (case 21,carton 122)
Short-title catalogue no.19177.

1.Catholic church--Doctrinal and controversial works.

NL 0406977 MiU

En Liten och kårt hand-bok, utaf adelig öfning, at bruka wid många tilfällen til stor hjälpreda i åtskilliga mål. Stockholm, 1760
1 v.

NL 0406978 MH

PT 9993 .C5L58 En Liten pilgrim; berättelse för ungdom. Översättning. Rock Island, Ill., Augustana Book Concern «19--?»
126 p. illus. 18 cm.

1. Children's stories.

NL 0406979 MnHi

FILM 4338 DL Roll 28 En liten sångbok. [Stockholm, Amund Laurentsson, 1553]
30 ℓ. 2°.
Collijn, II, 202 ("Uppl. 1")

NL 0406980 CU

FILM 4338 DL Roll 34 En liten sångbok. [Stockholm, Amund Laurentsson] 1553.
64 l. 4°.
Collijn, II, 203 ("Uppl. 2")

NL 0406981 CU

Liter, Calvin Pollard, 1900- comp.
Louisiana. *State board of agriculture and immigration.*
Louisiana 1925–1926. Issued by Department of agriculture and immigration. Harry D. Wilson, commissioner. Baton Rouge ⌐Ramires-Jones printing co., 1926⌐

VOLUME 336

Liter, Calvin Pollard, 1900- comp.

Louisiana. *State board of agriculture and immigration.*
Louisiana 1927-1928. Issued by Department of agriculture and immigration, Harry D. Wilson, commissioner. Baton Rouge, La. ₍Ramires-Jones printing co.₎ 1928.

M25 .L5 Liter, Monia.

[Piano music] London, I. Dash Music Co., c1943.
2 v. in 1. 31cm.
Publisher's pl. nos.: I. D. C. 1-2.
CONTENTS.—Blue fugue.—Swing prelude.

1. Piano music. 2. Canons, fugues, etc. (Piano) I. Title: Blue fugue. II. Title: Swing prelude.

NL 0406983 MB

Liter, Oneta.
Cold facts

see under

U.S. Rural Electrification Administration.

Litera. v. 1- 1954-
İstanbul, English Dept., University of Istanbul.
v. 24 cm. annual.

1. Literature—Hist. & crit.—Period. 2. Language and languages—Period. I. Istanbul. Universite. Ingiliz Filolojisi Şubesi.

PN2.L55 405 59-40088

NL 0406985 DLC OrU

---

851 P759s 1577 Rare Books Col

Litera dol la gloriosa et trionfante entrada del serenissimo prencipe di Spagna in bins citta di Fiandra.
[n.p.] M. D. XLIX. 26p. 15cm. in foldor in case 17cm. [With Poliziano, Angelo. Stanze ... Fiorenza, MDLXXVII]

Signatures: a^8, b^6 (b_6 blank)
Initial.

NL 0406986 TxU

BX 9435 G29 1707 Cage

Literae a celeberrimis pastoribus & professoribus Ecclesiae & Academiae Genevensis ad Universitatem Oxoniensem transmissae: Una cum responso ejusdem Universitatis Oxon. ad easdem literas ... Oxonii, E Theatro Sheldoniano, 1707.

A-B^2. Fo.

NL 0406987 DFo ICRL

Literae a conventu theologum in Anglia, et Ecclesiae Scoticanae delegatis, ad ecclesias in Belgio, Gallia
see under Westminister Assemby of Divines.

Literae Cantuarienses; the letter books of the monastery of Christ church, Canterbury...
see under Canterbury, Eng. Christ church priory.

Literae de re nummaria, in opposition to the common opinion that the Denarii Tomani were never larger than seven in an ounce
see under [Smith, William] 1651?-1735.

Political Pamphlets P105967

Literae humaniores: an appeal to teachers. 2d ed. London, W. Reeves, 1898.
32p. 19cm. (The Humanitarian League's publications, no. 14)

1. Animals, Treatment of. (Series: Humanitarian League. Pulications, no. 14)

NL 0406991 IEN NN

Wing ZP 539 .E 8073

LITERAE illustriss. principis, Ludouici Borbonii ad Carolū IX Galliae regem, quibus eius fidē implorat. Eiusdem Testificatio causarum quae eum arma sumere coegerunt. Literae Reginae Nauarrae ad regē Galliae quibus causas exponit. cur sese principi Cōdaeo cōiūxerit. Narratio caedis in Lud. Borbonium perpetratae. Varia variis linguis scripta in eundem epitaphia.
[Paris?H. Estienne,1569?]
75,[1],32p. 15cm.
Signatures: a-e^8 (last 2 *l.* blank) A-B^8.
Edited by Henry Estienne, the younger.
Bound in brown morocco with triple gilt fillet borders and fleurons on the sides.

NL 0406992 ICN

Literae procerum Europae ab imperatoribus, electoribus, principibus, statibusque sacri imperii Romano-Germanici ab anno 1552 ad annum 1712.
Lipsiae, 1712.
3 vols. 8vo.

NL 0406993 NN

Literae Sacrae; or, The doctrines od moral philosophy...
see under [Norman, A.]

Literae virorvm ervditorvm ad Franciscvm Craneveldivm, 1522-1528
see under Vocht, Henry de, 1878-ed.

016.8917 L711

Literärischer Begleiter zum Russischen Merkur.
1. Jahrg., Bd. 1 (Nr. 1-51); 2. Jan.-18. Dez., 1831. St. Petersburg.
viii, 202p. 22cm. weekly.

"Herausgegeben von August von Oldekop."
No more published?

NL 0406996 IU

Literärisch-praktische Bürgerverbindung in Riga.
Führer durch Lettland. Riga, G.Löffler, 1929.

vii, 168, 39, 16 p. 7 folded maps.
"Inseratenteil" (advertisements) pp. [127]-168

NL 0406997 MH CSt-H NN

Literärisch-Praktische Bürgerverbindung in Riga.
Die ₍H₎undertjaehrige jubelfier... am 12. Dezember 1902. ₍ ₎Riga, 1903.
64p.
[Separatabzug aus den "Rigaschen stadtblaettern" nr. 51 und 52]

YA 22779

NL 0406998 DLC

Literärisch-Praktische-Bürgerverbindung in Riga.
Rigasche stadblätter
see under title

Literaerisch-praktische Buergerverbindung in Riga.
Verfassung und Gesetze der Literärischpraktischen Bürger-Verbindung zu Riga. Riga: W. F. Häcker, 1828. 10 p. f°.

1. Industries and mechanic arts—Assoc. and org.—Russia—Riga.
N. Y. P. L. June 23, 1925

NL 0407000 NN

PT9550 L6 Scandinavian Dept.

Literärt album, redig. af Gustaf Meyer. Årg. 1-
Stockholm, O. L. Lamm [1877-
v. illus.

1. Swedish literature - 19th cent. I. Meyer, Gustaf, ed.

NL 0407001 CU DLC-P4 MnU

Literaire reacties op de wereld van heden; vijf lezingen, gehouden door H. Oldewelt ₍et al. voor de School voor Taal- en Letterkunde te 's Gravenhage₎ Den Haag, Servire, 1953.
109 p. 23 cm.

CONTENTS.—De verhouding tussen 's mensen gemoedsbehoeften en de moderne bestaansleisen van de samenleving, door H. Oldewelt.—Cultuurcritiek en wensdroom in Hesse's Glasperlenspiel, door J. H. Schouten.—Stromingen in het moderne Franse toneel, door H. Brugmans.—Toekomstangst in de hedendaagse Engelse roman, door M. D. E. de Leve.—Drievoudig verzet, door G. Stuiveling.

1. Literature, Modern—20th cent.—Addresses, essays, lectures. I. Oldewelt, Hendrik Marie Jan, 1897-

A 54-1291

Illinois. Univ. Library for Library of Congress

NL 0407002 IU NN

Den literaire retskrivning.
Gyldendal, 1889.

NL 0407003 NdU

Literairt maaneskrift, redigiret og udgivet af Adolph ₍Hertz; 1 bd...Kiobenhavn, 1853-54.
9 nos. in 1 v. 8°

NL 0407004 NN

VOLUME 336

A LITERAL exposition of two prophecies cited by St. Matthew out of the Old Testament, and said by him to be fulfill'd in the person of Jesus Christ. London, 1726.

pp. 304

NL 0407005 MH

Literal Interpretation of The Sermon on The Mount ...
see under Dods, Marcus, 1834-1909.

A literal prose translation of five select pieces from the works of Tasso ...
see under Capuzzi, F

A literal translation into English of the earliest known book on fowling and fishing written originally in Flemish and printed at Antwerp in the year 1492. [London], Privately printed for A. Denison, 1872.

[24] p.l 1. illus. 25 cm.
Unpaged. Arthur Denison, translator.
Only 25 copies printed.
Contains the printer's marks of Matthias van der Goes.

NL 0407008 MH

Literal translation of the German patent law with German technical phraseology ...
see under Germany. Laws, statutes, etc.

Literal translation to scientific German.
n.p. 18-

NL 0407010 NjP

Literal translations of selections from Roman historical literature. Trenton, 1915.

NL 0407011 NjP

The Literalist. v.1-5; 1840-1842. Philadelphia, O. Rogers.
5v.

Binder's title.
Vols. 1-2, 4-5 lack title page.

NL 0407012 ICRL ICU OOxM NjNbS

BT875 .A3 Literalist.
Essays and Sermons on the Advent and Kingdom of Christ, ... Phila., 1840-41

NL 0407013 DLC

Literarhistorische Bibliothek.
Bd. 1

Berlin: Junker und Dünnhaupt, 1929- 8°.
v.

Editor : Bd. 1 , M. Sommerfeld.

Contents:
Bd. 1. SOMMERFELD, M. Deutsche Barocklyrik nach Motiven ausgewählt und geordnet. 1929.

Bd. 3. SOMMERFELD, M. Deutsche Lyrik 1880-1930. 1931.

1. No subject. I. Sommerfeld, Martin, 1894- , editor.
N. Y. P. L. December 16, 1931

NL 0407014 NN OO KyU OU NcD ICN OCU

Literarhistorische forschungen. Hrsg. von. dr. Josef Schick ... und dr. M. frh. v. Waldberg ...
Weimar [etc.] E. Felber, 1897-19
v. 22cm.

Title varies: hft. 1-28, Litterarhistorische forschungen ...
Imprint, hft. 11- : Berlin, E. Felber.
Publication suspended, 1915-1927.

1. Literature—Hist. & crit. I. Schick, Josef, 1859- ed. II. Waldberg, Max, freiherr von, 1858- ed.

G-2006 (rev. '29)

Library of Congress PN35.L6

OCU OO
NL 0407015 DLC NjP OClW CoU CaBVaU TxU TU CU MiU

Literarhistorische gesellschaft, Bonn.
Bonner forschungen, hrsg. von Berthold Litzmann...
see under title

Literarhistorische gesellschaft, Bonn.

Festschrift für Berthold Litzmann zum 60. geburtstag 18. 4. 1917. Im auftrage der Literarhistorischen gesellschaft Bonn, herausgegeben von Carl Enders. Bonn, F. Cohen, 1920.

---

809 L711m Literarhistorische Gesellschaft, Bonn.
Mitteilungen der Literarhistorischen Gesellschaft Bonn, unter dem Vorsitz von Professor Berthold Litzmann. Bonn, F. Cohen, 1906-
v. 22cm.

Ceased publication in 1929. Cf. Union List of Serials.

1. Literature - Hist. & crit. - Period.
I. Litzmann, Berthold, 1857-1926.

NL 0407018 TxU PU NcD NcU

Literarhistorische Gesellschaft, Bonn.
[Schriften] v. 1-10 Dortmund 1906-11.
5 v. 23 cm.
Title given on back of volumes.
Editor: v. 1-10 Berthold Litzmann.

Continued as Bonner forschungen.

NL 0407019 CU ICU OO

Literarhistorische Gesellschaft, Bonn.
Schriften ... Neue Folge
see Bonner Forschungen.

Literarhistorisches taschenbuch. Hrsg. von R. E. Prutz. 1.-6. jahrg.; 1843-48. Leipzig, O. Wigand [1843-44]; Hannover, C. F. Kius [1845-48]
6 v. 18-20½cm.
No more published.

I. Prutz, Robert Eduard, 1816-1872, ed.

5-22267

Library of Congress PN4.L5

NL 0407021 DLC CU MdBJ OClW TxU UU

Literarhistorisch-musikwissenschaftliche Abhandlungen. Bd. 1- Würzburg, 1938-
v. illus. (incl. music) 25 cm.
Publication suspended 1944-1952.
1. Music - History and criticism - Collections.

NL 0407022 OU MoSW

Literaria A. G., firm, publishers, Vienna.

AC30 .P5 Piszk, Karl Oskar, 1894- *ed.*
Künstlerhilfe-Almanach der Literaria. Wien, Literaria-Verlag, 1924.

Literarii sodalitii apud Marpurgum aliquot cachinni super quodam duorum Lypsensium Poetarum in Lutherum scripto Libello, effusi.
M. D. XXVIII. At end: Excusum Marpurgi, Anno, M, D, XXVIII. septimo Calendas Octobres.
14h. [16] p. t.-p. border. Text in italics. Wdct initials. This little collection of Latin verses seems nowhere mentioned. Cordus (who here, as elsewhere, calls himself 'Eustathius Cordus') is the chief writer, the others bearing the names of 'Hadrianus Consus,' 'Chalcondyles Anthyllius,' 'Demetrius Marianus,' Valentinus Lorichius,' 'Androsthenes Buccacius,'

'Anneus Barba,' and 'Faustulus Canens.' The Leipsic poets attacked are 'Myricinus and 'Hasenbergius.'

NL 0407025 NIC

Gz 056.86 L712 El Literario; semanario de literatura, artes e historia. t.1- (no.1-); mayo 6, 1916-
Bogotá.
v. illus. 24cm. weekly (irregular).

Ceased publication 1919?
"Director: Diego Uribe."

1. Colombian literature - Period. I. Uribe, Diego, 1867-

NL 0407026 TxU

Literarische...
see also Litterarische...

Literarische Adalbert-Stifter-Gesellschaft, Eger
see Adalbert-Stifter-Gesellschaft, Eger.

Literarische anzeigen
see under [Anding, Ernest] 1860-

VOLUME 336

4-Serials
Literarische Beilage des Staats-Anzeiger für Württemberg.

NL 0407030 DLC-P4

Literarische berichte aus dem gebiete der philosophie; das umfassende philosophische literaturblatt für wissenschaft und allgemeines geistesleben ... hft. 1- herbst 1923- Erfurt, K. Stenger, 1923-
v. 23cm. irregular.
Nos. 9/10, 11/12, 13/14 were issued in one number each.
Nos. 1-2 have title: Literarische berichte der Deutschen philosophischen gesellschaft.
Editor: 1923- Arthur Hoffmann.

1. Philosophy—Period. 2. Philosophy—Bibl. I. Hoffmann, Arthur K. Wilhelm, 1889- ed. II. Deutsche philosophische gesellschaft, Jena.
27-21554
Library of Congress B3.L5

NL 0407031 DLC CSt OCU ICU

LITERARISCHE berichte aus dem gebiete der philosophie. Herausgegeben von Arthur Hoffman-Erfurt. Sonderdruck von heft 9/10. Dem Internationalen kongress für philosophie (Harvard University, Cambridge, Mass., September, 1926) ergebenst überreicht von verlag und schriftleitung. Erfurt, K. Stenger, 1926.

Title taken from cover.

NL 0407032 MH

Literarische berichte aus Ungarn. Über die thätigkeit der Ungarischen academie der wissenschaften und ihrer commissionen, des Ung. national-museums, der Kisfaludy-gesellschaft, der Histor. gesellschaft, der Naturwissenschaftlichen und anderer gelehrter gesellschaften und anstalten, sowie auch einzelner schriftsteller. Hrsg. von Paul Hunfalvy ... 1.-4. jahrg.; 1877-80. Budapest, Druck des Franklin-verein, 1877-80.
4 v. illus., plates (part col.) 22½cm. quarterly.
Each volume contains "Literatur."
Continued as Ungarische revue.

——— Register zu Literarische berichte aus Ungarn, bd. I-IV. 1878-1881 und Ungarische revue, jahrg. I-XIII. 1882-1894. Budapest, 1894.
54 p. 26½cm. [With Ungarische revue. Budapest, 1894. 14. jahrg.]

1. Hungary—Hist.—Period. I. Hunfalvy, Pál, 1810-1891, ed. II. Magyar tudományos akadémia, Budapest.
3-8291

NL 0407034 DLC MH ICRL ICN NIC NNC ICJ NN OU

Literarische Blätter. [1.]- Jahrg. [Nr. 1- 20 Mai 1946-
[Genf] Die Auslese, Gesellschaft für Lesefreunde.
v. in illus. 23 cm. monthly (irregular)

I. Die Auslese, Gesellschaft für Lesefreunde. Geneva.
AP32.L57 52-22455

NL 0407035 DLC NN

Das Literarische Comptoir in Zürich und Winterthur, der Bericht eines preussischen Geheimagenten aus dem Jahre 1844. [Hrsg. von] Hans Gustav Keller. Aarau, Graphische Werkstätten H. R. Sauerländer [1943]
22 p. 23 cm.
"Sonderabdruck aus Schweizer Beiträge zur allgemeinen Geschichte, Band I (1943)"

1. Literarisches Comptoir. 2. Espionage, Prussian—Switzerland. I. Keller, Hans Gustav, 1902- ed.
Z232.L72L5 54-52736

NL 0407036 DLC NN OU MH

*7270a.10
Literarische Correspondenz. Herausgegeben und redigirt von Hans Adam Stoehr. Jahrgang I, no. 1-7.
Leipzig. Foltz. [1877.] (3), 147 pp. 4°.
After vol. I, no. 13, this was continued as Allgemeine literarische Correspondenz für das gebildete Deutschland.

June 26, 1900
*D5948 — Periodicals. — Stoehr, Hans Adam, ed.

NL 0407037 MB

Literarische Denkmale...
see under [Bodmer, Johann Jakob] 1698-1783.

Das literarische Deutschland. v.1- ; Nov. 1950-
Heidelberg, Ger.
v. semimonthly.

Ceased 1951.
Continued by Neue literarische Welt.
"Zeitung der Deutschen Akademie für Sprache und Dichtung."

NL 0407039 ICRL

Literarische Durchflüge. (Der Neue teutsche Merkur. Weimar, 1797. 12°. Jahr 1797. Bd. 1, p. 293-300.)
References to Benjamin Franklin, p. 294-295.

NL 0407040 NN

Das Literarische Echo
see Die Literatur; Monatsschrift für Literaturfreunde ...

Literarische Geheimberichte aus dem Vormärz
see under Glossy, Karl, 1848-1937, ed.

PT4 .L77
Die LITERARISCHE gesellschaft; hrsg. von der Literarischen gesellschaft zu Hamburg. 1.-6. jahrg., hft. 6; 1915-1920. [Hamburg, 1915-20]
6 v. in 2. 22½cm. monthly (irregular)
No more published.

1. German literature--Period.

NL 0407043 ICU

PT3877 A3L5
Literarische Gesellschaft, Aarau.
Aargauisches Dichterbuch. Festschrift zur aargauischen Centenarfeier, 1903. Aarau, E. Wirz, 1903.
166 p.

1. German literature - Swiss authors. 2. Aargau - Festivals, etc. I. Title.

NL 0407044 CU

Literarische Gesellschaft, Bern.
Festschrift für Edouard Tièche
see under title

Literarische Gesellschaft, Bern.
Neujahrsblatt auf das Jahr 1917, zum Andenken Georg Finsler's, 1852-1916. Bern, Wyss, 1916.
129 p. 10.5 in.

NL 0407046 CoU

~~GEU~~ PT35 L45
Literarische Gesellschaft, Bern.
Schriften. 1-
Bern, H. Lang, 1938-
no. in v.

Supersedes its Neujahrsblätter; also called Neue Folge der Neujahrsblätter.

NL 0407047 GEU OU NN CaOTU

Literarische gesellschaft, *Cologne.*
Jahrbuch der Kölner blumenspiele.

Köln, J. G. Schmitz, 19
v. ports. 26cm.
Includes music.

1. German literature—Societies. 2. German literature—Year-books. 3. Cologne—Festivals, etc. 4. Floral games.
43-50081
Library of Congress PT23.L5

NL 0407048 DLC

Hkl he63 893i
Literarische Gesellschaft, Nuremberg.
... Heine-Almanach. Als Protest gegen die Düsseldorfer Denkmalverweigerung. Hrsg. in Verbindung mit hervorragenden Schriftstellern von der "Literarischen Gesellschaft" in Nürnberg. Nürnberg, C. Koch, 1893.
v, 217, [1]p. port. 23cm.
At head of title: Zum Besten des Fonds für ein Heine-Denkmal.

NL 0407049 CtY

Literarische Gesellschaft Chicago.

DD61 .D462
Deutsche Beiträge zur geistigen Überlieferung. [1.]- Jahrg.; 1947-
Chicago, H. Regnery [etc.]

Literarische gesellschaft Chicago.
Mitteilungen.
[Chicago, 19
v. 28 cm.

1. Germany—Intellectual life.
DD239.L5 48-32224

NL 0407051 DLC

Literarische Gesellschaft Regensburg, Germany.
Die Volksbücherei Regensburg ruft auch dich; Regensburg's library is calling on you. [Regensburg, n. d.] 24 p. illus. 20cm.
"Die vorliegende Broschüre wurde von Dr. Rudolf Binapfl, Regensburg, zusammengestellt.

1. Libraries—Germany—Regensburg. I. Binapfl, Rudolf, comp.

NL 0407052 NN

VOLUME 336

Literarische Gesellschaft von Morrisania.
Bücher-Verzeichniss. New York, Druck von William Wieser, 1895.
33 p. 12°.
--- ---- Supplement. [New York, W. Wieser], 1900.
16 p. 12°.

NL 0407053 NN

Literarische Gesellschaft von Morrisania.
Charter und revidierte Statuten ...
New York, Buchdruckerei von A. Heubner, 1897.
11 p. 16°.
Title taken from cover.

NL 0407054 NN

Literarische Gesellschaft von Morrisania.
Einladung und Program zur Feier des Deutschen Tages ... 7. October 1899.
[New York] A. Heubner, printer [1899]
2 l. f°.

NL 0407055 NN

Literarische Gesellschaft von Morrisania.
Programm zur Feier des Deutschen Tages ... 7. October 1899. [New York, 1899]
2 l. 8°.

NL 0407056 NN

LITERARISCHE GESELLSCHAFT ZU EUTIN.
Johann Heinrich Voss-gedächtnisschrift zur 100. wiederkehr seines todestages (29.märz 1826). Eutin, G.Struve,1926.
pp. 61. Port.
"Bibliography, p.58."

NL 0407057 MH

Literarische gesellschaft zu Halberstadt.
Gemeinnützige unterhaltungen für 1804
see under title

Literarische Gesellschaft zu Hamburg.
Die Literarische gesellschaft
see under title

Literarische Kommission der deutschen Heimarbeitsausstellung.
Bilder aus der deutschen Heimarbeit. Leipzig, F.Diedrich, 1906.
31 p. 21 cm. (Sozialer fortschritt, no. 63-64)
Cover title.

NL 0407060 MH

PN 6034 L57
Literarische Leckerbissen; Sammlung von Kabinettstücken deutscher und ausländischer Literatur. Charlottenburg-Berlin, T. Lissner, 1912-
v. illus. 19cm.

1. Literature - Collections 2. German literature - Translations from foreign language

NL 0407061 WU TNJ

Literarische mitteilungen der Annalen des Deutschen Reichs. Monatsbericht über neuerscheinungen auf dem gebiete der rechts- und staatswissenschaften.
München, J. Schweitzer verlag (A. Sellier)
v. 24½cm.
Vols. 14- with Annalen des Deutschen Reichs, v. 34-
Issued independently as "Literarische mitteilungen für juristen und verwaltungsbeamte" from 1888 to 1900. Joined as a supplement to "Annalen des Deutschen Reichs" in 1901.
Editors: 1901-02, K. T. von Eheberg.—1903- K. T. von Eheberg, Anton Dyroff.
1. Social sciences—Bibl.—Period. I. Eheberg, Karl Theodor von, 1855- ed. II. Dyroff, Anton, 1864- ed.
CA 7-6733 Unrev'd
Library of Congress H5.A6

NL 0407062 DLC CU

Literarische mitteilungen fuer juristen und verwaltungsbeamte
see
Literarische mitteilungen der Annalen des Deutschen Reichs.

Literarische Revue. Jahrg. 1-
München, Willi Weismann [1946-
v. 24 cm. monthly.
Title varies: v. 1-2, Die Fähre.

AP30.L68 52-39436

NL 0407064 NIC TxU DLC NcD KU CU NcU ICarbS CtY PU NBuG NN

Literarische revue.
Entwicklungstendenzen im modernen roman.
[München, W. Weismann, 1949]
64 p.
From Literarische revue. 4. jahrg., heft 1, Jan. 1949.

1. Fiction - Hist. and crit. 2. Fiction - Addresses, essays, lectures. I. Title.

NL 0407065 NNC

PT1141 L57
Literarische Revue.
Schriftsteller und Diktatur, Schicksale deutscher Dichtung ...
[München] W. Weismann [1948]
449-512 p. (Literarische Revue, 3. Jahrg., Heft 8, November 1948)

1. German literature - 20th cent. I. Title.

NL 0407066 CU

Literarische Rundschau.
Freiburg i. Br., etc., Ger., Herder, etc.
v. monthly.
Published 1875-1880.
Continued by Literarische Rundschau für das katholische Deutschland.

NL 0407067 ICRL OO

Literarische Rundschau für das katholische Deutschland. Ser., v.7- ; 1881-
Freiburg i Br., Herder.
v. monthly.
Ceased 1914.
Continues Literarische Rundschau.
Center has:

NL 0407068 ICRL OO

Literarische rundschau für den familienforscher.
Marktschellenberg [etc.] Degner & co., 19
v. in 23½cm. monthly (irregular)
Vols. -5, no. 12 published in Leipzig.
Supplement to Familiengeschichtliche quellen.

1. Genealogy—Bibl.—Period. 2. Germany—Geneal.—Bibl. I. Familiengeschichtliche quellen. Supplement.
43-43829
Library of Congress Z5311.L5

NL 0407069 DLC

LITERARISCHE Rundschau für den Familienforscher.
Jahrg. 1-4, Heft 45; Juli, 1927-Feb. 15, 1937
Leipzig, Degener. v. 24cm.
Film reproduction. Negative.
"Halbmonatsberichte über Neuerscheinungen des genealogischen Schrifttums und verwandter Gebiete (Wappen- und Siegelkunde, Namenusen, Vererbungslehre u. derg.)"

Issued as a suppl. to Familiengeschichtliche Quellen (see that entry).
Editor: July, 1927-Feb. 15, 1937, F. Wacken.
Ceased publication with v. 6, Sept. 1944?

1. Germany--Geneal.--Bibl. I. Wecken, Friedrich, 1875- ,ed.

NL 0407071 NN

Literarische sachverstaendigen-kammer fuer den Koenigl. Preussischen staat
see
Prussia. Literarische sachverstaendigen-kammer

Literarische silhouetten; deutsche dichter und denker und ihre werke. Ein literarkritisches jahrbuch. (Ausgabe 1907) Herausgegeben und bearbeitet von dr. philos. Heinz Voss und dozent a. d. Bruno Volger ... Oetzsch-Leipzig, B. Volger, 1907.
2 p. l., 334 p. 20½cm.
The second "ausgabe" appeared in the same year; the third and last in 1908.

1. German literature—Year-books. 2. Authors, German. I. Voss, Heinz, ed. II. Volger, Bruno, 1875- joint ed.
8-22155 Revised
Library of Congress PT13.L5

NL 0407073 DLC

Literarische silhouetten; deutsche dichter und denker und ihre werke. Ein literarkritisches schriftsteller-jahrbuch. Zweite ausgabe 1907. Herausgegeben von dr. phil. Heinz Voss und dozent a. d. Bruno Volger. Oetzsch-Leipzig, B. Volger 1907.
3 p. l., 339 p. illus. (port.) 19cm.
The first "ausgabe" appeared in the same year; the third and last in 1908.

1. German literature—Year-books. 2. Authors, German. I. Voss, Heinz, ed. II. Volger, Bruno, 1875- joint ed.
28-10240
Library of Congress PT13.L5 1907 a

NL 0407074 DLC

VOLUME 336

Literarische texte des mittleren reiches i, ii.
Leipzig, 1908-09
see under Erman, Adolf, 1854-1937, ed.

Literarische Texte und ptolemäische Urkunden
see under Larsen, Tage, 1909- ed.

Literarische Vereinigung, Brunswick, Ger.
Ina Seidel [zum 65.Geburtstage am 15.Sept.1950 von der Stadt Braunschweig und der Literarischen Vereinigung Braunschweig E.V. Braunschweig, 1950]

NL 0407077 MH

LITERARISCHE VEREINIGUNG,BRUNSWICK,GER.
Robert Jordan, zum fünfundsechzigsten Geburtstage, 11. September 1950, von der Literarischen Vereinigung Braunschweig E.V. [Braunschweig, 1950] 23 p. illus. 20cm.

Title-page on two pages.
"Zusammengestellt von Ewald Lüpke."
"Bibliographie,: p. 22-23.
CONTENTS.—Trapp, Albert. Robert Jordan, sein Wesen und seine Leistung.—Ernst, Heinrich. Robert Jordan und sein Verhältnis zur bildenden Kunst.—Keil, Arno. Offener Brief an ein Geburtstagkind.—Schmidtke,

Gotthard.Die spitze Feder.—Wedemeyer, Max. Ein persönliches Bekenntnis zu Robert Jordan.

I. Jordan, Robert, 1885- . I. Lüpke, Ewald, , ed.

NL 0407079 NN

Literarische Vereinigung Winterthur.
In memoriam Dr.Alfred Mombert, 1872-1942. [Einleitende Worte von Rudolf Hunziker, gesprochen in der von der Literarischen Vereinigung Winterthur veranstalteten Feier. Winterthur, 1942]

30 p. ports.
Cover title

1. Mombert, Alfred, 1872-1942. I. Hunziker, Rudolf, 1870-1946. II. Title.

NL 0407080 MH

Literarische vereinigung Winterthur
Jahrbuch der Literarischen vereinigung Winterthur. ...
Winterthur, A.Vogel [ ]
v. illus.(music),plates,ports.(1 mounted) 22½cm.

1. Swiss literature (German). 2. German literature - Swiss authors

NL 0407081 NRU GU

---

*GC9 R4574 A920l

Literarische Vereinigung Winterthur.
Jahrbuch der Literarischen Vereinigung, Winterthur, 1920, mit neun Bildern und einer Musikbeilage.
Verlag von A.Vogel,Winterthur[1920]
168p. plates(incl.music)ports. 22.5cm.,in case 23.5cm.
"Die Toten, von Émile Verhaeren (uebertragen durch Rainer Maria Rilke)": p.53 (Ritzer T73).
Original printed green wrappers; in cloth case.

NL 0407082 MH

PT2621 .E584S4

Literarische Vereinigung Winterthur.
Kempter, Lothar, 1900-
Die Schwester, Erzählung. Hrsg. von der Literarischen Vereinigung Winterthur. [Winterthur] 1940.

PT3860 .L75 v.24

LITERARISCHE VEREINIGUNG WINTERTHUR.
Winterthurer Lyriker; eine Auswahl. Winterthur, W. Vogel [1954]
59 p. (24.Gabe der Literarischen Vereiniging Winterthur)

1. German poetry--Swiss authors. 2. Swiss poetry (German)

NL 0407084 ICU

Literarische Warte
see Die Warte.

Die Literarische Welt
see Das deutsche Wort der Literarischen Welt, Neue Folge, und die Grosse Uebersicht.

Literarische wochenschrift; kritisches zentralblatt für die gesamte wissenschaft. 6. juni 1925–31. dez. 1926. Weimar, Verlag von R. Wagner sohn, 1925–26.
2 v. 30cm.
Founded and edited by Eduard Zarncke.
No more published.

1. Books—Reviews. I. Zarncke, Eduard, 1857–1936, ed.
27-16614 Revised
Library of Congress Z1007.L76

NL 0407087 DLC IEN

ליטעראַרישע זאַמלונגען ... רעדאַקטירט: מ. גיציס, מאַטעס דייטש. שיקאַגא. [Chicago] 1943–
v. illus., port. 22½cm.
Vols. 1–3 have cover-title: Literarishe zumlungen; edited by M. Ghitzis and Mates Deitch.

1. Yiddish literature. I. Ghitzis, Moisey, 1894– ed. II. Deitch, Mattes, 1894– joint ed. *Title transliterated:* Literarische zamlungen.
46-12965
Library of Congress PJ5125.L5

NL 0407088 DLC CaBVaU NNYI

Literarische Zeitfragen, hrsg. von Hermann Graef. 1- Lpz. 1908-
v. in 16 cm.
Contents.
1. Rendtorff, K.G. Hauptmanns Kaiser Karls geisel. 1908.
2. Kronacher, Alwin. Das deutsche theater zu Berlin und Geothe. 1908.

NL 0407089 CU

Der **Literarische** Zeitgenosse
see
Литературный современник (*transliterated:* Literaturnyĭ sovremennik)

AC30 .L5

Der **Literarische** Zeitspiegel. Folge 1/2-
1933-
Zürich.
v. illus. 17 cm.

AC30.L5 51-39952

NL 0407091 DLC

Literarische zeitung ... [1.]–16. jahrg.; 2. jan. 1834–28. juni 1849. Berlin, Duncker und Humblot [etc.] 1834–49.
16 v. 24–27½cm.
Weekly, 1834–42; semiweekly, 1843–Apr. 12, 1848; weekly, Apr. 20, 1848–June 1849.
Editors: Jan. 2, 1834–Nov. 15, 1837, Karl Büchner.—Nov. 22–Dec. 23, 1837, Carl Duncker.—Jan. 3–Dec. 26, 1838, Eduard Meyen.—Jan. 2, 1839–June 28, 1849, K. H. Brandes.
Published by Duncker und Humblot, 1834–45; E. H. Schroeder, 1846; F. Schneider & comp., 1847–48; F. Dümmler, 1849.
Includes supplements.
No more published.

1. Bibliography—Period. 2. Book reviews. I. *Büchner, Karl, 1806–1837, ed. II. Brandes, Karl Heinrich, ed.
34-41009
Library of Congress Z1007.L763 010.5

NL 0407092 DLC NcU CU ICU NN

Literarischer...
see also Litterarischer...

Literarischer Almanach.

NL 0407094 InU

PT19 L68 Rarebk room

Literarischer almanach für 1827-1832. So nützlich und angenehm,als unterhaltend und lustig zu lesen./ Von Lic.Simon Ratzeberger,dem jüngsten[pseud.] 1.-6.jahrg. Leipzig[etc. 1826-31]
v.in 16½cm.
Contains music.
Vol.5-6 have also special t.-p.:Literarisches taschenbuch auf das jahr 1831-1832;1.-2.jahrg.
Vol.5-6 have imprint:München,M.Lindauer.
No more published.

NL 0407095 ICU

Literarischer Anzeiger.
Graz, Austria, Verlags-Buchhandlung "Styria"
v. monthly.
Published 1886-1914?
Title varies slightly.

NL 0407096 ICRL OCl

Literarischer handweiser zunächst für alle **katholiken** deutscher zunge.
Münster, Theissing
v. 25cm.
12 no. a year, 24 no. a year, 19
Editor: Franz Hülskamp.—19 Edmund Niesert.

1. Catholic literature—Bibl.—Period. 2. Bibliography—Best books—Catholic literature. I. Hülskamp, Franz, 1833– ed. II. Niesert, Edmund H . M., 1866– ed.
CA 7-2645 Unrev'd
Library of Congress Z7837.L55

NL 0407097 DLC KU CSt IU TxU OClJC MoConA

VOLUME 336

Literarischer jahresbericht ... hrsg. von der **redaktion** "Nord und süd" ... Berlin [1907-
v. illus., plates, ports. 28½cm.

1. German literature—Year-books. 2. Bibliography—Best books—German literature. I. Nord und süd, Berlin.

8-7618

Library of Congress Z1035.L78

NL 0407098 DLC FU MiU ICJ MB

Literarischer Jahresbericht des Dürerbundes. [1]-
Berlin, Sieben-Stäbe, 1907-31.
v. 25cm.

Publisher varies.

√1.Literature - Yearbooks. √I.Title.

NL 0407099 CLSU NN IU

Literarischer Ratgeber des Dürerbundes
see under Dürerbund.

Literarischer ratgeber für die katholiken Deutschlands ... jahrg., 19
München, Allgemeine verlags-gesellschaft m. b. h., 19
v. fronts., plates (part col.) ports. (part col.) 24cm.

Volumes for -1904 have title: Literarischer ratgeber für Weihnachten.
-1904, hrsg. von der redaktion der "Literarischen warte"; 1905- hrsg. von J. Popp.

1. German literature—Year-books. 2. Catholic literature—Bibl. I. Literarische warte. II. Popp, Joseph, 1867- ed.

CA 9—855 Unrev'd

Library of Congress Z7837.L58

NL 0407101 DLC

Literarischer ratgeber fuer Weihnachten
see
Literarischer ratgeber fuer die katholiken Deutschlands

---

806 [Literarischer Verein]
L776t Tagebuch [Mittwoch d.10 Juni 1868 bis Donnerstag d.31 März, 1870. N.p., 1868-70]
1v.(unpaged) 21cm.

NL 0407103 CLSU

Literarischer Verein, New York.
...Jahrbuch
19
New York, 1 16°.
v. illus.

Cover-title.
Title varies: 19 Literarisch-geselliger Verein...Taschen-Kalender; 1927- Literarischer Verein...Jahrbuch.
1926- title of institution also in English: German Literary Society.

1. New York (city)—Societies, Literary.
N. Y. P. L. July 31, 1928

NL 0407104 NN

PT23 Literarischer Verein in Nürnberg.
L57 Album ...
Nürnberg, In Kommission bei Bauer und Raspe, 18
v.

Supersedes the society's Jahresbericht.
No more published

NL 0407105 NcD InU ICU WU CU NNU-W NjP MB PU-F ICN OClW MWelC

Literarischer Verein in Stuttgart.
Bibliothek. Publikation 1-
Stuttgart [etc.] Hiersemann [etc.] 1843-19
v. 23 cm.

Publication suspended 1916-24 and 1942-52.
Vols. 1-266 (1843-1915) issued by the society under its variant name: Litterarischer Verein in Stuttgart.

1. German literature (Collections)

PT1101.L5 56-28670

NL 0407106 NjP CoU UU OU OCU MB NcGU TU MH MdBP NBuG TxU DLC CSt FU TNJ CU PPeSchw DCU MiU ViU

LITERARISCHER VEREIN IN STUTTGART.
Rechenschafts bericht über das sechste Verwaltungsjahr (1851) des Vereins. Stuttgart, 1853.

pp. 5. (In its Bibliothek, e[ ] 25.)

NL 0407107 MH

PT2266 Literarischer verein in Wien.
.Z8L7 Grillparzers ahnen; eine festgabe zu August Sauers 60. geburtstage hrsg. vom Literarischen verein in Wien. Wien, 1915.
56, [1] p. illus., pl., port., fold. facsims., fold. geneal. table. 27cm.

NL 0407108 ICU MoU FU OCU NIC CtY IU MH

Literarischer verein in Wien.
Schriften des Literarischen vereins in Wien. 1.-
Wien, Verlag des Literarischen vereins in Wien, 1904-
v. 20½ cm.

8—19525

NL 0407109 DLC OCU OU ICarbS NcD PU CU NjP

---

*pGB8 Literarischer Verein in Wien.
V6755R Zur Aufklärung der politischen Bedeutung der
4.21.48 bevorstehenden Wahlen zum deutschen Parlament in Frankfurt am Main. Der unterzeichnete Literaten-Verein hält es für seine Pflicht ...
[Wien,1848]

broadside. 47x29cm.
Dated: Wien, den 21. April 1848.

NL 0407110 MH

Literarischer Verein "Phoebus", Munich
Hkl Festgabe des Literarischen Vereins "Phoebus",
he74 München, bei seiner Heine-Feier 19.Januar 1908.
+904f München, Verlag des Literarischen Vereins "Phoebus", Druck und Vertrieb für den Buchhandel C.A.Seyfried & Comp.,1908.
22p. illus.(incl.facsims.) 30½cm. Bound with: Franzos, Karl Emil, 1848-1904. Heine-Bilder. [Wien,1904?]

Hkl
he63 -- -- Another copy.
+908f

NL 0407111 CtY

Literarischer weihnachts-katalog. jahrg.; ?
Leipzig [K. F. Koehler]
v. illus., col. plates. 23½cm.
Issued for distribution by various firms.

1. Bibliography—Best books—German literature. 2. German literature—Bibl.

CA 13-491 Unrev'd

Library of Congress Z1035.L81F

NL 0407112 DLC

Literarischer Zodiacus; Journal für Zeit und Leben, Wissenschaft und Kunst. Leipzig
Jg.1-2 no.1; Jan. 1835-Jan. 1836
Redigiert von Theodor Mundt
No more published?
Reprinted in 1971 by Athenäum, Frankfurt/Main, in its series Zeitschriften des Jungen Deutschland, as v.1-2

The same. Original ed. Sept., Oct. 1835
I. Mundt, Theodor, 1808- 61, ed.

NL 0407113 MH CU

Literarisches...
see also Litterarisches...

Literarisches beiblatt zum jahrbuch des Deutschen vereins für buchwesen und schrifttum ... jahrg. 1-
jan./feb. 1924- Leipzig, Verlag des Deutschen vereins für buchwesen and schrifttum, 1924-
v. illus., pl. 31cm. 3 double no. a year (1925: 4 no.)

Vols. 1-4 (1924-27) issued as "Literarisches beiblatt der Zeitschrift des Deutschen vereins für buchwesen und schrifttum".
Vols. 5- (1928-) issued as supplement to Buch und schrift; jahrbuch des Deutschen vereins für buchwesen und schrifttum.
Editor: 1924- H. H. Bockwitz.

1. Bibliography—Period. 2. German literature—Bibl.—Period. I. Bockwitz, Hans Heinrich, 1884- ed. II. Deutscher verein für buchwesen und schrifttum. III. Buch und schrift.

31-12178

Library of Congress Z119.D54B

010.5

NL 0407115 DLC CSmH NN OCl ICJ MiU

Literarisches centralblatt für Deutschland
see
Literarisches zentralblatt für Deutschland.

Z 1007 Literarisches Conversations-Blatt. Nov. 1, 1820
.L 7 Juni 1826. Leipzig, F. A. Brockhaus, 1821-26.
v. 22½-20cm.

No more published.
Includes Literarischer Anzeiger (zu den in der Buchhandlung Brockhaus in Leipzig erscheinenden Zeitschriften) and occasional Beilagen.
Supersedes Literarisches Wochenblatt (Z1007.L75)
Superseded by Blätter für literarische Unterhaltung (Z1007.B62)

NL 0407117 MdBJ MBU NN

PT19 **LITERARISCHES** jahrbuch. Central-organ für die wis-
.L71 senschaftlichen, literarischen und künstlerischen interessen Nordwestböhmens und der deutschen grenzlande. Begründet und hrsg.von Alois John. I.[-VI.] bd.;1891-1896. Eger,Selbstverlag des herausgebers, 1891-96.
6 v. fronts.(ports.)illus.,plates. 19½cm.
Sub-title varies slightly.
No more published.
1.German literature--Year-books.

NL 0407118 ICU

VOLUME 336

2876.276

Literarisches Jahrbuch. Jahres-Rundschau über die literarischen Erzeugnisse deutscher Zunge auf schöngeistigem, dramatischem und musikdramatischem Gebiet verbunden mit einem Lexikon der lebenden deutschen Schriftsteller und Schriftstellerinnen. Jahrgang 1. 1902.
— Köln. Hoursch & Bechstedt. [1902.] 1 v. Illus. Portraits. 20 cm., in 8s.

Editors: Jahrgang 1– , Peter Thiel.

E1165 — Annuals and year-books. (rmany. Lit. Bibl. — Thiel, Peter, ed. — Authors. German. Biog. Dict. — Ge..nany. Biog. Dict. — Lexikon der lebenden deutschen Schriftsteller und Schriftstellerinnen.

NL 0407119 MB IEN InU CtY DLC

PT 15 L5 Literarisches Jahrbuch 1929. Hrsg. Emil Steiner. Basel, Verein Schweiz. Literaturfreunde, 19
v. illus.,ports. (Die Dichter der Schweiz)

1. Swiss literature (German)--Yearbooks. I Verein Schweiz. Literaturfreunde.

NL 0407120 UU

Literarisches magazin für buchhaendler und schriftsteller, oder Sammlung von vorschlägen und entwürfen zu büchern, die bisher noch nicht geschrieben und verlegt worden sind. Von Erduin Julius Koch ... 1.-2. semester; 1792-93. Berlin, F. Franke, 1792-93.

2 v. in 1. 20½cm.

Title varies.
No more published.

1. Literature—Hist. & crit.—Period. I. Koch, Erduin Julius, 1764-1834, ed.

11-7659

Library of Congress PN109.L6

NL 0407121 DLC

Literarisches vademecum für juristen und verwaltungsbeamte.

München, J. Schweitzer

v. 14½cm.

On cover, : Schweitzer's vademecum.

1. Law—Bibl.—Catalogs. 2. Law—Bibl.—Period. 3. Law—Germany—Bibl. I. Schweitzer (J.) sortiment.

44-17872

Library of Congress Z6458.G3L5

016.34

NL 0407122 DLC

PN4 .L82 **Literarisches wochenblat,** oder Gelehrte anzeigen mit abhandlungen. 1.-2. bd. Nürnberg, M. J. Bauer, 1769-70.

2 v. in 1. 20½cm.

Edited by G. A. Will.

1. Literature—Period.

NL 0407123 ICU CLU

Literarisches Wochenblatt ... Weimer, 1818-20
5 v.

NL 0407124 NjP MdBJ NN

Literarisches Zentralblatt für Deutschland. Jahrg. 1-95, Heft 13/14; 1. Oct. 1850-31. Juli 1944. Leipzig, Harrassowitz [etc.]

95 v. in 94. 29-30 cm.

Frequency varies.
Title varies: 1850-1903, Literarisches Centralblatt für Deutschland.
Editors: Oct. 1850-Oct. 1891, F. Zarncke.—Oct. 1891-July 1924, E. Zarncke (with W. Frels, 1924)—July 1924-Dec. 1926, W. Frels.—1927-44, H. Praesent.
"Herausgegeben von der Deutschen Bücherei zu Leipzig," 1927-44.
Vols. for 1897 and 1898 each accompanied by 2 supplements: Vorlesungsverzeichniss sämmtlicher Universitäten des deutschen Sprachgebietes (title varies slightly) for 1897-1898/99.

Issues for 1900-01 include a supplement which was issued separately beginning in 1902 as Die Schöne Literatur (later Die Neue Literatur)
L. C. set incomplete: 1897, 2d suppl.; v. 92, no. 11-24 wanting.

——— Jahresberichte des Litterarischen Zentralblattes über die wichtigsten wissenschaftlichen Neuerscheinungen des gesamten deutschen Sprachgebietes. 1.-19. Jahrg.; 1924-42. Leipzig, Harrassowitz [etc.]
19 v. in 23. 22-31 cm.
Vol. for 1942, issued without subtitle, has also a distinctive title: Das Deutsche wissenschaftliche Schrifttum.
"Herausgegeben von der Deutschen Bücherei zu Leipzig," 1927-42.
Editors: 1924-26, W. Frels.—1927-42, H. Praesent.
Z1007.L7702

Vol. 1 in 24 pts., each also with a special t. p.

1. Bibliography — Period. 2. Books — Reviews. 3. German literature—Bibl.—Period. I. Zarncke, Friedrich Karl Theodor, 1825-1891, ed. II. Zarncke, Eduard, 1857-1936, ed. III. Frels, Wilhelm, 1886-1942, ed. IV. Praesent, Hans, 1888-1946, ed. V. Leipzig. Deutsche Bücherei. VI. Title: Literarisches Centralblatt für Deutschland. VII. Title: Vorlesungsverzeichniss sämmtlicher Universitäten des deutschen Sprachgebietes. VIII. Title: Jahresberichte des Literarischen Zentralblattes. IX. Title: Das Deutsche wissenschaftliche Schrifttum.

Z1007.L77 6-1196 rev 2*

MNS TxDaM CtY
CU NN MB NBuG ICJ OrU MeB ICU NcU OCU InU NRU NdU IC
NL 0407127 DLC KU KyU PSt FTaSU GEU NcD OU MiU OO

Literarisches Zentralblatt für Deutschland.
Geographie...
see under title

Literarisches zentralblatt für Deutschland.

Monatsverzeichnis der an den deutschen universitäten und technischen hochschulen erschienenen schriften. Hrsg. von der Preussischen staatsbibliothek. [jahrg.] 1- jan./feb. 1922-
Leipzig, E. Avenarius [1922-

Literarisches Zentralblatt für Deutschland.
Musik, Theater, Tanz, Musikwissenschaft
see under title

Literarisches Zentralblatt für Deutschland.

Z1007 L7703 Die Neue Literatur. 3.-44. Jahrg.; 4. Jan. 1902-März 1943. Leipzig, E. Avenarius.

Literarisch-geselliger Verein, New York
see Literarischer Verein, New York.

Literarisch-geselliger verein in Oldenburg.
Die Schillerfeier im casino, 9. november 1859. Veranstaltet von dem Literarisch-geselligen verein in Oldenburg. Oldenburg, Schulz (W. Berndt) 1859.

26 p. 23½cm.

1. Schiller, Johann Christoph Friedrich von, 1759-1805. I. Title.

15-9518

Library of Congress PT2486.A59Z6

NL 0407133 DLC

ליטעראַרישע בלעטער; אילוסטרירטע וואכנשריפט פאר
ליטעראַטור, טעאַטער און קונסט. 1 יארג.; 9טער
אפּריל 1924-
וואַרשע, ב. קלעצקין. [Warszawa]

v. illus., ports. 32 cm.

Editors: Apr. 9-May 16, 1924, N. Meisel and ot..ers May 23, 1924-July 9, 1926, M. Ravitch; July 16, 1926- N. Meisel.

1. Yiddish literature—Period. I. Meisel, Nachman, 1887- ed.
Title transliterated: Literarishe bleter.

PJ5120.A25L5 52-46027

NL 0407134 DLC

Literarium duellum inter Salernitanos et Neapolitanos medicos, Vicentii de Petrone ociosi academici Neapolitani, et in Salernitano gymnasio primi philosophiæ interpretis. In quo de intestinorum phlegmone controvertitur casus. Una cum Michaelis Rocci in eodem gymnasio theoricam profitentis medicinam apologia. Et alio ejusdem auctoris literario addito de hepatis inflammatione duello. 3 p. l., 144 pp. sm. 4°. *Venetiis. Bertanos.* 1646.

NL 0407135 DNLM

PR 3070 R62 L7 Literarius, Thersites, pseud.
A familiar address to the curious in English poetry: more particularly to the readers of Shakspeare. By Thersites Literarius ... London, Printed for H. Payne, 1784.
1 p.l., 37 p. 20½cm.
A reply to Joseph Ritson's Observations on the three first volumes of the History of English poetry, and his Remarks, critical and illustrative, on the text and notes of the last edition of Shakspeare.
1. Ritson, Joseph, 1752-1803. Observations on the three first volumes of the History of English poetry. 2. Ritson, Joseph, 1752-1803. Remarks, critical and illustrative, on the text and notes of the last edition of Shakspeare. I. Title.

NL 0407136 MiU NN DFo CtY RPB

Literarna pratika. V Ljubljani
Leto 1914 (1st)
Uredil Milan Pugelj

NL 0407137 MH

Literárne historická společnost, Prague.
Albert Pražák, 1880-1940
see under title

Literárně historická společnost, Prague.
Karel Hynek Mácha; osobnost, dílo, ohlas
see under title

Literárně historická společnost, Prague.

PN9 .S5 Slovesná věda; sborník pro literární historii, theorii literatury a literární kritiku.

V Praze [Literárně historická společnost]

Literárně historická společnost československá v Praze
see
Literárně historická společnost, *Prague.*

Literární a řečnický spolek "Slavia" v Praze (*Founded 1869*)
see **Slavia, literární a řečnický spolek v Praze** (*Founded 1869*)

VOLUME 336

Literárni atlas československý; sebral a sestavil Bohumil Vavroušek s literárním přispěním Arna Nováka ... Vydáno s podporou Ministerstva školství a národní osvěty a České akademie věd a umění. Praze, J. Otto [etc.] 1932-38. 2 v. illus. 44cm.

1. Literary landmarks—Czecho-Slovakia. 2. Authors, Bohemian. I. Novák, Arne, 1880- . II. Vavroušek, Bohumil. III. Česká akademie věd a umění, Prague. IV. Czecho-Slovakia Ministerstvo školství a národní osvěty.

NL 0407143 NN NjP DN

Literární knihovna. V Praze, Bursík & Kohout,

1 (1896) - Vlček, Jaroslav, 1860-1930
Pavel Josef Šafařík

NL 0407144 MH

Literární kroužek, Chicago
see Knihovna "Literární kroužku "

AP52
.L769
Literární listy; týdenník věnovaný literatuře, umění, poučení a zábavě. 186 -1865. Praha.

Monthly: 186 - ; biweekly: -Mar. 1865; weekly: Apr. 1865-Nov.1865.
Issued 186 -Mar. 5, 1865 as suppl. to Národní listy.
Some issues have vol. numbering.
Title varies: 186 - Kritická příloha k Národním listům-- -Mar. 5, 1865, Literární příloha k Národním listům.
Superseded by Květy on Nov. 30, 1865.

NL 0407146 ICU IU CtY NNC InU OClBHS

891.8605
LIN
Literární noviny; měsíčník pro literaturu a kulturní reportáž. roč. 1- 1928- V Praze, ELK. v. illus. 26cm.

NL 0407147 IU InU

AP52
.L6
Literární noviny; týdeník pro kulturně politické a umělecké otázky. roč. 1- 1952- V Praze, Svaz československých spisovatelů.
v. illus., ports., maps. 47 cm.

I. Svaz československých spisovatelů.

AP52.L6 56-42451

NL 0407148 DLC CLU NN MiU CaBVaU InU MB TxU

PG 5003
.L77
LITERÁRNÍ PORTRETY: TOLSTOJ, GOGOL, NĚMCOVÁ, Jirásek, Krásnohorská, Zeyer, Holeček. Praha, Nakl. Melantrich, 1931.
1 v. (various pagings) port.

1. Czech literature--Hist. & crit. 2. Tolstoi, Lev Nikolaevich, graf, 1828-1910. 3. Gogol', Nikolai Vasil'evich, 1809-1852.

NL 0407149 InU

Literární příloha k Národním listům
see Literární listy.

LITERÁRNI rozhledy. roč. 8-15; říj. 1923-1931 (incomplete)
V Praze. v. illus., ports. 30cm.

Film reproduction. Positive.
Monthly (summer issues in combined form).
"Organ Svazu knihkupcův a nakladatelů ČSR v Praze."

Superseded by Rozhledy po literatuře a umění.

1. Bibliography, Czechoslovakian--Per. and soc. publ. 2. Booksellers and book trade--Per. and soc. publ. I. Svaz knihkupcův a nakladatelů Republiky Československe, Prague.

NL 0407152 NN CSt IU MH PNST

PG5020
A47
Literární umělecký kruh Aktivisté. Almanach. [Jožka Antek et al. V Praze, Máj [1936]
65 p. plates. 28cm.

1. Czech literature - 20th cent. 2. Art, Czech. 3. Art, Modern - 20th cent. - Czechoslovak Republic. I. Antek, Jožka.

NL 0407153 CSt

Literárnohistorický sborník.

Bratislava.

v. in 25 cm. irregular.

Issued by Slovenská akadémia vied a umení.

1. Slovak literature—Hist. & crit.—Period. 2. Literature—Hist. & crit.—Period. I. Slovenská akadémia vied a umení.

PG5400.L5 58-22086

NL 0407154 DLC TxU IU CoU InU CLU

The Literary. A miscellany for the town ... no. 1; Nov. 15, 1836. New-York, H. Greene, 1836.

cover-title, 48 p. 19cm.

Only thirty copies printed.
E. A. Duyckinck, editor.
No more published.

I. Duyckinck, Evert Augustus, 1816-1878, ed.

15-3158

Library of Congress AP2.L552

NL 0407155 DLC IaU NN

Literary address, 1889, delivered at Bennettsville, Lancaster and Newberry. [1889]
13 p. O.
Possibly by Evander Roderic McIver, who was appointed state treasurer June 27, 1889.
[Dawson pamphlets, v. 55, no. 4]
I. Southern imprints - S.C. - ? - 1889.

NL 0407156 NcU

PS661
.L5
Office
Literary addresses. [v. p., pam. in v. 21cm.

Binder's title.

NL 0407157 DLC

Literary addresses, delivered at various popular institutions. 1st-3d series.
London. Griffin & Co. 1855. 3 v. [British eloquence of the Nineteenth Century. Literary oratory.] Sm. 8°.
The 1st series is of the 2d edition.
The addresses are by Sir J. F. W. Herschel, Right Hon. Benjamin Disraeli, Lord John Manners, Sir Thomas Noon Talfourd, John Phillips, The Earl of Carlisle, Archbishop Whately, Charles Knight, Sir Archibald Alison, Lord Mahon, J. P. Nichol, The Duke of Argyll, Sir David Brewster, and Henry Glassford Bell.

F3279 — S.r.

NL 0407158 MB PPiPT CSmH NjP

Literary addresses, delivered at various popular institutions. Second series. Rev. and cor. by the authors. London and Glasgow, R. Griffin and company, 1855.

3 p. l., 314 p. 17½cm. (*Half-title:* British eloquence of the nineteenth century)

CONTENTS.—The right use of books, by Sir James Stephen.—The study of abstract science essential to the progress of industry, by Lyon Playfair.—Address of Sir Edward Bulwer Lytton to the associated societies of the University of Edinburgh.—Address of Richard Cobden to the Mechanics' institution at Barnsley.—Address of Lord John Russell to the members of the Leeds mechanics' institution.—Inaugural address of Thomas Babington Macaulay as lord rector of the University of Glasgow.—Address of Henry, lord Brougham, to the Manchester mechanics institution.—Inaugural address of Sir Robert Peel as lord rector of the University of Glasgow.—Lecture on university education, by A. J. Scott.—Introductory lecture by Professor Wilson to the Edinburgh philosophical institution.—Inaugural address of Thomas Campbell as lord rector of the University of Glasgow.—The study of the languages and literature of Greece and Rome, by J. G. Greenwood.—College-education and self-education, by David Masson.

1. English orations. 2. English literature—Addresses, essays, lectures.

34-23563

Library of Congress PR1326.L52 1855 825.80822

NL 0407160 DLC CtY ViU InU OClW

Literary adelphi, *New Hampton, N. H.*
see
New Hampton literary institution, New Hampton, N. H. Literary adelphi.

Coll
LI877
Harris Collection
The Literary age, vol. 1878- Liberty, Va., Hoffman & Murrell, 1878- v. illus. 24 cm.

Partial contents: 1.1. The voiceless [a poem] by O.W. Holmes.--Nature [a poem] by H.W. Longfellow.-- William Cullen Bryant [a memorial notice]

1. Bryant, William Cullen, 1794-1878. I. Holmes, Oliver Wendell, 1809-1894. The voiceless. II. Longfellow, Henry Wadsworth, 1807- 1882. Nature.

NL 0407162 RPB

The literary amaranth; or Prose and poetry ...
see under Brooks, Nathan Covington, 1809-1898.

Literary America.
Forms in poetry
see under title

Literary America.
Writing for the experimental market...
see under Appel, Benjamin, 1907-

VOLUME 336

The Literary American.

New York, A. J. Townsend, 18

v. illus. 29cm. weekly.

Editor: G. P. Quackenbos.

Merged into the Message bird.

I. Quackenbos, George Payn, 1826-1881, ed.

CA 7-4054 Unrev'd

Library of Congress AP2.L555

NL 0407166 DLC MB

Literary amusements, a collection of essays, etc., on a variety of entertaining and instructive subjects, in prose and verse, by different authors. Dublin, Printed for R. Cross, 1803. 144p.

NL 0407167 PSt

Y 145 .L 71 Literary amusements; or, Evening entertainer. By a female hand... Dub. 1782. 2v. nar. S.

"A plan for the prevention of future taxes in carrying on the American war, and a way pointed out for the bringing it to a speedy conclusion." v.2, p.104-109.

"On taxing the Americans. Written in the year 1775." v.2, p.171-175.

"On the im portance of the colonies to Great Britain..." v.2, p.194-200.

NL 0407168 ICN IU

Literary and antiquarian society of Perth.

Transactions of the Literary and antiquarian society of Perth. v. I. Perth [Scotland] The Society, 1827.

[241] p. front., 2 pl., 2 plans, 2 facsim. 29½ cm.

Various paging.
No more published.

4—14503

Library of Congress DA750.L7

NL 0407169 DLC WaU

Literary and artistic products and copyright problems. [Durham, N. C.] School of Law, Duke University, 1954.

[139]-322 p. 27 cm. (Law and contemporary problems, v. 19, no. 2)

Cover title.
Bibliographical footnotes.

CONTENTS.—Foreword, by R. Kramer. International copyright in the United States: a critical analysis, by J. Schulman. Protection of "neighboring rights," by G. H. C. Bodenhausen. Rights in new media, by T. R. Kupferman. Old licenses and new uses, by M. E. Cohn. The right of publicity, by M. B. Nimmer. Copyright protection of architectural plans, drawings, and designs, by A. S. Katz. Literary and artistic property, including copyright, as security: problems facing the lender, by L. Kaplan. The composer and the public interest; regulation of performing right societies, by H. Finkelstein. The antitrust aspects of merchandising modern music: the ASCAP judgment of 1950, by S. Timberg.

1. Copyright—U. S. I. Duke University, Durham, N. C. School of Law. (Series)

54-4490

NL 0407171 DLC OrCS MiU OU MoU TxU

Literary and Catholic sentinel
see also the periodical it superseded:
The Jesuit; or, Catholic sentinel.

Literary and Critical Remarks, on Sundry eminent Divines and Philosophers, of the Last and Present Age. Particularly Sir Walter Raleigh, Cudworth, Hobbes, Locke, Newton, Bolinbroke, Shaftsbury, Bishop Butler, Dr. Blair, Dr. Gregory, Bishop Porteus, Dr. Johnson, Bishop Hurd, Mrs. M. Graham, Dr. Priestley, &c. &c. Combining observations on Religion and Government, The French Revolution, &c.

With an Appendix. . . .
London: Printed for R. Crosby, No. 4, Stationers Court, Ludgate Street. 1794.
pp. (4); XVI; 489; (3).

NL 0407174 PPL

B1111 .L75 Literary and critical remarks, on sundry eminent divines and philosophers, of the last and present age...combining observations on religion & government, the French revolution, &c. With an appendix containing a short dissertation on the existence, nature, and extent of the prophetic powers in the human mind, with examples of several eminent prophesies ... London, Printed for B. Crosby [1795]

[3], xvi, 489 p. 21½cm.

1. Philosophers, English. 2. Philosophy, English.

NL 0407175 ICU MH NCH

Literary and Dramatic Society.

Prologue and epilogue to Time works wonders, as represented by the...society, at the Theatre Royal, Thursday, 13th August. Liverpool: W. Fearnall and Co., 1857. 15 p. 16°.

At head of title: In remembrance of the late Douglas Jerrold.
In: *C p. v. 1476, no. 19.

1. Jerrold, Douglas William: Time works wonders.
N. Y. P. L. May 13, 1914.

NL 0407176 NN

The Literary and educational year book for 1859

London, Kent and co. [1859]–

v. 21½cm.

1. Literature—Year-books. 2. English literature—Bibl. I. Title: Educational year book.

CA 17-210 Unrev'd

Library of Congress Z2011.L75

NL 0407177 DLC DHEW MH

The Literary and evangelical magazine. v. 1-11; Jan. 1818-Dec. 1828. Richmond, Va., N. Pollard [etc.] 1818-28.

11 v. 22½ cm. monthly.

Title varies: 1818-20 (v. 1-30) The Virginia evangelical and literary magazine, ed. by John H. Rice.
1821 (v. 4) The Evangelical and literary magazine, and missionary chronicle: conducted by John H. Rice ...
1822-23 (v. 5-6) The Evangelical and literary magazine.
1824-28 (v. 7-11) The Literary and evangelical magazine.

1. Theology—Period. I. Rice, John Holt, 1777-1831, ed. II. The Virginia evangelical and literary magazine. III. Title: The Evangelical and literary magazine.

BR1.L7 5—3423

NL 0407178 DLC ICN N NcD MH-AH MiU

The Literary and evangelical magazine. v. 1-11; Jan. 1818-Dec. 1828. Richmond, N. Pollard [etc.]

2 reels. (American periodical series: 1800-1825. 124-125)

Microfilm copy, made in 1949 by University Microfilms, Ann Arbor, Mich. Positive.
Collation of the original: 11 v.
Monthly.
Title varies: Jan. 1818-Dec. 1820, The Virginia evangelical and literary magazine.—Jan. 1821-Dec. 1823, The Evangelical and literary magazine (varies slightly)
Founded and for some years edited by J. H. Rice.
Copy filmed incomplete: v. 9-11 wanting.

1. Theology—Period. I. Rice, John Holt, 1777-1831, ed. II. Title: The Virginia evangelical and literary magazine. III. Title: The Evangelical and literary magazine. (Series: American periodical series: 1800-1850. 124-125)

Microfilm 01104 no. 124-125 AP Mic 56-4895

NL 0407179 DLC NN ICRL MiU TxU OU

The Literary and Evangelical register.
Vol. I: July, 1826-June, 1827. Milton, Pa., 1827.
576 p.
Ed. by Eugenio Kincaid.

NL 0407180 PHi PPPrHi PP NcMHi

Literary and graphical illustrations of Shakspeare, and the British drama: comprising an historical view of the origin and improvement of the English stage, and a series of critical and descriptive notices of upwards of one hundred of the most celebrated tragedies, comedies, operas, and farces. Embellished with more than two hundred engravings on wood, by eminent artists. London, Printed by and for Maurice and co., and pub. by E. Wilson [etc.] 1831.

xvi, 204 p. incl. front., illus. 20cm.
Reprinted in 1833 under title: The Dramatic souvenir.
1. Shakespeare, William—Illustrations.

22-11731

Library of Congress PR2883.L5

NL 0407181 DLC InU MdBP NIC CtY MiU OCU

Literary and graphical illustrations of Shakspeare, and the British drama: comprising an historical view of the origin and improvement of the English stage, and a series of critical and descriptive notices of . . . celebrated tragedies, comedies, operas, and farces. London. Hurst, Chance & Co. 1831. xvi, 204 pp. Illus. Plate Vignette. 21 cm., in 6s.

A later edition having the title Dramatic souvenir, The . . . Literary and graphical illustrations of Shakespeare and other . . . English dramatists. . . may be found on shelf-numbers **G.3951.44; **T.47.42.

L8603 — Shakespeare, William. Illus. — Drama. English. Hist and crit.

NL 0407182 MB NN

Literary and historical activities in North Carolina
see under North Carolina. Historical Commission.

Literary and Historical Association of North Carolina, Raleigh, N. C.
Anglo-American relations in commemoration of the tercentenary of Sir Walter Raleigh.
(In North Carolina. Historical Commission. Publications. Bulletin. No. 25. Pp. 23-146. Portrait. Plates. Autograph facsimile. Raleigh. 1919.)

Contents. — Introductory, by President James Sprunt. — Raleigh and British imperialism, by Edwin Greenlaw. — Sir Walter Raleigh as a man of letters, by Frank Wilson Chaney Hersey. — Raleigh's place in American colonization, by Charles M. Andrews. — England and the birth of the American nation, by William Thomas Laprade. — The converging democracies of England and America, by William E. Dodd. — Anglo-American diplomatic relations during the last half century, by Charles H. Levermore. — Social and political ideals of the English-speaking peoples, by George Armstrong Wauchope.

NL 0407185 MB

*4372.201

Literary and Historical Association of North Carolina, Raleigh, N. C
Proceedings of the 11th, 12th annual sessions.
— Raleigh, N. C. 1912. v. Portrait. [North Carolina Historical Commission. Publications. Bulletin no. 11.] 22½ cm., in 8s.

H7429 — S.r. — North Carolina. Hist.

NL 0407186 MB

Literary and historical society of Quebec.
... Blockade of Quebec in 1775-1776 by the American revolutionists ...
see under Würtele, Frederick Christian, 1842-

VOLUME 336

Literary and historical society of Quebec.

Le Moine, James MacPherson, 1825–1912.
Brighton, the southern queen of English watering places. Scarborough, the northern empress of the seaside. Versailles, and the lion mount of Waterloo. Inaugural address, lecture season, 1882–3. Read before the Literary and historical society of Quebec, 27th November, 1882, by J. M. Le Moine ... Quebec, Printed at the "Morning chronicle" office, 1882.

Literary and historical society of Quebec.
Bulletin. no. 1–
Apr. 14, 1900–
[Quebec; 1900–
23½cm.

12-28283

Library of Congress Z883.Q25

NL 0407189 DLC

Literary and Historical Society of Quebec.
By-laws of the Literary and Historical Society of Quebec: to which is prefixed a copy of the royal charter of incorporation of the Society. Quebec: Printed for the Literary and Historical Society, by T. Cary & Co., 1832. 2 p.l., [3–]31 p. 8°.

1. Societies, Historical—Canada—Quebec.
N. Y. P. L. October 27, 1925

NL 0407190 NN

Literary and Historical Society of Quebec.
By-laws of the...Society...to which is prefixed a copy of the royal charter of incorporation of the society as also an act amending the same. Quebec: Hunter, Rose & Co., 1863. 23 p. 8°.
Bound with: Transactions of the society, 1862-63.

1. Societies (Historical), Canada: Quebec.
N. Y. P. L. April 25, 1913.

NL 0407191 NN CaOTU ICN

Literary and Historical Society of Quebec.
Catalogue of the mineralogical collection belonging to the ...Society... n. t.-p. [New Haven, Conn.: H. Howe, 1829.] 72 p. 8°.
Excerpt: Transactions of the Literary and Historical Soc. v. 1, 1829.

1. Mineralogy.—Collections, Canada: Quebec.
N. Y. P. L. May 5, 1913.

NL 0407192 NN Nh CtY

Literary and historical society of Quebec.
The centenary volume of the Literary and historical society of Quebec, 1824–1924. Quebec, L'Evenement press, 1924.
196 p. front., illus., pl., fold. facsim. 22½cm.

I. Title.

25-4492

Library of Congress F1051.L715

OCl
NL 0407193 DLC CaBVaU NcD TxU MWA MiU MiU-C NN MB

Literary and historical society of Quebec.
Le Courrier du livre. Canadiana. Pub. monthly in French and English. Canadian history, archæology, bibliography, numismatics, philately and genealogy ... Pub. mensuellement en anglais et en français ... Histoire, archéologie, bibliographie, numismatique, philatélie et généalogie canadiennes ... v. 1–5; mai 1896–juin 1900. Québec, L. Brousseau [etc.] 1897–1901.

Literary and Historical Society of Quebec.
Histoire de l'eau-de-vie en Canada
see under title

971.4 L71h

Literary and Historical Society of Quebec.
Historical documents. 1st-10th ser. Quebec 1838-1927.
v. 23 cm.
DLC:F1051.L8
Some issued without series title or numbering.
Some have title: Manuscripsts relating to the early history of Canada.
Some are reprints.
1. Canada--Hist.--1763-1791. 2. Canada--Hist. --To 1763 (New France) 3. Quebec (Province)--Hist. I. Literary and Historical Society of Quebec. Manuscri[p]ts relating to the early history of Canada.

OCl DAU ICN NN CtY CaOTU DLC
NL 0407196 LU NhD PBL CaBViP RPJCB OOxM MWA MiEM GU

F1054 .O7B7

Literary and historical society of Quebec.

Bowen, Noel Hill, *d.* 1872.
An historical sketch of the isle of Orleans, being a paper read before the Literary and historical society of Quebec, on Wednesday evening, the 4th of April, 1860; by N. H. Bowen ... Quebec, Printed at the "Mercury" newspaper office, 1860.

Literary and historical society of Quebec.
Index of the lectures, papers and historical documents ...
see under Würtele, Frederick Christian, 1842– comp.

Literary and historical society of Quebec.
Index to the archival publications of the Literary and historical society of Quebec, 1824–1924. Quebec, L'Evenement press, 1923.

1. Literary and historical society of Quebec. Historical documents. 2. Literary and historical society of Quebec. Transactions. I. Title.

24-18934

Library of Congress F1051.L82

CaBVaU
NL 0407199 DLC CaOTU FMU NIC LU MWA MH NN MB CaBViP

971.406 L7761

Literary and Historical Society of Quebec.
Index to the archival publications of the Literary and Historical Society of Quebec, 1824-1924. Quebec, 1924.
215p. 22cm.

I. Literary and Historical Society of Quebec: Historical documents. Indexes. II. Literary and Historical Society of Quebec. Transactions Indexes.

NL 0407200 IEN

Literary and historical society of Quebec.

F1051 L382

List of Historical documents and new series of "Transactions" published by the Literary & historical society of Quebec (founded 1824) ... Quebec, Printed for the Society by the Chronicle-telegraph pub. co., 1927.
12 p. 22 1/2 cm.

NL 0407201 CSmH

Literary andhistorical society of Quebec.
Manuscripts relating to the early history of Canada
see its
Historical documents.

Literary and historical society of Quebec.
Mémoires sur le Canada, depuis 1749 jusqu'a 1760 ...
see under Courville, Louis de, fl. 1754.

Literary and historical society of Quebec.

Campbell, John, 1840–1904.
Origin of the aborigines of Canada. A paper read before the Literary and historical society, Quebec, by Prof. J. Campbell, M. A., (of Montreal,) ... Quebec, Printed at the "Morning chronicle" office, 1881.

The literary and historical society of Quebec.
[Papers presented to the Society, 1837-1855]. [N.p.]L'Evenement press, 1927. 366p.O.

NL 0407205 CaBViP

Literary and Historical Society of Quebec.
Report of the council for
1836, 1862
Quebec, 1837-63. 8°.
For 1865-date see Transactions of the society, Appendix, no. 4-date (1865-date)
1862 bound with Transactions of the society, 1862-63.

1. Societies (Historical), Canada: Quebec.
N. Y. P. L. April 25, 1913.

NL 0407206 NN MWA MiD OCl DLC PBL

Literary and Historical Society of Quebec.
Report of the council of the Literary and Historical Society of Quebec, at the anniversary meeting for the election of officers, January 11th, 1837. [Quebec? 1837?] 15 p. 12°.
Caption-title.

NL 0407207 NN

Literary and historical society of Quebec
Report of the Council...together with the treasurer's report, list of members, &c

Library has
1858, 1862, 1865, 1904-1905.

1865, 1904-1905 found in its Transactions.

NL 0407208 MiD

VOLUME 336

Literary and Historical Society of Quebec. 4469a.284
The Plains of Abraham. The historic battle-field of Canada — 1759, its history, etc.
— [Quebec. 1899.] 31 pp. 22 cm.
A collection of press notices and resolutions passed by various societies in Canada advocating the purchase of the Plains of Abraham for a public park.
There is no title-page.

K6617 — Plains of Abraham, Battle of, Sept. 13, 1759. — Quebec, City. Parks.

NL 0407209 MB OC1

Literary and historical society of Quebec.
Siege of Quebec on 31st December, 1775. The centenary fete of the Literary and historical society, held in their rooms, on the evening of Wednesday, 29th December, 1875. Quebec, Printed at the "Morning chronicle" office, 1876.
2 p. l., [3]-104 p. illus., fold. pl., plan. 24cm.

1. Quebec (City)—Siege, 1775-1776. I. Title.

A 34-2141

Title from Providence Pub. Libr. Printed by L. C.

NL 0407210 NjP MH MiU-C RP

Literary and historical society of Quebec.
Trade and shipping, port of Quebec, 1793-1882. (Literary and historical society of Quebec. Historical documents. Series 6)

NL 0407211 OC1

F1051
.L77
Literary and Historical Society of Quebec.
Transactions. v. 1-5, 1829-62; ser., no. 1-
1863-19
Quebec.
v. in illus., fold. maps. 20-23 cm.
Published 1829-1924. Cf. Union list of serials.
Issues for sessions 1876/77-82/83 have no numbering.

1. Quebec (Province) 2. Quebec (Province)—Hist.—Period.
3. Canada—Hist.—Period.

F1051.L77 50-37479 ‡

CSmH CaNS Wa IU GU NhD MiU PBL CaBVaU
NL 0407212 DLC MiD NcD MWA CaOTU IU ULS NIC ICN

Literary and historical society of Quebec.
Roche, Alfred R.
A view of Russian America, in connection with the present war. By A. R. Roche ... Montreal, Printed by J. Lovell, 1855.

Literary and historical society of Quebec. *Library.*
Catalogue of books in the library of the Literary and historical society of Quebec. Quebec, Printed by G. T. Cary, 1864.
2 p. l., [iii]-vi p., 1 l., 114, [22] p. 25cm.
Classified, with index of authors and subjects.

33-32872

Library of Congress Z883.Q36 1864 017.1

NL 0407214 DLC NN MH

Literary and historical society of Quebec. *Library.*
Catalogue of books in the library of the Literary and historical society of Quebec. Quebec, Printed at the "Morning chronicle" office, 1873.
v, 195, iv, [43] p. 25cm.
Classified, with index of authors and subjects.

33-29830

Library of Congress Z883.Q36 1873 017.1

NL 0407215 DLC CaNSWA NN CtY KyHi

Literary and historical society of Quebec. Library.
... Hand list of additions to the library, 1900-1914. Quebec, 1914.
142 p. 22cm.

CA 19-450 Unrev'd

Library of Congress Z883.Q24

NL 0407216 DLC

Literary and library prizes. 1935-
New York, R. R. Bowker Co.
v. 23 cm.
Formerly issued in the Author's annual.
Title varies: 1935-39, Famous literary prizes and their winners.—1946, Literary prizes and their winners.

1. Literary prizes.

PN171.P75L5 807.9 59-11370

GU KyFSC CtY NcC IU KyWA CaBVaU WaTC OrPR OrSaW
KyLxT ArU CSf AzU NBuC NcRS OrAshS WaS ViU MoU
ViU MsSM PV RPB MiU DS ScU MBtS IaU CtNIC NBuG
KEmT PRosC MeB NNC-M WaE FTaSU KU CtY NN MB DS
NL 0407217 DLC PSC PPT MH PP PU PBL IdB PPAmP MB

The Literary and mathematical asylum no. 1. Dublin, 1822
3pts. 18cm.
Editor: Matthew M. Meagher
Bound with The New Rosorea almanac for 1824

NL 0407218 PV

Literary and musical magazine. v. 1-4; July 5, 1817-June 9, 1820. Philadelphia, H. C. Lewis.
4 v. in 1. music. 27 cm. weekly.
Publication suspended Oct.-Dec. 1818.
Vol. 4, no. 15-38 (Aug. 24? 1819-June 9, 1820) also called new ser., v. 1, no. 1-24.
Title varies: July 5, 1817-July 13, 1818, Ladies' literary museum; or, Weekly repository.—July 27-Sept. 30, 1818, Lady's and gentleman's weekly museum, and Philadelphia reporter.—Jan. 1-Mar. 1, 1819, Lady's and gentleman's weekly literary museum and musical magazine.
Edited by H. C. Lewis.
L. C. set incomplete: v. 4, no. 14-38 wanting.
I. Lewis, Henry C., ed. II. Title: Ladies' literary museum; or, Weekly repository. III. Title: Lady's and gentleman's weekly museum, and Philadelphia reporter.

AP2.L558 1-27274 rev*

NL 0407219 DLC

Literary and musical magazine. v. 1-4; July 5, 1817-June 9, 1820. Philadelphia, H. C. Lewis.
(American periodical series: 1800-1850. 213)
Microfilm copy, made in 1952 by University Microfilms, Ann Arbor, Mich. Positive.
Collation of the original: 4 v. music.
Weekly.
Publication suspended Oct.-Dec. 1818.
Vol. 4, no. 15-38 (Aug. 24? 1819-June 9, 1820) also called new ser., v. 1, no. 1-24.
Title varies: July 5, 1817-July 13, 1818, Ladies' literary museum; or, Weekly repository.—July 27-Sept. 30, 1818, Lady's and gentleman's

Continued in next column

Continued from preceding column

weekly museum, and Philadelphia reporter.—Jan. 1-Mar. 1, 1819, Lady's and gentleman's weekly literary museum and musical magazine.
Edited by H. C. Lewis.
Film incomplete: v. 4, no. 14, 21-33 wanting.

1. Music—Period. I. Lewis, Henry C., ed. II. Title: Ladies' literary museum; or, Weekly repository. III. Title: Lady's and gentleman's weekly museum, and Philadelphia reporter. (Series)

Microfilm 01104 no. 213 AP Mic 56-4617

NL 0407221 DLC ICRL MiU NN

Literary and musical magazine.
see also
Lady's and gentleman's weekly literary museum and musical magazine. v. 3, no. 1-19; July 27, 1818-March 1, 1819. Philadelphia [H. C. Lewis] 1818-19.

Literary and philosophic club, Bristol, Eng.
The Literary and philosophic club...
Bristol, 1892

AS122
.B8

NL 0407223 DLC

... **Literary** and philosophical essays, French, German and Italian, with introductions, notes and illustrations. New York, P. F. Collier & son [c1910]
1 p. l., 419, [1] p. front., ports. 22½cm. (The Harvard classics, ed. by C. W. Eliot. [vol. XXXII]) $2.00
CONTENTS.—That we should not judge of our happiness until after our death. That to philosophise is to learne how to die. Of the institution and education of children. Of friendship. Of bookes. By Montaigne.—Montaigne. What is a classic? By C.-A. Sainte-Beuve.—The poetry of the Celtic races, by E. Renan.—The education of the human race, by G. E. Lessing.—Letters upon the æsthetic education of man, by J. C. F. von Schiller.—Fundamental principles of the metaphysic of morals. Transition from popular moral philosophy to the metaphysic of morals. By I. Kant.—Byron and Goethe, by G. Mazzini.

1. Essays. I. Montaigne, Michel Eyquem de, 1533-1592. II. Sainte-Beuve, Charles Augustin, 1804-1869. III. *Renan, Ernest, 1823-1892. IV. Lessing, Gotthold Ephraim, 1729-1781. V. Schiller, Johann Christoph Friedrich von, 1759-1805. VI. Kant, Immanuel, 1724-1804. VII. Mazzini, Giuseppe, 1805-1872.

10-7942

Library of Congress AC1.A4 vol. 32

WaSp OrPR OrCS Or
OFH MiU OCU OC1h NN KMK CaBVa WaT WaS WaTC IdB Wa
NL 0407225 DLC NBuC MB NBuU PRosC OC1W OC1ND OC1 OU

The **Literary** and philosophical repertory: embracing discoveries and improvements in the physical sciences; the liberal and fine arts; essays moral and religious; occasional notices and reviews of new publications; and articles of miscellaneous intelligence. Ed. by a number of gentlemen. v. 1-2; Apr. 1812-May 1817. Middlebury, Vt., Printed for S. Swift by T. C. Strong [etc., 1812-17]
2 v. 21½cm.
Vol. 2 has imprint: Middlebury, Vt., Printed and published by T. C. Strong.

7-22278

Library of Congress AP2.L559

Mi
NL 0407226 DLC NBu NIC CtY NN MB VtMidSM RPB NbCrD

The Literary and philosophical repertory: embracing discoveries and improvements in the physical sciences, the liberal and fine arts, essays moral and religious, occasional notices and reviews of new publications, and articles of miscellaneous intelligence. v. 1-2; Apr. 1812-May 1817. Middlebury, Vt., Printed for S. Swift by T. C. Strong [etc.]
(American periodical series: 1800-1825. 126)
Microfilm copy, made in 1949 by University Microfilms, Ann Arbor, Mich. Positive.
Collation of the original: 2 v.
(Series: American periodical series: 1800-1850. 126)
Microfilm 01104 no. 126 AP Mic 56-5075

NL 0407227 DLC NN ICRL

VOLUME 336

Literary and philosophical society, Kingston, Jamaica.
Inaugural address of the president of the Literary and philosophical society,...
Kingston, 1843

AS73
.K5

NL 0407228 DLC

Literary and philosophical society at Kingston-upon-Hull
see
Hull literary and philosophical society, Hull, Eng.

Literary and philosophical society of Liverpool.
Proceedings. no. 1- 1844/45- 34th- sess. Liverpool, 1845-
v. illus., plates (part col.) photos., ports., maps, facsims., tables, diagrs. 21-23cm.
Nos. 2-5, 18-58, published in London and Liverpool.
The 36th-40th sess. (nos. 3-6) are incorrectly numbered 35th-39th, respectively.
Vol. 1 has title "Report of the proceedings of the Literary & philosophical society of Liverpool, for 1844-45, being session XXXIV. vol. I." It includes "List of papers read at the society, from the end of the 10th session (1821) to the end of the 33d session, May, 1844" (a list of the earlier communications was printed in pamphlet form)
List of members in nos. 1, 6-

No. 62 includes "Proceedings at the centennial banquet of the society held in Liverpool ... 13th March, 1912," p. xxxii-lxviii.
Monographs, separately paged, are appended to several of the volumes; for the monographs on natural history a general t.-p. was issued with title "Monographs on the natural history of Liverpool and its vicinity. Extracted from the published Proceedings of the Literary and philosophical society of Liverpool." In the Library of Congress set these appendices are bound with the volumes with which they were issued, and the general t.-p. above mentioned is bound at the end of no. 14, 1859/60.
Appendices: no. 6, app. (I) The flora of Liverpool, by Joseph Dickinson.—no. 6, app. II. Meteorological results deduced from observations taken at the Liverpool observatory during the five years ending December 31st, 1850, by John Hartnup.—no. 7, app. Meteorological results deduced

from observations taken at the Liverpool observatory during the two years ending December 31st, 1852, by John Hartnup.—no. 8, app. The fauna of Liverpool, by Isaac Byerley.—no. 9, app. (I) On the *Musci* and *Hypaticæ* found within twelve miles of Liverpool and Southport, by F. P. Marrat.—no. 9, app. II. Supplement to The flora of Liverpool, by Joseph Dickinson.—no. 12, app. (I) Synopsis and list of British *Hymenomycetes*, by H. H. Higgins.—no. 12, (app. II) The *Fungi* of Liverpool and its vicinity. pt. I. *Hymenomycetes*, by H. H. Higgins.—no. 13, app. Synopsis and list of British *Gasteromycetes*, by H. H. Higgins.—no. 14, app. On the hepatics and lichens of Liverpool and its vicinity, by F. P. Marrat.—no. 16, app. I. Appendix; containing an account of the proceedings of the jubilee festival of the Literary and philosophical society of Liverpool, March 11th and 13th, 1862.—no. 16, app. II. Suggestions offered on the

part of the Literary and philosophical society of Liverpool to members of the mercantile marine.—no. 18, app. The *Lepidoptera* of the hundred of Wirral, Cheshire, by J. F. Brockholes.—no. 19, app. The Kabbalah: its doctrines, development, and literature. An essay, by C. D. Ginsburg.—no. 28, app. Synopsis of an arrangement of invertebrate animals in the Free public museum of Liverpool; with introduction; by H. H. Higgins.—no. 34, app. On the varieties of the shells belonging to the genus *Nassa*, Lam., by F. P. Marrat.—no. 40, app. The first report upon the fauna of Liverpool Bay and the neighbouring seas, written by the members of the Liverpool marine biology committee, and ed. by W. A. Herdman. (L. M. B. C. reports. no. 1)—no. 46, app. Spola. Easter day in Rome, 1849. A link in the chain of Italian unity, by J. F. Palmer.

—— Index to papers contained in the Proceedings of the Literary & philosophical society of Liverpool. vols. I.-XXV. 1844-71. Comp. by Alfred Morgan, honorary librarian. Liverpool, D. Marples, printer, 1871.
28 p. 22cm. (*With* Proceedings, no. 26)
AS122.L41 no. 26
—— Index to papers contained in the Proceedings of the Literary & philosophical society of Liverpool, vols. I-L. 1844-96. Vols. I to XXV—1844-1872 comp. by Alfred Morgan ... vols. XXVI to L—1872-1896 comp. by Josiah Marples. Liverpool, D. Marples & co., 1896.
51, (1) p. 22½cm.

—— An index to the Proceedings of the Literary and philosophical society of Liverpool (volumes I to LXII). Comp. by Alfred W. Newton, M. A., honorary librarian. Liverpool, D. Marples & co., printers, 1912.
102 p., 1 l. 21½cm.
On cover: Centenary index volume.

I. Morgan, Alfred, comp. II. Marples, Josiah, comp. III. Newton, Alfred W., comp.

17-14198-201
Library of Congress AS122.L41 Index
—— —— Copy 2.

00 MiU DSI
NL 0407235 DLC PPAmP ICRL ICJ NBuU OU MH MWA ICJ

Literary and philosophical society of Liverpool.
Report of proceedings ... 1844/5
see its
Proceedings.

Literary and Philosophical Society of Liverpool.
Roscoe lecture.
19

Liverpool, 19 8°.
no.

NL 0407237 NN

Literary and philosophical society of Liverpool.
Roscoe lecture.

Drinkwater, John, 1882-1937.
Art and the state, by John Drinkwater ... Liverpool, E. A. Bryant, 1930.

Literary and philosophical society of Liverpool.
... Suggestions offered on the part of the Literary and philosophical society of Liverpool, to members of the mercantile marine, who may be desirous of using the advantages they enjoy for the promotion of science, in furtherance of zoology. (Liverpool, Printed for the members of the Society, by T. Brakell, 1862)
49 p. 22cm. (Proceedings of the Literary and philosophical society of Liverpool. no. XVI, appendix II)
Caption title.
1. Zoological specimens—Collection and preservation.

17-14216
Library of Congress AS122.L41 no. 16

NL 0407239 DLC ICJ

Literary and philosophical society of Liverpool.
Suggestions offered on the part of the Literary and philosophical society of Liverpool, to members of the mercantile marine, who may be desirous of using the advantages they enjoy for the promotion of science, in furtherance of zoology. Liverpool, Printed for the Society, by T. Brakell, 1862.
51 p. 21cm.

1. Zoological specimens—Collection and preservation.

6-16973†
Library of Congress QL61.L77

NL 0407240 DLC CU

Literary and philosophical society of Manchester
see Manchester literary and philosophical society, Manchester, Eng.

Literary and Philosophical Society of New York. *4477.38
The charter, laws, and regulations . . . with a list of the officers and members.
New York. Van Winkle. 1818. 19, (1) pp. 22 cm., in 4s.

D3249

NL 0407242 MB MWA MH CtY NNC

Literary and philosophical society of New York.
Circular letter of the Literary and philosophical society, of New York; on the subject of a statistical account of the state of New-York. New-York, Printed by T. and W. Mercein, 1815.
8, 2 p. 23½cm. (*With* Clinton, De Witt. An introductory discourse, delivered before the Literary and philosophical society of New-York. New-York, 1815. 29½ x 23cm.)
Signed: De Witt Clinton, president.

I. Clinton, De Witt, 1769-1828.

2-6379
Library of Congress Q171.C7

NL 0407243 DLC MWA MB NN CSmH

Literary and philosophical society of New York.
Clinton, De Witt, 1769-1828. FOR OTHER EDITIONS SEE MAIN ENTRY
An introductory discourse, delivered before the Literary and philosophical society of New-York, on the fourth of May, 1814, by De Witt Clinton ... New-York, Printed by Van Winkle and Wiley, 1815.

Literary and philosophical society of New York.
Clinton, De Witt, 1769-1828. FOR OTHER EDITIONS SEE MAIN ENTRY
Memoir on the antiquities of the western parts of the state of New-York. Read before the Literary and philosophical society of New-York. By De Witt Clinton ... Albany, Printed by E. & E. Hosford, 1820. Tarrytown, N. Y., Reprinted, W. Abbatt, 1916.

Literary and philosophical society of New York.
Transactions of the Literary and philosophical society of New-York. Instituted in the year MDCCCXIV. v. 1-v. 2, pt. 1. New-York, Pub. for the Society, by Van Winkle and Wiley, 1815-(25)
2 v. plates. 28cm.
Vol. 2, pt. 1, half-title.

1. Science—Societies.

7-37097
Library of Congress Q11.N48

NNC NhD MeB FU MB MdBP PMA KyU
NL 0407246 DLC CtY MH NcD DI-GS MoU OC1W ICJ NBu

Literary and philosophical society of New York.
Transactions of the Literary and philosophical society of New-York. Instituted in the year MDCCCXIV. v. 1-v. 2, pt. 1. New-York, Pub. for the Society, by Van Winkle and Wiley, 1815-[25]
2 v. plates. 28 cm.
Vol. 2, pt. 1, half title.
(American periodical series: 1800-1850, roll 840)
Microfilm.
1. Science - Societies.

NL 0407247 LU IaAS

Literary and philosophical society of Newcastle upon Tyne.
A historical sketch of the transactions of the Literary and philosophical society of Newcastle upon Tyne, during the first twelve years from its commencement. To which are added, the laws of the society, and a catalogue of its library, apparatus, &c. ... Newcastle, Printed by S. Hodgson, 1807.
8, xxxix, (1) p. 20½cm. (*With its* Annual reports, 1793 to 1808)

20-2009
Library of Congress AS122.N5

NL 0407248 DLC DNLM

A
9
.622
LITERARY AND PHILOSOPHICAL SOCIETY OF NEWCASTLE-UPON-TYNE.
Laws of the Literary and philosophical society of Newcastle upon Tyne; with a list of members... [Newcastle-upon-Tyne,]1794.
18p. 21cm.

Binder's title: Literary and philosophical society of Newcastle-upon-Tyne. Pamphlets.

NL 0407249 ICN

VOLUME 336

Literary and philosophical society of Newcastle-upon-Tyne.
Lectures delivered to the Literary and philosophical society, Newcastle-upon-Tyne, on Northumbrian history, literature, and art, by Thomas Hodgkin ... Robert Spence Watson ... R. Oliver Heslop, Richard Welford ... Lent term, 1898. Published by the society. Newcastle-upon-Tyne, Printed by A. Reid & company, limited, 1898.
3 p. l., 214 p. illus., ports. 22cm.
CONTENTS.—Roman occupation of Northumberland, by T. Hodgkin.—Northumbrian story and song, by R. S. Watson.—Dialect speech in Northumberland, by R. O. Heslop.—Newcastle a hundred years ago, by R. Welford.
1. Northumberland, Eng. I. Hodgkin, Thomas, 1831-1913. II. Watson, Robert Spence, 1837-1911. III. Heslop, Richard Oliver, 1842- IV. Welford, Richard, 1836- V. Title.
Library of Congress DA670.N8L5 20-1644

NL 0407250 DLC MtU MB

Literary and philosophical society of Newcastle upon Tyne.
Obits of some of the more distinguished members of the Literary and philosophical society of Newcastle-upon-Tyne, noticed in the reports of the committee of the Society between the years 1844-1851. Newcastle-upon-Tyne, E. Charnley, 1857.
12 p. 20cm. [Typographical society of Newcastle upon Tyne. Publications. 52]

NL 0407251 MnU

Literary and philosophical society of Newcastle upon Tyne.
Plan of the Literary and philosophical society of Newcastle upon Tyne. Instituted Feb. 7, MDCCXCIII ... [Newcastle-on-Tyne?] 1793.
16 p. 21cm.
[Miscellaneous pamphlets, v. 401, no. 4]
3-23136

NL 0407252 DLC

Literary and philosophical society of Newcastle-upon-Tyne.
Report.
Newcastle-upon-Tyne, 18
v. 21½cm.
Full title: Ninety-seventh year's report of the Literary and philosophical society, Newcastle-upon-Tyne; with a statement of the accounts of the Society.
Library of Congress AS122.N5 CA 15-457 Unrev'd

NL 0407253 DLC

Literary and philosophical society of Newcastle-upon-Tyne. Library.
A catalogue of the library of the Literary and philosophical society of Newcastle upon Tyne. Newcastle, Printed by T. & J. Hodgson, 1829.
xiv p., 1 l., 339 p. 23 cm.

NL 0407254 CtY

Literary and Philosophical Society of Newcastle-upon-Tyne. Library.
Catalogue of the library.
Newcastle. 1848. (5), xxxiii-xlvi, 837, (1) pp. 8°. *6137.11 .35
H2815 — Catalogues. Society libraries.

NL 0407255 MB

Literary and philosophical society of Newcastle-upon-Tyne. Library.
Catalogue of the library of the Literary and philosophical society of Newcastle-upon-Tyne ... Arranged according to the Decimal classification of Melvil Dewey ... Newcastle-upon-Tyne, A. Reid & company, limited, 1903.
xxvii, 1046 p. incl. plans. 26 cm.

NL 0407256 CtY

Literary and philosophical society. Newcastle-upon-Tyne. Library.
List of books added to the library. 18 -

NL 0407257 DI-GS

NJI 737 .825 .9
Literary and Philosophical Society of New New Jersey. Constitution. [Princeton, D.A. Borrenstein, 1825]
2 p. 27 cm
Caption title

NL 0407258 NjP

Literary and philosophical society of South-Carolina, Charleston.
Ford, Timothy, 1762-1830.
Address, delivered before the Literary and philosophical society, of South-Carolina, on the 19th of November, 1817, on physical science, and particularly the science of chymistry. By Timothy Ford ... Charleston, S. C., Printed for the Society, by J. Hoff, no. 118, Broad-Street. 1818.

Toner
Literary and philosophical society of South Carolina, *Charleston.*
Address of the Literary and philosophical society of South-Carolina, to the people of the state, on the classification, character and exercises, or the objects and advantages of the lyceum system, with a view to its general introduction into our towns, villages, and the country at large. Charleston, Observer press, 1834.
iv, [5]-56 p. 22cm.
1. Lyceums.
CA 9—6045 Unrev'd
Library of Congress LC6552.S6L5
——— Copy 2. [Miscellaneous pamphlets, v. 535, no. 15] AC901.M5 vol. 535

NL 0407260 DLC WHi ViW CtY

Literary and philosophical society of S.C. Charleston.
Elliott, Stephen, 1771-1830.
An address to the Literary and philosophical society of South-Carolina; delivered in Charleston, on Wednesday, the 10th August, 1814. By Stephen Elliott ... Charleston: Printed by W. P. Young, No. 44 Broad-street. 1814.

Literary and philosophical society of South-Carolina, Charleston.
An address, to the Literary and philosophical society of South-Carolina
see under Johnson, Joseph, 1776-1862.

Literary and philosophical society of S.C. Charleston.
Johnson, William, 1771-1834.
Nugæ georgicæ; an essay, delivered to the Literary and philosophical society of Charleston, South-Carolina, October 14, 1815. By the Honorable William Johnson ... Charleston, S. C. Printed for the Society by J. Hoff, No. 117, Broad-street. 1815.

The Literary & Pictorial Mirror and Repository of Science, Art, and General Knowledge. Illustrated with seventy engravings. [vignettes]
London: for the Proprietor [Sears, printer, 1837]
viii, 464 p. front., illus., plates. 8vo.
3/4 green calf, gilt, red label, gilt top, by Rivière.
From Anderson Galleries, 10-11 Mr 19, no. 282.
Contains several articles on railroads; and at p. 49 an illustration of trains of the period.

NL 0407264 CSmH

---

823 L7121
The literary and pictorial souvenir; a museum of entertainment and instruction. London, T. Holmes [1849?]
313p. illus. 22cm.

1. Short stories. 2. Gift-books (Annuals, etc.)

NL 0407265 IU MB

Literary and Political Life of A. von Kotzebue
see under [Cramer, Friedrich Matthias Gottfried] 1779-1836.

Literary & scientific institution, London
see London. City of London Literary and scientific institution.

The Literary and scientific register & almanack.
Year
London: D. Bogue[, 18 32°.
v.
Editor : 18 J. W. G. Gutch.
Issued from 1842-57.
1. Almanacs—Gt. Br.
N. Y. P. L. February 11, 1930

NL 0407268 NN MH

The Literary and scientific repository, and critical review. v. [1]-4 (no. 1-8); June 1820-May 1822. New-York, Wiley and Halsted [etc.] 1820-22.
4 v. pl., port. 23½cm. quarterly.
No. 1 dated June 1820 on caption, July 1820 on t.-p. and cover; no. 8 dated May 1822 on caption, June 1822 on cover.
C. K. Gardner, editor.
No more published?
I. Gardner, Charles Kitchell, 1787-1869, ed.
2-4279
Library of Congress AP2.L562

NL 0407269 DLC NN NBu NcD ViU

The Literary and scientific repository, and critical review. v. 1-4 (no. 1-8); June 1820-May 1822. New-York, Wiley and Halsted [etc.]
(American periodical series: 1800-1825. 126)
Microfilm copy, made in 1949 by University Microfilms, Ann Arbor, Mich. Positive.
Collation of the original: 4 v. illus.
Quarterly.
Edited by C. K. Gardner.
Superseded by the United States magazine and literary and political repository. Cf. Union list of serials.
I. Gardner, Charles Kitchell, 1787-1869, ed. (Series: American periodical series: 1800-1850. 126)
Microfilm 01104 no. 126 AP Mic 56-5076

NL 0407270 DLC ICRL NN

VOLUME 336

Literary and scientific society of Madisonville, Ohio.
Archæological explorations by the Literary and scientific society of Madisonville, Ohio ... 1878– Cincinnati, Printed by J. Barclay, 1880–
pt. illus., 3 pl. 22½cm.
Paged continuously.
Cover-title.
Running title: Cincinnati society of natural history. Archæological explorations near Madisonville, Ohio.
4 parts only were issued, all of which were also published in the Journal of the Cincinnati society of natural history, v. 3–4, 1880–1881.
Pt. I–III prepared by Charles F. Low, at the request of the Committee on publication of the Literary and scientific society of Madisonville. *cf.* pt. III, p. [41] foot-note.
1. Mounds—Ohio. 2. Madisonville, O.—Antiq. 3. Hamilton Co., O.—Antiq. I. Low, Charles F.
6–3141
Library of Congress E74.O3L7

NL 0407271 DLC MH-P OClWHi ICJ MB

Literary and social Boston
see under Lathrop, G[eorge Parsons], 1851-1898.

The **Literary** and theological review. v. 1–6; Jan. 1834–Dec. 1839. New-York, D. Appleton & co. [etc.]; Boston, W. Pierce [etc.] 1834–39.
6 v. 22cm. quarterly.
Editors: 1834–37, L. Woods, jun.—1838–39, C. D. Pigeon.
No more published.
1. Theology—Period. I. Woods, Leonard, 1807–1878, ed. II. Pigeon, Charles D., ed.
2–13553
Library of Congress BR1.L8

NL 0407273 DLC NhD OCl ViRUT OU OCl OO OClWHi MiU

FILM The Literary and theological review. v. 1-6; Jan. 1834-Dec. 1839. New York, Appleton. 6 v. (American periodical series: 1800-1850)
Microfilm copy. Ann Arbor, Mich., University Microfilms.
#Theology--Periodicals.

NL 0407274 MoU IaAS LU

The Literary and travel club, Seattle.
Year book.
Library has: 1912/13-1933/34. Lacking: 1917/18-1920/21; 1924/25.

NL 0407275 WaS

Literary anniversary club of San Francisco.
Robert Louis Stevenson; catalogue of the Stevenson exhibition under the auspices of the Literary anniversary club of San Francisco, displayed in the San Francisco public library from November 13th to December 10th, 1932. [San Francisco, 1932]
22 p. incl. front. 20½cm.
1. Stevenson, Robert Louis, 1850–1894—Bibl. I. San Francisco. Public library.
33–22703
Library of Congress Z8843.L77
012

NL 0407276 DLC CU-A CU NNP CtY

Literary anniversary club of San Francisco.
To remember R. L. S. November 13th, 1932. [Atherton, Calif.] Clare Shield: Camino de Lago press [1932]
[16] p. 21cm.
"10 copies printed."
Speeches by Dr. Sandholdt and F. W. Herron and poem by E. V. Weller, given at Monterey, Calif., in celebration of the anniversary of Stevenson's birth.
Autographs of F. W. Herron and E. V. Weller on fly-leaf.

NL 0407277 CU-B

The Literary annual register. London, 1808
see
The Literary panorama and national register.

A literary antiquarian.
The manners and customs of Westmorland
see under Gough, John, of Middleham, Eng.

A literary antiquary.
The history of origins
see under title

The **Literary** apprentice.
Quezon City [etc.] U. P. Writers' Club, University of the Philippines.
v. illus. 22–24 cm.
Vol. 8 (1935) has also a distinctive title: Flame wings.
I. Quezon, Philippine Islands. University of the Philippines. Writers' Club. II. Title: Flame wings.
LH7.Q8L5 378.914 A 40–2656 rev*‡
Grosvenor Library for Library of Congress [r53c1]†

NL 0407281 NBuG DLC OCU OOxM KyU IEN LU TxU IU OrU IEN FU NcU OCU KyU NjP LU WU MiU CU MH IU CLU OU KU CtY NN OrU NIC MNS

The Literary apprentice, silver jubilee edition
see under Ingles, R. Rafael, comp.

A Literary Association.
The American system of education. A hand-bool ...
see under title.

A Literary association.
... First thoughts; or, Beginning to think ...
see under title

A literary association.
... A hand-book of Anglo-Saxon derivatives, on the basis of the handbook of Anglo-Saxon root-words. In three parts. First part. Materials of Anglo-Saxon derivatives. Second part. Studies in Anglo-Saxon derivatives. Third part. The beginning of words ... By a literary association. New York, D. Appleton & co., 1854.

A Literary Association.
... A hand-book of Anglo-Saxon orthography
see under title

A literary association.
... A hand-book of Anglo-Saxon root-words
see under title

A literary association.
... A hand-book of the engrafted words of the English language
see under title

Literary association.
... The sentential reader ... By a literary association. New-York, A. Montgomery; Boston [etc.] F. Parker, 1853.

Literary Association of the Friends of Poland, London.
Address, ... 1832
see under Campbell, Thomas, 1777-1844

943.8
L712 Literary association of the friends of Poland, London.
Address of the Literary association of the friends of Poland, to the people of Great Britain and Ireland; drawn up by Lord Dudley Stuart. London, E. Detkens, bookseller, 1846.
47 p. 21cm.
1.Poland. History. 1795-1864. 2.Poles in Gt. Brit. I.Stuart, Lord Dudley Coutts, 1803-1854.
MnU 51-39

NL 0407291 MnU MH

LITERARY ASSOCIATION OF THE FRIENDS OF POLAND, London.
Address to the Poles. Odezwa do Polaków. Drawn up by Lord Dudley Coutts Stuart. London, E. Detkens, 1850. 47 p. 23cm.
English and Polish on opposite pages.
1. Poles in Great Britain, 19th cent. I. Stuart, Lord Dudley Coutts, 1803-1854.

NL 0407292 NN MH

Literary Association of the Friends of Poland, London.
The Hull Polish record
see under title

Literary association of the friends of Poland, London.
Polonia; or, Monthly reports on Polish affairs. Pub. by the Literary association of the friends of Poland. v. 1– Aug. 1832– London, C. Fox [etc., 1832]–

Literary association of the friends of Poland, *London.*
Report.
London, 18
v. 20½–22cm.
Title varies: 18 Report of the proceedings of the ... annual general meeting of the London Literary association of the friends of Poland. 18 Report of the ... annual meeting of the Literary association of the friends of Poland.
1. Poles in England.
CA 13–371 Unrev'd
Library of Congress HV640 1830

NL 0407295 DLC

VOLUME 336

Literary association of Wisconsin, *Milwaukee.*
Constitution and by-laws of the Literary association of Wisconsin. 1897. [Milwaukee? 1897]
cover-title, 9, [2] p. 14½cm.

Library of Congress PN121.L5 CA 15-392 Unrev'd

NL 0407296 DLC NN

Literary attraction, The celebrated George Lippard, author of 'Quaker City, ...etc, will deliver a lecture/... on Friday...... on the Battle of the Brandywine.... October 13, 1847
West Chester, Pa., Printed at the Office of the Village Record, (1847)
hand-bill. 34.5 x 36 cm.

NL 0407297 MiU-C

The Literary blue book, or Kalendar of literature, science, and art. For 1830. London, Marsh and Miller; [etc., etc., 1829]
iv, ii, 200 p. 14½cm.
No more published?

1. Literature—Year-books. 2. London—Direct.

18-10500

Library of Congress DA679.A1285

NL 0407298 DLC NN

Sw 824 L712 (The)literary bouquet;a selection of essays in prose from admired authors. London,Darton,1796.
v,172p.

NL 0407299 IRA

Ia107 L695 **The Literary** bouquet: gathered from favourite authors. Illustrated with numerous drawings on wood by eminent artists. ... Edinburgh: William P. Nimmo,1872.
160p. illus. 21½cm.

NL 0407300 CtY

Y .95L665 CUTTER The literary bouquet: gathered from favourite authors. Illustrated ... by eminent artists. Edinburgh, W. P. Nimmo, 1873.
160 p. illus. 22 cm.

1. Gift-books (Annuals, etc.)

NL 0407301 WU PP

The LITERARY box;containing the contributions of the Evelyn family,consisting of instructing and amusing tales,in prose and verse suited to all ages. By the author of "The Welcome Visitor". London,John Harris,1824.

pp.(4),90.

NL 0407302 MH

PR3991 A7 W45 1826 **The Literary box:** containing the contributions of the Evelyn family, consisting of instructing and amusing tales, in prose and verse, suited to all ages. By the author of "The welcome visitor". Philadelphia, Ash & Mason, 1826.
105p. front., plates 16 cm.

NL 0407303 RPB ICU NN

Case +7A 29 LITERARY BUDGET
v. 2, no. 1-21; 23-41.
Jan. 7 -May 27, 1854; June 10 - Oct. 14, 1854.
Chicago, 1854.
1v.(328p.) illus. 43cm.
Continuously paged.
Editor: W.W.Danenhower.
P.45-46 mutilated with loss of text.
No. 41 incomplete, p.323-326 missing.

NL 0407304 ICN ICHi

The Literary bureau; a magazine for the writing craft. v. 1, no. 1-6; Apr.-Sept. 1911. Philadelphia, Pa., Literary bureau incorporated, 1911.
cover-title, 408 p. illus. 25cm. monthly.
No more published.

12-19437

Library of Congress AP2.L567

NL 0407305 DLC

Literary bye-hours, a book of instructive pastime . see under [Japp, Alexander Hay] 1839-1905.

The Literary cabinet, v. 1; 1-15 (Nov. 15, 1806-July 4, 1807) [New Haven] 1806-07.
120 p. 21 cm.
Covers and t.p. lacking.
Caption title.

NL 0407307 RPB

Literary cabinet. v. 1, no. 1-20; Nov. 15, 1806-Oct. 31, 1807. [New-Haven, Printed by O. Steele]
(American periodical series: 1800-1825. 22)
Microfilm copy, made in 1946 by University Microfilms, Ann Arbor, Mich. Positive.
Collation of the original, as determined from the film: 160 p.
Biweekly (irregular)
Edited by members of the senior class, Yale University.

I. Yale University. (Series: American periodical series: 1800-1850. 22)

Microfilm 01104 no. 22 AP Mic 56-4580

NL 0407308 DLC LU ICRL OrU NN

The literary cabinet; a collection of original and selected literature. London, 1839.
20 cm.
1. English literature - Selections: Extracts, etc.

NL 0407309 CtY

Literary cabinet and evening fireside companion, v.1, no.1-12, 1832-1833. St. Clairsville, O., 1832-1833.
v. weekly?

NL 0407310 MiD-B

The Literary cabinet and western olive branch. new ser., v. 1, no. 1-26 (no. 15-34); Feb. 16, 1833-Feb. 8, 1834. St. Clairsville, Ohio, Printed for the editor by H. J. Howard.
(American periodical series: 1800-1850. 565)
Microfilm copy (positive) by University Microfilms, Ann Arbor, Mich.
Collation of the original: 2 v. illus.
Semimonthly.
Began publication in 1832. Cf. Union list of serials.
Edited by T. Gregg.
Superseded by the Western gem and cabinet of literature, science and news?
I. Gregg, Thomas, b. 1808, ed. (Series)

Microfilm 01104 no. 565 AP Mic 61-7438

NL 0407311 DLC NN ICRL TxU ICHi OU

Ia107 L696 **The Literary casket. A gift for all seasons. In two parts. New York:Moore & Atkins[188-?]**
2v. in 1. plates. 23cm.

Issued in monthly parts but published as an annual.

NL 0407312 CtY MB MH TxU MiD

Literary casket and pocket magazine of classic and polite literature. v. 1, no. 1-2; April-May, 1821
New York, Published by S. Woodworth. no. illus. 16cm.

Lacking: cover and p. 71-72 of v. 1, no. 1.
Monthly.
Cover title: Woodworth's Literary casket and pocket magazine of classic and polite literature.

Caption title: The literary casket, devoted to classic and polite literature.
Ceased publication sometime in 1822 or 1823 when v. 2 was completed.—*cf. Taft, K. B. Samuel Woodworth. Chicago, 1938. p. 168.*

I. Periodicals—U. S. I. Woodworth, Samuel, 1785-1842, ed. II. Title: The literary casket, devoted to classic and polite literature. III. Title: Woodworth's literary casket and pocket magazine of classic and polite literature.

v. 1, no. 2, Ford Collection

NL 0407314 NN CtY

The Literary casket: devoted to literature, the arts, and sciences. v. 1; Mar. 4, 1826-Feb. 3, 1827. Hartford, Norton & Russell, 1827.
1 p. l., 208 p. 28cm. biweekly.
No more published.

7-22235†

Library of Congress AP2.L573

NL 0407315 DLC OClWHi WHi

The Literary casket: devoted to literature, the arts, and sciences. v. 1; Mar. 4, 1826-Feb. 3, 1827. Hartford, Norton & Russell.
1 v. (American periodical series: 1800-1850)
Microfilm copy. Ann Arbor, Mich., University Microfilms.

NL 0407316 MoU IaAS LU AAP

Case 6A 28 LITERARY CASKET; for literary associations, academies, and high schools; the drawing-room and the fireside. V.1 no. 1-6, Jan.-June, 1852. Boston, 1852.
6 issues. 36cm.

No more published. Cf. Union list of serials.
Edited by Henry C. Shepard.

NL 0407317 ICN

Literary cavalcade. v. 1-
Oct. 1948-
[Dayton, Ohio, Scholastic Corp.]
v. illus. 29 cm. monthly (during the school year)

AP2.L574 051 54-30796

NL 0407318 DLC IU TxU AzTeS

VOLUME 336

The Literary census; a satirical poem
see under Mathias, Thomas James, 1754?-1835.

A literary centre of a literary capital. Edinburgh, R. Grant, 1946.
27 p. ports. 28 cm.
"Edinburgh as a literary centre, by W. Forbes Gray": p. 1-6.

1. Grant (Robert) and Son, Edinburgh. 2. English literature—Edinburgh. I. Gray, William Forbes, 1874-

Z325.G8L5 655.441 47-6493*

NL 0407320 DLC NNC

M920
L77m
The Literary century.
Michigan Woman's Press Association. ⌊Ann Arbor, Mich.⌋ 1893.
⌊381⌋-428p. | illus.,ports. 28cm. (Its v.2,no.13, May 1893)

"Columbian souvenir number."

1.Authors, Women. 2.Press-Mich. 3.Women in Mich. 4.Mich.-Biog. 5.Michigan Woman's Press Association. I. Title.

NL 0407321 Mi

The literary character
see under [Disraeli, Isaac] 1766-1848.

Literary characters
see under Cape, Jonathan, supposed author.

Literary chart of the Iliad
see under [Connell, Francis M] 1866-1935.

The Literary chronicle; containing a review of all new publications of value and interest; original poetry, essays, and anecdotes
see Literary chronicle and weekly review.

AP2
.A858
Literary chronicle and weekly review.
London,Davidson,
v. 26cm. weekly.
Title of individual numbers:The Literary chronicle and weekly review...
In July 1828 absorbed by The Athenaeum,London.

1.Periodicals.

NL 0407326 ICU

Microfilm
9-63
no.88E
Literary chronicle and weekly review. v. 1-10, May 22, 1819-May 24, 1828; new ser., v. 1 (no. 1-480) May 31-July 26, 1828. London.
11 v. on 5 reels. (English literary periodicals, 88E)

Merged into Athenaeum; a journal of literature, science, the fine arts, music and the drama.
Microfilm. Ann Arbor, Mich., University Microfilms.

NL 0407327 ViU MiU CaBVaU NIC NBuU PSt

BR1
.L775
Literary churchman. v.1-38, 1855-92. London, 1855-92.
38v. 25cm. bi-weekly.

1. Christianity--Period. 2. Christian literature--Period.

NL 0407328 IEG

BV4241
L57
Literary Churchman Sermons. A selection of plain sermons. 3d ser. Reprinted from the Literary Churchman from 1883 to 1889. London, Skeffington, 1889.
231p. 19cm.

1. Sermons, English. 2. Sermons, Collections.

NL 0407329 IaU

Literary clinic, *Buffalo.*
Shakespeare studies; papers read before the Literary clinic. Buffalo, The Literary clinic, 1916.
156 p., 1 l. 20½cm. $0.75
CONTENTS.—Foreword, by C. E. Rhodes.—Shakespeare's England, by Pauline H. and B. L. Nichols.—Hamlet, by F. H. Smith.—As you like it, by F. H. Smith.—King Lear, by F. H. Smith.—Romeo and Juliet, by F. H. Smith.—Othello, by F. H. Smith.—The tempest, by F. H. Smith.—These our actors, by F. H. Smith.—A tribute, by F. H. Smith.

1. Shakespeare, William—Criticism and interpretation.

Library of Congress PR2976.L5 16-10342

NL 0407330 DLC GU OC1W NN MiU

Literary club, Cincinnati.

Poole, William Frederick, 1821-1894.
Anti-slavery opinions before the year 1800; read before the Cincinnati literary club, November 16, 1872, by William Frederick Poole ... to which is appended a fac simile reprint of Dr. George Buchanan's Oration on the moral and political evil of slavery, delivered at a public meeting of the Maryland society for promoting the abolition of slavery, Baltimore, July 4, 1791. Cincinnati, R. Clarke & co., 1873.

Literary club, *Cincinnati.*
... Constitution, catalogue of members, etc. Cincinnati, C. T. Woodrow & co., printers, 1879.
40 p. 23½cm.
At head of title: The Literary club of Cincinnati.
Includes "Extracts from records," 1849-64.

Library of Congress PN22.C6 1879 14-2664

NL 0407332 DLC OCU OC1WHi

Literary club, *Cincinnati.*
... Constitution, catalogue of members, etc. Cincinnati, R. Clarke & co., printers, 1890.
92 p. 20cm.
At head of title: The Literary club of Cincinnati.
Includes "Extracts from records," 1849-64.

PN22.C6 1890 14-2665

NL 0407333 DLC MH OC1WHi OFH

Literary club, *Cincinnati.*
The Literary club of Cincinnati 1849-1903. Constitution, catalogue of members, etc. Cincinnati, The Ebbert & Richardson co. ⌊1903⌋
4 p. l., 7-170 p. front. (4 port.) 3 pl. 28½cm.
CONTENTS.—Introductory to edition of 1903.—Introductory to edition of 1890.—Extracts from records.—Fiftieth anniversary of the club.—Constitution.—Lists of officers since February, 1864.—Members during first club year.—Honorary members.—Active members, May, 1903.—Catalogue of members, past and present.—Papers read before the club.—Catalogue of books and pamphlets in club library written by members, etc.—Military record of those who were or had been members prior to the close of the war.—Paintings, engravings, etc., in the club rooms.

4-731 Revised

Library of Congress PN22.C6 1903

NL 0407334 DLC OC OCU OC1WHi OC1 MB IU

374.23
L712
1911
Literary club, Cincinnati.
Constitution, June, 1911. ⌊Cincinnati⌋ The Literary Club, 1911.
12 p. 16 cm.

342677

NL 0407335 KyU

---

*
374.23
L712
1937
Literary Club, Cincinnati.
The Literary Club. Constitution as adopted June, 1936, and amended May, 1937. Cincinnati, Ohio, 1937.
⌊7⌋ p. 16 cm.

Cover title.

342678

NL 0407336 KyU

Literary Club, Cincinnati.
In memoriam. Dr. Landon Rives Longworth... Edmund Dexter... Papers read before the Literary club of Cincinnati. ⌊Cincinnati, R. Clarke & Co., 1879?⌋ 12 p. 12°.

Cover-title.

KREHBIEL COLLECTION.
1. Longworth, Landon Rives, 1835-79. 2. Dexter, Edmund, 1846-79.
N. Y. P. L. May 3, 1924.

NL 0407337 NN OCU MH

Literary Club, Cincinnati.
The Literary Club of Cincinnati, 1849-1924. Cincinnati, Ebbert & Richardson Co. ⌊1925?⌋
265 p. illus. 26 cm.

PN22.C5525 72-190341 MARC

NL 0407338 DLC NcD OCH OCU

Literary Club, Cincinnati.
The Literary Club of Cincinnati, 1849-1949; centennial book. ⌊Cincinnati, Roessler Bros., Printers, 1949?⌋
101 p. illus. 24 cm.

I. Title.
PN22.C5527 73-155861 MARC

NL 0407339 DLC OCU OCH NRU

VOLUME 336

Literary club, Cincinnati,
...The Literary club of Cincinnati.
Fiftieth anniversary, Oct. 29, 1899.
[Cinci.? 1899?]
27, [1] p.

NL 0407340 OClWHi

Literary Club, Cincinnati.
Memorial of Manning F. Force, presented to the Literary Club of Cincinnati, May 26, 1899
see under title

Literary Club, Cincinnati.
Papers read ... by Robert Ralston Jones
see under Jones, Robert Ralston
[Supplement]

LITERARY CLUB OF CINCINNATI.
Report of the committee [J.W.Herron and 4 others] on the death of L.E.Mills. Adopted April 17, 1878. [Cinn. 1878.]
24°. pp. 8. Large paper.

NL 0407343 MH CtY

Literary Club, *London.*
Annals of The Club, 1764–1914 ... London, Printed for The Club, 1914.
vi p., 1 l., 231 p. IX pl. (incl. front. (port.) 8 double facsim.) 28 x 22 cm.
The present work is a consecutive account of The Club's transactions from its foundation, embodying the information contained in Sir Mountstuart Grant Duff's short history of the society presented to the Roxburghe Club ("The Club, 1794–1905") with much additional matter; the biographical sketches of deceased members contained in the short history are here reprinted, with the necessary additions. *cf.* Preliminary note.
The frontispiece is a reproduction of a sketch of Sir Joshua Reynolds, the originator of The Club, by Thomas Sandby, from the Royal collections at Windsor Castle; the facsimiles include signatures of Sir Joshua Reynolds, Dr. Samuel Johnson, James Boswell, Edmund Burke, and others.
1. Reynolds, Sir Joshua, 1723–1792. 2. Johnson, Samuel, 1709–1784. 3. Autographs—Gt. Brit.—Facsimiles. I. Grant Duff, Sir Mountstuart Elphinstone, 1829–1906.
HS2865.L7L5 25–21307*

NL 0407345 DLC CtY

Literary Club of the Church of the Messiah, Buffalo, New York. *P.39.507.2
Club calendar. 1884–87, 1888–1890, 1892–93, 1894–1907.
= Buffalo, N. Y. 1884–1907. v. 16°.
A women's club.
G5786 — Women's clubs.

NL 0407346 MB

Literary Club of the Church of the Messiah, Buffalo, N. Y. *2169.62
Reference list. French history and literature from 1774 to present time.
= [Buffalo. 1890.] (5) pp. 32°.
The title is on the cover.
H46 — France. Lit. Bibl. — France. Hist. Bibl.

NL 0407347 MB

L010.5
L776 The Literary collector; a monthly magazine of book-lore and bibliography. v. 1–9, v. 10, no. 1–3; Oct. 1900–Sept. 1905. New York, G. D. Smith [1900–01] Greenwich, Conn., and New York, The Literary collector company [1902–05]
10 v. in 7. illus., plates, ports., facsims. 22–24cm.
Subtitle varies.
Editors: Nov. 1901–Oct. 1904, F. C. Bursch.—Nov. 1904–Sept. 1905, F. C. Bursch, Ann D. Bursch.
No more published.
1. Bibliography—Period. I. Bursch, Frederick C., ed. II. Bursch, Annie (Dennis) 1870– ed.
Library of Congress Z1007.L772 7-4560

NL 0407348 DLC OClWHi NcU

LITERARY collector; a monthly magazine devoted to the interests of collectors. v. 1, no. 5. New York, 1901. 23cm.
Film reproduction. Negative.
Contains an article on shorthand book collecting by C. C. Beale.
1. Collectors and collecting--Per. and soc. publ.

NL 0407349 NN

The LITERARY comment.
v.
[Ann Arbor, Mich.,] 192 4°.
v. illus.
Irregular.
Issued as a suppl. to The Hillel news.
Ceased publication.
1. Colleges and universities--Student publications--U.S.--Michigan.

NL 0407350 NN

Literary committee, Connecticut board of Lady managers for the Columbian exposition
see Connecticut. Board of lady managers, World's Columbian exposition.

The Literary companion. Editors, William H. Egle, Clarence May. v. 1; Aug. 1853–Jan. 1854. Harrisburg, Pa., W. H. Egle & co., 1854.
iv, 188 p. plates. 24½cm. monthly.
No more published.
I. Egle, William Henry, 1830–1901, ed. II. May, Clarence, ed.
13-6642
Library of Congress AP2.L576

NL 0407352 DLC OClWHi

The Literary companion. v. 1, no. 1–13; June 16–Sept. 8, 1821. [New-York, G. & J. Huntley]
(American periodical series: 1800–1825. 131)
Microfilm copy, made in 1950 by University Microfilms, Ann Arbor, Mich. Positive.
Collation of the original, as determined from the film: 208 p.
Weekly.
(Series: American periodical series: 1800–1850. 131)
Microfilm 01104 no. 131 AP Mic 56–5123

NL 0407353 DLC ICRL NN ViW

A literary companion. 1944
see under [Gaskell, Goddard] comp.

Literary conglomerate; or, A combination of various thoughts and facts on various subjects
see under [Duncan, Philip Bury] 1772–1863.

Literary convention, *New York,* 1831.
Report of the Committee on the propriety of studying the Bible in the institutions of a Christian country, presented to the Literary convention at New York, October, 1831. Boston, Allen and Ticknor; [etc., etc.] 1832.
24 p. 24cm.
W. C. Woodbridge, chairman.
1. Bible in [the] schools.
E 14-1631
Library, U. S. Bur. of Education LC107.L71

NL 0407356 DHEW CtY

Literary cookery
see under Brae, Andrew Edmund, d. 1881.

808.8
L714 The Literary coronal, for Glasgow, Printed for R. Griffin, 18
v. illus. 14cm.

NL 0407358 IU DLC

Literary coterie. Detroit.
[Year book] 19 – [Detroit]
v.
Library has
1930/31.
Organized Mar. 26, 1930.

NL 0407359 MiD-B

The Literary criterion.
[Mysore] Rao & Raghavan.
v. 22 cm. semiannual.
NSyU
1. English literature—Hist. & crit.—Period.
PR1.L5 S A 63-3332
Library of Congress [2] PL 480: I-E-E-349

NL 0407360 DLC ICU MiU NN NSyU

*
PS3525
.E43Z63 A literary critic. From the Christian
1920 register of June 24, 1920.
[2] p. 16½cm.
Inscribed: "H. L. Mencken."
1. Mencken, Henry Louis, 1880–1956.

NL 0407361 ViU

Literary curiosities and eccentricities [1875]
see under Clouston, William Alexander, 1843–1896, comp.

VOLUME 336

Literary curiosities and notes
see under Gomme, George Lawrence, ed.

The literary diary; or, Improved common-place book
see under [Mathews, Charles James] 1803-1878, comp.

AP
2
L58
The Literary digest. v. 1-124, v. 125, no. 1-8; Mar. 1, 1890-Feb. 19, 1938. New York, Funk & Wagnalls [etc., 1890-1938]

125 v. in 128. illus. (incl. ports.) 29½-31 cm. weekly.

Title varies: 1890-99, The literary digest; a repository of contemporaneous thought and research as presented in the periodical literature of the world.
1900-01, The Literary digest; a weekly compendium of the contemporaneous thought of the world.
1902-July 10, 1937, The Literary digest.
The Literary digest and the Review of reviews were united July 17, 1937. From this date till Nov. 6, 1937 title reads: The Digest. Review of reviews incorporating the Literary digest (v.1 no. 1-17) Nos. 1-15 were edited by Albert Shaw, with Albert Shaw, jr., as publisher: no. 16-17 were edited by D. P. Page. With this issue for Nov. 13, 1937 the title Literary digest was resumed, with D. P. Page as editor and the Literary digest, inc., as publisher.
Editors: 1895-1905? E. J. Wheeler.—1906?-12, I. K. Funk.—1913-33. W. S. Woods.—1933-35, A. S. Draper.—1936-37, W. J. Funk.
Absorbed Public opinion in July 1906, and Current opinion in May 1925.
No more published: merged into "Time" in May 1938.

I. Wheeler, Edward Jewitt, 1850-1922, ed. II. Funk, Isaac Kaufman, 1839-1912, ed. III. Woods, William Seaver, 1872- ed. IV. Draper, Arthur Stimson, 1882- ed. V. Funk, Wilfred John, 1883- ed.

7-22244

AP2.L58

TxLT MWH FM CU KT NC ODW ILS
MiU OO OOxM OC1ND OC1U OCU OC1JC MeP ABS LNL I
DCU-H ICJ OC1 NIC NdU NBuG NcRS ICN NjP OC1WHi
MB GU-L NNH PPiD GDS MtU TxDW MiU AzTeS KyLoU MH
NL 0407365 DLC OrAshS OrCS DAL OrLgE NbHi CoU

Microfiche
*AP2
.L57
The Literary digest. v. 1-
Mar. 1, 1890-
New York, Funk & Wagnalls [etc.] 1890-
sheets. 10 1/2 x 15 1/2 cm.
Subtitle varies.
Microfiche copy made by Microcard Editions, Inc., Washington, D. C.

1. Periodica ls, English.

NL 0407368 MB

Literary digest.

Applied psychology ... a series of twelve volumes on the applications of psychology to the problems of personal and business efficiency, by Warren Hilton ... Rev. ed. Issued under the auspices of the Literary digest for the Society of applied psychology ... New York and London [°1927]

Sp Col
Wilson
LL776a
The Literary digest.
[Articles about Woodrow Wilson, April 8, 1916 through Feb. 1925. New York, Funk & Wagnalls, 1925]
1 v. (various pagings) illus. 31cm.

Made up title; typewritten table of contents tipped in.

1. Wilson, Woodrow, pres. U.S., 1856-1924.

NL 0407370 IEN

The Literary digest.

Williams, Henry Smith, 1863-
The book marvels, by Henry Smith Williams ... New York and London, Funk & Wagnalls company [°1931]

The Literary Digest.
Building supplement.
no.

New York, 192 f°.
v. illus.

Semi-annual.
Ceased publication, Spring, 1930.

1. Building—Per. and soc. publ.
N. Y. P. L. May 13, 1931

NL 0407372 NN MiU

The Literary digest.
Circulation analysis; the Literary digest. [New York] 1929.
69 p. 28cm.
"Circulation figures in this book are for the issue of April 14, 1928."

1. Advertising—Mediums— Newspapers and periodicals.
N. Y. P. L. February 14, 1945

NL 0407373 NN

Literary digest.
Edison's posers answered in various ways. [New York, 1921]
[6] p. 31 cm.
Extracted from the Literary digest for May 28, 1921.
1. Mental tests. I. Title.

NL 0407374 CU

[The Literary digest.]
Education in Americanism; lessons in patriotism prepared for the Literary digest and especially designed for school use. [New York: The Literary digest, 1920?] 30 l. illus. (map.) f°.

A scrapbook of photostat reproductions and actual clippings from the Literary digest, mounted on one side of blank sheets.

1. Emigration and immigration, U. S. 2. Title.
N. Y. P. L. September 22, 1922.

NL 0407375 NN

Literary digest
Fructuous years, 1927-1929; the news and advertising of aviation as it was recorded by the Literary digest. N. Y., The Author [1930?]
126 p. illus. ports. maps, facsims.

NL 0407376 MiD

The Literary digest.
Insuring the to-morrow of the American chemical industry. New York, The Literary digest, 1919.
3 p. l., 11-38, [1] p. front., plates. 23½cm.

1. Chemicals—Manufacture and industry—U. S. I. Title.
19—3534
Library of Congress TP23.L7

NL 0407377 DLC DNLM PHi OC1 ODW ICJ ViU

Literary digest.
Light on the career of Richard Realf
see under title

The LITERARY DIGEST.
The Literary digest book of art. New York: Funk & Wagnalls Co.[, cop. 1927.] 121 p. 32½cm.

"This scrapbook...provides a place for the cover-pictures of The Literary digest...with the description of each, cut from the same issue and pasted on the opposite page."

641315A. 1. Paintings, U.S. I. Title.

NL 0407379 NN

The Literary digest.
The Literary digest poll on the Roosevelt policies; report ... New York, N. Y., Funk & Wagnalls company [°1934-
v. 30½cm.

1. U. S.—Pol. & govt.—1933- I. Title.
CA 34-777 Unrev'd
Library of Congress HC106.3.L55
——— 2d set.
Copyright 330.973

NL 0407380 DLC

654.0973
5
Literary digest.
The lord of telephone manor ... New York, Literary digest, 1927-1930.
Library has ed. 2-3, 1927-1930. front., illus., maps, tables. 13-26cm.
Telephone statistics.

NL 0407381 ICJ NcU MiU OC1 OC1U OU TU OC1FRB

The Literary digest.
The lord of Telephone manor. New York, The Literary digest, 1925.
4 p. l., 67 p. incl. illus., tables. front. 23½cm.
The standing of the Literary digest in the telephone market.

1. Advertising. 2. Telephone—U. S. I. Title.
25-17643
Library of Congress HF6146.T4L5

NL 0407382 DLC OC1 MiU ViU OC1FRB

Map
G
6795
1918
L5
Literary Digest.
Map of the Balkan front. New York, Funk & Wagnalls, 1918.
col. map 19 x 26cm.

Scale ca. 1:1,900,000.
From Literary Digest for October 5, 1918.

1. Balkan peninsula--Maps.

NL 0407383 NIC

Map
G
5833
M35
1918
L5
Literary Digest.
Map of the Marne-Champagne drive. New York, Funk & Wagnalls, 1918.
col. map 19 x 26cm.

Scale ca. 1:516,880.
From Literary Digest for August 3, 1918.

1. European War, 1914-1918--Maps.

NL 0407384 NIC

VOLUME 336

The Literary digest.
Military map of Europe compiled from the most authentic sources
see under General Drafting Co., Inc.

Literary digest.

Tipper, Harry, 1879-
Psychology in advertising, by Harry S. Tipper ... issued under the auspices of the Literary digest for the Society of applied psychology. New York and London, 1920.

G1019 .F78 1934 MAP DIV.

Literary digest.

Funk and Wagnalls Company.
The standard atlas and gazetteer of the world; especially prepared with many unusual features by Rand M'Nally & Co. Literary digest ed. New York [°1934]

The Literary Digest.
Who builds the ten homes in which you live? A summary of building contracts awarded in the three years of 1911 to 1925, with special reference to the post war period... [New York:] The Literary Digest, 1926. 100 p. col'd illus., tables. 4°.

Cover-title.

1. Building—U. S. 2. Advertisements and advertising—Building trades. 3. Title.
N. Y. P. L. March 31, 1927

NL 0407388 NN ICJ MH

The Literary digest.
The work they do and where they live. Section one, occupational analysis, etc. Section two, state, county, and city circulation. Section three, general merchandising statistics. New York and Chicago, The Literary digest, °1922.

115 p. facsim., tables, diagrs. 28cm.

I. Title.

NL 0407389 MiU MH NN

Literary digest. L050.433 S700
The work they do and where they live. 1926-1927. Circulation analysis. The Literary digest. [New York, Funk & Wagnalls, 1927?]
cover-title, 67 p. 28cm.

NL 0407390 ICJ ICRL OU

The Literary digest.

[Eastman, R. O., inc.]
Zanesville and 36 other American communities; a study of markets and of the telephone as a market index. New York, The Literary digest. 1927.

The Literary digest: a repository of contemporaneous thought and research as presented in the periodical literature of the world
see The Literay digest.

The Literary digest atlas of the new Europe and the Far East ...
see under Updegraff, Allan Eugene, 1883-

The literary digest atlas of the world
see under Funk and Wagnalls Company.

The Literary digest atlas of the world and gazetteer ...
see under Funk and Wagnalls Company.

Literary digest books.

New York and London, Funk & Wagnalls company, 19-
v. 19cm.

NL 0407396 OO

The Literary digest day-by-day history of the war. [pt. 1- New York, The Literary digest, °1915-
illus. 31cm.
Cover-title.

1. European war, 1914-

Library of Congress D525.L5 15-14289

NL 0407397 DLC

Literary [The] digest european war maps. 3 maps. sm. fol. New York, Literary digest [1914] 4232

NL 0407398 DLC ICU OO

---

912 qL712h The literary digest historical and political atlas of new Europe and the Far East. New York [etc.] Funk & Wagnalls company [192-?]

cover-title,[3] 48 p. incl. col. maps. 28cm.

Includes advertising matter.

1. Atlases. I. Funk & Wagnalls company

NL 0407399 MnU

The Literary digest international book review. v. 1-4 (no. 1-48); Dec. 1922-Nov. 1926. New York [etc.] Funk & Wagnalls company [1922-26]
4 v. illus. 31cm. monthly.
Clifford Smyth, editor.
No more published.

1. American literature—Bibl.—Period. 2. English literature—Bibl.—Period. 3. Books—Reviews. I. Smyth, Clifford, 1866- ed. II. Title: International book review.

Library of Congress Z1007.L773 25-1181 Revised

KT MtU NdU ILS
ICJ ViU ICN MB NN OC1W OC1JC OCU NcCU CU GEU LNL N
NL 0407400 DLC WaS I MtBC PBL NIC OO MiU ODW OOxM

The Literary digest liberty map of new Europe, revealing the great changes brought about by the world war, 1914-1919, with complete index ... New York, Funk & Wagnalls company, °1920.
col. map. 99 (i. e. 101) x 126½cm.
"Natural scale, 1: 4,560,000, 72 miles=1 incl."
"Engraved and printed by Matthews-Northrup works, Buffalo, N. Y."
"References: Boundaries as they existed before the war, 1914.—Boundaries definitely decided by the Peace treaties.—Possible new boundaries not yet determined.—Territories affected by plebiscite.—International territory."

Inset: The Literary digest new map of Africa, showing mandates proposed by the Peace conference ... New York, Funk & Wagnalls company, 1920. Natural scale 1:21,500,000, 340 miles=1 inch.
With this is issued: Index for the Literary digest liberty map of new Europe, also separate index for New map of Africa. New York, London, Funk & Wagnalls company [°1920] (44 p. 25½cm.)

1. Europe—Descr. & trav.—Maps. 2. Africa—Descr. & trav.—Maps. I. Funk & Wagnalls company. II. Matthews-Northrup company, Buffalo, N. Y.
Library of Congress Div. of maps Map 22-12 Revised

NL 0407402 DLC NIC OCl

The Literary digest liberty map of the western front of the great world war, showing the battle line of liberty as it stood May 1st, 1918. Also showing the lines of farthest advance of the German and the French offensives; with complete index. New York: Funk & Wagnalls Co., 1918. 1 map, with index of 32 p. nar. 4°.

Map, size within border: →48¾ × ↑38¼ in.
Scale: 8 m. = 1 in.
Engraved and printed on cloth by the Matthews-Northrup Works, Buffalo, N. Y.
Insets in upper right corner show the coal and iron fields in the western war territory, and the world production of pig iron and coal.

1. European war, 1914- .—Maps. 2. Europe.—Maps, 1918.
N. Y. P. L. August 8, 1918.

NL 0407403 NN IU OCl NjP MtU

---

*Map 1033-79
The Literary Digest liberty map of the western front of the great world war, showing the battle line of liberty as it stood September 5th, 1918. Also showing the lines of farthest advance of the German and Allied offensives.
New York. Funk & Wagnalls Co. 1918. col map 102 x 126 cm.
Scale, 1:500000 (or, 8 miles to 1 inch). Chart. On linen. Folded.
Submaps. — Map of the complete war area. — Coal and iron fields in the western war territory.
Accompanied by Index. 35 pp. 25½ cm.

L5443 — European War, 1914- . Maps. — France. Geog. Maps.

NL 0407404 MB NIC MdBJ OCl

The Literary digest map of U. S. S. R. ... New York, Funk & Wagnalls company, °1934.
1 sheet incl. 5 col. maps. 100 x 127cm.
Compiled, engraved and printed by the J. W. Clement co., Matthews-Northrup works, Buffalo, N. Y.
CONTENTS.—Union of soviet socialist republics. Scale 1:8,236,800.—Europe. Scale 1:12,038,400.—Economic map of Asia. Scale 1:47,000,000.—The world. Scale 1:175,000,000.—Asia. Scale 1:22,809,600.
——— Copy 2.
Copyright F 7390
——— Handbook and index to The Literary digest new map of soviet Russia. New York and London, Funk and Wagnalls company, 1935 [°1934]
47 p. 25½ x 15½cm.
1. Russia—Descr. & trav.—Maps. I. Funk & Wagnalls company.
Library of Congress Div. of Maps Map 35-90
——— Copy 2.
Copyright AA 163559

NL 0407405 IU

---

*Map.405.1934
The Literary Digest Map of the U.S.S.R., Union of Soviet Socialist Republics.
— New York. Funk & Wagnalls Co. 1935. Text: Handbook and index... 1935. Tables. 25.5 cm. Map: Size, 39 × 50 inches, folded to 10¾ × 13 inches. Scale, 1:8,236,800, or, 130 statute miles to 1 inch. In envelope.
Submaps: — Europe. — Economic map of Asia, including U.S.S.R. in Europe. — The world, showing routes and distances from the United States to U.S.S.R. — Asia.
The title on the envelope reads: The Literary Digest New map of Soviet Russia...

D9247 — U.S.S.R. (Union of Socia... Soviet Republics.) Geog. Maps. — Russia. Geog. Maps.

NL 0407406 MB

VOLUME 336

The Literary digest 1931 atlas of the world. [New York, Funk & Wagnalls company, °1930]
cover-title, 92 p. incl. 143 col. maps. 31cm.
Text on p. [2] and [3] of cover.

1. Atlases. I. Funk & Wagnalls company.

Library of Congress Div. of Maps Map 35-27

NL 0407407 DLC OU

The Literary Digest political cyclopedia
see under Thwing, Eugene, 1866-

The Literary emporium; a compendium of religious, literary, and philosophical knowledge ... v. 1-4; [Jan.?] 1845-[Dec.?] 1846. New York, J. K. Wellman [1845]-46.
4 v. in 2. plates (part col.) port. 23cm. monthly.

Library of Congress AP2.L582 7-41321

NL 0407409 DLC MWA MNS ViU NNC TU PU Vi KyU

Literary era. 1894-
see Era magazine.

Literary essays. London, 1906
see under [Morley, John] 1838-

The Literary examiner: consisting of the Indicator, a review of books, and miscellaneous pieces in prose and verse. No.1-26, July 5-Dec 27, 1823. London, Printed for H.L.Hunt,1823
26 no.in 1 vol.(1 l., 412p., 1 l.) 22cm.

Edited by Leigh Hunt.
Superseded The Indicator (Oct.1819-Oct.1821).
For further description see L.A.Brewer, My Leigh Hunt library, First editions, 1932, p.117-120.

I. Hunt, Leigh, 1784-1859, ed. II. The Indicator.

NL 0407412 MWelC TxDW TxLT ScU CSmH NjP NN ICU NCH

The Literary examiner, consisting of the Indicator, a review of books, and miscellaneous pieces in prose and verse. v. 1, no. 1-26; July 5-Dec. 27, 1823. London, Printed for H. L. Hunt.
1 reel. (English literary periodicals, 89E)
Microfilm copy, made in 1954 by University Microfilms, Ann Arbor, Mich. Positive.
Collation of the original, as determined from the film: 412 p.
Weekly.
Edited by L. Hunt. Cf. Union list of serials.

I. Hunt, Leigh, 1784-1859, ed. (Series)

Microfilm 01105 no. 89E AP Mic 56-4413

CSt MiU ViU
NL 0407413 DLC ICRL CaBVaU ScU PSt AAP NBuU CLSU

The Literary examiner and western monthly review. Ed. by E. Burke Fisher. v. 1; May-Dec. 1839. Pittsburgh, Pa., Whitney & M'Cord, 1839.
vii, 464 p. 27cm.

I. Fisher, E. Burke, ed.

Library of Congress AP2.L584 7-22279

NL 0407414 DLC WaSp TxU NcU MnHi OClWHi

Cg86
231
Literary exercises, held under the auspices of the Tinmouth valley grange, at the "Old home day" celebration, in Tinmouth, Vermont, Thursday, September 7, 1905. [Middletown Springs,Vt.,1905]
Pamphlet
Cover-title: Souvenir of Tinmouth "Old home day", Thursday, September 7, 1905.

NL 0407415 CtY NcD

The Literary exposé and fashionable Proteus, being a new series continued from ... the Literary humbug; or, Weekly take-in. v. 1 (no. 1-); May 14, 1823-
London [Chappell and son, etc.] 1823-
v. front., illus. 21½cm.
From May 14 to June 18, 1823, title reads: The Literary humbug; or, Weekly take-in.
"By Jaspero, the younger, esq."

I. Jaspero, the younger, esq., pseud.

Library of Congress AP4.L417 22-16115

NL 0407416 DLC MB

Literary extracts, in prose and verse
see under Griffith, Mary Louise, ed.

Literary Florida. Tampa, Florida. v.1, 1939-

v.[8], 9-10, [11], 12-13, [14]- 15#3 ||

NL 0407418 FTaSU

---

*EF75
M6793b
The Literary fly. no.1-17; 18 Jan.-8 May 1779.
London,C.Etherington,1779.
f°. 17 nos.in 1v. 32cm. weekly.
Written by Sir Herbert Croft.
No more published.
Bound with The Mirror, 1779-80.

NL 0407419 MH

Literary focus. v.1, no. 1-12; June 1827-May 1828. Oxford, Ohio «Miami University»
1 reel. (American periodical series: 1800-1850. 777)

Microfilm copy (positive by University Microfilms, Ann Arbor, Michigan.

NL 0407420 AAP IaAS MoU

Ap
A100
864l
Rare
Books
Col
Literary foundlings: verse and prose, collected in Canterbury, N.Z. ...
Christchurch: Printed at the "Times" Office, Gloucester Street. MDCCCLXIV. 73p. 16½cm.
"This Collection has been made with the object of helping the funds of the Christchurch Orphan Asylum, and will be first offered for sale at the Bazaar about to be held in behalf of that institution. Consisting ... entirely of the productions of Canterbury writers."—Advertisement.
List of contributors in manuscript on verso of t.p.
1. English literature - Collections.

NL 0407421 TxU

Pam.
Coll.
17409
... A literary fraud unmasked. How it falsifies history and traduces the South and how it is imposed upon the public. [Houston, Tex., 1895]
58 p. 24 cm.

1. Encyclopaedia britannica. 2. Southern states. History.

NL 0407422 NcD

Literary fund, Royal
see
Royal literary fund, London.

Pam.
Coll.
19386
Literary Fund of North Carolina.
Report of the president and directors of the Literary fund, to the legislature of North Carolina. Raleigh, Weston R. Gales, 1842.
8, 7 p. tables (1 fold.) 22½cm.

1. Education. North Carolina. Finance

NL 0407424 NcD

The Literary garland
see The Literary garland and British North American magazine.

The Literary garland, and British North American magazine ... v. 1- 4, Dec. 1838- Nov.1842; new ser., v. 1- 9, Jan. 1843- Dec.1851.
Montreal, Lovell & Gibson; [etc., etc.]
v. plates. 25cm. monthly.
Includes music.
Title varies: 1838- The Literary garland ...
1846, The Literary garland, and Canadian magazine ...
1847- The Literary garland, and British North American magazine.

No more published. Cf. Union list of serials.

Library of Congress AP5.L57 45-43251

NL 0407426 DLC TxU

The Literary garland and Canadian magazine ...
see The Literary garland and British North American magazine.

The Literary gazette. v. 1-2 (no. 1-32); Aug. 1, 1834-June 26, 1835. Concord, N. H., D. D. Fisk [etc.] 1834-35.
2 v. in 1. 1 illus. 32½cm.
Weekly, Aug. 1834-Mar. 1835; semimonthly, Apr.?-June 1835.
Caption title.
Edited by Asa Fowler and others.

I. Fowler, Asa, 1811-1885, ed.

Library of Congress AP2.L587 26-19400

NL 0407428 DLC MoSW NcD MB NN

VOLUME 336

Film
829
Reel 400

Literary gazette. v.1-2 (no.1-32) Aug. 1, 1834-June 26, 1835. Concord, N.H., D.D. Fisk.
1 reel. (American periodical series: 1800-1850. 400)

Microfilm copy (positive) by University Microfilms, Ann Arbor, Mich.
Weekly, Aug. 1834-Mar. 1835; semimonthly, Apr.?-June 1835.
Edited by Asa Fowler and others.

I. Fowler, Asa, 1811-1885, ed. II. Series.

NL 0407429 TxU LU FU NN

The Literary gazette. A weekly journal of literature, science, and the fine arts. no. 1-2162. Jan. 25. 1817-June 26, 1858; new ser., v. 1- July 3, 1858

London, H. Colburn; ͵etc., etc.͵ 1817-
v. illus., plates, facsims. 29cm (no. 1-1510: 25 x 19½cm)

Title varies: Jan. 1817-Feb. 1856, The Literary gazette and journal of belles lettres, arts, sciences, &c. (Title varies slightly) Caption title sometimes reads: The London literary gazette ...
Mar. 1856-Dec. 1857, The Literary gazette and journal of archæology, science, and art.
Jan.-June 1858, Literary gazette and journal of belles lettres, science, and art.
July 1858- The Literary gazette. A weekly journal of literature, science, and the fine arts.

Edited by William Jerdan, July 1817-Dec. 1850; by L. A. Reeve, 1851-56; by J. M. Jephson, 1856?-58. The new series was edited successively by Shirley Brooks, Henry Christmas, W. R. Workman, Frederick Arnold, John Morley, C. W. Goodwin. *cf.* Brit. mus. Catalogue.
Merged into the Parthenon. after Apr. 26, 1862

I. Jerdan, William, 1728-1869, ed. II. Reeve, Lovell Augustus, 1814-1865, ed. III. Jephson, John Mounteney, 1819-1865, ed. IV. Brooks, Shirley *i. e.* Charles William Shirley, 1816-1874, ed. V. Christmas, afterwards Noel-Fearn, Henry, 1811-1868, ed. VI. Workman, William Ring, ed. VII. Arnold, Frederick, 1833- ed. VIII. Morley, John, 1838- ed. IX. Goodwin, Charles Wycliffe, 1817-1878, ed.

Library of Congress AP4.L42 CA 7-4053 Unrev'd

NL 0407431 DLC NcU KyLoU

Micro
Film
F352

The Literary gazette. A weekly journal of literature, science, and the fine arts. no.1-2360; Jan. 25, 1817-Apr. 26, 1862. London. 14 reels. 35mm. (English literary periodicals, 90E)
Issues for July 3, 1858-Apr. 26, 1862 also called new ser. v.1-8 (no.1-200)
Title varies: Jan. 1817-Feb. 1856, The Literary gazette and journal of belles lettres, arts, sciences, &c. (varies slightly). Caption title sometimes reads: The London literary gazette ...; Mar. 1856-Dec. 1857, The Literary gazette and journal of archaeology, science, and art; Jan.-June 1858, Literary gazette and journal of belles lettres, science, and art.
Merged into the Parthenon.
Microfilm (positive). Ann Arbor, Mich., University Microfilms, 1973.
Filmed with The Farmer's magazine.
I. Title: London literary gazette.

NL 0407433 PSt

The Literary gazette; or, Journal of criticism, science, and the arts. Being a collection of original and selected essays. v. 1; Jan. 6-Dec. 29, 1821. Philadelphia ͵J. Maxwell͵
829 p. 27 cm. weekly.
Supersedes the Analectic magazine.

AP2.A48 5-6121 rev*

NL 0407434 DLC MdBP NcU PCaD

The Literary gazette; or, Journal of criticism, science, and the arts. Being a collection of original and selected essays. v. 1; Jan. 6-Dec. 29, 1821. Philadelphia ͵J. Maxwell͵
(American periodical series: 1800-1825. 131)
Microfilm copy, made in 1950 by University Microfilms, Ann Arbor, Mich. Positive.
Collation of the original: 829 p.
Weekly.
Supersedes the Analectic magazine.

(Series: American periodical series: 1800-1850. 131)

Microfilm 01104 no. 131 AP Mic 56-5124

NL 0407435 DLC ICRL NN ViU

FILM

Literary gazette and American athenaeum. v. 1-3, no. 26; Sept. 1825-Mar. 1827? New York [J. G. Brooks & G. Bond]
3 v. (American periodical series: 1800-1850)
Title varies: Sept. 10, 1825-Mar. 4, 1826, The New York literary gazette (subtitle varies)
Supersedes Minerva.
Absorbed American athenaeum, March 1826.
Microfilm copy. Ann Arbor, Mich., University Microfilms.

NL 0407436 MoU

F010.5
L776

The Literary gazette and quarterly advertiser. v.1-2; 1841-43.
Philadelphia, Carey & Hart, 1841-43.
2v. 31cm. quarterly.

Consists mainly of advertisements of books.

NL 0407437 NcU

808.8
L7122

The literary gem; or, Legends and lyrics, etc. ... for the amusement of winter nights and summer mornings. Boston, Printed by J. H. Eastburn for B. Davenport, 1827.
238p. 15cm.

Imperfect: p.1-4 missing.

1. Gift-books (Annuals, etc.)

NL 0407438 IU NN TU MH

The literary gem for 1830. London ͵Printed by Oilver and Boyd, n.d.͵
542p. 20cm.

NL 0407439 IaU ICN OCl

808.8
L7123

The Literary gem; an illustrated souvenir for all seasons. New York, D. Appleton, 1850.
280p. 19 plates. 24cm.

NL 0407440 IU NNC

The Literary gem: consisting of tales, historical and biographical sketches, poetry, music, &c., and engravings. v. 1; 1851. Philadelphia, J. Van Court, 1853.
1 p. l., 5-576 p. illus., pl. (part col.) port. 23½ cm.

The single nos. were issued under title: Van Court's new monthly magazine.

Library of Congress AP2.L589 2—8668

NL 0407441 DLC

The Literary geminæ: a monthly magazine in English and French. v. 1; June 1839-May 1840. Worcester, Mass., E. Burritt ͵1839-40͵
cover-title, 288, 288 p. 23½cm

Elihu Burritt, editor.
Each number contains an English and a French section, each section having separate paging.
No more published.

I. Burritt, Elihu, 1810-1879, ed.

Library of Congress AP2.L59 6-38505

NL 0407442 DLC NNC MiU MB

051.08
A5121
Reel
657

The Literary geminae: a monthly magazine in English and French. v.1, no.1-12; June 1839-May 1840. Worcester, Mass., E. Burritt.
1 v. 24cm.

Edited by E. Burritt.
Microfilm. Ann Arbor, Mich., University Microfilms [1962] 1 reel. 35mm. (American periodical series: 1800-1850. 657)

I. Burritt, Elihu, 1810-1879, ed.

NL 0407443 FU LU

FILM

Literary gems. v. 1, no. 1-28; Apr. 10-July 1833? New York.
1 v. (American periodical series: 1800-1850)
Microfilm copy. Ann Arbor, Mich., University Microfilms.

NL 0407444 MoU IaAS

LITERARY gems. In two parts. Edinburgh, printed for Hurst, Robinson & co., London, and McLachlan & Stewart, Edinburgh, 1826.

The two parts are paged continuously.
Preface signed: J.S.

NL 0407445 MH IU CtY NcD CLU

Literary gems.
[Series]

N.Y., Putnam's sons, 18- v.

NL 0407446 DLC

A Literary Gentleman
See
Paterson, G.

The Literary Germ. Ed. and publ. by the students of Salem inst. Salem, Ohio. 1852-

Lib. has: vol. 1, no. 1, March 5, 1852.

NL 0407448 OClWHi OCl

Literary gleanings, by an invalid
see under [Henslowe, Fanny H]

The Literary gossip. 1821
see The Gossip: a series ...

FILM
X467

The Literary guardian, and spectator of books, science, fine arts, the drama, etc., etc. v.1-͵2͵ (no.1-45?); Oct.1,1831-Aug.4,1832? London, W.Tindall.

Title varies slightly.
Microfilm. Ann Arbor, University Microfilms. (English literary periodicals, 91 E).

NL 0407451 MiU PSt

VOLUME 336

The Literary guide and rationalist review ... London
see Humanist; a rational approach to the modern world.

The Literary Guild magazine
see The Literary Guild preview.

Literary guild of America.
The Guild annual ... New York, The Literary guild of America, 1928.
217 p. illus. (ports.) 18½cm.

1. English literature (Selections: Extracts, etc.) 2. American literature (Selections: Extracts, etc.) I. Title.
28-13527
Library of Congress PR1149.L5

NL 0407455 DLC OrU NIC NcD OCl MiU OU OO ViU NN

Literary Guild of America,
The Literary Guild; an innovation in book publishing. [New York, 1928?] 39 p. 8°.
Cover-title.

396895A. 1. Booksellers and book trade—U. S.
N. Y. P. L. February 11, 1929

NL 0407456 NN

Literary guild of America.
The patriotic anthology
see under title

Literary guild of America.

Robinson, Edwin Arlington, 1869-1935.
Tristram, by Edwin Arlington Robinson. New York, The Literary guild of America, 1927.

Literary Guild of America.
Wings; the story of the Literary Guild. New York: The Literary Guild of America, Inc.[, 1929.] 15 l. 16°.
On cover: The new wings.

406988A. 1. Booksellers and book-trade—U. S. 2. Title.
N. Y. P. L. December 30, 1929

NL 0407459 NN IdU NNC

PZ1 .S15 Be
Literary guild of the Philippines.

Santa Romana, Osmundo O ed.
The best Filipino short stories, edited by Osmundo O. Sta. Romana, with the index of short stories published in Philippine magazines selected by Jose Garcia Villa and the Literary guild of the Philippines. Manila, Wightman printing company, inc., 1935.

---

805 WI
The Literary Guild preview.
Feb.1927-
Garden City, N.Y., Literary Guild of America.
v. illus. 19-24cm. monthly (slightly irregular)

Title varies: Feb.1927-July 1965, Wings; the Literary Guild review.- Aug.-Sept.1965, The Literary Guild review.- Oct.1965-May 1968, The Literary Guild preview.
Issues for

NL 0407461 IU NN

The Literary Guild review
see The Literary Guild preview.

The literary guillotine
see under [Whitelock, William Wallace] 1869-

A literary handbook; or, How and what to read. By a [reader. Ossian, Ind., J. H. Keefer, 1897.
32 p. 17cm.

1. Books and reading. I. Keefer, James H., 1869-
0-6267
Library of Congress Z1003.L775

NL 0407464 DLC

The Literary harvester. A semi-monthly journal of literature, science, and the fine arts. Containing original and select tales, biography, history, sketches of travels and adventure, criticism, moral and humorous essays, poetry, natural science, news, etc., etc. ...v.2, no.17-24; Jan.2-Apr.22, 1843 v.3, no.1-13; June 1-Dec. 1 1843 Hartford, Conn., Printed by J. G. Wells, 1842-43.
2 v. in 1 illus. 34½cm.

No numbers were issued for May 1843.
Editors: Jan. 1843-July 1, 1843, G. W. Foss.—July 15, 1843-Dec. 1843. J. G. Wells.

I. Foss, German Wheatcroft, ed. II. Wells, John Gaylord, ed.
CA 28-71 Unrev'd
Library of Congress AP2.L595

NL 0407465 DLC CtH

Literary hearthstones...
see under Terhune, Mary Virginia Hawes.

Literary history
see under [Cogswell, Joseph Greene] 1786-1871.

The literary history of the New Testament
see under [Conder, Josiah] 1789-1855.

Literary history of the United States. Editors: Robert E. Spiller, Willard Thorp, Thomas H. Johnson [and] Henry Seidel Canby; associates: Howard Mumford Jones, Dixon Wecter [and] Stanley T. Williams. New York, Macmillan, 1948.
3 v. 25 cm.
Vol. [3]: Bibliography.
—— Bibliography supplement; edited by Richard M. Ludwig. New York, Macmillan, 1959.
288 p. 24 cm.
PS88.L5 Suppl.
1. American literature—Hist. & crit. 2. American literature—Bibl. I. Spiller, Robert Ernest, 1896- ed. II. Thorp, Willard, 1899- ed. III. Johnson, Thomas Herbert, ed. IV. Canby, Henry Seidel, 1878- ed. V. Ludwig, Richard M., 1920- ed.
PS88.L5 48-11370 rev 2*

WaS WaE CaBVaU
OrStbM OrPS OrPR OrSaW OrU WaWW WaSpG WaRC WaT CaBViP IdB IdPS IdU MtBC MtU MtBuM Or OrCS OrP MH-AH ViU TxU MH ICU NIC PSt PSC MiU NjP CaBVa PIm NN MoSWx FTaSU InU MeB NcGU CU OU OEac MiHM PPSteph ICN CoU KyWAT RPJCB IaU OrU NIC TxU PHC
NL 0407469 DLC PPLas PU PPD PRosC PBL PPAmP Mi

LITERARY history of the United States; editors: Robert E. Spiller [and others] New York, Macmillan co., 1949. 3 v. 25cm.

Vol. [3]: Bibliography.

—— Bibliography supplement, edited by Richard M. Ludwig. New York, Macmillan co. [1960] xix, 268 p. 25cm.

1. American literature--Bibl. I. Spiller, Robert Ernest, 1896- ed. II. Ludwig, Richard M.

NL 0407471 NN

Literary history of the United States. Editors: Robert E. Spiller, Willard Thorp, Thomas H. Johnson [and] Henry Seidel Canby; associates: Howard Mumford Jones, Dixon Wecter [and] Stanley T. Williams. Rev. ed. New York, Macmillan, 1953.
xxii, 1456 p. 25 cm.
Bibliography: p. 1407-1429.
—— Bibliography supplement; edited by Richard M. Ludwig. New York, Macmillan, 1959.
268 p. 24 cm.
PS88.L5 1953 Suppl.
1. American literature—Hist. & crit. 2. American literature—Bibl. I. Spiller, Robert Ernest, 1896- ed. II. Thorp, Willard, 1899- ed. III. Johnson, Thomas Herbert, ed. IV. Canby, Henry Seidel, 1878- ed. V. Ludwig, Richard M., 1920- ed.
PS88.L5 1953 810.9 53—13350

KyMurT
CU NBuC MsSM OEac KyU KyU-C KyLxCB KyFSC KyMdC PU PJA PPPL TU OClU OClND MiU OCl OOxM OrCS OCU NcD PBL PPD TxU NcC NjR MiU MB NcU NIC MsU ViU OU
NL 0407472 DLC DSI AU NNC AAP OClW PPT PP PPLas

---

xXZ .27 .L71B
Literary history of the United States. Editors: Robert E. Spiller, Willard Thorp, Thomas H. Johnson [and] Henry Seidel Canby. Bibliography. New York, Macmillan Company, 1953.
xxii, 817 p. 24cm.

NL 0407474 MB TxU

Literary hours
see under
Ablett, Joseph, comp.

The Literary humbug; or, Weekly take-in
see
The Literary exposé and fashionable Proteus.

Literary ideals in Ireland
see under Magee, William Kirkpatrick.

VOLUME 336

FILM Literary inquirer. v. 1-3, no.? 13; 1833-Oct. 15, 1834? Buffalo, N. Y.
3 v. (American periodical series: 1800-1850)
Microfilm copy. Ann Arbor, Mich., University Microfilms.

NL 0407478 MoU IaAS

Literary Institute, Nashville, 1838.
Proceedings of the literary institute, and Association of Professional Teachers...
see under Association of Professional Teachers.

Literary Institute and Commercial College, Denver
see Denver. Literary Institute and Commercial College.

A
AP3
.L57

A Literary Journal. v. 1-5; Oct. 1744-Mar. 1748/June 1749. Dublin, Printed by S. Powell for the Author, 1744-49.
5 v. 23cm.
Published by Rev. J?P? Droz.
Each volume in 2 parts.

I. Droz, J? P?

NL 0407481 MB P ICN

Micro Film F128

Literary journal; a review of domestic and foreign literature. v.1-5, Jan. 1804-Dec. 1806; new ser. v.1-2, Jan.-Dec. 1806. London.
2 reels. 35mm. (English literary periodicals, 92E)
Title varies: July 1804-Dec. 1805, Literary journal, or, Universal review of literature, domestic and foreign.
Subtitle varies: Jan. 1803-June 1834, a review of literature, science, manners, politics.
Founded and edited by James Mill.
Microfilm (positive). Ann Arbor, Mich., University Microfilms, 1961.

NL 0407482 PSt ViU NBuU MiU NIC NcU MiU PSt CSt

Literary journal: a review of literature, science, manners, politics
see Literary journal; a review of domestic and foreign literature.

---

*7220a.8

Literary Journal, The, and general miscellany of science, arts, history, politics, morals, manners, fashion, and amusements. [Weekly.]
Vol. I. March 29 – December 26, 1818.
= London. Limbird . . . [1818.] v. Illus. Map. 4°.

F8850 — Great Britain. Period. — Periodicals.

NL 0407484 MB NIC

Micro Film F129

The literary journal, and general miscellany of science, arts, history, politics, morals, manners, fashion, and amusements. v.1-2 (no.1-59), Mar. 29, 1818-May 8, 1819. London.
1 reel. 35mm. (English literary periodicals, 93E)
Title varies slightly.
No more published?
Microfilm (positive). Ann Arbor, Mich., University Microfilms, 1961.

NL 0407485 PSt ViU NBuU

The Literary journal, and weekly register of science and the arts. Ed. by Albert G. Greene. v. 1 -May 31, 1834. Providence, J. Knowles and company, 1833-34.
2 p. l., 412 p. 34½cm.
No more published.

I. Greene, Albert Gorton, 1802-1868, ed.

Library of Congress AP2.L6 CA 9—6282 Unrev'd

NL 0407486 DLC LU RPB PP N MB

051.08
A5121
Reel
799
MICROFILM

The Literary journal, and weekly register of science and the arts. v.1, no.1-52; June 8, 1833-May 31, 1834. Providence, J. Knowles.
1 v. 35cm.

Edited by A. G. Greene.
Microfilm. Ann Arbor, Mich., University Microfilms [1966] 1 reel. 35mm. (American periodical series: 1800-1850. 799)
I. Greene, Albert Gorton, 1802-1868, ed.

NL 0407487 FU MoU IaAS

The Literary journal, or, Universal review of literature, domestic and foreign ...

London, Printed by and for C. and R. Baldwin. 18
1 v. 25cm. monthly.
Wants v.5, no.2,5,9.

Library of Congress AP4.L423 CA 7-4052 Unrev'd

NL 0407488 DLC

808.8
L7124

The literary keepsake. London, M. Marshall, 1833.
iv, 276p. 17cm.

Imperfect: front. wanting.

1. Gift-books (Annuals, etc.)

NL 0407489 IU CaBVaU

Literary landmarks of Jerusalem
see under Hutton, Laurence, 1843-1904.

Literary landmarks of London
see under Hutton, Laurence, 1843-1904.

A literary lady.
Saint Valantine's budget
see under title

Literary lantern. Greensboro, 1924-
Extracts from Greensboro daily news, Jan. 13, 1924-

Library has:
Jan.13, 1924-May 23, 1927 (incomplete).

Missing numbers and later issues may be found in Greensboro daily news and other state papers (Sunday issues).

NL 0407493 NcU

Literary leaves by tomorrow's writers ... the best material submitted by students under twenty-one years of age, in a nation-wide contest conducted by the weekly magazine, Current literature. 1st- ed., 1928-
Columbus, O., American education press, inc., °1928-
v. ports. 19½cm.
Contains short stories, verse and essays.

1. American literature—20th cent. I. Current literature.

29—2936

Library of Congress PS536.L55

NL 0407494 DLC OClJC MBU

Bonaparte Collection No.789

LITERARY leaves for general readers. March-April, 1870. [London, Nelson & co., 1870]
2 no. in 1v. 21x16cm. monthly.

The two issues contain The Basque problem solved, by Arthur Hall.

NL 0407495 ICN

Literary leisure, or, The recreations of Solomon Saunter, esq. [pseud.] ... London, W. Miller, 1802.
2 v. 20cm.
Originally published in 60 numbers, September 26, 1799 to November 18, 1800. Ascribed to Hewson Clarke. cf. Hope cat. of early newspapers, p. 128.

I. Clarke, Hewson, 1787-1832? supposed author. II. Saunter, Solomon, esq., pseud.

28-17217

Library of Congress PR5299.S35 1802

NL 0407496 DLC NIC CtY NcU NN

Literary liberty considered; in a letter to H. S. Woodfall. 2 p.l., 32 pp. *London: J. Johnson*, 1774. 8°.
In: TH. p. v. 18.

NL 0407497 NN

Literary life. Cleveland; Chicago; N,Y. 1-6, 1884-86; ns, no.1-48, 1900-03.

NL 0407498 CtNIC

Literary life of Charles Philip Brown
see under [Brown, Charles Philip] 1798-1884.

VOLUME 336

The **Literary** lounger ... Jan.–Sept. 1826. London, L. Relfe [etc.] 1826.
iv, 435 p. 23cm. monthly.
No more published.

Library of Congress AP4.L426 7-22280

NL 0407500 DLC

Film
829 **Literary magazine.** v.1, no.1; Jan. 1, 1835.
Reel 400 Boston.
1 reel. (American periodical series: 1800-1850. 400)

Microfilm copy (positive) by University Microfilms, Ann Arbor, Mich.
No more published. Cf. Union list of serials, 3d ed.

NL 0407501 TxU

The Literary magazine. London, 1735–1736
see The Literary magazine: or, The history of the works of the learned.

Literary magazine. Omaha, Neb.
see Literary magazine section.

Literary magazine. Portland, Ore., 1933-
see The Literary monthly.

The Literary magazine; a journal established for the advancement of knowledge
see under Detroit Young Men's Society.

The **Literary** magazine, and American register ... v. 1–8; Oct. 1803–Dec. 1807. Philadelphia, J. Conrad & co.; [etc., etc.] 1804–08.
8 v. 22cm. monthly.
Charles Brockden Brown, editor.
No more published.

I. Brown, Charles Brockden, 1771–1810, ed.

Library of Congress AP2.L623 2—16172

00 Vi ViW
NL 0407506 DLC OrU ICN NcGU DAU FU ICRL ViU MiU

The **Literary** magazine, and American register. v. 1–8 (no. 1–51); Oct. 1803–Dec. 1807. Philadelphia, Printed by T. & G. Palmer [etc.]
2 reels. (American periodical series: 1800–1825, 22–23)
Microfilm copy, made in 1946 by University Microfilms, Ann Arbor, Mich. Positive.
Collation of the original: 8 v.
Monthly.
Edited by C. B. Brown.

I. Brown, Charles Brockden, 1771–1810, ed. (Series: American periodical series: 1800–1850. 22–23)
Microfilm 01104 no. 22–23 AP Mic 56–4587

NL 0407507 DLC DNAL NN

The **Literary** magazine and British review ... v. 1–11; July 1788–Dec. 1793. London, Printed for the proprietors [1788–93]
11 v. plates, ports., maps. 22cm. monthly.
Engraved title-pages.
Vols. 1–5 have caption title: The Literary magazine, and British review; v. 6–11: The Literary and biographical magazine, and British review.
Library of Congress set incomplete: v. 12 (1794) wanting.

26-19995
Library of Congress AP3.L62

NL 0407508 DLC KyU IaAS IaU NPV AU NjP

FILM The Literary magazine and British review.
Pos. v. 1–12; July 1788–1794. London.

English literary periodicals, no. 135E.
Microfilm reproduction by University Microfilms, Inc., Ann Arbor. Positive copy.
For full bibliographical information, see main card for original edition.

NL 0407509 ViU PSt NcU CSt MiU

The **Literary** magazine of Allegheny college. v. 1–
Oct. 1896–
[Meadville, Pa., 1896–
v. in illus., plates. 22½–27½cm.
Monthly during the school year, 1896–1923; irregular, 1924–
Volume numbers irregular: v. 14, no. 3–4 called v. 15, no. 3–4; v. 15, no. 1 called v. 16, no. 1; v. 24, no. 1–7 called v. 19, no. 1–7; v. 25, no. 1 called v. 19, no. 8; v. 25, no. 2–7 called v. 20, no. 2–7; v. 16 omitted in numbering.
"Successor to 'Allegheny [i. e. Alleghany] magazine'," 1816–17.
Published by the student body of Allegheny college.
Title varies: 1896–Mar. 1925, The Allegheny literary monthly.
Nov. 1925–May 1941, The Allegheny literary magazine.
Dec. 1941– The Literary magazine of Allegheny college.
I. Allegheny college, Meadville, Pa.

Library of Congress LH1.A36L5 43-48013
378.748

NL 0407510 DLC

The **Literary** magazine: or, Select British library. Containing an early, accurate, and impartial account of the most noted and valuable books and pamphlets publish'd in Great-Britain and Ireland. As also, a succinct detail of such controversies as arise in the republick of letters; a view of the state of learning; and a catalogue of the best books publish'd in foreign parts. Occasionally interspersed with an abstract of the lives of such eminent persons, as may occur in the progress of this work ... Vol. I. For the first six months in 1735. London, J. Wilford, 1735.
312 p. 20½cm.
1. English literature—Bibl.—Period. 2. English literature—Bibl.—Early. 3. English literature—18th cent.—Bibl. 4. Bibliography—Period. I. Wilford, John, fl. 1723–1742, pub.

Library of Congress Z2005.L77 13-19675

NL 0407511 DLC MiU ICRL

The **Literary** magazine: or, The History of the works of the learned; containing an account of the most valuable books published both at home and abroad, in most of the languages in Europe, and in all arts and sciences, with proper observations on each author. To which are occasionally added, biographical memoirs, dissertations, and critical enquiries. By a society of gentlemen. v. [1]–2; Jan. 1735–Dec. 1736. London, Printed for T. Cooper.
2 v. 21 cm. monthly.
Vol. 1, Jan.–June 1735, issued originally by J. Wilford with title: The Literary magazine; or, Select British library.

"One of the principal editors was Ephraim Chambers, author of the Cyclopaedia." Cf. W. T. Lowndes, The bibliographer's manual, 1864.
Superseded by the History of the works of the learned.

1. Bibliography—Period. I. Chambers, Ephraim, 1680 (ca.)–1740, ed.
Z1007.L7735 56–55296

NL 0407513 DLC TxLT

The **Literary** magazine: or, The history of the works of the learned. v. 1–2; Jan. 1735–Dec. 1736. London, Printed for T. Cooper [etc.]
(English literary periodical series, 136E)
Microfilm copy, made in 1954 by University Microfilms, Ann Arbor, Mich. Positive.
Collation of the original, as determined from the film: 2 v.
Monthly.
Title varies: Jan.–Nov. 1735, The Literary magazine; or, Select British library.
"One of the principal editors was Ephraim Chambers, author of the Cyclopaedia." Cf. W. T. Lowndes, The bibliographer's manual, 1864.
Superseded by the History of the works of the learned.
1. Bibliography—Period. I. Chambers, Ephraim, 1680 (ca.)–1740, ed. II. Title: The Literary magazine; or, Select British library.
Microfilm 01105 no. 136E AP Mic 56–4417

CaBVaU
NL 0407514 DLC CSt NBuU MiU OU AAP ICRL PSt CLSU

The **Literary** magazine: or, Universal review ... v. 1–
[Apr. 15?], 1756–
London, J. Richardson [1756–
v. front., illus., plates, ports., fold. maps. 21½cm. monthly.
Vol. 1, no. 1 has t.-p. with imprint: London, W. Faden, 1756.

27-1985
Library of Congress AP3.L6

NL 0407515 DLC ICU NBuU

The **Literary** magazine; or, Universal review. v. 1–3; Apr. 15/May 14, 1756–July 1758. London, Printed for J. Wilkie [etc.]
(English literary periodicals, 137E)
Microfilm copy (positive) by University Microfilms, Ann Arbor, Mich.
Collation of the original as determined from the film: 3 v. illus., ports., maps (part fold.)
Monthly.

(Series)
Microfilm 01105 no. 137E AP Mic 62–7507

NL 0407516 DLC ICRL AAP ViU PSt

AP2 Literary magazine section ... 1908–
.S97 May 15, 1910. Omaha, Neb., 1908–10.
3 v. illus. 34 cm. weekly.
Title varies: Magazine section.
Sept. 27, 1908–May 15, 1910, Literary magazine section (running title: Literary magazine)
Issued with the Sunday world-herald, Omaha, Buffalo courier, Elmira telegram, Pittsburg dispatch, Washington herald, Louisville herald, and the Colorado Springs gazette.
I. World-herald, Omaha, Neb.
CA 10-163 Unrev'd.

NL 0407517 DLC

LH
1 The Literary magazine, the College of William
W64 and Mary in Virginia. v. 1-44?; Nov.?
L7 1890-summer 1937? Williamsburg, Va.
44? v. illus. (part col.) ports. 22–28 cm.
Frequency varies.
Title varies: Nov.? 1890–May? 1891, Nov? 1895?–May? 1908, The William and Mary College monthly. – Dec. 1891–May 1895? The William and Mary College bi-monthly – Nov. 1908– 1936, The William and Mary literary magazine.
Published by the Phoenix and Philomathean Literary Societies of the College of William and Mary, 1890–19 by the students and alumni of the College of William and Mary in Virginia, 19 –1937.
Superseded by the Royalist?

1. Periodicals (Titles) I. William and Mary College, Williamsburg, Va. Phoenix Literary Society. II. William and Mary College, Williamsburg, Va. Philomathean Literary Society. III. William and Mary College, Williamsburg, Va.

NL 0407519 Vi

The **Literary** magnet of the belles lettres, science, and the fine arts: consisting of I. Original satirical essays of permanent interest; II. Sketches of society, humorous and immaginative; III. Original poetry; IV. Miscellaneous matter: forming a body of original and elegant literature ... Ed. by Tobias Merton, gent. ... v. 1–
1824–
London, W. C. Wright [etc.] 1824–
v. illus., plates (part col.) port. 22cm.
Each number of v. 3 includes a second part, separately paged, entitled: Monthly journal.
I. Merton, Tobias, gent., pseud., ed.
CA 7—4697 Unrev'd
Library of Congress AP4.L428

NL 0407520 DLC ICN NcD

VOLUME 336

MIC-1 AP 4 .L428 Govt. Doc. Rm. The Literary Magnet; or, monthly journal of The Belles-Lettres. Volumes 1-4, 1824-1825; new series volumes 1-5, January 1826-April 1828. London. 2 reels. (English literary periodicals)
Title varies: Wright's London Magnet.
Microfilm copy (positive) made by University Microfilms, Ann Arbor, Mich.

NL 0407521 NBuU PSt MiU CaBVaU ViU

**T.96.31
Literary Magnet, The; or, monthly journal of the belles lettres, from January to July, 1828. New series.
= London. Wright. 1828. (1), 140 pp. Plates. Vignette. 21½ cm., in 8s.

J362 — Periodicals.

NL 0407522 MB

The literary man's Bible (W.L. Courtney, ed.)
see under Bible. O.T. English. Selections. 1907. (also 1908, and 19--)

Literary market place; the directory of American book publishing. ₍1st₎- ed.; 1940-
New York, Bowker.
v. 19-23 cm. annual.
None published for 1941.
Subtitle varies.
Editors: 1940-42, J. K. Hanrahan.—1943- A. J. Richter.

1. Publishers and publishing—U. S.—Direct. I. Hanrahan, John Keith, ed. II. Richter, Anne (Jones) 1905- ed.

PN161.L5 655.473 41-51571 rev 3*

MnU-A MtU
OkU-M MoU CBGTU AAP MH-AH DNAL ICJ NcC Ky-LE MNS
OrU-M FTaSU GAT KyLoS Ky-Le KEmT MntcA MdBP CoU
NjR MB CSt TxDaS NcD PBm PHC PJB IdB OrP OrStbM
OClW OCl OEac OOxM OO NcRS MiU KU DDO PHC OU NBuC
NL 0407524 DLC TxU TU DNLM OCH ViU-L OLak OCU OCC

PN161 .L52 Literary market place. Supplement.
Names & numbers; the book industry telephone directory. 1952/53-
New York, Bowker.

The Literary market place of Denmark
see
Danmarks blad- og bogverden.

Literary masterpieces; Franklin: Irving: Bryant: Webster: Everett: Longfellow: Hawthorne: Whittier: Emerson: Holmes: Lowell: Poe: Henry: Wirt: Johnson: Timrod: Lanier: Tabb, with biographical sketches and portraits. Boston, New York ₍etc.₎ Houghton, Mifflin and company ₍1904₎
viii p., 1 l., 433, ₍1₎ p. front., ports. 20cm.
"This book is a modified form of 'Masterpieces of American literature,' pub. in 1891. "The additions include material from Southern authors."—Pref.

1. American literature (Selections: Extracts, etc.) 2. Authors, American.

Library of Congress PS507.M4 1904 4-10485

NL 0407527 DLC OrU OClJC ViU

---

508 L712 Literary memoirs of Germany and the North, being a choice collection of essays on the following interesting subjects, viz., alchemy, algebra & analysis... animal economy... chemistry ... geography... logic... mechanics, medicine... mineralogy... natural history... agriculture, &c., &c. Done from the Latin and High-Dutch, by a Society of gentlemen... London, Printed for J. Warcus ₍etc.₎ 1759.
2 v. in 1. 1 illus., plates ₍part fold.₎ 25 x 21cm.

NL 0407528 MnU

Literary memoirs of living authors of Great Britain, ...
see under [Rivers, David]

The literary merit of the English Bible
see under Bible. English. Selections. 1931.

Literary messenger. New York. 1840-41
see
The Iris; or, Literary messenger

AP2 .A2L59 Rare Bk. Coll. The Literary mirror. v. 1; Feb. 20, 1808-Feb. 11, 1809. ₍Portsmouth, N. H.₎
208 p. 30 cm. weekly.
Edited by S. Sewall.
L.C. set imperfect: p.1-2 wanting.

I. Sewall, Stephen, ed.

AP2.A2L59 55-55613

NL 0407532 DLC NhD MB

The Literary mirror. v. 1; Feb. 20, 1808-Feb. 11, 1809. ₍Portsmouth, N. H.₎
(American periodical series: 1800-1825. 24)
Microfilm copy, made in 1946 by University Microfilms, Ann Arbor, Mich. Positive.
Collation of the original: 208 p.
Weekly.
Edited by S. Sewall
Film incomplete: p. 1-2 wanting.

I. Sewall, Stephen, ed. (Series: American periodical series: 1800-1850. 24)

Microfilm 01104 no. 24 AP Mic 56-4593

NL 0407533 DLC DAU NN ICRL

Rare Book Collection PR974 .L58 Literary miscellany. Manchester, Printed and sold at the Office of G.Nicholson: sold also by T.Knott, and Champante & Whitrow, London ₍1793-97₎
₍203₎p. 14cm.

Title from label on spine.
Appears in Hofmann & Freeman dealer's catalogue no.35 under title: Manchester chapbooks.
Contents.- Moral tales. 1797.- Moral tales. 1796.- Gothic stories. 1797.- The story of

NL 0407534 NcU

---

x821.08 L712 Literary miscellany. ₍Poughnill, Eng.₎ Printed and sold by G. Nicholson, 1799-1802₎
7 pamphlets in 1v. illus. 14cm.

Binder's title.
A miscellany of poetry.

NL 0407535 IU

The Literary miscellany; or, Monthly review, a periodical work. By Charles N. Baldwin. v. 1, no. 1-4; May-Aug. 1811. New-York, Riley & Adams, 1811.
338 p. 15cm.
Vol. 1 includes supplement.
No more published?

I. Baldwin, Charles N., ed.

10-10418

Library of Congress AP2.L626

NL 0407536 DLC NN OClWHi

The Literary miscellany; or, Monthly review, a periodical work. v. 1, no. 1-4; May-Aug. 1811. New-York, Riley & Adams.
(American periodical series: 1800-1825. 131)
Microfilm copy, made in 1950 by University Microfilms, Ann Arbor, Mich. Positive.
Collation of the original: 338 p.
Edited by C. N. Baldwin.

I. Baldwin, Charles N., ed. (Series: American periodical series: 1800-1850. 131)

Microfilm 01104 no. 131 AP Mic 56-5125

NL 0407537 DLC ICRL NN ViU

The Literary miscellany; or, Selections and extracts, classical and scientific with originals, in prose and verse ... Stourport, Printed by G. Nicholson, 1812
v. illus. 14½cm.
Issued in parts, 1800- several with special engr. t.-p., incl. port.
George Nicholson in 1797, or earlier, commenced the publication of his "Literary miscellany"; each number consisted of a distinct subject, and the whole series extended to about sixty parts, or twenty volumes. cf. Dict. nat. biog.

1. English poetry (Selections: Extracts, etc.) I. Nicholson, George, 1760-1825.

CA 16-137 Unrev'd

Library of Congress PR1175.L5

NL 0407538 DLC OrU NjP CtY ICU MB IU

The Literary miscellany, containing elegant selections of the most admired fugitive pieces, and extracts from works of the greatest merit, with originals. Prose and poetry ... v. 1 (no. 1-8); 1795. Philadelphia, Printed for T. Stephens, 1795.
₍256₎ p. 13cm.
Various paging.
No more published?

12-19182

Library of Congress PR1171.L5

NN DLC OrU CaBVaU
NL 0407539 DLC NjP PPL TxLT DGU MiU-C PU PPL NcD

The Literary miscellany, containing elegant selections of the most admired fugitive pieces and extracts from works of the greatest merit, with originals. v. 1, no. 1-8; 1795. Philadelphia, Printed at the office of W. W. Woodward, for T. Stephens ₍etc.₎
(American periodical series: eighteenth century, 14)
Microfilm copy (positive) made by University Microfilms, Ann Arbor, Mich.
Collation of the original: 16 no. Cf. Union list of serials.

(Series)

Microfilm 01103 no. 14 AP Mic 57-5524

NL 0407540 DLC DAU ICRL NN ViU OrU

VOLUME 336

The Literary miscellany, including dissertations and essays on subjects of literature, science, and morals; biographical and historical sketches; critical remarks on language; with occasional reviews ... v. 1-2; 1805-06. Cambridge [Mass.] W. Hilliard, 1805-06.
2 v. port. 21cm. quarterly.
"By the Phi beta kappa society of Harvard college."—Sabin, Dict. of books relating to America, v. 10.
I. Phi beta kappa. Massachusetts Alpha, Harvard university.
Library of Congress AP2.L625 7-22241

NL 0407541 DLC OrU CtY PU OO OCl NN MB ICN MiU-C

The Literary miscellany, including dissertations and essays on subjects of literature, science, and morals; biographical and historical sketches; critical remarks on language; with occasional reviews. v. 1-2. Cambridge [Mass.] W. Hilliard, 1805-06.
(American periodical series: 1800-1825. 24)
Microfilm copy, made in 1946 by University Microfilms, Ann Arbor, Mich. Positive.
Collation of the original: 2 v.
Quarterly.
By the Phi Beta Kappa Society of Harvard College. Cf. Sabin. Bibliotheca americana.
I. Phi Beta Kappa. Massachusetts Alpha, Harvard University. (Series: American periodical series: 1800-1825, 24)
Microfilm 01104 no. 24 AP Mic 56-4594

NL 0407542 DLC DAU ViU ICRL NN

PS 1 L58 The Literary monthly.
v.1, no.1-4.
Dec. 1933-May/June 1934.
Portland, Or.
1 v. illus. 20cm.
Title varies slightly: v.1 no.4 called The Literary magazine.
I. Title: The Literary magazine.

NL 0407543 CoU OrU Or

The Literary museum. 1848- Boston
see Dodge's literary museum.

... The Literary museum, an annual volume of the useful and entertaining, including the wonders of nature and art; tales of all countries and all ages; travels, adventures, &c. ... v. 1-3, v. 4, no. 1-19; Jan. 6, 1844-Oct. 2, 1847. Boston, J. B. Hall & co. [etc.] 1844-47.
4 v. in 2. plates (partly col.) 34cm. semimonthly.
Title varies: Jan. 1844-Apr. 8, 1845, The World we live in. A semi-monthly journal of useful and entertaining literature.
Apr. 19, 1845-Oct. 1847, The Literary museum, and annual volume of the useful and entertaining ... (Caption title: The Literary museum; a repository of the useful and entertaining)
J. B. Hall and A. J. Loud, editors, 1844.
I. Hall, John B., ed. II. Loud, Andrew J., ed.
Library of Congress AP2.L628 7-29812

NL 0407545 DLC CtY MB

The Literary museum, and register of arts, sciences, and general literature; comprising analytical reviews, with copious extracts from every new publication, critical notices on the drama, fine arts, &c. ... v. 1-[2] (no. 1-88) Apr. 27, 1822-Dec. 27, 1823; new ser. [v. 1] (no. 1-7) Jan. 3-Feb. 14, 1824. London, Printed by A. J. Valpy [etc., 1822-24]
3 v. 28½cm. weekly.
Absorbed the Literary register in Aug. 1823.
Title-page of v. 1 reads: The Museum; or, Record of literature, fine arts, science, antiquities, the drama, &c. Caption title: Apr. 27-June 1, 1822, The London museum; or, Record of literature ...; June 8-Dec. 28, 1822, The Museum; or, Record of literature ...
Title-page of v. 2 reads: The Literary museum, and register of arts, sciences, and general literature ... Caption title: Jan. 4-July 26, 1823, The Museum; or, Record of literature ...; Aug. 2, 1823, The Literary museum, and register of arts ...; Aug. 9-Dec. 27, 1823, The Museum, and register of arts ...
Title-page of v. 1 of the new ser. wanting.
Caption title: The Museum, and register of belles-lettres ...
No more published?
17-4966
Library of Congress AP4.L429

NL 0407547 DLC MH

The literary museum; or, A selection of scarce old tracts ...
see under [Waldron, Francis Godolphin] 1744-1818, ed.

The literary museum; or, Ancient and modern repository, etc.
see under [Waldron, Francis Godolphin] 1744-1818.

The Literary museum; or Monthly magazine ... January-June, 1797 ... West-Chester [Pa.] Printed by Derrick & Sharples. And sold by the principal booksellers in Philadelphia [1797]
336 p. pl. 24cm. 2-7259

NL 0407550 DLC ICN PCaD TxLT NcD

The Literary museum; or, Monthly magazine. Jan.-Jun 1797. West-Chester [Pa.] Printed by Derrick & Sharples.
(American periodical series: eighteenth century, 14)
Microfilm copy (positive) made by University Microfilms, Ann Arbor, Mich.
Collation of the original: 336 p.
Monthly.
(Series)
Microfilm 01103 no. 14 AP Mic 57-5525

NL 0407551 DLC DAU ViU MiU NN ICRL OrU

Literary New England ... Portland, Me., c1905.
illus., port., pl. 20 cm.
Cover-title, illus.

NL 0407552 RPB

The Literary news, a monthly journal of current literature.
new ser., v. 1-25; Jan./Feb. 1880-[Dec.] 1904. New York, F. Leypoldt [etc.] 18 -1904.
v. illus. 25-27½cm.
Cover-title, 1883-1904: The Literary news, an eclectic review of current literature (later "A monthly eclectic review of current literature illustrated")
Editors: 1868-84, Frederick Leypoldt.—1884-1903, Augusta H. Leypoldt.
Begun by Frederick Leypoldt in Dec. 1868 as the Literary bulletin, a monthly record of current literature. A special trade edition of the publication, entitled the Trade circular and literary bulletin (later the "Trade circular and publishers' bulletin") was issued from Sept. 1869 to Dec.? 1871 (5 v.) In Jan. 1872 Mr. Leypoldt incorporated the American literary gazette and publishers' circular (published by George W. Childs of Philadelphia) with the Trade circular. The joint publication became the Publishers' and stationers' weekly trade circular, and in 1873 the Publishers' weekly.
The Literary bulletin was replaced in Oct. or Nov. 1872 by the Monthly book circular, which continued under this title till Mar. 1875. In Apr. 1875 the title was changed to the Literary news. Publication ceased with Dec. 1904.
L. C. set incomplete, 1868-79 wanting except the following numbers: Apr., July 1875; Feb., Apr., May, June, July/Sept. 1876; Sept. 20, 1879.
1. American literature — Bibl. — Period. I. Leypoldt, Frederick, 1835-1884, ed. II. Leypoldt, Mrs. Augusta Harriet (Garrigue) 1849-1919, ed.
Library of Congress Z1219.L77 CA 7-4050 Unrev'd

NL 0407554 NhD P InU MB ICJ OClWHi OClW MiU OCl DLC NjNbT I CaBViPA WaS ICRL Nc NbHi Nh

YA 23250 Literary news.
... Helen Hunt Jackson's life and writings. (Boston, 1887)
p. 97-102. (The Literary News)

NL 0407555 DLC

347.05 L1 Literary news and law intelligencer, v.1, no.1, 1845. Philadelphia, Lea & Blanchard, 1845. v.1, 1845.
Suspended after one issue

NL 0407556 WaU-L

The Literary Northwest. v. 1- Mar. 1892-
St. Paul, Hall's library company; [etc., etc.] 1892-
v. illus., plates, ports. 25cm (v. 1: 35cm) monthly
Editor: Dec. 1892- Mary H. Severance.
I. Severance, Mrs. Mary Frances (Harriman) ed.
CA 7-4698 Unrev'd
Library of Congress AP2.L632

NL 0407557 DLC MnU

Literary notes, from Boston. Newspaper clipping. Boston, Sept. 23 [1899]
23 cm.

NL 0407558 RPB

Graff 2917 LITERARY notices. The Motto of Jubilee College, &c. ... [n.p.,1849]
470-76p. 21cm.
Detached copy from v.7 of an unidentified periodical, published in August 1849.

NL 0407559 ICN

PN2 .L45 Literary observer. v. 1, no. 1-6, Apr. 1934-Apr. 1935. Hartford, E. V. Mitchell, 1934-35.
6 nos. illus., ports. 30cm. bimonthly.
1. Literature—Hist. & crit.—Period.

NL 0407560 ViU NcGU NBu

PR109 .L5 "Literary originals of the counties"... [Gravesend, 1936-
1 v. 25 1/2 cm.

NL 0407561 DLC NN

The literary pageant
see under Hyatt, Stanley Portal, 1877-1914, ed.

The Literary pamphleteer. no.1-6. Paris, Ky., 1823.
6 v.
1. Holley, Horace, 1781-1827.

NL 0407563 PMA PPrHi WHi ICU

VOLUME 336

The Literary pamphleteer, containing some observations on the best mode of promoting the cause of literature in the State of Kentucky; and a review of the late administration of the Transylvania University. no. 1-6. Paris, Ky., Lyle & Keenon, 1823.

(American periodical series: 1800-1825. 132)

Microfilm copy (positive) made in 1950 by University Microfilms, Ann Arbor, Mich.
Collation of the original, as determined from the film: 6 no.
Edited by J. M'Farland.

1. Transylvania University, Lexington, Ky., 1783-1865. I. M'Farland, John, ed. (Series: American periodical series: 1800-1850. 132)

Microfilm 01104 no. 132 AP Mic 56-4917

NL 0407564 DLC ICRL MiU NN ViU

The Literary panorama, and national register: a review of books, register of events, magazine of varieties: comprising interesting intelligence from the various districts of the United Kingdom; the British connexions in America, Africa, the East Indies, the West Indies, Western Asia, &c. and from all parts of the world ... v. 1-15, Oct. 1806-Sept. 1814; new ser., v. 1-9, Oct. 1814-July 1819. London, Printed by Cox, son, and Baylis for C. Taylor [etc.] 1807-19.

24 v. plates, ports., maps, plans, facsim., tab. 24cm. monthly.

Vols. 1-15 have title: The Literary panorama. A review of books, register of events, magazine of varieties ... (later "The Literary panorama, being a compendium of national papers and parliamentary reports, illustrative of the history, statistics, and commerce of the empire; a universal epitome of interesting and amusing intelligence, from all quarters of the globe ...")
Edited by C. Taylor.
Absorbed the Literary annual register in 1809.
Merged into the New monthly magazine.

I. Taylor, Charles, 1756-1823, ed.

Library of Congress AP4.L43 7-22240†

NL 0407566 DLC N MoSW RP TxU TxDW ICN NN

Micro Film F134 Literary panorama, and national register. v.1-15, Oct. 1806-Sept. 1814; new ser., v.1-9, Oct. 1814-July 1819. London.
5 reels. 35mm. (English literary periodicals, 199E)
Subtitle varies.
Merged into New monthly magazine.
Pagination frequently incorrect.
Microfilm (positive). Ann Arbor, Mich., University Microfilms, 1966.
New ser., v.7, p.165-168 filmed after p.144.

NL 0407567 PSt MiU NcU CSt

099.2 L77 The Literary pocket-book; or, Companion for the lover of nature and art. London, Printed for C. Ollier [1822]-
v. T.

In case.
Edited by Leigh Hunt.
Ceased publication with 1823 issue.
For list of vols. in this library see next card.

NL 0407568 PBL IaU

Literary Polish Association.
Address of the Literary Polish Association to the people of Great Britain. Campbell, T.
(*With* Hill, R., *Home colonies.* 3165

NL 0407569 MdBP

Literary port folio. no. 1-26; Jan. 7-July 1, 1830. Philadelphia [E. Littell & brother, etc.] 1830.

208 p. front., port. 28½cm. weekly.

Running title: Philadelphia port folio: a weekly journal of literature, science, art, and the times.

Library of Congress AP2.L635 7-22283

NL 0407570 DLC ICN ViU MB OU

Literary portraits. No. 1-William Cullen Bryant.
In- The New world. New York, Apr. 24, 1841. (v.2:17) port.

NL 0407571 RPB

Literary portraits, being biographical and critical studies of contemporary and classical authors with illustrative selections from their works ... v. 1-2; 1888-89. New York, J. B. Alden, 1888-89.

2 v. illus. (incl. ports.) 21cm.

Reprinted from Literature—an illustrated weekly magazine.

1. Authorship. I. Literature—an illustrated weekly magazine.

Library of Congress PN137.L5 7-33443

NL 0407572 DLC ViU

Literary prizes and their winners
see
Literary and library prizes.

Literary property. Address to Parliament on the claims of authors to their own copyright. [anon.] 1813.

(Pamphleteer, v. 2)

NL 0407574 MnHi

The literary rambler: being a collection of the most popular and entertaining stories in the English language. [London] Oliver & Boyd, 1833.

2 p. l., [vii]-viii, 542 p. 19cm.

Library of Congress PZ1.L71 7-16033†

NL 0407575 DLC

The Literary record and journal of the Linnean Association of Pennsylvania College
see under Gettysburg College. Linnean Association.

Literary record of Cleveland Abbe, jr.
see under [Abbe, Cleveland] 1872-1934.

Office Literary recreations. v. 1 (no. 1-27); Jan. 24-Aug. 29, 1829. Round Hill, Northampton [1829]

108 p. 28½ x 28½cm. weekly.

Caption title.
Literary paper of the Round Hill school, Northampton, Mass.
No more published?

I. Northampton, Mass. Round Hill school.

Library of Congress AP2.L637 40-21248

NL 0407578 DLC NN NNU-W

Bd.w. DA 65 K2 Cage The literary register. No. 1- [n.p.] 1747-

Issued monthly.
Library has: January 1747-March 1747.

NL 0407579 DFo

Z1007 .L73 The literary register and record of new books, v.1-
Phila. William H. Gilder, editor and publisher, 1847-
v.

1. Bibliography - Period. I. Gilder, William Henry, 1812-1864.

NL 0407580 PSt

R.B.R. The Literary register; or, Weekly miscellany. v. 1-5; 1769-73. Newcastle-upon-Tyne, 5 v. in 3. 31 cm.

Irregular paging.

NL 0407581 NcD P

L630.52 3 v.19-24

Literary register supplement: and Ceylon "notes and queries." [Colombo, Ceylon, A. M. & J. Ferguson, 1900-1905.]
Nov. 1899-Dec. 1904. 6 vol. 25½cm.
Caption title.
Published as supplement to, and bound with The Tropical agriculturist, vol. 19-24.
Ceased publication.

NL 0407582 ICJ

The literary remembrancer. [An autograph album] Hartford, O. D. Cooke & Co., 1827.
1 v. illus. 20 cm.

Title-vignette.

1. Autograph albums.

NL 0407583 RPB

Literary remittances by a banker
see under [Reihl, Charles Wesley] 1867-

090.5 L712 Literary repository.

1. Book collecting. Per soc etc.

NL 0407585 OrU

AAq G783 J927l Rare Books Col Literary reputations in the balance, by Sir Edmund Gosse, Robert Graves [and others. London, 1927]
p.256-258. 33½cm. in envelope in folder 42cm.

In a whole no. of The Bookman, v.72, no.431, Aug. 1927.
About Edgar Allan Poe.

I. Graves, Robert, 1895-

NL 0407586 TxU

VOLUME 336

Literary researches into the history of The book of Saint Albans
see under [Haslewood, Joseph] 1769-1833.

Literary retrospection
see under [Green, Mrs. Sarah]

The Literary review; a monthly news journal of belles lettres. v. 1- Jan. 15, 1897- ; new ser., v. 1, no. 1-2, Mar.-Apr. 1901. Boston, R. G. Badger [etc.]
5 v. in illus., ports. 25-31 cm.
Title varies: Mar.-Apr. 1901, The New literary review.

I. Title: The New literary review; a monthly news journal of belles lettres.

AP2.L638 66-81767

NL 0407589 DLC Nh MB

The Literary review and book plate collector. v. 1, no. 1; Nov. 1902. Boston, The C. E. Peabody co. [1902]
cover-title, 28 p. illus. 25½cm.
C. E. Peabody, A. E. Churchill, G. H. Westley, W. P. Truesdell, editors.
No more published.

1. Books—Reviews. 2. Book-plates—Period. I. Peabody, Charles Edward, ed. II. Churchill, Aimee Evelyn, ed. III. Westley, George Hembert, 1865- ed. IV. Truesdell, Winifred Porter, 1877- ed. V. Title: Book plate collector.

14-21339

Library of Congress Z993P.L77

NL 0407590 DLC CSmH OO

Literary robbery in Paris
see under [Libri, Guillaume] 1803-1869.

The Literary review; published by New York evening post. v. 1-7; Sept. 11, 1920-May 28, 1927. New York, 1920-27.
7 v. illus. 45cm. weekly.
H. S. Canby, editor, 1920-Apr. 1924.
Supersedes the Books section (called in 1920 "Book review") of the New York evening post.
No more published.

1. American literature—Bibl.—Period. 2. English literature—Bibl.—Period. 3. Books—Reviews. I. Canby, Henry Seidel, 1878- ed. II. The New York evening post.

Library of Congress Z1219.N57 23-12247 Revised

NL 0407592 DLC WaS ICRL OCl MiU OY

FILM 3417 Z Library School

The Literary review; published by the New York evening post.
v.1-7;
Sept.11, 1920-May 28, 1927.
New York.
7 v. on 5 reels. On film (Positive)

Microfilm. Original in Library of Congress.
Editor: 1920-1924, H.S. Canby.
Supersedes the Books section (called in 1920 "Book review") of the New York evening post.
No more published.

NL 0407593 CU NN MH PSt

891.4409 L776

The literary scene in East Pakistan; an introduction to the language and literature of East Pakistan [Dacca; n.p. [1955]
88 p. 19 cm. (An East Pakistan P.E.N. publication)

1. Bengali literature. History and criticism
2. Authors, Bengali. Biography.

NL 0407594 NcD NNC

Literary scholarship, its aims and methods, by Norman Foerster [and others] ... Chapel Hill, The University of North Carolina press, 1941.
ix p., 2 l., [3]-269 p. 22cm.
CONTENTS.—The study of letters, by Norman Foerster.—Language, by J. C. McGalliard.—Literary history, by René Wellek.—Literary criticism, by Austin Warren.—Imaginative writing, by W. L. Schramm.—Notes.—Bibliography (p. 239-255)

1. Literature—Philosophy. 2. Philology—Study and teaching. I. Foerster, Norman, 1887- II. McGalliard, John Calvin. III. Wellek, René. IV. *Warren, Austin, 1899- V. Schramm, Wilbur Lang, 1907-

Library of Congress PN45.L5 41-25535
[40] 801

WU NBuC OrSaW MtU OrU OrPR WaS WaSpG
OCIW OCIJC ODW ViU WaWW OrCS CaBVaU IdPI WaTC MB CoU
NL 0407595 DLC CU MiU NcD OCl OOxM OU OCU OCICC

Literary, Scientific and Classical School, Baltimore
see Baltimore. Literary, Scientific and Classical School.

Literary selections for the students of the Normal college for young ladies
see under [Hunter, Thomas] 1831-1915.

The literary snail... 1939
see under [Burtoh, Katherine] ed.

Literary Society of Bombay
see
Asiatic Society of Bombay.

Literary society of St. Francis Xavier's church, New York
see
New York. St. Francis Xavier's church. Literary society.

Literary society of Washington, Washington, D.C.

Ainsworth Rand Spofford, 1825-1908; a memorial meeting at the Library of Congress on Thursday, November 12, 1908, at four o'clock, the librarian of Congress presiding. [New York city, Printed for the District of Columbia library association by the Webster press, 1909]

PN22 .L53A5

Literary society of Washington, Washington, D.C.
...List of present and past members and honorary associates with dates of meeting for the season, 1926/27. Washington, D.C., The Society, 1927-
1 v.

NL 0407602 DLC

Literary society of Washington, *Washington, D. C.*
Officers and members of the Literary society of Washington, D. C., 1878-'79. [Washington? 1878?]
[2] p. 23½cm.

Library of Congress PN21.L5 15-5081

NL 0407603 DLC

Literary society of Washington, *Washington, D. C.*
A tribute of respect from the Literary society of Washington, to its late President, James Abram Garfield. Proceedings of a meeting of the Society held November 19, 1881. Washington, 1882.
53, [2] p. front. (port.) 26cm.

1. Garfield, James Abram, pres. U. S., 1831-1881.
(Toner)

Library of Congress E687.L77 10-30620

NL 0407604 DLC MWA NN OClWHi

Literary society of Washington, D. C.

Clarke, Isaac Edwards, 1830-1907.
A tribute to Bayard Taylor; an essay and poem, by Isaac Edwards Clarke. Read before the Literary society of Washington at a regular meeting held at the residence of Charles W. Hoffman, esq., on the evening of March 8th, 1879. Washington, D. C., Mohun brothers, 1879.

Literary Society of Washington, Washington, D. C.
Whence cometh my help

see under

Johnson, Nelson Trusler, 1887-1954.

The Literary souvenir. London, 1825-
see The Cabinet of modern art, and literary souvenir.

Ia107 L712

The Literary souvenir, a Christmas and New Year's present for 1838, 1840, 1844-1845.
Philadelphia, E.L.Carey and A.Hart, 1838-45.
4v. fronts., plates. 16-21½cm.

Added title-page with vignette.
No issue published for 1839, 1841-1843?
Edited by Wm. E.Burton, Esq.
No more published?

NcD MoU PSt DLC NN MdBJ MWA IEM PU PHi NcU
PPL NcU OClWHi NN ICN CtY MB MiD MH MiU IU NBuG
NL 0407608 CtY MiDW ODW IU PPiU MnHi PSt ViW CSmH

VOLUME 336

The Literary souvenir. A weekly journal of literature, science, and the arts.

Lowell [Mass.] A. B. F. Hildreth; [etc., etc.] 18

v. illus. 34½cm.

Editors: -Feb. 1842, A. B. F. Hildreth.—Feb.-Apr. 1842, W. B. Pike.—May-Oct. 1842, S. H. N. B. Everette.—Oct.- Isaac Kinsman.

Pub. in Concord, N. H., etc., Feb.-Apr. 1852; in Manchester, N. H., etc., May-

I. Hildreth, Azro Benjamin Franklin, 1816- ed.

CA 9-6568 Unrev'd

Library of Congress AP2.L639

NL 0407609 DLC OO NBu

Literary souvenir, and cabinet of modern art
see The Cabinet of modern art and literary souvenir.

The Literary souvenir; or, Cabinet of poetry and romance.

The Cabinet of modern art, and literary souvenir. Ed. by Alaric A. Watts. [1825-37] London, Hurst, Robinson and co.; [etc., etc.] 1825-37.

The Literary speculum. Original essays, criticism, poetry. "By various hands" ... v. 1-2; 1821-22. London, Richardson [1821-22]

2 v. 20cm. monthly.

Library of Congress AP4.L435 7-22239†

NL 0407612 DLC CaBVaU NcD OCU

Microfilm 9-63 no.96E

Literary speculum. v. 1-3; Nov. 1821-Jan. 1823. London.
3 v. on 1 reel. (English literary periodicals, 96E)

Microfilm. Ann Arbor, Mich., University Microfilms.

NL 0407613 ViU NBuU CaBVaU PSt

The literary spotlight, with a preface by John Farrar ...
see under Farrar, John Chipman, 1896- ed.

A literary squabble
see under [Planché, James Robinson] 1796-1880.

Literary Swansea
see under Association of Bookmen of Swansea and West Wales.

The Literary tablet: devoted to the cause of education, literature ... tales, poetry, etc.
1834 (v. 2) New Haven, 1834.
29 cm.

NL 0407617 RPB ICRL WHi

The literary tablet; or, A general repository of useful entertainment; consisting of essays, original and selected, in poetry and prose. By Nicholas Orlando [pseud.] Hanover ⟨N. H.⟩ Printed by Moses Davis, for the editor [18

v. 32½cm. biweekly.

"The literary tablet, published ... by Moses Davis from August 6, 1803, to August 5, 1807 ... was edited by Davis himself, with the assistance of other gentlemen, under the nom de plume of 'Nicholas Orlando'."—Child's Gazetteer of Grafton county, N. H., 1886; pt. 1, p. 112[22].

I. Davis, Moses, ed. A 33-2482

Title from Grosvenor Libr. Printed by L. C.

NL 0407618 NBuG MB

The Literary tablet; or, A general repository of useful entertainment; consisting of essays, original and selected, in poetry and prose. v. 1-4: Aug. 6, 1803-Aug. 5, 1807. Hanover, N. H., M. Davis.

(American periodical series: 1800-1825. 24)

Microfilm copy, made in 1946 by University Microfilms, Ann Arbor, Mich. Positive.
Collation of the original: 4 v.
Biweekly.
Edited by N. Orlando [pseud.]

I. Davis, Moses, of Hanover, N. H., ed. (Series: American periodical series: 1800-1850. 24)

Microfilm 01104 no. 24 AP Mic 56-4584

NL 0407619 DLC ICRL NN WHi DAU

The literary tradition of Canterbury
see under [Conrad, Mrs. Jessie (George)]

Literary treasures.
see under Hearst's International combined with Cosmopolitan.

A literary treasury. New York, The Literary guild of America, inc., 1937.

viii, 184 p. 18cm.

"Twelve excerpts of recent Literary guild selections."—Introd.
Introduction signed: John Beecroft.

CONTENTS.—Escape from Siberia, by W. Duranty.—A woman's innermost life, by W. S. Maugham.—Murder in Naples, by V. Sheean.—A dying woman sees into the future, by T. Gulbranssen.—How kings are made, by P. Guedalla.—To sea in a sieve, by C. Belfrage.—The Cossack girl, by N. Farson.—Royal blood! by D. du Maurier.—Famous American birdsmen, by D. C. Peattie.—The story of the false armistice, by R. Howard.—A woman doctor and spy, by R. W. Rowan.—Dr. Johnson speaks, by J. Boswell.

1. English literature (Selections: Extracts, etc.) I. Literary guild of America.

A 40-1889

Hamilton college. Library for Library of Congress

NL 0407622 NCH OKentU IaU

US 36822.6.5

The literary undertakings of H.H.Bancroft. [San Francisco, 188- ?]

8 p.

NL 0407623 MH

The Literary union: a journal of progress, in literature and education, religion and politics, science and agriculture ...
v. 1- Apr. 7, 1849-
Syracuse [N. Y.] W. W. Newman, 1849-

v. 31½ cm. weekly.

J. M. Winchell, James Johannot, editors.

I. Winchell, J. M., ed. II. Johannot, James, 1823-1888, ed.

AP2.L64 CA 7—5450 Unrev'd

NL 0407624 DLC LU

AP2 Am358 Reel 742

The Literary union; a journal of progress in literature and education, religion and politics, science and agriculture. v. 1-2, no. 13, Apr. 7-Dec. 29, 1849; new ser., v. 1-2, no. 1, Jan.-July 1850.// Syracuse [N.Y.] W.W. Newman, 1849-50.
(American periodical series: 1800-1850, reel 742, APS 990)
Microfilm copy made by University Microfilms, Ann Arbor, Mich. Positive.

Weekly.
J.M. Winchell, James Johonnot, editors.

NL 0407626 IaAS ICRL MoU

---

*AC8 P2934 A813l

The Literary visitor, or Entertaining miscellany, comprising meritorious selections and original productions in prose and verse. v.1-2 (no.[1-6]); 1812-13.
Published by E.J.Coale,Baltimore,1813.

2v. 15cm.,in case 15.5cm.
Nos.1-3 were advertised in the Baltimore & Georgetown newspapers on Nov.23, 1812, Jan. 12 & Mar. 11, 1813, respectively; publication was probably bi-monthly.
Pages [245]-264 of v.1 contain "Juvenile poems by Mr. John Howard Payne, principally written between the age of thirteen and seventeen years." A separate printing of these, from the same setting, was issued in 1813 with title "Juvenile poems ... by John Howard Payne. Communicated to the publisher for The Literary visitor."
No more published.
In case with this are bibliographical notes by C. E. Walter.

NL 0407628 MH MdHi

The Literary West. v. 1- Aug. 1902-

San Francisco, The Whitaker and Ray company, 1902-

v. 37cm. monthly.

Editors: Aug. 1902-July 1903, Herbert Bashford.—Oct. 1903- J. G. Jury.

I. Bashford, Herbert, 1871- ed. II. Jury, John George, 1866- ed.

Library of Congress AP2.L641 7-28787†

NL 0407629 DLC WaT

The Literary who's who (formerly Literary year-book)
see
The Literary year-book.

AP2 .L6415

... The Literary workshop. v. 1 1934-
[New York, The Writers laboratory guild, inc., 1934-
v. 25½cm.

At head of title: The National organ for student expression.

Editors: 1934 E. A. Sand and R. C. Lidon.

NL 0407631 DLC OU IEN KU NN

VOLUME 336

La
818
L712c
Literary Workshop of Baton Rouge, La.
The corner light. Baton Rouge, °1946.
[27]p. illus. 22cm.

Some of the poems previously published.

1. American poetry. I. Title.

NL 0407632 LU

The Literary world. v. 1-35; June 1, 1870-Dec. 1904. Boston, L. C. Page [etc.]
35 v. illus. 30 cm.
Frequency varies.
Absorbed Robinson's epitome of literature, Sept. 27, 1879.
Merged into the Critic, New York.

1. Literature—Hist. & crit.—Period.

PN2.L6 54—50417

KAS OC1W
NL 0407633 DLC WaS LU OO CtH MsSM MB MiU ICJ I

The LITERARY world. [Boston] v.1, no.4-5, v.5-35; Sept.-Oct. 1870, June, 1874-1904
Boston. v. 31cm.

Vols. 13-18, 1882-87, on film made by Library of Congress. Negative. (In *ZAN-1334).
Monthly, 1870-78, Apr. 1900-1904; biweekly, 1879-Mar. 1900.
Absorbed by: The Critic; an illustrated monthly review of literature, art and life, in Jan. 1905.
1. Periodicals--U.S.

NL 0407634 NN

Literary World; [Boston]
Dr. Holmes, the spade, and Zoan
see under Holmes, Oliver Wendell, 1809-1894.

The Literary world. v. 1-13; Feb. 6, 1847-Dec. 31, 1853. New York, Osgood & co. [etc.] 1847-53.
13 v. in 12. illus. 28-29cm. weekly.
Vol. 1-2 have title: The Literary world. A gazette for authors, readers, and publishers. v. 3-10: The literary world: a journal of society (later "of science"), literature, and art. (Caption title, v. 3-11, The Literary world. A journal of American and foreign literature, science, and art)
Editors: Feb.-Apr. 1847, E. A. Duyckinck.—May 1847-Sept. 1848, C. F. Hoffman.—Oct. 1848-Dec. 1853, E. A. Duyckinck, G. L. Duyckinck.
No more published.

I. Duyckinck, Evert Augustus, 1816-1878, ed. II. Hoffman. Charles Fenno, 1806-1884, ed. III. Duyckinck, George Long, 1823-1863, ed.

7-22238

Library of Congress AP2.L642

NjP NN NjR MB ICJ
NL 0407636 DLC ICRL Nc CCC ICRL NhD WU MiU OC1 OC1W

The Literary world. v. 1-13; Feb. 6, 1847-Dec. 31. 1853. New York, E. A. & G. L. Duyckinck [etc.]
4 reels. (American periodical series: 1800-1850. 483-486)
Microfilm copy (positive) by University Microfilms, Ann Arbor, Mich.
Collation of the original: 13 v.
Weekly.
Editors: Feb.-Apr. 1847, E. A. Duyckinck.—May 1847-Sept. 1848, C. F. Hoffman.—Oct. 1848-Dec. 1853, E. A. Duyckinck, G. L. Duyckinck.

I. Duyckinck, Evert Augustus, 1816-1878, ed. II. Hoffman, Charles Fenno, 1806-1884, ed. III. Duyckinck, George Long, 1823-1863, ed.

Microfilm 01104 no. 483-486 AP Mic 60-7148

NL 0407637 DLC OU LU NN

Literary world; a gazette for authors, readers and publishers
see The Literary world. 1847-1853. New York.

The Literary world: a journal of American and foreign literature, science and art
see The Literary world. 1847-1853. New York.

The Literary world: a journal of popular information and entertainment. With numerous engravings. Conducted by John Timbs ... v. 1-3 (no. 1-79); Mar. 30, 1839-Sept. 26, 1840. London, G. Berger, 1839-40.
3 v. illus. 23½cm. weekly.
No more published.

I. Timbs, John, 1801-1875, ed.

37-34537

Library of Congress AP4.L436

052

ICU NN OC1
NL 0407640 DLC CaBViP OrU CSt NcRS IU FU CSmH ICN

The Literary world: a journal of society, literature, and art
see The Literary world. 1847-1853. New York.

Literary world; a monthly magazine of literature, science and art. v. 1-5, no. 5; 1880-Aug. 1884.
Monroe, N. C.

holdings:
v. [2]

NL 0407642 Nc

The Literary world; a monthly review of current literature
see The Literary world. Boston.

PN2
.L63
The Literary world; a survey of international letters. no. 1-9, May 1934-June 1935. New York, Froben Press, 1934-35.
9 nos. 45cm. monthly.
Suspended Jan.-May 1935.
Title varies slightly.

1. Literature—Hist. & crit.—Period.

NL 0407644 ViU ICU MiU

LITERARY world; a survey of international letters. no. 1-9; May, 1934-June, 1935. New York, Froben press. 9 no. illus., ports. 26-44cm.

Microfilm (negative)
Monthly.
Publication suspended Jan.-May, 1935.
Title varies slightly.
Edited by A. Flores, May-Nov. 1934; by V. Robinson, Dec. 1934-June, 1935.

1. Periodicals--U.S. I. Flores, Angel, 1900- , ed. II. Robinson, Victor, 1886- , ed.

NL 0407646 NN

The Literary world: choice readings from the best new books and critical reviews
see The Literary world. Boston.

The Literary year-book. [1st]-24th v.; 1897-1923. London, G. Routledge and sons, limited; New York, E. P. Dutton and co.; [etc., etc.] 1897-[1923]
25 v. ports. (incl. fronts.) 20-26 cm.

Publication suspended during 1918-19.
Volume numbers irregular: 1897-1917 called [1st]-21st v.; 1920-21 without designation; 1922-23 called 23d-24th v.
Title varies: 1897-98, 1906-10, The Literary year-book.
1899-1907, 1911-12, The Literary year-book and bookman's directory.
1913, The Literary year-book illustrators' directory and bookman's guide.
1914-17, The Literary year-book, authors' who's who and illustrators' directory.

1920, The Literary Who's who ...
1921-23, The Literary year-book.
Editors: 1897, F. G. Aflalo.—1898-99, Joseph Jacobs.—1900-02, Herbert Morrah.—1903-04, Henry Gilbert.—1905-08, not ascertained.—1909-20, Basil Stewart.—1921-23, Mark Meredith.
Imprint varies: 1897-1904, London, G. Allen.—1905-12, London, G. Routledge and sons, limited; New York, E. P. Dutton & co.—1913, London, G. Ouseley, limited.—1914-17, London, Heath, Cranton and Ouseley, limited [etc.]—1920-21, London, G. Routledge and sons, limited; New York, E. P. Dutton and co.—1922-23, Liverpool [etc.] Published by the proprietor; New York, R. R. Bowker co.
The issue for 1923 is autographed from type-written copy, with printed t.-p., and is called "Supplement to the basic issue of 1922."

Continued in four separate publications: Who's who in literature ... A continuation of the bibliographical section of the Literary year book; What editors and publishers want; The Librarians' guide; British booksellers.

1. Literature—Year-books. I. Aflalo, Frederick George, 1870-1918, ed. II. Jacobs, Joseph, 1854-1916, ed. III. Morrah, Herbert Arthur, 1870- ed. IV. Gilbert, Henry, 1868- ed. V. Stewart, Basil, 1880- ed. VI. Meredith, Mark, 1888- ed.

1—15590

Library of Congress Z2011.L77

MB NN NcD UU DHEW KEmT MB ICN NjP
NL 0407650 DLC WaS OO OU OCU ICJ MB MiU OC1W UU MeB

The Literary year-book.
The Librarians' guide, 1923- edition ...
see under title

The Literary year-book.
What editors and publishers want. (1924 ed.), being the continuance of sections of the Literary year book ... Liverpool, The Literary year book press [1923-

---

DS135
H9L77
Literati, pseud.
Keresztény kiáltvány, irta: Literati [pseud.] Budapest? 19--]
15,[1] p. 16cm.
Caption title.

1.Jews in Hungary. 2.Christians. I.Title.

NL 0407653 CSt-H

Pamphlet
Mexico
1811
L71
El literato insurgente, desenganado y arrepentido. [Mexico,1811]

NL 0407654 CtY

Literatur
see also Litteratur.

Die Literatur. Beilage der Hamburger nachrichten.
[Hamburg, Hermann's erben]
v. 50cm.
Weekly, -June 1905; biweekly, July 1905-

I. Hamburger nachrichten.

CA 12-626 Unrev'd

NL 0407656 DLC MWelC

VOLUME 336

Die Literatur; monatsschrift für literaturfreunde ... 1.- jahrg.; 1. okt. 1898-
Berlin, F. Fontane & co. ₍etc., 1898-1921₎; Stuttgart und
NN
Berlin, Deutsche verlags-anstalt ₍1921-
v. illus., ports. 28ᶜᵐ.
Semimonthly, Oct. 1898-Dec. 1922; monthly, Jan. 1923-
Title varies: Oct. 1898-Sept. 1923, Das Literarische echo; halbmonatsschrift für literaturfreunde (Oct. 1898-Sept. 1905 spelled "Litterarische" and 'litteraturfreunde")
Oct. 1923- Die Literatur ...
Editors: Oct. 1898-Apr. 1911, Josef Ettlinger.—May 1911- Ernst Heilborn.
Official organ of the Deutsch-oesterreichische literatur-gesellschaft, Oct.-Dec. 1899.
₍r29d2₎
1. Literature—Hist. & crit.—Period. I. Ettlinger, Josef, 1869-1912, ed. II. Heilborn, Ernst, 1867- ed. III. Deutsch-oesterreichische literatur-gesellschaft, Vienna.
Library of Congress AP30.L66 11-24520 Revised

PSC MoU NN
PBL MH CU IC TxLT FU PPT KU PSt NcD MdBJ NjP PBm
NL 0407657 DLC MH OrPR CaBVaU CtY MnU OO TU CU KyU

Die Literatür. Sammlung illustriertér Einzeldarstellungen. Berlin, Bard, Marquardt ₍1904-21₎
v.in illus.,ports.

Vol.35 never published.
No more published.
Edited by George Morris Cohen Brandes

NL 0407658 CU

MICROFILM
F4685
Die Literatur. Wochenschrift für das nationale Geistesleben der Gegenwart. Herausgeber: Hermann Riotte und Paul Wislicenus.
Bd. 1-2.
1 Juli 1873-25 Dez. 1874.
Leipzig, Richter & Harrassowitz ₍etc.₎ 1873-74.
2 v.

No more published.
Microfilm (negative) ₍n. p., 195-?₎ 2 reels. 35mm.

NL 0407659 NNC

Literatur [Ägyptologie], mit Beiträgen von Heilmut Brunner [et al] ...
see Brunner, Hellmut.
Ägyptologie. 2. Abschnitt: Literatur.

ליטעראטור; זאמעלבוך ארויסגעגעבען פון פעראיין ליטעראטור.
רעדאגירט פון יואל ענטין, יואל סלאנים ₍און₎ מ. י. חאאימאוויטש.
₍ניו יארק, הויפט פערקויף אין מייזעל'ס בוכהאנדלונג₎ 1910.
143 p. 27 cm.

1. Yiddish literature—Collections. 2. Yiddish literature—Addresses, essays, lectures. I. Entin, Joel, 1875-1959, ed. II. Slonim, Joel, 1884-1944, ed. III. Haimowitz, Morris Jonah, 1881-1958, ed.
Title romanized: Literatur.

PJ5125.L55 71-244494

NL 0407661 DLC

805
L71
Die Literatur der gegenwart.
Jahrg.
Recklinghausen, Bitter & co. ₍19
v. 28cm.

1. Literature, Modern - History and criticism - Periodicals.

NL 0407662 NNC DCU PU

Literatur der V Orte.
19
₍Stanz, 19 8°.
no.
Editor : 19 J. Troxler.

1. Bibliography, Swiss. 2. Switzerland—Bibl.
N. Y. P. L. April 21, 1927

NL 0407663 NN

Literatur der Gegenwart in Einzeldarstellungen
see under
Gültig, Heinz, ed.

Z
2244.S5
L776
Literatur der Landes- und Volkskunde der Provinz Schlesien. Heft 1.-7., 1892-1900; 1900/03-1904/06.
.Breslau, Aderholz.
9 v. in
Issued as Ergänzungsheft to Jahresbericht der Schlesischen Gesellschaft für Vaterländische Cultur, 69-70, 72-75, 77, 81, 84.
Edited 1892-1900 by J. Partsch; 1900/03-1904/06 by H. Nentwig.
1. Bibliography, National - Germany I. Nentwig, Heinrich, 1855- ed. II. Partsch, Joseph, 1882-1925, ed. III. Schlesische Gesellschaft für Vaterländische Cultur in Breslau. Jahresbericht. Supplement

NL 0407665 DNLM

Die Literature der Psychiatrie, Neurologie und Psychologie von 1459-1799
see under Laehr, Heinrich, 1820-1905.

Literatur (Die) der Veterinär-Wissenschaft und verwandter Gebiete vom 1. April 1889 bis 1. Juli 1898. 69 pp. 8°. *Berlin, R. Schoetz,* 1898.

NL 0407667 DNLM

HX
8
.L514
Literatur der Weltrevolution. 1931-
Moskau, Staatsverlag.
v. illus.

Zentralorgan der Internationalen Vereinigung Revolutionaerer Schriftsteller.
Issued also in English, French and Russian editions.

#Communism--Period.

#Russian literature--Translations into German--Period.
(A)Internationale Vereinigung Revolutionaerer Schriftsteller.

NL 0407669 MoU

... Die literatur der zehn wichtigsten nutzfische der Nordsee ...
see under [Hoek, Paulus Peronius Cato] 1851-1914, comp.

93083 Literatur des Frauenzimmers, oder Entwurf zu einer auserlesenen Frauenzimmerbibliothek. Frankfurt und Leipzig, 1794.
72 p. 19½ x 15ᶜᵐ.

NL 0407671 ICJ

Literatur für kaufleute oder aufführung zur handlungswissenschaftlichen bücherkunde ...
see under [Gruber, Johan Sigmund] d. 1805.

PN9
.L56
Literatur og kritik. 1.-4. Bind. København, O.B. Wroblewski, 1889-90.
4v. ports.

Edited by C.Riis-Knudsen.

1.Literature - Hist. & crit. - Period.
2.Scandinavian literature - Hist. & crit. - Period. I.Riis-Knudsen, C., ed.

NL 0407673 NcU KU MnU

Literatur og Kritik (For)
see For literatur og kritik

Literatur om likbränning.
(In Svenska likbränningsföreningen. Meddelanden, No. 3 and ff. 1885+)

NL 0407675 ICJ

Literatur über Ultraschall: Überreicht durch Siemens-Reiniger-Werke A. G. ₍Lausanne? 1950?₎
23 p. 25 cm.
"Aus dem Kongressbericht der Erlanger Ultraschall-Tagung 1949. S. Hirzel Verlag, Zürich."

1. Ultrasonic waves—Bibl. I. Siemens-Reiniger-Werke A. G.

Z7144.W2L5 57-24566 ‡

NL 0407676 DLC

Literatur- und anzeigeblatt fuer das baufach
see
Allgemeine bauzeitung.

Literatur- und Dokumentationsstelle für Rechenanlagen, *Darmstadt*
see
Deutsche Forschungsgemeinschaft (*Founded 1949*) *Kommission für Rechenanlagen. Literaturstelle.*

Literatur- und Kirchengeschichte des Mittelalters
see
Archiv für Literatur- und Kirchengeschichte des Mittelalters.

830.9
L712
Literatur und Leben. Bd.1-11, 1933-39, n.F. Bd.1- 1949-
Köln, Böhlau,
v. 23cm.

Imprint varies.
Editor: n.F.. v.1- , Richard Alewyn.

1. German literature - Hist. & crit. I. Alewyn, Richard, 1902- ed.

NL 0407680 TxU DAU KyU GU

VOLUME 336

Literatur - und notizblatt des Civilingenieur
see
Der Civilingenieur

NL 0407681

Y 9511 .51 LITERATUR und Theater Forschungen. 1.-3.
Heidelberg, C. Winter, 1914-19.
3v. in 1. 23cm.

Edited by Eugen Wolff.
Includes bibliographies.
Contents.--1. Heinrich von Kleist und C.M. Wieland, von H. Behme. 1914.--2. Kleists Lustspiel "Der zerbrochene Krug" auf der Bühne, von G. Buchtenkirch. 1914.--3. Die Heimathymnen der preussischen Provinzen und ihrer Landschaften, eine literarische Charakteristik, von G. Stendal. 1919.

NL 0407682 ICN NhD

Literatur zur kriegsschuldfrage
see under [Wegerer, Alfred von]

NL 0407683

EIY
LITERATUR zur schlesischen Geschichte. 1920/22-
Breslau. no. 23cm.

Published by the Historische Kommission für Schlesien (1926/27- with the Verein für Geschichte Schlesiens).
Compiler: 1920/22-1923/25, H. Bellée; 1926/27- H. Jessen.
Literatur zur schlesischen Geschichte 1907-1918/19 was published annually in: Verein für Geschichte Schlesiens. Zeitschrift. 1908-20.
Similar bibliographical material was also published in: Schlesische Gesellschaft für vaterländische Kultur. Jahresberichte. Beihefte. 1892-1914.
[Not in the library]

1. Silesia—Hist.—Bibl. I. Historische Kommission für Schlesien. II. Verein für Geschichte Schlesiens, Breslau. III. Bellée, Hans, 1889- , ed. IV. Jessen, Hans, 1897- , ed.

NL 0407685 NN CU

Literatura. (Periodical). Ano 1-3 (no. 1-8); set. 1946-março, 1948.
Rio de Janeiro. 3 v. 24cm.

Film reproduction. Master negative. Original discarded.
Positive in *ZAN-488.
Monthly (irregular).
Editor: Sept. 1946-Mar. 1948, A. Pereira.

NL 0407686 NN

Literatura; beszámoló a szellemi életröl.
évf. 1
Budapest, 1926 4°.
v. illus.

Monthly (except July - August).
Editor : 1926 G. Supka

1. Bibliography—Per. and soc. publ.
N. Y. P. L. August 23, 1927

NL 0407687 NN

015.437 L712 Literatura; bibliograficko-vzdělávácí věstník.
roč. 1-
1923-
Praha.
v. 27cm.

Frequency varies.

NL 0407688 IU

...Literatura... Edicion del gobierno dominicano. [Santiago] 1944. 2 v. 24cm. (Colección Trujillo; centenario de la republica, 1844-1944. [no.] 17-18.)

Cover-title.
Serie 4 of the Colección.
Each v. has also special t.-p.
CONTENTS.—v. 1-2. Antologia de la literatura dominicana. v. 1. Verso. v. 2. Prosa.

332312-3B. 1. Dominican literature —Collections. I. Ser.
N. Y. P. L. June 28, 1946

NL 0407689 NN

LITHUANIAN 891.98 L712 Literatūra; lietuvių literatūros, meno ir mokslo metraštis. Chicago, Lietuvių literatūros draugija [c1950-
v.

Added t. p. in English: Literatura; yearbook of Lithuanian literature, art, and science.

NL 0407690 MiD

A LITERATURA almanachja.
19
Budapest: Lantos R.-T. kiadasa, 19 19cm.
v. illus. (incl. ports.)

1. Almanacs—Hungary.

N. Y. P. L. June 9, 1933

NL 0407691 NN InU NNC IU

LITERATURA almanako de lingvo internacia
Paris. v. 18cm.

At head of title: Lingvo internacia.

MRS. DAVE H. MORRIS COLLECTION

1. Esperanto--Per. and soc. publ.

NL 0407692 NN

392.708 L712 Literatura árabe. Madrid, Editorial Ibero-Americana [1914]
191p. 19cm. (Joyas de la literatura universal, v.1)

1. Arabic literature - Translations into Spanish. 2. Spanish literature - Translations from Arabic.

NL 0407693 TxU

Literatura arábigo-española. Madrid, La españa ed. [1902?]
128 p. 24°. (Todas las literaturas)

NL 0407694 NN NjP

La Literatura argentina; revista bibliográfica. año 1- (núm. 1-); set. 1928-
Buenos Aires, Talleres gráficos argentinos L. J. Rosso [1928-
v. illus. (incl. ports.) 29cm. monthly.

Editor: Sept. 1928- L. J. Rosso.
Vols. 2- include current supplement, with special t.-p. and separate paging: Bibliografía general argentina, compilada por Fortunato Mendilaharzu. Buenos Aires, 1929- (Also issued separately in volume form)

1. Argentine literature—Bibl.—Period. 2. Argentine republic—Bibl. I. Rosso, Lorenzo J., ed.

Library of Congress Z1615.L77 34-3816
015.82

IU NSyU DPU OCl MWelC NN
NL 0407695 DLC ICRL MB NcD InU IaU FU ICN NNH ICRL

La Literatura argentina. Supplement

... Bibliografía general argentina, por Manuel Selva ... Fortunato Mendilaharzu ... y Lorenzo J. Rosso ... inventario analítico-crítico de todas las publicaciones argentinas desde el origen de la primera imprenta en el rio de la Plata, hasta el presente. Publicación auspiciada por la Comisión protectora de bibliotecas populares. Buenos Aires, Talleres gráficos argentinos de L. J. Rosso, 1931-

NL 0407696

... Literatura castellana... Madrid: La España editorial [1902?] 2 v. in 1. 13cm. (Todas las literaturas.)

CONTENTS.—[v.] 1. Desde la formación de la lengua hasta fines del siglo XVI.—[v.] 2. Desde fines del siglo XVI hasta nuestros dias.
With this is bound: Literatura noruega. Madrid [1902?]

193286B. 1. Spanish literature— Hist. and crit.
N. Y. P. L. March 2, 1943

NL 0407697 NN

Literatura česká devatenáctého století; [od josefinského obrození až po českou modernu] Napsali: Josef Hanuš [et al.] V Praze, Nákl. J. Laichtera, 1902-07.
3 v. in 4. illus., facsims., ports. 21 cm. (Laichterův výbor nejlepších spisů poučných, kn. 19, 21, 16 [i. e. 26, 31])
Vol. 3, pt. 2 by Leandr Čech [et al.]
Each vol. has also special t. p.
Includes bibliographical references.
CONTENTS: díl 1. Od Josefa Dobrovského k Jungmannově škole básnické.—díl 2. Od M. Zd. Poláka k K. J. Erbenovi.—díl 3, č. 1. Od K. H. Máchy ke K. Havlíčkovi; č. 2. Od Boženy Němcové k Janu Nerudovi.
1. Czech literature—History and criticism. I. Hanuš, Josef, 1862-1941. II. Čech, Leandr, 1854-1911.
PG5006.L5 52-57930

NL 0407698 DLC NSyU OO MH CSt ICU RPB NNC ViU

Literatura česká devatenáctého století; [od josefinského obrození až po českou modernu] Napsali: Josef Hanuš [et al.] 2. vyd., oprav. a dopl. V Praze, Nákl. J. Laichtera, 1911-17.
2 v. illus., facsims., ports. 21 cm. (Laichterův výbor nejlepších spisů poučných, kn. 19, 21)
L. C. copy imperfect: t. p. and all before p. 49 in v. 2, wanting. No more published.
Each vol. has also special t. p.
Includes bibliographical references.
CONTENTS: díl 1. Od Dobrovského k Jungmannové škole básnické.—díl 2. Od Poláka k Langrovi.
1. Czech literature—History and criticism. I. Hanuš, Josef, 1862-1941.
PG5006.L53 1911 22-24490
rev 2

TNJ MiU PU MH CtY FTaSU ViU IU OU
NL 0407699 DLC NN IEN InU CtY KU WU TxU MB CaBVaU

La literatura colombiana
see under Gómez Restrepo, Antonio, 1869-1947.

NL 0407700

VOLUME 336

... **Literatura** cubana ... Madrid, Barcelona, Editorial ibero-americana [n. d.]

191 p. incl. ports. 18½cm. (Joyas de la literatura universal. [II])

CONTENTS.—Gabriel de la Concepción Valés (Plácido)—Enrique Piñeyro.—José Martí.—José María Heredia y Campuzano.—José Jacinto Milanés.—Gertrudis Gómez de Avellaneda.

1. Cuban literature (Selections: Extracts, etc.) I. Valdés, Gabriel de la Concepción, 1809–1844. II. Piñeyro, Enrique, 1839–1911. III. Martí, José Julián, 1853–1895. IV. Heredia, José María, 1803–1839. V. Milanés, José Jacinto, 1814–1863. VI. Gómez de Avellaneda y Arteaga, Gertrudis, 1814–1873.

18–1061

Library of Congress PQ7384.L5

NL 0407701 DLC FMU NcU NBuU IU MU InU WU TxU

891.869
L776 **Literatura** czeska i słowacka; obraz piśmiennictwa. W zarysie przedstawił Jan Magiera. Warszawa, Nakładem księgarni F.Hoesicka, 1929.
292 p.
Bibliography: p.[7]

1.Czech literature--Addresses,essays, lectures. 2.Slovak literature--Addresses, essays,lectures. I.Magiera,Jan.

NL 0407702 MiU

La **Literatura** del Brasil. Buenos Aires, Impr. de la Universidad, 1945–

v. 19 cm. (Instituto de Cultura Latino-Americana ... Las literaturas americanas, 5,

At head of title: Facultad de Filosofía y Letras de la Universidad de Buenos Aires.

CONTENTS.—v. 1. A. A. de Melo Franco. Algunos aspectos de la literatura brasileña, traducción de Raúl Navarro. Bibliografía de autores brasileños citados en esta obra (p. [91]–98)—v. 2. M. A. d'Elía. El sentido de la tierra en la narrativa. Bibliografía (p. [83]–85)

1. Brazilian literature—Hist. & crit. I. Mello Franco, Affonso Arinos de, 1905– (Series: Buenos Aires. Universidad Nacional. Instituto de Literatura. Sección Argentina y Americana. Las literaturas americanas, t. 5 [etc.])

PQ9511.L5 869.09 47–26221 rev*

NL 0407703 DLC NcD NcD OO MoSU WU IaU MiEM MiU ICarbS TxU ICU OU

Literatura didactica, arreglada conforme a los programas oficiales de Guatemala...
see under [Espinosa R Emilio]

Literatura Dominicana
see under [Tejera, Apolinar]

LITERATURA escogida; bibliografía de obras selectas para quienes se interesen en la mejor literatura conducente á la cultura moral é intelectual. New York, Comité de Cooperación en la América Latina, [1916?].

pp. 78.

NL 0407706 MH ICU

Literatura escogida; bibliografía de obras selectas para quienes se interesen en la mejor literatura conducente a la cultura moral e intelectual. 2. ed. ... New York, Comite de cooperacion en la America latina, 1925.

56 p. 23cm.

1. Bibliography—Best books—Spanish. 2. Spanish literature—Bibl.

26–23076

Library of Congress Z1035.7.L77 1925

NL 0407707 DLC

Q016
L712
1928 **Literatura** escogida; bibliografía de obras selectas para quienes se interesen en la mejor literatura conducente a la cultura moral e intelectual. 3. ed. New York, Comité de Cooperación en la América Latina, 1928.
76p. 23cm.

1. Bibliography - Best books. 2. Spanish literature - Bibl. 3. Spanish-American literature - Bibl.

NL 0407708 TxU DLC OCU

Literatura española. Barcelona
v.1 (1945) and later volumes
Issued in various unnumbered series: Publicaciones de la Sección de Filología Románica; Publicaciones de la Escuela de Filología de Barcelona; etc.
Title varies: 2-4,6 lack series title: v.5,7-8, Filología moderna.(v.1-7 listed as Publicaciones de la Sección de Filología Moderna in v.8)
Some volumes issued by the Instituto Antonio de Nebrija, others by Instituto Miguel de Cervantes de Filología Histanica, del C.S.I.C.

NL 0407709 MH FU

...**Literatura** francesa... Madrid: La España editorial [1902?] 2 v. in 1. 13cm. (Todas las literaturas.)

CONTENTS.—v. 1. Desde los orígenes hasta el siglo XVIII.—v. 2. Siglos XVIII y XIX.
Bound with: Literaturas escandinavas. Madrid [1902?]

196978B. 1. French literature— Hist. and crit.
N. Y. P. L. March 3, 1943

NL 0407710 NN

Literatura hispanoamericana; articulo publicado en la "Revista nacional" de Buenos Aires. Chartres, Imprenta de Durand, 1887.
"Edicíon privada."

NL 0407711 NNH

L51
.L5 **Литература** и язык в политехнической школе.

Москва, Гос. учеб.-педагог. изд-во [etc.]

v. in ports. 23-26 cm.

Frequency varies.
Organ of Glavnoe upravlenie sotsial'nogo vospitaniia and Institut metodov shkol'noi raboty, 19 -28; Narodnyi komissariat po prosveshcheniiu RSFSR, 1929-
Title varies: 19 -28, Родной язык и литература в трудовой школе.—1929–31, Русский язык в советской школе.
Editors: 19 -28, I. N. Kubikov.—1929–31, P. I. Lebedev-Polianskii.—1932- F. M. Golovenchenko.
(L. C. Set incomplete: V. 2, nos. 1-2, 6; v. 3, nos. 5-6 wanting.)

1. Russian language—Study and teaching—Period. 2. Russian literature—Study and teaching—Period. I. Kubikov, Ivan Nikolaevich, 1877- ed. II. Lebedev-Polianskii, Pavel Ivanovich, 1881–1948, ed. III. Golovenchenko, Fedor Mikhailovich, ed. IV. Russia (1917- R. S. F. S. R.) Glavnoe upravlenie sotsial'nogo vospitaniia. V. Russia (1917- R. S. F. S. R.) Narodnyi komissariat po prosveshcheniiu.

Title transliterated: Literatura i iazyk v politekhnicheskoi shkole.

L51.L5 49–56181*

NL 0407713 DLC

.L44 **Литература** и искусство. г. 1–2; 1930–31. Москва, Гос. изд-во худож. лит-ры.

v. illus., ports., music. 25 cm. monthly.
Supersedes Печать и революция.
Organ of Institut literatury, iskusstva i iazyka Kommunisticheskoi akademii (later Nauchno-issledovatel'skii institut literatury i iskusstva Kommunisticheskoi akademii)
Superseded in 1932 by Марксистско-ленинское искусствознание.
Editor: 19 -31, no. 3, P. M. Kerzhentsev.
L. C. set incomplete: v. 1, v. 2, nos. 4–12 wanting.
1. Literature—Period. 2. Russian literature—Hist. & crit.—Period. 3. Art—Period. I. Kerzhentsev, Platon Mikhailovich, 1881–1940, ed. II. Kommunisticheskaia akademiia, Moscow. Nauchno-issledovatel'skii institut literatury i iskusstva.

Title transliterated: Literatura i iskusstvo.

PN9.L44 49–36958*

NL 0407714 DLC

Литература и марксизм. г. 1–
1928–
Москва, Гос. изд-во худож. лит-ры [etc.]

v. 23 cm. bimonthly.

L.C. set incomplete: v.4, no.6 wanting.)

1. Literature—Hist. & crit.—Period. 2. Russian literature—Hist. & crit.—Period. *Title transliterated:* Literatura i marksizm.

PN9.L46 48–42181*

NL 0407715 DLC

Literatura i sztuka; monografie. Stanisławów, Staudacher

6 (1907) - Brzozowski, Stanisław Leon, 1878-1911
Fryderyk Nietzsche

NL 0407716 MH DLC

Literatura informilo. no. 1- ; 1924-
see under Hirt, Ferdinand, firm, publishers.

La **Literatura** internacional
see **Literatura** soviética.

...**Literatura** italiana. Madrid: La España editorial [1902?] 144 p. 13cm. (Todas las literaturas.)

197711B. 1. Italian literature—Hist. and crit.
N. Y. P. L. March 25, 1943

NL 0407719 NN CU

Literatura Judaica. Madrid: La España Editorial, [189-?]
121 p. (Todas las literaturas)

NL 0407720 OCH CtY

...**Literatura** mexicana: Sor Juana Inés de la Cruz—Juan Ruiz de Alarcón—Juan de Dios Peza—Vicente Riva Palacio—Ignacio M. Altamirano—Manuel Gutiérrez Nájera—Salvador Díaz Mirón—Manuel Acuña—Justo Sierra. Madrid [etc.] Editorial Ibero-americana [1906] 191 p. illus. 19cm. (Joyas de la literatura universal. 3.)

303575B. 1. Poetry, Mexican—Collections.
N. Y. P. L. June 6, 1945

NL 0407721 NN FU ICarbS CSt IU

Literatura mieszczańska w polsce od końca XVI do końca XVII wieku
see under Budzyk, Kazimierz, ed.

VOLUME 336

LITERATURA moderna; novelas de E.Ramirez Angel, A. Martinex Olmedilla, A. Hoyos Vinent etc. Barcelona, librería de Feliu y Susanna, 1911,

1.8°. Illustr.

NL 0407723 MH

LITERATURA mondo. Jaro 1-7; 1931-37 +
Budapest. v. illus. 31cm.

Monthly (irreg.) 1931-35; bimonthly 1936-37.
Jaro 1- called Dua periodo.

1. Esperanto--Per. and soc. publ.

NL 0407724 NN

Literatura Moskovskago gosudarstva.
Arkhangel'skiĭ, Aleksandr Semenovich, 1854-1926.
Изъ лекцій по исторіи русской литературы: литература Московскаго государства (кон. XV-XVII вв.) Казань, Типо-лит. Имп. университета, 1913.

Литература национальностей СССР. ₍г. -4₎; -дек. 1935. Москва.

v. in illus., ports. 26 cm. monthly.

Began publication in 1932.
Supersedes in part Книга строителям социализма.
At head of title, 1933: Критико-библиографический бюллетень.
Title varies: 19 -33, Национальная литература.
Issued by Nauchno-issledovatel'skiĭ kritiko-bibliograficheskiĭ institut (called, 1933, Kritiko-bibliograficheskiĭ institut; 1934-35, Kritiko-bibliograficheskiĭ nauchno-issledovatel'skiĭ institut)

1. Russian literature—Bibl.—Period. I. Moscow. Nauchno-issledovatel'skiĭ kritiko-bibliograficheskiĭ institut.
Title transliterated: Literatura nat͡sional'nosteĭ SSSR.

Z2495.L7 51-34527

NL 0407726 DLC CU

A literatura no Brasil

see under

Coutinho, Afranio ed.

... **Literatura** noruega. Madrid: La España editorial ₍1902?₎ 108 p. 13cm. (Todas las literaturas.)

Bound with: Literatura castellana. Madrid ₍1902?₎

193286B. 1. Norwegian literature— Hist. and crit.
N. Y. P. L. March 3, 1943

NL 0407728 NN

Literatura o divadle a divadelní hry. 1945/55-

₍V Praze, etc., Státní pedagogické nakl., etc.₎

v. 21 cm.

Vols. for 1945/55- issued as Publikace Universitní knihovny v Olomouci; as Publikace Státní vědecké knihovny v Olomouci.
Vols. for 1945/55- issued by Universitní knihovna, Olomouc; by Státní vědecká knihovna, Olomouc (Z796.O44)

1. Theater—Bibliography. 2. Drama—Bibliography. I. Olomouc, Moravia. Palackého universita. Knihovna. II. Olomouc, Moravia. Státní vědecká knihovna. (Series: Olomouc, Moravia. Státní vědecká knihovna. Publikace)

Z5781.L55 65-50715

NL 0407729 DLC ICU

Литература о Калужской области.
Калуга.

v. 20 cm.

Issued by Spravochno-bibliograficheskiĭ otdel of Kaluzhskai͡a oblastnai͡a biblioteka imeni V. G. Belinskogo.

1. Kaluga, Russia (Province)—Bibl. I. Kaluga, Russia (City) Oblastnai͡a biblioteka imeni V. G. Belinskogo. Spravochno-bibliograficheskiĭ otdel.
Title transliterated: Literatura o Kaluzhskoĭ oblasti.

Z2514.K2L5 67-51430

NL 0407730 DLC CSt-H

Литература о музыке (*transliterated:* Literatura o muzyke)
see
Советская литература о музыке (*transliterated:* Sovetskai͡a literatura o muzyke)

G868.805
L712 **La Literatura** peruana. año 1-

₍Lima, 1923-

v. 20½cm. weekly.

1. Peruvian literature - Period.

45-50811

Library of Congress AP63.L75

NL 0407732 DLC TxU MH AzU

Literatura pharmacopoearum
see under Scherer, Alexander Nicolaus, 1771-1824, comp.

Literatura piękna; przewodnik bibliograficzny. 1954-

Warszawa.

v. 22 cm.

Issued by Instytut Bibliograficzny of the Biblioteka Narodowa.
Editor: 1954- A. Wróblewski.

1. Polish literature—Bibl.—Period. 2. Polish literature—Translations from foreign literature—Bibl.—Period. I. Wróblewski, A., ed. II. Warsaw. Biblioteka Narodowa. Instytut Bibliograficzny.

Z2523.L5 56-28967

NL 0407734 DLC MiU OU NSyU

Literatura piękna dla dzieci i młodzieży; adnotowany rocznik bibliograficzny.
Warszawa, Stowarzyszenie Bibliotekarzy Polskich.

v. 21 cm.

Issued, 195 by Instytut Bibliograficzny of the Biblioteka Narodowa.
Subtitle varies.
Vols. for 195 reprinted from Literatura piękna, 195

1. Children's literature, Polish—Bibl.—Period. I. Warsaw. Biblioteka Narodowa. Instytut Bibliograficzny.

Z1037.6.L5 60-41417

NL 0407735 DLC NSyU OU

Литература по лесной и бумажной промышленности.

Москва, 19

no. in v. 26 cm.

Began in 1955. Cf. Letopis' periodicheskikh izdaniĭ SSSR, 1955-60.
Issued by T͡Sentral'nai͡a nauchno-tekhnicheskai͡a biblioteka lesnoĭ i bumazhnoĭ promyshlennosti.

1. Lumbering—Bibl.—Period. 2. Wood-using industries—Bibl.—Period. I. Moscow. T͡Sentral'nai͡a nauchno-tekhnicheskai͡a biblioteka lesnoĭ i bumazhnoĭ promyshlennosti.
Title romanized: Literatura po lesnoĭ i bumazhnoĭ promyshlennosti.

SD538.L75 67-119778

NL 0407736 DLC

Литература по педагогическим наукам (*transliterated:* Literatura po pedagogicheskim naukam)
see
Литература по педагогическим наукам и народному образованию (*transliterated:* Literatura po pedagogicheskim naukam i narodnomu obrazovanii͡u)

NL 0407737

.L5 **Литература** по педагогическим наукам и народному образованию; библиографический указатель.
Москва, Изд-во Академии педагог. наук РСФСР.

v. in 21 cm. quarterly.

Began publication in 1951. Cf. Летопись периодических изданий СССР, 1950-1954, № 2164.
Issued by Gosudarstvennai͡a biblioteka po narodnomu obrazovanii͡u.
Title varies: 19 -59, Литература по педагогическим наукам.

1. Education—Bibl. I. Moscow. Gosudarstvennai͡a biblioteka po narodnomu obrazovanii͡u.
Title transliterated: Literatura po pedagogicheskim naukam.

Z5811.L5 60-45175 rev

NL 0407738 DLC DNLM

Литература по железнодорожному транспорту.

Москва, Транспорт.

v. in 21 cm. monthly.

"Библиографический указатель отечественной и зарубежной литературы."
Began in 1949. Cf. Letopis' periodicheskikh izdaniĭ SSSR, 1955-60.
Issued by T͡Sentral'nai͡a nauchno-tekhnicheskai͡a biblioteka of Ministerstvo puteĭ soobshchenii͡a SSSR.

1. Railroads—Bibliography—Periodicals. I. Russia (1923- U. S. S. R.) Ministerstvo puteĭ soobshchenii͡a. T͡Sentral'nai͡a nauchno-tekhnicheskai͡a biblioteka.
Title romanized: Literatura po zheleznodorozhnomu transportu.

Z7233.L56 78-206710

NL 0407739 DLC

Literatura polska dla klasy i liceów ogolnokształcących ...
see under Kleiner, Juliucz, 1886-1957.

G869.808
C676 **Literatura popular em verso.**
v.4
[Rio de Janeiro] Ministério da Educação e Cultura, Casa de Rui Barbosa.
v. illus., facsim. 24cm. (Coleção de textos da lingua portuguesa moderna, v.4)

Editor:
sect.2, v.1, Manoel C. Proença.
CONTENTS.—[sect.1] Catálogo. t.1-
—[sect.2] Antologia. t.1-

NL 0407741 TxU

PC3945 Literatura popular mallorquina. Soller,
.M25L7 Imp. de "La Sinceridad", 1900.
3 v. in 1.
Edited by José Rullán y Mir.
Contents.--t.1. Glôses d'en Pau Noguera y Ripoll.--t.2. Glôses de n'Andreu Coll y Bernat.--t.3. Glôses de'n Sebastiá Marqués y Ortegas.

1. Catelan literature--Majorca. 2. Folk-literature--Majorca. I. Noguera y Ripoll, Pau, 1781-1868. II. Coll y Bernat, Andreu, 1749?-1872.

NL 0407742 ICU

... **Literatura** portuguesa. Madrid: La Espana editorial ₍1902?₎ 139 p. 13cm. (Todas las literaturas.)

197711B. 1. Portuguese literature— Hist. and crit.
N. Y. P. L. March 25, 1943

NL 0407743 NN CU

VOLUME 336

LITERATURA radziecka. lip. 1949-date
Moskwa, "Litieraturnaja gazieta" [etc.] v.
illus. (part col.)ports. (part col.) 27cm.

Monthly.
Published by the Związek pisarzy ZSRR (Soyuz sovetskikh pisateleĭ), Sept. 1956-date.
Occasional issues have title also in Russian: Советская литература. На польском языке. (Sovetskaya literatura. Na pol'skom yazyke.)

Also published in English, French, German, and Spanish editions with titles: Soviet literature. La Littérature soviétique. Sowjet Literatur. Literatura sovietica. (French and German editions not in the library. See separate entries for English and Spanish editions.)

1. Russian literature—Per. and soc. publ. 2. Periodicals—Russia, Polish. I. Soyuz sovetskikh pisateleĭ. II. Title: Sovetskaya literatura [Polish ed.]

NL 0407745 NN

Литература революционной Испании; указатель художественной литературы. ₍Составитель С. Г. Романов₎. Ленинград, Библиотечная методическая база Ленинградского Облпрофсовета, 1936.

23 p. ports. 11 x 14 cm.

1. Spanish literature—20th century—Translations into Russian—Bibliography. 2. Russian literature—Translations from Spanish—Bibliography. I. Romanov, S. G.
Title romanized: Literatura revoliutsionnoĭ Ispanii.

Z2694.T7L5 72-220553

NL 0407746 DLC

A90 L71 **Literatură si stiintă.** v.1-
1893-
Bucharesti, Graeve.
23cm. annual

1. Periodicals - Rumania.

NL 0407747 CtY

... Literatura sobre Pago Largo
see under [Gómez, Hernán Felix]
1888- comp.

Literatura sovietica; revista mensual. 1942–
Moscú.

v. 26 cm.

Issues for 194 also called año (issues for 1943, no. also called no.
Title varies: 1942– La Literatura internacional.
Indexes:
Vols. 1-3, 1942-44, *in* v. 3.

AP64.L5 056 48-37344 rev*‡

NL 0407749 DLC NN WU IEN

Literatūra un māksla; Latvijas padomju rakstnieku, komponistu, mākslinieku, arhitektu un kinematogrāfijas darbinieku savienību laikraksts. Riga
1964, nr.2 (also numbered 1000) and later numbers

NL 0407750 MH

LITERATURA un māksla. 1955-date
Riga. v. illus.

Film reproduction. Positive.

Weekly
"Latvijas padomju rakstnieku, komponistu, mākslinieku un architektu savienību laikrasts."
1. Periodicals--Latvia. I. Latvijas padomju rakstnieku savienība.

NL 0407751 NN

Literatura universal; un estudio completo y comprensivo de las literaturas de las naciones, desde la aurora de la civilización hasta el momento actual ... Preparado por prominentes educadores y escritores norteamericanos y sudamericanos; ampliamente ilustrado. ₍Caracas₎ La Llave del saber, cía. ₍1940–41₎

9 v. fronts. (part col.) plates (1 col.) ports. 24½ cm.

Paged continuously.
"Impreso en Estados Unidos de América."

1. Literature—Hist. & crit. 2. Literature—Collections. 3. Authors. I. La Llave del saber, compañía.

PN593.L5 809 40-32398 rev 2

NL 0407752 DLC

Literatura universal; un estudio completo, que comprende las literaturas de las naciones, desde la aurora de la civilización hasta el momento actual ... Preparado por eminentes profesores y escritores norteamericanos y sudamericanos. ₍Elsinore? Calif.₎ Cía La Llave del Saber ₍1954₎

9 v. (3129 p.) illus. (part col.) ports. 24 cm.

1. Literature—Hist. & crit. 2. Literature—Collections. 3. Authors. I. La Llave del Saber, Compañía.

PN593.L52 54-35723

NL 0407753 DLC

La Literatura uruguaya del 900 ₍i. e. novecientos₎ por A. Ardao ₍et al.₎ Montevideo, Número, 1950.

340 p. ports. 22 cm.

"Este libro es reedición del volumen especial (año 2, no. 6-7-8) de la revista Número."

1. Uruguayan literature—Hist. & crit. I. Ardao, Arturo.

PQ8510.L5 52-44447

NL 0407754 DLC IU TxU NcU MH MiU IEN CSt ICN InU

PN59 .L5 Литература в школе.

Москва, Учпедгиз.

v. illus., ports. 26 cm. bimonthly.

Publication suspended 1942–45 inclusive.
Supersedes in part Русский язык и литература в средней школе.
Organ of Narodnyĭ komissariat po prosveshchenii︠u︡ RSFSR, 19 –46, no. 1; Ministerstvo prosveshchenii︠a︡ RSFSR, 1946, no. 2-19

1. Literature—Study and teaching—Period. 2. Literature—Hist. & crit.—Period. I. Russia (1917– R. S. F. S. R.) Narodnyĭ komissariat po prosveshchenii︠u︡. II. Russia (1917– R. S. F. S. R.) Ministerstvo prosveshchenii︠a︡.
Title transliterated: Literatura v shkole.

PN59.L5 49-36956*

NL 0407755 DLC MdBJ

PG3021 .L5 Литература, вдохновленная коммунизмом; статьи о лауреатах сталинских премий 1948 года. Москва, Литературная газета, 1949.

44 p. 20 cm.

1. Russian literature—20th cent.—Hist. & crit. 2. Stalin prizes.
Title transliterated: Literatura, vdokhnovlennai︠a︡ kommunizmom.

PG3021.L5 52-16629

NL 0407756 DLC

Literatura ye škole; časopis pro metodiku vyučování literatuře.
Praha, Státní pedagogické nakl.

v. in illus., ports. 21 cm. 10 no. a year.

Published 1953-58.
In 1959 merged with Český jazyk to form Český jazyk a literatura.

1. Czech literature—Study and teaching—Period. 2. Literature—Study and teaching—Period.

PG4065.L55 61-41808

NL 0407757 DLC

Literatura venezolana ...
see under [Güell y Mercader, José]

La literatura y el arte en Francia al servicio de la propaganda instigadora de la guerra
see under [Spectator Galliae] pseud.

Literatur-archiv-gesellschaft, Berlin.

Schleiermacher, Friedrich Ernst Daniel, 1768-1834.
Friedrich Schleiermachers ästhetik, im auftrage der Preussischen akademie der wissenschaften und der Literatur-archiv-gesellschaft zu Berlin nach den bisher unveröffentlichten urschriften zum ersten male herausgegeben von Rudolf Odebrecht. Berlin und Leipzig, W. de Gruyter & co., 1931.

PN24 L52 Literaturarchiv-Gesellschaft, Berlin.
Bericht über die Tätigkeit...1917-1922 und Satzungen...nach den Beschlüssen der ausserordentlichen Generalversammlung vom 10. Februar 1922. ₍n.p., n.d.₎
11 p. 21cm.

1. German literature - Societies, etc.

NL 0407761 CSt

Literaturarchiv-gesellschaft in Berlin.

Jahresbericht über die wissenschaftlichen erscheinungen auf dem gebiete der neueren deutschen literatur, hrsg. von der Literaturarchiv-gesellschaft in Berlin. neue folge, bd. 1- bibliographie 1921-
Berlin und Leipzig, W. de Gruyter & co., 1924-

Literaturarchiv-Gesellschaft in Berlin.
Litterarische Mittheilungen. Festschrift zum zehnjährigen Bestehen der Litteraturarchiv-Gesellschaft in Berlin. Berlin, 1901. 146 p. facsims. 24cm.
"In 200 Exemplaren für die Mitglieder gedruckt."

1. German literature—Collections.

NL 0407763 NN MH GU KU CU

FILM 943 L71m Literaturarchiv-Gesellschaft, Berlin.
Mitteilungen aus dem Litteraturarchive in Berlin. Band 3: 1901-1905. Berlin, 1905.

Microfilm copy made in 1956 by the University of Illinois Library from the original in the University of Minnesota Library. Negative.
Collation of original, as determined from the film: 394p.
"In 100 Exemplaren für die Mitglieder gedruckt. No.24."

NL 0407764 IU

VOLUME 336

Literaturarchiv-Gesellschaft, Berlin.
Satzungen. Berlin, 1903.

NL 0407765 MH

PG 9031 L57 Literaturas chrestomatija. 8. klasei. Sakartojis Rigas skolotāju kolektivs. Rīgā, Latvijas valsts izdevnieciba, 1951.
714 p. 23cm.

1. Latvian literature (Selections: Extracts etc.)

NL 0407766 CoU

... Literaturas escandinavas: danesa, sueca, finlandesa, islandesa. Madrid: La España editorial [1902?] 128 p. 13cm. (Todas las literaturas.)
With this is bound: Literatura francesa. Madrid [1902?]

196978B. 1. Scandinavian literature—Hist. and crit. 2. Finnish literature—Hist. and crit.
N. Y. P. L. March 3, 1943

NL 0407767 NN

Literatur-Bericht [der Zeitschrift für wissenschaftliche Insektenbiologie I]–LXVIV. [Husum, 1905–1911?]
359 p. 24½cm.
Caption title.
No more published.

NL 0407768 ICJ

Literaturberichte für die Jahre 1839–1947
see under Janssen, Jozef Marie Antoon.

Literaturberichte über Wasser, Abwasser, Luft und Boden.
Bd. 1– 1950–
Stuttgart, Fischer [etc.]
v. in 25 cm. Irregular.
Editor: v. 1– E. Tiegs.
"Im Auftrage des Vereins für Wasser-, Boden- und Lufthygiene" and v. 2–"In Gemeinschaft mit dem Institut für Wasser-, Boden- und Lufthygiene im Bundesgesundheitsamt."

1. Hygiene, Public—Bibl. 2. Hygiene, Public—Abstracts. 3. Water-supply—Bibl. 4. Sewage—Bibl. I. Tiegs, Ernst, ed. II. Verein für Wasser-, Boden- und Lufthygiene.

Z6673.L5 57-15427

NL 0407770 DLC NN

Literaturberichte zur Flora oder Allgemeinen botanischen Zeitung. Im Auftrage der Königl. Bayer. Botanischen Gesellschaft zu Regensburg herausgegeben .... Erster–[zwölfter] Band, Nro. 9 1831–1842. Regensburg, 1831–1842.
12 vol. in 8. 17½cm.–19½cm.
Published as supplement to Flora; vol. 12 bound with Flora, vol. 25, which has shelf number 580.53 7 v.25
Vol. 4–11 edited by David Heinrich Hoppe and August Emanuel Fürnrohr.

NL 0407771 ICJ PPULC NcU MiU LU PPAN CSmH

Literaturbladet. Et Ugeblad fornemmelig for udenlandsk Literatur. Nr. 1–40.
Udgivet af R. Rask. København, S. L. Møller, 1829. 8°. IcA41L776
Contains many important reviews by the editor, e.g., of several of Finnur Magnússon's works, of Jón Þorláksson's version of Milton's "Paradís armissir," etc., etc.

NL 0407772 NIC

Literatur-blatt. Stuttgart, 1832-49
see
Morgenblatt fuer gebildete leser

Literaturblatt des Orients
see
Der Orient.

Literaturblatt für germanische und romanische philologie...
1.– jahrg.; jan. 1880–
Heilbronn, Gebr. Henninger [1880–1889]; Leipzig, O. R. Reisland [1890–19
v. 28cm. monthly.
"Hrsg. von dr. Otto Behagel ... und dr. Fritz Neumann ... Verantwortlicher redacteur: dr. Fritz Neumann", 1880–
Vols. 1–6 "Unter mitwirkung von prof. dr. Karl Bartsch".

1. Germanic philology—Bibl.—Period. 2. Romance philology—Bibl.—Period. 3. Books—Reviews. I. Behagel, Otto, 1854– ed. II. Neumann, Fritz, 1854– ed. III. Bartsch, Karl Friedrich, 1832–1888, ed.

G—856

Library of Congress Z7037.L7

MnU FU IU NhD CtNIC OOxM
NL 0407775 DLC PPeSchw PPT CU KU PSt TxLT KyU ICN

Literatur-blatt für orientalische philologie; unter mitwirkung von Dr. Johannes Klatt in Berlin, hrsg. von Prof. Dr. Ernst Kuhn in München. I.–4. bd.; oct. 1883–oct. 1888. Leipzig, O. Schulze [1884–88]
4 v. in 2. 21½cm.
Vol. 1–2 monthly, 3–4 quarterly (irreg.)
"Bibliographie für 1883 bis 1886." (The first 3 volumes contain besides the bibliography proper "Recensionen" and "Kleinere mittheilungen") Vol. 4, p. 193–222: Alphabetisches register zu bd. I–IV. Vol. 2–4 published "mit unterstützung der Deutschen morgenländischen gesellschaft."

Superseded by A. Müller's Orientalische bibliographie.
Forms with Zenker, "Bibliotheca orientalis," 1846–61; "Wissenschaftlicher jahresbericht über die morgenländischen studien" 1859–81 (irreg. suppl. to the "Zeitschrift der Deutschen morgenländischen gesellschaft"); Friederici, "Bibliotheca orientalis" 1876–83; and "Orientalische bibliographie" (A. Müller, E. Kuhn, L. Scherman) 1887– , a continuous bibliography of Oriental philology.

Subject entries: Oriental philology—Bibl.

2-19246

Library of Congress, no. Z7046.L77.

NL 0407777 DLC TxU WU NcU CU IEN CtY MH NcD

... Literaturdenkmäler aus Ungarns Türkenzeit, nach handschriften in Oxford und Wien, bearbeitet von Franz Babinger, Robert Gragger, Eugen Mittwoch und J. H. Mordtmann. Berlin und Leipzig, W. de Gruyter & co., 1927.
vi p., 1 l., 231 p. 4 facsim. on 2 l. 29cm. (Ungarische bibliothek ... 1. reihe. 14)
Pagination includes facsimiles of the Bodleian ms. (p. 143–187) and of fol. 29a–68b of the Vienna ms. (p. 191–231)
Table of transliteration ("Türkisch—Deutsch — Magyarisch — Kroatisch—Lateinisch"): p. 98.
CONTENTS. — Gragger, R. Türkisch-ungarische kulturbeziehungen. — Babinger, F. Der Pfortendolmetsch Murād und seine schriften.—Gragger, R. Der magyarische text von Murāds "Glaubenshymnus" mit deutscher übersetzung.—Mittwoch, E., und Mordtmann, J. H. Die Wiener sammelhandschrift [Flügel 2006]—Mittwoch, E. Die deutschen, magyarischen, kroatischen und lateinischen texte der Wiener sammelhandschrift.—Mordtmann, J. H. Aus der türkischen anthologie der Wiener sammelhandschrift.—Die handschrift Marsh 179 der Bodleiana.—Die handschrift Flügel 2006 der Wiener national-bibliothek, bl. 29a–68b.
1. Hungarian literature (Selections: Extracts, etc.) 2. Turkish literature (Selections: Extracts, etc.) 3. Hungary—Hist.—1000–1683. 4. Turks in Hungary. 5. Transliteration—Turkish. I. Gragger, Robert, 1887–1926. II. Babinger, Franz Carl Heinrich, 1891– III. Mittwoch, Eugen, 1876– IV. Mordtmann, Johannes Heinrich, 1852– V. Oxford. University. Bodleian library. Mss. (Turkish Marsh 179) VI. Vienna. Nationalbibliothek. Mss. (Arabic Flügel 2006) VII. Murād, bey, dragoman of the Sublime Porte, 16th cent.

Library of Congress PH3136.L5 28-12769

NL 0407779 DLC CU IU CtY NN OCl

Literature. [American ed.] v. 1–3; new ser., v. 1–2. Oct. 23, 1897–Nov. 24, 1899. New York, Harper & bros., 1897–99.
5 v. 31cm. weekly.
1897–98 are identical with English edition, except outside cover; 1899 is largely new matter.
Editors: 1897–98, H. D. Traill.—1899, J. K. Bangs.
No more published.

I. Traill, Henry Duff, 1842–1900, ed. II. Bangs, John Kendrick, 1862–1922, ed.

Library of Congress AP4.L438 1-2687

NL 0407780 DLC I TxU MB Nh OCl OO OClW

AP4 L57 Literature. [English periodical]
v.1-10; Oct. 23, 1897–Jan. 11. 1902.
London, The Times.
10 v. in 9. illus. 30cm.
Merged into Academy in 1902, later called Academy and literature.

NL 0407781 CoU OCU CtH

Literature; an illustrated weekly magazine. v. 1– (no. 1– Feb. 25, 1888–
New York [etc.] J. B. Alden, 1888–
v. illus. 20½cm.

1. Literature—Period. 2. Authors. 3. Authors, American.

27-25216

Library of Congress PN2.L65

NL 0407782 DLC ViU OClWHi MiU

Literature--an illustrated weekly magazine.

Literary portraits, being biographical and critical studies of contemporary and classical authors with illustrative selections from their works ... v. 1–2; 1888–89. New York, J. B. Alden, 1888–89.

Literature, ancient and modern, with specimens
see under [Goodrich, Samuel Griswold] 1793-1860.

PN 35 .F3 Literature and ideas series. v.1-
Greenwich, Conn., Fawcett Publications, 19 -

1. Literature-Hist. & crit.-Collections.

NL 0407785 DAU

804 L712 Literature and life; addresses to the English Association by Sir H. Idris Bell [and others] London, G. G. Harrap [1948]–
165 p. 20 cm.

1. Literature—Addresses, essays, lectures. I. Bell, Sir Harold Idris, 1879– II. English Association.

PN501.L5 804 48-25530*

ICU AAP IEN NIC IU MH PHC
NL 0407786 DLC NcU CtY MiU ICarbS NBC GU OU NNC TU

VOLUME 336

LITERATURE and Program Aids for the 50th Herzl Commemorative Year July 1954-July 1955 (New York) Joint Herzl Committee of the American Zionist Council and the Jewish Agency,(1954) 41s. (mimeographed) 28cm

1.Herzl, Theodor, 1860-1904.

NL 0407787 NNJ

Literature and psychology.

[Amherst, Mass., etc.]
v. in 28-29 cm. quarterly.
Began in 1951. Cf. New serial titles, 1950-60.
Vols. for -1959 sponsored by the Modern Language Association Conference on Literature and Psychology; 1960- by the association's General Topics 10.
Vols. for summer/fall 1964- published with assistance of English Dept. of the City College of the City University of New York; 1966, no. 3/4- with assistance of English Dept. of University of Massachusetts.
Editor: L. F. Manheim.
1. Literature—Psychology—Period. I. Manheim, Leonard Falk, 1902- ed. II. Conference on Literature and Psychology. III. Modern Language Association of America. General Topics 10.
PN49.L5 67-9054

CL TxU CU-Riv NN KU NhD
NL 0407788 DLC CoU WaU PU MiU NN PPT IU NcGU IEN

FILM 1.48 Literature and psychology. v.1- 1951- New York.

Microfilm. Ann Arbor, University Microfilms.

NL 0407789 MiU

Literature association of the Church union

see

Church union. Church literature association.

Literature book, The. [Edited by Roma Gans.]
— [Chicago. Shuman & Co. 1936.] (2), x, (1), 398 pp. Illus. Portraits, 1 colored. Plates. Autograph facsimile. Illustrated title-page. Illustrated end-papers. [The new wonder world. Vol. 8.] 25 cm., in 8s.
Extracts from the best literature, and seventeen biographies.

E1922 — English literature. Colls. — Biography. Colls. — S.r.c. — United States. Lit. Colls. — Gans, Roma, ed.

NL 0407791 MB

Literature concerning the new remedy for tuberculosis. n. t.-p. [Philadelphia, 1891.] 122-130 p. 8°.

Title from cover.
Repr.: Amer. naturalist. February, 1891.

1. Tuberculosis.—Tubercle bacillus: Bibliography.
N. Y. P. L. December 18, 1912.

NL 0407792 NN DNLM

Literature east & west. v. 1- spring 1954-
New Paltz, N. Y. [etc.]
v. in 28 cm. quarterly (irregular)
Issued by the Conference on Oriental-Western Literary Relations of the Modern Language Association of America.

1. Literature—Period. I. Modern Language Association of America. Conference on Oriental-Western Literary Relations.

PN2.L67 65-9986

NL 0407793 DLC NcGU IU CL NcRS TxU NN OU FU

Literature for children.... guides for the study of history, literature, travel ...
see under [Gibbons, Emma]

Literature for ladies, 1830-1930 ... illustrations by Ethel M. Arnold ... cover page lettering by Edgar T. Keith ... Manhattan, Kan., K. S. A. C. press [1930]

54 p., 1 l. illus. 22½cm. (On cover: Kansas state agricultural college bulletin. vol. XIV, no. 12; December 15, 1930)

CONTENTS.—Godey's lady's book, 1830-1898, by Elizabeth H. Davis.—Modern women's magazines, by Lilian Hughes Neiswanger.—The woman reader of 1930, by Mrs. Leslie Wallace.

1. Godey's magazine. 2. American periodicals.

Library of Congress PN4888.W6L5 35-1028

NL 0407795 DLC KMK ICRL NIC OCl

Literature for the high school. NY, American Book Company

no.2 (1935): Bennett, Henry Garland. On the high road

NL 0407796 MH

The literature of America.

Quinn, Arthur Hobson, 1875- ed.
The literature of America; an anthology of prose and verse ... edited by Arthur Hobson Quinn ... Albert Croll Baugh ... [and] Will David Howe ... New York, Chicago [etc.] C. Scribner's sons [°1938]

The literature of American history; a bibliographical guide, with supplement

see under

Larned, Josephus Nelson, 1836-1913, ed.

---

416 1 The literature of American numismatics ... (In Norton's literary letter. New York, 1859. 21cm. no.3,p.4-7. illus.)

NL 0407799 CtY

895.108 C539 1900 The Literature of Arabia. With critical and biographical sketches by Epiphanius Wilson, A.M. Rev. ed. New York, The Colonial press [°1900]
iv, 149p. illus. 24cm. (Oriental literature, v. IV)
On spine: The World's great classics.
Bound with: The Literature of China.
Contents.--The romance of Antar.-Arabian poetry.-Arabian nights.
1. Arabic literature--Translations into English. I. Wilson, Epiphanius, 1845-1916.

NL 0407800 TxDaM MiD OCU TxU Vi AU

PL 3277 E1L7 1900 The literature of China; with critical and biographical sketches by Epiphanius Wilson. Rev. ed. New York, Colonial Press [1900]
300 p. front. 24cm. (The World's great classics, Oriental literature, v. 4)
Bound with The literature of Arabia [New York, 1900]

1. Chinese literature. 2. Arabic literature. I. Wilson, Epiphanius, 1845-1916, ed. II. Title: The literature of Arabia.

NL 0407801 CMenSP Vi MiD TxU CLU TxDaM OCU

...The literature of India; with critical and biographical sketches by Epiphanius Wilson. Rev. ed. N. Y., Colonial press, °1900.
467 p. plate (World's great classics)

At head of title: Oriental literature [v.3]
Also pub. under title: Hindu literature.

I. Dutt, Toru, 1856-1877. II. Arnold, Sir Edwin, 1832-1904, tr. III. Monier-Williams, Sir Monier, 1819-1899, tr. IV. Wilson, Ephihanius, 1845-1916, ed.

NL 0407802 MiD ICU OCU Vi TxU FMU

850.8 J68l Ranney The literature of Italy, 1265-1907. Ed. by Rossiter Johnson and Dora Knowlton Ranous. With a general introduction by William Michael Rossetti... New translations, and former renderings compared and rev... [New York, The National alumni, c1906-07]
16v. mounted fronts, plates, ports. 0.

Frontispieces are identical.
Each vol. has also special t.-p. and frontispiece.

In cases.
"The Quirinal edition...limited to twenty-five copies." This set is no.1.
For contents and list of vols. in this library see next card.

Contents:
[v.1] Guerrazzi, F.D. Beatrice Cenci. [c1906]
[v.2] Manzoni, Alessandro. The betrothed. [c1906]
[v.3] Goldoni, Carlo. Three comedies. [c1907] Alfieri, Vittorio. Three tragedies. [c1907]
[v.4] Serao, Matilde. The conquest of Rome. [c1906]
[v.5] Castiglione, Baldassare, conte. The courtier. [c1907]

[v.6] Carcano, Giulio. Damiano, the story of a poor family. [c1907]
[v.7] Annunzio, Gabriele d'. The flame. [c1906]
[v.8] Flamini, Francesco. A history of Italian literature (1265-1907) [c1906]
[v.9] Tasso, Torquato. Jerusalem delivered. [c1907]
[v.10] Grossi, Tommaso. Marco Visconti. [c1907]

[v.11] Cellini, Benvenuto. Memoirs. [c1906]
[v.12] Johnson, Rossiter, and Ranous, Mrs. D.K. (Thompson) eds. An anthology of Italian authors from Cavalcanti to Fogazzaro (1270-1907) [c1907]
[v.13] Pellico, Silvio. My prisons and Francesca da Rimini. [c1906]
[v.14] Dante Alighieri. The new life. [c1907] Petrarca, Francesco. One hundred sonnets. [c1907]

[v.14] Boccaccio, Giovanni. La Fiammetta. [c1907]
Buonarroti, M.A. Poems. [c1907]
[v.15] Ariosto, Lodovico. Orlando furioso. [c1906]
[v.16] Machiavelli, Niccolò. The prince. [c1907]
Campanella, Tommaso. The city of the sun. [c1907]
Foscolo, Ugo. Essays. [c1907]
Mazzini, Giuseppe. Essays. [c1907]
Garibaldi, Giuseppe. Recollections. [c1907]

NL 0407808 IaU WaU IdU OClW ODW Wa ICU IU

...Literature of Japan; with critical and biographical sketches by Epiphanius Wilson. Rev. ed. N. Y., Colonial press, °1900.
296 p. port. (World's great classics)

At head of title: Oriental literature [v.2]
Also pub. under title: Japanese literature.
Bound with Literature of Persia, v.2.

NL 0407809 MiD TxU Vi OCU

VOLUME 336

Literature of libraries in the seventeenth and eighteenth centuries. Edited by John Cotton Dana and Henry W. Kent. Chicago, A. C. McClurg, 1906-07.
6 v. 18 cm.

1. Library science—Collections. I. Dana, John Cotton, 1856-1929, ed. II. Kent, Henry Watson, 1866-1948, ed.

Z674.L55 67-4901

NL 0407810 DLC NNC OC1W OC1 PPD MiU NjP OO ICJ CU

... The literature of medicine and science illustrating the romance of pain. New York, Old Hickory Bookshop [1941]
cover-title, 57 p., [1] illus. on cover.
At head of title: Catalogue No. 67, Autumn, 1941.
Anaesthesia Collection. Visulog, volume 1 (Autograph volume)
1. Pain, romance of - catalogue. I. Old Hickory Bookshop.

NL 0407811 KU-M

The literature of Oscar Wilde
see under [Callaghan, Kenneth Ford]

PK 6449 E1 P4 1900 The literature of Persia. With a special introd. by Richard J. H. Gottheil. Rev. ed. New York, The Colonial Press [c1900]
2 v. illus.
Published also with title: Persian literature.
Oriental literature, v.1-2
PERSIAN LITERATURE--TRANSLATIONS INTO ENGLISH
ENGLISH LITERATURE--TRANSLATIONS FROM PERSIAN

NL 0407813 KMK OCU Vi TxU

The literature of Persia
see also Persian literature.

The literature of philanthropy, 1893
see under Goodale, Frances Abigail (Rockwell) ed.

1888 The literature of the Christmas festival and of the customs connected with it. [anon.] Philadelphia, ledger, 1886.
23 p. 12°. [Philadelphia Ledger and Transcript, Dec. 25, 1886]
[Toner Excerpts]

NL 0407816 DLC

Literature of the heat pump
see under [Electrical world]

Literature of the Italian war
see under Bury, de, attributed author.

The literature of the local history of New York
see under [Ludewig, Hermann Ernst] 1810-1856.

*
PS1138 .Z9L57 1835 Literature of the nineteenth century. America. [n. p., 1835]
15 pieces. 27½cm.
Excerpted from various numbers of the Athenaeum.

1. Brown, Charles Brockden, 1771-1810.

NL 0407820 ViU

808.8 L776 1900 **Literature** of the Orient. Byzantine ed. Edited, grouped & classified, with introductions & translations by Sir Edwin Arnold, Max Müller, LL. D., René Basset, PH. D., Richard Gottheil, PH. D. & other oriental scholars. Epiphanius Wilson, A. M., literary editor; Clarence Cook, art editor. London, New York [etc.] The Colonial press [c1900-1901]
10 v. fronts. (part col.) plates, ports., facsims. 24 cm.
"Revised edition."

NL 0407821 FTaSU OCU

Literature of the Orient. Byzantine ed. Edited, grouped & classified, with introductions & translations by Sir Edwin Arnold, Max Müller, LL. D., René Basset, PH. D., Richard Gottheil, PH. D. & other oriental scholars. Epiphanius Wilson, A. M., literary editor; Clarence Cook, art editor. London, New York [etc.] The Colonial press [1902]
10 v. fronts. (part col.) plates, ports., facsims. 24cm.
"Limited to five hundred copies."
Each plate accompanied by guard sheet with descriptive letterpress.
CONTENTS.—[I] Babylonian and Assyrian literature. Armenian literature.—[II] Chinese literature. Arabian literature.—[III] Egyptian literature.—[IV] Hebrew literature.—[V] Hindu literature.—[VI] Moorish literature. Malayan literature.—[VII-VIII] Persian literature. Japanese literature.—[IX] Sacred books of the East.—[X] Turkish literature.
I. Wilson, Epiphanius, 1845-1916, ed.

Library of Congress PJ408.L5 30-8219

NL 0407822 DLC NIC PPDrop

The literature of the rail
see under [Phillips, Samuel] 1814-1854.

RC16.8 L776 Literature of the renaissance in 19 - ; a bibliography and index. [Chapel Hill North Carolina, 1917?-]
v.
Reprinted from Studies in philology.
Title varies: 1940(for the year 1939) Recent literature of the renaissance; 1941-53(for the years 1940-52) Recent literature of the renaissance; a bibliography and index.
1. Literature, Modern--15th and 16th cent.--Bibl. 2. English literature--Early Modern(to 1700)--Bibl. I. Title: Recent literature of the renaissance.

NL 0407824 ICarbS MiU NcU

Literature of the renaissance
see also Craig, Hardin, 1875-
Recent literature of the renaissance.

Literature of the road. Illustrated scenes and incidents on the lines of the Philadelphia and Reading rail road... Philadelphia, Baker, 1882.
98 p. illus., map.

1. Philadelphia and Reading railroad company.

NL 0407826 NjP

The **literature** of the second century. Short studies in Christian evidences. By F. R. Wynne, D. D., J. H. Bernard, D. D., and S. Hemphill, B. D. New York, J. Pott & co., 1891.
1 p. l., [vii]-viii, 270 p. 19½cm.
CONTENTS.—The evidence to Christianity supplied by the literature of the sub-apostolic age. The gradual growth of the New Testament canon. By Rev. F. R. Wynne.—The apocryphal gospels. The miraculous in early Christian literature. By Rev. J. H. Bernard.—The long-lost harmony. Early vestiges of the fourfold gospel. By Rev. S. Hemphill.

1. Christianity—Evidences. 2. Christian literature, Early — Hist. & crit. I. Wynne, Frederick Richards, bp., 1827-1896. II. Bernard, John Henry, 1860-1927. III. Hemphill, Samuel, 1859-1927.

Library of Congress BT1115.L7 1-15223

NL 0407827 MH ICU DLC IU PPRETS PHC ODW PPL PPDio IEG MB

The literature of the Servians and Croats
see under [Morfill, William Richard] 1834-1909.

The literature of the sixteenth and seventeenth centuries, illustrated by reprints of very rare tracts
see under Halliwell-Phillips, James Orchard.

The **literature** of the South African war, 1899-1902. By a British officer ... [New York, 1907]
cover-title, p. 299-321. 27cm.
Reprinted from the American historical review, vol. XII, no. 2, January, 1907.

1. South African war, 1899-1902—Bibl. I. British officer.

Library of Congress Z3918.L65 15-25896

N 0407830 DLC

AP4 .L44 Literature of the world revolution ...
Moscow, The State publishing house [1931]
v. illus., plates. 25cm.
"The central organ of the International union of revolutionary writers."
Edited by Bruno Jasienski and others.
Published also in Russian, French and German.
A special no. is bound in place of no.3, entitled: "Second international conference of revolutionary writers; reports, resolutions, debates ... 1931".
Ceased publication with no.5 ([Oct?] 1931); superseded by International literature.
I. Jasiénski, Bruno, 1901- ed. II. International union of revolutionary writers.

NL 0407832 DLC UU

... The literature of Uruguay in the year of its constitutional centenary ...
see under [Luisi, Luisa]

The literature of Utopia... 188?
see under [Upton, M.G.]

VOLUME 336

The Literature of working men; being the supplementary numbers of "The Working man's friend" ...
see under The Working man's friend, and family instructor.

QA1 .L52 Math.-Stat. Library

Literature on Hilbert space, 1940-1949.
[n.p., n.d.]
1 v. (unpaged)

Binder's title.
Abstracts of published papers, taken from Mathematical reviews.

1. Mathematics - Bibl. 2. Mathematics - Abstracts. 3. Spaces, Generalized. I. Title. II. Title: Hilbert space.

NL 0407836 CU

QA1 .L53 Math.-Stat. Library

Literature on linear space, 1940-1949.
[n.p., n.d.]
1 v. (unpaged)

Binder's title.
Abstracts of published papers, taken from Mathematical reviews.

1. Mathematics - Bibl. 2. Mathematics - Abstracts. 3. Spaces, Generalized. I. Title. II. Title: Linear space.

NL 0407837 CU

Literature on politics and industry in Danzig.
v. 1

Danzig: A. W. Kafemann, G.m.b.H., 1930 8°.
no. diagrs.

Editor : v. 1 , T. Rudolph.

Contents:
v. 1. Pelser, K. Danzig's shipping and foreign trade. 1930.

1. Economic history—Danzig. 2. Danzig—Govt. I. Rudolph, Theodor, editor.
N. Y. P. L. October 3, 1931

NL 0407838 NN

Literature on the natural history of the Arctic region with special reference to Alaska ...
see under Jackson, Hartley H[arrad] T[hompson], 1881-

Literature primers.
6 vol. London, etc. 1875-79. 16°. *Namely:—*
Edited by J. R. Green.

NL 0407840 MH NN

Literature primers, ed. by J.R. Green.
Jobb. Sir R.C. Greek literature, 1881.
Nichol John English composition. 1889.
Morris Richard English grammar. 4th ed. 1876.

NL 0407841 OClW OO

The literature relating to New Zealand
see under [Collier, James] 1846-

Literature review on oils and fats
see under India (Republic) Council of Scientific and Industrial Research.

Literature: I. Robert Burns. II. Sir Walter Scott. ... Lord Byron; from the Chicago record. New York, The Doubleday & McClure co., 1899.

xviii p., 1 l., 295 p. incl. front., illus., plates, ports. 20½cm. (Home study circle, ed. by Seymour Eaton)

Half-title: Popular studies in literature.
Critical studies, with selections from the authors.
Introductory study and biographical sketches of Scott and Byron signed by John Ebenezer Bryant.

1. Burns, Robert, 1759-1796. 2. Scott, Sir Walter, bart., 1771-1832. 3. Byron, George Gordon Noël Byron, 6th baron, 1788-1824. I. Bryant, John Ebenezer, 1849-1909, ed.

Library of Congress PR447.L6 99-5285 Revised

NL 0407844 DLC NjP PRosC MWelC PPD ViU OO NN OCl MB

QC 373 .O6 L77

LITERATURE SURVEY OF MATERIAL PUBLISHED RElating to specifications of hand held binoculars Prepared by Howard S. Coleman. From the confidential reports of the 33rd meeting [of the] Armed Forces-NRC Vision Committee, Nov. 12-13, 1953, Fort Knox, Kentucky. Ann Arbor, Mich., The Executive Secretariat, University of Michigan [1953?]
59 p. illus.

1. Field-glasses. I. Coleman, Howard S 1917- II. Armed Forces-National Research Council Vision Committee.

NL 0407845 InU

Die literaturen des Ostens in einzeldarstellungen.
Leipzig, 19-

see

Die litteraturen des Ostens [etc.]

Литературен збор.
Скопје, 195
v. in 23 cm. quarterly.

Began publication in 1954. Cf. New serial titles, 1950-1960.
Issued by the Društvo za makedonski jazik i literatura.

1. Macedonian language. 2. Macedonian literature. I. Društvo za makedonski jazik i literatura.
Title transliterated: Literaturen zbor.

PG1161.L5 65-31954

NL 0407847 DLC

AC8 .W362

Literature's golden age.

Watts, L Owen.
Literature's golden age, and other articles by L. Owen Watts. Ilfracombe, N. Devon, A. H. Stockwell, ltd. [1944]

Literatures of the world

see

Short histories of the literatures of the world

Literaturgeschichte; die deutsche und die fremde Dichtung...
see under [Henschke, Alfred] 1891-1928.

Literatur-Gesellschaft "Neue Bahnen".
Ordentliche Veröffentlichungen der Literatur-Gesellschaft "Neue Bahnen"...
Leipzig: R. Voigtländer, 19 8°.
v.

NL 0407851 NN

PN 462 .L 77

LITERATURKALENDER: SPEKTRUM DES GEISTES. Ein Querschnitt durch das Geistes- und Verlagsschaffen der Gegenwart. - Jahrgang. [Ebenhausen bei München] Langewiesche-Brandt [19]
v.

Editor: H. Voss.

I. Voss, Hartfrid. 1903- ed.

NL 0407852 InU

Literatur-Katalog. 1904/05-
[Köln, etc.] Koehler & Volckmar [etc.]
v. in 25 cm.

Publication suspended 1943-1958.
Issued also with title: Barsortiments-Lagerkatalog.
Title varies: 1904/05-19 Deutscher Literatur-Katalog.
Vols. for 1904-19 issued by F. Volckmar.
"Überreicht von F. A. Brockhaus, Leipzig," 1904-
Supplements accompany some vols.

1. German literature—Bibl.—Catalogs. I. Koehler & Volckmar. II. Volckmar, F., firm, booksellers, Leipzig. III. Brockhaus, firm, publishers, Leipzig.

Z2221.D5 5-10363 rev 2*

OCl OClW OU NjR PPTU MoS PHC PU OClW MBdAF
NjR MiU NBuU CBGTU NcU MnU-A OO OCU NNC OrU MB
WaS OrU IdU CtY OU ICU IU ICRL ICJ NN DS NcD
NL 0407853 DLC DNLM NcD CaBVaU OrCS OrPR OrP MtU

Literatur-Merkbüchlein. Wegweiser auf dem Gebiete der deutschen Literatur. Zweite, wesentlich vermehrte Auflage. Reudnitz an Leipzig: H. Pfeil, 1869. iv, 112 p. 15½cm.

Bibliography, p. iv.

1. Authors, German.
N. Y. P. L. February 4, 1942

NL 0407855 NN

Літературна Одеса; літературно-художній та публіцистичний альманах. (4-5, 15-21)
[Одеса] Одеське обл. вид-во, 19(51-58)
(19 v. in illus., ports., music. 26 cm.

Began publication in 1948. Cf. Летопись периодических изданий СССР, 1955, № 684.
Vols. 17-18 issued together.
Issued by Odes'ka filiia of the Spilka radians'kykh pys'mennykiv Ukraïny.
Ukrainian or Russian.

1. Ukrainian literature—Odessa. 2. Russian literature—Odessa. I. Spilka pys'mennykiv Ukraïny. Odes'ka filiia.
Title transliterated: Literaturna Odesa.

PG3957.O2L5 60-23907

NL 0407856 DLC

Литературна Стара Загора; сборник. Стихотворения, разкази, очерци. [Редактори: К. Коняров, Ив. Мирчев, Тр. Даскалов] Стара Загора, Литературен колектив "Георги Бакалов," 1955.

230 p. 21 cm.

1. Bulgarian literature—Stara Zagora. I. Komiarov, Konstantin, ed.
Title transliterated: Literaturna Stara Zagora.

PG1044.L5 58-35336 ‡

NL 0407857 DLC

VOLUME 336

Z 7164 P65 L5
Literatur-nachrichten; philatelic digest. Nr. 1- 1951-
[München,]
v. 21-30 cm. irregular.

"Im Verlag des Bundes deutscher Philatelisten e. V. ... unter Mitwirkung der Stadtbibliothek München, philat. Abteilung."
Subtitle varies.

NL 0407858 OU

Z7914 .P9L6
Literaturnachweis der Papier- und Zellstoffindustrie.
Wiesbaden, Dr. Sändig Verlag K. G., 1954-
v. 22 cm.
Editor: v. H. Fiebiger.

1. Paper making and trade—Bibl. I. Fiebiger, H., ed.

A 55-95 rev

Washington. Univ., for Library of Congress Seattle. Library [r55b1]

NL 0407859 WaU DLC NN

Literaturnachweis des wohnungs- und siedlungswesens für die jahre 1933 und 1934- 1. und 2.- jahrg. ... Berlin-Charlottenburg, E. Wasmuth gmbh, 1936-
v. 23cm.
Editor: 1933/34- Rose von Mangoldt.
"Mit unterstützung der Stiftung zur förderung von bauforschungen herausgegeben vom Deutschen verein für wohnungsreform."

1. Housing—Bibliography. I. Mangoldt, Rose von, ed. II. Deutscher verein für wohnungsreform.

A C 37-1168

Michigan. Univ. Library for Library of Congress Z7164.H8L77

NL 0407860 MiU IU MH

Литературная Аджария; сборник произведений писателей Аджарии. Батуми, Гос. изд-во, 1954.
210 p. 23 cm

1. Georgian literature—Translations into Russian. 2. Russian literature — Translations from Georgian. 3. Georgian literature — Adzharia. *Title transliterated:* Literaturnaîa Adzharîa.

PK9184.R1L5 57-29929 ‡

NL 0407861 DLC

Литературная Башкирия; альманах.
Уфа, Башкирское книжное изд-во, 19
v. illus. 23 cm.
Began publication in 1948. Cf. Летопись периодических изданий СССР, 1955, № 680.
Issued by Russkaîa sekfsiîa of the Soîuz sovetskikh pisateleĭ Bashkirii.

1. Russian literature—Bashkiria. I. Soîuz pisateleĭ Bashkirii. *Title transliterated:* Literaturnaîa Bashkiriîa.

PG3504.B3L5 60-23898

NL 0407862 DLC InU

Литературная энциклопедия. Редакционная коллегия: П. И. Лебедев-Полянский [и др.] Ответственный редактор В. М. Фриче. [Москва] Изд-во Коммунистической академии, 1929-
v. illus., ports. 26 cm.
At head of title of v. 1-3: Коммунистическая академия. Секция литературы, искусства и языка; v. 4-8: Коммунистическая академия. Институт литературы, искусства и языка (v. 6-8: Научно-исследовательский институт литературы и искусства)
Vols. 3-9, 11: Главный редактор А. В. Луначарский.

1. Literature—Dictionaries. 2. Literature—Bio-bibl. 3. Russian literature—Dictionaries. *Title transliterated:* Literaturnaîa ênfsiklopediîa.

PN41.L45 50—42482

NL 0407863 DLC GU CSt OrP

Литературная энциклопедия. Редакционная коллегия: П. И. Лебедев-Полянский [и др.] Ответственный редактор В. М. Фриче. [Москва] Изд-во Коммунистической академии, 1929- [Ann Arbor, J. W. Edwards, 1948-
v. illus., ports. 26 cm. (American Council of Learned Societies reprints: Russian series, no. 20)
At head of title of v. 1-3: Коммунистическая академия. Секция литературы, искусства и языка; v. 4-8: Коммунистическая академия. Институт литературы, искусства и языка (v. 6-8: Научно-исследовательский институт литературы и искусства)
Vols. 3-9, 11: Главный редактор А. В. Луначарский.
"Photo-lithoprint reproduction."

1. Literature—Dictionaries, indexes, etc. 2. Literature—Bio-bibl. 3. Russian literature—Dictionaries, indexes, etc. (Series: American Council of Learned Societies Devoted to Humanistic Studies. Reprints: Russian series, no. 20)
— .... *Title transliterated:* Literaturnaîa ênfsiklopediîa.

PN41.L46 50-41535
Library of Congress [3]

NL 0407864 DLC TU OrU PSt OrCS

Литературная эстрада; в помощь художественной самодеятельности. [Составитель П. Т. Щипунов] Ленинград, Искусство, 1948.
637 p. 21 cm.
Errata slip inserted.

1. Russian literature — 19th cent. 2. Russian literature — 20th cent. I. Shchipunov, P. T., comp. *Title transliterated:* Literaturnaîa êstrada.

PG3226.L5 49-14384*

NL 0407865 DLC

Литературная газета. т. 1-
1 янв. 1830-
Санктпетербургъ.
v. 30 cm. every five days.

Title transliterated: Literaturnaîa gazeta.

AP50.L5 51-36937

NL 0407866 DLC

Литературная газета.

Санктпетербургъ.
v. illus., ports. 30 cm.
Frequency varies.
Published 1831-49. Cf. Lisovskiĭ, N. M., Russk. period. pechat', 1703-1900, no. 325 and 435.
Title varies: 1831-39, Литературныя прибавленія къ Русскому инвалиду.

I. Russkiĭ invalid. Supplement. *Title transliterated:* Literaturnaîa gazeta.

AP50.L515 52-50851

NL 0407867 DLC

AP50 .R3
Literaturnaîa gruppa "Kuznifsa," Moscow.
Рабочий журнал.
Москва, Госиздат.

Литературная Калуга; альманах.
Калуга, Изд-во газеты "Знамя,"
v. illus., music. 23 cm.
Began publication in 1951. Cf. Летопись периодических изданий СССР, 1955, № 681.
Issued by Kaluzhskoe literaturnoe ob"edinenie.
Subtitle varies.
Vols. for (1956-) called also (no.3-)

1. Russian literature—Kaluga (Province) I. Kaluzhskoe literaturnoe ob"edinenie. *Title transliterated:* Literaturnaîa Kaluga.

PG3504.K33L48 60-23904

NL 0407869 DLC

Литературная Мордовия; литературно-художественный альманах.
Саранск, Мордовское книжное изд-во, 19
v. 23 cm.
Began publication in 1940. Cf. Летопись периодических изданий СССР, 1955. № 683.
Vols. called also 19
Issued by Soîuz pisateleĭ Mordovskoĭ ASSR.

1. Mordvinian literature—Translations into Russian. 2. Russian literature—Translations from Mordvinian. 3. Russian literature—Mordovskaya A. S. S. R. I. Soîuz pisateleĭ Mordovskoĭ ASSR. *Title transliterated:* Literaturnaîa Mordoviîa.

60-24846

NL 0407870 DLC NIC

Литературная Рязань; литературно-художественный и публицистический альманах.
Рязань, Изд. газеты "Приокская правда," 195
v. illus., ports. 21 cm.
Began publication in 1955. Cf. Летопись журнальных статей, 1956.
Issued by Rîazanskoe oblastnoe literaturnoe ob"edinenie.

1. Russian literature — Ryazanskaya oblast'. I. Rîazanskoe oblastnoe literaturnoe ob"edinenie. *Title transliterated:* Literaturnaîa Rîazan'.

PG3504.R9L5 60-23906

NL 0407871 DLC

Литературная Тула; литературно-художественный и общественно-политический альманах.
[Тула] Тульское книжное изд-во, 19
v. illus. 23 cm.
Began publication in 1948. Cf. Летопись периодических изданий СССР, 1950-1954, № 2823.
Issued by Tul'skoe oblastnoe literaturnoe ob"edinenie.

I. Tul'skoe oblastnoe literaturnoe ob"edinenie. *Title transliterated:* Literaturnaîa Tula.

AP50.L52 60-21009

NL 0407872 DLC

Литературная учеба. г. 1-
1930-
Москва, Советский писатель [etc.]
v. in ports. 22-24 cm.
Frequency varies.
Editor: 1930-36, M. Gor'kiĭ.

1. Literature—Hist. & crit.—Period. 2. Russian literature—Hist. & crit.—Period. I. Gorkiĭ, Maxim, 1868-1936, ed. *Title transliterated:* Literaturnaîa ucheba.

PN9.L48 48-42186*

NL 0407873 DLC PSt

Литературная Вологда; альманах.
Вологда, Вологодское книжное изд-во, 195
v. illus., ports. 21 cm.
Began publication in 1955. Cf. Летопись периодических изданий СССР, 1957, № 972.

1. Russian literature—Vologda (City) *Title transliterated:* Literaturnaîa Vologda.

PG3505.V6L5 60-42800

NL 0407874 DLC

Literaturno-dramaticheskoe obshchestvo v S.-Peterburgê.
Уставъ. С.-Петербургъ, Тип. И. Н. Скороходова, 1887.
20 p. 19 cm.

Title romanized: Ustav.

PN2017.R8L5 72-297014

NL 0407875 DLC

VOLUME 336

891.708 L776Е Литературно-художественные альманахи издательства "Шиповникъ." кн. 1-26. Петроградъ (Санктпетербургъ) 1907-17.
v. plates. 25 cm.
Cover title: v. 17-26, Альманахи издательства "Шиповникъ." Vol. 25 has also a distinctive title: Метель.
1. Russian literature—20th cent.—Period. I. Shipovnik, Izdatel'stvo. II. Title: Al'manakhi izdatel'stva "Shipovnik." III. Title: Metel'.
Title transliterated: Literaturno-khudozhestvennye al'manakhi izdatel'stva "Shipovnik."
PG3227.L48 54-54865

NL 0407876 DLC OCH CaBVaU KU CoU TU NcD IaAS

Литературно-критические чтения. [Сессия 1- 16/19 марта 1951- Москва, Гос. изд-во детской лит-ры.
v. 21 cm.
Sponsored by Dom detskoĭ knigi in Moscow.
1. Children's literature, Russian—Hist. & crit. I. Dom detskoĭ knigi. *Title transliterated:* Literaturno-kriticheskie chtenii͡a.
PN1009.R8D58 52-37520

NL 0407877 DLC

Літературно-науковий вістник. річник 1- (т. 1-) 1898- [Київ, etc.]
v. in 23-25 cm.
Vols. 1-29 issued by Naukove tovarystvo imeni Shevchenka; v. 30-36 by Ukraïns'ko-rus'ka vydavnycha spilka u L'vovi.
I. Naukove tovarystvo imeni Shevchenka. II. Ukraïns'ko-rus'ka vydavnycha spilka.
Title romanized: Literaturno-naukovyĭ vistnyk.
AP58.U5L49 67-116379

NL 0407878 DLC NNC OU MH InU NN

Літературно-науковий збірник. 1- Нью-Йорк, 1952-
v. 25 cm.
Issued by the Ukrainian Academy of Arts and Sciences in the United States.
1. Ukrainians in the U. S.—Period. I. Ukrainian Academy of Arts and Sciences in the United States.
Title transliterated: Literaturno-naukovyĭ zbirnyk.
E184.U5U352 54-35437

NL 0407879 DLC CaBVaU

Литературное наследство. [т.] 1- 1931- Москва, Институт литературы Академии наук СССР [etc.]
v. in illus., ports. (part col.) 26-28 cm. irregular.
Vols. 1-2 sponsored by Institut literatury i iskusstva Kommunisticheskoĭ akademii and Rossiĭskai͡a assot͡siat͡sii͡a proletarskikh pisateleĭ.
1. Literature—Hist. & crit.—Period. 2. Russian literature—Hist. & crit.—Period. I. Akademii͡a nauk SSSR. Institut literatury. II. Kommunisticheskai͡a akademii͡a, Moscow. Nauchno-issledovatel'skiĭ institut literatury i iskusstva. III. Rossiĭskai͡a assot͡siat͡sii͡a proletarskikh pisateleĭ. *Title transliterated:* Literaturnoe nasledstvo.
PN9.L5 48-34746*

KyU MdBJ WaTC KU OU CtNIC ICRL OOxM CSt
NL 0407880 DLC IdPI CaBVaU OrPR IU ICU GU OrU IaU

Литературное обозрение. г. 1- янв. 1936- Москва.
v. in illus., ports. 22-26 cm. semimonthly.
Issued Jan. 1936-Nov. 20, 1940 as a supplement to Литературный критик; Dec. 5, 1940- by Institut mirovoĭ literatury of Akademii͡a nauk SSSR.
1. Bibliography—Period. 2. Books—Reviews. I. Literaturnyĭ kritik. Supplement. II. Akademii͡a nauk SSSR. Institut mirovoĭ literatury. *Title transliterated:* Literaturnoe obozrenie.
Z1007.L7736 52-18152

NL 0407881 DLC

Литературное обозрѣніе. т. 1- 1 янв. 1895- С. Петербургъ.
v. 31 cm.
Weekly, 1895-96; monthly, 1897- Cf. Lisovskiĭ, N. M. Русская періодическая печать.
1. Bibliography—Period. 2. Books—Reviews.
Title transliterated: Literaturnoe obozrenie.
Z1007.L7737 51-38980

NL 0407882 DLC InU

Literaturnoe obshchestvo pri I. IUr'evskom universitetie
see under Tartu. Ülikool. Ucheno-literaturnoe obshchestvo.

AP50 .L53 Литературные листки. г. 1-2; авг. 1823-дек. 1824. Санктпетербургъ.
2 v. in 23 cm.
Monthly, 1823; semimonthly, 1824.
L. C. set incomplete: v. 1 wanting.
Title transliterated: Literaturnye listki.
AP50.L53 51-53699

NL 0407884 DLC

Literaturnye manifesty.
Литературные манифесты: От символизма до "Октября." Составили Н. Л. Бродский и Н. П. Сидоров. [Москва] Новая Москва, 1924-
v. 24 cm.
CONTENTS: 1. Россия.
1. Russian literature—20th century—History and criticism. I. Brodskiĭ, Nikolaĭ Leont'evich, 1881-1951, comp. II. Sidorov, Nikolaĭ Pavlovich, comp. III. Title: Ot simvolizma do Oktiabri͡a.
PG3016.L48 72-216315

NL 0407885 DLC

Htb26 L712 Литературные портфели; статьи, заметки и неизданные материалы по новой русской литературе из собраний Пушкинского Дома. Петербург, Атеней, 1923-
v. 25 cm.
Contents.—1. Время Пушкина.
1. Russian literature—Hist. & crit. I. Akademii͡a nauk SSSR. Pushkinskiĭ Dom. *Title transliterated:* Literaturnye portfeli.
PG2932.L5 50-29750

NL 0407886 DLC CaBVaU IaU CtY

Литературный альбомъ для публичныхъ чтеній, въ 2-хъ частяхъ, извѣстнаго чтеца и артиста Императорскихъ С.-Петербургскихъ театровъ П. А. Никитина. Съ его біографіей и портретомъ, исполненнымъ художникомъ Н. С. Матвѣевымъ. Москва, Изданіе Е. И. Никитиной, Типографія Ф. Іогансонъ, 1881.
xii p., 2 l., 208 p. incl. port. 20½ cm.
1. Russian poetry (Collections) 2. Nikitin, Pavel Aleksandrovich, 1836-1880. I. Matveev, Nikolaĭ Sergeevich.
Title transliterated: Literaturnyĭ al'bom.
PG3230.5.L5 47-44912

NL 0407887 DLC

Литературный альманахъ "Грани." кн. 1-2. Берлинъ, Изд-во "Грани," 1922-23.
2 v. in 1. 23 cm.
1. Russian literature—20th cent.
Title transliterated: Literaturnyĭ al'manakh "Grani."
PG3227.L49 61-56310

NL 0407888 DLC

Литературный архив; материалы по истории литературы и общественного движения. 1- Москва, 1938-
v. illus., ports., facsims. 23-30 cm.
Issued 1938-40 by Institut literatury of Akademii͡a nauk SSSR; 1951- by its Institut russkoĭ literatury.
Publication suspended 1941-50.
1. Russian literature—Hist. & crit.—Period. 2. Authors, Russian—Correspondence, reminiscences, etc. I. Akademii͡a nauk SSSR. Institut literatury. II. Akademii͡a nauk SSSR. Institut russkoĭ literatury.
Title transliterated: Literaturnyĭ arkhiv; materialy po istorii literatury i obshchestvennogo dvizhenii͡a.
PG2900.L55 47-44270 rev

NL 0407889 DLC OrU CaBVaU ICU GEU TU CSt PU PPULC

Литературный Азербайджан; литературно-художественный журнал. Баку.
v. in illus., ports. 25 cm. monthly.
Began publication in 1931. Cf. Летопись периодических изданий СССР, 1950-1954, № 2695.
Publication suspended 1942-June 1953.
Organ of Soi͡uz sovetskikh pisateleĭ Azerbaĭdzhana.
Vols. no. called also no.
I. Soi͡uz sovetskikh pisateleĭ Azerbaĭdzhana, Baku.
Title transliterated: Literaturnyĭ Azerbaĭdzhan.
AP50.L54 59-23229

NL 0407890 DLC CLU CtY

Literaturnyĭ fond, *Leningrad*
see
Obshchestvo dli͡a posobii͡a nuzhdai͡ushchimsi͡a literatoram i uchenym, *Leningrad.*

Литературный Ярославль.
[Ярославль] Ярославское книжное изд-во, 19
v. illus., ports. 23 cm.
Began publication in 1947. Cf. Летопись периодических изданий СССР, 1950-1954, № 2837.
Issued by I͡Aroslavskoe otdelenie of the Soi͡uz pisateleĭ RSFSR.
1. Russian literature—Yaroslavl'—Period. 2. Russian literature—20th cent.—Period. I. Soi͡uz pisateleĭ RSFSR. I͡Aroslavskoe otdelenie. *Title transliterated:* Literaturnyĭ I͡Aroslavl'.
PG3505.Y3L5 59-45228

NL 0407892 DLC

Литературный календарь.
Ленинград, Художественная литература.
v. illus., ports. 18 x 23 cm.
1. Almanacs, Russian. 2. Literary calendars.
Title transliterated: Literaturnyĭ kalendar'.
AY946.L5 61-56055

NL 0407893 DLC InU

Литературный Киргизстан; литературно-художественный и общественно-политический журнал. [г. 1]- 1955-
Фрунзе, Советтик Кыргызстан [etc.]
v. in illus., ports. 27 cm.
Bimonthly, 1955-62; quarterly, 1963-
Vols. 1-2 (1955-56) called v. 16-17, continuing the vol. numbering of Альманах Киргизстан, which it supersedes; v. 3- called also no. 18-
Organ of Soi͡uz pisateleĭ Kirgizii (called prior to Aug. 1956 Soi͡uz sovetskikh pisateleĭ Kirgizii)
Title varies: 1955-56, no. 4, Киргизстан.
I. Soi͡uz pisateleĭ Kirgizii. II. Title: Kirgizstan.
Title transliterated: Literaturnyĭ Kirgizstan.
AP50.L545 64-46868

NL 0407894 DLC

VOLUME 336

Литературный критик; ежемесячный журнал литературной теории критики и истории литературы.

Москва.

v. in illus., plates, ports. 28 cm. monthly.

Began publication in 1933.

1. Literature—Hist. & crit.—Period. 2. Russian literature—Hist. & crit.—Period. *Title transliterated:* Literaturnyĭ kritik.

PN9.L53 52-19036

NL 0407895 DLC CSt CaBVaU

Film
2706 **Литературный** критик; ежемесячный журнал литературной теории критики и истории литературы.

Москва.

v. in illus., plates, ports. 28 cm. monthly.

Began publication in 1933.
Microfilm. Positive.

NL 0407896 IU CaBVaU LU

Literaturnyĭ kritik. Supplement.

Z1007
.L7736 Литературное обозрение. г. 1- янв. 1936-
Москва.

Literaturnyĭ muzeĭ, *Tartu*
see
Tartu. Fr. R. Kreutzwaldi nimeline Kirjandusmuuseum.

Literaturnyĭ muzeĭ L. N. Tolstogo, *Yasnaya Polyana*
see
Yasnaya Polyana, Russia. Muzeĭ-usad'ba L. N. Tolstogo "I͡Asnai͡a Poli͡ana."

Литературный музеумъ на 1827 годъ, Владиміра Измайлова. Москва, Изд. А. Ширяева, 1827.

320 p. 14 cm.

"Гишпанская пѣсня. Слова А. С. Пушкина, музыка А. Н. Верстовскаго" (for voice and piano) : fold. plate following p. 320.

1. Russian literature—19th cent. 2. Pushkin, Aleksandr Sergeevich, 1799-1837—Musical settings. I. Izmaĭlov, Vladimir Vasil'evich, 1773-1830, ed. II. Verstovskiĭ, Alekseĭ Nikolaevich, 1799-1862. Gishpanskai͡a pi͡esni͡a. *Title transliterated:* Literaturnyĭ muzeum.

PG3226.L52 61-56034

NL 0407900 DLC

Литературный распадъ; критическій сборникъ. 2. изд. С.-Петербургъ, Изд. "Т-ва Издательское бюро," 1908-09.

2 v. in 1. 23 cm.

Vol. 2 without edition statement, published by "EOS."
Bibliographical footnotes.

1. Russian literature—20th cent.—Addresses, essays, lectures. *Title transliterated:* Literaturnyĭ raspad.

PG3016.L5 66-49790 rev

NL 0407901 DLC CaBVaU MoU TxU TNJ

Літературний рапорт XII і XVII з'їздам партії. [За ред. І. Кириленко, І. Кулика, І. Микитенко. Харків?] ДВОУ, ЛІМ, 1934.

278 p. ports. 25 cm.

"XVII з'їздові Всесоюзної комуністичної партії (більшовиків), XII з'їздові КП(б)У" ([iv] p. laid in)

1. Ukrainian literature (Collections) I. Kyrylenko, Ivan, ed. II. Kulyk, Ivan I͡Ulianovych, 1897-1941, ed. III. Mykytenko, Ivan Kindratovych, 1897-1937, ed. IV. Kommunisticheskai͡a partii͡a Ukrainy. 12. s"ezd, Kharkov, 1934. V. Kommunisticheskai͡a partii͡a Sovetskogo Soi͡uza. 17. s"ezd, Moscow, 1934.
Title transliterated: Literaturnyĭ raport dvanadtsi͡atomu i simnadtsi͡atomu z'ïzdam partiï.

PG3932.L49 65-49405

NL 0407902 DLC

FILM
891.7908
L712 **Літературний** рапорт XII і XVII з'їздам партії. [За ред. І. Кириленко, І. Кулика, І. Микитенко. Харків?] ДВОУ, ЛІМ, 1934.

278 p. ports. 25 cm.

"XVII з'їздові Всесоюзної комуністичної партії (більшовиків), XII з'їздові КП(б)У" ([iv] p. laid in)

Microfilm (negative). Washington, D.C., Library of Congress, 1967. 1 reel. 35mm.

Title transliterated: Literaturnyĭ raport dvanadtsi͡atomu i simnadtsi͡atomu z'ïzdam partiï.

NL 0407903 IU

Литературный Саратов (*transliterated:* Literaturnyĭ Saratov)
see
Новая Волга (*transliterated:* Novai͡a Volga)

Литературный сборникъ издаваемый Галицко-русскою матицею ... Львовъ, Тип. Ставропигійского института, 1887-

v. front. (port.) pl. 24cm.

Literary miscellany pub. by the Ruthenian society.
Editor: 1887- B. A. Dīditskiĭ.
The volume for 1887 contains I. E. Levitskiĭ's Галицко-русская библіографія за 1887-ый годъ (p. [278]-344)

1827-1908.
I. Dīditskiĭ, Bogdan A., II. Galitsko-russkai͡a matitsa, Lemberg.

5-7443

NL 0407905 DLC

Литературный сборникъ памяти Н. А. Некрасова (1877-1902) Москва, Изд. ред. Кружка писателей изъ народа, 1903.

154 p. 18 cm. (Писатели изъ народа. Сер. 1, вып. 2)

1. Nekrasov, Nikolaĭ Alekseevich, 1821-1877. 2. Russian literature—19th cent.
Title transliterated: Literaturnyĭ sbornik pami͡ati N. A. Nekrasova.

PG3226.L53 54-53698 ‡

NL 0407906 DLC

Литературный Смоленск; альманах.
[Смоленск] Смоленское книжное изд-во, 19

v. 23 cm.

Began publication in 1940. Cf. Летопись периодических изданий. СССР, 1957, № 983.
Issued by Smolenskoe otdelenie of Soi͡uz pisateleĭ SSSR.

1. Russian literature—Smolensk, Russia (City) I. Soi͡uz pisateleĭ SSSR. Smolenskoe otdelenie.
Title transliterated: Literaturnyĭ Smolensk.

PG3505.S6L5 60-24718

NL 0407907 DLC

Literaturnyĭ t͡sentr konstruktivistov, *Moscow.*

Бизнес; сборник, под ред. Корнелия Зелинского и Ильи Сельвинского. [Москва] Гос. изд-во, 1929.

200 p. 23 cm.

1. Russian literature—20th cent. 2. Constructivism (Russian literature) I. Zelinskiĭ, Korneliĭ Li͡ut͡sianovich, 1896- ed. II. Sel'vinskiĭ, Il'i͡a L'vovich, 1899- ed. III. Title.
Title transliterated: Biznes.

PG3227.L5 52-45810

NL 0407908 DLC

Literaturnyĭ t͡sentr konstruktivistov, Moscow.

Zelinskiĭ, Korneliĭ Li͡ut͡sianovich, 1896- *ed.*

Госплан литературы; сборник Литературного центра конструктивистов (ЛЦК) под редакцией Корнелия Зелинского и Ильи Сельвинского. Москва-Ленинград, "Круг" [1924]

Литературный современник. г. [1]- янв. 1933-
Ленинград.

v. in illus., plates, ports. 23 cm. monthly.

Supersedes Ленинград, 1930-32. Cf. no. 9-10/11, 1932, p. [3] of cover.
Organ of Soi͡uz sovetskikh pisateleĭ SSSR (of its Leningradskoe otdelenie, Jan. 1939)

I. Soi͡uz sovetskikh pisateleĭ SSSR.
Title transliterated: Literaturnyĭ sovremennik.

AP50.L55 51-54995

NL 0407910 DLC

Литературный современник. № 1-
Мюнхен, 1951-

v. in 25 cm.

Title also in French, English and German.

1. Russian literature in foreign countries—Period.
Title transliterated: Literaturnyĭ sovremennik (Munich)

PG3516.L5 54-18105

NL 0407911 DLC

Литературный Сталинград; альманах.

Сталинград.

v. 22 cm. irregular.

Issued by Stalingradskoe otdelenie of Soi͡uz sovetskikh pisateleĭ.

1. Russian literature—20th cent. 2. Russian literature—Stalingrad. I. Soi͡uz .. pisateleĭ, Stalingradskoe otdelenie.
Title transliterated: Literaturnyĭ Stalingrad; al'manakh.

PG3505.S82S623 52-28411

NL 0407912 DLC

Литературный Таджикистан; альманах. [кн.] 1-

Сталинабад, Таджикгосиздат, 1950-

v. 22-24 cm.

Title varies: v. 1, Таджикистан.
Issued by Soi͡uz pisateleĭ Tadzhikistana (called 1950-51 Soi͡uz sovetskikh pisateleĭ Tadzhikistana)

1. Tajik literature—Translations into Russian. 2. Russian literature—Translations from Tajik. I. Soi͡uz pisateleĭ Tadzhikistana.
Title transliterated: Literaturnyĭ Tadzhikistan; al'manakh.

PK6978.9.L5 57-39100 rev

NL 0407913 DLC

VOLUME 336

Литературный Татарстан,
Казань, Татарское книжное изд-во, 19 -58.
no. in 21 cm.
Published 1947-58. Cf. Летопись периодических изданий СССР, 1955-1960, № 7978.
Issued by Soi͡uz sovetskikh pisateleĭ TASSR.
Superseded by Литературная Казань.

1. Russian literature—Tatar Republic. I. Soi͡uz sovetskikh pisateleĭ Tatarskoĭ ASSR.
Title transliterated: Literaturnyĭ Tatarstan.

PG3504.T3L5 64-59565

NL 0407914 DLC

Literaturnyĭ vi͡estnik.

Z6956
.R9L5

Lisovskiĭ, Nikolaĭ Mikhaĭlovich, 1854-1920.
Списокъ указателей къ русскимъ періодическимъ изданіямъ XVIII-XIX ст. Изъ журнала "Литературный вѣстникъ." С.-Петербургъ, Тип. А. Э. Винеке, 1903.

Литературный Воронеж; альманах.
[Воронеж] Воронежское обл. книгоизд-во.
v. 20 cm.
Published 1937-56. Cf. Летопись периодических изданий СССР, 1955-1960, № 7992.
Issued by Voronezhskoe otdelenie of Soi͡uz sovetskikh pisateleĭ.

1. Russian literature—Voronezh, Russia (Province) I. Soi͡uz pisateleĭ SSSR. Voronezhskoe otdelenie.
Title transliterated: Literaturnyĭ Voronezh.

PG3504.V65L5 64-59566

NL 0407916 DLC

Літературний журнал.
Харків, Держ. літературне вид-во.
v. in illus., ports. 23 cm. monthly.
Organ of Spilka radi͡ans'kykh pys'mennykiv Ukraïny.
Editor: 19 P. Khodchenko.

I. Khodchenko, Pavlo Semenovych, ed. II. Spilka pys'mennykiv Ukraïny.
Title transliterated: Literaturnyĭ zhurnal.

AP58.U5L5 49-35642*

NL 0407917 DLC

Literatūros almanachas.
[Nr.] 1

Minsk: Baltarusijos valstybinė leidykla nacionalinis sektorius, 1934 22½cm.
v.

1. Periodicals—Latvia. 2. Bolshevism—Latvia.
N. Y. P. L. November 13, 1936

NL 0407918 NN

Literatūros lankai; neperiodinis poezijos, prozos ir kritikos žodis. nr. 1- 1952-
Buenos Aires.
no. in v. illus., ports. 37 cm.

AP95.L5L5 65-57091

NL 0407919 DLC

Literatursammlung aus dem gesamtgebiet der agrikulturchemie. Freising.

NL 0407920 OU NcD

Literatur-Verzeichnis der politischen Wissenschaften. 1952-
München.
v. 21 cm. annual.
"Herausgegeben von der Hochschule für Politische Wissenschaften München."

1. Social sciences—Bibl. I. Munich. Hochschule für Politische Wissenschaften.

Z7163.L53 55-31220

NL 0407921 DLC OrU ICIU DAU ViU PSt UU

Literaturverzeichnis eines deutschen wasserbauingenieurs
see under [Deutscher verband technisch-wissenschaftlicher vereine]

PT
13
L5

Literaturwissenschaftliches Jahrbuch der Görres-Gesellschaft. Freiburg. 1. B., Herder. Bd. 1- 1926-
v. 24 cm.

1. German literature—Yearbooks. I. Görres-Gesellschaft.

NL 0407922 IEdS CU PPDrop MdBP CLSU NcU OO ICU

Literaturzusammenstellungen aus dem Gebiet der technischen Mechanik und Akustik.
Heft

Berlin: In Kommission bei VDI-Verlag G.m.b.H., 193
no. 29½cm.
Editor: Heft W. Zeller.

1. No subject. I. Zeller, Werner, 1906- , ed.
N. Y. P. L. May 11, 1939

NL 0407923 NN

Literaturzusammenstellung über Papierchromatographie.
Heft 1- 1946-51—
Dassel [Ger.] C. Schleicher & Schüll.
v. 29 cm. annual.
Title varies: 1953-54, Literaturzusammenstellung über Papierchromatographie und Papierelektrophorese.
Beginning with 1956 the bibliography on paper electrophoresis is published separately under title: Literaturzusammenstellung über Papierelektrophorese.

1. Paper chromatography—Bibliography. I. Schleicher (Carl) & Schüll, Dassel, Ger.

Z5524.C55L5 63-37866

NL 0407924 DLC

Literatuur en samenleving. Zes lezingen, gehouden door C. Soeteman [et al., voor de School voor Taal- en Letterkunde te 's-Gravenhage] Den Haag, Servire, 1952.
118 p. 23 cm.
CONTENTS.—De Duitse ridderroman in het kader van de middeleeuwse samenleving, door C. Soeteman.—De hoveling en de burger in de Franse literatuur van de 16e eeuw, door R. Lebègue.—Renaissance en barok in Holland, door W. Asselbergs.—De verburgerlijking van de literatuur in de 18e eeuw in Engeland, door D. E. de Leve.—Sociale en geestelijke stromingen, weerspiegeld in de Franse literatuur der negentiende eeuw, door H. Brugmans.—Literatuur en samenleving i onze tijd, door P. Minderaa.

1. Literature—Hist. & crit. I. Soeteman, C.

A 52-10328

Illinois. Univ. Librar.
for Library of Congress [1]

NL 0407925 IU NN NNC

Literatuur over Rubens
see under [Arents, Prosper] 1889-

Literatuurlijst voor het adatrecht van Indonesie ...
see under Adatrechtstichting te Leiden.

Literatuuropgave voor het Adatrecht
see under Instituut voor Taal-, Land- en Volkenkunde.

Z3273
.L77

Literatuur-overzicht ... van de taal-, land- en volkenkunde en geschiedenis van Nederlandsch-Indië ... 193
Uitgegeven door het Koninklijk instituut voor de Taal-, land-en volkenkunde van Nederlandsch-Indië te 's-Gravenhage.
's-Gravenhage, M. Nijhoff, 193
v. 25cm.
1. Dutch East Indies--Bibl. I. Instituut voor de taal-, land-en volkenkunde van Nederlandsch-Indië, The Hague. II. Naerssen, F H van III. Meurs, H van

NL 0407929 DLC WaU NIC ICU NSyU OCl CtY DSI NIC

Litere, *pseud.*
see
Sommers, Lillian E.

Literes, Antonio, 18th cent.
Canción de la zarzuela heroica "Acis y Galatea" (1709) [por] Antonio Literes... Armonizada por Felipe Pedrell. (In: Asociación patriótica española. Clásicos españoles de la música. Buenos Aires, 1939. v. 2, p. 71-[76])
For 1 voice with piano accompaniment. Spanish words.
First line: Si de rama en rama.
Biographical sketch of the composer, p. 70.

1. Songs, Spanish. I. Pedrell, Felipe, 1841-1922, arr. II. Ser.
N. Y. P. L. September 20, 1943

NL 0407931 NN

Litericultura. anno 1-
1 jan. 1912-
Therezina, Piauhy [Brazil] Typographia Paz, 1912-
v. 22½cm. monthly.

45-42339

Library of Congress AP66.L5

NL 0407932 DLC

Lites ac res gestae inter Polonos Ordinemque cruciferorum ... Posnaniae, typis L. Merzbachi, 1855-56.
3 v. plates, port., facsims. 34½cm.
Engr. title vignettes (seals) "Sigilla ducum et regum privilegiis eorundem subappensa aeri incisa ..." (6 pl. in t. II)
"Tomi primi pars altera" has separate t.-p.
Edited by Count Adam Tytus Działyński.
A supplement appeared with title: Lites [etc.] Supplementum quo continetur causa inter Wladislaum, regem Poloniae, et Cruciferos anno 1320 acta ... Posnaniae, 1880.
CONTENTS.—t. 1 [pars 1] Continet librum et regestrum Joannis Dlugosz ... de anno MCCCCLXXIX; pars 2. Continet privilegia et alia producta pro parte fratrum de Prussia, de anno MCCCCXXI.—t. 2. ["Regestrum eorum que gesta sunt et acta in causa que vertitur inter ... Wladislaum d. g. Regem Polonie ex una et Magistrum ac fratres ordinis beate marie Theutunicorum de Prussia partibus ex altera coram ... Antonio Zeno . . Nuncio Apostolico per ... Martinum d. p. papam Quintum ... delegato ... Anno Domini MCCCCXXII ..."—t. 3. Liber rev: patris Dom: Sbignei olim cardinalis et epis: cracoviensis, munimenta varia, articulos et questiones regis Polonie contra magistr. Prussie in se continens.

1. Poland—Hist.—Sources. 2. Teutonic knights—Hist.—Sources. 3. Poland—Hist.—Jagellons, 1386-1572. 4. Seals (Numismatics)—Poland. I. Działyński, Adam Tytus, hrabia, 1797-1861, ed. II. Długosz, Jan, 1415-1480. Historiae polonicae libri XII. III. Oleśnicki, Zbigniew, cardinal, 1389-1455.

5-42026 Revised

Library of Congress DK402.L6

NL 0407934 DLC MH

VOLUME 336

Lites ac res gestae inter Polonos Ordinemque Cruciferorum. Ed. 2. Posnaniae, Sumptibus Bibliothecae Cornicensis, 1890–1935.

3 v. 29 cm.

Added title pages: Sprawy i spory pomiędzy Polakami a Zakonem Krzyżackim.
Introductions, notes, and table of contents in Polish.
Vols. 1–2 edited by I. Zakrzewski; v. 3, by J. Karwasińska (published in Warsaw)
Bibliography: v. 3, p. [xxvii]–xxix.

1. Poland—Hist.—Sources. 2. Teutonic Knights—Hist.—Sources. I. Zakrzewski, Ignacy, 1823–1889, ed. II. Karwasińska, Jadwiga, ed. III. Title: Sprawy i spory pomiędzy Polakami a Zakonem Krzyżackim.

DK402.L7 5–13105 rev 2

NL 0407935 DLC CSt CoU CU CtY MH MiU IU Mi WaU ICU OU

Litevka, Mordecai Menahem
see
Litevsky, Mordecai Menahem, 1856–

Litevsky, Mordecai Menahem, 1856–
הזמיר; קבוצה ראשונה. החלק הראשון שירים והשני מכתמים.
יוצא לאור ע"י מ. ב. רוזן. ווארשא. בדפוס האלטער ואייזענשטאדט.
Варшава, 1894. תרנ"ד.

200 p. 23 cm.
Vocalized text.

——— Microfilm copy (positive)

Negative film in the New York Public Library.

I. Title. *Title transliterated:* ha-Zamir.

PJ5053.L5Z2 A 55–4196

New York. Public Libr. for Library of Congress

NL 0407937 NN DLC

Litewka, Mordecai Menahem
see
Litevsky, Mordecai Menahem, 1856–

Litewski, M. M.
see Litevsky, Mordecai Menahem, 1856–

Litewski, Maria, 1906–
... Über die zirkuläre Caries des Milchgebisses ... Hamburg, 1930.
Inaug.-Diss. - Hamburg.
Lebenslauf.
"Literatur": p. 21.

NL 0407940 CtY

Litewski (M[ichael]) [1860–]. *Ein Fall von Framboesia syphilitica. 31 pp. 8°. *Greifswald, J. Abel,* 1895.

NL 0407941 DNLM

Litfass, E pub.
Kriegshumor, 1914.
see under title

Lith, Adriaan Johan Jacob van.
De praktijk der ontluizing ... door **Adriaan Johan Jacob van Lith** ... Rotterdam, Drukkerij J. de Jong, 1922.

4 p. l., 120 p. fold. pl. 24½cm.

Proefschrift—Amsterdam.
"Geraadpleegde litteratuur": p. [117]
"Stellingen": p. [119]–120.

1. Lice. 2. Hygiene, Public. I. Title.

33–37108

Library of Congress RC117.L6L5 1922 [614.43] 616.9681

NL 0407943 DLC MiU ICRL ICU

JQ 760 .A5 L7 LITH, F VAN
De politiek van Nederland ten opzichte van Nederlandsch-Indië. 's-Hertogenbosch, L. C. G. Malmberg [192?]
45 p.

1. Netherlands--Colonies--East Indies. 2. Autonomy. I. Tc.

NL 0407944 InU

Oyd70 1 Lith, F van
De politiek van Nederland ten opzichte van Nederlandsch-Indië. 's-Hertogenbosch, L.C.G. Malmberg [1935?]
46 p.

NL 0407945 CtY

Tr.R. Lith, Heinricus à, praeses.

F. D. V. dissertatio moralis De jure hominis in bruta, quam consensu amplissimo facultatis philosophicae, pro loco in eadem, more majorum rite & solenniter consequendo, praeses m. Heinricus à Lith, verdensis, respondente Hermanno Gerhardo Stoding ... in alma Salana A.M.DC.LXXV; d. 21. augusti publicae disquisitioni subjiciet. Jenae, literis Johannis Jacobi Bauhoferi [1675?]
[48] p. 20 x 17cm. [With Hobbes, Thomas. Leviathan. Londini, 1676]

NL 0407946 NcD

Lith, Johann Karl von der, respondent.
Praedestinatianos qvinto fvisse saecvlo...
see under Bernhold, Johann Balthasar, 1687-1769, praeses.

---

van der Lith (Joan. Govert.) *Bijdragen tot de kennis van de ziekelijke ontwikkeling der organa uro-genitalia en den normalen descensus testiculorum. xiii, 219 pp., 3 pl. 8°. *Utrecht, Kemink en Zoon,* 1867.

NL 0407948 DNLM

Lith, Johann Karl von der, ed.
Disquisitio theologica et historica de adoratione panis ...
see under Lith, Johann Wilhelm von der, 1709-1775.

---

van der Lith (Joh. Petrus Theodorus). *De vitiis nervorum organicis. [Utrecht.] xiv, 175 pp., 2 l., 1 pl. 8°. *Amstelodami, Elix et soc.,* 1838.

NL 0407950 DNLM

FLGZ 148 no.23 Lith, Johann Wilhelm von der, praeses. 1709-1775
... De officio principis circa bellum suscipiendum ... Halae Magdeburgicae, C. Henckel [1698]
[32]p. 20cm.
(Foreign law pamphlet collection, v.148, no.23)

Diss. - Halle (D. Zöllner)

NL 0407951 CtY-L MH-L

609.2 C151.4vi 1700 LITH, Johann Wilhelm von der, 1709-1775
...De superstitione jubilaei pontificii, inprimis bullae novissimae Innocentii XII ... & libello Herbipoli nuper edito (cui titulus: Eigentl. Beschreibung der Ceremonien des H. Jubel=Jahrs.) opposita. ... praeside ... Paulo Antonio ... Cal. Nov. MDCC ... Halae Magdeb. literis Chr. Henckelii, acad. typ. [1700?]
3p.l., 8,130p. 19.5cm.

At head of title: "Dissertatio theologica inauguralis".
Number 2 in a bound volume of 17th-century tracts and disputations.

NL 0407953 MH-AH

Lith, Johann Wilhelm von der, 1709–1775.
Ioh. Gvilielmi de Lith... Disqvisitio theologica et historica de adoratione panis consecrati et interdictione sacri calicis in Evcharistia; piaqve cvm ad Romano-Catholicos tvm ad Evangelicos monita, edita a Ioh. Carolo de Lith... Svobaci: Svmtibvs Iohannis Iacobi Enderesii, 1753. 424 p. 8°.

Bound with: Jabłoński, P. E. Pavli Ernesti Iabłoński... Pantheon Aegyptiorum. Francofurti ad Viadrum, 1750–52.

281555A. 1. Lord's Supper. 2. Lith, Johann Karl von der, editor.
N. Y. P. L. May 31, 1927

NL 0407954 NN MH

LH32 L776 Lith, Johann Wilhelm von der, 1709-1775.
Erläuterung der Reformations-Historie, vom 1524. bis zum 28.Jahr Christi incl. Aus dem Hoch-Fürstlich-Brandenburg-Onolzbachischen Archiv an das Licht gebracht von Johann Wilhelm von der Lith ... Schwobach, C.H. Steinmarch, 1733.
8p.l., 258 [i.e.300], [2]p. 17cm.
Title in red and black, on two leaves.

NL 0407955 NNUT NcD PU

270.6 L776E Lith, Johann Wilhelm von der, 1709-1775
Gründlicher Beweiss, dass das Niederknien vor denen Hostien in der Messe ... ist eingeführet worden ... 2. Aufl. Anspach, S. Keul, 1743.
256 p. 17 cm. (With his Erläuterung der Reformations-Historie ... Schwobach, 1733)
1. Lord's Supper. 2. Catholic Church. Doctrinal and controversial works. Protestant authors. 3. Catholic Church. Liturgy and ritual.

NL 0407956 NcD

Lith, Johann Wilhelm von der, 1709–1775.
Neue vollständig erwiesene abhandlung von denen steuern und deren vortheilhafter einrichtung in einem lande, nach den grundsätzen einer wahren die verbesserung der macht eines regenten und die glückseligkeit seiner unterthanen wirkenden staatskunst, entworfen von Johann Wilhelm von der Lith ... Ulm, A. L. Stettin, 1766.

10 p. l., 432, [20] p. 20cm.

1. Taxation. 2. Internal revenue.

33–38085

Library of Congress HJ2300.L48 336.2

NL 0407957 DLC ICU NIC MH-BA MiU MH

VOLUME 336

Lith, Johann Wilhelm von der, 1709–1775.
Politische betrachtungen über die verschiedene ⌊!⌋ arten der steuern. Entworfen von Johann Wilhelm von der Lith ... Breslau, J. J. Korn, 1751.
10 p. l., 214 p., ⌊62⌋ p. 20cm.

1. Taxation. 2. Internal revenue. I. Title.
33-38084
Library of Congress HJ2300.L5 336.2

NL 0407958 DLC ICU

DS633 .E5 Lith, Pieter Antonie van der, 1844-1901, ed.
Encyclopædie van Nederlandsch-Indië, met medewerking van verschillende ambtenaren, geleerden en officieren ... 's Gravenhage-Leiden, M. Nijhoff ⌊etc., 1895–1905⌋

Lith, P⌊ieter⌋ A⌊ntonie⌋ van der, 1844–1901.
Nederlandsch Oost-Indië beschreven en afgebeeld voor het Nederlandsche volk. Doesborgh, J. C. Van Schenk Brill, 1875.
l. 8°. pp. (4), 452. Colored plates.

NL 0407960 MH MiU DNW CSt-H CtY CU-S CU

DS 619 +L47 **Lith, Pieter Antonie van der, 1844-1901**
Nederlandsch Oost-Indië, beschreven en afgebeeld voor het Nederlandsche volk. Doesborgh, J. C. van Schenk Brill, 1877. 452p. illus. 29cm.

1. Dutch East Indies 2. Dutch East Indies - Hist. 3. Ethnology - Dutch East Indies I. Title

NL 0407961 WU

Lith, Pieter Antonie van der, 1844–1901.
Nederlandsch Oost-Indië, beschreven en afgebeeld voor het Nederlandsche volk, door P. A. van der Lith ... 2. geheel omgewerkte druk, met 32 platen ... Leiden, E. J. Brill, 1893–95.
2 v. col. fronts., plates (partly col.) fold. map. 25½cm.
"Alphabetisch zaak- en plaatsregister" at end of v. 2 has special t.-p. and separate paging.

1. Dutch East Indies. 2. Dutch East Indies—Hist. 3. Ethnology—Dutch East Indies.
1-D-282
Library of Congress DS619.L77

NL 0407962 DLC CU CtY NIC NSyU InU

Lith, Pieter Antonie van der, 1844-1901, ed.

Revue coloniale internationale. (Fondée par l'Association coloniale néerlandaise à Amsterdam) Direction ... C. M. Kan ... P. A. van der Lith ... D. Josephus Jitta ... Rédacteur de la bibliographie mensuelle ... H. C. Rogge ... 1. juil. 1885-1887. Amsterdam, J. H. de Bussy ⌊1885–87⌋

Lith, P⌊ieter⌋ A⌊ntonie⌋ van der, 1844–1901.
De staatsinstellingen van Nederlandsch-Indië beschreven door P. A. van der Lith en J. Spanjaard. 's Gravenhage, Gebroeders Belinfante, 1871.
pp. (8), xi, 355, viii.

East Indies (Dutch)- Hist. 1816- ||Spanjaard

NL 0407964 MH CtY CU NNC

Z 491 .L 713 **LITH, THEODOR VAN DER.**
Catalogus duarum bibliothecarum in omni disciplinarum & linguarum genere librorum, inter quos reperiuntur libri valdè curiosi & benè conditionati...Theodori van der Lith...et Joannis Tuldeni...quorum publica auctio fiet Hagæ, die 10 Aprilis & sequentibus 1724. In aulâ magnâ (vulgo) de groote zaal van't hof per Rutger. Christoph. Alberts. Hagæ Comitum, Apud R. C. Alberts, 1724.
219p. 19cm.

NL 0407965 ICN

W 4 L68 v. 2 no. 5 LITH, Tido Henrich von der
Dissertatio inauguralis medico-chirurgica, de empyemate ... Lugduni Batavorum, Apud Conradum Wishoff, 1725.
20 p. 23 cm.
Diss. - Leyden.

NL 0407966 DNLM

Lith de Jeude, Theodorus Willem van
see
Lidth de Jeude, Theodorus Willem van, 1853–

Lithander, Arne, 1906–
... Acute adrenal insufficiency in rabbits produced by some bacterial toxins, by Arne Lithander; translated by Bernard Norbelie. Stockholm ⌊P. A. Norstedt & söner⌋ 1945.
114 p. incl. illus., tables, diagrs. 5 pl. on 3 l. 23½ cm. (*On cover:* Acta medica scandinavica. Supplementum CLX (160))
"From the State bacteriologic laboratory ... Stockholm, Sweden."
Bibliography: p. ⌊110⌋–114.

1. Adrenal glands—Diseases. 2. Toxins and antitoxins. I. *Norbelie, Bernard, 1904– tr.
A 48—658
John Crerar Library for Library of Congress ⌊48c1⌋

NL 0407968 ICJ IdPI OU PU-Med IU PPT-M ViU

Lithander (Daniel)
*Om nödwändigheten af skogarnas bettre wård och ans Finland. *Åbo*, 1753. 2 p.l., 44 pp. 4°.

NL 0407969 NN

Lithander, Daniel, respondent.
Theses miscellaneae; quas ... sub praesidio Petri Kalm ...
see under Kalm, Pehr, 1716-1779, praeses.

Lithander, Pehr Jonas, respondent.
Chirurgiska iakttagelser...
see under Bergstrand, Carl Hënrik, 1800- praeses.

Lithapelo tsa Bakriste. 4th ed. Maseru, Basutoland, Mazenod Institute, 1940.
276 p. illus. 15 cm.

1. Catholic Church—Prayer-books and devotions—Sotho.
BX1990.S66A2 1940 72-208745

NL 0407972 DLC

Lithberg, Nils, *1883-1934.*
Almanackan från astrologisk rådgivare till svensk kalender. Stockholm, P.A. Norstedt & söners förlag ⌊1933⌋

64 p. illus. 22cm. (Svenska humanistiska förbundet. ⌊Skrifter⌋ 40)

"Litteraturanvisningar": p. 62.

1.Calendar. I.Title.

NL 0407973 MnU

Lithberg, Nils, 1883–1934.
Computus med särskild hänsyn till runstaven och den borgerliga kalendern. Enligt uppdrag utg. av Sam Owen Jansson. Stockholm, 1953.
326 p. illus., facsims., tables. 29 cm. (Nordiska museets handlingar: 29)
"Rättelser": slip tipped in.
Summary in German.
"Källor och litteratur": p. ⌊287⌋–302.
1. Calendar. 2. Almanacs. I. Jansson, Sam Owen, ed. (Series: Stockholm. Nordiska museet. Handlingar, 29)
Full name: Nils Jacob Mauritz Lithberg.
A 57-2981
Harvard Univ. Library for Library of Congress ⌊1⌋

NL 0407974 MH CtY KU NN RPB DSI

Lithberg, Nils, 1883-
Gotlandica; till Nils Lithberg, den 3 aug. 1933
see under title

Lithberg, Nils, 1883–1934.
... Den gotländska runkalendern 1328, av Nils Lithberg och Elias Wessén. Stockholm, Wahlström & Widstrand (i kommission) 1939.
xx, ⌊1⌋, 153 p. illus. (part col.) facsims. 24cm. (Kungl. vitterhets historie och antikvitets akademiens handlingar, del 45: 2)
Bibliographical foot-notes.

1. Calendars, Runic. 2. Calendar, Germanic. I. *Wessén, Elias, 1889– joint author. II. Title.
⌊*Full name:* Nils Jacob Mauritz Lithberg⌋
A C 39-2110
Princeton univ. Library for Library of Congress [DL601.V78 vol. 45, no. 2]
(948.50062)

NL 0407976 NjP NIC TxU NcU NcD MnU

Lithberg, Nils, *1883- 1934*
Gotlands stenålder ... af Nils Lithberg ... ⌊Stockholm, J. Bagges söners aktiebolag, 1914⌋
136, ⌊2⌋ p. plates, 8 fold. maps. 26cm.
Akademisk afhandling—Uppsala.
Descriptive letterpress on versos facing the plates.
Published also without thesis note.
Errata slip attached to p. 136.

1. Stone age—Sweden—Gotland. 2. Gotland—Antiq.
34-9157
Library of Congress GN776.S2L5 1914 a 913.486

NL 0407977 DLC CtY

Lithberg, Nils, *1883-1934*
Gotlands stenålder, af Nils Lithberg. ⌊Stockholm, J. Bagges söners aktiebolag, 1914⌋
3 p. l., ⌊3⌋–143, ⌊3⌋ p. plates, fold. maps. 26cm.

1. Stone age—Sweden—Gotland. 2. Gotland—Antiq.
27-13060
Library of Congress GN776.S2L5

NL 0407978 DLC ICRL MH

VOLUME 336

LITHBERG, NILS, 1883-1934
Johannes Pihls beskrivning över Gotland. (IN: Gotländskt arkiv. Visby. 24cm. [bd.] 6 (1934) p.[33]-45)

1. Pihl, Johannes, 1684-1751. Sciagraphia Gothlandiæ illustratæ.

NL 0407979 NN

Lithberg, Nils, 1883-1934
Kalendariska hjälpmedel
Nilsson, Martin Persson, 1874- ed.
... Tideräkningen, utgiven av Martin P:n Nilsson ... Stockholm, A. Bonnier; [etc., etc., 1934]

CC260 .S8L5
Lithberg, Nils, 1883-1934.
Koskällan, af Nils Lithberg. [Stockholm, P.A. Norstedt & söner, 1914]
18 p. illus. 24 cm.
Caption title.
From Fataburen, 1914, hft. 1.

NL 0407981 DLC

Lithberg, Nils, 1883-
Schloss Hallwil... Stockholm, Tisell, [1924-32]
5 v.in 6. illus.,plates(part double) maps(1 double)plans(part double)facsims., geneal.tables. 29½ x 24 cm.
One of an edition of 800 copies.
Vol.5, by Nils Lithberg and Anders Roland.

"Literaturnachweise": v.3, pt.1, p.[141]-159.
Contents.- I. Die wiederherstellung.- II. Die ausgrabungen.- III. Die fundgegenstände. 2 v.- IV. Die baugeschichte.- V. Der baubestand im bilde.

1.Hallwil castle. I.Roland,Anders. II.Title.

NL 0407983 NjP MH CtY

Lithberg,Nils, 1883-
Die steinzeit Gotlands,von Nils Lithberg. Aus dem schwedischen übersetzt von dr.phil. Heinz Hungerland. Stockholm, J.Bagges söners aktiebolag, 1916.
3 p.l.,[3]-109 p.,2 l. plates,8 fold.maps. 16½cm.
Descriptive letterpress on versos facing plates.
"In der vorliegenden auflage sind die vielen einzelkeiten ... ausgeschlossen ... Das 7.cap.,'Der namen Gotland im lichte der prähistorie',ist neu geschrieben."—Vorwort.
1.Stone age--Sweden--Gotland. 2.Gotland--Antiq. I. Hungerland,Heinz,1873- tr.

NL 0407984 MiU

LITHBERG, NILS, 1883-1934
Två krönikor; ett minnesår i den gotländska historieskrivningens annaler. (IN: Gotländskt arkiv. Visby. 24cm. [bd.] 5 (1933) p. [3]-10)

Bibliographical footnotes.
1. Strelow, Hans Nielsen, 1587-1656. Cronica Guthilandorum.
2. Spegel, Haqvin, abp., 1645-1714. Rudera gothlandica.

NL 0407985 NN

Lithberg, Nils Jacob Mauritz
see Lithberg, Nils, 1883-1934.

Lithell, Carol. Gustav, respondent.
Observations pathologioco anatomicae...
see under Akerman, Jacobus, 1770-1829, praeses.

Lithenius (Martinus)
*De lagopode gallinacea et congeneribus. *Upsaliae*, 1729]. 1 p.l., 26 pp. 4°.

NL 0407988 NN

283.04 L713
Lithenius, Nicolaus
Synopseos Reformationis Ecclesiae Anglicanae et historiae schismaticae prodromus sistens Lutherum magnum Dei instrumentum ad Ecclesiam Britannicam reformandem ex genuinis historiae Anglicanae monumentis ab ipso repurgationis initio historice deductus et in gloriam Dei atque memoriam divi Lutheri secundo hoc jubilaeo publicae luci expositus....Jenae, I.B. Helleri [17--?]
40 p. 19 cm.
Provenance: Bp. ttingham, Maryland Diocesan Library.
1. Church of Eng. - Hist. - Reformation. I. Tit.

NL 0407989 NNG

Litherland, Dorothy Albietz, 1906-
A half century of accrual accounting theory, 1886-1936. Urbana, 1951.
11 p. 23 cm.
Abstract of thesis—University of Illinois.
Vita.

1. Accounting—Hist
HF5605.L48 A 51-10571
Illinois. Univ. Library for Library of Congress [1]†

NL 0407990 IU NIC WaU NNC DLC

Litherland, Herschel.
... A study of the nature and scope of "principles of secondary education" ... by Herschel Litherland ... [Cincinnati? 1930?]
23 p. 23cm.
At head of title: University of Cincinnati. College of education.
Abstract of thesis (PH. D.)—University of Cincinnati, 1930.
Bibliography: p. 21-23.

1. Education, Secondary.
31-15583
Library of Congress LB1609.L5 1930
Univ. of Cincinnati Libr. [2] 373

NL 0407991 OCU DLC

Litherland, John Charles, ed.
The law relating to child welfare, affiliation & adoptions (Child welfare act, 1939) with annotations, regulations and forms made under the Child welfare act, 1939, and rules and forms made by the Supreme court of N. S. W. for use in adoption proceedings, by John Charles Litherland ... Sydney [etc.] The Law book co. of Australasia pty ltd., 1940.
2 p. l., iii-xiv, 380 p. 22cm.
"Addenda" slips inserted.
1. Children—Law—New South Wales. 2. Children—Charities, protection, etc.—New South Wales. 3. Illegitimacy — New South Wales. 4. Adoption — New South Wales. 5. Forms (Law) — New South Wales. I. New South Wales. Laws, statutes, etc. II. Title.
41-4833

NL 0407992 DLC

Litherland, John Charles.
The law relating to maintenance of wives and children who are deserted or left without means of support in Australia and New Zealand. Sydney, Law Book Co. of Australasia, 1949.
xlviii, 576 p. 22 cm.

1. Desertion and non-support—Australia. 2. Desertion and non-support—New Zealand.
50-22726

NL 0407993 DLC

LITHGOW, ARTHUR.
The felicity brag; a humorous play. [n.p., 194-?] 42, 25, 23 l. 28cm.
"This play is an adaptation in American terms of Gogol's The government inspector."
"Copyright under the title A marshal at Squaw's Crossing."

1. Drama, American. 2. Drama--Promptbooks and typescripts. I. Gogol, Nikolaĭ Vasil'yevich, 1809-1852. The government inspector. II. Title. III. Title: A marshal at Squaw's Crossing.

NL 0407994 NN

B610.24 Ed4 1813-14
Lithgow, David.
De sanguinis detractione ... Edinburgi, Excudebant J. Ballantyne et Socii, 1814.
[8], 49 p. 21 cm. (In Edinburgh. University. Dissertationes medicae, 1813-14)

Inaug. Diss. - Edinburgh.

NL 0407995 MnU-B

AM .LI
Lithgow, David Cunningham, 1868-
History of the Indian groups with a description of the technic, by David C. Lithgow; The Indian groups of the New York State Museum and a description of the technic, by Noah T. Clarke. Albany, University of the State of New York, 1937.
[83]-120 p. plates. 23 cm.
"From the New York State Museum Bulletin 310, pages 82-120. Thirtieth report of the Director."

NL 0407996 WHi

Lithgow, David Cunningham, 1868-

State bank of Albany.
Murals in the State bank of Albany ⟨painted by David Cunningham Lithgow⟩ including a short history of the founding of the bank in eighteen hundred and three and its one hundred and forty years of service to the community; written by Arthur Pound, state historian, New York. [Albany, Priv. print. at the Argus press, 1943.

E 7 .F 6311
LITHGOW, EDWARD FLAGG, 1894-
The genealogy of the Flagg family, 1615-1941 [revised edition] Chicago,1941.
70l. port.,facsim.,col.coat of arms. 31cm.
Includes mounted clippings.

1. Flagg family.

NL 0407998 ICN

E 7 .N 518
LITHGOW, EDWARD FLAGG, 1894-
The genealogy of the Nichols family, 1680-1941. Chicago,Ill.,1941.
33l. illus.,facsims. 31cm.
Includes mounted clippings.
Bibliography: p.3.

1. Nichols family.

NL 0407999 ICN

VOLUME 336

LITHGOW, J. R. The Sabbath question ꞏꞏꞏ nally published in the "Acadian recorde. . Hali., Bowes, 1861. 48 p. 19 cm.

NL 0408001 CaNSWA

LITHGOW, Sir JAMES, 1st bart., 1883–
...Industry and the Empire, by Col. Sir James Lithgow, bt. ... Greenock: "Telegraph" Prtg. Works, 1932. 18 p. 21cm. (Watt anniversary lectures. 1932.)

766220A. 1. Economic history—Gt.Br., 1918– . I. Ser.

N. Y. P. L. April 19, 1935

NL 0408002 NN NRU

Lithgow, Llewellyn William, 1796-1881.

[Hill, Mark Langdon] 1772–1842.
Lithgow family.

(*In* Collections of the Maine historical society. Portland, 1857. 23cm [1st ser.] v. 5, p. [413]–423)

Lithgow, Michael, 1920–
Mach one. With a foreword by Charles Gardner. London, A. Wingate [1954]
151 p. illus. 22 cm.
Autobiography of a test pilot.

1. World War, 1939–1945—Personal narratives, English. I. Title.
Full name: Michael John Lithgow.

TL540.L53A3 55–20296 ‡
Library of Congress

NL 0408004 DLC CaBVa CaBViP MB NN PP FMU NIC

Lithgow, R M
The parabolic gospel; or, Christ's parables, a sequence and a synthesis, by the Rev. R. M. Lithgow ... Edinburgh, T. & T. Clark, 1914.
xv, 196 p. 21½cm.
On spine: Scribners.
First published in a series of nine articles in the Expository Times.—*cf.* Pref.

1. Jesus Christ—Parables. I. Title. II. Title: Christ's parables, a sequence and a synthesis.

NL 0408005 ViU NjPT CSaT CLSU OO MH

Lithgow, Robert Alexander Douglas-
see
Douglas-Lithgow, Robert Alexander, 1846– 1917.

Lithgow, William, *1582-1645.*
Adventures and painful peregrinations of nineteen years' travels from Scotland to the most famous kingdoms in Europe,...n.t.-p. Edinburgh, 1632.
12°

NL 0408007 NN

Lithgow, William, 1582-1645?
A Briefe and summarie discourse upon that lamentable and dreadfull disaster at Dunglasse. Anno 1640. the penult. of August. Collected from the soundest and best instructions, That time and place could certainly affoord, the serious enquirie of the painfull and industrious Author. By William Lithgovv. Edinburgh, by Robert Bryson [1640]
Sm. 4to. Green morocco.
Britwell sale, March 1921, no. 141.

NL 0408008 CSmH

AW 1 R475: 1278
Lithgow,William,1582-1645?
A briefe and summarie discourse upon that lamentable and dreadfull disaster at Dunglasse. Anno 1640. the penult of August ... Edinburgh, Printed by R. Bryson [1640]
In verse.
CaBVaU
Microfilm of original in the British Museum. Ann Arbor,Mich., University Microfilms, 1972. (Early English books,1475-1640,reel 1278)
Micro/ STC no.15708.
mr73jme Microfilm

1.Murder. I. Title. mco

NL 0408009 MiU CaBVaU

1582-1645
LITHGOW, WILLIAM. Experimental and exact relation upon that famous and renowned siege of Newcastle, the divers conflicts and occurances fell out there during the time of ten weeks and odde dayes; and of that mightie and marveilous storming thereof, with power, police, and prudent plots of warre: Together with a succinct commentarie upon the battell of Bowdon hill, and that victorious battell of York, or Marston Moore, never to bee forgotten. Edinburgh, [July 15] 1645.
Somers 5:279-96.
Another copy, Newcastle reprints 1.

NL 0408010 MnU ICN

STC 15709
Lithgow, William, 1582-1645?
The gushing teares of godly sorrovv. Containing, the causes, conditions, and remedies of sinne, depending mainly upon contrition and confession. And they seconded, with sacred and comfortable passages, under the mourning cannopie of teares, and repentance ... By William Lithgovv.
Edinburgh,Printed by Robert Bryson,anno Dom. 1640. At the expences of the authour.
[100]p. 20cm.
Signatures: A-M^4.N^2.

In verse.
Imperfect: H2-3 slightly mutilated.
Mounted on front flyleaf is an engr. port. of Lithgow in Turkish dress.

NL 0408012 MH CSmH DFo

AW 1 R475: 1246
Lithgow,William,1582-1645?
The gushing teares of godly sorrow. Containing, the causes,conditions,and remedies of sinne,depending mainly upon contrition and confession ... Edinburgh, Printed by R.Bryson, 1640.
CaBVaU In verse.
Microfilm of original in the British Museum. Ann Arbor,Mich., University Microfilms, 1971. (Early English books,1475-1640,reel 1246)
Micro/ mr72 jme
STC no.15709.
Microfilm.

NL 0408013 MiU CaBVaU

Ecd 609L
Lithgow, William, 1582-1645?
A most delectable, and trve discourse, of an admired and painefull peregrination from Scotland, to the most famous kingdomes in Europe, Asia and Affricke ... By William Lithgovv Scotus. London,Printed by Nicholas Okes,and are to be sold by Thomas Archer,at his shop in Popes-Head Pallace,neere the Royall Exchange.1614.
[152]p. 18cm.
Signatures: $A^4a^2B\text{-}S^4T^2$.

Imperfect: a few head-lines very slightly bled.

NL 0408015 CtY DFo MH CSmH

FILM
Lithgow,William,1582-1645?
A most delectable,and trve discourse,of an admired and painefull peregrination from Scotland, to the most famous kingdomes in Europe,Asia and Affricke. With the particular descriptions (more exactly set downe then hath beene heeretofore in English) of Italy,Sycilia,Dalmatia,Ilyria,Epire, Peloponnesus,Macedonia,Thessalia,and the whole continent of Greece,Creta,Rhodes,the Iles Cyclades,with all the ilands in the Ionian, Aegean,and Adriaticke Seas,Thracia.the renowned

citty Constantinople,Cholchis,Bythinia,and the Black Sea,Troy,Phrygia,and the chiefest countries of Asia Minor: From thence to Cyprus,Phaenicia, Syria,Mesopotamia,Arabia Petrea,and the desert of Egypt,the Red Sea,Grand Cayro,the whole prouince of Canaan,the Lake of Sodom and Gomorrha,the famous riuers Nylus,Euphrates and Iordan,and the sacred citty of Ierusalem,&c. London, Printed by

N.Okes,and are to be sold by T.Archer, 1614.
Editions of 1632 and 1640 were published under title: The total discourse,of the rare adventures, and painefull peregrinations of long nineteene yeares trauayles. Microfilm.
Short-title catalogue no.15710 (carton 807)

1.Voyages and travels.

NL 0408018 MiU

STC 15711 Bd.w. STC 3136
Lithgow, William, 1582-1645?
A most delectable and true discourse, of an admired and painefull peregrination from Scotland to the most famous kingdomes in Europe, Asia and Affricke ... The second impression, correctrd [!] and enlarged ... London, Printed by Nicholas Okes and are to be sold by Thomas Archer, 1616.

A-R^4. 4to.
Duke of Hamilton-Harmsworth copy.

NL 0408019 DFo CSmH

FILM
Lithgow,William,1582-1645?
A most delectable and trve discourse,of an admired and painefull peregrination from Scotland, to the most famous kingdomes in Europe,Asia and Affricke. With the particular descriptions (more exactly set downe then hath beene heeretofore in English) of Italy,Sycilia,Dalmatia,Ilyria,Epire, Peloponnesus,Macedonia,Thessalia,and the whole continent of Greece,Creta,Rhodes,the Iles Cyclades,with all the ilands in the Ionian,Aegean, and Adriaticke Seas,Thracia,the renowned citie

Constantinople,Cholchis,Bythinia,and the Blacke Sea,Troy,Phrygia,and the chiefest countries of Asia Minor. From thence,to Cyprus,Phaenicia, Syria,Mesopotamia,Arabia Petrea,and the desart of Egypt,the Red Sea,Grand Cayro,the whole prouince of Canaan,the Lake of Sodom and Gomorrha,the famous riuers,Nilus,Euphrates,and Iordan,and the sacred citie Ierusalem,&c. The 2d impression,

Continued in next column

VOLUME 336

Continued from preceding column

corr.and enl.by the authour. London, Printed by N.Okes,and are to be sold by T.Archer, 1616.
Editions of 1632 and 1640 were published under title: The total discourse,of the rare aduentures and painefull peregrinations of long nineteene yeares trauayles. Microfilm.
Short-title catalogue no.15711 (carton 807)
1.Voyages and travels.

NL 0408022 MiU

Ecd 609Lc
Lithgow, William, 1582-1645?
A most delectable and trve discovrse of an admired and painefull peregrination from Scotland, to the most famous kingdomes in Europe, Asia and Affrica ... Newly imprinted, and exactly inlarged, by the author William Lithgow; with certaine rare relations of his second, and third trauels ... London,Printed by Nicholas Okes,1623.
4p.ℓ.,205p. port. 18½cm.
Signatures: A-Z⁴; Aa-Dd⁴ (last blank and genuine)

Pagination irregular.
Published later under title: The totall discourse of long nineteene yeares travailes.
Portrait of the author published July 20, 1792 by I. Caulfield, London, laid in.
Bookplates of Brayton Ives and John Camp Williams.

NL 0408024 CtY CSmH

FILM
Lithgow,William,1582-1645?
A most delectable and trve discovrse of an admired and painefull peregrination from Scotland, to the most famous kingdomes in Europe,Asia and Affrica. With the particular descriptions (more exactly set downe then haue beene heretofore in English) of Italy,Sycilia,Dalmatia,Ilyria,Epire, Peloponensus,Macedonia,Thessalia,and the whole continent of Greece,Creta,Rhodes,the Iles Cyclades,with all the ilands in the Ionian,Aegean, and Adriaticke Seas,Thracia,the renowned city

Constantinople,Colchis,Bythinia,and the Blacke Sea,Troy,Phrygia,and the chiefest countries of Asia Minor. Fron thence,to Cyprus,Phaenicia, Syria,Mesopotamia,Arabia Petrea,and Deserta, Aegypt,the Read Sea,Grand Cayro,the whole prouinces of Canaan,the Lake of Sodome and Gomorha,the famous riuers Nylus,Euphrates,and Iordan,and the sacred city Ierusalem,&c. Newly

imprinted and exactly inl.,by the author; with certaine rare relations of his second,and third trauels. London, Printed by N.Okes, 1623.
Editions of 1632 and 1640 were published under title: The total discourse,of the rare aduentures, and painefull peregrinations of long nineteene yeares trauayles. Microfilm
Short-title catalogue no.15712 (carton 807)
1.Voyages and travels.

NL 0408027 MiU

Case D 4940 .513
Lithgow, William, 1582-1645.
A narrative of the tortures by the popish bloody inquisition. With an account of the dreadful sufferings by their rack, and the grievous tortures inflicted on the body of William Lithgow... Edinburgh,1771. 32,16p.

The first part is taken from The totall discourse of the rare adventures and painfull peregrinations by William Lithgow.
Part 2 (in verse) has title: The loyal martyrs; or, Bloody inquisition of Spain...

NL 0408028 ICN

Lithgow, William, 1582-1645?
Willem Lithgouws 19. jaarige lant-reyse vyt Schotland, naer de vermaerde koninckrijcken Europa, Asia ende Africa. Voltrocken in drie dier-gekochte voyagien, ende in het besichtigen van 48 oude en moderne koninckrijcken, 21 republijcken, 10 absolute vorstendommen, ende 200 eylanden. Waer in begrepen is een pertinent verhael vande wetten, religien, policien, ende regeeringe van alle hare princen, potentaten en natien. Als mede, d'onuytsprekelijcke tormenten die den autheur gheleden heeft door de inquisitie van Malagom, in Spangien; sijn won-

derbaerlijcke bekent-wordingh ende verlossingh: ende vande laetste wederkomste uyt de Noordse eylanden, ende andere by-leggende plaetsen. Uyt 't Engels overgeset, ende met kopere platen versiert. t'Amsterdam, By J. Benjamijn, 1652.
4 p. l., 187, 97, [1] p. illus. 20½cm.
Added t.-p., engr.
Armorial book-plate of William Edward Kelly.
1. Voyages and travels.
25-3698
Library of Congress G640.L75

NL 0408030 DLC NNH

LITHGOW,William,1582-1645?
Willem Lithgouws 19.jaarige landt-reyse uit Schotlandt,naer de vermaerde koninkrycken Europa,Asia en Africa [etc.]. Uit't Engels over geset. t'Amsterdam,P.Verbeek,1705.
21 x 16 cm. Plates.
Added engraved title-page.

NL 0408031 MH

G 460 .L77 1682
Lithgow,William,1582-1645?
Lithgow's nineteen years travels through the most eminent places in the habitable world. Containing an exact description of the customs,laws,religion,policies and government ... also of the countries and cities,trades,rivers,and commerce in all places through which he travell'd. Also an account of the tortures he suffered under the Spanish Inquisition ... London, Printed for J.Wright and T.Passinger, 1682.

[8],481,[7] p. illus.,plates. 17 cm.
First published in 1614,with title: A most delectable and true discourse,of an admired and painefull peregrination from Scotland to the most famous kingdomes in Europe,Asia,and Affricke. The enlarged ed.of 1632 has title: The totall discourse, of the rare

aduentures,and painefull peregrinations of long nineteene yeares trauayles,from Scotland to the most famous kingdomes in Europe,Asia,and Affrica.
Imperfect: upper margin closely trimmed with some loss of running title and pagination.
Plate designated as belonging between p.252 and 253 wrongly bound between p.152 and 153.

Armorial bookplate: Batemen of Middleton Hall (by Youlgrave) in the County of Derby.

1. Voyages and travels.

NL 0408035 MiU CLU-C NcD N NjP

WA 4921
Lithgow, William, 1582-1645?
Lithgow's nineteen years travels through the most eminent places in the habiable world. Containing an exact description of the customs, laws, religion, policies...and commerce in all places through which he travell'd. Also an account of the tortures he suffered under the Spanish Inquisition...10th ed. London, Printed by J. Millet, for M. Wotton, 1692.
488, [8]p. fold. plates. 18cm.

NL 0408036 CtY DFo CU

Lithgow, William, 1582-1645.
The pilgrimes farewell, to his natiue countrey of Scotland: Wherein is contained, in way of dialogue, the joyes, and miseries of peregrination ... By William Lithgow, the Bonaventvre of Evrope, Asia, and Africa, &c. ... Imprinted at Edinburgh, by Andro Hart. Anno Domini 1618 ...
[32] leaves. illus. 20 cm.
Initials; head and tail-pieces.
Full page woodcut of author and servant on verso of t.-p.
In verse.
On verso of third leaf are 14 lines of

verse "To his singular friend, William Lithgow" signed "W.R." (possibly Sir Walter Raleigh)
Signatures: A-H⁴.
1. Voyages andtravels. I. Title.

NL 0408038 MB CSmH

FILM
Lithgow,William,1582-1645?
The pilgrimes farewell,to his natiue countrey of Scotland: wherein is contained,in way of dialogue,the joyes and miseries of peregrination. With his lamentado in his second trauels,his passionado on the Rhyne,diuerse other insertings, and farewels,to noble personages,and,The heremites welcome to his third pilgrimage,&c. Worthie to be seene and read of all gallant spirits,and pompe-expecting eyes. Edinburgh, Imprinted by A.Hart, 1618.
In verse. Microfilm.
Short-title catalogue no.15715 (carton 808)
I.Title.

NL 0408039 MiU

Lithgow, William, 1582-1645?
The poetical remains of William Lithgow, the Scotish traveller. M. DC. XVIII. — M. DC. LX. Now first collected. Edinburgh: T. G. Stevenson, 1863. liv, 134 l. facsims., pl. 8°.
Facsims. of original title-pages.

189171A. 1. Poetry, Scottish.
N. Y. P. L. August 11, 1925

NL 0408040 NN CtY IU OU ViU KU NcU ICN MnU WaU MiU ICU NjP

Lithgow, William, 1582-1645?
Rare adventures and painefull peregrinations, by William Lithgow, edited by B. I. Lawrence. London, J. Cape [1928]
287, [1] p. 17½cm. (Half-title: The travellers' library)
"This abridgment has been made from the edition of The totall discourse of the rare adventures and painfull peregrinations by William Lithgow, published in 1906, by Messrs. James MacLehose & sons, Glasgow."—p. 7.

1. Voyages and travels. I. Lawrence, Barbara Innes, 1902- ed. II. Title.
29-22443
Library of Congress G460.L72 1928

NL 0408041 DLC CaBVaU CaBViP KU CtY MH

Brit. Tracts 1660 L72
[Lithgow, William] 1582-1645?
Scotlands paraenesis to her dread soveraign, King Charles The Second ... [n.p.]1660.
12p. 18cm.
In verse.

1. Solemn league and covenant.
I.Title(2)

NL 0408042 CtY MH

VOLUME 336

Lithgow, William. 1582-1645?
Scotland's teares, by Williame Lithgow, in his countreyes behalf. 8 pp.
(In Various pieces of fugitive Scottish poetry. Edinburgh. 1853.)

F5907 — T.r.

NL 0408043 MB

STC 15716 Lithgow, William, 1582-1645?
Scotlands welcome to her natiue sonne, and soueraigne lord, King Charles. Wherein is also contained, the maner of his coronation, and convocation of Pa[rl]iament; the whole grievances, and abuses of the Common-wealth of this kingdome, with diverse other relations, never heretofore published ... Edinburgh, Printed by Iohn Wreittoun [1633]
$*^4$, A-G^4. (*1, probably blank, lacking.) 4to.
In verse.
Harmsworth copy.

NL 0408044 DFo CSmH MH

FILM Lithgow, William, 1582-1645?
Scotlands welcome to her native sonne and soveraigne lord, King Charles. Wherein is also contained, the maner of his coronation, and convocation of Parliament; the whole grievances, and abuses of the common wealth of this kingdome, with diverse other relations, never heretofore published. Worthy to be by all the nobles and gentry perused; and to be layd vp in the hearts, and chests of the whole Commouns, whose interests may best claime it, either in meane, or maner, from which their priuiledges, and fortunes are drawne, as from the loadstar of true direction. Edinbvrgh, Printed by I.Wreittovn [1633]
In verse. Microfilm
Short-title catalogue no.15716 (carton 808)

1. Charles, I, King of Great Britain, 1600-1649--Poetry. I. Title.

NL 0408046 MiU

Lithgow, William, 1582-1645?
The siege of Newcastle, by William Lithgow. Newcastle: Printed by S. Hodgson, Union-street, for Emerson Charnley. MDCCCXX.
xiii, 44 p. 20cm.
Title vignette (editor's device)
With reproduction of original t.-p.: An experimentall and exact relation upon that famous and renowned siege of Newcastle ... Together with a succinct commentarie upon the battell of Bowden Hill, and that victorious battell of York or Marston Moore ... By ... William Lithgow. Edinburgh, Printed by Robert Bryson. 1645.

Preface signed: J. T. B. (John Trotter Brockett)
"Two hundred copies printed."—Lowndes, Bibl. man., App., 1878, p. 162.
One of a typographically uniform series of volumes, with woodcut vignettes by Bewick and his pupils, published in Newcastle, the earliest in 1817; after the foundation of the Typographical society of Newcastle upon Tyne in 1818 the publications were issued under the auspices of the society.

1. Newcastle-upon-Tyne—Siege, 1644. I. Brockett, John Trotter, 1788-1842, ed. II. Typographical society of Newcastle upon Tyne.

NL 0408048 MiU CtY IaU OU MnU TxU ICN MdBP

Lithgow, William, 1582-1645?
The Totall Discourse, Of the Rare Aduentures, and painefull Peregrinations of long nineteene Yeares Trauayles, from Scotland, to the Most Famous Kingdomes in Europe, Asia, and Affrica. Perfited by three deare bought Voyages, in Surueighing of Forty eight Kingdomes ancient and Moderne; twenty one Rei-publickes, ten absolute Principalities, with two hundred Ilands. The particular Names whereof, are Described in each Argument of the ten Diuisions of this History: And it

Continued in next column

Continued from preceding column

also diuided in Three Bookes; two whereof, neuer heretofore Published. Wherein is Contayned, an exact Relation, of the Lawes, Religion, Policies, and Gouernment of all their Princes, Potentates, and People. Together with the grieuous Tortures he suffered, by the Inquisition of malaga in Spaine, his miraculous Discouery and Deliuery thence: And of his last and late Returne from the Northerne Iles ... By William Lithgovv. Imprinted at London by Nicholas Okes, and are to be sold by Nicholas Fussell and Humphery Mosley at their shops in Pauls Churchyard, at the Ball, and the white Lyon. 1632.
7 p. l., 507, [5] p. front. (port.) illus. 19cm.
Earlier editions pub. 1614, 1616 and 1623.
Armorial book-plate of George Arnold, esq., and book-plate of Huth collection.

1. Voyages and travels.
Library of Congress G460.L65 5-29030 Revised
——— Copy 2.
Imperfect: p. 363-366 wanting.

NL 0408051 DLC WU DFo CtY NN MB NNH NjP

Lithgow, William, 1582-1645?
The total discourse, of the rare aduentures, and painefull peregrinations of long nineteene yeares trauayles, from Scotland, to the most famous kingdomes in Europe, Asia, and Affrica. Perfited by three deare bought voyages, in surueighing of forty eight kingdomes ancient and moderne; twenty one rei-publickes, ten absolute principalities, with two hundred ilands. The particular names whereof, are described in each argument of the ten diuisions of this history: and it also diuided in three bookes; two whereof, neuer heretofore published. Wherein is contayned, an exact relation, of the lawes, religion, policies, and gouernment of all their princes, potentates, and people. Together with the grieuous tortures he suffered, by the inquisition of Malaga in Spaine, his miraculous discouery and deliuery thence: and of his last and late returne from the northerne iles. London, Imprinted by N.Okes, and are to be sold by N.Fussell and H.Mosley, 1632.
Earlier editions published under title: A most delectable and trve discourse, of an admired and painefull peregrination. Microfilm
Short-title catalogue no.15713 (carton 807)

1. Voyages and travels.

NL 0408054 MiU

Lithgow, William, 1582-1645?
The total discourse... London, J. Okes 1640. 4to. in eights.

Second Complete Edition

STC 15713

NL 0408055 MWiW-C

Lithgow, William, 1582-1645?
The Totall Discourse, Of the rare Adventures, and painefull Peregrinations of long nineteene yeares Travailes from Scotland, to the most famous Kingdomes in Europe, Asia, and Affrica. Perfited by three deare bought Voyages, in surveying of forty eight Kingdomes ancient and modern; twenty one Rei-publicks, ten absolute Principalities, with two hundred Islands. The particular Names whereof, are described in each Argument of the ten Divisions or Parts of this

Continued in next column

Continued from preceding column

History; and it also divided into three Bookes: being newly corrected, and augmented in many severall places, with the addition of a Table thereunto annexed of all the chiefe heads. Wherein is contayned an exact Relation of the Lawes, Religions, Policies and Governments of all their Princes, Potentates and People. Together with the grievous Tortures he suffered by the Inquisition of Malaga in Spaine: His miraculous Discovery and Delivery. And of his last and late returne from the Northern Isles, and other places adjacent. By William Lithgow. Imprinted at London by I. Okes, 1640.
7 p.l., 514(i.e.512), [8] p. front., illus. 19½cm.
Fifth edition.
Signatures: A-Z^8, Aa-Kk^8, Ll^4 (A_1, frontispiece; H_2 incorrectly signed P_2)
Pages 86-87, 94, 96, 312, 322, 324, 429, 432 incorrectly numbered 84-85, 92, 66, 212, 222, 224, 426, 429, respectively; no.445-446 omitted in the paging.
Headpieces; initials. Marginal notes.
Commendatory poems by Patrick Hannay and others.
First published, 1614, with title: A Most Delectable, and Trve Discourse, of an admired and painefull peregratioh.
Armorial book-plate of Sir Henry Mainwaring, bart.
Bound in old sprinkled calf, rebacked.

NL 0408060 CLU-C MH MB ICN CSmH WU CU DFo

Lithgow, William, 1582-1645?
The totall discourse, of the rare adventures, and painefull peregrinations of long nineteene yeares travailes from Scotland, to the most famous kingdomes in Europe, Asia, and Affrica. Perfited by three deare bought voyages, in surveying of forty eight kingdomes ancient and modern; twenty one rei-publicks, ten absolute principalities, with two hundred islands. The particular names whereof, are described in each argument of the ten divisions or parts of this history; and it also divided into three bookes: being newly corr., and augm. in many severall places, with the additions of a table thereunto annexed of all the chiefe heads. Wherein is contayned an exact relation of the lawes, religions, policies and governments of all their princes, potentates and people. Together with the grievous tortures he suffered by the inquisition of Malaga in Spaine: his miraculous discovery and delivery. And of his last and late returne from the northern iles, and other places adjacent. London, Imprinted by I.Okes, 1640.
Earlier editions published under title: A most delectable, and trve discourse, of an admired and painefull peregrination.
Pages 445-446 lacking. Microfilm
Short-title catalogue no.15714 (carton 808)
1. Voyages and travels.

NL 0408063 MiU

Lithgow, William, 1582-1645?
The totall discourse of the rare adventures & painefull peregrinations of long nineteene yeares travayles from Scotland to the most famous kingdomes in Europe, Asia and Affrica, by William Lithgow. Glasgow, J. MacLehose and sons, 1906.
xxxi, 448, [2] p. front., plates, ports. (1 fold.) 23cm.
"Reprint of the 'editio princeps' of 1632," with reproduction of original t.-p.

1. Voyages and travels. I. Title.
Library of Congress G460.L7 7-28951

NL 0408064 NBuU GU PPT NjNbS TU OO OCl MH NN ViU DLC CaBVaU OrCS Vi IEN WaU NjR TxU NcP

VOLUME 336

Lithgow, William, 1582-1645?
The totall discourse of the rare adventures & painefull peregrinations of long nineteene yeares travayles from Scotland to the most famous kingdomes in Europe, Asia and Affrica, by William Lithgow. Glasgow, J. MacLehose and sons, New York, The Macmillan co., 1906.
448, p.

NL 0408065 OU OC1W MiU CtY

Lithgow, William, 1582?-1645?
The travels and adventures of Wm. Lithgow, en Europe, Asia, and Africa, during nineteen years. Glasgow, Printed for the booksellers [ca. 1850]
23 p. 17cm. [Chap books. v.1, no.12]
"[No.] 122."

NL 0408066 MnU

910.9
L776
1770

Lithgow, William, 1582-1645?
Travels and voyages through Europe, Asia, and Africa, for nineteen years. 11th ed. Edinburgh, A. Murray and J. Cochran, 1770.
xvi,490p. illus. 18cm.

"Embellished with copperplates, and illustrated with notes from later travellers."

1. Voyages and travels. I. Title.

NL 0408067 IEN DSI NjP NIC MBCo

Lithgow, William, 1582-1645?
Travels & voyages through Europe, Asia, and Africa, for nineteen years ... By William Lithgow. 12th ed. ... Leith, W. Reid; London, Longman, Hurst, Rees, Orme & Brown; [etc., etc.] 1814.
viii, 412 p. front. (port.) 22cm.

1. Voyages and travels. 5—29029

Library of Congress G460.L67

NL 0408068 DLC MdBP

Lithgow, William, 1582-1645?
A true and experimentall discourse, upon the beginning, proceeding, and victorious event of this last siege of Breda. With the antiquity and annexing of it, to the house of Nassaw, and the many alterations it hath suffered by armes, and armies, within these three-score yeares ... Written by him who was an eye-witnesse of the siege. William Lithgow. London: printed by I. Okes for I. Rothwel, and are to be sold at his shop in Pauls Church-yard at the signe of the Sunne. 1637.
3 p. l., 55 p. 18 x 15cm.
1. Breda—Siege, 1624-1625. I. Title.
43-18736
Library of Congress DH206.B8L5

NL 0408069 DLC CtY InU MiU DFo NjP MH CSmH ICN

Lithgow, William, 1582-1645?
A True Experimentall and Exact Relation upon That famous and renovvned Siege of Newcastle, The diverse conflicts and occurrances fell out there during the time of ten weeks and odde days: And of that mightie and marveilous storming thereof, with Power, Policie, and prudent plots of Warre. Together with a succinct commentarie upon the Battell of Bowdon Hill, and that victorious Battell of York or Marston Moore, never to bee forgotten. By him who was an eye witnesse to the siege of Nevvcastle, William Lithgovv. Edinburgh, by Robert Bryson, 1645.
31 p. (A-D, each 4 leaves). small 4to. Half russia and marbled boards.

NL 0408070 CSmH

W 4
S23
1947

LITHGOW BALDWIN, Luis Rodolfo
Contribución al estudio de la retención urinaria post-operatoria y su tratamiento por la inyección intravesical de glicerina-boricada. [Ciudad Trujillo? 1947?]
56 l. (Santo Domingo. Universidad. Facultad de Medicina. Tesis. 1947/48 [i. e. 1946/47] no. 51)
Typewritten copy.

NL 0408071 DNLM

Lithgow corporation.
Lithcoted strips of mild steel were suspended in the following solutions for test at room temperatures. Results of these tests ... Laboratory report, November, 1939.
7 p.

NL 0408072 DAL

Lithgow family
see under [Hill, Mark Langdon] 1772-1842.

Lithgow library and reading room, *Augusta, Me.*
Annual reports.
[Augusta,
v. 22½cm.

CA 25-187 Unrev'd
Library of Congress Z733.A923

NL 0408074 DLC NN

Lithgow library and reading room, *Augusta, Me.*
Catalogue of Lithgow library and reading room. Augusta, Maine. 1884. Augusta, Kennebec journal print., 1884.
111, [1] p. 23cm.

CA 17-2289 Unrev'd
Library of Congress Z881.A93

NL 0408075 DLC

Z733
A771A3
Library
School

Lithgow Library and Reading Room, Augusta, Me.
The Lithgow Library and Reading Room, Augusta, Maine.
[Augusta, Me., Maine Farmers' Almanac Press, 1897]
174 p. plates, ports., facsims.

NL 0408076 CU MH

Lithiby, Sir John, 1852-1936, ed.

Law

Gt. Brit. *Laws, statutes, etc.*
The Education act, 1921, the Grammar schools act, the Public schools acts, the Endowed schools acts, the Charitable trusts acts, the School sites acts and the acts relating to the superannuation of teachers; with other acts relating to education, and notes on the statutory provisions; also an appendix, containing selections from the Orders in Council and rules, regulations and memoranda of the Board of Education, the Home Office, the Ministry of Health, etc. Together with an abstract of the grant regulations. 22d ed. by Sir John Lithiby. London, C. Knight, 1923.

Lithiby, Sir John, 1852-1936.
The law of district and parish councils, being the local government act, 1894.
see under Gt. Brit. Laws, statutes, etc., 1837-1901 (Victoria)

Lithiby, John, 1852-1936.
Fry, Danby Palmer, 1818-1903.
The law relating to lunacy and mental deficiency comprising the Lunacy acts, 1890 to 1911; the Mental deficiency act, 1913; the Asylums officers' superannuation act, 1909; the Education of epileptic and defective children acts; the Criminal lunatic acts; extracts from poor law statutes relating to pauper lunatics; as well as from various other statutes dealing with the subject, together with an introductory commentary, notes to the statutes and references to cases decided in the superior courts. Being the 4th ed. of "Fry's lunacy laws," 1st and 2nd ed. by Danby P. Fry... 4th ed. by John Lithiby... London, Knight & co., ltd., 1914.

LB2582
.O8
1936

Lithiby, Sir John, 1852-1936, ed.

Gt. Brit. *Laws, statutes, etc.*
Owen's Education acts manual. First 20 editions by Sir Hugh Owen. 21st & 22d editions by Sir John Lithiby. 23d ed. by Sir Ross Barker. London, C. Knight, 1936.

Lithiby, Sir John, 1852-1936.

Law

Gt. Brit. *Laws, statutes, etc.*
Shaws' manual of the vaccination law, containing the Vaccination acts, 1867, 1871, 1874, 1898 & 1907, the vaccination orders, 1898, 1899, 1905 & 1907, and the instructional circulars and memoranda issued by the Local Government Board, with introduction, notes and index, by John Lithiby. 8th ed. London, Butterworth, 1908.

Lithic Laboratory, Ohio State Museum
see
Ohio Historical Society. *Museum. Lithic Laboratory.*

D669.8
L714

[Lithium company]
Lithium metallic vapor atmosphere furnaces; principles and data. [Newark, N. J., Lithium co., c1944]
cover-title, 20 p. illus., diagrs.

1. Furnaces. I. Title.

NL 0408083 NNC

Lithium Corporation of America, inc.
Annotated bibliography on the use of organolithium compounds in organic synthesis; a review of literature published prior to January, 1948. Minneapolis, 1949.
[80] p. 28 cm.
——— Supplement. no. 1 Jan. 1950– Minneapolis.
v. 28 cm. biennial.
Z5524.L6L52
1. Lithium organic compounds—Bibl. 2. Chemistry, Organic—Synthesis—Bibl. I. Title: Organolithium compounds in organic synthesis.
Z5524.L6L5 016.5472 60-18170 rev

MsU KU ICIU MiU NcD OU OrCS
NL 0408084 DLC OrP OrU MsU TxDaM MsU MoSW AU OU

VOLUME 336

Lithium corporation of America, inc.
Lithium dispersions. Minneapolis, Minn. [1955] 3 l. 28cm. (ITS: Product data. 101–456)

Caption title.

1. Lithium. 2. Colloids. I. Lithium corporation of America, inc. Product data. t. 1956.

NL 0408085 NN

Chem QD Z 5524 L6L53 Lithium Corporation of America. Ellestad Research Laboratories. Library.
Annotated bibliography of literature on lithium. 19 - Bessemer City, N.C.
v. 22 x 28 cm.

1.Lithium--Bibl.

NL 0408086 LU

Lithium in modern industry
see under Foote Mineral Company.

Lithium metallic vapor atmosphere furnaces.
See under
[Lithium company]

PD 5117 L57 Lithner, Augusta.
Rim och dikter; poetisk läsebok för skolans lägre klasser, utg. af Augusta Lithner och Laura Löwenhielm. 2. samlingen. Stockholm, Wilhelm Billes Bokförlags Aktiebolag [1905]
117 p.

NL 0408089 WaU

Lithner, Magnus.
Måste vi uppge hoppet i fredssaken? Demokratiernas fred bevarad genom gemensam, stark militärmakt under full nationell avrustning samt genom internationell folkminskning. Efterskrift: Är folkminskning att beklaga? Revid. och vidgad uppl. Stockholm, Seelig, 1937.
79 p. 19 cm.

1. Peace — Addresses, essays, lectures. 2. World politics — Addresses, essays, lectures. I. Title.

JX1963.L462 1937 65–59389 ‡

NL 0408090 DLC CSt-H

Lithner, Magnus.
Måste vi uppge hoppet i fredssaken? Reviderad och vidgad uppl. Efterskrift: Är folkminskning att beklaga? Stockholm, Seelig, 1939.

NL 0408091 MH

Litho-media, inc., *New York.*
Litho-media; a demonstration of the selling power of lithography. New York, Litho-media, inc., 1939.
206 (i. e. 207) p. illus. (incl. mounted specimens; part col.) col. plates. 38½ cm.
The mounted specimens include folders, leaflets, music, post-cards, labels, trade-marks, etc.
One double illustration not included in paging.
"Roger Stephens, the publisher of Litho media, was aided by the following staff in the publication of this book: H. Homer Buckelmueller, editor, Colin Campbell, managing editor, Margaret Halmy [and] Donald L. Gutelius, associate editors, Lewis C. Gandy, typography and design."
1. Lithography. 2. Advertising layout and typography. I. Stephens, Roger, 1889– II. Buckelmueller, H. Homer.
Library of Congress HF5825.L5 39—30208
[a49f½] [763] 659.1

NL 0408092 DLC OrP ICJ OCl

Lithobolia: or, The stone-throwing devil
see under [Chamberlayne, Richard]

PA 2084 L8 1625 Cage Lithocomus, Ludolf.
... Etymologia latina, nova et ad captum puerilem accommodatiori methodo disposita. Accesserunt annotationes et exemplorum Belgica interpretetio. Editio nova prioribus correctior. Amstelodami, Apud Joannem Janssonium, 1625.
4 pts. in 1 v. Pt.1: 120 p. A-G8, H4; pt.2: 59 [1] p. I-L8, M6; pt.3: [2] 195-239 [1] p. N-P8; pt.4: 30 [2] p. a-b8 (A1 lacking or cancelled) 8vo
Added engraved title-page.

Title-page of pt.2 is dated 1624. Pt.3 bears title: Antonii Caucii Suntaxis dilucido compendio scripta. Accesserunt annotationes suis locis insertae... Pt.4 bears title:... Prosodia latina, annotationibus illustrata...

NL 0408095 DFo

Lithogaea
see Moscow. Institut prikladnoĭ mineralogii.

Lithograph showing examples of Egyptian, Hindu, Mexican, Grecian Roman, romanesque, Saracenic and gothic archtiecture
see under Long, Robert Cary, d. 1849.

[Lithographed copy of an Egyptian deed, in the demotic character.] [n.p., n.d.]
sheet 73 x 23 cm. fold. in envelope 27 cm.

NL 0408098 CtY

The Lithographer. v. 1– (no. 1–); July 1, 1870–
[London?] 1870–
v. in 27cm. monthly.
Caption title.
Merged into the Printing times, Aug. 15, 1874.

1. Lithography—Period.

Library of Congress NE2250.L5 45–49913
[2] 763.05

NL 0408099 DLC NNC ICN

Z 1 L7141 The Lithographer; artist and engraver, and magazine of the graphic arts.
v. 1-
Sept. 15, 1891-
[London] 1891-
v. 28cm. monthly.

With which is incorporated "The Printing times and lithographer." Preceded by The Printing times and lithographer, which was formed by a merger of The Lithographer and The Printing times July 1, 1870.

NL 0408100 NNC

The Lithographer and printer
see
The American lithographer & printer.

Wing ZP 8831 .96 LITHOGRAPHERS ASSOCIATION OF PHILADELPHIA.
Banquet tendered by the Lithographers Association of Philadelphia to their guests in commemoration of the centennial of lithography, Monday July 13th 1896 ...
[Philadelphia, 1896]
[2] l. 22cm.

NL 0408102 ICN

Lithographers' international protective and beneficial association of the United States and Canada.
Addresses of the officers. Jurisdictions and places of meeting of the several S.A.'s of the L.I.P. & B. associations. [New York city, n.d.]

[Lithographers' association. Constitutions 1891-1907.]

NL 0408103 MdBJ

Lithographers' International Association of the United States and Canada.
By-laws of the Lithographers' International Association of the United States and Canada. (D. A. 189.) Organized February 19, 1887. New York, Concord Co operative Printing Company (ltd.), 1887.
18 p. 17cm.

NL 0408104 ICJ

LITHOGRAPHERS' INTERNATIONAL PROTECTIVE AND BENEFICIAL ASSOCIATION OF THE UNITED STATES AND CANADA.
OFFICIAL PUBLICATION ... 1910-
NEW YORK, [191 ?-
V. 28½CM.

NL 0408105 MdBJ WHi

LITHOGRAPHERS' INTERNATIONAL PROTECTIVE AND BENEFICIAL ASSOCIATION OF THE UNITED STATES AND CANADA.
Proceedings of the conference consisting of a representative from each local of the L.I.P. and B.A. held at Indianapolis, Apr.10-14, 1911. New York, [1911?].

pp. 40. Table.

NL 0408106 MH DL

VOLUME 336

Lithographers' international protective and beneficial association of the United States and Canada
see also Amalgamated Lithographers of America.

HFBL72 .L713 4L71 Lithographers International Protective and Beneficial Association. Subordinate association no. 1, New York.
Arbitration a success! History of the lithographers' strike. New York, 1896.
171 p. 20 cm.

1. Lithographers - New York (city)
I. Title.
II. Title: Lithographers' strike, History of the.

NL 0408108 WHi

HFBL72 .L713L N489 Lithographers International Protective and Beneficial Association. Subordinate association no. 1, New York.
By-laws. New York,
v. 15 cm.

Library has: 1901, 1905,

NL 0408109 WHi

Lithographers' journal; pertaining to lithography and the field of supplies for lithographers ...
Philadelphia [W. M. Patton] 18
v. illus. (part col., incl. ports.) col. plates. 35cm. monthly.

1. Lithography—Period.

Library of Congress Z119.L56 6—29995

NL 0408110 DLC

THOGRAPHERS' journal. v.1-49, no.4; June, 1915-July/Aug. 1964. New York. 49 v. illus., ports. 23-29cm.

Lacking: v.48, no.2, May, 1963.
Monthly (some issues combined).
Organ of the Amalgamated lithographers of America.
Title varies slightly.
Includes an occasional suppl.

United with the American photo engraver to form the Graphic arts unionist.

1. Trade unions, Lithographers'--U.S. I. Amalgamated lithographers of America.

NL 0408112 NN ICRL IU TU MCM KMK CU PPiCI

R655.33 L713 The lithographers manual; a compendium of lithography. New York, Waltwin Pub. Co.
Library has
1st- 3d 1937-1958
Title varies: 1937, The photo-lithographer's manual.
Editor: 1937-1940, Walter E. Soderstrom; 1958- Victor Strauss.
655.33 L713 ----- Same.
Library has

NL 0408113 MiD OCl ICJ

Lithographers national association.
American lithography; its growth; its development; its need of tariff protection. Essential facts set forth in the hearings before the Committee on ways and means, showing the fairness of the appeal of American lithographers for higher tariff duties. A question of wages ... [Rochester? N. Y.] Issued by the National association of employing lithographers, 1909.
32 p. 16½ x 9 cm.

1. Tariff on lithographs—U. S.

HF2651.L55U5 9—27636 rev

NL 0408114 DLC

Lithographers National Association.
Annual awards book
see its
National competition of offset-lithography.

Lithographers national association, inc.
Lithographic awards competition
see Lithographers National Association. National competition of offset-lithography.

Lithographers National Association.
National competition of offset-lithography.
New York.
v. illus. 31 cm. annual.
Cover title, 195 Annual awards book.

1. Lithography—Societies, etc. 2. Lithography—Competitions. I. Title.

TR940.L43 54-43815

NL 0408117 DLC NN

Microfilm Lithographers National Association.
Stevenson, Harry Clifford, 1884–
Uniform manufacturing cost and estimating system adopted by the National association of employing lithographers, 1914, by Harry C. Stevenson, of Harpham, Barnes & Stevenson company ... [New York, Printed by the American lithographic company, °1914]

Lithographers National Association
see also Joint Cost Committee of the Label Manufacturers National Association Folding Box Manufacturers National Association and the National Association of Employing Lithographers.

Lithographer's supply catalog.
New York, National Lithographer Pub. Co.
v. 28 cm.
Title varies: —1954-55, The National lithographer's yearbook.

1. Lithography—Apparatus and supplies. 2. Lithography—Metal plate processes.

NE2495.N3 763.078 49-23207 rev*‡
[r56b1]

NL 0408120 DLC

Lithographia
see Graphische Künste.

Lithographic abstracts
see Graphic arts abstracts.

HFBL72 .LI Lithographic Artists' League of America.
Constitution and by-laws...adopted at a regular meeting, May 20, 1900. New York, Concord print., 1900.
11 p. 14cm.

1. Lithographers - New York (city)

NL 0408123 WHi

Wing ZX 8451 .26 The LITHOGRAPHIC drawing book. London, Printed at C.Hullmandel's Lithographic Establishment for J.Dickinson[1824-26]
8 no.in 1v. plates. 19-28cm.

One no. is for the year 1824, edited by J.D. Harding, S.Prout, C.Hullmandel; the other nos. are for the year 1826, edited by R.R.Reinagle, J.D.Harding, S.Prout, etc.
In box.

NL 0408124 ICN

Lithographic facsimiles of documents and papers relating to the purchase of Louisiana ...
N.p., n.pub., n.d.
Facsims. F°.

NL 0408125 CaBViPA

Lithographic Printing Productivity Team
see British Lithographic Printing Productivity Team.

A lithographic sketch of the north bank of the Thames
see under [Baynes, Thomas Mann]

238 L71 Lithographic Technical Foundation, inc.
Albumin plate making. New York, 1944.
35 p. (Its Shop manual. no.3)

NL 0408128 DNAL NBNC

Lithographic technical foundation, inc.
[MacDonald, David James] 1875–
... Analysis of the single-color offset pressman's trade, with suggested course of study. New York city, Lithographic technical foundation, inc., 1928.

Lithographic technical foundation, inc.
Basic texts for apprentices in lithography ... [Chicago] Lithographic technical foundation, inc. [°1926–
v. 23cm.

1. Lithography. I. Title.

Library of Congress NE2425.L5 27-3708

NL 0408130 DLC ICRL MB NNC ICJ OCl

VOLUME 336

Lithographic technical foundation, inc.
Bulletin
see its
Research bulletin.

[Lithographic technical foundation, inc.]
Chemistry for lithographers ... [New York, °1945–
v. illus., diagrs. 29½ x 25cm.
Loose-leaf.
On cover: L. T. F. training course, 403 A.
"Reading references": v. 1, 2 leaves at end.

1. Chemistry—Outlines, syllabi, etc. 2. Chemistry—Study and teaching. I. Title.
Library of Congress QD41.L69 46-855
[2] 540.71

NL 0408132 DLC

Lithographic technical foundation, inc.
The dampening system of the lithographic offset press. New York, Lithographic foundation, inc. [c1945]
36 p. diagrs (Shop manual, no. 8)

NL 0408133 OCl

Lithographic Technical Foundation.
Effect of humidity on sensitivity of bichromated colloids; progress report no.2, Oct.14–Dec,27, 1946. [Chicago] Armour Research Foundation, 1947.
17 p.

I. IIT Research Institute, Chicago. 655.226

NL 0408134 ICJ

Lithographic technical foundation, inc.
Financial statement
see its Reports.

Z117
.L5
Lithographic Technical Foundation, inc. Foundation publications. (Indexes)
Lithographic Technical Foundation, inc.
General index of the publications issued by the Lithographic Technical Foundation. New York [1955, °1954]

Lithographic Technical Foundation, inc.
General index of the publications issued by the Lithographic Technical Foundation. New York [1955, °1954]
116 p. 22 cm. (*Its* Foundation publication, 601)

1. Lithography—Technique—Bibl. I. Lithographic Technical Foundation, inc. Foundation publications. (Indexes)
Z117.L5 *016.65532 016.775 55-27356

NL 0408137 DLC CaBVa NN ICJ

NE2285
.L5
no.109
1945
Lithographic Technical Foundation, inc.
Guides, grippers and insertion devices for lithographic offset presses. [1st ed.]
New York [1945]
38 p. illus. 17cm. (Its Foundation publications, no. 109. Its Shop manuals, no. 9)

1. Lithography—Technique. I. Title. II. Ser. III. Ser.

NL 0408138 ViU

Lithographic Technical Foundation.
Gum arabic substitute. Chicago, Armour Research Foundation, 1946.
40 p. illus. (IIT Research Institute, Chicago. Project no.2-350 C. Report, no.1)

I. IIT Research Institute, Chicago. 655.226

NL 0408139 ICJ

NE2285
.L5
no.124
1946
Lithographic Technical Foundation, inc.
Halftone photography for offset lithography. [1st ed.] New York [1946]
52 p. illus. 17cm. (Its Foundation publications, 124. Its Shop manuals, no. 24)

1. Photography. 2. Lithography—Metal plate process. 3. Chromolithography. I. Title. II. Ser. III. Ser.

NL 0408140 ViU NBNC LU

NE2285
.L5
no.117
1946
Lithographic Technical Foundation, inc.
Hand transfers for offset lithography. [1st ed.] New York [1946]
52 p. illus. 17cm. (Its Foundation publications, no. 117. Its Shop manuals, no. 17)

1. Lithography—Technique. I. Title. II. Ser. III. Ser.

NL 0408141 ViU MiD

Lithographic technical foundation, inc.
Handbook of air conditioning for lithographers, by Robert F. Reed ...
see under Reed, Robert Findley, 1890–

655.32
L776 H
Lithographic Technical Foundation, inc.
How to make deep-etch plates on ungrained zinc and aluminum. [1st ed.] N.Y. [c1953]
45p. illus. 22cm.

1.Lithography I.Ti.

NL 0408143 NB ICJ N CaBVa

Lithographic technical foundation, inc.
Improved desensitization with cellulose gum; instructions for use. New York, Lithographic foundation [c1948] 29 p. illus. 21cm. (Its: Instructions. no. 801)

1. ed.

1. Lithography—Technique.

NL 0408144 NN

667.5
L713i
LITHOGRAPHIC technical foundation, inc.
Inks for offset lithography; drying, conditioning, mixing.
N.Y. c1945. 48p. tables (1 fold.) diagrs.
(its Shop manual, no.13)

"Glossary": p.47-48.
"Reading references": p.46.

NL 0408145 WaS

Lithographic Technical Foundation, inc.
Изготовление альбуминных пластин; цеховое руководство литоофсетной техники. Перевод с английского по, ред. А. Д. Троицкого. [Москва] Гизлегпром, 1946.
39 p. illus. 17 cm.
Original published as no. 3 of its Shop manual.

1. Lithography—Technique. I. Title.
Title transliterated: Izgotovlenie al'buminnykh plastin.
NE2425.L56 54-35283

NL 0408146 DLC

Lithographic Technical Foundation, inc. LTF shop manual
see its Shop manual.

Lithographic Technical Foundation, inc.
Lithographic abstracts.
New York.
v. 22 cm.

1. Photolithography—Abstracts. I. Title.
TR940.L46 54-31385 ‡

NL 0408148 DLC N

Lithographic Technical Foundation, inc.
Lithographic abstracts
see also Graphic arts abstracts.

Lithographic Technical Foundation, inc.
News letter. no. 6 Dec. 1951 New York
Irregular.

NL 0408150 OCl

VOLUME 336

Lithographic Technical Foundation, inc.
Offset photography line. ₍1st ed.₎ New York ₍1945₎
32 p. illus., diagrs. 17cm. (Its Shop manual no. 12)

1. Photography. 2. Lithography—Metal plate process. I. Title. II. Series.

NL 0408151 MB CaBVa

763.072 L776 Lithographic Technical Foundation, inc.
Optical density as a measure of tone values in lithography. New York ₍1950, °1945₎
36 p. illus. 22 cm. (Its Foundation publication, no. 304. Technical bulletin, no. 4)

1. Lithography. I. Title. Series: Lithographic Technical Foundation, inc. Foundation publications, no 304. Series: Lithographic Technical Foundation, inc. Technical bulletin, no. 4.

NL 0408152 N

Hum NE 2250 L77 no.4 Lithographic Technical Foundation, inc.
Optical density as a measure of tone values in lithography. New York, ₍1955,c1945₎
36p. illus. (Lithographic Technical Foundation, inc. Technical bulletin. no.4)

1. Lithography. I. Title. ser.

NL 0408153 FTaSU

NE 2425 .L5 P3 Lithographic Technical Foundation, Inc.
Paper and humidity in the pressroom. New York, c1944.
34 p. diags., graphs. 16 cm. (Its shop manual no. 1)

1. Paper--Testing. 2. Lithography--Technique. 3. Paper, Lithographic. I. Title.

NL 0408154 NBNC

Lithographic technical foundation, inc.
Paper and paper problems; a stenographic report of ₍a series of₎ conferences of paper manufacturers and lithographic pressmen, conducted under the auspices of the Lithographic technical foundation, inc. New York ₍194-₎
28 p. 23cm.

1. Paper - Testing. I. Title: Paper problems.

NL 0408155 NNC NBuG NN OCl

NE 2425 .L5 P364 Lithographic Technical Foundation, Inc.
Paper conditioning for offset lithography. New York ₍°1946₎
39p. diags., graphs. 17cm. (Its Shop manual no. 26)

1. Paper, Lithographic. 2. Lithography --Apparatus and supplies. I. Title.

NL 0408156 NBNC

NE 2425 .L5 P36 Lithographic Technical Foundation, Inc.
Papers for offset lithography. New York ₍°1946₎
44p. illus. 17cm. (Its Shop manual no.25)

1. Paper, Lithographic. 2. Lithography Apparatus and supplies. I. Title.

NL 0408157 NBNC

Lithographic Technical Foundation, inc.
pH: what it is, how to measure it, where to control it. New York ₍°1951₎
41 p. illus. 22 cm.

1. Hydrogen-ion concentration. 2. Photolithography. I. Title.

TR940.L48 *655.32 775 53-15191

NL 0408158 DLC NN MiD

Lithographic Technical Foundation, inc.
pH: what it is, how to measure it, where to control it. ₍Rev.₎ New York ₍1955, °1951₎
41 p. illus. 22 cm.

1. Hydrogen-ion concentration. 2. Photolithography. I. Title.

[TR940] 655.325 A 62-5651 ‡ Cancel

Printed for Card Div. Library of Congress ₍2₎

NL 0408159 DLC OCl MB NB ICJ NBNC

---

238 L71P Lithographic Technical Foundation, inc.
Photo-composing for offset lithography. [1st ed.] New York [1946]
39 p. (Its Shop manual. no.20)

NL 0408160 DNAL

---

332 L71 Lithographic Technical Foundation, inc.
Photography for offset lithography color separation. [1st ed.] New York [1945]
40 p. (Its Shop manual. no.16)

NL 0408161 DNAL LU

Lithographic technical foundation, inc.
Photography for offset lithography; color separation. New York, N. Y., Lithographic technical foundation, inc. ₍1945₎
72 p. illus., diagrs. 21½cm.
"First edition, September 1945."

1. Photography. 2. Lithography—Metal plate processes. 3. Chromolithography.

Library of Congress TR977.L5 46-15132
₍3₎ 775

NL 0408162 DLC NN TxU

Lithographic technical foundation, inc.
A plan of action for an in-plant training program. New York [1953?] [13] p. 22cm.

Cover-title.

1. Schools, Factory--U.S. 2. Lithography--Study and teaching--U.S.

NL 0408163 NN

NE 2540 .L5 P41 Lithographic Technical Foundation, Inc.
Plate troubles in offset lithography. New York ₍c1947₎
61 p. 17 cm. (Its Shop manual no. 31)

1. Lithography--Metal plate processes. 2. Lithography--Technique. I. Title.

NL 0408164 NBNC

---

238 L71PL Lithographic Technical Foundation, inc.
Platemaking for offset lithography, deep etch. [1st ed.] New York [1946]
48 p. (Its Shop manual. no.23)

NL 0408165 DNAL NBNC

Lithographical technical foundation, inc.
Progress bulletin. New York.
Monthly?

NL 0408166 NN

655.3 L776 P **Lithographic Technical Foundation, inc.**
Proving for offset lithography. ₍1st ed.₎ N.Y. ₍c1946₎
37p. illus. 17cm. (Its Shop manual no. 22)

1.Lithography. Metal plate processes I.Ti.

NL 0408167 NB NBNC

---

763 L71r 1949 Lithographic Technical Foundation, inc.
The relations between dot area, dot density and tone value in lithgraphy. ₍2d ed.₎ New York ₍1949₎
46p. illus. 22cm. (Its Technical bulletin, no.5)

1. Lithography--Technique. I. Title.

NL 0408168 IU N

LITHOGRAPHIC TECHNICAL FOUNDATION, INC.
Reports.
New York. v. illus. 23- 28cm.

Continued in next column

VOLUME 336

Continued from preceding column

Annual.
Reports for 1950, 1959-61 called 27th, 36th-38th.
Title varies 1946, 1948-50, Financial statement. (Other variations).
Includes suppl.: Lithographic technical foundation, inc.; its origin and accomplishments. [1940].

For later file, which continues its numbering, see: Graphic arts technical foundation. Report.

1. Lithography--Study and teaching--U.S.--N.Y.--New York. 2. Printing--Assoc. and org.--U.S. I. Lithographic technical foundation, inc. Financial statement. II. Lithographic technical foundation, inc. Lithographic technical foundation, inc.; its origin and accomplishments. 1. subs. for its Reports for the Education and research departments---

NL 0408170 NN ICJ

Lithographic Technical Foundation, Inc.
[Reports for the Education and Research Departments for the year ending April 1
19

New York, 19 23cm.
no.

1. Lithography—Study and teaching—U. S.—N. Y.—New York.
N. Y. P. L. November 10, 1936

NL 0408171 NN OC1

Lithographic technical foundation, inc.
Research bulletin. no. 1–
New York, N. Y. [1925–
nos. illus., plates, tables, diagrs. 21½–23cm. Irregular.
Nos. 1-12 issued as its Research series, no. 1-5, 7-8, 10, 10[a], 10[b], 11, 5[a]
Title varies: nos. 1-4, Bulletin.
nos. 5- Research bulletin.

1. Lithography.

Library of Congress NE2250.L75 46-29384
[2] 763.072

NL 0408172 DLC ICJ

LITHOGRAPHIC TECHNICAL FOUNDATION, INC.
Research progress. no.1-50; May/June, 1947-Nov. 1960. Chicago. 50 no. in 1 v. illus. 28cm.

Lacking: no.48-49, Aug.-Sept. 1960?
Bimonthly (irregular).
No. 1-10, May/June, 1947-1948, called v. 1.
Prepared by its Research dept.
No more published?
1. Lithography--Per. and soc. publ.

NL 0408173 NN MiD

Lithographic Technical Foundation, Inc.
Research series. no. 1-2, 4-6, 10.
New York [c1925-34]
6 no. in 1 v.

NL 0408174 ICN

Lithographic technical foundation, inc.
Sales bulletin. no. 1–
New York, N. Y. [1931–
nos. illus. 23cm. (Its Research series, no. 6, 9

1. Lithography.

Library of Congress NE2250.L76 46-29385

NL 0408175 DLC OCU

Lithographic technical foundation, inc.
Science of photolithographic processes and materials. Issued by Lithographic technical foundation, inc. New York, N. Y. [c1937]
3 p. l., 72 p. illus., diagrs. 23cm.

1. Photolithography. I. Title.
Library of Congress TR940.L5 38-17993
——— Copy 2.
Copyright AA 230867 [3] 775

NL 0408176 DLC OC1 OOxM ICJ

Lithographic technical foundation, inc.
Selling lithography ... [New York, N. Y., Lithographic technical foundation, inc., c1933–
v. 23cm.
CONTENTS.—I. Creative or planned selling.

1. Advertising. 2. Lithographs. 3. Salesmen and salesmanship.

Library of Congress HF5827.L5 42-31459

NL 0408177 DLC NN OC1

Lithographic Technical Foundation, inc.
Shop manual.
New York, 19
nos. illus. 17 cm.
Began publication in 1944.
Title varies: no. -4, LTF shop manual.

1. Lithography—Technique.
NE2425.L53 763 45-15539 rev*

NL 0408178 DLC NN

Lithographic Technical Foundation, Inc.
Subscribers' bulletin.
no.

New York, 192 23cm.
nos.
Annual.

1. Lithography—Per. and soc. publ.
N. Y. P. L. April 15, 1937

NL 0408179 NN

763
L71t
Lithographic technical foundation, inc.
Technical bulletin.
New York, N. Y. [ ]
nos. illus., diagrs. 21½–23cm.
Nos. 1-3 issued as its Research series no. 0[a], 4[a], 9[b]

1. Lithography.

NL 0408180 KEmT FTaSU NN

NE2425
.L55
Lithographic Tecnnical Foundation, inc.
Травление точек; цеховое руководство лито-офсетной техники. Перевод с английского и ред. А. Д. Троицкого. Москва, Гизлегпром, 1946.
54 p. illus. 17 cm.
Original published as no. 2 of its series: Shop manual.

1. Lithography—Technique. I. Troiŝkiĭ, A. D., ed. II. Title.
Title transliterated: Travlenie tochek
NE2425.L55 53-29878]

NL 0408181 DLC

Lithographie
see under [Rémusat, Jean Pierre Abel] 1788-1832.

La lithographie en France. Mulhouse, Librairie F. Gangloff, 1946–
v. illus. 17 cm.
At head of title: Société Godefroy Engelmann.
CONTENTS.—1. Des origines au début du romantisme, par L Lang.—2. L'époque du romantisme, par J. E. Bersier.

1. Lithography — France. I. Lang, Léon. II. Bersier, Jean Eugène.
NE2349.L5 52-30217

NL 0408183 DLC MH

AP103
.C17
vol. 11
Rosenwald Coll
Lithographie mensuelle. no. 1-24, août 1832-1834. Paris, Bureau de la Caricature [etc.]
[25] l., 24 plates. 22 x 32-30 x 52 cm. monthly.
The plates, designed by the artists of La Caricature, are each accompanied by a leaf of descriptive text. These plates are also described in La Caricature. No. 1-19 are variously called "Dessin de l'Association," or "Dessin de la souscription." Cf. G. Vicaire. Manuel de l'amateur, col. 81-87.
Published by subscription for the Association de la liberté de la presse.
Bound as v. 10 (i. e. 11) of La Caricature.
L. C. set incomplete: leaves to accompany plates 20-24 are wanting.
1. Caricatures and cartoons—France. I. Association de la liberté de la presse.
AP103.C17 vol. 11 Rosenwald Coll. 50-14322 rev

NL 0408184 DLC

La Lithographie parisienne, Association d'ouvriers lithographes, Paris.
...Statuts. (Paris, n.d.)
28 p. 21 cm
Caption title.

NL 0408185 DL

Lithographing industry parity committee, Quebec
Statistical report on the number of establishments, the number of employees, the hours of work and the wages paid in the lithographing industry of the province of Quebec, 1938-1946. Montreal [1946]
55 p. tables, diagrs.

NL 0408186 NNC

Lithographing industry parity committee, Quebec.
Statistics relative to wages, hours of work and employees in the various branches of the lithographing industry, 1938-1947. Prepared by the Lithographing industry parity committee for the Province of Quebec. [Quebec, 1947]
68 numb. l.

Consists entirely of tables.

NL 0408187 MH-BA

VOLUME 336

Lithography. [London] 1820.
[61]-84 p. 21 cm.
Running title. Binder's title: Review of Senefelder's & Hullmandel's [i. e. his translation of Raucourt's] Lithography.
Detached from unidentified periodical, v. 4, no. 1 (July, 1820)
Bookplate of Howard C. Levis.

1. Senefelder, Alois, 1771-1834. Vollständiges Lehrbuch der Steindruckerey. 2. Raucourt, Antoine, 1790-1841. Mémoire sur les expériences lithographiques.
NE2420.S523L5 Rosenwald Coll. 50-47851

NL 0408188 DLC

Lithography; or, The art of making drawings on stone
see under [Bankes, H]

Div. of Maps

Lithoprint Map Company, *New York.*
Farm plat book of Marshall County. [Plymouth, Ind.] Distributed by Marshall County Rural Youth, 1949.
[11] l. of maps (1 col.) 41 cm.
Cover title.
"John W. Hildebrand, surveyor and engineer; David J. Rinkenberg, deputy and draftsman."

1. Marshall Co., Ind.—Maps. 2. Real property—Marshall Co., Ind.—Maps. I. Marshall County Rural Youth.

Map 50-966

NL 0408190 DLC

AC-L W557L L713

Le Lithostrotos. D'après des fouilles récentes Avec une préface du R.P.H. Vincent ... Paris, Dillen & cie., [1933]
4p.*l.*, [11]-92, [8]p. illus., plans, photos. 19½cm.
"Lettre de son eminence le Cardinal Pacelli" 3d-4th p.*l.*, in Italian and French.
Paper wrappers.
From the library of Evelyn Waugh.
I. Pius XII, Pope, 1876-1958. II. Vincent, Hughes, 1872-

NL 0408191 TxU

Lithotomus castratus; or, Mr. Cheselden's treatise on the high operation for the stone
see under [Houstoun, Robert]

WJ 500 L776 1876

LITHOTOMY; its successes and its dangers. Being a verbatim report, from shorthand notes, of an inquest held before the city coroner. With a preface and commentary by an M. R. C. S. E. Melbourne, Bailliere, 1876.
xxviii, 131 p. illus.

NL 0408193 DNLM OCIW-H CSt

---

*F.88 .174

Lithotype Printing Co., Gardner, Mass.
Natick illustrated, Twenty-seven views. Gardner, Mass., Lithotype Printing Co. [1880?]
[1] l., 27 mounted photos. 18 x 28cm.

1. Natick, Mass.--Descr.--Views.

NL 0408194 MB

Lithotype printing and publishing co., Gardner, Mass., pub.
Waterbury and her industries. Fifty attractive and carefully selected views, by the photogravure process, as photographed from nature, of the many leading manufacturing establishments, public buildings, churches, residences, park, street and general bird's-eye views of Waterbury, Conn., together with a Historical sketch of the city and its various industries, by Homer F. Bassett, representing the Waterbury of to-day. Negatives by Adt & brother. Gardner, Mass., Lithotype printing and publishing co. [1889?]

---

fNA9127 S36L5 City & Regional Planning Library

Lithotype Process Company, San Francisco.
Zoning map book for city and county of San Francisco contains complete city map, sectional zoning maps, district boundary map, set back map [and] zoning ordinance. [San Francisco, The author, c1948]
27 p. (chiefly maps) 46cm.

Letter of approval from San Francisco City Planning Commission on verso of t. p.

1. Zoning - San Francisco. 2. Zoning law - San Francisco. I. San Francisco. City Planning Commission. II. Title.

NL 0408196 CU

Lithovius (Samuel)
*Om nyttan och nödwändigheten för en präst, at äga insikt i medicine... *Åbo*, 1762. 20 pp. 4°.

NL 0408197 NN

Lithuania
see also **Ostland.**

Lithuania.
Affaire du chemin de fer Panevėžys-Saldutiškis. Contre-mémoire du gouvernement lithuanien. [Kaunas? "Spindulio"] 1938.
82 p., 1 l. 32cm.

NL 0408199 MH-L

Lithuania.
Affaire du chemin de fer Panevėžys-Saldutiškis. Duplique du gouvernement lithuanien. [Kaunas? "Spindulio"] 1938.
65, [1] p. 32cm.

NL 0408200 MH-L

DK511 .L27A5 1920

Lithuania.
The boundaries of Lithuania. A memorandum to the State department presented by the representative of Lithuania in America, April, 1920. [Washington? 1920]
1 p.l., 3, III, 29 numb. l. 28 cm.

NL 0408201 DLC

Lithuania.
Demande d'admission de la Lithuanie dans la Société des Nations. Mémorandum, avec annexes
see under League of Nations. Secretary-General, 1919-1933 (Earl of Perth)

Lithuania.
Dispute between Lithuania and Poland. Letter from the Lithuanian Government regarding the resolution of the Council of February 3rd, 1923. Geneva, 1923.
10 l. 33 cm.
Caption title.
At head of title: League of Nations.
Official no.: C.218.M.125.1923.VII.
Refers to Lithuania's refusal to accept the Council's resolution of Feb. 3, 1923 in regard to the line of demarcation and its request that the matter be submitted to the Permanent Court of International Justice (official no.: C.161.M.85.1923.VII)
"Statement to the Council of the League of Nations": leaves 2-10.
1. Lithuania—Bound.—Poland. 2. Poland—Bound.—Lithuania. 3. League of Nations. Council. I. League of Nations.

A 48-7803*

Woodrow Wilson Memorial Library for Library of Congress [2]

NL 0408203 NNUN-W

Lithuania.
The dispute between Poland and Lithuania: memorandum ...
see under League of Nations. Secretary-General, 1919-1933 (Earl of Perth)

Lithuania.
Economic and financial situation of Lithuania.

[Kaunas, 4°.

1. Commerce—Lithuania. 2. Economic history—Lithuania.
N. Y. P. L. September 30, 1927

NL 0408205 NN DLC

Lithuania.
Exposé écrit du gouvernement de la République Lithuanienne concernant la demande d'avis consultatif adressée par le Conseil de la Société des nations à la Cour permanente de justice internationale et portant: "Les engagements internationaux en vigueur obligent-ils, dans les circonstances actuelles, la Lithuanie, et, en cas de réponse affirmative, dans quelles conditions, à prendre les mesures nécessaires pour ouvrir au trafic, ou à certaines catégories de trafic, la section de

ligne de chemin de fer Landwarow-Kaisiadorys?" Kaunas, 1931.
91 p. 32 cm.
"Trafic ferroviaires entre la Lithuanie et la Pologne. I. Exposé du gouvernement polonais" (25 leaves, typewritten) inserted in back cover pocket.

NL 0408207 PU

Law

Lithuania.

Poland. *Konfederacja Generalna, Warsaw, 1764.*
Konfederacya Generalna Omnium Ordinum Regni, & Magni Ducatûs Litt. na Konwokacyi Głowney Warszawskiey uchwalona. Dnia siódmego miesiąca maja roku pańskiego tysiącznego siedmsetnego sześćdziesiątego czwartego. W Warszawie, W druk. Rzeczypospolitey w Collegium xx. Schol. Piarum [1764?]

Lithuania.
... Lithuania. [Geneva, 1939]
47 p. illus. 24 cm. (League of nations. Series of publications. European conference on rural life. 12)
League of nations. National monographs drawn up by governments.
At head of title: ... League of nations. European conference on rural life, 1939 ...
Official no.: C.28.M.16.1939. Conf.E.V.R.12.

1. Lithuania. 2. Agriculture—Lithuania. I. European conference on rural life, Geneva, 1939.
HD105.E8 1939a no. 12 39-32951 rev
——— Copy 2. JX1975.A2 1939.C.28.M.16

NL 0408209 DLC IdU OrU MoU

VOLUME 336

Lithuania.
… Lithuanie. Genève, 1939.

47 p. illus., tables. 24cm. ([League of nations] Série de publications. Conférence européenne de la vie rurale. 12)

League of nations. Monographies nationales établies par les gouvernements.
At head of title: … Société des nations. Conférence européenne de la vie rurale 1939 …
Official no.: C.28.M.16.1939. Conf. E.V.R.12.
Issued also in English.

1. Lithuania. 2. Agriculture—Lithuania. I. European conference on rural life, Geneva, 1939.

A 46-3585

Woodrow Wilson memorial library for Library of Congress [HD105.E8] [3] 331.76309475

NL 0408210 NNUN-W

Lithuania.
Memel territory. [Memorandum from the Lithuanian Government to the Council of the League of Nations, Geneva, 1923.

24 l. 33 cm.

Caption title.
At head of title: League of Nations.
Official no.: C.727.M.297.1923.VII.
Rejects the League intervention.
Reprinted in League of Nations. The status of the Memel territory, 1924, p. 38–44 (official no.: C.159.M.39.1924.VII)

1. Memel (Territory) I. League of Nations.

A 48-5572

Woodrow Wilson Memorial Library for Library of Congress [1]

NL 0408211 NNUN-W

Lithuania.
… Minorités en Lithuanie. Genève, 1925.

1 p. l., 6 numb. l. 33cm.

Caption title.
At head of title: Société des nations.
Official no.: C.744.1925.I.
Mimeographed.
"Communiqué aux membres du Conseil."
"Memorandum présentant les observations du Gouvernement lithuanien au sujet des diverses plaintes concernant la situation des minorités de race, de langue et de religion en Lithuanie": leaves 1–6.

1. Poles in Lithuania. 2. Jews in Lithuania. I. League of nations.

A 47-872

Woodrow Wilson memorial library for Library of Congress [2]

NL 0408212 NNUN-W

Lithuania.
… Minorities in Lithuania. Situation of the Polish minority in Lithuania. Geneva, 1925.

15 p. 33cm.

At head of title: … League of nations.
Official no.: C.149.1925.I.
"Communicated to the members of the Council."
Issued also in French.
Memorandum submitted to the Council of the League of nations by the Lithuanian government.
Final text issued in the League's Official journal, 1925, p. 587–606.

1. Poles in Lithuania. I. League of nations.

A 46-5809

Woodrow Wilson memorial library for Library of Congress [2]

NL 0408213 NNUN-W

Lithuania. . . . Note adressée au gouvernement polonais par la gouvernement de Lituanie [le 24 juillet, 1919] Kaunas, 1919.
2 p. 27 cm. (Délégation de Lituanie à la Conférence de la paix. [pt.] VII, 14)
Caption title.
Mimeographed.
At head of title: Copie

NL 0408214 CSt-H

Lithuania.
The Polish-Lithuanian dispute. Geneva, 1920.

2 l. 33 cm.

Caption title.
At head of title: League of Nations.
Official no.: 20/4/428/1.
Telegram dated Dec. 3, 1920, from the Lithuanian Government regarding the popular expression of opinion in the Vilna region.

Continued in next column

Continued from preceding column

1. Plebiscite—Vilna. I. League of Nations.

A 48-7172*

Woodrow Wilson Memorial Library for Library of Congress [1]

NL 0408215 NNUN-W

Lithuania.
Preliminary objection to the jurisdiction of the court filed by the Lithuanian government in conformity with article 38 of the rules, in the case concerning the interpretation of the statue of Memel. Leyden, 1932.

9, (3) p. f°.
(French and English).

NL 0408216 MH-L

Lithuania.
Request of the Lithuanian Government under article 11 of the Covenant. Geneva, 1927.

17 l. 33 cm.

Caption title.
At head of title: League of Nations.
Official no.: C.525.M.183.1927.VII.
Letter, dated Oct. 15, 1927, protesting against the suppression of Lithuanian schools in Poland and against Polish persecution of Lithuanian clergy.

——— Letter from the Lithuanian Government dated November 21, 1927. Geneva, 1927.

[1] l. 33 cm.

At head of title: League of Nations.
Official no.: C.525(a)M.183(a)1927.VII.
Contains verification of statements made in League document C.525.M.183.1927.VII.

1. Lithuanians in Poland. 2. Minorities—Poland. I. League of Nations.

A 48-7711*

Woodrow Wilson Memorial Library for Library of Congress [1]

NL 0408218 NNUN-W

Lithuania.
… Vyriausybės žinios …
[Kaunas, etc.] 1918–

v. 32cm.

Number 1 issued at Vilna.
Numbers 1–37 have title: Laikinosios vyriausybės žinios …

1. Lithuania—Pol. & govt. I. Lithuania. Laws, statutes, etc. II. Title. III. Title: Laikinosios vyriausybės žinios.

31-20598

Library of Congress J7.L5 354.474

NL 0408219 DLC

Lithuania. *Army*
see **Lithuania.** *Kariuomenė.*

Lithuania. Board of state railways
see Lithuania. Geležinkelių valdyba.

Lithuania. *Centralinis statistikos biuras.*
297-nių [i. e. Dviejų šimtų devyniasdešimt septynių] darbininkų, tarnautojų ir valdininkų šeimų biudžetų tyrinėjimo Lietuvoje 1936–1937 m. rezultatai. Kaunas, 1939.

135 p. tables. 29 cm.
Title and table of contents also in French and German.

1. Cost and standard of living—Lithuania. I. Title.

HD7035.6.A52 54-47370 ‡

NL 0408222 DLC NjP MH NN

Lithuania. *Centralinis statistikos biuras.*
Lietuva skaitlinėmis; diagramų albumas. La Lithuanie en chiffres. [Kaunas, Finansų ministerijos leidinys, 1924?]

1 v. (unpaged, chiefly illus.) 21 x 31 cm.
Lithuanian, French, and English.

1. Lithuania—Stat. I. Title. II. Title: La Lithuanie en chiffres.

HA1448.L5A53 56-53187 ‡

Library of Congress

NL 0408223 DLC NN

Lithuania. *Centralinis statistikos biūras.*
… Lietuva skaitmenimis 1918–1928 m. La Lithuanie en chiffres 1918–1928. Diagramų albomas. Album de diagrammes. [Kaunas?] Finansų ministerija–Centralinis statistikos biuras [1929?]

1 p. l., ii, 184, [4] p. incl. illus., map, plan, tables, diagrs. (part col.) 32cm.

At head of title: Lietuvos respublika. République lithuanienne.
Lithuanian and French.

1. Lithuania—Stat. I. Title. II. Title: La Lithuanie en chiffres 1918–1928.

30-31500

Library of Congress HA1448.L5A5 1928 [2] 314.75

NL 0408224 DLC NN PU WaU MH

Lithuania. *Centralinis statistikos biūras.*
… Lietuvos apgyventos vietos. Pirmojo visuotinojo Lietuvos gyventojų 1923 m. surašymo duomenys. Kaunas [A. Bako spaustuvė] 1925.

viii, 735, [2] p. incl. tables. 24cm.

At head of title: Finansų ministerija. Centralinis statistikos biūras
Introduction and table headings in Lithuanian and French.
"Pastebėtų klaidų atitaisymas": [2] p. at end.

1. Cities and towns—Lithuania—Stat. 2. Lithuania—Population. I. Title.

31-32851

Library of Congress HA1448.L5A5 1923 314.75

NL 0408225 DLC PU NN

Lithuania. Centralinis statistikos biuras.
Lietuvos gyventojai, pirmojo 1923 m. rugsėjo 17 d. visuotino gyventojų surašymo duomenys. Population de la Lithuanie. Données du premier recensement du 17 septembre 1923. [Kaunas, 1926.] lxix, 311 p. incl. forms, tables. illus. 4°.

On cover: Lietuvos Respublika. République Lithuanienne. Finansų ministerija. Ministère des finances. Centr. statistikos biūras. Bureau centr. de statist.
Lithuanian and French on opposite pages.
Errata, 1 p. at end.

1. Lithuania—Census, 1923.
N. Y. P. L. October 5, 1927

NL 0408226 NN MH-BA DLC MH

VOLUME 336

Lithuania. *Centralinis statistikos biuras.*
Lietuvos pasėlių plotų ir gyvulių surašymas, 1935 m. birželio mėn. 30 d. Kaunas [1935?]
69 p. maps, diagrs. 29 cm.
Errata slip inserted.

1. Agriculture—Lithuania—Stat. I. Title.

HD1995.L5A52 53-52969

NL 0408227 DLC NNC NN MH-L

Lithuania. Centralinis statistikos biuras.
... Lietuvos statistikos metraštis ...
Annuaire statistique de la Lithuanie ... [Kaunas, "Spindulio" b-ves spaustuvė
v. tables. 26 cm.
At head of title: Lietuvos respublika. République lithuanienne.
, issued by Centralinis statistikos biuras.
In French and Lithuanian.
1. Lithuania - Statistics. I. Title. II. Title: Annuaire statistique de la Lithuanie.

NL 0408228 CU DS DLC MH

Lithuania. Centralinis statistikos biuras.
... Lietuvos uzsienio prekyba ... Commerce extérieur de Lithuanie ... [Kaunas,]
v. tables. 26 cm. annual.
At head of title: Lietuvos respublika. République lithuanienne.
Issued by Centralinis statistikos biuras.
In French and Lithuanian.
1. Lithuania - Commerce. I. Title. II. Title: Commerce extérieur de Lithuanie.

NL 0408229 CU NN MH DLC

Lithuania. Centralinis statistikos biuras.

Lietuvos ūkis ir rinka. Litauens wirtschaft und markt. Leidžia Centralinis statistikos biuras ... nr. 1-10/11; sausis/kovas 1930-balandis/rugsėjis 1932. Kaunas ["Spindulio" b-vės spaustuvė, etc., 1930-32]

Lithuania. *Centralinis statistikos biūras.*
Naturalis gyventojų judėjimas Lietuvoje 1915-1922 m. (Centrinio statistikos biuro daviniais) Kaunas [Valstybės spaustuvė] 1923.
24 p. incl. tables. 25½cm.

1. Lithuania—Population. 2. Lithuania—Statistics, Vital. I. Title.

39-82089

Library of Congress HB3608.6.A5 1923

NL 0408231 DLC

Lithuania. Centralinis statistikos biuras.
...Statistikos biuletenis. Bulletin statistique.

Kaunas, 4°.

Monthly.
In Lithuanian, French and English.

1. Lithuania—Stat.
N. Y. P. L. January 27, 1925

NL 0408232 NN DLC

LITHUANIA. Centralinis statistikos biuras.
Statistinės žinios apie Lietuvą ligi karui 1914 m. Kaunas,Prekybos ir pramonės ministerijos Bendros statistikos departamento leidinys,1919.
200p. tables(1 fold.) 21cm.

NL 0408233 PU

Lithuania. Centralinis statistikos biuras.
Valstybės statistikos kalendorius... Lithuanian government statistical almanac.

[Kaunas, 23½cm.
Lithuanian and English.

1. Lithuania—Stat. 2. Lithuania —Yearbooks.
N. Y. P. L. June 3, 1938

NL 0408234 NN DLC DL

Lithuania. Centralinis statistikos biuras.

HA1448
.L5V5

Visa Lietuva; informacinė knyga. 1922-
Kaunas, "Spaudos fondo" leidinys [etc.]

Lithuania. Centralinis statistikos biuras.
Visuotinis Lietuvos žemės ūkio surašymas 1930 Vytauto Didžiojo met. gruodžio mėn. 30 d. ... Recensement agricole en Lithuanie le 30 décembre 1930. Kaunas: Centralinis statistikos biuras [193-] 4 v. forms, illus. (charts), tables. 29 x 23cm.

Lithuanian and French in parallel columns; some tables in Lithuanian only.
CONTENTS.—Tomas 1. Žemės ūkių plotai. Valdymo santykiai. Žemės reforma. —Tomas 2. Plotų naudojimas. Pasėliai. Derlius. Vaisiniai medžiai. Trąšos.— Tomas 3. Darbo rankos. Gyvuliai ir paukščiai. Mašinos ir įrankiai. Trobesiai.— Tomas 4. Mažieji ūkiai iki 1 ha.

1. Agriculture—Stat.—Lithuania.
N. Y. P. L. May 22, 1935

NL 0408236 NN

LITHUANIA. Centralinis statistikos biuras.
Visuotinis Lietuvos žemės ūkio surašymas 1930 Vytauto Didžiojo met. gruodžio mėn. 30 d. Recensement agricole en Lithuanie le 30 décembre 1930. Kaunas: Centralinis statistikos biuras [193-] 4 v. maps, diagrs., tables. 29cm.

Film reproduction. Positive.
Lithuanian and French in parallel columns; some tables in Lithuanian only.

CONTENTS.--1. Žemės ūkiu plotai. Valdymo santykiai. Žemės reforma.--2. Plotu naudojimas. Pasėliai. Derlius. Vaisiniai medžiai. Trąšos.--3. Darbo rankos. Gyvuliai ir paukščiai. Mašinos ir įrankiai. Trobesiai.--4. Mažieji ūkiai iki 1 ha.
1. Agriculture--Stat.--Lithuania. t. 193

NL 0408238 NN

Lithuania. Centrinė kariuomenės biblioteka.
... Centrinės kariuomenės bibliotekos Katalogas 1922-1932. I. Sistematine dalis. Kaunas 1933-34.
556 p. 18½ cm.
Added t. - p. in French

NL 0408239 DNW

Lithuania. Chamber of commerce, industry and crafts
see
Lithuania. Prekybos pramonės ir amatų rūmai, *Kaunas.*

Lithuania. Constituent assembly
see Lithuania. Steigiamasis seimas, 1920-1922.

Lithuania. Constitution.
Rolnik, Hirsch, *ed.*
Die baltischen staaten; Litauen, Lettland und Estland und ihr verfassungsrecht, von dr. Hirsch Rolnik ... Leipzig, R. Noske, 1927.

Lithuania. Constitution.
Constitution de la Lithuanie. Kaunas: "Spindulys", s. a., 1938. 38 p. 20½cm.

1. No subject.
N. Y. P. L. April 29, 1941

NL 0408243 NN

Lithuania. Constitution.
Rouzier, A.
... La constitution de la Lithuanie et le statut de Memel ... par A. Rouzier ... Toulouse, Les frères Douladoure, imprimeurs, 1926.

Lithuania. Constitution.

Rouzier, A.
... La constitution de la Lithuanie et le statut de Memel (textes et commentaires) [Toulouse] Faculté de droit, 1926.

Lithuania. Constitution.
...Constitution de la république de Lithuanie. Kaunas, 1922. 16 p. 8°.
At head of title: Ministère des affaires étrangères.

1. Constitutions—Lithuania, 1922. 2. Lithuania. Uzsieniu reikalu ministerija.
N. Y. P. L. June 23, 1925

NL 0408246 NN

Lithuania. *Constitution.*
Constitution of the republic of Lithuania. Lithuanian information bureau ... London ... [London, Eyre & Spottiswoode, ltd., 1924]
12, [1] p. 25cm.

I. Lithuanian information bureau. II. Title.

28-11277

Library of Congress JN6745.A5 1924

NL 0408247 DLC

Lithuania. Constitution.
...Constitution of the state of Lithuania. [Kovno, 1922.] 14 f. f°.

Caption-title.
At head of title: ...Adopted by the Constituent Assembly August 1, 1922.
Mimeographed.

1. Constitutions, Lithuania, 1922.
N. Y. P. L. June 20, 1923.

NL 0408248 NN DLC

VOLUME 336

Lithuania. Constitution.
... La costituzione lituana
see under Giannini, Amedeo, 1886-1960.

Lithuania. Constitution.

FOR OTHER EDITIONS
SEE MAIN ENTRY

Kazlauskas, Bronius.
... L'Entente baltique; préface de m. Robert Redslob ... Paris, Recueil Sirey, société anonyme, 1939.

Lithuania. *Constitution.*
Lietuvos valstybės konstitucijos. Išrašai iš "Vyriausybės žinių" 1922, 1928 ir 1938 metų. Toronto, Žiburiai, 1952.
48 p. 22 cm.

I. Title.

54-15193

NL 0408251 DLC PU

Lithuania. *Constitution.*
Loi constitutionelle de l'État lithuanien. ⌊Berlin, Impr. O. Elsner, 1922?⌋
23, ⌊1⌋ p. 23½cm.

I. Title.

28-11276

Library of Congress JN6745.A5 1922 a

NL 0408252 DLC NN

Lithuania. *Constitution.* Lois fondamentales de la constitution provisoire de l'État lituanien. [n.p., 1919?]
[3] p. 27 cm.
"Jusqu'à l'établissement du régime et de la constitution de l'État lituanien ... la Taryba lituanienne ... établit son gouvernement sur la base des lois fondamentales provisoires suivantes."

NL 0408253 CSt-H

Lithuania. Constitution.

Miller, Artur.
... Nowa konstytucja Państwa litewskiego. Warszawa, Nakł. Księgarni F. Hoesicka, 1930.

Lithuania. Constitution.

Batilliat, René.
... Origine et développement des institutions politiques en Lithuanie. Lille ⌊etc.⌋ Mercure universel, Valentin Bresle, éditeur ⌊°1932⌋

Law

Lithuania. Constitution, 1588.

Bershadskiĭ, Sergeĭ Aleksandrovich, 1850-1896.
Литовскій статутъ и польскія конституціи; историко-юридическое изслѣдованіе. С.-Петербургъ, Тип. М. Стасюлевича, 1893.

JN6745
.A12G5

Lithuania. Constitution, 1928.

Giedra, Balys, 1890-
Valstybė ir pilietis; visuomenės mokslo vadovėlis. 2., pataisyta ir papildyta laida. Raseiniai, Š. Kadušino spaustuvė ⌊pref. 1930-

---

Lithuania. Consulate. New York.
Short list of English references on Lithuania. Prepared by consulate general of Lithuania ... New York, N. Y. ⌊New York, 1938⌋ 7 f. 28cm.

Caption-title.
Classified.
Introductory notice in Lithuanian and English.

1. Lithuania—Bibl.
N. Y. P. L. October 4, 1940

NL 0408258 NN

Lithuania. Délégation de Lithuanie à la Conférence de la paix. Bureau d'informations
see Lithuanian Information Bureau.

Lithuania. *Delegation to the League of nations.*
... Différend entre la Pologne et la Lithuanie. Lettre de M. Galvanauskas... Dispute between Poland and Lithuania. Letter from M. Galvanauskas. ⌊Genève, Imp. Atar, 1921⌋
⌊3⌋, 3-7, 3-7 p. 33cm.
At head of title: ... A. 111. 1921. Genève, le 21 septembre 1921. Société des nations... League of nations.
Paged in duplicate; French and English on opposite pages.
1. European war, 1914-1918—Territorial questions—Lithuania. 2. European war, 1914-1918—Territorial questions—Poland. 3. Poles in Lithuania. I. Galvanauskas, Ernest. II. League of nations.
(L. of N. author file Biv)

22-16936

Library of Congress D651.L5A5 1921 d

NL 0408260 DLC

Lithuania. *Delegation to the League of nations.*
Les droits de la Lithuanie sur Vilna et son territoire. Mémoire présenté par la Délégation lithuanienne à la Société des nations. ⌊n. p., 1921?⌋
cover-title, 18 p., 2 l. illus. (map) 28 x 21½cm.
"Littérature": 2d leaf at end.

1. Vilna. 2. European war, 1914-1918—Territorial questions—Lithuania. I. League of nations. II. Title.
(L. of N. author file Biv)

28-22984

Library of Congress DK511.L27A5 1921 a
⌊2⌋

NL 0408261 DLC

Lithuania. *Delegation to the League of nations.*
... Exposé du conflit lithuano-polonais. Deuxième Assemblée de la Société des nations à Genève. Genève, Imprimerie Atar, 1921.
99, ⌊1⌋ p. 1 illus., fold. map. 29cm.
At head of title: Délégation de Lithuanie.
Folded map has caption: Carte ancienne de la Lithuanie ⌊par Ioh. Baptista Homann⌋ dont l'original se trouve au British museum (Londres)
1. European war, 1914-1918—Territorial questions—Lithuania. 2. European war, 1914-1918—Territorial questions—Poland. 3. Lithuania. I. League of nations. II. League of nations. 2d Assembly, 1921. III. Title. IV. Title: Conflit lithuano-polonais.
(L. of N. author file Biv; topic file C: Lithuania, Poland)

28-22985 Revised

Library of Congress D651.L5A5 1921 l
⌊r34c2⌋

NL 0408262 DLC

Lithuania. *Delegation to the League of nations.*
... The Lithuanian-Polish dispute. Second Assembly of the League of nations at Geneva, 1921. London, Eyre and Spottiswoode, ltd., 1921.
101 p. 4 fold. maps. 28½ x 22cm.
At head of title: Lithuanian delegation.
Map no. 1 is "Ancient map of Lithuania, the original of which, no. 33670 ⌊9⌋ can be seen at the British museum, London" (a map by Joh. Baptist Homann)
This volume forms v.1 of the three volumes issued by the Lithuanian information bureau entitled: The Lithuanian-Polish dispute.
1. European war, 1914-1918—Territorial questions—Lithuania. 2. European war, 1914-1918—Territorial questions—Poland. 3. Lithuania. I. League of nations. Delegations. Lithuania, 1921. II. League of nations. Assembly. 2d sess., 1921. III. Title.
— —— Copy 2.

22-8974

Library of Congress D651.L5A5

NL 0408263 DLC

Lithuania. *Département des forêts*
see
Lithuania. *Miškų departamentas.*

Lithuania. Department of railways
see Lithuania. Geležinkelių valdyba.

Lithuania. Diet
see
Lithuania. Seimas.

Lithuania. Finance ministry
see
Lithuania. Finansų ministerija.

Lithuania. *Finances, Département des*
see
Lithuania. *Finansų departamentas.*

Lithuania. *Finansų departamentas.*
Informations économiques de Lithuanie; publiées par le Département des finances, Ministère des finances. 1.- année (n. 1-); 1932-
Kaunas ⌊1932-
v. in tables, diagrs. 31cm. semimonthly.

1. Lithuania—Econ. condit.

HC337.L5A34 330.9475 46-43453

NL 0408269 DLC NN

Lithuania. *Finansų departamentas.*
Lietuvos valstybės ... metų pajamos ir išlaidos ... Receipts and expenditures of the republic of Lithuania ...

Kaunas, 19

v. tables. 21 x 33cm.

On cover, 19 : Lietuvos valstybės ... biudžetas ... The Lithuanian state budget ...
19 Finansų ministerijos, Finansų departamento leidinys. Publication of the Finance department of the Ministry of finance."

1. Lithuania—Appropriations and expenditures.

HJ55.5.C2 336.475 43-30247 rev

NL 0408270 DLC NN

VOLUME 336

Lithuania. Finansų ministerija.
...Économie et coopération de Lithuanie; étude statistique. Kaunas[: Valstybės spaustuvė, 1924?]. 40 p. illus. 8°.

At head of title: République Lithuanienne. Ministère des finances.
Issued also in English.

1. Economic hist.—Lithuania. 2. Cooperation—Lithuania.
N. Y. P. L. December 1, 1927

NL 0408271 NN

Lithuania. *Finansų ministerija.*
... Economy and cooperation of Lithuania. Statistical study. Kaunas [Lietuvos valstybės spaustuvė, 1924?]
cover-title, 36 p. incl. illus., tables. 21cm.
At head of title: Lithuanian Republic. Ministry of finance.

1. Lithuania—Econ. condit. 2. Cooperation—Lithuania. I. Title.

Library of Congress HC337.L5A6 1924 25-13956

NL 0408272 DLC OrU NN

Lithuania. *Finansų ministerija.*
... Lietuva skaitlinėmis. La Lithuanie en chiffres. Diagramų albomas. Album de diagrammes. [Kaunas, Valstybės spaustuvė, 1924?]
1 p. l., [2] p. 39 col. diagr. 21½ x 31cm.
At head of title: Lietuvos Respublika. République Lithuanienne.
Lithuanian, French, and English.
Introduction signed: Finansų ministerijos Centralinis statistikos biūras.

1. Lithuania—Stat. 2. Lithuania—Econ. condit. I. Title. II. Title: La Lithuanie en chiffres.

Library of Congress HC337.L5A6 1924 a 25-13955

NL 0408273 DLC

Lithuania. Finansų ministerija.

Lietuvos ūkis; mėnesinis visuomenės ūkio ir finansų laikraštis
... Finansų ministerijos leidinys ... [1.]–6. tomas ([1.]–7. metai); gruodis 1921–gruodis 1928. Kaunas, Valstybės spaustuvė [etc., 1921–28]

HJ1215 Lithuania. Finansų ministerija.
.A3
.1932q Lietuvos valstybės 1928, 1929, 1930 ir 1931 m.biudžetai ir jų palyginimas. [Kaunas? 1932?]
76 numb.ℓ.incl.tables. 20½ x 32½ cm.

Mimeographed.

1.Budget in Lithuania.

NL 0408275 NjP

Lithuania. Finansų ministerija.
Litauens wirtschaftlich-finanzielle lage im jahre 1924. Hrsg. vom Litauischen finanz-ministerium. [Kaunas] Staatsdruckerei [1925?]
55 p. tables. 28 cm.
Errata slip inserted.

NL 0408276 PU

Lithuania. Finansų ministerija.
Lithuania. *Technikos-chemijos laboratorija.*
... Valstybinės technikos chemijos laboratorijos darbai ... [1– ; m., 1922–
Kaunas, 1923–

Lithuania. Finansų ministerija.
Wirtschaftliche Informationen. Jahrg. 1–

April, 1930–

Kaunas, 1930– f°.

Issued twice a month.
1930 – Aug., 1931 reproduced from typewritten copy.

1. Economic history—Lithuania.
N. Y. P. L. July 19, 1932

NL 0408278 NN

Lithuania. Finansu ministerija.
Centralinis statistikos biuras
see
Lithuania. Centralinis statistikos biuras.

Lithuania. *Finansų ministerija. Finansų departamentas*
see
Lithuania. *Finansų departamentas.*

Lithuania. Finansu ministerija. Matu, saiku, svarstikliu ir probavimo rūmai
see
Lithuania. Matu, saiku, svarstikliu ir probavimo rūmai.

Lithuania. Finansų ministerija.
Prekybos departamentas
see
Lithuania. Prekybos departamentas.

Lithuania. Finansų ministerija. Statistikos biūras
see Lithuania. Centralinis statistikos biūras.

Lithuania. Finansų ministerija. Technikos-chemijos laboratorija
see Lithuania. Technikos-chemijos laboratorija.

Lithuania. Foreign affairs ministry
see
Lithuania. Uzsienių reikalų ministerija.

Lithuania. *Forestry department*
see
Lithuania. *Miškų departamentas.*

Lithuania. *Forêts, Département des*
see
Lithuania. *Miškų departamentas.*

HE3139
.5
.A24 Lithuania. *Geležinkelių valdyba.*
Données principales concernant le compte rendu annuel des opérations des chemins de fer de l'État Lithuanien

Kaunas.
v. diagrs., tables. 31 cm.

1. Railroads—Lithuania. I. Title.

HE3139.5.A24 64-38011

NL 0408288 DLC NN

Lithuania. *Geležinkelių valdyba.*
... Geležinkelių įstatymas ir jam vykdyti taisyklės (paskelbta: įstatymas V. ž. ɪd. n 634, taisyklės V. ž. ɪɪd. n. 583) Veikia nuo 1939 m. liepos mėn. 1d. [Kaune] Ekonominės direkcijos leidinys, 1939.
xvi, 144 p. 4 forms (3 fold.) 23½cm.
At head of title: Susisiekimo ministerija. Geležinkelių valdyba.

1. Railroad law—Lithuania. 2. Railroads—Lithuania—Management. I. Lithuania. Laws, statutes, etc. II. Title.

Library of Congress HE3139.5.A5 1939 42-32979

NL 0408289 DLC

Lithuania. *Geležinkelių valdyba.*
... Geležkelių valdybos darbuotės apyskaita 1919–1923 m. Kaunas, Valstybės spaustuvė, 1925.
114 p., 1 l. incl. tables. fold. diagrs. 24cm.
At head of title: Lietuvos respublika. Susisiekimo ministerija.

1. Railroads—Lithuania. I. Title.

Library of Congress HE3139.5.A5 1923 34-37158 385.09475

NL 0408290 DLC

Lithuania. *Geležinkelių valdyba.*
Kaunas. Ausgabe der Verwaltung der litauischen eisenbahnen. Kaune, "Spindulio", b-vės spaustuvė, 1930.
29 p. illus., diagr. 26 x 13cm.
On cover: Kaunas, provisorische hauptstadt von Litauen ...
Map on p. [3] of cover.
Illustrated cover.
Published also in English.

1. Kaunas—Descr.

Library of Congress DK651.K125A5 1930 a 37-32255
[2] 947.5

NL 0408291 DLC NcRS PU

VOLUME 336

Lithuania. *Geležinkelių valdyba.*
Kaunas. Published by Lithuanian department of railways. Kaune, "Spindulio", b-vės spaustuvė, 1930.
31 p. illus., diagr. 26 x 13cm.
On cover: Kaunas, the provisional capital of Lithuania. Published by the Board of the state railways of Lithuania.
Map on p. [3] of cover.
Illustrated cover.
Published also in German.

1. Kaunas—Descr.

37-32256
Library of Congress DK651.K125A5 1930
[2] 917.5

NL 0408292 DLC

Lithuania. *Geležinkelių valdyba.*
Keleivių ir bagažo geležinkeliais pervežimo tarifas. Veikia nuo 1931 m. gegužės 1 d. [Kaunas, 1931?]
77 p. 24 cm.
——— Papildymų ir pakeitimų rinkinys. 1932- [Kaunas]
v. 24 cm.
HE2055.6.A522
1. Railroads—Lithuania—Fares. 2. Railroads—Lithuania—Baggage. I. Title.
HE2055.6.A52 61-56089

NL 0408293 DLC

Lithuania. *Geležinkelių valdyba.*
Lietuvos geležinkelių atstumų lentelės. Tarifo 6. dalis. Veikią nuo 1931 m. rugpiūčio mėn. 1 d. Paskelbta Vyriausybės žinių 2. d. nr. 182 iš 1931. VII. 24 d. [Kaunas, Ekonominės direkcijos leidinys [1931]
89 p. tables. 30 cm.

1. Railroads—Lithuania—Distances, etc. I. Title.
HE3139.5.A5 1931 64-58342

NL 0408294 DLC

Lithuania. *Geležinkelių valdyba.*
Lietuvos geležinkelių pirmasis dešimtmetis. Kaunas [Spaudino "Meno" spaustuvė] 1929.
88, [2] p. plates (incl. ports., diagrs.) 23cm.
On cover: Lietuvos geležinkelių dėšimtmetis. 1919-1929 ... Geležinkelių valdybos leidinys.

1. Railroads—Lithuania. I. Title.
33-707
Library of Congress HE3139.5.A5 1929 385.09475

NL 0408295 DLC

Lithuania. Geležinkelių valdyba
Lietuvos pajūris. Kaunas, 1931
31 p. illus.

1. Lithuania - Coasts. I. Title

NL 0408296 MH

Lithuania. Hidrometrine partija
See
Lithuania. Hidrometrinis biuras.

Lithuania. Hidrometrinis biuras.
...Hidrometrinis metrastis 1925-1927.
Jahrbuch des hydrometrischen buros Lithauens
1925-
1927- Kaunas, 1929-
v. illus. tables, diagrs, 26½cm

NL 0408298 DI-GS

Lithuania. *Hidrometrinis biuras.*
... Die hydrometrischen arbeiten in Litauen ... Kaunas, V. Spaustuvė, 1927.
32 p. incl. illus., tables, diagrs. 23cm.
At head of title: Wasserstrassenverwaltung des verkehrsministeriums Litauens. Hydrometrisches büro. Ing. Steponas Kolupaila, leiter des Hydrometrischen büros.

1. Stream measurements. I. Title.
G S 28—68 Revised
U. S. Geol. survey. Library for Library of Congress P(575) W28hk [r40b2]

NL 0408299 DI-GS

Lithuania. *Hidrometrinis biuras.*
... Nemuno ties Kaunu 1877–1925 m. Matavimai. Les résultats des observations hydrométriques sur le Nemunas près de Kaunas. 1877–1925. Kaunas, Valstybės spaustuvė, 1925.
192 p. incl. plan, tables, diagrs. plates. 26cm.
At head of title: Lietuvos respublikos Susisiekimo ministerija. Plentų ir vandens kelių valdybos Hidrometrinė partija. Bureau hydrométrique de la République leithuanienne. Inž. Steponas Kolupaila, Hidrometrinės partijos vedėjas, chef du Bureau hydrométrique.
Preface and table headings in Lithuanian and French; short French summaries interspersed.
1. Stream measurements—Lithuania. I. Kolupaila, Steponas. II. Title. III. Title: Les résultats des observations hydrométriques sur le Nemunas près de Kaunas.
31-29100
Library of Congress GB1333.L5A5 1925
[2] 551.4809475

NL 0408300 DLC

Lithuania. Hidrotechnikos ir melioracijos mokslinio tyrimo institutas
see Kaunas. Lietuvos hidrotechnikos ir melioracijos mokslinio tyrimo institutas.

Lithuania. Hydrometrisches Buro
See
Lithuania. Hidrometrinis biuras.

Lithuania. *Jewish Ministry*
see
Lithuania. *Ministerija žydų reikalams.*

U11 .L5K3
Lithuania. Kariuomenė. Štabas.
Karininkų metraštis.
Kaunas.

U135 .L5K3
Lithuania. Kariuomenė. Štabas.
Kario kalendorius.
Kaunas, Kariuomenės štabas.

Lithuania. *Kariuomenes štabas*
see
Lithuania. *Kariuomenė. Štabas.*

Lithuania. *Karo Mokslo Skyrius*
see **Lithuania.** *Krašto Apsaugos Ministerija. Karo Mokslo Skyrius.*

Lithuania. Knygų leidimo komisijo.
Bibliografijos žinios ... 1.- metai. 1928-
Kaunas, 1928-

Lithuania. Knygu leidimo komisija.
Knygos: bibliografijos ir kritikos žurnalas ... [serija 1-nr. 1- 1922- m. Kaunas, 1922-

Lithuania. Knygu leidimo komisija.
Andersen, Hans Christian, 1805–1875.
... Rinktinės Anderseno pasakos, su paveikslais. Vertė J. Balčikonis. 2. leidimas. Kaunas ["Lituanijos" spaustuvė Klaipėdoje] 1923.

Lithuania. Knygų rūmai
see Lietuvos TSR Knygų rūmai.

UF86 L5A53
Lithuania. *Krašto apsaugos ministerija.*
Artilerijos statutas. Kaunas, Kariuomenės štabas, Sp. ir šviet. sk., 19
v. illus. 16 cm.

1. Artillery—Lithuania. I. Title.
UF86.L5A53 66-55780

NL 0408312 DLC

Lithuania. *Krašto apsaugos ministerija.*
Internuotųjų stovyklų vidaus tvarkos taisyklės. Regulamin obozów dla internowanych. Kaunas, Kariuomenės štabas, SP. ir šviet. sk., 1939.
18 p. 19 cm.
Lithuanian and Polish.
Photostat (negative)

1. World War, 1939–1945—Prisoners and prisons, Polish. I. Title. II. Title: Regulamin obozów dla internowanych.
D805.P7L53 1939a 61-56348 ‡

NL 0408313 DLC

VOLUME 336

Lithuania. *Krašto Apsaugos Ministerija.*
Kariškas lietuviškai-rusiškas ir rusiškai-lietuviškas žodynėlis. Kaunas, 1919.
106 p. 17 cm.
At head of title: Krašto Apsaugos Ministerijos Literatūros Skyriaus leidinys.

1. Military art and science—Dictionaries—Lithuanian. 2. Military art and science—Dictionaries—Russian. 3. Lithuanian language—Dictionaries—Russian. 4. Russian language—Dictionaries—Lithuanian. I. Title.
U25.L64 1919 50-49221

NL 0408314 DLC

Lithuania. Krašto apsaugos ministerija.
...Karių uniforma. Kaunas, Ekonominės karių b-vės leidinys, 1931. 9, 38 p. illus. 26cm.
At head of title: Neoficialus leidinys.
Signed, p. 8: Krašto apsaugos ministeris.

1. Military uniforms, Lithuanian.
N. Y. P. L. May 24, 1948

NL 0408315 NN

Lithuania. Krašto apsaugos ministerija.
Karo baudžiamasis statutas
see under Lithuania. Laws, statutes, etc.

Lithuania. *Krašto Apsaugos Ministerija.*
Karo meto etapų dėsniai. Kaunas, 1921.
23 p. 23 cm.

1. Lithuania. Kariuomenė—Barracks and quarters. I. Title.
UC405.L5A5 1921 53-49869

NL 0408317 DLC

Lithuania. Krašto apsaugos ministerija.
Laikinasis rikiuotės statutas. Krašto apsaugos ministerijos Literatūros skyriaus leidinys. Kaunas, 1919. 91 p. 18cm.

1. Army, Lithuanian—Inf.—Drill and tactics. I. Title.
i. 1919.

NL 0408318 NN

LITHUANIA. Krašto apsaugos ministerija.
...Pestininku rikiuotes kamandos ir terminai; 2. pataisyta laida. Kaunas, 1919. 11 p. 23cm.
At head of title: Krašto apsaugos ministerijos literatūros skyriaus leidinys...

1. Army, Lithuanian—Inf.—Drill and tactics.

NL 0408319 NN

Lithuania. *Krašto apsaugos ministerija.*
Pistoletai; technika. Kaunas, Kariuomenės štabas, Spaudos ir švietimo skyrius, 1939.
159 p. illus. 16 cm.

1. Pistols. I. Title.
UD415.L58A55 64-42375

NL 0408320 DLC

Lithuania. Krašto apsaugos ministerija.
Vyties kryžiaus ordeno įstatymas ir statutas Kaunas, 1928
see under Lithuania. Laws, statutes, etc.

Lithuania. *Krašto apsaugos ministerija. Kariuomenes štabas*
see
Lithuania. *Kariuomenė. Štabas.*

Lithuania. *Krašto Apsaugos Ministerija. Karo Mokslo Skyrius.*
Kariuomenės tiekimas, sanitarija ir veterinarija. Sistematizuotas rinkinys įsakymų, įstatymų ir taisyklių, išleistų kariuomenei iki 1922 m. sausio m. 1 d. Paruošė V. Augustauskas ir V. Tarasevičius. Kaunas, 1923.
xvi, 749 p. 25 cm.

1. Lithuania. Kariuomenė—Accounting. 2. Military hygiene—Law and legislation—Lithuania. 3. Veterinary laws and legislation—Lithuania. I. Augustauskas, V. II. Tarasevičius, V. III. Title.
614.09475 34-15733 rev*

NL 0408323 DLC

Lithuania. *Krašto Apsaugos Ministerija. Karo Mokslo Skyrius.*
Karo archyvas. Redagavo V. Steponaitis. Kaunas, 1925–
v. illus., maps. 27 cm.

1. European War, 1914–1918—Lithuania. 2. European War, 1914–1918—Personal narratives, Lithuanian. I. Steponaitis, V. II. Title.
D552.L5A5 1925 940.481475 43-30202 rev*

NL 0408324 DLC

Lithuania. Krašto apsaugos ministerija. Karo mokslo skyrius.
Ružancovas, Aleksandras.
... Lietuvos karo bibliografija 1917–1922. Kaunas ͺLietuvos valstybės spaustuvėͺ 1923.

Lithuania. *Krašto apsaugos ministerija. Karo mokslo skyrius.*
Minosvaidžių vadovėlis. Kaunas, 1924.
124 p. illus. 23 cm.

1. Mortars (Ordnance) I. Title.
UF565.L5A75 59-58428 ‡

NL 0408326 DLC

Lithuania. Krašto Apsaugos Ministerija. Karo Mokslo Skyrius.
Mūsų žinynas; karo mokslo ir istorijos žurnalas ... t. ͺ1ͺ– 1921–
Kaunas, Leidžia Krašto apsaugos ministerijos Karo mokslo skyrius ͺetc.ͺ 1921–

Lithuania. *Krašto Apsaugos Ministerija. Literatūros Skyrius*
see **Lithuania.** *Krašto Apsaugos Ministerija.*

UH 600 qL776 **LITHUANIA.** Krašto Apsaugos Ministerija. Sanitarijo Skyriaus
ͺCollection of publicationsͺ

The Library has a collection of miscellaneous publications of this organization kept as received. These publications are not listed or bound separately.

NL 0408329 DNLM

Lithuania. Kredito įstaigų ir kooperatyvų inspekcija.
...Lietuvos kooperacija...Coopération de Lithuanie. 19
Kaunas, 19 8°.
Annual.
Text in Lithuanian, t.-p. and captions in Lithuanian and French.

1. Co-operation—Lithuania.
N. Y. P. L. May 16, 1932

NL 0408330 NN

Lithuania. Kunstiticijóns
See
Lithuania. Constitution.

Lithuania. Landwirthschaftlicher central-verein fuer Littauen und Masuren
see
Landwirthschaftlicher central-verein fuer Littauen und Masuren.

Lithuania. Laws, statutes, etc.
... Baudžiamasis statutas su papildomaisiais baudžiamaisiais istatymais ir komentarais, sudarytais iš rusijos senato ir lietuvos vyriausiojo tribunolo sprendimų bei kitų aiškinimų. Spaudai parengė S. Bieliackinas ... ͺirͺ Martynas Kavolis ... Kaune, D. Gutman, 1934.
xix, 887 p. 18cm.
At head of title: Neoficijalinis leidimas.

NL 0408333 MH-L PU-L

Lithuania. Laws, statutes, etc.
Bendrasai saskaitybos istatymas (Istat. rinkinio VIII t. II d.) su aiškinimais. Vertė ... J. Bolelis. Redagavo ... Jur. Grabauskas. Kaunas, D. Gutman, 1932.
196 p. 22½cm.

NL 0408334 MH-L

Lithuania. *Laws, statutes, etc.*
Civiliniai įstatymai (x tomo 1 dalis) Civilinių įstatymų tekstą su papildymais iki 1933. 1. 1. ir kasacinių sprendimų nuo 1924 m. iki 1931 m. bei Vyriausiojo tribunolo išspręstų klausimų ištraukas sudarė K. Šalkauskis. Kasacinių sprendimų ištraukas nuo 1931 metų iki 1933 metų vasario mėn. sudarė V. Fridšteinas; rusų Senato sprendimų ištraukas vertė J. Abramavičius. Neoficialinis leidimas. Kaunas, "Literatūros" knygyno leidimas, 1933.
689 p. 24 cm.
1. Civil law—Lithuania. I. Šalkauskis, Kazys, 1885– ed.
52-47533

NL 0408335 DLC MH-L CtY

VOLUME 336

Lithuania. Laws, statutes, etc.
Law

Confoederacya Generalna, Omnivm Ordinvm Regni, et Magni Dvcatvs Lith. ná Conwokácyey głowney Wárszáwskiey vchwalona, roku pánskiego M.DC.XLVIII., dnia 16. mieśiącá lipcá. ⌈n. p., 1648⌉

Law
Lithuania. Laws, statutes, etc.

Poland. *Sejm, 1661.*
Constitvcye Wielkiego Xięstwá Lithewskiego, 1661. ⌈W Krakowie? 1661⌉

Lithuania. Laws, statutes, etc.

Lithuania. *Geležinkelių valdyba.*
... Geležinkelių įstatymas ir jam vykdyti taisyklės (paskelbta: įstatymas V. ž. rd. n. 634, taisyklės V. ž. rd. n. 583) Veikia nuo 1939 m. liepos mėn. 1d. ⌈Kaune⌉ Ekonominės direkcijos leidinys, 1939.

Lithuania. Laws, statutes, etc.
Lithuania. *Prekybos departamentas.*
... Instrukcija konfiskacijos byloms vesti (Pritaikymo mui tinių įst. 157–200 §§ tvarka) Kaunas, Valstybės spaustuvė 1926.

Lithuania. *Laws, statutes, etc.*
Įstatymai darbo srityje Lietuvoj. Sutaisė V. Akelaitis. Kaunas, 1927.
128 p. 23 cm.
At head of title: Neoficialinis leidinys.

1. Labor laws and legislation—Lithuania. I. Akelaitis, Vincas, 1888– ed. II. Title.

57-56333

NL 0408340 DLC

Lithuania. Laws, statutes, etc.

.. Įstatymas apie valstybini mokestį nuo nejudomųjų turtų miestuose ir miesteliuose. Spaudai parengė J. Baltrušaitis. Kaunas, D. Gutman, 1934.
29, ⌈3⌉ p. 17cm.
At head of title: Neoficialinis leidimas.

NL 0408341 MH-L

Law Case
Lithuania. Laws, statutes, etc.

Zalaszowski, Mikołaj, 1631–1703.
Jus Regni Poloniæ, ex statutis et constitutionibus ejusdem regni & M. D. L. collectum et additionibus ex jure civili, Romano, canonico, Saxonico necnon ex constitutionibus provincialibus Gnesnensibus auctum, historijsq; illustratum ... a Nicolao Zalaszowski in lucem publicam editum Posnaniæ anno Domini 1699. Varsaviæ, Reimpressum typis S. R. M. Collegij Societatis Jesu, 1741–42.

Lithuania. Laws, statutes, etc.
Karo baudžiamasis statutas...sutaisė Kapitonas Papečkys. Kaunas, 1922
141, viii p. 23cm.

NL 0408343 DNW

Law
Lithuania. Laws, statutes, etc.

Konfederacya Generalna Ordinvm Regni, & Magni Dvcatvs Litvaniae, po niedoszłey Konwokácyey głowney Warszáwskiey umowiona roku páńskiego 1696., dńiá 29. miesiącá sierpńia. ⌈n. p., 1696⌉

Lithuania. Laws, statutes, etc.
...1. Law of the Bank of Lithuania. 2. Byelaws of the Bank of Lithuania. 3. Law of the monetary unit. [London: Printed by Eyre and Spottiswoode, Ltd. 1922] 23 p. 24½cm.

765630A. 1. Banks and banking—Lithuania.

NL 0408345 NN

Lithuania. Laws, statutes, etc.
(Laws translated by International labor office)(London, 1920-35)
15 v. 24½ cm. (I.L.O. Legislative series, 1920, Lith. 1-2; 1922, no. 1-3; 1923, no. 1; 1924, no. 1-4; 1925, no. 1-3; 1926, no. 1-3; 1927, no. 1-3; 1928, no.1; 1929, no. 1-3; 1930, no. 1-4; 1931, no.1-4; 1932, no. 1-2; 1933, no. 1-4; 1934, no. 1-3; 1935, no.3-4.

NL 0408346 DL

Law
Lithuania. Laws, statutes, etc.

Poland. *Laws, statutes, etc.*
Leges, statuta, constitutiones, privilegia Regni Poloniae, Magni Ducatus Lithuaniae, omniumq; provinciarum annexarum, à Comitiis Visliciae anno 1347 celebratis usq; ad ultima regni comitia. ⌈Varsaviae⌉ In typographia S. R. M. & Reipublicae Collegij Varsaviensis Scholarum Piarum, 1732–1782.

Lithuania. *Laws, statutes, etc.*
... Lietuvos įstatymai. Sistematizuotas įstatymų, instrukcijų ir įsakymų rinkinys. Yra surinkęs teisininkas A. Merkys. Redagavęs ·Vyriausiojo tribunolo pirmininkas A. Kriščiukaitis.
Kaunas, Išleido A. Merkys ir V. Petrulis, 1922–
v. 22½cm.
At head of title: Neoficialinis leidinys.
Vol. 2 has imprint: Klaipėda Išleido Akc. b-vė "Rytas", 1925.

I. Kriščiukaitis, A., ed. II. Merkys, A. III. Title.

27-21960

NL 0408348 DLC WaS CtY PU

Lithuania. *Laws, statutes, etc.*
... Das litauische Straf-prozess-gesetz aus dem litauischen übersetzt und hrsg. von G. Gronau ... Memel ⌈F. W. Krumpholz-druck⌉ 1934.
288, 56 p. 19½cm.
At head of title: Nicht offizielle ausgabe.
"Stichwörterverzeichnis": 56 p. at end.

1. Criminal procedure—Lithuania. I. Gronau, G., ed. and tr. II. Title.

36-24257

Library of Congress

NL 0408349 DLC DS

DK3 .R8 т. 20, etc.
Lithuania. *Laws, statutes, etc.*
Литовская метрика. Петербургъ, 1903–15.
4 v. 28 cm. (Русская историческая библиотека, т. 20, 27, 30, 33)
Vol. 3 issued in Tartu.
No more published?
CONTENTS.—Отдѣлъ 1. ч. 1. Книги записей. ⌈ч. 2.⌉ книга 1.–⌈3.⌉ судныхъ дѣлъ. ч. 3. Первая книга публичныхъ дѣлъ. Переписи Войска литовскаго.—Отдѣлъ 1.–2. ч. 3. Книги публичных дѣлъ: 2., 4., часть 5-ой, 6., 7.

I. Title. (Series: Russkaia istoricheskaia biblioteka, t. 20, 27, 30, 33)
Title transliterated: Litovskaia metrika.

DK3.R8 т. 20, etc. 52-50807

NL 0408350 DLC

Lithuania. *Laws, statutes, etc.*
Литовскій статутъ въ московскомъ переводѣ-редакціи. Юрьевъ, Тип. К. Маттисена, 1916.
xxx, 395 p. 26 cm.
Editor's name, И. И. Лаппо, at head of title.
"Оттискъ изъ 28. выпуска Лѣтописи занятій Императорской археографической коммиссіи."

I. Lappo, Ivan Ivanovich, ed. II. Title.
Title transliterated: Litovskiĭ statut v moskovskom perevodiě-redakfŝii.

54-53999

NL 0408351 DLC IU

Lithuania. Laws, statutes, etc.

Lfubavskiĭ, Matveĭ Kuz'mich, 1860–1936.
Литовско-русскій сеймъ; опытъ по исторіи учрежденія въ связи съ внутреннимъ строемъ и внѣшнею жизнью государства. Москва, Изд. Имп. Об-ва исторіи и древностей россійскихъ при Московскомъ университетѣ, 1900.

Lithuania. *Laws, statutes, etc.*
... Muitinių įstatai. Kaunas ⌈Valstybės spaustuvė⌉ 1924.
52 p. 15½cm.
At head of title: Vyr. žin. 164 nr.

1. Customs administration—Lithuania. I. Title.

39-9541

Library of Congress HJ6969.5.L5A5 1924

NL 0408353 DLC

Lithuania. *Laws, statutes, etc.*
... Muitų tarifai. Kaunas, Valstybės spaustuvė, 1926.
164 p., 1 l. 21 x 11cm.
At head of title: Prekybos departamento leidinys.

1. Tariff—Lithuania—Law. I. Lithuania. Prekybos departamentas. II. Title.

39-9540

Library of Congress HJ6256.L5A3 1926

NL 0408354 DLC

Lithuania. Laws, statutes, etc.
...Muitų tarifai. Kaunas, „Spindulio" b-vės spaustuvė, 1931.
240, ⌈2⌉ p. 22cm.
At head of title: Prekybos departamento leidinys.

NL 0408355 DS

Lithuania. Laws, statutes, etc.
Lithuania. *Piliečių apsaugos departamentas.*
Nusikaltimams kelti ir tirti vadovėlis. Kaunas ⌈Valstybės spaustuvė⌉ 1925.

VOLUME 336

Law

Lithuania. Laws, statutes, etc.

Lûbavskiĭ, Matveĭ Kuz'mich, 1860-1936.
Областное дѣленіе и мѣстное управленіе Литовско-Русскаго государства ко времени изданія перваго Литовскаго статута; историческіе очерки. Москва, Унив. тип., 1892.

DK511
.L23L5

Lithuania. Laws, statutes, etc.

Lûbavskiĭ, Matveĭ Kuz'mich, 1860-1936.
Очеркъ исторіи Литовско-Русскаго государства до Люблинской уніи включительно. Съ приложеніемъ текста хартій, выданныхъ Великому Княжеству Литовскому и его областямъ. Москва, Изд. Имп. Об-ва исторіи и древностей россійскихъ, 1910.

Lithuania. *Laws, statutes, etc.*
Prawa z Statutu W. X. Litewskiego y Konstytucyi, dla wygody pilnuiących z urzędu albo potrzeby sądów y dla innych obywatelów koronnych y litewskich. Wiadomości porządnie podług alfabetu zebrane, a ile w processa prawne wchodzących o pretensye wszelakie. Za pozwoleniem Zwierzchności. Za Przywileiem. W Warszawie, Nakł. y drukiem M. Grölla, 1783.

796 p. 16 cm.

I. Title.

65-67314

NL 0408359 DLC

Law

Lithuania. Laws, statutes, etc.

Poland. *Laws, statutes, etc.*
Prawo polityczne i cywilne Korony Polskiey y Wielkiego Xięztwa Litewskiego, to iest: Nowy zbiór praw oboyga narodów od roku 1347. aż do teraźnieyszych czasów ⌊przez Antoniego Trębickiego ułożone⌋ W Warszawie, W druk. P. Dufour, 1789-91.

Lithuania. Laws, statutes, etc.
Statut litewski, drugiej redakcyi, 1566
see its Statutum lituanicum alterius editionis.

Law

Lithuania. *Laws, statutes, etc.*
Статутъ Великого Князьства Литовскаго 1588 года. Новое изд. Имп. московскаго об-ва исторіи и древностей россійскихъ. ⌊Москва, 1854⌋

24, 382 p. 28 cm.

The text of this ed. follows that of the 1st pub. by Mamonicz, Krakow, 1588.
Detached from Временникъ Императорскаго московскаго общества исторіи и древностей россійскихъ, кн. 19, 1854.

I. Moscow. Universitet. Obshchestvo istorii i drevnosteĭ rossiĭskikh. *Title transliterated:* Statut Velikogo Kníaz'stva Litovskago.

48-30883*

NL 0408362 DLC

Law

Lithuania. Laws, statutes, etc. Statut Velikogo Kníaz'stva Litovskago.

Kistíakovskiĭ, Aleksandr Fedorovich, 1833-1885, *ed.*
Права, по которымъ судится малороссійскій народъ, высочайшимъ всепресвѣтлѣйшія, державнѣйшія Великія Государыни Императрицы Елисаветъ Петровны, Самодержицы Всероссійскія, Ея императорскаго священнѣйшаго Величества повелѣніемъ, изъ трехъ книгъ, а именно: Статута Литовскаго, Зерцаля Саксонскаго и приложенныхъ при томъ двухъ правъ, таkodже изъ Книги порядка, по переводѣ изъ полскаго и латинскаго языковъ на россійскій діалектъ въ едину книгу сведенныя, въ градѣ Глуховѣ, лѣта отъ Рождества Христова 1743 года. Изданныя подъ ред. и съ приложеніемъ изслѣдованія о семъ Сводѣ и о законахъ дѣйствовавшихъ въ Малороссіи А. Ѳ. Кистяковскаго. Кіевъ, Въ Унив. тип. (І. І. Завадзкаго) 1879.

Law

Lithuania. Laws, statutes, etc. Statut Velikogo Kníaz'stva Litovskago.

Bershadskiĭ, Sergeĭ Aleksandrovich, 1850-1896.
Литовскій статутъ и польскія конституціи; историко-юридическое изслѣдованіе. С.-Петербургъ, Тип. М. Стасюлевича, 1893.

DK511
.L24S9

Lithuania. Laws, statutes, etc. Statut Velikogo Kníaz'stva Litovskago.

Šliupas, John, 1861-1944.
Gadynė šlėktos viešpatavimo Lieutuvoje, 1569-1795. m., ir Lietuviškasis statutas Zigmanto I (pagal T. Čackį) Chicago, Turtu ir spauda "Lietuvos," 1909.

Lithuania. *Laws, statutes, etc.*
Statut Wielkiego Księstwa Litewskiego, z dołączeniem treści konstytucyi przyzwoitych. W Sankt-Petersburgu, W Druk. Rządzącego Senatu, 1811.

2 v. 27 cm.

Added t. p.: Статутъ Великаго Княжества Литовскаго, съ подведеніемъ въ надлежащихъ мѣстахъ ссылки на конституціи, приличныя содержанію онаго.
Polish and Russian.

I. Title. II. Title: Statut Velikago Kníazhestva Litovskago.

78-455518

NL 0408367 DLC

(V)
JN6745
A3
1786

Lithuania. Laws, statutes, etc.
Statut Wielkiego Księstwa Litewskiego, naprzód, za Nayjaśnieyszego Hospodara Zygmunta III, w Krakowie w roku 1588; ... po dwakroć za Nayjasnieyszego Króla Stanisława Augusta, z przydatkiem Summaryuszów, Praw i Konstytucyy od roku 1764 do roku 1786; taraz za szczęśliwego panowania Nayjaśnieyszego Cesarza i Samowładcy Wszech-Rossyy, Króla Polskiego Alexandra I., bez żadney odmiany, podług wydania wileńskiego, roku 1786, nakładem Wileńskiego Towarzystwa Typograficznego przedrukowany. W Wilnie, W Drukarni A. Marcinkowskiego, roku pańskiego 1819.
⌊20⌋ 356 ⌊96⌋ 18 ⌊11⌋ 47 p. 34cm.

NL 0408368 CSt-H

Law
Case

Lithuania. *Laws, statutes, etc.*
Statut Wielkiego Xięstwa Litewskiego, naprzod, za naiaśnieyszego hospodara krola jegomości Zygmunta III. w Krakowie w roku 1588. Drugi raz w Wilnie, w roku 1619. z pokazaniem zgody y różnice Statutow Koronnych y W. K. L. Trzeci raz, za naiaśnieyszego K. J. M. Władysława IV. w Warszawie, w roku 1648. z przydaniem Konstytucyi od roku 1550 do 1647. Czwarty raz, za naiaśnieyszego krola jegomości Jana Trzeciego w Wilnie w roku 1698. Z przyłożeniem pod Artykuły Konstytucyi seymowych od Seymu roku 1550. aż do Seymu roku 1690, oboygu narodom służących (textu samego niwczym nie naruszaiąc) Teraz zaś piąty raz, za szczęśliwie panuiącego naiaśnieyszego krola jegomosci Augusta Trzeciego, przedrukowany. W Wilnie, W Drúkarni J. K. M. Akademickiey Societatis Jesu, 1744.
1 v. (various pagings) coats of arms. 33 cm.
CONTENTS.—⌊Statut Wielkiego Xięstwa Litewskiego⌋—Rejestr.—Trybunał obywatelom Wielkiego Xięstwa Litewskiego na Seymie Warszawskim, dany roku 1581.—Coaequatio jurium una cum ordinatione judiciorum tribunalitiorum et repartitione locationeque exercituum Magni Ducatus Litvaniae.—Constytucye Seymu walnego ordynaryinego sześćniedzielnego w Grodnie roku Pańskiego 1726.—Constytucye Wielkiego Xięstwa Litewskiego.

65-69101

Library of Congress

NL 0408370 DLC

Lithuania. *Laws, statutes, etc.*
Statut Wielkiego Xięstwa Litewskiego, naprzod, za naiaśnieyszego hospodara krola jegomości Zygmunta III. w Krakowie w roku 1588. Drugi raz w Wilnie, w roku 1619. z pokazaniem zgody y różnice Statutow Koronnych y W. K. L. Trzeci raz, za naiaśnieyszego K. J. M. Władysława IV. w Warszawie, w roku 1648. z przydaniem Konstytucyi od roku 1550. do 1647. Czwarty raz, za naiaśnieyszego krola jegomości Jana Trzeciego w Wilnie w roku 1698. Z przyłożeniem pod Artykuły Konstytucyi seymowych od Seymu roku 1550. aż do Seymu roku 1690, oboygu narodom służących (textu samego niwczym nie naruszaiąc) Teraz zaś piąty raz, za szczęśliwie panuiącego naiaśnieyszego krola jagomości Augusta Trzeciego, przedrukowany. W Wilnie, W Drukarni J. K. M. Akademickiey Societatis Jesu, 1744 ⌊i. e. 1780⌋
1 v. (various pagings) coats of arms. 33 cm.
CONTENTS.—Summaryusz Statutu W. X. Lit.—⌊Statut Wielkiego Xięstwa Litewskiego⌋—Konstytucye Seymu walnego ordynaryinego sześćniedzielnego w Grodnie roku Pańskiego 1726.—Trybunał obywatelom Wielkiego Xięstwa Litewskiego na Seymie Warszawskim, dany roku 1581.—Porządek sądzenia spraw w Trybunału W. X. Lit.—Coaequatio jurium sta- nów Wielkiego Xięstwa Litewskiego z Korona Polska.—Sum- mariusze niektórych Konstytucyi Wielkiego Xięstwa Litew skiego.—Rejestr.

65-69102

NL 0408372 DLC CU

LITHUANIA - Laws, statutes, etc.
Statutum lituanicum, alterius editionis, 1566. [Cracoviae, 1900.]

Forms vol. 7 of Collectanea ex archivo collegii iuridici, issued by Akademija umiejętności, Krakow.
Title taken from half title-page.
Title also in Polish.

NL 0408373 MH

Lithuania. Laws, statutes, etc.
Teisiniai santykiai šeimoje
see under Veržbavičius, L

LIT
397
D44

Lithuania. Laws, statutes, etc.
Trybunał obywatelom Wielkiego xięstwa litewskiego na Seymie warszawskim dany roku 1581. Wilno, drukarnia akademickiey Societatis Iesu, 1744.
1 p.l., 30, ⌊1⌋, 68 p. 33cm.
Partial contents:- Coaequatio jurium una cum ordinatione judiciorum tribunalitiorum, et repartitione, locationeque exercituum magni ducatus Litvaniae.- Konstytucye Seymu walnego ordynaryinego szescniedzielnego w Grodnie roku pańskiego 1726, dnia 28, września, złozonego.

NL 0408376 MH-L

Lithuania. *Laws, statutes, etc.*
1588 ⌊i. e. Tūkstantis penki šimtai aštuoniasdešimt aštuntųjų⌋ metų Lietuvos statutas. Литовскій статутъ 1588 года. Kaunas, Akc. "Spindulio" b-vės spaustuvė, 1934-38.
2 v. in 3. facsims. 25 cm.
Editor's name, J. Lappo, at head of title.
Vol. 2 issued in series: švietimo ministerijos Knygų leidimo komisijos leidinys nr. 497.
In Russian.
CONTENTS.—1. t. Изслѣдованіе. 2 v.—2. t. Текстъ.
I. Lappo, Ivan Ivanovich, ed. II. Title. III. Title: Litovskiĭ statut tysiacha piat'sot vosem'desiat vos'mogo goda.

58-50103

NL 0408377 DLC ICU NN

VOLUME 336

LITHUANIA. Laws, statutes, etc.
1588 metų Lietuvos statutas. Литовскій статуть 1588 года. Kaunas, 1938. 1 v. illus. 25cm. (Lithuania. Švietimo ministerija. Knygų leidimo komisijos leidinys. Nr. 497)
Tom 2.
Microfilm (Master negative)
Editors name J. Lappo, at head of title.
In Russian.
CONTENTS.--T.2. Текстъ.

NL 0408378 NN

Law
Lithuania. Laws, statutes, etc.
Ãsinskiĭ, Mikhail Nikitich, 1862–
Уставныя земскія грамоты Литовско-Русскаго государства. Кіевъ, Въ Унив. тип., 1889.

Lithuania. Laws, statutes, etc.
Lithuania. *Piliečių apsaugos departamentas.*
... Vadovėlis policijai ... Kaunas, K. Narkevičiaus ir V. Atkočiūno spaustuvė, 1926.

LITHUANIA. Laws, statutes, etc.
I. Veikiantieji Lietuvoj įstatymai darbo srityje. II. Žemės reformos įstatymas. Sutaisė: V. Akelaitis ,ir, L. Velpertas. Kaunas, 1922. 134p. 15cm.
At head of title: Neoficialinis leidinys.

NL 0408381 PU

Law
Lithuania. Laws, statutes, etc.
Poland. *Laws, statutes, etc.*
Volumina legum. Przedruk Zbioru praw staraniem xx. pijarów w Warszawie od roku 1732 do roku ,1793, wydanego. Petersburg, Nakł. J. Ohryzki, 1859–1952.

Lithuania. Laws, statutes, etc.
Lithuania.
... Vyriausybės žinios ...
,Kaunas, etc., 1918–

Lithuania. Laws, statutes, etc.
Vyties kryžiaus ordeno įstatymas ir statutas Kaunas, 1928.
35p. 12 col. plates. 28cm.

NL 0408384 DNW

Lithuania. *Laws, statutes, etc.*
Законодательные акты Великого княжества Литовского XV–XVI вв. Сборник материалов подготовлен к печати И. И. Яковкиным. Ленинград, Ленинградское отд-ние Гос. социально-экон. изд-ва, 1936.
xi, 152 p. 20 cm. (Документы и материалы по истории народов СССР)
At head of title: Ленинградский гос. университет. Исторический факультет.
Some laws also in Latin or Polish.
Bibliographical footnotes.
1. Lithuania—Hist.—Sources. 2. Law—Lithuania—Sources. I. ÎAkovkin, Innokentiĭ Ivanovich, 1881– ed. II. Title.
Title transliterated: Zakonodatel'nye akty Velikogo kn̂iazhestva Litovskogo.
53–47794

NL 0408385 DLC

Lithuania. *Laws, statutes, etc.*
Zbiór praw litewskich od roku 1389. do roku 1529. Tudzież rozprawy sejmowe o tychże prawach od roku 1544. do roku 1563. Poznań, Drukarnia na Garbarach, 1841.
2 p. l., iv, 542 p. illus., plates, facsims. 24 x 20½ᶜᵐ.
Polish and Latin.
I. Title.
36-30838

NL 0408386 DLC CU KU CtY NjP

Law
Lithuania. Laws, statutes, etc.
Poland. *Laws, statutes, etc.*
Zbiór praw polskich i W. X. Litewskiego od roku 1347 Seymu Wiślickiego, aż do roku 1786. Podług sławnych Heyneccyusza i Höpfnera prawników porządku ułożony przez Fr. B. Piekarskiego. W Krakowie, W Drukarni Akademickiey, 1813.

Lithuania. *Laws, statutes, etc.*
Zbior praw y przywileiow miastu stołecznemu W. X. L. Wilnowi, nadanych na żądanie wielu miast koronnych, jako też Wielkiego Księstwa Litewskiego. Ułozony y wydany przez Piotra Dubinskiego. W Wilnie, w Druk. J. K. Mci, 1788.
312 p. 32 cm.
Latin or Polish.
1. Vilna—Charters, grants, privileges. I. Dubiński, Piotr, ed. II. Poland. Laws, statutes, etc. III. Title.
66-34882

NL 0408388 DLC

Lithuania. Laws, statutes, etc.
... Žyminio mokesčio įstatymas, su visais pakeitimais, papildymais ir su vyriausiojo tribunolo bei rusų senato aiškinimais. Spaudai parengė L. Veržbavičius ... ,ir, J. Rižis ... Redagavo J. Baltrušaitis ... Kaune, D. Gutman, 1935.
viii, 164 p. 23cm.
At head of title: Neoficialinis leidimas.

NL 0408389 MH-L

Law
Lithuania. Laws, statutes, etc. (Indexes)
Poland. *Laws, statutes, etc.* (*Indexes*)
Constitvcye koronne, y Wielkiego Xięstwa Litewskiego od Roku Pańskiego 1550 do roku 1683. Przez Macieia Marcyana Ładowskiego krotko zebráne. W Warszawie, W druk. Collegium Scholarum Piarum, 1685.

Law
Lithuania. Laws, statutes, etc. (Indexes)
Poland. *Laws, statutes, etc.* (*Indexes*)
Inwentarz konstytucyy koronnych y W. X. Litewskiego. Przez Macieia Marcyana Ładowskiego, sekretarza J. K. M., metrykanta kancelaryi koronney, od roku panskiego 1550. do r. 1683., krotko zebrany. A przez J. W. J. MCI. X. Jozefa Jędrzeia na Załuskach Załuskiego, referendarza koronnego, opata Przemeckiego &c., w roznych mieyscach y cytacyach zkorygowany, przydatkiem opuszczonych artykułow popr. y suplementem obszernym od roku 1683., aż do ostatniey konstytucyi seymu 1726. inclusive opatrzony. W Lipsku, Ex officina Weidmanniana, 1733.

Law
Lithuania. Laws, statutes, etc. (indexes)
Poland. *Laws, statutes, etc., 1764–1795* (*Stanisław II Augustus*) (*Indexes*)
Inwentarz nowy praw, traktatow, y konstytucyi Koronnych y W. X. Lit. w czasie bez-krolewia r. 1764 y za panowania nayiaśnieyszego Stanisława Augusta do r. 1780 uchwalonych, na wzor inwentarza dawnieyszego ułożony przez Teodora Ostrowskiego. W Warszawie, W druk. u XX. Scholarum Piarum, 1782.

Lithuania. Laws, statutes, etc. (Indexes)
Lietuvos įstatymų raidynas; "Vyriausybės žinių" I dalies 1918–1932 m. rodyklė. Kaunas, Spaudos fondas, 1933.
165, [2] p. 23 cm.
Cover title: Lietuvos įstatymų raidynas 1918–1932 m.
At head of title: Jokubas Robinzonas.

NL 0408393 PU

Lithuania. *Laws, statutes, etc.* (*Indexes*)
Vyriausybės žinių 1927–1929 metų rodyklė. Kaunas, "Spindulio" b-vės spaustuvė, 1930.
46 p. 31 x 23½ᶜᵐ.
1. Law—Lithuania—Indexes. I. Title.
36-31124

NL 0408394 DLC

Lithuania. Legation. U.S.
see Lithuania. Pasiuntinybė. U.S.

GR203 L4B312
Lithuania. Lietuvių tautosakos archyvas.
Balys, Jonas, 1909– *ed.*
Lietuvių liaudies sakmės. I. Lithuanian folk legends. Kaunas, A. S. lituanistikos instituto Lietuvių tautosakos archyvas, 1940.

Lithuania. Lietuviu tautosakos archyvas.
Tautosakos rinkėjo vadovas. Kaunas, 1936
79 p. (Its Leidinys)
1. Folklore - Lithuania. 2. Folklore - Field work. I. Title. X ref.: Kaunas. Lietuvių Tautosakos Archyvas (to main entry)

NL 0408397 MH

VOLUME 336

Lithuania. *Lithuanian Folklore Archives*
see
Lithuania. *Lietuvių tautosakos archyvas.*

Lithuania. *Matų, saikų, svarstyklių ir probavimo rūmai.*
... Vyriausiųjų matų, saikų ir svarstyklių rūmų penkerių $19\frac{23}{\text{VIII}}19$–$19\frac{23}{\text{VIII}}24$ metų darbuotės apyskaita. Kaunas ⌊Valstybės spaustuvė⌋ 1924.

46 p. incl. tables. 23cm.

At head of title: Finansų ministerijos leidinys.

1. Weights and measures—Lithuania. I. Title.

36-34965

Library of Congress QC89.L5A45

⌊2⌋ 389.09475

NL 0408399 DLC

Lithuania. Ministère des affaires étrangères
see
Lithuania. Užsienų reikalų ministerija.

Law
Hebr

Lithuania. *Ministerija žydų reikalams.*
תקנות הבחירות לועדי הקהלות. קובנה, תרפ"א.
⌊Kaunas, 1921⌋

19 p. 17 cm.

Cover title.
Bound with its תקנות פאר די וואלן אין די ועדי הקהלות ⌊Kaunas⌋ 1921.

1. Jews—Legal status, laws, etc.—Lithuania. 2. Local elections—Lithuania.

Title transliterated: Takanot ha-beḥirot le-vaʻade ha-kehilot.

59-58730

Library of Congress ⌊2⌋

NL 0408401 DLC

Lithuania. *Ministerija žydų reikalams.*
תקנות פאר די וואלן אין די ועדי הקהלות. קאוונע.
⌊Kaunas⌋ 1921.

24 p. 17 cm.

Added t. p. in Lithuanian.
Cover title.
Bound with its תקנות הבחירות לועדי הקהלות ⌊Kaunas, 1921⌋

1. Jews—Legal status, laws, etc.—Lithuania. 2. Local elections—Lithuania.

Title transliterated: Takones far di valn in di vaadey ha-kehiles.

59-58733 rev

Library of Congress ⌊r60b2⌋

NL 0408402 DLC

Law
(Hebr)

Lithuania. *Ministerija žydų reikalams.*
די צייטווייליקע תקנות פאר די וואלן אין די קהלות. קאוונא.
⌊Kaunas⌋ 1919.

27 p. 18 cm.

1. Jews—Legal status, laws, etc.—Lithuania. 2. Local elections—Lithuania.

Title transliterated: Di tsaytvaylike takones far di valn in di kehiles.

58-52642

Library of Congress ⌊2⌋

NL 0408403 DLC

Lithuania. *Ministerium für Jüdische Angelegenheiten*
see
Lithuania. *Ministerija žydų reikalams.*

Lithuania. *Ministras Pirmininkas.*
Convention regulating the status of the Memel Territory. Letter from the Prime Minister and Minister for Foreign Affairs of Lithuania. Geneva, 1926.

18 l. 33 cm.

Caption title.
At head of title: League of Nations.
Official no.: C.459.1926.VII.
Concerns procedural and substantive questions for consideration by the Council of the League of Nations in the dispute between the Territory of Memel and the central Lithuanian Government.

1. Memel (Ter.) 2. League of Nations. Council. I. League of Nations.

A 48-9139*

Woodrow Wilson Memorial Library
for Library of Congress ⌊2⌋

NL 0408405 NNUN-W

Lithuania. *Ministras Pirmininkas.*
Dispute between Poland and Lithuania. Geneva, 1922.

5 l. 33 cm.

Caption title.
League of Nations' official no.: C.16.M.3.1922.VII.
Declaration by the Lithuanian Prime Minister before the Constitutional Asembly, Dec. 17, 1921, protesting against the elections at Vilna.

1. Elections—Vilna. 2. Lithuania—For. rel.—Poland. 3. Poland—For. rel.—Lithuania. I. League of Nations.

A 48-7716*

Woodrow Wilson Memorial Library
for Library of Congress ⌊4⌋

NL 0408406 NNUN-W

Lithuania. *Ministras Pirmininkas.*
Dispute between Lithuania and Poland. Geneva, 1923.

3, 5-7 l. 33 cm.

At head of title: League of Nations.
Official no.: C.313.M.151.1923.VII.
Letter, dated Apr. 18, 1923, from the Lithuanian Prime Minister referring to the decision of the Conference of Ambassadors giving Vilna to Poland.
Includes note, dated Apr. 16, 1923, to the Conference of Ambassadors refusing to recognize the decision regarding Vilna.

1. Vilna. 2. Lithuania — Bound. — Poland. 3. Poland — Bound. — Lithuania. I. League of Nations.

A 48-7727*

Woodrow Wilson Memorial Library
for Library of Congress ⌊1⌋

NL 0408407 NNUN-W

Lithuania. *Ministras Pirmininkas.*
Dispute between Lithuania and Poland. Geneva, 1923.

3 l. 33 cm.

Caption title.
At head of title: League of Nations.
Official no.: C.324.M.153.1923.VII.
Letter, dated Apr. 19, 1923, from the Lithuanian Prime Minister, concerning inaccuracies in the League's historical summary of question of the neutral zones between Poland and Lithuania (official no.: C.219.M.128.1923.VII)

1. League of Nations. Secretariat. Historical summary ... of the question of the neutral zones between Poland and Lithuania. I. League of Nations.

A 48-7726*

Woodrow Wilson Memorial Library
for Library of Congress ⌊1⌋

NL 0408408 NNUN-W

Lithuanian. Ministras Pirmininkas.
Exchange of telegrams between the Lithuanian Government and the Secretary-General
see under League of Nations. Secretary-General, 1919-1933 (Earl of Perth)

Lithuania. *Ministras Pirmininkas.*
Letter from the Prime Minister of Lithuania. Geneva, 1924.

2 l. 33 cm.

Caption title.
At head of title: League of Nations.
Official no.: C.323.1924.VII.
Protest against new acts of Polish aggression on the Lithuanian-Polish line of demarcation.

1. Lithuania—For. rel.—Poland. 2. Poland—For. rel.—Lithuania. I. League of Nations.

A 48-7725*

Woodrow Wilson Memorial Library
for Library of Congress ⌊1⌋

NL 0408410 NNUN-W

Lithuania. *Ministras pirmininkas.*
... Lithuanian schools in the territory of Vilna and in the district of Punsk-Sejny ... Letter from the Lithuanian Prime minister to the Secretary-general. Geneva, 1923.

1 l., 2-3 numb. l. 33 cm.

At head of title: League of nations.
Official no.: C.779.1923.I.
Mimeographed.
"Communicated to the members of the Council."

1. Minorities—Poland. 2. Lithuanians in Poland. 3. Schools—Poland. I. League of nations. II. Title.

A 49-127

Woodrow Wilson Memorial Library
for Library of Congress ⌊2⌋

NL 0408411 NNUN-W

Lithuania. *Ministras Pirmininkas.*
Polish-Lithuanian dispute. Elections in the Vilna district. Geneva, 1922.

2 l. 33 cm.

Caption title.
At head of title: League of Nations.
Official no.: C.719.M.431.1922.VII.
Letter, dated Oct. 7, 1922, from the Lithuanian Prime Minister, protesting against Poland's organized elections of Vilna district.

1. Elections—Vilna. 2. Lithuania—For. rel.—Poland. 3. Poland—For. rel.—Lithuania. I. League of Nations.

A 48-7806*

Woodrow Wilson Memorial Library
for Library of Congress ⌊2⌋

NL 0408412 NNUN-W

Lithuania. *Ministras Pirmininkas.*
Request of the Lithuanian Government in virtue of article 11 of the Covenant. Letter from the Lithuanian Government dated October 24th, 1927. Geneva, 1927.

8 l. 33 cm.

Caption title.
At head of title: League of Nations.
Official no.: C.536.M.190.1927.VII.
Letter from the Lithuanian Prime Minister giving a list of expelled Polish nationals together with their petitions to the League of Nations, urging their return to Poland and the reinstatement of heir properties.

1. Expulsion—Poland. I. League of Nations.

A 48-7723*

Woodrow Wilson Memorial Library
for Library of Congress ⌊1⌋

NL 0408413 NNUN-W

Lithuania. *Ministras Pirmininkas.*
Telegram from the Lithuanian Government. Geneva, 1927.

⌊1⌋ l. 33 cm.

At head of title: League of Nations.
Official no.: C.528.M.192.1927.VII.
Telegram from the Lithuanian Prime Minister, concerning Poland's expulsion of undesirable Polish nationals into Lithuanian territory.
Issued also in French.

1. Expulsion—Poland. I. League of Nations.

A 48-7724*

Woodrow Wilson Memorial Library
for Library of Congress ⌊1⌋

NL 0408414 NNUN-W

VOLUME 336

Lithuania. *Ministras Pirmininkas.*
Territory of Memel. Paris, 1923.
7 l. 33 cm.
Caption title.
At head of title: League of Nations.
Official no.: C.816.M.306.1923.VII.
Letter dated Dec. 11, 1923, from Mr. Galvanauskas, Prime Minister of Lithuania, refuting certain points in the report by the Extraordinary Commission to Memel, Mar. 6, 1923 (official no.: C.664.M.295.1923.VII)

1. Memel (Ter.) 2. Extraordinary Commission to Memel. I. League of Nations.

A 48-9137*

Woodrow Wilson Memorial Library
for Library of Congress [2]

NL 0408415 NNUN-W

Lithuania. *Ministry for Jewish Affairs*
see
Lithuania. *Ministerija žydų reikalams.*

Lithuania. Ministry of finance
see
Lithuania. Finansų ministerija.

Lithuania. Ministry for foreign affairs
see
Lithuania. Užsienių reikalų ministerija.

Lithuania. *Miškų departamentas.*
Lietuvos miškų statistika. Statistique forestière de la Lithuanie. m. 1- 1937-
Kaunas.
v. 27 cm.
Preface, table of contents, and captions in Lithuanian and French.

1. Forests and forestry—Lithuania—Stat. I. Title.

SD83.L5A3 56-48798

NL 0408419 DLC

Lithuania. *Miškų departamentas.*
Miškų departamento metraštis, 1918–1938 m. Annuaire du Département des forêts, 1918–1938. Kaunas, Miškų departamento leidinys, 1940.
viii, 127 p. incl. illus. (incl. ports.) tables, diagrs. 2 fold. maps. 28½cm.
Table of contents and preface in Lithuanian and French.

1. Forests and forestry—Lithuania. 2. Woodwork—Lithuania.

42-5696

Library of Congress SD217.L8A5 1938

NL 0408420 DLC DNAL

Lithuania. *Miškų departamentas.*
Statistique forestière de la Lithuanie
see its
Lietuvos miškų statistika.

Lithuania. Miškų ūkio mokslinio tyrimo institutas
see Lietuvos miškų ūkio mokslinio tyrimo institutas.

UB325
.L5A5
1925

Lithuania. Naujokų ėmimo komisija.
... Vyriausios naujokų emimo komisijos nutarimai, aiškiną karinės prievolės įstatymą, jo papildymus bei pakeitimus, ir aplinkraščiai bei paaiškinimai apskričių Naujokų emimo komisijoms naujokų šaukimo reikalu ligi 1925 m. gruodžio men. 31 d. Surinko ... Kaunas, Valstybes spaustuvė, 1926.
132 p. incl. forms 19½cm. [see pub.cat.card]
1. Lithuania--Army--Recruiting, enlistment, etc. 2. Military law—Lithuania. I. Lithuania. Piliečių ap- saugos departamentas. II. Title.

NL 0408423 DLC

TP609
.L5
1923

Lithuania. Netiesioginių mokesnių ir valstybinių monopolių valdyba.
Nurodymai kaip naudotis Tralles'o spirtometru ir lentelėmis ... Kaunas [Valstybės spaustuvė] 1923.
cover-title, 55 p. incl. tables 22cm.
"Netiesioginių mokesnių ir valstybinių monopolių valdybos leidinys."
Errata slip mounted on verso of p.
1. Liquors—Gaging and testing. 2. Alcoholometer. I. Title: Tralles'o spirtometru ir lentelemis, Nurodymai kaip naudotis.

NL 0408424 DLC

Lithuania. Pasiuntinybė. U.S.
Appeal of the representatives of the Baltic nations
see under title

D731
.C85

Lithuania. Pasiuntinybė. U. S.
Lithuanian situation. [v. 1]-
no. [1]- Aug. 3, 1940-
Washington, D. C., 1940-

Lithuania. *Pašto valdyba*
see **Lithuania.** *Paštų, telegrafų ir telefonų valdyba.*

Lithuania. *Paštų, telegrafų ir telefonų valdyba.*
... Instrukcijos tarnautojams lydintiems paštą ir nešiotojams korespondencijos. P. T. ir T. valdybos leidinys. Kaunas [Valstybės spaustuvė] 1923.
14 p. 15½cm.
At head of title: Lietuvos respublika.

1. Postal service—Lithuania. I. Title.

39-9542

Library of Congress HE7065.6.A5 1923 a

NL 0408428 DLC

Lithuania. *Paštų, telegrafų ir telefonų valdyba.*
Lietuvos pašto, telegrafo ir telefono įstaigų, agentūrų ir punktų sąrašas.
Kaunas.
v. 21 cm.
Title varies: Lietuvos pašto, telegrafo ir telefono įstaigų ir agentūrų sąrašas.

1. Postal service—Lithuania. 2. Telegraph—Lithuania. 2. Telephone—Lithuania. I. Title.

HE7065.6.A3 52-57675

NL 0408429 DLC

Lithuania. Paštu, telegrafu ir telefonu valdyba.
U. S. *Treaties, etc., 1933-* (*Franklin D. Roosevelt*)
Parcel post agreement between the United States of America and Lithuania. Washington, U. S. Govt. print. off., 1940.

Lithuania. *Paštų, telegrafų ir telefonų valdyba.*
... Pašto taisyklės ... Kaunas [Valstybės spaustuvė] 1923.
128, 40, iii p. forms. 21½cm.
"Paštų, telegrafų ir telefonų valdybos oficialis leidinys."
Errata slip mounted at end.

1. Postal service—Lithuania—Laws and regulations. I. Title.

39-9543

Library of Congress HE7065.6.A4 1923

NL 0408431 DLC

Lithuania. *Paštų, telegrafų ir telefonų valdyba.*
Pašto-telegrafo įstaigose laikraščių užsakymo priėmimui atidengti ir jų ekspedijavimo operacijos instrukcija. Kaunas [Valstybės spaustuvė] 1925.
cover-title, 25 p. incl. tables, forms. 21 x 16½cm.
"Tvirtinu: 1925 m. vasario 14. d. (Pasirašė) B. Tomaševičius, P., T. ir T. valdybos direktorius."

1. Postal service—Lithuania.

39-9544

Library of Congress HE7065.6.A5 1925

NL 0408432 DLC

Lithuania. *Paštų, telegrafų ir telefonų valdyba.*
... Pašto, telegrafo-telefono įstaigų telegramų išnešiotojams instrukcija ... Kaunas [Valstybės spaustuvė] 1923.
12 p. 15½cm.
At head of title: ... Lietuvos respublika.
"Paštų, telegrafų ir telefonų valdybos leidinys."

1. Telegraph—Lithuania. I. Title.

39-9545

Library of Congress HE8225.7.A5 1923

NL 0408433 DLC

Lithuania. *Paštų, telegrafų ir telefonų valdyba.*
Sąrašas valstybių ir vietų, į kurias gali būti priimami mažo svorio siuntiniai (colis pastaux) Kaunas, 1924.
100 p. 28 cm.

1. Parcels-post—Lithuania. I. Title.

HE7065.6.A52 53-52697

NL 0408434 DLC

VOLUME 336

HE6176
.L5

Lithuania. Paštu, telegrafu ir telefonu valdyba.
Sarašas valstybių, su kuriomis galima apsimainyti įvertintais laiškais (lettres avec valeur déclarée) Kaunas, 1929.
16½x21½cm.

1. Postal service--Lithuania--Registry system. 2. Postal service--Lithuania--Foreign mail.

NL 0408435 DLC

HE9275
.7
.A6

Lithuania. Paštu, telegrafu ir telefonu valdyba.
... Telefonų abonentų knyga ... 19
Kaunas [19
v. fold. maps 21½-23cm.
"Paštu telegrafų ir telefonų valdybos leidinys."
--- ----Papildomoji ... 19
Kaunas, 19
v. 23cm.

1. Lithuania--Directories--Telephone. I. Title.

NL 0408436 DLC

Lithuania. *Paštų, telegrafų ir telefonų valdyba.*
... Telegrafo taisyklės ... Kaunas ⌐Valstybės spaustuvė⌐ 1924.
cover-title, 104, ⌐6⌐ p. forms (part fold.) 22½cm.
"Paštų, telegrafų ir telefonų valdybos leidinys."

1. Telegraph—Lithuania—Laws and regulations. I. Title.

39-9546

Library of Congress HE8225.7.A5 1924

NL 0408437 DLC

HE8225
.6
.A5
1923

Lithuania. Paštu, telegrafu ir telefonu valdyba.
... Telegrafo tarifas užsieniui ...
Kaunas [Valstybės spaustuvė] 1923.
48 p. 27½x22cm.

At head of title: Lietuvos Paštų, telegrafų ir telefonų valdyba.
"Oficialus leidinys."

1. Telegraph--Rates. I. Title.

NL 0408438 DLC

Lithuania. *Paštų, telegrafų ir telefonų valdyba.*
... Telegrafo tarifas užsieniui. Kaunas, Akc. "Spindulio" b-vės spaustuvė, 1929.
50 p. 32cm.
"Paštų, telegrafų ir telefonų valdybos leidinys."

1. Telegraph—Lithuania—Rates. I. Title.

39-9547

Library of Congress HE8225.7.A5 1929
⌐2⌐ 384.169475

NL 0408439 DLC

Lithuania. *Paštų, telegrafų ir telefonų valdyba.*
... Telegrafo-telefono statyba ir priežiūra. Kaunas ⌐A. Bako spaustuvė⌐ 1929.
148, ⌐4⌐ p. illus. 22½cm.
At head of title: Paštų, t. ir t. valdyba. Technikos tarnyba.

1. Telegraph lines—Construction. 2. Telephone lines—Construction. I. Title.

33-36800

Library of Congress TK5401.L5 1929

NL 0408440 DLC

Lithuania. *Piliečių apsaugos departamentas.*
Geležkelių policijos instrukcija. Kaunas ⌐Valstybės spaustuvė⌐ 1925.
32 p. 17cm.
Signed: J. Danauskas, Piliečių apsaugos departamento direktorius.

1. Railroads—Lithuania—Police. I. Title.

36-30181

Library of Congress HE1771.L5 1925

NL 0408441 DLC

Lithuania. *Piliečių apsaugos departamentas.*
... Instrukcija milicijos tarnautojams. Kaunas ⌐Valstybės spaustuvė⌐ 1925.
cover-title, 60, ⌐2⌐ p., 1 l. incl. forms. 17½cm.
At head of title: Vidaus reikalų ministerijos Piliečių apsaugos departamento leidinys.

1. Lithuania—Militia. I. Title.

36-4520

Library of Congress U145.L8A5 1925 355.12

NL 0408442 DLC

Lithuania. Piliečių apsaugos departamentas.

HV8227
.6
.A2T6

Tomašauskas, Ig *ed.*
Lietuvos policija, 1918–1928. Kaunas, V. R. M. Piliečių apsaugos d-to leidinys, 1930–

Lithuania. *Piliečių apsaugos departamentas.*
Nusikaltimams kelti ir tirti vadovėlis. Kaunas ⌐Valstybės spaustuvė⌐ 1925.
75 p. 17cm.
"Piliečių apsaugos departamento leidinys."

1. Police—Lithuania. I. Lithuania. Laws, statutes, etc. II. Title. III. Title: Vadovėlis, Nusikaltimams kelti ir tirti.

36-36016

Library of Congress HV7762.6.A5 1925
⌐2⌐ 351.7409475

NL 0408444 DLC

Lithuania. Piliečių apsaugos departamentas.

Policija, lietuvos policijos mėnesinis laikraštis. nr. 1–
(1– metai); rugsėjo 1924–
Kaunas, 1924–

Lithuania. *Piliečių apsaugos departamentas.*
... Vadovėlis policijai ... Kaunas, K. Narkevičiaus ir V. Atkočiūno spaustuvė, 1926.
2 p. l., viii, 102, 76, 43, 194, 43 p. incl. tables, forms. 23½cm.
At head of title: V. R. M. Piliečių apsaugos departamento leidinys.
CONTENTS.—Valstybės teisė.—Baudžiamoji teisė.—Baudžiamasis procesas.—Policijos teisė.—Trumpos žinios iš policijos raštvedybos.

1. Police—Lithuania. I. Lithuania. Laws, statutes, etc. II. Title.

36-31468

Library of Congress HV7355.6.A6 1926
⌐2⌐ 351.7409475

NL 0408446 DLC

VK381
.L5

Lithuania. Plentų ir vandens kelių valdyba.

Lithuania. *Susisiekimo ministerija.*
Lietuvos vidaus vandens kelių laivininkystės signalai ir nurodomieji ženklai. Sustatyta Plentų ir vandens kelių valdyboje. Kaunas, 1923.

Lithuania. Plentų ir vandens kelių valdyba.
Hidrometrinis biuras

See

Lithuania. Hidrometrinis biuras.

Lithuania. *Prekybos departamentas.*
Autovežimių per Lietuvos sieną perleidimo taisyklės. Galioja nuo 1933. VII. 1. Kaunas, Akc. "Spindulio" b-vės spaustuvė, 1933.
68, 9 p. forms, tables. 17 cm. (*Its* Leidinys nr. 7)

1. Customs administration—Lithuania. I. Title.

60-59445

NL 0408449 DLC

Lithuania. *Prekybos departamentas.*
... Instrukcija konfiskacijos byloms vesti (Pritaikymo muitinių įst. 157–200 §§ tvarka) Kaunas, Valstybės spaustuvė, 1926.
19 p. 20cm.
At head of title: Prekybos departamento leidinys.
Errata slip (mimeographed) mounted on p. ⌐2⌐ of cover.

1. Searches and seizures—Lithuania. 2. Customs administration—Lithuania. I. Lithuania. Laws, statutes, etc. II. Title.

36-32461

Library of Congress HJ6969.5.L5A5 1926
⌐2⌐ 336.2600474

NL 0408450 DLC

Lithuania. Prekybos departamentas.

Lithuania. *Laws, statutes, etc.*
... Muitų tarifai. Kaunas, Valstybės spaustuvė, 1926.

Lithuania. *Prekybos departamentas.*
Prekybos departamento 1926–1927 metų aplinkraščių rinkinys. Kaunas ⌐F. Sokolovskienės ir G. Lano spaustuvė⌐ 1929.
xxix, 291 p. incl. forms. 16½cm.
"Prekybos departamento leidinys."

1. Commercial law—Lithuania. 2. Customs administration—Lithuania. 3. Finance—Lithuania—Accounting. I. Title.

36-36895

NL 0408452 DLC

Lithuania. Prekybos ir pramonės ministerija.
Bendros statistikos departamentas
see Lithuania. Centralinis statistikos biuras.

VOLUME 336

Lithuania. Prekybos, pramonės ir amatų rūmai, Kaunas.
Lietuvos importas ir importeriai. Litauens Import und Importeure. Lithuanian imports & importers... Išleido... I. Leibenzonas. Kaunas: V. D. M., 1930. 268 p. incl. tables. illus. 23½cm.

Title also in French.
Lithuanian, German, English and French.
Advertising matter interspersed.

955203A. 1. Commerce—Lithuania, 1925–1929. 2. Commerce—Direct. —Lithuania. I. Title.
N. Y. P. L. January 5, 1939

NL 0408454 NN

Lithuania. Prekybos, pramonės ir amatų rūmai, *Kaunas.*
Lietuvos importeriai, eksporteriai ir pramoninkai; adresų ir informacijos knyga. Lithuanian importers, exporters and manufacturers; trade directory. Sudarė ir išleido I. Leibenzonas. Kaunas, 1938.

280 p. 24 cm.

Lithuanian, German, English, and French.

1. Lithuania—Comm.—Direct. 2. Lithuania—Indus.—Direct. I. Leibenzonas, I., ed. II. Title. III. Title: Lithuanian importers, exporters and manufacturers.

HF3635.7.L49 65–58653

NL 0408455 DLC

LITHUANIA . Prekybos, pramonės ir amatų rumai, Kaunas.
Report of the Chamber of Commerce, Industry and Crafts; ten years of Lithuanian economy Kaunas, 1938.

23 cm. Plate.

NL 0408456 MH

Lithuania. Prekybos, pramonės ir amatų rūmai, *Kaunas.*
... Ten years of Lithuanian economy. Kaunas, 1938.

167 p. incl. tables. pl., diagrs. 23 cm.

At head of title: Report of the Chamber of commerce, industry and crafts.

1. Lithuania—Econ. condit.—1918– I. Title.

HC337.L5L52 A 42–4159

Cincinnati. Univ. Libr. for Library of Congress [a55c½]†

WaU CoU
NL 0408457 OCU OC1 MiD CtY CU PU DLC NIC PSt NN

HC337
L5L7763

Lithuania. Prekybos, pramonės ir amatų rūmai, Kaunas.
_ Zehn jahre litauischer wirtschaft. Kaunas, 1938.

171,[1] p. incl.tables. pl., diagrs. 23½cm.

Hoover Library

At head of title: Konjunkturbericht der : Handels-industrie- und handwerkskammer.

1.Lithuania - Econ. condit. - 1918-
I.Title.

NL 0408458 CSt-H PU CSt

Lithuania. *Prezidentas, 1926–1940 (Smetona)*
see also
Smetona, Antanas, *pres. Lithuania,* 1874–1944.

Lithuania. *Savivaldybių departamentas.*
Lietuvos savivaldybės 1918–1928. Savivaldybių įsikūrimo ir pirmojo dešimtmečio darbų apžvalga ... Kaunas [Spaustuvė "Grafika"] 1928.

2 p. l., 294, [2] p. incl. tables. 23½cm.

"Savivaldybės leidinys."

1. Local government—Lithuania. I. Title.

33–705

Library of Congress JS6130.52.A8 1928 352.0475

NL 0408460 DLC OC1

JS7
.L5A3

Lithuania. Savivaldybių departamentas.
[Leidiniai] ... [Mariampolije, 1925?–]
1 v. front. (port.) 23 cm.

NL 0408461 DLC

JS6130
.5
.A1S3

Lithuania. Savivaldybiu departamentas.
Savivaldybė; mėnesinis Lietuvos savivaldybių laikraštis. birž. 1923–
[Kaunas, 1923–

JS7
.L5A3
no. 2

Lithuania. Savivaldybių departamentas.
... Savivaldybių kalendorius. 192
[Mariampolėje, 192]
1 v. port. 23 cm. (Leidinys nr.)

NL 0408463 DLC

Lithuania. Seimas.
Seimo stenogramos. Seimas 1–

1922/23

Kaunas, 1922– f°.

NL 0408464 NN ICU DLC

Lithuania. Seimas.
Trumpos Steigiamojo seimo nariu biografijos su atvaizdais. Klaipedoje, Spaude "Lituania", 1924.
71 p. ports. 31 cm.

NL 0408465 PU

Lithuania. Statistikos biūras
see Lithuania. Centralinis statistikos biūras.

LITHUANIA. Steigiamasis seimas, 1920-1922.
Darbai.
[Kaunas] no. 30cm.

Film reproduction. Positive.

NL 0408467 NN ICU DLC

Lithuania. Susisiekimo ministerija.
...Lietuvos geležinkelių...darbuotės apyskaita. Compte rendu annuel des opérations des chemins de fer de L'état Lithuanien pour l'exercice. 1919/23–

Kaunas, 1925– 8° & f°.

1919/23 has title: Geležkelių valdybos darbuotės apyskaita.
In Lithuanian and French; 1919/23–1926 in Lithuanian only.

1. Railways—Lithuania.
N. Y. P. L. May 26, 1931

NL 0408468 NN

Lithuania. *Susisiekimo ministerija.*
Lietuvos vidaus vandens kelių laivininkystės signalai ir nurodomieji ženklai. Sustatyta Plentų ir vandens kelių valdyboje. Kaunas, 1923.

14 p. diagrs. 21 cm.

1. Signals and signaling. I. Lithuania. Plentų ir vandens kelių valdyba. II. Title.

VK381.L5 59–58425

NL 0408469 DLC

Lithuania. *Susisiekimo ministerija.*
Susisiekimo ministerijos. 1937 metų metraštis. Kaunas [Spaudė "Spindulys"] 1938.

411 p. incl. tables. ports., diagrs. 29cm.

At head of title: Nepriklausomosios Lietuvos XX metų sukaktis. Lietuvos respublika. Susisiekimo ministerija.
French summary: p. 84–96.

1. Lithuania. Susisiekimo ministerija. 2. Postal service—Lithuania. 3. Railroads—Lithuania. 4. Roads—Lithuania. 5. Transportation—Lithuania.

41–27187

Library of Congress HE70.6.A5 1937

NL 0408470 DLC

Lithuania. *Susisiekimo ministerija. Geležinkelių valdyba*
see
Lithuania. *Geležinkelių valdyba.*

Lithuania. Susiekimo ministerija.Hidrometrinis biuras
See
Lithuania. Hidrometrinis biuras.

Lithuania. *Susisiekimo ministerija. Plentų ir vandens kelių valdyba*
see Lithuania. *Plentų ir vandens kelių valdyba.*

Lithuania. *Sveikatos departamentas.*
Egzaminų programa medicinos felčerio teisėms įgyti. Kaunas, 1924.

39 p. 17 cm.

1. Medicine—Study and teaching—Lithuania. I. Title.

R804.L5A58 59–57885

NL 0408474 DLC

VOLUME 336

Lithuania. Sveikatos departamentas.
Lietuvos medicinos, farmacijos, ir veterinarijos personalo ir istaigų sąrašas [Kaune, "Varpo" b-vės spaustuvė] 1922-23.
23cm.
"Vid. reik. min-jos Sveikatos departamento oficialis leidinys."
1. Medicine—Lithuania. 2. Physicians—Lithuania—Direct. 3. Veterinarians—Lithuania—Direct. 4. Pharmacists—Lithuania—Direct. 5. Dentists—Lithuania—Direct. I. Title.

NL 0408475 DLC

Lithuania. *Sveikatos departamentas.*
... Lietuvos medicinos, veterinarijos ir farmacijos personalo ir įstaigų sąrašas. ₍Kaunas, "Varpo" b-vės spaustuvė, 1925?₎
98, ₍2₎ p. 24½cm.
At head of title: V. R. M. ₍*i. e.* Vidaus reikalų ministrija₎ "Sveikatos departamento oficialus leidinys 1924-1925 met."
1. Medicine—Lithuania. 2. Physicians—Lithuania—Direct. 3. Veterinarians—Lithuania—Direct. 4. Pharmacists—Lithuania—Direct. 5. Dentists—Lithuania—Direct. I. Title.
34-36002
Library of Congress R713.67.L5A5 1925 610.5

NL 0408476 DLC DNLM

Lithuania. *Sveikatos departamentas.*
Lietuvos viešosios sveikatos stovio metų apžvalga. Aperçu sur l'état sanitaire public de la Lithuanie en Kaunas, 19
v. illus. (map) tables. 31½cm.
"Sveikatos departamento leidinys. Édition du Département de l'hygiène publique", 19
1. Lithuania—Sanit. affairs.
32-13718
Library of Congress RA299.L5A3 614.09475

NL 0408477 DLC

Lithuania. Švietimo ministerija.
Homerus.
... Homèro Odisėja. Vertė d-ras J. Ralys. Kaunas, Švietimo ministerijos leidinys, 1921.

Lithuania. *Švietimo ministerija.*
... Mūsų senovė, žurnalas Lietuvos istorijos medžiagai rinkti ... 1.– knygos. Tilžėje ₍etc.₎ 1921–
v. illus. (incl. map, facsims.) tables. 23cm.
"Švietimo ministerijos leidinys."
Subtitle varies slightly.
Includes bibliographies.
1. Lithuania—Hist. 2. Lithuania—Hist.—Sources. I. Title.
37-32257
Library of Congress DK511.L2A3
₍3₎ 947.5

NL 0408479 DLC CtY

Lithuania. Švietimo ministerija.
Skaitymai; literatūros ir kritikos žurnalas ... 1.– **knygos;** 1920–
Kaunas, Švietimo ministerijos leidinys, 1920–

Lithuania. Švietimo Ministerija.
Švietimo darbas
see under title

Lithuania. *Švietimo ministerija.*
Švietimo ministerijos žinios. Oficijalinis mėnesinis Švietimo ministerijos leidinys ... 1931–
Klaipėda, Spaude akcinė "Ryto" bendrovė; ₍etc., etc.₎ 1931–
v. ports., tables, forms. 24cm.
1. Education—Lithuania. I. Title.
42-32683
Library of Congress L466.L5A32

NL 0408482 DLC

Lithuania. Švietimo ministerija.
Hauff, Wilhelm, 1802-1827.
V. Haufo Pasakos, su 57 paveikslais. Vertė J. Balčikonis. 2. leidimas. Švietimo ministerijos leidinys. Kaunas, Valstybės spaustuvė, 1925.

Lithuania. *Švietimo ministerija. Lietuvių tautosakos archyvas*
see
Lithuania. *Lietuvių tautosakos archyvas.*

Lithuania. *Švietimo ministerija. Tautosakos archyvas*
see
Lithuania. *Lietuvių tautosakos archyvas.*

Lithuania. *Švietimo ministerija. Valstybės teatras, Kaunas*
see
Kaunas. Valstybės teatras.

Lithuania. *Tarptautinio Intelektualinio Bendradarbiavimo Tautinė Komisija.*
Organisation of international intellectual assistance. Proposals submitted by the Lithuanian National Committee. ₍Geneva, 1923?₎
1 l. 33 cm.
At head of title: League of Nations. Committee on Intellectual Co-operation.
Official no.: C.I.C.I.83.
1. Intellectual cooperation—Societies. I. League of Nations. International Committee on Intellectual Co-operation.
A 50-590
Woodrow Wilson Memorial Library for Library of Congress ₍1₎

NL 0408487 NNUN-W

Lithuania.Tautinės olimpiados komitetas
see Lietuvos tautinė olimpijada, 1st, Kaunas, 1938.

Lithuania. *Technikos-chemijos laboratorija.*
... Valstybinės technikos chemijos laboratorijos darbai . ₍I– ₎ m., 1922–
Kaunas, 1923–
v. tables. 26cm.
At head of title, ₍I– ₎ m.: Finansu, prekybos ir pramonės ministerijos leidinys.
I. Lithuania. Finansų ministrija. II. Title.
34-19615
Library of Congress TP198.L6A2 660.61

NL 0408489 DLC

Lithuania. *Teisingumo ministerija. Vyriausiasis Tribunolas*
see
Lithuania. *Vyriausiasis Tribunolas.*

Lithuania. Treaties, etc.
Gronskiĭ, Pavel Pavlovich, 1883-
Instrumentum Lithuanicae deditionis anno 1655. Kaunas, 1923.

Lithuania. Treaties, etc.
Poland. *Sejm,* 1773-1775.
Konstytucye publiczne Seymu extraordynaryinego warszawskiego pod węzłem Generalney Konfederacyi oboyga narodów, trwaiącego roku 1773, dnia 19. kwietnia zaczętego, a z limity y sześciu prorogacyi w roku 1775 przy utwierdzeniu dzieł generalnych Konfederacyi y rozwiązaniu onychże skończonego; za zgodą zgromadzonych y skonfederowanych stanów uchwalone ... W Warszawie, Drukarnia J. K. Mci y Rzeczypospolitey u xx. scholarum piarum, 1775.

Lithuania. Treaties, etc.
Poland. *Sejm,* 1767-1768.
Konstytucye Seymu extraordynaryinego w Warszawie roku MDCCLXVII. Dnia piątego października złożonego y zaczętego, a z limitacyi y prorogacyi w roku MDCCLXVIII. Dnia piątego marca, przy rozwiązaniu Konfederacyi Generalnych Koronney y Wielkiego Xięstwa Litewskiego zakończonego, ex consensu ordinum totius Republicae ustanowione. W Warszawie, Drukarnia J. K. Mci y Rzeczypospolitey u xx. scholarum piarum ₍1768?₎

Lithuania. *Treaties, etc.*
Lietuvos sutartys su svetimomis valstybėmis. Užsienių reikalų ministerijos leidinys. Surinko ir sutvarkė Pranas Dailidė, Užs. reik. min-jos referentas ... Recueil des traités conclu par la Lithuanie avec les pays étrangers. Publié par le Ministère des affaires étrangères sous la direction de m. Pranas Dailidė, chef de division au Ministère des affaires étrangères ... Kaunas ₍"Spindulio" b-vės spaustuvė₎ 1930–
v. 29½cm.
1. Lithuania—For. rel. I. Lithuania. Užsienių reikalų ministerija. II. Title. III. Title: Recueil des traités conclu par la Lithuanie avec les pays étrangers.
41-33380
Library of Congress JX760.L52A3
₍2₎ 341.2475

NL 0408494 DLC DS IaU WaU NNC PU

Lithuania Treaties, etc. 1920-1926 (Stulginskis)
Gt. Brit. *Treaties, etc., 1910-* (*George v*)
... Agreement between the British and Lithuanian governments respecting commercial relations. Signed May 6, 1922 ... London, H. M. Stationery off., 1922.

VOLUME 336

Lithuania. Treaties, etc., 1920-1926 (Stulginskis)
U. S. *Treaties, etc., 1923-* (*Coolidge*)
... Agreement effected by exchange of notes between the United States and Lithuania. According mutual unconditional most-favored-nation treatment in customs matters. Signed December 23, 1925 .... Washington, Govt. print. off., 1926.

Lithuania. Treaties, etc., 1920-1926 (Stulginskis)
Allied powers (1919-) *Treaties, etc.*
... Convention between the British Empire, France, Italy, Japan and Lithuania respecting the Memel Territory and the Statute of the Memel Territory. Signed at Paris, May 8, 1924. ⟨British ratification deposited at Paris, August 25, 1925.⟩ ⟨In continuation of "Lithuania no. 1 (1924) Cmd. 2235."⟩ ... London, H. M. Stationery off., 1925.

Lithuania. Treaties, etc., 1920-1926 (Stulginskis)
Allied powers (1919-) *Treaties, etc.*
... Convention between the British Empire, France, Italy, Japan and Lithuania respecting the Memel Territory and the Statute of the Memel Territory. Signed at Paris, May 8, 1924. (Ratification has not yet been effected.) ... London, Printed & pub. by H. M. Stationery off., 1924.

Lithuania. Treaties, etc., 1920-1926 (Stulginskis)
Allied powers (1919-) *Treaties, etc.*
... Convention et Disposition transitoire relatives à Memel, signées à Paris, le 8 mai 1924 ... Convention and Transitory provision concerning Memel, signed at Paris, May 8th, 1924. [Geneva, 1924]

Lithuania. *Treaties, etc., 1920-1926 (Stulginskis)*
Différend polono-lithuanien. Genève, 1920.
[10] l. 33 cm.
At head of title: Société des Nations.
Official no.: 20/4/458.
Protocol of November 29, 1920, signed by the Lithuanian and Polish representatives on the League Commission of Control.
French and English.
Includes declaration by the Lithuanian representative urging the evacuation of Zeligovski's troops.

1. Vilna. 2. Zeligovski, Lucjan. I. Poland. Treaties, etc., 1919-1922 (Pilsudski) II. League of Nations.

A 48-6672*

Woodrow Wilson Memorial Library for Library of Congress [2]

NL 0408500 NNUN-W

Lithuania. Treaties, etc., 1920-1926 (Stulginskis)
Hague. Permanent court of international justice.
... Interprétation du Statut du territoire de Memel ... Interpretation of the Statute of the Memel territory. Leyde, A. W. Sijthoff [1932]

Lithuania. Treaties, etc. 1920- (Stulginskis
Hague. Permanent court of international justice.
... Interprétation du Statut du territoire de Memel (exception préliminaire) ... Interpretation of the Statute of the Memel territory (preliminary objection) Leyde, A. W. Sijthoff [1932]

Lithuania. Treaties, etc., 1920-1926 (Stulginskis)
Konvencija del Klaipedos krašto
see under Allied powers (1919-)
Treaties, etc.

Lithuania. Treaties, etc., 1920-1926 (Stuginskis) Lietuvos taikos sutartis su Rusija... [1920?]
(In Lithuanian and Russian)
DK511
L27A 1920

NL 0408504 CSt-H

Lithuania. Treaties, etc., 1920-1926 (Stulginskis)
... Non-aggression treaty between the Lithuanian Republic and the Union of Soviet Socialist Republics. [n.p., 1926]
3 p. 33 cm.
Typewritten carbon copy.
Caption title. At head of title: Translation.

NL 0408505 CSt-H

Lithuania. Treaties, etc., 1920-1926 (Stulginskis)
U. S. *Treaties, etc., 1923-* (*Coolidge*)
... Treaty between the United States and Lithuania. Extradition. Signed at Kaunas, April 9, 1924 ... Washington, Govt. print. off., 1924.

NL 0408506

Lithuania. Treaties, etc., 1926 (Grinius)
Gt. Brit. *Foreign office.*
... Notification extending to Canada as from the 18th September, 1928, the treaty between His Majesty and Lithuania for the extradition of fugitive criminals, signed at Kovno the 18th May, 1926. Ottawa. F. A. Acland, printer, 1929.

Lithuania. Treaties, etc., 1926- (Grinius)
Gt. Brit. *Treaties, etc., 1910-* (*George v*)
... Treaty between the United Kingdom and Lithuania for the extradition of fugitive criminals. Signed at Kaunas (Kovno), May 18, 1926. ⟨Ratifications exchanged at Kaunas (Kovno), March 29, 1927⟩ ... London, H. M. Stationery off., 1927.

Lithuania. Treaties, etc., 1926- (Smetona)
Gt. Brit. *Treaties, etc., 1910-* (*George v*)
... Agreement between His Majesty's government in the United kingdom and the Lithuanian government relating to trade and commerce, with protocol. London, July 6, 1934. ⟨The agreement has not been ratified by His Majesty's government in the United kingdom⟩ ... London, H. M. Stationery off., 1934.

Lithuania. Treaties, etc., 1926- (Smetona)
Gt. Brit. *Treaties, etc., 1910-* (*George v*)
... Agreement between His Majesty's government in the United kingdom and the Lithuanian government relating to trade and commerce, with protocol. London, July 6, 1934. ⟨Ratifications exchanged at London, August 2, 1934⟩ ... London, H. M. Stationery off., 1934.

Lithuania. Treaties, etc., 1926- (Smetona)
Gt. Brit. *Treaties, etc., 1910-* (*George v*)
... Convention between His Majesty in respect of the United kingdom and the president of Lithuania regarding legal proceedings in civil and commercial matters. Kovno, April 24, 1934. ⟨The convention has not been ratified by His Majesty⟩ ... London, H. M. Stationery off., 1934.

Lithuania. Treaties, etc., 1926- (Smetona)
Gt. Brit. *Treaties, etc., 1910-1936* (*George v*)
... Convention between His Majesty in respect of the United kingdom and the president of Lithuania regarding legal proceedings in civil and commercial matters. Kovno, April 24, 1934. ⟨Ratifications exchanged at London on May 7, 1936⟩ ... London, H. M. Stationery off., 1936.

Lithuania. Treaties, etc., 1926- (Smetona
FOR OTHER EDITIONS SEE MAIN ENTRY
Kazlauskas, Bronius.
... L'Entente baltique; préface de m. Robert Redslob ... Paris, Recueil Sirey, société anonyme, 1939.

Lithuania. Treaties, etc., 1926- (Smetona)
Gt. Brit. *Treaties, etc., 1910-* (*George v*)
... Exchange of notes between His Majesty's government in the United kingdom and the Lithuanian government respecting commercial relations between Tanganyika territory and Lithuania. Riga, December 14—Kovno, December 28, 1931 ... London, H. M. Stationery off., 1932.

Lithuania. Treaties, etc. 1926- (Smetona)
U. S. *Treaties, etc., 1933-* (*Franklin D. Roosevelt*)
... Extradition. Supplementary treaty between the United States of America and Lithuania. Signed at Washington, May 17, 1934 ... Washington, U. S. Govt. print. off., 1935.

Lithuania. Treaties, etc., 1926- (Smetona)
U. S. *Treaties, etc., 1933-* (*Franklin D. Roosevelt*)
... Liability for military service and other acts of allegiance of naturalized persons and persons born with double nationality. Treaty between the United States of America and Lithuania. Signed at Kaunas, October 18, 1937 ... Washington, U. S. Govt. print. off., 1938.

Lithuania. Treaties, etc., 1926- (Smetona)
U. S. *Treaties, etc., 1933-* (*Franklin D. Roosevelt*)
Parcel post agreement between the United States of America and Lithuania. Washington, U. S. Govt. print. off., 1940.

Lithuania. Treaties, etc., 1926- (Smetona)
FOR OTHER EDITIONS SEE MAIN ENTRY
U. S. *Treaties, etc., 1923-1929* (*Coolidge*)
... Treaty between the United States and Lithuania. Arbitration. Signed at Washington, November 14, 1928 ... Washington, U. S. Govt. print. off., 1930.

VOLUME 336

Lithuania. Treaties, etc., 1926–1940 (Smetona)

U. S. *Treaties, etc., 1923–1929 (Coolidge)*
... Treaty between the United States and Lithuania. Conciliation. Signed at Washington, November 14, 1928 .. Washington, U. S. Govt. print. off., 1930.

Lithuania. University of Kaunas
see Kaunas. Universitetas.

Lithuania. *Užsienių Reikalų Ministerija.*
Communication émanant du chargé d'affaires de Lithuanie à Londres au sujet du différend entre la Lithuanie et la Pologne. Correspondence from the Lithuanian Chargé d'Affaires in London regarding the dispute between Lithuania and Poland. [Londres, 1920]
[14] l. 33 cm.
At head of title: Société des Nations.
Official no.: Document du Conseil T2 (20/4/245)
Contains note addressed by the Lithuanian Government to the Polish Government on Sept. 6, and telegrams dated Sept. 1 and Sept. 7, 1920, concerning Polish-Lithuanian territorial dispute.
1. Lithuania—For. rel.—Poland. 2. Poland—For. rel.—Lithuania. I. League of Nations.
A 48-5215*
Woodrow Wilson Memorial Library for Library of Congress [1]

NL 0408520 NNUN-W

Lithuania. Užsienių reikalų ministerija.

League of nations. *Council.*
... Conflit lithuano-polonais; correspondance échangée entre le Conseil de la Société des nations et le gouvernement lithuanien, postérieure au rapport du Conseil du 20 septembre & à la résolution du 24 septembre 1921 de l'Assemblée de la Société des nations. 15 décembre 1921–8 avril [*i. e.* 18 mai] 1922. Kaunas, 1922.

Lithuania. *Užsienių reikalų ministerija.*
... Conflit lithuano-polonais. Correspondance échangée entre les gouvernements lithuanien et polonais du 27 janvier au 8 avril 1922. Kaunas, 1922.
1 p. l., 19 p. 27½cm.
At head of title: Ministère des affaires étrangères de Lithuanie.
1. European war, 1914–1918—Territorial questions—Lithuania. 2. European war, 1914–1918—Territorial questions—Poland. 3. Lithuania—For. rel.—Poland. 4. Poland—For. rel.—Lithuania. I. Poland (1918–) Ministerstwo spraw zagranicznych. II. Title.
28-11790 Revised
Library of Congress D651.L5A6 1922

NL 0408522 DLC

Lithuania. *Užsienių Reikalų Ministerija.*
Demande adressée à l'Assemblée par le Gouvernement lithuanien concernant: a) la résolution du Conseil en date du 13 janvier 1922; b) le renvoi de certaines questions à la Cour permanente de justice internationale en vue d'obtenir un avis consultatif. Genève, 1923.
[2] p. 33 cm.
Caption title.
At head of title: Société des Nations.
Official no.: A.7.1923.VII.
Concerns authority of the League of Nations to intervene in the Polish-Lithuanian dispute.
French and English.
1. Lithuania—For. rel.—Poland. 2. Poland—For. rel.—Lithuania. I. League of Nations.
A 49-4510*
Woodrow Wilson Memorial Library for Library of Congress [2]

NL 0408523 NNUN-W

Lithuania. *Užsienių Reikalų Ministerija.*
Demande d'admission de la Lithuanie dans la Société des Nations. Lettre en date du 12 octobre 1920. Request from Lithuania for admission to the League of Nations. Letter, dated 12th October 1920. [Londres? 1920]
[3] l. 33 cm.
At head of title: Société des Nations.
Official no.: Document de l'Assemblée 34 (20/48/34)
1. League of Nations—Lithuania. I. League of Nations.
A 49-4245*
Woodrow Wilson Memorial Library for Library of Congress [1]

NL 0408524 NNUN-W

Lithuania. *Užsienių Reikalų Ministerija.*
Le différend entre la Lithuanie et la Pologne. [Genève 1920]
[2] l. 33 cm.
League of Nations official no.: Document du Conseil Y.3 (20/4/379)
French and English.
Telegram from the Lithuanian Chargé d'Affaires in London, reporting attacks by Polish troops.
1. Lithuania—For. rel.—Poland. 2. Poland—For. rel.—Lithuania. I. League of Nations.
A 48-4655*
Woodrow Wilson Memorial Library for Library of Congress [1]

NL 0408525 NNUN-W

Lithuania. *Užsienių Reikalų Ministerija.*
Le différend entre la Lithuanie et la Pologne ... [Genève, 1920]
2, 2 l. (numb. in duplicate) 33 cm.
Caption title.
League of Nations official no.: Document du Conseil Z.3 (20/4/381)
French and English.
Telegram from the Lithuanian Chargé d'Affaires in London, reporting continued fighting.
1. Lithuania—For. rel.—Poland. 2. Poland—For. rel.—Lithuania. I. League of Nations.
A 48-4656*
Woodrow Wilson Memorial Library for Library of Congress [1]

NL 0408526 NNUN-W

Lithuania. *Užsienių Reikalų Ministerija.*
Différend entre la Lithuanie et la Pologne. Genève, 1921.
3, [3] l. 33 cm.
Caption title.
At head of title: Société des Nations.
Official no.: 21/68/30.
Reply by the Lithuanian Foreign Minister to note from the League of Nations (20/4/468) concerning the proposed plebiscite in the Vilna region.
French and English.
1. Plebiscite—Vilna. I. League of Nations.
A 48-7174*
Woodrow Wilson Memorial Library for Library of Congress [1]

NL 0408527 NNUN-W

Lithuania. *Užsienių Reikalų Ministerija.*
Le différend entre la Lithuanie et la Pologne: deux télégrammes, en date des 3 et 4 novembre 1920, émanant du chargé d'affaires de Lithuanie à Londres. Genève, 1920.
[5] l. 33 cm.
Caption title.
At head of title: Société des Nations.
Official no.: 20/31/83.
Text in French and English.
Appeal to the League of Nations to enforce Poland's adherence to Council decisions.
1. Lithuania—For. rel.—Poland. 2. Poland—For. rel.—Lithuania. I. League of Nations.
A 48-4945*
Woodrow Wilson Memorial Library for Library of Congress [1]

NL 0408528 NNUN-W

Lithuania. *Užsienių Reikalų Ministerija.*
Différend entre la Lithuanie et la Pologne; lettre, en date du 8 août 1922, transmettant pétition du Comité intérimaire lituanien de Vilna. Dispute between Lithuania and Poland; letter dated 8th August, 1922, transmitting petition from the Provisional Lithuanian Committee of Vilna. Genève, 1922.
4, 4 p. (numb. in duplicate) 33 cm.
At head of title: Société des Nations.
Offical no.: A.20.1922.VII.
1. Vilna. 2. Lithuanians in Poland. I. League of Nations.
A 49-3949*
Woodrow Wilson Memorial Library for Library of Congress [2]

NL 0408529 NNUN-W

Lithuania. *Užsienių Reikalų Ministerija.*
Différend entre la Lithuanie et la Pologne: lettre, en date du 13 septembre 1920, émanant du chargé d'affaires de Lithuanie à Londres. Dispute between Lithuania and Poland: letter, dated 13th September 1920 from the Lithuanian Chargé d'Affaires in London. [Londres, 1920]
[3] l. 33 cm.
At head of title: Société des Nations.
Official no.: 20/4/254.
Appointment of Professor Voldemar as Lithuanian representative at the forthcoming Council meeting to discuss the Polish-Lithuanian conflict.
1. Voldemaras, Augustinas, 1883– I. League of Nations.
A 48-4947*
Woodrow Wilson Memorial Library for Library of Congress [1]

NL 0408530 NNUN-W

Lithuania. *Užsienių Reikalų Ministerija.*
Le différend entre la Pologne et la Lithuanie: lettre en date du 11 octobre 1920, émanant du représentant de la Lithuanie à Paris. Londres, 1920.
3, 2 l. (numb. in duplicate) 33 cm.
Caption title.
At head of title: Société des Nations.
Official no.: 20/4/335.
French and English.
Reports the capture of Vilna by Polish irregulars.
1. Vilna. 2. Lithuania—For. rel.—Poland. 3. Poland—For. rel.—Lithuania. I. League of Nations.
A 48-6673*
Woodrow Wilson Memorial Library for Library of Congress [2]

NL 0408531 NNUN-W

Lithuania. *Užsienių Reikalų Ministerija.*
Le différend entre la Pologne et la Lithuanie: lettre en date du 2 novembre 1920, émanant du chargé d'affaires de Lithuanie à Londres. Genève, 1920.
[5] l. 33 cm.
Caption title.
At head of title: Société des Nations.
Official no.: 20/4/341.
Text in French and English.
Includes Lithuanian note addressed to the Polish Government concerning exchange of war prisoners, and telegram from Kowno reporting air bombardment of a church at Wilkomir.
1. Lithuania—For. rel.—Poland. 2. Poland—For. rel.—Lithuania. I. League of Nations.
A 48-4946*
Woodrow Wilson Memorial Library for Library of Congress [1]

NL 0408532 NNUN-W

Lithuania. *Užsienių Reikalų Ministerija.*
Le différend entre la Pologne & la Lithuanie: lettre en date du 18 novembre, émanant du représentant diplomatique de la Lithuanie auprès de la République française. Genève, 1920.
2 l. 33 cm.
Caption title.
At head of title: Société des nations.
Official no.: 20/4/372.
Concerns the composition of the army of General Zeligowski, and request for immediate application to Poland, of article 16 of the Covenant.
1. Zeligovski, Lucjan. 2. Lithuania—For. rel.—Poland. 3. Poland—For. rel.—Lithuania. 4. Vilna. I. League of Nations.
A 48-4698*
Woodrow Wilson Memorial Library for Library of Congress [2]

NL 0408533 NNUN-W

VOLUME 336

Lithuania. *Užsienių Reikalų Ministerije.*
Le différend entre la Pologne et la Lithuanie: télégramme en date du 20 octobre emanant du Chargé d'affaires de Lithuanie à Londres. Genève, 1920.

[2] l. 33 cm.

Caption title.
At head of title: Société des nations.
Official no.: M.20/4/64/1.
Text in French and English.
Concerns official Polish aid to Zeligowski's army.

1. Zeligovski, Lucjan. 2. Lithuania—For. rel.—Poland. 3. Poland—For. rel.—Lithuania. I. League of Nations.

A 48-4704*

Woodrow Wilson for Library of Congress — Memorial Library [2]

NL 0408534 NNUN-W

Lithuania. *Užsienių Reikalų Ministerija.*
Le différend entre la Pologne et la Lithuanie: télégramme en date du 22 octobre 1920, émanant du Chargé d'affaires de Lithuanie à Londres. Genève, 1920.

[1] l. 33 cm.

At head of title: Société des nations.
Official no.: M.20/4/78/1.
French and English.
Reports concentration of Polish troops in Vilna.

1. Vilna. 2. Lithuania—For. rel.—Poland. 3. Poland—For. rel.—Lithuania. I. League of Nations.

A 48-4677*

Woodrow Wilson for Library of Congress — Memorial Library [1]

NL 0408535 NNUN-W

Lithuania. *Užsienių Reikalų Ministerija.*
Différend entre la Lithuanie et la Pologne ... télégramme du chargé d'affaires de Lithuanie auprès du gouvernement de la République helvétique, au sujet d'une concentration de troupes polonaises contre la Lithuanie. Genève, 1921.

[2] l. 33 cm.
Caption title.
At head of title: Société des Nations.
Official no.: 21/68/49.
French and English.

1. Lithuania—For. rel.—Poland. 2. Poland—For. rel.—Lithuania. I. League of Nations.

A 48-6659*

Woodrow Wilson for Library of Congress — Memorial Library [1]

NL 0408536 NNUN-W

Lithuania. *Užsienių Reikalų Ministerija.*
The dispute between Lithuania and Poland. Geneva, 1922.

3 l. 33 cm.

Caption title.
At head of title: League of Nations.
Official no.: C.133.M.79.1922.VII.
Letter, dated Mar. 1, 1922, from the Lithuanian Minister of Foreign Affairs, replying to the League Council's recommendation for the establishment of diplomatic relations between Lithuania and Poland.

1. Lithuania—For. rel.—Poland. 2. Poland—For. rel.—Lithuania. I. League of Nations.

A 48-7729*

Woodrow Wilson for Library of Congress — Memorial Library [1]

NL 0408537 NNUN-W

Lithuania. *Užsienių Reikalų Ministerija.*
Dispute between Lithuania and Poland. Geneva, 1922.

4 l. 33 cm.

Caption title.
At head of title: League of Nations.
Official no.: C.488.1922.VII.
Letter, dated July 17, 1922, from the Lithuanian Delegation, replying to Poland's allegations of violation of the neutral zone by Lithuania.

1. Lithuania—For. rel.—Poland. 2. Poland—For. rel.—Lithuania. I. League of Nations.

A 48-7721*

Woodrow Wilson for Library of Congress — Memorial Library [1]

NL 0408538 NNUN-W

Lithuania. *Užsienių Reikalų Ministerija.*
Dispute between Lithuania and Poland. Geneva, 1922.

7 l. 33 cm.

Caption title.
At head of title: League of Nations.
Official no.: C.597.1922.VII.
Letter, dated Aug. 19, 1922, from the Lithuanian Minister of Foreign Affairs protesting against ill-treatment of the Lithuanian population in districts occupied by Poland and requesting that a League Commission be sent to investigate conditions.
Includes a Memorandum addressed to the Lithuanian Republic by delegates of the communes in the districts of Vilna and Grodno.

1. Lithuanians in Poland. I. League of Nations.

A 48-7717*

Woodrow Wilson for Library of Congress — Memorial Library [1]

NL 0408539 NNUN-W

Lithuania. Užsienių Reikalų Ministerija.
Dispute between Lithuania and Poland. Arrest of Lithuanians and White Russians at Vilna. [Letters ...
see under League of Nations. Delegation from Lithuania.

Lithuania. *Užsienių Reikalų Ministerija.*
The dispute between Poland and Lithuania: communication dated 7th October, 1920, from the Lithuanian Chargé d'Affaires in London. London, 1920.

[1] l. 33 cm.

At head of title: League of Nations.
Official no.: 20/4/294.
Issued also in French.
Offer to submit to League arbitration.

1. Lithuania—For. rel.—Poland. 2. Poland—For. rel.—Lithuania. I. League of Nations.

A 48-4923*

Woodrow Wilson for Library of Congress — Memorial Library [1]

NL 0408541 NNUN-W

Lithuania. *Užsienių Reikalų Ministerija.*
The dispute between Poland and Lithuania: communication dated 8th October 1920, received from the Lithuanian Chargé d'Affaires, London. London, 1920.

2 l. 33 cm.

Caption title.
At head of title: League of Nations.
Official no.: 20/4/296.
Issued also in French.
Protest against Polish military action in contravention of agreement sponsored by the League of Nations.

1. Lithuania—For. rel.—Poland. 2. Poland—For. rel.—Lithuania. I. League of Nations.

A 48-4941*

Woodrow Wilson for Library of Congress — Memorial Library [1]

NL 0408542 NNUN-W

Lithuania. *Užsienių Reikalų Ministerija.*
The dispute between Poland and Lithuania: communication dated 8th October, 1920, from the Lithuanian Chargé d'Affaires, London. London, 1920.

[1] l. 33 cm.

At head of title: League of Nations.
Official no.: 20/4/295.
Issued also in French.
Report on military action on the Polish-Lithuanian border.

1. Lithuania—For. rel.—Poland. 2. Poland—For. rel.—Lithuania. I. League of Nations.

A 48-4922*

Woodrow Wilson for Library of Congress — Memorial Library [1]

NL 0408543 NNUN-W

Lithuania. *Užsienių Reikalų Ministerija.*
The dispute between Poland and Lithuania: copy of Lithuanian note addressed to the Polish Government, dated Kowno October 12, in reply to the note of Prince Sapieha of 9th October, 1920. London, 1920.

2 l. 33 cm.
Caption title.
At head of title: League of Nations.
Official no.: 20/4/327.
Issued also in French.
Refers to Prince Sapieha's note included in League document 20/4/324.

1. Lithuania—For. rel.—Poland 2. Poland—For. rel.—Lithuania. I. League of Nations.

A 48-4654*

Woodrow Wilson for Library of Congress — Memorial Library [1]

NL 0408544 NNUN-W

Lithuania. *Užsienių Reikalų Ministerija.*
Dispute between Poland and Lithuania: letter, dated 24th September 1920, from the Lithuanian Chargé d'Affaires, London. London, 1920.

[1] l. 33 cm.

At head of title: League of Nations.
Official no.: 20/4/258.
Issued also in French.
Appeal for immediate intervention by the League to stop Polish aggression.

1. Poland—For. rel.—Lithuania. 2. Lithuania—For. rel.—Poland. I. League of Nations.

A 48-4924*

Woodrow Wilson for Library of Congress — Memorial Library [1]

NL 0408545 NNUN-W

Lithuania. *Užsienių Reikalų Ministerija.*
Dispute between Poland and Lithuania: letter, dated 24th September 1920, from the Lithuanian Chargé d'Affaires, London. London, 1920.

[2] l. 33 cm.

Caption title.
At head of title: League of Nations.
Official no.: 20/4/259.
Includes answer by the Polish Government to the Lithuanian proposal of Sept. 21, 1920 to submit the Polish-Lithuanian dispute to arbitration by the League of Nations.

1. Lithuania—For. rel.—Poland 2. Poland—For. rel.—Lithuania. I. League of Nations.

A 48-4653*

Woodrow Wilson for Library of Congress — Memorial Library [1]

NL 0408546 NNUN-W

Lithuania. *Užsienių Reikalų Ministerija.*
The dispute between Poland and Lithuania: letter dated 27th September 1920, from the Lithuanian Chargé d'Affaires, London. London, 1920.

[1] l. 33 cm.

At head of title: League of Nations.
Official no.: 20/4/269.
Issued also in French.
Request for immediate convocation of the League of Nations Council, in accordance with articles 11 and 17 of the Covenant, to consider the Polish invasion of Lithuania.

1. Lithuania—For. rel.—Poland. 2. Poland—For. rel.—Lithuania. I. League of Nations.

A 48-4940*

Woodrow Wilson for Library of Congress — Memorial Library [1]

NL 0408547 NNUN-W

Lithuania. *Užsienių Reikalų Ministerija.*
The dispute between Poland and Lithuania: letter, dated 29th September 1920, from the Lithuanian Chargé d'Affaires, London. London, 1920.

[4] l. 33 cm.

Caption title.
At head of title: League of Nations.
Official no.: 20/4/271.
Issued also in French.
Report on progress of negotiations.

1. Lithuania—For. rel.—Poland. 2. Poland—For. rel.—Lithuania. I. Poland. Ministerstwo Spraw Zagranicznych. II. League of Nations.

A 48-4688*

Woodrow Wilson for Library of Congress — Memorial Library [2]

NL 0408548 NNUN-W

Lithuania. *Užsienių Reikalų Ministerija.*
The dispute between Poland and Lithuania: letter dated 1st October, 1920, from the Lithuanian Chargé d'Affaires, London. London, 1920.

[3] l. 33 cm.
Caption title.
At head of title: League of Nations.
Official no.: 20/4/274.
Issued also in French.
Includes telegram from the Soviet Foreign Commissar, dated Sept. 28, 1920, regarding neutrality of Lithuanian territory.
1. Lithuania—Neutrality. 2. Lithuania—For. rel.—Poland. 3. Poland—For. rel.—Lithuania. I. Russia (1917– R. S. F. S. R.) Narodnyi komissariat po inostrannym delam. II. League of Nations.

A 48-4982*

Woodrow Wilson for Library of Congress — Memorial Library [2]

NL 0408549 NNUN-W

VOLUME 336

Lithuania. *Užsienių Reikalų Ministerija.*
Dispute between Poland and Lithuania: letter, dated 2nd October, 1920, from the Lithuanian Chargé d'Affaires, London. London, 1920.
[1] l. 33 cm.
At head of title: League of Nations.
Official no.: 20/4/277.
Issued also in French.
Reports unwillingness of Polish Government to cease hostilities.

1. Lithuania—For. rel.—Poland. 2. Poland—For. rel.—Lithuania. I. League of Nations.
A 48-4939*
Woodrow Wilson Memorial Library for Library of Congress [1]

NL 0408550 NNUN-W

Lithuania. *Užsienių Reikalų Ministerija.*
The dispute between Poland and Lithuania: letter dated 4th October 1920, from the Lithuanian Chargé d'Affaires, London. London, 1920.
[2] l. 33 cm.
Caption title.
At head of title: League of Nations.
Official no.: 20/4/283.
Issued also in French.
Includes two telegrams from Vilna reporting aggression by Polish troops.
1. Vilna. 2. Poland—For. rel.—Lithuania. 3. Lithuania—For. rel.—Poland. I. League of Nations.
A 48-4699*
Woodrow Wilson Memorial Library for Library of Congress [2]

NL 0408551 NNUN-W

Lithuania. *Užsienių Reikalų Ministerija.*
The dispute between Poland and Lithuania: letter dated 6th October 1920, from the Lithuanian Chargé d'Affaires, London. London, 1920.
[1] l. 33 cm.
At head of title: League of Nations.
Official no.: 20/4/288.
Issued also in French.
Concerns Polish refusal to evacuate Orany.

1. Poland—For. rel.—Lithuania. 2. Lithuania—For. rel.—Poland. . League of Nations.
A 48-4657*
Woodrow Wilson Memorial Library for Library of Congress [1]

NL 0408552 NNUN-W

Lithuania. *Užsienių Reikalų Ministerija.*
The dispute between Poland and Lithuania: letter dated 9th October 1920, from the Lithuanian Chargé d'Affaires, London. London, 1920.
[2] l. 33 cm.
Caption title.
At head of title: League of Nations.
Official no.: 20/4/300.
Issued also in French.
Includes copy of official telegrams received from Vilna reporting Polish military action near Vilna.
1. Vilna. 2. Lithuania—For. rel.—Poland. 3. Poland—For. rel.—Lithuania. I. League of Nations.
A 48-4915*
Woodrow Wilson Memorial Library for Library of Congress [2]

NL 0408553 NNUN-W

Lithuania. *Užsienių Reikalų Ministerija.*
The dispute between Poland and Lithuania: 1. Letter dated 11th October, 1920, from the Lithuanian Chargé d'Affaires, London. 2. Letter dated 12th October, 1920, addressed to the Lithuanian Chargé d'Affaires, London, by the Secretary-General. London, 1920.
[2] l. 33 cm.
Caption title.
At head of title: League of Nations.
Official no.: 20/4/319.
Issued also in French.
Protest against the occupation of Vilna by Polish forces.
1. Vilna. 2. Lithuania—For. rel.—Poland. 3. Poland—For. rel.—Lithuania. I. League of Nations. Secretary-General, 1919–1933 (Earl of Perth)
A 48-4697*
Woodrow Wilson Memorial Library for Library of Congress [2]

NL 0408554 NNUN-W

Lithuania. *Užsienių Reikalų Ministerija.*
The dispute between Poland and Lithuania: letter dated 13th October 1920, from the Lithuanian Chargé d'Affaires, London. London, 1920.
[1], 2 l. 33 cm.
At head of title: League of Nations.
Official no.: 20/4/324.
Issued also in French.
Contains copy of official telegram from Kowno, dated October 11, 1920, including Polish proposal to resume direct negotiations.

1. Lithuania—For. rel.—Poland. 2. Poland—For. rel.—Lithuania. I. League of Nations.
A 48-4938*
Woodrow Wilson Memorial Library for Library of Congress [1]

NL 0408555 NNUN-W

Lithuania. *Užsienių Reikalų Ministerija.*
The dispute between Poland and Lithuania: letter dated 15th October 1920 from the Lithuanian Chargé d'Affaires, London. London, 1920.
[3] l. 33 cm.
Caption title.
At head of title: League of Nations.
Official no.: 20/4/334.
Issued also in French.
Request of "de jure" recognition of Lithuania's independence by the League of Nations as the only way for peaceful settlement of the Vilna dispute.
1. Lithuania—Hist. 2. Vilna. 3. Lithuania—For. rel.—Poland. 4. Poland—For. rel.—Lithuania. I. League of Nations.
A 48-4694*
Woodrow Wilson Memorial Library for Library of Congress [2]

NL 0408556 NNUN-W

Lithuania. *Užsienių Reikalų Ministerija.*
Dispute between Lithuania and Poland ... letter from the Lithuanian Minister for Foreign Affairs, together with the Secretary-General's reply. Geneva, 1921.
[12] l. 33 cm.
Caption title.
At head of title: League of Nations.
Official no.: C.514.M.381.1921.VII.
Report of Poland's disregard for the provisional demarcation line agreed upon, and violation of minority rights of Lithuanians in Poland.
1. Lithuanians in Poland. 2. Lithuania—For. rel.—Poland. 3. Poland—For. rel.—Lithuania. I. League of Nations. Secretary-General, 1919–1933 (Earl of Perth)
A 48-6515*
Woodrow Wilson Memorial Library for Library of Congress [2]

NL 0408557 NNUN-W

Lithuania. *Užsienių Reikalų Ministerija.*
Dispute between Lithuania and Poland ... letter from the Minister for Foreign Affairs to the President of the Council of the League. Geneva, 1921.
[5] l. 33 cm.
Caption title.
At head of title: League of Nations.
Official no.: C.528.M.374.1921.VII.
Protest against the attempts made by the Polish Government to give legal stability to the situation brought about in Vilna by General Zeligowski's action.
1. Vilna. 2. Zeligovski, Lucjan. 3. Lithuania—For. rel.—Poland. 4. Poland—For. rel.—Lithuania. I. League of Nations.
A 48-6514*
Woodrow Wilson Memorial Library for Library of Congress [2]

NL 0408558 NNUN-W

Lithuania. *Užsienių Reikalų Ministerija.*
Dispute between Lithuania and Poland. The neutral zone. Geneva, 1922.
[1] l. 33 cm.
At head of title: League of Nations.
Official no.: C.582.1922.VII.
Letter, dated Aug. 12, 1922, from the Lithuanian Minister of Foreign Affairs, protesting against Polish violation of the neutral zone.

1. Lithuania—For. rel.—Poland. 2. Poland—For. rel.—Lithuania. I. League of Nations.
A 48-7720*
Woodrow Wilson Memorial Library for Library of Congress [1]

NL 0408559 NNUN-W

Lithuania. *Užsienių Reikalų Ministerija.*
Dispute between Lithuania and Poland. The neutral zone. Geneva, 1923.
2 l. 33 cm.
Caption title.
At head of title: League of Nations.
Official no.: C.161.M.85.1923.VII.
Telegram, dated Feb. 10, 1923, from the Lithuanian Minister of Foreign Affairs, refusing to accept the Council's resolution of Feb. 3, 1923 concerning the replacement of the neutral zone by a line of demarcation, and requesting that the matter be submitted to the Permanent Court of International Justice.
1. Lithuania—Bound.—Poland. 2. Poland—Bound.—Lithuania. I. League of Nations.
A 48-7715*
Woodrow Wilson Memorial Library for Library of Congress [1]

NL 0408560 NNUN-W

Lithuania. *Užsienių Reikalų Ministerija.*
Dispute between Lithuania and Poland. Proposed substitution of provisional line of demarcation for neutral forces. Letter from the Lithuanian Minister for Foreign Affairs. Geneva, 1922.
3 l. 33 cm.
Caption title.
At head of title: League of Nations.
Official no.: C.219.1922.VII.
Concerns Lithuania's reasons for not assenting to neutral zones established by the League's Military Control Commission.
1. Lithuania—For. rel.—Poland. 2. Poland—For. rel.—Lithuania. 3. League of Nations. Military Control Commission on the Polish-Lithuanian Dispute. I. League of Nations.
A 48-7805*
Woodrow Wilson Memorial Library for Library of Congress [2]

NL 0408561 NNUN-W

Lithuania. *Užsienių Reikalų Ministerija.*
Dispute between Lithuania and Poland. Polish prisoners at Kovno. Geneva, 1923.
[2] l. 33 cm.
At head of title: League of Nations.
Official no.: C.35.M.16.1923.VII.
Letter, dated Jan. 12, 1923, from the Lithuanian Minister of Foreign Affairs concerning the pardons granted to the Polish political prisoners.

1. Poles in Lithuania. I. League of Nations.
A 48-7777*
Woodrow Wilson Memorial Library for Library of Congress [1]

NL 0408562 NNUN-W

Lithuania. *Užsienių Reikalų Ministerija.*
Dispute between Lithuania and Poland. Provisional line of demarcation in the neutral zone. Geneva, 1923.
[1] l. 33 cm.
At head of title: League of Nations.
Official no.: C.165.M.89.1923.VII.
Telegram, dated Feb. 18, 1923, from the Lithuanian Foreign Minister, protesting against Polish occupation of the neutral zone.

1. Lithuania—For. rel.—Poland. 2. Poland—For. rel.—Lithuania. I. League of Nations.
A 48-7780*
Woodrow Wilson Memorial Library for Library of Congress [1]

NL 0408563 NNUN-W

Lithuania. *Užsienių Reikalų Ministerija.*
Dispute between Lithuania and Poland. Provisional line of demarcation in the neutral zone. Geneva, 1923.
[1] l. 33 cm.
At head of title: League of Nations.
Official no.: C.175.M.99.1922 [i. e. 1923] VII.
Telegram, dated Feb. 23, 1923, from the Lithuanian Minister of Foreign Affairs, protesting against the Polish advance beyond the line of demarcation.

1. Lithuania—For. rel.—Poland. 2. Poland—For. rel.—Lithuania. I. League of Nations.
A 48-7714*
Woodrow Wilson Memorial Library for Library of Congress [1]

NL 0408564 NNUN-W

VOLUME 336

Lithuania. *Užsienių Reikalų Ministerija.*
Dispute between Lithuania and Poland. Publication of documents. Letter from the Lithuanian Chargé d'Affaires in Berne. Geneva, 1922.
3 l. 33 cm.
Caption title.
At head of title: League of Nations.
Official no.: C.112.M.66.1922.VII.
Letter, dated Feb. 4, 1922, replying to Poland's protest (C.79.M.28.1922.VII) against the publication of the Lithuanian Prime Minister's speech on the elections of Vilna.
1. Elections—Vilna.
A 48-7861*
Woodrow Wilson Memorial Library for Library of Congress [1]

NL 0408565 NNUN-W

Lithuania. *Užsienių Reikalų Ministerija.*
Dispute between Lithuania and Poland ... Reply of the Lithuanian Government to the proposal of the Council, dated September 20th ... Geneva, 1921.
[3] l. 33 cm.
Caption title.
At head of title: League of Nations.
Official no.: C.544.M.389.1921.VII.
Rejection of the draft agreement proposed at the Brussels conference.
1. Lithuania—For. rel.—Poland. 2. Poland—For. rel.—Lithuania. I. League of Nations.
A 48-6768*
Woodrow Wilson Memorial Library for Library of Congress [1]

NL 0408566 NNUN-W

Lithuania. *Užsienių Reikalų Ministerija.*
Dispute between Lithuania and Poland. Situation in the neutral zone. Geneva, 1923.
[1] l. 33 cm.
At head of title: League of Nations.
Official no.: C.34.1923.VII.
Letter, dated Jan. 12, 1923, from the Lithuanian Minister of Foreign Affairs, protesting against the Polish violation of the neutral zone on Dec. 3, 1922.
Issued also in French.
1. Lithuania—For. rel.—Poland. 2. Poland—For. rel.—Lithuania. I. League of Nations.
A 48-7713*
Woodrow Wilson Memorial Library for Library of Congress [1]

NL 0408567 NNUN-W

Lithuania. *Užsienių Reikalų Ministerija.*
Dispute between Lithuania and Poland: treatment of Lithuanians in Vilna. Geneva, 1921.
[4] l. 33 cm.
Caption title.
At head of title: League of Nations.
Official no.: C.435.M.314.1921.VII.
Issued also in French.
Letter from the Lithuanian Minister for Foreign Affairs requesting the League of Nations to protect the Lithuanian element in the Vilna region under Polish occupation.
1. Lithuanians in Vilna. 2. Lithuania—For. rel.—Poland. 3. Poland—For. rel.—Lithuania. I. League of Nations.
A 48-6516*
Woodrow Wilson Memorial Library for Library of Congress [2]

NL 0408568 NNUN-W

Lithuania. *Užsienių Reikalų Ministerija.*
Dispute between Lithuania and Poland in the territory of Vilna. Geneva, 1922.
4 l. 33 cm.
Caption title.
At head of title: League of Nations.
Official no.: C.727.M.431.1922.VII.
Letter, dated Oct. 23, 1922, from the Lithuanian Minister of Foreign Affairs referring to Polish ill-treatment of minorities.
Includes petition addressed to the President of Lithuania by the delegates of the districts of Vilna and Grodno.
1. Lithuanians in Poland. 2. White Russians in Poland. I. League of Nations.
A 48-7733*
Woodrow Wilson Memorial Library for Library of Congress [1]

NL 0408569 NNUN-W

Lithuania. *Užsienių reikalų ministerija.*
Documents diplomatiques. Conflit polono-lithuanien; question de Vilna, 1918–1924. Kaunas, 1924.
xx, 440 p. maps (part fold. col.) 32 cm.
1. Lithuania—For. rel.—Poland. 2. Poland—For. rel.—Lithuania. 3. Vilna—Hist. I. Title. II. Title: Conflit polono-lithuanien.
DK418.5.L5A52 54-52645

NL 0408570 DLC PU MU IaU

Lithuania. *Užsieniu reikalų ministerija.*
Documents diplomatiques. Conflit polono-lithuanien. Question de Vilna 1918–1924. République de Lithuanie. Ministère des affaires étrangères. Kaunas, 1924.
xx p., 1 l., 440 p., 1 l. 3 fold. maps. 32cm.
1. Vilna. 2. European war, 1914–1918—Territorial questions—Lithuania. 3. Lithuania—For. rel.—Poland. 4. Poland—For. rel.—Lithuania. I. Title. II. Title: Conflit polono-lithuanien.
25-14899
Library of Congress DK511.L27A5 1924

NL 0408571 DLC PSt NN WaU

Lithuania. *Užsienių reikalų ministerija.*
... Documents diplomatiques. Question de Memel ... Kaunas, 1923–24.
2 v. 32cm.
At head of title, v. 1: République de Lithuanie. Ministère des affaires étrangères.
CONTENTS.—v. 1. Depuis la Conférence de la paix (1919) jusqu'au renvoi de la question par la Conférence des ambassadeurs devant le Conseil de la Société des nations (29 septembre 1923) 1923.—v. 2. Règlement de la question de Memel par le Conseil de la Société des nations. 1924.
1. Memel (Territory) 2. European war, 1914–1918—Territorial questions—Lithuania. I. Paris. Peace conference, 1919. II. Allied powers (1919–) Council of ambassadors. III. Title. IV. Title: Question de Memel.
25-14900
Library of Congress DK511.L273A5 1924

NL 0408572 DLC CSt-H PU

Lithuania. *Užsienių Reikalų Ministerija.*
Enlargement of the Council. Letter from the Lithuanian Government. Geneva, 1926.
3 l. 33 cm.
Caption title.
At head of title: League of Nations.
Official no.: C.182.1926.
Disputes Poland's right to admission to the Council.
1. League of Nations. Council. 2. League of Nations—Poland. I. League of Nations.
A 48-2051*
Woodrow Wilson Memorial Library for Library of Congress [1]

NL 0408573 NNUN-W

Lithuania. *Užsienių Reikalų Ministerija.*
Financial arrangements for the settlement of the Polish-Lithuanian dispute. Correspondence between the Lithuanian Minister for Foreign Affairs and the Secretary-General of the League of Nations. Geneva, 1923.
6 l. 33 cm.
Caption title.
At head of title: League of Nations.
Official no.: C.188.M.111.1923.X.
Issued also in French.
Allocation of expenses for the Military Commission appointed for the Polish-Lithuanian dispute.
1. League of Nations—Finance. 2. League of Nations. Military Control Commission on the Polish-Lithuanian Dispute. I. League of Nations. Secretary- General, 1919–1933 (Earl of Perth)
A 48-5494*
Woodrow Wilson Memorial Library for Library of Congress [1]

NL 0408574 NNUN-W

Lithuania. *Užsienių Reikalų Ministerija.*
Incident de frontière polono-lithuanien [!] Polish-Lithuanian frontier incident. Geneva, 1925.
[1] l. 33 cm.
At head of title: Société des Nations.
Official no.: C.212.M.71.1925.VII.
Telegram, dated Mar. 19, 1925, from the Lithuanian Minister of Foreign Affairs thanking the League of Nations for its intervention in the border incident (official no.: C.207.M.66.1925.VII)
Issued also in French.
1. Lithuania—For. rel.—Poland. 2. Poland—For. rel.—Lithuania. I. League of Nations.
A 48-7750*
Woodrow Wilson Memorial Library for Library of Congress [1]

NL 0408575 NNUN-W

Lithuania. Užsienių reikalų ministerija.
Klaipėdos krašto statuto aiškinimo byla Hagos tribunole ... Kaunas ["Šviesos" spaustuvė] 1932.
286, [3] p. 30½cm.
"Užsienių reikalų ministerijos leidinys."

NL 0408576 MiU-L

Q947.52 L715.5
LITHUANIA. Užsienių reikalų ministerija.
Lietuvių lenkų byla dėl tranzito Nemuno upynu ir Kaišiadorių-Lentvaravo geležinkelio ruožu. Nuo Tautų sąjungos Tarybos 1927 m.gruodžio 10d. rezoliucijos iki Hagos tarptautinio tribunolo patariamosios nuomonės pareiškimo. Kaunas, 1931.
2v. fold.maps. 32cm.

NL 0408577 PU

Lithuania. Užsienių reikalų ministerija.

Lithuania. *Treaties, etc.*
Lietuvos sutartys su svetimomis valstybėmis. Užsienių reikalų ministerijos leidinys. Surinko ir sutvarkė Pranas Dailidė, Užs. reik. min-jos referentas ... Recueil des traités conclu par la Lithuanie avec les pays étrangers. Publié par le Ministère des affaires étrangères sous la direction de m. Pranas Dailidė, chef de division au Ministère des affaires étrangères ... Kaunas ["Spindulio" b-vės spaustuvė] 1930–

947.52 L715
LITHUANIA. Užsienių reikalų ministerija.
Lietuvos valstybės kūrimasis ligi vyriausybei susidarius, nuo 1915 ligi 1918 m.lapkričio mėn. 11 d. Vilnius, Lietuvos valstybės Užsienių reikalų ministerija,1918.
xxxiiip. 23cm.

NL 0408579 PU

JX1808 .6 .A23
Lithuania. Užsienių riekalų ministerija.
... Liste du corps diplomatique accredité à Kaunas avec annexe contenant la liste des consuls généraux, consuls et vice-consuls en Lithuanie sept. 1924. [Kaunas, 1924]
1 v. 24 cm.
At head of title, 1924- : Ministère des affaires étrangères.

NL 0408580 DLC

Lithuania. *Užsienių reikalų ministerija.*
Lithuanie et Pologne. Notes des gouvernements lithuanien et polonais relatives au conflit lithuano-polonais. Kaunas, Valstybės spaustuvė, 1927.
26, [2] p. 31½cm.
1. European war, 1914–1918—Territorial questions—Lithuania. 2. European war, 1914–1918—Territorial questions—Poland. 3. Lithuania—For. rel.—Poland. 4. Poland—For. rel.—Lithuania. I. Poland (1918–) Ministerstwo spraw zagranicznych. II. Title.
29-21717
Library of Congress D651.L5A6 1927

NL 0408581 DLC WaU

VOLUME 336

Lithuania. *Užsienių reikalų ministerija.*
... Minorities in Lithuania. Letter from the Lithuanian minister for foreign affairs, dated July 28th, 1923. Geneva, 1923.
2 l. 33cm.
Caption title.
At head of title: League of nations.
Official no.: C.516.1923.I.
Mimeographed.
"Communicated to the members of the Council."
1. Minorities—Lithuania. I. League of nations.
A 46-6065
Woodrow Wilson memorial library for Library of Congress [2]
NL 0408582 NNUN-W

Lithuania. Užsieniu reikalu Ministerija.
Gt. Brit. *Foreign office.*
... Notification extending to Canada as from the 18th September, 1928, the treaty between His Majesty and Lithuania for the extradition of fugitive criminals, signed at Kovno the 18th May, 1926. Ottawa, F. A. Acland, printer, 1929.

Lithuania. *Užsienių Reikalų Ministerija.*
Polish-Lithuanian dispute. Geneva, 1922.
[1] l. 33 cm.
At head of title: League of Nations.
Official no.: C.198.M.107.1922.VII.
Telegram from the Lithuanian Minister of Foreign Affairs, protesting against the annexation of Vilna, voted by the Diet of Warsaw on Mar. 24, 1922.
1. Vilna. 2. Lithuania—For. rel.—Poland. 3. Poland—For. rel.—Lithuania. I. League of Nations.
A 48-7722*
Woodrow Wilson Memorial Library for Library of Congress [1]
NL 0408584 NNUN-W

Lithuania. *Užsienių Reikalų Ministerija.*
Polish-Lithuanian dispute. Polish prisoners detained in Lithuania. Geneva, 1922.
3 l. 33 cm.
Caption title.
At head of title: League of Nations.
Official no.: C.192.M.106.1922.VII.
Letter, dated Mar. 20, 1922, from the Lithuanian Minister of Foreign Affairs concerning health conditions of the Polish political prisoners at Kowno.
1. Poles in Lithuania. 2. Prisons—Lithuania.
A 48-7730*
Woodrow Wilson Memorial Library for Library of Congress [1]
NL 0408585 NNUN-W

Lithuania. *Užsienių Reikalų Ministerija.*
Polish-Lithuanian incident. Geneva, 1925.
[1] l. 33 cm.
At head of title: League of Nations.
Official no.: C.207.M.66.1925.VII.
Telegram dated Mar. 17, 1925, from the Lithuanian Minister of Foreign Affairs, protesting against a Polish incursion beyond the line of demarcation and requesting the League's intervention.
Issued also in French.
1. Lithuania—For. rel.—Poland. 2. Poland—For. rel.—Lithuania. I. League of Nations.
A 48-7728*
Woodrow Wilson Memorial Library for Library of Congress [1]
NL 0408586 NNUN-W

Lithuania. Užsieniu reikalu ministerija.
... The question of Memel. Diplomatic and other documents from the Versailles Peace Conference ...
see under Lithuanian Information Bureau, London.

Lithuania. Užseinių reikalų ministerija.
Situation économique & financière de la Lithuanie au début de l'année 1922. Publié par le Ministère des affaires étrangères. Kaunas[, 1922?]. 63 p. incl. tables. sq. 4°.
Cover-title.
1. Economic history—Lithuania. 2. Finance—Lithuania.
N. Y. P. L. September 6, 1927
NL 0408588 NN CtY InU MH DLC

Lithuania. *Užsienių Reikalų Ministerija.*
Territory of Memel. Geneva, 1924.
4 l. 33 cm.
Caption title.
At head of title: League of Nations.
Official no.: C.108.M.31.1924.VII.
Letter from the Lithuanian Foreign Minister dated Feb. 29, 1924.
Reprinted in League of Nations. The status of the Memel territory, 1924, p. 73-74 (official no.: C.159.M.39.1924.VII)
1. Memel (Territory) I. League of Nations.
A 48-5570*
Woodrow Wilson Memorial Library for Library of Congress [1]
NL 0408589 NNUN-W

Lithuania. *Užsienių Reikalų Ministerija.*
Le typhus en Lithuanie: lettre en date du 10 mai 1921, émanant de M. Sidzikauskas, chargé d'affaires de la Lithuanie à Berne. Typhus in Lithuania: letter dated May 10th, 1921, from M. Sidzikauskas, Lithuanian Chargé d'Affaires at Berne. Genève, 1921.
5, [2]-5 p. (numb. in duplicate) 33 cm.
At head of title: Société des Nations.
Official no.: C.56.M.27.1921.IV.
Includes appeals by the Lithuanian Health Department and the Governing Body of the Lithuanian Red Cross.
1. Typhus fever—Lithuania. I. League of Nations.
A 49-6674*
Woodrow Wilson Memorial Library for Library of Congress [1]
NL 0408590 NNUN-W

JX1808 .6 .A25
Lithuania. *Užsienių reikalų ministerija.*
Žinynas.
[Kaune]
v. 19 cm.
1. Lithuania—Diplomatic and consular service.
JX1808.6.A25 56-54991
NL 0408591 DLC PU

HJ55 .5 .B16
Lithuania. Valstybės kontrolė.
Valstybės kontrolės ... 1928 m.- valstybės biudžeto vykdymo apyskaita. [Kaunas?] 1929-
1 v. tables (part. fold.) 31 cm.
NL 0408592 DLC

Lithuania. Valstybės Taryba.
DK511 .L27K6
Kovo 20 [i. e. dvidešimtoji] diena; Mažosios Lietuvos prisiglaudimui paminėti. [Kaunas, Išleista Lietuvos Valstybės Tarybos lėšomis, 1921.

Lithuania. *Valstybės taryba.*
Valstybės tarybos nuomonės teisės klausimais, 1929-1937. Kaunas, Lietuvos teisininkų draugija, 1937.
x, 190 p. 24 cm.
Preface signed: J. Byla.
1. Advisory opinions—Lithuania. I. Byla, Jurgis, 1890- ed. II. Title.
55-53605
Library of Congress [1]
NL 0408594 DLC

Lithuania. Verwaltung der lithauischen eisenbahnen
see Lithuania. Geležinkelių valdyba.

Lithuania. Vidaus reikalų ministerija.
Siemaška, D.
... Gaisrų gesinimo taktika ... Kaunas, Valstybės spaustuvė, 1926.

Lithuania. *Vidaus reikalų ministerija.*
... Medžioklės įstatymui vykdyti instrukcija. Kaunas [K. Narkevičiaus ir V. Atkočiūno sp.] 1925.
cover-title, 8 p. 15½cm.
At head of title: Priedelis prie "Policijos" nr. 9 (13)
Signed: A. Endziulaitis, Vidaus reikalų ministeris.
1. Game-laws—Lithuania. I. Title.
Library of Congress SK543.L5A5 1925 36-36342
[2] 799.09475
NL 0408597 DLC

Lithuania. *Vidaus reikalų ministerija.*
Vidaus reikalų ministerijos pasienio policijos instrukcijos. Kaunas [Valstybės spaustuvė] 1924.
32 p. 15cm.
1. Police—Lithuania. 2. Customs administration—Lithuania. 3. Smuggling. I. Title: Pasienio policijos instrukcijos.
36-30790
Library of Congress HV7762.6.A5 1924
[2] 351.7409475
NL 0408598 DLC

Lithuania. *Vidaus reikalų ministerija. Administracijos departamentas.*
Vidaus reikalų ministerijos Administracijos departamento aplinkraščiai 1938- ... Kaunas, 1938-
v. forms. 24cm.
"Vidaus reikalų ministerijos leidinys."
1938- includes the following supplements: A. Vyriausiojo tribunolo nutarimai.—B. Valstybės tarybos nuomonės.—C. Apskričių viršininkų išleisti priv. įsakymai.
1. Lithuania—Pol. & govt. 2. Administrative law—Lithuania.
41-22985
Library of Congress J400.L5B3
NL 0408599 DLC

Lithuania. *Vidaus reikalų ministerija. Piliečių apsaugos departamentas*
see
Lithuania. *Piliečių apsaugos departamentas.*

VOLUME 336

Lithuania. *Vidaus reikalų ministerija. Sveikatos departamentas*
see **Lithuania.** *Sveikatos departamentas.*

Law

Lithuania. *Vyriausiasis Tribunolas.*
Civilinių kasacinių bylų sprendimų rinkinys.

Kaunas.

v. 32 cm. annual.

Editors: 19 Z. Toliušis and V. Požela.

1. Law reports, digests, etc.—Lithuania. I. Toliušis, Zigmas, ed. II. Požela, Vladas, ed. III. Title.

58-50435

NL 0408602 DLC

Lithuania. *Vyriausiasis Tribunolas.*
Vyriausiojo Tribunolo 1924–1927 metų baudžiamųjų kasacinių bylų sprendimų rinkinys. Redagavo J. Byla. Kaunas, D. Gutmano leidinys, 1932.

894 p. 23 cm.

"Neoficialinis leidimas."

1. Criminal law—Lithuania—Cases. 2. Criminal procedure—Lithuania—Cases. I. Byla, Jurgis, 1890– ed. II. Title: Baudžiamųjų kasacinių bylų sprendimų rinkinys.

57-56332

NL 0408603 DLC

Lithuania. *Vyriausiasis Tribunolas.*
Vyriausiojo Tribunolo praktika Civilinių įstatymų (x t. 1 d.) reikalu. Kaunas, D. Gutmano leidinys, 1934.

303 p. 18 cm.

Editor's name, L. Veržbavičius, at head of title.

1. Civil law—Lithuania—Cases—Digests. I. Veržbavičius, Levas, ed. II. Title.

57-55800

NL 0408604 DLC

Lithuania. Wa'ad ha-kehilloth ha-roshiyoth
see
Council of main districts of Lithuania.

Lithuania. War Dept.
see Lithuania. Krašto apsaugos ministerija.

Lithuania. *Wojsko litewskie*
see **Lithuania.** *Kariuomenė.*

Lithuania. Žemės ūkio departamentas.

Strazdas, J.
... Daržovių auginimas, su 197 paveikslais. Kaunas, "Varpo" b-vės spaustuvė, 1925.

Lithuania. *Žemės ūkio departamentas.*
Lietuvos žemės ūkis ir žemės reforma ... Kaunas [Valstybės spaustuvė] 1922.

57, [2] p. tables (1 fold.) 15 cm.

1. Land tenure—Lithuania. 2. Agricultural laws and legislation—Lithuania. I. Title.

HD725.7.A4 1922 39-9548

NL 0408609 DLC

Lithuania. Žemės ūkio ir valstybės turtų ministerija. Žemės ūkio departamentas
see **Lithuania. Žemės ūkio departamentas.**

Lithuania. *Žemės ūkio ministerija.*
Metraštis, 1918–1924 M. M. Kaunas, Valstybės spaustuvė, 1927.

615 p. illus. 26 cm.

1. Agriculture—Lithuania. 2. Lithuania—Public lands.

S242.L35A5 1924 54-50779 ‡

NL 0408611 DLC NN

LITHUANIA. Žemės ūkio ministerija.
Metraštis. 1918/24-
Kaunas, Valstybės spaustuvė. v. illus., maps.

Film reproduction. Master negative.
Positive in *ZAN-1785.

NL 0408612 NN

Lithuania. *Žemės ūkio ministerija.*
Metraštis, 1918–1938. [Kaunas? 1938]

411 p. illus. 28 cm.

1. Agriculture—Lithuania. 2. Lithuania—Public lands.

S242.L35A5 1938 54-48805 ‡

NL 0408613 DLC DNAL

Lithuania. Žemės ūkio departamentas.

Končius, Ignas, 1886–
... Palangos kraštas. Palangos kraštui pažinti medžiaga. Su paveikslais, diagramomis, žemėlapiais, profiliais. Kaunas, Valstybės spaustuvė, 1925.

Lithuania. Žemės ūkio departamentas.

Reisonas, K.
... Žemės ūkio statyba. Lieutuvos tautiniai motyvai paruošti prof. arch. V. Dubeneckio ir dail. P. Galaunės. Kaunas ["Svyturio" bendrovės spaustuvė] 1926.

Lithuania. *Žemės ūkio departamentas.*
Žemesniosios žemės ūkio mokyklos; taisyklės, programos ir kit. Kaunas, "Spindulio" bendrovės spaustuvė, 1929.

56 p. illus. 24 cm.

1. Agricultural education—Lithuania. I. Title.

S535.L5A57 59-58287

NL 0408616 DLC

Lithuania. *Žemės ūkio ministerija. Miškų departamentas*
see
Lithuania. *Miškų departamentas.*

Lithuania. Žemės ūkio ministerija. Žemės ūkio departamentas
see Lithuania. Žemės ūkio departamentas.

Lithuania. *Žydų reikalams ministerija*
see
Lithuania. *Ministerija žydų reikalams.*

Lithuania (Territory under German occupation, 1915-1918) Laws, statutes, etc.
Verordnungsblatt der deutschen Verwaltung für Litauen. Paliepimų laiškas vokiečiu valdžios Lietuvoje. no. 1–9, [N. F.] no. 1–15; 26. Oktober, 1915–30. Juni, 1916. Tilsit [etc.] Verlag der deutschen Verwaltung für Litauen, 1915–16. 24 nos. in 1 v. 30½ cm.

Irregular.
Caption-title.
German and Lithuanian in parallel columns.
Jan. 28 – June 30, 1916 published at Kowno.

837417A. 1. European war, 1914–1918 —Law and legislation—Lithuania. I. Germany. Statutes.
N. Y. P. L. November 19, 1936

NL 0408620 NN MiU-L

Lithuania (*Territory under German occupation, 1941–1945*) *Generalkommissar in Kauen.*
Amtsblatt. Jahrg. 1– 1. Sept. 1941–
Kauen, Kauener Zeitung.

v. in col. illus. 31 cm.

Text in German and Lithuanian.

I. Lithuania (Territory under German occupation, 1941–1945) Laws, statutes, etc.

61-57579

NL 0408621 DLC NcD NN CU NNC MiU-L

Law

Lithuania (Territory under German occupation, 1941–1945) Laws, statutes, etc.

Lithuania (*Territory under German occupation, 1941–1945*) *Generalkommissar in Kauen.*
Amtsblatt. Jahrg. 1– 1. Sept. 1941–
Kauen, Kauener Zeitung.

VOLUME 336

Law

Lithuania (Territory under German occupation, 1941-1945) Laws, statutes, etc.

Meyer, Alfred, *ed.*
Das recht der besetzten Ostgebiete: Estland, Lettland, Litauen Weissruthenien und Ukraine; sammlung der verordnungen, erlasse und sonstigen vorschriften über verwaltung, rechtspflege, wirtschaft, finanzwesen und verkehr mit erläuterungen der referenten, herausgegeben von dr. Alfred Meyer ... unter mitarbeit von dr. Walter Wilhelmi ... dr. Walter Labs ... [und] dr. Hans Schäfer ... München und Berlin, C. H. Beck, 1943-

---

Lithuania. [Kaunas? Lithuanian Tourist Association, 1937?]
32 p. illus., map. 19 cm.
Cover title.

1. Lithuania.

DK511.L2L47 73-242436

NL 0408624 DLC

947.5 L715

LITHUANIA and its day of independence on the 16th February 1918-1946. Hanau, Lithuanian committee, 1946.
44p. illus., ports., maps, diagrs. 21cm.

Contents. -The past way of Lithuania. -Who are we? -Our camp life.
With this is bound Pašilaitis, Juozas, pseud. Hearken the judge. Tübingen, 1949?.

NL 0408625 PU

Lithuania, country and nation. [Edited by A. Stanys] Augsburg [Community of the Lithuanian DPs] 1946.
62 p. illus., map. 21 cm.

1. Lithuania. I. Stanys, A., ed.

DK511.L2L48 55-42698

NL 0408626 DLC CtY

Lithuania; guiding facts for tourists
see under Lietuvos automobilių klubas.

The Lithuanian, Memmingen
see Lietuvis, Memmingen.

Lithuanian agency "Elta" service
see Lithuanian telegraph agency ("Elta") service, Kaunas.

HS2008 .L53A5

Lithuanian Alliance of America.
Kas yra Susivienijimas lietuvių Amerikoje. New York [n. d.]
47 p. 18 cm.
By M. J. Vinikas, Secretary of the Lithuanian Alliance of America.

I. Vinikas, Matas J.

HS2008.L53A5 60-18077

NL 0408630 DLC

Lithuanian Alliance of America.
Susivienijimo lietuvių Amerikoje auksinio jubiliejaus albumas. Išleidimu rūpinosi SLA Jubiliejaus komisija. Redagavo ir tekstus parašė S. E. Vitaitis. Vinietes nupiešė ir medžiagą surinko A. B. Strimaitis. New York, 1936.
303 p. illus., ports. 24 x 31 cm.

1. Lithuanians in the U. S. I. Vitaitis, Stasys E., ed. II. Title.

HS2008.L53A52 53-50141 rev

NL 0408631 DLC NIC

Lithuanian Alliance of America
see also
Lithuanian Roman Catholic Alliance of America.

---

768 8402.9

Lithuanian American Catholic congress, New York, 1946
For a just peace. Policy declarations and resolutions ... New York [1946]
24 p. 22½cm.

NL 0408633 MH-L NIC NN

DK511 L2A26

Lithuanian American Council.

Lithuanian bulletin. Apr. 15, 1943- Chicago [etc.]

Lithuanian American council
see also
Lithuanian American information center, *New York.*

Lithuanian American information center, *New York.*
An appeal to fellow Americans on behalf of the Baltic states by united organizations of Americans of Lithuanian, Latvian and Estonian descent. New York, The Lithuanian American information center, 1944.
54 p. illus. (facsims.) 21½ cm.
On cover: Lithuanian American information center; a service of the Lithuanian American council, inc., New York, N. Y.
——— Supplement ... no. 1- New York, The Lithuanian American information center, 1944-
v. illus. (facsims.) 21½ cm.
Bibliography: v. 1, p. 28-31.

1. World war, 1939- war, 1939-1945—Baltic states. 2. World war, 1939-1945—Occupied territories.
D802.B3L5 D802.B3L5 Suppl. 1945—
Harvard Univ. Library for Library of Congress 940.53474 A 44-5409 [a54r45g1]†

NL 0408636 MH NIC DLC

DC102 .8 .L3K552

Lithuanian American information center, New York.
Klimas, Petras, 1891-
Ghillebert de Lannoy in medieval Lithuania; voyages and embassies of an ancestor of one of America's great presidents, by Petras Klimas. An introduction by Constantine R. Jurgela ... New York, N. Y., The Lithuanian American information center, 1945.

DK511 L2J75

Lithuanian American information center, New York.
Jurgela, Constantine Rudyard, 1904-
Lithuania in a twin Teutonic clutch; a historical review of German-Lithuanian relations, by Constantine R. Jurgėla, Rev. Kazys Gečys [and] Simas Sužiedėlis. (With five maps) New York, N. Y., The Lithuanian American information center, 1945.

D742 L5H3

Lithuanian American information center, New York.
Harrison, Ernest John, 1873-
Lithuania's fight for freedom, by E. J. Harrison ... New York, 1945.

Lithuanian American information center, New York.
[Release] New York, N.Y. Monthly?

NL 0408640 NN

Lithuanian art in exile. [Managing editor: Paulius Augius, in collaboration with Viktoras Petravicius and others. Translated by W. Rickmer Rickmers. Munich, T. J. Vizgirda, 1948]
[3] p. (p. [17]-78 illus. (part col.)) 30 cm. (Lithuania, country and nation, 12)
"Biographies": p. 11-15.

1. Art, Lithuanian. I. Augius, Paulius, 1909- ed. (Series)

N6995.L5L5 709.475 51-34804

NL 0408641 DLC OC1 PU-FA DGU OKentU OC1W PPPM

Lithuanian automobile club
see Lietuvos automobilių klubas.

Lithuanian bibliography service
see Lietuvių bibliografinė tarnyba.

[Lithuanian books. Catalogue distributed by Brockhaus. n. p., 190-?]
29, [4] p. 17cm.

1. Lithuanian literature—Bibl.—Catalogs.

CA 12-1113 Unrev'd

Library of Congress Z2514.L4Z93

NL 0408644 DLC

Lithuanian bulletin. Apr. 15, 1943- Chicago [etc.]
v. in illus., maps. 22-28 cm.
Frequency varies.
Publication suspended 1952-Jan. 1963.
Issues for 1943-51 called v. 1-9.
Issues for Apr. 1943-Jan. 1946 published by the Lithuanian National Council; Feb. 1946- by the Lithuanian American Council.

1. Lithuania — Pol. & govt. — Period. I. Lithuanian National Council. II. Lithuanian American Council.

DK511.L2A26 49-22970 rev*

NL 0408645 DLC MdBJ ICU MH OU FU NN WaS

Lithuanian bulletin.
The situation of the church and religious practices in occupied Lithuania
see under Trakiškis, A

VOLUME 336

Lithuanian Catholic Press Society.
Amerikos lietuvių katalikų Metraštis 1916 m. Tvarkė ir redagavo Kun. P. Lapelis. Išleido Lietuvių katalikų spaudos Draugija. Chicago, Ill., "Draugo" spauda, [1916].
438, [10] p. illus. (incl. ports.) 23½cm.

NL 0408647 ICJ ICRL

Lithuanian Catholic truth society.

DK511 FOR OTHER EDITIONS
L9J8 SEE MAIN ENTRY
1911 **Jusaitis, Antanas.**
The history of the Lithuanian nation and its present national aspirations, by Kunigas Antanas Jusaitis ... Translated from the Lithuanian. 2d ed., enl. [Philadelphia?] The Lithuanian Catholic truth society, 1919.

Lithuanian Catholic youth magazine
see
Ateitis; katalikiškojo jaunimo žurnalas.

Lithuanian Chamber of Commerce of Illinois.
Chicagos vadovas. Chicago, 1952.
247 p. illus., ports., fold. col. map. 17 cm.
Chapter headings in English.

1. Chicago—Direct. I. Title.

F548.18.L5 58-42017

NL 0408650 DLC KMK OKentU PU

Lithuanian Committee, Hanau.
Lithuania and its day of independence on the 16th February 1918-1946
see under title

Lithuanian council
see
Council of main districts of Lithuania.

LITHUANIAN COUNCIL OF CHICAGO.
Memorandum on the independence of Lithuania. Resolution adopted Aug. 20th, 1920. [Chicago, 192-.].

Pamphlet.

NL 0408653 MH

Lithuanian cultural institute.

Pakštas, Kazys, 1893–
The Baltoscandian confederation, by Prof. Kazys Pakštas ... [Chicago] Lithuanian cultural institute, 1942.

Lithuanian cultural institute.

Pakštas, Kazys, 1893–
The Lithuanian situation, by K. Pakštas ... [Chicago] Lithuanian cultural institute, 1941.

Hvc10 **Lithuanian Cultural Institute,**
L71 Publications. Sect.1. **Lithuanian language** and literature. no.1-
Chicago, Ill., 1942-
illus. 22cm.

NL 0408656 CtY OrU ArU

Lithuanian "Elta" agency service
see Lithuanian telegraph agency ("Elta") service, Kaunas.

Lithuanian Executive Council
see
Supreme Lithuanian Committee of Liberation. *Executive Council.*

Lithuanian exports & exporters.

HF3635
.7
.L48 **Lietuvos** eksportas ir eksporteriai. Lithuanian exports & exporters.
1927-
Kaune.

Lithuanian Folklore archives
see
Lithuania. *Lietuvių tautosakos archyvas.*

Lithuanian information bureau. ... Articles exportés de Lituanie par les Allemands pendant l'occupation. [Paris, 1919?]
9 p. 27 cm. (Délégation de Lituanie à la Conférence de la paix. [pt.] V, 7)
Caption title.
Mimeographed.
At head of title: Bureau d'informations, près la Délégation de Lituanie à la Conférence de la paix.

NL 0408661 CSt-H

Lithuanian information bureau.

Lithuania. *Constitution.*
Constitution of the republic of Lithuania. Lithuanian information bureau ... London ... [London, Eyre & Spottiswoode. ltd., 1924]

Lithuanian information bureau.

—— ... Des frontières lituano-allemandes et lituano-polonaises. [Paris, 1919?]
[3] p. 27 cm. (Délégation de Lituanie à la Conférence de la paix. [pt.] II, 1)
Caption title.
Mimeographed.
At head of title: Bureau d'informations, près la Délégation de Lituanie à la Conférence de la paix.

NL 0408663 CSt-H

Lithuanian information bureau.
Economic & financial condition of the Lithuanian republic at the beginning of 1922. London, Lithuanian information bureau [1922?]
vi, 57, [1] p. 25cm.

1. Lithuania—Econ. condit. I. Title.

45-53530

Library of Congress HC337.L5L5

NL 0408664 DLC MH-BA NN

Lithuanian information bureau.

Lithuanian telegraph agency ("Elta") service, *Kaunas.*
... Economic and general bulletin.
London, Lithuanian information bureau, 19

Lithuanian information bureau.

—— ... La formation et le caractère du Conseil d'état de Lituanie (Taryba) [Paris, 1919?]
7 p. 27 cm. (Délégation de Lituanie à la Conférence de la paix. [pt.] IV, 2)
Caption title.
Mimeographed.
At head of title: Bureau d'informations, près la Délégation de Lituanie à la Conférence de la paix.

NL 0408666 CSt-H

Lithuanian information bureau.
The Lithuanian-Polish dispute ... London, Eyre and Spottiswoode, ltd., 1921–23.
3 v. fold. maps. 27½ x 21½cm.
Issued by the Lithuanian information bureau (London) whose name and address are given on v. [2]–3 and suppl. to v. 3. (*cf. also* v. 3, p. [5] foot-note)
CONTENTS.—[v. 1] Second Assembly of the League of nations at Geneva, 1921. 1921. (At head of title: Lithuanian delegation).—[v. 2] Correspondence between the Council of the League of nations and the Lithuanian government since the second Assembly of the League of nations, 15th December, 1921–17th July, 1922. With an introductory statement of the facts. 1922.—v. 3. Including correspondence between the Lithuanian government and the League of nations and the Conference of ambassadors. August, 1922–July, 1923. With introductory statements. 1923.
D651.L5L4

—— The Memel convention. Correspondence between the Conference of ambassadors and the Lithuanian government, August 9th to September 21st, 1923. (Supplementary to that contained in volume 3 of the Lithuanian-Polish dispute, September 1923.) ... London, Eyre and Spottiswoode, ltd., 1923.
28 p. 27 x 21cm.
1. European war, 1914–1918—Territorial questions—Lithuania. 2. European war, 1914–1918—Territorial questions—Poland. 3. Lithuania. 4. Memel (Territory) I. League of nations. II. Allied powers (1919–) Conference of ambassadors. III. Title. IV. Title: Memel convention.
(L. of N. author file Biv; topic file C: Lithuania, Memel, Poland)

24-20430-31 Revised

Library of Congress DK511.L273L5

NL 0408668 DLC IdU ICJ NIC OU MiU OO WaU

DK511 Lithuanian information bureau.
.L2L78 The Lithuanian-Polish dispute. Correspondence between the Council of the League of nations and the Lithuanian government since the second Assembly of the League of nations 15th December, 1921–17th July, 1922 ... London, Eyre and Spottiswoode, 1922.
65 p. 28cm.

1. European war, 1914–1918—Territorial questions—Lithuania. 2. European war, 1914–1918—Territorial questions—Poland.

NL 0408669 ICU IU

VOLUME 336

Lithuanian information bureau.
Lithuanian recognition advocated by Hon. William G. McAdoo, Dr. Herbert Adams Gibbons, Hon. Walter M. Chandler. Washington, D. C., Lithuanian information bureau [1921]
8 p. l., 70 p. map. 28cm.
CONTENTS.—Letter of McAdoo, Cotton and Franklin to Secretary of state Colby.—Memorandum to secretary of state in behalf of recognition of Lithuania from McAdoo, Cotton and Franklin.—Notes extending recognition to Lithuania by Great Britain, France, Finland, Latvia, Norway, Poland, Sweden, Argentina, Mexico, Russia.—Letter of W. G. McAdoo to Secretary of state Hughes.—Economic basis for Lithuania's claim to independence.—Lithuania, the United States and the League of nations, by H. A. Gibbons.—Plea of W. M. Chandler for recognition of Lithuania, Latvia and Esthonia.
1. Lithuania. 2. Baltic provinces. I. McAdoo, William Gibbs, 1863– II. Gibbons, Herbert Adams, 1880–1934. III. Chandler, Walter Marion, 1867–1935. IV. Title.
21—21224
Library of Congress DK511.L26L5

NL 0408670 DLC IdU MtU KU ICJ NN CU OO MiU

---

lithuanian inform ation bureau.

—— ... Lituanie & Pologne. [Paris, 1919]
22 p. 27 cm. (Délégation de Lituanie à la Conférence de la paix. [pt.] VII, 1)
Caption title.
Mimeographed.
At head of title: Bureau d'informations, près la Délégation de Lituanie à la Conférence de la paix.

NL 0408671 CSt-H

Lithuainian information bureau.

—— ... Les Lituaniens d'Amérique. [Paris, 1919?]
4 p. 27 cm. (Délégation de Lituanie à la Conférence de la paix. [pt.] V, 5)
Caption title.
Mimeographed.
At head of title: Bureau d'informations, près la Délégation de Lituanie à la Conférence de la paix.

NL 0408672 CSt-H

947.5 Lithuanian information bureau.
L71m The Memel problem, with a map of Lithuania and of the Memel territory. London, Lithuanian information bureau [1922]
21p. fold.map.

1. Memel (Territory) 2. European war, 1914-1918--Territorial questions--Lithuania.

NL 0408673 IU WaPS MH OU CSt-H

Lithuanian Information Bureau.
The Memel problem. With a map of Lithuania and of the
152799 Memel territory. London, Lithuanian Information Bureau, [1923].
21, [1] p. 1 fold. map. 24cm.
——— Supplement .... [London, 1923.]
21, [1] p. 24cm.
——— Reply of the Lithuanian government delegation to the questionnaire ... on the Memel problem .... [London, 1923?]
3, [1] p. 24cm.
Bound together.

NL 0408674 ICJ MiU

Lithuanian information bureau.
... A plea for the Lithuanians, a monthly review pub. by the Lithuanian information bureau ... no. 1– Feb. 1916–
[Philadelphia, 1916–
v. ports., maps. 23cm.
Editor: 1916– J. J. Kaulakis.

1. Lithuania—Hist. 2. Lithuanians. 3. European war, 1914– —Atrocities. I. Kaulakis, J. J., ed. II. Title.
17–15248
Library of Congress DK511.L2L5

NL 0408675 DLC ICJ

[Lithuanian Information Bureau]
Il problema di Vilna. Genova, Tip. G. B. Marsano, 1922.
38, 9, [1] p. 4 fold. maps. 26 cm.
Bound with its Le probleme de Vilna. Paris, 1922.
Map no. 5 wanting.
"Memorandum sulla questione di Memel" p. 1-[10] (2nd paging)

NL 0408676 PU

Lithuanian information bureau.
Le problème de Memel devant la Conférence des ambassadeurs ... Paris, Bureau d'information lithuanien, 1923.
cover-title, 37 p. map. 27 x 21cm.
CONTENTS.—Documents se rapportant aux travaux de la commission chargée d'étudier le statut de Memel.—Correspondance échangée entre le gouvernement lithuanien et la Conférence des ambassadeurs au sujet de la reconnaissance de jure de la Lithuanie et de l'internationalisation du Niémen.

1. Memel (Territory) 2. European war, 1914–1918—Territorial questions—Lithuania. 3. Memel River. I. Title.
30–4576
Library of Congress DK511.L273L57

NL 0408677 DLC MH-L PU

Lithuanian information bureau.
Le problème de Vilna. Paris, Bureau d'information lithuanien, 1922.
1 p. l., 32 p. 2 fold. maps. 24cm.
Published also in English.

1. Vilna. 2. European war, 1914–1918—Territorial questions—Lithuania. 3. Lithuania—For. rel.—Poland. 4. Poland—For. rel.—Lithuania.
29—9702
Library of Congress DK511.L27L53

NL 0408678 DLC PU

Lithuanian information bureau.

—— ... Quelques données statistiques sur la Lituanie. [Paris, 1919?]
4 p. 27 cm. (Délégation de Lituanie à la Conférence de la paix. [pt.] V, 1)
Caption title.
Mimeographed.
At head of title: Bureau d'informations, près la Délégation de Lituanie à la Conférence de la paix.

NL 0408679 CSt-H

Lithuanian information bureau.
... The question of Memel. Diplomatic and other documents from the Versailles peace conference till the reference of the question by the Conference of ambassadors to the Council of the League of nations (1919–1923), including historical sketches of the Memel region, and other introductory statements ... London, Eyre and Spottiswoode, ltd., 1924.
189 p. map. 27½ x 21cm.
At head of title: Lithuanian Ministry for foreign affairs.
Issued by the Lithuanian information bureau (London)
1. European war, 1914–1918 — Territorial questions — Lithuania. 2. Memel (Territory) I. Paris. Peace conference, 1919. II. Allied powers (1919–) Conference of ambassadors. III. Title.
24—20432
Library of Congress DK511.L273L6

NL 0408680 DLC N DS MH CU MiU CtY ICJ WaU

Lithuanian information bureau.

—— ... Revendications. [Paris, 1919?]
4 p. 27 cm. (Délégation de Lituanie à la Conférence de la paix. [pt.] III, 1bis)
Caption title.
Mimeographed.
At head of title: Bureau d'informations, près la Délégation de Lituanie.

NL 0408681 CSt-H

Lithuanian information bureau.
Sidelights on life in Lithuania
see under title

Lithuanian informatim bureau.

—— ... Sur le prétendu recensement de Vilna, en 1916. [Paris, 1919?]
6 p. 27 cm. (Délégation de Lituanie à la Conférence de la paix. [pt.] V, 3)
Caption title.
Mimeographed.
At head of title: Bureau d'informations, près la Délégation lituanienne à la Conférence de la paix.

NL 0408683 CSt-H

Lithuanian information bureau.

—— ... Vilna, capitale de la Lituanie. [Paris, 1919?]
5 p. 27 cm. (Délégation de Lituanie à la Conférence de la paix. [pt.] V, 2)
Caption title.
Mimeographed.
At head of title: Bureau d'informations, près la Délégation de Lituanie à la Conférence de la paix.

NL 0408684 CSt-H

Lithuanian information bureau.
The Vilna problem, with five maps. London, Lithuanian information bureau [1922]
1 p. l., 24, [2] p. 5 fold. maps. 24½cm.
Published also in French.
"Memorandum on the Memel question" (6, [1] p.) laid in.

1. Vilna. 2. European war, 1914–1918—Territorial questions—Lithuania. 3. Lithuania—For. rel.—Poland. 4. Poland—For. rel.—Lithuania. I. Title.
24—2183
Library of Congress DK511.L27L5

NL 0408685 DLC OU GU NN CtY OCl MiU WaU

Lithuanian Information Bureau, Lausanne
see **Bureau d'informations de Lithuanie, Lausanne.**

Lithuanian Information Service
see
Supreme Lithuanian Committee of Liberation.

LITHUANIAN information service, Brooklyn. Bulletin no.1-2, Ag 1940-F 1941//

NL 0408688 MiU CU

LITHUANIAN Jew. v. 1-3, no. 7/8; June, 1943-April/May, 1946. New York.
Microfilm (master negative)

NL 0408689 NN

Lithuanian Literary Association
see
American Lithuanian Literary Association.

VOLUME 336

Lithuanian Literary Society of Chicago.
Senųjų lietuviškų knygų istorija

see under

Biržiška, Vaclovas, 1884-1956.

Lithuanian Literary Society of Chicago.
Vincas Krėvė-Mickevičius; rašytojo 70 metų sukaktis. ₍Chicago₎ 1953.
187 p. port. 17 cm.
Added t. p. in English.
"Pagunda," by Vincas Krėvė: p. ₍85₎-182.

1. Krėvė-Mickevičius, Vincas, 1882-1954. I. Krėvė-Mickevičius, Vincas, 1882-1954. Pagunda.

PG8721.K7Z74 58-40437

NL 0408692 DLC OCl PU MiD UU

Lithuanian national anthem; voice and piano
see under [Kudirka, Vincas] 1858-1899.

Lithuanian national council.

Bartuška, V.
Observations du délégué du Conseil national lituanien à la suite de son voyage dans les régions de la Lituanie occupée par l'armée allemande, par Dr V. Bartuška. Lausanne, Bureau d'informations lituanien, 1918.

Lithuanian national council.
Projet de reconstitution de la Lithuanie indépendante, élaboré par la délégation permanente du Conseil national suprême lithuanien. [Lausanne, 1916]
19 p. illus. (maps) 27 cm.
"Il a été tire de cet ouvrage; 50 exemplaires sur papier hollande, numérotés de I à L. 200 exemplaires sur papier mikado, numerotés de 1 à 200. No. 10."
By J. Gabrys. cf. Brit. Mus.
Half-title: Mémoires relatif à la reconstitution de la Lithuanie indépendante.

At head of title: Confidentiel.
Gift of Smetona.
1. Lithuania - History. 2. European war, 1914-1918 - Territorial questions - Lithuania. I. Gabrys, J. II. Title. III. Title: Mémoire relatif à la reconstitution de la Lithuanie indépendante.

NL 0408696 CSt-H MH

Lithuanian national council. . . . Prusse orientale. Déclaration du Conseil national des Lituaniens sur la propagande allemande dans les régions lituaniennes de la Prusse orientale. [Paris, 1919?]
3 p. 27 cm. (Délégation de Lituanie à la Conférence de la paix. [pt.] II, 2)
Caption title.
Mimeographed.
At head of title: Bureau d'informations, près de la Délégation de Lituanie à la Conférence de la paix.
Signed: Assemblée des Lituaniens de la Prusse orientale. La Taryba nationale.

NL 0408697 CSt-H

Lithuanian national council. [Revendications des Lituaniens de la Prusse Orientale] à son excellence Monsieur Georges Clemenceau, président de la Conférence de la paix et président du Conseil des ministres, Paris. [Paris? 1919]
5 p. 27½ cm. (Délégation de Lituanie à la Conférence de la paix. [pt.] III, 3)
Caption title.
Mimeographed.
At head of title: Délégation de Lituanie à la Conférence de la paix. Copie.
Dated: Tilsit, le 6 février 1919.
Signed: La présidence du Conseil national de la Lituanie prussienne.
"Conforme à l'original."

NL 0408698 CSt-H

DK511 .L2A26

Lithuanian National Council, Chicago.
Lithuanian bulletin. Apr. 15, 1943-
Chicago ₍etc.₎

Lithuanian national council of America.

Exposé sommaire du développement de la conscience nationale lituanienne dans le passé et le présent. ₍n. p., 191-₎

Lithuanian national council of America.

₍Norus, T ₎
... Independence for the Lithuanian nation; statement setting forth the claim for independent government and freedom in the terms of peace for Lithuania by the Lithuanian national council in the United States ... Washington, Govt. print. off., 1918.

Lithuanian national council of America.
Lithuania; facts supporting her claim for reestablishment as an independent nation. Washington, D. C., The Lithuanian national council ₍1918₎
cover-title, ₍3₎-48 p. 21½cm.
"Compiled by Dr. J. J. Bielskis, member Lithuanian national council."
"Books, pamphlets and journals published by the Lithuanian information bureaus": p. 48.

1. Lithuania—Hist. I. Bielskis, Julius J., comp.

Library of Congress DK511.L2L7 18-22748 Revised

MH OClWHi OO
NL 0408702 DLC DNW CU PU OCl OU OCU MiU ICN NN

Lithuanian national council of America.
Lithuania against Poland; an appeal for justice, addressed to ... the President of the United States, to the senators and representatives of the United States Congress, and to all American citizens. ₍Washington₎ Executive committee, Lithuanian national councils ₍1919₎
₍3₎ p. 28cm.
Signed: Matthias J. Vinikas, chairman. Julian J. Bielskis, acting secretary.

1. European war, 1914- —Territorial questions—Lithuania. I. Title.

Library of Congress D651.L5L5 20-10795

NL 0408703 DLC NN

Lithuanian national council of America.
Norus, T.
Lithuania's case for independence, by T. Norus and J. Zilius; issued by Lithuanian national council in United States of America. Washington, D. C., B. F. Johnson, inc., 1918.

Lithuanian, Polish and Russian folk dances
see under Boyd, Neva Leona.

Lithuanian Populist Peasant Union
see Lietuvos Valstiečių Liaudininkų Sąjunga.

Lithuanian R. C. Priests' League of America
see
Lithuanian Roman Catholic Priests' League of America

Lithuanian Roman Catholic Alliance of America
see also
Lithuanian Alliance of America.

Lithuanian Roman Catholic Federation of America.
For a just peace
see under Lithuanian American Catholic Congress, New York, 1946.

Lithuanian Roman Catholic Priests' League of America.
Amerikos lietuvių katalikų darbai. Catholic action of the Lithuanians of America. ₍New York?₎ 1943.
336 p. illus. 24 cm.

1. Lithuanians in the U. S. 2. Catholics, Lithuanian. I. Title. II. Title: Catholic action of the Lithuanians of America.

BX1407.L5L5 61-56274 ‡

NL 0408710 DLC PU

Lithuanian Roman Catholic Priests' League of America.
Metraštis. [Brooklyn, N.Y.] 1951.

NL 0408711 PU

Lithuanian Roman Catholic Priests' League of America.
Žinynas, 1918-
South Boston, Darbininkas. v. illus. 23cm.

1. Priesthood, Lithuanian. 2. Catholic Church, Roman--U.S.--Direct. 3. Lithuanians in the U.S. I. Title. II. Darbininkas.

NL 0408712 NN PU

Lithuanian SSR
see also Lithuania.

VOLUME 336

Lithuanian S. S. R. Architektūros reikalų valdyba.
Vilnius; architektūra iki xx amžiaus pradžios. ₍Redakcinė komisija: V. Bytautas et al. Sudarytojas A. Janikas. Dailininkas E. Jurėnas. Kaune₎ Valstybinė grožinės literatūros leidykla, 1955.

Lithuanian S. S. R. *Aukščiausioji Taryba.*
Lietuvos TSR Aukščiausiosios Tarybos stenogramos.

Vilnius, Valstybinė politinės ir mokslinės literatūros leidykla.
v. in 22 cm.

1. Lithuania—Pol. & govt. I. Title.

J400.L5H45 64-6460

NL 0408715 DLC NIC

Lithuanian S. S. R. *Aukščiausioji Taryba.*
Стенографический отчет.

Вильнюс, Гос. изд-во полит. и науч. лит-ры Литовской ССР.
v. in 23 cm.

1. Lithuania—Pol. & govt. 2. Lithuania—Econ. condit.—1918– 3. Cost and standard of living—Lithuania.
Title transliterated: Stenograficheskiĭ otchet.

J400.L5H452 64-5197

NL 0408716 DLC

Lithuanian S. S. R. Aukščiausioji Taryba. Organizacinis-informacinis skyrius.
Lietuvos TSR administracinis-teritorinis suskirstymas.

Vilnius, Valstybinė politinės ir mokslinės literatūros leidykla.

Lithuanian S. S. R. Aukščiausioji Taryba. Prezidiumas.
Lithuanian S. S. R. *Laws, statutes, etc.*
Хронологическое собрание законов Литовской ССР, указов Президиума Верховного Совета и постановлений Правительства Литовской ССР. т. 1– 1940/47–
Вильнюс, Гос. изд-во полит. и науч. лит-ры.

Lithuanian S. S. R. *Aukščiausioji Taryba. Prezidiumas. Organizacinis-informacinis skyrius*
see
Lithuanian S. S. R. *Aukščiausioji Taryba. Organizacinis-informacinis skyrius.*

Lithuanian S. S. R. Centrinė statistikos valdyba.
Экономика и культура Литовской ССР; статистический ежегодник.
Вильнюс, Статистика.

Lithuanian S. S. R. Centrinė statistikos valdyba.
Литовская ССР в цифрах; краткий статистический сборник.

Вильнюс, Госстатиздат; Литовское отд-ние.

Lithuanian S. S. R. *Centrinė statistikos valdyba.*
Lietuvos TSR ekonomika ir kultūra; statistikos metraštis.
Vilnius, Leidykla "Statistika."
v. 15 cm.

1. Lithuania—Stat. I. Title.

HA1448.L5A3 65-82290

NL 0408722 DLC CU MiU OU

Lithuanian S. S. R. *Constitution.*
Constitution (fundamental law) of the Lithuanian Soviet Socialist Republic of August 25, 1940. As amended through Apr. 7, 1948. New York, American Russian Institute, 1950.
15 l. 28 cm.
Cover title.
Errata slip inserted.

342.47 50-32255

NL 0408723 DLC MH NN PU-L ViU

Lithuanian S. S. R. *Constitution.*
Конституция (основной закон) С изменениями и дополнениями, принятыми на I, II и IV сессиях Верховного Совета Литовской ССР третьего созыва. Вильнюс, Гос. изд-во полит. и науч. лит-ры, 1954.

Lithuanian S. S. R. *Constitution.*
Konstytucja (ustawa zasadnicza) Litewskiej Socjalistycznej Republiki Radzieckiej. Z uwzględnieniem zmian i uzupełnień uchwalonych przez I, II i IV sesje Rady Najwyższej Litewskiej SRR trzeciej kadencji. Wilnius, Państwowe Wydawn. Literatury Politycznej i Naukowej, 1954.
27 p. 21 cm.

I. Title.

57-38722 ‡

NL 0408725 DLC MH-L

Lithuanian S. S. R. *Constitution.*
Lietuvos Tarybų Socialistinės Respublikos Konstitucija (pagrindinis įstatymas) Su Lietuvos TSR Aukščiausiosios Tarybos 2. sušaukimo I, III, IV ir VI sesijose ir 3. sušaukimo I sesijoje priimtais pakeitimais ir papildymais. Vilnius, Valstybinė politinės ir mokslinės literatūros leidykla, 1951.
23 p. 22 cm.

54-40076

NL 0408726 DLC

Lithuanian S. S. R. *Gosudarstvennyĭ komitet po koordinatsii nauchno-issledovatel'skikh rabot*
see
Lithuanian S. S. R. *Valstybinis mokslinio tyrimo darbų koordinavimo komitetas.*

Lithuanian S. S. R. *Gosudarstvennyĭ komitet po delam stroitel'stva i arkhitektury*
see
Lithuanian S. S. R. *Valstybinis statybos ir architektūros reikalų komitetas.*

Lithuanian S. S. R. *Laws, statutes, etc.*
Butų ūkis; įstatyminės ir instruktyvinės medžiagos rinkinys 1955 m. gegužės 1 dienai. Жилищное хозяйство; сборник законодательных и инструктивных материалов по состоянию на 1 мая 1955 г. Sudarė V. P. Fatiejevas. ₍Redaktoriai: A. Žiurlys, L. Davimas, J. Bluvšteinas₎ Vilnius, Lietuvos Respublikinės profesinių sąjungų tarybos leidykla, 1955.
721 p. forms. 23 cm.
At head of title: Lietuvos TSR Komunalinio ūkio ministerija.
Lithuanian and Russian.

Includes legislation of U. S. S. R.
Errata slip inserted.

1. Housing—Lithuania—Law and legislation. 2. Housing—Russia—Law and legislation. I. Fateev, V. P., comp. II. Žiurlys, A., ed. III. Lithuanian S. S. R. Komunalinio ūkio ministerija. IV. Russia (1923– U. S. S. R.) Laws, statutes, etc. V. Title. VI. Title: Zhilishchnoe khozîaĭstvo.

57-17066

NL 0408730 DLC

Lithuanian S. S. R. *Laws, statutes, etc.*
Хронологическое собрание законов Литовской ССР, указов Президиума Верховного Совета и постановлений Правительства Литовской ССР. т. 1– 1940/47–
Вильнюс, Гос. изд-во полит. и науч. лит-ры.
v. 23 cm.
Issued by Ministerstvo fustifsii Litovskoĭ SSR.
Editor: 1940/47– A. Žiurlys.
I. Žiurlys, Alfonsas, ed. II. Lithuanian S. S. R. Teisingumo ministerija. III. Lithuanian S. S. R. Aukščiausioji Taryba. Prezidiumas. IV. Title.
Title transliterated: Khronologicheskoe sobranie zakonov Litovskoĭ SSR.

59-29889 rev

NL 0408731 DLC

Lithuanian S. S. R. *Ministerstvo fustifsii*
see
Lithuanian S. S. R. *Teisingumo ministerija.*

Lithuanian S. S. R. *Ministerstvo vnutrennikh del*
see
Lithuanian S. S. R. *Vidaus reikalų ministerija.*

Lithuanian S. S. R. *Ministrų taryba. Architektūros reikalų valdyba*
see
Lithuanian S. S. R. *Architektūros reikalų valdyba.*

Lithuanian S. S. R. *Ministrų Taryba. Centrinė statistikos valdyba*
see
Lithuanian S. S. R. *Centrinė statistikos valdyba.*

Lithuanian S. S. R. *Ministrų Taryba. Radijo ir televizijos komitetas*
see
Lithuanian S. S. R. *Radijo ir televizijos komitetas.*

VOLUME 336

Lithuanian S. S. R. *Ministrų taryba. Upravlenie po delam arkhitektury*
see
Lithuanian S. S. R. *Architektūros reikalų valdyba.*

Lithuanian S. S. R. *Ministrų Taryba. Valstybinis mokslinio tyrimo darbų koordinavimo komitetas*
see
Lithuanian S. S. R. *Valstybinis mokslinio tyrimo darbų koordinavimo komitetas.*

Lithuanian S. S. R. *Mikslinio tyrimo darbų koordinavimo komitetas*
see
Lithuanian S. S. R. *Valstybinis mokslinio tyrimo darbų koordinavimo komitetas.*

Lithuanian S.S.R. Mokslu Akademija
see
Lietuvos TSR Mokslu akademija, Vilna.

Lithuanian S. S. R. *Mokslinio tyrimo darbų koordinavimo komitetas*
see
Lithuanian S. S. R. *Valstybinis mokslinio tyrimo darbų koordinavimo komitetas.*

PN1992 .K3

Lithuanian S. S. R. Radijo ir televizijos komitetas.

Kalba Vilnius; radijo ir televizijos programos.

[Vilnius]

Lithuanian S. S. R. *Sovet Ministrov*
see
Lithuanian S. S. R. *Ministrų taryba.*

Lithuanian S. S. R. *Statisticheskoe upravlenie*
see
Lithuanian S. S. R. *Centrinė statistikos valdyba.*

Lithuanian S. S. R. *Statistikos valdyba*
see
Lithuanian S. S. R. *Centrinė statistikos valdyba.*

Law

Lithuanian S. S. R. Teisingumo ministerija.

Lithuanian S. S. R. *Laws, statutes, etc.*
Хронологическое собрание законов Литовской ССР, указов Президиума Верховного Совета и постановлений Правительства Литовской ССР. т. 1- 1940/47-
Вильнюс, Гос. изд-во полит. и науч. лит-ры.

Lithuanian S. S. R. *Ts̄entral'noe statisticheskoe upravlenie*
see
Lithuanian S. S. R. *Centrinė statistikos valdyba.*

Lithuanian S. S. R. *Upravlenie po delam arkhitektury*
see
Lithuanian S. S. R. *Architektūros reikalų valdyba.*

M574

Lithuanian S. S. R. Valstybinis mokslinio tryimo darbų koordinavimo komitetas.

Mokslas ir technika.

[Kaunas]

Lithuanian S. S. R. *Verkhovnyĭ Sovet*
see
Lithuanian S. S. R. *Aukščiausioji Taryba.*

Lithuanian S. S. R. *Vidaus reikalų ministerija. Arkhivnyĭ otdel*
see
Lithuanian S. S. R. *Vidaus reikalų ministerija. Archyvų skyrius.*

DK190 L5

Lithuanian S. S. R. *Vidaus reikalų ministerija. Archyvų skyrius.*
Документы штаба М. И. Кутузова, 1805–1806; сборник. [Под общей ред. Жюгжда, Ю. И.] Вильнюс, Гос. изд-во полит. лит-ры, 1951.
338 p. illus. 21 cm.
At head of title: Институт истории Академии наук Литовской ССР. Архивный отдел МВД Литовской ССР.
1. Russia — History, Military — 1801–1825 — Sources. 2. Kutuzov, Mikhail Illarionovich, svetleĭshiĭ kniaz' Smolenskiĭ, 1745–1813. I. Žiugžda, Juozas, ed. II. Lietuvos TSR Mokslų akademija, Vilna. Istorijos institutas. III. Title.
Title transliterated: Dokumenty shtaba M. I. Kutuzova.

DK190.L5 54–29956 ‡

NL 0408752 DLC

The Lithuanian situation. v. [1]- (no. [1]-);
Aug. 3, 1940-
Washington.
v. in 28–36 cm. monthly (irregular)
Publication suspended Sept. 1940–May 1941.
Title varies: July 1941–Nov./Dec. 1954, Current news on the Lithuanian situation.
Issued by the Lithuanian Legation.

1. World war, 1939-1945 - Periodicals, etc.
1. Lithuania—Hist.—Periodicals. I. Lithuania. Pasiuntinybė. U. S. II. Current news on the Lithuanian situation.
DK511.L2L72 UCS 45-29325 rev*

NL 0408753 DLC ICU ICN CLU FU CtY

Lithuanian societies' acting committee of Greater New York.
Lietuvių demonstracija Didžiajame New Yorke, liepos 4d., 1918. Išleido Didžiojo New Yorko lietuvių draugijų veikiantysis komitetas ... redagavo J. O. Širvydas, spaudon tvarkė ir sustatė P. Mulevičius ir M. Milukas ... Brooklyn, N. Y., 1918.
64 p. illus. (incl. ports., music) 23ᶜᵐ.

1. Lithuanians in New York (City) 2. Fourth of July celebrations. I. Širvydas, Joseph Otto, 1875- ed. II. Title.
Library of Congress F128.9.L7L7 19-489

NL 0408754 DLC MB

DK511 .L2A265

Lithuanian Student Association.

Lituanus. v. [1]- Nov. 1954-
[Brooklyn, N. Y., etc.]

HS3313 .B7L5

Lithuanian Student Scout Association.

Kviklys, Bronius.
Akademinė skautija 1924–1954 metais; trisdešimties metų gyvenimo, veiklos ir darbų apžvalga. Čikaga, Akademinis skautų sąjūdis, 1954.

HC337 .L5A17

Unbound parts listed on above Book Number

Lithuanian Telegraph Agency ("Elta") Service, Kaunas.
Economic and general bulletin. July 1936-
London, Lithuanian Information Bureau [1936-
v. in 29cm. monthly (irregular)
Vol. 3 incomplete.
Issues for 1936 called no. 7-12; 1937- called v. 1-
1. Lithuania. 2. Lithuania—Econ. condit. 3. Periodicals, English. I. Lithuanian Information Bureau.

NL 0408757 MB

Lithuanian telegraphic agency ("Elta") service
see Lithuanian telegraph agency ("Elta") service, Kaunas.

Lithuanian trade directory; exports, imports, industry. Adressbuch der Exporteure, Importeure und der Industrie Litauens. Indicateur d'exportateurs, d'importateurs et d'industries de la Lithuanie.

Kaunas, D. Gruodis.

v. 19 cm.

1. Lithuania—Comm.—Direct.

HF3635.7.L5 56-51449 ‡

NL 0408759 DLC NN OCl

Lithuanian University, *Kaunas*
see **Kaunas. Universitetas.**

Lithuanian Workers Literature Society
see
American Lithuanian Literary Association.

LITHUANIANS IN CHICAGO.
Miscellaneous pamphlets, etc.

NL 0408762 ICHi

La LITHUANIE et Memel. Paris, 1922.

(4) + 11 p. Map.
"Extrait de l'Europe nouvelle du 18 novembre 1922."

NL 0408763 MH-L

VOLUME 336

Lithuanie et Ruthénie Blanche. Varsovie, 1919. 42 p. 29cm.

1. Lithuania—Hist. 2. Ruthenia (Province)—Hist.

NL 0408764 NN CSt-H

Lithuanus, pseud.
La vérité polonaise sur les Lithuaniens, par Lithuanus ... Lausanne, Bureau d'information de Lithuanie, 1917.
cover-title, 16p. 24cm.

NL 0408765 DNW

Lithzenius, Andreas, respondent.
... Dissertatio gradualis, circumlata per Graeciam Gothorum arma
see under Amnell, Johannes J praeses.

Lithzenius, Andreas, respondent.
... Monumenta politico ecclesiastica ex archivo Palmskiöldiano...
see under Celsius, Olof Olofsson, 1716-1794, praeses.

Lithzenius (Johannes)
* De corona triplici pontificis Romani. *Upsaliæ*, [1736].
6 p.l., 44 pp. 8°.

NL 0408768 NN

Lithzenius, Petrus Vilhelmus, respondent.
De Norkopia, urbe Ostro-Gothorum principe...
see under Ekerman, Petrus, 1696-1783, praeses.

Le liti del comune di Monopoli ...
see under [Onghia, G d']

Litiana, *pseud.*
... L'Egitto colto sul vivo. Firenze, R. Bemporad & fº ₍1928₎
211 p., 1 l. 19cm.
Contents.—Le stelle nel pozzo (scene di vita egiziana)—Malese!—Più di lui!—L'harem di Abdu.—Colei che non dà ombra.

I. Title.
Library of Congress PQ4827.I 7E5 1928 29-15998

NL 0408771 DLC

Litiatco, Alfredo Elfren.
The heiress of Joaquin Lerma (a play in four scenes) by Alfredo Elfren Litiatco. (In: Gwekoh, S. H., comp. Philippine plays. Manila, 1930. 23½cm. p. ₍45₎-54.)

1. Drama, Philippine. I. Title.
N. Y. P. L. February 11, 1941

NL 0408772 NN

Litiatco, Alfredo Elfren.
With harp and sling. ₍Verses. Limited memorial ed.₎ Manila, Effandem, 1943.
91 p. 20 cm.

I. Title.
PS9993.L45W5 811.5 49-35199*

NL 0408773 DLC MH RPB

LÍTIÐ ungsmannsgaman; vikulestrar handa unglingum, frá ábyrgðarmanni Þjóðólfs. I.-III, (in 1 vol.). Reykjavík, prentað í prentsmiðju Islands, 1852-57.
Scan 5997.66.15
III. is frá Svb. Hallgrímssyni. Akureyri, a H. Helgasyni, 1857.
Contents: 1. Sunnundagur.- 2. Mánudagur.- 3. Þriðjudagur.

NL 0408774 MH

El Litigante.
Guadalajara, Mexico.
v. ports. 33cm. 4 no. a month.
"Periodico de legislacion, jurisprudencia y variedades."
Some no. accompanied by supplements.

NL 0408775 IU

El litigante generoso. Comedie en tres actos y en verso...
see under [Puchol Valdes, Nicandor] supposed author.

LITIGATION statistics furnished by clerks of several counties to the commissioners upon the subject of town or local courts. 1860.

NL 0408777 MH Nh

PQ 4627 L56 N4 Cage

Litigio, Fulvio.
... Nimicissimo capital de le donne approua le loro male operation fare contra gl'uomini. Hortensia in difesa de le donne inanzi la giustitia approua ogni tiranide & mala operatione de gli huomini operina piaceuole, & dotta ₍n.p., n.d.₎
$A-D^4$. 8vo.
See G. Passano, I novellieri Italiani... 1864, p. 265.

NL 0408778 DFo

G 1700 L77++

Litigio de límites. Atlas de mapas. Réplica de Bolivia. ₍Buenos Aires, Lit. Comp. Sud. Americana de Billetes de Banco (etc.)₎ 1907.
7 ₍i. e. 8₎ maps (6 fold.; part col.) 48cm.
Includes 4 maps of Peru or departments thereof, a map of Bolivia and 3 maps of South America or a part thereof.
1. South America--Maps. 2. Peru--Maps. 3. Bolivia--Maps. I. Title: Atlas de mapas. II. Title: Réplica de Bolivia.

NL 0408779 NIC

El litigio fronterizo del Ecuador con el Perú
see under Junta Investigadora de la Colonia Ecuatoriana en Bogotá.

El litigio paraguayo-boliviano ... Santiago de Chile: Dirección general de Talleres fiscales de prisiones, Seccion imprenta, 1928. 23 p. 23cm.
With autograph of Jacinto López.
"Tirada especial del artículo publicado en el n. 93-94 de la Revista chilena."

649780A. 1. Chaco, El Gran. I. López, Jacinto, 1864-
N. Y. P. L. July 19, 1933

NL 0408781 NN

F 3451 B75 L576 LAC

El Litigio perú - ecuatoriano ante los principios jurídicos americanos. Lima, 1942.
12p. maps. 20cm.

1. Peru - Bound. - Ecuador. 2. Ecuador - Bound. - Peru. Sp.: Lucuix Collection.

NL 0408782 TxU NN

El Litigio territorial entre el Ecuador y el Perú. El protocolo de Río de Janeiro, su origen y sus consecuencias; polémica entre los embajadores del Ecuador y del Perú. Caracas ₍Editorial Ancora₎ 1953.
47 p. mapa. 24 cm.
Consists chiefly of letters from Antonio Parra Velasco and Eduardo Garland to two newspapers in Caracas.

1. Ecuador—Bound.—Peru. 2. Peru—Bound.—Ecuador. I. Parra Velasco, Antonio. II. Garland R., Eduardo.
F3451.B75L58 54-27865

NL 0408783 DLC ViU NN

El Litigio territorial entre el Ecuador y el Perú. El protocolo de Río de Janeiro, su origen y sus consecuencias; polémica entre los embajadores del Ecuador y del Perú. Guayaquil, Impr. de la Universidad, 1954.
54 p. mapa. 25 cm.
Consists chiefly of letters from Antonio Parra Velasco and Eduardo Garland to two newspapers in Caracas.
Errata slip inserted.

1. Ecuador — Bound. — Peru. 2. Peru — Bound. — Ecuador. I. Parra Velasco, Antonio. II. Garland Roel, Eduardo.
F3451.B75L58 1954 58-24626

NL 0408784 DLC MH DPU

The LITIGIOUS suitor defeated; or, A new trick to get a wife. London, 1742. (In The STROLERS pacquet open'd, 1742, 203-226.)

NL 0408785 MH

VOLUME 336

A litil boke the whiche traytied and reherced many gode thinges necessaries for the ... pestilence ...
see under [Knutsson, Bengt] bp. of Vesterås, fl. 1461.

Lítil jólabók
see under Jónsson, Ásmundur (of Lyngar)

Lítil saga umm herhlaup tyrkjans á Íslandi árið 1627
see under [Egilsson, Ólafur] d. 1639.

LITILL leiðarvísir í skógrækt. Tileinkaður U. M. F. Í. [Reykjavík], Prentsm. Hafnarfjarðar, 1909.

pp. 10/.

NL 0408789 MH

DS135 R93P6 Hebraic Sect.

Litinski, Menahem Nahum, 1852–ca. 1900.
קורות פאדאליא וקדמוניות היהודים שם; או, המר לדברי ימי היהודים ברוסיא ... אדעססא, בדפוס מ. א. בעלינסאן, תרנ"ה. Одесса, 1895.

68 p. 23 cm.

Vol. 1; no more published.

1. Jews in Podolia.
Title transliterated: Korot Podoliyo vekadmoniyot ha-Yehudim sham.

DS135.R93P6 52-51703

NL 0408790 DLC

Litinski (O[sip Arnoldovich]) [1868–].
*Essai d'une classification rationnelle des appareils physiologiques de l'organisme (avec schéma). 64 pp. 4°. *Paris*, 1895, No. 381.

NL 0408791 DNLM

-VM 452 .L 77q2

LITINSKIĬ, GENRIKH, 1901-
[Quartet, string; no.2, D minor] [Deuxième quatuor...pour 2 violons, viola et violoncelle... Partition... Moskau, Staatsmusikverlag[1932]
48p. 20cm.

At head of title: H.Litinsky.
Title also in Russian.
Miniature score.
Plate no.: M.9635 Г; U.E. 9244.

NL 0408792 ICN CaBVaU MB PP NN

Litinskiĭ, Genrikh Il'ich, 1901–
[Quartet, strings, no. 5]

Квартет № 5, "Туркмениана." Для двух скрипок, альта и виолончели. Партитура. Москва, Гос. музыкальное изд-во [1932]

miniature score (45 p.) 19 cm. (U[niversal] E[dition] 10169)

1. String quartets—Scores. I. Title: Turkmeniana.
Title transliterated: Kvartet no. 5.

M452.L76 no. 5 1932a M 56-1357

NL 0408793 DLC MB ICN

Litinskiĭ, Genrikh Il'ich, 1901–
[Quartet, strings, no. 4]

Квартет-сюита № 4, для 2 скрипок, альта и виолончели. Москва, Гос. изд-во, 1931.

miniature score (14 p.) 20 cm. (Universal Edition, No. 10114)

1. String quartets—Scores.
Title transliterated: Kvartet-siûita no. 4.

M452.L76 no. 4 1931a M 56-1348

NL 0408794 DLC NN

Litinskiĭ, Genrikh Il'ich, 1901–
[Sonata, violin & violoncello]

Соната для скрипки и виолончели. Москва, Гос. музыкальное изд-во Р. С. Ф. С. Р., 1933.

score (19 p.) 31 cm.

1. Sonatas (Violin and violoncello)
Title transliterated: Sonata dlia skripki i violoncheli.

M287.L78S63 M 56-1387

NL 0408795 DLC

Litinetskiĭ, Izot Borisovich.

М. В. Ломоносов—основоположник отечественного приборостроения. Москва, Гос. изд-во технико-теорет. лит-ры, 1952.

157, [3] p. illus., ports., facsims. 21 cm.

Bibliography: p. 157–[158]

1. Lomonosov, Mikhail Vasil'evich, 1711–1765.
Title transliterated: M. V. Lomonosov—osnovopolozhnik otechestvennogo priborostroeniia.

QC16.L64L5 55-18182 rev

NL 0408796 DLC

Litinsky, Heinrich
see
Litinskiĭ, Genrikh Il'ich, 1901–

Litinsky, Leonid, 1887–

Feuerfeste baustoffe für kammern der kokerei- und gaswerksöfen, von L. Litinsky ... Mit 15 abbildungen. Halle (Saale) Kommissionsverlag W. Knapp, 1926.

49, [1] p. illus., diagr. 24½cm.

"Die vorliegende arbeit stellt eine erweiterte und verbesserte umarbeitung des aufsatzes dar, der unter dem gleichen titel in den zeitschriften 'Brennstoff- und wärmewirtschaft' 1925, hefte 7–9 und 'Feuerfest' 1925, hefte 4, 7, 11 ff. erschienen ist. Es ist ferner in aussicht genommen worden, die arbeit auch als einen abschnitt meines zurzeit beim verlag W. Knapp, Halle im druck befindlichen buches 'Kokerei- und gaswerksöfen' zu verwerten."—Foot-note, p. [5]

1. Building, Fire-proof. 2. Furnaces. I. Title.

38-37049

Library of Congress TN677.L48

[2] 660.8

NL 0408798 DLC NN OU

Litinsky, Leonid, 1887–

Gasfernversorgung Westsachsens, bericht erstattet von ob. ing. L. Litinsky ... mit 8 karten. Leipzig, Kreishauptmannschaft Leipzig, Landesplanung Westsachsen, 1928.

31 p. illus., fold. map. 23cm.

1. Gas manufacture and works—Saxony. 2. Gas distribution. Title.

Library of Congress TP733.G3L5 29-11069

NL 0408799 DLC OU

Litinsky, Leonid, 1887-
Der Industrieofen in Einzeldarstellungen
see under title

Litinsky, Leonid, 1887–

Kokerei- und gaswerksöfen, von L. Litinsky ... mit 149 in den text gedruckten abbildungen und 32 zahlentafeln. Halle (Saale) W. Knapp, 1928.

4 p. l., 336 p. incl. illus., tables, diagrs. 24cm. (*Added t.-p.:* Kohle, koks, teer ... bd. 17)

1. Coke-ovens. 2. Gas-retorts. I. Title.

Library of Congress TP336.L57 28-30857

NL 0408801 DLC ICJ

Litinsky, Leonid, 1887–

Markenbezeichnungen im Feuerfest-Fach und im Ofenbau; alphabetisches Verzeichnis von annähernd 1500 bekanntester Markennamen der Feuerfest-Industrie und des Industrieofenbaues der Welt nebst Angabe deren Eigenschaften und Bezugsquellen. Zusammengestellt von L. Litinsky. Leipzig: L. Litinsky, 1934. 112 p. 21½cm.

1. Refractory materials—Direct. 2. Furnaces—Direct. 3. Trademarks.
N. Y. P. L. October 26, 1937

NL 0408802 NN IU PSt WaPS

Litinsky, Leonid, 1887-
...Mess-, prüf- und kontrollgerate auf der Leipziger frühjahrsmesse 1930. Ausstellungsbericht von L. Litinsky ...
Halle (Saale) W. Knapp, 1930.
35 p. illus.
Sonderdruck aus "Die messtechnik" 1930. heft 5 bis8.

NL 0408803 OU

Litinsky, Leonid, 1887–

Messung grosser gasmengen, anleitung zur praktischen ermittlung grosser mengen von gas- und luft-strömen in technischen betrieben von L. Litinsky ... mit 138 abbildungen, 37 rechenbeispielen, 8 tabellen im text und auf einer tafel, sowie 13 schaubildern und rechentafeln im anhang. Leipzig, O. Spamer, 1922.

xv, 274 p. illus., tables, diagrs. 24cm. (*Half-title:* Chemische technologie in einzeldarstellungen ... Allgemeine chemische technologie)

"Literaturübersicht": p. [260]–266.

1. Gas-meters. 2. Gases, Flow of.

Library of Congress TH7940.L5 24-20671

NL 0408804 DLC ICRL ICJ MiU

VOLUME 336

Litinsky, Leonid, 1887-
Die Nebenproduktenkokerei in Südrussland; Entwicklung, Stand, Organisation und Aussichten der russischen Teerkokerei. Leipzig, B. G. Teubner, 1921.
42 p. diagrs. 22 cm. (Osteuropa-Institut in Breslau. Vorträge und Aufsätze, 3. Abt.: Bergbau u. Hüttenkunde, Heft 1)
"Quellen": p. 42.

1. Coal-tar products. 2. Chemical industries—Russia. I. Title. (Series: Breslau. Osteuropa-Institut. Vorträge und Aufsätze. 3. Abt: Bergbau u. Hüttenkunde, Heft 1)

HD9665.R92L5 52-46884

NL 0408805 DLC ICU NN CSt-H

Litinsky, Leonid, 1887-
Ofenbau und feuerfeste erzeugnisse auf der ausstellung "Gas und wasser" Berlin. Auszug aus dem ausstellungsbericht, von L. Litinsky... Mit neun abbildungen... Leipzig, O. Spamer ͵1929?͵
16 p. illus.

NL 0408806 OU

Litinsky, Leonid, 1887-
... Prüfanstalt für feuerfeste materialien, von L. Litinsky ... mit 83 abbildungen im text. (Durchgesehener und erweiterter sonderdruck aus der zeitschrift "Feuerfest-ofenbau" 1930, heft 1-4) Leipzig, O. Spamer, 1930.
127 p. illus. 21cm. (Monographien zur feuerungstechnik, bd. 11)
Bibliographical foot-notes.

1. Fireproofing. 2. Testing laboratories. I. Title.
Library of Congress TH1092.L5 30-33968
Copyright A—Foreign 8954
͵2͵ 620.19

NL 0408807 DLC NN OU

Litinsky, Leonid, 1887-
Schamotte und silika, ihre eigenschaften, verwendung und prüfung, von ob.-ing. L. Litinsky ... Mit 75 abbildungen im text und auf 4 tafeln und 43 zahlentafeln im text. Leipzig, O. Spamer, 1925.
vii, 286 p. illus., IV pl., diagrs. 24cm.
"Literaturübersicht": p. ͵256͵-276.

1. Refractory materials. 2. Fire-clay. 3. Silica.
Library of Congress TN677.L5 25-21204

NL 0408808 DLC ICJ NN

Litinsky, Leonid, 1887-
... Trockene Kokskühlung mit Verwertung der Koksglut, von L. Litinsky ... Mit 18 Abbildungen und 7 Tabellen im Text. Leipzig, O. Spamer, 1922.
52 p. incl. illus., tables, diagrs. 22cm. (Monographien zur Feuerungstechnik. Heft 4)

NL 0408809 ICJ NN

Litinsky, Leonid, 1887-
Über die wahl eines gaswerksofensystems. Von L. Litinsky ... Mit 9 abbildungen. Halle (Saale) Kommissionsverlag von W. Knapp, 1926.
29 p. illus., diagr. 24½cm.
"Die vorliegende arbeit bildet einen abschnitt aus meinem im verlage Wilhelm Knapp in Halle (Saale) im druck befindlichen buch 'Kokerei- und gaswerksöfen'."—Foot-note p. 6.

1. Gas-producers. 2. Furnaces. I. Title.
Library of Congress TP762.L5 41-40062

NL 0408810 DLC NN OU

Litinsky, Leonid, 1887-
... Wärmewirtschaftsfragen, von L. Litinsky ... Mit 40 Abbildungen und 17 Tabellen im Text und Anhang. Leipzig, O. Spamer, 1923.
194 p. incl. tables, diagrs. 22cm. (Monographien zur Feuerungstechnik. Heft 5)

NL 0408811 ICJ NN IU

Lititchevsky, Nina, 1911-
... Contribution à l'étude de la fibrosite ... Paris, 1938.
Thèse - Univ. de Paris.

NL 0408812 CtY

Lititz, Pa. Linden Hall Moravian Seminary for Young Ladies.
Catalogue. Lancaster, Pa., 1869.
8°

NL 0408813 MnHi

Lititz, Pa. Moravian church.
Marriage register of the Moravian church, Litiz. 1743-1800.
(*In* Pennsylvania archives. Harrisburg, 1896. 21cm. 2d ser., v. 9, p. ͵137͵-148)

1. Registers of births, etc.—Lititz, Pa. I. Title. 19-7631
Library of Congress F146.P41 2d ser., vol. 9

NL 0408814 DLC

Lititz, Pa. Moravian church.
Reminiscences of the Moravian Church at Lititz...
see under Hart, Francis P.

BX8581
L5W3 Lititz, Pa. Warwick Moravian congregation.
Souvenir of the Sesquicentennial...1899.
Lititz, Pa.,? 1899.
1 pam. 8°

NL 0408816 DLC

... Lititz as an early musical centre ...
see under [Beck, Herbert Huebener]

Litiz, Pa.
see
Lititz, Pa.

Litiz Academy for Boys
see John Beck's School Lyceum, Lititz, Pa.

Lititz-Warwick directory and surrounding country
see Directory of Lititz and northern Lancaster County.

En litjen book som kallas Bonde-practica, eller Vädher-book innehållandes några sköna reglor, huruledes man skal känna, ochläraheela-åhrsens lopp, alltijdh varandes åhr ifrå åhr. Stockholm, B. Lagerström, 1924.
113p. illus. 24cm.

Reprint of the 1662 edition.

1.Calendar, Germanic. I.Title: Bonde-practica.

NL 0408821 CSdS

Litjens, H P M
Onmaatschappelijke gezinnen; sociologisch onderzoek naar de onmaatschappelijkheid te Maastricht. ͵With summary in English͵ Assen, Van Gorcum, 1953.
298 p. illus. 23 cm. (Bouwstenen voor de kennis der maatschappij, 13)

1. Family. 2. Maastricht—Soc. condit. I. Title.

HQ636.M3L5 55-18354 ‡

NL 0408822 DLC NNC MH PU NIC CtY OrU MH-BA

Litke, Fedor Petrovich, graf, 1797-1882.
Четырекратное путешествіе въ Сѣверный Ледовитый океанъ, совершенное по повелѣнію императора Александра I, на военномъ бригѣ Новая Земля, въ 1821, 1822 1823 и 1824 годахъ. Съ присовокупленіемъ путешествій лейтенанта Демидова въ Бѣлое море и штурмана Иванова на рѣку Печору. Санктпетербургъ, Въ Морской тип., 1828.
2 v. in 1. plates, maps (part fold.) 31 cm.
L. C. copy imperfect: p. 321-331 of v. 1 wanting. cf. Sokolov, A. P. Russkaia morskaia biblioteka, 1883, p. 183.
1. Voyages around the world. 2. Novaia Zemlia (Ship) I. Title.
Title transliterated: Chetyrekratnoe puteshestvie.
G420.L75 1828 49-37652

NL 0408823 DLC

Litke, Fedor Petrovich, graf, 1797-1882.
Четырехкратное путешествие в Северный Ледовитый океан на военном бриге "Новая Земля" в 1821-1824 годах. ͵Под ред. и с примечаниями Я. А. Марголина; вступ. статья Б. П. Орлова͵ Москва, Гос. изд-во геогр. лит-ры 1948.
383 p. illus., port., fold. maps. 27 cm.

1. Voyages around the world. 2. Novaia Zemlia (Ship) I. Title.
Title transliterated: Chetyrekhkratnoe puteshestvie v Severnyĭ Ledovityĭ okean.
G420.L75 1948 49-21252
rev

NL 0408824 DLC OOxM CSt

SPECIAL COLLECTIONS
B526.73
L97 Litke, Fedor Petrovich, graf, 1797-1882.
Observations du pendule invariable exécutées dans un voyage autour du monde, pendant les années 1826, 1827, 1828, 1829, par M. le contre-amiral Luetke. Traduit du russe par M. Loustaunau. Saint-Pétersbourg, Impr. de l'Académie impériale des sciences, 1836.
242 p. plates, tables. 27cm.

Translation of Opyty nad postoiannym maiatnikom ...
"Extrait des Mémoires de l'Académie impériale des sciences de St.-Pétersbourg."

NL 0408825 NNC

VOLUME 336

Litke, Fedor Petrovich, *graf*, 1797–1822.
Опыты надъ постояннымъ маятникомъ, произведенные въ путешествіе вокругъ свѣта на военномъ шлюпѣ Сенявинѣ въ 1826, 1827, 1828 и 1829 годахъ флота капитаномъ Ѳ. Литке. Санктпетебургъ, Въ Тип. Имп. Академіи наукъ, 1833.
232 p. 28 cm.

1. Pendulum. 2. Voyages around the world. 3. Seníavin (Corvette) I. Title.
Title romanized: Opyty nad postoíannym maíatnikom.

QB335.L57 72-264027

NL 0408826 DLC

Litke, Fedor Petrovich, graf, 1797–1882.
Путешествіе вокругъ свѣта, совершенное по повелѣнію императора Николая I, на военномъ шлюпѣ Сенявинѣ, въ 1826, 1827, 1828 и 1829 годахъ, флота капитаномъ Ѳедоромъ Литке. Отдѣленіе мореходное съ атласомъ. Санктпетербургъ, Печатано въ тип. Х. Гинце, 1835.
vi p., 1 l., [iii]–x, 356 p. incl. tables. diagrs., plates (partly fold.) maps (1 fold.) 29 x 22½ cm. and atlas of 6 p. l., 34 double maps. 65 cm.
The atlas, published without place or date [St. Petersburg, 1832] has engr. title: Атласъ къ путешествію вокругъ свѣта шлюпа Сенявина ... with added t. p. in French.
Imperfect: Atlas wanting.
1. Voyages around the world. 2. Seníavin (Corvette) 3. Navigation.
Title romanized: Puteshestvie vokrug svíeta.
G420.L76 5–34890

NL 0408827 DLC

Litke, Fedor Petrovich, *graf*, 1797–1882.
Voyage autour du monde, exécuté par ordre de Sa Majesté l'empereur Nicolas 1er, sur la corvette le Séniavine, dans les années 1826, 1827, 1828 et 1829, par Frédéric Lutké ... commandant de l'expédition ... Paris, Typ. de Firmin Didot frères, 1835–36.
4 v. plates (part fold.) maps (part fold.) plans (part fold.) tables, diagrs. 23 cm. ([v. 4]: 27 x 21 cm.) *and* 2 atlases. 57½ x 65 cm.
The two atlases have engraved title-pages. The atlas of the "partie nautique" (6 p. l., 34 double maps) published without place or date [St. Petersburg, 1832] has title in Russian with added t.-p. in French; the table of contents and the headings of the maps are given in Russian and French. The atlas of the "partie historique" with title: ... Atlas lithographié d'après les dessins originaux d'Alexandre Postels ... et du baron Kittlitz. Paris, Lith. de Engelmann et compagnie [1835] has text in French only.
CONTENTS.—t. 1–2. Partie historique, avec un atlas ... Tr. du russe sur le manuscrit original, sous les yeux de l'auteur, par ... F. Boyé.—t. 3. Contenant les travaux de mm. les naturalistes, rédigé par A. Postels: Notices géognostiques, par A. Postels (tr. de l'allemand par J. M. de Genève). Notices sur les îles Carolines, par le dr. Mertens. Observations zoologiques, par F. H. de Kittlitz. Observations du docteur Brandt sur le polypes, acalèphes et astéries recueillies par le dr. Mertens. Biographie du docteur Mertens. [t. 4] Partie nautique avec un atlas. Tr. du russe, sous les yeux de l'auteur, par ... J. Boyé, St. Pétersbourg, Impr. de C. Hintze, 1836.

1. Voyages around the world. 2. Seníavin (Corvette) 3. Kamchatka—Descr. & trav. 4. Bering sea. 5. Caroline islands. 6. Natural history. 7. Navigation. I. Boyé, F., tr. II. Postels, Aleksandr Filippovich, 1801–1871. III. Mertens, Karl Heinrich, 1796–1830. IV. Kittlitz, Friedrich Heinrich, freiherr von, 1799–1874. V. Brandt, Johann Friedrich von, 1802–1879.

G420.L93 5—34891

NL 0408830 DLC PPAN WaU CtY NNC CU-S OrP NN

JS5484
L776

Litke, Karl.
In deiner Sache, Berliner; das Wirken der SED-Fraktion. Berlin, Landesvorstand der SED [1947]
48 p. 21cm.

Hoover Library

1.Berlin - Pol. & govt. - 1945- 2. Socialism in Berlin. 3.Sozialistische Einheitspartei Deutschlands. I.Sozialistische Einheitspartei Deutschlands. Landesvorstand. II.Title.

NL 0408831 CSt-H NN

LITKE, KARL.
In deiner Sache, Berliner; das Wirken der SED-Fraktion. Berlin, Landesvorstand der SED [1947] 48 p. 21cm.

Film reproduction. Positive.

1. Berlin--Politics. I. Sozialistische Einheitspartei Deutschlands. Landesvorstand.

NL 0408832 NN

[Litkenhous, Edward Earl] 1907- , ed.
...Bagasse utilization including bagasse patents... Washington, Hobart publ. co. [1945?] 2 parts in 1 v. 28cm. (PB16389.)

"Report...[of a study] carried out under War production board project no. 547."
Foreword signed: E. E. Litkenhous.
"Bibliography," part 2.

387399B. 1. Bagasse. 2. Bagasse—Bibl. I. United States. War production board.
N. Y. P. L. March 30, 1948

NL 0408833 NN MiD

[Litkenhous, Edward Earl] 1907- ed.
Bagasse utilization including bagasse patents, bibliography. Washington, Hobart, [1950]
63 p. Q.

NL 0408834 PPF

Litkenhous, Edward Earl. 1907- joint author.

Furnas, Clifford Cook, 1900–
A bibliography of unit operations of chemical engineering, by C. C. Furnas ... E. E. Litkenhous ... G. H. Montillon ... R. A. Ragatz ... R. C. Ernst ... A project sponsored by the Research committee of the Society for the promotion of engineering education, F. T. Mavis, chairman ... [Louisville, The Department of chemical engineering of the University of Louisville, °1939]

Litkenhous, Edward Earl, 1907–
The hydrogenation of nickel carbonyl ... by Edward Earl Litkenhous ... [New York, 1938]
cover-title, p. [934]–938 incl. tables, diagrs. 29½cm.
Thesis (PH. D.)—University of Minnesota, 1934.
Vita.
By E. E. Litkenhous and Charles A. Mann.
"Reprinted from Industrial and engineering chemistry, vol. 29 ... August, 1937."
"Literature cited": p. 938.

1. Hydrogenation. 2. Nickel carbonyl. I. Mann, Charles August, 1886- joint author.
39-10696
Library of Congress QD181.N6L5 1934
Univ. of Minnesota Libr.
——— Copy 2. [2] 546.741

NL 0408836 MnU DLC

Ae litl big man. Cincinnati, Longley Brothers, 1856.
1 v. (unpaged) illus. 17 cm.
A poem for children written phonetically.
1. English language - Phonetics.
2. Spelling reform. I. Longley Brothers, Cincinnati.

NL 0408837 OC

Litla jólabókin. Útgefandi: S. O. S. Akureyri, Prentsmiðja Björns Jónssonar, 1925. 12°. pp. 24.
IcH31V521

NL 0408838 NIC

Litla tímaritið. ; Útgefandi: Jón H. Guðmundsson. I. ár, 1.–2. hefti; II. ár, 1. hefti. Reykjavík, 1929–30. 2 *vols.* sm. 8° *and* 8°.
IcR1L641

NL 0408839 NIC

Litle, Guilielmus
see William, of Newburgh, 1136-1198.

Litle, Roy Finis, 1906-
A study of six-director school districts not maintaining high schools in Missouri. Ann Arbor, University Microfilms, 1949.
([University Microfilms, Ann Arbor, Mich.] Publication no. 1472)
Microfilm copy of typewritten ms. Positive.
Collation of the original: viii, 172 l. map, tables.
Thesis—University of Missouri.
Abstracted in Microfilm abstracts, v. 9 (1949) no. 3, p. 73–75.
Vita.
"Selected bibliography": leaves [169]–172.
1. Public schools—Missouri.
Microfilm AC-1 no. 1472 Mic A 49-229*

Michigan. Univ. Libr.
for Library of Congress [1]†

NL 0408841 MiU DLC

---

q657
L71p

Litle, Goodwin & company, Pittsburgh.
Pamphlets. Pittsburgh, 1922.
no.1-

No.1-3 have title System.

NL 0408842 IU

Litli hringurinn. Þýtt. Akureyri, Bókaforlag Odds Björnssonar, 1919. 8°. pp. 32.
IcF85S921

NL 0408843 NIC

Litli Kútur og Labbakútur. Danskt æfintýri handa börnum. Freysteinn Gunnarsson þýddi. Reykjavík, Þorvaldur Kolbeins, 1930. sm. 8°. pp. 52, *illustr.*
IcF85L525
"Lesbækur barnanna. 1. bók."

NL 0408844 NIC

Litlington, Nicholas, 1316?-1386.
Catholic church. *Liturgy and ritual. Missal. Westminster.*
Missale ad usum Ecclesie westmonasteriensis, nunc primum typis mandatum curante Iohanne Wickham Legg ... Londini [Harrison and sons, printers] 1891–97.

LITLIR gimsteinar. 1.-8. Útgefandi: C.H.Cox. Reykjavík,Gutenberg,1912.

48°. Illustr.
Contents:- 1.Litli hjarðsveinninn.- 2.Særði fuglinn.- 3.Sagan af týnda sauðnum.- 4.Snjóflóð 5.Litla smalastúlkan.- 6.Göfug fórn.- 7.Síðasta óskin.- 8.Góður drengur.

NL 0408846 MH NIC

VOLUME 336

Litlyngton, Nicholas
See
Litlington, Nicholas, 1316?-1386.

Litman, *pseud.*
see Geltman, Litman, 1898-1946.

Litman, Alexander, 1899-
Cicero's doctrine of nature and man, by Alexander Litman ... New York, 1930.
3 p. l., 5-41, [1] p. 23cm.
Thesis (PH. D.)—Columbia university, 1930.
Vita.

1. Cicero, Marcus Tullius. 2. Philosophy, Ancient.

Library of Congress PA6320.L5 1930 31-11375
Columbia Univ. Libr. [2] 186.3

NL 0408848 NNC NIC MH OkU CU NcD DLC

Litman, Alexander, 1899-
Man's value and destiny. Moral atheism in Spinoza. New York, 1935. f. 77-85.
Title taken from first page.
Advance proof: American scholar. Winter, 1935.

NL 0408849 OCH

Litman, Bernard.
An analysis of rotating amplifiers. [n. p., 1949]
7 p. diagrs. 28 cm.
Cover title.
Thesis—Columbia University.
"Reprinted from the Transactions of the American Institute of Electrical Engineers, volume 68, 1949."
"References": p. 7.

1. Amplifiers, Vacuum-tube. I. Title: Rotating amplifiers.

TK6565.A55L5 A 50-5787
Columbia Univ. Libraries
for Library of Congress [1]†

NL 0408850 NNC DLC

Litman, Henri.
Les lumières et les ombres du ghetto de Varsovie; souvenirs vécus des années 1939-1943. (Traduit du polonais) Tourcoing, G. Frère [1945]
95 p. 23 cm.

1. World War, 1939-1945—Atrocities. 2. Jews in Warsaw. 3. World War, 1939-1945—Personal narratives, Jewish. I. Title.

A 52-270
New York. Public Libr.
for Library of Congress [1]

NL 0408851 NN

Litman, Henri.
Les lumières et les ombres du ghetto de Varsovie; souvenirs vécus des années 1939-1943. (Traduit du polonais) Tourcoing, G. Frère [1945]
95 p. 23 cm.
Film reproduction. Positive

1. WORLD WAR, 1939-1945—ATROCITIES 2. GHETTO—WARSAW
3. WARSAW—GHETTO 4. JEWS IN POLAND—WARSAW
5. WORLD WAR, 1939-1945—PERSONAL NARRATIVES, JEWISH
6. WORLD WAR, 1939-1945—PERSONAL NARRATIVES, POLISH

NL 0408852 NN

Litman, Martin, 1906-
... Contribution á l'étude des ostéites des maxillaires ... Versailles, 1931.
Thése - Univ. de Paris.
"Bibliographie": p. [33]-34.

NL 0408853 CtY

Litman, Neil N
A preliminary report on the association of growth failure and poliomyelitis. Minneapolis, Minn.? n.p.,1948? [3]p.

"Reprinted from the Journal-Lancet, Minneapolis May,1948,vol.LXVIII,no.5,p.185."

NL 0408854 OClW

Litman, Mme. Rifka (Vincler) 1909-
... Contribution au traitement des tétanies graves; sympathectomie cervicale moyenne et greffe d'os purum ... Paris, 1939.
Thèse - Univ. de Paris.

NL 0408855 CtY

Litman, Samuel, joint author.

Ball, Thomas Fauntleroy, 1894-
Laboratory experiments in direct and alternating currents, by Thomas Fauntleroy Ball ... and Samuel Litman ... Ann Arbor, Mich., Edwards brothers, inc., 1940.

Litman, Samuel A[aron]
Finality of Decisions for the Purpose of Review in the Federal Courts. Typewritten. n. p., [1926]
19 f. 4°.
Thesis - Law School of Harvard Univeristy.

NL 0408857 MH-L

Litman, Simon, 1873-

Moody, Walter Dwight, 1874-1920, *ed.*
Business administration; theory, practice and application: editor-in-chief, Walter D. Moody ... managing editor, Samuel MacClintock ... Chicago, La Salle extension university [°1910-11]

380
L714c
Litman, Simon,1873-
Commerce and industry. [Albany, N. Y., 1908?]
p.349-360.

Caption title.
At head of title: New York state education department. New York state library. Review of legislaton 1907-8. Legislation 39zh.

NL 0408859 IU

Litman, Simon, 1873-
Competition in trade.
(In Litman, Simon, and others. Trade and commerce. Pp. 419-434. [La Salle Extension University. Business administration text-books.] Chicago. 1910.)

L920 — Competition.

NL 0408860 MB

380
L714e
Litman, Simon,1873-
The effects of the world war on trade. Philadelphia, 1926.
7p.

"Reprinted from the Annals of the American academy of political and social science, Philadelphia, September, 1926. Publication no.1992."

NL 0408861 IU

Litman, Simon, 1873-
Essentials of international trade, by Simon Litman ... New York, J. Wiley & sons, inc.; [etc., etc.] 1923.
2 p. l., iii-vi, 398 p. diagrs. 23½cm.
"References" at end of each chapter.

1. Commerce. 2. U. S.—Comm. I. Title.
Library of Congress HF1007.L77 23-18089

NL 0408862 OU ODW MiU OCU NN OU OOxM ICJ MtU IdU-SB WaS CaBVaU DLC NcD NcRS FMU ViU OKentU TU CU OCl

---

Litman, Simon, 1873-
Essentials of international trade, by Simon Litman ... 2d rev. and enl. ed. New York, J. Wiley & sons, inc.; London, Chapman & Hall, limited, 1927.
xii, 380 p. diagrs. 23½cm. $3.50
"References" at end of each chapter.

1. Commerce. 2. U. S.—Comm. I. Title.
Library of Congress HF1007.L77 1927 27-22626

NL 0408863 OOxM NN MB ICJ MiU OrCS MtU DLC WaWW WaS CaBVa NIC OCU OU OO OCl

---

382
L714f
Litman, Simon,1873-
... The foreign trade of the United States since the signing of the armistice. Philadelphia, 1921.
7p.

Caption title.
"Reprinted from the Annals of the American academy of political and social science, Philadelphia, March, 1921. Publication no.1500."

NL 0408864 IU

Litman, Simon, 1873-
Interstate commerce, trade and commerce
see under Lasalle Extension University, Chicago.

331.2
L71m
Litman, Simon,1873-
Die möglichkeit der lohnsteigerungen und die lohnfondstheorien. München, 1902.
82p.

Inaug.-diss.—Zürich.

NL 0408866 IU NN ICRL

HF3031
.L5
Litman, Simon, 1873-
The past decade of the foreign commerce of the United States. [Evanston, Ill., American Economic Association] 1920.
[313]-331 p. tables. 25 cm.
Reprinted from Americ an economic review, v. 10, no. 2, June 1920.
Bibliographical footnotes.

1. U.S.--Commerce. I. Title.

NL 0408867 MB DPU IU MH

VOLUME 336

Litman, Simon, 1873–
... Prices and price control in Great Britain and the United States during the world war, by Simon Litman ... New York [etc.] Oxford university press, 1920.
ix, 331 p. diagrs. 25½cm. (Preliminary economic studies of the war, ed. by David Kinley ... no. 19)
At head of title: Carnegie endowment for international peace. Division of economics and history.
1. Prices—Gt. Brit. 2. Prices—U. S. 3. European war, 1914–1918—Economic aspects—Gt. Brit. 4. European war, 1914–1918—Economic aspects—U. S. I. Title.
20–16218
Library of Congress HC56.P7 no. 19
——— Copy 2. HB236.G7L5

OCU DN DL NN ICJ MB ViU Ok CaBVaU WaU-L IdU-SB WaWW WaTC OrP ViU NIC KEmT CoU AU OClW OCl MiU OU ODW WaS
NL 0408868 DLC CU WaSp Wa OrPR MtU IdB WaTC OrP

Litman, Simon, 1873–
... The republic of Ukraine, by Simon Litman ... Urbana, The War committee of the University of Illinois [1919]
cover-title, 8 p. incl. map. 23cm. (University of Illinois bulletin. vol. XVI, no. 21)
1. Ukraine—Politics and government. I. Title.
A 19–330
Title from Illinois Univ. Printed by L. C.

NL 0408869 IU MH OO OCl

947
L71r
Litman, Simon,1873-
Revolutionary Russia. Urbana, Ill., 1918.
10p.
Reprinted from The American political science review, vol.XII, no.2, May, 1918.

NL 0408870 IU

387
L71s
Litman, Simon,1873-
San Francisco as a foreign port. n.p. n.d.
p.326-33
Reprinted from the University of California Chronicle, vol.X, no.3.

NL 0408871 IU

385.57
L714s
Litman, Simon,1873-
La Sibérie et le Transsibérien. Paris, 1903.
cover-title, p.[573]-589.
Extract from "Annales des sciences politiques ... 18. année, 15 septembre 1903."

NL 0408872 IU

Litman, Simon, 1873– , and others.
Trade and commerce.
— Chicago. 1910. (12), iii, 492 pp. Diagrams. Tables. [La Salle Extension University. Business administration text-books.] 23½ cm., in 8s.
Contents. — Trade and commerce, by Simon Litman. — Government and industry, by Stephen Leacock. — The value of commercial geography to business men, by Theodore H. Boggs. — Mercantile agencies and their work, by John Boulter. — The value of commercial museums to com-
*5632.43
merce and industry, by Wilfrid H. Schoff. — Competition in trade, by Simon Litman. — Our commercial relations with South America, by John Barrett. — Water-borne freight in the foreign trade as affecting our national independence and prosperity, by Lewis Nixon. — Quiz questions.
Bibliography, pp. 167–170.
Each work is catalogued separately.

NL 0408874 MB IU MH

Litman, Sloim, 1908-
... Contribution à l'étude des épithéliomas de l'appendice ... Paris, 1939.
Thèse - Univ. de Paris.

NL 0408875 CtY

Litmanowicz, H(erschlik): 1884- Aus d. Kgl. Med. Klin. zu Breslau. Über das Verhalten des Ptyalins unter normalen und krankhaften Bedingungen. ⟨Untersuchungen mit Hilfe d. 'Stärkekleisterplatte'.⟩ Weimar 1909: Wagner. 24 S. 8°
Breslau, Med. Diss. v. 16. Febr. 1909, Ref. v. Strümpell
[Geb. 19. Apr. 84 Petrikau; Wohnort: Lodz; Staatsangeh.: Rußland; Vorbildung: Gymn. Petrikau Reife Juni 03; Studium: Berlin 6, Leipzig 2, Breslau 2 S.; Rig. 21. Jan. 09.] [U 09. 561

NL 0408876 ICRL DNLM NN

Litmanowicz, Władysław.
Obrona słowiańska szachowe; studium teoretyczne. [Warszawa] Wydawnictwo Głównego Komitetu Kultury Fizycznej [1951]
194, [4] p.

NL 0408877 OCl

Litmanowitsch, Menasche, 1908-
Optische Untersuchungen über Ionenassoziation. Zürich, 1939.
Inaug.-Diss. - Zürich.

NL 0408878 CtY

Ic
C19
D361
Litmyndir af íslenzkum jurtum. I. [Reykjavík, Ísafoldarprentsmiðja, 1948]
[1] l., 19 col. plates. 22cm.
Preface by Ingólfur Davíðsson.
Cover title.

NL 0408879 NIC

QA999 Litoff, Oscar, 1925-
The general linear group. 1953.
37 l.
Thesis--Univ. of Chicago.
1. Groups, Theory of.

NL 0408880 ICU

Litogea
see Moscow. Institut prikladnoĭ mineralogii.

Litografia Cuciniello e Bianchi
see Cuciniello e Bianchi (Firm)

Litografía nacional Franco, Guayaquil.
Atlas (mapa provincial) del Ecuador. Guayaquil, Litografía nacional Franco [192–] 17 l. incl. maps. 20cm.
Cover-title.
——— ——— Same. 18 l.
"Compliments of Banco de descuento, Guayaquil, Ecuador" printed on cover; "Banco de descuento...Schedule of collection charges..." l. 18.
325036B. 1. Ecuador—Maps, 192–. I. Banco de descuento, Guayaquil, Ecuador.
N. Y. P. L. April 8, 1947

NL 0408883 NN

Litografía Nacional Franco, *Guayaquil.*
Atlas (mapa provincial) del Ecuador. Guayaquil [1940?]
[34] p. col. maps. 21 cm.
Cover title.
1. Ecuador—Maps. 2. Ecuador—Descr. & trav. I. Title.
G1735.L5 1940 70–653022

NL 0408884 DLC DPU

Litografiskt allehanda. Album för svensk konst.
1.- årg.
Stockholm [1859]-
illus.
1.Art. Periodicals. 2.Art in Sweden.

NL 0408885 MnU

Litolff, Henry Charles, 1818-1891
[Nocturne, sur le lac, sans souci, piano]
Au pays des souvenirs. 3 morceaux caracteristiques pour piano. Braunschweig, Litolff [n.d..
23p. 31cm. (Collection Litolff, no. 1892)

NL 0408886 OrSaW

Litolff, Henry Charles, 1818-1891.
Ave Maria. [Pour S., T. ou Bar. Accomp. de piano.]
Paris. Choudens. [187–?] (1), 5 pp. F°.
April 11, 1902.
E3573 — S.r. — Church music. Anthems, &c.

NL 0408887 MB

Film
8799
Litolff, Henry Charles, 1818-1891.
[Die Tempelheeren. Selections; arr.]
Ballet-Musik aus Die Tempelherren, grosse Oper von Henry Litolff. Braunschweig, H. Litolff [n.d.]
27p. (Collection Litolff no.1893)
Arranged for piano.
Microfilm copy (negative) made in 1963 of the original in the Free Library of Philadelphia.
On reel with the composers Rêve d'un captif, op.41, Brunswick, G.M.Meyer, jr. [n.d.]
Contents.- 1. Adagio.- 2. Auftritt der Zigeuner & Csardas.- 3. Die Bogenschützen des Königs.- 4. Schmetterlings- Tanz.- 5. Kleine Tanz-Scene.- 6. Gigue.
1. Operas - Excerpts - Piano scores.
2. Ballets - Excerpts - Piano scores.

NL 0408889 IaU

VOLUME 336

Litolff, Henry Charles, 1818-1891. 6
La boite de Pandore. Opéra bouffe en 3 actes. Paroles de Th. Barrière. Musique de Henri Litolff. Partition piano et chant. Paris. Bathlot. [1871.] (3), 243 pp. L. 8°.

April 11, 1902.
E3574 — Barrière, Théodore. — Operas.

NL 0408890 MB

M1503 L68 B6 1880
Litolff, Henry Charles, 1818-1891.
[La boîte de Pandore. Piano-vocal score. French]
La boite de Pandore; opéra bouffe en 3 actes. Paroles de Th^re^. Barrière, musique de Henry Litolff. Partition piano et chant. Paris, L. Bathlot [ca. 1880] Pl. no. L. B. 437.
score (243 p.)

At head of title: Théâtre des Folies Dramatiques.

NL 0408891 WaU

VW 1503 L 77b
LITOLFF, HENRY CHARLES, 1818-1891.
Die Braut von Kynast, grosse romantische Oper in drei Akten von Friedr: Fischer, in Musik gesetzt von Henri Litolff. Vollständiger Clavier-Auszug von L. Winkler. Braunschweig, G.M. Meyer [1847]
score(214p.) 33cm.

First performed 1847.

NL 0408892 ICN MB NN

Film 8799
Litolff, Henry Charles, 1818-1891.
[Chant d'amour, piano, op.78]
Chant d'amour, etude de salon pour le piano...op.78. Brunswick, G.M.Meyer, jr. [n.d.] Pl.no.965.
11p.

At head of title: "Julie".
Microfilm copy (negative) made in 1963 of the original in the Free Library of Philadelphia.
On reel with the composer's Rêve d'un captif op.41, Brunswick, Meyer [n.d.]

NL 0408893 IaU

Litolff, Henry Charles, 1818-1891.
[Spinnlied, op. 81, piano]
Chant de la fileuse, op. 81, für pianoforte. Braunschweig, Henry Litolff [c1898]
11p. 31cm. (Collection Litolff, no. 2224)

NL 0408894 OrSaW CU

Litolff, Henry Charles, 1818-1891.
Chant des Belges. Ouverture dramatique. Op. 101. Partition. Brunswick. Litolff. [1858?] (1), 64 pp. L. 8°.

E3574 — T.r. — Overtures.

NL 0408895 MB

*M1011 .L53 No.3
Litolff, Henry Charles, 1818-1891.
[Concerto, piano, no. 3, op. 45, E♭ major; arr.
Concerto symphonique, no. 3 (National Hollandais) op. 45, für Klavier & Orchester. Mit unterlegtem 2. Klavier nach der Partitur bearb. Neuausgabe von Th. Leschetitzky. Braunschweig, H. Litolff [18--?]
score (76 p.) 31cm. (Collection Litolff, no. 2335)

1. Concertos (Piano)—2-piano scores. I. Leschetitzki, Theodor, 1830-1915, ed.

NL 0408896 MB

Litolff, Henry Charles. 1818-1891.
Concerto symphonique [No. IV.] pour piano et orchestre. Op. 102. [Partition] piano.
Brunswick. Litolff. [185-?] 87 pp. 34 cm.
The instrumentation is indicated.

H5402 — Concertos. Two pianofortes. — Pianoforte. Music. Two pianofortes.

NL 0408897 MB MH

Film 8879
Litolff, Henry Charles, 1818-1891.
[Concerto symphonique, piano, no.5, op. 123, C minor; arr.]
[Concerto symphonique n:V, op.123 pour piano et orchestre. Braunschweig, Henry Litolff's Verlag, n.d.] Pl. no.2388.
Score (57p.)
Orchestral part arranged for second piano.
Caption title.
Microfilm made in 1963 of the original in the Memorial Library of Music of Stanford University. 1 reel. 35mm.
1. Concertos (Piano), Arranged.

NL 0408898 IaU

785.1 L77d
Litolff, Henry Charles, 1818-1891
...Le dernier jour de la terreur, drame symphonique. Op.55. Paris, Costallat [n.d.]
72p. Q.
Caption title.
Score.

NL 0408899 IaU

VW 1530.3 L 776s
LITOLFF, HENRY CHARLES, 1818-1891.
[Scenen aus Göthe's Faust. Faust in seinem Studirzimmer] Erste Scene. Faust in seinem Studirzimmer. Für Orchester, Sopran- und Bariton-Stimme und Chor mit Declamation. Op.103, No.1. Braunschweig, H.Litolff's Verlag [18--?]
score(136p.) 30cm.

NL 0408900 ICN

* M1 .S444 v.70 no.14
Litolff, Henry Charles, 1818-1891.
Erstes Spinnlied, Ausgewählts Compositionen für das pianoforte, Op. 81. Price 20 Ngr. Braunschweig, Henry Litolff's Verlag ... [18--?] Pl. no. 966.
11 p. 32cm. (Sheet music collection, v. 70, no. 14)
Stamped: Strassburg, Handlung Leinanstalt, Gebrüder Bug.
1. Piano music. I. Title.

NL 0408901 ViU

M1503 L53E8
Litolff, Henry Charles, 1818-1891.
[L'escadron volant de la reine; acc. arr. piano]
L'escadron volant de la reine; opéra-comique en 3 actes. Paroles de A. d'Ennery [pseud.] & J. Brésil. Paris, L. Bathlot & Vve. Héraud [1888] Pl. no. L. B. 6640.
317 p.
French words.

NL 0408902 CU MB

Litolff, Henry Charles, 1818-1891.
[La fiancée du roi de Garbe. Vocal score]
...La fiancée du roi de Garbe; opéra comique en 4 actes. Paroles de M. M. Dennery et Chabrillat. Musique de Henry Litolff... Paris, Maison Royol, L. Bathlot, successeur [1874?] Publ.pl.no. L.B.842. 340 p. 28cm.

Arranged by C. Genet.

J. S. BILLINGS MEM. COLL.
429344B. 1. Operas, Comic—Vocal scores. I. Dennery, Adolphe Philippe, 1811-1899. La fiancée du roi de Garbe. II. Chabillat, Henri, 1842-1893. La fiancée du roi de Garbe. III. Genet, C., arr.
April 23, 1943

NL 0408903 NN MB CU

Film 8799
Litolff, Henry Charles
[Frascati valse, piano]
Frascati valse [for] piano. [n.pub. n.p., n.d.]
9p.

Caption title.
Microfilm copy (negative) made in 1963 of the original and the Free Library of Philadelphia.
On reel with the composer's Rêve d'un captif, op.41, Brunswick, Meyer, [n.d.]

NL 0408904 IaU

Film 8824
Litolff, Henry Charles, 1818-1891.
[Caprice sur des motifs de Lucrezia Borgia, piano, op.20]
Grand caprice sur des motifs de l'opera di Lucrezia di Borgia. Transcrite pour le piano, op.20. [Berlin, A.M.Schlesinger [1846?] Pub. no. S3212.
[2,10p.] 32 x 33cm.

Caption title: "Grand caprice de l'opera Lucrezia Borgia de Donizetti, op.20".

Microfilm (negative) made in 1963 by the Library of Congress Photodup. Service.
On reel with the composer's Opuscules, piano, op.25, Berlin [1846?]
1. Piano music. 2. Donizetti, Gaetano, 1797-1848. Lucrezia Borgia.

NL 0408906 IaU

Litolff, Henry Charles, 1818-1891.
...Héloise et Abailard; opéra-comique en 3 actes, paroles de M. M^rs^. Clairville et W. Busnach. Musique de Henry Litolff. Partition piano et chant... Paris: L. Bathlot [ca. 1872]. Publ. pl. no. L. B. 633. 311 p. front. (port.) 4°.

Vocal score. French words.
"Représenté pour la première fois à Paris, au théâtre des Folies-dramatiques, le 17 octobre, 1872."
"Partition piano et chant réduite par C. Genet."

JUILLIARD FOUNDATION FUND.
100802A. 1. Operas.—Piano and voice. 2. Operas (Comic).—Piano and voice. 3. Clairville, pseud. of Louis François Nicolaie, 1811-79. 4. Busnach, William Bertrand, 1832-1907. 5. Title.
N. Y. P. L. January 31, 1924.

NL 0408907 NN MB ICN NcU CU

VOLUME 336

Litolff, Henry Charles, 1818-1891.
König Lear. Oper in drei Akten nach Shakespeare und Holinshed . . . Ouverture. Partitur.
Braunschweig. Litolff. [189-?] 32 pp. F°.

G768 — T.r. — Overtures. — Shakespeare, William. King Lear.

NL 0408908 MB

Film 8799 Litolff, Henry Charles, 1818-1891.
[Marche funèbre, piano, op.116]
Marche funèbre pour le piano... [op.116]
A la mémoire de Giacomo Meyerbeer.
Braunschweig, H.Litolff [n.d.] Pl.no.2426.
7p.

Microfilm copy (negative) made in 1963 of the original in the Free Library of Philadelphia.
On reel with the composer's Rêve d'un captif, op.41, Brunswick, Meyer [n.d.]

NL 0408909 IaU

LITOLFF, HENRY CHARLES, 1818-1891.
Les octaves; morceau de concert pour le piano, op.106
Braunschweig, H.Litolff's Verlag; New York, Scharfenberg & Luis [186-] Pl. no.1454. 11 p. 33cm.
Film reproduction. Negative.
1. Piano. I. Title.

NL 0408910 NN

Film 8799 Litolff, Henry Charles, 1818-1891.
[Les octaves, piano]
Les octaves. [Morceau de concert.
New York, G.Schirmer, 1902]
11p. (Exhibition Pieces: A collection of Brilliant and Difficult Compositions for Pianoforte)

Microfilm copy (negative) made in 1963 of the original in the Free Library of Philadelphia.
On reel with the composer's Rêve d'un captif., op.41, Brunswick, Meyer [n.d.]

NL 0408911 IaU

Film 9824 Litolff, Henry Charles, 1818-1891.
[Opuscules, piano, op.25, no.1-6]
[Opuscules, op.25. For piano.] Berlin, A.M.Schlesinger [1846?] Pl.nos.5321?-3222.
various pagings.

Microfilm (negative) made in 1963 by the Library of Congress Photoduplication Service
On reel with the composer's Caprice sur des motifs de Lucrezia Borgia, Berlin [1846?]

1. Piano music.

NL 0408912 IaU

Litolff, Henry Charles, 1818-1891.
[Die Girondisten.] Ouverture zu Die Girondisten, Trauerspiel von Robert Griepenkerl. Op. 80. Partitur.
Braunschweig. Meyer. [187-?] (1), 70 pp. L. 8°.

April 11, 1902.
E3574 — Overtures. — Girondisten, Die. Overture.

NL 0408913 MB

---

fM209 L79M3 Litolff, Henry Charles, 1818-1891.
[Maximilian Robespierre (Overture); arr., piano, 4 hands]
Ouverture[zu] Maximilian Robespierre, op.55. Trauerspiel von Robert Griepenkerl, componirt ... von H.Litolff [und bearb. von L.Winkler] für Pianoforte zu vier Händen. Branschweig, G.M.Meyer, jr. [1850?] Pl.no.860.
25p. 32cm.

Also published with the title: Le dernier jour de la terreur.

NL 0408914 IaU

Litolff, Henry Charles, 1818-1891.
Ouverture zu Maximilian Robespierre, Trauerspiel von Robert Griepenkerl, componirt...von Henry Litolff. Op. 55. Partitur... Braunschweig: H. Litolff's Verlag [1856]. Publ. pl. no. 1246.
1 p.l., 80 p. f°.

Full score.

JULIAN EDWARDS COLL.
1. Orchestra (Full).—Overtures. 2. Griepenkerl, Wolfgang Robert, 1810-68: Maximilian Robespierre.
N. Y. P. L. April 25, 1916.

NL 0408915 NN ICN MB

---

sVM 1004 L 77m LITOLFF, HENRY CHARLES, 1818-1891.
[Maximilian Robespierre], Ouverture zu "Maximilian Robespierre"... Für salonorch. bearb. von Otto Dobrindt... [Berlin, R.Birnbach, c1924]
12 pt. 32cm.

A second copy of the 1st violin part.
Composed as an overture to W.R.Griepenkerl's play Maximilian Robespierre.
Plate no.: R.B. 1657.

NL 0408916 ICN

LITOLFF, Henry Charles, 1818-1891.
Die preussische post. Caprice pour piano. Oeuv. 35. n.p., n.d.

NL 0408917 MH

Litolff, Henry Charles, 1818-1891.
Premier grand quatuor pour deux violons, alto et violoncelle, composé... par Henri Litolff, oeuv.60. Brunswick, C.M.Meyer, jr., etc. n.d. 4 parts in portfolio. 36cm.
Publ.no. 882.

NL 0408918 CU

Film 8799 Litolff, Henry Charles, 1818-1891.
[Rêve d'un captif, violin & piano, op.41]
Rêve d'un captif. [n.d.] (Card 2)
On reel with the composer's Frascati valse [n.p., n.d.]— Chant d'amour, op.78, Brunswick [n.d.]— Le repos, op.54, no.2, Brunswick [n.d.]— Terpsichore, op.57, Brunswick [n.d.]— Spinnlied, no.2, op.104, Braunschweig [n.d.]— Ballet Musik aus Die Templeheeren, Braunschweig [n.d.]

1. Violin and piano music.

NL 0408919 IaU

VM 2003 L 776r LITOLFF, HENRY CHARLES, 1818-1891.
...Ruth et Booz, scène biblique de H.Lefebvre. Musique de H.Litolff. Paris, Choudens [1869?]
59p. 28cm.

Vocal score with piano accompaniment.
French words.
Plate no.: A.C. 1805.

NL 0408920 ICN MB

Litolff, Henry Charles, 1818-1891.
[Ruth et Booz. Vocal score]
...Ruth et Booz; scène biblique de H. Lefebvre. Musique de H. Litolff. Paris, Choudens [ca. 1900] Publ. pl. no. A.C.1805.
59 p. 28cm.

Reissue of the original edition, 1869.

CARNEGIE CORP. OF NEW YORK.
372398B. 1. Oratorios—Vocal score. I. Lefebvre, Hippolyte. Ruth et Booz.
N. Y. P. L. January 10, 1947

NL 0408921 NN NcU

LITOLFF, Henry Charles, 1818-1891.
Scenen aus Goethe's Faust. Scene 1, 2. Partitur. Op. 103.
Braunschweig. Litolff. [187-?] 2 parts in 1 v. F°.
Contents. — 1. Faust in seinem Studirzimmer, für Orchester, Sopran- und Bariton Stimme und Chor mit Declamation. 2. Vor dem Thore, für Orchester, Tenor- und Bass Stimme und Chor.

NL 0408922 MB

Litolff, Henry Charles, 1818–1891.
[Concerto symphonique, piano & orchestra, no. 4, op. 102, D minor. Scherzo, arr.]

Scherzo concerto for piano and orchestra; an adaptation of the famous Scherzo from Concerto symphonique no. 4. [Arr. by] Curzon. London, Hawkes; sole selling agents: Boosey & Hawkes, °1948.
violin-conductor score (12 p.) and parts. 32 cm. (Hawkes concert edition)
Abridged version for piano and small orchestra; originally for piano and large orchestra.

"This arrangement can be effectively performed by strings and small combinations with solo pianoforte."
"Duration: 4¼ mins."

1. Piano with chamber orchestra, Arranged—Scores (reduced) and parts. I. Curzon, Frederic, 1899– arr.
M1010.L8 op.102.C8 48–21282*

NL 0408924 DLC IU

Film 8799 Litolff, Henry Charles, 1818-1891.
[Sérénade, piano, op.61]
Sérénade, pour le piano, oeuv.61.
Brunswick, G.M.Meyer, jr. [n.d.] Pl.no.885.
10p.

Microfilm copy (negative) made in 1963 of the original in the Free Library of Philadelphia.
On reel with the composer's Rêve d'un captif, op.41, Brunswick, Meyer [n.d.]

NL 0408925 IaU

Litolff, Henry Charles, 1818-1891.
Souvenir de l'opéra de Donizetti Lucia di Lammermoor pour piano seul, composé et executé aux concerts par H. Litolff. Op. 19. Berlin, Ad. Mt. Schlesinger [18-]
15 p. f°.

NL 0408926 NN

VOLUME 336

VM 25 L 77s LITOLFF, HENRY CHARLES, 1818-1891.
Spinning song. (Spinnlied) Revised and fingered by Wm. Scharfenberg... ₍New York, G. Schirmer, inc., c1884₎
11p.

Caption title.
Plate no.: 3663.

NL 0408927 ICN

---

qM786.41 L715s 1910 Litolff, Henry Charles, 1818-1891.
₍Spinnlied₎
Spinnlied. Spinning song. ₍Rev. ed. by Rafael Joseffy. Rev. and fingered by Wm. Scharfenberg₎ New York, G. Schirmer ₍c1910₎
9p. 35cm. (Brilliant pieces for the piano with scale-, arpeggio- and passage-work, 2d ser.)

For piano.

NL 0408928 IU

VM 1003 L 769t LITOLFF, HENRY CHARLES, 1818-1891.
₍Les templiers. Airs de ballet₎ Les templiers, opéra en 5 actes. Airs de ballet. Partition d'orchestre. Paris, Enoch frères & Costallat₍188-₎
score(258-322p.) 36cm.

Contents.--Adagio.--Entrée des Bohémiens.--Czardaz.--Les archers du roi.--Petite danse scénique.--Gigue.

NL 0408929 ICN

Litolff, Henry Charles, 1818-1891.
...Les templiers; opéra en 5 actes. Poème de M. M. Jules Adenis, Armand Silvestre & Lionel Bonnemère. Musique de Henry Litolff. Partition piano & chant réduite par l'auteur... Paris: Enoch frères & Costallat, 1886. Publ. pl. no. E. F. & C. 1201. 401 p. 4°.

Vocal score. French words.
"Représenté pour la première fois sur le Théâtre royal de la Monnaie à Bruxelles. (Janvier 1886).

JUILLIARD FOUNDATION FUND.
100797A. 1. Operas.—Piano and voice. 2. Adenis, Jules, 1823–1900. 3. Silvestre, Paul Armand, 1837–1901. 4. Bonnemère, Lionel, 1843– 5. Title.
N. Y. P. L. February 7, 1924.

NL 0408930 NN MB ICN WaU NIC CU NcU IaU

LITOLFF, Henry Charles, 1818-1891.
The three sisters, a set of admired quadrille taken from the French opera of "Les trois soeurs." N.Y. [18-?]

4°. pp. 11.

NL 0408931 MH

Film 8799 Litolff, Henry Charles, 1818-1891.
₍Le repos, piano, op.54, no.2₎
Trois morceaux caractéristiques pour le piano, oeuv.54, no.₍2₎:...Le repos. Brunswick, G.M.Meyer, jr. ₍n.d.₎ Pl.no.835₍B₎
10p.

Microfilm copy (negative) made in 1963 of the original in the Free Library of Philadelphia.
On reel with the composer's Rêve d'un captif, op.41, Brunswick, Meyer ₍n.d.₎

NL 0408932 IaU

LITOLFF, Henry Charles, 1818-1891.
Valse de bravoure pour le piano. Oeuv. 66. n.p., n.d.

NL 0408933 MH

Film 9017 Litolff, Henry Charles, 1818-1891.
₍Valse sur des motifs de Heloise et Abelard, piano; arr.₎
Valse sur des motifs de l'opera comique Heloise et Abelard. ₍n.d.₎

Nationalbibliothek, Wien. 1 reel. 35mm.
On reel with the composer's Tarentelle Calabraise ₍n.p., n.d.₎— Das neue Lied ₍n.p., n.d.₎— La boîte de Pandore Waltz ₍n.p., n.d.₎
1. Piano music (4 hands); Arranged. 2. Litolff, Henry Charles, 1818-1891. Heloise et Abelard.

NL 0408934 IaU

Litolff, Henry Charles, 1818-1891.
Das Welfenlied von Gustav von Meyern, musikalisch illustrirt für grosses Orchester. Op. 99. Partitur.
Braunschweig. Litolff. [1856.] (3), 84 pp. L. 8°.

April 11, 1902.
E3575 — T.r. — Symphonic poems.

NL 0408935 MB

Film 8799 Litolff, Henry Charles, 1818-1891.
₍Spinnlied, no.2, op.104, piano₎
₍Zweites Spinnlied, op.104₎. Braunschweig, H.Litolff, n.d.₎ Pl.no.1453.
13p.

Caption title.
Microfilm copy (negative) made in 1963 of the original in the Free Library of Philadelphia.
On reel with the composers Rêve d'un captif, Brunswick, Meyer ₍n.d.₎

NL 0408936 IaU

---

*GB8 V6755R 3.15.48 Litolff, Henry Charles, 1818-1891.
Zur Feier der 4 Tage im März 1848! 12. 13. 14. 15. der heldenmüthigen Studirenden-Legion an der Wiener Hochschule brüderlich geweiht von Henry Litolff und Siegfried Kapper. Dritte Auflage.
Wien, am 15. März 1848, dem ersten Tage der Constitution.
folder([4]p.) 22.5x15.5cm.
Helfert (Wiener Parnass) 311.
Printer's imprint on p.[4]: K. k. Hof=Buchdruckerei des L. Sommer (vormals Strauss) in Wien.

The poem by Kapper has title "Chorgesang der Wiener Studenten-Legion"; includes the music by Litolff.

NL 0408938 MH

Litolff, firm, Brunswick.
Collection Litolff...
Braunschweig & New York, [1870]

ML 10106

NL 0408939 DLC

Litolff, firm, Brunswick
Collection Litolff: Hauptcatalog. Braunschweig [1909?]

3 v. in 1, paged contin.

NL 0408940 MH

Litolff, firm, Brunswick.
many.
Haupt-Catalog der Collection Litolff. Braunschweig ₍1895?₎
106 p. 26cm.

Caption-title.
Excerpt: Verband der deutschen Musikalienhändler. Musik-Katalog. Gesammelte Verlags-Kataloge... Leipzig, 1895–97. Bd. 6.

——— ——— Nova. 1896–97.

Excerpt: Verband der deutschen Musikalienhändler. Musik-Katalog. Gesammelte Verlags-Kataloge... Leipzig, 1895–97. Ergänzungsbd. 2.
Bound with the above.

348460B. 1. Music—Bibl.
N. Y. P. L. November 22, 1946

NL 0408941 NN

Litolff, firm, Brunswick
Haus-Chronik von Henry Litolff's Verlag, Braunschweig. [Braunschweig, 1914]

58 p. illus., ports.

NL 0408942 MH

Litolff's musical world. A monthly magazine of new compositions for the pianoforte.

Boston, A. P. Schmidt ₍18

v. 31 cm.

On spine : Musikalische Welt.
Editor : C. Schultze.

1. Piano music. I. Schultze, Clemens, 1839–1900, ed.

M20.L73 M 53–1197 ‡

NL 0408943 DLC

Litoměřice, Czechoslovak Republic. Ackerbau-, Obst- und Weinbauschule. *Landwirtschaftlich-Chemische Untersuchungs- und Samencontrolstation.*
Jahresbericht. 1.–2.; 1894/95–1895/96. Leitmeritz.
2 v. 25 cm.
Report year ends Nov. 30.
No more published?

1. Agricultural chemistry. 2. Seed adulteration and inspection—Czechoslovak Republic.

S225.E2L6 57–55428

NL 0408944 DLC

Litoměřice, Czechoslovak republic. Bruckner-fest, *1930.*
Festschrift, Bruckner-fest in Leitmeritz, 25. bis 27. april 1930. Leitmeritz, Selbstverlag der Deutschen Brucknergemeinde in Leitmeritz ₍1930₎
64 p. incl. front., ports. 23 cm.
"Verantwortlicher schriftleiter: Prof. Adalbert Sattermann."

1. Bruckner, Anton, 1824–1896. I. Deutsche Bruckner-gemeinde, Litoměřice. II. Sattermann, Adalbert.

ML410.B88L4 32–18304 rev

NL 0408945 DLC

Litoměřice, Czechoslovak Republic. Deutsche Bruckner-Gemeinde
see
Deutsche Bruckner-Gemeinde, *Litoměřice.*

VOLUME 336

943.71 L71z Litoměřice, Czechoslovak Republic--Fest-ausschuss.
1227 ɛi.e. Zwölf hundert sieben und zwanzigɜ -1927 Stadt Leitmeritz; Festschrift zur Feier des 700jährigen Bestandes als Stadt. Hrsg. vom Festausschuss. ɛLeitmeritzɜ Verlag des Vereines zur Förderung der Stadt Leitmeritz ɛ1927ɜ
iv, 192p. illus., plates. 23cm.
Includes bibliography.

NL 0408947 IU InU MH

Litoměřice, Czechoslovak Republic. Grenzpolitische Tagung der Oststelle der Reichsstudentenführung, 2d, 1939
see Grenzpolitische Tagung der Oststelle der Reichsstudentenführung. 2d, Litoměřice, 1939.

Litoměřice, Czechoslovak Republic. Sudetendeutsche Tagung für Öffentliches Recht. *3d, 1937*
see
Sudetendeutsche Tagung für Öffentliches Recht. *3d, Litoměřice, 1937.*

Litoměřice, Czechoslovak Republic. Veřejná městská knihovna.
Co čisti? Abecední seznam knih. Knihovní rada veřejné městské knihovny. ⌊Vyd. 1.⌋ V Litoměřicích, 1948.
51 p. 21 cm.

I. Title.

Z926.L58 53-25200

NL 0408950 DLC

Litoměřice, Czechoslovakia (Diocese).
Catalogus universi cleri dioecesani Litomericensis, tum saecularis tum regularis anno 1880. Warnsdorfii, Typis A. Opitz ɛ1880ɜ.
237 p. 24 cm.

NL 0408951 PLatS

Litoměřický, Hilarius
see
Hilarius, *Litoměřický,* 1411?-1468.

Litomierczicze
see
Litoměřice, *Czechoslovak Republic.*

Litomierzyce
see
Litoměřice, *Czechoslovak Republic.*

Litomyšle, Mikuláš z
see Mikuláš z Litomyšle, fl. 1386.

Літопис друкованих творів образотворчого мистцтва. Летопись печатных произведений изобразительного искусства.
Харків, Редакційно-видавничий відділ Книжкової палати УРСР.
v. 22 cm. semiannual.
"Орган державної бібліографії Української РСР."
Began in 1952.
Issued by Knyzhkova palata Ukraïns'koï RSR.
1. Art, Ukrainian—Bibliography—Periodicals. I. Knyzhkova palata Ukraïns'koï RSR. II. Title: Letopis' pechatnykh proizvedeniĭ izobrazitel'nogo iskusstva.
Title romanized: Litopys' drukovanykh tvoriv obrazotvorchoho mystetstva.

Z5961.U7L58 79-289119

NL 0408956 DLC

Літопис нот. Летопись нот.
Харків, Редакційно-видавничий відділ Книжкової палати УРСР.
v. 22 cm. semiannual.
"Орган державної бібліографії Української РСР."
Began in 1954.
Issued by Knyzhkova palata Ukraïns'koï RSR.

1. Music—Ukraine—Bibliography. I. Knyzhkova palata Ukraïns'koï RSR. II. Title: Letopis' not.
Title romanized: Litopys' not. Letopis' not.

ML120.R8L3 77-613026

NL 0408957 DLC

Літопис рецензій. Летопись рецензий.
Харків.
v. in 23 cm.
Began publication in 1936 superseding in part Літопис українського друку (later called Літопис друку УРСР) Cf. Періодичні видання УРСР, 1918–50.
Issued by Knyzhkova palata Ukraïns'koï RSR.

1. Books—Reviews—Indexes. I. Knyzhkova palata Ukraïns'koï RSR. II. Title: Letopis' retsenziĭ.
Title transliterated: Litopys retsenziĭ.

Z1035.6.A1L5 68-130612

NL 0408958 DLC

.DK508 .A2L5
Літопис революції.
Харків, Партвидав ЦК КП(б)У.
no. in v. ports. 22-27 cm.
Frequency varies.
Organ of Instytut istoriï partiï (under its earlier names: Institut istorii partii i Oktiabr'skoĭ revoliutsii TSentral'nogo komiteta Kommunisticheskoĭ partii (bol'shevikov) Ukrainy, and Vseukrainskaia komissiia po izucheniiu istorii Oktiabr'skoĭ revoliutsii i Kommunisticheskoĭ partii (bol'shevikov) Ukrainy) 19 [illegible]
Title varies: 1922-24 Летопись революции.
1. Ukraine—Hist.—Period. 2. Ukraine—Hist.—Revolution, 1917-1921—Sources. 3. Kommunisticheskaia partiia Ukrainy. I. Kiev. Instytut istoriï partiï. *Title transliterated:* Litopys revoliutsiï.

DK508.A2L5 48-42154 rev*

NL 0408959 DLC

Z2514 .U5L52
Літопис українського друку: орган державної бібліографії УСРР. рік 1- 1924-
Харків.
v. in 23 cm.
Frequency varies.
Publication suspended 1931-34.
Issued by Ukr. knyzhkova palata.
Ceased publication in 1935. Superseded by Літопис друку. Книги (later called Літопис книг); Літопис друку. Газетні статті (later called Літопис газетних статей); Литопис друку. Журнальні статті (later called Літопис журнальних статей); Літопис друку. Рецензії (later called Літопис рецензій); and Літопис друку. Твори образотворчого мистецтва. Cf. Періодичні видання УРСР, 1918-1950.
1. Ukraine—Imprints. I. Knyzhkova palata Ukraïns'koï RSR.
Title transliterated: Litopys ukraïns'koho druku.

Z2514.U5L52 66-47620

Library of Congress ⌊1⌋

NL 0408960 DLC

Літопис великої дружби, 1654–1954. ⌊Твори українських радянських письменників про віковічну дружбу українського і російського народів. Редакційна колегія: Бажан, М. П та ін.⌋ Київ, Радянський письменник, 1954.
601 p. illus. 32 cm.
1. Ukrainian literature (Selections: Extracts, etc.) I. Bazhan, Mykola Platonovych, 1904- ed.
Title transliterated: Litopys velykoï druzhby.
PG3931.L5 55-20589 ‡

NL 0408961 DLC CSt NIC

Літопис Волині. Volhynian chronicle. p. 1- (число 1-); 1953-
Winnipeg.
v. in illus., ports. 23 cm.
"Науково-популярний збірник волинезнавства."
In Ukrainian.
Issued by Instytut doslidiv Volyni and Tovarystvo "Volyn."

1. Volhynia—Hist.—Period. I. Winnipeg. Ukrainian Research Institute of Volyn. II. Association "Volyn."
Title romanized: Litopis Volyni.

DK511.V7L5 67-123698

NL 0408962 DLC OCl KU

Літопис журнальних статей. Летопись журнальных статей.
Харків.
v. 22 cm. monthly.
Issued by Knyzhkova palata Ukraïns'koï RSR.
Began publication in 1936 superseding in part Літопис українського друку (later called Літопис друку УРСР) Cf. Періодичні видання УРСР
1. Russian periodicals—Indexes. 2. Ukrainian periodicals—Indexes. I. Knyzhkova palata Ukraïns'koï RSR.
Title transliterated: Litopys zhurnal'nykh stateĭ.

AI 15.L5 58-32399

NL 0408963 DLC

Litoral.
Torremolinos.
no. illus. 24 cm. monthly.
"Revista de la poesía y el pensamiento."

1. Literature, Modern—Periodicals.

PN6054.L57 72-624388

NL 0408964 DLC

PQ6607 .I38Z64 Litoral; cuadernos de poesía, música y pintura, publicados por José Moreno Villa, Emilio Prados, Manuel Altolaguirre, Juan Rejano, Francisco Giner de los Ríos. Mexico [Fondo de Cultura Economica-1944]
irreg. paging illus.
Published August 1944, as a special issue "a la memoria de Enrique Diez Canedo.
1. Diez Canedo, Enrique, 1879-1944.

NL 0408965 NBuU TNJ NcU MiU TxU GU NN

Litoral; revista de cultura. 1-
Junho, 1944-
Lisboa.
no. in v. illus. 21 cm. monthly.
Director: 1944- C. Queiroz.

I. Queiroz, Carlos.

AP65.L53 53-23829

NL 0408966 DLC WU MiU CU IU TxU ICU InU

VOLUME 336

LITORAL; revista del espíritu. Año 1-3 (núm. 1-9); 1951-54. Valencia. 3 v. illus. 23cm.

Irregular.
Issued by the Delegación provincial de educación of Valencia.
No more published?

1. Periodicals--Spain. I. Falange española tradicionalista de las juntas ofensivas nacional-sindicalistas. Delegación provincial de educación, Valencia.

NL 0408967 NN MoU

W 1
LI823
LITORAL médico; revista de difusión científica.
Cartagena, Colombia, 1946-
v.
Issued by the Facultad de Medicina, Universidad de Cartagena and the Asociación Médica de Cartagena.
1. Medicine - Period. I. Asociación Médica de Cartagena II. Cartagena, Colombia. Universidad. Facultad de Medicina

NL 0408968 DNLM

Il litorale jugoslavo
see under Rojc, Milau, 1855-

Li Tors, Lambert
see
Lambert le Tort, 12th cent.

Litostroj, Titovi zavodi, *Ljubljana*
see
Titovi zavodi Litostroj, *Ljubljana.*

BX2350
.L77
LITOU, EUGÈNE CLÉMENT AUGUSTE.
... L'édifice de la morale évangelique(d'après les paroles mêmes de N.-S.J.-C.) Avignon, Aubanel frères[1929]
[iii]-viii, 104 p. 16½cm.

1. Christian ethics. 2. Commandments, Ten.

NL 0408972 ICU

Litou, Henri.
... Les Livres en 1881- études critiques et analytiques par MM. Gaston d'Hailly, A. Le-Clère & Henri Litou, rédacteurs de la Revue des livres nouveaux, publiées dans ce recueil pendant l'année 1881-
t. 1- 1881-
Paris, 1883-

Litova almanako.
Kaunas.
v. 18 cm.
Issued by the Litova Esperanto Asocio.

1. Esperanto—Texts. I. Litova Esperanto Asocio.

PM8251.L5 51-36601

NL 0408974 DLC NN

PM8251
.L5
Litova Esperanto Asocio.
Litova almanako.
Kaunas.

El litova poezio
see under Lapienė, P

PM8201
L5
Litova stelo. Kaunas, 1925-26.
2 v. in 1. illus. 35 cm.
monthly.
Editor: Apr. 1925-Mar. 1926, A. Dombrovski.

NL 0408977 DLC

Z244
.3
L53
Litoval'tsev, Petr Fedorovich.
В бригаде печатников. ₍Рассказ записал и литературно обработал Л. Бородкин. Москва₎ Профиздат, 1954.
69 p. illus. 16 cm. (Рассказы новаторов)

1. Printing, Practical. I. Borodkin, L. II. Title.
Title transliterated: V brigade pechatnikov.

Z244.3.L53 57-36611

NL 0408978 DLC

45
L71Ag
Litovchenko, Grigoriĭ Romanovich
Grundlegende Fragen der Schafzucht.
[Berlin] Deutscher Bauernverlag [1952]
72 p.

Translation of his Osnovnye voprosy plemennoĭ raboty v ovt͡sevodstve.

1. Sheep. Breeding. 2. U.S.S.R. Sheep.
I. Vasil'ev, A V joint author.

NL 0408979 DNAL

S405
.V822
1955,
no. 28
Litovchenko, Grigoriĭ Romanovich.
Передовые приемы повышения продуктивности овцеводства. Москва, Знание, 1955.
31 p. 22 cm. (Всесоюзное общество по распространению политических и научных знаний. Серия 5, № 28)

1. Sheep—Russia. I. Title.
Title transliterated: Peredovye priemy povysheni͡a produktivnosti ovt͡sevodstva.

S405.V822 1955, no. 28 56-24270 ‡

NL 0408980 DLC

Law
Litovchenko, M
Деньги въ гражданскомъ правѣ. Кіевъ, Типо-лит. И. Н. Кушнерева, 1887.
iii, 50 p. 26 cm.
Bibliography: p. ₍1₎-2.

1. Money—Law.
Title transliterated: Den'gi v grazhdanskom pravi͡e.

49-57807*

NL 0408981 DLC

Litovchenko, Nikita Vasil'evich.
Горячая прокатка толстых и средних листов. Одобрено в качестве учеб. пособия для школ ФЗО. Москва, Гос. научно-техн. изд-во лит-ры по черной и цветной металлургии, 1955.
170, ₍2₎ p. illus. 23 cm.
Bibliography: p. ₍171₎

1. Rolling (Metal-work) 2. Sheet-metal. I. Title.
Title transliterated: Gori͡achai͡a prokatka tolstykh i srednikh listov.

TS340.L527 56-37671

NL 0408982 DLC

Litovchenko, Nikita Vasil'evich.
Прокатка периодических профилей арматурной стали. Москва, Гос. научно-техн. изд-во лит-ры по черной и цветной металлургии, 1955.
46, ₍2₎ p. diagrs., tables. 20 cm.
At head of title: Н. В. Литовченко, Б. П. Бахтинов.
Bibliography: p. ₍47₎

1. Rolling (Metal-work) 2. Steel bars. I. Bakhtinov, Boris Petrovich, joint author. II. Title.
Title transliterated: Prokatka periodicheskikh profileĭ armaturnoĭ stali.

TS340.L53 56-35226

NL 0408983 DLC

Litovitz, Theodore A 1923-
Ultrasonic absorption of glycerin in the liquid and quasi-solid state. Washington, Catholic University of America Press, 1950.
1 card. 7½ x 12½ cm.
Microprint copy of typescript.
Collation of the original: 16 l. diagrs., tables. 28 cm.
Thesis—Catholic University of America.
Bibliographical footnotes.

1. Ultrasonic waves. 2. Glycerin. I. Title.

Microcard QC233 Micp A 53-87

Catholic Univ. of America. Library
for Library of Congress ₍⅔₎†

NL 0408984 DCU DLC MiU TxFTC NcU

Litovsk, R
"Handicap"...by R. Litovsk. [n.p.,19--]
1 v. 26cm.

Typescript.

1. Drama, American. I. Title.

NL 0408985 NN

Litovsk, R
"Her wedding day;" a play... [n.p., n.d.] 1 v. 28cm.

Typescript.

1. Drama, American. I. Title.

NL 0408986 NN

Литовская ССР в цифрах; краткий статистический сборник
Вильнюс, Госстатиздат; Литовское отд-ние.
v. 15 cm.
Issued by T͡Sentral'noe statisticheskoe upravlenie of the Lithuanian S. S. R.

1. Lithuania—Stat. I. Lithuanian S. S. R. Centrinė statistikos valdyba.
Title transliterated: Litovskai͡a SSR v t͡sifrakh.

HA1448.L5A318 65-36249

NL 0408987 DLC CSt-H

VOLUME 336

Litovskaiā sel'skokhoziāĭstvennaiā akademiiā, *Kaunas*
see
Kaunas. Lietuvos žemės ūkio akademija.

DK511
.L2L74

Литовская Советская Социалистическая Республика, 1940–1950. ₍Вильнюс, Гос. изд-во полит. и научной лит-ры, 1950₎

1 v. of illus., ports. (unpaged) 34 x 50 cm.

1. Lithuania—Descr. & trav.—Views.
Title transliterated: Litovskaiā Sovetskaiā Sotsialisticheskaiā Respublika.

DK511.L2L74 51-29508

NL 0408989 DLC

PG8771
.R8L5

Литовские рассказы. Перевод с литовского. Москва, Советский писатель, 1953.

364 p. 21 cm.

1. Short stories, Lithuanian—Translations into Russian. 2. Short stories, Russian—Translations from Lithuanian.
Title transliterated: Litovskie rasskazy.

PG8771.R8L5 54-21617 ‡

NL 0408990 DLC

Litovskiĭ, Alekseĭ Ivanovich Dzens-
see
Dzens-Litovskiĭ, Alekseĭ Ivanovich, 1892–

PG3476
.L63A4

Litovskiĭ, Osaf Semenovich.

... Александр Невский; пьеса в пяти действиях, девяти картинах. ₍Москва₎ Государственное издательство "Искусство," 1942.

70, ₍2₎ p. 16½ x 12½cm.

At head of title: О Литовский, К. Осипов.

1. Alexander Nevski, Saint, grand duke of Vladimir, 1219–1263—Drama. I. Osipov, K., pseud. joint author.
Title transliterated: Aleksandr Nevskiĭ.

44-21196

Library of Congress PG3476.L63A4

NL 0408992 DLC

PG3476
.O76R8

Litovskii, Osaf Semenovich, joint author.

Osipov, K

... Русские орлы; военно-историческая пьеса в четырех действиях, семи картинах. Москва, Ленинград, Государственное издательство "Искусство," 1943.

Litovskiĭ institut zemledeliiā, *Dotnuva*
see
Dotnuva, Lithuania. Lietuvos žemdirbystės institutas.

Litovskiĭ nauchno-issledovatel'skiĭ institut zemledeliiā, *Dotnuva*
see
Dotnuva, Lithuania. Lietuvos žemdirbystės institutas.

Litovtsev, Solomon L'vovich Poliākov-
see
Poliākov, Solomon L'vovich.

Litowich, Carolina.

Ugly face, by Carolina Litowich. Boston, The Christopher publishing house ₍©1932₎

52 p. 21cm.

I. Title.

Library of Congress PZ3.L714Ug 32-30024

NL 0408997 DLC

Litra (de) & cie, *Paris.*

Le marché des monnaies d'or de 1900 à nos jours. Paris ₍1951₎

122 p. 22 cm.

1. Currency question—France. I. Title.

HG979.L52 332.4944 54-15652 ‡

NL 0408998 DLC OU NN

LB775
.T668

Litrán, Cristóbal, tr.

Toulouse, Édouard, 1865–

... Cómo se forma una inteligencia; versión española de Cristóbal Litrán. Barcelona, Casa editorial Maucci ₍193–?₎

HX704
.P74

Litrán, Cristóbal, tr.

Proudhon, Pierre Joseph, 1809–1865.

... El comunismo es la religión de la miseria; versión española de Cristóbal Litrán. Barcelona, Biblioteca Séneca, 1934.

Litrán, Cristóbal.

Historia de Victor Hugo... traduzida e precedida de um estudo critico sobre Victor Hugo e a sua obra por Teixeira Bastos.
Lisboa, Empreza noites romanticas, n.d.

YA12850

NL 0409001 DLC

HQ
1393
.L5

Litrán, Cristóbal.

La mujer en el cristianismo. Con el prólogo La mujer ante la ciencia, por Odón de Buen. Barcelona, Tip. La Academia, 1892.

91 p. 16 cm.. (Biblioteca de "La Tramontana")

1. Women and religion. I. Title.

NL 0409002 WU

Litrán, Cristóbal.

El regionalismo catalán y su política (notas y comentarios) por Cristóbal Litrán. Vendrell: Ramon, 1918. 92 p., 2 l. 8°.

1. Nationality, Catalonia. 2. Catalonia.—Politics, 1899–1918.
N. Y. P. L. October 3, 1919.

NL 0409003 NN MiU

Litre, Émile François, 1846–

L'aviation et le mouvement terrestre; théorie aérodynamique du virage, des effets gyroscopiques directs, du capotage et des retours spontanés. Paris: Gauthier-Villars, 1912. vii, 44 p., 2 l. 4°.

1. Aeronautics.—Machines, 1912. 2. Earth.—Motion.
N. Y. P. L. September 17, 1913.

NL 0409004 NN

Litre, Émile François, 1846–

... La locomotion à grandes vitesses et ses accidents inhérents, par le commandant E. Litre ... Paris, Gauthier-Villars et cie, 1929.

xi, 92 p., 2 l. 1 illus., diagrs. 23cm. (Rudiments de mécanique réelle)

1. Motion. 2. Accidents. I. Title.

34-11951

Library of Congress QA841.L75 531.1

NL 0409005 DLC ICJ

Litre, Émile François, 1846–

Les régiments d'artillerie à pied de la Garde, le régiment monté de la Garde et le 23e régiment d'artillerie. Notice historique par E. Litre ... Paris, E. Plon, Nourrit et cie; ₍etc., etc.₎ 1895.

3 p. l., 735, ₍1₎ p., 1 l. front. (port.) plates. 25cm.

Plates and portrait accompanied by guard sheet with descriptive letterpress.

1. France—Army—Artillery—23d regt.

22-9256

Library of Congress UA705.Z6.23d

NL 0409006 DLC

Litre, Émile Francois, 1846–

Rudiments de mécanique réelle. La locomotion à grandes vitesses et ses accidents inhérents, par le commandant E. Litre... Paris: Gauthier-Villars et cie, 1929. xi, 92 p. diagrs. 8°.

506651A. 1. Speed.
N. Y. P. L. December 26, 1930

NL 0409007 NN

Litrento, Oliveiros Lessa, 1923–

Alguns ensaios. 1. série. Recife, Região, 1954.

167 p. 18 cm.

"Os trabalhos reunidos nêste volume fôram publicados, durante o ano de 1953, no 'Jornal do comercio,' Recife, exceto parte de 'Aloisio Branco.'"

I. Title.

PQ9697.L587A69 54-44598 rev 2 ‡

NL 0409008 DLC

VOLUME 336

Litri, *pseud.*
Los toros a través del micrófono
see
Uruñuela, Emiliano de.

PB 1235 L587 1947
LITRIU na Gaeilge. Lámhleabhar an chaighdeáin oifigiúil. Baile átha Claith, Arna Fhoilsiú ag Oifig an tSoláthair [réamhrá 1947]
vi, 121 p. 22 cm.

Irish-English vocabulary: p. 68-121.

1. Irish language - Orthography and spelling.

NL 0409010 CaBVaU MH

Lits, Ernö.
Richard B. Adam, ein Träger deutsch-ungarischer Kunstbeziehungen, von Ernö Lits. München: A. Dresler, 1928. xxvi, 86 p. incl. geneal. table. illus. (incl. ports., part col'd, part mounted.) 8°.

431343A. 1. Adam, Richard Benno, 1873- . 2. Paintings, German.
N. Y. P. L. September 20, 1929

NL 0409011 NN KyLoU MH

Litsmer (Carolus). * De cortice chinæ historice, chemice et pharmacologice considerato. 32 pp., 1 l. 8°. *Budæ, typ. Reg. Univ. Hung.*, 1824. [P., v. 1312.]

NL 0409012 DNLM

Litsch, Emil.
De Cassio Dione imitatore Thucydidis. Freiburg, 1893.
Inaug.-Diss. - Freiburg.

NL 0409013 ICRL NjP

Litsch, Erich, 1900-
Redressement forcé ... Schwetzingen [n. d.]
Inaug.-Diss. - Heidelberg.
Lebenslauf.
"Literaturverzeichnis": p. 31-32.

NL 0409014 CtY

W 4 B51 1940
Litsch, Hans, 1914-
Über die operative Behandlung von Cystennieren. Heidelberg, Brausdruck, 1940.
38 p.

Inaug.-Diss. - Berlin.
Bibliography: p. 37-38.

NL 0409015 DNLM

Litsch (Joh. Jacobus). De salium effectu frigorifico in liquoribus. 26 pp. 4°. *Argentorati, typ. M. Pauschingeri*, [1748].

NL 0409016 DNLM

Litschauer, Franz
see **Litschauer, Gottfried Franz,** 1903-

Litschauer, Gottfried Franz, 1903-
... Bibliographie zur geschichte, landes- und volkskunde des Burgenlandes 1800-1929, bearb. von dr. G. Fr. Litschauer. Linz a. Donau, F. Winkler, 1933-
24cm. (Bibliographie zur geschichte landes- und volkskunde Österreichs, 6. abt., lfg. 1-
Cover-title.
At head of title: Archiv für bibliographie. Beiheft 8, lfg. 1-
Bibliography: p. v-vii.

1. Burgenland—Bibl.

Library of Congress Z2124.B9L7 34-5777
[2] 016.94391

NL 0409018 DLC CtY CU OU ICU MiU

DB35 L5 1938
Litschauer, Gottfried Franz, 1903-
Daten der österreichischen Geschichte [von der Urzeit bis zur Heimkehr in das Deutsche Reich] 2. Aufl. Leipzig, A. G. Ploetz, 1938.
vi, 93 p. 18 cm.
Published also as "Anhang III zu Ploetz, Auszug aus der Geschichte."

1. Austria—Hist.—Chronology.

DB35.L5 1938 A 53-738
Harvard Univ. Library
for Library of Congress [3]†

NL 0409019 MH DLC ICRL NNC CtY CU NN

Litschauer, Gottfried Franz, 1903-
Geschichtsbilder aus Niederdonau. Textteil. In Ergänzung dieses Textteiles erscheint ein eigenes Bilderheft. [St.Pölten, St.Pöltner Zeitungs-Verlags-Ges. [1933?]
79 p. (Niederdonau, Ahnengau des Führers, Schriftenreihe für Heimat und Volk, 24/25)
HCL lacks Bilderheft.

NL 0409020 MH NcD CtY CU NN

Litschauer, Gottfried Franz, 1903-
...Kleine österreichische Geschichte. Wien, Obelisk-Ausgabe, 1946. 400 p. 22cm. (Reihe interessante Wissenschaft. Bd. 1.)

419296B. 1. Austria—Hist.
N. Y. P. L. January 23, 1948

NL 0409021 NN CoFS CU

Litschauer, Gottfried Franz, 1903-
Österreichische Geschichte; die geschichtlichen Ereignisse der Jahre 1930-1936. Leipzig, Ploetz [193-]
184 p.
"Nachtrag zur 21.Aufl. von K.Ploetz, Auszug aus der alten, mittleren, neueren und neuesten Geschichte."

NL 0409022 MH

Litschauer, Gottfried Franz, 1903-
... Spanische kulturgeschichte ... Wien-Leipzig, Bernina verlags-ges. m. b. h. [1939]
2 v. col. front., plates, ports., maps (1 fold. in pocket) 22½cm.
At head of title: Franz Litschauer.
Paged continuously.
CONTENTS.—[I] Urzeit bis Kolumbus.—[II] Kolumbus bis Franco.

1. Spain—Hist. 2. Spain—Civilization.

DP66.L65 A 42-1604 †
New York. Public library
for Library of Congress [r47c1]†

NL 0409023 NN DLC ICU CU WaU NcD MH

Litschauer, Risa von, 1895-
Vocabularium polyglottum vitae silvarum; waldbiologisches Fachwörterbuch auf der Grundlage der wissenschaftlichen Nomenklatur: Latein, Deutsch, Englisch, Französisch, Spanisch [und] Russisch. Hamburg, P. Parey, 1955.
126 p. 26 cm.

1. Natural history—Dictionaries—Polyglot. 2. Latin language—Dictionaries—Polyglot. 3. Forest ecology — Dictionaries — Polyglot. I. Title.

QH13.L5 55—3961

CtY CU MH NcD PSt NBPol CaBVaU IdU MtU OrCS
NL 0409024 DLC DNAL NNBG FTaSU NN MB MiU TU NcU WaU

Litschel, Erwin, 1912-
... Versuche über das filtrierbare Virus des Tuberkelbazillus ... Sibiu (Hermannstadt) [1938]
Inaug.-Diss. - München.
Lebenslauf.

NL 0409025 CtY

---

ar V 10993
Litschel, J W
Valentinus Greff; ein Bild aus Birthälms Vergangenheit, 1524-1530. Geschichtliches Schauspiel in 5 Aufzügen. Valentinus Greff; e beld ois Birthalms vergongenhft... Bistritz (Nösen) Haupt, 1889.
143 p. 20cm.

German and Transylvania Saxonian dialect on opposite pages.
I. Title.

NL 0409026 NIC

Litscher, Martin.
Die alpkorporationen des bezirkes Werdenberg.
Inaug.-diss., Bern, 1919.
Bibl.

NL 0409027 ICRL DLC CtY

Litscher, Martin.
... Die alpkorporationen des bezirkes Werdenberg. Von dr. jur. Martin Litscher. Bern, Stämpfli & cie., 1919.
xi, 134 p. 23½cm. (Abhandlungen zum schweizerischen recht, hrsg. von dr. Max Gmür ... 91. hft.)
"Literaturverzeichnis": p. v-ix.

1. Werdenberg, Switzerland—Econ. condit. 2. Dairying—Werdenberg, Switzerland. 3. Corporations—Werdenberg, Switzerland. 4. Dairying—Alps. I. Title.

27-10151

NL 0409028 DLC

Litscher, Otto Gübeli-
see **Gübeli-Litscher, Otto.**

VOLUME 336

329.6
L769r
Litschert, Frank P
The Republican party. Washington, Republican National Committee [1923?]
95p. illus.

1. Republican party--Hist.

NL 0409030 ICarbS

Litschfousse, Claude Marie Edmond, joint author.

U255
.F7C6
Costa de Serda, Paul Émile.
Carnet aide-mémoire de manœuvres et de campagne à l'usage de toutes armes, par le commandant E. Costa de Serda et le capitaine Litschfousse ... Paris, J. Dumaine, 1880.

Litschfousse, Victor, 1874 –
Alain, ou Les vertus guerrières. Paris, Dorbon-Ainé [1924]
208 p.

NL 0409032 MH

Litschfousse, Victor, 1874–
... Pouilles; roman ... Paris, A. Michel [c1923]
3 p. l., [9]–158 p., 1 l. 19cm. (*On cover:* Nouvelle collection Albin Michel)

I. Title.
Library of Congress PQ2623.I7P6 1923 23-17867

NL 0409033 DLC

Litschgi (François-Joseph). * Essai sur la dysenterie, considérée dans son état de simplicité. 36 pp. 4°. *Strasbourg,* 1823, v. 52.

NL 0409034 DNLM

Litschgy, Albert.
Als Kriegsgeisel in Frankreich. Wer hat die Kriegsgreuel begangen? Selbsterlebtes von 1914 bis 1920, von Rektor Litschgy ... Schwäb. Gmünd: Rems-Zeitung, G.m.b.H.[, 1928.] 51 p. 12°.

435904A. 1. European war, 1914–1918—Prisoners and prisons, French.
N. Y. P. L. October 5, 1929

NL 0409035 NN

Litschgy, Mich.
Die elsass-lothringischen kriegsgeiseln. Von Mich. Litschgy ... 4. aufl. Strassburg i. Els., Strassburger druckerei u. verlagsanstalt, 1918.
64 p. illus. 20cm. (*On cover:* Elsass-lothringische gegenwartsfragen. 2. hft.)

1. European war, 1914–1918—Alsace-Lorraine.
24-5042
Library of Congress DD801.A57L65 1918

NL 0409036 DLC

W 4
M22
1949
LITSCHKE, Paul, 1919-
Die Veränderungen des Takata-Ara während des Cyklus. [Mainz, 1949]
34 ℓ.
Inaug.-Diss. - Mainz.
Typewritten copy.
1. Takata - Ara test

NL 0409037 DNLM

AP50
.L58
Лицей. ч. 1-4; 1806. Санктпетербургъ.
4 v. 21 cm. monthly.
Supersedes Сѣверный вѣстникъ.
Issued by I. I. Martynov.

I. Martynov, Ivan Ivanovich, 1771-1833.
Title transliterated: Litsei.
AP50.L58 52-50853

NL 0409038 DLC

Litseĭ kni͡azi͡a Bezborodko
see
Nezhin, Ukraine. Istoriko-filologicheskiĭ institut kni͡azi͡a Bezborodko.

888.4
L776G
Litsenburg, Petrus Johannes Gerardus Maria van
God en het goddelijke in de Dialogen van Plato. The Divinity and the divine in the Dialogues of Plato. Nijmegen [1955]
224 p. 24 cm.

Proefschrift--Nijmegen.
"Stellingen" ([2] ℓ.) laid in.
Summary in English.
Bibliography: p. 218-222.
1. Plato. Dialogues. 2. Plato. Religion and ethics. I. Title.

NL 0409040 NcD DLC-P4 MH NNC DCU CtY

B398
.G6L8
Litsenburg, Petrus Johannes Gerardus Maria van.
God en het goddelijke in de dialogen van Plato. (The Divinity and the divine in the dialogues of Plato) Nijmegen, Dekker & Van de Vegt [1955]
224 p.
"Summary" in English; p.200-212.
Includes bibliography.

1. Plato. 2. God. I. Title. II. Title: The Divinity and the divine in the dialogues of Plato.

NL 0409041 ICU NIC NN NjR

Litsevoĭ podlinnik
see
Podlinnik ikonopisnyĭ.

929
H42L
6844
Litsey, David Randolph
The Hays family in Kentucky and their descendants. [Springfield, Ky.?] 1949.
387 p.

NL 0409043 KyHi

Litsey, David Randolph.
Litsey family formerly Litching and Litsey and their descendants with Colonial and Revolutionary records. Compiled by David Randolph Litsey. 1952.
924 p.
Reproduced from type written copy.

NL 0409044 KyHi

Litsey, Edwin Carlile, 1874–
A bluegrass cavalier, by Edwin Carlile Litsey ... Philadelphia, Dorrance [c1922]
320 p. 19½cm.

I. Title.
Library of Congress PZ3.L715Bl 22-6526

NL 0409045 DLC MB OClJC

Litsey, Edwin Carlile, 1874–
The eternal flame, a novelette, by Edwin Carlile Litsey ... Louisville, Ky., The Standard printing company, incorporated, 1937.
3 p. l., 98 p. 22cm.
"Based on the life of Jesus of Nazareth."
"First edition, 300 copies."

1. Jesus Christ—Fiction. I. Title.
38-8334
Library of Congress PS3523.I 82E7 1937

NL 0409046 DLC NcD

Litsey, Edwin Carlile, 1874–
The filled cup; a book of poems for Sarah, by Edwin Carlile Litsey. Louisville, Ky., The Standard printing company, incorporated, 1935.
7 p. l., 90 p. 22½cm.
"First edition 300 copies."

I. Title.
36-10878
Library of Congress PS3523.I 82F5 1935
——— Copy 2.
Copyright A 95282 [2] 811.5

NL 0409047 DLC KyBgW

813
L776g
Litsey, Edwin Carlile, 1874–
Grist. by Edwin Carlile Litsey. London, Hutchinson & Company.
221 p. 19½cm.

I. Title.

NL 0409048 KyHi

Litsey, Edwin Carlile, 1874–
Grist, by Edwin Carlile Litsey. Philadelphia, Dorrance and company [c1927]
231 p. 19½cm.

I. Title.
Library of Congress PZ3.L715Gr 27-3097

NL 0409049 DLC

VOLUME 336

Litsey, Edwin Carlile, 1874–
The love story of Abner Stone, by Edwin Carlile Litsey. New York, A. S. Barnes and company, 1902.
viii, 170 p. 21½cm.

I. Title.
Library of Congress PZ3.L715L 2—17064

NL 0409050 DLC WaS NcD OO OCl

Litsey, Edwin Carlile, 1874–
The love story of Abner Stone. New York, Log cabin press [c.1921]

NL 0409051 MH

Litsey, Edwin Carlile, 1874–
A maid of the Kentucky hills, by Edwin Carlile Litsey ... illustrated by John Cassel. Chicago, Browne & Howell company, 1913.
5 p. l., 380 p. col. front. 19½cm. $1.25

I. Title.
Library of Congress PZ3.L715M 13-24796

NL 0409052 DLC KyBgW

Litsey, Edwin Carlile, 1874–
The man from Jericho, by Edwin Carlile Litsey. New York, The Neale publishing company, 1911.
290 p. 19cm. $1.50

Library of Congress PZ3.L715M 11-31964

NL 0409053 DLC

Litsey, Edwin Carlile, 1874–
The princess of Gramfalon. By E. Carl Litsey. Cincinnati, The Editor publishing co., 1898.
4 p. l., 323 p. front. 18cm.

I. Title.
Library of Congress PZ3.L715P 98-1337 Revised

NL 0409054 DLC

FILM 4274 PR v.3 reel L22

Litsey, Edwin Carlile, 1874–
The princess of Gramfalon. By E. Carl Litsey. Cincinnati, The Editor publishing co., 1898.
4 p. l., 323 p. front. 18cm.
(Wright American Fiction, v. III, 1876-1900, no. 3363, Research Publications, Inc. Microfilm, Reel L-22)
Microfilm.

NL 0409055 CU

Litsey, Edwin Carlile, 1874–
The race of the swift, by Edwin Carlile Litsey ... illustrated from drawings by Charles Livingston Bull. Boston, Little, Brown, and company, 1905.
7 p. l., 3-151 p. front., 3 pl. 19½cm.
CONTENTS.—The race of the swift.—The robber baron.—The ghost coon.—The spoiler of the folds.—The fight on the tree-bridge.—The guardian of the flock.—The king of the northern slope.

Library of Congress Copyright 5-32679

NL 0409056 DLC NN WaS

Litsey, Edwin Carlile, 1874–
Shadow shapes, by Edwin Carlile Litsey. Chicago, R. Packard & company, 1929.
3 p. l., [3]-308 p. 20½cm.

I. Title.
Library of Congress PZ3.L7158h 29-28787

NL 0409057 DLC

Litsey, Edwin Carlile, 1874–
Spindrift; verses and poems, by Edwin Carlile Litsey. Louisville, Ky., John P. Morton & company, incorporated, 1915.
4 p. l., 105 p. 19½cm. $1.00
Reprinted in part from various periodicals.

I. Title.
Library of Congress PS3523.I 82S5 1915 15-27992

NL 0409058 DLC KyLx ViU

Litsey, Edwin Carlile, 1874–
Stones for bread, by Edwin Carlile Litsey. Caldwell, Id., The Caxton printers, ltd., 1940.
284 p. 21½cm.

I. Title.
Library of Congress PZ3.L7154St 40-1702

NL 0409059 DLC KyBgW KyHi KyLx NcD OOxM OCl

Tzz 811 L715f

Litsey, Sarah.
For the lonely. London, Favil Press, 1937.
56p. 23cm.

A narrative poem.
With author's autograph.

NL 0409060 TxU CtY NjP KyU

Litsey, Sarah.
The intimate illusion. New York, Appleton-Century-Crofts [1955]
311 p. 21 cm.

I. Title.
PZ3.L7156 In 55-5438 ‡

NL 0409061 DLC CaBVa Or PP

811.08 L77

Litsey, Sarah, comp.
Kentucky poets, an anthology of 29 contemporary poets; foreword by Sarah Litsey. New York, Henry Harrison, poetry publisher, c 1936.
95p.

NL 0409062 KyHi

Litsey, Sarah.
There was a lady, by Sarah Litsey. Indianapolis, New York, The Bobbs-Merrill company [1945]
253 p. 21cm.
"First edition."

I. Title.
Library of Congress PZ3.L7156Th 45-7025

NL 0409063 DLC NcD TxU OEac OCl

Litshow, I
see Lychev, Ivan Akimovich, 1882?-

Lifšin, Lazar' Naumovich.
Оформление графических работ. Разрешено в качестве учеб. пособия для учащихся строит. техникумов. Харьков, Изд-во Харьковского гос. университета, 1951–52.
2 v. illus. 25 x 33 cm.
At head of title: СССР. Министерство строительства предприятий тяжелой индустрии. Управление учебными заведениями. Харьковский строительный техникум.
Includes bibliographies.

1. Mechanical drawing. 2. Building—Details—Drawings. I. Title.
Title romanized: Oformlenie graficheskikh rabot.

T353.L78 56-25714

NL 0409065 DLC

QM511 .L6

Litsinger, George G.
Ocular anatomy. Copyrighted...[by] George G. Litsinger.
Chicago, Ill.,c 1930.
3 p.l.,3-54 numb. l.,2 l. illus. 27 1/2 cm.

NL 0409066 DLC DNLM

Litskii, Vladimir Romanovich, tr.

Law

Netherlands (*Kingdom, 1815–*) *Laws, statutes, etc.*
Нидерландское уложеніе отъ 3 марта 1881 г. С.-Петербургъ, 1881.

Лицо советского киноактера. Б. Бабочкин, В. Гардин [и др.] о себе. Москва, Кинофотоиздат, 1935.
245, [3] p. illus. (incl. ports.) 19 x 14 cm.
"Редактор—Ш. Ахушков."—p. [248]

1. Actors, Russian. I. Babochkin, Boris Andreevich, 1902 or 3– II. Akhushkov, Shamil', ed.
Title transliterated: Lifšo sovetskogo kinoaktera.

PN2727.L5 49-31700

NL 0409068 DLC

Litson, Edith.
Record of tombstone inscriptions in the old cemetery at the Strand, Waterford, Conn. Copied by Edith Litson. Brooklyn, N. Y., 1927. 4 l. illus. 4°.
Illustration is mounted photograph.

1. Epitaphs—U. S.—Conn.—Waterford.
N. Y. P. L. October 10, 1927

NL 0409069 NN

VOLUME 336

Litster, David Michael.
Foundations of Daly College, Indore, [India]. London, Inst. [Civil Eng.] 1889.
4 p. 8°.
Excerpt: Minutes Proc. Inst. Civil Eng., v. xcvii, Session 1888-89, Pt. iii.

NL 0409070 NN

F881 O692 v. 7:76 x
Litster, John
The House of Mystery, the famous 125-foot circle with its unsolved natural phenomena. [Medford, Or., Knocker Printery, 194-?]
folder([4] p.) illus., map. 16cm. [Oregon miscellany. v. 7, no. 76]
In portfolio.
1. House of Mystery, Or. (Series)

NL 0409071 CU-B

Litster, John.
A vagabond's testament, by John Litster. Private ed. Medford, Or., Printed by the Klocker printery, °1939.
38 p. 24cm.
Poems.
I. Title.
39-32637
Library of Congress PS3523.I 82V3 1939
——— Copy 2.
Copyright A 134275 [2] 811.5

NL 0409072 DLC Or

F881 O692 v. 7:77 x
Litster, Mildred
The House of Mystery, located within the famous circular area, the Oregon Vortex, with its unique phenomena. [Medford, Or., Klocker Printery, 1954]
folder([6] p.) illus., col. map. 21cm. [Oregon miscellany. v. 7, no. 77]
In portfolio.
1. House of Mystery, Or. (Series)

NL 0409073 CU-B

Litster, Mildred.
The Oregon vortex ... Copyright ... by Mildred Litster. Gold Hill, Or., °1944.
16 p. illus., diagrs. 23cm.
"Corrected diagram" mounted over diagram no. 1.
On cover: Notes and data, relative to the phenomena at the area of the House of mystery, Sardine creek, Gold Hill, Oregon. 1944 ed.
1. Gold Hill, Or. I. Title.
44-9274
Library of Congress QC816.L5
[2] 538.7

NL 0409074 DLC OrU Or

538.7 L7152
Litster, Mildred.
The Oregon vortex. [4th ed.] Gold Hill, Ore., c1953.
30p. illus., diagrs. 23cm.
On cover: Notes and data, relative to the phenomena at the area of the House of mystery, Sardine Creek, Gold Hill, Oregon.
1. Gold Hill, Ore. I. Title.

NL 0409075 OrU

Litster, Thomas Harkness.
Songs in your heart and mine, by Thomas Harkness Litster. Toronto, Can.: McClelland, Goodchild & Stewart [1917] 142 p. 19½cm.
122396B. 1. Poetry, Canadian. I. Title.
N. Y. P. L. September 29, 1941

NL 0409076 NN CaOTU TxU RPB

HB 3593 +L5
Litt, Alfred.
Die Idee der Bevölkerungspolitik in der neueren Staatswissenschaft. Leipzig, S. Hirzel, 1943-
v. 24cm. (in binder, 26cm.) (Archiv für Bevölkerungswissenschaft und Bevölkerungspolitik, Beiheft 12)
Includes bibliography.
1. Germany - Population 2. Race discrimination - Germany I. Title

NL 0409077 WU ICN NcD MH NN CU MnU

BP 634 L77
Litt, Fernand.
...La question des rapports entre la nature et la grâce de Baius au synode de Pistoie; doctrines théologiques et documents ecclésiastiques... Fontaine-L'Évêque, Louis Daisne, 1934.
216 p. 22 cm.
At head of t.-p.: Pontificia universitas gregoriana.
1.Supernatural order. 2.Man (Theology).
3.Grace - History of doctrines. 4.Jansenism
5.Bay, Michel de 1513-1589.

NL 0409078 IMunS DCU

[Litt, Johannes] ed.
Gesetze und verordnungen über die milchwirtschaft; eine sammlung der zum neuaufbau der deutschen milchwirtschaft erlassenen gesetze und verordnungen. 6. aufl. Hildesheim, Molkerei-zeitung, 1937.
335 p. illus. 22½cm.
"Vorwort zur sechsten auflage" signed: Johs. Litt.
1. Dairy laws—Germany. 2. Milk trade—Germany. I. Germany. Laws, statutes, etc. II. Title.
38-521

NL 0409079 DLC

Litt, Robert Stephen.
Urbanization and social control; an analysis of Kingston, New York, 1820-1872
Honors thesis - Harvard, 1971
1. Kingston, N.Y. - Hist.

NL 0409080 MH

Litt, Theodor, 1880-1962
Das Allgemeine im Aufbau der geisteswissenschaftlichen Erkenntnis. Leipzig, S.Hirzel, 1941.
71 p. 24 cm. (Berichte über die Verhandlungen der Sächsischen Akademie der Wissenschaften zu Leipzig. Philologisch-historische Klasse, 93, 1941, 1.Heft)

NL 0409081 MH

Litt, Theodor, 1880-
Die Befreiung des geschichtlichen Bewusstseins durch J. G. Herder. Leipzig, E. A. Seeman [°1942]
185 p. 19 cm. (Kleine Bücherei zur Geistesgeschichte, Bd. 11)
1. Herder, Johann Gottfried, 1744-1803. 2. History—Philosophy. I. Title. (Series)
PT2354.L5 A F 48-5066*
Yale Univ. Library for Library of Congress [1]†

NL 0409082 CtY CaBVaU OU UU TxU DLC

Litt, Theodor, 1880-1962
Berufsbildung und Allgemeinbildung. Wiesbaden, E. Brockhaus, 1947.
59 p. 20 cm.
"Das Folgende ist die erweiterte Ausarbeitung eines Vortrags, den ich bei einer Tagung von Berufsschullehrern der russischen Besatzungszone gehalten habe."
1. Vocational education—Germany. I. Title.
LC1047.G3L5 52-23053

NL 0409083 DLC NNC-T

Litt, Theodor, 1880-1962
Der Bildungsauftrag der Deutschen Hochschule. Vortrag, gehalten bei der Tagung des Hochschulverbandes in Marburg am 2. Mai 1952. Göttingen, O. Schwartz, 1952.
31 p. 21 cm. (Schriften des Hochschulverbandes, Heft 2)
1. Education—Germany—1945- I. Title.
LA721.82.L5 55-27772 ‡

NL 0409084 DLC NcU CtY

Litt, Theodor, 1880-
Das Bildungsideal der deutschen Klassik und die moderne Arbeitswelt. [Bonn] Bundeszentrale für Heimatdienst [1955]
148 p. 21 cm. (Schriftenreihe der Bundeszentrale für Heimatdienst, Heft 15)
1. Classicism. 2. Science—Philosophy. 3. Man. I. Title.
JN3966.A3 Heft 15 57-26594 ‡

NL 0409085 DLC OCU NcU

PA 6965 V3L77
Litt, Theodor, 1880-1962.
De Verrii Flacci et Cornelii Labeonis fastorum libris. Bonnae, C. Georg, 1904.
34 p. 23cm.
Diss.--Bonn.
1. Verrius Flaccus, Marcus. 2. Labeo, Cornelius.

NL 0409086 NIC CtY CU

4B-258
Litt, Theodor, 1880-1962.
Denken und sein. Stuttgart, S. Hirzel, 1948.
266 p.

CLSU MH-AH TxU KyU
NL 0409087 DLC-P4 NNC MH ViU PU NjP ICU MB NN OU

VOLUME 336

Litt, Theodor, 1880–
... Der deutsche geist und das christentum; vom wesen geschichtlicher begegnung. 5. bis 7. tausend. Leipzig, L. Klotz, 1938.
63, [1] p. 23½cm.

1. Germany—Religion—1933– I. Title. 39-29603

Library of Congress BR856.L53 1938
[2] 274.3

NL 0409088 DLC CaBVaU CSt NcD NN NcU NNUT CtY

BR 856 L768
Litt, Theodor, 1880–
Der deutsche Geist und das Christentum; vom Wesen geschichtlicher Begegnung. Leipzig, L. Klotz, 1939.
63 p. 22cm.

1. Christianity--Germany--20th cent. I. Title.

NL 0409089 NIC MH-AH

Litt, Theodor, 1880–
Einleitung in die philosophie, von Theodor Litt. Leipzig und Berlin, B. G. Teubner, 1933.
viii, 331, [1] p. 21cm.
"Literaturverzeichnis": p. [326]–329.

1. Philosophy, Modern. 34-235
Library of Congress B804.L47
Copyright A—Foreign 22800
[2] 190

NL 0409090 DLC CtY TxU

---

190 L776e 1949
Litt, Theodor, 1880–
Einleitung in die philosophie. 2. verb. Aufl. Stuttgart, E. Klett [1949]
viii,271p. 22cm.

1.Philosophy, Modern.

NL 0409091 CLSU PU

Litt, Theodor, 1880–
Erkenntnis und leben; untersuchungen über gliederung, methoden und beruf der wissenschaft, von Theodor Litt. Leipzig, Berlin, B. G. Teubner, 1923.
vii, [1], 214 p. 22cm.

1. Intellect. 2. Culture. 3. Life. I. Title.
41-33921
Library of Congress CB19.L5
[2] 121

NL 0409092 DLC LU ICN CU NIC OU NN NjP IU MH ICU

LITT, THEODOR, 1880-
Erkenntnis und Leben; Untersuchungen über Gliederung, Methoden und Beruf der Wissenschaft. Leipzig, B.G. Teubner, 1923. vii, 214 p. 8°.

Film reproduction. Negative.

1. Science--Philosophy. t. 1923. . i. subs. for L-, Thodor, 1880- .

NL 0409093 NN

4BJ 319
Litt, Theodor, 1880–
Ethik der Neuzeit. [München, R. Oldenbourg, 1926]
184 p.

NL 0409094 DLC-P4 MoSCS ICN CLSU

Litt, Theodor, 1880–
... Ethik der neuzeit, von Theodor Litt. München und Berlin, R. Oldenbourg, 1927.
2 p.l., [3]-184 p. 25cm.
"Sonderausgabe aus dem Handbuch der philosophie."
Contains bibliographies.

1. Ethics. 2. Philosophy, Modern. I. Handbuch der philosophie.

NL 0409095 MiU OCH MH

Litt, Theodor, 1880–
Die Frage nach dem Sinn der Geschichte. München, R. Piper [1948]
54 p. 22 cm.

1. History—Philosophy. I. Title.

D16.8.L47 56-31951 ‡

NL 0409096 DLC OU KMK MH CLSU NN ICU MiDW

Litt, Theodor, 1880–
Die Freiheit des Menschen und der Staat. Berlin, Gebrüder Weiss, 1953.
44 p. 23 cm. (Schriftenreihe der Deutschen Hochschule für Politik, Berlin)
Vortrag—Deutsche Hochschule für Politik, Berlin (Lemesterfeier) June 12, 1953.

1. Liberty. I. Title.

JC571.L57 56-19763 ‡

NL 0409097 DLC OU NcD CU NNC PU NN ICU

Litt, Theodor, 1880–
"Führen" oder "wachsenlassen," eine erörterung des pädagogischen grundproblems, von Theodor Litt. Leipzig, Berlin, B. G. Teubner, 1927.
iv p., 1 l., 100 p. 20½cm.

1. Teaching. 44-49533
Library of Congress LB1027.L55

NL 0409098 DLC OOxM

---

371 L776f
Litt, Theodor, 1880–
"Führen" oder "Wachsenlassen," eine Erörterung des pädagogischen Grundproblems. 2. verb. Aufl. Leipzig, B.G. Teubner, 1929.
v.107p. 21cm.

1.Teaching.

NL 0409099 IEN

LB1027 L55 1931
Litt, Theodor, 1880–
"Führen" oder "Wachsenlassen" eine Erörterung des pädagogischen Grundproblems. 3. durchgesehene Aufl. mit einem Anhang: Das Wesen des pädagogischen Denkens. Leipzig, B.G. Teubner, 1931.
v,148 p.

1. Teaching.

NL 0409100 CU

Litt, Theodor, 1880–
Führen oder Wachsenlassen; eine Erörterung des pädagogischen Grundproblems. 4. durchgesehene und erweiterte Aufl. Stuttgart, E. Klett, 1949.
136 p. 22 cm. (Erziehungs Wissenschaftliche Bücherei. Reihe 4. Theoretische Pädagogik)

1. Teaching. I. Title.

LB1027.L55 1949 56-24818 ‡

NL 0409101 DLC OU

Litt, Theodor, 1880–
Führen oder Wachsenlassen; eine Erörterung des pädagogischen Grundproblems. 5. ~~durchgesehene und erweiterte~~ Aufl. Stuttgart, E. Klett, 1952.
136 p. 22 cm. (Erziehungs Wissenschaftliche Bücherei. Reihe 4. Theoretische Pädagogik)
"Anmerkungen"(Bibliography): p. 127-136.

1. Teaching. I. Title.

NL 0409102 PPT

PT2139 B4915
Litt, Theodor, 1880–
Die Geschichte und das Übergeschichtliche, eine Rede. Hamburg, E. Hauswedell, 1949.
31 p.

"Rede, gehalten im Hamburger Rathaus am 13. Januar 1949 anlässlich der Feier zur Eröffnung des Goethe-Jahres."

NL 0409103 CU DGW MiU WU DLC-P4 CFIS

F 018 .508
LITT, THEODOR, 1880–
Geschichte und Leben. Von den Bildungsaufgaben geschichtlichen und sprachlichen Unterrichts. Leipzig, B.G.Teubner, 1918.
iv,199p. 22cm.

NL 0409104 ICN ICarbS

Litt, Theodor, 1880–
Geschichte und Leben; Probleme und Ziele kulturwissenschaftlicher Bildung, von Theodor Litt... Leipzig: B. G. Teubner, 1925. vi, 222 p. 2. ed., rev. and enl. 8°.
Bibliographical footnotes.

302004A. 1. History—Philosophy of.
N. Y. P. L. August 19, 1927

NL 0409105 NN MH NjP ICU NNU-W

Litt, Theodor, 1880–
Geschichte und leben; probleme und ziele kulturwissenschaftlicher bildung, von Theodor Litt. 3. verb. aufl. Leipzig und Berlin, B. G. Teubner, 1930.
vii p., 1 l., 238 p. 22½cm.

1. History—Philosophy. 2. Life. 3. History—Study and teaching. I. Title.
39-5547
Library of Congress D16.9.L47 1930
[2] 901

NL 0409106 DLC NcD CtY

VOLUME 336

4D 2158 Litt, Theodor, 1880-
Geschichte und Verantwortung; ein Vortrag gehalten bei der Eröffnung der Leipziger Ortsgruppe des Kulturbundes zur Demokratischen Erneuerung Deutschlands. Wiesbaden, Dieterich'sche Verlagsbuchhandlung [1947]
32 p.

NL 0409107 DLC-P4 MH CLSU CU NN OU

4D-1446 Litt, Theodor, 1880-1962.
Geschichtswissenschaft und Geschichtsphilosophie. München, F. Bruckmann [c1950]
45 p.

NL 0409108 DLC-P4 ICU ICN NN PU MnU MH OU MiDW

B2648 .L58
Litt, Theodor, 1880–
Hegel; Versuch einer kritischen Erneuerung. Heidelberg, Quelle & Meyer, 1953.
314 p. 23 cm.

1. Hegel, Georg Wilhelm Friedrich, 1770–1831.

A 53–2621

Chicago. Univ. Libr. for Library of Congress [2]

WaU CSt IEN TxU CaBVaU
NL 0409109 ICU MU LU OU MsU OCU PU NN NIC DLC NjR

Litt, Theodor, 1880–
Individuum und gemeinschaft; grundfragen der sozialen theorie und ethik, von Theodor Litt. Leipzig und Berlin, B. G. Teubner, 1919.
vi, 224 p., 1 l. 22cm.
"Literaturnachweise": p. 223–224.

1. Sociology. 2. Individualism. 3. Civilization—Philosophy. I. Title.

Library of Congress HM24.L5 1919 40–25127
[2] 301.15

NL 0409110 DLC NIC TxU MH

Litt, Theodor, 1880–
Individuum und gemeinschaft; grundlegung der kulturphilosophie von Theodor Litt. 2. völlig neu bearb. aufl. Leipzig, Berlin, B. G. Teubner, 1924.
x, 265, [1] p. 22cm.

1. Individualism. 2. Sociology. 3. Psychology. 4. Civilization. 5. Knowledge, Theory of.

Library of Congress HM24.L5 1924 25–8068

NL 0409111 DLC NN MiU

Litt, Theodor, 1880-
Individuum und gemeinschaft; grundlegung der kulturphilosophie. 3. abermals durchgearb. und erweiterte aufl. Leipzig, B. G. Teubner, 1926.
xii, 415p.

NL 0409112 ScU GEU OCU OO IaU OU ViU MH CtY NN

Litt, Theodor, 1880–
... Kant und Herder als deuter der geistigen welt. Leipzig, Quelle & Meyer, 1930.
vii, [1], 290, [1] p. 22½cm. (Half-title: Das wissenschaftliche weltbild, hrsg. von P. Hinneberg)

1. Kant, Immanuel, 1724–1804. 2. Herder, Johann Gottfried von, 1744–1803.

Library of Congress B2798.L67 38–31693
[2] 193.2

IU MiU MH NRU NcU
NL 0409113 DLC CU TxU UU CU-S NcD CaBVaU OCU ICU

Litt, Theodor, 1880–
Kant und Herder als Deuter der geistigen Welt. 2. verb. Aufl. Heidelberg, Quelle & Meyer, 1949.
270 p. 21 cm.
Bibliographical references included in "Anmerkungen" (p. 265–270)

1. Kant, Immanuel, 1724–1804. 2. Herder, Johann Gottfried von, 1744–1803.

B2798.L67 1949 193.2 A 50–3999

Harvard Univ. Library for Library of Congress [1]†

NL 0409114 MH WaU UU MoKU GU NN ICN CtY TU OU DLC

Litt, Theodor, 1880–
Der lebendige Pestalozzi; drei sozialpädagogische Besinnungen. Heidelberg, Quelle & Meyer, 1952.
79 p. 22 cm.

1. Pestalozzi, Johann Heinrich, 1746–1827. I. Title.

LB627.L5 56–43744 ‡

NL 0409115 DLC OU CU U

Litt, Theodor, 1880–
Leibniz und die deutsche Gegenwart, ein Vortrag, gehalten in der Deutschen Akademie der Wissenschaften zu Berlin zur Feier von Leibniz' 300. Geburtstag. Wiesbaden, Dieterich [1947]
47 p. 18 cm.

1. Leibniz, Gottfried Wilhelm, Freiherr von, 1646–1716.

B2598.L5 52–22936

NL 0409116 DLC

Litt, Theodor, 1880-
Leibniz und die deutsche Gegenwart; ein Vortrag, gehalten in der Deutschen Akademie der Wissenschaften zu Berlin zur Feier von Leibniz' 300.Geburtstag. Wiesbaden, Dieterich [1946]
47 p. 17 cm.

NL 0409117 MH NNC ICU NjP OU NN CaBVaU

AC831 C642 1909 Stack
Litt, Theodor, 1880-1962.
Lucians philosophische Entwicklung. Cöln, 1909.
28 p.
"1909. Progr. Nr. 608."
Programmschrift - Königliches Friedrich-Wilhelms-Gymnasium, Cöln.

1.Lucianus Samosatensis.

NL 0409118 CSt

Litt, Theodor, 1880-
Mensch und charakter ... München und Berlin, R. Oldenbourg, 1931.

4B-242 Litt, Theodor, 1880-1962.
Mensch und Welt, Grundlinien einer Philosophie des Geistes. München, I. & S. Federmann, 1948.
336 p. (Ernst Reinhardt Bücherreihe)

OCU OU NN MH CtY MH-AH MsU
NL 0409120 DLC-P4 WaU ICN NNC IU CLSU TxU CLU ICU

Litt, Theodor, 1880-
Der Mensch vor der Geschichte. Bremen, Schünemann [1950]
38 p. (Schriften der Wittheit zu Bremen)

NL 0409121 MH

Litt, Theodor, 1880–
Möglichkeiten und grenzen der pädagogik; abhandlungen zur gegenwärtigen lage von erziehung und erziehungstheorie, von Theodor Litt. Leipzig, Berlin, B. G. Teubner, 1926.
iv p., 1 l., 174 p. 22cm.
CONTENTS.—Die gegenwärtige lage der pädagogik und ihre forderungen.—Die philosophischen grundlagen der staatsbürgerlichen erziehung.—Bildungspolitik.—Wissenschaft und höhere schule.—Lehrfach und lehrpersönlichkeit.—Gedanken zum "kulturkundlichen" unterrichtsprinzip.

1. Education—Study and teaching. I. Title.

Library of Congress LB775.L55 27–9972

NL 0409122 DLC

Litt, Theodor, 1880–
Möglichkeiten und Grenzen der Pädagogik; Abhandlungen zur gegenwärtigen Lage von Erziehung und Erziehungstheorie. 2. erweiterte Aufl. Leipzig, B. G. Teubner, 1931.
iv, 202 p. 22 cm.

1. Education—Study and teaching. I. Title.

LB775.L55 1931 49–42163*

NL 0409123 DLC

LC93 .G2L7
Litt, Theodor, 1880–
... Nationale erziehung und internationalismus, von Theodor Litt. Berlin, E. S. Mittler & sohn, 1920.
36 p. 21cm. (Sozialpädagogische abende im Zentralinstitut für erziehung und unterricht. 3. heft)

1. Education. 2. Nationalism and nationality.

NL 0409124 ICU

Litt, Theodor, 1880–
Naturwissenschaft und Menschenbildung. Heidelberg, Quelle & Meyer, 1952.
99 p. 21 cm.

1. Science—Philosophy. 2. Education, Humanistic. I. Title.
Q175.L57 A 54–2816

Harvard Univ. Library for Library of Congress [1]†

NL 0409125 MH ICJ NN NIC OU DLC

Litt, Theodor, 1880–
Naturwissenschaft und Menschenbildung. 2. verb. und erweiterte Aufl. Heidelberg, Quelle & Meyer, 1954.
144 p. 21 cm.

1. Science—Philosophy. 2. Education, Humanistic. I. Title.

Q175.L57 1954 54–28263 ‡

NL 0409126 DLC OCU NN ICN

VOLUME 336

Litt, Theodor, 1880-
Pestalozzi zum 200jährigen Geburtstag. Berlin, Volk und Wissen Verlag, 1946.
31 p. 21 cm.

1. Pestalozzi, Johann Heinrich, 1746-1827.
LB629.L58 53-16531 ‡

NL 0409127 DLC

LITT, Theodor, 1880-
Die Philosophie der Gegenwart und ihr Einfluss auf das Bildungsideal. Leipzig, etc., B.G. Teubner 1925.
21 cm. pp.(4), 74.

NL 0409128 MH CU

Litt, Theodor, 1880-
Die philosophie der gegenwart und ihr einfluss auf das bildungsideal, von Theodor Litt. 2. verb. aufl. Leipzig, Berlin, B.G. Teubner, 1927.
2 p.l., 79, [1] p. 20½ cm.
"Literatur": p. [78]-79.

1. Philosophy, Modern. 2. Culture. I. Title.

NL 0409129 MWelC MA IU IaU MH OClW

LITT, Theodor, 1880-
Die philosophie der gegenwart und ihr einfluss auf das bildungsideal. 3e abermals verbesserte aufl. Leipzig, etc., B.G. Teubner, 1930.
pp.(4), 89+.

NL 0409130 MH NcD

Litt, Theodor, 1880-
... Philosophie und zeitgeist. Leipzig, F. Meiner [1935]
61 p. 21cm. (Wissenschaft und zeitgeist. 1)
"Die vorliegende schrift bringt den inhalt eines im november dieses jahres in Berlin gehaltenen vortrages in stark erweiterter fassung."—Vorbemerkung.

1. Philosophy—Addresses, essays, lectures. I. Title.
36-11776
Library of Congress BD41.L55
[2] 104

NL 0409131 DLC CU ICU NcU

Litt, Theodor, 1880-
Die politische Selbsterziehung des deutschen Volkes. [Bonn] Bundeszentrale für Heimatdienst [1954?]
38 p. 21 cm. (Schriftenreihe der Bundeszentrale für Heimatdienst, Heft 1)

1. Civics, German. I. Title. (Series: Germany (Federal Republic, 1949-) Bundeszentrale für Heimatdienst. Schriftenreihe, Heft 1)
JN3777.L5 55-57738

NL 0409132 DLC MH WU

LITT, Theodor, 1880-1962.
Protestantisches Geschichtsbewusstsein; eine geschichtsphilosophische Besinnung. Leipzig, Leopold Klotz, 1939.
61p. 23cm.

NL 0409133 MH-AH CU

Litt, Theodor, 1880-
... Die selbsterkenntnis des menschen. Leipzig, Felix Meiner verlag, 1938.
120 p. 19½cm.
Bibliographical notes included in "Anmerkungen" (p. 118-120)

1. Self. I. Title.
A C 39-3064
Johns Hopkins univ. Libr. for Library of Congress [2]

NL 0409134 MdBJ CU MB

Litt, Theodor, 1880-
Die Selbsterkenntnis des Menschen [2. verb. Aufl.] Hamburg, R. Meiner [1948]
89 p. 21 cm.
Includes bibliography.

NL 0409135 CaBVaU CU MB DLC-P4

4QH-18 Litt, Theodor, 1880-1962.
Die Sonderstellung des Menschen im Reiche der Lebendigen. Wiesbaden, Dieterich [1948]
53 p.

NL 0409136 DLC-P4 MH CLSU

JC341 L776 MiDW NcU Hoover Library
Litt, Theodor, 1880-
Staatsgewalt und Sittlichkeit. München, Erasmus, 1948.
127 p. 21cm.

1. State, The. 2. Political science. I. Title.

OU NNUN CU
NL 0409137 CSt-H MiDW NcU CLSU NN MnU MiU NNC MH

370.943 L71s 1934
Litt, Theodor, 1880-
Die stellung der geisteswissenschaften im nationalsozialistischen staate ... 2. unveränderte aufl. Leipzig, Quelle & Meyer [1934]
24p.
"Sonderdruck aus heft 1 der zeitschrift 'Die Erziehung', 9. jahrgang."

1. Education and state--Germany. 2. National-sozialistische deutsche arbeiter-partei. I. Title: Geisteswissenschaften im nationalsozialistischen staate.

NL 0409138 IU WU OCU

CB 19 .L52
Litt, Theodor, 1880-1962.
Das Verhältnis der Generationen ehedem und heute. Wiesbaden, Dieterich [1947]
67 p. 18 cm.

1. Civilization—Philosophy. I. Title.
CB19.L52 55-38668 ‡

NL 0409139 DLC MH DAU

Litt, Theodor, 1880-1962.
Von der Sendung der Philosophie, ein Vortrag. Wiesbaden, Dieterich [194-]
51 p.

NL 0409140 NNC NjP ICU MH

Litt, Theodor, 1880-
Von der Sendung der Philosophie, ein Vortrag. Wiesbaden, Dieterich [1946]
51 p. 18 cm.

1. Philosophy--Addresses, essays, lectures.

NL 0409141 NN PU NNC OU

Litt, Theodor, 1880-
Von der Sendung der Philosophie, ein Vortrag. Wiesbaden, Dieterich [1947]
51 p. 18 cm.

1. Philosophy.
B53.L5 52-22935

NL 0409142 DLC

Litt, Theodor, 1880-1962.
Wege und Irrwege geschichtlichen Denkens. München, R. Piper [1948]
155 p. 23 cm.

1. History—Philosophy. I. Title.
D16.9.L48 901 48-21190*

NL 0409143 DLC PU CU IaU KMK OU CtY NBC ICU

Litt, Theodor, 1880-1962.
Wissenschaft, bildung, weltanschauung, von Theodor Litt. Leipzig [etc.] B. G. Teubner, 1928.
vi, 136 p. 22cm.

1. Metaphysics. 2. Philosophy, Modern. 3. Culture. 4. Science—Philosophy. I. Title.
29-7705
Library of Congress BD113.L5

NL 0409144 DLC MH-AH CtY ICJ

D16 .4 G4L5
Litt, Theodor, 1880-1962.
Zur Gestaltung des Geschichtsunterrichts in der Schule. Berlin, E.S. Mittler, 1918.
35 p. (Geschichtliche Abende im Zentral-institut für Erziehung und Unterricht, 4. Heft)
Bibliographical references in "Anmerkungen" (p.34-35)

1. History - Study and teaching - Germany

NL 0409145 CU

Litt, Willard David, 1899- ed.
Yale university. Class of 1921.
History of the class of nineteen hundred and twenty-one ... [v. 1- New Haven, Conn., Tuttle, Morehouse and Taylor, 1921-

VOLUME 336

Litt, Willard David, 1899- ed.
Yale university. Class of 1921.
... Milestones. no. 1- June, 1922-
[New Haven, Class secretaries bureau] 1922-

Y 155 .L 71 LITT, William.
Henry and Mary, a local tale; illustrative of the peculiar habits, customs, and diversions of the inhabitants of the west of Cumberland, during the greater part of the eighteenth and preceding century... Whitehaven,R.Gibson,1825.
382p. 21cm.

Ms. notes.

NL 0409148 ICN

Litt, William.
Henry and Mary; a local tale illustrative of the habits, customs, and diversions of the inhabitants of the west of Cumberland during the greater part of the eighteenth and preceding century. Whitehaven, M. and W. Alsop, 1860.
nar. 12°. pp. xi, 175.
"Reprinted from *the Whitehaven news.*"

NL 0409149 MH

QTA L776w 1823 **LITT, William.**
Wrestliana; or, An historical account of ancient and modern wrestling. Whitehaven [Eng.] Gibson, 1823.
170 p.

NL 0409150 DNLM InNd MnU NN CU MH MSIntY

Litt om den Norske Amerikalinjes tillblivelse
see under [Mowinckel, Johan Ludwig] 1870-

Litt om overleveringen i Håvards saga
see under [Holtsmark, Anne] 1896-

Litt om Voss og Vosseskiferen, 1895-1945
see under [Gierløff, Christian Per Grønbeck] 1879-

---

626 L71m Litta, Agostino, conte, d.1781.
Memoria idrostatica ... concernente lo sperimento pubblico fatto nel 1774 di spurgare la fossa interiore del naviglio della città di Milano colla semplice forza, ed uso dell'acqua sua corrente. [Milano, Stamperia di G. Marelli, 1775]
69p.

1. Canals--Milan.

NL 0409154 IU

LITTA, Agostino,conte,d.1781.
Memorie galanti, centuria prima di pensieri, ed annotazioni sopra le opere dell'abate Metastasio. Venezia, V. Radici, 1768.

NL 0409155 MH

---

626 L71r [Litta, Agostino, conte] d.1781.
Risposta al sig. ingegnere Dionigi Maria Ferrario intorno al metodo proposto della spurgazione del naviglio di città. [Milano, Stamperia di G. Marelli, 1763]
xlvii p.

Dedication signed: Conte cavaliere Agostino Litta.

1. Canals--Milan. 2. Ferrario, Dionigi Maria, 1710-1782. I. Title.

NL 0409156 IU

729.15 B294d 1771 cop.2 Litta, Agostino, conte, d.1781.
Risposta del conte cavaliere Agostino Litta alle Brevi riflessioni del sig. ingegnere Dionigi Maria Ferrario, e Piano di naturale spurgo della fossa interiore della città coll'uso dell'acque liberamente correnti proposto dal suddetto cavaliere. [Milano, Stamperia di G. Marelli, 1763]
lxxvi p. [With Bassi, Martino. Dispareri in materia d'architettura, e prospettiva. Milano, 1771. cop.2]

Head and tail-pieces.

NL 0409157 IU

Litta, Alfonso, cardinal, d. 1679, comp.
Andromeda a Perseo liberata, in laureâ legali Alexandri Mazvchelli academici hermathenaici, svb avspiciis ill.mi, et rev.mi D. D. comitis Alphonsi Littæ S. M. E. archiepiscopi vigilantissimi. Mediolani, Ex typographia Ludouici Montiæ, 1665. 43 p. front. 36cm.(f°.)

Comprises poetry and prose in honor of A. Mazuchellus.
Illustrations: frontispiece engraved by Agnellus. Ornamental initials and head- and tailpieces. Title vignette (compiler's arms). Each page within border of typographical ornaments.

1. Mazuchellus, Alexander. 2. Festival books, Italian, 17th cent. 3. Engravings, Italian. I. Agnelli, Federico, illus. II. Title.

NL 0409158 NN

Litta, Alfonso, Cardinal, d. 1679.
Missae Sanctorum qui novissime Ambrosiano calendario accesserunt ... (1672)
see under Catholic Church. Liturgy and ritual. Missae novae. [Ambrosian rite] [with date 1672 and Litta named in title, in supplement; with date 1675 (presumably also by order of Litta) in v. 99, NC 0219125]

Litta, Giulio
see Litta-Visconti-Arese, Giulio, duca, 1822-1891.

[**Litta, Lorenzo,** *cardinal*] 1756-1820.
Lettres diverses et très-intéressantes, sur les quatre articles dits, du clergé de France; par un professeur en théologie, ex-jésuite; accompagnées d'une dissertation très-importante, sur cette question: Le souverain pontife a-t-il le droit de priver un évêque de son siége, dans un cas de nécessité pour l'église, ou de grande utilité? Cette dissertation tr. du latin de m. A. Muzzarelli... Paris, 1809.
144p. 21cm.

1 Popes. 2. Councils and synods. I. Muzzarelli, Alfonso, 1749-1813. II. Title.

Printed by Wesleyan University Library

NL 0409161 CtW

[LITTA,Lorenzo] cardinal, 1756 - 1820.
Lettres diverses sur les quatre articles dits du clergé de France. n.p.,n.d.

pp.74.
Without title-page. Caption title.

NL 0409162 MH

262.131 L716l **Litta, Lorenzo, cardinal, 1756-1820.**
Lettres sur les quatre articles dits du clergé de France. 2d. éd., rev. et augm. par l'auteur. [n. p., n. d.]
123 p. 19cm.
Authority for author's name: Barbier, Dictionnaire des ouvrages anonymes. 1872. v. 2, col. 1304.

1. Gallicanism. 2. Declaratio cleri gallicani, 1682. 3. Catholic church in France. I. Title.

NL 0409163 MoSU

Litta, Lorenzo, cardinal, d.1820

Lettres sur les quatre articles dits du clergé de France. 3.éd. rev., cor. et augm. par l'auteur. Bruxelles, n.p., 1813.
iii p., 142 p. 22cm.

1. Catholic church in France. 2. Catholic church. Clergy. I. Title.

NL 0409164 NcD MH

Litta, Lorenzo, Cardinal, d.1820

Lettres sur les quatre articles dits du clergé de France, (par son Em. Mgr. le Cardinal Litta.) Nouv.éd. d'après la 3e de Rome, rev. et considerablement augm. par l'auteur. Avec un discours preliminaire, par M. Robiano de Borsbeek. Avignon, Seguin aîné, 1823.
168 p. 18cm.

1. Catholic church in France. 2. Catholic church. Clergy.

NL 0409165 NcD MH

Litta, Lorenzo, *cardinal,* 1756-1820.
Sr. eminenz des cardinal Litta briefe über die sogenannten vier artikel des klerus von Frankreich. Nach der neuen vom **verfasser selbst durchgesehenen und bedeutend vermehrten ausgabe aus dem französischen übersetzt. Nebst einer einleitung vom Robiano von Borsbeck, und einem anhange, verschiedene documente und die consistorial-acten der retractation des Febronius** [*pseud.*] enthaltend ... Münster, J. H. **Deiters, 1844.**
1 p. l., 271, [1] p. 19cm.
1. Gallicanism. 2. Declaratio cleri gallicani, 1682. 3. Catholic church in France. I. Robiano de Borsbeek, Louis François de Paule Marie Joseph, comte de, 1781-1855. II. Hontheim, Johann Nikolaus von, 1701-1790.
Library of Congress BX1529.L53 43-41742

NL 0409166 DLC

Litta, Lorenzo, cardinal, 1756-1820.
Vingt-neuf lettres sur les quatre articles dits du clergé de France, par S. Em. le cardinal Litta, d'après la seconde édition revue et augmentée par l'auteur en 1814; précédées d'un discours préliminaire par Mr. Louis Fr. de Robiano de Borsbeek... Louvain: Vanlinthout et Vandenzande, 1822. xliii, 172 p. 8°.

1. Church history, France, 1682. 2. Church and state, France, 1682. 3. Robiano de Borsbeek, Louis François de Paule Marie Joseph, comte de, 1781-1855.
N. Y. P. L. March 7, 1923.

NL 0409167 NN

VOLUME 336

Litta, Louise.
A simplified French conversational manual; or, How to converse in French whilst travelling, at the hotel, restaurant shopping, with the principal routes to Paris and places of interest. London, David Nutt, 1900.
160 p.

NL 0409168 OCl

BV 280 L77 Litta, Luigi, d. 1785.
Del diritto di stabilire impedimenti dirimenti il matrimonio, e di dispensarne. Ed. 2. riveduta, ed accresciuta dall'autore. Pavia, P. Galeazzi, 1784.
2 v. 20cm.
Contents. -- v.1. Lettere. - v. 2. Ragionamenti.

1. Marriage - Impediments. 2. Church and state

NL 0409169 DCU

945.21 L71d Litta, Marco.
Marci Littæ ivreconsvlti De vrbe mediolanensi libellvs. Mediolani, apvd Moschenios, 1554.
27 numb.l. 16½cm.

Signatures: A-C[8], D[4](D[4] blank)
Device of printer on t.-p. Initials.
Armorial book-plate of Frederick Pollock.

1. Milan--Hist.

NL 0409170 IU ICN

Litta, María Elvira.
... Viajes famosos, por María Elvira Litta. Buenos Aires, Editorial "Verbo" [1943]
94, [2] p. 20½cm. (Biblioteca "Escuela")

1. Voyages and travels. 2. Discoveries (in geography) I. Title.
44-30582
Library of Congress G170.L5
[2] 910.9

NL 0409171 DLC

Litta, Orio.
... Manuale teorico-pratico per la riscossione delle imposte di consumo e per la preparazione agli esami di agente. 4. ed. ampliata e aggiornata. [Roma] Stamperia reale di Roma, 1940.
106 p. 17½cm.

1. Taxation of articles of consumption—Italy. 2. Municipal finance—Italy.
45-47120
Library of Congress HJ5715.I 8L5 1940
[2] 336.271

NL 0409172 DLC NN IU MH

Litta, Paolo, 1871-1931.
Batka, Richard, 1868-
L'aria ancienne. Ida Isori et son art du "bel-canto." Par le Dr Richard Batka ... précédé d'une préface de Paolo Litta ... Paris, Costellat & cie [pref. 1913]

Litta, Paolo, 1871-1931
La déesse nue. Die entschleierte Göttin. Poème ésotérique pour une danseuse, piano, violon et triangle. Ein esoterisches Tanz-Gedicht für eine Tänzerin, Klavier, Violine u. Triangel. [Partition et partie.]
— Florenz. Libera estetica. 1912. 45 pp. 34 cm.

K4308 — Tr. — Dance music.

NL 0409174 MB

LITTA, PAOLO, 1871-1931.
La déesse nue. Florence, Édition "Libera estetica," 1912. 78 p. diagr. 18cm.

"La danse comme moyen esotèrique d'expression musicale."

1. Dancing--Psychology.

NL 0409175 NN

M1503 L534E4 Litta, Paolo, 1871-1931.
[Ellys; acc. arr. piano]
Ellys; conte dramatique en un acte et en prose rythmée d'Alfred Mortier. Partition chant et piano, arr. par l'auteur. Liège, Belgique, Veuve L. Muraille [1897?] Pl. no. 240-107.
110 p.

Vocal score with piano accompaniment. French words.

NL 0409176 CU MB

sVM 1003 L 77s LITTA, PAOLO, 1871-1931.
Sérénade [par] P.Litta. Bruxelles,J.B. Katto[n.d.]
5p. 35cm.

Op.2, no.2.
Full score for orchestra.
Plate no.: Ch. V. & L. 1740.

NL 0409177 ICN

Litta, Paolo, 1871-1931.
...Der Tod als Fiedler. Death as fiddler. Le ménétrier, la mort. Il giullare, la morte. Rapsodia da concerto per violino e pianoforte (con danza ad libitum) [di] Paolo Litta. Wien: Universal-Edition A.-G.[, introd. 1924.] 3 parts in 1 v. diagr. f°.

Violin, cymbals and piano in score, and violin and cymbals parts.
Introduction in German, French, Italian and English.

1. Violin and piano. 2. Title.
N. Y. P. L. December 26, 1929

NL 0409178 NN

Litta, Pompeo, conte, 1781-1852.
Albero della famiglia Alighieri, tratto da Pompeo Litta, colle aggiunte del Pelli.
(In L'inferno, 1858-65, vol. II, 3-5 p.)

NL 0409179 NIC

Litta, Pompeo, conte, 1781-1852.
Albero della famiglia di Dante Alighieri, tratto da Pompeo Litta, colle aggiunte del Pelli.
(In L'inferno, 1842)

NL 0409180 NIC

929.75 L716 F Litta, Pompeo, conte, 1781-1852.
Famiglie celebri italiane, del conte Pompeo Litta ... Milano, Si vende presso l'autore, 1819-
mounted front., plates (part col.) ports (part col.) col. maps, plans., facsims., geneal. tables, col. coats of arms. 49cm.

Issued in fascicles.
Original title-page bound in v. 1: Famigli celebri di Italia. Milano, Giusti, 1819.
Commemorative material by Carlo Belgiojoso and Luigi Passerini inlaid at beginning of v. 1.
Vol. 9 and 10 have imprint: Tipografia delle Famiglie celebri italiane.
"Nel 1819 uscì il primo fascicolo con la famiglia degli Attendolo Sforza da Cotignola ... Agli Attendolo seguirono altre centodieci famiglie, fino alla morte del Litta, in centotrentacinque dispense, e cioè alla seconda parte dei Malaspina, uscita nel 1852. Dopo continuò ... fino al 1883, per virtù dei seguenti collaboratori: conte Luigi Passerini Orsini de' Rilli ... cav. Federico Odorici ... cav. Fedrigo Stefani, cav. Francesco Di Mauro de Polvica e professor Costantino Coda, raggiungendosi così il numero di centottantaquattro dispense o centocinquanta famiglie."- Boschetti, A. F. I cataloghi dell'opera di P. Litta. 1930. p. [19]-21.

NL 0409183 NNC PPT MH IU

MICROFILM F 8979 Litta, Pompeo, conte, 1781-1852.
Famiglie celebri di Italia. Milano, Giusti, 1819-
v.

Vol. 9 and 10 on microfilm (negative) Ithaca, N. Y., Cornell University Libraries, 1966. 1 reel.

NL 0409184 NNC NjP

RARE BOOKS DEPT. [Litta, Pompeo, conte] 1781-1852.
Famiglie celebri di Italia. Milano, Paolo Emilio Giusti [etc.] 1819[-1883]
10 v. plates, col. coats of arms, geneal. tables. 49cm.

Issued unbound in 123 sections, each within its own paper cover; gathered, but not bound, into 10 tie binders.
Section covers have title: Famiglie celebri italiane.
Sections 1-41, pt. 3 and sections 42-43 designated on their paper covers as fascicles only; sections 41, pt. 4 and sections 44-76 designated as fascicles and numbers (dispense); remaining sections designated as numbers only.
Fascicles 1-75 also called numbers 1-137. Cf. Boschetti. Anton Ferrante. I cataloghi dell' opera di Pompeo Litta "Famiglie celebri italiane", p.[27]-28, 42-57. 1930.
Imprint varies. Cf. Boschetti, op. cit., p.[23]-25.
Imperfect: 1 plate of fasc. 33, pt. 1 and no. 178, 180-184 wanting.
Continued after Litta's death by Luigi Passerini Orsini de'Rilli, Federico Odorici, Federigo Stefani, Francesco Di Mauro di Polvica and Costantino Coda. - Boschetti, op. cit., p.[19]-21.

1. Italy - Nobility. 2. Italy - Biog. 3. Italy - Geneal.

NL 0409186 CU

Litta, Pompeo, conte, 1781-1852.
Famiglie celebri italiane. Del conte Pompeo Litta... Milano: Presso l'autore, 1819-85. 11 v. in 10. col'd coats of arms, geneal. tables, maps, plans, plates (part col'd), ports. (part col'd.) 49cm.

Imprint varies; v. 9-10: Milano, Tipografia delle Famiglie celebri italiane; v. 11: Torino, F. Basadonna.
Vol. 11 has no t.-p.; imprint from cover.
Continued by Luigi Passerini, Federico Odorici, Federigo Stefani and Francesco di Mauro.

Continued in next column

VOLUME 336

Continued from preceding column

——— Famiglie celebri italiane, seconda serie... Napoli: Stab. tipo-litogr. Richter, 1902. 3 v. col'd coats of arms, geneal. tables, maps, plans, plates (part col'd), ports. (part col'd.) 49cm.
Issued in 78 parts, 1902-23.
No more published?

1. Italy—Geneal. I. Odorici, Federico, 1807-1884, ed. II. Stefani, Federico, d. 1897, ed. III. Passerini, Luigi, 1816-1877, ed. IV. Mauro, Francesco di, ed. V. Title.
N. Y. P. L. *Revised* December 29, 1936

NL 0409188 NN ICN

Rare
CS
757
L77++
Litta, Pompeo, conte, 1781-1852.
Famiglie celebri italiane. ₍Milano₎ Basadonna ₍1819₎-99.
188 pts. in v. illus. (part col.) 48cm.

Cover title.
Imprint varies.
Continued by L. Passerini, Orsini de Rilli, F. Odorici and F. Stefani. Cf. Brit. Mus. Cat., London Library Cat.

--- -----2. ser. Napoli, L. Basadonna, 1902-23.
78 pts. in v. illus. (part col.) 50 cm.

Pts. 12-5 published by Detken & Rocholl; pts. 5 -74 , by E. Detken; pts. 75-78, by Detken & Rocholl (B. Johannowsky).

NL 0409190 NIC OCl

Litta, Pompeo, comte.
Famiglie celebri italiane. Milano, Ferrario & Torino, Bassadonna, 1819-1912.
Opera continuata da Luigi Passerini, Fed. Odorici, Fed. Stefani.
Library has: [1. ser.[1819-74. arranged alphabetically in 11 vol. 2. ser. [ed. by Luciano Basadonna. Napoli, 1902?-1912?. 3 v.
--- --- Indice generale.
Photostat facsimile (negative) made by N.Y. public library.
--- --- [Covers and Contents, v. 1-11]

NL 0409191 CtY

Litta, Pompeo, conte, 1781-1852.
Famiglie celebri italiane. Milano, Typ. del dottore G. Ferrario, 1820/1856-85.
11 v. of plates (illus., geneal. tables, maps, ports.) 48 cm.
Continued by F. Oderici, L. Passerini, F. Stefani, and others after the author's death.
Imprint varies: v. 10, Milano, Tip. delle Famiglie celebri italiane; v. 11, Torino, F. Bassadonna.
Issued in 185 parts.
L. C. set imperfect; v. 11 wanting except for first fascicle.
Each genealogy is accompanied by a hand-colored, engraved coat-of-arms.
CONTENTS: t. 1. Da Camino della Marca di Trevigi. Ecelini. Sanvitale di Parma. Arcimboldi di Milano. Simonetta di Calabria. Gallio di Como. Trivulzio di Milano. Cesarini di Roma. Peretti di Montalto. Trinci di Foligno. Cavaniglia di Napoli. Giovio di Como. Cesi di Roma. Castiglioni di Milano. Visconti di Milano. Pico della Mirandola. Attendolo di Cotignola in Romagna, famiglia detta poi Sforza. Pio di Carpi. Bonacolsi di Mantova. Cavalcabò di Cremona. Valori di Firenze.—t. 2. Medici di Firenze. Candiano di Venezia. Facchinetti di Bologna. Gaddi di Firenze. Dal Verme di Verona. Orseolo di Venezia. Piccolomini già Todeschini di Siena. Boiardo di Reggio. Guicciardini di Firenze. Carraresi di Padova (Carraresi detti Pappafava) Rossi di Parma. Alighieri di Firenze. Visconti già Aicardi di Milano. Vitelli di Citta di Castello. Appiani di Pisa. Cantelmi di Napoli. Buonarroti di Firenze. D'Este.—t. 3. Foscari di Venezia. Macchiavelli di Firenze. Bentivoglio di Bologna. Corraro di Venezia. Fogliani di Reggio. Gonzaga di Mantova. Tiepolo di Venezia. Boncompagni di Bologna. Tornabuoni di Firenze. Vettori di Firenze. Colonna di Roma. Della Pusterla di Milano.—t. 4. Borromeo di S. Miniato. Erizzo di Venezia. Lannoy di Napoli. Roverella di Ferrara. Pallavicino. Aldobrandini di Firenze. Marescotti di Bologna. Strozzi di Firenze. Massimo di Roma.—t. 5. Duchi di Savoia. Gozzadini di Bologna.—t. 6. Giustiniani di Venezia. Bonelli di Roma. Gambacorta di Pisa. Ferrero di Biella. Mauruzi di Tolentino. Altemps di Roma. Navagero di Venezia. Ghilini d'Alessandria. Sinibaldi di Pistoia. Villani di Firenze. Bourbon del Monte. Archinto di Milano. Casali

Continued in next column

Continued from preceding column

di Cortona. Normanni re di Sicilia. Acquaviva di Napoli. Torelli di Ferrara. Acciaioli di Firenze. Ariosto di Bologna.—t. 7. Orsini di Roma. Marchesi di Monferrato. Calcagnini di Ferrara. Contrari di Ferrara. Lando di Venezia. Adorno di Genova. Fregoso di Genova. Buondelmonte di Firenze. D'Alviano d'Orvieto. Grassi di Bologna. Re di Napoli della casa di Svevia. Concini di Arezzo. Del Monte di Montesansavino. Rangoni di Modena.—t. 8. Guidi di Romagna. Torriani di Valsassina. Conti del Montefeltro, duchi d'Urbino. Conti di Carpegna nel Montefeltro. Signori della Faggiola nel Montefeltro. Birago di Milano. Pazzi di Firenze. Alidosio d'Imola. Lodovisi di Bologna. Stampa di Milano. Malaspina. Bevilacqua di Verona. Gambara di Brescia. Conti della Gherardesca di Pisa.—t. 9. Scaligeri di Verona. Accolti di Arezzo. Da Correggio. Martelli di Firenze. Ottoboni di Venezia. Varano di Camerino. Farnesi, duchi di Parma. Soderini di Firenze. Manfredi di Faenza. Da Polenta, signori di Ravenna. Euffreducci di Fermo. Ordelaffi di Forlì. Barbo di Venezia. Steno di Venezia. Della Rovere di Savona, duchi d'Urbino. Camposampiero della Marca trevigiana. Condulmero di Venezia.—t. 10. Panciatichi di Pistoia. Mocenigo di Venezia. Pucci di Firenze. Malatesta di Rimini. Cima di Cingoli. Smeducci di Sanseverino. Ottoni di Matelica. Lupi, marchesi di Soragna. Capponi di Firenze. Savelli di Roma. Morozzo di Mondovì. — t. 11. Marchesi di Saluzzo. Da Uzzano di Firenze. Ferrucci di Firenze. Pagani di Susinara. Zampeschi di Forlì. Albizzi di Firenze. Alessandri già Albizzi di Firenze. Bossi di Milano. Da Monteverde di Fermo. Migliorati di Sulmona. Rusca, o Rusconi di Como. Duchi di Savoia, pt. 2. Della Rovere, pt. 2. Farnesi, pt. 2. Guidi di Romagna, pt. 2. Scaligeri, pt. 2. Visconti, pt. 2. Madruzzo di Trento. Meli, poi Meli Lupi di Cremona e Soragna. Perillo di Napoli.

——— ———2. serie. Proprietà letteraria ed artistica dell'editore Luciano Basadonna. Napoli, Stab. tipo-litogr. Richter e C., 1902-₍15₎
2 v. of plates (illus., geneal. tables, ports.) 50 cm.
Issued in 78 parts.
CONTENTS: 1. D'Aquino di Capua. D'Aquino di Napoli. Caracciolo di Napoli.—2. Carafa di Napoli. Foscarini di Venezia. Moncada di Sicilia. Provana. Ruffo di Calabria. Toraldo di Napoli.
CS757.C72
1. Italy—Genealogy. 2. Italy—Nobility. I. Odorici, Federico, 1807-1884. II. Passerini, Luigi, 1816-1877. III. Stefani, Federico, d. 1897. IV. Basadonna, Luciano. V. Title.

CS757.C7 72-293082

NL 0409198 DLC

CS
757
.L78
Litta,Pompeo,conte,1781-1852.
Famiglie celebri italiane ... Milano, Dalla tip.del dottore G.Ferrario; si vende in Milano presso l'autore ₍etc.,etc.₎ 1850-
v. plates (part col.) coats of arms,geneal., tables,maps. 50 cm.
Continued after the author's death by L.Passerini,F.Odorici and F.Stefani.
Issued in parts,1819- ; imprint varies: dispensa 177- ,Torino,Basadonna,1875-
Index at end of v.1.

Bookplate: Ex libris Alberti Giovanelli.
The Bevilacqua arms stamped on front covers (v.1-11)

1.Italy--Nobility. I.Passerini,Luigi,1816-1877. II.Odorici,Federico,1807-1884. III.Stefani,Federico. IV.Title.

NL 0409200 MiU

Case
E
6835
.5
ser.2
LITTA, POMPEO, conte, 1781-1852.
...Famiglie celebri italiane. Seconda serie... Napoli,Richter e c.,1902-₍23₎
3v. illus.(col.coats-of-arms)plates,ports., geneal.tab. 49cm.

Issued in 78 parts, 1902-23.
Edited by Luciano Basadonna.
Type-written table of contents in each vol.

NL 0409201 ICN

---

f929.2 Litta, Pompeo, conte, 1781-1852.
L71f Famiglie Dal Verme, Trivulzio, Castiglioni, Gallio, Giovio. [Milano, Stamperia Giusti, 1821?]
15 double geneal.tables, plates, maps. (His Famiglie celebri italiane)

Binder's title.

NL 0409202 IU

---

f929.2 Litta, Pompeo, conte, 1781-1852.
V8221 Famiglie Visconti, Sforza. [Milano, P. E. Giusti, 1819-1827?]
28 double geneal.tables, plates(part col.) map. (His Famiglie celebri italiane)

Binder's title.

NL 0409203 IU

Litta, Pompeo, conte, 1781-1852.
Dante Alighieri, 1265-1321.
L'Inferno di Dante Alighieri disposto in ordine grammaticale e corredato di brevi dichiarazioni da G. G. Warren, lord Vernon ... Londra, T. e G. Boone; ₍etc., etc.₎ 1858-65.

---

f929.2 Litta, Pompeo, conte, 1781-1852.
M291 Malaspina. [Milano, 1852-55]
XXIII double geneal.tables, plates, map. (His Famiglie celebri italiane. Dispensa 133-135)

Edited by Federico Odorici.

NL 0409205 IU

LITTA, Pompeo, conte, 1781-1852.
L'occupazione, suo concetto e suòi effetti sulle proprietà pubbliche e private nella guerra continentale; saggio critico. Milano, 1881.

61+(3) p.

NL 0409206 MH-L DS

Litta, Pompeo, comte, 1781-1852, ed.
₍Affò, Ireneo₎ 1741-1797.
Vita di Pierluigi Farnese, primo duca di Parma, Piacenza e Guastalla, marchese di Novara ecc. Milano, P. E. Giusti, 1821.

945.112 ₍Litta, V ₎
L716a Appunti storici su Garessio per un garessino. Mondovì, G. Bianco, 1880.
100p.

"Prefazione" signed: Prof. V. Litta.
"Opere consultate": p.₍101₎

NL 0409208 IU

Litta Biumi Resta (Carlo Mateo). Riflessioni sul magnetismo animale; fatte ad oggetto di illuminare i suoi cittadini avendolo trovato salutare in molti mali. 234 pp. 16°. *Italia,* 1792.

NL 0409209 DNLM

M1503
L535B5
1843
Litta-Visconti-Arese, Giulio, duca, 1822-1891.
[Bianca di Santafiora; acc. arr. piano]
Bianca di Santafiora; melodramma in due atti di Pietro Rotondi. Posto in musica dal Conte Giulio Litta. Riduzione del maestro Luigi Truzzi. Milano, G. Canti [1843?] Pl. nos. 821-836.
202 p.

Italian words.

NL 0409210 CU MB

VOLUME 336

M1503
L535M3
Litta-Visconti-Arese, Giulio, duca, 1822-1891.
[Maria Giovanna. Selections; acc. arr. piano]
Maria Giovanna; melodramma semiserio in tre atti. Posto in musica da Giulio Litta. Riduzione per canto e pianoforte di Luigi Truzzi. Milano, G. Ricordi [1851?] Pl. nos. 23893/23914.
1 v. (various pagings)

Italian words.
Imperfect copy: t.p. and many numbers wanting.

NL 0409211 CU

M2003
L574P3
Litta-Visconti-Arese, Giulio, duca, 1822-1891.
[La passione; acc. arr. piano]
La passione; inno sacro di Alessandro Manzoni. Posto in musica da Giulio Litta. Milano, G. Canti [ca. 1857] Pl. nos. 1981-1990.
106 p.

Italian words printed also as text.
Vocal score with piano accompaniment. Italian words.

I. Title. II. Manzoni, Alessandro, 1785-1873.

NL 0409212 CU

M1503
L535S3
1844
Litta-Visconti-Arese, Giulio, duca, 1822-1891.
[Sardanapalo; acc. arr. piano]
Sardanapalo; melodramma di Pietro Rotondi. Posto in musica dal Conte Giulio Litta. Milano, G. Canti [1844?] Pl. nos. 971-992.
223 p.

Italian words.

NL 0409213 CU MB NN

Litta-Visconti-Arese, Giulio, duca, 1822-1891.
[Sardanapolo. Libretto. Italian & Spanish]
Sardanapolo; opera en cuatro partes ...
Madrid, Ignacio Boix, 1846.
47 p. 17 cm. (Teatro Borrás [Operas] v. 20, no. 12)

NL 0409214 NcU

Litta-Visconti-Arese, Giulio, duca, 1822-1891.
Il viandante
For libretti see under Coppée, François, 1842-1908.

M1503
L535V5
1880
Litta-Visconti-Arese, Giulio, duca, 1822-1891.
[Il viandante, acc. arr. piano]
Il viandante [scena lirica] Parole de E. Praga. Canto e pianoforte. Milano, Ricordi [188-?] Pl. no. 42843.
47 p.

Cover title.
Vocal score with piano acc. Italian words.
The libretto is a translation by E. Praga of a work by Francois Coppée.

I. Praga, Emilio, 1839-1875. II. Title.

NL 0409216 CU MB NN NcU

Litta-Visconti-Arese, Janie (Perry) duchessa, 1865- tr.
Negri, Gaetano, 1838-1902.
Julian the Apostate, by Gaetano Negri, tr. from the 2d Italian ed. by the Duchess Litta-Visconti-Arese, with an introduction by Professor Pasquale Villari ... New York, C. Scribner's sons, 1905.

LITTA-VISCONTI-ARESE, POMPEO, duca, 1856-
Beyond the wall, by duca Litta-Visconti-Arese...
London: T. W. Laurie, ltd. [1919] 256 p. 19cm.

81868B. 1. Fiction, Italian. I. Title.

NL 0409218 NN

Litta-Visconti-Arese, Pompeo, duca, 1856- ed.
Mario, *Signora* **Jessie** (White) 1832-1906.
The birth of modern Italy, posthumous papers of Jessie White Mario; ed., with introduction, notes and epilogue by the Duke Litta-Visconti-Arese ... London, T. F. Unwin; [etc., etc.] 1909.

Litta-Visconti-Arese, Pompeo, *duca,* 1856-
Monsignor Villarosa, by the Duke Litta ... London, T. F. Unwin [1914]
331, [1] p. 19½cm.

1. Title.

Library of Congress PZ3.L716M 14-2885

NL 0409220 DLC

Litta-Visconti-Arese, Pompeo, *duca,* 1856-
Monsignor Villarosa, by Pompeo, duke Litta ... New York and London, G. P. Putnam's sons, 1914.
vii, 396 p. 19½cm. $1.35

1. Title.

Library of Congress PZ3.L716M 2 14-11092

NL 0409221 DLC OC1

Litta-Visconti-Arese, Pompeo, *duca,* 1856-
The soul of a priest, by the Duke Litta. New York, Doubleday, Page & company [Edinburgh printed] 1908.
4 p. l., 312 p. front. 19½cm.

8-33161 Additions

Library of Congress PZ3.L716S

NL 0409222 DLC

Littann, Emil: Hypnostereotypismen. [Maschinenschrift.] 45 S. 4°. — Auszug: Greifswald 1922: Adler. 4 S. 8°
Greifswald, Med. Diss. v. 16. Febr. 1922

NL 0409223 ICRL

W 4
H46
1951
LITTANN, Karl Ernst, 1923-
Der Verlauf und die Verbreitung der Lepra in Mittel- und Nord-Europa.
[Heidelberg] 1951.
59 l. illus.
Inaug.-Diss. - Heidelberg.
1. Leprosy - Europe

NL 0409224 DNLM

Case
Y
682
.L 715
LITTARA, VINCENZO, 1550-1602.
Vincentii Littarae...Conradis, post authoris obitum in lucem edita, annotationibus, & lectionum varietatibus in margine ab authore scriptis, ac argumentis in singulos libros nuper additis, illustrata. Panormi, Apud I.A. de Franciscis, 1608.
459, [13] p. 15cm.

Title vignette: seal of the city of Netum, now Noto, Sicily.

NL 0409225 ICN

Littara, Vincenzio, 1550-1602. De rebus Netinis libri II. 92 pp. (Graevius, J. G., Thes. antiq. Sicil. v. 12.)

NL 0409226 MdBP

Littattafan hira.
Zariya, Nijeriya ta Arewa, An shirya a Gaskiya Corp. [19
no. 18 cm.

1. Hausa language—Texts.

PL8234.A2L57 53-31045 ‡

NL 0409227 DLC

Littauer, Alfred, 1890- Referendar, Berlin: Der Einfluß des Irrtums, der Täuschung und der Drohung auf Rechtsgeschäfte des Vormunds, die der vormundschaftsgerichtlichen Genehmigung bedürfen. Borna-Leipzig 1913: Noske. IX, 46 S. 8°
Rostock, Jur. Diss. v. 15. Mai 1913, Ref. Bernhöft
[Geb. 17. März 90 Berlin; Wohnort: Peitz; Staatsangeh.: Preußen; Vorbildung: Königstädt. G. Berlin Reife 08; Studium: Berlin 1, Freiburg 1, Berlin 4 S.; Rig. 15. Juli 12.] [U 13. 1231

NL 0409228 ICRL MH-L

Littauer (Arthur). Die Kürzung der runden Mutterbänder vom Leistenkanal aus behufs Rechtlagerung der Gebärmutter nach Laparotomie.
In Samml. klin. Vortr., Leipz., 1909, n. F., No. 544. (Gynäk., No. 201).

NL 0409229 DNLM

Littauer (Arthur). Leipziger "Geburtshilfliche Statistik" für das Jahr 1894. Auf Grund des behördlichen bearbeitet.
In: Samml. klin. Vortr., n. F., Leips., 1898, No. 219 (Gynäkol., No. 79, 1251-1276).

NL 0409230 DNLM

Littauer, Fritz, 1892- Volontärassist.: Ueber ein Aneurysma in der absteigenden Aorta mit Durchbruch in den Magen. Aus d. Pathol. Inst. des Wenzel-Hancke-Krankenh. zu Breslau. (Prosektor: Heinrichsdorff.) [In Maschinenschrift.] 20 S. 4°(2°). — Auszug: Breslau 1921: Breslauer Genossensch.-Buchdr. 2 Bl. 8°
Breslau, Med. Diss. v. 26. Sept. 1921, Ref. Henke
[Geb. 7. Mai 92 Liegnitz; Wohnort: Breslau; Staatsangeh.: Preußen; Vorbildung: RG. am Zwinger Breslau Reife 11; Studium: Breslau 3, Berlin 1, Breslau 15 S.; Coll. 28. Juli 20; Approb. 17. Aug. 20.] [U 21. 3001

NL 0409231 ICRL

VOLUME 336

LITTAUER, Hans-Alfred, 1900-
Der alkohol im deutschen strafrecht der gegenwart und zukunft, unter besonderer berücksichtigung der dem reichsrat und reichstag vorgelegten entwürfe eines allgemeinen deutschen strafgesetzbuchs. Radebeul bei Dresden, 1927.

Inaug.-diss. --- Kiel.

NL 0409232 MH-L CtY ICRL

Littauer (Josephus) [1805-]. *De trichomate. 30 pp. 8°. Berolini, typ. Nietackianis, [1833].

NL 0409233 DNLM

Littauer (Julius). *Ueber Diabetes insipidus. 36 pp. 12°. Würzburg, P. Scheiner, 1886.

NL 0409234 DNLM

Littauer, Kaethe, 1893-
Ueber zwei faelle von graviditas interstitialis Inaug.-Diss.- Leipzig, 1925.

NL 0409235 ICRL CtY

Littauer, Louise, 1857-1876.
Louise Littauer, her book. New York, Priv. print., 1924.

xii p., 1 l., 225 p. front., pl., ports., fold. facsim. 24cm.
Edited by Lucius Nathan Littauer.
"This edition consists of 400 copies, of which this volume is number 72."

I. Littauer, Lucius Nathan, 1859- ed.

Library of Congress PS2248.L33 1924 25-39

NL 0409236 DLC NN

Littauer, Lucius Nathan, 1859-

U. S. *Congress. House. Committee on appropriations.*
Hearings [Jan. 13-15, 1906] before subcommittee of House Committee on appropriations ... in charge of deficiency appropriations for 1906 and prior years on urgent deficiency bill. Washington, Gov't print. off., 1906.

Littauer, Lucius Nathan, 1859-

U. S. *Congress. Conference committees,* 1905-1906.
... Legislative, executive, and judicial appropriation bill. [1907] Conference report (to accompany H. R. 16472.) [Washington, Govt. print. off., 1906]

Littauer, Lucius Nathan, 1859- ed.

Littauer, Louise, 1857-1876.
Louise Littauer, her book. New York, Priv. print., 1924.

337.4
L717s
Littauer, Lucius Nathan, 1859-
The ship-subsidy bill: speech in the House of representatives, Tuesday, February 26, 1907. Washington, 1907.
24p.

NL 0409240 IU

LITTAUER, LUDWIG.
Parallel yarn tables and equivalents for use in the textile and dyeing industries, compiled by Ludwig Littauer... New York: L. Littauer, 1910. 24 p. incl. tables. 20cm.

Imperfect: p. 5-10 wanting.

1. Yarn—Tables, calculations, etc. I. Title.

N. Y. P. L. May 24, 1940

NL 0409241 NN DLC

Littauer (Ludwika). *Des mouvements de l'iris et de l'action de l'atropine et l'ésérine sur la pupille. 45 pp. 4°. Paris, 1892, No. 340.

NL 0409242 DNLM

LITTAUER, M.I.
Vegetarianism and the evils of flesh eating, by M.I. Littauer... [New York,] 1928. 22 p. 12°.

584407A. 1. Vegetarianism.

N. Y. P. L. March 15, 1932

NL 0409243 NN

Littauer, Max, 1877-
Ueber den regenerationsmodus der leukocyten. Inaug. diss. Leipzig, 1902. (Berlin)
Bibl.

NL 0409244 ICRL CtY

Littauer, Richard: 1891- Die private Volksversicherung und die Reformversuche auf gemeinnütziger Grundlage. Berlin 1915: Falk. VIII, 118 S. 8°
Freiburg i. B, Rechts- u. staatswiss. Diss. v. 8. März 1915, Ref. Diehl
[Geb. 23. Aug. 91 Berlin; Wohnort: Berlin; Staatsangeh.: Preußen; Vorbildung: Askan. G. Berlin Reife 09; Studium: Berlin 4, Freiburg 4 S.; Rig. 4. Mai 14.] [U 15. 306

NL 0409245 ICRL CtY

QA295
.L5
Littauer, Sebastian Barkann, 1900-
A new tauberian theorem with application to the summability of Fourier series and integrals.
[Cambridge] 1929
1 pam 8°

(Mass.Inst. of tech. Dept. of math. Series II, no. 169)

NL 0409246 DLC

QA311
L5
Littauer, Sebastian Barkann, 1900-
Note on a theorem of Jacob
Boston, 1929. 1pam. 8°

NL 0409247 DLC

QA311
.L65
Littauer, Sebastian Barkann, 1900-
...Note on a theorem of Jacob...
[London, 1929]
p[226]-231. 25 1/2 cm.

NL 0409248 DLC

Littauer, Sebastian Barkann, 1900- joint author.
Statistical models

see under

Hertz, David Bendel, 1919-

Littauer, Vladimir Stanislas, 1892-
Be a better horseman; an illustrated guide to the enjoyment of modern riding, by Capt. Vladimir S. Littauer, with two hundred and thirty photographs by Bert Clark Thayer. New York, The Derrydale press [°1941]

2 p. l., ix-xii p., 1 l., 251 p. incl. illus., plates, diagrs. front. (port.) 24 x 19cm.

1. Horsemanship. I. Title. 42-3605

Library of Congress SF309.L495
——— Copy 2. [5] 798.23

NL 0409250 DLC MtBC

Littauer, Vladimir Stanislas, 1892-
Be a better horseman; an illustrated guide to the enjoyment of modern riding. With 230 photos. by Bert Clark Thayer. New York, Essential Books, Duell, Sloan and Pearce [°1941]

xii, 251 p. illus., port. 24 x 19 cm.

1. Horsemanship. I. Title.
[SF309.L] 798.23 A 48-8767*
Wellesley College. Libr. for Library of Congress [3]

NBuG
NL 0409251 MWelC WaS OrP Or WaT KMK MiU N MB PSt

Littauer, Vladimir Stanislas, 1892-
Be a better horseman; an illustrated guide to the enjoyment of modern riding. With 218 photos. by Bert Clark Thayer. London, New York, Hurst & Blackett [1953]

304 p. illus. 24 cm.

1. Horsemanship. I. Title.
SF309.L495 1953 798.23 53-32472 ‡

NL 0409252 DLC

VOLUME 336

[Littauer, Vladimir Stanislas] 1892–
Boots and saddles, ten talks on horsemanship delivered over the network of the National broadcasting company (station WEAF) February–March–April–May 1930. New York city, The Boots and saddles riding school, inc. [°1930]
144 p. 18½cm.
"The authors are Russians [V. S. Littauer and S. N. Kournakoff]"—Foreword.
1. Horsemanship. I. Kournakoff, Sergei Nicholas, 1892– joint author. II. Boots and saddles riding school, inc., New York. III. Title.
Library of Congress SF309.L5 30-13626
Copyright A 23238 [3] 798.2

NL 0409253 DLC OCl NN MH

Littauer, Vladimir Stanislas, 1892–
Common sense horsemanship; a distinct method of riding and schooling horses and of learning to ride. With two chapters by Alexis Wrangel. Sketches by Berri Chamorel. [1st ed.] New York, Van Nostrand [1951]
333 p. illus. 24 cm.
1. Horsemanship. I. Title.
SF309.L52 798.2 51-12768 ‡

NL 0409254 DLC WaS OrP Or OrCS Wa CU TU PP MB

LITTAUER, VLADIMIR STANISLAS, 1892–
Common sense horsemanship, by Vladimir S. Littauer, with two chapters by Alexis Wrangel; sketches by Berri Chamorel. A distinct method of riding and schooling horses and of learning to ride. London, Macmillan [1953] vii, 333 p. illus., port. 24cm.
1. Horsemanship.

NL 0409255 NN

Littauer, Vladimir Stanislas, 1892–
The defense of the forward seat by means of an analysis of the jump, by Capt. V. S. Littauer and Capt. S. N. Kournakoff. Drawings by Capt. S. N. Kournakoff. New York: Boots & Saddles Riding School, Inc., 1934. 142 p. charts, diagrs., plates, table. 24½cm.
CONTENTS.—An introduction to the analysis of the jump, by V. S. Littauer.—Ballistics of the jump, by S. N. Kournakoff.—Film-study of the jump, by V. S. Littauer.—Tachelectrographic study, by S. N. Kournakoff.—Ballistics of the rider, by S. N. Kournakoff.
814484A. 1. Horsemanship. I. Kurnakov, Sergeĭ Nikolayevich, 1892– II. Title.
N. Y. P. L. April 14, 1936

NL 0409256 NN

SF 309 .L53 1934
Littauer, Vladimir Stanislas, 1892–
Forward riding, by Captain Vladimir S. Littauer. New York, William Morrow & Co., 1934.
166 p. illus. 20 cm.
1. Horsemanship. I. Title

NL 0409257 OKentU

Littauer, Vladimir Stanislas, 1892–
Forward riding, by Captain Vladimir S. Littauer ... [Wilmington, Del.] National vulcanized fibre co., °1937.
19 p. illus. 23½cm.
1. Horsemanship. I. Title.
Library of Congress SF309.L53 37-33914
——— Copy 2.
Copyright AA 246365 [3] 798.23

NL 0409258 DLC

Littauer, Vladimir Stanislas, 1892–
Jumping the horse, by Captain V. S. Littauer; edited by Phyllis French. New York, The Derrydale press, 1931.
2 p. l., iii–xii, [1] p., 1 l., 125 p., 1 l. incl. illus., plates. front., plates. 25cm.
Title in red and black.
"Nine hundred and fifty copies ... have been printed."
1. Horsemanship. I. French, Phyllis, ed. II. Title.
Library of Congress SF309.L55 32-433
——— Copy 2.
Copyright A 46383 [3] 798.23

NL 0409259 DLC WaS ViW OCl

Littauer, Vladimir Stanislas, 1892–
Modern horsemanship for beginners (Riding forward) by V. S. Littauer ... Garden City, N. Y., Garden City publishing co., inc. [1946]
vi p., 2 l., 166 p. front., illus., plates, diagrs. 19½cm. (Star books)
"Formerly published under the title Riding forward."
Bibliography: p. 161–164.
1. Horsemanship.
Library of Congress SF309.L57 1946 46-5272
[4] 798.23

NL 0409260 DLC PP NcC WaE NcRS KMK PCM

Littauer, Vladimir Stanislas, 1892–
More about riding forward; the modern way to ride and school a field horse, by V. S. Littauer ... Syosset, N. Y., Pub. priv. by V. S. Littauer [°1938]
x, 11–192 p. front., illus., plates. 20cm.
1. Horsemanship. I. Title. II. Title: Riding forward, More about.
Library of Congress SF309.L56 38-34557
——— Copy 2.
Copyright A 122582 [3] 798.2

NL 0409261 DLC OKentU

Littauer, Vladimir Stanislas, 1892–
Riding forward; modern horsemanship for beginners, by V. S. Littauer ... Boots and saddles ed. New York, W. Morrow & co., 1934.
vi p., 3 l., 3–166 p. front., illus., plates. 19½cm.
"This edition, numbered and signed by the author, is limited to three hundred and fifty copies for sale. Copy number 362."
Bibliography: p. 161–164.
1. Horsemanship. I. Title.
Library of Congress SF309.L57 35-138
——— Copy 2.
Copyright A 77570 [3] 798.23

NL 0409262 DLC Or OClW

Littauer, Vladimir Stanislas, *1892–*
Riding forward: modern horsemanship for beginners. By V. S. Littauer.
— New York. Morrow & Co. 1935. vi, (3), 166 pp. Illus. Plates. Diagrams. 19 cm.
Bibliography, pp. 161–164.
D7860 — T.r. — Horsemanship.

NL 0409263 MB NIC CU WaSp CaBVa NN OrP

Littauer day, Gloversville, N.Y.
see under Gloversville, N.Y. Littauer day organization.

Littauer day organization, Gloversville, N.Y.
see Gloversville, N.Y. Littauer day organization.

LITTAYE,
Notice sur la pêche de la morue, par M. le commissaire Littaye... Paris, A. Challamel, 1891.
56 p, 24 cm.
Extrait de la Revue des pêches maritimes.

NL 0409266 MH

Littaye, Guy.
... Contribution à l'étude des jets liquides ... Paris, Gauthier-Villars, 1942.
3 p. l., [5]–vi, 102, [2] p. illus., diagrs. 27cm.
Thèse—Univ. de Paris.
"Bibliographie": p. [103]
1. Hydrodynamics. 2. Jets.
Library of Congress TC171.L5 46-42525
[2] 532.5

NL 0409267 DLC MCM NN WaS CtY

Littaye, Guy.
Contribution à l'étude des jets liquides. Préf. de A. Foch. Paris, Blondel La Rougery, 1942.
vi, 102, [1] p. illus. 27 cm. (Publications scientifiques et techniques du Secrétariat d'état à l'aviation, no 181)
Issued also as thesis, Paris.
Bibliography: p. [103]
1. Hydrodynamics. 2. Jets. (Series: France. Ministère de l'air. Publications scientifiques et techniques, no 181)
TL502.F77 no. 181 532.5 50-50854
——— Copy 2. TC171.L5 1942a

NL 0409268 DLC MoU NNC

Littchen, Oscar A
"Basic air navigation—understandably," by Oscar A. Littchen ... Stockton, Calif., O. A. Littchen, °1943.
1 v. diagrs., forms. 26½ x 20½cm.
Leaves variously numbered; reproduced from type-written copy.
1. Navigation (Aeronautics) I. Title.
Library of Congress TL586.L48 1943 43-11437
[3] 629.1325

NL 0409269 DLC

Littchen, Oscar A.
... Celestial air navigation; "the quickest 1942 method," by Oscar A. Littchen. [Hollywood, Calif.] O. A. Littchen, °1942.
95 l. incl. diagrs. 29 x 23cm.
At head of title: 2d ed.
Leaves variously numbered; reproduced from type-written copy.
1. Navigation (Aeronautics) I. Title.
Library of Congress TL588.L5 1942 42-20231
[2] 629.13252

NL 0409270 DLC

VOLUME 336

Littchen, Oscar A
Interception—understandably, by O. Littchen. 1944 ed. ... Hollywood, Calif., O. Littchen [1944]
cover-title, [3], 3, 55, [1] p. diagrs. 28 x 21½cm.
Loose-leaf; mimeographed.

1. Navigation (Aeronautics) 2. Aeronautics—Problems, exercises, etc. 3. Air warfare. I. Title.
44-4123
Library of Congress TL586.L49
[3] 629.1325076

NL 0409271 DLC

Littchen, Oscar A
"Primary air navigation — understandably," by Oscar A. Littchen ... [Stockton, Calif.] O. A. Littchen, °1943.
1 v. tables, diagrs. 28 x 20cm.
Leaves variously numbered; reproduced from type-written copy.
"A course ... suggested for use in pre-flight and primary schools in the preparation of flying cadets for the U. S. army air forces."
"Reading assignments": leaves 82-84.
"Answers": 20 leaves at end.

1. Navigation (Aeronautics) I. Title.
43-10207
Library of Congress TL586.L5
[3] 629.1325

NL 0409272 DLC

Litte, Erich.

Liedertafel Harmonia, *Bernburg.*
... Festschrift und vereinsgeschichte zur hundert-jahrfeier. Bernburg an der Saale, "Liedertafel Harmonia", 1938.

Litte, William
see William, of Newburgh, 1136-1198.

Litteau, Max Guérin de
see Guérin de Litteau, Max.

LITTEL, THERESE.
...Mansions; a comedy for young women in three acts, by Therese Littel... St. Louis: The Queen's Work Press[, cop. 1929]. 94 p. 18cm. (The Queen's Work dramatic series. no. 9.)

1. Drama, American. I. Title. II. Ser.

NL 0409276 NN RPB DLC

Litteljohn, Arthur Rieussett.
Meat and its inspection; a practical guide for meat inspectors, students, and medical officers of health, by Arthur R. Litteljohn ... London, Baillière, Tindall and Cox, 1911.
xii, 399 p. illus., VI pl. 21cm.

1. Meat. Inspection. I. Gt. Brit. Laws, statutes, etc.
Agr 11-1676
Library, U. S. Dept. of Agriculture 50L71

NL 0409277 DNAL ICJ KMK DNLM ICRL OU

S.C.
p92
J13L1
Littell, Charles Willing.
Major William Jackson, Secretary of the Federal Convention. (In: Pennsylvania Magazine of History and Biography, vol. II, no. 4, 1878. p. 353-369)

Detached copy in pamphlet binder.

1. Jackson, William, 1759-1828.

NL 0409278 ScU MdBP

---

*
PS2248
.L37S3
1853
Littell, Charles Willing.
Scotland. The poem delivered at the third annual Commencement, at Burlington College, 29 September, 1852. For private distribution. Philadelphia, King & Baird, 1853.
34 p. 19cm.
Presentation copy inscribed to Miss Rosa M. Nourse from her cousin John S. Littell.
Manuscript corrections in text.
1. Scotland—Poetry. I. Title.

NL 0409279 ViU NN

Littell, Clair Francis, 1887–
The neutralization of states; a study in diplomatic history and international law, by Clair Francis Littell ... Meadville. Pa., 1920.
181 p. 23cm.
Thesis (PH. D.)—Columbia university, 1921.
Vita.
Bibliography: p. 171-176.

1. Neutrality. I. Title.
21—6367
Library of Congress JX4031.L5

NL 0409280 DLC NIC NcU CtY ODW MiU PMA

Littell, Clarence Guy, 1882–
The distinguished collection of Americana, formed by C. G. Littell ... public auction sale by his order February 5 and 6 [1945] ... New York, Parke-Bernet galleries, inc., 1945.
3 p. l., 276 p., 1 l. incl. front., illus. (facsims.) 24cm.
"Sale number 631."
Annotated.

1. America—Bibl.—Catalogs. I. Parke-Bernet galleries, inc., New York.
45-10799
Library of Congress Z1207.Z9L75
[3] 016.97

NL 0409281 DLC AU MdBP KMK CU-A GU CaOTP CU-B OO

CS71
.L7765
1933
Littell, Doreen Haight, 1905–
Descendants of William Littell of Essex County, N. J., who served in the revolutionary war in Captain Benjamin Laing's company, First regiment, Essex county militia (1757-1819) [Compiled by Miss Doreen Haight Littell] [Bridgeport, Conn., 1933]
4 l. 28cm.
Type-written.

1. Littell family.

NL 0409282 DLC NN

Littell, Eliakim, 1797-1870, ed.

Microfilm
01104
no. 319–323
AP
Littell's living age. v. 1-27 (no. 1-345); May 11, 1844–Dec. 28, 1850. Boston, E. Littell [etc.]

Littell, Eliakim, 1797-1870.

The Living age

Littell, Eliakim, 1797-1870, ed.

Microfilm
01104
no. 146–148
AP
The Museum of foreign literature and science. v. 1-7; July 1822–Dec. 1825. Philadelphia, E. Littell [etc.]

Littell, Eliakim, 1797-1870, ed.

The Museum of foreign literature, science, and art. v. 1-45; July 1822–Dec. 1842. Philadelphia, E. Littell; [etc., etc., 1822-42]

Littell, Eliakim, 1797-1870, ed.

The **National** recorder. Containing essays upon subjects connected with political economy, science, literature, &c.; papers read before the Agricultural society of Philadelphia; a record of passing events; selections from foreign magazines, &c. &c. v. 2-5; July 3, 1819–June 30, 1821. Philadelphia, Littell & Henry [1819-21]

Littell, Eliakim, 1797-1870, ed.
Panorama of Life and Literature
see under title

Littell, Eliakim, 1797-1870, ed.

The **Philadelphia** register, and national recorder ... v. 1; Jan. 2–June 26, 1819. [Philadelphia] Littell & Henry [1819]

Littell, Eliakim, 1797-1870, ed.

Microfilm
01104
no. 237–238
AP
The Saturday magazine: being in great part a compilation from the British reviews, magazines, and scientific journals. v. 1-5, Jan. 2, 1819–June 30, 1821; [new ser.] v. 1-2, July 7, 1821–June 29, 1822. Philadelphia, Littell & Henry [etc.]

Littell, Elton Gardiner.
Interesting school children in health—Abstract.
(*In* National education association of the United States. Addresses and proceedings, 1924. p. 440-442)

1. School hygiene. I. Title.
E 26-406
Library, U. S. Bur. of Education

NL 0409291 DHEW

Littell, Frank Bowers, 1869–

U. S. *Naval observatory.*
Catalogue of 23521 stars between 13° 35′ and 45° 25′ south declination for the equinox 1850. From zone observations made at the United States Naval observatory, 1846-1852. Comp. by W. S. Eichelberger and F. B. Littell. [Washington, Govt. print. off., 1911]

VOLUME 336

Littell, Frank Bowers, 1869-

U. S. *Naval observatory.*

... Determination of the difference of longitude between Washington and Paris, 1913–1914. Reduced under the direction of F. B. Littell and G. A. Hill. [Washington, Govt. print. off., 1918]

NL 0409294 DN-Ob

Littell, Frank Bowers, 1869-

Naval observatory eclipse expedition to Sumatra, by F. B. Littell. (Northfield, Minn.) 1926.

cover-title, 3 p. pl. XX - XXI. 25½ cm.

Reprinted from Popular astronomy, v. XXXIV, no. 7. August-September, 1926.

NL 0409294 DN-Ob

Littell, Frank Bowers, 1869-

U. S. *Naval observatory.*

... Observations made with the nine-inch transit circle, 1908–1911, under the direction of F. B. Littell. Reduced under the direction of W. S. Eichelberger. [Washington, Govt. print. off., 1918]

Littell, Frank Bowers, 1869-

U. S. *Naval observatory.*

... Observations made with the nine-inch transit circle, 1912–1913, under the direction of F. B. Littell. Reduced under the direction of H. R. Morgan. [Washington, Govt. print. off., 1918]

Littell, Frank Bowers, 1869-

U. S. *Naval observatory.*

... Observations with the six-inch transit circle. 1900–1901. By Milton Updegraff, assisted by Frank B. Littell and George K. Lawton. [Washington, Govt. print. off., 1903]

Littell, Frank Bowers, 1869-

U. S. *Naval observatory.*

... Total solar eclipses of January 24, 1925, January 14, 1926 and May 9, 1929. [Washington, U. S. Govt. print. off., 1932]

Littell, Frank Bowers, 1869- joint author.

U. S. *Naval observatory.*

Vertical circle observations made with the five-inch altazimuth instrument, 1898–1907, by F. B. Littell, G. A. Hill, and H. B. Evans, reduced by F. B. Littell. [Washington, Govt. print. off., 1914]

Littell, Frank Bowers, 1869-

U. S. *Naval observatory.*

... World longitude operation of 1926. Results of observations at San Diego and Washington, by F. B. Littell, J. C. Hammond, C. B. Watts and P. Sollenberger. [Washington, U. S. Govt. print. off., 1929]

Littell, Frank Bowers, 1869-

U. S. *Naval observatory.*

Zone observations with the nine-inch transit circle. 1894–1901. By Aaron N. Skinner, assisted by Frank B. Littell and Theo. I. King. [Washington, Govt. print. off., 1902]

Littell, Franklin Hamlin.

The Anabaptist view of the church; an introduction to sectarian Protestantism. [Hartford?] American Society of Church History, 1952.

xii, 148 p. 25 cm. (Studies in church history, v. 8)

"In original form this study was submitted to ... Yale University ... for the degree of doctor of philosophy."

Bibliography: p. 113–145.

1. Anabaptists. 2. Church. I. Title. (Series: Studies in church history (Hartford) v. 8)

BX4931.L5 284.3 52–3597

NL 0409302 DLC ICU PP PPWe PPLT OU MiU MH IdU OBlC

Pamph f.v.415 LITTELL, Franklin Hamlin, 1917-

Social pathology. [N.p., n.d.]

1*l*. 28cm.

"The quill."

NL 0409303 MH-AH

Littell, Harold.

Development of the city school system of Indiana - 1851-1880. By Harold Littell.

(From Indiana magazine of history Bloomington, 1916. vol. XII, p. (193) 213 299-325)

NL 0409304 DHEW

Littell, Harold, joint author.

Smith, Henry Lester, 1876–

Education in Latin America [by] Henry Lester Smith ... and Harold Littell ... New York, Cincinnati [etc.] American book company [©1934]

Littell, Harold, joint ed.

Smith, Henry Lester, 1876– ed.

... The philosophy of human relations, individual and collective; a source book by Henry Lester Smith and Harold Littell ... [Bloomington] Bureau of coöperative research, Indiana university [1931]

Littell, Jane.

Carnival girl, by Jane Littell. New York, L. MacVeagh, The Dial press; Toronto, Longmans, Green and co., 1931.

280 p. 19½cm.

I. Title.

Library of Congress PZ3.L717Car 31–7409

NL 0409307 DLC MB

Littell, Jane.

Million dollar meal ticket, by Jane Littell ... New York, Hillman-Curl, inc., 1938.

252 p. 19½cm.

"A streamlined romance."

I. Title.

Library of Congress PZ3.L717Mi 38–34798

NL 0409308 DLC

Littell, Jane.

That notorious Lola Paget, by Jane Littell ... New York, L. MacVeagh, Dial press, inc., 1932.

311 p. 19½cm.

I. Title.

Library of Congress PZ3.L717Th 32–5298

NL 0409309 DLC NN

Littell, John, defendant.

A brief state of the case, imprisonment, and sufferings of John Littell, who hath been a prisoner above seven years for conscience sake ... London, 1753.

I. Title.

NL 0409310 PHC

Littell, John, genealogist.

Family records; or, Genealogies of the first settlers of Passaic Valley (and vicinity), above Chatham, with their ancestors and descendants, as far as can now be ascertained. By John Littell. Feltville, N. J., D. Felt and co., 1851.

3 p. l., 504 p. 23½cm.

Added t.-p., engr.

1. Passaic Valley, N. J.—Geneal.

Library of Congress F142.P3L7 4–11456

MnHi

NL 0409311 DLC OrP MeB WHi MWA NjP OFH OClWHi NjR

---

ar W 4642 [Littell, John] genealogist.

Genealogy of John Miller. Boston, Goodspeed, 1945.

[8] p. 25cm.

First published as an appendix to his Family records: or, Genealogies of the first settlers of Passaic valley. Feltville N. J., 1851. Reprinted here in an edition of sixty copies.

NL 0409312 NIC

E 6967 .5 Index LITTELL, JOHN, genealogist.

Index to family records or genealogies of the first settlers of Passaic Valley & vicinity above Chatham, N.J., by John Littell, 1852.

[Comp. by Mrs. John V.O. Parker. Morristown, N.J., ca.1939]

117p. 28cm.

Photostat (positive) of typed copy.

NL 0409313 ICN

VOLUME 336

355.73
L717

Littell, John McGregor.
The draft (compulsory training) by J. McGregor Littell. Mount Arlington, N. J., Littell, c1940.
cover-title, 31 l. 28cm.

Various paging.
Reproduction of typewritten copy.

1. Military service, Compulsory. 2. U. S. - Army - Recruiting, enlistment, etc. I. Title.

NL 0409314 NNC NN MH

HE396
.S25
L57
Q

Littell, John McGregor
... The Great lakes-St. Lawrence waterway and power project, by John McGregor Littell. South Orange, N.J., J.M. Littell, c1941.
2p.ℓ.,49numb.ℓ. 32cm. (The Littell digest, no.13)

Reproduced from type-written copy.

1. St. Lawrence River - Navigation. 2. St. Lawrence River - Power utilization. 3. Great Lakes - Commerce. I. Title. II. Series: The Littell digest, no.13. S

NL 0409315 PSt NNC

Littell, John McGregor.

H1
.L5

The Littell digest. ⌈no. 1⌉–
South Orange, N. J. ⌈etc.⌉ J. M. Littell ⌈°1940–

331.2
L717

Littell, John McGregor
A new plan that will provide true health insurance for all our people, the American way, by John McGregor Littell. South Orange, N. J., Littell's service, c1940.
1 p. l., 9, ⌈1⌉ numb. l. 28cm.

Reproduced from typewritten copy.

1. Insurance, Health - U. S.

NL 0409317 NNC NN

Littell, John McGregor.
Reconversion (postwar jobs for all). ⌈South Orange, N.J., John McGregor Littell, c1943⌉
39 numb. l. (The Littell digest, no. 32)

Caption title.
Reproduced from typewritten copy.
At head of each leaf: ⌈No.⌉ 4401.

NL 0409318 OCl

Littell, John McGregor
Cd43
0172
Roosevelt or Willkie ... [n.p.,c1940]

Mimeographed.
"He believes that town meetings will save democracy, by H.L.Williams ... Reprinted from June, 1940 issue of Church management": 1ℓ. inserted at end.

NL 0409319 CtY

Littell, John McGregor.
Roosevelt or Willkie. Mount Arlington, N.J., c.1940.

28 cm.
Paper cover serves as title-page.
Manifold copy.
Various pagination.
"Authorized for use only in the forums of the Littell chain."
Contains also statements by Joseph W.Martin, jr. and Edward J.Flynn; as well as "He believes that town meetings will save democracy," by H.L.Williams, "reprinted from June 1940 issue of Church management."

NL 0409321 MH

329
L717

Littell, John McGregor.
Roosevelt or Willkie, by J. McGregor Littell. Mount Arlington, N. J., Littell, c1940.
cover-title, 13 l. 28cm.

Various paging.
Reproduction of typewritten copy.

1. Roosevelt, Franklin Delano, pres. U. S., 1882- 2. Willkie, Wendell Lewis, 1892- 3. U. S. - Politics and government - 1933- 4. Presidents - U. S. - Election - 1940.

NL 0409322 NNC

Littell, John McGregor.
Summary of views on labor relations, by J. McGregor Littell. Mount Arlington, N. J., J. M. Littell, °1940.
cover-title, 15 numb. l. 28 x 21½cm. ⌈The Littell digest, no. 2⌉
Reproduced from type-written copy.
Imprint stamped on cover: South Orange, N. J., The Littell digest.

1. Labor laws and legislation—U. S. I. Title.
43-28919 Revised
Library of Congress H1.L5 no. 2
⌈r45c2⌉ (305) 331.154

NL 0409323 DLC

Littell, John McGregor.
What is social security? By J. McGregor Littell. Mount Arlington, N. J., J. M. Littell, °1940.
cover-title, 10 numb. l. 28 x 21½cm. ⌈The Littell digest, no. 1⌉
Reproduced from type-written copy.
Imprint stamped on cover: South Orange, N. J., The Littell digest.

1. Insurance, State and compulsory—U. S. 2. Public welfare—U. S. I. Title.
43-28918 Revised
Library of Congress H1.L5 no. 1
⌈r45d2⌉ (305) 331.2544

NL 0409324 DLC

⌈**Littell, John Stockton**⌉ 1806–1875.
The Clay minstrel; or, National songster. To which is prefixed a sketch of the life, public services, and character of Henry Clay ... Philadelphia and New York, Turner & Fisher, 1842.
iv, ⌈vii⌉–viii, ⌈9⌉–167, ⌈1⌉ p. front., illus. (port.) 15½cm.

1. Clay, Henry, 1777–1852. 2. Campaign songs, 1842—Whig. I. Title.
17-5272
Library of Congress E340.C6L68

NL 0409325 DLC ViU PHi

⌈**Littell, John Stockton**⌉ 1806–1875.
The Clay minstrel; or, National songster ... New York, Greeley & M'Elrath; Philadelphia, Thomas, Cowperthwait and co., 1844.
288 p. front. (port.) illus. 12½cm.
On cover: New edition.

1. Campaign songs, 1844—Whig. I. Title.
16-25395
Library of Congress E340.C6L73

NL 0409326 DLC RPB TxU OClWHi OO

Littell, John Stockton, 1806–1875.
The Clay minstrel; or, National songster, to which is prefixed a sketch of the life, public services, and character of Henry Clay, by John S. Littell ... 2d ed.; enl. New York, Greeley & M'Elrath; Philadelphia, Thomas, Cowperthwait and co., 1844.
384 p. incl. front. (port.) illus. 13½cm.

1. Clay, Henry, 1777–1852. 2. Campaign literature, 1844—Whig. I. Title.
7-17115
Library of Congress E340.C6L7
——— Copy 2.
The portrait of Clay in this copy differs from that in copy 1.

NL 0409327 DLC MHi NjP TxU NIC ViU ViW PPL DSI InU

Littell, John Stockton, 1806-1875.
Doane, George Washington, *bp.*, 1799–1859.
E pluribus, unum: the address, at Burlington college; on the seventy-eighth anniversary of American independence, and eighth anniversary of the institution; July 4, 1854: by the Right Reverend George W. Doane ... Burlington ⌈N. J.⌉ Printed at the Gazette office, 1854.

Littell, John Stockton, 1806-1875, ed.
Graydon, Alexander, 1752–1818.
Memoirs of his own time. With reminiscences of the men and events of the revolution. By Alexander Graydon. Ed. by John Stockton Littell ... Philadelphia, Lindsay & Blakiston, 1846.

Littell, John Stockton, 1806-1875.
Ode.
(In: Doane, George Washington. Address at Burlington College.)

NL 0409330 RPB

Littell, John Stockton, 1870–
500 questions & answers in religion, by the Reverend John S. Littell ... Milwaukee, Wis., Morehouse publishing co.; London, A. R. Mowbray & co., ltd. ⌈°1931⌉
84 p. 23cm.
"Books which have helped": p. 77; "Materials in religious education by the Rev. John S. Littell, D. D.": p. 82–84.

1. Protestant Episcopal church in the U. S. A.—Catechisms and creeds. I. Title.
32-9568
Library of Congress BX5939.L55
Copyright A 50521 ⌈3⌉ 238.3

NL 0409331 DLC

VOLUME 336

Littell, John Stockton, 1870–
The historians and the English reformation, by the Rev. John Stockton Littell ... Milwaukee, The Young churchman company; [etc., etc.] 1910.
viii, 307 p. 23cm. $2.50

1. Gt. Brit.—Hist.—Historiography. 2. Reformation—England. I. Title.

Library of Congress BR375.L7 10-10544

NL 0409332 DLC MoU MeB PPEB NIC IaU OKentU KyU CtY MB KyLx OCl ODW OO OU OCU WaE OrP WaT OrU MtU NjNbS

Littell, John Stockton, 1870–
How Washington makes us think of the church ... A supplement to George Washington: Christian, by the Rev. John S. Littell ... Keene, N. H., The American S. C. L., 1916.
29, [2] p. illus. (incl. ports., facsim., coats of arms) 25½cm. (Stories of cross and flag, no. 4) $0.25

1. Washington, George, pres. U. S.—Religion. I. Title.

Library of Congress E312.17.L75 16-9964

NL 0409333 DLC MBAt

Littell, John Stockton, 1870–
The Kingdom in pictures, by the Rev. John Stockton Littell ... Keene, N. H., The author, °1914.
[40] p. illus. (part col.) 26cm. (Stories of cross and flag. no. 7) $0.50

I. Title.

Library of Congress 14-578

NL 0409334 DLC

Littell, John Stockton, 1870–
St. Patrick and his followers, by the Rev. John Stockton Littell ... Keene, N. H., The author, °1914.
47, [1] p. illus. (incl. ports.) 15½cm. (Stories of cross and flag, no. 5) $0.50
"Book list": 1 p. at end.

I. Title.

Library of Congress 14-5355

NL 0409335 DLC

Littell, John Stockton, 1870–
Some great Christian Jews, by the Rev. John Stockton Littell ... [Bellows Falls, Vt., P. H. Gobie press] °1913.
31 p. illus. (incl. ports.) 26½cm. (Stories of cross and flag, no. 2)
CONTENTS.—The Jew in America.—The virtues of the Jew.—Jews who are venerated by us all.—The persecution of the Jew.—The Jew fixes his own destiny.—Our own relations to the Jew.—The Jew as a Christian: I. Professor Neander. II. Dr. Edersheim. III. Bishop Isaac Hellmuth. IV. Bishop Samuel Isaac J. Schereschewsky. V. Meyer Lerman. VI. The Rev. Michael Rosenthal. VII. The Jerusalem and the East mission.

1. Jews. I. Title.

Library of Congress DS115.L5 13-12514

NL 0409336 DLC MiU

Littell, John Stockton, 1870–
Some great Christian Jews, by the Rev. John Stockton Littell ... 2d ed. Rev. and enl. Keene, N. H., The author, °1913.
63, [1] p. illus. (incl. ports.) 26½cm. (Stories of cross and flag, no. 2) $0.25
p. 58-63, advertising matter.

Continued in next column

Continued from preceding column

CONTENTS.—The Jew in America.—The virtues of the Jew.—Jews who are venerated by us all.—The persecution of the Jew.—The Jew fixes his own destiny.—Our own relations to the Jew.—The Jew as a Christian: I. Professor Neander. II. Dr. Edersheim. III. Bishop Isaac Hellmuth. IV. Bishop Samuel Isaac J. Schereschewsky. V. Meyer Lerman. VI. The Rev. Michael Rosenthal. VII. Joseph Wolff. VIII. Bishop Michael Solomon Alexander.—A general summary of Christianized Jews.—Two societies for the conversion of the Jews.—The awakening of the Jews.—Christian work awaiting the Jews.—The hope of the nation.—The desire of all nations.—What can we American Christians do?—Books consulted and recommended.

1. Jews. I. Title.

Library of Congress DS115.L5 1913 a 13-2485

NL 0409338 DLC MH-AH NN

Littell, John Stockton, 1870–
Washington:—Christian, by the Rev. John Stockton Littell ... Keene, N. H., The Hampshire art press, 1913.
[36] p. illus. (incl. ports.) 26cm. (Stories of cross and flag, no. 1) $0.25
Cover-title: George Washington: Christian.
Bibliography: p. [3]

1. Washington, George, pres. U. S., 1732–1799.

Library of Congress 13-5417

NL 0409339 DLC MiU

Littell, Joseph.
Leland; an historical sketch, by Joseph Littell. [Indianapolis, Indianapolis printing company, °1920]
3 p. l., [9]–61 p. 21cm.

1. Leland, Mich.

Library of Congress F574.L53L7 20-5207

NL 0409340 DLC

Littell, Lydia B
Bushwhacking for the WAACS. Portland, Oregon writers' project, 1942]
[58] l.
Typescript, carbon copy.
Loose-leaf.

NL 0409341 Or

Littell, Mrs. Malvina (Pray)
see
Florence, Mrs. Malvina (Pray) Littell

Littell, Margaret.
The campus medal, by Margaret Littell. Elgin, Ill., David C. Cook publishing co. [°1930]
96 p. incl. plates. 19½cm.

I. Title.

Library of Congress PZ7.L713Cam 31-3180

NL 0409343 DLC

Littell, Margaret.
Private hospital, by Margaret Littell. New York city, Gramercy publishing co. [°1939]
250 p. 19½cm.

I. Title. 39-12000

Library of Congress PZ3.L7175Pr

NL 0409344 DLC

Littell, Mary Clark.
Robert Harper, founder of Harper's Ferry, West Virginia, by Mary Clark Littell... [n. p., c1944] 4 l. 14cm.

1. Harper, Robert, 1713–1782— Poetry. I. Title.
N. Y. P. L. June 21, 1948

NL 0409345 NN

Littell, Mary V
From pot-closet to Palais Royal, or How a tired house-keeper went to Europe. New York, J.S.Ogilvie publishing co., c.1899.

NL 0409346 MH

Littell, Mary V.
"Tag". New York, c1899.
41 p., 5 l. 18 cm.

NL 0409347 RPB

LITTELL, MARY V.
Tramplets. By Mary V. Littell... New York: J. S. Ogilvie pub. co. [1899] viii, 10–32 p. 18½cm.

1. Poetry, American. I. Title.

NL 0409348 NN RPB

Littell, Norman Mather, 1899–
The German invasion of American business. [Address] delivered before the Indiana state bar association, annual-mid winter banquet, Indianapolis, Ind., Saturday, January 25, 1941. [Indianapolis, 1941] 26 l. 27cm.
Cover title.

1. Cartels, International. 2. World war, 1939–1945—Economic aspects—U. S. I. Title.

NL 0409349 NN WaU-L

Littell, Norman Mather, 1899–
Legal incentives for private investments abroad; a paper by Norman M. Littell, chairman, Committee on International Economic Cooperation, and delegate from the United States to International Bar Association, Monte Carlo, Monaco, July 19-24, 1954. [1954]
20 p.

Cover title.

NL 0409350 NNC MH-L

VOLUME 336

Littell, Norman Mather, 1899-
... Mejoras en el ambiente legal para las inversiones en el extranjero, por Norman M. Littell. Madrid, Consejo general de los ilustres colegios de abogados de España, 1952.
⌊7⌋ p. 27½cm.
"IV congreso de la International bar association, Madrid, julio de 1952."

NL 0409351 MH-L

Littell, Norman Mather, 1899- ed.

09
?N346

Navaho Indians.
Navajo Tribal Council executive volume.
Washington.

Littell, Norman Mather, 1899-
Nazi conspiracies in the United States, by Norman M. Littell, assistant United States attorney general. ⌊Washington, The National committee against persecution of the Jews, 1944⌋
15, ⌊1⌋ p. 23 x 10cm.
"Originally delivered as an address, before the Commonwealth club of California at San Francisco on May 19, 1944."
Bibliographical foot-notes.

1. World war, 1939- —Economic aspects—U. S. 2. Germans in the U. S. I. National committee against persecution of the Jews. II. Title.

Library of Congress D753.3.L5 45-14394
⌊3⌋ 338.885

NL 0409353 DLC NN CSt WHi

Littell, Norman Mather, 1899-

HF1411
.I 445

International Bar Association. *Committee on International Economic Cooperation.*
Preliminary report by Norman M. Littell. The Hague, M. Nijhoff ⌊1950⌋

Littell, Norman Mather, 1899-.
Shadows of the crooked cross. Washington, D.C. National committee against Nazi persecution and extermination of the Jews [1942?]
12 p. 23 x 10 cm.

NL 0409355 MH OrU

LITTELL, NORMAN MATHER, 1899-
Shadows of the crooked cross. Delivered before the American-Jewish congress, New York City, Monday, Feb., 14, 1944. [New York, 1944?] 13 p. 27cm.
Film reproduction. Positive.

1. Jews in the U. S.--Anti-Semitism. 2. United States--Anti-Semitism.

NL 0409356 NN

Littell, Philip, 1868-
Books and things, by Philip Littell. New York, Harcourt, Brace and Howe, 1919.
5 p. l., 3-283 p. 19½cm.
First published in the New republic.

1. Books and reading. I. Title.
Library of Congress PS3523.I 825B6 1919 19-15891

OC1W OC1 MB MiU IdU ViU
NL 0409357 DLC WaTC WaS Wa Or PBm IdB NcRS NcU NN

Littell, Philip, 1868-
This way out, by Philip Littell. New York, Coward-McCann, inc., 1928.
3 p. l., 314 p. 20cm.

I. Title.
Library of Congress PZ3.L718Th 28-21182

NL 0409358 DLC WaS ViU MB

Littell, Robert, 1896-
Candles in the storm, a novel, by Robert Littell. New York and London, Harper & brothers, 1934.
4 p. l., 3-322 p. 21½cm.
"First edition."

I. Title.
Library of Congress PZ3.L719Can 34-24860

NL 0409359 DLC WaS WaE OC1h OC1 OLak NN

Littell, Robert, 1896-
Read America first, by Robert Littell. New York, Harcourt, Brace and company, 1926.
x, 289 p. 19½cm.
"Articles" reprinted from the New republic.

1. United States. I. Title.
Library of Congress E169.L75 26-17689

OC1 OCU OOxM OU OC1W
NL 0409360 DLC OrPR IdU WaS WaT Wa OrP MB FTaSU NN

Littell, Robert Elwood, 1912- joint author.

Stack, John, 1906-
... The compressibility burble and the effect of compressibility on pressures and forces acting on an airfoil, by John Stack, W. F. Lindsey and Robert E. Littell. 1938. ⌊Washington, U. S. Govt. print. off., 1939⌋

Littell, Robert S., 1831-1896.

AP2
.L65

The Living age. v. 1-360; May 11, 1844-Aug. 1941. New York, The Living age company, inc.; ⌊etc., etc., 1844-1941⌋

Littell, Sara L
Educative play for the little child, by Sara L. Littell. Numbers and letters learned through play... Cooperstown, N.Y., Today's housewife, (1920?)
7 p. 23 cm

NL 0409363 DHEW

Littell, Squire, 1803-1886.
A manual of the diseases of the eye. By S. Littell, jr. ... Philadelphia, J. S. Littell, 1837.
xiv, ⌊2⌋, 255 p. 20½cm.

1. Eye—Diseases and defects.
Library of Congress RE46.L77 7-14031†

OC1W-H
NL 0409364 DLC MnU-B KyU KU-M NcU DNLM ViU MB MiU

WW
L779m
1838

LITTELL, Squire, 1803-1886
A manual of the diseases of the eye; or, Treatise on ophthalmology. Rev. and enl. by Hugh Houston. London, Churchill, 1838.
xvi, 307 p.
I. Houston, Hugh, ed.

NL 0409365 DNLM CtY

Hist.
19th c.
WW
L777M
1840

Littell, Squire, 1803-1886.
A manual of the diseases of the eye; or, Treatise on ophthalmology. Rev. & enl. by Hugh Houston. London, Churchill, 1840.
xvi, 307 p. 18 cm.

Hugh Houston's presentation copy to the Royal Medical Society of Edinburgh.

1. Eye Diseases. I. Houston, Hugh, ed. II. Title.

NL 0409366 WU-M DNLM

Littell, Squire, 1803-1886.
A manual of the diseases of the eye: or, Treatise on ophthalmology. By S. Littell, jr. ... 2d ed., rev. and enl. Philadelphia, Hogan and Thompson, 1846.
xii, ⌊25⌋-372 p. 20½cm.

1. Eye—Diseases and defects.
Library of Congress RE46.L78 7-14032†

NL 0409367 DLC CtY NN ICRL DNLM OOxM MH ICJ

Littell, Squire, 1803-1886.
Memoir of Captain Eliakim Littell of Essex county, N.J. by his grandson, S. Littell of Philadelphia. n.p., n.d.
p. 83-104. 24 cm.
Cover-title.

NL 0409368 RPB

B
W844l2

Littell, Squire, 1803-1886.
Memoir of George B. Wood, M.D., LL.D., late president of the College of Physicians of Philadelphia. Read before the College, October 1, 1879. Philadelphia, 1879.
56p.
"Extracted from the Transactions, third series, volume V."

1. Wood, George Bacon, 1797-1879.

NL 0409369 PP

1885

Littell, Squire, 1803-1886.
Memoir of Isaac Remington, M.D. [Philadelphia, 1862?]
10 p. 8°.

NL 0409370 DLC

VOLUME 336

Film 1338 no. 2 LITTELL, Squire, 1803-1886.
Memoir of Isaac Remington, M. D., read before the College of Physicians, December 3, 1862. [Philadelphia? 1862?]
10 p. Film 1338
Caption title.
Reprinted from the Transactions of the College of Physicians of Philadelphia.
1. Remington, Isaac, 1804-1862

NL 0409371 DNLM

Littell, S quire, 1803 - 1886.
Memoir of John Rodman Paul, M.D. Philadelphia, 1878. 21 p. 8°.
Repr.: College of Physicians of Philadelphia. Transac. Series 3, v. 4.

1. Paul, John Rodman, M.D.
N. Y. P. L. December 18, 1912.

NL 0409372 NN

YA9100 Littell, Squire, 1803-1886.
Memoir of Theophilus Elmer Beesley, read by Dr. Littell before the College of Physicians, Dec. 4, 1867 ... Philadelphia, 1868.
12 p.
1. Beesley, Theophilus Elmer, 1796-1867.

NL 0409373 DLC

R154 .Y35L5 Toner Coll. Littell, Squire, 1803-1886.
Memoir of Thomas H. Yardley, M. D. Read by Dr. Littell, before the College of physicians, February 1, 1860. [Philadelphia, 1860]
cover-title, p.[335]-344. 23½cm.

From the Transactions of the College of physicians of Philadelphia, v. 3, 1860.

1. Yardley, Thomas Howe, 1800-1860.

NL 0409374 DLC

Littell, Squire, 1803-1886, ed.
The Monthly journal of foreign medicine
see under title

Littell, S[quire], 1803 - 1886.
On the influence of electrical fluctuations as a cause of disease. n. t.-p. [Philadelphia, 1857.] 27 p. 8°.
Repr.: North Amer. Medico-Chirurgical Review. 1857.

1. Electricity.—Influence on life. 2. Diseases.—Causes.
N. Y. P. L. December 20, 1912.

NL 0409376 NN DLC

Littell, Thomas.
The clergyman's remembrancer. A sermon [on I Tim.iv.16] preach'd at a visitation held at Boston in Lincoln-shire; April 23. 1708 ... London, J. Bowyer, 1708.
28 p. 22cm.

NL 0409377 CLU-C TxU CSmH

[Littell, Tillie Roome]
... Uses of crêpe and tissue paper. London and New York, The Butterick publishing co. (limited) ©1894.
cover-title, 93 p. illus., diagrs. 24½ cm. (Metropolitan pamphlet series, vol. 8, no. 1)

1. Fancy work. 2. Paper work. 3. Crepe paper. I. The Butterick publishing company, limited.

TT870.L6 8—32159

NL 0409378 DLC

Littell, Walter Ricks, 1768 - 1824, ed.
A history of Cooperstown; including "The chronicles of Cooperstown", by James Fenimore Cooper; "The history of Cooperstown", 1839-1886, by Samuel M. Shaw; "The history of Cooperstown", 1886-1929, by Walter R. Littell. [Cooperstown, N. Y., The Freeman's journal company] 1929.

Littell, Walter Ricks, 1880–
A visit to Cooperstown. [Cooperstown, N. Y.] 1946.
40 p. illus., fold. map, ports. 23 cm.
Bibliography: p. 13–14.

1. Cooperstown, N. Y.—Descr. I. Title.
F129.C77L5 917.4774 47-27314*

NL 0409380 DLC

Law Littell, William, 1768-1824, ed.

Kentucky. *Court of appeals.*
Cases selected from the decisions of the Court of appeals of Kentucky. [1795–1821] Not heretofore reported. Published by by [!] William Littell ... in compliance with an act of the legislature. Cincinnati, O., The W. H. Anderson co. [1909]

Littell, William, 1768-1824, ed.
A digest of the statute law of Kentucky
see under Kentucky. Laws, statutes, etc.

Littell, William, 1768 - 1824.
Directions to the sheriffs of the different counties in the state of Kentucky. By William Littell. Louisville, K. Printed by Butler & Hughes. 1817.
12.5 x 20 cm. 7 p.

NL 0409383 OCHP

MICD 976.9 Littell, William, 1768-1824.
An epistle from William, surnamed Littell, to the people of the realm of Kentucky ... Frankfort, K., Printed by William Hunter, 1806.
40 p. (Kentucky culture series, no. 300)

#Kentucky--Politics and government--1792-1865.
An epistle from William.
Kentucky culture series. no. 300.

NL 0409384 MoU ICU WHi

Micro-card Ed. MIAMI Littell, William, 1768-1824.
An epistle from William, surnamed Littell, to the people of the realm of Kentucky... Frankfort, Ky., printed by William Hunter, 1806.
40p. 19cm. (Kentucky culture series, no. 300)
Microcard edition (1 cd.)

1. Kentucky. Politics and government. 1792-1865.

NL 0409385 OOxM

Littell, William, 1768-1824.
Festoons of fancy, consisting of compositions amatory, sentimental, and humorous, in verse and prose. Louisville, From the press of W. Farquar, 1814.
179 p. 18 cm.

I. Title.
PS2248.L34A6 1814 54-54449

CSmH ICU OFH
NL 0409386 DLC MiU-C PPRF CtY KyHi KyBgW ICN Ky NN

Littell, William, 1768–1824.
Festoons of fancy, consisting of compositions amatory, sentimental, and humorous, in verse and prose, by William Littell, esq. Lexington, Ky., University of Kentucky publications committee, Margaret Vorhies Haggin trust, 1940.
xv, 114, [2] p. facsim. 23cm. [Kentucky reprints, no. 1]
Includes facsimile of original t.-p., Louisville, 1814.

I. Title.
41-52473
Library of Congress PS2248.L34A6
[4] 817.2

NcD OCIW OOxM OO OCl ViU KyBgW OrU WaS OCU NN ViU
NL 0409387 DLC OC NIC KyLx KyHi KyLxT KyU ScU PPRF

LITTELL, William, 1768 - 1824.
Lecture delivered at Frankfort, Ky., Jan.15, 1818, on the necessity of establishing law colleges in the United States. Frankfort, Printed by Bledsoe & Farnham, 1818.

Manuscript note on title-page:-Judge White from his friend & humble servant J.H.Farnham.

NL 0409388 MH-L CSmH

Littell, William, 1768-1824.
Political transactions in and concerning Kentucky, from the first settlement thereof, until it became an independent state, in June, 1792 ... Frankfort, (K.), From the press of William Hunter, 1806.
81, 66 p.

1. Kentucky - Politics and government - To 1792.
2. Political transactions in and concerning Kentucky.

PPiU OC
NL 0409389 ICU KyHi DLC MB MWA NN PHi WHi MBAt OFH

MICD 976.9 Littell, William, 1768-1824.
Political transactions in and concerning Kentucky, from the first settlement thereof, until it became an independent state, in June, 1792 ... Frankfort, (K.), From the press of William Hunter, 1806.
81, 66 p. (Kentucky culture series, no. 344)
Microopaque

Continued in next column

VOLUME 336

Continued from preceding column

#Kentucky--Politics and government--To 1792.
Political transactions in and concerning Kentucky.

Kentucky culture series. no. 344.

NL 0409392 MoU OOxM

Littell, William, 1780 (*ca.*)–1824.
Principles of law and equity, recognised and established by the Court of appeals of Kentucky, in the various cases determined in that court, commencing with its first existence, and concluding with the close of the October term, one thousand eight hundred and six, (except the land cases published by James Hughes, esq.) digested and arranged in alphabetical order. By William Littell, esq. From the press of William Gerard ... Frankfort. 1808.
vii, ⌊13⌋–101, ⌊1⌋ p. 17ᶜᵐ.
Errata slip mounted on end-paper.
1. Law reports, digests, etc.—Kentucky. 2. Equity. ⌊2. Equity—Kentucky⌋ I. Kentucky. Court of appeals. II. Title.
80-6462

NL 0409393 DLC MH-L KyLo

Littell, William, 1768–1824.
... Reprints of Littell's Political transactions in and concerning Kentucky and Letter of George Nicholas to his friend in Virginia, also General Wilkinson's memorial; with an introduction by Temple Bodley. Louisville, Ky., J. P. Morton & company, incorporated, 1926.
2 p. l., cxxxix, 172 p. facsims. 23½ᶜᵐ. (Filson club publications: no. 31)
1. Kentucky—Pol. & govt.—To 1792. 2. Kentucky—Hist. 3. Southwest, Old—Hist. I. Nicholas, George, 1755?–1799. II. Wilkinson, James, 1757–1825. III. Bodley, Temple.
26-10120 Revised
Library of Congress F454.L75
——— Copy 2. F446.F48 no. 31
Copyright A 890603 ⌊r35l2⌋

OrU CU NcD MiU OOxM OU OO ViU
NL 0409394 DLC IdU MB IaU KyU KyLxT KyLx KyHi INS

Law

Littell, William, 1768–1824, reporter.

Kentucky. *Court of appeals.*
Reports of civil and criminal cases decided by the Court of appeals of Kentucky ... v. ⌊1⌋–
⌊June 1785⌋–
Frankfort, Ky. ⌊etc.⌋ 1810–⌊19

Littell, William, 1768–1824, comp.

Kentucky. *Laws, statutes, etc.*
The statute law of Kentucky; with notes, prælections, and observations on the public acts. Comprehending also, the laws of Virginia and acts of Parliament in force in this commonwealth; the charter of Virginia, the federal and state constitutions, and so much of the King of England's proclamation in 1763, as relates to the titles to land in Kentucky. Together with a table of reference to the cases adjudicated in the Court of appeals ... By William Littell ... Frankfort, (Ken.) Printed by and for William Hunter. 1809–1819.

Littell & Gay.
Tales of the Living age
see under title

The Littell digest. ⌊no. 1⌋–
South Orange, N. J. ⌊etc.⌋ J. M. Littell ⌊ᶜ1940–
nos. in v. 28ᶜᵐ.
Reproduced from type-written copy.
No. 7 lacks title.

1. Social sciences—Collected works. I. Littell, John McGregor.
45-31152
Library of Congress H1.L5
⌊2⌋ 305

NL 0409398 DLC TxU OCl NN WaS OrP OCU

Littell's living age.

The Living age ... v. 1–
May 11, 1844–
Boston, Littell, son & company; ⌊etc., etc., 1844–19

Littell's living age. v. 1–27 (no. 1–345); May 11, 1844–Dec. 28, 1850. Boston, E. Littell ⌊etc.⌋
5 reels. (American periodical series: 1800–1850. 319–323)
Microfilm copy, made in 1954 by University Microfilms, Ann Arbor, Mich. Positive.
Collation of the original: 360 v. illus.
Edited by E. Littell.
Ceased publication with v. 360 in Aug. 1941 under title: Living age.

I. Littell, Eliakim, 1797–1870, ed. (Series)
Microfilm 01104 no. 319–323 AP Mic 56-5110

NL 0409400 DLC NN ICRL WU-M MoU

Anesth. IV. 47c

Littell's living age, no. 161, 12 June, 1847.
A treatise on the inhalation of the vapor of ether, by J. Robinson ... London, 1847. Notes on the inhalation of sulphuric ether ... by J. Y. Simpson ... Edinburgh, 1847. The medical periodicals, passim. [Boston, E. Littell]1847.
p. [481]–496. 27cm.
Running title: Painless operations in surgery. Reviews from the North British Review.

NL 0409401 CtY-M KU-M

A 5 .5298

LITTELL'S Saturday magazine, or, Spirit of the magazines and annuals... July 1836-Dec.1837. Philadelphia,E.Littell⌊1836-37⌋ 2v.in 1.

"A collection of light reading from British periodicals."

NL 0409402 ICN

AP2 .L718

Littell's spirit of the magazines and annuals: consisting of the best parts of Blackwood's, Metropolitan, New monthly ... and other magazines, and all the annuals ...
Philadelphia, E. Littell & co., 1838–
v. 24ᶜᵐ. monthly.

NL 0409403 ICU AzU NNU-W PV

Littelton, George, 1st baron
see Lyttelton, George Lyttelton, 1st baron, 1709-1773.

Littelton, Thomas Littelton, 2d baron
See
Lyttelton, Thomas Lyttelton, 2d baron, 1744-1779.

Litten, Anthony, ed.
The Cork surgeon's antidote
see under Cox, Sir Richard, bart., 1702-1766.

941.58 C692 v.54 no.25

Litten, Dick, pseud.
The mirrour for the mirror; or, An antidote extraordinary. By Dick Litten, brother to Sir Anthony Litten, baronet, who was created on Sept.15th 1749, by His Highness, Charles Lucas, lord protector of independancy. 2d ed. Dublin, 1749.
15p.

[Collins pamphlets. v.54, no.25]

NL 0409407 IU CtY

Litten, E.
Vademecum für den deutschen Burschenschafter zusammengestellt von E. Litten. Mit Nachträgen bis Sommer-Semester 1885 ... Jena, 1885.
9 l. col. illus. 18 cm.

NL 0409408 CtY

LITTEN, F. W.
Über die passivconstruction im spanischen. [Santiago de Chile, 1895.]

1.8°. pp. (9).
Verhandlungen des Deutschen wissensch. vereins zu Santiago de Chile, 1895. pp.140-148.

NL 0409409 MH

Litten, Frederic Nelson, 1885–
Air mission Red. Chicago, Rand, McNally ⌊1951⌋
254 p. 21 cm.

I. Title.
PZ3.L7194Ai 51-10351

NL 0409410 DLC

Litten, Frederic Nelson, 1885–
Air mission to Algiers, by Frederic Nelson Litten. New York, Dodd, Mead & company, 1943.
xii p., 1 l., 274 p. 21ᶜᵐ.
Story for older boys.

I. Title.
43-15502
Library of Congress PZ7.L718Ah

NL 0409411 DLC WaSp

VOLUME 336

Litten, Frederic Nelson, 1885–
Air trails north, by Frederic Nelson Litten. New York, Dodd, Mead & company, 1939.
viii p., 1 l., 236 p. 21cm.

I. Title.
Library of Congress PZ7.L718Ai 39-25956

NL 0409412 DLC

Litten, Frederic Nelson, 1885–
Airmen of the Amazon, by Frederic Nelson Litten. New York, Dodd, Mead & company, 1942.
viii, 280 p. 21cm.

I. Title.
Library of Congress PZ7.L718Ai 42-23862

NL 0409413 DLC OO OLak

Litten, Frederic Nelson, 1885–
Brooks of the Valley airways, by Frederic Nelson Litten; illustrated by Svén Elven. New York, London, D. Appleton and company, 1931.
v, [1] p., 1 l., 280, [1] p. front., illus. 19½cm.

I. Title.
Library of Congress PZ7.L718Br 31-8328

NL 0409414 DLC

Litten, Frederic Nelson, 1885–
Code of a champion. Philadelphia, Westminster Press [1950]
224 p. illus. 21 cm.

I. Title.
PZ3.L7194Co 50-10334

NL 0409415 DLC OrU Or

Litten, Frederic Nelson, 1885–
... The kingdom of flying men, a story of air cargo. Philadelphia, The Westminster press [1946]
5 p. l., [9]-247 p. 21cm.

I. Title.
Library of Congress PZ7.L718Ki 46-7179

NL 0409416 DLC CaBVa

Litten, Frederic Nelson, 1885–
The kingdom of flying men; illustrated by Hedley Rainnie. [Complete and unabridged. New York, Pocket Books, 1950]
342 p. illus. 17 cm. (Pocket book, jr., J-51)

I. Title.
PZ7.L718Ki 2 50-58128

NL 0409417 DLC

Litten, Frederic Nelson, 1885–
Pilot of the high Andes, by Frederic Nelson Litten. New York, Dodd, Mead & company, 1941.
viii p., 1 l., 298 p. 21cm.
Illustrated t.-p.

I. Title.
Library of Congress PZ7.L718Pg 41-18123

NL 0409418 DLC CaBVa OrP WaS Wa

Litten, Frederic Nelson, 1885–
Pilot of the high Sierras, by Frederic Nelson Litten. New York, Dodd, Mead & company, 1937.
viii p., 1 l., 350 p. 21cm.

I. Title.
Library of Congress PZ7.L718Pi 37-30400

NL 0409419 DLC NN WaS

Litten, Frederic Nelson, 1885–
Pilot of the North country; a Johnny Caruthers flying story, by Frederic Nelson Litten. New York, Dodd, Mead & company, 1938.
viii p., 1 l., 244 p. 21cm.

I. Title.
Library of Congress PZ7.L718Pik 38-32615

NL 0409420 DLC NN

Litten, Frederic Nelson, 1885–
... Rendezvous on Mindanao. New York, Dodd, Mead & company, 1945.
x, 237 p. 19cm.

I. Title.
Library of Congress * PZ7.L718Re 45-10322

NL 0409421 DLC

Litten, Frederic Nelson, 1885–
Rhodes of the Flying cadets, by Frederic Nelson Litten, foreword by W. E. Gillmore ... New York, London, D. Appleton and company, 1929.
5 p. l., 251, [1] p. front. 19½cm.

I. Title.
Library of Congress PZ7.L718Rh 29-19880

NL 0409422 DLC

Litten, Frederic Nelson, 1885–
Rhodes of the Leathernecks, by Frederic Nelson Litten ... New York, Dodd, Mead & company, 1935.
vi p., 1 l., 376 p. front. 19½cm.

I. Title.
Library of Congress PZ7.L718Ri 35-19963

NL 0409423 DLC NN

PZ 7 L718 Rh
Litten, Frederic Nelson, 1885–
Rhodes of the 94th. Illustrated by Clayton Knight. New York, Junior Literary Guild and Sears Pub. Co., 1933.
306p. illus. 20cm.

NL 0409424 WU

Litten, Frederic Nelson.
Rhodes of the 94th, by Frederic Nelson Litten; illustrated by Clayton Knight. New York, Sears publishing company, inc. [c1933]
306 p. front., plates. 19½cm.

I. Title.
Library of Congress PZ7.L718Rk 33-22044

NL 0409425 DLC WaS WU OO MB

LITTEN, FREDERIC NELSON, 1885–
...Rhodes of the 94th, by Frederic Nelson Litten; illustrated by Howard Leigh. London: J. Hamilton, Ltd. [1934] 252 p. col'd front., plates. 19cm. (The "Ace" series.)

796485A. 1. Fiction, American. 2. Aeronautics in literature. I. Title.

N. Y. P. L. October 8, 1935

NL 0409426 NN

Litten, Frederic Nelson, 1885–
... Sinister island squadron, by Frederic Nelson Litten. New York, Dodd, Mead & company, 1944.
x p., 1 l., 251 p. 19cm.
At head of title: A flying story of the Pacific area.
"First appeared in shorter serialized form in ... the Open road for boys."

I. Title.
Library of Congress PZ7.L718Si 44-6747

NL 0409427 DLC CaBVa

Litten, Frederic Nelson, 1885–
Sun-up on the range, by Frederic Nelson Litten; illustrations by Albin Henning. New York, London, D. Appleton and company, 1930.
5 p. l., 263, [1] p. front., illus. 19½cm.

I. Title.
Library of Congress PZ7.L718Su 30-29825

NL 0409428 DLC MB

Litten, Frederic Nelson, 1885–
Transatlantic pilot, by Frederic Nelson Litten. New York, Dodd, Mead & company, 1940.
viii p., 1 l., 307 p. 21cm.

I. Title.
Library of Congress PZ7.L718Tr 40-34112

NL 0409429 DLC CaBVa WaS

VOLUME 336

Litten, Frederic Nelson, 1885–
Treasure Bayou. Philadelphia, Westminster Press [1949]
223 p. 22 cm.

I. Title.

PZ7.L718Tre 49-11234*

NL 0409430 DLC PJA CaBVa Wa

LITTEN, Fritz, 1873-
Beiträge zur lehre von der schadensberechnung nach römischem und bürgerlichem recht. Jena, 1905.

NL 0409431 MH-L

Litten, Fritz, 1873-
Der Dissens über die Person des Empfängers beim Traditions-Erwerb durch Stellvertreter. Eine Studie im Gebiete des gemeinen Civilrechts ... von Frita Litten ... Königsberg, Hartung, 1895.
4 p.l., 100 p., 2 l. 21cm.
Inaug.-Diss. - Halle-Wittenberg.
"Lebenslauf": 2d leaf at end.
Bibliographical footnotes.

NL 0409432 MH-L ICRL

LITTEN, F[ritz], 1873-
Gutachten über die frage: Empfiehlt sich eine änderung des im Deutschen Reiche geltenden rechtes betr. die aus anlass einer grundstücksveräusserung stattfindende übernahme einer durch hypothek gesicherten forderung durch den grundstückserwerber? [Berlin], n.d.

NL 0409433 MH-L

Litten, Fritz, 1873–
Römisches recht und pandekten-recht, in forschung und unterricht. Von dr. Fritz Litten ... Berlin, F. Vahlen, 1907.
79, [1] p. 23cm.
"Literarische nachweise": p. [70]-79.

10-3385

NL 0409434 DLC NNF CtY

LITTEN, F[ritz] 1873-
Ueber "lo Codi" und seine stellung in der entwicklungs-geschichte des culpa-problems. [Halle, 1908]
(4) + 34 + (2) p.
"Extrait des Mélanges Fitting."

NL 0409435 MH-L

Litten, Fritz, 1873-
Über "Lo Codi" und seine Stellung in der Entwicklungs-Geschichte des Culpa-Problems. Von Fritz Litten. Berlin, F. Vahlen, 1910.
45, [1] p. 23cm.
"Diese Abhandlung ist bereits im zweiten Bande der 'Mélanges Fitting (Montpellier, 1908)' erschienen; aber die von ihr hergestellten Sonderdrucke sind vergriffen, und das ganze Werk ist in Deutschland schwer zugänglich."-p. [3]
Bibliographical footnotes.

NL 0409436 MH-L

Litten, Fritz, 1873–
Die wahlschuld im deutschen bürgerlichen rechte. Von dr. Fritz Litten ... Berlin, F. Vahlen, 1903.
v, 223 p. 23cm.

1. Debtor and creditor—Germany. 2. Civil law—Germany. 3. Debtor and creditor (Roman law) I. Title.

33-365

NL 0409437 DLC MH-L CtY

LITTEN, Fritz, 1873-
Die wirkung geistiger störungen auf den rechtlichen bestand der ehe. Heidelberg, 1904.

NL 0409438 MH-L

LITTEN, Fritz, 1873-
Zum dolus-begriff in der actio de dolo. Berlin, 1910.

NL 0409439 MH-L

Litten (Fritz) [1900-]. *Ein Beitrag zur Statistik und Kasuistik des Oesophaguscarcinoms. 16 pp. 8°. Frankfurt a. M., H. Münch. 1926.

NL 0409440 DNLM MiU

Litten, Hans.
Die Ansprüche des Abzahlungsverkäufers im Falle seines Rücktrittes vom Vertrage nach dem Reichsgesetz vom 16. Mai 1894 ... von Hans Litten ... Emsdetten, Heinr. & J. Lechte, 1933.
iii, 60 p. 22½cm.
Inaug.-Diss. - Erlangen.
"Literatur-Verzeichnis": p. 55-60.

NL 0409441 MH-L ICRL

Litten, Heinz Wolfgang, 1905-
Die aenderung des buehnenwerkes durch die auffuehrung.
Inaug. diss. Koenigsberg, 1927.
Bibl.

NL 0409442 ICRL MH-L CtY

Litten, Irmgard (Wüst)
"All the Germans"—are they really guilty? By Irmgard Litten. With a foreword by W. Arnold-Forster. London, V. Gollancz ltd., 1945.
22, [1] p. 18½cm.

1. Concentration camps—Germany. I. Title.

46-2751
Library of Congress DD253.L567
[3] 943.086

NL 0409443 DLC

Litten, Irmgard (Wüst)
Beyond tears, by Irmgard Litten; introduction and epilogue by Pierre van Paassen; foreword by His Grace the Archbishop of York; preface by W. Arnold-Forster. New York, Alliance book corporation [°1940]
xviii, 325 p. front. (port.) 21cm.

1. National socialism. I. Van Paassen, Pierre, 1895– II. Title.
40-32665
Library of Congress DD253.L57
——— Copy 2.
Copyright [20] 943.085

NcD NcC OU OEac OClW OOxM Wa Or WaSpG
NL 0409444 DLC ViU NIC CoU OKentU CU WaT IdU WaS

Litten, Irmgard (Wüst)
... Die hölle sieht dich an: der fall Litten. Vorwort von Rudolf Olden. Paris, Éditions nouvelles internationales, 1940.
298 p., 3 l., incl. port., facsims. 19½cm.
At head of title: Irmgard Litten.

1. Litten, Hans Achim, 1903–1938. 2. National socialism. I. Title.
A 43-578
Harvard univ. Library for Library of Congress [DD253.L]
[2] 943.086

NL 0409445 MH OCl

Litten, Irmgard (Wüst)
... Una madre contra Hitler. México, Ediciones Minerva, 1941.
xxiii, 299 p., 1 l. 19cm.
At head of title: Irmgard Litten.
"Versión española de Miguel G. Santesmases."

1. Litten, Hans Achim, 1903–1938. 2. National socialism. I. Santesmases, Miguel G., tr. II. Title.
43-43074
Library of Congress DD253.L574
[2] 943.086

NL 0409446 DLC

Litten, Irmgard (Wüst).
Une mère résiste aux Nazis; le lent martyre d'un prisonnier politique poursuivi par la haine d'Hitler dans un camp de concentration. [n. p., 194–?] 27 p. 26cm.
Cover-title.
Page [4] of cover: no. 73.

1. World war, 1939–1945—Prisoners and prisons, German. 2. Burial and funerals—Germany. I. Title.

NL 0409447 NN

Litten, Irmgard (Wüst)
A mother fights Hitler, by Irmgard Litten. With a foreword by His Grace the Archbishop of York and an introduction by W. Arnold-Forster. London, George Allen and Unwin ltd. [1940]
2 p. l., vii-xii, 286 p. front. (port.) 20cm.
"First published in 1940."
"Translated from the German manuscript by Bernard Miall."
American edition (New York, Alliance book corporation) has title: Beyond tears.
1. Litten, Hans Achim, 1903–1938. 2. National socialism. I. Miall, Bernard, 1876– tr. II. Title.
A 40-3196 Revised
Harvard univ. Library for Library of Congress [r43c2] 943.085

NL 0409448 MH ScU GU

VOLUME 336

DD253
L777
Litten, Irmgard (Wüst)
Eine Mutter kämpft. Rudolstadt/Thür., Der Greifenverlag [1941]
264 p. 19cm.

Hoover Library
1.Litten, Hans Achim, 1903-1938. 2.National socialism. 3.Political crimes and offenses - Germany. I.Title.

NL 0409449 CSt-H

943.085
L777m
Litten, Irmgard (Wüst)
Eine Mutter kämpft. Rudolstadt, Greifenverlag [1946?]
263p. 19cm.

1. Litten, Hans, 1903-1938. 2. National socialism. I. Title.

NL 0409450 IEN

943.085
L718m
Litten, Irmgard (Wüst)
Eine mutter kämpft. Rudolstadt Thür, Der Greifenverlag [1947]
264 p. 19cm.

1. National socialism. I. Title.

NL 0409451 MnU

Div.S.
264
L777W
Litten, John Howard
Within Thy gates; a book of worship for the use of youth fellowships entering the communion of Christ's Church. London, Epworth Press [1941]
135 p. 20 cm.

Includes music.
1. Worship (Religious education) 2. Worship programs. 3. Public worship. I. Title.

NL 0409452 NcD

Litten, Julius.
Der Modedichter; eine literarische humoreske. Elberfeld, Baedeker'schen Buch-u. Kunsthandlung, 1890.
62 p. 15 cm.

NL 0409453 TU

Litten, Julius Edward.
Die Rohrbrüche in Halle a. S., ihre Ursache und Remedur. Von J. Edward Litten ... Halle a. S., Druck von O. Hendel, 1907.
31, [1] p. 24cm.

NL 0409454 ICJ

Litten, Käte, 1902-
Welches sind die soziologischen ursachen für die kriminalität in der Rheinpfalz? ... Charlottenburg [1928?]
Diss. - Frankfurt a.M.

NL 0409455 MiU

Litten, Manfred, 1909-
Die politischen parteien Hollands von 1848 bis 1914. ... 1936.
Inaug. Diss. - Berlin, 1936.
Lebenslauf.
Literaturverzeichnis.

NL 0409456 ICRL CtY

Litten (Meier) [1813-]. *De symblepharo totali, adjecta symblephari totalis acquisiti historia. 29 pp., 1 l. 8°. *Berolini, typ. Nietackianis,* [1836].

NL 0409457 DNLM

Litten, Moritz, 1845-1907

Senator, Hermann, 1834-1911.
... Diseases of the kidneys and of the spleen, hemorrhagic diseases, by Dr. H. Senator ... and Dr. M. Litten ... ed., with additions by James B. Herrick ... Authorized translation from the German, under the editorial supervision of Alfred Stengel ... Philadelphia and London, W. B. Saunders & company, 1905.

Litten, Moritz, 1845-1907.
Die Krankheiten der Milz und die haemorrhagischen Diathesen, von Prof. Dr. M. Litten ... Mit 2 Abbildungen und einer Tafel in Farbendruck. Wien, A. Hölder, 1898.
[6], 392 p. 1 illus., 1 col. pl., 1 col. diagr. 26cm. (In Specielle Pathologie und Therapie, hrsg. von Hermann Nothnagel. VIII. Bd.)
"Literatur": p. 309-310, 391-392.

NL 0409459 ICJ OC1W-H MB IU-M DNLM IaU ICRL CtY

Litten (M[oritz]) [1845-]. Pathologisch-anatomische Beobachtungen. 16 pp., 1 pl. 8°. [*Berlin,* 1876.]
Repr. from: Arch. f. path. Anat. [etc.], Berl., 1876, lxvi.

NL 0409460 DNLM

Litten (Moritz) [1845-1907]. *Ueber den Vorfall der schwangeren Gebärmutter. 46 pp. 8°. *Berlin, G. Lange,* [1869].

NL 0409461 DNLM ICRL

Litten, Moritz, 1845-1907.
—— & **Salomon** (G.) Ueber eine schwere Hauterkrankung im Gefolge allgemeiner Infection. 10 pp. 8°. [n. p., 1878, vel subseq.]

NL 0409462 DNLM

Litten, Wilhelm, 1880-1932, *ed.*
Das drama in Persien, von Wilhelm Litten; mit einem geleitwort von Friedrich Rosen. Berlin und Leipzig, W. de Gruyter & co., 1929.
xix, 371 p. 27cm.
Reproduction in facsimile of the editor's collection of fifteen Persian manuscripts.

1. Persian drama (Collections) 2. Manuscripts, Persian—Facsimiles.
43-35721
Library of Congress PK6440.L5

NL 0409463 DLC OC1 TxU NNC LU IU ICU NN

Litten, Wilhelm, 1880-
Einführung in die persische diplomatensprache, von Wilhelm Litten ... Berlin, G. Reimer, 1919.
2 v. 22½cm. (*Added t.-p.:* Lehrbücher des Seminars für orientalische sprachen zu Berlin ... bd. xxxi, 1-2)
CONTENTS.—I. Vorwort, umschreibung und übersetzung.—II. Wortlaut in persischer schikästä-schrift.

1. Persian language—Chrestomathies and readers.
35-23725
Library of Congress PK6237.L5 491.5586

NL 0409464 DLC CU NN ICN MH OC1

Litten, Wilhelm, 1880 - 1932.
...Lettisch, von Wilhelm Litten... Berlin-Schöneberg: Langenscheidtsche Verlagsbuchhandlung [1923]. 160 p. 24°. (Metoula Sprachführer.)

140253A. 1. Lettish language.—Conversation books. 2. Series.
N. Y. P. L. October 6, 1924

NL 0409465 NN

Litten, Wilhelm, 1880 - 1932.
...Persien von der "pénétration pacifique" zum "Protektorat"; Urkunden und Tatsachen zur Geschichte der europäischen "pénétration pacifique" in Persien 1860-1919, von Wilhelm Litten ... Berlin: W. de Gruyter & Co., 1920. xi, 396 p. incl. tables. maps. 4°.
At head of title: Veröffentlichung der Deutsch-persischen Gesellschaft, e. V.

1. Corporations (Foreign), Persia, 1860-1919. 2. Economic history, Persia. 3. Germans in Persia. 4. Deutsch-persische Gesellschaft.
N. Y. P. L. December 7, 1921.

NL 0409466 NN WaU NjP CSt-H MH OC1W

Litten, Wilhelm, 1880 -1932.
... Persisch, von Wilhelm Litten ... Berlin-Schöneberg, Langenscheidt [1919]
152 p. illus. (incl. map) 13½cm. (Metoula-sprachführer)

1. Persian language—Conversation and phrase books. 2. German language—Conversation and phrase books.
Library of Congress PK6239.L5 23-2606

NL 0409467 DLC CU

4DS-303
Litten, Wilhelm, 1880-1932.
Persische Flitterwochen. Berlin, G. Stilke, 1925.
444 p.

NL 0409468 DLC-P4 MH NjP OU CLU NN

Litten, Wilhelm, 1880- 1932.
... Eine verkürzte methode Toussaint-Langenscheidt. Lettisch, von Wilhelm Litten ... Berlin-Schöneberg, Langenscheidt [1925]
3-160 p. illus. (map) 13½cm. (Metoula-sprachführer)
"Inhaltsangabe" on front lining-paper.

1. Lettish language—Conversation and phrase books—German.
36-23442
Library of Congress PG8839.L5 491.938243

NL 0409469 DLC

VOLUME 336

PK
6525
.L58 Litten, Wilhelm, 1880-1932.
Was bedeutet Chäjjam? Warum hat Omar Chäjjam, der Verfasser der berühmten persischen Vierzeiler, gerade diesen Dichternamen gewählt? Versuch einer Erklärung. Berlin, W. de Gruyter, 1930.
25 p.

Includes bibliographical references.

NL 0409470 NNC OCl NN

Litten, Wilhelm, 1880–1932.
Wer hat die persische Neutralität verletzt? 14 Punkte zur Frage der persischen Neutralität und zur persischen schwarzen Liste. Nebst 320 wortgetreuen amtlichen diplomatischen Schriftsätzen zur Aufklärung über die Kriegführung an der östlichsten Front. Berlin, W. de Gruyter, 1920.
164 p. (p. 164 advertisement) 24 cm.
Errata slip inserted.
Documents in French.
1. Persia—Neutrality. I. Title.
D621.P4L5 49-55608*

NL 0409471 DLC CSt NN MH

Litter, Dora Kleimans de
see **Kleimans de Litter, Dora.**

1882–
Litter, Fritz, bacc. jur.: Die Pflichten des stillen Gesellschafters.
Borna-Leipzig 1911: Noske. VIII, 48 S. 8°
Leipzig, Jur. Diss. v. 29. Dez. 1911
[Geb. 13. Nov. 82 Bautzen; Wohnort: Hamburg; Staatsangeh.: Sachsen; Vorbildung: Gymn. Bautzen Reife O. 02; Studium: Grenoble 1, München 1, Leipzig 5 S.; Rig. 17. Juli 06.] [U 12. 2966

NL 0409473 ICRL MH

RC124
L71
Litter, Leo, 1911-
... Die neurologischen folgezustände der meningitis cerebrospinalis epidemica ... Stetten/Basel, Karl Schahl, 1936.
4 p. l., 44 p. tables (2 fold.)

Inaug.-diss., Basel.
"Literaturverzeichnis": p. 36-44.

1. Meningitis, Cerebrospinal.

NL 0409474 NNC CtY MiU

Litter, Manuel.
... Determinación del ácido ascórbico en la sangre en casos normales y patológicos, con especial referencia a las afecciones reumáticas; tesis de doctorado, por el dr. Manuel Litter ... Buenos Aires, "La Semana médica," imp. de E. Spinelli, 1938.
67 p., 1 l. diagr. 16½cm.
At head of title: Universidad nacional de Buenos Aires. Facultad de ciencias médicas. Escuela de medicina.
"Bibliografía": p. [61]–67.

1. Blood—Analysis and chemistry. 2. Ascorbic acid.
43-26989
Library of Congress RB145.L64

NL 0409475 DLC

Litter, Manuel, tr.
Elementos esenciales de electrocardiografía para estudiantes y médicos prácticos...
see under Ashman, Richard, 1890–

Litter, Manuel.
Estudios cuantitativos sobre el equilibrio entre los transmisores químicos autonómicos y las células efectoras; análisis estadístico y curvas dosis-respuesta de la acetilcolina, *l*-adrenalina, *l*-noradrenalina, e histamina. Buenos Aires, El Ateneo, 1955.
83 p. illus. 27 cm.
Tesis de profesorado—Universidad de Buenos Aires.

1. Pharmacology. 2. Probabilities. I. Title.
QP909.L55 57-24591 ‡

NL 0409477 DLC DNLM

Litter, Manuel.
... Medicación cardiovascular y renal ... Buenos Aires, "El Ateneo," 1946.
xvi, 265 p. illus. (part col.) 23 cm.
Contains author's signature (initials)

1. [Cardiovascular system, Effects of drugs on] 2. [Kidneys, Effect of drugs on] I. Title.
Med 47-2659
U. S. Army Medical Library for Library of Congress [WB905L777m 1946] [1]

NL 0409478 DNLM

Litter, Manuel.
... Tratado de neurologia, para estudantes e médicos práticos. Tr. da 2. ed. pelos doutores Odilon Gallotti ... e C. Magalhães de Freitas ... Rio [de Janeiro] Guanabara, 1946.
2 v. illus. (part col.) 25½cm.
At head of title: Manoel Litter ... e Mario Wexselblatt ...

1. Nervous system—Diseases. I. Wexselblatt, Mario, joint author. II. Gallotti, Odilon, tr.
Med 47-1515
U. S. Army medical library for Library of Congress [WL140qL777t 1946] [2]

NL 0409479 DNLM

Litter, Manuel.
Tratado de neurologia para estudiantes y medicos practicos, por Manuel Litter y Mario Wexselblatt. 4. ed. Buenos Aires, Ateneo, 1950.
xxv, 1231 p. illus. (part col.)

I. Wexselblatt, Mario, joint author. 616.8

NL 0409480 ICJ DNLM

Litter, Víctor A
Clasificación decimal de la bibliografía antropológica; proyecto de extensión. Buenos Aires, I. D. E. A., 1953.
44 p. 20 cm.

1. Classification—Books—Anthropology. 2. Classification, Decimal.
Z697.A6L5 025.46571 54-21772 ‡

NL 0409481 DLC OCIW CU MH-P ICU MB TxU NN KyU

LITTERA de Ragugia de gli orribili segni apparsi in Bossia & appresso a Bel Grado. [Ragugia?,1531.]

20 cm. pp.(7).
The title-page has been reinforced.
Dated:"De Ragugia,alli xvi de novemb.1531."

NL 0409482 MH

Littera mãdata della Insula de Cu ‖ ba de India in laquale se cotie ‖ ne de le insule Citta Gente ‖ et animali nouamente ‖ trouate de lanno. ‖ M. d. xix. p li ‖ Spagnoli. ‖ ✠ [n. p., 1520] [Boston, 1921]
facsim.: 16 l. 25½cm. [Americana series; photostat reproductions by the Massachusetts historical society. no. 42]
Woodcut below title.
Collation of original: 8 l. Signatures: A-B⁴.
An account of the expedition of Juan de Grijalva to Cuba, with his discovery of the "insula ... da Yucaton" and other parts of the coast of Mexico.
For description *cf.* Harrisse, Bibl. amer. vetus. ... additions. no. 60.
One of 10 photostat copies reproduced from the original in the Biblioteca nazionale di San Marco, May 1921.
1. America—Disc. & explor.—Spanish. 2. Cuba—Disc. & explor. 3. Yucatan—Disc. & explor. 4. Grijalva, Juan de, d. 1527.
24-5140
Library of Congress E125.G8L6

NL 0409483 DLC NN RPJCB MiU-C

Litterae a celeberrimis pastoribus et professoribus Ecclesiae et Academiae Genevensis ad Universitatem Oxoniensem transmissae ... 1707
see Literae a celeberrimis ...

Litterae annuae Iaponicae
see under Jesuits. Letters from missions (The East)

Litterae Apostolicae quibus institutio confirmatio et varia privilegia continentur societatis Jesu
see under Catholic church. Pope.

Litteræ Apostolicæ Diversorvm Romanorvm Pontificvm Pro officio sanctissimæ Inquisitionis
see under Catholic Church. Pope.

Litterae eminentissimi legati ad episcopum N. de neo-catechismo, et in easdem litteras animadversiones. np [180?]

39 p.

NL 0409488 MH

FILM
4338
DL
Roll
19
Litterae fraternitatis conuentus hospitalis S. Spiritus extra oppidum Sudercopensem. [Uppsala, Paul Grijs, ca. 1510-1515]
1 l. 165 x 185mm.
Collijn, I, 211 (edition described as "Bb" according to Collijn; in the Palmskiöld collection, vol. 293)

NL 0409489 CU

VOLUME 336

FILM 4338 DL Roll 15 Litterae fraternitatis hospitalis S. Johannis in Eskilstuna. Uppsala, Paul Grijs, ca. 1519.
1 l. 8°.
Collijn, I, 269.

NL 0409490 CU

Litterae laborum solamen
see under Oberlin college. L. L. S. society.

Litterae orientales; orientalistischer literaturbericht.
Leipzig, O. Harrassowitz [19
v. 22½cm. quarterly.

1. Oriental philology—Bibl.—Period.
42-47175
Library of Congress Z7048.L5 [3] 490.5

NL 0409492 DLC NNC IEN

AW 1 R2462:136:2 Litterae participationis monasterii Sanctarum Mariae virginis et Birgittae in Vadstena. [Lübeck, Bartholomaeus Ghotan, 1491]
Broadside. 55 x 125mm.
Microfilm

NL 0409493 CaBVaU CU

Litterae quadrimestres ex universis praeter Indiam et Brasiliam locis in quibus aliqui de Societate Jesu versabantur Romam missae. Matriti, A. Avrail, 1894–
v. 24 cm. (Monumenta historica Societatis Jesu, [v. 4, 6, 8, 10, 59, 61, 62
Vols. 5-6 have imprint: Madrid; v. 7– Roma.
CONTENTS.—t. 1. 1546-1552.—t. 2. 1552-1554.—t. 3. 1554-1555.—t. 4. 1556.—t. 5. 1557-1558.—t. 6. 1559-1560.—t. 7. 1561-1562.

1. Jesuits—Hist.—Sources. 2. Jesuits—Missions. (Series)
BX3701.M7 vol. 4, etc. 3-9233 rev*

MB OCIJC
NL 0409494 DLC KU NcD MU MiU RPB NN MoSU OCX MH

Litterär kritik.1-6.
Malmö,1935-1940.

NL 0409495 CU

804 L777S Litterära soiréer i Helsingfors under hösten 1849. [Imprimatur: N. A. Gyldén] Helsingfors, Finska litteratur-sällskapet, 1849.
332 p. 21 cm.
Includes lectures by M. A. Castrén and others.
1. Literature. Addresses, essays, lectures. 2. Languages. Addresses, essays, lectures. I. Gyldén, Nils Abraham, 1802- ed. II. Castrén, Matthias Alexander, 1813-1852.

NL 0409496 NcD

4PT Nor. 201 Den Litteraere Klubb i Trondheim.
Den Litteraere Klubb i Trondheim, hvori opptatt bokmannsklubben; en ti-arsberetning ved Arvid Dahle. Med illustrasjoner av Erik Bergersen. Trondheim, 1955.
67 p.

NL 0409497 DLC-P4 NN

De Litteraire revue; alg. maandblad voor dicht- en prozakunst. jaarg. 1 (Jan. – Juni, 1937)
Vlissingen: Firma F. van de Velde jr., 1937. 1 v. 26½cm.
Edited by J. H. Eekhout and others.
Ceased publication with jaarg. 1, nr. 6 (Juni, 1937)

1. Periodicals—Netherlands.
N. Y. P. L. March 25, 1938

NL 0409498 NN

LITTERÆRT liv i Norden. aarg. 1, no. 1-11/12; dec. 1945-nov. 1946. København. 1 v. illus. 26cm.
Lacks: v. 1, no. 8, 11/12.
Monthly.
"Dansk-norsk-svensk udgave af Boganmelderen."
Includes under one cover: Bog-anmelderen (Copenhagen), Bokanmälaren (Stockholm), and Bokanmelderen (Oslo). These publications also appeared separately before and after the existence of Litterært liv i Norden.

Separate edition of Bokanmelderen (Oslo) not in the library.
Ceased publication with v. 1, no. 11/12. -cf. Union list of serials.

1. Literature--Per. and soc. publ.

NL 0409500 NN

Litterært Samfund, Copenhagen. Scattered
...Smaaskrifter.
no.
[Copenhagen, 19 12°.
no.

1. No subject.
N. Y. P. L. April 20, 1922.

NL 0409501 NN

Litterair paspoort. 1.– Jaarg. (nr. 1–)
Jan. 1946–
[Amsterdam, Meulenhoff, etc.]
v. in illus. 29 cm.
Bimonthly, 1946-47; 10 no. a year, 1948–
Editor: Jan. 1946– A. Morriën.

1. Literature—Hist. & crit.—Period. I. Morriën, Adriaan, 1912– ed.
PN9.L42 55-18328

NL 0409502 DLC NIC NN

L Ger K115Zl Litterair paspoort.
Franz Kafka, 1883-1924. [Amsterdam, Meulenhoff, 1949]
97-120p. illus., ports. 29cm.
Litterair paspoort, v.4, no.29, Aug./Sept. 1949.
Text in Dutch, French, German or English.
1. Kafka, Franz, 1883-1924.

NL 0409503 IEN

Litterair paspoort.

Z6519 .H3 Hague. Gemeentemuseum.
Wereldschrijvers van nabij [tentoonstelling ... gehouden in het Gemeente Museum te 's-Gravenhage 20 Juni–23 Juli 1950 ter gelegenheid van het Holland Festival 1950. Inrichters van de tentoonstelling Bert Bakker, et al.] Catalogus uitg. onder auspicien van Litterair paspoort. [Amsterdam, Meulenhoff, 1950]

Le Littéraire
see
Le Figaro littéraire.

Litterarhistorische forschungen
see
Literarhistorische forschungen.

Litteraria historica Slovaca. roč. 1/2; 1946/47. Bratislava, Slovenská akadémia vied a umení.
384 p. 26 cm.
Bibliographical footnotes.

1. Slovak literature—Addresses, essays, lectures. I. Slovenská akadémia vied a umení, Bratislava.
PG5003.L5 57-58098

IU CSt CaBVaU OrU OrPS
NL 0409507 DLC NN OU DDO CtY CLU NIC TxU ICU NcU

053 LITH Litteraria Hungarica. 1.Jahrg.
1941
Budapest, Königl. Ung. Universitätsdruckerei.
v. 25cm. quarterly.
"Herausgegeben vom Landesverbande der Ungarischen Wissenschaftlichen Gesellschaften und Institute."

NL 0409508 IU

Litterarische ...
see also Literarische ...

Litterarische Analekten
see under Wolf, Friedrich August, 1759-1824.

VOLUME 336

ZW 1 W816 Litterarische Annalen der gesammten Heilkunde. 1.-24. Bd.; 1825-32. Berlin, T. C. F. Enslin.
24 v.
Continued by Wissenschaftliche Annalen der gesammten Heilkunde.
Edited by J. F. K. Hecker.
1. Medicine - abstracts I. Hecker, Justus Friedrich Karl, 1795-1850, ed.

NL 0409511 DNLM

Litterarische Annalen der Geschichtkunde in und ausser Teutschland...
1786

Bayreuth: J. A. Lübecks Erben, 1786 19cm.
v.

Bimonthly?
Supersedes Historische Litteratur.
Edited by J. G. Meusel.
United with Historisch-litterarisches Magazin to form Historisch-litterarisch-bibliographisches Magazin.

1. History—Bibl.—Per. and soc. publ. I. Meusel, Johann Georg, 1743-1820, ed.
N. Y. P. L. October 20, 1937

NL 0409512 NN IU

Litterarische beilage zur Paedagogischen zeitung
see
Paedagogische zeitung

Das Litterarische Berlin
see under Dahms, Gustav, 1853-1901.

AP30 .L77 Litterarische blætter 1.-6.bd. 13.märz,1802-8.juni,1805... Nürnberg,J.L.S.Lechner,1802-05.
6 v.in 3. plates. 22x18cm. weekly.
No more published.
Vol.3-6 have added t.-p.:Neuer oder fortgesetzter allgemeiner literarischer anzeiger.

NL 0409515 ICU PU

Zg All 785l Litterarische Chronik. 1.- Bd. Bern,Haller,1785-
18cm.

NL 0409516 CtY CU IU

Das Litterarische echo
see
Die Literatur ...

Der litterarische eilbote für Teutschland...1810; hrsg. von J. G. Pahl.

Gmünd, [1810?]

3420.592

NL 0409518 NjP

Litterarische Gesellschaft Masovia.
Mitteilungen. 1815-
Lötzen,
v. illus. 23 cm. annual.

Title varies: Vol. 1 published by the society under its earlier name: Verein für Kunde Masurens, as Beiträge zur Kunde von Masuren.

1. Masurenland.

DD491.O7L5 57-53659 ‡

NL 0409519 DLC MH IU

Das litterarische Leipzig. Illustriertes handbuch der schriftsteller- und gelehrtenwelt, der presse und des verlagsbuchhandels in Leipzig. Leipzig, W. Fiedler, 1897.
298, [1] p. ports. 22½cm.

Contents.—1. Widmung.—2. Einleitung.—3. Die dichtung und ihre vertreter.—4. Die presse und ihre vertreter.—5. Die wissenschaft und ihre vertreter.—6. Das litterarische und journalistische vereinswesen.—7. Der Leipziger verlagbuchhandel.—8. Nachtrag.—Generalregister.

1. Leipzig—Bio-bibl. 2. Authors, German. 3. Poets, German. 4. Press—Leipzig. 5. Booksellers and bookselling—Germany.

Library of Congress Z2244.L5L7 G—36

NL 0409520 DLC NcU CSt CtY

Litterarische Mittheilungen; Festschrift
see under Literatur-Archiv-Gesellschaft, Berlin.

Eine litterarische Reise durch Deutschland.
Berlin, Erkstein [1894 ?]
32 p. 8°. [Neue Litterarische Volkshefte. Nr. 9]

NL 0409522 MB

Litterarische Spiessruthen; oder, Die hochadligen und berüchtigten Xenien
see under [Schiller, Johann Christoph Friedrich von] 1759-1805.

Das litterarische Urteil und anderes. Im Interesse des Publikums, der Autoren und Buchhändler. Ungeschminkte Wahrheiten von einem Buchhändler... Spandau, Neugebauer, 1889. 69 p. 19cm.

1. Criticism, Literary. 2. Book sellers and book trade. 3. Juvenile literature—Hist. and crit. I. Ein Buchhändler.
N. Y. P. L. December 24, 1946

NL 0409524 NN

---

*6874.1
Litterarische Volkshefte. Gemeinverständliche Aufsätze über litterarische Fragen der Gegenwart. Herausgegeben unter Mitwirkung der Herren Georg Brandes, Bulthaupt, Moritz-Carrière u. a. von Eugen Wolff und Leo Berg.
Berlin. Eckstein. [1887]-89. 10 parts in 1 v. 8°.
Contents. — 1. Oscar Blumenthal der Dichter des deutschen Theaters und der deutschen Presse, von Eugen Wolff. 2. Henrik Ibsen und das Germanenthum in der modernen Litteratur, von Leo Berg. 3. Julius Wolffe und die "moderne Minnepoesie, von Julius Hart. 4. Dumas, Sardou und die jetzige Franzosenherrschaft auf der deutschen Bühne, von Heinrich Bulthaupt. 5. Die jüngste deutsche Litteraturströmung, von Eugen Wolff. 6. Was kann die Dichtung für die moderne Welt noch bedeuten? von Wolfgang Kirchbach. 7. Ernst von Wildenbruch und das Preussenthum in der modernen Litteratur, von Leo Berg. 8. Was kann das deutsche Volk von Richard Wagner lernen? von Max Koch. 9. Theodor Storm und der moderne Realismus, von Alfred Biese. 10. Émile Zola, von Georg Brandes.

NL 0409525 MB DLC

Die Litterarische Welt. 1946-
Wien, W. Frick.
v. illus. 25 cm. quarterly.
Editor: 1946- L. W. Rochowanski.

I. Rochowanski, Leopold Wolfgang, 1885- ed.

AP30.L75 053 48-23161*

NL 0409526 DLC PU NN MH IU NNC NjP CtY

Litterarischer ...
see also Literarischer ...

Litterarischer anzeiger für christliche theologie und wissenschaft überhaupt. Hrsg. von dr. A. Tholuck. 1. jan. 1830-31. dec. 1849. Halle, Anton & Gelbcke [etc.] 1830-49.
20 v. in 10. 25½cm.
Issued every 4 or 5 days.
No more published.

1. Theology—Period. I. *Tholuck, August, 1799-1877, ed.
10-19579
Library of Congress BR4.L5

NL 0409528 DLC RPB CSt OO

Z1007 .L77 Litterarischer merkur;kritisches und bibliographisches wochenblatt. 1- jahrg. Weimar [etc.]1880-
v. illus. 28½cm.(v.1-4:24½cm.)

Irregular,1880/81-1887/88.
Subtitle varies.
1880/81 pub.in Berlin.

NL 0409529 ICU

Litterarischer Monats-Bericht.
Litterarischer Monats-Bericht über neue Erscheinungen auf dem Gesammtgebiete der Elektrotechnik und des Beleuchtungswesens einschliesslich verwandter Zweige. [Steglitz-Berlin, 1901-.]
Continued from v. 1. May, 1901. 28cm.
Caption-title.
No index.

NL 0409530 ICJ

Litterarischer sachverstændigen-verein fuer den Koenigl. Preussischen staat
see
Prussia. Literarische sachverstaendigen-kammer.

Litterarischer Verein in Stuttgart
see
Literarischer Verein in Stuttgart.

Litterarischer verein "Minerva," Leipzig.

Internationale literatur- und musikberichte ... 1.- jahrg.; apr. 1894-
Leipzig, C. F. Müller [etc.] 1894-

VOLUME 336

LITTERARISCHER wegweiser fürs evangelische pfarrhaus.. Herausgegeben von ?. Stöckicht. Gratisgabe für die abonnenten der homiletischen zeitschrift Mancherlei gaben und ein geist "[Jahrg.I.] nr. 1-4; II:no.1-4." [Wistaden.] [1883]-84.

Vols. 2.

NL 0409534 MH-AH

Litterarisches ...
see also Literarisches ...

Literarisches Archiv der Akademie zu Bern
see under Bern. Akademie.

Litterarisches leben des königlich-baierischen geheimen rathes und ritters Anton von Klein, mit rückblicken auf die schönste und wichtigste epoche der deutschen, besonders der Pfälzischen litteratur. Wiesbaden, Schellenberg, 1818.
156 p.

NL 0409537 OClW

053 LITM Litterarisches Magazin von Böhmen und Mähren. 1.-3. Stück. Prag, Schönfeld, 1786-87. 3v. 18cm.

"Herausgegeben von Joseph Dobrowsky."

NL 0409538 IU

Litterarum societas esthonica
see
Tartu. Ülikool. Õpetatud eesti selts.

The Litterateur. Akron, O., Chi Delta Phi, 192

NbHi has vol.8 no.1 (Nov.1931); vol.12 no.2 (Jan.1937)

NL 0409540 NbHi

Un littérateur américain George Ticknow [Lausanne, 1877]
see under [Circourt, Adolphe Marie Pierre de count] 1801-1879.

Le Littérateur français. v. 1

Boston [M. W. H. S. Jordan, etc.] 18
v. 33cm. weekly.

CA 11-2095 Unrev'd

Library of Congress AP21.L5

NL 0409542 DLC CtY MB

Litteratur ...
see also Literatur ...

Die Litteratur der geonäischen Zeit
see under [Kaminka, Armand] 1866-1950.

Litteratur der musik, oder Anleitung zur kentnis der vorzüglichen musikalischen bücher
see under [Gruber, Johann Sigmund] 1759-1805.

Litteratur der musik, oder Systematische anleitung zur kenntnis der vorzüglichen musikalischen bücher
see under Gruber, Johann Sigmund, 1759-1805.

ZSF 615 L777 1858-89 Die Litteratur der Veterinärwissenschaft und der Hilfswissenschaften von 1858-1. Apr. 1889. [Berlin, R. Schoetz, 189]
94 p.

ZSF 615 L777 Suppl. —— [Fortsetzung] 1889/Apr. 1892- Berlin, R. Schoetz.
v.

NL 0409547 DNLM

Die litteratur des jahres 1892 über morphologie, systematik und verbreitung der phanerogamen nebst register. 8°. pp. [532]. Berlin, 1895.
"Sonderabdruck aus Just's Botanischen jahresbericht."

NL 0409548 MBH TU

Litteratur, konst, teater. 1945-48. Helsingfors, H. Schildts förlag, 1945-48. 4 v. illus. 25cm.

Quarterly (slightly irregular).
Edited by Ole Torvalds.
No more published.

1. Periodicals—Finland. I. Torvalds, Ole Torvald Elis, 1916- ed.
N. Y. P. L. May 3, 1950

NL 0409549 NN

P 2085 .L 7 1931 Litteratur og kritik af i dag. En radio-debat mellem Richardt Gandrup, Hartvig Frisch, Henning Kehler [og] Bertel Budtz-Müller. København, Levin & Munksgaards forlag, 1931.
77 p. 23cm.

1. Literature - Addresses, essays, lectures. 2. Criticism - Addresses, essays, lectures. I. Gandrup, Richardt, 1885- II. Frisch, Hartvig, 1893-1950. III. Kehler, Henning, 1891- IV. Budtz Müller, Bertel, 1890-1946.

NL 0409550 MdBJ CU

809 qL718 LITTERATUR og sprog af Alfred Bindslev, J. Byskov, Th. Døssing [och andra] Odense, Skandinavisk bogforlag a/s [1939]

346 p. illus., ports. 27cm.
(Added t.-p.: Alverdens viden om naturen og menneskelivet; dansk kultur-bibliotek. III)

1. Literature. Hist. & crit.

NL 0409551 MnU

Litteratur-Recensioner; från den Kristna ungdomens litteraturnämnd.
årg. 1

Stockholm: E. Westerbergs boktryckeri, 1936 25cm.
v.

Semimonthly (irregular).

1. Bibliography, Swedish—Per. and soc. publ. I. Kristna ungdomens litteraturnämnd, Stockholm.
N. Y. P. L. December 7, 1938

NL 0409552 NN

Litteratur-revue. v.1-2, no.13; Oct. 1, 1887-Dec. 29, 1888. Copenhagen.
2v. weekly.

In English, French and German.

NL 0409553 ICRL IU

Litteratur-tidende.
Kjobenhavn, 1811-36.
26 vols. 8vo.

NL 0409554 NN

X Per L777T Litteratur-tidning. 1.-3. bd.; 1795-97. Stockholm, G. A. Silfverstolpe.
3 v. 18 cm. 4 no. a year.

I. Silfverstolpe, Gustaf Abraham, 1772-1824.

NL 0409555 NcD NN MnU

PN29 S25 no.13 Litteratur-tolkning. Debattinlägg av Martin S. Allwood [et al] Stockholm, H. Geber [1948]
98 p. (Skrifter utg. av Samfundet för stilforskning. 13)

1. Literature - Aesthetics. 2. Criticism - Addresses, essays, lectures. I. Allwood, Martin Samuel, 1916-

NL 0409556 CU MH

Litteratur- und theater-zeitung.
Berlin, A. Wever, 17
v. 18½-20cm. weekly.

Each year in four parts with separate title-pages. Paging continuous.
C. A. von Bertram, editor.

1. Theater — Period. 2. Theater — Germany — Period. 3. Literature — Period. I. Bertram, Christian August von, ed.

CA 12-795 Unrev'd

Library of Congress ML48.S4772

NL 0409557 DLC NjP MdBJ CU

VOLUME 336

Litteraturblad för allmän medborgerlig bildning.
Årgång

Helsingfors, 18 4°, 8°.
v.

Monthly.
Ceased publication in 1863.

1. Periodicals—Finland.
N. Y. P. L. May 15, 1930

NL 0409558 NN CtY

Litteratura do norte
see under Tavora, Franklin, 1842-1888.

Da litteratura dos livros de cavallarias
see under Varnhagen, Francisco Adolpho de, visconde de Porto Seguro, 1816-1878.

Littérature. Paris
see its later title Plaisir de lire.

AC-LP
L718
Littérature; revue mensuelle. nº 1-20. mars 1919-août 1921; nouv. sér., nº 1-11/12, mars 1922-oct. 1923. [Paris]
32no. illus. 23cm.

Directeurs: mars 1919-août 1921, Louis Aragon, André Breton, Philippe Soupault; mars-mai 1922, André Breton & Philippe Soupault; septembre 1922-octobre 1923, André Breton.
No more published. Cf. Union list of serials, 3d ed.

NL 0409562 TxU PU

FILM
1164
PQ
Littérature; révue mensuelle. Apr.1919-Mai 1922. Paris, Levé, 1919-22.
1 reel. illus. On film (Negative)

Microfilm. Original in Univ. of Michigan Library.
No more published.

1. French literature - Period. 2. French literature - Hist. & crit. - Period.

NL 0409563 CU NN NcU MH

..La Littérature à Lyon depuis le XVIe siècle jusqu'à nos jours. Lyon [Audin] 1920.
139 p. 19 cm. (Société des études locales dans l'enseignement public. Section lyonnaise. Publications. 3)

Bibliography: p.5-6; "Bibliographie" at the end of each chapter.

1.French literature-Hist.& crit.
2.French literature-Lyons.

NL 0409564 NjP ICN

La LITTÉRATURE anglaise traduite en français. [Paris, La maison des amis des livres, 1925].

Without title-page. Caption title.
Half-title: Bibliographie.
Appended: Bibliographie. La littérature. américaine traduite en français.
Cut from LE NAVIRE D'ARGENT. No.1 etc.1925.

NL 0409565 MH

La littérature arabe
see under Bordeaux. Université. Faculté des Lettres.

La Littérature canadienne de 1850 à 1860. Publiée par la direction du "Foyer canadien." Québec, Desbarats et Derbishire [etc.] 1863-64.
2 v. 21½cm.

1-27264—M 2

NL 0409567 DLC CaBVaU CU NN CtY

Littérature de choc.

[Paris] Gallimard.
Editor : v. 4 Maurice Thorez.

x Thorez, Maurice, 1900- , ed.

NL 0409568 NN

LITTÉRATURE des dames; ou, Morceaux choisis des meilleurs auteurs anciens et modernes. Paris, Le Fuel [18--] 252 p. illus. 14cm.

1. Literature--Collections.

NL 0409569 NN

Littérature du dialecte alsacien
see under [Mohr, Louis] 1828-1886.

... Littérature espagnole
see under [Jubinal, Achille] 1810-1875.

PH307
f.L77
Littérature et beaux-arts en Finlande... Helsingfors, Impr. F. Tilgmann, 1900.
[1], 110 p. illus. (incl. ports.) 33½cm.
Extrait de l'ouvrage illustré "La Finlande au 19me siècle."

CONTENTS.—Les belles-lettres: La littérature suedoise en Finlande, par C. G. Estlander. La littérature finnoise en Finlande, par E. Aspelin. La presse périodique, par Valfrid Vasenius.—Les beaux-arts: Les arts plastiques, par J. J. Tikkanen. La musique, par R. F. von Willebrand. L'art scénique, par Werner Söderhjelm.

1. Swedish-Finnish literature. 2. Finnish literature—Hist. & crit. 3. Art, Finnish.

NL 0409572 ICU MH NjP

Littérature française, publiée sous la direction de Joseph Bédier [et] Paul Hazard. Nouv. éd. refondue et augm. sous la direction de Pierre Martino. Paris, Larousse [1948-49]
2 v. illus. (part col.) ports. 30 cm.

Previously published under title: Histoire de la littérature française, illustrée.

1. French literature—Hist. & crit. I. Bédier, Joseph, 1864-1938, ed.

PQ101.H52 840.9 50-24609 rev

PSt MsU CLSU
CU-I CoU NcRS WaS ViU NcU NbU CU-S MU ICU GAT
CSf OCU InStme PSC C CU OO TxU OClJC FTaSU MB
PBm FMU NjP CU CtY NN IU PU TU NNC MiU OU NBC
NNU-W RPB OClW IdU CaBVaU OrCS OU PPLas OClMA
NL 0409573 DLC CSt WaSpG IdPI OrU MH KMK IEN ICN

La littérature française contemporaine, 1827-1849
see Quérard, Joseph Marie, 1797-1865.
La littérature française contemporaine.
XIX siècle. v. 5-6.

La littérature française contemporaine, recueil en prose et en vers
see under [Leypoldt, Frederick] 1835-1884, comp.

PQ116
L5
1906
Littérature française depuis ses origines jusqu'à nos jours [par] J. M. J. A. 13. éd. Paris, C. Poussielgue, 1906.
vii, 634 p. (Histoire des littératures anciennes et modernes ... [2])

At head of title: Alliance des maisons d'éducation chrétienne.

1. French literature - Hist. & crit. I. A., J. M. J.

NL 0409576 CU

Littérature Française depuis ses origines jusqu'à nos jours; ouvrage approuvé et recommandé par Mgr. l'Evêque de Nantes; couronné par la Société libre d'instruction et d'éducation; trentieme ed. Paris. J. de Gigord, 1921.
vii, 634 p.

NL 0409577 PPLas

La Littérature internationale
see La Littérature sovietique.

Littérature juridique de la Finland
see
Suomen lainopillinen kirjallisuus.

... Littérature officielle sous la Commune ... Paris: Librairie des bibliophiles, 1871. 140 p. 19cm. (Documents sur les événements de 1870-71.)

"Les principaux articles littéraires, publiés par l'organe officiel de l'insurrection."

J. S. BILLINGS MEM. COLL.
949721A. 1. Paris—Hist.—Commune, 1871. Journal officiel. 2. Paris—Hist.—Commune, 1871—Sources. I. Paris.
N. Y. P. L. December 20, 1938

NL 0409580 NN MnU IaU N NcD MH

VOLUME 336

Littérature orale de la Picardie; contes secrets. Paris, H. Welter, 1907-
v. 16 cm.
Extrait de Κρυπτάδια, vol. 10-
On spine, v. 1- Contes picards.

1. Tales, French—Picardy. I. Title: Contes secrets. II. Title: Contes picards.
GR162.P5L5 55-51420 ‡

NL 0409581 DLC CtY

LITTÉRATURE orale de la Savoie. Proverbes, devinettes, contes, etc. *Annecy: J. Dépollier et cie.* 1882. 32 pp. 16°.

NL 0409582 MB MH

Litterature orale et traditions du Nivernais
see under Millien, Achille, 1838-1927.

La littérature renversée, ou L'art de faire des pièces de théatre sans paroles
see under [Nougaret, Pierre Jean Baptiste] 1742-1823.

PQ1304 .L8 [Littérature romane. Recueil de pièces du 13eme siècle. Paris,1834-38]
12 pam.in 1 v. fold.facsim. 21½cm.

Binder's title.
Each pamphlet has special t.-p.

1.French literature-Old French.

NL 0409585 ICU

La Littérature soviétique. -1958. Moscou.
v. in illus., ports. 23 cm. monthly.
Began publication in 1931. Cf. Union list of serials.
Vols. for -no. 5, 1948, called also "année -18."
"Revue de l'Union des écrivains de l'U. R. S. S." no. 9, 1956-1958.
Title varies: La Littérature internationale.
Issued also in English.
Publishers vary.
Superseded in 1959 by Œuvres et opinions.

I. Soiûz pisateleĭ SSSR. II. La Littérature internationale.
AP25.L5 48-35179 rev*

NL 0409586 DLC NN MiU

Littérature tamoule ancienne
see under [Vinson, Julian] 1843-1926, ed. and tr.

PN9 .L588 Litteraturen; nordens kritiske revue. 1.-arg.;Apr. 1918-
København, G.E.C. Gads forlag.
v.

1.Literature - Hist.& crit.- Period.
2.Scandinavian literature - Hist. & crit.- Period.

NL 0409588 NcU MiU KU

890.9 L777 Die Litteraturen des Ostens in Einzeldarstellungen. 1.-10. Bd.
Leipzig, Amelang, 1901-09.
10v.

Bd. 9, Nr.2-3 published 1913-20.

1. Arabic literature--Hist. & crit. 2. Byzantine literature--Hist. & crit. 3. Greek literature, Modern--Hist. & crit. 4. Persian literature--Hist. & crit. 5. Turkish literature-- Hist. & crit.

NL 0409589 ICarbS CtNIC NjP DLC OO

Litteraturen i Danmark, og de øvrige nordiske lande. Hvem skrev hvad før 1914? Redigeret af Henning Fonsmark. København, Politikens forlag, 1954.
510 p. illus., ports. 18 cm. (Politikens håndbøger nr. 51)
Bibliography: p. 506-507.

1. Scandinavian literature—Hist. & crit. 2. Finnish literature—Hist. & crit. 3. Authors, Scandinavian. 4. Authors, Finnish. I. Title: Hvem skrev hvad før 1914? II. Fonsmark, Henning B., ed.
PT7060.L5 55-28074

NL 0409590 DLC MnU NN CU MH PU OCl

Les Littératures de l'Orient. t. 1-
Paris, Maisonneuve, 1876-
v. 25 cm.

NL 0409591 NcD NN

808.8 L777 Les littératures populaires de toutes les nations. Traditions, legends, contes, chansons, proverbes, devinettes, superstitions. Paris, Maisonneuve, 1881-1892.
30v.

Contents.- t.1. Littérature orale de la Haute-Bretagne.- t.2-3. Legendes chretiennes de la Basse Bretagne.- t.4. Contes Egyptiens.- t.5-7. Poésies populaires de La Gascogne.-

t.8. Hitopadésa.- t.9-10. Haute Bretagne.- t.11. Littérature oral de la Basse-Normandie.- t.12. Gargantua dans les traditions populaires.- t.13. Littérature orale de la Picardie.- t.14. Times et jeux de l'enfance.- t.15. Folk-lore du pays Basque.- t.16. Contes populaires de la Corse.- t.17-18. Chansons populaires d'Alsace.- t.19-21.

Contes populaires de la Gascogne.- t.22. Coutumes populaires de la Haute-Bretagne.- t.23. Traditions indiennes du Canada nord-Ouest.- t.24-26. Contes populaires de Basse-Bretagne.- t.27. t.28. Traditions populaires de l'Asie Mineure.- t.29. t.30. Six nouvelles nouvelles.

NL 0409594 FTaSU

Les littératures populaires de toutes les nations; traditions, légendes, contes, chansons, proverbs, devinettes, superstitions. 47v. Paris, J. Maisonneuve, 1881-1902.

Imprint varies slightly; v.47 has imprint: Paris, E. Guilmoto.

MiU UU
NL 0409595 OCl NjP MH ICarbS MiD FTaSU DCU DLC

Scattered
Les **Littératures** populaires de toutes les nations. Traductions, légendes, contes, chansons, proverbes, devinettes, superstitions. Série in-8° raisin.
Tome 1

Paris: Maisonneuve frères, 1931 25cm.
v.

Contents:
Tome 1. Creangă, I. Contes populaires de Roumanie (Poveşti) ... 1931.

1. No subject.
N. Y. P. L. December 16, 1932

NL 0409596 NN OO

Litteraturhandboken, ny utökad uppl. av Vem skrev vad? [Redaktion: Jan Cornell och Bengt Olof Vos. Stockholm, Forum [1952]
607 p. illus., ports. 17 cm. (När-var-hur-serien)
"Den utökade upplagan redigerad av Gunvor Grenholm."

1. Literature—Hist. & crit. I. Cornell, Jan, ed. II. Vos, Bengt Olof, ed. III. Grenholm, Gunvor, ed. IV. Title: Vem skrev vad.
PN574.V4 1952 54-28727

NL 0409597 DLC MnU CSt CU NNU

Litterer, Mirosława.
Zmiany w rozmieszczeniu i strukturze ludności Polski Ludowej w latach 1946 do 1950. Bogusław Welpa. Zagadnienie struktury wieku ludności Polski Ludowej w roku 1950. [Wyd. 1.] Warszawa, Państwowe Wydawn. Naukowe, 1955.
112 p. maps, diagrs., tables. 25 cm. (Polska Akademia Nauk. Instytut Geografii. Prace geograficzne)
Titles also in Russian and English; summaries in Russian and English.

1. Poland—Statistics, Vital. I. Welpa, Bogusław. Zagadnienie struktury wieku ludności Polski Ludowej w roku 1950. II. Title.
HB3608.7.L5 57-18856

NL 0409598 DLC MiU GU MnU NN NcD

Litterer, Oscar F
The Missouri Basin development program; a background study reveals its mammoth proportions and its great potentialities. [Minneapolis] Federal Reserve Bank of Minneapolis [1953]
23 p. illus. 27 cm.
Bibliographical footnotes.

1. Water resources development—Missouri Valley. I. Title.
HD1695.M5L5 54-37285 ‡

NL 0409599 DLC IU MiD NNC ODW NN N MtBC DNAL

HN79 .A172L5 Litterer, Oscar F
Missouri basin development program. [Minneapolis?] 1953.
103 p. illus.

1. Water resources development - Missouri Valley. 2. Regional planning - Missouri Valley. I. Title

NL 0409600 NbU OrU NIC

---

286 L712 Litterer, Oscar F
The Ninth District's stake in world trade. Minneapolis, 1949.
31 p.

1. European recovery program. 2. Tariff. U.S. 3. U.S. Commerce. I. Federal Reserve Bank of Minneapolis. II. Title: World trade.

NL 0409601 DNAL

VOLUME 336

658
L71w
Litterer, Oscar F
Where does small business obtain its capital? Minneapolis, Federal Reserve Bank, 1948.
18p. tables. 22cm.

1. Business. 2. Capital. I. Federal Reserve Bank of Minneapolis. II. Title.

NL 0409602 IU MH-BA OCU NN PPFRB

332.7
L718
Litterer, Oscar F
Where does small business obtain its capital? Minneapolis, Federal Reserve Bank, 1949.
iv,18p. illus. 24cm.

1. Credit. U.S. I. Title.

NL 0409603 OrU

Litterer-Marwege, Wanda.
Nowe osiedla mieszkaniowe i ich mieszkańcy. Warszawa, Polskie Wydawn. Gospodarcze, 1952.
208 p. illus. 21 cm. (Biblioteka Instytutu Budownictwa Mieszkaniowego, t. 3)
At head of title: Wanda Litterer.

1. Apartment houses—Poland. I. Title.

HD7287.6.P7L55 68-46846

NL 0409604 DLC

Litterick, James , 1901-
Whither Manitoba?; speech delivered in the Manitoba legislature on February 24th, 1937. [Tor. New Era pub.]n.d.
32p.port.sq.S.

NL 0409605 CaBViP

Litteris; an international critical review of the humanities. v. 1–7; Sept. 1924–Dec. 1930. [Lund, The Berling press, 1924–31]
7 v. 24½cm. 3 nos. a year.
Published 1924–25, at Lund, by the New society of letters.
Edited by S. B. Liljegren, Lauritz Weibull and others.
Some reviews in English, some in French, some in German.
No more published.

1. Humanities—Bibl.—Period. 2. Books—Reviews. I. Liljegren, Sten Bodvar, 1885- ed. II. Weibull, Lauritz Ulrik Absalon, 1873- ed. III. Vetenskaps-societeten i Lund.

26-542 Revised

Library of Congress Z1007.L774

NL 0409606 DLC NIC NcD OCU OU MiU OClW NN

I
747
.948
LITTERS, JONAS.
Catalogus rectorum, et illustrium virorum archigymnasii Viennensis: in quo præter elegantissimam temporum seriem, summa quædam continentur, quasi capita earum rerum, quæ celeberrimæ huic Academiæ sub cujusq; magistratu, memoriâ contigerunt dignæ. Ab anno MCCXXXVII. vsque ad annum MDCXLIV. inclusive. Viennæ, Austriæ, Typis M.Rictii,1645.
113p. 20cm.

NL 0409607 ICN MH

LITTERSCHEID, Franz.
Beiträge zur kenntnis der anagyris-alkaloide. Inaug.diss. Marburg, 1899.

NL 0409608 MH-C

Litterscheid, Franz.
Die Erkennung der Haare unserer Haussäugetiere und einiger Wildarten. Eine praktische Einführung in die einfache Methodik der mikroskopischen Tierhaaruntersuchungen mit einem Bestimmungsschlüssel und 16 Tafeln nach Handzeichnungen, von Dr. Franz Litterscheid, ... und Dr. Hans Lambardt, ... Hamm (Westf.), Reimann & Co., 1921.
32 p. illus., XVI pl. in pocket. 30cm.
"Literaturverzeichnis," p. 27.

NL 0409609 ICJ

Litterscheid, Franz, composer.
Lebewohl. [Männerchor.] Op. 30.
Leipzig. Siegel. [1890?] 3 pp. [Leichte und volkstümliche Chorgesänge für Männerstimmen.] L. 8°.

E3575 — Part songs. — T.r. April 11, 1902.

NL 0409610 MB

Litterscheid, Franz, composer.
Ma Schätzerl [T. T. B. B.]. Op. 29.
Leipzig. Siegel. [1890?] 3 pp. [Leichte und volkstümliche Chorgesänge für Männerstimmen.] L. 8°.

E3576 — T.r. — Part songs. April 11, 1902.

NL 0409611 MB

Litterscheid, Franz, composer.
Der Nibelungenhort [T. T. B. B.]. Mit Solo-Quartett [T. T. B. B.]. Op. 45.
Leipzig. Siegel. [189-?] 5 pp. [Konzertgesänge für Männerchor. 6.] L. 8°.

E3576 — T.r. — Part songs. April 11, 1902.

NL 0409612 MB

ML410
.W8L5
Litterscheid, Richard, 1904–
Hugo Wolf, von dr. Richard Litterscheid, mit 15 notenbeispielen und 20 abbildungen. Potsdam, Akademische verlagsgesellschaft Athenaion [©1939]
2 p. l., 124 p. illus. (music) plates, ports., facsims. (incl. music) 19½cm. (*Added t.-p.:* Unsterbliche tonkunst; lebens- und schaffensbilder grosser musiker, hrsg. ... von dr. habil. Herbert Gerigk)
"Werkverzeichnis": p. 119–120. "Literaturhinweis": p. 120–121.

1. *Wolf, Hugo, 1860–1903.

[*Full name:* Richard Ludwig Theodor Litterscheid]

A 41-2759

New York. Public library
for Library of Congress [2]

NL 0409613 NN DLC InU IU MH PP MB

Litterscheid, Richard, 1904- ed.

ML410
.B8
A3215
Brahms, Johannes, 1833–1897.
Johannes Brahms in seinen schriften und briefen, eingeleitet und mit biographischen und kritischen erläuterungen versehen von dr. Richard Litterscheid. Mit 64 abbildungen auf 32 tafeln und 40 notenbeispielen. Berlin, B. Hahnefeld [©1943]

ML279
.8
.E77M8
Litterscheid, Richard, 1904- ed.

Essen. Musikfest, 1938.
Musikfest der stadt Essen vom 12. bis 17. märz 1938. Festschrift, aus anlass des 100jährigen bestehens des Essener städtischen musikvereins ... herausgegeben vom Stadtamt für kunst, Essen ... Essen, Druck: National-zeitung [1938]

LITTERSCHEID, Richard, 1904-
Zur geschichte des Basso ostinato. Inaug.-diss. Marburg, druck von K.Strauch, Dortmund, 1928.

pp.76-.
"Literaturverzeichnis",pp.73-76.
"Lebenslauf",at end.

NL 0409616 MH DLC CtY

LITTERSCHEIDT, Franz.
Die hinterlegung zum zwecke der schuldbefreiung. Köln, n.d. [1906?].

8°. 38 p.
Inaug.-diss. — Jena.

NL 0409617 MH-L NN ICRL

Litterski (Stephan). Ueber die Auflösbarkeit der rothen Blutkörperchen abhängig von ihrem Gasgehalte. 27 pp. 8°. *Greifswald, F. W. Kunike,* 1875.

NL 0409618 DNLM ICRL

Littey, Janvier.
Reponse de Janvier Littey, Homme de couleur de la Martinique... [Paris, 1794]
Bd. with Affaires des colonies, v. 10, pam. 4

NL 0409619 RPJCB

Litthauer (Carolus) [1836-]. * De apoplexiæ ischæmicæ et sanguineæ diagnosi. 32 pp. 8°. *Berolini, G. Lange,* [1860].

NL 0409620 DNLM

Litthauer, F
Allgemeines deutsches Handelsgesetzbuch. Text-Ausg. mit Anmerkungen, von F. Litthauer. Allgemeine deutsche Wechselordnung. Text-Ausg. mit Anmerkungen, von S. Borchardt. Berlin, J. Guttentag, 1871.
viii, 248, 54 p. 13 cm. (Deutsche Reichsgesetzgebung. Text-Ausgaben mit Anmerkungen)
Each part has special t.-p.
Both laws originated as models for the member states of the German Confederation and were adopted successively by the North German Confederation and the German Reich. Cf. Litthauer, F. Allg. deut. Handelsgesetzbuch. 1890. p. 1–17; Gr. Brockhaus, 16th ed. v. 5, p. 236. v. 20, p. 88–89.

1. Commercial law—Germany. I. Borchardt, Siegfried Max, d. 1880. Allgemeine deutsche Wechselordnung. II. Germany. Laws, statutes, etc. Allgemeines deutsches Handelsgesetzbuch. III. Germany. Laws, statutes, etc. Allgemeine deutsche Wechselordnung. IV. Title. V. Title: Allgemeine deutsche Wechselordnung. (Series)

42-45557 rev

NL 0409622 DLC

VOLUME 336

4K-531 Litthauer, F.
Allgemeines deutsches Handelsgesetzbuch, nebst Einführungs- und Ergänzungs-Gesetzen unter Ausschluss des Seerechts. Text-Ausg. mit Anmerkungen, den von dem Reichs-Oberhandelsgericht zu Leipzig angenommenen Rechtsgrundsätzen und Sachregister; hrsg. von F. Litthauer. 3. Aufl. Berlin, J. Guttentag, 1875.
439 p. (Deutsche Reichsgesetzgebung. Text-Ausgaben mit Anmerkungen)

NL 0409623 DLC-P4

Litthauer, F
Allgemeines deutsches Handelsgesetzbuch nebst Einführungs- und Ergänzungs-Gesetzen, unter Ausschluss des Seerechts. Text-Ausgabe mit Anmerkungen, den von dem Reichsgericht und dem früheren Reichs-Oberhandelsgericht angenommenen Rechtsgrundsätzen und Sachregister. Hrsg. von F. Litthauer. Berlin: J. Guttentag, 1883. vii, 544 p. 5. ed. half clo. 24°. (Deutsche Reichsgesetzgebung.)

1. Statutes, Germany.—Codes (Commercial). 2. Litthauer, F.
N. Y. P. L. July 8, 1914.

NL 0409624 NN

KD1313 Litthauer, F
.3 Allgemeines deutsches Handelsgesetzbuch nebst
.A2L74 Einführungs- und Ergänzungsgesetzen unter Ausschluss des Seerechts. ... hrsg. von F. Litthauer. 5.Aufl. Berlin, Guttentag, 1885.
vii. 655. (Deutsche Reichsgesetzgebung, Nr.4)

1. Commercial law--Germany. I. Litthauer, F ed.

NL 0409625 ICU

Litthauer, F
Allgemeines deutsches handelsgesetzbuch nebst einführungs- und ergänzungsgesetzen unter ausschluss des seerechts. 6e aufl. Berlin, etc., J. Guttentag, 1886.

24°.
(Guttentag'sche sammlung deutscher reichsgesetze, 4.).

NL 0409626 MH-L

Litthauer, F
Allgemeines deutsches Handelsgesetzbuch, nebst Einführungs- und Ergänzungsgesetzen unter Ausschluss des Seerechts. Text-Ausg. mit Anmerkungen, den von dem Reichsgericht und dem früheren Reichs-Oberhandelsgericht angenommenen Rechtsgrundsätzen und Sachregister. Hrsg. von F. Litthauer. 7. Aufl. Berlin, J. Guttentag, 1890.
vii, 604 p. 13 cm. (Guttentag'sche Sammlung deutscher Reichsgesetze, Nr. 4)
Commentary, with text, on articles 1-431 of the Allgemeines deutsches Handelsgesetzbuch as valid in the German Empire.
1. Commercial law—Germany. I. Germany. Laws, statutes, etc. Allgemeines deutsches Handelsgesetzbuch. Articles 1-431. II. Title.
33-29699 rev

NL 0409627 DLC

LITTHAUER, F.
Allgemeines deutsches handelsgesetzbuch nebst einführungs-und ergänzungsgesetzen unter ausschluss des seerechts. 8. aufl. Berlin, 1894.

24°.
Guttentag'sche sammlung deutscher reichsgesetze, Nr. 4."

NL 0409628 MH-L

Litthauer, F. FOR OTHER EDITIONS SEE MAIN ENTRY
Germany. *Laws, statutes, etc.*
... Handelsgesetzbuch (ohne seerecht). Mit den ergänzenden vorschriften des Bürgerlichen gesetzbuchs und einem anhang enthaltend das Einführungsgesetz, das Depotgesetz, die bestimmungen über börsentermin- und differenzgeschäfte u. a., nebst erläuterungen. Im anschluss an die textausgabe von F. Litthauer. Von dr. Albert Mosse ... Neu bearb. von dr. Ernst Heymann ... 17. aufl. Unter mitwirkung von dr. Karl August Crisolli in Berlin. Berlin und Leipzig, W. de Gruyter & co., 1926.

Litthauer, F. ed. FOR OTHER EDITIONS SEE MAIN ENTRY
Germany. *Laws, statutes, etc.*
... Handelsgesetzbuch vom 10. mai 1897 unter ausschluss des seerechts. Mit den ergänzenden vorschriften des Bürgerlichen gesetzbuchs und erläuterungen herausgegeben von F. Litthauer ... 10. (der neuen fassung 1.) aufl. 2. unveränderter abdruck. Berlin, J. Guttentag, 1899.

Litthauer, F ed.
Sammlung kleinerer Reichsgesetze...
Textausg...
see under Germany. Laws, statutes, etc.

Litthauer (Heimannus) [1833-]. *De calomelane modo Mialhiano in sanguinem inducendo. 36 pp. 8°. *Berolini, G. Lange,* [1859].

NL 0409632 DNLM

Litthauer (Max) [1865-]. *Ein Beitrag zur Lehre von der Retention abgestorbener Früchte im Uterus. 29 pp., 1 l. 8°. *Berlin, G. Schade,* [1887].

NL 0409633 DNLM

Litthauer, Siegfried, 1869-
Ueber die einwirkung von phosphoniumjodid auf benzaldehyd.
Inaug.-diss.-Berlin, 1890.

NL 0409634 ICRL CtY

W 4 LITTICH, Josef, 1926-
M96 Untersuchungen über den thyreo-
1951 statischen Effekt von Thioluminal an Kaulquappen. Klinische Untersuchungen zur Behandlung von Hyperthyreosen mit Prothyrisat. München, 1951.
29 ℓ. illus.
Inaug.-Diss.- Munich.
Typewritten copy.
1. Barbiturates - Effects
2. Thyrotoxicosis - Treatment

NL 0409635 DNLM

Littig, Frank Leo, 1878-
Have you got it? Words by Daniel E. Lanza. Music by Frank Littig. Hollywood, Nordyke music publ. [c1945]
First line: Just be careful what you say.
Chorus: Have you got what we call it?

Printed for the Music Division
1. Slang phrases. 2. Personality. I. Lanza, Daniel E. II. Song index (3).
N. Y. P. L. December 2, 1947

NL 0409636 NN

Littig, Frank Leo, 1878-
How to sing, by Frank Littig ... Friend, Neb., Studio news [1945]
cover-title, 7 p. illus. (music) 23ᶜᵐ.
Reproduced from type-written and manuscript copy.

1. Singing—Methods. I. Title.
46-1166
Library of Congress MT825.L65
[2] 784.9

NL 0409637 DLC

784.8 [Littig, Frank Leo,] 1878-
L777 Littig's comic songs for ukulele or tenor banjo. Enlarged ed. Chicago, The chart music publishing house, inc. [c1929]
cover-title, 26 p. 26 cm.
Includes music.

1. Songs. I. Title: Comic songs for the ukulele or tenor banjo.

NL 0409638 LNHT

Littig, Frank Leo, 1878-
Song poem or lyric course. [2. ed.] Friend, Nebr., Studio news, 1947. 32 p. 23cm.
Cover title.

1. Language and music. 2. Music and language. 3. Song writing and publishing. 4. Songs—Writing and publishing.

NL 0409639 NN

LITTIG, FRANK Leo, 1878-
Song-writing technic for lyricists. 2. ed. [Friend, Neb., Studio news, c1946-48] 3 pts. in 1 v. mounted port. 23cm.
Microfiche (neg.) 11 x 15cm. (NYPL FSN-11, 023)
CONTENTS.--Song writing technic.--Thoro music study song poem or lyric course, by Frank Littig.--Life story of Carrie Jacobs Bond, by B. Grainger.
1. Songs--Writing and publishing. 2. Song writing and publishing.
3. Bond, Carrie (Jacobs), 1862-1946.

NL 0409640 NN

Littig, Friedrich.
Andronikos von Rhodos ... München, 1890-95.
3v. in 1. 25½cm.
Imprint varies; v. 2-3 published in Erlangen.
Vol. 1, separate, from Programm-Königliches Maximilian-gymnasium; v. 2-3, separate, from Programm-Kgl. humanistisches gymnasium in Erlangen.
1. Andronicus Rhodius.

Printed by the Wesleyan University Library, 1937

NL 0409641 CtW CSt MH NjP OClW

---

878 Littig, Friedrich
C12sCsM Die Philosophia des Georgios Pachymeres.
In: Festgruss an die XLI. Versammlung deutscher Philologen und Schulmänner von dem Lehrerkollegium des K. Maximiliansgymnasiums in München. [n.p.,] [n.d.]
1v.(various paging) 23cm.
Bound with: Melber, Johann, Der Bericht des Dio Cassius über die Gallischen Kriege Caesars.

1. Pachymeres, Georgius.

NL 0409642 NcU RPB

VOLUME 336

Littig, Kent S
Domestic flies and their control

see under

United States. Communicable disease center, Atlanta.

Mann
Microfilm
QL 508 P5 L77
Littig, Kent S 1909-
External anatomy of the Florida walking stick, Anisomorpha buprestoides Stoll. [Gainesville, 1935.
Microfilm copy of typescript. Negative. Collation of the original, as determined from the film: 39 l. illus., tables.
Thesis - University of Florida.
Vita.
Bibliography: leaves 38-39.
1. Phasmidae.

NL 0409644 NIC

LC2781 .L57
Littig, Lawrence William, 1927-
A pilot study of personality factors related to occupational aspirations of Negro college students. [n.p., n.p., n.d.]
42 l. 27cm.
At head of title: Final report.
"Vocational and Technical Education contract number OE-6-85-003. Vocational Education Act of 1963, section 4(c)"
"Project ... supported by a contract with the U. S. Department of Health, Education, and Welfare, Office of Education."

NL 0409645 NcU

Littig, Marquis D , 1871-
Descendants of Peter Littig, Godfrey Rogge and others, by M. D. Littig and collaborators. [Concord, N. H.] 1944. 40 p. illus. 21cm.
"Privately printed."

344043B. 1. Littig family. 2. Rogge family.
N. Y. P. L. July 3, 1946

NL 0409646 NN WaS OClWHi MB Or MnHi

Littig, Theodor, 1900-
...Zur blutzuckerfrage bei roentgenbestrahlung. Inaug. diss. - Freiburg, 1926.

NL 0409647 ICRL MiU CtY

Littigs' comic songs for ukulele or tenor banjo
see under Littig, Frank Leo, 1878-

Litting, George.
Consider your ways. A course of twenty-one brief sermons, or church readings, being one for each Wednesday, Friday, and Sunday, from Ash Wednesday to Easter day. By the Rev. George Litting ... London, Skeffington & son, 1894.
x, 119p. 19½cm.

NL 0409648 CtW OClW ViU

Litting, George, tr.
Childe, Edward Lee.
The life and campaigns of General Lee. By his nephew, Edward Lee Childe. Tr. from the French, with the consent and approval of the author, by George Litting ... London, Chatto and Windus, 1875.

Litting, George.
Sins worthily lamented. A course of forty-seven brief sermons or church readings, being one for each week-day and Sunday from Ash Wednesday to Easter-day. By the Rev. George Litting ... London, Skeffington & son, 1893.
xii, 174p. 19cm.

NL 0409650 CtW

Littitz, Hektor Emanuel Bubna-
see Bubna-Littitz, Hektor Emanuel.

DB 870 .L5
Littke, Aurél,
Buda-Pest a török uralom korában. Budapest, Fritz Ármin Könyvnyomdája, 1908.
49 p. 2 fold. plans.
Bibliographical footnotes.

NL 0409652 NNC

Littke, Aurél, joint author.
Cholnoky, Jenő, 1870-
A föld. A föld multja, jelene és felfedezésének története. Irták Cholnoky Jenő, Littke Aurél, Papp Károly és Treitz Péter ... Budapest, Athenaeum részvénytársulat [1906]

Littke-Persson, A. K., joint author.
TK2799 .D3
Dahlgren, Fredrik, 1893-
Static frequency transformers for small electric motors, by F. Dahlgren and A. K. Littke-Persson. Göteborg, Elanders boktr. [H. Lindståhls bokhandel i distribution, Stockholm] 1951.

[**Little,** *Mrs.*]
Grenadier Rolf, by his mother. London, The Kingsley press, ltd., 1920.
xiv p., 1 l., 340 p. incl. front. plates, ports. 22cm.

1. Little, Rolf, 1895-1915. I. Title.
32-19326
Library of Congress BF1311.L5G7 133.9

NL 0409655 DLC

There are no cards for numbers NL 0409656 to NL 0410000

Little, A. Alexander.
Life insurance. Life insurance upon the mutual system
see under Connecticut Mutual Life Insurance Company, Hartford.

Little, A. Clarke. Iceland and the Faröe Islands. *Extr. fr.* The Dublin Review. Vol. CXXV. London, 1899. 8°. pp. 385-401.
IcC9L778

NL 0410002 NIC

---

*
M1 .S444 v.105 no.9
Little, A F
Farewell to summer. Written by Chester Deming. Washington, D. C., W. G. Metzerott, Music Depot [c1858]
5 p. 35cm. [Sheet music collection, v. 105, no.9]
"To Miss M. J. Turpin."
W. French, engraver.
Stamp of W. C. Metzerott on cover.
1. Songs with piano. I. Title.

NL 0410003 ViU

---

*
M1.642 .L577M6 1864
Little, A F
Morning prayer; song with piano-forte accompaniment, written and composed by A. F. Little. Richmond, Va., Geo. Dunn & Compy., c1864.
[3] p. 31cm.

NL 0410004 ViU GEU CSmH

Little, A. F.
A treatise on vocal and instrumental music.
— Washington. McGill. 1859. 36 pp. 19 cm., in 6s.

E1220 — T.r. — Music. Hist.

NL 0410005 MB

976.7 L721c
Little, A G
Corrupt domination of Arkansas politics; speech in the House of Representatives, Wednesday, May 3, 1911. [Little Rock? Ark., 1911?]
27p. 22cm.

1. Arkansas - Pol. & govt. 2. Liquor laws - Arkansas. I. Title. Sp.: Littlefield Fund.

NL 0410006 TxU

---

*
M1 .S444 v.69 no.25
Little, A G
[A farmer's wife I'll be; arr.]
A farmers wife I'll be, ballad. Music composed for the melodeon or piano. [Arr. for the] guitar [by H. Werner] Figure 2½ in five pointed star. St. Louis, Balmer & Weber, 56 Fourth St.; Louisville, Webb, Peters & Co.; New Orleans, Ph. P. Werlein [c1857]
Pl. no. 941=3.
5 p. 35cm. [Sheet music collection, v.69, no.25]
At head of title: To Alfred Little Boscowan, esq., N.H.
1. Songs with guitar. I. Werner, Heinrich, fl. 1844, arr. II. Title.

NL 0410007 ViU

VOLUME 336

Little, A. J.

Celebrated men of the day: Matthew F. Maury.

Excerpt from Belford's magazine, Oct. 1890.

NL 0410008 DAS

Little, A J.

Manual on breaking and educating horses ... with a description of the construction and use of the patent "breaking machine," with a limited right to use the same. By A. J. Little. Fort Worth, Tex., Press of C. M. Brown, & co., 1892.

143 p. illus. 15cm.

1. Horse-training.

4-31594

Library of Congress SF287.L77

NL 0410009 DLC

Little, Alan, joint author.

Rostovtsev, Mikhail Ivanovich, 1870–

La maison des fresques de Doura-Europos, par mm. M. Rostovtzeff et Alan Little.

(In Académie des inscriptions et belles-lettres, Paris. Mémoires. Paris, 1933. 27cm. t. 43, 1. ptie., p. [167]–190. illus. (incl. plan))

Little, Alan MacNaughton Gordon.

The decoration of the Hellenistic peristyle house in south Italy [by] A. M. G. Little. [Concord, N. H., 1935]

cover-title, 360-371 p. illus., pl. XLIII–XLVI. 29 x 23cm.

Title type-written on slip mounted on cover.
Thesis (PH. D.)—Yale university, 1933.
Thesis note on label attached to recto of blank leaf following cover.
From the American journal of archaeology, v. 39, 1935 (photostat, on one side of leaf only)
Bibliographical foot-notes.

1. Decoration and ornament, Architectural. 2. Architecture, Greco-Roman. 3. Architecture, Domestic—Rome. 4. Mural painting and decoration. I. Title: Hellenistic peristyle house in south Italy.

42-17966 Revised

Library of Congress NA3360.L5

NL 0410011 DLC

Little, Alan MacNaughton Gordon.

Myth and society in Attic drama, by Alan M. G. Little. New York, Columbia university press, 1942.

vii p., 2 l., 95 p. illus. 22cm.

Bibliography: p. [87]–88.

1. Greek drama—Hist. & crit. 2. Mythology in literature. 3. Civilization, Greek. I. Title.

43-2754

Library of Congress PA3131.L5

00xM ODW OCU OO
NL 0410012 DLC MtU OrPR OrU MtBC CU GU DAU NcD

HB171 .5 .P314 1944

Little, Albert William Selwyn, joint author.

Patterson, Samuel Howard, 1892– FOR OTHER EDITIONS SEE MAIN ENTRY

... American economic problems, by S. Howard Patterson, A. W. Selwyn Little and Henry Reed Burch. [Madison, Wis.] Pub. for the United States Armed forces institute by the Macmillan company [1944]

Little, Albert William Selwyn, joint author.

Patterson, Samuel Howard, 1892–

American social problems [by] S. Howard Patterson ... A. W. Selwyn Little ... [and] Henry Reed Burch ... New York, The Macmillan company, 1939.

H83 .E445

Little, Albert William Selwyn.

Edmonson, James Bartlett, 1882–

... Civics in American life [by] James B. Edmonson ... [and] Arthur Dondineau ... New York, The Macmillan company, 1941.

Little, Albert William Selwyn, joint author.

Edmonson, James Bartlett, 1882–

Civics through problems; a social and governmental civics. Pennsylvania ed. [By] James B. Edmonson ... Arthur Dondineau ... [and] A. W. S. Little ... New York, The Macmillan company, 1935.

Little, Albert William Selwyn.

Laboratory study of current social issues [by] A. W. Selwyn Little ... S. Howard Patterson ... [and] Henry Reed Burch ... New York, The Macmillan company, 1941.

1 p. l., 302 p. incl. forms. 28 x 21cm.

"Foreword" and "Final score" on p. [2] and [3] of cover, respectively.
Includes "References." "General bibliography": p. 300-302.

1. Social problems—Outlines, syllabi, etc. I. Patterson, Samuel Howard, 1892– joint author. II. Burch, Henry Reed, 1876– joint author. III. Title.

41-6427 Revised

Library of Congress H62.L5
[r42e2] 302

NL 0410017 DLC OrU

Little, Albert William Selwyn, joint author.

Patterson, Samuel Howard, 1892– FOR OTHER EDITIONS SEE MAIN ENTRY

... Problems in American democracy [by] S. Howard Patterson ... A. W. Selwyn Little ... [and] Henry Reed Burch ... New York, The Macmillan company, 1940.

Little, Alfred.

About the jubilee, sir! Song [with accompaniment for pianoforte]. Boston. Ditson & Co. 1869. 5 pp. 35 cm.

L4969 — T.r. — Songs. With music.

NL 0410019 MB

---

* M1 .S444 v.165 no.12

Little, Alfred E

Absence. Text by Catherine Young Glen. Music by Alfred E. Little. High voice, in E. [Price] .60. Boston: Oliver Ditson Company, New York: Chas.H. Ditson & Co. [etc.] [c1897] Pl. no. 4-7-59838-3.

5 p. 30cm. [Sheet music collection, v. 165, no. 12]

"To Gardner E. Meeks, Columbus, O."

1. Songs (High voice) with piano. I. Title.

NL 0410020 ViU

M1 .W35 vol. 2, no. 13

Little, Alfred E. I look into my glass.

Gilbert, Henry Franklin Belknap, 1868-1928.
[The lament of Deirdré]

... Three songs: The lament of Deirdré, by Henry F. Gilbert. I look into my glass, by Alfred E. Little. Love's secret, by Arthur Farwell ... Newton Center, Mass., The Wa-wan press, 1903.

Little, Alfred E

A lake and a fairy boat. Song for baritone by Alfred E. Little. New York. Phelps music co. [c1897]

With piano accompaniment.
Words by Thomas Hood.
1. Songs, U.S. 2. Songs, Secular—1870- . I. Hood, Thomas.

NL 0410022 NN

Little, Alfred E

The message, song; the words by Marie Van Vorst New York, The William Maxwell music co. [c1903]

6p. 35½cm.

NL 0410023 OrU

Little, Alfred E.

My love's like a red red rose. Song for tenor by Alfred E. Little. New York, Phelps music co. [c1897]

With piano accompaniment.
Words by Robert Burns.

1. Songs, U.S. 2. Songs, Secular—1870- I. Burns, Robert.

NL 0410024 NN

Little, Alfred E

Tender and true. Song for soprano. By Alfred E. Little. New York, Phelps music co. [c1897]

With piano accompaniment.
Words by Dinah Mulock.
First line: Could you come back to me, Douglas, Douglas.
1. Songs, U.S. 2. Songs, Secular—1870- I. Mulock, Dinah.

NL 0410025 NN

LITTLE, ALFRED E.

... Thy coming. Boston, H. B. Stevens co. c 1900.

Song with piano accompaniment.
Words by Charles Grant.
First line: The air was never so soft before.

1. Songs, U. S. 2. Songs, Secular—1870- I. Grant, Charles.

NL 0410026 NN

M1621 .L58T9

Little, Alfred E

Two songs for mezzo-soprano, by Alfred E. Little ... Boston, H. B. Stevens company; London, S. Lucas, W. Pitt & Hatzfeld, c1900.

2 v. in 1. 35cm.
Piano accompaniment.
Publisher's plate nos.: H. B. S. co. 869, 870.
CONTENTS.—Only for thee.—Thy coming.

1. Songs (Medium voice) with piano.

NL 0410027 MB

LITTLE, Alfred F.

From serfdom to culture; the remarkable story of a blind Chinese girl who rose from a waif in Canton to the position of a proof reader in a large American institution. With reminiscences and anecdotes. n.p., [1939].

22 cm. pp.16. Port.

NL 0410028 MH

VOLUME 336

Little, Alfred Timothy, 1913–
The administrator takes a look

see under

Uvalde Work Conference for Administrators, Uvalde, Tex., 1952.

TD1955
L721
Little, Alfred Timothy, 1913-
Conferences and study participation by superintendents of schools. Austin, Tex., 1955.
304,[10]l. illus.,tables. 28cm.
Thesis (D.Ed.) - University of Texas, 1955.
Vita.
One of the studies undertaken in connection with the Southwestern Cooperative Program in Education. cf.p.4.
Bibliography: [302]-304.

NL 0410030 TxU

Little, Alicia Helen Neva (Bewicke) d. 1926.

Little, Archibald John, 1838–1908.
Across Yunnan: a journey of surprises, including an account of the remarkable French railway line now completed to Yunnan-fu; by Archibald Little ... Ed. by Mrs. Archibald Little ... London, S. Low, Marston & co., ltd., 1910.

Wason
DS703
Z138
Little, Alicia Helen Neva (Bewicke) d. 1926.
The fairy foxes. A Chinese legend. Shanghai, Kelly & Walsh, 1890.
41 double l. illus. 18cm.

On cover: Told in English by Mrs. Archibald Little. Second edition.
In vol. lettered: China and the Chinese. Pamphlets. Vol. 38.

NL 0410032 NIC OrU OCl

Little, Alicia Helen Neva (Bewicke) d. 1926.

... The fairy foxes. A Chinese legend. Told in English by Mrs. Archibald Little. Yokohama[etc.] Kelly & Walsh,l'd.;Tokyo,T.Hasegawa,1895.
1p.l.,43p.incl.illus.(part. col.;1 double) 18x15cm.
Printed in Japan.
At head of t.-p.: Third ed.
Printed on double leaves, on crêpe paper, Japanese style.
Illustrated col. wrappers.

NL 0410033 CtY MSaE IEN MB

823
L72f
Little, Alicia Helen Neva (Bewicke) d.1926.
Flirts and flirts; or, A season at Ryde. London, R. Bentley, 1868.
2v. 21cm.

NL 0410034 IU

Little, Alicia Helen Neva (Bewicke) d. 1926

Little, Archibald John, 1838–1908.
Gleanings from fifty years in China, by the late Archibald Little ... revised by Mrs. Archibald Little. London, S. Low, Marston & co., ltd., 1910.

Little, [Alicia Helen Neva (Bewicke)] d. 1926.
Guide to Peking, by Mrs. Archibald Little ... Tientsin, Tientsin press, limited, 1904.
4 p. l., iii, 91 p. fold. map, fold. plan. 17½cm.

1. Peking—Descr.—Guide books.

Library of Congress DS795.L54 6-5479

NL 0410036 DLC OrU WaU NIC OO NN MSaE

Soc
DS
709
L76
Little, Alicia Helen Neva (Bewicke) d.1926.
In the land of the blue gown, by Mrs. Archibald Little. New York, D. Appleton, 1909.
304p. plates.

Cover title: The land of the blue gown.

1. China - Descr. & trav. 2. China - Soc. life & cust. I. Title. II. Title: The land of the blue gown.

NL 0410037 FTaSU CU MB

Little, Alicia Helen Neva (Bewicke) d. 1926.
Intimate China. The Chinese as I have seen them. By Mrs. Archibald Little ... with 120 illustrations. London, Hutchinson & co., 1899.
xv, 615 p. incl. front., illus., plates. 25cm.

1. China—Descr. & trav. I. Title.

4-16690 Revised
Library of Congress DS709.L76
915.1 [r30f2] G66

NL 0410038 DLC WaS NIC CU OU MSaE NjP MdBP DN CtY

Little, Alicia Helen Neva (Bewicke) d. 1926
Intimate China. The Chinese as I have seen them. By Mrs. Archibald Little ... with 120 illustrations. London, Hutchinson & co.; Philadelphia, J. B. Lippincott compy., 1899.
xv, 615 p. incl. front., illus., plates. 25cm.

1. China—Descr. & trav. I. Title.

17-7115
Library of Congress DS709.L762

NL 0410039 DLC NN MB OO OClW OClMN OCl

DS709
L76
1901
Little, Alicia Helen Neva (Bewicke), d. 1926.
Intimate China - the Chinese as I have seen them. With 120 illus. London, Hutchinson; Philadelphia, J. B. Lippincott, 1901.
xv, 424 p. illus. 22cm.

1. China - Descr. & trav. I. Title.

NL 0410040 CoU NcC Nh IaU CLU MU OU DNW NcU MH

Little, Alicia Helen Neva (Bewicke) d. 1926.
The land of the blue gown, by Mrs. Archibald Little. London, T. F. Unwin, 1902.
xx, 370 p. illus., plates. 24 cm.

1. China—Soc. life & cust. I. Title.

DS721.L65 2-18219 rev

NL 0410041 DLC OrU Or CtY MSaE OO OCl CU MH MB

Little, Alicia Helen Neva (Bewicke) d. 1926.
The land of the blue gown [China] by Mrs. Archibald Little. [2d ed.] London, T. F. Unwin, 1908.
xv,304p. illus.

Partly reprinted from the "Times", "St. James's gazette", "North China herald", "Shanghai mercury" and "Hong Kong telegraph".

NL 0410042 NBC NjP NN MiU OU WU

823
L72l
Little, Alicia Helen Neva (Bewicke) d. 1926
The last of the Jerninghames London, C. J. Skeet, 1873.
2v. in 1.

NL 0410043 IU

Little, Alicia Helen Neva (Bewicke) d. 1926.
Li Hung Chang; his life and times, by Mrs. Archibald Little ... With several portraits and a map. London, Paris, New York and Melbourne, Cassell & company, limited, 1903.
1 p. l., viii, 356 p. 5 port. (incl. front.) fold. map. 22cm.

1. Li Hung Chang, 1821–1901.

4—13598
Library of Congress DS763.L6L7

NL 0410044 DLC WaS NIC IaU MSaE OO MiU MB

Z
823
L721l
Little, Alice Helen Neva (Bewicke) d. 1926.
Lonely Carlotta: "A crimson bud of a rose"; a novel by A.E.N. Bewicke ... London, R. Bentley & son, 1874.
3v. 19cm.

CONTENTS.--v.1. Prelude. Transplanted.--v.2. Transplanted (continued) Carried by the current.--v.3. Carried by the current (continued) Conclusion.

NL 0410045 TxU

[Little, Alicia Helen Neva (Bewicke)] *"Mrs. Archibald Little,"* d. 1926.
Love me for my love. By the author of "Flirts & flirts," "One foot on shore" ... London, R. Bentley, 1869.
2 v. 18cm.

I. Title.

7—16065
Library of Congress PZ3.L72L

NL 0410046 DLC CtY

Little, Alicia Helen Neva (Bewicke) d. 1926.
A marriage in China, by Mrs. Archibald Little (A. E. N. Bewicke) ... London, W. Heinemann, 1899.
viii, 312 p. 19½cm.

I. Title.

Library of Congress PZ3.L72M 1-20919 Revised

NL 0410047 DLC NIC NcU

Little, Mrs. Alicia Helen Neva (Bewicke) d. 1926.
My diary in a Chinese farm, by Mrs. Archibald Little (A. E. N. Bewicke) ... Shanghai, Kelly & Walsh, ltd. [1894?]
3 p. l., 74 p. illus., plates.

Illustrated end-papers.
"Collotypes and photo-engravings by K. Ogawa."
Printed in Japan.
"500 copies printed." This copy unnumbered.

NL 0410048 NNC OrU Or CtY ICU OrU OO CU MH NIC MnU

VOLUME 336

W823
L778o «Little, Alicia Helen Neva (Bewicke), d. 1926.
One foot on shore. A novel, by the author of "Flirts and flirts; or, A season at Ryde." London, R. Bentley, 1869.
3 v. 21 cm.

According to dealer's slip tipped in, this is a 1st edition.

NL 0410049 NcU

Wason
PR6023
I91
09
Little, Alicia Helen Neva (Bewicke) d. 1926.
Out in China! By Mrs. Archibald Little. London, Anthony Treherne, 1902.
182 p. 19cm.

NL 0410050 NIC MH

Little, Alicia Helen Neva (Bewicke), d. 1926.
Out in China! By Mrs. Archibald Little... New and cheaper ed. London, S. Low, Marston & co. [1912] 182 p. 19cm.

A novel.

NL 0410051 NN

Little, Alicia Helen Neva (Bewicke) d. 1926.

Round about my Peking garden; by Mrs. Archibald Little ... Illustrated ... London, T. Fisher Unwin; Philadelphia, J. B. Lippincott company, 1905.

[5]-284 p. col. front., 85 pl. 22½cm.

1. Peking—Description. I. Title.

W 6—21

Washington, D. C. Public library for Library of Congress [a41c1]

MB NN OCl OClW
NL 0410052 DWP NIC CSt CLSU MSaE WaS WaT OrU OU ICJ

Wason
DS703
Z138
Little, Alicia Helen Neva (Bewicke) d. 1926.
To Kalgan and the Mongolian grassland. By Mrs. Archibald Little. Shanghai, Printed at the Shanghai Mercury, 1904.
30 p. 19cm.

Cover title.
"Reprinted from the 'Shanghai mercury.'"
In vol. lettered: China and the Chinese. Pamphlets. Vol. 38.

1. Mongolia-- Descr. & trav. I. Title.

NL 0410053 NIC MSaE

Little, Alla Pearl.
Sketch of the Herman family ... by Pearl Little ... [Hickory, N. C., 1939]
cover-title, 13 numb. l. ports. (part mounted) 36cm.
Reproduced from type-written copy.

1. Herman family.

41-31423

Library of Congress CS71.H55 1939

NL 0410054 DLC OClWHi

Little, *Mrs.* Amos R.
see
Little, Anna P "*Mrs.* Amos R."

Little, Andrew George, 1863-1945.
Brother William of England, companion of St. Francis, and some Franciscan drawings in the Matthew Paris manuscripts.
— [Sevenoaks. 1891.] 8 pp. Facsimiles. 22 cm.
The author's name appears only on page 8.

E3651 — William of England, Brother, -1232? — Matthew Paris, -1259. — Franciscans. Fine arts.

NL 0410056 MB PPPD

Little, Andrew George, 1863-1945.
A century of English Franciscan history (1224-1324).
— London. 1924. 10 ff. 24.5 cm.
Reprinted from the Contemporary Review, October, 1924.
Printed on only one side of the paper.

E3480 — Franciscans in England.

NL 0410057 MB

[Little, Andrew George] 1863-1945.
... Charles Lethbridge Kingsford, 1862-1926. London, Pub. for the British academy, by H. Milford, Oxford university press [1926]
cover-title, 9 p. 25cm.
At head of title: The British academy.
Signed: A. G. Little.

1. Kingsford, Charles Lethbridge, 1862-1926. I. British academy, London.

28-10467

Library of Congress DA3.K5L5

NL 0410058 DLC CtY OrU

BX3601
.C6
Little, Andrew George, 1863-1945, ed.
FOR OTHER EDITIONS SEE MAIN ENTRY
Collectanea Franciscana. Aberdoniae, Typis Academicis, 1914-22.

BX3601
.B3
1911a
Little, Andrew George, 1863-1945.
FOR OTHER EDITIONS SEE MAIN ENTRY
Bacon, Roger, 1214?-1294.
Compendium studii theologiae. Edidit H. Rashdall. Una cum appendice de operibus Rogeri Bacon edita per A. G. Little. Aberdoniae, Typis Academicis, 1911.

Little, Andrew George, 1863-1945.
The constitution of provincial chapters in the Minorite Order.
— [Manchester. 1925.] 249-267 pp. 24.5 cm.
Bound with the original paper cover.
Reprinted from Essays in medieval history presented to Thomas Frederick Tout.
Contains a MS. presentation inscription to Paul Sabatier from A. G. L.

E3480 — Franciscans. Constitutions.

NL 0410061 MB DHN

Little, Andrew George, 1863-1945.
Decrees of the General Chapters of the Friars Minor, 1260 to 1282.
— (*In* English Historical Review, Vol. 13, pp. 703-708. London. 1898.)

Same. (*Cut from* Same.)
Contains MS. notes by Paul Sabatier.

E3481 — Franciscans. Official documents.

NL 0410062 MB

Little, Andrew George, 1863-1945.
Description du manuscrit Canonici. miscell. 525 de la Bibliothèque bodléienne à Oxford.
— Paris. Fischbacher. 1903. (3), 251-297 pp. [Opuscules de critique historique. Fasc. 5.] 23 cm.
Bound with the original paper covers.
Contains MS. notes and insertions by Paul Sabatier.
The MS. deals principally with the life of St. Francis.

E3527 — S.r.c. — Bodleian Library, Oxford. Manuscripts. Canonici miscell. 525. — Francesco d'Assisi, Saint, 1182-1226. Biog.

NL 0410063 MB CSmH PPPD

Little, Andrew George, 1863-1945.
Educational organisation of the mendicant friars in England (Dominicans and Franciscans). By A. G. Little ...
(*In* Royal historical society, London. Transactions. London, 1894. 22cm. n. s., v. 8, p. [49]-70)

1. Dominicans in England. 2. Franciscans in England. I. Title.

A C 36-326

Newberry library for Library of Congress [DA20.R9 n. s., vol. 8]
[a38c1] (942.0062)

NL 0410064 ICN CLSU DLC

Little, Andrew George, 1863-1945, ed.

Essays in medieval history presented to Thomas Frederick Tout; edited by A. G. Little and F. M. Powicke. Manchester [Eng.] Printed for the subscribers, 1925.

Little, Andrew George, 1863-1945.
The first hundred years of the Franciscan school at Oxford.
— *Galley proofs.* [London? 1910?] (8) ff. 72 cm.
Proofs for an unidentified publication.

E3527 — Franciscans in England. Oxford. — Oxford. England. Hist. Relig.

NL 0410066 MB

Little, Andrew George, 1863-1945, *ed.*
Franciscan history and legend in English mediaeval art, edited by A. G. Little ... [Manchester] Manchester university press, 1937.
xix, 118, [1] p. plates (part fold.) 23 x 17 cm. (*Half-title:* British society of Franciscan studies. [Publications] vol. xix)
CONTENTS.—Franciscan influence in English mediaeval wall-painting, by Professor E. W. Tristram.—Screen paintings, by the Rev. W. W. Lillie.—Franciscan saints in English mediaeval glass and embroidery, by the Rev. C. Woodforde.—Illuminated manuscripts, by A. G. Little.—The seals of the Franciscans, by H. S. Kingsford.—Sculpture and miscellaneous, by A. G. Little.
1. Christian art and symbolism. 2. Art—England. 3. Franciscans in England. 4. Illumination of books and manuscripts—England. I. Title.
BX3601.B7 vol. 19 246.0942 38—1811
N6763.L5

ICU OO OrCS MU CaBVaU
NL 0410067 DLC OrU GU MsSM CoU CLSU NIC MdBWA OU

Little, Andrew George, 1863-1945.
Franciscan papers, lists, and documents, by A. G. Little ... [Manchester] Manchester university press, 1943.
xiii, 262 p. illus. (map) 6 pl. (incl. port., facsim.) on 4 l. 22½cm. (*Half-title:* Publications of the University of Manchester, no. CCLXXXIV. Historical series, no. LXXXI)
Bibliographical foot-notes.

1. Franciscans. 2. Franciscans in England. I. Title.

A 44-2927

Harvard univ. Library for Library of Congress

OCU NcD
NL 0410068 MH OrU MU MH KyWAT LU IEG DHN TxU OU

VOLUME 336

Little, Andrew George, 1863-1945.

BX3618 O 3L5

... The Franciscan school at Oxford in the thirteenth century ... Ad Claras Aquas prope Florentiam, Typ. Collegii s. Bonaventurae, 1926.

74 p. 24.2 cm.
"Extractum ex periodico Archivum Franciscanum historicum, Vol. XIX, 1926."
Bibliographical foot-notes.

1. Franciscans in Oxford. 2. Oxford. University

NL 0410069 CSmH CtY

Little, Andrew George, 1863-1945.

... The Franciscans and Dominicans of Exeter, by A. G. Little ... and R. C. Easterling, M. A. Exeter, A. Wheaton & company, limited, 1927.

91, [1] p. 2 plans, facsim. 24½cm. (History of Exeter research group, monograph no. 3)

1. Franciscans in Exeter. 2. Dominicans in Exeter. I. Easterling, Ruth Clarke.

Library of Congress DA690.E9A4 no. 3 28-22717

NL 0410070 DLC CaBVaU CLU MoU DHN NN

Little, Andrew George, 1863-1946, ed.

BX3601 .P4 1910a

FOR OTHER EDITIONS SEE MAIN ENTRY

Peckham, John, *Abp. of Canterbury, d.* 1292.

Fratris Johannis Pecham ... Tractatus tres de paupertate. Cum bibliographia ediderunt C. L. Kingsford, A. G. Little, F. Tocco. Aberdoniae, Typis Academicis. 1910.

Little, Andrew George, 1863-1945.

Bacon, Roger, 1214?-1294.

Fratris Rogeri Bacon Compendium studii theologiae edidit H. Rashdall, una cum appendice De operibus Rogeri Bacon edita per A. G. Little. Aberdoniae. Typis academicis. 1911.

Little, Andrew George, 1863-1945.

The Grey friars in Oxford; part I: A history of the convent, part II: Biographical notices of the friars, together with appendices of original documents, by Andrew G. Little ... Oxford, Printed for the Oxford historical society at the Clarendon press, 1892.

xvi, 369 p. 23cm. (*Lettered on cover:* Oxford historical society. xx)
"Catalogues of manuscripts consulted": p. [viii]-ix.

1. Franciscans in Oxford. I. Title.

Library of Congress BX3618.O8L5 12-32784 Revised

NL 0410073 DHN FU ScU NcU MB MdBP OCIW OU MiU ViU MH OCU OCl DLC KyLoU MsSM PPPD N InStme GU MB WaSpG

Little, Andrew George, 1863-1945.

... A guide to Franciscan studies, by A. G. Little. London, Society for promoting Christian knowledge; New York, The Macmillan company, 1920.

v, 7-63 p. 18½cm. (Helps for students of history. no. 23)

1. Franciscans. I. Title.

Library of Congress BX3606.L5 21-9803

NL 0410074 OU OClJC DHN DLC CaBVaU OrPR NIC DCU MB NN OCl MiU

Little, Andrew George, 1863-1945.

An illuminated letter of fraternity, by A. G. Little ... London, H. Milford [1942]

7, [1] p. front. (facsim.) 25½cm.
"From the Proceedings of the British academy. Volume XXVII."
"The document here reproduced from a photograph in the British museum purports to be a letter of fraternity granted by John Zouch, provincial minister of the Friars minor in England, to William Lord Ferrers and Philippa his wife ... on 13 January, A. D. 1406/7 ... The original is now the property of the Port Adelaide institute, Port Adelaide, South Australia."—p. [3]

1. Illumination of books and manuscripts—Gt. Brit. 2. Ferrers of Groby, William de Ferrers, 5th baron, 1372-1445. 3. Franciscans in England. 4. Patronage, Ecclesiastical. I. Port Adelaide institute, Port Adelaide, Australia. II. Title. III. Title: Letter of fraternity.

Harvard univ. Library for Library of Congress ND3385.L4L5 [a45d1]† A 43-1383 096.1

NL 0410075 MH CaBVaU DLC

Little, Andrew George, 1863-1945.

An illuminated letter of fraternity, by A. G. Little ... (*In* British academy, London. Proceedings, 1941. London [1944] 26cm. [v. 27] p. [269]-273. facsim.)

"Communicated 28 September 1941."
"The document here reproduced from a photograph in the British museum purports to be a letter of fraternity granted by John Zouch, provincial minister of the Friars minor in England, to William Lord Ferrers and Philippa his wife ... on 13 January, A. D. 1406/7 ... The original is now the property of the Port Adelaide institute, Port Adelaide, South Australia."

1. Illumination of books and manuscripts—England. 2. Ferrers of Groby, William de Ferrers, 5th baron, 1372-1445. 3. Franciscans in England. 4. Patronage, Ecclesiastical. I. Port Adelaide institute, Port Adelaide, Australia. II. Title. III. Title: Letter of fraternity.

Wisconsin. Univ. Libr. for Library of Congress AS122.L5 vol. 27 † A 45-1167

NL 0410076 WU PLatS CtY NcD DLC

Little, Andrew George, 1863-1945, *ed.*

Initia operum latinorum quae saeculis XIII. XIV. XV. attribuuntur, secundum ordinem alphabeti disposita, edidit A. G. Little ... Manchester, University press, 1904.

xiii p., 1 l., 275 numb. l. 23½ cm. (*Half-title:* Publications of the University of Manchester. Historical series, no. II)

Printed on one side of leaf only.
"Fontes": p. [vii]-ix.

1. Latin literature, Medieval and modern—Bibl. 2. Literature, Medieval—Bibl. 3. Manuscripts, Latin—Bibl.

Z6517.L55 5—28376

NL 0410077 DLC MB PPT DDO NN NcU MiU OCl ICJ MH

Little, Andrew George, 1863-1945.

... Introduction of the Observant friars into England, by A. G. Little ... <From the Proceedings of the British academy, vol. XI> London, Pub. for the British academy by H. Milford, Oxford university press [1923]

cover-title, 17 p. 25cm.
At head of title: The British academy.
"Read July 11, 1923."

I. British academy, London. II. Title.

Library of Congress BX3616.L5 24-32102

NL 0410078 DLC CaBVaU PLatS ICRL DHN CtY CU

Little, Andrew George, 1863-1945.

Introduction of the Observant friars into England, by A. G. Little ...

(*In* British academy, London. Proceedings, 1921-1923. London [1926?] 26cm. [v. 10] p. [455]-471)

"Read July 11, 1923."

1. Franciscans in England.

Title from Wisconsin Univ. Library of Congress [AS122.L5 vol. 10] A 34-2627

NL 0410079 WU MiU

Little, Andrew George, 1863-1945.

Introduction of the Observant friars into England: a bull of Alexander VI, by A. G. Little ...

(*In* British academy, London. Proceedings, 1941. London [1944] 26cm. [v. 27] p. [155]-166)

"Communicated 16 April 1941."

1. Franciscans in England.

Wisconsin. Univ. Libr. for Library of Congress AS122.L5 vol. 27 † A 45-1162

NL 0410080 WU NNC NcD MH DLC

Little, Andrew George, 1863-1945.

Introduction of the Observant Friars into England: a bull of Alexander VI. London, Humphrey Milford [1941]

14 p. 25 cm.
"From the Proceedings of the British Academy, vol. XXVII."
Bound with his Introduction of the Observant Friars into England. 1923.

NL 0410081 PLatS DDO

Little, Andrew George, 1863-1945, ed.

Liber exemplorum ad usum praedicantium saeculo XIII compositus a quodam fratre minore anglico de provincia Hiberniae, secundum codicem dunelmensem editus per A. G. Little. Aberdoniae, Typis academicis, 1908.

Little, Andrew George, 1863-1945, ed.

Fitzmaurice, E B *ed.*

Materials for the history of the Franciscan province of Ireland, A. D. 1230-1450, collected and ed. by the late Rev. Father E. B. Fitzmaurice, O. F. M., and A. G. Little. Manchester, The University press, 1920.

Little, Andrew George, 1863-1945.

... Measures taken by the prelates of France against the friars (c. A. D. 1289-90). (In: Miscellanea Francesco Ehrle. Roma: Biblioteca apostolica vaticana, 1924. 4°. v. 3. p. [49-]66.)

Bibliographical footnotes.

1. Friars—France, 13th cent.

September 29, 1928

NL 0410084 NN MB

Little, Andrew George, 1863-1945.

Mediæval Wales, chiefly in the twelfth and thirteenth centuries; six popular lectures, by A. G. Little ... London, T. F. Unwin, 1902.

vii p., 2 l., 148 p. incl. maps and plans. 19½cm.

CONTENTS.—Introductory.—Geoffrey of Monmouth.—Giraldus Cambrensis.—Castles.—Religious houses.—Llywelyn ap Gruffydd and the barons' war.

1. Wales—Hist. 2. Geoffrey, of Monmouth, 1100?-1154. 3. Giraldus Cambrensis, 1146?-1220? 4. Monasteries—Wales. I. Title.

Library of Congress DA715.L77 2—22096

NL 0410085 DLC PU NcD CaOTP OCl NN CtY

Little, Andrew George, 1863-1945, ed.
A new 'Fioretto' of St. Francis
see under Francesco d'Assisi, Saint. Legend.

Little, Andrew George, 1863-1946.

... Notes on the exhibition of Franciscan manuscripts in the British Museum, by A. G. Little ... [London: Printed by order of the Trustees of the British Museum, 1926.] 8 p. 22cm.

Caption-title.
At head of title: Septingentenary of St. Francis, October, 1926.

710565A. 1. Franciscans. 2. Manuscripts—Collections—Gt. Br.—Eng.—London. I. British Museum. Manuscripts, Department of.

September 20, 1934

NL 0410087 NN

VOLUME 336

Little, Andrew George, 1863-1945.
Un nouveau manuscrit franciscain, ancien Phillipps 12290, aujourd'hui dans la bibliothèque A. G. Little, décrit et étudié par A. G. Little.
— Paris. Fischbacher. 1919. (4), 110 pp. [Opuscules de critique historique. Fasc. 18.] 22.5 cm.
Bound with the original paper covers.
The MS. includes the Actus Beati Francisci and chapters of the Speculum Perfectionis.
Contains MS. notes by Paul Sabatier.
[Numerous selections of text are included.--The MS. became, eventually, Codex Oxford 23]

E3572 — S.r. — Phillipps, Sir Thomas, Baronet, 1792-1872. — Actus Beati Francisci. — Speculum Perfectionis.

NL 0410088 MB DHN ICU CSmH

Little, Andrew George, 1863-1945.
Oxford theology and theologians, c. a. d. 1282-1302, by A. G. Little ... and F. Pelster ... Oxford, The Clarendon press for the Oxford historical society, 1934.
xi, [1], 389, [1] p. 22cm. (*Half-title:* Oxford historical society. [Publications] v. 96)
"Dr. Pelster's introductions and notes, originally written in German, were translated partly by Mr. A. B. Gough, partly by myself."—Pref., signed: A. G. Little.
Bibliography: p. [ix]-xi.
Contents.—Ms. Assisi 158. Quaestiones at Oxford and Cambridge, c. a. d. 1282-90.—Sermons and preachers at the University of Oxford in the years 1290-3.—Ms. Worcester cathedral library Q. 99. Quaestiones at Oxford, c. a. d. 1300-2.
1. Oxford. University. 2. Manuscripts, Gt. Brit. 3. Theologians, English. i. Pelster, Franz, 1880- joint author. ii. Gough, Alfred Bradly, 1872- tr. iii. Title.
34-22388
Library of Congress DA690.O97O8 vol. 96
(942.57) 378.42

GU PLatS NcD OCl MiU OU OCU MB OO
NL 0410089 DLC PPiPT CtY-D DHN FU ScU NBuU OClW

[LITTLE, Andrew George, 1863-1945, ed.
Palaeographical facsimiles in use in the University of Manchester; twenty-eight specimens from MSS of the 6th to the 16th century mostly of English origin.]

NL 0410090 MH

BX3601 .B32 1912a
Little, Andrew George, 1863-1945, ed.
FOR OTHER EDITIONS SEE MAIN ENTRY
Bacon, Roger, 1214?-1294.
Part of the Opus tertium of Roger Bacon, including a fragment now printed for the first time. Edited by A. G. Little. Aberdeen, University Press, 1912.

Little, Andrew George, 1863-1945.
... Paul Sabatier, historian of St. Francis; a lecture delivered before the British society of Franciscan studies on 29th April, 1929, by A. G. Little ... with a personal appreciation by Sir Oliver Wardrop ... Manchester, The University press, 1929.
14 p. 19cm.
At head of title: British society of Franciscan studies.

1. Sabatier, Paul, 1858-1928. Vie de s. François d'Assise. i. British society of Franciscan studies, London.
30-2160
Library of Congress BX4700.F6S255

NL 0410092 DLC NN NIC DHN MB CtY NBuG MH

Little, Andrew George, 1863-1945.
Professor Tout... [London, Macmillan and co., ltd.; New York, The Macmillan co., 1930]
[313]-324 p. 25cm. (From: History, Jan.1930, N.S. v.14,no.56)
Caption-title.
Ms. presentation note to the Henry E.Huntington library, on cover, from Mary Tout.
1.Tout, Thomas Frederick, 1855-1929.

NL 0410093 CSmH NIC

Little, Andrew George, 1863-1945.
—— Records of the Franciscan province of England. (In "Collectanea Franciscana," v. 1.) (Brit. Soc. of Franciscan studies, v. 5.)

NL 0410094 PPPD

Little,Andrew George,1863-1945.
Roger Bacon,by A.G.Little ... London, H. Milford [1928]
33,[1] p.,1 l. 26cm. (British academy. Annual lecture on a master mind. Henriette Hertz trust)
"From the Proceedings of the British academy. Volume XIV."

1.Bacon,Roger,1214?-1294. I.British academy,London.

NL 0410095 MiU DHN CSmH MH DDO NN

Little, Andrew George, 1863-1945.
Roger Bacon, by A. G. Little ... London, H. Milford [1929]
33, [1] p., 1 l. 26cm. (The British academy. Annual lecture on a master-mind, Henriette Hertz trust. 1928)
"From the Proceedings of the British academy. Volume xiv."
"Read July 4, 1928."

1. Bacon, Roger, 1214?-1294.
35-14072
Library of Congress B765.B24L62
189

NL 0410096 DLC

Little, Andrew George, 1863-1945
... Roger Bacon, by A. G. Little ...
(*In* British academy, London. Proceedings, 1928. London [1930] 26cm. [v. 14] p. [265]-296)
At head of title: Annual lecture on a master mind, Henriette Hertz trust.
"Read July 4, 1928."
Bibliographical foot-notes.

1. Bacon, Roger, 1214?-1294.
A 34-2677
Title from Wisconsin Univ. Library of Congress [AS122.L5 vol. 14]

NL 0410097 WU MB

Little, Andrew George, 1863-1945, *ed.*
Roger Bacon essays, contributed by various writers on the occasion of the commemoration of the seventh centenary of his birth, collected and ed. by A. G. Little. Oxford, Clarendon press, 1914.
viii, 425, [1] p. 23 cm.
Contents.
On Roger Bacon's life and works, by A. G. Little.—Der einfluss des Robert Grosseteste auf die wissenschaftliche richtung des Roger Bacon, von Ludwig Baur.—La place de Roger Bacon parmi les philosophes du xiiie siècle, par François Picavet.—Roger Bacon and the Latin vulgate, by Francis Aidan, cardinal Gasquet.—Roger Bacon and philology, by S. A. Hirsch.—The place of Roger Bacon in the history of mathematics, by David Eugene Smith.

Roger Bacon und seine verdienste um die optik, von Eilhard Wiedemann.—Roger Bacons lehre von der sinnlichen spezies und vom sehvorgange, von Sebastian Vogl.—Roger Bacons art des wissenschaftlichen arbeitens dargestellt nach seiner schrift De speculis, von J. Würschmidt.—Roger Bacon et l'horreur du vide, par Pierre Duhem.—Roger Bacon, his relations to alchemy and chemistry, by M. M. Pattison Muir.—Roger Bacon and gunpowder, by H. W. L. Hime.—Roger Bacon and medicine, by E. Withington.—Roger Bacon in English literature, by Sir John Edwin Sandys.—Roger Bacon's works, with reference to the mss. and printed editions, by A. G. Little (p. [375]-425, [1])
1. Bacon, Roger, 1214?-1294. 2. Bacon, Roger, 1214?-1294—Bibliography.
B765.B24L6 A 14—1674
Columbia Univ. for Library of Congress Libraries [a54i1]

NIC NBuU MiU InStme
ICJ CtY NN DHN IU IdU WaS CaBVaU TNJ MeB NcD ICarbS
NL 0410099 NNC MoSU NBuC MB DLC OClW OCU ODW OU OO

Little, Andrew George, 1863-1945.
Scholastic philosophy and universities.
(*In* Tilley, Arthur, editor. Medieval France. Pp. 212-252. Cambridge. 1922.)
Relates to France.
Bibliography, p. 252.

M7737 — Scholasticism. — France. Phil. — Universities.

NL 0410100 MB

Little, Andrew George, 1863-1945.
—— The seventh centenary of St. Francis of Assisi (1226-1926). (In "Franciscan Essays," v. 2.) (Brit. Soc. of Franciscan studies; Extra series, v. 3.)

NL 0410101 PPPD

Little, Andrew George, 1863-1945.
... Some recently discovered Franciscan documents and their relations to the second Life by Celano and the "Speculum perfectionis", by A. G. Little ... <From the Proceedings of the British academy> London, Pub. for the British academy by H. Milford, Oxford university press [1926?]
cover-title, 32 p. 25cm.
At head of title: The British academy.
"Communicated on the Feast of St. Francis, 1926."

1. Francesco d'Assisi, Saint. Legend. i. British academy, London.
28-20543
Library of Congress BX4700.F6L5

NL 0410102 DLC KU PLatS MB DHN CtY OO

Little, Andrew George, 1863-1945.
Some recently discovered Franciscan documents and their relations to the second Life by Celano and the Speculum perfectionis, by A. G. Little ...
(*In* British academy, London. Proceedings, 1926. London [1928] 26cm. [v. 12, p. [147]-178)
"Communicated on the Feast of St. Francis, 1926."

1. Francesco d'Assisi, Saint. Legend.
A 34-2656
Title from Wisconsin Univ. Library of Congress [AS122.L5 vol. 12]

NL 0410103 WU MB

Little, Andrew George, 1863-1945.
The sources of the history of St. Francis of Assisi; a review of recent researches.
[London]. 1902. 35 pp. 24.5 cm.
Reprinted from The English historical review, vol. 17, October, 1902, pp. 643-677.
Contains MS. notes by Sabatier, and a MS. presentation inscription from the author.

E3481 — Francesco d'Assisi, Saint, 1182-1226. Biog. Sources.

NL 0410104 MB

Little, Andrew George, 1863-1945.
Studies in English Franciscan history; being the Ford lectures delivered in the University of Oxford in 1916, by A. G. Little ... Manchester, The University press; London, New York [etc.] Longmans, Green & co., 1917.
ix, 248 p. 23cm. (*Half-title:* Publications of the University of Manchester. Historical series. no. xxix)
On verso of t.-p.: Publications of the University of Manchester, no. cxiii.

1. Franciscans in England.
18-1241
Library of Congress BX3616.L6

OO MB WaU
NL 0410105 DLC DHN IdU NIC NcD MBtS OCU OClW MiU OU

Little, Andrew George, 1863-1945, ed.
Vaughan, Charles Edwyn, 1854-1922.
Studies in the history of political philosophy before and after Rousseau, by C. E. Vaughan ... edited by A. G. Little ... Manchester, The University press; London, New York, etc., Longmans, Green & co., 1925.

Little, Andrew George, 1863-1945.
Thomas Docking and his relations to Roger Bacon.
(*In* Davis, Henry W. C., editor, 1874- . Essays in history. Pp. 301-331. Oxford. 1927.)

NL 0410107 MB NN

VOLUME 336

BX3616
T52

Little, Andrew George, 1863–1945, ed.

Thomas, *of Eccleston, fl.* 1250.
Tractatus de adventu Fratrum Minorum in Angliam, denuo edidit, A. G. Little. ₍1st English ed.₎ Manchester, University Press ₍1951₎

M1621
.L582L6 Little, Anita Gray.
Love. [Poem by] Mary Baker Eddy. [Music by] Anita Gray Little. Boston, H. I. Hunt, c1938.
7 p. 31cm.
Caption title.
For low voice.
At head of title: Poems by Mary Baker Eddy set to music in solo form.

1. Songs (Low voice) with piano. I. Eddy, Mary (Baker) 1821-1910. II. Title.

NL 0410109 MB

Little, ₍**Anna P** ₎ *"Mrs.* **Amos R. Little."**
The world as we saw it; by Mrs. Amos R. Little ... Boston, Cupples and company, 1887.
xiii, 476 p. front., illus., plates. 26cm.

1. Voyages around the world.

Library of Congress G440.L77 5-37790†

NL 0410110 DLC OFH OClW OCl

Little, *Mrs.* **Archibald**
see
Little, Alicia Helen Neva (Bewicke) *d.* 1926.

Little, Archibald Alexander, 1860–
The highway to happiness; sermons ... by Archibald Alexander Little ... Grand Rapids, Mich., Zondervan publishing house, 1935.
204 p. incl. port. 19½cm.

1. Presbyterian church—Sermons. 2. Sermons, American. I. Title.

Library of Congress BX9178.L55H5 35-34020

Copyright A 89618 252.051

NL 0410112 DLC

Little, Archibald John, 1838–1908.
Across Yunnan: a journey of surprises, including an account of the remarkable French railway line now completed to Yunnan-fu; by Archibald Little ... Ed. by Mrs. Archibald Little ... London, S. Low, Marston & co., ltd., 1910.
164 p. front., 10 pl., port. gr., fold. map. 19½cm.

1. Yunnan, China (Province)—Descr. & trav. I. Little, Alicia Helen Neva (Bewicke) "Mrs. Archibald Little," d. 1926. II. Title.

Library of Congress DS793.Y8L6 10—20190

NL 0410113 DLC WaS MSaE NIC NcU CLSU CtY MB NN OCl

Little, Archibald John, 1838– *1908*
Across Yunnan & Tonking by Archibald Little. Part I. Between two capitals. Part II. Yunnanfu to the coast. Chungking, 1904.
[6], 33 p. 2 fold. maps incl. front. 24cm.

NL 0410114 ICJ CU

Little, Archibald John, 1838–1908.
The Far East, by Archibald Little ... Oxford, The Clarendon press, 1905.
viii. 334 p. illus. (incl. maps) 3 pl., 9 maps (8 fold.) 23½cm. ₍(The regions of the world)

CONTENTS.—Preface. — Editorial note. — Definition. — The central kingdom: China.—The northern basin. The Yellow River.—The middle basin: I. The Yangtse River. II. The province of Szechuan. III. The Chengtu plateau. IV. The lower Yangtse provinces.—The intermediate provinces.—The southern basin. Yunnan to Canton.—The dependencies: I. Manchuria. II. Mongolia. III. Turkestan. IV. Tibet.—Whilom dependencies: I. Indo-China. II. Corea.—The buffer kingdom: Siam.—The Island empire: Japan.

1. East (Far East) 2. China.

Library of Congress DS508.L7 5—35280

OOxM OU MiU ODW WaSp Or OrP CU CaBVaU CU-S OrU Or
NL 0410115 DLC WaS NcU DI-GS DNW NcD OO DN NN MB ICJ

Little, Archibald John, 1838–1908.
Gleanings from fifty years in China, by the late Archibald Little ... revised by Mrs. Archibald Little. London, S. Low, Marston & co., ltd., 1910.
xvi p., 1 l., 335, ₍1₎ p. front., plates, ports. 22½cm.

Advertising matter: p. 331–335.
Reprinted, in part, from various periodicals.

CONTENTS.—Foreword, by R. S. Gundry.—Editional note.—pt. I. Trade and politics: Western China: its products and trade. British trade with China. Ex oriente lux. Two cities: London and Peking. The value of Tibet to England. The partition of China. How to register your trade mark.—pt. II. Travel: The romance of Chinese travel. A new road. A Chinese sulphur bath. The New Rapid and the arrival of the first steamer in Chungking. The dangers of the upper Yangtse. Szechuan revisited. Yachting in the Chusan Archipelago. Retrospect of events in China.—pt. III. Drama and legend: The Chinese drama. Borrowing boots. ₍Tr. from the original Chinese; a two-hundred-year-old Chinese farce, still popular in China, and played at the present day₎ Plot and counterplot. ₍A comedy in two acts, written by Archibald Little, in imitation of the Chinese style₎ The rat's plaint. ₍Tr. from the original Chinese₎—pt. IV. Religion and philosophy: In a Buddhist monastery. Missionaries. Confucianism.

1. China. 2. China—Descr. & trav. I. Little, Alicia Helen Neva (Bewicke) "Mrs. Archibald Little," d. 1926, ed. II. Title.

Library of Congress DS710.L7 11—35434

OO CtY
NL 0410117 DLC WaT WaSp WaS NN KU OCl CU OrU DN

Little, Archibald John, 1838–1908.
Gleanings from fifty years in China, by the late Archibald Little ... Rev. by Mrs. Archibald Little. Philadelphia, J. B. Lippincott co. ₍etc., etc., 1910₎ xvi, 335 p. illus. 21cm.

"Part III. Drama and legend: The Chinese drama. Borrowing boots ₍Tr. from the original Chinese; a two-hundred-year-old Chinese farce₎ Plot and counterplot ₍A comedy in two acts, written by Archibald Little, in imitation of the Chinese style₎ The rat's plaint ₍Tr. from the original Chinese₎" p. 216–285.
"Books by Mr. Archibald Little," p. 331–335.

282669B. 1. China — Descr. and trav., 1900–1910. 2. Religion — China. 3. Chinese literature—Drama—Hist. and crit. 4. Chinese literature—Drama—Translations into English. 5. Drama, English—Translations from Chinese. I. Little, Alicia Helen Neva (Bewicke), d. 1926, ed. II. Title: Borrowing boots. III. Title: Plot and counterplot. IV. Title: The rat's plaint.
May 9, 1945

NL 0410118 NN NjP MB OClW NIC CSt-H

Little, Archibald John, 1838–1908.
Mount Omi and beyond; a record of travel on the Thibetan border, by Archibald John Little ... with a map and illustrations. London, W. Heinemann, 1901.
xiv p., 1 l., 272 p. front. (port.) plates, fold. map. 23cm.
"These chapters originally appeared ... in the columns of the North China herald."—Pref.

1. China—Descr. & trav. 2. Tibet—Descr. & trav. I. Title.

Library of Congress DS709.L773 17–9519

OClW OCl MH NN MB
NL 0410119 DLC Wa NIC IaU NBuU MSaE MiU NSyU CU CtY

LITTLE, ARCHIBALD JOHN. Notes on Szechuen and the Yangtse Valley. Shanghai, 1884. [18] p. 8°.
"Read 3d Dec., 1883."
From Journal of the North China branch of the Royal Asiatic society, 1883, n.s., v. 18, p. 165-182.

NL 0410120 MSaE

LITTLE, ARCHIBALD JOHN. Notes on western China, and opening of Ch'ungk'ing. [London, 1890.] 22 p. 8°.

NL 0410121 MSaE

Little, Archibald John, 1838–1908,
The rat's plaint, tr. from the original Chinese. [2d ed. Tokyo, T. Hasegawa, pref. 1891]
[34]p. (on double leaves) col.illus. 15 x 20 cm.

Printed on crepe paper, on one side of double leaves folded once in Japanese style.

NL 0410122 IEN MH OCl CtY

Little, Archibald John, 1838–1908.
Rat's plaint; an old legend, tr. from the Chinese. Tokoyo, 1892.
il. pl. ob.T.

NL 0410123 RPB

Little, Archibald John, 1838–1908.
Through the Yang-tse gorges; or, Trade and travel in western China, by Archibald John Little ... London, S. Low, Marston, Searle, & Rivington (limited), 1888.
xv, 368 p. fold. map. 23½cm.

1. China—Descr. & trav. 2. Yangtze River.

Library of Congress DS709.L775 1—1800

OCU OCl MH
NL 0410124 DLC CaBVaU DN CLU NBC CU OO MSaE CtY

Little, Archibald John, *1838–1908,*
Through the Yang-tse gorges; or, Trade and travel in western China. London, Low, Marston, Searle & Rivington, 1888
xv, 368 p. map
Microfilm, positive, of Harvard College Library copy
Film Mas 1135
——**Microfilm, master copy, of Harvard College Library copy**

NL 0410125 MH

Little, Archibald John, 1838–1908.
Through the Yang-tse gorges; or, Trade and travel in western China, by Archibald John Little ... 3d and rev. ed., with map and illustrations. London, S. Low, Marston & company, limited, 1898.
xxiv, 315, ₍1₎ p. front., plates, fold. map. 19½cm.

1. China—Descr. & trav. 2. Yangtze River. I. Title.

Library of Congress DS709.L78 1—1801

ICJ NN CaBVaU
NL 0410126 DLC OrU Or WaWW NIC OU CU NjP MdBP NcU

Little, Arlington P , 1879–1939.
Electricity in the mineral industries ... by Arlington P. Little. ₍Boulder, Col.₎ Colorado school of mines, c1929-34.
2v. illus.,pl.,diagrs. 27½cm.

Reproduced from typewritten copy.

--- ----- Problems and laboratory. ₍1934₎
1v. forms,diagrs. 27½cm.

Reproduced from typewritten copy.

NL 0410127 PSt DLC

Ca
PS3523
L7775
S8 **Little, Arnold Wilson.**
Stepping stones to right living; poetry, prose, song. ₍n.p., c1935₎
32 p. port. 23cm.

Author's autograph inscription on frontispiece.

NL 0410128 GU

VOLUME 336

Little, Arthur.
Early New England interiors. Sketches in Salem, Marblehead, Portsmouth and Kittery. By Arthur Little ... Boston, A. Williams and company, 1878.
45 l. 36 pl. 28 x 36cm.
Added t.-p., engraved.

1. Architecture—New England. 2. Architecture, Colonial. I. Title.

11—28648

Library of Congress NA707.L7

OC1W MdBP Nh CU MB
NL 0410129 DLC NN PSt MH OU OC1 MBAt OC1 PPPM MWA

RS201 Little, Arthur, of Liverpool
T2L58 Tablet making, by Arthur Little and K.A. Mitchell. Liverpool, Eng., The Northern
Pharm. pub. co. c1949.
121p. plates. 22cm.

1. Tablets (Medicine) I. Mitchell, K jt. auth. II. Title.
A

CoU WaU
NL 0410130 IaU DSI MiU CU-M OU PPSKF NcU ICJ NN PPC

QV LITTLE, Arthur, of Liverpool
785 Tablet making, by Arthur Little and
L778t K. A. Mitchell. Liverpool, Northern
1949 Pub. Co. [1951]
123 p. illus.
First published, 1949.
1. Tablets I. Mitchell, K
A

NL 0410131 DNLM IdPI OrCS MtU CaBVaU ICU CaBVa

E [Little, Arthur] 1837-1915.
5
.R 607 [In memoriam] August 19, 1867. Grace P. Rockwood. June 6, 1886. n.p. [1886?] sq.S.

Printed on rectos only.
Two sketches signed respectively Arthur Little and E.W. Blatchford.

NL 0410132 ICN

LITTLE, ARTHUR, 1837-1915.
In memoriam [Col. Bradford Hancock, born January 18, 1831, at Sackett's Harbor, N.Y.; died May 15, 1887, at Chicago, Ill. Laid to rest in Graceland cemetery May 17, 1887. Address of Rev. Arthur Little. n.p., n.d.] [9] p.

Microfilm.
Cover title.

"Resolutions... passed by the surviving members of the Twenty-ninth regiment of Wisconsin volunteer infantry at... Waterloo, Wis.," p. [8].

1. Hancock, Bradford, 1831-1887. I. In memoriam. [Col. Bradford Hancock]

NL 0410134 NN

Little, Arthur, 1837-1915.
The law of productiveness in spiritual husbandry. Annual sermon before the American board of commissioners for foreign missions, Oct. 8, 1890. Boston, Todd. 1890.
23 p. 8°.

NL 0410135 MB CtY NN DLC ICN

Little, Arthur, 1837-1915.
The leadership demanded by the hour. An address before the General Conference of the Congregational churches of Maine. Delivered at Bangor, June 20, 1894.
— Portland, Me. Marks. 1894. 16 pp. 8°.

G6453 — Leadership. — Congregational Church in Maine. Addresses.

NL 0410136 MB

Little, Arthur, 1897-1949.
Christ unconquered, by Arthur Little, s. j. Dublin, Browne and Nolan limited [1945]
5 p. l., 211 p., 1 l. 22cm.
Poem.
"First published March, 1945."

1. Jesus Christ—Poetry. I. Title.

A 46-3786

New York. Public library
for Library of Congress

NL 0410137 NN MH

Little, Arthur, 1897-1949.
Christ unconquered. [Poem] Illustrated by Fritz Kredel, introd. by Fulton Oursler. [1st American ed.] New York, Prentice-Hall [1952]
232 p. illus. 24 cm.

1. Jesus Christ—Poetry. I. Title.
PR6023.I 68C5 1952 [232.991] 821.91 52-7584 ‡

Or OrStbM
NL 0410138 DLC WaS IU MB OC1ND CtY NBuU N WaSpG

Little, Arthur, 1897-1949.
The nature of art, or, The shield of Pallas. London, New York, Longmans, Green [1946]
x, 264 p. illus. 20 cm.
A development of a series of lectures given to the Study Club of the Central Catholic Library in Dublin.

1. Art—Philosophy. 2. Esthetics. I. Title.

N66.L5 701 47-6738*

NL 0410139 DLC WaSpG NNC OC1JC CtY MB TxU

Little, Arthur, 1897-1949.
Philosophy without tears, being broadcast dialogues on philosophy, by Arthur Little, s. j. Dublin, J. Duffy & co., ltd., 1946.
viii, 9-128 p. 19cm.

1. Philosophy—Addresses, essays, lectures. I. Title.
46-7574
Library of Congress B4691.L51P5
104

NL 0410140 DLC NN

Little, Arthur, 1897-1949.
Philosophy without tears. Buffalo, Desmond & Stapleton, 1947.
viii, 128 p. 22 cm.
Originally prepared for broadcasting over Radio Eireann.

1. Philosophy—Addresses, essays, lectures. I. Title.
[B4691.L51P] 104 A 50-9740
Ohio State Univ. Libr.
for Library of Congress

NL 0410141 OU WaSpG MH-AH OrStbM MiD-P

230.7 Little, Arthur, 1897-1949.
L72 The Platonic heritage of Thomism. Dublin, Golden Eagle Books [1949]
xv, 290 p.

Includes bibliographical references.

1. Thomas Aquinas, Saint--Philosophy. 2. Plato. 3. Aristoteles. 4. Participation (Metaphysics) I. Title.

OU NN CtY KU CU InU WaSpG IMunS MBtS
NL 0410142 MoSU-D OrStbM MH DGU CtY-D DCU KAS ICU

Little (Arthur D.) inc.
Ammonia and methanol from northern lignite; report to Resources Research Committee. Cambridge, Mass., 1954.
ix, 98 p. map, diagrs., tables. 29 cm.

1. Ammonia. 2. Wood—alcohol. 3. Lignite. I. Resources Research Committee. II. Title.

TP329.L5 56-16624 rev

NL 0410143 DLC

Little (Arthur D.) inc.
The Arab League market; report to U. S. Government Foreign Operations Administration, under contract SCC-21504, C-58780-11. Cambridge, Mass., 1954.
xi, 78 p. tables. 29 cm.

1. Near East—Comm. 2. Egypt—Comm. I. U. S. Foreign Operations Administration. II. Title.

HF3760.8.L5 58-38076 rev

NL 0410144 DLC NN

Little (Arthur D.) inc.
Arthur Dehon Little memorial lecture at the Massachusetts Institute of Technology
see under title

Little (Arthur D.) inc.
Attracting an atomic energy plant to the North Dakota area; report to Resources Research Committee. Cambridge, Mass., 1954.
ii, 10 l. table. 29 cm.

1. Atomic power industry—North Dakota. I. Resources Research Committee. II. Title.

HD9698.U53N94 56-17863 rev

NL 0410146 DLC

Little, Arthur D., Inc.
Bibliographic series no. 1-7 ... Arthur D. Little, Inc., chemists and engineers ... [Cambridge, 1919-1921]
7 no. in 1 v. 23½cm.
Reprinted from various periodicals.
No more published.
Wanting: no. 4.

NL 0410147 ICJ DI-GS OrPR OrCS MB OO DLC MiD

660.5 **Little (Arthur D.) inc.**
L1 **The bulletin.** no. 1- 1927-
Cambridge, Mass.
no. 29cm.

Frequency varies.
Title varies: 1927-Oct./Nov. 1970, Industrial bulletin.

NL 0410148 IU

VOLUME 336

Little (Arthur D.) inc.
The bulletin
see also its Industrial bulletin of Arthur D. Little, inc.

Little (Arthur D.) inc.
Chemicals from North Dakota lignite; report to Resources Research Committee. [Cambridge, Mass.] 1955.
iii, 24 l. diagrs., tables. 29 cm.

1. Lignite. 2. Chemicals—Manufacture and industry—North Dakota. I. Resources Research Committee. II. Title.

TP329.L52 56-16622 rev

NL 0410150 DLC

Little (Arthur D.) Inc.
Chemistry in overalls. [Cambridge, Mass.: Arthur D. Little, Inc. [1918.] 31(1) p. illus. 8°.
Cover-title.

1. Chemistry.—Research. 2. Chemical technology. 3. Title.
N. Y. P. L. March 10, 1919.

NL 0410151 NN NcD MH MB OO

WB 26 qL778 LITTLE (Arthur D.) inc.
[Collection of publications]
The Library has a collection of miscellaneous publications of this organization kept as received. These publications are not listed or bound separately.

NL 0410152 DNLM

TH117 .L5
Little (Arthur D.) inc.
Demonstration of stabilized mud brick in Egyptian village housing. Washington, Technical Aids Branch, Office of Industrial Resources, International Cooperation Administration [195-?]
58 p. illus. 28 cm.
Cover title.
"Prepared for the Technical Cooperation Administration."
Bibliography: p. 58.

1. Building, Adobe. 2. Dwellings—Egypt. I. U. S. Technical Cooperation Administration. II. Title.

TH117.L5 61-61966 rev

NL 0410153 DLC NN

Little, (Arthur D.) Inc.
Diversification: an opportunity for the New England textile industry. A report. [Boston] Published by The Federal Reserve Bank of Boston, 1955.
ix,109p. illus.

1. Textile industry and fabrics - New England. I. Title.

IU NcD
NL 0410154 ScU GAT NN MiU NcU ICU MiD NBC MH-BA

338.47 L72ec Little (Arthur D.) inc.
The economic feasibility of establishing a tire manufacturing facility in Puerto Rico; report to the Government Development Bank for Puerto Rico and Tire Mart., inc. Cambridge, Mass., 1954.
ix, 71p. 28cm.

1. Tire industry--Puerto Rico. I. Government Development Bank for Puerto Rico. II. Tire Mart, inc. III. Title.

NL 0410155 IU

Little (Arthur D.) inc.
Economic study of inland transportation in Egypt; report to U. S. Government Foreign Operations Administration under contract SCC-21504, C-58780-13. Cambridge, Mass., 1954.
v, 57 p. tables. 29 cm.

1. Transportation—Egypt. I. U. S. Foreign Operations Administration. II. Title.

HE283.L5 58-37754 rev

NL 0410156 DLC

Little (Arthur D.) inc.
The Egyptian capital market; report to U. S. Government Technical Cooperation Administration, under contract SCC-21504, C-58780-8. Cambridge, Mass., 1953.
iv, 52 p. tables. 29 cm.
"Errata" slip inserted.

1. Savings and investment—Egypt. I. U. S. Technical Cooperation Administration. II. Title.

HG5832.L48 58-38078 rev

NL 0410157 DLC

HE 367 .L78 Little (Arthur D.) inc.
Egyptian highway study; report to U.S.Government Foreign Operations Administration. Based on material presented in memorandum by Charles M.Upham Associates,inc.,subcontractor to Arthur D.Little, inc. Cambridge, 1954.
143 p. illus.,fold.maps. 29 cm.
"Under Contract SCC-21504,C-58780-1."
This final report supplements the Progress report of July 15,1953. cf.p.l.
1.Roads--Egypt. I.Upham (Charles M.) Associates,inc. II.U.S. Foreign Operations Administration. III.Title.

NL 0410158 MiU

Little (Arthur D.) inc.
Egyptian vegetable oil industry; report to U. S. Government Foreign Operations Administration, under contract TA62-102-4001, C-59200-1. Cambridge, Mass., 1955.
ix, 83 p. fold. map, diagrs., tables. 29 cm.

1. Oil industries—Egypt. I. U. S. Foreign Operations Administration. II. Title.

HD9490.E32L5 58-38077 rev

NL 0410159 DLC

J 745.7 D43p no.12 Little, Arthur D., Inc.
An evaluation of tropical fruit production and processing potential in Western Nigeria and a suggested prerequisite programme.
25 p. (Western Nigeria Development Project. Project analysis, no.12)

1.Agriculture - Nigeria, Western.

NL 0410160 MBU

Little (Arthur D.) inc.
Factors influencing investment in Egypt; report to U. S. Government Foreign Operations Administration, under contract SCC-21504, C-58780-10. Cambridge, Mass., 1954.
vii, 79 p. 29 cm.

1. Investments, Foreign—Egypt. I. U. S. Foreign Operations Administration. II. Title.

HG5832.L5 58-37755 rev

NL 0410161 DLC

Little (Arthur D.) inc.
Feasibility of an aluminum smelter in the North Dakota area; report to Resources Research Committee. Cambridge, Mass., 1954.
iii l., 34 p. tables. 29 cm.

1. Aluminum industry and trade—North Dakota. I. Resources Research Committee. II. Title.

HD9539.A7U59 56-17864 rev

NL 0410162 DLC

Little (Arthur D.) inc.
Fertilizer production in Egypt; report to U. S. Government Technical Cooperation Administration. Subsidiary agreement no. 3, under contract SCC-21504 C-58780-3. Cambridge, Mass., 1953.
33 l. tables. 29 cm.

1. Fertilizers and manures. I. U. S. Technical Cooperation Administration. II. Title.

S633.L595 58-38209 rev

NL 0410163 DLC

M08.71 L778f Little (Arthur D.), Inc.
Final report on development and manufacture of electric hygrometer elements for meteorological use to Camp Evans Signal Laboratory #24 Belmar, New Jersey. bridge, Mass., 1952.
26 p. illus., diagrs. 28cm.

Work done on contract No. DA-36-039-sc-165. File No. 136- 12-PH-50-5(1156) Department of the Army Project No. 3-36-06-026.

Signal Corps Project No. 24-732K-1, C-58178.
"References": p.26.

NL 0410165 DAS

Little (Arthur D.) inc.
Industrial bulletin of Arthur D. Little, inc. ... [v. 1- no. 1- ; Jan. 1927-
Cambridge, Mass., 1927-
v. illus., diagrs. 28cm. monthly.

1. U. S.—Indus.—Period. 2. Research, Industrial—Period. I. Title.

Library of Congress T21.L5 32-7026
605

PU-Sc NNCC
NL 0410166 DLC IU CU OrCS NN ICJ DSI OU OCU OC1

Little (Arthur D.) inc.
Industrial bulletin of Arthur D. Little, inc.
see also its The bulletin.

Little (Arthur D.) inc.
Industrial opportunities in North Dakota; report to Resources Research Committee. [Cambridge, Mass.] 1955.
x, 166 p. diagrs., tables. 29 cm.
Bibliographical footnotes.

1. North Dakota—Indus. I. Resources Research Committee. II. Title.

HC107.N9L5 56-17855 rev

NL 0410168 DLC NN

VOLUME 336

Pamphlet
T
25+
Little (Arthur D.) inc.
Industrial opportunities in Rhode Island. Part I: Selection of industries suited to Rhode Island. Report to Textron, inc., C-58938. Cambridge, 1953.
ix,50 l. 28cm.

1. Industries, Location of--Rhode Island. 2. Rhode Island--Industries. I. Title.

NL 0410169 NIC

Little, (Arthur D.) inc.
Industrial research; what it means to British industry
see under Hartley, Sir Harold, 1878-

Little (Arthur D.) inc.
Industrial uses of radioactive materials, a selected bibliography. Cambridge, Mass. [1949]
v, 13 p. 28 cm.
Cover title.

1. Radioactive tracers—Bibl. 2. Radioactivity—Bibl. I. Title.

Z7144.R2L5 016.6 49-6281 rev*

CU ICJ OrCS
NL 0410171 DLC IdPI OrP ICU OCl NNC MH-BA NcD PBL

Little (Arthur D.) inc.
Lignite and U. S. energy supplies; report to Resources Research Committee. Cambridge, Mass., 1953.
93 p. diagrs., tables. 29 cm.

1. Lignite. 2. Power resources—U. S. I. Resources Research Committee. II. Title.

TP329.L523 56-15720 rev

NL 0410172 DLC

Little (Arthur D.) inc.
The Little journal; pub. occasionally by Arthur D. Little, inc. ... Boston, 1914-19.
5 nos. 34 cm.

NL 0410173 CtY

Little (Arthur D.) inc.
Locating a chloralkali plant in North Dakota; report to Resources Research Committee. [Cambridge, Mass.] 1955.
iii, 21 l. diagrs., tables. 29 cm.

1. Salt industry and trade—North Dakota. I. Resources Research Committee. II. Title.

TN903.N6L5 56-16623 rev

NL 0410174 DLC

Little (Arthur D.) inc.
Management of industrial research; a selected and annotated bibliography. Cambridge, Mass., 1950.
vi, 14 p. illus. 28 cm.

1. Research, Industrial—Abstracts. 2. Research, Industrial—Bibl. I. Title.

T175.L55 016.607 50-8943 rev

MH-BA
NL 0410175 DLC ICJ OrP NN GAT DNAL CU ViU NNC MiD

Little (Arthur D.) inc.
The manufacture of phosphate rock derivatives in North Dakota; report to Resources Research Committee. [Cambridge, Mass.] 1955.
iii, 22 l. diagrs., tables. 29 cm.

1. Phosphate industry—North Dakota. I. Resources Research Committee. II. Title.

TN914.N57L5 56-16615 rev

NL 0410176 DLC

Little (Arthur D.) inc.
Marketing potential for oilseed protein materials in industrial uses. Washington [U. S. Govt. Print. Off.] 1951.
i, 120 p. 24 cm. (U. S. Dept. of Agriculture. Technical bulletin no. 1043)
Cover title.
"Literature cited": p. 119-120.

1. Proteins. 2. Oilseed plants. [1. 2. Oil-seed proteins] I. Title. (Series)

S21.A72 no. 1043 338.476653 Agr 51-404 rev
U. S. Nat'l Agr. Libr. for Library of Congress 1Ag84Te no. 1043 [r62f]†

NL 0410177 DNAL DLC Or WaS

Little, (Arthur D.) Inc.
On the making of silk purses from sows' ears. A contribution to philosophy.
Cambridge, Mass. 1921. (1), 9 pp. Colored plate. Vignettes. Facsimiles. 23 × 10 cm.

M3259 — Silk. Artificial. — Silk purses from sow's ears. On the making of.

NL 0410178 MB NNU-W MiU ICJ OClWHi OO CU

Little (Arthur D.) inc.
Opportunities for Egypt in the European market; report to U. S. Government Foreign Operations Administration, under contract SCC-21504, C-58780-20. Cambridge, Mass., 1954.
ix, 117 p. tables. 29 cm.

1. Egypt—Comm. 2. Cotton trade—Egypt. I. U. S. Foreign Operations Administration. II. Title.

HF3886.L5 58-38079 rev

NL 0410179 DLC

Little (Arthur D.) inc.
Opportunities for industrial development in Egypt; report to U. S. government Foreign operations administration under contract SCC-21504 C-58780. Cairo, Govt. press, 1955. ix, 168 p. tables. 27cm.
At head of title: Republic of Egypt. Ministry of commerce and industry.

1. Economic history—Egypt. 2. Egypt—Economic history. 3. Industries—Egypt. I. Egypt. Commerce and industry ministry. II. United States. Foreign operations administration. t. 1955.

NL 0410180 NN DNAL MH-BA NjP

Little (Arthur D.) inc.
Opportunities for the Egyptian chemical industry; report to U. S. Government International Cooperation Administration, under contract TA62-102-4001, C-59200. Cambridge, Mass., 1955.
xiii, 120 p. illus. 29 cm.

1. Chemical industries—Egypt. I. U. S. International Cooperation Administration. II. Title. III. Title: Egyptian chemical industry.

HD9658.E3L5 338.4766 57-37574 rev

NL 0410181 DLC

HC107
.T3L5
Little (Arthur D.) Inc.
The opportunity for industrial development in Benton, Houston, and Humphreys counties, Tennessee; report to the Area Redevelopment Administration, C-65063. [Cambridge? Mass.]
viii, 135 p. incl.maps(part fold.) tables. 29 cm.

1. Benton County, Tenn.--Ind. 2. Houston County, Tenn.--Ind. 3. Humphreys County, Tenn.--Ind. I. U.S. Area Development Administration.

NL 0410182 T

Little (Arthur D.) inc.
... The paper making qualities of Hawaiian bagasse, by Arthur D. Little, inc. ... Honolulu, Hawaii, 1919.
51 p. 23 cm. (Report of the Experiment station of the Hawaiian sugar planters' association. Agricultural and chemical series. Bulletin no. 46)

1. Bagasse. 2. Paper making and trade. I. Title: Hawaiian bagasse.

SB231.H3 no. 46 Agr 20-122 rev 2
U. S. Nat'l Agr. Libr. for Library of Congress 100H31B no. 46 [r62e1]†

NL 0410183 DNAL DLC MB

Little (Arthur D.) inc.
Paper production and consumption in Egypt; report to U. S. Government Foreign Operations Administration under contract SCC-21504, C-58780-21. Cambridge, Mass., 1954.
iii, 25 l. diagrs., tables. 29 cm.

1. Paper making and trade—Egypt. I. U. S. Foreign Operations Administration. II. Title.

HD9837.E32L5 58-37753 rev

NL 0410184 DLC NN

Little (Arthur D.) inc.
The petroleum outlook. Cambridge, Mass. [1920]
18 p. illus., fold. maps. 30 cm.

1. Petroleum—U. S. I. Title.

TN872.A5L5 21-1905 rev*

NL 0410185 DLC DNLM MH ICJ

660
L73p
Little, (Arthur D.) inc.
Professional papers, no.1-7: Contributions to engineering chemistry by members of the staff of Arthur D. Little, inc., chemists and engineers Boston, 1908-17.
7 no.

Cover-title.
No.1-3 have title: Professional papers ... Contributions to engineering chemistry by members of the staff of the Arthur D. Little laboratory.
No more published.

NL 0410186 IU MB OCl OO OrCS DI-GS DBS CU ICJ

408.71
L778i
Little (Arthur D), Inc.
Progress report no.7-50 on improvement of electric hygrometer elements for meteorological use. Covering month of October 1946 - July 1950. To Camp Evans Signal Laboratory, Belmar, New Jersey. C-57590. [Cambridge, Mass.] 1946-1950.
44 v. in 5. illus., diagrs. 28cm.

Work done on contract No. W-36-039-SC-32054. File No. 12102-PH-46-91(SCEL) Department of the Army Project 3-99-07-022. Signal Corps Project 172B.
Reports no.1-6 not available.
Contains Final and summary report.
Processed.

NL 0410188 DAS

VOLUME 336

Little (Arthur D.) Inc.,
The purchase of coal.
Boston. [1909.] 15 pp. 23 cm.

L4204 — Coal.

NL 0410189 MB MH NN

Little (Arthur D.) inc.
Recommendations for design and operation of milk pasteurizing plant of the Société misr laitière et alimentaire; report prepared under contract no. TA62-102-4001, C-59200, with the Foreign Operations Administration of the United States. [Cambridge, Mass.] 1955.
iii, 42 l. illus. 29 cm.

1. Société misr laitière et alimentaire, Cairo. 2. Dairy plants. I. U. S. Foreign Operations Administration. II. Title.

SF247.L5 637.1323 57-42126 rev

NL 0410190 DLC

LITTLE (ARTHUR D.) INC.
Report.
Cambridge. no. illus. 23cm.

Annual.

NL 0410191 NN ICJ FTaSU

Little (Arthur D.) inc.
Report on a survey of industrial opportunities in New England, to the Federal Reserve Bank of Boston. Cambridge, 1952.
399 p. 28 cm.
Cover title.
Errata slip laid in.

1. New England—Indus. I. Federal Reserve Bank of Boston. II. Title: Industrial opportunities in New England.

A54-3565

Michigan. Univ. Libr. for Library of Congress

NL 0410192 MiU CaBVaU OrCS NN MH-BA NNC NBuG MB KU PU-W NcD MiD OU PSt OCl

Little (Arthur D.) inc.
Report on design for volume reduction of combustible radioactive wastes by incineration. Oak Ridge, Tenn, Technical Information Service, 1950.
iv, 194 p. illus., diagrs. 28 cm. (U. S. Atomic Energy Commission. ALI-C-57867)

1. Radioactive waste disposal. 2. Refuse destructors. I. Title. (Series)

TD812.L5 53-60764 rev

NL 0410193 DLC

Little (Arthur D.) inc.
Report on limestone deposits in New England and shipping costs of cement to Federal Reserve Bank of Boston./ Cambridge, Mass., 1953.
29 l. maps. (C-58761)

Report prepared at the request of the Federal Reserve Bank in order to supplement the findings of the Survey of industrial opportunities in New England. - Letter of transmittal.

NL 0410194 MH-BA

Little (Arthur D.) inc.
Report on new industries for Puerto Rico to Puerto Rico development corporation, C-57289. [Cambridge, Mass.] 1942.
2 p. l., 4, 124 (i. e. 131) numb. l. 29 x 23 cm.
Reproduced from type-written copy.
A preliminary report. cf. leaf 5.

1. Puerto Rico—Indus. I. Puerto Rico development company, San Juan. II. Title.

HC157.P8L5 330.97295 43-53233 rev

NL 0410195 DLC

Little (Arthur D.) inc.
Report on survey of alternatives for olive oil in processes of wool manufacture to The National association of wool manufacturers. National association of wool manufacturers, °1938.
84 p. fold. charts.

Cover title.
Bibliography: p.59-77.

I. National association of wool manufacturers.

NL 0410196 MiD

TH145 L7
Little (Arthur D.) Inc.
Report on technological developments in the building industry to President's Materials Policy Commission. Cambridge, Mass., 1951.
137 l. tables. 29 cm.
"C-58374."

1. Building materials. 2. Building trades. I. U.S. President's Materials Policy Commission. II Title: Technolog- ical developments in the building industry.

NL 0410197 DI

BMA 856 L77
Little (Arthur D.) inc.
Report on Ten-Year Industrial Plan for Puerto Rico to Puerto Rico Economic Development Administration, January 2, 1951. Cambridge, Mass., 1951.
vi, 100 p. illus. (C57315-51)

1.Puerto Rico - Industries. 2.Puerto Rico - Economic conditions. 3.Economic planning - Puerto Rico. I.Puerto Rico. Economic Development Administra- tion.

NL 0410198 MH-BA

Little (Arthur D.) inc.
Report to State of West Virginia. [Cambridge, Mass.] 1955.
1 v. (various pagings)
Contents. - Survey of industrial development. - Community development program. - The metal-working industry. - Chemicals and related processing. - The apparel industry. - Wood and wood products.

NL 0410199 OCl PPFRB

Little (Arthur D.) inc.
Research in the physical and structural analysis of high polymers by punched card methods; final report by Gilbert W. King. [Washington, U. S. Dept. of Commerce. Office of Technical Services] 1953.
41 p. tables. 27 cm.
At head of title: Office of Naval Research, contract N6-onr-228, T. O. II, project NR 330-006.
"PB 111485."
Bibliography: p. 41.

1. Punched card systems—Polymers and polymerization. I. King, Gilbert William, 1914- II. Title.

TP156.P6L5 55-60023 rev

NL 0410200 DLC

Little (Arthur D.) Inc.
Safety manual for ship salvage operations, section two. Cambridge, Mass., Arthur D. Little, Inc., 1943.
82p.

NL 0410201 ICRL

Little (Arthur D.) Inc.
Samples of paper made from sugar cane fibre prepared by the Simmons process. Boston, Mass.: A. D. Little, Inc., 1913. 5 l., 4 pl., 43 sample sheets. 4°.

1. Paper.—Manufacture. January 29, 1919.

NL 0410202 NN

Little (Arthur D.) inc.
Science & industry; being abstracts of addresses delivered to the American association for the advancement of science at Kansas City, between December 28, 1925, and January 2, 1926. Cambridge, Mass. [1926]
24 p.
Reprinted from Mechanical engineering of February, 1926.

NL 0410203 MH-BA

Little (Arthur D.) inc.
A short bibliography of sulfite alcohol; a list of articles on the production of alcohol from sulfite wast liquor
see under West, Clarence Jay, 1886-

Little (Arthur D.) Inc.
Studies in operations research.
Cambridge, Mass. [195-?
6 v. in 1.

NL 0410205 MH-BA

Little (Arthur D.) inc.
Study of proposed slaughterhouse for the municipality of Cairo; report to U. S. Government International Cooperation Administration, under contract TA-62-102-4001, C-59200. Cambridge, Mass., 1955.
17 l., 5 fold. plans. 29 cm.

1. Slaughtering and slaughter-houses—Egypt—Cairo. I. U. S. International Cooperation Administration. II. Title: Proposed slaughterhouse for the municipality of Cairo.

TS1967.C3L5 58-38168 rev

NL 0410206 DLC

Little (Arthur D.) inc.
Study of the feasibility of utilizing lignite in the iron ore industry; report to Resources Research Committee. [Cambridge, Mass.] 1955.
v, 49 p. diagrs., tables. 29 cm.
Bibliography: p. 48-49.

1. Lignite. 2. Iron ores. I. Resources Research Committee. II. Title: Feasibility of utilizing lignite in the iron ore industry.

TP329.L526 56-16616 rev

NL 0410207 DLC NN

VOLUME 336

Little (Arthur D.) inc.
Sulfuric acid production; report to U. S. Government Foreign Operations Administration, under contract SCC-21504, C-58780-6. Cambridge, Mass., 1954.
iv, 16 l. tables. 29 cm.

1. Sulphuric acid industry. I. U. S. Foreign Operations Administration. II. Title.

HD9660.S79L5 58-37756 rev

NL 0410208 DLC NN

G338
qL721s Little (Arthur D.) inc.

Summary of industrial opportunities in North Dakota and adjoining areas; report to Resources Research Committee. [Cambridge] 1955.

xiii, 50 p. maps, tables. 29cm.

1. North Dakota. Industries. I. Resources Research Committee. II. Ti: Industrial (thru areas)

NL 0410209 MnU MH-BA

Little (Arthur D.) inc.
A summary of the status of research on the mechanism of combustion. [Silver Spring, Md.] 1946.
36, [20] p. 28 cm. (Bumblebee series, rept. no. 47)
At head of title: The Johns Hopkins University, Applied Physics Laboratory, Silver Spring, Maryland. [Section T, Operating under contract NOrd 7386 with the Bureau of Ordnance, U. S. Navy.
"This report is one part of a survey of the literature on combustion prepared by Arthur D. Little, inc., for the Applied Physics Laboratory, the Johns Hopkins University. The survey was conducted and the report written under the direction of Dr. W. H. Avery."
Letter of transmittal and Foreword ([4] p.) inserted.
Bibliography: p. [37]-[56]
1. Combustion research. 2. Combustion—Bibl. I. Johns Hopkins University. Applied Physics Laboratory, Silver Spring, Md. II. Title. (Series)

QD516.L6 56-43395 rev

NL 0410210 DLC

Little (Arthur D.) inc.
Summary report on the metalworking study; report to the U. S. Government International Cooperation Administration, under contract no. TA-62-102-4001. [Cambridge, Mass., 1955.
ii, 37 l. 29 cm.

1. Iron industry and trade—Egypt. 2. Steel industry and trade—Egypt. I. U. S. International Cooperation Administration. II. Title: Metalworking study.

HD9527.E32L5 57-37870 rev

NL 0410211 DLC

Little (Arthur D.) inc.
Survey of industrial development. Report to state of West Virginia
see its Report to State of West Virginia.

Little (Arthur D.) inc.
FOR OTHER EDITIONS SEE MAIN ENTRY
Griffin, Roger Castle, *ed.*
Technical methods of analysis, as employed in the laboratories of Arthur D. Little, inc., Cambridge, Mass., edited by Roger Castle Griffin ... 2d ed. New York [etc.] McGraw-Hill book company, inc., 1927.

Little (Arthur D.) inc.
Technology of lignite; report to Resources Research Committee. Cambridge, Mass., 1954.
vii, 82 p. maps, diagrs., tables. 29 cm.
Bibliography: p. 79-82.

1. Lignite. I. Resources Research Committee. II. Title.

TP329.L528 56-16617 rev

NL 0410214 DLC NN

M75.1
L778w Little (Arthur D.), Inc.
Warm fog and stratus cloud dissipation. Quarterly report no.3 to Signal Corps Supply Agency. Cambridge, Mass., 1953.
3 p. 26cm.

At head of title: Security information. Restricted [unclassified]
Contract No. DA-36-039 SC-42585; file No. 13155-PH-53-91(2209)
Photostat.

NL 0410215 DAS

Little (Arthur D.) inc., Industrial Economics Group
The technology behind investment; three reviews of the petrochemicals, drugs and synthetic fiber industries. Presented at the Investment Banking Seminar held under the sponsorship of the Investment Bankers Association of America and Wharton School of Finance and Commerce at the University of Pennsylvania, June 23-27, 1952. Cambridge, Mass. [1952?]
25 [1] p. illus.

Cover title.

NL 0410216 MiD MH-BA OrCS PWpM

Little (Arthur D.) inc. Mechanical Division.
Low temperature bibliography for the field of cryogenics. Cambridge, Mass.[1952]
63 p.

——— Supplement. no.1-9; 1953-Mar.1957. Cambridge, Mass.

Supplement no.9, Mar.1957 published by A.D. Little Inc., Engineering Division.

Superseded by A bibliography of low temperature engineering and research.

I. Little (Arthur D.) inc., Cambridge, Mass. Engineering Division. II. Title. 016.53656 536.56 016.54279 542.79

NL 0410218 ICJ MiU IU IEN NcD

Little, Arthur Dehon, 1863-1935.
... The basis of quality in paper, by Arthur D. Little ... Boston, 1910.
cover-title, 10 p. 23cm. (Professional papers, no. 4. Contributions to engineering chemistry by members of the staff of Arthur D. Little, inc.)

1. Paper.

11-9981

Library of Congress TS1109.L75

NL 0410219 DLC CU OU MiU NN MB

Little, Arthur Dehon, 1863-1935.
Canada ascendant; an address, by Arthur D. Little... given at the College of Business Administration as the introductory lecture in a course on Canadian resources and industries, and later given, by request, before the members and guests of the Canadian Club of Boston, at the twenty-third annual banquet of the club. [Boston, Mass: Boston University, 1922.] 17 p. 8°.

1. Economic history, Canada.

October 30, 1923.

NL 0410220 NN

Little, Arthur Dehon, 1863-1935
... The chemist and the community, by Arthur D. Little. Boston, 1908.
cover-title, 11 p. 22½cm. (Professional papers, no. 1; contributions to engineering chemistry by members of the staff of the Arthur D. Little laboratory)
"An address delivered at Columbia university, December 27, 1906, before the American chemical society and section C of the American association for the advancement of science."

1. Chemistry.

A 11-1513

Illinois. Univ. Library for Library of Congress [a40b1]

NL 0410221 IU CU MB

Little, Arthur Dehan, 1863-1935.
The chemistry behind the dollar. An address delivered under the auspices of the American chemical society at the 30th annual convention of the New York state bankers' association, Atlantic City, June 13, 1923. Cambridge, Mass. Arthur D. Little, inc. [1923]
15 p.

NL 0410222 MH-BA

Little, Arthur Dehon, 1863-1935, joint author.
Griffin, Russell B.
The chemistry of paper-making, together with the principles of general chemistry; a handbook for the student and manufacturer, by R. B. Griffin and A. D. Little. New York, H. Lockwood & co., 1894.

Little, Arthur D[ehon], 1863-1935.
The cotton fibre substance and its properties. [Boston, 1909]
9 p. 8°. (Nat. Assoc. of Cotton Manufacturers)
n.t.-p.
Advance copy.

NL 0410224 NN

Little, Arthur Dehon, 1863-1935.
Developing the estate, by Arthur D. Little... [Boston, 1919.] 12 p. 8°.
Repr.: Atlantic monthly. March, 1919.

1. Land settlement, U. S.

July 6, 1920.

NL 0410225 NN

Little, A[rthur] Dehon, 1863-1935.
The durability of paper. By A. D. Little. Boston, Little & Walker [1903]
cover-title, [4] p. 28½ x 21½cm.
"From the Printing art (June, 1903, vol. I, no. 4)"

Subject entries: Paper.

3-21649

Library of Congress, no. Z247.L5.

NL 0410226 DLC NN

VOLUME 336

Little, Arthur Dehon, 1863-1935.
The dyestuff situation and its lesson; address before Chamber of commerce of the United States of America at Washington, February 5, 1915, by Arthur D. Little. Boston, Mass., Arthur D. Little, inc., 1915.
cover-title, 1 p. l., 10 p. 23cm.

1. Dyes and dyeing. I. Title.
16-1132
Library of Congress TP910.L5

NL 0410227 DLC MB OU NjP

Little, Arthur Dehon, 1863-1935.
... The earning power of chemistry, by Arthur D. Little ... Boston, 1911.
cover-title, 19 p. 23cm. (Professional papers, no. 5. Contributions to engineering chemistry by members of the staff of Arthur D. Little, inc.)
"A public lecture to business men delivered under the auspices of the American chemical society at Indianapolis, June 29, 1911."
"Reprinted from the Journal of industrial and engineering chemistry. vol. 3, no. 8. August, 1911."

1. Chemistry—Addresses, essays, lectures.
13-22
Library of Congress TP185.L6

NL 0410228 DLC CU Or OO MiU

Little, Arthur Dehon, 1863-1935.
The earning power of chemistry. By Arthur D. Little. [Easton? Pa., 1911]
cover-title, 18 p. 23cm.
"Reprinted from the Journal of industrial and engineering chemistry, vol. 3, no. 8, August, 1911."
Also issued as Professional papers, no. 5. Contributions to engineering chemistry by members of the staff of Arthur D. Little, inc.

1. Chemistry—Addresses, essays, lectures. I. Title.
22-23497
Library of Congress TP185.L6 1911 a

NL 0410229 DLC WaS NN MB

Little, Arthur Dehon, 1863-1935.
The fifth estate.
463
+F8728 From Science, n.s., v.60, p.299-306, Oct.3, 1924.
"Delivered in connection with centenary celebration of the founding of the Franklin institute and the inauguration exercises of the Bartol research foundation on September 19, 1924."

NL 0410230 CtY

Little, Arthur Dehon, 1863-1935.
The fifth estate.
463
+F8728 From The Atlantic monthly, Dec., 1924, p.771-781.
Address delivered on the occasion of the centenary celebration of the founding of the Franklin institute and the inauguration exercises of the Bartol research foundation, September 17, 18, 19, 1924.

NL 0410231 CtY

Little, Arthur Dehon, 1863-1935.
The fifth estate; an address by Arthur D. Little ... on the occasion of the centenary celebration of the founding of the Franklin institute and the inauguration exercises of the Bartol research foundation, September 17, 18, 19, 1924. Philadelphia, The Franklin institute [1925]
22 p. 25cm.

1. Science—Addresses, essays, lectures. 2. Scientists. 3. Franklin institute, Philadelphia. 4. Franklin, Benjamin, 1706-1790. I. Title.
25-10374
Library of Congress Q171.L7

GAT NIC OO OCl
NL 0410232 DLC DL ViU OCU IdB NN ICJ MH OClW OU

Little, Arthur Dehon, 1863-1935.
463
+F8728 The fifth estate, delivered in connection with the centenary celebration of the founding of the Franklin institute and the inauguration exercises of the Bartol research foundation, September 19, 1924, and published in the Journal of the Franklin institute, volume 198, number 5 ... [New York, 1925]
[18]p., 1l. 23cm.
"Reprinted by the Chemical foundation, inc. through the courtesy of the Atlantic monthly."

NL 0410233 CtY DLC OO

Little, Arthur Dehon, 1863-1935.
The handwriting on the wall; a chemist's interpretation, by Arthur D. Little, CH. D. Boston, Little, Brown, and company, 1928.
viii p., 2 l., [3]-287 p. 21½cm.

1. Chemistry, Technical—Addresses, essays, lectures. I. Title.
28-23441
Library of Congress TP7.L5

KEmT CU DAU PSt
OClW OO OCU MiU OU ViU NN MB ICJ MH-BA NIC NcRS NcU
NL 0410234 DLC CaBVaU WaS OrPR OrP ICJ ODW OOxM OCl

Little, Arthur Dehon, 1863-1935.
... Impending changes in our use of fuels, presented by Arthur D. Little ... to the meeting of the Foundation at the University club in New York, May 19, 1927 ... New York city, 1927.
16 p. 15½cm. (Engineering foundation. Publication no. 14)

1. Fuel.
27-15182
Library of Congress TA1.E582 no. 14

NL 0410235 DLC NN NIC MiU OU OrCS

Little, Arthur Dehon, 1863-1935.
Industrial applications of cellulose thiocarbonates and products derived therefrom, by Arthur D. Little. (In: Clayton Beadle. New cellulose derivatives. 1894. 8°. p. 12-17).

1. Cellulose.—Derivatives.
March 27, 1914

NL 0410236 NN

Little, Arthur Dehon, 1863-1935.
... "Industrial research," an address by President Arthur D. Little of the American chemical society. President Scherer's address to the freshmen. Pasadena, Cal., 1913.
35 p. 21cm. (Throop college bulletin, vol. XXII, no. 61)

1. Research. I. Scherer, James Augustin Brown, 1870- II. Title.
17-10932
Library of Congress T65.L65

NL 0410237 DLC OrU NN

Little, Arthur D[ehon], 1863-1935.
Industrial research in America; presidential address before the American Chemical Society, at Rochester, New York, September 9, 1913. Boston: A. D. Little, Inc., 1913. 23 p. 8°.
Repr.: Jour. of industrial and engineering chemistry. October, 1913.
Title from cover.
——— [Easton, Pa., 1913.] 21 p. 8°.
Repr. Jour. of industrial and engineering chemistry. October, 1913.
Title from cover.

1. Industries and mechanic arts.—History. 2. Laboratories.
January 8, 1914

NL 0410238 NN NNC WaS OO IU

[Little, Arthur Dehon] 1863-1935.
Industrial research laboratories Arthur D. Little, inc., dedicated to industrial progress. [Cambridge, Mass., The Murray printing company, 1918]
31, [1] p. illus. 23cm.
Caption title.
Signed: Arthur D. Little, inc.
On cover: Chemistry in overalls.

1. Research, Industrial. 2. Technology. I. Title.
22-11578
Library of Congress T178.L5

NL 0410239 DLC

Little, Arthur Dehon, 1863-1935.
The industrial resources and opportunities of the South; address before American chemical society at New Orleans, Louisiana, April 1, 1915, and Atlanta Chamber of commerce, and Georgia section American chemical society, at Atlanta, Georgia, April 5, 1915, by Arthur D. Little. Boston, Mass., Arthur D. Little, inc., 1915.
cover-title, 1 p. l., 18 p. 23cm.

1. Southern states—Econ. condit. 2. Natural resources. I. Title.
16-1091
Library of Congress HC107.A8L5

NL 0410240 DLC OU

[Little, Arthur Dehon,] 1863-1935.
...Lo que aporta la ciencia a las industrias manufactureras ... Washington, D. C.: La Unión panamericana[, 1926]. ii, 13 p. 8°. (Pan American Union. Finanzas, industria, comercio. no. 14.)
"Por A. D. Little," p. 1.
Repr.: Pan American Union. Boletin.
Translated from his article in the Annals of the Amer. Acad. of Political and Social Science, May, 1925.

1. Industries and mechanic arts—Research. 2. Ser.
N. Y. P. L. January 18, 1928

NL 0410241 NN

Little, Arthur Dehon, 1863-1935.
Natural resources in their relation to military supplies. By Arthur D. Little.
(In Smithsonian institution. Annual report, 1919. Washington, 1921. 23½cm. p. 211-237)

1. Military supplies. 2. Natural resources.
22-386
Library of Congress Q11.S66 1919

NL 0410242 DLC ICJ WaS

Little, Arthur Dehon, 1863-1935.
On the making of silk purses from sows' ears
see under Little, (Arthur D.) Inc.

Little, Arthur Dehon, 1863-1935.
Organization of industrial research. By ... n.p. [1918]
10 p.

Reprinted from the copyrighted Proceedings of the American society for testing materials. Philadelphia, col. 18, part 2, 1918. At head of title: topical discussion on Cooperation in industrial research.

NL 0410244 OO

VOLUME 336

Little, Arthur Dehon, 1863- 1935.
... The relation of research to industrial development, by Arthur D. Little ... address before Canadian manufacturers association, Toronto. Boston, 1917.
cover-title, 17 p. 23cm. (Professional papers no. 7. Contributions to engineering chemistry by members of the staff of Arthur D. Little, inc.)
1. Research, Industrial. 2. Chemistry, Technical. I. Title.
Library of Congress T65.L67 17—21995

NL 0410245 DLC NN MB OO OU Or CU

Little, Arthur Dehon, 1863- 1935.
Report of Arthur D. Little, official chemist of the American paper and pulp association, read at the annual meeting, February 6th, 1908. [Boston? 1908]
cover-title, 8 p. 23cm.
1. Paper-making and trade. I. American paper and pulp association.
8-27579
Library of Congress TS1109.L78

NL 0410246 DLC

Little, Arthur Dehon, 1863-1935.
Research; the mother of industry. [n.p., 1924]
[5] p.
Reprinted from The scientific monthly, August 1924, v. 19, p. 165-169.

NL 0410247 MH-BA

Little, Arthur Dehon, 1863- 1935.
The romance of carbon, by Arthur D. Little ...
(*In* Smithsonian institution. Annual report, 1926. Washington, 1927. 23½cm. p. 235-255)
"Reprinted ... from Industrial and engineering chemistry, vol. 18, no. 5 ... May, 1926."
1. Carbon.
Library of Congress Q11.S66 1926 27-24978

NL 0410248 DLC ViU OClMN MiU ODW OClJC OU OCl ICJ

Little, Arthur Dehon, 1863-1935.
... Some important research problems of today. [Brooklyn, Polytechnic Institute, 1927]
[6] p.
An address delivered at the Polytechnic institute of Brooklyn, May 3 and 4, 1927.

NL 0410249 MH-BA

Little, Arthur D[ehon] 1863-1935.
The untilled field of chemistry. Address of the Chairman of the Division of Industrial Chemists and Chemical Engineers, Baltimore, Dec. 29, 1908. [Easton, Pa.? 1909]
5 p. 8°.
Repr.: Jour. of Industrial and Engineering Chemistry. V. 1[2], 1909.

NL 0410250 NN

Little, Arthur H., ed.
System and business management. v. 1-3, June 1928-Dec. 1929; v. 57-64; Jan. 1930-June 1935. [Chicago, The System company; etc., etc., 1928-29; New York, McGraw-Hill publishing company, inc., etc., 1929-35]

Little, Arthur H.
Technical publicity association.
25 years of the Technical publicity association, inc., the world's oldest technical advertising association 1905-1930 ... [New York, Printed by Tri-arts press, 1930]

Little, Arthur Mitchell, 1865-
Mendelssohn's music to the Antigone of Sophocles, by Arthur M. Little ... Washington, D. C., Printed by Gibson brothers, 1893
2 p. l., 91, [1] p. 24cm.
Inaug.-diss.—Leipzig.
Vita.
"Books of reference": p. [90]-91.
1. *Mendelssohn-Bartholdy, Felix, 1809-1847. Antigone. 2. Greek drama (Tragedy)—Hist. & crit. 3. Sophocles. Antigone.
Library of Congress ML410.M5L4 6-5763

NL 0410253 DLC NcGU NjP

Little, Arthur Reginald.
[The city of sleep]
... Four songs: The city of sleep, by Arthur Reginald Little. Take, O, take those lips away, from Measure for measure, two settings by John Beach and Frederic Ayres. Eskimo love song, by Stanley R. Avery ... Newton Center, Mass., The Wa-wan press, 1906.
1 p. l., 13 p. 34½ x 27cm. (Wa-wan series of American compositions ... Vol. v <winter quarter, pt. 1> no. 33)
Words of the songs are by Rudyard Kipling, Shakespeare and Frances C. Lamont, respectively.
1. Songs with piano. I. Beach, John Parsons, 1877- Take, O, take those lips away. II. Ayres, Frederic, 1876-1926. Take, O, take those lips away. III. Avery, Stanley R., 1879- Eskimo love song. IV. Kipling, Rudyard, 1865-1936. The brushwood boy. V. Shakespeare, William. Measure for measure. VI. Lamont, Frances C. Eskimo love song.
Library of Congress M1.W35 vol. 5, no. 33 45-52712

NL 0410255 DLC OClW MB NN ICN

Little, Arthur Reginald.
[Ulalume]
Three pianoforte compositions: I. Ulalume, by Arthur Reginald Little. II. Negro episode, by Henry F. Gilbert. III. Ichibuzzhi, by Arthur Farwell. Newton Center, Mass., The Wa-wan press, 1902.
3 p. l., 5-16 p. 34½ x 26½cm. [Wa-wan series of American compositions, v. 1, no. 6]
Ichibuzzhi, by A. G. Farwell, op. 13, is based on the composition of the same name in his set of American Indian melodies. cf. Introd.
1. Piano music. I. Gilbert, Henry Franklin Belknap, 1868-1928. Episodes, orchestra, op. 2, no. 2. Negro episode, arranged. II. Farwell, Arthur George, 1872- Ichibuzzhi.
Library of Congress M1.W35 vol. 1, no. 6 45-52728

NL 0410256 DLC MB ICN MH

Little, Arthur Reginald.
Three songs: Helen, and Drink to me only with thine eyes, by Arthur Reginald Little, and Salammbô's invocation to Tänith, by Henry F. Gilbert. Newton Center, Mass., The Wa-wan press, 1902.
3 p. l., 5-15 p. 34½ x 26½cm. [Wa-wan series of American compositions, v. 1, no. 5]
Salammbô's invocation to Tänith originally with orchestral accompaniment.
Words of the songs are by E. A. Poe, Ben Jonson and Gustave Flaubert, respectively. The Flaubert text is in English translation.
1. Songs with piano. I. Gilbert, Henry Franklin Belknap, 1868-1928. Salammbô's invocation to Tänith; arranged. II. Poe, Edgar Allan, 1809-1849. To Helen. III. Jonson, Ben, 1573?-1637. To Celia. IV. Flaubert, Gustave, 1821-1880. Salammbô.
Library of Congress M1.W35 vol. 1, no. 5 45-52784

NL 0410257 DLC ICN MH MB

Little, Arthur Shepard, 1872-
Formulae for obtaining from ordinary bond tables values for bonds at various unusual coupon rates from 3.01% to 6.50% ... devised and publisht by Arthur S. Little. St. Louis, ©1915.
[12] p. 14 tab. 17½cm. $2.50
1. Investments—Tables, etc.
Library of Congress HG4537.L6 15-18937

NL 0410258 DLC ICRL CU ICJ NN

Little, Arthur Shepard, 1872-
Table of factors for obtaining true values to the exact day of bonds or notes having a life of any number of years, months or days, on a basis of semiannual compound interest, computed by Arthur S. Little ... and Financial publishing company, Boston ... Boston, Financial publishing company; London, G. Routledge & sons, ltd. [©1926]
127 p. 21½cm.
1. Bonds. 2. Investments—Tables, etc. I. Financial publishing company.
Library of Congress HG4537.L67 26-22683

NL 0410259 DLC NNC ICJ

Little, Arthur Shepard, 1872-
Table of factors for obtaining true values to the exact day of bonds or notes having a life of any number of years, months or days, on a basis of semiannual compound interest, computed by Arthur S. Little ... and Financial publishing company, Boston. 2d ed. ... Boston, Financial publishing company; London, G. Routledge & sons, ltd. [©1927]
127, [1] p. 26cm.
1. Bonds. 2. Investments—Tables, etc. I. Financial publishing company.
Library of Congress HG4537.L67 1927 27-6861

NL 0410260 DLC

Little, Arthur Shepard, 1872-
A table of interpolation multipliers for obtaining through the means of calculating machines intermediate rates bond values at yield intervals of one ten-thousandth percent, devised and computed by Arthur S. Little ... Boston, Financial publishing company [©1927]
29 p. diagrs. 22cm.
Lettered on cover: Multipliers for intermediate yield rates.
1. Investments—Tables, etc. I. Title: Interpolation multipliers.
Library of Congress HG4537.L675 29-13882

NL 0410261 DLC IU

Little, Arthur Shepard, 1872-
A table of key numbers for obtaining with readiness and ease level-tax maturities for serial bonds, at various usual coupon rates to be retired in any number of instalments from 5 to 40 years ... devised and computed by Arthur S. Little ... St. Louis, ©1922.
63 p. incl. tables. 17cm.
On cover: Serial bond maturities.
1. Investments—Tables, etc. 2. Bonds.
Library of Congress HG4537.L5 22-13753

NL 0410262 DLC ICRL OCU

Little, Arthur West, 1873- 1943
Address of Arthur W. Little, chairman of board, J. J. Little & Ives Co., to his associates in the business of book printing and binding upon the occasion of the 65th anniversary of the founding of the business by Joseph J. Little, April 15, 1867. [1932?]
cover-title, 31 p. 18cm.

NL 0410263 NNC

Little, Arthur West, 1873-1943.
From Harlem to the Rhine; the story of New York's colored volunteers, by Arthur W. Little. New York, Covici, Friede [1936]
xviii, 382 p. front. (facsim.) plates, ports. 24½cm.
Illustrated lining-papers.
1. U. S. Army. 369th infantry (Colored) 2. European war, 1914-1918—Regimental histories—U. S.—369th infantry (Colored) 3. European war, 1914-1918—Negroes. I. Title. II. Title: New York's colored volunteers.
Library of Congress D570.33 369th.L5 36-12290
[a44o1] 940.41273

MB NN ICU MtU IU OkU GU IEN
NL 0410264 DLC WaS OrU NBuU OCU IaU MiU MoU LNHT

*
PS2248
.L373
1897
Little, Arthur West, 1873- 1943
His last appearance (in a single role). Presented by Arthur West Little at the Aldine Club, April 14th, 1897. With a primer biographical sketch of each of the well known artists assisting in the production. [New York?, Stag Publishing Co., 1897.
unpaged. 16cm.
Limited edition to 25 copies. This is no. 1.
Inscribed by the author.
I. Title.

NL 0410265 ViU MH

VOLUME 336

AP2 .P35 Little, Arthur West, 1873–1943, ed.
Pearson's magazine. v. [1]–51, no. 3; Mar. 1899–Apr. 1925. [New York, etc., 1899–1925]

Little, Arthur W[ilde] 1856-1910
The character of Washington, by Arthur W. Little . an extempore sermon preached before the society [of the Sons of the revolution in the state of Illinois] on Washington's birthday, 1903. Stenographed by Mr. R. H. Wyman ... Printed by order of the Society. Milwaukee, Wis., Young churchman co. [1903]
13 p. 25cm.
3-15415

NL 0410267 DLC

Little, Arthur Wilde, 1856-1910.
The intellectual life of the priest; its duties and its dangers, by Arthur W. Little.
Milwaukee, Young Churchman Co., 1897.
37 p. 19 cm.
1. Clergy. Intellectual life. I. Title.

NL 0410268 IEG

Little, Arthur Wilde, 1856- 1910
... The maintenance and the propagation of the church idea, the peculiar work of the American church in the twentieth century, by the Rev. Arthur W. Little ... 2d ed. Milwaukee, Pub. for the Western theological seminary, Chicago, by the Young churchman co. [1906?]
40 p. 22½cm. (The Hale memorial sermon, no. 1)

I. Title.
19-13418
Library of Congress BX5937.A1H3 no. 1

NL 0410269 DLC ICJ

Little, Arthur Wilde, 1856-1910.
The maintenance and the propagation of the Church idea the peculiar work of the American Church in the twentieth century. 1st edition.
Chicago. 1906. 39 pp. [Western Theological Seminary. Chicago, Ill. Hale Memorial Sermon. No. 1.] 8°.
Refers especially to the Protestant Episcopal Church in the United States.
The Hale Memorial Sermons were established by the will of Charles Reuben Hale in memory of his wife, Anna McK. T. Hale.

G2458 — Church, The. — Protestant Episcopal Church in the United States. — S.r.

NL 0410270 MB C ICN MiU OC1 MH NN

Little, Arthur Wilde, 1856-1910.
Reasons for being a churchman. Addressed to English speaking Christians of every name. By the Rev. Arthur Wilde Little ... 8th thousand. Milwaukee, Wis., The Young churchman company [188-?]
xvi, 269 p. front. 19½cm.

1. Protestant Episcopal church in the U. S. A.—Doctrinal and controversial works. I. Title.
38-20527
Library of Congress BX5930.L5

NL 0410271 DLC OrP WaS OrU NNUT NN MeB NjNbS

LITTLE, Arthur Wilde, 1856-1910
Reasons for being a churchman; addressed to English speaking Christians of every name. 16th thousand. Milwaukee, Wis., etc., 1890.
sm. 8°. Front.

NL 0410272 MH OO

BX 5133 L72 1893 Little, Arthur Wilde, 1856-1910.
Reasons for being a churchman; addressed to English speaking Christians of every name ... 21st thousand. Milwaukee, Wis., The Young churchman co 1893.
xvi, 269 p. 20cm.

NL 0410273 DNC

Little, Arthur Wilde, 1856-1910.
Reasons for being a churchman. Addressed to English speaking Christians of every name. By the Rev. Arthur Wilde Little ... 23d thousand. Milwaukee, Wis., The Young churchman company, 1894.
xvi, 269 p. front. 19½cm.

NL 0410274 ViU OGK

Little, Arthur Wilde, 1856–
Reasons for being a churchman; addressed to English speaking Christians of every name, by Arthur W. Little ... Rev. ed. 25th thousand. Milwaukee, Wis., The Young churchman co., 1905.
xvi, 309 p. front. 20cm.

1. Protestant Episcopal church in the U. S. A. 2. Church of England. I. Title.
5-2766
Library of Congress BX5930.L5

NL 0410275 DLC MeB OO MH-AH MB NcD

Little, Arthur Wilde, 1856-1910.
Reasons for being a churchman; addressed to English speaking Christians of every name, by Arthur W. Little...46th thousand. Milwaukee, Wis., The Young churchman co., London, A. R. Mowbray & co., 1911.
xvi, 309 p. front. 20cm.
1. Protestant Episcopal church in the U. S. A. 2. Church of England. I. Title.

NL 0410276 ViU

609.5 W514.9 L778t 1905 LITTLE, Arthur Wilde, 1856-1910.
The times and the teaching of John Wesley.
Milwaukee, Wis., Young Churchman Co., 1905.
xiv, 68p. port. 19.3cm.

NL 0410277 MH-AH

Little, Arthur Wilde, 1856-1910.
The times and the teaching of John Wesley, by Arthur W. Little ... 2d ed. Milwaukee, Wis., The Young churchman co., 1905.
xiv, 68 p. front. (port.) 19cm.

1. Wesley, John, 1703-1791.
5-39042
Library of Congress BX8495.W5L5 1905

NL 0410278 DLC MtBC NjPT TxU NcD

*
PS3511 .A86Z7348 19— Little, Ashford H
[Launching of motor ship Minmargony. n. p., 19—?]
1 reel sd b & w. 8mm.

Shows William Faulkner supervising the construction of motot ship Minmargary.

1. Faulkner, William, 1897-1962—Biography. I. Title: Minmargany.

NL 0410279 ViU

Little, B H
Performance and boundary-layer data from 12° and 23° conical diffusers of area ratio 2.0 at Mach numbers up to choking and Reynolds numbers up to 7.5 x 10⁶, by B. H. Little, Jr., and Stafford W. Wilbur. Washington, U. S. Govt. Print. Off., 1954.
ii, 23 p. diagrs. 30 cm. ([U. S.] National Advisory Committee for Aeronautics. Report 1201)
Cover title.
Bibliography: p. 15.
1. Aeroplanes—Turbojet engines—Diffusers. I. Wilbur, Stafford W., joint author. II. Title: Conical diffusers. (Series)
TL521.A33 no. 1201 55-63668
——— Copy 3. TL709.5.D5L5

NL 0410280 DLC

Little, B. P., joint author.
Pike, Robert Dickson, 1885–
... Electrolytic iron from sulfide ores, by Robert D. Pike, George H. West, L. V. Steck, Ross Cummings and B. P. Little ... New York, American institute of mining and metallurgical engineers, inc., °1930.

Little, Barbara, ed.
Commission of inquiry and conciliation, Bolivia and Paraguay, 1929.
Actuaciones de la Comisión de investigación y conciliación boliviano-paraguaya, 13 de marzo de 1929–13 de septiembre de 1929. Washington [Baltimore, The Sun book and job printing office, inc., 1929]

Little, Barbara, ed.
Commission of inquiry and conciliation, Bolivia and Paraguay, 1929.
Proceedings of the Commission of inquiry and conciliation, Bolivia and Paraguay, March 13, 1929–September 13, 1929. Washington [Baltimore, The Sun book and job printing office, inc., 1929]

Little, Bascom, 1879-
Inaugural addresss ... delivered at the sixty-seventh annual meeting of the Cleveland Chamber of commerce, April 20th, 1915. Cleveland, 1915.
11 p.

NL 0410284 OCl

Little, Bascom, 1879-
Cleveland. *Special tax commission.*
Report of the Special tax commission of the city of Cleveland, appointed by the mayor at the request of the City council. Filed November 22, 1915 ... R. E. Collins, clerk of Council. [Cleveland, 1915]

Little, Bertha E
See
Robie, Bertha E (Little), 1866-

Little, *Mrs.* Blanche E.
Mistletoe (ethereal plant) Oklahoma's state flower, by Blanche E. Little. Cedar Rapids, Ia., The Torch press [°1927]
45 p. front., plates, port. 20½cm.

1. Mistletoe.
27-23788
Library of Congress QK85.L5

NL 0410287 DLC

VOLUME 336

Little, Mrs. Blanche E. Mistletoe (ethereal plant) Oklahoma's state flower. Revised ed. Cedar Rapids, Iowa. [1928.] 8°. pp. 52. Portrs. and plates.

NL 0410288 MH-A

Little, *Mrs.* Blanche E.
The staff of Joseph of Arimathea, the holy Glastonbury thorn ₍by₎ Blanche E. Little. Cedar Rapids, Ia., The Torch press ₍°1926₎
₍11₎ p. front., plates. 23cm.
Cover-title: The miracle tree.

1. Washington, D. C. Cathedral of St. Peter and St. Paul. I. Title. II. Title: Glastonbury thorn.
Library of Congress F204.C3L5 27-887

NL 0410289 DLC

₍Little, *Mrs.* Blanche E₎
When the Star spangled banner cheered his lonely heart and sounded best to him, being the experience of a soldier of the A. E. F. and a French child. Cedar Rapids, Ia., The Torch press, 1925.
24 p. incl. 1 illus., ports. 23½cm.
"Copyright ... by Blanche E. Little."

1. European war, 1914-1918. 2. Star spangled banner (Song) I. Title.
Library of Congress D640.L535 26-3573

NL 0410290 DLC

Little, Bryan D G
The building of Bath, 47-1947; an architectural and social study. London, Collins, 1947.
176 p. illus., maps. 22 cm.
Bibliography: p. 167-169.

1. Architecture—Bath, Eng. 2. Bath, Eng.—Hist. 3. Bath, Eng.—Descr. I. Title.
A 48-4766*
Harvard Univ. Library for Library of Congress

NL 0410291 MH CaBViP CaBVaU KEmT CLO NcD ICU TU IaU

A
720.942
L723
LITTLE, BRYAN D G
The building of Bath, 47 - 1947; an architectural and social study. London, Collins₍1948₎
176p. illus., maps. 22cm.
Bibliography: p.167-169.

NL 0410292 PU OrPS IEN MH MiD OU FMU PSt MH MB

Little, Bryan D G
Cheltenham. London, New York, Batsford ₍1952₎
127 p. illus. 19 cm. (British cities)
Includes bibliography.

1. Cheltenham, Eng.—Hist.
DA690.C48L5 942.41 52-32358 ‡

NL 0410293 DLC NN PU-FA CaBViP

Little, Bryan D G
The city and county of Bristol; a study in Atlantic civilisation. London, W. Laurie ₍1954₎
xix, 390 p. illus., maps. 22 cm.
Bibliography: p. 363-378.

1. Bristol, Eng.—Hist.
DA690.B8L5 1954 942.41 55-21196

CtY ICU NN TxU OCl PBL PU PPT PP
NL 0410294 DLC KU NcD OCU FTaSU PHC MB TU WaU MH CU

Little, Bryan D G
Exeter, Crediton, Cullompton, Exmouth, Ottery St. Mary, Tiverton, and Topsham. London, Batsford ₍1953₎
167 p. illus. 23 cm.
Includes bibliography.

1. Exeter, Eng.—Descr. & trav. 2. Devon, Eng.—Descr. & trav.
DA670.D5L65 942.35 53-37332 ‡

KU NBuU
NL 0410295 DLC CaBViP MiU CtY OCl PP MH MB NN MiD

Little, Bryan D G
The life and work of James Gibbs, 1682-1754. London, Batsford ₍1955₎
210 p. illus. 23 cm.

1. Gibbs, James, 1682-1754.
NA997.G5L5 55-2967 ‡

CaBVa MtU
CtY ViU OO ICU PU-FA TU FU PSt OrU NcD LU CaBVaU
NL 0410296 DLC MB FTaSU OCl OOxM MiU TxU NN IU NNC

LF128
.K65
Little, Bryan D. G.

Kersting, A F
Portrait of Cambridge, a selection of photographs by A. F. Kersting, with text by Bryan Little, and foreword by S. C. Roberts. London, Batsford ₍1955₎

Little, Bryan D G
The three choirs cities: Gloucester, Hereford and Worcester. London, New York, Batsford ₍1952₎
132 p. illus. 19 cm. (The British cities series)
Includes bibliography.

1. Gloucester, Eng.—Descr. 2. Hereford, Eng.—Descr. 3. Worcester, Eng.—Descr. 4. Three choirs (Worcester, Gloucester, Hereford) I. Title.
DA690.G5L5 914.24 52-43880 ‡

NL 0410298 DLC MH FMU CaBVa CaBViP

Little, Bryce, 1743?-1820.
A sermon, preached before the Clydesdale Volunteers, in the Church of Covington, on Saturday, 19th May, 1804: by the Rev. Bryce Little... Edinburgh: P. Hill, 1804. 44 p. 8°.

391650A. 1. Sermons. January 29, 1929

NL 0410299 NN

657.6
L721s
1952
Little, Burnett Allan.
Some aspects of internal auditing in selected colleges and universities. Champaign, Ill., Distributed by Illini Union Bookstore, c1952.
119p. 28cm.

Bibliography: p.114-119.

1. Universities and colleges--Finance. 2. Auditing. I. Title.

NL 0410300 IU

Little, Burtis McGie, 1884-
Francisco the Filipino, by Burtis M. Little ... New York, Cincinnati ₍etc.₎ American book company ₍°1915₎
viii, 104 p. incl. col. front., illus. 19cm. $0.40

1. Philippine Islands—Soc. life & cust. 2. Children in the Philippine Islands. I. Title.
Library of Congress DS663.L6 15-13687 Revised

NL 0410301 DLC NN OClh

Cp37
20
Little, Burtis McGie, 1884-
The National old trails road and the part played by Lexington in the westward movement ... ₍n.p.₎ 1928.
2p.l.,28p.incl.front.,illus.(incl.ports., facsims. 24½cm
Cover-title: Brief sketch of the National old trails road. Souvenir of Lexington, Missouri, September 17, 1928.

NL 0410302 CtY NNC

₍Little, C.₎
...Denver Dan and his mystic band. New York: F. Tousey, 1881. 15 p. illus. 4°. (The five cent wide awake library. no. 433.)

NL 0410303 NN

₍Little, C.₎
Denver Dan and the counterfeiters. ₍By the author of "Denver Dan and his mystic band"...₎ New York: F. Tousey, 1881. 15 p. illus. 4°. (The five cent wide awake library. no. 439.)

NL 0410304 NN

HD
9999
.C6L5
Little (C.W.) & Co.
Illustrated catalogue. New York ₍1890?₎
₍31 p.₎ illus. 22 cm.

Cover title.

1. Clocks & watches--Catalogs of supplies, etc. 2. Firearms industry and trade--Catalogs of supplies.

NL 0410305 OkU

Little, Caroline Frances

La Fontaine, Rachel Adelaide, *ed.*
The four evangelists in classic art, ed. by Rachel A. La Fontaine ... New York, T. Whittaker ₍1900₎

VOLUME 336

Little, Caroline Frances.
Little Winter-green, by Caroline Frances Little ... New-York, T. Whittaker [°1896]
iv, 98 p. front., 2 pl. 19cm. (The "little heroine" series)

Library of Congress PZ7.L72L 7-19393†

NL 0410307 DLC

Little, Caroline Frances
The soldier's aid society.

In King, Charles, ed. An intitial experience. Phila., 1896. p. 207-214. 12°

NL 0410308 DLC

Little, Caroline Frances.
The three vocations. By Caroline Frances Little. Milwaukee, Wis., The Young churchman co., 1888.
252 p. 20cm.

Library of Congress PZ3.L722T 7-19403†

NL 0410309 DLC

Little, Carroll Herman, 1872-
Disputed doctrines; a study in Biblical and dogmatic theology, by C. H. Little ... Burlington, Ia., The Lutheran literary board, 1933.
127 p. front. (port.) 20½cm.

1. Lutheran church—Doctrinal and controversial works. 2. Theology, Doctrinal. I. Title.
Library of Congress BX8065.L5 33-34981
Copyright A 66821 230.41

NL 0410310 DLC

Little, Carroll Herman, 1872-
Explanation of the book of Revelation. St. Louis, Concordia Pub. House [°1950]
vi, 232 p. 21 cm.

1. Bible. N. T. Revelation—Commentaries. I. Bible. N. T. Revelation. English. 1950.
BS2825.L53 228 51-3484

NL 0410311 DLC

BS2825
.I 53 Little, Carroll Herman, 1872-
Explanation of the book of Revelation. St. Louis, Concordia Pub. House [1954, c1950]
vi, 232 p. 21cm.

1. Bible. N. T. Revelation—Commentaries. I. Bible. N. T. Revelation. English. 1954.

NL 0410312 MB PPWe

Little, Carroll Herman, 1872-
Lutheran confessional theology, a presentation of the doctrines of the Augsburg confession and the Formula of concord, by C. H. Little ... with introduction by Theodore Graebner ... St. Louis, Mo., Concordia publishing house, 1943.
xvi, 185 p. 19½cm.

1. Augsburg confession. 2. Lutheran church. Formula of concord. 3. Lutheran church—Doctrinal and controversial works. I. Title.
Library of Congress BX8069.L5 43-14357
238.41

NL 0410313 DLC PPiPT PPLT OCl OO

Little, Carroll Herman, 1872-
Lutheran confessional theology. St. Louis, Mo. Concordia, 1945.

NL 0410314 PGladM

Little, Catherine T
Postwar developments affecting the world sugar market.

Thesis - Radcliffe, 1952

NL 0410315 MH

Little, Cecile Elizabeth, 1891-
Miss Flavia Farmer. [1st ed.] New York, Pageant Press [1952, °1951]
184 p. 21 cm.

I. Title.
PZ3.L7223Mi 52-1599 ‡

NL 0410316 DLC

Little, Charles
Relation of the citizen to the government. A discourse delivered on the day of national thanksgiving, November 24th, 1864... New Haven. W. H. Stanley, 1864.
14 p.

NL 0410317 OClWHi CtY

Little (Charles C.) and Company, *publishers, Boston*
see **Little, Brown and Company,** *publishers, Boston.*

Little, Charles Coffin, 1799-1869
see also **Little, Brown and Company,** *publishers, Boston.*

Little, Charles Edgar, 1865-1945, joint author.
Parsons, Carrie Ambrose.
... First Latin lessons, by Carrie Ambrose Parsons ... and Charles Edgar Little ... New York state ed. by Alvah T. Otis ... Boston, New York [etc.] D. C. Heath and company [°1928]

Little, Charles Edgar, 1865-1945, joint author.
Parsons, Carrie Ambrose.
First Latin lessons for junior and senior high schools, by Carrie Ambrose Parsons ... and Charles Edgar Little ... Boston, New York [etc.] D. C. Heath and company [°1926]

Little, Charles Edgar, 1865-1945, comp.
George Peabody college for teachers, *Nashville.*
George Peabody college for teachers; its evolution and present status, September, 1912. Nashville, Tenn., George Peabody college for teachers, 1912.

Little, Charles Edgar, 1865-1945.
A grammatical index to the Chāndogya-upanisad, by Charles Edgar Little ... New York, Cincinnati [etc.] American book co. [°1900]
x, 192 p., 1 l. 19cm. (The Vanderbilt Oriental series, ed. by Herbert Cushing Tolman and James Henry Stevenson)

1. Upanishads. Chāndogya-upanishad — Concordances, indexes, etc. I. Title.
Library of Congress PK3521.C5L6 1-29342 Revised

NL 0410323 DLC OrU IdU NIC ICN ICU OU ViU OClW OCU OCl MiU MB NcD

Little, Charles Edgar, 1865-1945.
PA6650
.E5L5 **Quintilianus, Marcus Fabius.**
Institutio oratoria; with an English summary and concordance by Charles Edgar Little. Nashville, Printed for George Peabody College for Teachers [°1951]

Little, Charles Edgar, 1865-1945, ed.
Life and literature readers; primer Advisory ed., Charles E. Little... San Francisco, Doub & company (c1914-16)
2 v. illus. (part col.) 20 cm.

NL 0410325 DHEW CSt

Little, Charles Edgar, 1865-1945.
... Second Latin lessons, by Charles Edgar Little ... and Carrie Ambrose Parsons ... Boston, New York [etc.] D. C. Heath and company [°1927]
xvi, 657 p. illus., maps (part double) 19cm. (The Heath Latin series, W. L. Carr, general editor)

1. Latin language—Grammar—1870- 2. Latin language—Composition and exercises. I. Parsons, Carrie Ambrose, joint author. II. Title.
Library of Congress PA2087.P32 28-4395

NL 0410326 DLC ViU DN

Little, Charles Edgar, 1865-1945.
... Second Latin lessons, by Charles Edgar Little ... and Carrie Ambrose Parsons ... New York state ed. by Alvah T. Otis ... Boston, New York [etc.] D. C. Heath and company [°1928]
xvi, 685 p. front., illus., maps (part double) 19cm. (The Heath Latin series)

1. Latin language—Grammar—1870- 2. Latin language—Composition and exercises. I. Parsons, Carrie Ambrose, joint author. II. Otis, Alvah Talbot. III. Title.
Library of Congress PA2087.P32N7 28-15897

NL 0410327 DLC

Little, Charles Edgar, 1865-1945.
George Peabody college for teachers, *Nashville.*
The semicentennial of George Peabody college for teachers 1875-1925. The proceedings of the semicentennial celebration February 18, 19, and 20, 1925. Committee in charge of the celebration, Charles Edgar Little ... chairman ... Nashville, Tenn., George Peabody college for teachers, 1925.

PA2087
.P32 Little, Charles Edgar, 1865-1945.
Teacher's manual to accompany Second Latin lessons.
Boston, N.Y.[etc.][c1930.]
1 pam. 12°

NL 0410329 DLC

VOLUME 336

Little, Charles Eugene, 1838–1918, *ed.*
Biblical lights and side-lights: ten thousand illustrations, with thirty thousand cross-references, consisting of facts, incidents, and remarkable declarations taken from the Bible: for the use of public speakers and teachers, and also for those in every profession, who, for illustrative purposes, desire ready access to the numerous incidents and striking statements contained in the Bible. By Rev. Charles E. Little ... New York, Funk & Wagnalls, 1883.
2 p. l., [iii]–iv, 632 p. 25½cm.
1. Bible—Indexes, Topical. I. Title.
37-19930
Library of Congress BS432.L5
Copyright 1883: 23121 220.2

NL 0410330 DLC MH-AH CtY-D NcD OCl OO MiU OClW

BS432
.L76
LITTLE,CHARLES EUGENE,1838-1918.
Biblical lights and side-lights: ten thousand illustrations, with thirty thousand cross-references, consisting of facts, incidents, and remarkable declarations taken from the Bible;for the use of public speakers and teachers... By Rev.Chas.E.Little. 2d ed. ... New York,Funk & Wagnalls,1886.
[2],iv,632 p. 25½cm.
1.Bible--Concordances.

NL 0410331 ICU ODW

Little, Charles E[ugene], 1838-1918.
Biblical lights and side-lights; ten thousand illustrations, with thirty thousand cross-references, consisting of facts, incidents, and remarkable declarations taken from the Bible, for the use of public speakers and teachers, and also for those in every profession, who, for illustrative purposes, desire ready access to the numerous incidents and striking statements contained in the Bible. Toronto: Funk & Wagnalls Co. [cop. 1886.] 3 p.l., 632 p. 3. ed. 8°.

NL 0410332 NN

Little, Charles Eugene, 1838-1918, ed.
Biblical lights and side-lights; ten thousand illustrations with thirty thousand cross-references, consisting of facts, incidents, and remarkable declarations taken from the Bible; for the use of public speakers and teachers, and also for those in every profession, who, for illustrative purposes, desire ready access to the numerous incidents and striking statements contained in the Bible. By Rev. Chas. E. Little. 3d ed. ... New York, Funk & Wagnalls, 1889.
2 p. l., [iii]-iv, 632 p. 25½cm.
1. Bible—Indexes, Topical. I. Title.

NL 0410333 ViU

Little, Charles Eugene, 1838–1918.
Cyclopedia of classified dates, with an exhaustive index, by Charles E. Little ... for the use of students of history, and for all persons who desire speedy access to the facts and events, which relate to the histories of the various countries of the world, from the earliest recorded dates. New York and London, Funk & Wagnalls company, 1900.
vii, [1], 1454 p. 26 cm.
1. Chronology, Historical. I. Title.
0—649
Library of Congress D9.L7

MiU OO OCU OCl OClW NN DN MB ICJ NjP NcD
NL 0410334 DLC IU FU OrU DAU WaS OrPR KyLx DI-GS

Little, Charles Eugene, 1838–1918.
The cyclopedia of classified dates. By Charles E. Little ... For the use of students of history, and for all persons who desire speedy access to the facts and events which relate to the histories of the various countries of the world from the earliest recorded dates; with an exhaustive index. New York and London, Funk & Wagnalls company, 1905.
vii, [1], 1454 p. 26½cm.
"Third edition."
With this is bound: The perfect calendar for every day of the Christian era, by Henry Fitch. New York and London, 1900.
1. Chronology, Historical. I. Title.
39-6689
Library of Congress D9.L7 1905
902

NL 0410335 DLC

Little, Charles Eugene, 1838–1918, *comp.*
Historical lights: a volume of six thousand quotations from standard histories and biographies ... Comp. by Rev. Charles E. Little ... New York [etc.] Funk & Wagnalls, 1886.
vi, 958 p. 25½cm.
1. Quotations, English. I. Title.
10—7730
Library of Congress PN6083.L5

ViU
OLak MWA OClStM ODW MdBP NN NIC MdBP TU KyLxCB OkU
NL 0410336 DLC MtU OrU WaU-L MiU OClW OCl Or WaS OCU

Little, Charles Eugene, 1838-1918, comp.
Historical lights: a volume of six thousand quotations from standard histories and biographies ... Comp. by Rev. Charles E. Little ... New York [etc.] Funk & Wagnalls, 1892.
vi, 958 p. 25.5 cm.
1. Quotations, Engl. I. Title.

NL 0410337 PRosC NjNbS

Little, Charles Eugene, 1838-1918, comp.
Historical lights; six thousand quotations from standard histories and biographies ... Compiled by Rev. Charles E. Little ... 2d ed. New York, London, Funk & Wagnalls, 1886.
vi, 958 p. 25.5 cm.
1. Quotations, English. I. Title.

NL 0410338 Vi

Little, Charles Eugene, 1838-1918, comp.
Historical lights; six thousand quotations from standard histories and biographies. 2d ed. New York, etc., Funk & Wagnalls, 1888.

NL 0410339 MH

Little, Charles Eugene, 1838-1918, comp.
Historical lights: six thousand quotations from standard histories and biographies, with twenty thousand cross-references, and a general index, also an index of personal names... 3d ed. New York, Funk and Wagnalls, 1892.
vi, 958 p.
1. Quotations, English. I. Title.

NL 0410340 AAP PRosC OOxM OClWHi NN

808.8
L722h
1896
Little, Charles Eugene, 1838-1918, comp.
Historical lights: six thousand quotations from standard histories and biographies ... Compiled by Rev. Charles E. Little ... Toronto, New York [etc.] Funk & Wagnalls company [1896, c1886]
1p.l.,vi, 958p. 24½cm. (On cover: The Standard library, no.196)
1. Quotations, English. I. Title.

NL 0410341 TxU DLC

Little, Charles Eugene, 1838–1918, *comp.*
Historical lights; six thousand quotations from standard histories and biographies ... Compiled by the Rev. Charles E. Little ... New York and London, Funk & Wagnalls company [19—]
3 p. l., v–vi, 958 p. 23 cm.
1. Quotations, English. I. Title.
PN6083.L53 820.822 33—30526

NL 0410342 DLC WaU-L CaBVaU NcRS

Little, Charles Joseph, 1840–1911.
Abraham Lincoln: an address delivered on Lincoln day, 1907, in Memorial hall, Chicago, by Charles Joseph Little ... Chicago, M. Umbdenstock & co., printers, 1907.
16 p. 23½cm.
Published by request.
1. Lincoln, Abraham, pres. U. S.—Addresses, sermons, etc.
20-20898
Library of Congress E457.8.L77

NL 0410343 DLC MH

Little, Charles Joseph, 1840–1911.
The angel in the flame; sermons preached at Evanston, Ill., in the First Methodist Episcopal church, by Charles J. Little ... Cincinnati, Jennings and Pye; New York, Eaton and Mains [1904]
143 p. front. (port.) 19cm. (*Half-title:* The Methodist pulpit)
I. Title.
4-5001
Library of Congress BX8333.L5A6

NL 0410344 DLC IEG CBPac OCl ODW NcD

BV4070
.G38L77
1900
Little, Charles Joseph, 1840-1911.
Baccalaureate Sermon for the class of 1900. Preached by the President, April 29, 1900 in the First M. E. Church of Evanston, Illinois. [Evanston] Garrett Biblical Institute, [1900.
unpaged [17p.] 23cm.
1. Sermons, American. 2. Garrett Biblical Institute, Evanston, Ill. 3. Methodist Church--Sermons. I. Title. II. Garrett Biblical Institute, Evanston, Ill.

NL 0410345 IEG

BV4070
.G38L7
1900
Little, Charles Joseph, 1840-1911.
Baccalaureate sermon for the class of 1900, preached by the president, Charles J. Little, April 29, 1900, in the first M. E. Church of Evanston, Ill. Published by the trustees at the request of the class and the board of visitors, 1900.
Unpaged (8p.) 23cm. (Garrett Biblical Institute)
Title from cover.
1. Sermons, Methodist. 2. Garrett Faculty Publications I. Title.

NL 0410346 IEG

Little, Charles Joseph, 1840–1911.
Biographical and literary studies by the late Charles Joseph Little ... ed. and arranged by Charles Macaulay Stuart ... New York, Cincinnati, The Abingdon press [1916]
352 p. front. (port.) 19½ cm.
"The studies dealing with Galileo, The women of Dante's Commedia, and The place of Christ in modern thought were first published in the Methodist review."—Introd.
CONTENTS.—Introduction, by C. M. Stuart.—The Apostle Paul.—Hildebrand.—Dante.—The women of Dante's Commedia.—Savonarola.—Martin Luther.—Galileo.—Henrik Ibsen.—The women of Ibsen.—Ibsen compared with Sophocles and Shakespeare.—The place of Christ in modern thought.
1. Biography. 2. Dante Alighieri. Divina commedia. 3. Ibsen, Henrik, 1828–1906. I. Stuart, Charles Macaulay, 1853–1982, ed.
CT104.L45 16—11062

NL 0410347 DLC OrSaW ICN NcD IEG

Little, Charles Joseph, 1840–1911.
Christianity and the nineteenth century, being the thirtieth Fernley lecture, delivered in Burslem, July, 1900, by Charles Joseph Little... London: C. H. Kelly, 1900. 96 p. 8°.
1. Christianity.—History, 19th century. January 29, 1924.

NL 0410348 NN CtY-D NcD IU N OO

VOLUME 336

BY2050 .L77 Little, Charles Joseph, 1840-1911.
Episcopal problems, an address before the Methodist Social Union of New York City, March 12, 1900. New York, 1900.
11 p. 20 cm.

1. Methodist Episcopal Church--Bishops. I. Title.

NL 0410349 IEG

833H41 DL72 Little, Charles Joseph, 1840-1911.
Herder and religious thought. Address delivered before Northwestern university. Evanston, Illinois, upon the hundredth anniversary of the death of Johann Gottfried Herder, December 18, 1903. [New York] 1904.
unp.

Reprinted from the Methodist review, March-April 1904.

NL 0410350 IU IEN MiU PPC MH

Little, Charles Joseph, 1840-1911.
... The historical method of writing the history of Christian doctrine, by Prof. Charles J. Little ...
(*In* American historical association. Annual report ... for the year 1893. Washington, 1894. 24½cm. p. 67-75)

1. Theology, Doctrinal—History. 2. Theology—History.
C D 17-387
Library of Congress Card Div. E172.A60. 1893

NL 0410351 DLC OCl OCU MiU MB

Little, Charles Joseph, 1840-1911, ed.

Weber, Georg, 1808-1888.
History of the world from the creation of man to the present day, by Dr. George Weber ... Including a comprehensive history of America, by Chas. J. Little ... Profusely illustrated with over 700 engravings, from drawings by DeNeuville, Vierge, Meissonier, Phillopoteaux, Lix, Delort, and others. Philadelphia and St. Louis, P. W. Ziegler & co. [°1894]

Little, Charles Joseph, 1840-1911.
In memoriam, Charles Joseph Little, born September 21, 1840, died March 11, 1911; ed. by Charles M. Stuart. Chicago, Forbes & company, 1912.
2 p. l., 305 p. front. (port.) 20cm. $1.50
"Papers and addresses by Charles J. Little": p. [81]-305.

I. Stuart, Charles Macaulay, 1853- ed.
12-12154
Library of Congress

VIU ICJ NN NcD
NL 0410353 DLC MeB NIC IEG MB MiD MWA OU OO MiU CU

Little, Charles Joseph, 1840-1911.
John Milton; a paper read before the Chicago literary club, Monday evening, December 7, 1908, in celebration of the tercentenary of the poet's birth, by Charles Joseph Little. [Chicago] Chicago literary club, 1909.
2 p. l., 7-39, [1] p., 1 l. 18½cm. (*On cover:* Club papers)
"This edition consists of four hundred and thirty copies, privately printed for members of the Chicago literary club, in the month of January, nineteen hundred and nine."

1. Milton, John, 1608-1674.
9-7084
Library of Congress [Copyright 1909 A 229971)

NL 0410354 DLC IEdS IEN ICN NcD OO MiU

Little, Charles J[oseph] 1840-1911.
John Wesley, preacher of Scriptural Christianity; an address before the Rock River conference at Aurora, Ill., Oct. 11, 1903, by Charles J. Little ... [Evanston? Ill., 1903]
24 p. 20cm.

1. Wesley, John, 1703-1791.
4-6729

NL 0410355 DLC NcD NN

LITTLE, CHARLES JOSEPH, 1840-1911.
John Wesley, preacher of scriptural Christianity. An address before the Rock River Conference at Aurora Ill., Oct. 11, 1903. [Aurora? Ill., c1903] 24 p. 25cm.

Microfiche (negative). 1 sheet. 11 x 15cm. (NYPL FSN 993)

1. Wesley, John, 1703-1791.

NL 0410356 NN

1886 Little, Charles Joseph, 1840-1911.
The methodist pioneers and their works.
n.p., n.d.
18 p. 12°.

NL 0410357 DLC

Little, Charles Joseph, *1840-1911.*
Papers and addresses.
(*In* Stuart, Charles Macaulay, editor, 1853- In memoriam Charles Joseph Little. Pp. 81-305. Chicago. 1912.)

NL 0410358 MB OClW

Little, Charles Joseph, 1840-1911.
The religious revival in history.
(In MacDonald. The revival. Pp. 40-63. Cincinnati. [1905.])

G64 — Revivals of religion.

NL 0410359 MB

Little, Charles Joseph, 1840-1911.

MacDonald, James Henry, 1864- ed.
The revival; a symposium ... collected and edited by Rev. J. H. MacDonald ... Cincinnati, Jennings and Graham: New York, Eaton and Mains [1905]

Little, Charles Joseph, 1840-1911.
[Schiller the historian.]
(In Chicago's Schiller-Gedenkfeier. Souvenir. Pp. 76-84. Chicago. 1905.)

F8936 — Schiller, Johann Christoph Friedrich von.

NL 0410361 MB

Little, Charles Joseph, 1840-1911.

Roads, Charles, 1855-
Sunday-school organization and methods, by Chas. Roads ... introduction by Rev. Charles J. Little ... Cincinnati, Jennings and Graham; New York, Eaton and Mains [1905]

975.5 V V.6 Little, Charles Joseph, 1840-1911.
Thomas Jefferson.

Detached copy: Chautauquan, Nov., 1891, p. (141)-(145); Virginia pamphlets, V.6.

1. Jefferson, Thomas, Pres. U.S., 1743-1826.

NL 0410363 ViN

BJ1581 L5 Little, Charles L
Essays from work, by Charles Little. New York, R. L. Stillson Company [1922]
50 p. col. front. 16 cm.

1. Work - Addresses, essays, lectures. I. Title.

NL 0410364 MeB NN

Little, Charles L.
... Who's who in the army and navy; how you can tell by uniform and insignia. Copyright ... [by] Charles L. Little. [New York, Robert L. Stillson co.] °1917.
[13] p. illus. (part col.) 13cm.
At head of title: Vest pocket edition.

1. U. S.—Army—Insignia. 2. U. S.—Navy—Insignia. I. Title.
17-31925
Library of Congress UC533.L7

NL 0410365 DLC

352.042 L778c Little, Charles M ed.
The city of Manchester, 1934. How Manchester is managed. A record of municipal activity with a description of the city. [Manchester, Published for the Corporation by direction of the Town Hall Committee, 1934.
307p. illus. 25cm.

Contains advertising.

1. Manchester, England - Description. I. Title: How Manchester is managed.

NL 0410366 NcU NcD

Little, C[harles] N., and W. L. Zeigler.
Trap rocks of Palouse region as road material. Moscow: North Idaho Star Print, 1904. 12 p., 2 pl. 8°. (Idaho. Agricultural experiment station. Bulletin 45.)

1. Pavements. 2. Zeigler, W. L.
N. Y. P. L. March 11, 1911.

NL 0410367 NN

Little, C[harles] N., and W. G. Turley.
Trap rocks of Palouse region as road material. Part 2. Moscow: Evening Journal Press, 1905. 15(1) p. 8°. (Idaho. Agricultural experiment station. Bulletin 50.)

1. Pavements. 2. Turley, W. G.
March 11, 1911.

NL 0410368 NN

Qe24 +pam Little, Charles Newton
... Non-alternate knots, of orders eight and nine ... Edinburgh, R. Grant & son[etc., etc.] 1889.
cover-title, p.[663]-664. plate. 31cm.
Pamphlet
"Transactions of the Royal society of Edinburgh. Vol.35, Pt.II. (No.18).

NL 0410369 CtY

VOLUME 336

S510
Z8
v.155
1885L
Little, Charles Newton
... On knots, with a census for order ten, by C. N. Little ... [1885]
[27]-43 p. tables.

Thesis (Ph. D.) Yale university, 1883.
Without thesis note.
From Transactions of the Connecticut academy of arts and sciences, vol. VII, 1885.

1. Knots and splices. 2. Curves.

NL 0410370 NNC

Little, Charles Newton.
... On knots, with a census for order ten ...
(*In* Connecticut academy of arts and sciences. Transactions. New Haven, 1885-88. 25cm. v. 7, p. [27]-43. pl. I-VII, 6 tab.)

1. Knots and splices. 2. Curves. I. Title.

A 17-815

Library of Congress Q11.C9 vol. 7
Yale University A53n.366.7

NL 0410371 CtY NIC GU OO OU OCU MiU OCl DLC

Little, Charles Newton.
The supply of and demand for engineering graduates in the United States.
(*In* National education association of the United States. Journal of proceedings and addresses, 1911. p. 681-688)

1. Engineering.

E 12-439

Library, U. S. Bur. of Education

NL 0410372 DHEW

Little, Christopher
Church controversy: first Presbyterian church of Pottsville vs. T.M.Russel, in the common pleas of Schuylkill county. 2d trial. Pottsville,Pa.,Miners' journal printing rooms,1871.
cover-title,70,iip.

"From notes of evidence taken at the trial and reported exclusively for the Daily miners' journal."

NL 0410373 PSt

Little, Cicely.
The lass with the delicate air. Sydney, Angus and Robertson, 1948.
301 p. 19 cm.

I. Title.

PZ3.L7225Las 49-17931*

NL 0410374 DLC TxU CtY

Little, Clarence B.
History of the class of '81, Dartmouth college. Hanover, 1881.

NL 0410375 Nh

Little, Clarence Cook, 1888–
The awakening college [by] Clarence Cook Little. New York, W. W. Norton & company, inc. [c1930]
282 p. 22cm.
"First edition."

1. Universities and colleges—U. S. 2. Students—U. S. I. Title.

30-12473

Library of Congress LA226.L5
——— Copy 2.
Copyright A 22402 378.73

NL 0410376 DLC KMK IdPI ICRL NIC MiU-H MB MH ViU NN MtBC OrPR Or WaS OClJC MiU OCU OLak OO OCl OU NcD WaSpG WaTC OrP IdU

Little, Clarence Cook, 1888–

Roscoe B. Jackson memorial laboratory, *Bar Harbor, Me.*
Biology of the laboratory mouse, by the staff of the Roscoe B. Jackson memorial laboratory, Clarence C. Little, director, George D. Snell, editor [and others] ... with a chapter on Infectious diseases of mice, by J. H. Dingle ... Philadelphia, The Blakiston company [c1941]

RC263
.A6
1944
Little, Clarence Cook, 1888– ed.
FOR OTHER EDITIONS SEE MAIN ENTRY

American cancer society. *Women's field army.*
Cancer, a study for laymen, edited by Clarence C. Little. New York, N. Y., American cancer society, 1944.

Little, Clarence Cook, 1888–
Civilization against cancer, by Clarence Cook Little, sc. d. New York, Toronto, Farrar & Rinehart, inc., 1939.
vi p., 2 l., 3-150 p. 21cm.

1. Cancer. I. Title.

39-27142

Library of Congress RC261.L78
Copyright A 127239 616.994

NL 0410379 DLC NcD OOxM OU OCl OEac OLak NN ViU WaE WaSp WaS OrU OrU-M OrCS Wa

---

Little, Clarence Cook, 1888–
... The fight on cancer, by Clarence C. Little ... [New York, Public affairs committee, inc.] 1939.
cover-title, 31, [1] p. illus., diagrs. 21½cm. (Public affairs pamphlets, no. 38)
"First printing, December, 1939."
"For further reading": p. 30-31.

1. Cancer.

40—1788

Library of Congress RC261.L783
[a41h2] 616.99

NL 0410380 DLC OrCS OrU Or DNLM OO OU OCU OEac OOxM ViU

Little, Clarence Cook, 1888–
... The fight on cancer, by Clarence C. Little ... [New York, Public affairs committee, inc.] 1941.
cover-title, 31, [1] p. illus., diagrs. 21½cm. (Public affairs pamphlets, no. 38 (Revised))
"First edition, December, 1939. Revised edition, November, 1941."
"For further reading": p. 30-31.

1. Cancer.

42-10841

Library of Congress RC261.L783 1941
616.994

NL 0410381 DLC NBuC ODW

Little, Clarence Cook, 1888–
... The fight on cancer, by Clarence C. Little ... [New York, Public affairs committee, inc.] 1945.
cover-title, 31, [1] p. 1 illus., diagrs. 21½cm. (Public affairs pamphlets, no. 38 (Revised))
"Third printing, April, 1945."
"For further reading": p. 30-31.

1. Cancer.

S G 45-223

U. S. Surg.-gen. off. Libr. for Library of Congress RC261.L783 1945

NL 0410382 DNLM DLC PSt

Little, Clarence Cook, 1888–
... The fight on cancer, by Clarence C. Little ... [New York, Public affairs committee, incorporated] 1946.
cover-title, 31, [1] p. diagrs. 21½cm. (Public affairs pamphlets, no. 38 (revised))
"First edition, December, 1939 ... Second revised edition, May, 1946."
"For further reading": p. 30-31.

1. Cancer.

46-6491

Library of Congress RC261.L783 1946

NL 0410383 DLC MsU

RC263
.J6
Little, Clarence Cook, 1888– The fight on cancer.

Johnson, Dallas.
Facing the facts about cancer, by Dallas Johnson for the National Cancer Institute and the American Cancer Society. [1st ed. New York] c1947.

Little, Clarence Cook, 1888–
Genetics, biological individuality, and cancer. Stanford, Stanford University Press, 1954.
x, 115 p. illus. 23 cm. (Lane medical lectures, 1954)
Stanford University publications. University series. Medical sciences, v. 7.
Includes bibliographies.

1. Cancer. I. Title. (Series. Series: Stanford University. Stanford University publications. University series. Medical sciences, v. 7)

RC262.L5 616.994 54—10680
AS36.L57 vol. 7

NL 0410385 DLC FU-HC TU AAP NcD NcRS DNLM TxU PPC PP PBL PPT PPLankH TxU PWcS

QH431
.M94
Little, Clarence Cook, 1888–

Muller, Hermann Joseph, 1890–
Genetics, medicine, and man [by] H. J. Muller ... C. C. Little ... [and] Laurence H. Snyder ... Ithaca, N. Y., 1947.

E
13
.1925
A2
Little,Clarence Cook,1888-
Inaugural address of the president of the University of Michigan. Science press, 1925.
cover-title,16 p. 28 cm.
-- ---copy 2
"Reprinted from School and society,vol.xxii, no.567."

NL 0410387 MiU

Little, Clarence Cook, 1888– ed.
Project Mouse; RX mouse and X mouse. [Concord, N.H.?] New Hampshire Chapter of the Jackson Laboratory Association, c1951.
45 l. illus.

NL 0410388 Wa

VOLUME 336

QY 50 L778p 1952 LITTLE, Clarence Cook, 1888- ed.
Project mouse; Rx mouse and X mouse. [Deering] N. H., New Hampshire Chapter of the Jackson Laboratory Assn., 1952.
xiv, 83 p. illus., port.
1. Mice 2. Neoplasms - Experimental studies 3. Roscoe B. Jackson Memorial Laboratory, Bar Harbor, Me.

NL 0410389 DNLM OrPR MiD PGloS PPC NNC

Little, Clarence Cook, 1888-

Castle, William Ernest, 1867-
Reversion in guinea-pigs and its explanation, by W. E. Castle. Experimental studies of the inheritance of color in mice, by C. C. Little. Washington, D. C., Carnegie institution of Washington, 1913.

Little, Clarence Cook, 1888- ed.

Harvard university. Class of 1910.
Secretary's ... report ... Harvard college class of 1910. 1st- 1911- Cambridge, Mass., Printed for the class [1911-

---

QL1 .I6 no.53f LITTLE, CLARENCE GUY
The birds of Winona lake. (In Indiana univ.--Biological station--Winona Lake. Reports, 1902, p.41-66. 1903)

Contributions from the Zoological laboratory of Indiana univ., no.53f.

NL 0410392 InU

Z 79 .E 23 LITTLE, CLEMENT, d.1580.
[Cathologus librorum quos vir eximius et beate memorie magister Clemens Litill Edinburgene ecclesie et ministris ejusdem obiens legavit et consecravit] [n.p., n.d.]
facsim. 31½x25cm. fold. to 25x17cm.

Inserted: an autograph letter, dated Oct. 25, 1901, from David Cuthbertson, presenting the document to Mr. E.W. Blatchford.
A facsimile taken from the records of the Town-council of Edinburgh. These books given "to Edinburgh & kirk of God" formed the nucleus of the library of the University of Edinburgh.
For full description see Maitland club. Miscellany, v.1, p.[285]-301.

—— —— another copy. 35x28½cm. fold. to 29½x 19cm.
Inserted: two pages of ms. notes, headed: Formation of Edinburgh university library, and signed: David Cuthbertson.

NL 0410394 ICN

[Little, Clifton T]
Restless Americans ... [Washington, D. C., Public affairs committee] 1936.
cover-title, 32 p. diagrs. 21½cm. (Public affairs pamphlets, no. 9)
"Prepared by Clifton T. Little on the basis of the report of the Study of population redistribution. For a more detailed consideration of this subject see 'Migration and economic opportunity,' University of Pennsylvania press, 1936."—p. 1.

1. U. S.—Population. 2. U. S.—Soc. condit. 3. Migration, Internal. I. Title.
Library of Congress HN57.L57 37-12715 Revised

NL 0410395 ViU DLC Or OrU OU WaU NBuC OO OOxM OCU MiU

[Little, Clifton T]
Restless Americans ... [New York, Public affairs committee, incorporated] 1938.
cover-title, 32 p. diagrs. 21½ cm. (Public affairs pamphlets. No. 9, revised)
"Prepared by Clifton T. Little on the basis of the report of the Study of population redistribution. For a more detailed consideration of this subject see 'Migration and economic opportunity,' University of Pennsylvania press, 1936."—p. 1.
"First edition, January, 1937 ... fourth printing, December, 1938."

1. U. S.—Population. 2. U. S.—Soc. condit. 3. Migration, Internal—U. S. I. Title.
HN57.L57 1938 a 309.173 39—4367

NL 0410396 DLC MtBC OU ViU

Little, Clifton T
... Restless Americans, by Clifton T. Little. [New York, Public affairs committee, inc.] 1940.
cover-title, 32 p. diagrs. 21½ cm. (Public affairs pamphlets. No. 9 (revised))
"Prepared on the basis of the report of the Study of population redistribution. For a more detailed consideration of this subject see 'Migration and economic opportunity,' University of Pennsylvania press, 1936."—p. 1.
"First edition, January, 1937 ... second revised edition, October, 1940."

1. U. S.—Population. 2. U. S.—Soc. condit. 3. Migration, Internal—U. S. I. Title.
HN57.L57 1940 309.173 40—34864

NL 0410397 DLC

Little, Constance.

The black cat, by Constance & Gwenyth Little. Gift of Death, by Edward Ronns [pseud.] A killer is loose among us, by Robert Terrall. The case of William Smith, by Patricia Wentworth. New York, Unicorn Mystery Book Club, 1949.
4 v. in 1. 20cm.
I. Little, Gwenyth, joint author. II. Aarons, Edward Sidney, 1916- Gift of death. III. Terrall, Robert. A killer is loose among us. IV. Wentworth, Patricia, pseud. The case of William Smith. V. Title. VI. Title: Gift of death. VII. Title: A killer is loose among us. VIII. Title: The case of William Smith.

NL 0410398 ViU

Little, Constance.
The black coat [by] Constance & Gwenyth Little. [1st ed.] Garden City, N. Y., Pub. for the Crime Club by Doubleday, 1948.
189 p. 21 cm.

I. Little, Gwenyth, joint author. II. Title.
PZ3.L723Bf 48-9093*

NL 0410399 DLC WaE TxU OOxM

Little, Constance.
... Black corridors. New York, Pub. for the Crime club by Doubleday, Doran & co., inc., 1940.
4 p. l., 269 p. 19½cm.
At head of title: Constance and Gwenyth Little.
"First edition."

I. Little, Gwenyth, joint author. II. Title.
40-31453
Library of Congress PZ3.L723Bg

NL 0410400 DLC

Little, Constance.
The black curl, by Constance and Gwenyth Little. [1st ed.] Garden City, N. Y., Published for the Crime Club by Doubleday, 1953.
189 p. 21 cm.

I. Little, Gwenyth, joint author. II. Title.
PZ3.L723Bgm 53-9131 ‡

NL 0410401 DLC OOxM WaSp WaE ICU

Little, Constance.
The black dream [by] Constance and Gwenyth Little. [1st ed.] Garden City, N. Y., Published for the Crime Club by Doubleday, 1952.
191 p. 21 cm.

I. Title.
PZ3.L723Bh 52-8752 †

NL 0410402 DLC WaE PP OOxM

Little, Constance.
... The black eye. Garden City, New York, Pub. for the Crime club by Doubleday, Doran and company, inc., 1945.
224 p. 18½cm.
At head of title: Constance & Gwenyth Little.
"First edition."

I. Little, Gwenyth, joint author. II. Title.
45-9766
Library of Congress * PZ3.L723Bl

NL 0410403 DLC PP OEac

Little, Constance.
... The black gloves. [New York] Pub. for the Crime club, inc., by Doubleday, Doran & company, inc., 1939.
4 p. l., 265 p. 20cm.
At head of title: Constance and Gwenyth Little.
"First edition."

I. Little, Gwenyth, joint author. II. Title.
39-30328
Library of Congress PZ3.L723Bo

NL 0410404 DLC OEac OO OClU

Little, Constance.
The black goatee [by] Constance & Gwenyth Little. Garden City, N. Y., Pub. for the Crime club by Doubleday & company, inc., 1947.
221 p. 20cm.
"First edition."

I. Little, Gwenyth, joint author. II. Title.
PZ3.L723Bkf 47-1626

NL 0410405 DLC WaE WaSp TxU ViU

Little, Constance.
... The black-headed pins. New York, Pub. for the Crime club, inc., by Doubleday, Doran & company, inc., 1938.
4 p. l., 270 p. 19½cm.
At head of title: Constance & Gwenyth Little.
"First edition."

I. Little, Gwenyth, joint author. II. Title.
39-27040
Library of Congress PZ3.L723Bl

NL 0410406 DLC Or

Little, Constance.
The black honeymoon [by] Constance and Gwenyth Little. Garden City, New York, Pub. for the Crime club by Doubleday, Doran and co., inc., 1944.
3 p. l., 210 p. 20cm.
"First edition."

I. Little, Gwenyth, joint author. II. Title.
44-1672
Library of Congress PZ3.L723Bm

NL 0410407 DLC OEac OOxM

VOLUME 336

Little, Constance.
The black house, by Constance and Gwenyth Little. [1st ed.] Garden City, N. Y., Published for the Crime Club by Doubleday, 1950.
216 p. 21 cm.

I. Little, Gwenyth, joint author. II. Title.

PZ3.L723Bn 50-5030

NL 0410408 DLC CaBVa PP OEac

Little, Constance.
The black iris, by Constance and Gwenyth Little. [1st ed.] Garden City, N. Y., Published for the Crime Club by Doubleday, 1953.
190 p. 21 cm.

I. Little, Gwenyth, joint author. II. Title.

PZ3.L723Bo 52-13573 ‡

NL 0410409 DLC WaE WaT OrP OOxM ViU

Little, Constance.
The black paw [by] Constance and Gwenyth Little. New York, Pub. for the Crime club by Doubleday, Doran and co., inc., 1941.
4 p. l., 266 p. 19½ᶜᵐ.
"First edition."

I. Little, Gwenyth, joint author. II. Title.

Library of Congress PZ3.L723Br 41-2434

NL 0410410 DLC WaS OOxM

Little, Constance.
The black piano, by Constance & Gwenyth Little. [1st ed.] Garden City, N. Y., Pub. for the Crime Club by Doubleday, 1948.
192 p. 21 cm.

I. Little, Gwenyth, joint author. II. Title.

PZ3.L723Bri 48-5564*

NL 0410411 DLC OOxM

Little, Constance.
... The black rustle. Garden City, New York, Pub. for the Crime club, Doubleday, Doran & co., inc., 1943.
4 p. l., 214 p. 20ᶜᵐ.
At head of title: Constance and Gwenyth Little.
"First edition."

I. Little, Gwenyth, joint author. II. Title.

Library of Congress PZ3.L723Bs 43-9807

NL 0410412 DLC OrU OOxM

Little, Constance.
The black shrouds, by Constance and Gwenyth Little. Garden City, N. Y., Pub. for the Crime club by Doubleday, Doran & company, inc., 1941.
4 p. l., 278 p. 20½ᶜᵐ.
"First edition."

I. Little, Gwenyth, joint author. II. Title.

Library of Congress PZ3.L723Bt 41-20726

NL 0410413 DLC

Little, Constance.
The Black Smith [by] Constance and Gwenyth Little. [1st ed.] Garden City, N. Y., Published for the Crime Club by Doubleday, 1950.
218 p. 21 cm.

I. Little, Gwenyth, joint author. II. Title.

PZ3.L723Btc 50-10871

NL 0410414 DLC WaE

Little, Constance.
... The black stocking. Garden City, New York, Pub. for the Crime club by Doubleday & company, inc., 1946.
4 p. l., 7-220 p. 18½ᶜᵐ.
At head of title: Constance and Gwenyth Little.
"First edition."

I. Little, Gwenyth, joint author. II. Title.

Library of Congress PZ3.L723Btg 46-6292

NL 0410415 DLC

Little, Constance.
... The black thumb. Garden City, N. Y., Published for the Crime club by Doubleday, Doran and co., inc., 1942.
4 p. l., 272 p. 20ᶜᵐ.
At head of title: Constance and Gwenyth Little.
"First edition."

I. Little, Gwenyth, joint author. II. Title.

Library of Congress PZ3.L723Bu 42-21959

NL 0410416 DLC OEac OO OOxM

Little, Constance.
The blackout [by] Constance & Gwenyth Little. [1st ed.] Garden City, N. Y., Published for the Crime Club by Doubleday, 1951.
190 p. 21 cm.

I. Title.

PZ3.L723Bx 51-13255 ‡

NL 0410417 DLC ICU

Little, Constance.
... Great black Kanba. Garden City, N. Y., Pub. for the Crime club by Doubleday, Doran and co., inc., 1944.
188 p. 19ᶜᵐ.
At head of title: Constance and Gwenyth Little.
"First edition."

I. Little, Gwenyth, joint author. II. Title.

Library of Congress PZ3.L723Gn 44-47047

NL 0410418 DLC TxU NcU OEac OOxM

Little, Constance.
Great black Kanba. New York, Dell [c1944]
240 p. 16 cm.
At head of title: Constance and Gwenyth Little

NL 0410419 NcU

Little, Constance.
... The grey mist murders. Garden City, N. Y., Pub. for the Crime club, inc., by Doubleday, Doran & co., inc., 1938.
4 p. l., 305 p. 20ᶜᵐ.
At head of title: Constance & Gwenyth Little.
"First edition."

I. Little, Gwenyth, joint author. II. Title.

Library of Congress PZ3.L723Gr 38-11472

NL 0410420 DLC

Little, Cynthia Maria (Jones) Atwood, 1837-
History of the clan MacFarlane, (Macfarlane) MacFarlan, MacFarland, MacFarlin. By Mrs. C. M. Little. Tottenville, N. Y., Mrs. C. M. Little, 1893.
viii, [9]-252, [2] p. front., illus., plates, ports. 23ᶜᵐ.
For private circulation.

1. McFarland family. 2. Macfarlane clan.

Library of Congress CS71.M142 1893 9-11931

NL 0410421 DLC NcC TxU TU Nh MWA MB

285.09768
L722h
Little, D D
History of the Presbytery of Columbia, Tennessee. By D.D. Little ... Columbia, Maury Democrat, 1928.
46p. 22½cm.

Cover-title.

1. Presbyterian church in the U.S. Presbyteries. Columbia.

NL 0410422 TxU

Little, D D
Mr. Paxton's solution; or, How one minister solved the financial problem ... Richmond Va., Presbyterian committee of publ. [n.d.]
22 p.

NL 0410423 ViU

220.62
L72t
Little, David
The tabernacle in the wilderness. New York, Loizeaux Bros., n.d.

63 p.

1. Tabernacle.

NL 0410424 CLamB

LITTLE, David, *physician.*
An address on the operative treatment of zonular cataract. London. British medical association. 1888. (1), 4 pp. 8°.
Reprinted from the British medical journal. Vol. 39 [*7740.3.39].

NL 0410425 MB

LITTLE, David, *physician.*
On extraction of senile cataract, with the results of 1,248 extractions. London. British medical association. 1889. 4 pp. 8°.
Reprinted from the British medical journal. Vol. 41 [*7740.3.41].

NL 0410426 MB

VOLUME 336

Little, David Flemming

Poems. Halifax, Nova Scotia printing company, 1881.
vi, [7]-101 p. illus. 18 cm.

1. Canadian poetry.

NL 0410427 RPB CaBVa CaBVaU CCamarSJ

Little, David Flemming
The wanderer, and other poems, by David F. Little. Los Angeles [Calif.] Mirror printing and binding house, 1880.

32 p. 18cm.

1. Poetry of places—California. I. Title.

NL 0410428 CCamarSJ MnU NN RPB OrU

Little, David Lawrence, 1906-
... Die chirurgische Behandlung der bösartigen Geschwülste der weiblichen Genitalien unter besonderer Berücksichtigung der Morbidität und Mortalität nach der einfachen und nach der erweiterten (Wertheim'schen) Operation ... Zürich, 1937.
Inaug.-Diss. - Zürich.
Curriculum vitae.
"Literaturverzeichnis": p. 40-42.

NL 0410429 CtY

Little, David Mason.
Instantaneous marine studies; taken by David Mason Little ... Boston, Cupples, Upham, and company, 1883.
85 p. incl. 20 pl. 30½ x 25½cm.
Printed on one side of leaf only.

1. Ships. I. Title.

Library of Congress VM307.L7 17-9270

NL 0410430 DLC NN MnU

Little, David Mason, 1896- ed.

Garrick, David, 1717-1779.
Pineapples of finest flavour; or, A selection of sundry unpublished letters of the English Roscius, David Garrick, edited with an introduction and notes by David Mason Little. Cambridge, Harvard university press, 1930.

M05 L778a Little, Delbert Morse, 1898-
Aviation's meteorological service and its needs. New York, Greater New York Safety Council, 1938.
4 numb. ℓ. 28cm.

Caption title.
Paper given at the Ninth Annual Convention, Greater New York Safety Council, April 19, 20, 21, 1938. Aeronautical Section, N.S.C., Session No.2, Paper no.4.

NL 0410432 DAS

M/0400 L778 Little, Delbert Morse, 1898-
Recent advances in airway meteorological service in the United States. New York. 1937.
p.206-208. 30 cm.

NL 0410433 DAS

M05 L778w Little, Delbert Morse, 1898-
Weather service for international civil aviation. Simultaneous session of the Commission for Aeronautical Meteorology and the Meteorology Division of the International Civil Aviation Organization, Montreal, June-July 1954. [Washington, D.C., U.S. Dept. of State, 1954]
pp. 824-827. 26cm.

At head of title: International Organizations and Conferences.

Caption title.
Separate from the Department of State Bulletin, Vol.31, no.805, November 29,1954.

NL 0410435 DAS

Little, Donald Campbell, 1901-
Descendants of Col. John Little, Esq., of Shrewsbury Township, Monmouth County, New Jersey. [Edwardsville? Kan.] 1951.
123 p. coat of arms, facsims. 24 cm.

1. Little family (John Little, 1680-1751)

CS71.L777 1951 52-24605

NL 0410436 DLC NN

L384.5 L778r Little, Donald G 1893-
Reminiscences. [New York, Columbia University, 1952]
107ℓ. (loose leaf) 29cm.

"These reminiscences are the result of interviews... by Frank Ernest Hill."

NL 0410437 IEN

Little, Dorothy.
The social phase of the narcotic problem, and two other suggested course plans for narcotic education [by] Dorothy Little [and] Doris Purcell. Tallahassee, Fla., State dept. of education [1944?]
vii, 101 p. 23cm.
Includes bibliographies.

1. Temperance—Study and teaching. 2. Narcotics. I. Purcell, Doris, joint author. II. Florida. State dept. of education.

45-37388

Library of Congress HV5060.L5

178

NL 0410438 DLC CU

Little, E.
Harry Hale; or, the search for the golden isle. New York, N.L. Munro, 1877.
31 p. [New York Boys' Library, Vol. II, no. 28]
(Dime Novel Collection - PZ1)

NL 0410439 DLC

Little, E A
The country publisher ... Ridgewood, N.J., The Editor company[c1917]
64p. 20½cm.

1.Newspapers. 2.Journalism.

NL 0410440 CtY

Little, E. D., joint author.

Cotterill, Charles Clement.
Ships and sailors, ancient and modern. A sketch of the progress of naval art, with historical illustrations. By C. C. Cotterill, B. A., and E. D. Little, B. A. With forty-two engravings. London, Seeley, Jackson, and Halliday, 1868.

Little, E. E.
Cherries and cherry growing in Iowa
see under Price, Henry Charles.

Little, E. E.
Plum varieties. [Ames, 1910.] 2 p.l., (1)122-149 p. illus. 8°. (Iowa. Agricultural experiment station. Bull 114.)

1. Plum. United States: Iowa.

February 8, 1911.

NL 0410443 NN MH-A MBH

Little, E Robin.
Summit's story; a chronicle for the city of Summit on the occasion of its fiftieth anniversary. Designed and illustrated by Jesse P. Gourlay. Summit, N. J., Published by the City, 1949.
78 p. illus. 28 cm.

1. Summit, N. J.—Hist.

F144.S95L5 917.4936 52-31727 ‡

NL 0410444 DLC NN

Little, Edna Margaret (Steele), ed.
The works of Jesus
see under Bible. N. T. Gospels. English. Selections. 1908. (Abilene, Little)
Also with date 1909 (San Francisco, Elder)

Little, Edward.
The professional training of teachers...
York, n.d.

NL 0410446 PHC

Little, Edward Campbell, 1858-1924.

U. S. *Laws, statutes, etc., 1921 (67th Cong., 1st sess.)* (*Bills*)
... An act to consolidate, codify, revise, and reenact the general and permanent laws of the United States in force March 4, 1919. [Washington, Govt. print. off., 1921]

Little, Edward Campbell, 1858-1924.
U. S. *Laws, statutes, etc., 1923-1924 (68th Cong., 1st sess.)* (*Bills*)
... An act to consolidate, codify, revise, and reenact the general and permanent laws of the United States in force December 2, 1923. [Washington, Govt. print. off., 1924]

Little, Edward Campbell, 1858-1924.
The Armenian question in the American House of representatives; a speech by the Hon. Lieut.-Colonel Edward C. Little of Kansas, delivered on Thursday, February 7th, 1918, reprinted from the "Congressional review" of March 4th, 1918. London, Printed by the Frederick printing company, ltd. [1918]
32 p. 23cm.
Delegation propaganda authenticated by the Armenian delegation at the Paris Peace conference, 1919.

1. Armenian question. I. Title.

A 23-2070

Hoover war libr., Stanford univ. for Library of Congress DS176.L5

NL 0410449 CSt-H NN

VOLUME 336

Little, Edward Campbell, 1858-1924. FOR OTHER EDITIONS SEE MAIN ENTRY

U. S. *Laws, statutes, etc., 1921 (67th Cong., 1st sess.)* (*Bills*)
... A bill to consolidate, codify, revise and reenact the general and permanent laws of the United States in force March 4, 1919. [Washington, Govt. print. off., 1921]

Little, Edward Campbell, 1858-1924.

U. S. *Congress. House. Committee on revision of the laws.*
... The code of the laws of the United States ... Report. <To accompany H. R. 12.> ... [Washington, Govt. print. off., 1923]

Little, Edward Campbell, 1858-1924.

U. S. *Congress. House. Committee on revision of the laws.*
... The code of the laws of the United States ... Report. <To accompany H. R. 9389> ... [Washington, Govt. print. off., 1920-21]

Little, Edward Campbell, 1858-1924.

U. S. *Congress. House. Committee on revision of the laws.*
Codification and revision of the laws. Hearings before the Committee on revision of the laws, House of representatives, Sixty-sixth Congress, first session, on H. R. 9389, a bill to consolidate, codify, revise, and reenact the general and permanent laws of the United States in force March 4, 1919. Friday, September 26, 1919. Washington, Govt. print. off., 1919.

Little, Edward Campbell, 1858-1924.

U. S. *Congress. House. Committee on revision of the laws.*
... Index, appendix, and annotations to the code of the United States ... Report. <To accompany H. R. 13555.> [Washington, Govt. print. off., 1923]

Little, Edward Filene, 1920-
Fundamentals of skiing, by Edward F. Little and John A. Clark. [Hanover, N. H., L. C. G. Pub. Co., 1948]
46 p. illus. 28 cm.

1. Skis and ski-running. I. Clark, John Appleton, 1906- joint author. II. Title.
GV854.L58 796.93 48-1574*
Library of Congress

NL 0410455 DLC WaT

AC1 .D29 no.2 1941
Little, Edward Filene, 1920-
The recapture of time; re-embracing Latin. [Hanover, N. H.] Dartmouth College Publications, 1941.
10 p. 23cm. (Dartmouth College Senior fellow pamphlets, 2)

1. Latin philology—Addresses, essays, lectures. 2. Latin literature—Addresses, essays, lectures. I. Title. II. Ser.

NL 0410456 ViU

Little, Edward Milton, 1897-
Ionization efficiency of ultra-violet light in caesium vapor, by Edward Milton Little ... [Minneapolis, Minn., 1927]
1 p. l., p. 109-118, 1 l. 1 illus., diagrs. 25½cm.
Thesis (PH. D.)—University of Illinois, 1926.
Vita.
"Reprinted from Physical review ... vol. 30, no. 2, August, 1927."

1. Ionization of gases. 2. Ultra-violet rays. 3. Caesium.
28-6298
Library of Congress QC702.L5 1926
Univ. of Illinois

NL 0410457 IU DLC OU

Little, Edward Revere, 1881-1905, illus.

Eliot, Henry Ware, 1879-
Harvard celebrities; a book of caricatures & decorative drawings by Frederick Garrison Hall, '03 & Edward Revere Little, '04, verses by Henry Ware Eliot, jr. '02. Cambridge [Mass.] Printed for the editors by the University press [1901]

Little, Edward S., ed.

The National spectator. v. 1 (no. 1-18); Jan. 9-May 8, 1926. Washington, D. C. [The National spectator corporation, 1926]

Little, Edward Selby, 1864-
The Chinese revenue and the new treaty: a protest against an increased tariff from a merchant's point of view. With some suggested regulations for mining. By Edward S. Little. Shanghai, "North-China herald" office, 1902.
cover-title, 16 p. 23½ cm.

1. Tariff—China. 2. Finance, Public—China. 3. Mining law—China. I. Title.
HF2316.L56 337.0951 34-4572

NL 0410460 DLC MSaE

Little, Edward Selby, 1864-
—— The currency question; a plea for immediate action with a view to the establishment of the gold standard in China. Shanghai, 1903. 7 p. 8°.

NL 0410461 MSaE CtY NN

Little, Edward Selby, 1864-
The fight for Kuling in 1892-1895
see under Archibald, John.

Little, Edward Selby, 1864-
The story of Kuling [sanitarium]. [Yanchow] 1899. 43 p. 32°.
"Pub. by request of the Chinkiang literary assoc."

NL 0410463 MSaE

Little, Edwin Maurice.
Sonnets and other poems, by E. Maurice Little. Brisbane, Queensland book depot [1923] 18 p. 22cm.

1. Sonnets, Australian.
June 28, 1948

NL 0410464 NN

Little, Elbert Luther, 1907-
Arizona's native century plants. (In Arizona highways. Phoenix, Ariz., v. 14, no. 4. April, 1943. p. [8]-11, 38-41)
1. Agave. 2. Arizona. Botany. I. Arizona highways, v. 14, no. 4.

NL 0410465 DNAL

Little, Elbert Luther, 1907-
A botanical survey of Muskogee County, Oklahoma, 1929.
vi, 205 l. illus., fold. maps (part col.) 29 cm.
Typescript (carbon copy)
Thesis—University of Chicago.
Bibliography: leaves 199-203.

1. Botany—Oklahoma—Muskogee Co.—Ecology. I. Title.
QK941.O6L57 71-298201

NL 0410466 DLC DNAL ICU

QK481 L499
Little, Elbert Luther, 1907-
Checklist of the native and naturalized trees of the United States, including Alaska. [Preliminary ed. Washington] U.S.D.A. Forest Service [1944]
325 p. 27cm.

Mimeographed.
Supersedes Sudworth's "Check list of the forest trees of the United States, their names and ranges." (U.S.D.A. Misc. Circ. 92. 1927)

1. Trees - U.S. I. U.S.D.A. Forest Service. II. Title. III. Title:

NL 0410467 OrCS

Little, Elbert Luther, 1907-
Check list of native and naturalized trees of the United States (including Alaska) Prepared under the direction of the Forest Service Tree and Range Plant Name Committee. Washington, Forest Service, 1953.
472 p. 24 cm. (U. S. Dept. of Agriculture. Agriculture handbook no. 41)
"Supersedes Miscellaneous circular 92, Check list of the forest trees of the United States, their names and ranges [by G. B. Sudworth]"
"Literature cited": p. 24-26.

1. Trees—U. S. 2. Trees—Nomenclature (Popular) 2. Trees—Names. 3. Botany—Nomenclators. I. Title. (Series)
QK481.L5 *581.973 582.16 Agr 53-309
U. S. Dept. of Agr. Libr. 1Ag84Ah no. 41
for Library of Congress [20*]†

OO NIC MiHM DI DDO NBuU AAP IdPI PPT-D OrP WaS OrCS MtBC KEmT CaBViP DLC IdB NNBG PPAN NcC LU WaE WaTC OOxM PU-A PSt TxU OU PHC NNC
NL 0410468 DNAL NcU DI PPT PP PSC PPD IU TU NcD

Little, Elbert Luther, 1907- joint author.

Ortenburger, Arthur Irving, 1898-
... Notes on some reptiles and amphibians from western Oklahoma, by A. I. Ortenburger and Beryl Freeman. Notes on a collection of birds from western Oklahoma, by A. I. Ortenburger and Elbert L. Little, jr. A list of the birds of the campus of the University of Oklahoma, by Margaret Morse Nice. A key to the lizards and snakes of Oklahoma, by A. I. Ortenburger. Norman, University of Oklahoma press, 1930.

A99.24 L72Ae
Little, Elbert Luther, 1907-
Notes on tropical dendrology. Rio Piedras, 1955.
27 p.

Slightly revised translation of his Notas sobre dendrología tropical (

1. Trees. Tropics. I. U.S. Forest Service. II. Little, Elbert Luther, 1907- Notas sobre dendrología tropicale. III. U.S. Foreign Operations Ad- ministration.

NL 0410470 DNAL

VOLUME 336

QK484 .A4T3 1950 Little, Elbert Luther, 1907- joint author.

Taylor, Raymond Frank, 1897-
Pocket guide to Alaska trees, by Raymond F. Taylor and Elbert L. Little, Jr. Washington, U. S. Govt. Print. Off., 1950.

Little, Elbert Luther, 1907- joint author

Jeffs, Royal Edgar, 1879-
... A preliminary list of the ferns and seed plants of Oklahoma, by R. E. Jeffs and Elbert L. Little, jr. Norman, University of Oklahoma press, 1930.

Little, Elbert Luther, 1907-
Southwestern trees; a guide to the native species of New Mexico and Arizona. Washington [U. S. Govt. Print. Off.] 1950.
ii, 109 p. illus., maps. 24 cm. (U. S. Dept. of Agriculture. Agriculture handbook no. 9)
Contribution from Forest Service.
"Selected references": p. 104-105.
—— Key to Southwestern trees. [Tucson? Ariz.] 1951.
28 p. 27 cm. (U. S. Forest Service. Southwestern Forest and Range Experiment Station. Research report no. 8)
Cover title.
SD11.A4598 no. 8

1. Trees—Arizona. 2. Trees—New Mexico. I. Title. (Series: U. S. Forest Service. Southwestern Forest and Range Experiment Station. Research report no. 8)

QK484.A6L5 582.16 Agr 51-228 rev
U. S. Dept. of Agr. Libr. 1Ag84Ah no. 9
for Library of Congress [r52f3*]†

NL 0410474 DNAL NIC DLC NNC NNBG MiU WaS WaT OrP

LITTLE, Elbert Payson.
The optical properties of quartz in the Schumann region.

Typewritten. 29 x 22 cm. Charts and diagrs.
Thesis, Ph.D. - Harvard University, 1941, Department of Physics.

NL 0410475 MH

Little, Eleanor Ann.
A birthday present for Jannie, written and illustrated by Eleanor Ann Little. New York, Comet Press Books [c1954]
33 p. illus. 22 cm.

I. Title.

PZ7.L722Bi 54-9551 ‡

NL 0410476 DLC

Ndn43 C8 +937l **Little, Eleanor Howell, 1885-**
Relief without politics, by Eleanor H. Little, Relief administrator for the state of Connecticut, 1933-1936. [Hartford?1937?]
cover-title, 1p.l., 37 numb.l. 28cm.
Typewritten ms (carbon copy).

NL 0410477 CtY

HF 5547 A45 no. 27 Little, Eleanor Howell, 1885-
Some considerations in installing a salary administration plan. New York, American Management Association, 1927.
20p. 24cm. (American Management Association Office management series, no. 27)

1. Wages - Clerks. I. Title. (Series)

NL 0410478 MU OU

Little, Eleanor Howell, 1885-
The United States rubber company's use of a dismissal wage, by E. H. Little ... New York, N. Y., American management association, c1930.
12 p. 23cm. ([American management association] Personnel series: no. 6)
"Presented at the A. M. A. Personnel administration conference held at ... Cleveland, January 31, 1930."—p. 3.
Discussion: p. 9-11.

1. United States rubber company. 2. Unemployed—U. S. I. Title.

Library of Congress HD4928.D5L5 37-25640
Copyright A 22467 658.3137878

NL 0410479 DLC OU NcGU MU OrP

Little, Eleanor Howell, 1885-
Women in supervisory positions, by E. H. Little ... New York, N. Y., American management association, c1926.
16 p. 23cm. ([American management association] Production executives' series: no. 43)
"Presented at the A. M. A. Production executives' conference held at Silver Bay, July 1, 1926."—p. 3.
Discussion: p. 12-15.

1. Woman—Employment. 2. Foremen. 3. Executive ability. I. Title.

Library of Congress HD6058.L5 37-25511
396.53311243

NL 0410480 DLC NcD OU

Little, Eleanor N
The early reading of Justice Oliver Wendell Holmes. [1954]
163-203 p. facsims.

Cover title.
"Offprint from Harvard Library bulletin, volume VIII, no. 2, spring 1954."

NL 0410481 NNC ViU-L PPT-L MB CU FU NcU

Little, Eliza Adams, *ed.*
The first parish, Newbury, Massachusetts, 1635-1935; editors, Eliza Adams Little [and] Lucretia Little Ilsley. Contributors, Marion Stackpole Bailey, Harriot Withington Colman, Elizabeth Hale Little Ilsley [and others] ... Newburyport, News publishing co., inc., printers, 1935.
104 p. incl. front. plates, ports. 23½cm.
Bibliography: p. 103-104.

1. Newbury, Mass. First church. I. Ilsley, Lucretia Little, 1906- joint ed.

Library of Congress BX7255.N33F5 40-31210
285.87445

NL 0410482 DLC ICN ICU CtY MH-AH CtY-D

Little, Elizabeth N *comp.*
... Beacon lights for God's mariners, comp. and illustrated by Elizabeth N. Little ... Boston, S. E. Cassino & co., 1884.
38 l. 15 x 13½cm.
Marginal illustrations.

1. Quotations. I. Title.

Library of Congress PN6110.S2L6 13-18142
Copyright 1884: 18823

NL 0410483 DLC OO

Little, Elizabeth N.
Habitations of God and His worshippers.
Boston, n.d.

NL 0410484 RPB

[**Little, Elizabeth N**] *comp.*
Log-book notes through life. New York & London, White and Allen, 1888.
34 l. illus. 20½ x 37cm.
Printed on one side of leaf only. Illustrated t.-p.
Compiler's name on cover and on leaf following t.-p.

1. American literature (Selections: Extracts, etc.) I. Title.

Library of Congress PS507.L6 18-13447

NL 0410485 DLC

[**Little, Elizabeth N**] *comp.*
Log-book notes through life. New York & London, White and Allen, 1889 [c1888]
34 l. illus. 20½ x 37cm.
Printed on one side of leaf only. Illustrated t.-p.
Compiler's name on cover and on leaf following t.-p.

NL 0410486 N

LITTLE, Elizabeth N. , compiler.
Long shore. By author of Beacon-lights, Ruling lights, &c. Boston, S.E. Cassino, 1886.

ff. (35)
Cover and each leaf illustrated.
A verse and Bible quotations for each day in the month.

NL 0410487 MH RPB

[**Little, Elizabeth N**]
"Nor' east by east." [Newton, Mass., c1885]
13 l. illus. 13½ x 17cm.
Text runs parallel with back of cover.
Descriptive of York, Me.

1. York, Me.—Descr. I. Title.

Library of Congress F29.Y6L7 18-15131

NL 0410488 DLC

[**Little, Elizabeth N**]
"Off the weather bow," on life's voyage. New York and London, White and Allen, c1889.
16 l. illus., 17 col. pl. 21 x 37cm.
Author's name on cover. Illus. t.-p.

Library of Congress NC1075.L78 11-29137
Copyright 1889: 22652

NL 0410489 DLC NN

[**Little, Elizabeth N**]
Ruling lights. A year after year calendar. [Boston, A. L Cassino, 1885]
15 l. illus. 17 x 17½ cm.
Decorated in colors.

1. Literary calendars. I. Title.

PN6110.R4L5 CA 19—343 Unrev'd

NL 0410490 DLC

VOLUME 336

[Little, Elizabeth N]
Watch ho! watch! on life's deep sea ... [Selected and illustrated by Elizabeth N. Little] New York, Dodd, Mead and company, °1891.
17 l. front., 16 pl. 19½ x 37cm.
Illustrated t.-p.

I. Title.
11—25492
Library of Congress NC1075.L8.

NL 0410491 DLC CtY

Little, Ella.
Kindergarten spelling book. Part first. By Ella Little. Boston, Lee & Shepard, 1866.
48 p. 17½cm.

1. Spellers. I. Title.
CA 17-3300 Unrev'd
Library of Congress PE1145.L7

NL 0410492 DLC MB

Little, Ella (Davidson), 1867-1916.
In memoriam. Mrs. Lacy L. Little
see under title

Little, Ellon.
the good girl. [Juvenile]
Worc., n.d. [1843?] 15 p. 32°
(Cover title is The Girl's token)
(Bound with this are Good advice for boys and girls; also The Little Riddler)

NL 0410494 MWA

Little, Elliott M
... Commonsense in labour relations, by Elliott M. Little ... An address delivered before the Canadian manufacturers' association, Toronto, June 8th, 1942. [Ottawa, Printed by "Le Droit printing," 1942]
18 p., 1 l. 19½cm.
At head of title: Dept. of labour.
"Issued by the director of public information under authority of Hon. J. T. Thorson, minister of national war services."—Leaf at end.
1. Industrial relations—Canada. 2. World war, 1939- —Economic aspects—Canada. I. Canada. Dept. of labour. II. Canada. Office of director of public information. III. Title.
43-12908
Library of Congress HD8106.L5

NL 0410495 DLC OrU NN

Little, Elliott M
... Facing realities, by Elliott M. Little ... [Ottawa, Ont., Progressive printers, 1942]
15 p. 19½cm.
At head of title: Dept. of labour.
"An address delivered before the Canadian congress of labour, Ottawa, September 15th, 1942."
"Issued by the Wartime information board, Ottawa, for the Director of national selective service."—p. 15.
1. Labor supply—Canada. 2. Canada. Army—Recruiting, enlistment, etc. 3. World war, 1939-1945—Manpower—Canada. I. Canada. Wartime information board. II. Canada. Director of national selective service. III. Title.
43-1671
Library of Congress HD5728.L5
[a46d1] 331

NL 0410496 DLC OrU NN MH

Little, Elliott M.
Labour-management relations; an address. [N.p.n.pub.]1948.
4p.sq.Q.

NL 0410497 CaBViP

Little, Elliott M
... Labour responsibilities in wartime, by Elliott M. Little ... [Ottawa, Can., Progressive printers, 1942]
15, [1] p. 19½cm.
At head of title: Dept. of labour.
"An address delivered before the Trades and labor congress of Canada, Winnipeg, August 25th, 1942."
"Issued by the Director of public information, Ottawa, under authority of Hon. J. T. Thorson, minister of national war services for the Director of national selective service."—p. [16]
1. Labor and laboring classes—Canada. 2. World war, 1939- —Economic aspects—Canada. I. Canada. Office of director of public information. II. Canada. Director of national selective service. III. Title.
43-1672
Library of Congress HD5728.L52
331

NL 0410498 DLC OrU NN

Little, E[lliott] M.
The North American supply of newsprint; an address by E.M. Little, before the Newspaper Advertising Executives association, at Quebec, June 24,1948. [N.p.n.pub.]1948?
4p.sq.Q.

NL 0410499 CaBViP CaBVaU

Little, Ellis Beecher, 1914-
An experimental study of the permanence of information learned before and during an introductory college biology course. Ann Arbor, University Microfilms [1955]
([University Microfilms, Ann Arbor, Mich.] Publication no. 13,515)
Microfilm copy of typescript. Positive.
Collation of the original: vi, 153 l. diagrs., tables.
Thesis—University of Illinois.
Abstracted in Dissertation abstracts, v. 15 (1955) no. 10, p. 1786-1787.
Vita.
Bibliography: leaves [142]-143.
1. Learning, Psychology of. 2. Biology—Study and teaching. I. Title: The permanence of information learned.
Microfilm AC-1 no. 13,515 Mic 55-444
Illinois. Univ. Library for Library of Congress

NL 0410500 IU DLC

Little, Eric H
Liberty men, fall in! By Eric H. Little ... [Cape Town, Unie volkspers, beperk, 1945]
5 p. l., 130 p. front., plates. 21cm.

1. World war, 1939-1945—Fiction. I. Title.
A 47-3584
New York. Public library for Library of Congress

NL 0410501 NN

Little, Eric H
The luck of H. M. S. Dragon, by Able Seaman Eric H. Little. A South African's thrilling sea story containing numerous incidents of the war in the Far East, including the evacuations of Singapore and Batavia. [Cape Town, Stewart printing company (pty.) ltd., 1944]
93, [1] p. incl. port. plates. 22cm.
Map on lining-papers.
Part of the text deleted by censor.
Errata slip mounted on p. [4]
1. World war, 1939-1945—Naval operations. 2. World war, 1939-1945—Personal narratives, South African. 3. Dragon (Cruiser) 4. World war, 1939-1945—East (Far East)
A 45-5163
New York. Public library for Library of Congress D772.D7L5 940.545
†

NL 0410502 NN DLC

Little, Ernest, 1888-
The determination of the acidity of a tan liquor, by Ernest Little ... [New York; Columbia university, 1923.
33, [1] p. diagrs. 23½cm.
Thesis (PH. D.)—Columbia university, 1924.
Vita.

1. Tanning.
24-10336
Library of Congress TS985.L5
Columbia Univ. Libr.

NL 0410503 NNC DLC MiU OU

Little, Ernest, 1888-
RS1 .N513
New Jersey pharmaceutical association.
The New Jersey pharmaceutical association, 1870-1945, an historical review, by David L. Cowen ... with the cooperation of Dr. Ernest Little ... [and] John J. Debus ... [Trenton, 1945]

Little, Ernest Graham.
Health resorts of South Africa. Plate.
(In Creswicke. South Africa and its future. Pp. 157-173. London, 1903.)

June 4, 1903
E9242 — Health resorts.

NL 0410505 MB

Little, Ernest L *comp.*
Agricultural and industrial survey of Missouri, compiled for Missouri Chemurgic Council. [Jefferson City] Missouri Division of Resources & Development [1949]
vi, 55 p. illus. 23 cm.
"Presented ... to the State of Missouri at a meeting of the State Chemurgic Council held in Jefferson City, February 20, 1949."
Includes bibliographies.

1. Agriculture—Missouri. 2. Missouri—Indus. I. Missouri Chemurgic Council.
S451.M8L5 630.9778 50-63213

NL 0410506 DLC MoU

Little, Ernest Muirhead, 1854-
Artificial limbs and amputation stumps; a practical handbook; by E. Muirhead Little ... with 267 illustrations. London, H. K. Lewis & co., ltd., 1922.
vii, 319 p. illus., plates (part fold.) 22cm.

1. Artificial limbs. 2. Amputation [Prosthesis] 3. Orthopedia, [Military] 4. Surgery, Military.
Library, U. S. Surgeon-General's Office S G 22-156

NL 0410507 DNLM CtY

Little, Ernest Muirhead, 1854- *comp.*
History of the British medical association, 1832-1932, compiled by Ernest Muirhead Little, F. R. C. S. London, British medical association [1932]
5 p. l., 342 p. front., plates (part col.) ports. 24cm.
Illustrated lining-papers.

1. British medical association. 2. Medicine—Gt. Brit. 3. Medicine—Biog.
33-4584
Library of Congress R35.B83
610.6242

NL 0410508 NcD-MC ICJ OU CtY AU DLC OrU-M PPiU ViU-M CaBVaU KU-M TU

VOLUME 336

Little E[rnest] Muirhead, 1854-
On the causes of rotation of the vertebrae in scoliosis. London, J. Bale & Sons, 1891.
8 p. 8°.
Repr. from: Lancet, Lond., 1891, i.

NL 0410509 DNLM

Little, Esther Louise.
... Budgets of families and individuals of Kensington, Philadelphia, by Esther Louise Little ... and William Joseph Henry Cotton ... Lancaster, Pa., Press of the New era printing company, 1920.
vi, 273 p. tables, diagrs. 23cm.
The author's thesis (PH. D.)—University of Pennsylvania, 1914.

1. Cost and standard of living—Philadelphia. I. Cotton, William Joseph Henry, joint author. II. Title.
20—8623
Library of Congress HD6994.P5L5
Univ. of Pennsylvania Libr.

NL 0410510 PU DLC WaS CU NIC OCl MiU OClW MB ICJ

Little, Etta Viola, 1883-
... The structure of the ocelli of *Polyorchis penicillata*, by Etta Viola Little. Berkeley, University of California press, 1914.
cover-title, p. [307]-328, pl. 13-15. 27cm. (University of California publications in zoology. v. 11, no. 12)
Bibliography: p. 321-323.

1. Medusae. 2. [Polyorchis penicillata]
A 14—691
California. Univ. Libr. for Library of Congress QL377.H9L5
QL1.C15 vol. 11, no. 12

NN ViU
NL 0410511 CU CaBVaU OrU MU CoU OU OClW OO MiU DLC

Little, Evelyn Agnes (Steel) 1890-
Backgrounds of world literature from Homer to Tolstoy, by Evelyn Steel Little ... 1st preliminary ed. ... Ann Arbor, Mich., Mimeographed by the Department of English language and literature, distributed by Wahr's university book store, 1934.
3 p. l., ii numb. l., 1 l., 151 numb. l. maps. 27½cm.

1. Literature—Hist. & crit. I. Title.
43-29924
Library of Congress PN524.L54
809

NL 0410512 DLC CU

Z239
E8L77
Bender Room

Little, Evelyn Agnes (Steel) 1890-
Books under fire. Mills College, Calif., The Eucalyptus Press, January 1945.
[10] p., 1 l. 23cm.
"An address before the Book Day assembly, Mills College, November 29, 1944."
"Three hundred copies designed and printed by the Eucalyptus Press, 1945."

1. Books - Addresses, essays, lectures. I. Title.

NL 0410513 CSt CaBViP CU CU-B

Little, Evelyn Agnes (Steel) 1890-
**Books under fire; [an address before the Book Day Assembly, Mills College, Nov. 29, 1944. Oakland, Calif.] Eucalyptus Press, 1945.
[20]p. 23cm.**

NL 0410514 IEN NNC

PN
524
.L781

Little,Evelyn Agnes (Steel) 1890-
... Chronological chart of world literature,by Evelyn Steel Little. To accompany English 223 (Library science 137). Ann Arbor,Mich., 1933.
1 p.l.,12 numb.l. fold.table. 30½ x 21½cm.
At head of title: University of Michigan. Department of library science.
On cover: Distributed by Brumfield & Brumfield,mimeographers,Ann Arbor,Mich.

NL 0410515 MiU CU DLC

Little,Evelyn Agnes (Steel) 1890-
Homer and Theocritus in English translation: a critical bibliography designed as a guide for librarians in the choice of editions for the general reader ... Ann Arbor,Michigan, 1936.
3 p.l.,ii-vii,[1], l.,511 numb.l. 2 tables. 28cm.
(University Microfilms. Pub.no.307)
Abstracted in Microfilm abstracts,v.III,no.2,p.60,1941.
Thesis (PH.D.)--University of Michigan,1936.
Typewritten copy.
"Notes on series in which the translations appear": p.498-503.

Bibliography: p.504-508.

1.Homerus--Translations,English. 2.Theocritus--Translations,English. I.Title.

NL 0410517 MiU

Little, Evelyn Agnes (Steel) 1890-
... Instruction in the use of books and libraries in colleges and universities, by Evelyn Steel Little ... Ann Arbor, Mich., The University of Michigan library, 1936.
4 p. l., 39 numb. l., 6 l. 27½cm.
At head of title: University of Michigan, Department of library science.
Mimeographed.
"List of references": 5 leaves at end.
"Errata": 1 leaf laid in.

1. Libraries and readers. 2. Libraries, University and college. I. Michigan. University. Dept. of library science. II. Title.
36-28294 Revised
Library of Congress Z668.L77
[r43f3] 028.70711

MiU ICU CtY NNC ViU ICJ IU
NL 0410518 DLC OrCS OrLgE OrPR OrU CU OCl OU OClW

Little, Evelyn Agnes (Steel) 1890-
... Instruction in the use of books and libraries in colleges and universities, by Evelyn Steel Little ... Issued 1936 by the University of Michigan library. Rerun without change by American library association. Chicago, 1938.
5 p. l., 39 numb. l., 6 l. 28cm.
At head of title: University of Michigan, Department of library science.
Mimeographed.
"List of references": 5 leaves at end.

1. Libraries and readers. 2. Libraries, University and college. I. Michigan. University. Dept. of library science. II. Title.
38-22164 Revised
Library of Congress Z668.L77 1938
[r4312] 028.70711

NL 0410519 DLC MtU MoU TxU NcRS OO OClCC TU MiHM

LITTLE, EVELYN Agnes (Steel) 1890-
The power of books in a democracy. Address delivered at the dedication of the Oregon state library, April 3, 1939. Author, 1939.
14 l.

Typewritten copy.
Bibliography: p. 14.

NL 0410520 Or

Little, Evelyn Agnes (Steel) 1890-
26 lead soldiers, a salute to printers by Evelyn Steel Little. Mills College [Calif.] The Eucalyptus press, 1939.
[11] p. 22½cm.
Radio address delivered September 13, 1939, on the Stanford university hour.

1. Printing—Hist.—Origin and antecedents. 2. Printing—Hist.—Celebrations of invention. I. Title.
43-448
Library of Congress Z126.L77

NL 0410521 DLC CSt MH

Little, Evelyn Agnes (Steel) 1890-
United States housing in war and peace; some of the data available in the American library in London: a bibliography compiled by Evelyn Steel Little to accompany the housing exhibition sponsored jointly by the Royal institute of British architects and the Office of war information to be held at the Institute from July 19th to August 30th, 1944. London, The American library, 1944.
26 numb. l. 26cm.

1. Housing—Bibl.—Catalogs. I. American library in London. II. Title.
45-3247
Library of Congress Z7164.H8L72
016.331833

NL 0410522 DLC

Z675
U5L778
Hoover Library

Little, Evelyn Agnes (Steel) 1890-
War activities of college and research libraries [by] Evelyn Steele Little. Chicago, American library association [1943]
179-211 p. 25½cm.
"Reprinted from College and research libraries, June 1943."

1.Libraries, University and college. 2.World war, 1939- Libraries (in camps,etc.) I.American library association. II.Title.

NL 0410523 CSt-H OCl

Little, Ezekiel, 1762-1840.

Works by this author printed in America before 1801 are available in this library in the Readex Microprint edition of Early American Imprints published by the American Antiquarian Society.
This collection is arranged according to the numbers in Charles Evans' American Bibliography.

NL 0410524 DLC

Little, Ezekiel, 1762-1840.
The usher. Comprising arithmetic in whole numbers; federal money; decimal and vulgar fractions; a description and use of Coggeshall's sliding rule; some uses of Gunter's scale...geometrical definitions and problems; surveying; the surveyor's pocket companion... Calculated and designed for youth. By Ezekiel Little ... Exeter [N. H.]: Printed by H. Ranlet, and sold at his bookstore; sold also, by the booksellers in Boston, Newburyport, Portsmouth, and other places. 1799. 240 p. 18cm. (12°.)

Evans 35734.
Imperfect: p. 235-240 (list of subscribers) wanting.

314982B. 1. Mathematics—Early works, to 1800. 2. Surveying—Early works, to 1800. I. Title.
June 20, 1946

NL 0410526 NN DAU CtY RPJCB MWA PU MH IU MiU-C

Little (F. P.) electrical construction and supply company, et. al., defendants.
... Edison electric light company vs. F. P. Little electrical construction and supply company et al.
see under Edison electric light company, New York, complainant.

VOLUME 336

Little, F.T., ed.

Methodist Protestant church.

Constitution and discipline of the Methodist Protestant church; rev. by General conference of 1912; ed. by F. T. Little ... Baltimore, Pittsburgh, The Board of publication of the Methodist Protestant church [1912?]

Film CD 3119 B3 U5 reel 20

Little, Fernmorz, 1820-1887.
Mail service across the plains.
38ℓ.
Microfilm (positive) of holograph.
Experiences with Charles F. Decker and Ephraim K. Hanks carrying mails between Great Salt Lake City, Fort Laramie, and Independence, 1850-1857; many sidelights on mountain men, Territorial officials, and trading posts along the overland trail.
1. Mormons and Mormonism--Hist.--Sources. 2. Postal service--The West. I. Title.

NL 0410529 UU

D 2912 .5

[LITTLE, FLORENCE S] comp.
History of the First Congregational Church, Winona, Minnesota, 1854-1904... [Winona, Minnesota] Published by the Church, 1908.
72p. illus., ports. 26cm.

NL 0410530 ICN

Little, *Mrs.* Frances.

Early American textiles, by Frances Little ... New York, London, The Century co. [°1931]

xvi, 267 p. front., plates, facsims. 21½cm. (*Lettered on cover:* Century library of American antiques) $4.00

"First printing."
Bibliography: p. 249-253.

1. Textile industry and fabrics—U. S. 2. U. S.—Hist.—Colonial period. I. Title.

Library of Congress NK8812.L5 31-32892

Copyright A 45020 677.0973

CaOTP CoU NBuC WaSp Or MB MnU-A NcD TU WaTC WaWW OrP WaT OrU MtU IdU KEmT
NL 0410531 DLC NcRS ICJ NcC ViU NN WaS OO OCl MWA

Little, Mrs. Frances.

New York. Metropolitan museum of art.

... Eighteenth-century costume in Europe, a picture book of twenty plates. New York, 1937.

Little, Frances, 1863-

see

Macaulay, *Mrs.* Fannie Caldwell, 1863-

Little, Frances Delanoy.

Ancient stories from the Dardanelles, by Frances Delanoy Little ... London, A. Melrose, ltd. [1918?]

4 p. l., 7-287 p. front., plates, ports., fold. map. 19½cm.

CONTENTS.—Argo.—Troy.—The Persians.—Alcibiades.—Alexander.—Cities of Asia.—Mithradates the Great.—Constantine.—Some Byzantine empresses.—Heraclius, Leo, Constantine V, and Irene.—Anna Comnena.—The fourth crusade.—"Fuit imperium."

1. History, Ancient—Juvenile literature. I. Title. II. Title: Dardanelles, Ancient stories from the.

Library of Congress PZ9.L72A 19-6976

NL 0410534 DLC OCl NN

Little, Frances Delanoy, tr.

Tharaud, Jean, 1877-

The shadow of the cross; translated from the French of Jean & Jérôme Tharaud, by Frances Delanoy Little. New York, A. A. Knopf, 1924.

Little, Frances Delanoy.

Sketches in Poland, written and painted by Frances Delanoy Little, with an historical postscript. London, A. Melrose, ltd. [1914]

vii, 344 p. 14 col. mounted pl. (incl. front.) map. 22½cm.

Plates accompanied by guard sheets with descriptive letterpress.

1. Poland—Social life and customs. 2. Poland—Description and travel. I. Title.

A 15—511

Springfield, Mass. City library for Library of Congress [a41d1]

NL 0410536 MS ICU FU CU CtY

Little, Frances Delanoy.
Sketches in Poland, written and painted by Frances Delanoy Little, with an historical postscript. New York, F. A. Stokes [1914]
vii, 344 p. illus. 23 cm.
Plates accompanied by guard sheets with descriptive letterpress.

1. Poland--Social life and customs. 2. Poland--Description and travel. I. Title

MiU
NL 0410537 OKentU WaSp NN OClW OO OLak NjP MH MB RP

Little, *Mrs.* Frances Woodward.

The place of the blind and the partially-seeing child in the public school system [by] Mrs. Frances Woodward Little.

(*In* National education association of the United States. Addresses and proceedings, 1934. p. 531-532)

1. Eye—Care and hygiene. I. Title.

E 35-464

Library, U. S. Office of Education L13.N212 1934
Library of Congress [L13.N4 1934]

NL 0410538 DHEW

Little, Francis, *d.* 1630.

"A monument of Christian munificence;" or An account of the Brotherhood of the Holy Cross and of the Hospital of Christ in Abingdon, by Francis Little. 1627. Edited, with an introduction and appendix, for the governors of the hospital, from a ms. in their possession, by Claude Delaval Cobham, ... Oxford and London, J. Parker and Co., 1871.

xix, 127 p. 18cm.

NL 0410539 ICJ

[**Little, Francis H**]

The untold sequel of The strange case of Dr. Jekyll and Mr. Hyde. Boston, Pinckney publishing co. [°1890]

2 p. l., [3]-41 p. 19cm.

I. Title.

Library of Congress (PZ3.L724U) 7—19402

NL 0410540 MH

Little, Frank.

Celery culture at Kalamazoo, Mich.

(*In* U. S. Dept. of agriculture. Report, 1886, p. 343-345. 23cm. Washington, 1887)

1. Celery.

Agr 13-1039

Library, U. S. Dept. of Agriculture 1Ag84 1886

NL 0410541 DNAL OU OO

017.4 L7695

Little, Frank H
Catalogue of English and American books: a choice and carefully selected assortment of the best works, in every department of literature: comprising many very rare, curious and elegant works of art, bibliography, history, theology, belles-lettres ... For sale at the very low prices affixed. Albany, F. H. Little [1859?]
35 p. 23 cm.

1. Catalogs. Booksellers'. New York (State) Albany. I. Title.

NL 0410542 N

Littlé, Franz.

Bundschuh und Ritterschwert; dramatische Erzählung in 5 Aufzügen, von Franz Littlé... Leipzig: B. Volger, 1914. 80 p. 12°.

1. Drama (German). 2. Title.

September 8, 1915.

NL 0410543 NN

Little, Fred W.

The Little system of playing the piano by ear (F. W. Little, sole-owner) Pittsburg, Standard printing co., °1909.

cover-title, [12] p. illus. 15 x 31cm. $3.00

1. Pianoforte—Instruction and study.

Library of Congress MT278.L58 9-28089

NL 0410544 DLC

Little, Gail.

Design for motherhood: survive it and enjoy it. New York, Ronald Press Co. [1953]

211 p. 21 cm.

1. Children—Management. 2. Infants—Care and hygiene. I. Title.

HQ769.L55 649.1 53-10379 ‡

CaBVa
NL 0410545 DLC FMU OCU NcD PP OCl Wa WaS WaT Or

LITTLE, George.
Anglers' annual; comprising articles and practical information on all matters relating to fish and fishing, by the ablest writers. An almanack with notes of special interest is added. London, [1882].

sm.4°. Portrs. and wdcts.
Contains several portraits of "gentlemen eminent in the fishing world," with short sketches of their lives.

NL 0410546 MH

VOLUME 336

Little, George.
The angler's complete guide and companion: being a practical treatise on angling and its requirements, with beautifully-executed illustrations, in colours, of the artificial flies for the different months, and highly finished engravings of all other necessary tackle. By G. Little. London, The author [etc., 1881]
203 p. illus., 12 col. pl. 19cm.
p. 164-203, advertising matter.
1. Fishing. 2. Fishing—Implements and appliances. 3. Flies, Artificial.
12-19525
Library of Congress SH439.L77

NL 0410547 DLC NIC CtY

LITTLE, George.
The unique fly book. [London, 188-?].
16°.pp.(21). Col. illustr.
There is no title-page. The work consists of 76 illustrations of flies, with brief directions for the use of each.

NL 0410548 MH

Little, George, b. 1791?
The American cruiser; a tale of the last war. By Capt. Geo. Little ... Illustrations by Billings. Boston, W. J. Reynolds and company, and Waite, Peirce, and co., 1847.
390 p. incl. front., plates. 19½cm.
I. Title.
Library of Congress PZ3.L725A 7—16064

NL 0410549 DLC KEmT ViU NcU DN IaU IU InU TxU MnU MiU OClWHi NNC

[Little, George] b. 1791?
The American cruiser; or, The two messmates. A tale of the last war. By the author of "Life on the ocean." Boston, Waite, Peirce and company, 1846.
1 p.l., 9-408 p. incl. plates. front. 19cm.
I. Title. II. Title: The two messmates.

NL 0410550 ViU MH CSmH PLF PU N

FILM 4274 PR v.1 reel L7
[Little, George] b.1791?
The American cruiser; or, The two messmates. A tale of the last war. By the author of "Life on the ocean." Boston, Waite, Peirce, 1846.
408 p. incl. front., plates. (Wright American fiction, v.1, 1774-1850, no.1699, Research Publications Microfilm, Reel L-7)

NL 0410551 CU

RARE BOOK COLL. PS2248 L33A7 1849
Little, George, b. 1791?
The American cruiser's own book. By Capt. Geo. Little. Illustrations by Billings. New York: Nafis & Cornish; St. Louis, Mo., Van Dein & McDonald, 1849.
vi, [1]-390 p. incl. front., plates. 20 cm.
Title vignette.
First published under title: The American cruiser; or, The two messmates.

NL 0410552 OU CLSU

PS 2248 L77A5 1851
Little, George, b. 1791?
The American cruiser's own book. Illus. by Billings. New York, Richard Marsh, 1851.
390 p. illus. 19cm.
Pub. in Boston, 1847, under title: The American cruiser, a tale of the last war.

NL 0410553 NIC

PS2248 L33A7 1852
Little, George, b. 1791?
The American cruiser's own book. By Capt. Geo. Little ... Illustrations by Billings. New-York, R. Marsh, 1852 [c1846]
390 p. incl. front., plates. 20 cm.

NL 0410554 OU

Little, George, b. 1791?
The American cruiser's own book ... Illustrations by Billings. New-York, R. Marsh, 1856.
18.5 cm.

NL 0410555 CtY

Little, George, b. 1791?
The American cruiser's own book. By Capt. Geo. Little ... Illustrations by Billings. Philadelphia, J. B. Smith & co., 1859.
1 p. l., [v]-vi, 7-384+ p. incl. plates. 19cm.
Imperfect: wanting frontispiece and all text after p. 384.
Published in Boston 1847 under title: The American cruiser: a tale of the last war.
I. Title.
7-16063 Revised 2
Library of Congress PZ3.L725Am

NL 0410556 DLC

Little, George, b. 1791?
An exposition of English grammar, in conversational or familiar lectures, containing a systematic order for parsing and false syntax corrected ... also, rules for parsing by transposition, observations on letter writing and comprehensive lectures on rhetoric and elocution ... By George Little. Baltimore, J. Young, printer, 1841.
iv, [5]-219 p. 19cm.
1. English language—Grammar—1800-1870.
10-25556 Revised
Library of Congress PE1109.L65

NL 0410557 DLC MdBP

Little, George, b. 1791?
Life on the ocean, or Twenty years at sea; being the personal adventures of the author. By George Little ... Baltimore, Armstrong & Berry, 1843.
viii, [9]-395 p. front. 20cm.
Experiences as a privateersman in the war of 1812: p. 195-244.
1. Voyages and travels. 2. Seafaring life. 3. U. S.—Hist.—War of 1812—Personal narratives. I. Title.
5-22932 Revised 2
Library of Congress G540.L7

NL 0410558 DLC MdU ViU

G 540 L7
Little, George, b.1791?
Life on the ocean, or Twenty years at sea; being the personal adventures of the author. 14th ed. New York, R. Marsh[1843]
395p. front. 20cm.
Experiences as a privateersman in the war of 1812: p. 195-244.
1. Voyages and travels. 2. Seafaring life. 3. U. S. - Hist. - War of 1812 - Personal narratives. I. Title.

NL 0410559 MU

LITTLE, George, b. 1791?
Life on the Ocean; or, Twenty years at Sea: being the Personal Adventures of the Author. 2d Ed. B. 1844.
12°.

NL 0410560 MH CSmH

Little, George, b. 1791?
Life on the ocean; or, Twenty years at sea: being the personal adventures of the author. By George Little ... 3d ed. Boston, Waite, Peirce, and company, 1845.
395 p. front., plates. 20cm.
1. Voyages and travels. 2. Seamen.
Library of Congress G540.L72 10—34173

NL 0410561 DLC FTaSU MWA MH MiU OU ICU

Wason G540 L77
Little, George, b. 1791?
Life on the ocean; or, Twenty years at sea: being the personal adventures of the author. By George Little ... 12th ed. Boston, Waite, Peirce, and company, 1846.
395 p. illus. 20cm.
1. Voyages and travels. 2. Seafaring life.

NL 0410562 NIC NN NcU NcD MSaE OClWHi

Little, George, b. 1791?
Life on the ocean; or, Twenty years at sea; being the personal adventures of the author. Aberdeen: G. Clark and Son, 1847. 2 p.l., (i)viii-xii, (1)14-288 p., 1 pl. 12°.
1. Voyages and travels, 1807-27. 2. Sea life.
November 9, 1912.

NL 0410563 NN CaBViP CaBVaU LNHT NN

Little, George, b.1791?
Life on the ocean, or Twenty years at sea: being the personal adventures of the author. 14th ed. Boston, Strong and Brodhead, 1849.

NL 0410564 MH

Little, George, b. 1791?
Life on the ocean; or, Twenty years at sea: being the personal adventures of the author, by George Little... Boston: C. D. Strong, 1851. 395 p. illus. 14. ed. 12°.
487844A. 1. Voyages and travels, 1800-1850. 2. Sea life. I. Title.
January 9, 1931

NL 0410565 NN WaU DN

VOLUME 336

LITTLE, George, b. 1791?.
Life on the ocean; or, Twenty years at Sea: being the personal adventures of the author. 14th ed. New York, Clark, Austin & Smith, 1852.

395 p. front,, plates.

NL 0410566 MH-BA CaBViP

Little, George, b. 1791?

Life on the ocean; or, Twenty years at sea: being the personal adventures of the author, by George Little ... 14th ed. ... New York, Richard Marsh, 1854.

395 p. 19.5cm.

NL 0410567 CaBVaU

Little, George, b. 1791?
Life on the Ocean; or, Twenty Years at Sea. 14th. ed. N.Y., 1856.
12°.

NL 0410568 CtY

G540
L72
1908

Little, George, b. 1791 ?
Life on the ocean; or, Twenty years at sea; being the personal adventures of the author. Philadelphia, Lippincott, 1908.
xiv, 317 p. plates (part col.) 22cm.

1. Voyages and travels. 2. Seamen.

NL 0410569 CoU OClW

Little, George, 1838-1924.
Catalogue of ores, rocks and woods, selected from the Geological survey collection of the state of Georgia, U.S.A., with a description of the geological formations [by] George Little ... state geologist. Atlanta, Harrison, 1878.
16 p. 22.5 cm.
On cover: For the Paris exposition.
Volume of pamphlets.
1. Geology - Georgia. 2. Paris. Exposition universelle, 1878 - U.S. - Georgia.

NL 0410570 NNC ViU DI-GS NcD MH-A

Little, George, 1838-1924.

Georgia. *State geologist.*
The country. Geological survey of the state. [External and internal relations of Georgia. By George Little, state geologist]

(*In* Georgia. Dept. of agriculture. Handbook ... Atlanta, 1876. 23½cm. p. [17]-143. map (in pocket))

Little, George, 1838-1924.
Geography of Georgia, a supplement to the Eclectic series of geographies . . . [Cincinnati] Van Antwerp, Bragg & co., 1880.

16 pp. illus., map. fol. (Eclectic series of geographies. Supplements)
F291.L77

1-13437—M 1

NL 0410572 DLC

Little, George, 1838-1924.
A history of Lumsden's battery, C. S. A. Written by Dr. George Little and Mr. James R. Maxwell. Tuskaloosa, Ala., R. E. Rhodes chapter, United daughters of the confederacy [1905?]
70 (i.e. 74) p. front. (group port.) 22 cm.

Four unnumbered pages inserted between p. 56 and 57.
"Written from memory in 1905 ... with the help of a diary kept by Dr. James T. Searcy. From ... Nov. 4, 1861, to Oct. 15, 1863, this data is the work of Dr. George Little; from Oct. 15, 1863, to ... May 4, 1965 [!] ... the work of Mr. James R. Maxwell." - verso t.-p.

1. Regimental histories - Civil war -- Alabama artillery - Lumsden's battery. 2. Personal narratives - Civil war - Confederate. 3. Alabama artillery. Lumsden's battery, 1861-1865. I. Maxwell, James R

NL 0410574 Vi ICN WHi CaBVaU TU NjP ViU NNC IaU NN T MB CU

Little, George, 1838-1924.
Memoirs of George Little ... Tuscaloosa, Weatherford printing company, 1924.

125 p. 22½cm.

I. Title.

G S 25-211

Library, U. S. Geological Survey 081 L72

NL 0410575 DI-GS NNBG MiU OU GU NN AU

QE101
.A1

Little, George, 1838-1924.

Georgia. *State geologist.*
Report of progress of the mineralogical, geological and physical survey of the state of Georgia for 1874-[1875] By George Little, state geologist. [Atlanta] J. H. Estill, public printer, 1875-76.

Little, George A., 1890-1946.
There's another angel now in old Killarney
see under Bernard, Mike.

Little, George Albert, 1883-
The teacher's manual; a guide to the International Sunday school lessons, improved uniform series: course for 1934-
By George A. Little ... [and] Archer Wallace ... New York, Round table press, inc., 1933-

v. front., illus. 22½cm.
Includes bibliographies.

1. International Sunday school lessons. I. Wallace, Archer, 1884- joint author. II. Title.

34-2

Library of Congress BV1560.L5

Copyright [3] 268.61

NL 0410578 DLC WaSp

Little, George Aloysius.
Brendan the navigator, an interpretation by Dr. George A. Little ... Dublin, M. H. Gill and son, ltd., 1945.

xix, 253 p. front., illus., plates. 19cm.
Maps on lining-papers.
Bibliography: p. 237.

1. Brendan, Saint. Legend. I. Title.

46-2355

Library of Congress BX4700.B8L5

922.2415

NL 0410579 DLC OrStbM MH NBC CMenSP MB TU MeWC NNC OCl CtY OU

CT808
.H6A3
1944

Little, George Aloysius.

FOR OTHER EDITIONS SEE MAIN ENTRY

Horan, Malachi, 1847-
Malachi Horan remembers, by Dr. George A. Little Dublin, M. H. Gill and son, ltd., 1944.

Little, George Aloysius.
The Ouzel galley, by Dr. George A. Little. [Dublin] Old Dublin society, 1940.

40 p. front., plates. 25½cm.
"This special issue is vol. III, no. 2 of the Dublin historical record."—p. [4]
Plan on lining-papers.
Bibliography: p. 32.

1. Ouzel galley society, Dublin. 2. Ouzel (Galley) I. Old Dublin society. II. Dublin historical record.

43-1574

Library of Congress HF302.L65

NL 0410581 DLC

LITTLE, GEORGE ALOYSIUS.
The Ouzel galley. 2. (rev.) ed. Dublin, Cahill, 1953. 48 p. illus. 25cm.

Bibliography, p. 40.

1. Ouzel (Galley). 2. Ouzel galley society, Dublin.

NL 0410582 NN MH MeWC

Little, George Barker, 1821-1860.
Address; Penobscot musical association, Bangor, also, Minutes of the convention, Oct. 23-26, 1855. Bangor, 1855.
24 p. O.

NL 0410583 RPB

LITTLE, George Barker, 1821-1860.
Eulogy on Zachary Taylor, delivered July 19, 1850. Bangor, 1850.

pp. 16.

NL 0410584 MH

LITTLE, GEORGE BARKER, 1821-1860.
The kingdom of God not in externals. A sermon delivered at Bath, June 24, 1857, before the Maine missionary society, at its fiftieth anniversary. By George B. Little... Augusta: E. G. Hedge & co., printers, 1857. 64 p. 23cm.

List of members of the society, etc., p. [50]-64.

1. No subject. I. Maine missionary society.

NL 0410585 NN DLC MB RPB

Little, George Barker, 1821-1860.
A memorial of closing scenes in the life of Rev. George B. Little
see under title

Little, George C ed.
The history of the 316th engineers; a record of military operations from August, 1917 to April, 1919. Pub. by the 316th engineers. [n.p., 1919?]
4 p.l., 233 p. incl. plates. illus. (incl. map) 25.5 cm.
George C. Little, managing editor.

NL 0410587 CSt-H

VOLUME 336

Little, George E.
Dictation exercises in drawing. A hand-book for teachers containing over two hundred straight and curved line forms, outlines of familiar objects, animals, fruits, flowers, &c. By George E. Little. Washington, D. C., The author [°1882]
34 p. illus., diagrs. 17½cm.

1. Drawing—Instruction.

Library of Congress NC620.L5 CA 11-2538 Unrev'd

NL 0410588 DLC

Little, George E.
Illustrative hand-book of drawing, containing over three hundred illustrations, including dictation exercises, outlines of familiar objects—vegetables, fruits, flowers, and human and animal forms, by George E. Little ... New York, Boston [etc.] D. Appleton and company, 1889.
lxxiii, 4 p. illus. 20 x 18cm.

1. Drawing—Instruction.

Library of Congress NC620.L56 11-17029

NL 0410589 DLC

Little, George E.
Organization and administration of intercollegiate and interscholastic athletics, by George E. Little ... Summer school of athletic coaching & physical education, 1923, University of Michigan. Ann Arbor, Mich., Edwards brothers [°1923]
1 p. l., v, 90 numb. l. illus. (forms) diagrs. 27½cm.
Autographed from type-written copy.
Printed on one side of leaf only.
"References": p. 89.

1. Athletics. I. Michigan. University. II. Title.

Library of Congress GV347.L5 23-11421

NL 0410590 DLC MiU

---

ar V 21835 Little, George Herbert. comp.
The automotor and horseless vehicle pocket book of automotive formulae and commercial intelligence for 1899. London, F. King, 1899.
xxiv, 271 p. illus. 17cm.

NL 0410591 NIC

Little, George Herbert, compiler.
The automotor and horseless vehicle pocket-book of automotive formulæ and commercial intelligence for 1900. [3d edition.] London. King & Co. 1900. v. Illus. Plates. Plans. Diagrams. Table. 16 cm., in 8s.
Bibliography, pp. 299-310.

K4321 — T.r. — Automobiles.

NL 0410592 MB MiD

VM 455 L77 Little, George Herbert.
The marine transport of petroleum; a book for the use of shipowners, shipbuilders, underwriters, merchants, captains, and officers of petroleum-carrying vessels. London, New York, E. & F. N. Spon, 1890.
xii, 251 p. illus. 19cm.

1. Petroleum--Transportation.

NL 0410593 NIC WaS MH DI DN MH-BA DP

Little, George Kerr, 1875-
The transportation of coal on the Warrior system, by Mr. G. K. Little ...
(*In* Professional memoirs, Corps of engineers, U. S. army, and Engineer department-at-large. Washington, 1916. 23cm. v. 8, no. 39, p. 301-319. illus.)

1. Inland navigation. 2. Barges. 3. Warrior system. 4. [Water] transportation. I. Title.

E S 16-29

Title from U. S. Engineer School Libr. Printed by L. C.

NL 0410594 DES OU MiU

Little, Geo[rge] O.
The mission of our government: a fast-day sermon, delivered at the 2d Presbyterian church, Fort Wayne, Aug. 4th, 1864. By the pastor - Rev. Geo. O. Little. [Fort Wayne], D. W. Jones, printer, 1864.
14 p.

NL 0410595 OCl OClWHi

Little, George Obadiah, *b.* 1839.
The royal houses of Israel and Judah, an interwoven history with a harmony of parallel passages. By Rev. George O. Little ... New York and London, Funk & Wagnalls company, 1901.
xxii, 329 p. 22½ x 17 cm.

1. Jews—Hist.—953-586 B. C. 2. Bible. O. T.—History of Biblical events. I. Title. II. Title: Israel and Judah.

DS121.L77 1—29525

NL 0410596 DLC OrP MBrZ NjNbS OO

Little, George P.
The fireman's own book: containing accounts of fires throughout the United States, as well as other countries; remarkable escapes ... heroic conduct ... By Geo. P. Little ... New York, Philadelphia [etc.] 1860.
2 p. l., [13]-286 p. incl. front., illus., plates. 24cm.

1. Fires.

Library of Congress TH9448.L8 8-32852†

NL 0410597 DLC

Little, George P
The fireman's own book
see also Hall, John B
The fireman's own book.

Little, George T[homas], 1857-1915.
Bowdoin and her sons.
(From Munsey's Jan. 1903. 24 cm.
p[576]-585 ports.

NL 0410599 RPB

Little, George Thomas, 1857-1915.
Descendants of George Little, who came to Newbury, Massachusetts, in 1640. Compiled by George T. Little. Cambridge, Printed at the University press by C. J. Little, 1877.
82 p. incl. col. front. (coat of arms) illus. pl. 20cm.

1. Little family (George Little, d. 1693 or 1694)

Library of Congress CS71.L777 1877 1-15069

NL 0410600 DLC MB MH MnHi MeB MWA

Little, George Thomas, 1857-1915.
The descendants of George Little, who came to Newbury, Massachusetts, in 1640. By George Thomas Little ... Auburn, Me., The author, 1882.
xiv, 2, 620, 2 p. front. (col. coat of arms) illus., 5 pl., 19 port. 26½cm.
No. A of the edition.
Two pages of addenda which follow p. 620 are also inserted between p. 514 and 515.
Imperfect: 2 plates, 4 portraits wanting.
Five additional portraits inserted.

1. Little family (George Little, d. 1693 or 4)

Library of Congress CS71.L777 1882 1-15070 Revised

NL 0410601 DLC MB Mi MWA Nh MnHi MeB NN

Little, George Thomas, 1857-1915
Exercises in Latin prose composition, based upon the De senectute and De amicitia of Cicero [Lewiston, Me., Printed at the Journal office, 1883]

Preface: 1883.

NL 0410602 MH

Little, George Thomas, 1857-1915.
The first ascent of Rogers peak. By George T. Little. [Excerpt from Appalachia, vol. VIII, July, 1897]
209-216 p. plate, diagr. 24.5cm.
Caption title.
With this are bound p. 275-279 of the same issue, which also deal with the ascent.

NL 0410603 CaBVaU

Little, George Thomas, 1857-1915, *ed.*
Genealogical and family history of the state of Maine; comp. under the editorial supervision of George Thomas Little ... and including among other local contributors Rev. Henry S. Burrage ... and Albert Roscoe Stubbs ... New York, Lewis historical publishing company, 1909.
4 v. fronts., illus., plates, ports. 27½cm.
Paged continuously.

1. Maine—Geneal. I. Burrage, Henry Sweetser, 1837-1926. II. Stubbs, Albert Roscoe.

Library of Congress F18.L77 9—22211

NL 0410604 DLC WaS IU MeB CU NCH NN MB WaU OClWHi OCl

Little, Goerge Thomas, 1857-1915, comp.
Bowdoin college. FOR OTHER EDITIONS SEE MAIN ENTRY
General catalogue of Bowdoin college and the Medical school of Maine 1794-1894. Including a historical sketch of the institution during its first century prepared by George Thomas Little ... Brunswick, Me., Pub. by the College, 1894.

Little, George Thomas, 1857-1915.
A historical sketch of Bowdoin College during its first century. Brunswick, Me., 1894.

NL 0410606 RP MB MH

Little, George Thomas, 1857-1915.
Longfellow, Henry Wadsworth, 1807-1882.
Longfellow's boyhood poems, a paper by the late George Thomas Little, LITT D.; together with the text of hitherto uncollected early poems and bibliography, edited by Ray W. Pettengill ... Saratoga Springs, N. Y., R. W. Pettengill, 1925.

VOLUME 336

[Little, George Thomas] 1857–1915, *comp.*
Memorial, Alpheus Spring Packard, 1798–1884 ... Brunswick, Me., Printed for Bowdoin college library, 1886.
2 p. l., 95 p. front. (port.) 24cm.
CONTENTS.—Prefatory note.—Biographical sketch, by the compiler.—Address at the funeral. J. L. Chamberlain.—Poem. S. V. Cole.—Sermon. W. P. Fisher.—Remarks at College chapel. H. L. Chapman.—Tribute from undergraduates, Bowdoin orient.—Commemorative address, E. C. Smyth.—Lecture on character, A. S. Packard.—Remarks at Portland, A. S. Packard.—Bibliography.
1. Packard, Alpheus Spring, 1798–1884.
7—30356
Library of Congress LD5528.P3M5

NL 0410608 DLC DNLM NIC MeB NjP MWA MdBP ViU MiU OC1W ICJ MH

Special Coll. Little, George Thomas, 1857-1915
Note book for the study of Latin literature. [Brunswick? Me., 1884]
42 p. 21 cm.
Interleaved, with ms. notes.

NL 0410609 MeB

Little, George Thomas, 1857-1915.
Longfellow, Henry Wadsworth, 1807–1882.
Origin and growth of the languages of southern Europe and of their literature; an inaugural address by Henry Wadsworth Longfellow, professor of modern languages in Bowdoin college ... delivered September 2, 1830. Brunswick, Me., Bowdoin college library, 1907.

Little, George W
My world skeleton, by George W. Little, sr. New York, N. Y., The Hobson book press, 1946.
2 p. l., vii-xiii p., 2 l., 170 p. 21½cm.
1. Toleration. 2. Social problems—Miscellanea. I. Title.
HN64.L565 301.153 47-17975

NL 0410611 DLC

Little, George Warren.
A study ofcable test procedure ... by ... [Cincinnati, 1940]
43 numb. l. incl.mounted plates, tables, diagrs.
Thesis (ElectricalEngineer) - University of Cincinnati, 1940.
Typewritten.
Bibliography: l. 43.

NL 0410612 OCU

Little, George Watson.
Diet for dogs, by George Watson Little ... New York, R. M. McBride & company, 1929.
xiii, 260 p. 19½cm.
1. Dogs. I. Title.
29-8051
Library of Congress SF427.L67

NL 0410613 DLC OC1h OU OC1 OLak ViU ICJ DNAL OrP WaT Or

Little, George Watson.
Dr. Little's dog book, by George Watson Little, D. V. M. New York, R. M. McBride & company, 1924.
xx p., 1 l., 345 p. front., illus., plates. 21½cm.
Bibliography: p. 334-341.
Library of Congress SF991.L5 25—1322

NL 0410614 DLC CaBVa Or WaE CoFS OKentU OC1h OC1 OLak ICJ NN MB DNAL

Little, George Watson.
Dr. Little's dog book, ... D. V. M. New York, R. M. McBride and company, 1925.
345 p. illus.

NL 0410615 OU

Little, George Watson.
Dr. Little's dog book, by George Watson Little, D. V. M. New York, R. M. McBride & company [1924]
xx p., 1 l., 345 p. front., illus., plates. 21½cm.
Bibliography: p. 334-341.

NL 0410616 TU CU

Little, George Watson.
Dr. Little's dog book, by George Watson Little ... New York, Robert M. McBride & Company, 1929.
xx, 345 p. front., illus. 21½cm.
1. Dogs - Diseases. I. Title.

NL 0410617 ViW CU-A

Little, George Watson.
Dr. Little's dog book, by George Watson Little, D. V. M. New and rev. ed. New York, R. M. McBride & company [1934]
xxvi p., 1 l., 345 p. front., illus., plates. 21½cm.
Bibliography: p. 334-341.
1. Dogs—Diseases. 2. Dogs. I. Title.
Library of Congress SF991.L5 1934 34-12243
Copyright A 72301 [636.70896] 619.7

NL 0410618 DLC NN DNAL MoU UU OC1

SF991 L5 1937 Little, George Watson.
Dr. Little's dog book. New and rev. ed. New York, R.M. McBride & company [1937]
xxvi, 345 p. front., illus., plates. 22cm.
Bibliography: p. 334-341.
1. Dogs - Diseases. 2. Dogs. I. Title.

NL 0410619 CoU

Little, George Watson.
True stories of heroic dogs; with an introd. by Mrs. Albert Payson Terhune. New York, Grosset & Dunlap [1951]
256 p. illus. 21 cm.
1. Dogs. I. Title.
QL795.D6L5 636.78 51-7493 ‡

NL 0410620 DLC FTaSU WaSp IdB

Little, Gertrude, 1911–
Understanding our pupils. Anderson, Ind., Warner Press [1950]
110 p. 19 cm.
1. Religious education. I. Title.
BV1471.L56 268 50-9995

NL 0410621 DLC

LITTLE, Giles, & co.
G.Little & co.,fishing rod & tackle manufacturers and fly dressers. [Catalogue of fishing rods and tackle.-The angler's instructor, &c.] London, 1879.
pp. 63. Wdcts.
Some of the information for anglers is taken from the blue book of the Thames angling preservation society.

NL 0410622 MH

LITTLE, Giles, & co.,
G.Little & co.'s catalogue of prices [of fishing rods and tackle] and Anglers' instructor, 1879. [London, 1879].
Cover-title, 63 p. Illustr.

NL 0410623 MH

LITTLE, Giles & Co.
Wholesale illustrated price list, Giles Littl & co., city fishing rod & tackle works. London, [187-?].
pp. 30. Wdcts. Lithographed.

NL 0410624 MH

Little, Gladys F.
Bank of England reference library catalogue
see under Bank of England.

Little, Gladys M., joint author.
FOR OTHER EDITIONS SEE MAIN ENTRY
Myers, George Edmund, 1871–
Planning your future; an occupational civics text, by George E. Myers ... Gladys M. Little ... and Sarah A. Robinson ... Rev. ed. New York and London, McGraw-Hill book company, inc. [°1940]

Little, Gladys M.
The story of the Little watch. [Detroit, 1950]
[8] p.

NL 0410627 MiD-B

Little, Grace
see Rhys, Grace (Little) 1865-1929.

VOLUME 336

PZ3 .L723 Bf
Little, Gwenyth, joint author.
Little, Constance.
The black coat [by] Constance & Gwenyth Little. [1st ed.] Garden City, N. Y., Pub. for the Crime Club by Doubleday, 1948.

Little, Gwenyth, joint author.
Little, Constance.
... Black corridors. New York, Pub. for the Crime club by Doubleday, Doran & co., inc., 1940.

PZ3 .L723 Bgm
Little, Gwenyth, joint author.
Little, Constance.
The black curl, by Constance and Gwenyth Little. [1st ed.] Garden City, N. Y., Published for the Crime Club by Doubleday, 1953.

PZ3 .L723 Bi
Little, Gwenyth, joint author.
Little, Constance.
... The black eye. Garden City, New York, Pub. for the Crime club by Doubleday, Doran and company, inc., 1945.

PZ3 .L723 Bk
Little, Gwenyth, joint author.
Little, Constance.
... The black gloves. [New York] Pub. for the Crime club, inc., by Doubleday, Doran & company, inc., 1939.

PZ3 .L723 Bkf
Little, Gwenyth, joint author.
Little, Constance.
The black goatee [by] Constance & Gwenyth Little. Garden City, N. Y., Pub. for the Crime club by Doubleday & company, inc., 1947.

Little, Gwenyth, joint author.
Little, Constance.
... The black-headed pins. New York, Pub. for the Crime club, inc., by Doubleday, Doran & company, inc., 1938.

PZ3 .L723 Bm
Little, Gwenyth, joint author.
Little, Constance.
The black honeymoon [by] Constance and Gwenyth Little. Garden City, New York, Pub. for the Crime club by Doubleday, Doran and co., inc., 1944.

PZ3 .L723 Bn
Little, Gwenyth, joint author.
Little, Constance.
The black house, by Constance and Gwenyth Little. [1st ed.] Garden City, N. Y., Published for the Crime Club by Doubleday, 1950.

PZ3 .L723 Bo
Little, Gwenyth, joint author.
Little, Constance.
The black iris, by Constance and Gwenyth Little. [1st ed.] Garden City, N. Y., Published for the Crime Club by Doubleday, 1953.

Little, Gwenyth, joint author.
Little, Constance.
The black paw [by] Constance and Gwenyth Little. New York, Pub. for the Crime club by Doubleday, Doran and co., inc., 1941.

PZ3 .L723 Bri
Little, Gwenyth, joint author.
Little, Constance.
The black piano, by Constance & Gwenyth Little. [1st ed.] Garden City, N. Y., Pub. for the Crime Club by Doubleday, 1948.

Little, Gwenyth, joint author.
Little, Constance.
... The black rustle. Garden City, New York, Pub. for the Crime club, Doubleday, Doran & co., inc., 1943.

Little, Gwenyth, joint author.
Little, Constance.
The black shrouds, by Constance and Gwenyth Little. Garden City, N. Y., Pub. for the Crime club by Doubleday, Doran & company, inc., 1941.

PZ3 .L723 Btc
Little, Gwenyth, joint author.
Little, Constance.
The Black Smith [by] Constance and Gwenyth Little. [1st ed.] Garden City, N. Y., Published for the Crime Club by Doubleday, 1950.

PZ3 .L723 Btg
Little, Gwenyth, joint author.
Little, Constance.
... The black stocking. Garden City, New York, Pub. for the Crime club by Doubleday & company, inc., 1946.

Little, Gwenyth, joint author.
Little, Constance.
... The black thumb. Garden City, N. Y., Published for the Crime club by Doubleday, Doran and co., inc., 1942.

PZ3 .L723 Gn
Little, Gwenyth, joint author.
Little, Constance.
... Great black Kanba. Garden City, N. Y., Pub. for the Crime club by Doubleday, Doran and co., inc., 1944.

Little, Gwenyth, joint author.
Little, Constance.
... The grey mist murders. Garden City, N. Y., Pub. for the Crime club, inc., by Doubleday, Doran & co., inc., 1938.

Little, H.W.
... Preliminary map; Nelson (west half) British Columbia. Ottawa[Cloutier]1949. Q. (Canada - Geological survey - Paper 49-22)

NL 0410648 CaBViP

Little, H.W.
... Salmo map-area, British Columbia (report and map). Ottawa[Cloutier]1950. 43p.map,Q. (Canada - Geological survey - Paper 50-19)

NL 0410649 CaBViP

Little, Halsted, ed.
Princeton university.
Directory of the living graduates and former students of Princeton university. [4th ed.] Princeton, N. J., The University, 1902.

TX907 .W5
Little, Harrison, ed.
Where to eat; 2,300 restaurants preferred by businessmen. A Dartnell directory. Chicago, Dartnell [1948]

Little, Harry Abner, 1900-
Missouri. University.
An administrative survey of the schools of Boone county, Missouri ... This survey made at the University of Missouri summer session of 1931. By the class in county school surveys under the direction of Harry A. Little. July, 1931. [Columbia, Mo., 1931]

Little, Harry Abner, 1900- joint author.
Arkansas. *Dept. of public instruction.*
Financial and administrative needs of the public schools of Arkansas ... by Howard A. Dawson, PH. D., director, Harry A. Little, M. A., assistant director, the Division of research and surveys, Arkansas state Department of education. Issued by C. M. Hirst, state superintendent of public instruction, Little Rock, Arkansas. November, 1930. [Little Rock, 1930-

---

Little, Harry Abner, 1900-
Handbook for supervisors of student teacher. Milledgeville, Ga., °1947.
vi, 125 p. 28 cm.
Cover title: Handbook for supervisors of student teaching.
"Annotated bibliography": p. 121-125.

1. Student teaching.
LB2157.U5L5 370.733 47-29855

NL 0410654 DLC PWcS ICU MtU

VOLUME 336

370.733 Little, Harry Abner, 1900-
L723h Handbook for supervisors of student
1950 teaching. Nashville, Tenn., Bureau of Publications, George Peabody College for Teachers ͺ1950ͺ
125p. 23cm.

"Annotated bibliography": p.121-125.

1. Student teaching.

NL 0410655 KU KEmT KMK IEN OU

Little, Harry Abner, 1900–
Potential economies in the reorganization of local school attendance units, by Harry A. Little ... New York city, Teachers college, Columbia university, 1934.
vi, 78 p., 1 l. diagrs. 23cm.
Thesis (PH. D.)—Columbia university, 1934.
Vita.
Published also as Teachers college, Columbia university, Contributions to education, no. 628.
Bibliography: p. 74–78.

1. Schools—Centralization. 2. Rural schools—U. S. 3. Public schools—U. S.—Finance.
35-1364
Library of Congress LB2861.L5 1934
Columbia Univ. Libr. 379.175

NL 0410656 NNC DLC WaTC OCU MiU OCl OClW OU

Little, Harry Abner, 1900–
Potential economies in the reorganization of local school attendance units, by Harry A. Little ... New York city, Teachers college, Columbia university, 1934.
vi, 78 p. diagrs. 23½ cm. (Teachers college, Columbia university. Contributions to education, no. 628)
Issued also as thesis (PH. D.) Columbia university.
Bibliography: p. 74–78.

1. Schools—Centralization. 2. Rural schools—U. S. 3. Education—U. S.—Finance.
LB2861.L5 1934a 379.175 35—1365
——— Copy 2. LB5.C8 no. 628

NL 0410657 DLC OrU OrCS MtU OrP NcU MB ViU PSt KEmT

Little, Harry Abner, 1900–
LB2864
.A7 **Arkansas.** *Dept. of public instruction.*
1930 Public transportation of school pupils in Arkansas. Prepared by Harry A. Little, assistant director, Division of research and surveys. Arkansas state Department of education. C. M. Hirst, state superintendent of public instruction. Little Rock, Arkansas. September, 1930. ͺLittle Rock, 1930ͺ

Little, Harry Abner, 1900–
Summary tables of a survey of the public schools of Arkansas
see under Arkansas. Dept. of public instruction.

Little, Harry Frank Victor.
Aluminium and its congeners, including the rare earth metals. London. Charles Griffin & Co., Ltd. 1917. xx, 485 pp. Illus. Plates. Plan. Charts. Tables. [Friend, J. A. N., editor. A text-book of inorganic chemistry. Vol. 4.] 22 cm., in 8s.

M6344 — Aluminum. — Metals. Earthy. — Earths of the rare metals. — S.r.c.

NL 0410660 MB CU RPB

LITTLE, Harry Frank Victor.
Aluminium and its congeners, including the rare earth metals. 2. ed. London, C. Griffin, 1921.
xxviii, 485 p. illus. 23cm. (Friend, J. A. N., ed. A text-book of inorganic chemistry. v.4)

On cover: Griffin's scientific text-books.
Bibliographical footnotes.
1. Aluminum. 2. Earths, Rare. 3. Organometallic compounds. I. Ser. t. 1921.

NL 0410661 NN CtY

Little, Harry Frank Victor, *tr.*
... Operatic translations, by H. F. V. Little ... London, Gramophone (publications) ltd. ͺ1928ͺ
2 v. 21½cm. (The gramophone library)

1. Librettos. I. Title.
39-15452
Library of Congress ML54.6.L45O62
782.08

NL 0410662 DLC NN

M2116 Little, Henry, comp.
L5 The Wesleyan harmony, or a compilation of choice tunes for public worship; adapted to the various metres in the Methodist hymn book now in use ... By Henry Little ... Hallowell ͺMe.ͺ Printed by E. Goodale, 1820.

125ͺ9ͺp. 13x23cm.

I. Title.
1. Wesleyan Methodist church.-Hymns.

NL 0410663 NBuG CtY RPB MeB

Little, Henry, *comp.*

The Wesleyan harmony, or, A compilation of choice tunes for public worship; adapted to the various metres in the Methodist hymn book now in use: with a table of the particular metre hymns, and names of the tunes annexed in which they may be sung ... By Henry Little ... 2d ed.,—enl. and improved. Hallowell ͺMe.ͺ Printed by Goodale, Glazier & co., sold by them and the compiler at Bucksport; ͺetc., etc.ͺ 1821.
139, ͺ5ͺ p. 13½ x 23cm.
1. Hymns, English. 2. Methodist church—Hymns. I. Title.
43-32080
Library of Congress M2127.L5W3 1821

NL 0410664 DLC OCl NNUT NcD MBU-T

Little, Hͺenryͺ Aͺlexanderͺ.
China. Report on the physical, commercial, social and general conditions of Ichang and neighbourhood. London: Harrison and Sons, 1908. 24 p., 1 l., 1 map. 8°. (Great Britain. Foreign Office. Diplomatic and consular reports. Miscellaneous series. no. 671.)

1. Ichang (China).—Description, 1908. January 10, 1913.

NL 0410665 NN

Little, Henry F W 1842–
... The Seventh regiment New Hampshire volunteers in the war of the rebellion, by Henry F. W. Little ... regimental historian ... Pub. by the Seventh New Hampshire veteran association. Concord, N. H., I. C. Evans, printer, 1896.
xviii, 567, 110, xxi p. front., illus., plates, ports., plans (part fold.) 23½cm.
At head of title: 1861-1865.
"Biographical sketches": p. 460-567. "Complete roster of the Seventh regiment": 110 p.
1. New Hampshire infantry. 7th regt., 1861-1865. 2. U. S.—Hist.—Civil war—Regimental histories—N. H.—7th.
4-9841 Revised
Library of Congress E520.5 7th

NjP TxU NcD OClWHi MB NcU
NL 0410666 DLC CaBVaU FMU FTaSU WHi MWA NhDo Nh

Little, Henry Gilman, 1813–1900.
Early days in Newington, Connecticut, 1833–1836, by Henry G. Little, 1813–1900. Newington, Conn., Priv. print., 1937.
2 p. l., 122 p., 1 l. port. 24cm.
"One hundred copies printed."

1. Newington, Conn.—Hist. I. Title.
38-2746
Library of Congress F104.N62L5
974.62

NL 0410667 DLC ViU CtY

Little, Henry Gilman, 1813–1900.
Hollis ͺN. H.ͺ seventy years ago. Personal recollections, by Henry Gilman Little. Grinnell, Ia., Ray & MacDonald, printers, 1894.
x, 11–235 p. front., ports. 17½cm.
"A reprint of a series of letters pub. during the years 1891 and 1892 in the Hollis times."—Pref.

1. Hollis, N. H. 2. Hollis, N. H.—Geneal. I. Title.
1-8007
Library of Congress F44.H7L7

NL 0410668 DLC Nh NNC IU NN

Little, Henry Walmsley.
Come, let us sing the story. Carol. (For Christmas.)
(In Parish Choir, The. No. 134, p. 533. Medford, 1880.)

May 7, 1902
E3976 — T.r. — Christmas carols.

NL 0410669 MB

Little, Henry Walmsley.
The red shoes. A fairy tale by Hans Anderson [sic]. Incidental music by H. Walmsley Little. Pianoforte . . . accompt. Abridged and arranged for recitation by Mrs. Hasluck. London. The Vincent Music Co. Ltd. [189-?] 19 pp. [Recitations with music. No. 2.] 35½ cm.

M6767 — Double main card. — Little, Henry Walmsley. (M1) — Andersen, Hans Christian, 1805–1875. (M2) — T.r. Musical monologue. (1) — Monologues. Musical. (1) — Hasluck, Mrs., ed. (2)

NL 0410670 MB

Little, Henry William.
Arrows for the king's archers; analytic outline, addresses upon religious, temperance and social topics with some courses of addresses for special sesions for the use of busy and overworked clergymen, lay-readers, teachers, and parish-workers, by the Rev. Henry W. Little. New York, Thomas Whittaker [c1892]
xiii, 149 p. 19 cm.
1. Sermons. Outlines. I. Title.

NL 0410671 IEG

Little, Henry William.
Henry M. Stanley, his life, travels and explorations, by the Rev. Henry W. Little ... London, Chapman and Hall, limited; Philadelphia, J. B. Lippincott company, 1890.
xvi, 456 p. 23cm.

1. Stanley, Sir Henry Morton, 1841-1904.
6—5375
Library of Congress DT351.S6L7

NL 0410672 DLC MiU NIC CU OCl OClW

VOLUME 336

962.04 [Little, Henry William]
H277 How to save Egypt, by an old campaigner. London, A. Kingdon, 1884.
no.6 15 p. 25 cm.

Author's name supplied in MS. on t. p.
No. [6] in a vol. of pamphlets with binder's title: National union ...

1. Egypt. History. British occupation, 1882-1936. 2. Sudan. History. I. An old campaigner. II. Title.

NL 0410673 NcD

Little, Henry William.
The life and work of Emin Pasha in equatorial Africa
see his One man's power.

Little, Henry William.
Madagascar; its history and people, by the Rev. Henry W. Little ... Edinburgh and London, W. Blackwood and sons, 1884.
x, 356 p. fold. map. 20½cm.

1. Madagascar—Descr. & trav. I. Title.

Library of Congress DT469.M26L7 5—15925

NL 0410675 DLC NcU NNC IEN CtY OCU ViU NjP NN

Little, Henry William.
Madagascar; its history and people.
Edinburgh, W. Blackwood, 1884.
356p. illus. (CAMP book no. 70)

Microfilm ed., positive and negative copies.
Negative does not circulate.

NL 0410676 ICRL

Little, Henry William.
One man's power. The life and work of Emin Pasha in equatorial Africa, by the Rev. Henry W. Little ... With portrait and map. London, J. S. Virtue & co., limited, 1889.
viii, 112 p. front. (port.) map. 20½cm.

1. Schnitzer, Eduard, known as Emin Pasha, 1840-1892.

24-1583

Library of Congress DT363.L5

NL 0410677 DLC MdBP CU OCl

LITTLE, Henry W[illiam]
A short history of Russia. London, Swan Sonnenschein & Co., 1885.

NL 0410678 MH OCl

Little, Henry William.
What shall I say? Analytic outline addresses upon religious, temperance, thrift, health, and social topics, with some courses of addresses for special seasons. For the use of busy and over-worked clergymen, lay-readers, teachers, and parish-workers. By the Rev. Henry W. Little ... 3d ed. London, Skeffington and son, 1887.
xvii, 138 p. 19cm.

1. Sermons—Outlines. I. Title.

33-8586

Library of Congress BV4223.L5 1887 251

NL 0410679 DLC

BV
4223
.L5
1900
Little, Henry William.
What shall I say? Analytic outline addresses upon religious, temperance, thrift, health, and social topics, with some courses of addresses for special seasons. For the use of busy and over-worked clergymen, lay-readers, teachers, and parishworkers. By the Rev. Henry W. Little. 4th ed. London, Skeffington and son, 1900.
xvii, 138 p. 19 cm.

1. Sermons--Outlines. I. Title

NL 0410680 OKentU

Little, Herman C., comp.

Bowers' Manchester directory ... 1888, 1891, 1892/93, 1894, 1896/97-19
Manchester, Conn., A. E. Bowers, 1888-[19

Little, Herschel W
... Estimated lags between farm, wholesale, and retail prices for selected foods, by Herschel W.Little ... [and] Albert L.Meyers ... Washington, D.C., 1943.
1 p.ℓ., 16 p.incl.tables. 9 charts.

At head of title: United States Department of agriculture; Bureau of agricultural economics.
Manifold copy.

NL 0410682 MH-BA NIC

LITTLE, HOLMER, and M.J.CLOSSER.
Gun-shy; a comedy in three acts, by Holmer Little and Myla Jo Closser... Evanston, Ill. [etc.] Row, Peterson & co. [cop. 1934] 115, xxii p. incl. front. illus. 20½cm. (Row-Peterson plays. Professional series.)

"First performance of 'Raw meat,' later retitled 'Gun-shy,' at the Provincetown playhouse, N.Y."— p. [8]

879379A. 1. Drama, American. I. Closser, Myla Jo, jt. au. II. Title.

NL 0410683 NN OCl RPB IaU ViU Or DLC WaPS

QE122
.A5A2
Little, Homer Payson, 1884-

Maryland. *Geological survey.*
... Anne Arundel county. Baltimore, The Johns Hopkins press, 1917.

Little, Homer Payson, 1884- joint author.

Mathews, Edward Bennett, 1869-
... Geology and geography in the United States, by Edward B. Mathews and Homer P. Little (Preliminary edition) ... [Washington, D. C., National research council, 1921]

Little, Homer Payson, 1884-
The geology and mineral resources of Anne Arundel County ... by Homer Payson Little ... Baltimore, The Johns Hopkins press, 1917.
1 p. l., [23]-132 p., 1 l. vi pl. 25½cm.

Thesis (PH. D.)—Johns Hopkins university, 1910.
Biography.
Reprinted from "Anne Arundel County," published by Maryland Geological survey. 1917.
Bibliography: p. 34-46.

1. Geology—Maryland—Anne Arundel Co. 2. Mines and mineral resources—Maryland.

Library of Congress QE122.A5L5 18-7170
Johns Hopkins Univ. Libr.

NL 0410686 MdBJ DLC NIC NjP MiU

Little, Homer Payson, 1884- *comp.*
List of manuscript bibliographies in geology and geography. Washington, 1922.
17 p. 26 cm. (Reprint and circular series of the National Research Council, no. 27)

Cover title.

1. Bibliography—Bibl.—Geography. 2. Bibliography—Bibl.—Geology. 3. Geography—Bibl. 4. Geology—Bibl. (Series: National Research Council. Reprint and circular series, no. 27)

Q11.N293 no. 27 23-10832 rev*

NL 0410687 DLC TxU OrU WaS

Little, Homer Payson, 1884- joint author.

Miller, Benjamin LeRoy, 1874-
... Tolchester folio, Maryland, by B. L. Miller, E. B. Mathews, A. B. Bibbins, and H. P. Little, surveyed in cooperation with the state of Maryland. Washington, U. S. Geological survey, 1917.

LITTLE, HOWARD.
English for Iceland, by Howard Little... London: C. F. Roworth Ltd., 1934. vi, 8-103 p. 19cm.

768706A. 1. English language—Textbooks for foreigners, Icelandic. I. Title.

NL 0410689 NN

LITTLE, HOWARD.
Forty stories from easy to more difficult English, by Howard Little... London: C. F. Roworth Ltd., 1934. 50 p. 19cm.

The author is a teacher of English in Iceland.

768707A. 1. Reading books. I. Title.

NL 0410690 NN

Little, Hubert V.
The gospel according to Shakespeare; the bard and the good news. [London, n.d.]
21 p. 21 cm.
Mimeographed.
Text on inside back cover.
1. Shakespeare, William - Religion and ethics. I. Title.

NL 0410691 NcU

Little, I
Mrs. McLeod; a favorite Scotch dance and Virginia reel arr. as a rondo for the piano forte. Philadelphia, G. E. Blake [18—]
4 p. 33 cm.
Caption title.

1. Rondos (Piano), Arranged. 2. Dance music, Scottish. I. Title.

M1.A13L M 60-1606

NL 0410692 DLC

VOLUME 336

Little, Ian Malcolm David.
A critique of welfare economics. Oxford, Clarendon Press, 1950.
275 p. diagrs. 22 cm.

1. Economics. I. Title.
HB171.L73 330.1 50—10154

MtU MtBC CaBVa
ICU TxU MiU MB NcD NcRS OCl CaBVaU WaSpG OrU OrCS
NL 0410693 DLC CoU TU MiD MH NcU NN ScCleU CtY ViU

Little, Ian Malcolm David.
The price of fuel. Oxford, Clarendon Press, 1953.
197 p. 23 cm.

1. Fuel—Gt. Brit.—Prices. I. Title.
HD9551.6.L48 338.5276626 54-8886 ‡

NcRS ViU ICU NBC PPL MH NN CU NIC
NL 0410694 DLC NcD CtY OrU DI OrPR OrPS CoU MB PPL

Little, Irene.
Michael Finnegan, by Irene Little; pictures by Carol Yeakey. New York, Grosset and Dunlap [1946]
[32] p. incl. front., illus. (part col.) 24 x 21cm.

1. Cats—Legends and stories. I. Yeakey, Carol, illus. II. Title.
46-2254
Library of Congress PZ10.3.L715Mi

NL 0410695 DLC

Little, Irene
A rainy day story on the farm ... Illustrations by Elizabeth Matson. Racine, Wis., Whitman publishing company, c1944.
[31]p. col. illus. 17 cm. (Tell-a-Tale book)

Illustrated lining-papers in color.
Illustrated t.-p.

NL 0410696 RPB

Little, Mrs. Isabella F
Select Scriptures for daily meditation. By Mrs. I.F. Little. With a biographical preface... New York, J.A. Gray, 1853.
61 p. 24°.

NL 0410697 NN

Little, J Emmet, 1925–
The seventh gate. Philadelphia [1947]
76 p. 20 cm. (Contemporary poets of Dorrance, 343)

I. Title.
PS3523.I 828S4 811.5 47-30571*

NL 0410698 DLC

LITTLE, J. H.
The Bath waltz, as a rondo for the piano forte. London, Printed by Clementi [18--] 5 p. 33cm.

Caption title.

1. Waltzes (Piano) I. Title.

NL 0410699 NN

Little, J. J., & Ives company, *printers, New York.*
Book of type faces of J. J. Little & Ives co.; the plant complete. Linotype, monotype, initials, display borders, ornaments. New York, J. J. Little & Ives co. [c1940]
298 p. incl. illus., tables. 23½cm.
Binder's title: Type faces, machine and display.

1. Printing—Specimens. I. Title. II. Title: Type faces, machine and display.
41-2591
Library of Congress Z250.L767
Copyright 655.24

NL 0410700 DLC

Little, J. J., & Ives company, *printers, New York.*
How to take advantage of a business danger. New York N. Y., J. J. Little and Ives company [c1936]
12 p. 20cm.
An announcement of the joint activities of the Brearley service organization and the printing house of J. J. Little & Ives.

I. Brearley service organization, New York. II. Title.
37-4847
Library of Congress HF5353.L5
Copyright A 101028 [3] 650

NL 0410701 DLC

Little, J. J., & Ives company, *printers, New York.*
The J. J. Little book of types, specimen pages and book papers, with suggestions on book making and a glossary of printing and binding terms, by the plant complete. New York, J. J. Little & Ives company, 1923.
xiv p., [2], 151, 4, [153]-444 p. front. (port.) illus. 26½cm.
"Number 48, Complimentary edition."
"Prepared for the use of book publishers in their manufacturing departments by Luther H. Porter."
Z250.L77
Copyright A 704812

——— ——— Supplementary pages to The J. J. Little book of types, specimen pages and book papers, by the plant complete; additions since May 1923. New York, J. J. Little & Ives company, 1926.
32 p. 26cm.

1. Printing—Specimens. 2. Type and type-founding. I. Porter, Luther H. II. Title.
23-9649 Revised
Library of Congress Z250.L77 Suppl.

NL 0410703 DLC CU ViU OCl OU ICJ

Little, J. J., & Ives company, printers, New York.
Pertinent points for publishers. New York, J. J. Little & Ives co. [c1936]
cover-title, 48 p. 11½cm.

1. Printing, Practical - Style manuals.

NL 0410704 NNC

Little, J. J. & Ives company, printers, New York.
A prospectus of The J. J. Little book of types, specimen pages and book papers, with suggestions on book making and a glossary of printing and binding terms, by the plant complete. New York, J. J. Little & Ives company, 1924.
[16] p. (unpaged). 28cm.

Contains sample pages from The J. J. Little book of types ...

NL 0410705 NNC

Little, J. J., and Ives Company. New York.
Standardizing paper and book sizes from the forthcoming J. J. Little specimen book of types, pages and printing papers... New York, 1921. 4 l. 4°.

1. Printing. December 11, 1922.

NL 0410706 NN

Little, J S
A century of fires and fire brigades in Dunedin, 1848–1948, by J. S. Little... Dunedin, Dunedin Metropolitan fire board [1948] 234 p. illus. 19cm.

458106B. 1. Fires—Prevention and extinction—New Zealand—Dunedin. I. Dunedin, N. Z. Metropolitan fire board. April 25, 1949

NL 0410707 NN

Little, Jack, 1900–
Anything your little heart desires. By Little Jack Little, Dave Oppenheim and Ira Schuster. New York, Santly bros. inc., c1933.
First line: Do you ever think.

I. Oppenheim, Dave. II. Schuster, Ira. III. Song index (2). August 20, 1948

NL 0410708 NN

Little, Jack, 1900–
Are there any more at home like you? By Little Jack Little and Dave Oppenheim. New York, M. Witmark & sons, c1939.
First line: Betcha have a lovely dad and mother.

I. Oppenheim, David. II. Song index (2). April 17, 1946

NL 0410709 NN

Little, Jack, 1900–
Dancing with the daffodils (down at the garden ball). Lyric by Joe Young. Music by Little Jack Little. New York, Remick music corp. [c1931]
First line: Flowers dress'd in colors of the rainbow.

1. Flowers. 2. Daffodils. I. Young, Joseph, 1889–1939. II. Song index (2). November 3, 1950

NL 0410710 NN

Little, Jack, 1900–
Hold me. By Little Jack Little, Dave Oppenheim [and] Ira Schuster. New York, Metro-Goldwyn-Mayer corp., c1933.
First line: When you're near me.

I. Oppenheim, Dave. II. Schuster, Ira. III. Song index (2). August 20, 1948

NL 0410711 NN

Little, Jack, 1900–
Honestly. Words by Bud Green. Music by Little Jack Little. New York, Santly-Joy-Select, inc. [c1939]
First line: Why should I keep you guessing.
Chorus: Honestly, I'm so in love.

I. Green, Bud. II. Song index (3). April 10, 1946

NL 0410712 NN

VOLUME 336

Little, Jack, 1900–

I can't get enough of you. By Little Jack Little, Dave Oppenheim and Ira Schuster. New York, L. Feist, inc., c1933.

First line: You give a kid some candy.
Chorus: I never knew that I could love.

1. Love. I. Oppenheim, Dave. II. Schuster, Ira. III. Song index (3).
August 20, 1948

NL 0410713 NN

Little, Jack, 1900–

I hope to die if I told a lie. Music and lyric by Little Jack Little ... New York, Advanced music corp. [c1944]

First line: Somehow you wouldn't believe me.
Featured by Little Jack Little and his orchestra.
Portrait of Little Jack Little on t.-p.

1. Truth. 2. Little, Jack—Port. I. Song index (2).
April 18, 1947

NL 0410714 NN

Little, Jack, 1900–

I may be dancing with somebody else (but I keep thinking of you). By Little Jack Little, Dave Oppenheim and Ira Schuster ... New York, Miller music inc. [c1933]

First line: I'm dancing, the band is playing.
Successfully introduced by Kate Smith.
Portrait of Kate Smith on t.-p.

1. Dancing. 2. Smith, Kate—Port. I. Oppenheim, Dave. II. Schuster, Ira. III. Song index (2).
August 20, 1948

NL 0410715 NN

Little, Jack, 1900–

I promise you... Words and music by Little Jack Little. New York, P. Kornheiser, inc. [c1931]

First line: I had spent a life time.
Portrait of Morton Downey on t.-p.

1. Downey, Morton—Port. I. Song index (2).
August 25, 1950

NL 0410716 NN

Little, Jack, 1900–

I wouldn't trade the silver in my mother's hair for all the gold in the world. By Little Jack Little and J. Fred Coots. New York, I. Berlin, inc. [c1932]

First line: Mothers are made up in heaven.

1. Mother. 2. Old age. I. Coots, J. Fred. II. Song index (2).
February 24, 1948

NL 0410717 NN

LITTLE, JACK, 1900- .

I'm needin' you. Lyric by Jo Young. Music by Little Jack Little. New York, Remick music corp. [c1930]

First line: Just at the close of the day.
Chorus: A garden needs a lot of roses.
1. Songs, Popular—1890- . I. Young, Joseph, 1889-1939.

NL 0410718 NN

Little, Jack, 1900–

I'm so alone with the crowd. By Little Jack Little and Joe Young. New York, I. Berlin inc., c1932.

First line: The old land marks are gone.

1. Loneliness. I. Young, Joe. II. Song index (2).
February 13, 1948

NL 0410719 NN

Little, Jack, 1900–

If I ever meet the girl of my dreams. By Little Jack Little and Tea Little... New York, Shapiro, Bernstein & co. inc. [c1932]

First line: At the close of day.
Chorus: My life will be sweet.
Originally and successfully introduced by Rudy Vallee.
Portrait of Rudy Vallee on t.-p.

~~Printed for the Music Division~~

1. Dreams. 2. Vallee, Rudy—Port. I. Little, Tea. II. Song index (3).
December 2, 1947

NL 0410720 NN

Little, Jack, 1900–

It's a wonderful feeling (when you fall in love), by Little Jack Little, Dave Oppenheim and Ira Schuster. New York, Famous music corp. [c1933]

First line: I can thank the day.

1. No subject. I. Oppenheim, Dave. II. Schuster, Ira. III. Song index (2).
June 6, 1947

NL 0410721 NN

Little, Jack, 1900-
Jealous, fox trot; by Jack Little, Tommie Malie and Dick Finch; orch. by Arthur Lange. 10 partis in portfolio. N.Y. Henry Waterson, c1924.

NL 0410722 OC1

Little, Jack, 1900–

Let a little pleasure interfere with business. Words and music by Little Jack Little... New York, Santly bros., inc. [c1931]

First line: Something's wrong with you.
Featured by Al Shayne.
Portrait of Al Shayne on t.-p.

1. Shayne, Al—Port. I. Song index (2).
January 8, 1951

NL 0410723 NN

Little, Jack, 1900–

Let me hum a hymn to her tonight. Words by Joe Young. Music by Little Jack Little. New York, De Sylva, Brown and Henderson, inc. [c1931]

First line: There's a radio man.

1. Radio. 2. Mother. I. Young, Joseph, 1889–1939. II. Song index (2).
January 8, 1951

NL 0410724 NN

Little, Jack, 1900–

Let's make up. By Little Jack Little, Dave Oppenheim [and] Ira Schuster. New York, Metro-Goldwyn-Mayer corp., c1933.

First line: We met and we loved.

1. Quarrels. 2. Reconciliations. I. Oppenheim, Dave. II. Schuster, Ira. III. Song index (2).
August 30, 1948

NL 0410725 NN

Little, Jack, 1900–

My own. Words and music by Little Jack Little, Dave Oppenheim and Ira Schuster. New York, M. Witmark & sons, c1933.

First line: Ev'rything was wrong.

I. Oppenheim, Dave. II. Schuster, Ira. III. Song index (2).
August 20, 1948

NL 0410726 NN

Little, Jack, 1900–

Old roses. By Little Jack Little and Dave Franklin. New York, De Sylva, Brown and Henderson, inc. [c1934]

First line: I remember a garden fair.

1. Roses. 2. Keepsakes I. Franklin, Dave. II. Song index (2).
April 17, 1946

NL 0410727 NN

Little, Jack, 1900–

Take a picture of the moon. Words by Joe Young. Music by Little Jack Little. New York, Shapiro, Bernstein & co. inc. [c1932]

First line: Do you ever get a disappointment.
Portrait of Ruth King on t.-p.

1. Moon. 2. King, Ruth—Port. I. Young, Joe. II. Song index (2).
February 24, 1948

NL 0410728 NN

Little, Jack, 1900–

Ten tiny toes — one baby nose (that's all I'm living for). By Little Jack Little, Dave Oppenheim & Ira Schuster. New York, Harms inc. [c1932]

First line: Always at the close of day.

1. Babies. I. Oppenheim, Dave. II. Schuster, Ira. III. Song index (2).
February 24, 1948

NL 0410729 NN

Little, Jack, 1900–

There's a little bit of devil in your angel eyes. Words and music by Little Jack Little and J. Fred Coots. New York, Keit-Engel, inc. c1932.

First line: Where in heaven did you get those heavenly eyes?

1. Eyes. I. Coots, J. Fred. II. Song index (2).
December 1, 1947

NL 0410730 NN

Little, Jack, 1900–

There's oceans of love by the beautiful sea. By Little Jack Little and J. Fred Coots. New York, I. Berlin, inc. [c1932]

First line: There's something 'bout this balmy weather.
Portrait of Morton Downey on t.-p.

1. Seas & oceans. 2. Downey, Morton—Port. I. Coots, J. Fred. II. Song index (2).
December 5, 1947

NL 0410731 NN

VOLUME 336

Little, Jack, 1900–

Under a shady tree with you. ⌊By⌋ Little Jack Little & J. Fred Coots. ⌊New York⌋ De Sylva, Brown & Henderson inc., c1932.

First line: This is the kind of weather.
Chorus: Honey can't you see, I'd love to be.

1. Trees. I. Coots, J. Fred. II. Song index (3). Printed for the Music Division December 5, 1947

NL 0410732 NN

Little, Jack, 1900–

When the sun bids the moon goodnight. Words and music by Little Jack Little, Dave Oppenheim ⌊and⌋ Ira Schuster. New York, L. Feist, inc., c1933.

First line: Moonbeams are creeping.

1. Evening. 2. Memories. I. Oppenheim, Dave. II. Schuster, Ira. III. Song index (2). Printed for the Music Division August 30, 1948

NL 0410733 NN

Little, Jack, 1900–

When the wandering boy comes home, by Little Jack Little, Dave Oppenheim ⌊and⌋ Ira Schuster. New York, Metro-Goldwyn-Mayer corp., c1932.

First line: Where is my only boy tonight.

1. Prodigal sons. I. Oppenheim, Dave. II. Schuster, Ira. III. Song index (2). Printed for the Music Division
N. Y. P. L. February 24, 1948

NL 0410734 NN

Little, Jack, 1900–

When you understand each other. By Little Jack Little, Ira Schuster and Dave Oppenheim. New York, Shapiro, Bernstein & co. inc., c1932.

First line: Sweethearts come and sweethearts go.

I. Schuster, Ira. II. Oppenheim, Dave. III. Song index (2). Printed for the Music Division February 13, 1948

NL 0410735 NN

Little, Jack, 1900–

Without my gal. Words & music by "Little" Jack Little... New York, Handman, Kent & Goodman, inc. ⌊c1930⌋

First line: He was sleeping, and was weeping.
Chorus: Nothing matters anymore without my gal.
Portrait of Jack Little on t.-p.

1. Jilted. 2. Little, Jack—Port. I. Song index (3). Printed for the Music Division November 13, 1950

NL 0410736 NN

Ph.D. Ps '50 L778

Little, Jack Feramorz.
An experimental investigation of the libido theory. March 1950.
xiii,222 ℓ. illus. 29cm.

Thesis - Univ.of Southern California. Typewritten.

1. Neurosis. I. Title: Libido theory.

NL 0410737 CLSU

Little, Jack W 1877–

Who's your father? A novel. Detroit, S. J. Bloch Pub. Co. ⌊1951⌋

561 p. 25 cm.

I. Title.

PZ4.L778Wh 51-4761

NL 0410738 DLC

Little, Jacob.

E359 .4 .B3 Rare Bk Coll

⌊Ward, Richard R ⌋

Memorial, &c. To the honourable the Senate and House of representatives in Congress assembled. ⌊n. p., 1854?⌋

Little, Jacob, plaintiff.

Barker, Jacob, 1779–1871.

... R. G⌊!⌋ Ward, Fitz G. Halleck, and Jacob Little, assignees of Jacob Barker, *vs.* the United States. Brief of Jacob Barker, counsel for plaintiffs, on the rehearing granted the 16th March, 1859. ⌊n. p., 1859⌋

Little, Jacob, plaintiff.

U. S. *Congress. House. Committee on the judiciary.*

... R. R. Ward, F. G. Halleck, and Jacob Little. <To accompany bill H. R. no. 793.> February 28, 1855 ... Report ... ⌊Washington, 1855⌋

Little, Jacob, plaintiff.

Barker, Jacob, 1779–1871.

Speech of Mr. Barker. ⌊n. p., 1857⌋

Little, Jacob, petitioner.

⌊**Brown,**

To the honorable Court of claims, of the United States, sitting in Washington, D. C. ⌊Washington? 1855?⌋

Little, Jacob, & co., New York.

New York stock exchange.

Report of the committee of the New York stock and exchange board, in reference to the contracts for Kentucky bank stock, pending between J. Little & co. and Boorman, Johnston & co. New York, J. Elliott, printer, 1842.

Little, Jacob, 1795–1876.

... Home missionary sermon, prepared by direction of the General assembly, and preached before that body, at Chicago, May 27, 1858: by Rev. Jacob Little ... Alton and Chicago, 1858.

p. ⌊289⌋–299. 21cm. ⌊*With his* A New Year's sermon ... 1849. Newark, 1849?⌋

Caption title.
At head of title: The Presbytery reporter. Vol. IV, no. 1 ... Whole no. 75 ... July, 1858.
A detached copy.

1. Missions, Home. 2. Missions—Sermons. I. Title.

40-1645

Library of Congress BV4282.L5

NL 0410745 DLC

Little, Jacob, 1795–1876.

New Year, 1850. A discourse delivered at Granville, Ohio, on the first Sabbath of January, 1850. By Rev. Jacob Little, pastor of the Congregational church. Granville, Gill & Blackman, 1850.

31 p. 21cm. ⌊*With his* A New Year's sermon ... 1849. Newark, 1849?⌋

1. New-Year sermons. 2. Granville, O. I. Title.

40-1646

Library of Congress BV4282.L5

NL 0410746 DLC CSmH OClWHi

Little, Jacob, 1795–1876.

A New Year's sermon, delivered in Granville, Licking Co., Ohio, on the first Sabbath in January, 1838. By Rev. Jacob Little, A. M., pastor of the Congregational church. Columbus, Printed by Cutler and Pilsbury, 1838.

cover-title, 16 p. 23cm.

1. Granville, O. I. Title.

25-15938

Library of Congress F499.G7L5

NL 0410747 DLC

Little, Jacob, 1795–1876.

A New Year's sermon, delivered in Granville, Licking county, Ohio, on the first Sabbath of January, 1849. By Rev. Jacob Little, pastor of the Congregational church. Newark ⌊O.⌋ Printed at the Gazette office ⌊1849?⌋

30 p. 21cm.
Binder's title: New Year's sermons 1849–1854.

1. New-Year sermons. 2. Granville, O. I. Title.

40-1644

Library of Congress BV4282.L5

NL 0410748 DLC

285.173 P928 no.308

Little, Jacob, 1795-1876

Saints' perseverance. Philadelphia, Presbyterian Board of Publication ⌊n.d.⌋
21 p. 19 cm. (⌊Presbyterian tracts; no. 308)

NL 0410749 NcD

Little, Jacob, 1795–1876.

Saints' perseverance: a sermon, preached by appointment before the Synod of Ohio, at Delaware, Ohio, 1854, by Rev. Jacob Little ... Columbus, Printed by the Ohio state journal company, 1855.

15 p. 21cm. ⌊*With his* A New Year's sermon ... 1849. Newark, 1849?⌋

1. Perseverance (Theology) 2. Congregational churches—Sermons. I. Title.

40-1647

Library of Congress BV4282.L5

NL 0410750 DLC OClWHi

Little, Jacob, 1795–1876.

Twenty-fourth New Year's sermon. A discourse delivered at Granville, Ohio, on the first Sabbath of January, 1851. By Rev. Jacob Little, pastor of the Congregational church. Granville, D. Hunt, printer, Intelligencer office, 1851.

48 p. 21cm. ⌊*With his* A New Year's sermon ... 1849. Newark, 1849?⌋

1. New-Year sermons. 2. Granville, O. I. Title.

40-1648

Library of Congress BV4282.L5

NL 0410751 DLC

VOLUME 336

Little, Jacob, 1795-1876.
Twenty-fifth New Year's sermon. A discourse preached in Granville, Ohio, on the first Sabbath of January, 1852. By Rev. Jacob Little, pastor of the Congregational Presbyterian church. Granville, J. E. Wyche & co., printers, 1852.
cover-title, 32 p. 22½cm.

1. Granville, O. I. Title.
25-7749
Library of Congress F499.G7L53

NL 0410752 DLC OHi OO

Little, Jacob, 1795-1876.
Twenty-sixth New-Year's sermon: a discourse, preached in the Congregational church, Granville, Ohio, on the first Sabbath of January, 1853. By Rev. Jacob Little ... [Granville? 1853?]
31 p. 21cm. [With his A New Year's sermon ... 1849. Newark, 1849?]
Caption title.

1. New-Year sermons. 2. Granville, O. I. Title.
40-1649
Library of Congress BV4282.L5

NL 0410753 DLC OHi

Little, Jacob, 1795-1876.
Twenty-seventh New-Year's sermon. A discourse preached in the Congregational church, Granville, Ohio, on the first Sabbath of January, 1854. By Rev. Jacob Little ... [Granville? 1854?]
32 p. 21cm. [With his A New Year's sermon ... 1849. Newark, 1849?]
Caption title.

1. New-Year sermons. 2. Granville, O. I. Title.
40-1650
Library of Congress BV4282.L5

NL 0410754 DLC ICN DHU

Little, Jacob V
What the Bible tells us about the location of heaven and hell and the first, second, and third coming of Christ. By Jacob V. Little ... Deckertown, N. J., J. V. Little, 1890.
201 p. incl. front. (port.) 19cm.

1. Eschatology. I. Title.
45-30624
Library of Congress BT821.L7

NL 0410755 DLC

MANN SF 373 C8 L7
Little, James.
The story of the Corriedale; also a few suggestions as to the possible cause of Black sheep. Christchurch, Willis and Aiken, 1917.
8 p. 23 cm.
Cover-title.
1. Sheep. 2. Corriedale. I. Title.

NL 0410756 NIC

LITTLE, JAMES, of Caledonia.
Information for the public. The case of the Indian department, in reference to the Grand River settlers as submitted by Col. Bruce, chief superintendant [sic] of Indian affairs, in a letter to Sir Allan Napier MacNab, and three thousand memorialists, with their petition to the Executive, for an enquiry &c. and a review of the same by James Little, esq., of Caledonia, one of the momorialists [sic]. *Hamilton: "Spectator" steam press, corner of Court-house square. 1852.*
24 p. 8vo. Cover title. Printed in double columns. 21.3 x 14 cm.

NL 0410757 CaOTP

*AC85 Em345 S882l
Little, James, of New Hampshire.
The character and genius of Ralph Waldo Emerson, with selections from his works. An address by Councillor James Little. Manchester[N.H.].1882.
31p. 21.5cm.,in case 22.5cm.
Original printed white wrappers; wire-stitched, as issued; in cloth case.
Imperfect: p.29-30 mutilated.

NL 0410758 MH

Little, James, physician
Ascending and descending breathing; its value as a symptom and its mechanism. 9 pp. 8°. Dublin, J. Falconer, 1868.
Repr. from: Dublin Q. J. M. Sc., 1868, xlvi.

NL 0410759 DNLM

Little, James, physician
Lecture on the resources of the physician in the management of chronic diseases of the heart. Dublin, Fannin; London, Baillière, Tindall & Cox, 1894.
vi[1]78p. 17cm.
Cover title: Chronic diseases of the heart.
1.Heart diseases. I.Title II.Title: Chronic diseases of the heart.

NL 0410760 NcD-MC

Film 1121 no. 3
LITTLE, James, physician
Lecture on the resources of the physician in the management of chronic diseases of the heart. Dublin, Fannin, 1894.
vi, 78 p.
Film copy.

NL 0410761 DNLM

BT265 .L77
Little, James, religious writer
The cross in Holy Scripture; a study of the nature and significance of Christ's redemptive work ... London, R. Scott, 1911.
x, 147 p.
1. Atonement.

NL 0410762 ICU OrP

WW 10 L779
Little, James, religious writer
The day-spring and other sermons. Edinburgh, Oliphant, Anderson & Ferrier, 1907.
312p. 21cm.
1. Sermons, American. 2. Presbyterian church - Sermons. I. Title.

NL 0410763 ViRUT NjP

Little, James, religious writer
Glorying in the Lord. Edinburgh, Oliphant, Anderson & Ferrier, 1912.
254p. 21cm.
1. Sermons, American. 2. Presbyterian church - Sermons. I. Title.

NL 0410764 ViRUT NjP

Little, James, Rev.
An explanation of the nature and properties of logarithms, common, trigonometrical, and logistical ... To which is added, an appendix, containing remarks on the treatise on the Measures of ratios, by Mr. Maguire; and an explanation of the method of constructing logarithms by series, by Doctor Halley. Delivered in the form of lectures, by the Rev. James Little. Dublin, Printed by R. Graisberry, 1830.
254 p. 22cm.
1. Logarithms. 2. Maguire, James. Of the measures of ratios.
4-23861†
Library of Congress QA59.L7

NL 0410765 DLC CtY

Little, James, Rev., M.A.
The tercentenary of England's great victory over Spain and the Armada. 1588-1888. By Rev. James Little, M. A. Toronto, Canada, W. Briggs; [etc., etc.] 1888.
viii, [9]-238 p. 18½cm.

1. Armada, 1588.
A 33-351
Title from Univ. of Mich. DA360.L78 Printed by L. C.

NL 0410766 MiU NjP NN

Little, James, writer on forestry.
[. The timber question. [Montreal. 1881.]
8°.
Report of the Montreal horticultural society and fruit-growers' association of the province of Quebec, 1881, vi, 14-19.

NL 0410767 MH-A

Little, James, writer on forestry.
The timber supply question, of the Dominion of Canada and the United States of America. By James Little. Montreal, Lovell printing and publishing company, 1876.
23 p. 21½cm.

1. Canada. Forestry. 2. U. S. Forestry.
Agr 3-518
Library, U. S. Dept. of Agriculture 99L722

NL 0410768 DNAL MH-A DLC

Little, James A., joint author.
Watney, Charles.
Industrial warfare, the aims and claims of capital and labour, by Charles Watney and James A. Little ... London, J. Murray, 1912.

Little, James Alexander, 1831-
Biographical sketch of Feramorz Little, written under the patronage of his family by his brother ... Salt Lake City,Utah, Juvenile Instructor Office,1890.
viii,[9]-191p. 23½cm.
1.Little, Feramorz, 1820-1887.

NL 0410770 NjP NNC NN MH CtY ICN IEG

Little, James Alexander, 1831-
A compendium of the doctrine of the gospel, 1882
see under Richards, Franklin Dewey, 1821-1899.

VOLUME 336

Little, James Alexander, 1831-
From Kirtland to Salt Lake City, by James A. Little ... Salt Lake City, Utah, J. A. Little, 1890.
viii, [9]-260 p. illus. 23cm.
"This book may be considered an epitome of the motives and experiences of the saints who rejoiced and suffered in the prosecutions and exoduses attending the early growth of the Latter-day work."—Pref.

1. Mormons and Mormonism. 2. Utah—Hist. I. Title.
13—20443
Library of Congress BX8611.L55

OC1WHi CoU IEG WHi KMK
NL 0410772 DLC OrP MB OC1 NcD CtY ICN NNC NIC NN

Little, James Alexander, 1831-

FOR OTHER EDITIONS SEE MAIN ENTRY

Hamblin, Jacob, b. 1819.
Jacob Hamblin, a narrative of his personal experience, as a frontiersman, missionary to the Indians and explorer, disclosing interpositions of Providence, severe privations, perilous situations and remarkable escapes ... By James A. Little ... Salt Lake City, Utah, Juvenile instructor office, 1881.

Little, James Alexander, b. 1831.
The pawpaw (*Asimina triloba*) a native fruit of great excellence ... Some reasons why it has not been cultivated. Directions how to propagate it. Where found growing. Adaptation of soil ... A short history of the pawpaw in pioneer days. Reminiscences, by James A. Little ... [Clayton, Ind., O. G. Swindler] 1905.
[22] p. front. (port.) 17½cm.
Cover-title: A treatise on the pawpaw.

1. [Asimina triloba]
Agr 16-1339
Library, U. S. Dept. of Agriculture 93L72

NL 0410774 DNAL OO MH-A

Little, James Alexander, 1831-
What I saw on the old Santa Fe trail ... A condensed story of frontier life half a century ago. By James A. Little ... Plainfield, Ind., The Friends press [1904]
1 p. l., 127 p. incl. ports. front. 19½cm.

1. Santa Fé trail. 2. The West—Soc. life & cust. I. Title.
4-10848
Library of Congress F786.L77

NL 0410775 DLC KMK UU CtY NjP CoD NNC MB

Little, James Alfred, 1884-
Historical development of transport coordination & integration in the United States. Washington, 1950.
viii, 217 p. 27 cm. (U. S. Interstate Commerce Commission. Bureau of Transport Economics and Statistics. Statement no. 5015)
Cover title.
"This study was prepared principally by James A. Little ... Henry M. Cunningham ... and Chester E. Stiles."

1. Transportation—U. S.—Hist. 2. [Transportation—Coordination—Hist.] I. Title. (Series)
HE203.L5 385 A 50-9419
Bureau of Railway Economics. Library for Library of Congress †

NL 0410776 DBRE OrU NSyU PU-W PPD TU DLC

HE5623 .E24
Little, James Alfred, 1884- joint author.

Edfeldt, Theodore Roosevelt, 1904-
Motor operations by or for class 1 railroads, 1944 [by T. R. Edfeldt and J. A. Little] Washington, 1948.

Little, James Alfred, 1884-

HE197 .U5A53 1943 d
U. S. *Transportation investigation and research board.*
... Report on rate-making and rate-publishing procedures of railroad, motor, and water carriers. Letter from Board of investigation and research, transmitting report on rate-making and rate-publishing procedures of railroad, motor, and water carriers ... Washington, U. S. Govt. print. off., 1944.

Little, James Alfred, 1884-

U. S. *Office of federal coordinator of transportation.*
Report on the leasing of railroad owned grain elevator properties. Prepared by J. A. Little, research assistant, federal coordinator of transportation. Washington, D. C., 1936.

Law
Little, James Brooke, 1850- ed.

Gt. Brit. *Laws, statutes, etc.*
The law of allotments for the poor and labouring population, including The allotments acts, 1887 and 1890, The allotments and cottage gardens compensation for crops act, 1887, The operative parts of the Local government act, 1894, &c; together with the incorporated statutes, and the adaptations of the lands clauses acts and allotments acts by the Local Government Board, with tables of cases, and statutes and copious index. 2d ed., by James Brooke Little. London, Shaw, 1895.

Law
Little, James Brooke, 1850-

Gt. Brit. *Laws, statutes, etc.*
The law of burial: including all the burial acts as modified or affected by the Local government (England and Wales) act, 1894; all the church building, new parish and poor law acts relating to the subject; the Cremation act, 1902, and the official regulations of the Home Office and Local Government Board, with notes and cases. 3d ed. by James Brooke Little. London, Shaw, 1902.

Little, James Brooke, 1950-

Archbold, John Frederick, 1785-1870.
The Poor law; comprising the law relating to the poor law authorities; the relief of the poor, including the relief of pauper lunatics; the settlement and removal of the poor; and the poor rate. 15th ed. by James Brooke Little. London, Shaw, 1898.

Little, James Brooke, 1850- *comp.*
The poor law statutes, comprising the statutes in force relating to the poor; and to guardians, overseers, and other poor law authorities and officers, from Elizabeth to end of Victoria. With notes and cases ... By James Brooke Little ... [London] Shaw & sons [etc.] 1901-02.
3 v. 22cm.
Paged continuously: v. 1: xxxii, 548, [96] p.; v. 2: xviii, [549]-1464, [161 p.; v. 3: xlvii, [1465]-2355, [282] p.
Vols. 1-2 have each a Table of statutes, Table of general orders, Table of cases and Index; v. 3 has General table of statutes, General orders, Cases and General index.
1. Poor laws—Gt. Brit. I. Gt. Brit. Laws, statutes, etc.
2—21822
Library of Congress HV78.A5L7

NL 0410783 DLC

Little (James F.). A table of mortality according to height and weight. pp. 315-327. 8°. [n. p.], 1914.
Rept. from Trans. Actuar. Soc. Am., 1914, xv, pt. 2.

NL 0410784 DNLM

Little, James Kenneth, 1906-
... A critical study of public school costs in Kansas from 1898 to 1928 by J. Kenneth Little ... Topeka, Printed by Kansas state printing plant, B. P. Walker, state printer, 1932.
58 p. incl. tables, diagrs. 23cm. (On cover: [Kansas. State teachers college, Emporia] Studies in education. March, 1932, no. 6)
Bibliography: p. 57-58.

1. Public schools—Kansas. 2. Education—Kansas—Finance. I. Title.
E 32-504 Revised
U. S. Off. of educ. Library for Library of Congress LB5.K3 no. 6 [r43e2]† [370.73781621] 379.11

NL 0410785 DHEW DLC OC1JC ViU ODW OCU OU OrPR WaTC

Little, James Kenneth, 1906-
An investigation by means of special test-scoring and drill devices of the effect of certain instructional procedures on learning in educational psychology ... by ... [Columbus] The Ohio state university, 1934.
2-104 [56] numb. l.

Thesis (Ph.D.) - Ohio state university.

NL 0410786 OU

RD526 .L5 Toner Coll.
Little, James Laurence, 1836-1885.
A case of anchylosis of the right temporo-maxillary articulation, successfully treated by excision of the condyle, with remarks by James L. Little ... Albany, C. Van Benthuysen & sons, printers, 1874.
11 p. 2 pl. 23cm.

"Reprinted from the Transactions of New York state medical society, for 1874."

1. Jaws-- Ankylosis. I. Title.

NL 0410787 DLC DNLM

RD581 .L75 Toner Coll.
Little, James Laurence, 1836-1885.
A lecture on median lithotomy delivered before the Brooklyn anatomical and surgical society, by James L. Little ... New York, G. P. Putnam's sons, 1880.
24 p. illus. 23½cm.

"Reprinted from the Annals of the Anatomical and surgical society, Brooklyn, February, 1880."

1. Lithotomy.

NL 0410788 DLC NN

Tdb15 1
[Little, James Laurence] 1836-1885.
...On the use of plaster of Paris splints in military surgery ... [New York]1864.
Pamphlet
At head of title: Sanitary commission. T.
"Printed for circulation by the United States sanitary commission."
"Prepared by Dr. James L.Little."

NL 0410789 CtY

Little, James L[aurence] 1836-1885.
A paper on median lithotomy. By James L. Little ... Philadelphia, Collins, printer, 1870.
1 p. l., [5]-20 p. illus. 22½cm.
Extracted from the Transactions of the American medical association.

1. Lithotomy.

Library of Congress RD581.L77 7-4604†

NL 0410790 DLC DNLM NN

VOLUME 336

Little, James Laurence, 1836–1885.
Puncture of the bladder by Dieulafoy's aspirator; with a description of the instrument. By James L. Little ... New York, D. Appleton & company, 1872.
12 p. illus. 23½cm.
Reprinted from the N. Y. medical journal, November, 1872.

1. Bladder—Puncture and aspiration.

7-19098†* Cancel

Library of Congress RD581.L78

NL 0410791 DLC NN

Little, James Laurence, 1836–1885.
A remarkable case of morphine tolerance by an infant. By James L. Little ... New York, W. Wood & co., 1878.
6 p. 23cm.
Reprinted from the American journal of obstetrics and diseases of women and children, vol. XI, no. II, April, 1878.

1. Morphine.

7-18053†

Library of Congress RM666.M8L7

NL 0410792 DLC NN

Little, James Laurence, 1836–1885.
A report on the use of plaster of Paris in surgery. By James L. Little ... Philadelphia, Collins, printer, 1867.
12 p. illus. 23cm.
Extracted from the Transactions of the American medical association. On the "mode of constructing and applying plaster of Paris splints."

1. Splints (Surgery)

Library of Congress RD113.L77 7-919†* Cancel

NL 0410793 DLC NN

Little, James L[aurence] 1836–1885.
Two lectures on Lister's antiseptic method of treating surgical injuries, delivered at the College of physicians and surgeons, New York, by James L. Little ... Reprint from the Hospital gazette, May 9th and 16th, 1878. [New York, 1878]
cover-title, 15 p. 23cm.

1. Surgery, Aseptic and antiseptic.

7-388†

Library of Congress RD91.L77

NL 0410794 DLC NN

Little, James Macfarlane, 1885–
Erosional topography and erosion; a mathematical treatment with application to geomorphology, soil science, agronomy and engineering, with tables, by James M. Little ... San Francisco, Lithotone printed by A. Carlisle & co., 1940.
3 p. l., 5–104 p. incl. tables, diagrs. 23½cm.
Bibliographical foot-notes.
Symbols used: p. 8.

1. Erosion. 2. Physical geography. 3. Hydraulics. 4. Rain and rainfall. I. Title.

40–9048

Library of Congress QE581.L55

Copyright [40b5] 551.35

ICJ CU-I AAP DAS PP NcRS NcD OU MiU
NL 0410795 DLC OC1W CU CaBViP WaTC OrP OrCS CaBVaU

Little, James Macfarlane, 1885–
The geology and metal deposits of Chile, by James Macfarlane Little, E. M. New York, The Branwell company [c1926]
iv p., 1 l., v–ix, 188 p. illus., 2 fold. col. pl., 2 fold. maps (in pocket) diagrs. 23½cm.

1. Mines and mineral resources—Chile. 2. Geology—Chile. I. Title.

27–811

Library of Congress TN43.L5

MB MiU OU OC1 TU
NL 0410796 DLC IdU WaS CaBVaU CoU CU NIC OC1W ICJ

501.8
L7241
1961

Little, James Maxwell, 1910-
An introduction to the experimental method; for students of biology and the health sciences. Minneapolis, Burgess Pub. Co. [1916]
84p. illus. 28cm.

1. Science. Methodology. 2. Biology, Experimental. 3. Medicine. Experimental. I. Title: The experimental method.

NL 0410797 KU

Little, James Maxwell, 1910–
... The pathways of transportation of absorbed lipids ... by James Maxwell Little ... [Baltimore] 1941.
1 p. l., 773–780 p. incl. tables. 25cm.
Summary of thesis (PH. D.)—Vanderbilt university, 1941.
"Private edition, distributed by the Joint university libraries, Nashville, Tennessee."
"Reprinted from the American journal of physiology, vol. 134, no. 4, November, 1941."
"References": p. 780.

1. Absorption (Physiology) 2. Fat. 3. Lipoids.

A 42–2188

Joint university libraries, for Library of Congress Nashville QP165.L5 † 612.38

NL 0410798 TNJ DLC

[Little, James Park]
... California souvenir, occult and other poemettes, by "Alcione" [pseud.] ... San Francisco, 1898–99.
36 p. 19cm.

8-29647

NL 0410799 DLC MB RPB

Little, James Park
Poetic echoes from the western United States of America...
[San Francisco?] 1905

33

NL 0410800 DLC

NA
966
.L57x

Little, James Raymond.
Sketches of Georgian Bath by J. Raymond Little with a preface by T. Sturge Cotterell. Bristol [Eng.] Arrowsmith [1932]
1 v.(unpaged) 25 cm.

1. Architecture--Bath, England--History. 2. Architecture, Georgian. I. Title

NL 0410801 OOxM NcD NN

Little, James Stanley.
The doom of western civilization. London, W.H. & L. Collingridge, 1907.
63 (1) p. 12°.

NL 0410802 NN

Little, James Stanley. Future of landscape art. 12 pp. (Nineteenth Cent. v. 30, 1891, p. 197.)

NL 0410803 MdBP

Little, James Stanley.
... The life and work of William Q. Orchardson, R. A., by James Stanley Little ... London, The Art journal office, 1897.
2 p. l., 31, [1] p. front., illus., 3 pl. 33cm. (The Art annual, 1897)
The works of W. Q. Orchardson: 1 p. at end.

1. Orchardson, William Quiller, 1835–

16–10582

Library of Congress ND497.O7L5

NL 0410804 DLC IU ICN MB

Little, James Stanley.
Problems and possibilities. Plate.
(In Creswicke. South Africa and its future. Pp. 72–85. London, 1903.)

June 4, 1903
E9242 — Africa, South. Pol. hist.

NL 0410805 MB

Little, J[ames] Stanley.
Progress of British empire in the century, by J. Stanley Little . . . London, Philadelphia [etc.] The Linscott pub. co., 1901.
xxx pp., 1 l., 480 pp. front., port. 21½cm. (The nineteenth century series, v. 8)
Subject entries: Gt. Brit.—Hist.

2-1234—M 2

NL 0410806 DLC ViU

Little, J[ames] Stanley.
... Progress of the British empire in the century, by J. Stanley Little ... London & Edinburgh, W. & R. Chambers, limited; Philadelphia, Detroit [etc.] The Bradley-Garretson co., limited, 1903.
xxx p., 1 l., 480 p. 6 port. (incl. front.) 21½cm. (Added t.-p.: The nineteenth century series (vol. VIII))
Series title also at head of t.-p.

1. Gt. Brit.—Colonies—Hist. 2. Gt. Brit.—Hist.—19th cent.

Library of Congress DA16.L78 Copyright 5-12363

NL 0410807 DLC MB ICJ NN ODW MiU NcD

Little, James Stanley.
Psychical impressions: The day ghost, by James Stanley Little ... and Only a face, by Robert Baldwin. London, J. W. Jarvis & son, 1887.
2 p. l., 105, [1] p. 18½cm.

I. Baldwin, Robert. II. Title. III. Title: The day ghost. IV. Title: Only a face.

Library of Congress PZ3.L7252Ps 40-37581

NL 0410808 DLC

VOLUME 336

*EC8 Sh445 D875s
Little, James Stanley,
The Shelley centenary at Horsham, August 4th, 1892. Address on Shelley by Mr. Edmund Gosse, M.A., speeches by Professor J. Nichol, and Mr. Frederic Harrison. Press and personal notices. Reprinted, with additions, from the West Sussex gazette. Compiled and edited by the hon. secs., J. Stanley Little and J. J. Robinson.
Arundel: West Sussex gazette office. 1892.
52p. 18.5cm., in case 19.5cm.
Original printed gray wrappers; in cloth case with other Shelley pamphlets.

Another copy. 18cm., in folder 18.5cm.

NL 0410810 MH

Little, James Stanley.
Sketches and studies in So. Africa. 1889.
32916

NL 0410811 DN

Little, James Stanley.
South Africa; a sketch book of men, manners and facts: with an appendix upon the present situation in South Africa and upon the affairs of Zululand, the Transvaal, and Bechuanaland, with special reference to the Boer mission to England, by James Stanley Little ... London, W. S. Sonnenschein & co.; [etc., etc.] 1884.
2 v. 22½cm.
Paged continuously.
1. Africa, South. I. Title.
Library of Congress DT761.L77 5—15649

NL 0410812 DLC CtY DN IEN ICU OCl ViU

916.8 L778so
Little, James Stanley
South Africa; a sketch book of men, manners, and facts. 2d ed. in 1 v. with a new pref. London, Swan Sonnenschein, Lowrey, 1887.
xv, 504 p. 22 cm.
1. Africa, South. I. Title.

NL 0410813 NcD MH CtY

JN276 .L75
Little, James Stanley.
The United States of Britain. An address on England and her colonies ... delivered on the 19th May, 1886, and ... on the 18th June, 1886, with additions and revisions ... Guildford, Billing, 1887.
32 p.
1. Imperial federation.

NL 0410814 ICU

Little, James Stanley.
What is art? London, W. Swan Sonnenschein and Co. 1884.
pp. 181 +.

NL 0410815 MH

Little, James Stanley.
William Quiller Orchardson, R.A.
see his The life and work of William Q. Orchardson.

Ex 3829 .52932 .1792
Little, Janet
Poetical works of Janet Little, the Scotch milkmaid. Air, printed by J. & P. Wilson, 1792
207 p. 21 cm

NL 0410817 NjP ScU InU AU ICN MH IU CaBVaU

Little, Jay, *pseud.*
see Miller, Clarence L 1917-

1926 LI91321
Little, Jean, 1932-
"It's a wonderful world"; [poems. Guelph, Ont., 1947]
cover-title, 30 p. illus., incl. port. 16 cm.
Poems.
Author's autographed copy.
1. Canadian poetry. I. Title.

NL 0410819 RPB TxU

Spec. PS 3543 A 563 I 55 1942
Little, Jeannette.
Iowa rhythms; a book of sketches by Jeannette Little and poems by Mona Van Duyn. [n.p., 1942?]
1 v. (unpaged) illus. 23 cm.
Original paper wrappers.
"Cover design a wood block print by Jeannette Little."
Gift of Mona Van Duyn.
I. Van Duyn, Mona. II. Title.

NL 0410820 MoSW

Little, Jerome B
Model railway working, by Jerome B. Little. London, Vawser & Wiles, ltd. [1945]
95, [1] p. illus. (incl. plans) diagrs. 18cm.
1. Railroads—Models. I. Title.
Library of Congress TF197.T53 45-4312
625

NL 0410821 DLC

Little, Jesse Carter, 1815-1893, comp.
A collection of sacred hymns, for the use of the Latter day Saints.
see under Church of Jesus Christ of Latter-Day Saints.

Little, Mrs. Jessie
The conversion and deathbed experience of...
see under
Little, John.

Little, John.
The conversion and death-bed experience of Mrs. Jessie Little, of Glasgow, who died in January, 1842, at the age of eighteen, by John Little. From the 11th London ed., revised. New York, The American tract society [1851]
134 p. 15½cm.
1. Little, Mrs. Jessie (Cumming) 1824-1842.

NL 0410824 MiU NjNbS MWA MH OU CU IU

Little, John.
The conversion and death-bed experience of Mrs. Little of Glasgow, who died in January 1842, at the age of 18. London, J. Snow, 1845.
viii, 140 p. 24°.
7. ed.
p. 111-118 mutilated.

NL 0410825 NN

Little, John, Barrister at law
The constitution of the government of Newfoundland, in its legislative and executive departments. With an appendix, containing the rules and orders of the Legislative council, and the House of assembly. By John Little ... [St. Johns] Hazard & Owen, 1855.
3 p. l., [v]-xx, [3]-88 p. 16cm.
1. Newfoundland—Pol. & govt. 2. Newfoundland. General assembly—Rules and practice.
10-5140†
Library of Congress JL543.A3 1855

NL 0410826 DLC

CPA VF 933
Little, John, of New York.
Life for America's sons and daughters. [New York, New York State Young Communist League, 1939]
46 p. illus.
"Speech at the second annual convention of the New York State Young Communist League held on February 10-12, 1939."
1. Youth - U.S I. Title.

NL 0410827 MiEM MH

FILM HWT C697 Reel 2
Little, John, of New York.
Life for America's sons and daughters. [New York, New York State Young Communist League, 1939]
46, [1] p. illus., ports. 18½ cm.
Cover title.
Microfilm copy made by the Wisconsin State Historical Society. Negative.
"Keynote speech at the second annual convention of the New York State Young Communist League...1939."

NL 0410828 WHi

LITTLE, JOHN, of New York.
Wake up and live, by John Little. [New York: New York State committee, Young Communist league, 1937]
47 p. illus. (incl. ports.) 18½cm.
"Report...at the Empire state convention of the Young Communist league, held in...Brooklyn, November 26-28, 1937."
1. Bolshevism—U.S. I. Young Communist league of the U.S.A. New York (State).

NL 0410829 NN MiEM MH

VOLUME 336

Little, Rev. John.
The abuse of fiction, or, Effects of novel-reading. A lecture. New York, R. Bonner, 1853.
53 p. nar. 16°.
Presentation copy

NL 0410830 NN

Little, Rev. John, defendant.
Defence of Rev. John Little, pastor of the Reformed Presbyterian church, Waverly place, New York, delivered before the Presbytery, Oct. 13, in the case of his trial for heresy. With an appendix, containing a brief report of the trial ... New York, M. W. Dodd., 1851.
39,ixp. 22cm.
The trial resulted from a sermon by Rev. Little alleged at variance with a doctrine of his church that it is sin to obey a civil government not founded on strictly Christian principles.
With this are bound: New York. Broadway tabernacle church. Proceedings of the session of Broadway tabernacle against Lewis Tappan. 1839; Sterling, John Canfield, defendant. Defence on his trial upon presentment for alleged schismatical conduct. 1852; Boston. Hollis street society. Correspondence between a committee and the pastor of Hollis street society. 1840.

NL 0410833 NNU-W NNC

B252
L72
Little, Rev. John.
Obedience to law: a sermon, by Rev. John Little, pastor of the Reformed Presbyterian church, Waverly Place, New York. New York, Published by M. W. Dodd, 1851.
36 p. 23cm.

NL 0410834 NNC MiU NN

Little, Rev. John, ed.
Smith, *Mrs.* S E D *b.* 1817.
The soldier's friend; being a thrilling narrative of Grandma Smith's four years' experience and observation, as matron, in the hospitals of the South, during the late disastrous conflict in America. By Mrs. S. E. D. Smith. Rev. by Rev. John Little, and dedicated to the rebel soldiers. Memphis, Tenn., Printed by the Bulletin publishing company, 1867.

AC901
.W3
Little, Rev. John.
Spirit manifestations. A sermon. New York, E. Bonner, 1852.
8 p. (Waterman pamphlets, 164:18)

NL 0410836 DLC NN

SF375.5
G7
L57
Little, John, sheep farmer.
Practical observations on the improvement and management of mountain sheep, and sheep farms, also, remarks on stock of various kinds. Edinburgh, Printed by J. Moir, 1815.
198 p.

1. Sheep- Scotland. 2. Sheep- Wales. 3. Mountain sheep. I. Title: Improvement and management of mountain sheep, and sheep farms.

NL 0410837 CU-A PSt

Little, John, writer on paper currency.
The monetary crisis of 1847: its causes and a proposed new system of paper currency ... London, J.Snow [etc., etc.] 1847.
16 p. 16 cm.

NL 0410838 MH-BA CtY IU

Little, John Andrew, 1796–
The autobiography of a New churchman: or, Incidents and observations connected with the life of John A. Little. Philadelphia, Lippincott, Grambo, and co., 1852.
2 p. l., [13]–258 p. 19cm.

I. Title.
Library of Congress BX8749.L5A3 36-32221 922.8473

NL 0410839 DLC MeB

Little, John Buckner.
The history of Butler county, Alabama, from 1815 to 1885. With sketches of some of her most distinguished citizens and glances at her rich and varied resources . . . Cincinnati, Elm st. printing co., 1885. xi, [3]–256 pp. front., pl., port. 12°.
F332.B9L7 1-Rc-2468

NL 0410840 DLC AU NcD

Little, John D
Complete credit and collection letter book. Englewood, Cliffs, N.J., Prentice-Hall [c1953]
275 p. 24 cm.

NL 0410841 TxFTC

Little, John D
Complete credit and collection letter book. New York, Prentice-Hall, 1953.
275 p. 24 cm.

1. Credit. 2. Collecting of accounts. 3. Commercial correspondence. I. Title: Credit and collection letter book.
HF5556.L5 658.882 53-8395 ‡

IdB OCl TU PPT NN MB TxU
NL 0410842 DLC MtU WaS WaT Or OrP CaBViP IdPI CoU

Little, John Dutton Conant, 1928–
Use of storage water in a hydroelectric system. [Cambridge, Mass., Microreproduction Laboratory, M.I.T. Libraries, 1955]
118 ℓ. illus.
Thesis, Massachusetts Institute of Technology, 1954.
Microfilm (positive) of typescript. 1 reel.
Bibliography: ℓ. 117.
1. Water-power electric plants. 2. Electric power-plants - Water-supply - Mathematical models. 3. Time-series analysis. 4. Mathematical optimization. I. Title.

NL 0410843 NNC

Little, John Ernest, 1914–
A study of the action of pancreatic amylase ... by John Ernest Little. New York, N. Y., 1941.
2 p. l., 34 p., 1 l. diagrs. 21cm.
Thesis (PH. D.)—Columbia university, 1941.
"Lithoprinted by Edwards brothers, inc., lithoprinters, Ann Arbor, Michigan."
Vita.
Bibliography: p. 33–34.

1. Diastase. 2. Pancreas.
Columbia univ. Libraries for Library of Congress QP601.L5 A 42-927 † 612.01515

NL 0410844 NNC DLC CU OU

Little, *Mrs.* John F
see Little, Mamie Burkhalter, 1870–

Little, John Forsyth, 1880–
... Anatomy; a manual for students and practitioners, by John Forsyth Little ... 2d ed., rev. and enl., illustrated with seventy-five engravings. Philadelphia and New York, Lea & Febiger [1911]
xii, [17]–491 p. illus. 18½cm. (The medical epitome series) $1.50

1. Anatomy, Human.
Library of Congress QM28.L65 11-26508

NL 0410846 DLC DNLM

Little, John Forsyth, 1880–
... Anatomy; a manual for students and practitioners, by John Forsyth Little ... 3d ed., rev. and enl. including selected list of state board examination questions; illustrated with seventy-five engravings. Philadelphia and New York, Lea & Febiger [1913]
xii, [17]–491 p. illus. 18cm. (The medical epitome series) $1.00

1. Anatomy, Human.
Library of Congress QM28.L65 1913 13-19921

NL 0410847 DLC DNLM

Little, John Forsyth, 1880–
Anatomy and physiology; a text-book for nurses, by John Forsyth Little ... Illustrated with 149 engravings and 4 plates. Philadelphia and New York, Lea & Febiger [1914]
vi, [17]–483 p. illus., IV col. pl. 20½cm. (*On cover:* The nurses text book series) $1.75

1. Anatomy, Human. 2. Physiology.
Library of Congress QM26.L73 14-1473

NL 0410848 DLC OCIW-H DNLM MiU ICJ

Little, John Forsyth, 1880–
Library of health; complete guide to prevention and cure of disease, containing practical information on anatomy, physiology and preventive medicine
see under Scholl, Benjamin Franklin, 1860–

Little, John G., joint ed.
Material handling cyclopedia; a reference book covering definitions, descriptions, illustrations and methods of use of material handling machines employed in industry, comp. and ed. by Roy V. Wright, editor-in-chief ... John G. Little, managing editor ... and Robert C. Augur, associate editor ... New York, N. Y., Simmons-Boardman publishing co. [1921]

Little, John G., *Jr.*
The official history of the Eighty-sixth Division.
— Chicago. States Publications Society. 1921. ix, 319 pp. Illus. Portraits. Plates. Autograph facsimile. 25 cm.
Foreword by Charles H. Martin

M9956 — United States. A. & n. Army. American Expeditionary Forces. European War. 86th Division. — Martin, Charles Henry, pref., 1863–

NL 0410851 MB NN NjP OCIWHi MiU

VOLUME 336

Little, John Goulding, 1880–
Moment reactions; fixed points and moments at supports for continuous girders and frames held in position at supports from, Σ=0, at each support ... Copyright by John Goulding Little ... San Francisco, A. Carlisle & co., °1929.
cover-title, [8] p. diagrs. 27½cm.

1. Moments of inertia. I. Title.
Library of Congress TG267.L5 29-19600

NL 0410852 DLC

Little, John Howard.
K. & M. co. Check system; an analysis of co-operative buying, by J. H. Little ... [Pittsburgh, Printed by the Republic bank note company] °1914.
1 p. l., 5-15 p. 23cm.

1. Cooperation. I. Title. II. Title: Co-operative buying.
Library of Congress HF5432.L5 14-11256

NL 0410853 DLC

Little, John L., ed.
The Thresher world and farmers' magazine.
Chicago,

Little, John Peyton, 1818-1873.
History of Richmond, by John P. Little; reprinted from the Southern literary messenger. Introduction by Rev. A. A. Little, foreword by J. H. Whitty, woodblocks by Norma E. Dietz, index by George F. Scheer. Richmond, Va., The Dietz printing company, 1933.
1 p. l., xxi, 303 p. front. (port.) plates. 21½cm.
"Of this edition 682 copies were printed." This copy not numbered.
Includes reprint of original t.-p.: Richmond: the capital of Virginia: its history. By John P. Little, M. D. Richmond, MacFarlane & Fergusson, 1851.
1. Richmond—Hist. I. Whitty, James Howard, 1859-1937, ed.
33-20971
Library of Congress F234.R5L72
[a45d1] 975.5451

NL 0410855 DLC CU TU NcD NcU NNC OCl MB Vi NN

Little, John P[eyton] 1818-1873
Richmond: the capital of Virginia: its history . . . Richmond [Va.] Macfarlane & Fergusson, 1851.
102 pp. front., pl., port. 4°.
Enlarged from "The Southern literary messenger."
F234.R5L7 1-Rc-2921

NL 0410856 DLC Vi ViU

Little, John Philip Brooke-
see
Brooke-Little, John Philip.

Little, John R ed.
Los Angeles, the wonder city; a pictorial presentation of life in this great and growing metropolis on the West Coast. [Los Angeles, cop. 1931.]
31 cm.
Published by Charles P. Grossman.

NL 0410858 MH

[Little, John Scripps] 1864–
... Abraham Lincoln: rare pamphlets, books, autograph letters, portraits and prints, fine association items from the Hart, Burton and Lambert collections; sale Wednesday and Thursday, June 14-15, at 8 p. m. ... Chicago, Ill., Chicago book & art auctions, inc. [1933]
66 p., 1 l. 23cm.
At head of title: Sale no. 34.
Cover-title: ... Abraham Lincoln: books and pamphlets, medals, portraits and autographs; the collection made by John Scripps Little ... sold by order of John L. Scripps ...
1. Lincoln, Abraham, pres. U. S.—Bibl. I. Title.
33-23486
Library of Congress Z8505.L77
012

NL 0410859 DLC ICN OCl OClWHi

Little, John Sebastian, 1853-1916.
The battle of the masses...Speech...February 5, 1896.
Wash., 1896.

YA5000 (Congressional speeches, by author)
J 17

NL 0410860 DLC

Little, John Sebastian, 1853-1916
Indian appropriation bill...Speech...January 15, 1896.
Wash., 1895.

YA5000 (Congressional speeches, by author)
J 17

NL 0410861 DLC

Little, John Sebastian, 1853-1916
Indian appropriation bill...Speech...February 20, 1896.
Wash., 1896.

YA5000 (Congressional speeches, by author)
J 17

NL 0410862 DLC

Little, John Sebastian, 1853-1916
The insincerity and duplicity of the Republican party exposed. An appeal for Cuban liberty. Speech ... in the House ... January 10, 1898. Washington [Govt. print. off.] 1898.
4 p. 8°.
1-4636

NL 0410863 DLC

Little, John Sebastian, 1853-
Jurisdiction of federal courts in Indian territory - ...Speech...June 1, 1896.
Wash., 1896.

YA5000 (Congressional speeches, by author)
J 17

NL 0410864 DLC

Little, John Sebastian, 1853-
Pay the bonds of the government...Free homes for a free people...Speeches...Jan. 31 and March 10, 1898.
Wash., 1898.

YA5000 (Congressional speeches, by author)
J 17

NL 0410865 DLC

Little, John Sebastian, 1853-
Remarks...upon post office appropriation bill...
Wash., 1896.

YA5000 (Congressional speeches, by author)
J 17

NL 0410866 DLC

Little, John Sebastian, 1853-1916.
The tariff ... Speech of Hon. John S. Little, of Arkansas, in the House of representatives, Wednesday, March 24, 1897. Washington [Gov't print. off.] 1897.
8 p. 24cm.

1. Tariff—U. S.
Library of Congress HF1755.L77 1-4638

NL 0410867 DLC

Little, John Sebastian, 1853-1916.
Trade of Puerto Rico ... Speech of Hon. John S. Little, of Arkansas, in the House of representatives Friday, February 23, 1900. Washington [Govt. print. off.] 1900.
15 p. 25cm.

1. Philippine Islands—Pol. & govt. 2. U. S.—Colonial question. 3. Porto Rico tariff bill of 1900—Speeches in Congress.
Library of Congre DS681.5.U43L5 1-4963 Revised

NL 0410868 DLC

Little, John Sebastian 1853-1916.
War taxes. Shall the poor contribute more freely of their blood than the rich do of their money in defense of the country? Speech of Hon. John S. Little, of Arkansas, in the House of representatives, Thursday, April 28, 1898. Washington [Gov't print. off.] 1898.
8 p. 24cm.

1. War revenue law of 1898.
1-4639
Library of Congress HJ2375.L65

NL 0410869 DLC

BX5939 .L55 Little, John Stockton.
500 questions & answers in religion...
Milwaukee, Wis., London [c1936]
1 v. 8°.

NL 0410870 DLC

Little, John W.
Teaching as Jesus taught; a course in the curriculum of leadership education. [Canada] Leadership Education Committee, Dept. of Christian Education, the Canadian Council of Churches [1952] [c1936].
81 p., D.

NL 0410871 PPLT

VOLUME 336

W 4 LITTLE, Joseph
E23 Tentamen medicum, inaugurale, de variola ... Edinburgi,
1780 Balfour et Smellie, 1780.
L.1 40 p. 19 cm.
Diss. - Edinburgh.

NL 0410872 DNLM

Little, Joseph Edward, 1861?-1934?
QK306 The Ivel district of Bedfordshire. Arbroath
L5 [Eng.] T. Buncle & Co., 1936.
p. [50]-67. 22 cm.

Cover title.
Reprinted from the "Report of the Botanical exchange club" for 1935.
Bibliography p. 64-67.

1. Botany--Bedfordshire, Eng. 2. Ivel river.

NL 0410873 RPB

Little, Joseph James, 1841-1913.
Celebrates fiftieth anniversary
see under title

Little, Joseph James, 1841–1913.
Statement of facts regarding the indictment for criminal libel, found by the grand jury against Nicholas Murray Butler professor of philosophy in Columbia university, and others, upon the complaint of Joseph J. Little, president of the Board of education of the city of New York. [New York, 1899]
24 p. 21½cm.

1. Little, Joseph James, 1841-1913. 2. Butler, Nicholas Murray, 1862–

E 15—1438

U. S. Off. of educ. Library for Library of Congress LA2317.L72 [a41b1]

NL 0410875 DHEW MiU NN

Little, Joseph Kane.
The tinsmiths' pattern manual. Patterns for tinsmiths' work. By Joe K. Little ... Chicago, The American artisan press, 1894.
2 p. l., [vii]-ix, 248 p. incl. plates, diagrs. 20cm. (On cover: American artisan manuals)

1. Tinsmithing. 2. Sheet-metal work—Pattern-making.

Library of Congress TS600.L7 8-30325†

NL 0410876 DLC ICRL

Little, Joseph Kane.
The tinsmiths' pattern manual; patterns for tinsmiths' work. By Joe K. Little, C.E. For tinners, coppersmiths, plumbers, zinc workers, and sheet metal workers generally. [Second edition.] Chicago, American Artisan Press, 1901.
ix, 248 p. diagrs. 20cm. (On cover: American artisan manuals.)

NL 0410877 ICJ MiD OrP

[Little, Josiah]
To the members of the Honourable General Court of the Commonwealth of Massachusetts. [Petition for compensation for the loss of some of his lands.] [Boston, 1823]
31 p. 8°.
n.t.-p.

NL 0410878 NN MH

547.21 Little, Julian Royden, 1908-
L724a The action of sodium cyanide on 1,3-dibromo-1, 3-dibenzoylpropane ... Urbana, Ill. [1938]
86 numb.l. diagrs.
Thesis (Ph.D.)--University of Illinois, 1938.
Typewritten (carbon copy)
Vita.
Bibliography: leaves 84-86.
1938 ——— Thesis copy.
L724

1. Sodium cyanide. 2. Propane.

NL 0410879 IU

Little, Julian Royden, 1908–
The action of sodium cyanide on 1, 3-dibromo-1, 3-dibenzoylpropane, by Julian Royden Little ... Urbana, Ill., 1938.
5 p., 1 l. 23cm.
Abstract of thesis (PH. D.)—University of Illinois, 1938.
Vita.
Bibliography: p. 5.

1. Sodium cyanide. 2. Propane.

39-14896

Library of Congress QD341.N7L5 1938
Univ. of Illinois Libr.

547.1

NL 0410880 IU DLC

Little, Kate.

Talfourd, Froome, 1807–1902.
Memories of Froome Talfourd. Talfourd the artist of the Brownings [by Eliza L. Johnston] The late Froome Talfourd [from Eliza L. Johnston] Family reminiscences of Sutherland Johnston [by Kate Little] [London? Ont., 1942?]

Little, Katharine Day.
François de Fénelon, study of a personality. [1st ed.] New York, Harper [1951]
x, 278 p. port. 22 cm.
Bibliography: p. 261-264.

1. Fénelon, François de Salignac de la Mothe-, Abp., 1651-1715.

PQ1796.L58 928.4 51-2713

NL 0410882 OrSaW DLC MB ICU MoU MH ViU Wa WaS Or OrP

Little, Kenneth Lindsay.
Africans in transition; a study of local leadership in West Africa. By Kenneth Little, Tanya Baker and Alex Carey. [Dinburgh?] 1955.
155 p.

Microfilm: negative, 1 reel.
"Based on fieldwork carried out by the Dept. of social anthropology, University of Edinburgh, on behalf of UNESCO."

1. C15 - Native races.
2. Native races - Gold Coast.
3. C23 - Native races.
4. Native races - Nigeria.
5. C - Leadership.
6. Leadership - Africa.
7. Title.

NL 0410884 DS

Little, Kenneth Lindsay.
The Mende of Sierra Leone; a West African people in transition. London, Routledge & K. Paul [1951]
307 p. illus., maps (1 fold.) 23 cm. (International library of sociology and social reconstruction)
Bibliography: p. 292-294.

1. Mende. (Series: International library of sociology and social reconstruction (London))

DT516.L5 572.9664 52-2296

NL 0410885 MH DLC CaBVaU OrU DSI CSf CU C NN PPEB CU

AW
2 Little, Kenneth Lindsay.
H85 The Mende of Sierra Leone; a West African people in transition. London, Routledge & K. Paul [1951]
FC7 307 p. illus., maps. (International library
2: of sociology and social reconstruction)
Bibliography: p. 292-294.

Microfiche.

NL 0410886 CaBVaU

Little, Kenneth Lindsay.
Negroes in Britain; a study of racial relations in English society. London, K. Paul, Trench, Trubner [194-]
xiii, 292 p. map. 23 cm. (International library of sociology and social reconstruction. London)
The author's thesis, Univ. of London.
Bibliographical footnotes.

NL 0410887 ViHaI PPEB PPT IaU

Little, Kenneth Lindsay.
Negroes in Britain: a study of racial relations in English society. London, K. Paul, Trench, Trubner [1948]
xiii, 292 p. map. 23 cm. (International library of sociology and social reconstruction. London)
The author's thesis, Univ. of London.
Bibliographical footnotes.

1. Negroes in Great Britain. (Series)

A 48-9152*

Harvard Univ. Library for Library of Congress

NL 0410888 OU PU NcU NNUN MH NNC KEmT MB DAU KyWAT IU GU OrU MH OCIW CtY TxU IEN ViU ICU MiD OO MiU

Little, Kenneth Lindsay.
Race and society. Paris, UNESCO [°1952]
56 p. 21 cm. (The race question in modern science)

1. Race problems. I. Title.

HT1521.L5 *301.45 323.1 53—7467 †

NL 0410889 NIC NcD MiD LU ICU MB OrU Or IdU CaBVa CaBViP OrPR DLC IdPI GAU UU MoU NBC MiU OU ViU CtY

Little, Kenneth Lindsay
Race et Société. Paris, UNESCO [1952]
60 p. 21 cm. (La question raciale devant la science moderne)

Title in English: "Race and Society".

1. Race problems. I. Title.

NL 0410890 MB

Little, Kenneth Lindsey
323.108 The relations of white people and
R121 coloured people in Great Britain. Malvern,
no.2 Eng., Le Play House Press, 1946.
8 p. 22 cm. (Racial relations; studies in conflict and co-operation, no.2)

1. Gt. Brit. Race question. I. Title

NL 0410891 NcD MH

Little, Lacy L
"Rivershade," a historical sketch of Kiangyin station, China [by] Lacy L. Little. [Wilmington, N.C.?, 1929?]
viii, 63 p. incl. illus. (incl. group ports., map) 20 cm.

NL 0410892 NcD

VOLUME 336

Little, Mrs. Lacy L
see Little, Ella (Davidson) 1876-1916.

NL 0410893 [not shown]

Little, *Mrs.* Laura Jane (Roys)
A mother's peace offering to American houses; or, The martyr of the nineteenth century. By Mrs. L. J. Little. New-York, J. A. Gray, printer, 1861.
109 p. 23½cm.
Experiences of the writer in Sheffield, Mass., and other places.

1. Slavery in the U. S.—Controversial literature—1861.
11-19500
Library of Congress F74.S5L7

NL 0410894 DLC NjP

Z
5814
C57 L48
Little, Lawrence Calvin, 1897- comp.
A bibliography of doctoral dissertations on religion and public education (Preliminary) ₍n.p., n.d.₎
6l.

1. Church and education in the U.S.--Bibl.

NL 0410895 TxFTC NBuT

BV1463
.P55
1952
Little, Lawrence Calvin, 1897- ed.

Pittsburgh. University. *School of Education. Workshop in Moral and Spiritual Values in Education.*
Toward better education in moral and spiritual values; papers presented at the University of Pittsburgh Workshop in Moral and Spiritual Values in Education, summer, 1952. Edited by Lawrence C. Little, director of the workshop. Pittsburgh, Dept. of Religious Education, University of Pittsburgh, 1953.

Little, Leo Thomas.
Handbook for economics students. London, Jordan, 1955.
181 p. illus. 19 cm.

1. Economics. I. Title.
HB171.7.L5 330.2 56-23520 ‡

NL 0410897 DLC KU

Little, Leon Magaw, ed.
Harvard university. Class of 1910.
Secretary's ... report ... Harvard college class of 1910. 1st- 1911- Cambridge, Mass., Printed for the class ₍1911-

---

Little, Leroy L.
Carolina's vacation land...

Extract from Outing, July, 1917.

NL 0410899 NcU

Little, Leslie H
A bee book for bee-ginners

see under

Tennessee. Dept. of Agriculture.

AE5
E7
1929‡
Little, Leslie T

Report by Leslie T. Little ... on the new 14th edition of the Encyclopaedia britannica. No imprint [1930?]

caption-title[4]p. 23cm.

"Published in the Massachusetts library club bulletin, March 1929".

1. Encyclopaedia britannica.

NL 0410901 NBuG

Little, Levi, 1830-1883.
Three sermons. Erie.,1870.

NL 0410902 Nh

Little, Levi, 1830-1883.
Three sermons. Erie,1871.

NL 0410903 Nh DLC

BV4253
.L725
Little, Levi, 1830-1883.
Three sermons: 1. Human brotherhood; 2. The curse of Meroz; 3. Christian contentment, by a home missionary. Erie, Pa., Willard, Redway & Cook, 1872.
24 p.

Cover title.
1. Sermons, American - 19th cent. I. Title.

NL 0410904 CtHC DLC NjP PHi CSmH

Little, Levi, 1830-1883.
Three sermons: 1. Human brotherhood. 2. The curse of Meroz. 3. Christian contentment. By a home missionary. Revised edition. Ridgway, Pa., L. Little and company, 1874.

cover-title, 24 p. 23 cm. Orig. grey paper covers.

NL 0410905 CSmH DLC Nh

Little, Levi, 1830-1883.
Three sermons: 1. Human brotherhood. 2. The curse of Meroz. 3. Christian contenment. By a home missionary. Rev. ed. Claremont, N.H., 1877.
24 p. 8°.

NL 0410906 MB Nh

Little, Lewis Peyton.
History of Grafton Baptist church, York county, Virginia, constituted in 1777. By L. Peyton Little. [Richmond, Va., The William Byrd press, 1932]
15 p. 23 cm.
"This is the end of part I. The manuscript for parts II and III, which pertain to the second and third Grafton Baptist churches, located in this same community, have been deposited with the Virginia Baptist historical society, at Richmond, Va., by the author." - p. 15.
Reprinted from Minutes of the Peninsula Baptist association, state of Virginia. 29th annual session... June 14-15, 1932. p. [60]-72.

NL 0410907 Vi LU

Little, Lewis Peyton.
History of the First Baptist church of Newport News, Virginia, from 1883 to 1933, by Lewis Peyton Little. Newport News, Va., The Franklin printing company, inc., 1936.
xxi, ₍1₎, 218 p. incl. front., illus., ports., facsims. 23½cm.

1. Newport News, Va. First Baptist church. 2. Baptists—Newport News, Va. I. Title.
37-3274
Library of Congress BX6480.N575F5
Copyright A 103436 286.1755416

NL 0410908 DLC NcD WHi

Little, Lewis Peyton.
Imprisoned preachers and religious liberty in Virginia, a narrative drawn largely from the official records of Virginia counties, unpublished manuscripts, letters, and other original sources, by Lewis Peyton Little, with an introduction by Rev. R. H. Pitt ... Lynchburg, Va., J. P. Bell co., inc., 1938.
xix, ₍1₎, 534 p. incl. front., illus. 23½cm.

1. Baptists—Virginia. 2. Religious liberty—Virginia. 3. Persecution. I. Title.
Library of Congress BX6248.V8L5 39-993
Copyright A 125079 286.1755

NL 0410909 DLC CaBVaU PPEB TxU NcD ViU IObNB NcWsW

LITTLE, Lizzie Mary.
Persephone, and other poems.
Dublin: W. McGee. 1884. 115 pp. Sm. 8°.

NL 0410910 MB FU NBuG

Little, L₍izzie₎ M₍ary₎.
Poems. Dublin: Maunsel & Co., Ltd., 1909. 55 p., 1 port. 16°.

1. Poetry (Irish).
June 14, 1911.

NL 0410911 NN FU

LITTLE, Lizzie Mary.
Wild myrtle. London,J.M.Dent & Co.,1897.

pp.viii,96+.
Poems.
"500 copies."

NL 0410912 MH

W 6
P3
LITTLE, Lora C
The baby and the medical machine. Chicago, American Medical Liberty League ₍1911?₎
₍8₎ p.

NL 0410913 DNLM

---

*RA644
.S6L7
Little, Lora C
Crimes of the cowpox ring; some moving pictures thrown on the dead wall of official silence. Minneapolis, Liberator Pub. Co., 1906.
75 p. illus. 22cm.

NL 0410914 MnHi NN

VOLUME 336

Little, Louis, 1893–
How to watch football; the spectator's guide, by Lou Little ... with the collaboration of Robert Harron. New York, London, Whittlesey house, McGraw-Hill book company, inc. [°1935]
xviii, 315 p. front. (port.) illus., xxxi pl. (incl. ports.) on 18 l. 21cm.
"First edition."

1. Foot-ball. I. Harron, Robert, 1897– II. Title.

Library of Congress GV951.L728 35-27388

Copyright A 87515 [5-5] 796.33

NL 0410915 DLC OrLgE WaS Or WaT MiU NN NcRS NcD OU OCl OClh OLak MB

Little, Louis, 1893–
Lou Little's football, by Lou Little ... and Arthur Sampson ... Leominster, Mass., Printed by Leominster printing co. [°1934]
224 p. front., diagrs. 19½cm.

1. Foot-ball. I. *Sampson, Arthur, joint author.

Library of Congress GV951.L73 34-34906

Copyright A 75745 796.33

NL 0410916 DLC OrCS NIC ViU OCl OU OOxM MB NN

Little, Lowell, 1915–
[Rhythm moods]

Rhythm moods. Cleveland, Ludwig [1951]
condensed score (7 p.) and parts. 31 cm. (Ludwig symphonic band series, no. 37)

1. Suites (Band)—Excerpts—Scores (reduced) and parts. I. Title.

M1203.L 52-26960

NL 0410917 DLC

Little, Lowell, 1915–
[Valse Lynnette]

Valse Lynnette, solo for cornet (tenor sax.), baritone solo or alto saxophone, with band acc. New York, Belwin [1949]
condensed score (8 p.) and parts. 27 cm. (Famous band series, no. 177)
Cover title.

1. Cornet with band—Scores (reduced) and parts.

M1205.L 49-25810*

NL 0410918 DLC

Little, Lucius Powhattan, 1836–
Ben Hardin: his times and contemporaries, with selections from his speeches. By Lucius P. Little. Louisville [Ky.] Courier-journal job printing company, 1887.
xi, 640, xiii-xxii p. front., illus. (incl. ports., facsims.) 24cm.

1. Hardin, Benjamin, 1784-1852.

Library of Congress E340.H26L7 13-12788 Revised

NL 0410919 DLC KyHi MH I NcU CtY ViU MdBP NcD KyLx

Little, Lucius Powhattan, 1836–
Local preachers in old times in Kentucky. Nashville, Tenn., pub., House of the M.E. Church, South. Smith & Lemar, agents, 1905.

NL 0410920 KyHi

Little, Lucius Powhattan, 1836– *ed.*
The Practice act in force June 16, 1902, with notes on its construction and effect, and the practice thereunder, embracing directions to clerks, by Lucius P. Little ... Louisville, J. P. Morton & company, 1902.
24 p. 23cm.

1. Civil procedure—Kentucky. 2. Court rules—Kentucky. I. Kentucky. Laws, statutes, etc.

Library of Congress 2-19284 Revised

NL 0410921 DLC

C252
L779h
Little, Luther.
Humanity's sunrise. A book of sermons by Luther Little, pastor, First Baptist Church, Charlotte, N.C. Charlotte, 1930.
224 p. front. (port.) 20cm.

1. N.C.--Sermons I. Charlotte, N.C. First Baptist Church. II. Title.

NL 0410922 NcU NcC

Little, Luther.
Manse dwellers, by Luther Little; illustrations by Kenneth Whitsett. Charlotte, N. C., Presbyterian standard pub. co., 1927.
314 p. incl. front. plates. 20cm.

I. Title.

Library of Congress PZ3.L7253Ma 27-14797

NL 0410923 DLC FTaSU NcU

Little, Luther B.
For the forty-fifth anniversary of the settlement of Mr. Buxton in Webster. Chicago, 1883.
p. 52-55 O.
(In: Forty-fifth anniversary of the settlement of Rev. Edward Buxton as pastor of the second Congregational church of Boscawen, Dec. 13, 1882. 1883)

NL 0410924 RPB

Little, Luther B.
The Metropolitan Life Insurance Company. A public institution.
— [New York.] Metropolitan Life Insurance Co. 1921. (3), 42 pp. Illus. Portrait. Plates. 23.5 cm.
Reprinted from The Eastern Underwriter of April 8, 1921.
The author's name is signed to the preface.

D6644 — Metropolitan Life Insurance Company, New York.

NL 0410925 MB

Little, M.
At the sign of the burning bush. A novel by M. Little ... New York, H. Holt and company, 1910.
vi p., 1 l., 343, [1] p. 19cm.

Library of Congress PZ3.L7255A 10-20745

NL 0410926 DLC

Little, Malcolm C.
The land laws of Mexico, by Malcolm C. Little. [Los Angeles?] Association of American owners of lands in Mexico [1921]
22 p. 26½cm.

1. Land tenure—Mexico—Law. I. Title.

HD322.L5 22-4276

NL 0410927 DLC MH-L TxU DCU-IA CU NN

Little, Malcolm Edgeworth, 1893–
A laboratory manual for comparative anatomy, by Malcolm E. Little ... and Rudolf T. Kempton ... New York, The Macmillan company, 1928.
xix p., 1 l., 286 p. 19 pl. 22½cm.

1. Anatomy, Comparative—Laboratory manuals. I. Kempton, Rudolf Theodore, 1902– joint author.

Library of Congress QL812.L5 28—27751

NL 0410928 DLC OU ODW OClW

Little, Malcolm Edgeworth, 1893–
A laboratory manual for comparative anatomy. New York, Macmillan, 1929.
xix, 286 p. 19 pl. 23 cm.
I. Kempton, R.T.

NL 0410929 TU CU LU

Little, Malcolm Edgeworth, 1893–
A laboratory manual for comparative anatomy by ... and Rudolf T. Kempton ... New York, The Macmillan company, 1932.
xix p., 1 l., 286 p. 19 pl.

NL 0410930 OO

Little, Malcolm Edgeworth, 1893–
Structure of the vertebrates [by] Malcolm E. Little ... New York, R. Long & R. R. Smith, inc., 1932.
xiv, 392 p. illus. 22cm.
"Books for reference": p. 355-356.

1. Vertebrates—Anatomy. I. Title.

Library of Congress QL605.L5 32—16324
[a41k1] 596

NL 0410931 DLC OrCS MtBC CU NIC OO OCU OClJC ViU

QL
605
.L5
1934
Little, Malcolm Edgeworth, 1893–
Structure of the vertebrates [by] Malcolm E. Little ... New York, Farrar & Rinehart, Inc., [1934, c1932]
392 p. illus.

"Books for reference": p. 355-356.

NL 0410932 MoU CU NcRS OClUr MiU TxU

Little, Malcolm Edgeworth, 1893–
Structure of the vertebrates, by Malcolm E. Little ... Rev. ed. New York, Farrar & Rinehart, inc. [°1937]
x, 488 p. illus., diagr. 21½ cm.

1. Vertebrates—Anatomy. I. Title.

QL605.L5 1937 596 37—10313

NL 0410933 DLC OrP WaSpG FMU OCU ViU ODW OO NcD NN CU TU

VOLUME 336

CR4827 .H58 1949 Little, Mamie Burkhalter, 1870- The ladies of the Garter.

Hodgkins, Marie Wilkinson.
The most noble order, Knights of the Garter; alphabetical list, 1348-1725, compiled by Mrs. Howard L. Hodgkins, 1939, from the chronological list in "The knights of England" by William A. Shaw. The ladies of the Garter; chronological list, compiled by Mrs. John F. Little, 1949, from "The complete peerage," and "Order of the Garter" by Beltz. [Washington] National Society, Daughters of the Barons of Runnemede, °1949.

Little, Margaret.
A comparative study of the style of Goethe's Wilhelm Meisters theatralische sendung and Wilhelm Meisters lehrjahre. 1913.

NL 0410935 CU

Little, Marguerite, 1922-
Some Italian elements in the choral practice of Samson Agonistes, by Marguerite Little ... Urbana, Ill., 1946.
8 p. 23cm.
Abstract of thesis (PH. D.)—University of Illinois, 1946.
Vita.

1. Milton, John. Samson Agonistes. 2. Literature, Comparative—English and Italian. 3. Literature, Comparative—Italian and English.
A 46-5636
Illinois. Univ. Library for Library of Congress PR3566.L5

NL 0410936 IU DLC CtY NNC ICU NN NIC

Little, Marguerite F., ed.

The Biology student. v. 1, v. 2, no. 1-4; Sept. 15, 1930-Nov. 15, 1931. [Baltimore, Science publishers, incorporated, 1930-31]

Little, Marguerite F.
Development of language and vocabulary in young children
see under Williams, Harold Marshall, 1899-

Little, Marion.
Essays on Robert Browning, by Marion Little. London, S. Sonnenschein & co., lim., 1899.
2 p. l., 204 p. 19½cm.
CONTENTS.—Browning's public.—Paracelsus.—Caponsacchi.—Two poems on painters and their art.—Andrea del Sarto.—Christmas eve.

1. Browning, Robert, 1812-1889.
1-13227 Revised
Library of Congress PR4238.L6

NL 0410939 DLC TNJ OCU CtY MiU OCl OO NN PSt OU

Little, Marion L.
Fitting handwriting to children, a textbook for Teachers college students, by Marion L. Little ... Glassboro, New Jersey state teachers college, 1940.
4 p. l., 38 numb. l., 1 l., 39-51 numb. l. illus. 27½ x 21½cm.
Reproduced from type-written copy.
Bibliography: leaves 49-51.

1. Penmanship. I. New Jersey. State teachers college, Glassboro. II. Title.
41-46272
Library of Congress LB1590.L5
372.51

NL 0410940 DLC OCU OO

Little, Marion L
Reading-speech relationships of stutterers and non-stutters at different comprehension levels. [Philadelphia, 1950]
v. 98 l. tables. 29 cm. ([Pennsylvania. University. School of education. Studies in education, no. 33)
Typewritten.
Thesis (Ed.D.) - University of Pennsylvania 1950.
Includes bibliographies.

NL 0410941 PU

Film LB 23 LITTLE,MARTIN EBERT,1907-
The identification of propaganda in motion pictures. [Chicago,Library Dept. of Photographic Reproduction Univ. of Chicago] 1953.

Positive film reproduction.
Original in Univ. of Chicago.
Collation of original as determined from film: 5+103 p. tables, forms.
Thesis (Ph.D.)--Univ. of Chicago.

1. Moving-pictures in propaganda. I. Title.

NL 0410942 InU ICU

Little, Martin Ebert, 1907-
... A study of the eighth grade diploma situation in Kansas, by Martin Ebert Little ... Emporia, Kansas. Published by the college. Topeka, Printed by Kansas state printing plant, W. C. Austin, state printer, 1937.
37 p. incl. tables, forms. 23cm. (Kansas. State teachers' college, Emporia. Bulletin of information. [v. 17, no. 6])
At head of title: Kansas State teachers college of Emporia. Bulletin of information. Studies in education number. (Thirteenth of the series)
Bibliography: p. 25.
1. Grading and marking (Students) 2. Education—Kansas. 3. Education of children. I. Kansas. State teachers' college, Emporia. Studies in education, no. 13. II. Title.
37-28206
Library of Congress LB1873.E7 a vol. 17, no. 6
371.27

NL 0410943 DLC WaTC ViU OCU ODW

Little, Mary Beth
see **Little, Marybeth,** 1927-

HQ1061 L5 Little, Mary Hollis, ed.
Good living after fifty; essays on making the most of maturity, ed. by Mary Hollis Little and Margery Mack. Chicago, Industrial Relations Center, Univ. of Chicago, °1952.
96 l. 27½cm.

1. Old age. 2. Middle age. I. Mack, Margery, jt. ed. II. Chicago. University. Industrial Relations Center. III. Title.

NL 0410945 OrCS DCU CaBViP Wa

A782 L72d Little, Mary Lou, comp.
Draft of a catalogue of source materials for the history of opera and music in the theater in the Library of the University of Illinois. [Urbana, Ill., 1955.
42l. 28cm.

NL 0410946 IU MoSW

Little, Mary Wallace (Bundy) 1857-
The Rubaiyat of a huffy husband [by] Mary B. Little. Boston, R. G. Badger, 1908.
31 l. 20cm.
Printed on one side of leaf only.

8-18063

NL 0410947 DLC CU-S OCl MiU NN

Little, Mary Wilson.
A paragrapher's reveries ... by Mary Wilson Little. New York, Broadway publishing company [1904]
3 p. l., 114 p. 20cm.

4-36691

NL 0410948 DLC PSt

Little, Mary Wilson.
A paragrapher's reveries...by Mary Wilson Little. Philadelphia: D. McKay [cop. 1904]. 114 p. 12°.

65895A. 1. Wit and humor (American). 2. Aphorisms (American). 3. Title.
December 13, 1922.

NL 0410949 NN OO MiU

Little, Mary Wilson.
Retrospection [by] Mary Wilson Little; cover drawing by Edith Tadd-Little. New York, Broadway publishing company [°1909]
2 p. l., 88 p. 19½cm.

9-12200
Library of Congress PZ3.L726R

NL 0410950 DLC NN

Little, Marybeth, 1927-
Silk from a spool; illus. by Judith Jordan. Dallas, Tex., Kaleidograph Press [1944]
95 p. illus. 20 cm.
Poems.

I. Title.
PS3523.I 836S5 811.5 45-344 rev*

NL 0410951 DLC

Little, Marybeth, 1927-
Underside of leaves. [Poems] Dallas, Kaleidograph Press [1948]
76 p. 20 cm.

I. Title.
PS3523.I 836U5 811.5 48-3217*

NL 0410952 DLC NcU ViU TxU

Little, Maryella (Robinson)
The house of Charles Knox. n.p.[19-]

NL 0410953 MH

Little, *Mrs.* Maryella (Robinson)
Stephen Little of New York, his background and family; also short sketches of the MacMahon, Elliotte, Knox and Little lines of north Ireland, by Maryella R. Little. [n. p., 1932?]
85 p. 17½cm.
"One hundred copies privately printed. No. 34."

1. Little family. 2. Little family (Stephen Little, 1832-1917)
A 33-352
Michigan. Univ. Library for Library of Congress CS71.L77 1932
CS71.L777 1932 a

NL 0410954 MiU DLC OCl WHi ViU NN MH

VOLUME 336

Little, *Mrs.* Maud Greenwood (Burdick) 1867–
Literary leaves; a collection of programs for the Social and literary department of the Epworth league, from the writings of Mrs. Maud B. Little, as they have appeared from time to time in The Epworth era. Nashville, Tenn., Dallas, Tex., Publishing house of the M. E. church, South, Smith & Lamar, agents, 1911.
124 p. 17½cm. $0.25

I. Epworth league. Social and literary department. II. Title.

Library of Congress PN71.U5L5 13-1367

NL 0410955 DLC FMU

Little, *Mrs.* Maud Greenwood (Burdick) 1867–
Literary programs and diversions, from the writings of Mrs. Maud B. Little ... Nashville, Tenn., Cokesbury press, 1926.
199 p. 19½cm.

I. Title.

Library of Congress BV1620.L5 26—9389

NL 0410956 DLC NcD

PZ 3 .L685Ro Little, Maude
The rose-coloured room. New York, C. Scribner's, 1915.
viii,309p. 20cm.

NL 0410957 TNJ NN

Little, Maude Clay.
Effect of the depression on the condition, attitudes, and behaviour of young people in the United States. ⌈n. p.⌉ 1940.
245 l. 28cm.
Typewritten.
Thesis—Univ. of Virginia, 1940.
Bibliography: leaves 242-245.

1. Social psychology. 2. Panics—1929. 3. Attitude (Psychology) 4. Youth—U. S. I. Title.

NL 0410958 ViU

Little, Maximillien Paul Emile.
Dictionnaire de la langue francaise abrege ...
see under Beaujean, Amedee, 1821-1888.

Little, May.
The complete cake book. London: T. W. Laurie ⌈1912⌉. 3 p.l., xiii-xv p., 1 l., 3-161(1) p. 12°.

1. Cookery.—Cake. October 7, 1912.

NL 0410960 NN ICJ

Little, May.
The complete cake book, by May Little... London: T. W. Laurie, Ltd.⌈, 1929.⌉ xi, 161 p. 12°.

453433A. 1. Cookery—Cake. January 17, 1930

NL 0410961 NN

641.5 L778c Little, May.
Cookery up-to-date; a practical handbook of what to eat, and how to cook it. New and rev. ed. Liverpool, Bunney's ⌈n.d.⌉
247 p.

COOKERY
Cookery up-to-date.

NL 0410962 KMK

Little, May.
Cookery up-to-date. A practical handbook of what to eat, and how to cook it by May Little, ... London, T. W. Laurie, [1908].
v, 247 p. 19cm.

NL 0410963 ICJ NN

Little, May.
Everywoman's cook book; or, Economical cookery, by May Little... London: Jarrold & Sons ⌈1915?⌉. 78 p. 12°.

1. Cookery (English). 2. Title. November 26, 1915.

NL 0410964 NN

Little, May.
How to make and bake bread at home, by May Little... Jarrold & Sons ⌈1916⌉. 34 p. 12°. (War economy booklets.)

1. Bread making. 2. Series. March 29, 1917.

NL 0410965 NN

Little, May, joint author.

TX717 .G86 Rare bk. coll. **Groome, Dora**
More up-to-date and economical cookery, by Dora Groome and May Little. London, Jarrold ⌈1912⌉

Little, May.
Simple electric cookery. London: Jarrold & Sons ⌈1913⌉. 132 p., 11 pl. 12°.

1. Cookery by electricity. October 21, 1913.

NL 0410967 NN ICJ

Little, May, ed.
Up-to-date and economical cookery
see under Groome, Dora.

Little, May
A year's dinners. London, Harrods Ltd., ⌈n.d.⌉
3, 436 p. 22 cm.
Bitting collection.

NL 0410969 DLC

Little, May.
A year's dinners, 365 seasonable dinners, with instructions for cooking. A handy guide-book for worried housekeepers, by May Little ... London, T. W. Laurie ⌈1910⌉
4 p. l., 435, ⌈1⌉ p. 22cm.

1. Dinners and dining. 2. Menus. 3. Cookery, English.

11-19203

Library of Congress TX737.L6

NL 0410970 DLC ICJ NN

Little, Minnie R
Even as you and I. ⌈Spokane? Wash., 1953?⌉
cover-title, 94 p. 23 cm.
Prose and poetry.
Author's autographed copy.

NL 0410971 RPB Wa WaSp

Little, N., *Jr.*
Map of mining lands at Newbury, near Newburyport, Essex County, Massachusetts.
Boston. The Hatch Lith. Co. 1875. Size, 17⅞ × 22½ inches. Scale, 125 rods to 1 inch. Folded.
Inserted is a brief description of the attempts at mining, copied from the History of Newbury, Mass., 1902.

D4631 — Newbury, Mass. Mines. — Newbury, Mass. Descr. Maps.

NL 0410972 MB MiU

Little, N. V., of St. Johns, supposed author.
Imposition exposed, or Clerical rights examined.
see under title

Little, N. V., of St. Johns, supposed author.
Sacred and indefeasible rights of the Clergy examined, recognized and vindicated
see under title

Little, Nayan.
Our holy and our beautiful house
see under Austen, George, 1839-

Little, Neil, joint author.

Robbins, Charles Kendall, 1888–
Calculus, by Charles K. Robbins & Neil Little ... New York, The Macmillan company, 1940.

Little, Neil.

International labor office.
... The labour situation in Great Britain; a survey: May-October 1940. Montreal, 1941.

VOLUME 336

Little, Nellie Ursula.
Handbook for English, by N. Ursula Little ... James H. Elson ... Stuart Edgerly ... [and] John M. Baker ... New York, Chicago [etc.] C. Scribner's sons [c1933]
viii, 243 p. illus. 17cm.
Text on front lining-paper.
Includes bibliographies.
1. English language — Rhetoric. 2. English language — Grammar — 1870- I. Elson, James Hinsdale, joint author. II. Edgerly, Stuart, joint author. III. Baker, John Milton, joint author. IV. Title.
33-13634
Library of Congress PE1408.L58
Copyright A 61892 808

NL 0410978 DLC OClW ViU NcD NjR

Little, Nina Fletcher, 1903-
American decorative wall painting, 1700-1850. Sturbridge, Mass., Old Sturbridge Village, in cooperation with Studio Publications, New York City, 1952.
xvi, 145 p. illus. (part col.) 29 cm.
Bibliography: p. 138-140.
1. Mural painting and decoration. 2. Decoration and ornament—U. S. I. Title.
ND2606.L58 751.73 52-10836

NL 0410979 DLC NcGU OClMA OOxM NN PU ViU NIC NN MB WaSp TxU KyLx OrU PSt MoU Wa OrP WaS CaBVa CU

ND 207 L77 Little, Nina Fletcher, 1903-
Itinerant painting in America, 1750-1850. [Albany] New York State Historical Association, 1944.
[17] p. illus., ports. 23 cm.
Cover title.
Reprinted from New York History, April 1949.
1. Painting - U.S. - History. I. New York History. II. Title.

NL 0410980 DSI

ND 207 L77i Little, Nina Fletcher, 1903-
Itinerant painting in America, 1750-1850. [Cooperstown, N.Y.? 1949?]
[16]p. illus., ports. 23cm.
Cover title.
"A Farmers' Museum publication reprinted from New York history, April 1949."
1. Painting - U.S. 2. Mural painting and decoration. 3. Decoration and ornament - U.S. I. Title.

NL 0410981 NRU N

Little, Nina Fletcher, 1903-
Some old Brookline houses built in this Massachusetts town before 1825 and still standing in 1948; a compilation of existing data, to which has been added architectural and biographical notes, constructional details, photographs and floor plans. [Brookline] Brookline Historical Society, 1949.
160 p. illus., map. 24 cm.
Includes "References."
1. Brookline, Mass.—Historic houses, etc. I. Title.
F74.B9L58 974.47 49-4449*

NL 0410982 DLC CU MB OCl

W 01 .C 358 LITTLE, NINA FLETCHER, 1903-
Winthrop Chandler. [Springfield, Mass., 1947]
cover-title, [73]-168p. illus., plates, ports., fold.geneal.table. 28cm. (Art in America. v.35, no.2)
Bibliography: p.166-168.

NL 0410983 ICN MiDA OrU

Little, Noel Charlton, 1895-
College physics, by Noel Charlton Little ... New York, Chicago [etc.] C. Scribner's sons [c1928]
xiv p., 2 l., 3-408 p. incl. front., illus., diagrs. 23cm.
1. Physics. I. Title.
Library of Congress QC21.L5 28-22691

NL 0410984 DLC CU NN NcD OCX OU OO

Little, Noel Charlton, 1895-
Laboratory manual for college physics. n.p.
54p. tables, diagrs. 22.5cm.

NL 0410985 MeWC

Little, Noel Charlton, 1895-
Physics. Boston, Heath [1953]
648 p. illus. 24 cm.
1. Physics.
QC23.L74 530 53-10396 †

NL 0410986 DLC NcU PHC PJB OU OClW PSt ViU NcD MB WaS WaSpG KMK NBuU NSyU MH TNJ FTaSU

LITTLE, Noel C[harlton], 1895-
Regenerative phenomena in vacuum tubes. Thesis, Harvard University, 1923.
1/8°. ff. (2), 90, Plate and charts. Typewritten.

NL 0410987 MH

Little, Otis.
The rambling letters of an elderly husband, being the humorous philosophies of Otis Little. Boston, Mass. [c1919]
[13] p. front. 18cm.
I. Title.
Library of Congress HQ1233.L6 19-12935

NL 0410988 DLC

Little, Otis, 1712-1754.
Works by this author printed in America before 1801 are available in this library in the Readex Microprint edition of Early American Imprints published by the American Antiquarian Society.
This collection is arranged according to the numbers in Charles Evans' American Bibliography.

NL 0410989 DLC

[Little, Otis] 1712-1754.
The state of trade in the northern colonies considered; with an account of their produce, and a particular description of Nova Scotia ... London, Printed by G. Woodfall, 1748.
viii, [9]-84 p. 19cm.
Preface signed: Otis Little.
1. Canada—Comm. 2. New England—Comm. 3. Nova Scotia—Descr. & trav. I. Title.
Library of Congress HF3229.N9L7 6-26979

NL 0410990 DLC MWA MH CaOTU RPJCB MnU MH-BA NNC ICJ MiD-B CaNSWA MiU-C NN PBL

[Little, Otis] 1712-1754.
The state of trade in the northern colonies considered; with an account of their produce, and a particular description of Nova Scotia ... London Printed 1748. Boston, Re-printed and sold by Thomas Fleet, at the Heart and crown in Cornhill. 1749.
vi, [7]-43 p. 19½cm.
[Hazard pamphlets, v. 24, no. 2]
Preface signed: Otis Little.
1. Canada—Comm. 2. New England—Comm. 3. Nova Scotia—Descr. & trav. I. Title.
Library of Congress AC901.H3 vol. 24 6-26981

NL 0410991 DLC CtHT-W N MH ViU ICN CtY MB MBAt MHi NN RPJCB

[Little, Otis] 1712-1754.
The state of trade in the northern colonies considered; with an account of their produce, and a particular description of Nova Scotia ... London, Printed, 1748. Boston, Re-printed, and sold by Thomas Fleet, at the Heart and crown in Cornhill. 1749. [Boston, 1937]
facsim.: vi, [7]-43 p. 24½cm. [Photostat Americana. Second series ... Photostated at the Massachusetts historical society. no. 32]
Signatures: [A]-E[4], F[2].
Head-pieces.
Size of original: 20½cm.
Preface signed: Otis Little.
One of 15 copies from the original in the Massachusetts historical society, April, 1937.
1. Canada—Comm. 2. New England — Comm. 3. Nova Scotia—Descr. & trav. I. Title.
Library of Congress HF3229.N9L7 1749 a 39-5762
382.0971

NL 0410992 DLC NcD ViW MiU-C ViU

Little, Otway Henry.

Egypt. *al-Misāḥah al-Jiyūlūjīyah al-Miṣrīyah.*
The deep bores in Kharga and Dakhla oases and their effect on the future of the oases, by O. H. Little, director, Geological Survey, and M. I. Attia, assistant director, Geological Survey. Cairo, 1942.

Little, Otway Henry.
The development of Aswân district, with notes on the minerals of south-eastern Egypt, by O. H. Little ... director, Geological survey, and M. I. Attia ... Giza (Orman) Survey of Egypt, 1943.
cover-title, vi, 107 p. incl. tables. maps (part fold.) diagr. 32½ cm.
Report submitted by Committee for the improvement of Aswân town. cf. p. vi.
Reproduced from type-written copy.
"References": p. 97-99.
1. Geology—Egypt. 2. Mines and mineral resources—Egypt. 3. Aswân. I. Attia, Mahmoud Ibrahim, joint author. II. Egypt. Committee for the improvement of Aswân town. III. Egypt. al-Masāḥah al-Jiyūlūjīyah al-Miṣrīyah. IV. Egypt. Maslahat al-Masāhah.
QE328.L5 553 45—12540

NL 0410994 DLC ICU TxU

Little, Otway Henry.
... The geography and geology of Makalla (South Arabia) by O. H. Little ... With two appendices: I. Description of fossils from South Arabia and British Somaliland, by Professor G. Stefanini ... II. Note on some terrestrial *Mollusca* from the hinterland of Makalla, by P. Pallary ... Cairo, Government press, 1925.
xi, 250, [1] p. front., xxxv pl. (incl. 3 fold. maps) tables. 28cm.
At head of title: Ministry of finance. Egypt. Survey of Egypt. Geological survey.

Continued in next column

VOLUME 336

Continued from preceding column

Bibliographies throughout.

1. Geology — Arabia — Makallah region. 2. Physical geography — Arabia—Makallah region. 3. Paleontology—Arabia. 4. Paleontology—Somaliland, British. 5. Mollusks, Fossil. I. Stefanini, Giuseppe, 1882-1938. II. *Pallary, Paul, 1869- III. Egypt. Geological survey. IV. Title. V. Title: Fossils from South Arabia. VI. Title: Terrestrial *Mollusca* from the hinterland.

U. S. Geol. survey. Library (720) qL72g G S 25-235
for Library of Congress [r.38d1]

NL 0410996 DI-GS CU TxU IU LU OCl

Geology
D556.05
L72
Little, Otway Henry
Handbook of Cyrenaica. [Printed by the Printing and stationery services, M. E. F., 1945?-

Bibliography: v. 1., p. 84-91.
Contents.--pt. 1. Geology of Cyrenaica.

NL 0410997 NNC

Little, Otway Henry.

Egypt. *al-Misāḥah al-Jiyūlūjīyah al-Miṣrīyah.*
Preliminary report on the water supply of Kharga & Dakhla oases, by O. H. Little, director, Geological Survey. Giza (Mudiriya) Survey of Egypt, 1932.

Little, Otway Henry.

Egypt. *al-Misāḥah al-Jiyūlūjīyah al-Miṣrīyah.*
A report on some studies of underground water flow and subsoil pollution carried out in the State of Alabama, U. S. A., with special reference to the application of the results to conditions in Egypt, by O. H. Little, director Geological Survey and M. I. Attia, assistant director. Cairo, 1942.

Little, P F.

Fragmentary sketches and incidents, in Little Compton & Tiverton, during the revolution, and the war of 1812. By P. F. Little, esq. Never before published. Little Compton, R. I., 1880.

1 p. l., 32 p. 18½cm.

Subject entries: 1. Little Compton, R. I.—Hist. 2. Tiverton, R. I.—Hist.
3-30955

Library of Congress, no. F89.L8L7.

NL 0411000 DLC

0530
.L6
Little, P F
A sailors narrative of twenty four voyages; or, The adventures of Joseph J. Grinnell of Little Compton, R.I., giving an account of his ship-wrecks, sufferings and imprisonments in foreign ports. Little Compton, R.I., P.F.Little, 1856.

24p. 21cm.
Part 1 of a projected series of 4 parts.

1.Seafaring life. 2.Grinnell,Joseph J., 1770-
I.Title.

NL 0411001 CtNlCG NN

Little, P F

The Yankee privateer, Antelope of the Narragansett. A thrilling story of the last war on the land and sea... Little Compton, R. I., 1870.
4p.l.,[3]-92p. 18cm.

NL 0411002 RPB RNHi

Little, Patrick John.
Rome rule; a paper read at a meeting of the Young Ireland Branch U.I.L., November, 1911. Dublin, M.H. Gill, 1912.
20 p. 18 cm.

1. Catholic Church in Ireland. I. Title.

NL 0411003 MB

Little, Paul, *comp.*
The Pacific northwest pulpit, compiled by Paul Little, foreword by Charles Macaulay Stuart ... New York, Cincinnati, The Methodist book concern [°1915]
278 p. 19½cm.

1. Methodist church—Sermons. 2. Sermons, American. I. Title.
15-18643

Library of Congress BX8333.A1L5

InU NN OO NcD
NL 0411004 DLC WaWW WaTC OrP WaS Wa CaBViPA WaU

Little, Paul, 1917–
Federal income taxation of partnerships. Boston, Little, Brown, 1952.
xxv, 469 p. 25 cm.
Kept up to date by cumulative pocket supplements.
Bibliography: p. [419]-427.

—— —— Supplement. 1957–
Boston, Little, Brown.
v. 25 cm.

1. Partnership—U. S.—Taxation. I. Title.

*336.274 336.243 52-6209 rev

NL 0411005 DLC WaS OrU-L WaU-L NBuU OU PV TU OCIW

Little, Pauline DuBose, 1876-1897.
In memoriam. Pauline DuBose Little
see under title

Little, Pearl
see Little, Alla Pearl.

---

*A
1823-27
.D63
no.47
Little, Peter.

Ratio of representation under fifth census. Documents. February 17, 1827. Printed by order of the House of Representatives. Washington: Printed by Gales & Seaton, 1827.
7 p. fold. tab. 22cm. ([U.S.], 19th Cong., 2d sess., 1826-1827. House. Doc. no. 104)
Documents relating to the Judiciary, no. 47.
1. Proportional representation. I. Title.
II. Ser.

NL 0411008 ViU

Little, Peter Christopher.
Cholera: some remarks upon its nature and pathology, with a report of twenty cases out of a large number successfully treated under a certain system during the late epidemic. By P. C. Little ... London, J. Churchill & sons; [etc., etc.] 1867.
4 p. l., [5]-37 p. 21½cm.
"Read and discussed at the thirty-fifth annual meeting of the British medical association, held in the University of Dublin, 9th August, 1867."

1. Cholera, Asiatic.
35-36251

Library of Congress RC126.L6

NL 0411009 DLC DNLM

Little, Phebe A
[Flour City march, piano]

Flour City march; for the piano. Rochester, J. P. Shaw °1870.
6 p. 36 cm.

1. Marches (Piano) I. Title.

M28.L 52-58792

NL 0411010 DLC

Little, Philip, 1857- illus.

Harte, Bret, 1839-1902.
The heathen Chinee; plain language from truthful James, by Bret Harte; with an introduction by Ina Coolbrith and a bibliography by Robert Ernest Cowan; illustrated by Phil Little. San Francisco, Imprinted by J. H. Nash for the Book club of California, 1934.

Little, Philip, 1857-
Special exhibition of paintings...
see under Cincinnati. Art Museum.

821.9
L778t
Little, Philip Francis.
Thermopylae, and other poems. London, J. Long [1915]
227p. 21cm.

NL 0411013 IEN FU

Little, R
Deism examined by reason and morality, and proved inconsistent with either. Addressed to all who have any concern about Religion. No doubt, but ye are the people, and Wisdom shall die with you. Job xii. 2. By R. Little. Brooklyn, Printed and published by Pray and Bowen, 1814.
24 p. 10.5 x 17.5 cm.

NL 0411014 MWA

Little, R E
Oration ... Tallahassee, 1845.
[12] p.

NL 0411015 DSC NNFM

274
S603
Little, R. Emily.
Tactics for Nezah march.
[Indianapolis, c1907]
1 pam. 16°

NL 0411016 DLC

VOLUME 336

LITTLE, R. Craig.
Leonidas and others. Paisley, A. Gardner, Ltd., 1920-31.

6 pts.in 5.
Pts.ii-iii are in one volume.
Pt.v.Conclusion should be entitled "Hope".- Note on p.5 of Pt.vi.

NL 0411017 MH

Little, R H
Pioneering in the Everglades, by R. H. Little. Copy prepared by Historical Records Survey, Works Progress Administration, State Office, Jacksonville, Florida. [Jacksonville] 1938.
169 l. 29 cm.
Typescript.

1. Frontier and pioneer life—Everglades, Fla. I. U. S. Work Projects Administration. Florida. II. Title.

F317.E9L5 65-58697

NL 0411018 DLC

Tzz 973.772 L727y
Little, R H
A year of starvation amid plenty; or, How a Confederate soldier suffered from hunger and cruelty in a prison of war during the awful days of the sixties. Belton, Tex. [n.d.]
40p. 15cm.

1. U.S. - Hist. - Civil War - Prisoners and prisons. I. Title.

NL 0411019 TxU

Little, R J
Statistical view of the progress of Western Australia

see under

Western Australia. Registry Dept.

Little, Ralph Bulkley, *ed.*
Bovine mastitis; a symposium, edited by Ralph B. Little ... [and] Wayne N. Plastridge ... 1st ed. New York and London, McGraw-Hill book company, inc., 1946.
xiii, 546 p. illus. (incl. diagrs.) 23½ cm. (*Half-title: McGraw-Hill publications in the agricultural sciences; Leon J. Cole, consulting editor*)
"References" at end of each chapter except the sixteenth.
1. Udder—Diseases. [1. Mastitis] I. Plastridge, Wayne Norman, 1908- joint ed. II. [Title]
SF967.M3L5 636.2089819 Agr 47-132

U. S. Dept. of agr. Library for Library of Congress 41L722 [8]†

NL 0411021 DNAL CU MU TxU NcRS TU ICU DLC

Little, Ralph Bulkley, joint author.

R108 .R65 no. 19
Smith, Theobald, 1859-1934.
... Studies in vaccinal immunity towards disease of the bovine placenta due to *Bacillus abortus* (infectious abortion) by Theobald Smith, M. D., and Ralph B. Little, V. M. D. New York, The Rockefeller institute for medical research, 1923.

Little, Randel Quincy, 1927-
Reactions of hindered α,β-substituted succinic acid derivatives. Ann Arbor, University Microfilms [1955]
([University Microfilms, Ann Arbor, Mich.] Publication no. 11,312)
Microfilm copy of typescript. Positive.
Collation of the original: ix, 118 l. illus.
Thesis—University of Michigan.
Abstracted in Dissertation abstracts, v. 15 (1955) no. 4, p. 500.
Bibliography: leaves 114-118.

1. Succinic acid. 2. Chemical reactions.
Microfilm AC-1 no. 11,312 Mic A 55-633

Michigan. Univ. Libr. for Library of Congress [1]†

NL 0411023 MiU DLC

Little, Raymond, 1900-
Oil and gas burning under boilers, by Raymond Little ... Flavius B. Jones ... and I. C. S. staff ... Scranton, Pa., International textbook company [1933]
v, 49, 79, 70 p. illus., diagrs. 19½ cm. ([International textbook company. Bluebooks] 231B) $1.90
CONTENTS.—Elements of oil burning, Oil burning under stationary boilers, by I. C. S. staff.—Gas-burning under boilers, by R. Little and F. B. Jones.
1. Petroleum as fuel. 2. Gas as fuel. 3. Steam-boilers. I. Jones, Flavius B., 1902- II. International correspondence schools, Scranton, Pa. III. Title.
33-27428
Library of Congress TJ326.L5
[5] 621.18223

NL 0411024 DLC NN WaS Or MB

Little, Raymond Demorest, 1880-
Tennis tactics, by Raymond D. Little ... New York, Outing publishing company, 1913.
150 p. front., ports. 18½ cm. (Outing handbooks, no. 45) $0.70

1. Tennis.
Library of Congress GV995.L5 13-21862

NL 0411025 DLC OrCS OCl OClh OOxM OO OU MB NN

Little, Raymond Demorest, 1880-
Tennis tactics, by Raymond D. Little ... New York, The Macmillan company, 1919.
150 p. front., ports. 18 cm. [Outing handbooks]

1. Tennis.
A 23-2173
Chicago. Public library for Library of Congress [GV995.L]

NL 0411026 ICU IU

Little, Rhoda, 1879-
The wind in the pines. Dallas, Story Book Press [1954]
60 p. 20 cm.
Poems.

I. Title.
PS3523.I 837W5 811.5 54-37760 ‡

NL 0411027 DLC

Wing ZP 983 .H 7
[LITTLE, RICHARD HENRY] d. 1946.
The advertising conference, by the Goswogii [pseud.] [Chicago, 1927]
[24]p.(on double leaves) illus.(part col.) 16x15cm.
"Printed by the Holiday Press for the amusement of its friends."
"From 'A line o' type or two'. Used by permission of R.H.L. of 'The Chicago Tribune'. One hundred and seventy-five copies."
Illustrated by Ervine Metzl.
Bookplate of William A.Kittredge.

NL 0411028 ICN NcU NN

---

956 L7786 bet 1928
Little, Richard Henry, d.1946.
Better angels, by Richard Henry Little (R. H. L.) with an introduction by Carl Sandburg. New York, Minton, Balch & company, 1928.
43 p. incl. front. (port.) 18½ cm.
"A Lincoln story ... told through the words of an old negro woman."—Introd.

CoU WaS OrU WaT WaWW
NL 0411029 CU NcD MB OClh OCX OCl NN FU TxU NjP

Little, Richard Henry, d. 1946, ed.
The linebook
see under Chicago tribune.

Little, Rita.
... The postal service, by Rita Little. Developed in grade I, Young school, East Aurora, Ill. Principal, Alice Holden. Superintendent, K. D. Waldo. New York city, Bureau of publications, Teachers college, Columbia university [1932]
1 p. l., 21 p. 23 cm. ([Columbia university. Teachers college] Teachers' lesson unit series. no. 57)
Blank page for notes at end.
Bibliography: p. 18-20.
1. Postal service—U. S. I. Title.
E 33-33
Library, U. S. Office of Education LB1027.C7 no. 57
Library of Congress [HE6078.L5]

NL 0411031 DHEW OrMonO OCl

Little (Robert). On coral reefs as the cause of Blakan Mati fever, and of the fevers in various parts of the East. Part 4, Sumatra. 16 pp. 8°. [s. p., 1848.] [P., v. 1024.]

NL 0411032 DNLM

Little (Robert). On the habitual use of opium. (Abridged from the Journal of the Eastern Archipelago, January, 1848.) [*Also*:] Supplement to preceding paper on the habitual use of opium, more especially the mode of cure, by Robert Christison. 18 pp. 8°. *Edinburgh, Murray & Gibb*, 1850. [P., v. 1033.]
Repr. from: Month. J. M. Sc., Lond. & Edinb., 1850, x.

NL 0411033 DNLM

Little, Robert, M. D., *of Belfast.*
A treatise on the prevention and cure of pulmonary consumption. By Robert Little ... London, Longman and co.; [etc., etc.] 1836.
1 p. l., [v]-vi p., 1 l., 160 p. 22 cm.

1. Consumption.
7-34966†
Library of Congress RC311.L77

NL 0411034 DLC KyU DNLM

LITTLE, Robert, of Birmingham.
Death and a future life considered, in a sermon, Dec.20,1818, in Gainsborough. Gainsburgh, etc., 1819.

NL 0411035 MH-AH

LITTLE, Robert, of Birmingham.
The decline and fall of spiritual Babylon. a discourse, at Leicester, June 22,1814. Birmingham, 1814.

NL 0411036 MH-AH

VOLUME 336

Pam. Coll. 1573
Little, Robert, of Birmingham.
Remarks on Mr. Brown's vindication of the Presbyterian form of church government, &c. Containing reflections on the present state of the Church of Scotland. Edinburgh, Printed by J. Ritchie, 1806.
57 p. 18 cm.
1. Presbyterian Church. Government 2. Church of Scotland

NL 0411037 NcD MH

252.08 M681 v.6 no.2
Little, Robert, of Birmingham.
Salvation brought near to the guilty: a sermon. Edinburgh, J. Ritchie, 1806.
23p. 21cm. (In Miscellaneous sermons, v.6, no.2)

NL 0411038 OrU DLC

F 83361 .51
LITTLE, ROBERT, d.1827.
The duty of public usefulness. A sermon preached in the hall of the House of representatives in the capitol of the United States, Washington city, on Sunday, February 16, 1823. Washington,Thompson,1823.
20p.

NL 0411039 ICN DLC MH Nh MWA NNUT

Little, Robert, d. 1827.
A funeral sermon on the death of John Adams and Thomas Jefferson, ex-presidents of the United States, preached on Sunday evening, July 16, 1826. In the First Unitarian church, Washington City. By Robert Little. Washington, Bartow & Brannan, 1826.
22 p. 22½cm.
1. Adams, John, pres. U. S., 1735-1826. 2. Jefferson, Thomas, pres. U. S., 1743-1826.
6-43454
Library of Congress E322.L77

NL 0411040 DLC MdBP

Little, Robert, d. 1827.
Hymns, selected from various authors, for the use of the Unitarian Church in Washington
see under Unitarian Church in Washington, D.C.

WW10 L778 I
Little, Robert, d. 1827.
Ignorance, the parent of crime. A sermon occasioned by the death of William Seaver, who was murdered on the evening of July 6,1821, preached before the Unitarian society in the city of Washington,on ... July 15th,by Robert Little. Washington,Printed and sold by W.Cooper, sold also by P.Thompson[etc.]1821.
20p. 22cm.

NL 0411042 NNUT MH

Little, Robert, d. 1827.
The mystery of Christ. A sermon delivered in the city of Washington, October 7, 1821. With notes, chiefly in reference to a publication by the Rev. Anthony Kohlmann; the first number of which professes to contain a complete refutation of the fundamental principles of Unitarianism. By Robert Little. Washington, W. Cooper; Baltimore, P. Thompson [etc.] 1821.
22 p. 21½cm.
No. 5 in a volume lettered: Sermons.
1. Kohlmann, Anthony, 1771-1836. Unitarianism philosophically and theologically examined. 2. Unitarian churches—Sermons. I. Title.
45-52223
Library of Congress BX9843.A1S4 no. 5

NL 0411043 DLC NNUT RPB

Little, Robert, d. 1827.
The national anniversary. In two sermons preached July 4th, 1824, in the First Unitarian church, Washington city; with a short address respecting the views of the Colonization society. By Robert Little ... Washington, Way & Gideon, printers, 1824.
28 p. 23cm.
1. Fourth of July orations. 2. Negroes—Colonization—Africa.
18-4489
Library of Congress E286.W22 1824 L

NL 0411044 DLC N

*AC8 L7275 822r
Little, Robert, d.1827.
Religious liberty and Unitarianism vindicated. A sermon preached in the hall of the House of representatives of the United States, Washington city, Sunday, April 28, 1822. By Robert Little. 〈Published by request.〉
Washington:Published and sold by Pishey Thompson:sold also by F.Lucas,Baltimore,and A. Small,Philadelphia.A.Way,jr.printer.1822.
iv,[5]-22p. 22cm.

NL 0411045 MH CtY-D NNUT MH

*AC8 L7275 823s (A)
Little, Robert, d.1827.
The sacred origin and divine authority of the Jewish and Christian religions, argued from their internal evidences; in three sermons. By Robert Little ...
Washington:Printed by S.A.Elliot;& sold by Pishey Thompson,Penn.avenue;F.Lucas,Baltimore; and A.Small,Philadelphia.MDCCCXXIII.
x,39p. 22cm.
Another copy. 22.5cm.
Imperfect: p.37-39 mutilated.

NL 0411046 MH RPB

Little, Robert, d. 1827, ed. FOR OTHER EDITIONS SEE MAIN ENTRY
The Washington quarterly magazine of arts, science and literature. With illustrative engravings. Robert Little, editor ... v. 1, no. 1-2; July 1823-Apr. 1824. Washington city, P. Thompson; [etc., etc.] 1823.

PZ8 .3 .H88 Fl
Little, Robert, 1902- illus.
Humphrey, Dorothy.
Florida sand, by Dorothy Humphrey, illustrated by Robert Little. Philadelphia, Dorrance & company [1944]

724.173 L72o
[Little, Robert Bush]
On trail with the eighth Allerton scholars [by Robert B. Little and Donald R. Hodgson] [Urbana, Ill., 1936]
65 l. front., mounted photos., map, plans.
On cover: Eighth Allerton American traveling scholars.
Typewritten.
Photographs accompanied by guard sheets with descriptive matter.
1. Architecture, Colonial. I. Hodgson, Donald Rioker, jt. author II. Allerton American traveling scholarship.

NL 0411049 IU

PS 8523 I79R4
Little, Robert D 1888-
Rhyme and reason. Willowdale, Ont., Baker, Burney & McLaren Press, 1946.
58 p.
Poems.

NL 0411050 CaOTU RPB

975 L7271
Little, Robert Darden, 1908-
The ideology of the new South; a study in the development of ideas, 1865-1910. Chicago, 1950.
vi, 293p. 24cm.
Thesis - University of Chicago.
Bibliography: p.275-293.
Xerox copy.
1. Southern States - Hist. - 1865- 2. U.S. - Civilization. I. Title. Sp.: Littlefield Fund.

NL 0411051 TxU ICU

FILM P-856
Little, Robert Darden, 1908-
Ideology of the new South; a study in the development of new ideas, 1865-1910. Chicago, 1950.
Microfilm copy of typed manuscript. Positive.
Collation of original: 293 l.
Thesis—Univ. of Chicago, 1950.
Bibliography: leaves 275-293.
1. Southern states—Hist.—1865- I. Title.

NL 0411052 ViU

LITTLE, Robert Irving.
The moral ideas of Chrétien de Troyes. Thesis, Harvard University. Cambridge, 1918.
Typewritten.
4°. ff. (3), 215.

NL 0411053 MH

Little, Robert Weaver, 1916-
The destructive irradiation technique of spectrophotometric vitamin A assay; an application to the storage of vitamin A in animal tissues, by Robert Weaver Little ... New York, N. Y., 1942.
3 p. l., 36 p., 1 l. incl. tables, diagrs. 21½cm.
Thesis (PH. D.)—Columbia university, 1942.
Reproduced from type-written copy.
Vita.
Bibliography: p. [35]-36.
1. Vitamins.
A 42-5460
Columbia univ. Libraries for Library of Congress QP801.V5L55

NL 0411054 NNC DLC CU

Little, Robert Weaver, 1916- ed.
Flameproofing textile fabrics. Prepared by a staff of specialists under the editorship of Robert W. Little, Major, Q. M. C., under research project Q. M. C. #27 of the National Research Council, National Academy of Sciences. New York, Reinhold Pub. Corp., 1947.
xix, 410 p. illus. 24 cm. (American Chemical Society. Monograph series, no. 104)
At head of title: Office of the Quartermaster General. Military Planning Division. Research and Development Branch.
1. Fireproofing. 2. Textile industry and fabrics. I. U. S. Quartermaster Corps. Military Planning Division. II. Title. (Series)
A 48-6367*
Rochester. Univ. Libr. for Library of Congress TP267.L5 [10]

NL 0411055 TU NcRS MiU PU-Sc OCIU MiEM MiHM ICJ TxU NNC NN IU InU OU LU MB ICU NRU OrU OrCS MtBC WaT WaS DAU KMK NcGU

Wason PR4890 L25
Little, Robert William.
Poems. Shanghai, North-China Daily News & Herald, 1907.
47 p. 20cm.

NL 0411056 NIC

Little, Ronald Erl.
Moonglome. Boston, [c1926]
46 p. 20 cm.

NL 0411057 RPB

VOLUME 336

QK643 .C5U5 1945
Little, Ruby R.

U. S. *Foreign economic administration.*
Histology of barks of *Cinchona* and some related genera occurring in Colombia, by: Ruby R. Little, junior botanist. [Washington, Foreign economic administration, General commodities division, Cinchona section [1945?]

NL 0411060 ...

TX715 .G223
Little, Ruth, joint author.

Gardner, Esther L
Homemakers' cookbook and guide to nutrition, by Esther L. Gardner ... Daisy Schluntz ... Ruth Little ... [and] Mary Turner ... Mountain View, Calif., Brookfield, Ill. [etc.] Pacific press publishing assn. [1946]

Little, S supposed author.
The greatest blessing of life
see under title

Little, Samuel C 1915–
Abnormal movements of the face; with special consideration of abnormal facial movements occurring in paroxysmal disorders. University, Ala., University of Alabama Press, 1954.
79 p. illus. 21 cm.
Includes bibliography.

1. Face—Abnormities and deformities. I. Title.

RC936.L5 616.8 54-10881 ‡

NL 0411061 DLC OrU-M DNLM ViU LU GU MU

LITTLE, Mrs. Sarah Florella (Cowles) 1838-1912.
The education of the blind; an address read before the Wisconsin Teachers' Association, at La Crosse, July 10, 1879. Beloit, Wis., Free Press Steam Print, [1879].

pp. (1), 15.

NL 0411062 MH DNLM OO DGU

Little, Mrs. Sarah Florella (Cowles), 1838-1912.
Historical sketch of the Oberlin Missionary Home Association by ... 1902. n.p. n.d.
23 p.

NL 0411063 OO

Little, Seelye William, 1867–
Nephritis; a manual of the disease commonly called nephritis or Bright's disease, and of allied disorders of the kidneys, by Seelye W. Little, M. D. New York, The Grafton press, 1907.
xiii p., 1 l., 134 p. 19½cm. (*Half-title:* The Grafton medical books)

1. Kidneys—Diseases.

Library of Congress RC902.L5 7-18827

NL 0411064 DLC DNLM CtY-M ICJ

Little, Shelby.
George Washington [by] Shelby Little. New York, Minton, Balch & company, 1929.
x p., 2 l., 481 p. 24½cm.
Bibliography: p. 465-473.

1. Washington, George, pres. U. S., 1732-1799.

Library of Congress E312.L78 29-18687

Or TxU WaS MB WaTC NcRS OrSaW KEmT CaBVaU OCl OOxM ICU NcD OClJC OCl ViU OrP MtU TU IdU AU
NL 0411065 DLC NN MH MB ViU OLak OClWHi OClW OU

E 312 L78 1943
Little, Shelby
George Washington, [by] Shelby Little. New York, Halcyon House, [1943]
x p., 2l., 481 p. 24 1/2 cm.
Bibliography: p. 405-473

WASHINGTON, GEORGE, PRES. U.S., 1732-1799
George Washington

NL 0411066 KMK IU WaSp

Little, Shelby, comp.
The linebook
see under Chicago Tribune.

Little, Shelby.
This to that; the word-change book, by Shelby Little, with an introduction by Richard Henry Little. New York, Minton, Balch & company, 1927.
[128] p. 19½cm.

1. Puzzles. I. Title. II. Title: The word-change book.

Library of Congress GV1507.W8L5 27-18788

NL 0411068 DLC WaS NjP

[Little, Sidney H] d. 1841.
Appeal to the people of the state of Illinois. [Springfield? Ill., 1841?]
15 p. 25cm.
Signed: S. H. Little, E. D. Baker, J. J. Hardin, E. B. Webb, A. Lincoln, J. Gillespie.
"Objections of the Council of revision to the bill re-organizing the judiciary of the state" (signed: Wm. Wilson [and others]): p. [7]-10.
"Judge Smith's objections" (signed: Theo. W. Smith): p. [11]-15.

1. Courts—Illinois. I. Lincoln, Abraham, pres. U. S., 1809-1865. II. Title.

Library of Congress JK5781.L5 29-633

NL 0411069 DLC

Little, Sidney W
The four-language phrase book. [English, French, Spanish, Italian. Philadelphia] D. McKay Co. [1954, °1953]
79 p. 18 cm.

1. Languages, Modern—Conversation and phrase books. 2. English language—Conversation and phrase books—Polyglot. I. Title.

PB73.L5 413 53-11347 ‡

NL 0411070 DLC Wa MB PP Or

Little, Silas.
Ecology and silviculture of whitecedar and associated hardwoods in southern New Jersey. New Haven, Yale University, 1950.
103 p. illus., tables. 23 cm. (Yale University. School of Forestry. Bulletin no. 56)
"The original manuscript was submitted to Yale University as a dissertation ... for the degree of doctor of philosophy."
Bibliography: p. 96-101.

1. Cedar. 2. Hard woods. 3. Forest ecology. I. Title. (Series)

SD397.C4L5 634.9756 A 51-3607
Yale Univ. Library
for Library of Congress [3]†

DI
NL 0411071 CtY DLC AAP MiHM ICU NNBG MoU PU PPAN

1.9622 N2St22 no.35
Little, Silas.
Effect of prescribed burns and shelterwood cutting on reproduction of shortleaf and pitch pine. Upper Darby, Pa., 1950.
11 p. (U.S. Forest Service. Northeastern Forest Experiment Station. Station paper no.35)

Issued May 1950.

NL 0411072 DNAL

Little, Silas, joint author.

Lutz, Harold John, 1900–
... The influence of soil profile horizons on root distribution of white pine (*Pinus strobus L.*) by Harold J. Lutz ... Joseph B. Ely, jr. ... [and] Silas Little, jr. ... New Haven, Yale university, 1937.

1.9622 N2St22 no.31
Little, Silas.
Slash disposal in oak-pine stands of southern New Jersey. Upper Darby, 1949.
12 p. (U.S. Forest Service. Northeastern Forest Experiment Station. Station paper no. 31)

Issued Nov. 1949.

1. Slash disposal. I. Somes, H A joint author.

NL 0411074 DNAL

Little, Mrs. Sophia Louisa (Robbins) b. 1799.
The birth, Last days, and Resurrection of Jesus. Three poems ... By Sophia L. Little. Pawtucket, R. I., The author, 1841.
156 p. 15½cm.
Appeared in 1889, with addition of "Pentecost", under title: The last days of Jesus and other poems.

1. Jesus Christ—Poetry. I. Title: The birth of Jesus. II. Title: The last days of Jesus. III. Title: The resurrection of Jesus.

Library of Congress PS2248.L35B5 28-7941

NL 0411075 DLC NNUT ICN MH IU CSmH NBuG

Slavery E 441 M46 v.181 no.3
Little, Sophia Louisa (Robbins) b. 1799.
The branded hand: a dramatic sketch, commemorative of the tragedies at the South in the winter of 1844-5. By Sophia L. Little. Pawtucket, R.I., R.W. Potter, 1845.
46 p. 19cm.

May anti-slavery pamphlets, v. 181.

1. Slavery in the U.S.--Drama. I. Title.

NL 0411076 NIC RPB RP RHi

Little, Sophia Louisa (Robbins), b. 1799.
The last days of Jesus: a poem. By Sophia L. Little ... Pawtucket, R. I.: Printed for the author, 1839. 60 p. 17cm.
First edition.

1. Poetry, American. 2. Jesus Christ—Poetry. I. Title.
N. Y. P. L. March 21, 1941

NL 0411077 NN MH NcD

LITTLE, Sophia Louisa.
The last days of Jesus, and other poems. 2d ed. Newport, R.I., 1877.

Front.

NL 0411078 MH

VOLUME 336

Little, *Mrs.* Sophia Louisa (Robbins) *b.* 1799.
The last days of Jesus and other poems, by Sophia Louisa Little. 3d ed. New York, The author, 1889.
148 p. 19cm.
Published in 1841, without the last poem, under title: The birth, Last days and Resurrection of Jesus.
CONTENTS.—The advent.—The last days of Jesus.—The resurrection.—Pentecost.

1. Jesus Christ—Poetry. I. Title.

Library of Congress PS2248.L35L3 35-33074
Copyright 1889: 24871 811.49

NL 0411079 DLC MB OU NN

[Little, Mrs. Sophia Louisa (Robbins)] b. 1799.
Massacre at Fort Griswold and burning of New London, Sept. 6, 1781; [a poem] n.p., n.d.
Broadside. 33 x 19 fold. to 22 cm.
Written in the author's 82/year.

NL 0411080 RPB

Little, *Mrs.* Sophia Louisa (Robbins) *b.* 1799.
Pentecost ... By S. L. Little. Newport, R. I., Davis & Pitman's steam printing press, 1869.
49 p. 17½cm.

I. Title.

Library of Congress PS2248.L35P4 14-22481 Revised

NL 0411081 DLC NNUT MB

[Little, Sophia Louisa (Robbins)] b. 1799, supposed author.
A picture of slavery, for youth
see under [Walker, Jonathan] 1799-1878.

Little, *Mrs.* Sophia Louise Robbins. 1799—.
Poems. 6 pp. (Kettell, S., *Specimens of Am. poetry*, v. 3, p. 162.)

NL 0411083 MdBP

Little, Sophia L.
Poems by Sophia L. Little.
Pawtucket, 1841.
156 p. 18°

NL 0411084 MWA

Little, Mrs. Sophia Louisa (Robbins) b. 1799.
[Poems] (manuscript) [Newport, 1862?]
unp. 20 cm.

NL 0411085 RPB

Ex
3829
.5294
.376
[Little, Mrs. Sophia Louise (Robbins)] b.1799.
The reveille: or, Our music at dawn. Providence, R.I., Printed by B.T. Albro, 1854.
3 nos.(140 p.) 24 cm.

Part 1 contains ms. letter by the author presenting the copy to Mr. Pierpont.
In case.

NL 0411086 NjP MH RPB CtY

FILM
4274
PR
v.2
reel
L9
[Little, Sophia Louise (Robbins)] b.1799.
The Reveille; or, Our music at dawn. ...
Providence, B. T. Albro, 1854.
3 pts. (140 p.) (Wright American fiction, v.II, 1851-1875, no. 1560, Research Publications Microfilm, Reel L-9)

1. Temperance - Fiction. I. Title.

NL 0411087 CU

813
L727t
Little, *Mrs.* Sophia Louisa (Robbins) *b.* 1799.
Thrice through the furnace: a tale of the times of the iron hoof ... Pawtucket, R. I., A. W. Pearce, 1852.
190 p. 19cm.
Copyright by Mrs. Sophia L. Little. *cf.* also Bartlett, The literature of the rebellion; Sabin, A dict. of books relating to America.

1. Slavery in the U. S.—Fiction. I. Title.

NL 0411088 MiU InU IU NNC NcD CtY ICN NjP MB CtU TU PHi ViU

FILM
4274
PR
v.2
reel
L9
[Little, Sophia Louise (Robbins)] b.1799.
Thrice through the furnace: A tale of the times of the iron hoof... Pawtucket, R. I., A. W. Pearce, 1852.
190 p. (Wright American fiction, v.II, 1851-1875, no. 1561, Research Publications Microfilm, Reel L-9)

1. Slavery in the U. S. - Fiction. I. Title.

NL 0411089 CU

Little, Stephen.

HE2791
.A83
1894
Atchison, Topeka and Santa Fe railroad company.
General reorganization committee of the Atchison, Topeka & Santa Fé railroad company. Report of Stephen Little. [New York, 1894]

Little, Stephen.
Reorganization Committee...
see under Baltimore and Ohio Railroad Co.

Little, Stephen.

Massachusetts. *Commission on commerce and industry.*
... Report of the Commission on commerce and industry, with appendix. March, 1908. Boston, Wright & Potter printing co., state printers, 1908.

Little, Stephen.
Baltimore. *Commission to investigate the affairs of the Western Maryland railroad company.*
Report of the commission to investigate the affairs of the Western Maryland railroad company and the interest of the city therein, to the mayor and city council of Baltimore—together with the reports of—Stephen Little ... and H. T. Douglas ... employed by the commission to aid in the investigation. May 15th, 1893. Baltimore, John Cox, "City printer", 1893.

Little, Stephen.
Western Maryland railroad co. and Baltimore & Harrisburg railway co. Report of Stephen Little on the income accounts of these companies for the two years ended September 30th, 1899, and their financial condition at September 30th, 1897, and September 30th, 1899, respectively ... [New York, 1899?]
49 p. 23cm.

1. Western Maryland railroad company. 2. Baltimore and Harrisburg railway company.

A 16—1018

Bur. of railway econ. Libr.
for Library of Congress [a41b1]

NL 0411094 DBRE

Little, T. H.
Comments on extraterritorial operation in industrial insurance, by T. H. Little... Law institute, Olympia, Washington, July, 1940.
6 p. (In Legal institute Proceedings, 1940)

NL 0411095 WaU-L

Little, T W.
North country lyrics, by T. W. Little ... London, Stanesby & co.; Derby and Nottingham, F. Murray, 1889.
4 p. l., [vii]-viii, 92, [1] p. 18cm. (*On cover:* The Moray library)
"One hundred and forty copies of this small paper edition have been printed ..."

I. Title.

Library of Congress PR1145.M7L5 19-17134

NL 0411096 DLC NIC NBu

Little, Talbot.
Trixie in search of a title
see under Montagu, Edward.

Little, Thomas, esq., pseud.
See
Moore, Thomas, 1779-1852.

Little, Thomas, of the Opera Colonnade.
Confessions of an Oxonian
see under title

BV
4253
L5
Cage
Little, Thomas, 1665-1731.
The clergyman's remembrancer. A sermon preach'd at a visitation held at Boston in Lincoln-shire; April 23, 1708. Publish'd at the request of the clergy then present. By Thomas Littell...London, Printed for Jonah Bowyer...1708.
A-C⁴, D². 4to.
28 p.

NL 0411100 DFo

An
L728h
1828
Stark
Lib'y
Little, Thomas, fl. 1824-32.
Holly-grove. An epithalamic satire: with anecdotical notes. By Thomas Little, Esq. Part I. 2d ed. London, Printed and published by J. J. Stockdale, 1828.
134p. 21½cm.
TxU copy: half title wanting?

NL 0411101 TxU

VOLUME 336

Little, Thomas A. Chapel Hill, 1924.
Bunyan's indebtedness to his times.

NL 0411102 NcU

Little, Thomas Charles, 1925–
The administration of school supply purchase in Kentucky. Nashville, Bureau of Publications, George Peabody College for Teachers, 1949.
xi, 119 p. 24 cm. (George Peabody College for Teachers [Nashville] Contribution to education no. 408)
Bibliography: p. 115–119.

1. Schools—Furniture, equipment, etc. I. Title. (Series)

LB3261.L5 379.153 49-1695*

NL 0411103 DLC PPPL ViU OOxM TxU LU OrSaW

Little, Thomas Morton, 1910–
The distribution of North American rose species. By Thomas M. Little. 1942.
37-49 p., illus. (American rose annual, 1942)

NL 0411104 MH-A

Little, Thomas Morton, 1910–
Tetraploid segregation in *Antirrhinum majus* L., by Thomas M. Little ... [College Park, Md.] 1943.
3 p. l., 61 numb. l. incl. tables. 29½ x 23cm.
Thesis (PH. D.)—University of Maryland, 1943.
Type-written (carbon copy)
"Literature cited": leaves [58]-61.

1. Snapdragons. 2. Karyokinesis. I. Title.

A 44-184

Maryland. Univ. Library for Library of Congress QK495.S43L5 [2]†

NL 0411105 MdU DLC

Little, Thomas Sheperd, 1845-1910, joint author.
Porter, James Biggs, 1843–
The laws of insurance: fire, life, accident, and guarantee. Embodying cases in the English, Scotch, Irish, American, and Canadian courts. By James Biggs Porter ... assisted by William Fielden [!] Craies ... and Thomas Shepherd Little ... 3d ed. London, Stevens and Haynes, 1898.

B616.932
L588
LITTLE, Timothy Richards, 1841-1886.
A report on the microscopic objects found in cholera evacuations, &c. By Timothy Richards Lewis... Printed by order of government. Calcutta, Office of superintendent of government printing, 1870.
xvii, [1], 78 p. XXIV col. pl., fold. maps. 26cm.
Contents.- pt.1. Concerning the theory of the fungoid origin of cholera and the microscopic objects found in choleraic evacuations.- pt.2. Remarks regarding the soil, &c., of certain places in relation to Pettenkofer's theory.

1. Cholera, Asiatic. 2. Feces. Bacteriology. I. Title: Microscopic objects found in cholera evacuations.

NL 0411108 MnU

Little, Van Allen, 1898–
Cotton insects of the United States, by V. A. Little ... and D. F. Martin ... Minneapolis, Minn., Burgess publishing co., ©1942.
1 p. l., ii numb. l., 1 l., 130 numb. l. incl. plates. 27½ x 21cm.
Reproduced from type-written copy.
"Literature cited" at end of each section.

1. Cotton—Diseases and pests. 2. Insects, Injurious and beneficial. I. Martin, Dial Franklin, joint author. II. Title.

42—17142

Library of Congress SB608.C8L4 [43f3] 632.7

NL 0411109 DLC MtBC OrCS NIC CU TU NcRS OCl ICJ

Little, Van Allen, joint author.
Sievers, Arthur Frederick, 1885–
... Studies on the possibilities of devil's shoestring (*Tephrosia virginiana*) and other native species of *Tephrosia* as commercial sources of insecticides. By A. F. Sievers ... G. A. Russell ... M. S. Lowman ... E. D. Fowler ... C. O. Erlanson ... and V. A. Little ... Washington [U. S. Govt. print. off., 1938]

SCORE

MUSIC
m780.583
L778c
Little, Vilma Gertrude, 1883- comp. and ed.
Cantate Domino; a collection of supplementary hymns. Liverpool, Rushworth & Dreaper, 1933 [i.e.1935]
71p. 19cm.

Unaccompanied melodies; English words.
Intended as a bridge from familiar hymns to Gregorian chant. Cf. foreword.

1.Catholic Church - Hymns. 2.Hymns, English. 3.Chants (Plain, Gregorian, etc.) I.Title.

NL 0411111 CLSU

[Little, Vilma Gertrude] 1888–
The chant; a simple and complete method for teachers and students, by V.G.L. Tournai, Desclée, 1938.
140 [2] p. illus. (incl. music)

NL 0411112 MiD

783.25
L778C
[Little, Vilma Gertrude] 1888–
The chant, a simple and complete method for teachers and students, by V. G. L. 2d ed. Tournai, Society of St. John the Evangelist, Desclée, 1949.
126 p. music. 25 cm.

1. Chants (Plain, Gregorian, etc.) I. Title.

A 51-1180

Oregon. Univ. Libr.

NL 0411113 OrU MH-AH OrU OrStbM CCamarSJ NcD

[**Little, Vilma Gertrude**] 1888– comp.
Laudate Dominum, compiled by V. G. L. Accompaniments by H. P. Allen. Liverpool, Rushworth & Dreaper, ltd. [©1936]
1 p. l., 57 p. 31½ x 23½cm.
Chants for Benediction. Latin words, organ accompaniment.

1. Hymns, Latin. 2. Catholic church—Hymns. I. Allen, H. P. II. Title.

37-11933

Library of Congress M14.L34A6
Copyright E—Foreign 45368 [3] 783.9

NL 0411114 DLC

[Little, Vilma Gertrude] 1888-
Legendo. A simple approach to the Latin of the liturgy. By V.G.L. Liverpool, Rushworth & Dreaper, 1943.
x,202p. 22cm.

1. Latin language - church Latin. 2. Latin language, Medieval and modern - Grammar. I. V.G.L. II. L, V.G.
PA2823.A1L4

NL 0411115 KAS

PS3513
.R856G7
no.40
Little, Vivian
The singing of the skies. Winter Park, Fla., The Angel Alley Press [193-?]
[15] p. 36cm. [E. O. Grover collection, no. 40]
Vest pocket poets, no. 9. Edited by Edwin Osgood Grover.
"Five hundred copies of this first edition have been printed."

I. Angel Alley Press. II. Title.

NL 0411116 ViU FU

Little, Vivian Agincourt Spence, 1878–
The Christology of the apologists, doctrinal, by V. A. Spence Little ... with an introduction by W. B. Selbie ... London, Duckworth [1934]
240 p. 19cm. (*On cover:* Studies in theology)
"First published 1934."
"Bibliography": p. 229-236.

1. Jesus Christ—History of doctrines. 2. Apologetics—Early church. I. Title.

A 35-614 Revised 2

Princeton theol. sem. Libr for Library of Congress BT198.L5

NL 0411117 NjPT WaWW FTaSU DLC NcD

BT198
.L5
1935
Little, Vivian Agincourt Spence, 1878-
The Christology of the apologists, doctrinal; with an introd. by W. B. Selbie. New York, Scribner, 1935.
240p. 19cm.

"Bibliography": p.229-236.

1. Jesus Christ - History of doctrines. 2. Apologetics - Early church. i. Title.

NL 0411118 FMU

Little, W., of Saint Johns, supposed author.
Imposition exposed, or Clerical rights examined..
see under title

Little, W Buller.
see Little, William Buller, 1888-

LITTLE, W. C.
Roman fen-road in Cambridgeshire. n.p., [1879?].

8° pp.(4)
Extracted from a larger work.

NL 0411121 MH

VOLUME 336

Little, W N
Remedial work in oil fields of the eastern area of the United States.
(*In* Petroleum technology. York, Pa., 1938-48. 23 cm. v. 6, no. 3, May 1943. 11 p. illus.)
American Institute of Mining and Metallurgical Engineers. Technical publication no. 1596 (Class G, Petroleum Division, no. 189)

1. Petroleum engineering. I. Title.
[TN860.P55 vol. 6, no. 3] P O 52-110

U. S. Patent Office. Library
for Library of Congress [3]

NL 0411122 DP

Little, Mrs. Walter S
Study outlines and bibliography of American art
see under General Federation of Women's Clubs. Fine Arts Dept.

Little, *Mrs.* Water S.
The historical pageant. [A synopsis. Director of the pageant, Miss Lotta A. Clark. Author, Mrs. Water S. Little.]
(*In* Massachusetts. State Normal School, Bridgewater. Seventy-fifth anniversary . . . Pp. 79-87. Plates. Bridgewater. 1915.)

M3861 — Double main card. — Little, Mrs. Water S. (M1) — Clark, Lotta Alma. (M2) — Bridgewater, Mass. Pageants. (1) — Pageants. (1)

NL 0411124 MB

A912.77 Little, Weare C., and co., pub.
L778m Maps, &c. of the mineral region of Lake Superior. [Albany, N.Y., Weare C. Little & co., 1846?]
16p. 3 maps. 84cm.
Scale: 5mi. to 1¼ in.

Text consists of a list of persons to whom permits to locate mineral lands on the south shore of Lake Superior have been granted and leases issued upon them by the Secretary of war, up to June 16, 1846. In pocket.

NL 0411125 LNHT MnHi MH-B MB

Little, Will T., comp.
Oklahoma (*Ter.*) *Laws, statutes, etc.*
The statutes of Oklahoma, 1890. Compiled under the supervision and direction of Robert Martin, secretary of the territory, by Will T. Little, L. G. Pitman and R. J. Barker, from the laws passed by the First Legislative assembly of the territory. Guthrie, Okla., The State capital printing co., 1891.

LITTLE, WILLIAM.
A visit to Topos, and how the science of heredity is practised there. Ballarat, Berry, Anderson & co., printers, 1897. 28 p. 18cm.

1. Heredity.

NL 0411127 NN

Little, William, captain.
The interesting trials of the pirates, for the murder of William Little, captain of the ship American Eagle
see under title

Little, William, *defendant.*
A faithful report of the trial of Doctor William Little, on an indictment for an assault and battery, committed upon the body of his lawful wife, Mrs. Jane Little, a black lady ... New-York: Printed for the purchasers, 1808.
24 p. 21cm.
Charged, in the state of New York, city and county of New York, with assault committed on Apr. 5, 1808.

1. Little, Jane (Warner) I. Title.
46-34835

NL 0411129 DLC NIC CtY

Little, William, of Montreal. Alarming destruction of American forests. London. 1883. 8°. pp. 16.
"Reprinted from *Forestry*, 1883," pp. 243-257.

NL 0411130 MH-A

Little, William, *of Montreal.*
Letter to the president and council of the Montreal Board of trade objecting "To get rid of the timber." Presented by William Little at the meeting held on June 10, 1890. Montreal, Printed by J. Lovell & son, 1890.
43 p. 24½cm.

1. Forests and forestry—Canada. 2. Lumber trade—Canada. I. Montreal. Board of trade.
8—1966
Library of Congress HD1607.C2L2

NL 0411131 DLC MBH MH-A MH MB

[Little, William] of Montreal.
The political destiny of Canada being determined by its financial policy, by a British immigrant of fifty-six years' standing. Montreal, Canadian Spectator Co., 1879.
17 p. 22 cm.
Reprinted from the "Canadian Spectator".
I. A British immigrant of fifty-six years' standing. II. Title.

NL 0411132 CtY

Case
Wing
Z
40291
.511
LITTLE, WILLIAM, publisher.
William Little's double-action printing machine. [London,] 1846.
[441]-443p. illus., fold. plate. 22cm. (in The patent journal and inventor's magazine, v.[1], no.27, November 28, 1846)

NL 0411133 ICN

Little, William, 1136-1198?
see
William, of Newburgh, 1136-1198?

Little, William, *fl.* 1798.
Works by this author printed in America before 1801 are available in this library in the Readex Microprint edition of Early American Imprints published by the American Antiquarian Society.
This collection is arranged according to the numbers in Charles Evans' American Bibliography.

NL 0411135 DLC

Little, William, fl. 1798,
... The easy instructor; or, A new method of teaching sacred harmony. Containing, I. The rudiments of music on an improved plan ... II. A choice collection of psalm tunes and anthems ... By William Little and William Smith ... Albany, Printed for Websters & Skinners and D. Steele & son. Packard & Benthuysen, printers [pref. 1798]
127, [1] p. 13 x 22½cm.
At head of title: Revised and enlarged edition.

I. Smith, William, joint author.
A 18—2103
Western Reserve hist. soc. Library
for Library of Congress [a40c1]

MiU MnU MiU-C CtY NcU
NL 0411136 OClW MiU-C RPB ScU ICN ViU MB OClWHi

Little, William, *fl.* 1798, *comp.*
The easy instructor; or, A new method of teaching sacred harmony, containing the rudiments of music on an improved plan ... Together with a choice collection of psalm tunes and anthems ... By Edward Stammers, William Little. Copyright secured according to an act of congress. [Philadelphia? 1798]
[1] l. 9 x 11 cm.
Proposed title page deposited for copyright registration, June 15, 1798, by the proprietors. Stammers' relation to the work, other than as joint proprietor, has not been ascertained. Cf. Lowens. The easy instructor. Ann Arbor, 1953.

On verso, in ms.: Title page of The easy instructor &c. Deposited 15th June 1798, by Edwd Stammers and William Little as proprietors. A similar ms. statement (leaf, 20 cm.) is attached to the original.

I. Stammers, Edward, d. 1802. II. Title.
M2116.L7E28 M 54-1161

NL 0411138 DLC

Case
-VM
2136
W 72u
17--
[LITTLE, WILLIAM] comp.
[The easy instructor, compiled by William Little and William Smith. Albany?18--]
p.29-96. (with Williams, Aaron. The universal psalmodist. 17--)

Imperfect: t.-p. and pages preceding 29 and following 96, 43-46 wanting.
Supplied in ms.: Easy instructor. Albany.
The property of S.Jenks.
Character notes.

NL 0411139 ICN

Little, William, fl. 1798.
The easy instructor; or, A new method of teaching sacred harmony. Containing, I. the rudiments of music on an improved plan ... II. a choice collection of psalm tunes and anthems ... By William Little and William Smith. Albany, Websters & Skinner and D. Steele [pref. 1798] [1812?]
104 p. 13 x 23cm.

NL 0411140 NIC

Little, William, fl. 1798

The easy instructor; or, A new method of teaching sacred harmony. Containing, I. The rudiments of music on an improved plan, wherein the naming and timing of the notes are familiarized to the weakest capacity. II. A choice collection of psalm tunes and anthems, from the most celebrated authors, with a number composed in in[sic] Europe and America, entirely new; suited to all the metres sung in the different churches in the United States

... By William Little and William Smith. Printed, typographically, at Albany, by Websters & Skinner and Daniel Steele, (Proprietors of the copy-right,) and sold at their respective bookstores by T. & J. Swords, Evert Duyckinck and William Falconer, New-York; Mathew Carey, Johnson & Warner, William W. Woodward and Hopkins & Earl, Philadelphia; and Increase Cook, New-Haven [ca. 1802] 104 p. 13 x 22½cm.
Open score: 3 and 4 mixed voices.
"Advertisement," (p. [3]) dated: Philadelphia, August 15th, 1798.

200956B. 1. Hymns. I. Smith, William, of Philadelphia, jt. au.
N. Y. P. L. April 16, 1943

NL 0411142 NN ICN MWA

VOLUME 336

Little, William, *fl.* 1798, *comp.*

The easy instructor; or, A new method of teaching sacred harmony. Containing the rudiments of music on an improved plan ... With a choice collection of psalm tunes and anthems ... By William Little & William Smith. ⌊New York, G. & R. Waite, 1802⌋

score (105 ⌊i. e. 106⌋ p.) 14 x 24 cm.
"12" repeated in pagination.
L. C. copy imperfect: p. 12 (*bis*)–13 wanting.
For 3–4 voices.
Shape-note notation.
Edition A*b* in Lowens. The easy instructor. Ann Arbor, 1953.
1. Tune-books. I. Smith, William, fl. 1802, joint comp. II. Title.

M2116.L7E3 1802 M 54–979

NL 0411143 DLC RPB

MT 50 .L5 1803

Little, William, fl. 1798. comp.
The easy instructor; or, a new method of teaching sacred harmony ... By William Little and William Smith. Albany, Websters & Skinner, 1803.
108 p.

HARMONY--STUDY AND TEACHING
Smith, William
The easy instructor

NL 0411144 KMK

Little, William, fl. 1798, comp.

The easy instructor, or, A new method of teaching sacred harmony. Containing, the rudiments of music on an improved plan, wherein the naming and timing of the notes are familiarized to the weakest capacity. With a choice collection of psalm tunes and anthems from the most celebrated authors, with a number composed in Europe and America, entirely new; suited to all the metres sung in the different churches in the United States... By William Little and William Smith. Albany: Printed by Charles R. and George Webster, and Daniel Steele...and sold at Webster's bookstore, and at Steele's bookstore. 1805. 108 p. 13 x 24cm.

Shape-note notation.
First published in 1798 in Philadelphia. — *cf. Evans 34004.*

223075B. 1. Hymns. I. Smith, William, of Philadelphia, jt. au.
N. Y. P. L. August 5, 1943

NL 0411146 NN

Little, William, *fl.* 1798, *comp.*

The easy instructor; or, A new method of teaching sacred harmony, by William Little and William Smith. Containing the rudiments of music on an improved plan ... With a choice collection of psalm tunes and anthems ... Albany: Printed by Websters & Skinner and Daniel Steele, proprietors of the copy-right; and sold at their respective bookstores, at the corner of State and Pearl-Streets, and a few doors south of the court-house in Court-Street. 1807.

score (108 p.) 14 x 24 cm.

L. C. copy imperfect: p. 9–12 wanting.
For 3–4 voices.
Shape-note notation.

1. Tune-books. 2. Choruses, Sacred (Mixed voices), Unaccompanied. 3. Hymns, English. I. Smith, William, fl. 1802, joint comp. II. Title.

M2116.L7E3 1807 62–46284/M

NL 0411148 DLC ICN WaU MWA NN MiU-C

Little, William, *fl.* 1798, *comp.*

The easy instructor; or, A new method of teaching sacred harmony. Containing I. The rudiments of music on an improved plan ... II. A choice collection of psalm tunes and anthems ... By William Little and William Smith. Printed, typographically, at Albany, by Websters & Skinner and Daniel Steele, (proprietors of the copy-right,) and sold at their respective book-stores, at the corner of State and Pearl-Streets, and a few doors south of the Old City-Hall, in Court-Street; by T. & J. Swords, Evert Duyckinck and William Falconer, New-York: Mathew Carey, Johnson & Warner,

Continued in next column

Continued from preceding column

William W. Woodward and Hopkins & Earl, Philadelphia; and Increase Cook, New-Haven. ⌊1808⌋

score (104 p.) 14 x 24 cm.
For 3–4 voices.
Shape-note notation.
Edition F in Lowens. The easy instructor. Ann Arbor, 1953.

1. Tune-books. I. Smith, William, fl. 1802, joint comp. II. Title.

M2116.L7E3 1808 M 54–980

NL 0411150 DLC MiU-C NNUT MWA CtHT-W

Little, William, *fl.* 1798, *comp.*

The easy instructor; or, A new method of teaching sacred harmony. Containing, I. The rudiments of music on an improved plan ... II. A choice collection of psalm tunes and anthems ... By William Little and William Smith. Printed, typographically, at Albany, by Websters & Skinner and Daniel Steele, (proprietors of the copy-right,) and sold at their respective book stores, at the corner of State and Pearl-Streets, and a few doors south of the Old City-Hall, in Court-Street; by T. & J. Swords, Everet Duyckinck and William Falconer, New-York; Wm. J. M'Cartee, Schenectady; A. Seward, Utica; Tracy & Bliss, Lansingburgh; Parker & Bliss, Troy; and Increase Cook, New-Haven. Van Benthuysen & Newton, typographers. ⌊1808⌋

score (104 p.) 13 x 22 cm.
For 3–4 voices.
Shape-note notation.
Edition G in Lowens. The easy instructor. Ann Arbor, 1953.
Bound with Christmas anthem. ⌊n. p., 18—⌋ and Read, Daniel, comp. The Columbian harmonist. Boston, 1810.
1. Tune-books. I. Smith, William, fl. 1802, joint comp. II. Title.

M2116.L7E3 1808a M 54–1162

NL 0411152 DLC

Little, William, *fl.* 1798, *comp.*

The easy instructor; or, A new method of teaching sacred harmony. Containing, I. The rudiments of music on an improved plan ... II. A choice collection of psalm tunes and anthems ... By William Little and William Smith. Printed, typographically, at Albany, by Websters & Skinner and Daniel Steele, (proprietors of the copy-right,) and sold at their respective book-stores, at the corner of State and Pearl-Streets, and a few doors south of the old city-hall, in Court-Street; by T. & J. Swords, Everet Duyckinck and William Falconer, New-York; Wm. J. M'Cartee, Schenectady; A. Seward, Utica; Tracy & Bliss, Lansingburgh; Parker & Bliss, Troy; Increase Cook, New-Haven, and M. Cary, Philadelphia. Van Benthuysen & Newton, typographers. ⌊1809⌋

score (104 p.) 14 x 23 cm.
For 3–4 voices.
Shape-note notation.
Edition H in Lowens. The easy instructor. Ann Arbor, 1953.

1. Tune-books. I. Smith, William, fl. 1802, joint comp. II. Title.

M2116.L7E3 1809 M 54–1160

Library of Congress

NL 0411154 DLC NjR IU NN

Little, William, and W. Smith.

The easy instructor: or, A new method of teaching sacred harmony. Containing, I. The rudiments of music on an improved plan, wherein the naming and timing of the notes are familiarized to the weakest capacity. II. A choice collection of psalm tunes and anthems, from the most celebrated authors, with a number composed in Europe and America, entirely new; suited to all the metres sung in the different churches in the United States... By William Little and William Smith. Albany: Websters & Skinners and D. Steele ⌊1810⌋. 112 p. ob. 24°.

"Advertisement" dated: August 15th, 1798.
Words and music.

1. Hymns. 2. Psalmody. 3. Smith, William, of Philadelphia, jt. au. 4. Title.
N. Y. P. L. May 28, 1919.

NL 0411155 NN ICN

Little, William, *fl.* 1798, *comp.*

The easy instructor; or, A new method of teaching sacred harmony. Containing, I. The rudiments of music on an improved plan ... II. A choice collection of psalm tunes and anthems... By William Little and William Smith. Printed, typographically, at Albany, by Websters & Skinners and Daniel Steele, (proprietors of the copy-right,) and sold at their respective book-stores, at th ⌊sic⌋ corner of State and Pearl-Streets, and a few doors south of the Old City-Hall, in Court-Street; by T. & J. Swords, and Evert Duyckinck, New-York; Wm. J. M'Cartee, Schenectady; A. Seward, Utica; Tracy & Bliss, Lansingburgh; Parker & Bliss, Troy; Increase Cook, New-Haven; M. Cary, Philadelphia; J. Bogert, Geneva; J. D. Bemis, Canandaigua; P. Potter, Poughkeepsie; E. Lewis, Newburgh. Packard & Van Benthuysen, typographers. ⌊1812⌋

score (112 p.) 14 x 23 cm.
For 3–4 voices.
Shape-note notation.
Edition K in Lowens. The easy instructor. Ann Arbor, 1953.
1. Tune-books. I. Smith, William, fl. 1802, joint comp. II. Title.
M2116.L7E3 1812 M 54–988

NL 0411157 DLC

Little,William,fl.1798,comp.
The easy instructor; or,A new method of teaching sacred harmony. Containing,I.The rudiments of music on an improved plan ... II.A choice collection of psalm tunes and anthems ... By William Little and William Smith. Printed,typographically, at Albany,by Websters & Skinners and Daniel Steele,(proprietors of the copy-right,) and sold at their respective book-stores,at the corner of State and Pearl-Streets,and a few doors south of the old city-hall,in Court-Street; by T.& J.Swords, and Evert Duyckinck,New-York; A.Seward,Utica; Tracy & Bliss,Lansingburgh; Parker & Bliss and Solomon Wilber,jun. Troy; Increase Cook,New-Haven; Matthew Cary,Philadelphia; J.Bogert,Geneva; J.D.Bemis,Canandaigua; P.Potter,Poughkeepsie, William E.Norman,Hudson. Packard & Van Benthuysen, typographers. ⌊1813⌋
112 p. 13.5 x 22cm.
Shape-note notation.
This is edition "L" in Irving Lowens' The Easy instructor: (1801-1831): a check-list of editions and issues. (In his Music and musicians in early America. N.Y.⌊c1964⌋, p.292-310)

NL 0411159 MiU-C

Little,William,fl.1798.
The easy instructor; or,A new method of teaching sacred harmony. Containing,I. The rudiments of music ... II.A choice collection of psalm tunes and anthems ... By William Little and William Smith. Printed,typographically,at Albany,by Websters & Skinners and Daniel Steele,(proprietors of the copy-right,) and sold at their respective bookstores,at the corner of State and Pearl-streets,and a few doors south of the old city-hall,in Court-street; by T.& J.Swords and Evert Duyckinck,New-York; Riggs & Stevens,Schenectady; A.Seward,Utica; Tracy & Bliss,Lansingburgh; Parker & Bliss,Troy; M.Carey,Philadelphia; J. Bogert,Geneva; J.D.Bemis,Canandaigua; P.Potter, Poughkeepsie; E.Lewis,Newburgh. Packard & Van Benthuysen,typographers. ⌊1814⌋
112 p. 13.5 x 23cm.
Pages 107-112 lacking in Clements copy; several lines of text torn from p.5-6.
Shape-note notation.
This is either edition Ma or Mb in Irving Lowens' The Easy instructor (1798-1831),in his Music and musicians in early America. New York ⌊c 1964⌋,p.296-302. It is Ma according to Table IX ("soft" is under "m" in Denmark,p.61) but Mb according to the checklist (comma omitted after "T.& J.Swords" in imprint.)

1.Tune-books.2.Musical notation. I-II.Ptrs. III-V.Assn.

NL 0411162 MiU-C ICN RPB

VOLUME 336

Little, William, *fl.* 1798, *comp.*
The easy instructor; or, A new method of teaching sacred harmony, by William Little and William Smith. Printed, typographically, at Albany, by Websters & Skinners and Daniel Steele, (proprietors of the copy-right,) and sold at their respective book-stores, at the corner of State and Pearl-Streets, and a few doors south of the Old City-Hall, in Court-Street; by T. & J. Swords and Evert Duyckinck, New-York; Riggs & Stevens, Schenectady; A. Seward, Utica; Tracy & Bliss, Lansingburgh; Parker & Bliss, Troy; M. Carey, Philadelphia; J. Bogert, Geneva; J. D. Bemis, Canandaigua; P. Potter, Poughkeepsie; E. Lewis, Newburgh. Parckard & Van Benthuysen, typographers. [1814]
score (112 p.) 14 x 23 cm.
L. C. copy imperfect: p. 111-112 mutilated.
For 3-4 voices.
Shape-note notation.
Edition Ma in Lowens. The easy instructor. Ann Arbor, 1953.
1. Tune-books. I. Smith, William, fl. 1802, joint comp. II. Title.
M2116.L7E3 1814 M 61-2178

NL 0411164 DLC ICN MnHi OCHP

Little,William,fl.1798.
The easy instructor; or,A new method of teaching sacred harmony. Containing,I.The rudiments of music on an improved plan,wherein the naming and timing of the notes are familiarized to the weakest capacity.II A choice collection of psalm tunes and anthems,from the most celebrated authors,with a number composed in Europe and America,entirely new ... By William Little and William Smith. Printed, typographically,at Albany,by Websters & Skinners and Daniel Steele (proprietors of the copy-right,) ... Packard & Van Benthuysen,typographers. [1815]
112 p. 13.5 x 23cm.

Pages 107-112 lacking in Clements copy.
This is edition N in Lowens and Britton. The easy instructor. 1953.
Several lines of text torn from p.5-6.
Shape-note notation.

1.Tune-books.2.Musical notation. I-II. Ptrs.III-V. Assn.

NL 0411166 MiU-C

VM 2116 L 77e 1816 LITTLE, WILLIAM, comp.
The easy instructor; or, A new method of teaching sacred harmony. Containing, I. The rudiments of music on an improved plan... II. A choice collection of psalm tunes and anthems... By William Little and William Smith... Albany, Websters[1816?]
112p.

Character notes.
Imperfect: all after p.110 wanting; many pages mutilated.

NL 0411167 ICN NNNPsI MB NN

Little, William, *fl.* 1798, *comp.*
The easy instructor; or, A new method of teaching sacred harmony. Containing, I. The rudiments of music on an improved plan ... II. A choice collection of psalm tunes and anthems ... By William Little and William Smith. Rev. and enl. ed. Albany: Printed for Websters & Skinners and Daniel Steele, and sold at their respective book-stores, at the corner of State and Pearl-Streets, and at No. 472 South Market-Street. Packard & Van Benthuysen, printers. [1817]
score (127, [1] p.) 13 x 23 cm.

For 3-4 voices.
Shape-note notation.
Edition Q in Lowens. The easy instructor. Ann Arbor, 1953.

1. Tune-books. I. Smith, William, fl. 1802, joint comp. II. Title.
M2116.L7E3 1817 M 54-981
Library of Congress [2]

NL 0411169 DLC MiU-C

Little, William, *fl.* 1798, *comp.*
The easy instructor; or, A new method of teaching sacred harmony. Containing, I. The rudiments of music on an improved plan ... II. A choice collection of psalm tunes and anthems ... By William Little and William Smith. Albany: Printed for Websters & Skinners and Daniel Steele, (proprietors,) and sold at their respective book-stores, at the corner of State and Pearl-Streets, and at No. 472 South Market-Street; by T. & J. Swords, E. Duyckinck, Collins & Co. and D. Smith, New-York; M. Carey, B. Warner, W. W. Woodward and A. Small, Philadelphia; J. Cushing, Baltimore; H. Howe, New-Haven; Wells & Lilly, Boston; G. Goodwin & Sons, Hartford; P. Potter, Poughkeepsie; B. F. Lewis, Newburgh; E. Norman, Hudson; Parker & Bliss, Troy; Tracy & Bliss, Lansingburgh; Dodd & Stevens, Salem; H. Stevens, Schenectady; W. Williams, Utica; J. Bogert, Geneva; J. D. Bemis, Canandaigua; Skinner & Crosby, Auburn; S. H. & H. A. Salisbury, Buffalo. Packard & Van Benthuysen, printers. [1817]
score (120 p.) 14 x 23 cm.

For 3-4 voices.
Shape-note notation.
Edition P in Lowens. The easy instructor. Ann Arbor, 1953.

1. Tune-books. I. Smith, William, fl. 1802, joint comp. II. Title.
M2116.L7E3 1817a M 54-982

NL 0411172 DLC

Little, William, *fl.* 1798, *comp.*
The easy instructor; or, A new method of teaching sacred harmony. Containing I. The rudiments of music on an improved plan ... II. A choice collection of psalm tunes and anthems ... By William Little and William Smith. Utica: Printed by William Williams, No. 60, Genesee Street. 1818.
score (126, [1] p.) 14 x 22 cm.
For 3-4 voices.
Shape-note notation.
Edition S in Lowens. The easy instructor. Ann Arbor, 1953.
1. Tune-books. I. Smith, William, fl. 1802, joint comp. II. Title.
M2116.L7E3 1818 M 54-983

NL 0411173 DLC OClWHi NN MdBJ MHi ICU ICN

Little, William, joint author.
The easy instructor; or, a new method of teaching sacred harmony, containing: I. The rudiments of music on an improved plan...; II. A choice collection of psalm tunes and anthems....by William Little and William Smith .... Utica, printed by W. Williams, 1820.
126, [1] p. 23 cm.
Metcalfe, p. 37.
Williams, p. 88, (126 p. "1st ed. was Philadelphia, 1798.")

NL 0411174 CtY N NN OCl

Little,William,fl.1798,comp.
... The easy instructor; or,A new method of teaching sacred harmony. Containing,I.The rudiments of music on an improved plan ... II.A choice collection of psalm tunes and anthems ... By William Little and William Smith ... Albany: Printed for Websters & Skinners and Daniel Steele,and sold at their respective book-stores,at the corner of State and Pearl-streets,and at no.472 South Market-street. Packard & Van Benthuysen,printers. [1820]
127,[1] p. 13 x 22.5cm.
At head of title: Revised and enlarged edition.

Shape-note notation.
This is edition "V" in Irving Lowens' The Easy instructor: (1801-1831): a check-list of editions and issues. (In his Music and musicians in early America. N.Y. [c1964],p.292-310)

1.Tune-books.2.Musical notation.I.Assn.II-IV.Ptr.

NL 0411176 MiU-C ICN

Little, William, *fl.* 1798, *comp.*
The easy instructor; or, A new method of teaching sacred harmony. Containing, I. The rudiments of music on an improved plan ... II. A choice collection of psalm tunes and anthems ... By William Little and William Smith. Rev. and enl. ed. Albany: Printed for Websters & Skinners and D. Steele & Son. And sold at their respective book-stores, at the corner of State and Pearl-Streets, and at No. 436 South Market-Street. Packard & Van Benthuysen, printers. [1826]
score (127, [1] p.) 13 x 23 cm.

For 3-4 voices.
Shape-note notation.
Edition Yb in Lowens. The easy instructor. Ann Arbor, 1953.

1. Tune-books. I. Smith, William, fl. 1802, joint comp. II. Title.
A 18-2103 rev*
Western Reserve Hist. Soc. Library for Library of Congress [r54b½]

NL 0411178 OClW

Little, William, *fl.* 1798, *comp.*
The easy instructor; or, A new method of teaching sacred harmony. Containing, I. The rudiments of music on an improved plan ... II. A choice collection of psalm tunes and anthems ... By William Little and William Smith. Rev. and enl. ed. Albany: Printed by Websters & Skinners and Oliver Steele. And sold at their respective book-stores, at the corner of State and Pearl-Streets, and at No. 437 South Market-Street. 1828.
score (127, [1] p.) 14 x 23 cm.

For 3-4 voices.
Shape-note notation.
Edition Z in Lowens. The easy instructor. Ann Arbor, 1953.

1. Tune-books. I. Smith, William, fl. 1802, joint comp. II. Title.
M2116.L7E3 1828 M 54-984

NL 0411180 DLC

Little, William, *fl.* 1798, *comp.*
The easy instructor; or, A new method of teaching sacred harmony. Containing, I. The rudiments of music on an improved plan ... II. A choice collection of psalm tunes and anthems ... By William Little and William Smith. Rev. and enl. ed. Albany: Printed by Websters & Skinners and Oliver Steele, and sold at their respective book-stores at the corner of State and Pearl-Streets, and at No. 437 South Market-Street. [1830]
score (127, [1] p.) 13 x 24 cm.

For 3-4 voices.
Shape-note notation.
Edition AA in Lowens. The easy instructor. Ann Arbor, 1953.

1. Tune-books. I. Smith, William, fl. 1802, joint comp. II. Title.
M2116.L7E3 1830 M 54-985

NL 0411182 DLC

MT50 .L6 1831 Little, William, fl. 1798, comp
The easy instructor; or, A new method of teaching sacred harmony. Containing, I. The rudiments of music on an improved plan ... II. A choice collection of psalm tunes and anthems ... By William Little and William Smith. Albany, Printed by Websters & Skinners and Oliver Steele, 1831.
135, [1] p. 13 x 23cm.
At head of title: Revised and enlarged edition.
Cover and p. 35-38 wanting.
Shape-note notati on.
1. Harmony. I. Smith, William, joint author. II. Title.

NL 0411183 ViU

VOLUME 336

[Little, William] 1825-
A contribution to the history of Byfield parish. <An outside view.> [Newburyport, Mass., C. B. Huse, pr., 1893]
cover-title, 12 p. 23½cm.
Prepared for the West Newbury natural history club in 1891, and repeated at the annual gathering of the Byfield parish, July 12, 1893.

1. Byfield, Mass.—Hist. I. Title.
10—17555
Library of Congress F74.B99L7
[a41b1]

NL 0411184 DLC

Little, William, 1833-1893.
Address delivered at the centennial celebration of the town of Warren, N. H., on Tuesday, July 14, 1863, by William Little ... Manchester, N. H., Printed for the Town, by C. F. Livingston, 1863.
18 p. 22cm.

1. Warren, N. H.—Hist.
18-2260
Library of Congress F44.W22L68

NL 0411185 DLC Nh OClWHi

Little, William, 1833-1893.
Brief history of the schools of Manchester, N.H., formerly Derryfield. Manch.,1876(?)

NL 0411186 Nh

Little, William, 1833-1893.
History of the town of Warren, N. H., from its early settlement to the year 1854: including a sketch of the Pemigewasset Indians. By William Little. Concord, N. H., Steam printing works of McFarland & Jenks, 1854.
1 p. l., [vii]-viii, [9]-170 p. 19½cm.

1. Warren, N. H.—Hist.
16-8153
Library of Congress F44.W21L7

NL 0411187 DLC MWA Nh OClWHi

Little, William, 1833-1893.
The history of Warren; a mountain hamlet, located among the White Hills of New Hampshire. By William Little. Manchester, N. H., W. E. Moore, printer, 1870.
xiii, [3], [17]-592 p. front., illus. (incl. maps) photos., ports. 24cm.

1. Warren, N. H.—Hist.
1-8085
Library of Congress F44.W22L7

MB
NL 0411188 DLC WaS NN MU NIC KyHi MnHi OClWHi NhDo

F 44 W4L77 Little, William, 1833-1893.
The history of Weare, New Hampshire, 1735-1888. By William Little. David Cross, Abner P. Collins, Josiah G. Dearborn, Robert Peaslee, Sylvester C. Gould, town committee who furnished the material. Pub. by the town. Lowell, Mass., Printed by S. W. Huse & co., 1888.
x p., 2 l., 1064 p. front., plates, ports. 24cm.
Genealogy of families in Weare: p. [709]-1032.

1. Weare, N. H.—Hist. 2. Weare, N. H.—Geneal.
1—8078
Library of Congress F44.W4L7

NhDo MH
NL 0411189 DLC WaS MeB NNC-M CU OClWHi MWA Nh NIC

MICROFILM F7307 Little, William, 1833-1893.
The history of Weare, New Hampshire, 1735-1888. By William Little. David Cross, Abner P. Collins, Josiah G. Dearborn, Robert Peaslee, Sylvester C. Gould, town committee who furnished the material. Pub. by the town. Lowell, Mass., Printed by S. W. Huse & co., 1888.
x p., 2 l., 1064 p. front., plates, ports. 24cm.
Genealogy of families in Weare: p. [709]-1032.

Microfilm (positive) New York, Columbia University Libraries, 1971. 1 reel. Master negative

NL 0411191 NNC

Little, William, 1848-1922.
Oxford universal English dictionary on historical principles. From the original Oxford English dictionary ... this shorter Oxford English dictionary is adapted. Prepared by William Little, H. W. Fowler [and] J. Coulson; revised and edited by C. T. Onions. [New York] Oxford University Press, Doubleday, Doran & Co. [c1937]
10 v. (2475 p.) 27 cm.
Originally published in two volumes (Oxford, The Clarendon press, 1933) with title: The shorter Oxford English dictionary on historical principles.
1. English language—Dictionaries. I. Fowler, Henry Watson, 1858-1933, joint author. II. Coulson, Mrs. Jessie (Senior) 1903- joint author. III. Onions, Charles Talbut, 1873-1965, ed. IV. Title. V. Title: Oxford English dictionary.
PE1625.L53 1937 423 rev 38-34731

NL 0411192 DLC ICJ OClW

Little, William, 1848-1922.
The shorter Oxford English dictionary on historical principles; prepared by William Little, H. W. Fowler [and] J. Coulson; revised and edited by C. T. Onions. Oxford, The Clarendon Press, 1933.
2 v. (2475 p.) 28 cm.
"An abridgement officially authorized by the Delegates of the Oxford university press of A new English dictionary on historical principles, later known as The Oxford English dictionary."—Pref.
CONTENTS: I. A-M.—II. N-Z.

——— [Another issue] With note on verso of t. p. "First published, February 1933; reprinted with corrections, March, 1933."

1. English language—Dictionaries. I. Fowler, Henry Watson, 1858-1933, joint author. II. Coulson, Mrs. Jessie (Senior) 1903- joint author. III. Onions, Charles Talbut, 1873-1965, ed. IV. Title. V. Title: Oxford English dictionary.
PE1625.L33 423 33-11803

MB MH-BA NN KyLx PU
NL 0411194 DLC CtY MiU OCl OO OCU PBm PPD ViU IU

Little, William, 1848-1922.
The shorter Oxford English dictionary on historical principles; prepared by William Little, H. W. Fowler [and] J. Coulson; revised and edited by C. T. Onions. Oxford, The Clarendon Press [1934]
2 v. (2475 p.) 28 cm.
"First published, February 1933, reprinted, with corrections, March 1933 ... 1934."
"An abridgement officially authorized by the Delegates of the Oxford university press of A new English dictionary on historical principles, later known as The Oxford English dictionary."—Pref.
1. English language—Dictionaries. I. Fowler, Henry Watson, 1858-1933, joint author. II. Coulson, Mrs. Jessie (Senior) 1903- joint author. III. Onions, Charles Talbut, 1873-1965, ed. IV. Title. V. Title: Oxford English dictionary.
PE1625.L53 1934 423 35-12687

NL 0411195 DLC

Little, William, 1848-1922.
The shorter Oxford English dictionary on historical principles. Prepared by William Little, H. W. Fowler, J. Coulson. Revised and edited by C. T. Onions. 2d ed Oxford, The Clarendon press, 1935.

An abridgment of The Oxford English dictionary edited by James Augustus Henry Murray.

E1144 — T.r. — English lang. Dict. — Onions, Charles Talbut, ed., 1873-. — Fowler, Henry Watson, ed., 1858-1933. — Coulson, Mrs. Jessie (Senior), ed., 1903-. — Little, William, ed., 1848-1922.

NL 0411196 MB

Little, William, 1848-1922.
The shorter Oxford English dictionary on historical principles, prepared by William Little, H. W. Fowler [and] J. Coulson; revised and edited by C. T. Onions. 2d ed. Oxford, The Clarendon Press, 1936.
2 v. (2475 p.) 28 cm.
"An abridgement officially authorized by the Delegates of the Oxford university press of A new English dictionary on historical principles, later known as The Oxford English dictionary."—Pref.
1. English language—Dictionaries. I. Fowler, Henry Watson, 1858-1933, joint author. II. Coulson, Mrs. Jessie (Senior) 1903- joint author. III. Onions, Charles Talbut, 1873-1965, ed. IV. Title. V. Title: Oxford English dictionary.
PE1625.L53 1936 423 rev 37-6879 MARC

NL 0411197 DLC PPT MiU PBm PP IU OCl OClh

Little, William, 1848-1922.
The shorter Oxford English dictionary on historical principles prepared by William Little ... H. W. Fowler ... J. Coulson ... revised and edited by C. T. Onions ... 2d ed. ... Oxford, The Clarendon press, 1939.
2 v. 28½ cm.
"An abridgement officially authorized by the Delegates of the Oxford university press of A new English dictionary on historical principles, later known as The Oxford English dictionary."—Pref.

NL 0411198 ViU

R-889 M98 s 1947 Little, William, 1848-1922.
The shorter Oxford English dictionary on historical principles, prepared by William Little, H.W. Fowler, J. Coulson; rev. and ed. by C.T. Onions. 3d ed. [1944] rev. with addenda. Oxford, Clarendon Press [1947]
2 v. 29cm.
"An abridgment officially authorized by the Delegates of the Oxford University Press of A new English dictionary on historical principles, later known as The Oxford English dictionary."

NL 0411199 CU CtY PBm NcD ICU PP OU PPT

PE1625 .L53 1955 Little, William, 1848-1922.
The shorter Oxford English dictionary on historical principles, prepared by William Little, H. W. Fowler [and] J. Coulson, rev. and edited by C. T. Onions. 3d ed. rev., with addenda. Oxford, Clarendon Press [1955]
2515 p. 28 cm.

1. English language—Dictionaries. I. Fowler, Henry Watson, 1858-1933, joint author. II. Coulson, Mrs. Jessie (Senior) 1903- joint author. III. Onions, Charles Talbut, 1873-1965, ed. IV. Title. V. Title: Oxford English dictionary.
PE1625.L53 1955 423 A 56-6196
Mount Holyoke Coll. for Library of Congress rev 2 Library [r72u2]†

NL 0411200 MShM DLC

Little, William Buller, 1888-
General elementary science, by W. B. Little ... London, Sir I. Pitman & sons, ltd., 1934.
viii, 176 p. illus., diagrs. 19cm. [Science in everyday life]

1. Science—Juvenile literature. I. Title.
35-7282
Library of Congress Q163.L5
[3]

NL 0411201 DLC

Little, William Buller, 1888-
Handicraft in plywood, by W. B. Little. London, New York [etc.] Sir I. Pitman & sons, ltd., 1928.
xii, 115 p. col. front., illus. 19cm. (On cover: Pitman's homecraft series)

1. Plywood. I. Title.
29-17234 rev. 2
Library of Congress TT200.L5

NL 0411202 DLC MB OCl Or WaS

VOLUME 336

Little, William Butler, 1888
Handicraft in plywood. Pitman, 1935.
115 p. illus. (Pitman's "craft-for-all" series)

NL 0411203 MiU

Little, William Buller.
Science and health, by W. B. Little ... London, New York [etc.] Sir I. Pitman & sons, ltd., 1930.
xi, 183 p. illus. 19cm. [Science in everyday life ... Second series]

1. Physiology. 2. Hygiene. I. Title.

Library of Congress QP37.L5 32-2480
[2] 613

NL 0411204 DLC NN

Little, William Buller.
Science and living things, by W. B. Little ... London, New York [etc.] Sir I. Pitman & sons, ltd., 1931.
xv, 239 p. illus. (incl. ports.) 19cm. [Science in everyday life]

1. Natural history. 2. Biology. 3. Zoology. I. Title.

Library of Congress QH47.L75 32-2007
[3] 570

NL 0411205 DLC NN

Little, William Buller.
Science and the weather, by W. B. Little ... London, Sir I. Pitman & sons, ltd., 1933.
1 p. l., v-x, 155 p. illus., diagrs. 19cm.

1. Meteorology. 2. Weather. I. Title.

Library of Congress QC861.L5 33-36974
[3] 551.5

NL 0411206 DLC DNW

Little, William Buller.
Science and the weather. by W B Little and G Dury, 2.ed, London. Pitman [1951] ix, 110 p illus. 19cm. (Science in everyday life series)

1 Meteorology. I Dury. G H joint author t 1951

NL 0411207 NN

Little, William Buller.
Science in the city, by W. B. Little. London, New York [etc.] Sir I. Pitman & sons, ltd., 1930.
xii, 239 p. illus. 19cm. [Science in everyday life ... Second series]

1. Municipal engineering. 2. Hygiene, Public. 3. Cities and towns. I. Title.

Library of Congress TD148.L5 31-23406
[3] 628

NL 0411208 DLC

Little, William Buller.
Science in the country, by W. B. Little. London, New York [etc.] Sir I. Pitman & sons, ltd., 1930.
xii, 219 p. illus. (incl. ports.) 19cm. [Science in everyday life ... Second series]

1. Agriculture. 2. Farm life. 3. Science.

Library of Congress S495.L55 33-9827
[2] 631

NL 0411209 DLC

Little, William Buller.
Science in the home, by W. B. Little. London, New York [etc.] Sir I. Pitman & sons, ltd., 1929.
xii, 197 p. illus. (incl. ports., map) diagrs. 19cm. [Science in everyday life ... Second series]

1. Domestic economy. 2. Science.

Library of Congress TX149.L5 30-10929
[3] 640

NL 0411210 DLC

Little, William Buller, 1888–
A short course in biology, by W. B. Little ... Based on the suggestions of the Board of education on biology and health. London, Sir I. Pitman & sons, ltd., 1935.
viii, 168 p. illus., diagrs. 20cm.

1. Biology. 2. Hygiene—Study and teaching.

Library of Congress QH308.L55 36-8829
[2] 574

NL 0411211 DLC

Little, William Buller, 1888 –
The world's food. By W. B. Little ... London, New York [etc.] Sir I. Pitman & sons, ltd., 1931.
xii, 200 p. illus., map, diagrs. 19cm. (Lettered on cover: Pitman's commercial series)
Bibliography: p. 199–200.

1. Food. I. Title.

Library, U. S. Dept. of Agriculture 389L72 Agr 31-786

NL 0411212 DNAL NcD

Little, William Buller, 1888 –
The world's work in industry, by W. B. Little ... London, New York [etc.] Sir I. Pitman & sons, ltd., 1931.
xiii, 263 p. illus. 19cm.

1. Industrial arts. 2. Technology. I. Title.

Library of Congress T47.L5 33-1299
[3] 600

NL 0411213 DLC NN MB

Little, William C.

Gt. Brit. *Royal commission on labour.*
... The agricultural labourer ... [Assistant commissioners' reports] Presented to both houses of Parliament by command of Her Majesty. London, Printed for H. M. Stationery off., by Eyre and Spottiswoode, 1893–94.

Little, William C.
Local taxation: a paper read at the second meeting of the Wisbech district Chamber of agriculture, 21st April, 1870, by William C. Little ... Wisbech, A. Balding [1870]
20 p. 20cm.

1. Taxation—Gt. Brit. 2. Poor laws—Gt. Brit.

Library of Congress HJ9426.L6 10-12820

NL 0411215 DLC

HD1930 .A2L7 Little, William C
Report on agricultural depression, with reference to the western and southern counties; its cause and remedies. By W. C. Little, assistant commissioner, Royal commission on agriculture. Abridged by Sir T. D. Acland ... with a prefatory note to the Recommendations of the commissioners. Reprinted ... from the Journal of the Bath and west of England society and Southern counties association. London, W. Clowes, 1883.
54 p.
Full report contained in Gt.Brit. Royal commission on agriculture. Digest and appendix to part I of evidence taken ... 1881.

NL 0411216 ICU

Little, William C.

Gt. Brit. *Royal commission on labour.*
Report[s], [minutes of evidence, indexes, answers to questions] London, Printed for H. M. Stationery off., by Eyre and Spottiswoode, 1892–94.

Little, William Coffin, 1796–1838.
Settlement of the Accounts of Robert W. Wood, administrator...
see under Wood, Robert Williams, 1803–1892.

Little, William F.

... Helps for the teaching of Cæsar. New York, Columbia university press, 1902.

Little, William Francis, 1864– ed.

Müller, Elise.
Neue märchen für die liebe jugend, von Elise Müller; ed. for school use by special permission of the author, by W. F. Little ... New York, Cincinnati [etc.] American book company [c1907]

Little, William Francis, 1864–
Why go to high school? By W. F. Little ... Indianapolis, The Bobbs-Merrill company [c1928]
7 p. l., 281 p. 19½cm.

1. High schools. 2. Education, Secondary. 3. School-houses. I. Title.

Library of Congress LB1607.L55 28-16858

NL 0411221 DLC Or OrP ICJ MB OClJC OCl OClh ICJ MB

VOLUME 336

Little, William John, 1810-[18]94.
——. An address read at the inauguration of the London Hospital New Medical and Surgical College, Mile End, and the opening of the seventieth academic session of the London Hospital, Oct. 2, 1854. 26 pp. 12°. London, S. Highley, 1854.

NL 0411222 DNLM

Little, William John, 1810-94.
——. Introductory address at the opening of the medical session of the London Hospital Medical College, October 2, 1871. 43 pp. 12°. London, G. Levy, [1871].

NL 0411223 DNLM

WE L778m 1882
LITTLE, William John, 1810-1894
Medical and surgical aspects of in-knee (genu-valgum) its relation to rickets, its prevention and its treatment with and without surgical operation, by W. J. Little assisted by E. Muirhead Little. London, Longmans, Green, 1882.
xx, 161 p. illus.

NL 0411224 DNLM NcD

Little, William John, 1810–1894.
Medical and surgical aspects in-knee (genu-valgum): its relation to rickets, its prevention and its treatment with and without surgical operation. By W. J. Little, ..., assisted by E. Muirhead Little, ... Illustrated by upwards of fifty figures and diagrams. New York, D. Appleton & Co., 1882.
xx, 161 p. 52 illus. 22cm.

NL 0411225 ICJ OClW-H MoSU

Little, William John, 1810–1894.
On ankylosis, or stiff-joint: a practical treatise on the contractions and deformities resulting from diseases of joints. By W. J. Little, ... London, Longman, Brown, Green, and Longmans, 1843.
xii, 145 p. 32 illus. 23cm.

NL 0411226 ICJ NcD DNLM MH

Little, W. J.
On ankylosis or stiff joint.
London, 1845.
8vo.

NL 0411227 NN

WE L778o 1868
LITTLE, William John, 1810-1894
On spinal weakness and spinal curvatures, their early recognition and treatment. London, Longmans, Green, 1868.
xi, 121 p. illus.

NL 0411228 DNLM IU NcD KU-M

WE L778on 1853
LITTLE, William John, 1810-1894
On the nature and treatment of the deformities of the human frame: being a course of lectures delivered at the Royal Orthopaedic Hospital in 1843, with numerous notes and additions to the present time. London, Longman, Brown, Green, and Longmans, 1853.
x, 412 p. illus.

NL 0411229 DNLM OClW-H MnU ICJ

Little, W. J. Orthopaedic surgery.
[In Holmes, Timothy. System of surgery. v13. 1882, p. 326-377)
RD31 .H75

NL 0411230 DLC

Little, William John
Orthopaedic surgery.
(In Holmes, T. A system of surgery. London, 1860-64. 22 cm. v. III, 1862. p. 557-614)
RD31 .H745

NL 0411231 DLC

QSB L778r 1848
LITTLE, William John, 1810-1894
Remarkable congenital deformity, partly resulting from constriction by the umbilical cord. Presented to the Pathological Society, session 1847-48. London [Levy, Robson, and Franklyn] 1848.
15 p.

NL 0411232 DNLM

Little, William John, 1810-94.
——. Remarks on the treatment of infantile congenital club-foot. 35 pp. 8°. [London], 1876. [P., v. 2026.]

NL 0411233 DNLM

Little, William John, 1810-
——. Report of the Hunterian oration, delivered before the members of the Hunterian Society at the thirty-third aniversary, February 4, 1852. 34 pp. 8°. London, Robson, Levey & Franklyn, [1852]. [Also, in: P., v. 590.]

NL 0411234 DNLM

Little, William John, 1810-94.
——. Report of the Hunterian oration delivered before the members of the Hunterian Society, at the thirty-third anniversary, February 4th, 1852. 34 pp. 8°. London, Robson, Levey & Franklin, [1852]. [P., v. 20-32.]

NL 0411235 DNLM

Little (William John) [1810-]. *Symbolæ ad talipedem varum cognoscendum. Pars I. Genesis. 24 pp., 1 l. 4°. Berolini, typ. Nietackianis, [1837].

NL 0411236 DNLM

Little, W[illiam] J[ohn] 1810–1894.
A treatise on the nature of club-foot and analogous distortions ... By W. J. Little ... London, W. Jeffs; [etc., etc.] 1839.
2 p. l., [vii]-xxiii, [1], [xxi]-lxii, 276 p. illus. 22½cm.

1. Foot—Abnormities and deformities.

Library of Congress RD783.L77 7-5966†

NL 0411236-1 DLC OClW-H KyU DNLM WU-M NcD ICJ

Little, William John Knox, 1839-1918. 24.25
The broken vow. A story of here and hereafter. London. Chapman & Hall. 1887. Sm. 8°.

41078 — T.r.

NL 0411237 MB

Ip L728 887b
Little, William John Knox, 1839-1918.
The broken vow. A story of here and hereafter ... 2d ed. London, Chapman and Hall, limited, 1887.
viii, 263, [1]p. 20cm.

NL 0411238 CtY OO

PS2248 .L46 B7
Little, William John Knox, 1839-1918.
The broken vow. London, Chapman and Hall, 1888.
263p.

NL 0411239 NcU

Little, W[illiam] J[ohn] Knox, 1839-1918.
The broken vow. A story of here and hereafter. [3. ed.] London, Chapman & Hall, 1891.
viii, 264 p. 12°.

NL 0411240 NN

Little, William John Knox, 1839-1918.
The broken vow; a story of here and hereafter. [3d ed.] London, Chapman and Hall, 1893.
viii, 263 p. 20cm.

NL 0411241 ViU

Little, W[illiam] J[ohn] Knox, 1839-
The broken vow; a story of here and hereafter, by W. J. Knox Little ... Illustrated by Harold Piffard. London, Isbister & co. ltd. [1903]
84 p. incl. front., illus., pl. 24cm. [With The Sunday magazine. new ser., v. 32]
On cover: Paths of peace, 1903. Xmas no. Sunday magazine.

I. The Sunday magazine. Christmas number.

Library of Congress AP4.S85 6-35809

NL 0411242 DLC

Little, William John Knox, 1839-1918.
Characteristics and motives of the Christian life; ten sermons preached in Manchester Cathedral in Lent and Advent 1877, by the Rev. W.J. Knox Little. New and revised edition. New York, Pott, Young, 1880.
xii, 257 p. 18 cm.
1. Church of England. Sermons. 2. Advent sermons. 3. Lenten sermons. I. Title.

NL 0411243 RPB IEG

Little, William John Knox, 1839-1918.
Characteristics and motives of the Christian life; ten sermons preached in Manchester Cathedral in Lent and Advent, 1877. New and rev. ed. New York, E. and J. B. Young, 1881.
xii, 257 p. 19cm.
Pages v-vi (?) wanting.

1. Christian life. 2. Church of England—Sermons. 3. Sermons, English. I. Title.

NL 0411244 ViU OO

VOLUME 336

BV 4501 L55 1884 Little, William John Knox, 1839-1918.
Characteristics and motives of the Christian life. Ten sermons preached in Manchester Cathedral in Lent and Advent, by W. J. Knox Little. 3d ed. London, Rivingtons, 1884.
xii, 257 p. 18 cm.

1. Christian life. 2. Lenten sermons. 3. Advent sermons. I. Title.

NL 0411245 NRCR

LITTLE, WILLIAM JOHN KNOX, 1839-1918.
The child of Stafferton; a chapter from a family chronicle, by W. J. Knox Little... London: Chapman and Hall, ltd., 1888. xii, 330 p. 19cm.

1. Fiction, English. I. Title.

NL 0411246 NN NcU NjP OCl MH

Little, W[illiam] J[ohn] Knox.
The child of Stafferton; a chapter from a family chronicle. London: Chapman and Hall, Ltd., 1893. 330 p. 12°.

NL 0411247 NN RPB

Little, William John Knox.
The Christian home: its foundations & duties. N.Y. Young, pref. [1891].
287 p. D.

NL 0411248 OCl

Little, William John Knox , 1839-
The Christian Home, its foundation and outies. Lond. Longmans, 1895.
xv, 287p.

NL 0411249 PPPD IEG

Little, William John Knox-.
The Christian home; its foundation and duties. New impression. — London. Longmans, Green & Co. 1908. xiv, (1), 287 pp. 18 cm., in 8s.

L1550 — T.r. — Christian life.

NL 0411250 MB

Little, William John Knox, 1839-1918.
The Conflict of Ideals in Church of England. New York, Edwin S. Gorham, [n.d.]

NL 0411251 DNC

BX 5131. L37 Little, William John Knox, 1839-1918.
The conflict of ideals in the Church of England. London, Pitman, 1905.
xii,327p front(port) 22-1/2cm

Bibliographical footnotes.

1.Church of England. Doctrine. 2.Church of England. Ceremonies and practices. I.Title.

NL 0411252 MnCS MB

LS73 L77 Little, William John Knox, 1839-1918.
The conflict of ideals in the Church of England, by W.J.Knox Little ... New York, E.S.Gorham,1905.
xiii,327p. front.(port.) 22.5cm.

NL 0411253 NNUT

Little, William John Knox, 1839–
David, the hero-king of Israel, by Rev. W. J. Knox Little... London: J. M. Dent & Co. [pref. 1903.] viii, 125 p., 1 l., front., 2 maps. 24°. (The temple series of Bible handbooks.)

Title within ornamental borders.

SCHIFF COLLECTION.

1. David, king of Israel. 2. Series.
N. Y. P. L. October 10, 1917.

NL 0411254 NN NcD CtY NcU OCH

Little, William John Knox, 1839–1918.
Holy matrimony, by the Rev. W. J. Knox Little ... London, New York [etc.] Longmans, Green & co., 1900.
x p., 1 l., 296 p. 19½cm. (Half-title: The Oxford library of practical theology ...)

1. Marriage. I. Title.

A 21-414

Title from General Theol. Sem. Printed by L. C.

NL 0411255 NNG ICU MB OO

Little, William John Knox, 1839-1918.
Holy Matrimony. New York, Longmans, 1907.
296 p. (Oxford library of practical theology)

NL 0411256 PPLT

Little, William John Knox, 1839-1918.
Holy matrimony, by the Rev. W.J. Knox Little Longmans, Green, and co., 1913.
xp., 1l., 296 p. 19.5 cm. (On cover: Oxford library of practical theology)

NL 0411257 CtY-D

BT 430 A33L52 Little, William John Knox, 1839-1918.
The hopes and decisions of the Passion of our most holy Redeemer, by W. J. Knox Little. London, Rivingtons, 1886.
xii, 227 p. 18 cm.

1. Jesus Christ - Passion - Sermons. 2. Lenten sermons. I. Title.

NL 0411258 NRCR NjP CU

Little, William John Knox, 1839-
The hopes and decisions of the Passion of Our Most Holy Redeemer. New ed. Lond. Longmans, 1894.
xii, 227 p.

NL 0411259 PPPD

Little, William John Knox, 1839-1918.

Imitatio Christi.
The imitation of Christ by Thomas à Kempis. A facsimile reproduction of the first edition printed at Augsburg in 1471–2. With an introduction by Canon W. J. Knox Little, M. A. London, E. Stock, 1893.

Little, William John Knox, 1839-1918.
Immortality. A clerical symposium on What are the foundations of the belief in the immortality of man
see under title

Little, William John Knox, 1839-1918.
John Keble, the man & his work ...
see under title

BX 5133 L55J6 Little, William John Knox, 1839-1918.
The journey of life, by W. J. Knox Little. New York, E. P. Dutton & Co., 1892.
viii, 217 p. 19 cm. (Preachers of the age)

1. Church of England - Sermons. 2. Sermons, English. I. Title. (Series)

NL 0411263 NRCR IEG MA OO OCl NjP

BX5133 .L778l 1894 in: SWTS Little, William John Knox, 1839-1919.
Labour and sorrow. Sermons preached on various occasions. New York, Thomas Whittaker, 1894.
336p. 20cm.

1. Church of England--Sermons. 2. Sermons, English. I. Title.

NL 0411264 IEG PPPD

BX5133 .L778la 1889 in: SWTS Little, William John Knox, 1839-1919.
The light of life. Sermons preached on various occasions. London, Rivingtons; New York, E. & J.B. Young, 1889.
xii, 333p. 20cm.

1. Church of England--Sermons. I. Title.

NL 0411265 IEG

Little, William John Knox, 1839-
The Light of life; sermons preached on various occasions. New. Ed. Lond. 1895.
xii, 333 p.

NL 0411266 PPPD

731.4 K74ma 1900 LITTLE, William John Knox, 1839-1918.
A manual of devotion for Lent. London, Isbister & Co., 1900.
328p. 19.5cm.

NL 0411267 MH-AH

Little, William John
A manual of devotion for lent. N.Y. Dutton, 1901.
328 p.

NL 0411268 PPPD

VOLUME 336

Little, William John Knox, 1839-1918.
A manual of devotion for Lent, by W.J. Knox Little. 2d ed. New York, E.P. Dutton; London, Isbister, 1902.
328 p. 20 cm.
1. Lent. Prayer-books and devotions.

NL 0411269 IEG

BT 430 A33L53 Little, William John Knox, 1839-1918.
The mystery of the Passion of our most holy Redeemer, by W. J. Knox Little. London, Rivingtons, 1881.
xii, 199 p. 18 cm.

1. Jesus Christ - Passion - Sermons. 2. Lenten sermons. I. Title.

NL 0411270 NRCR ViU

Little, William John Knox, 1839-1918.
The mystery of the passion of Our Most Holy Redeemer ... New York, 1882.
18 cm.

NL 0411271 CtY

BT430 .L729 Little, William John Knox, 1839-1918.
The mystery of the passion of our most holy Redeemer. 3d ed. London, Rivingtons, 1885.
199 p.

1. Jesus Christ - Passion - Sermons. I. Title.

NL 0411272 CtHC

Little, William John Knox. 1839-

Notes of Catechisings.
N.Y. n.d. James Pott & Co.

NL 0411273 DNC

Little, William John Knox, 1839-1918.
On the love of God ... Lond., 1902
see under François de Sales, Saint, bp. of Geneva, 1567-1622.

BX 5133 L5589 Little, William John Knox, 1839-1918.
The outlook of the soul, and other sermons preached on various occasions, by W. J. Knox Little. (Previously entitled "Labour and Sorrow") London, H. R. Allenson [pref. 1894]
336 p. 19 cm. (Eminent preacher's series)
1. Church of England - Sermons. 2. Sermons, English. I. Title. II. Title: Labour and sorrow.

NL 0411275 NRCR OCl

Little, William John Knox, 1839-
The perfect life; sermons. Lond. Longmans, 1898.

xi, 368p.

NL 0411276 PPPD IEG

Little, William John [Knox.] "The priest in absolution:" a sermon . . . Manchester, Roworth, 1877. 35 p.

NL 0411277 PPPD

BX 5131 .L5x Little, William John Knox, 1839-1918.
Sacerdotalism; if rightly understood, the teaching of the Church of England. Being four letters originally addressed, by permission, to the late Very Rev. William J. Butler. London, New York, Longmans, Green, 1894.
318 p. 20 cm.
Pagination occasionally repeated where author revised and expanded.

1. Church of England--Doctrinal and controversial works. I. Title

NL 0411278 OKentU OrU ICN OCl MiD PPPD DN-Ob IEG

Little, William John Knox, 1839-1918.
St. Francis of Assisi; his times, life and work; lectures delivered in substance in the Ladye chapel of Worcester cathedral in the Lent of 1896 ... London, Isbister & co., 1897.
4 p. l., 328 p. front. (port.) 8°.

1. Francesco d'Assisi, Saint, 1182-1226.

1-13222

NL 0411279 NcD OU OCU MiU CSmH MB CtY DHN WaWW DLC CaBVaU MH-AH TU WaU KyLxCB CU CSaT

BQ 6595 .L77 Little, William John Knox, 1839-1918.
St. Francis of Assisi; his times, life and work; lectures delivered in substance in the Ladye chapel of Worcester cathedral in the Lent of 1896, by W.J. Knox Little ... New York, T. Whittaker, 1897.
4 p.l., 328 p. front. (port.) 22cm.

1. Francesco d'Assisi, Saint, 1182-1226.

NL 0411280 DCU MdBP

Little, William John Knox, 1839-1918.
St. Francis of Assisi; his times, life, work; lectures delivered in substance in the Ladye Chapel of Worcester Cathedral in the Lent of 1896... New York, T. Whittaker, 1898.
328 p. port. 23 cm.
Bibliographical footnotes.
1. Francesco d' Assisi, Saint, 1182-1226.

NL 0411281 NjPT

LITTLE, WILLIAM JOHN KNOX, 1839-1918.
St. Francis of Assisi; his times, life and work, by W. J. Knox Little... New and cheaper edition. London: Isbister and co., 1904. xiii, 328 p. front. (port.) 23cm.

Label of Thomas Whittaker, New York, over original imprint.
Bibliographical footnotes.

118234B. 1. Francis of Assisi, Saint, 1182-1226.

N. Y. P. L. June 4, 1941

NL 0411282 NN DHN

Little, William John Knox, 1839-1918.
Sermons preached for the most part in Manchester, by the Rev. W. J. Knox Little ... New York, Pott, Young, and company, 1880.
2 p. l., [vii]-xi, 340p. 19½cm.

Printed by the Wesleyan University Library, 1936

NL 0411283 CtW CLamB ViU

Little, William John Knox, 1839-1918.
Sermons preached for the most part in Manchester, by the Rev. W.J. Knox Little. New York, E. and J.B. Young, 1881.
xi, 340 p. 20 cm.
1. Church of England. Sermons. 2. Sermons, English.

NL 0411284 IEG MB

BX 5133 L5584 Little, William John Knox, 1837-1918.
Sermons preached for the most part in Manchester, by W. J. Knox Little. 2d ed. London, Rivingtons, 1882.
xv, 340 p. 20 cm.

1. Church of England - Sermons. 2. Sermons, English.

NL 0411285 NRCR

Little, William John Knox, 1839-
Sketches and studies in South Africa. London, Isbister, 1899.
328 p.
1. Africa, South - Descr. & trav. 2. Africa, South - Pol. & govt. I. Title.

NL 0411286 FTaSU NjP Nh MdBP TxU NcD

Little, William John Knox, 1839-1918.
Sketches and studies in South Africa, by W. J. Knox Little ... [2d ed.] London, Isbister and company, limited, 1899.
328 p. 24½cm.
First edition, June 1899; reprinted July 1899; reprinted December 1899.

1. Africa, South—Descr. & trav. 2. Africa, South—Pol. & govt. I. Title.

Library of Congress DT766.L77 4—19908

NL 0411287 OrU CaOTP MB NN MiU OCl NcU CtY DNW LU DLC CaBVaU OrU OrPR WaSp MiEM CoU WU

Little, W[illiam] J[ohn] Knox.
Sketches and studies in South Africa. London: Isbister and Co., 1900. 5 p.l., xiv p., 1 l., (1)16-328 p. [2. ed.] 8°.

1. Africa (South).—History, 19th century.
N. Y. P. L. April 16, 1913.

NL 0411288 NN CU ICJ TNF

Little, William John Knox, 1839-1918.
Sketches in sunshine and storm; a collection of miscellaneous essays and notes on travel, by W. J. Knox Little ... London and New York, Longmans, Green & co., 1892.
5 p. l., [3]-338 p. 20cm.
CONTENTS.—The martyr of Algiers.—The tombs of the kings.—The home of S. Nilus.—The shrine of the sacrament.—The grave of Dante.—Amalfi and its mountains.—The heights and hollows of the Lebanon.—The holy places of Palestine.

1. Voyages and travels. 2. Palestine—Descr. & trav. I. Title.

Library of Congress D973.L6 10—4209

NL 0411289 DLC IEG OCl NN

Little, William John Knox, 1839-
Sunlight and shadow in the Christian life; sermons preached for the most part in America. Lond. Rivingtons, 1889.

xii, 310p.

NL 0411290 PPPD OO NjP

VOLUME 336

Little, William John Knox, 1839-1918.
The Three Hours' agony of our Blessed Redeemer; being addresses in the form of meditations delivered in St. Alban's Church, Manchester on Good Friday, 1877, by Rev. W.J. Knox-Little. 2d. ed. Manchester, Thomas Roworth; London [etc.] Rivingtons [pref. 1877]
79 p. front. 17 cm.
1. Jesus Christ. Seven last words. I. Title.

NL 0411291 IEG

BT455 .L77 1877 in: SWTS
Little, William John Knox, 1839-1918.
The Three Hours' agony of our Blessed Redeemer. Being addresses in the form of meditations, delivered in St. Alban's Church, Manchester, on Good Friday, 1877. 3d ed. Manchester, Thomas Roworth [pref. 1877]
79p. 17cm.
1. Jesus Christ--Seven last words. I. Title.

NL 0411292 IEG

Little, William John Knox
The three hours' agony of Our Blessed Redeemer; being addressed in the form of meditations delivered in S. Alban's church, Manchester on Good Friday, 1877. New ed. Longmans, 1893

NL 0411293 WaSpG

LITTLE, W[illiam] J[ohn] Knox, 1839-
The threshold of the unseen; Some romances relating to the other world. London, Rees, Ltd. 1913.

NL 0411294 MH

Little, William John Knox, 1839-
A treasury of meditation; or, Suggestions as aids to those who desire to live a devout life. By W. J. Knox Little... London: Skeffington & Son, 1896. 1 p.l., (i)vi-xv p., 1 l., (1)4-363 p. 16°.
1. Meditations (Religious). 2. Title.
N. Y. P. L. August 22, 1917.

NL 0411295 NN PPPD

LITTLE, WILLIAM JOHN KNOX, 1839-1918.
The waif from the waves; a story of three lives touching this world and another, by W. J. Knox Little... London: Chapman & Hall, ltd., 1894. viii, 191 p. 19½cm.
118445B. 1. Fiction, English. I. Title.

NL 0411296 NN NcU

BT 430 A33L54
Little, William John Knox, 1839-1918.
The witness of the Passion of our most holy Redeemer, by W. J. Knox Little. London, Rivingtons, 1884.
x, 173 p. 18 cm.
1. Jesus Christ - Passion - Sermons. 2. Lenten sermons. I. Title.

NL 0411297 NRCR ViU

---

872 L778w
LITTLE, William John Knox, 1839-1918
The witness of the passion of our most holy redeemer. New York, E.& J.B. Young & Co., 1884.
x,173p. 18cm.

NL 0411298 MH-AH CtY NN IEG

Little, William John Knox, 1839-
The witness of the Passion of Our Most Holy Redeemer. Ed. 3. Lond. Longmans, 1894.
173p.

NL 0411299 PPPD

Little, William John Knox, 1839-1918.
A year of Eucharists; suggestions for prayer in preparation and thanksgiving for Holy Communion. Lond. Skeffington, 1891.
105p.

NL 0411300 PPPD

LE 3 T52 PhD 1956 L57 University Archives
Little, William Meldrum, 1924-
A study of inclusions in cassiterite and associated minerals. [Toronto, 1955.
83 leaves. illus., diagrs.
Thesis - University of Toronto.
Thesis accepted 1956.
Bibliography: leaves 71-82.

NL 0411301 CaOTU

Little, William Myers, 1867-
The Little scrapbook; being selections from the varied newspaper writings of William M. Little, sometime literary editor of The Sunday Charlotte Observer and later United States Consul to Honduras. With a forward by Laura Little. Atlanta, Privately printed, 1952.
103p. 24cm.

NL 0411302 NcWsW NcU

Little, William Robert
see
Little, Robert, 1902-

Little, W[illiam] S., M.D.
Address in ophthalmology. Philadelphia: Collins, 1884. 20 p. 8°.
Repr.: Medical Soc. of the State of Pennsylvania. Transac. 1884.
1. Eye.—Diseases.
N. Y. P. L. December 18, 1912.

NL 0411304 NN

Little (William S.) M.D. A case of persistent hyaloid artery. 3 pp., 1 pl. 8°. [Boston, 1881.]
Repr. from: Tr. Am. Ophth. Soc. 1880-84, Bost., 1885, iii.

NL 0411305 DNLM

YF 129 .C52 L77s
Little, Mrs. William S
The story of the massacre of Cherry Valley; a paper read by Mrs. William S. Little, December 12th, 1890, before the Rochester Historical Society ... [Rochester? N.Y.] Published at the request of the Society [1890?]
24,3p. 24cm.
Presentation copy inscribed by the author.
Bibliography: p.[1]
1. Cherry Valley Massacre, 1778. I. Title.

NL 0411306 NRU CSmH MWA NBuG

Little, Mrs. William S
The story of the Massacre of Cherry Valley; a paper read December 12th, 1890, before the Rochester historical society and published at the request of the society. [n.p., 1891?] 27,iii p. 23cm.
Bibliography, p. [2]
1. United States—Hist.—Revolution—Military, 1778, Nov. 11—Cherry valley. 2. Cherry Valley, N.Y.—Hist. I. Rochester historical society, Rochester, N.Y.

NL 0411307 NN

Little (W[illiam] S[wayne]). Letter on the recently proposed water supply of Sligo. 46 pp. 8°. Dublin, King, 1867.
Repr. from: Sligo Independent.

NL 0411308 DNLM

Little, Wilson.
Developmental guidance in secondary school [by] Wilson Little [and] A. L. Chapman. New York, McGraw-Hill, 1953.
324 p. illus. 24 cm.
1. Personnel service in secondary education. I. Chapman, Alvan Lothair, joint author. II. Title.
LB1620.5.L58 371.422 53—6014 ‡
[50k2]

CaBVaU OrSaW IdPI OrPR OrAshS MtU Or PSC NcRS OCl ODW OOxM IaAS WaU KEmT OrCS IdB OrU
NL 0411309 DLC MtBC OClW MB ViU OCU TxU PP PPT

Little, Wilson.
Spanish-speaking children in Texas, by Wilson Little ... Austin, Tex., The University of Texas press, 1944.
73 p. incl. tables, diagrs. 2 fold. maps. 23cm.
"Sponsored by the Committee on Inter-American relations in Texas, the University of Texas, in coöperation with the state Department of education."—Pref.
"Suggested sources of information": p. 70-73.
1. Mexicans in Texas. 2. Education—Texas. I. Texas. University. Committee on Inter-American relations in Texas. II. Texas. Dept. of education. III. Title.
A 44-5418
Texas. Univ. Library for Library of Congress [3]

NL 0411310 TxU

Little, Winston Woodard, 1892-
Applied logic [by] Winston W. Little, W. Harold Wilson [and] W. Edgar Moore. Boston, Houghton Mifflin [1955]
351 p. illus. 25 cm.
1. Logic—Study and teaching. I. Title.
BC108.L5 160.7 55-14414 ‡

KyU-A CaBVa CaBVaU OrLgE OrU WaSpG
NL 0411311 DLC GAT NcD OClUr PBm NcD MB ViU IU PJB

VOLUME 336

Little, firm, booksellers, Albany (1852.
Little & co.)

New York (*State*) *Supreme court.*
... Terms and circuits of the Supreme court, and Courts of oyer and terminer, of the state of New-York, from 1st Jan., 1852, to 1st Jan., 1854. Albany, Little & co., 1852.

... **Little** A. T. S. anthology; the first girl writers in battle-dress. ₍London₎ Distributed by Staples & Staples ₍1944₎
cover-title, 36 p. 18½cm. (A 'Khaki and blue' book, ed. by Peter Ratazzi)

1. English literature—20th cent. 2. English literature (Collections) I. Gt. Brit. Auxiliary territorial service.

A 45–1547

Harvard univ. Library for Library of Congress ₍2₎

NL 0411313 MH

Little Ada; or, The three new years
see under [Henry, Helen L]

PZ7
.H105I

Little Addie's poetry book, conceived in childish love by A.H. New York, Hebrew orphan asylum industrial school, 1875.
24p. 18cm.

NL 0411315 NNU-W

Epsteen Coll. in RareBooks Room

Little Aggie's fresh snow-drops, and what they did in one day. A tale for the young, by the author of "Hope on", "King Jack of Haylands" &c. London, T. Nelson and sons, 1875.
120 p. illus. 16cm. (Little Aggie's library, v.4)

Added title-page, in colors.

NL 0411316 CoU

Little Aimee, the persecuted child
see under Bullard, Anne Tuttle Jones.

Little Alano and His Dog. [being the 2nd part, pp. 11-16, of Mina and other stories]. Newport. 48mo. C. E. Hammett, Jr., Printer. 1098

NL 0411318 ViW

Yk
.S457

Little Alice. Boston, [c1854].
36p.

(Sunday school books; arr. numerically.)

NL 0411319 DLC

Little Alice's Christmas gift, Author of.

For Willie's sake. By the author of Little Alice's Christmas gift. Baltimore, Md., Cushings & Bailey, 1880.

Little Alice's palace; or, The sunny heart.
Philadelphia, American Sunday-school union, 1122 Chestnut Street [c. 1859]
[5],6- 36 p. 15 cm.

NL 0411321 DLC

The little altar boy's manual. Instructions for serving at mass, vespers, benediction, etc., with the proper responses. With prayers at mass, morning and evening prayers, etc. New York, Cincinnati ₍etc.₎ Benziger brothers ₍1891₎
119 p. incl. front., illus. 10½cm.
Translated by Brother D. Litz from Der kleine ministrant.

1. Altar boys. 2. Catholic church—Prayer-books and devotions—English. I. Litz, D., tr. *Translation of* Der kleine ministrant.

40–18691

Library of Congress BX1972.K65
Copyright 1891: 45711 ₍2₎ 264.02

NL 0411322 DLC

The little altar boy's manual. Instructions for serving at mass, vespers, benediction, etc., with the proper responses. With prayers at mass, vespers, morning and evening prayers, etc. New York, Cincinnati ₍etc.₎ Benziger brothers, 1898.
160 p. front., illus. 10½cm.
Translated by Brother D. Litz from Der kleine ministrant.

1. Altar boys. 2. Catholic church—Prayer-books and devotions—English. I. Litz, D., tr. *Translation of* Der kleine ministrant.

40–18692

Library of Congress BX1972.K65 1898
₍2₎ 264.02

NL 0411323 DLC

Little America times, 1933–1935; August Horowitz, editor, Herbert R. Loges, art editor. ₍New York₎ ©1935.
190 l. incl. illus., plates, ports., maps. 19cm.
A compilation of all the editions of the newspaper which came into existence with Admiral Byrd's second expedition to the south pole. It recounts in digest form the Byrd and Ellsworth experiences. *cf.* Foreword.

1. Byrd Antarctic expedition, 2d, 1933–1935. 2. Ellsworth trans-antarctic flight expedition, 1933–1935. I. Horowitz, August, ed.

CA 35–246 Unrev'd

Library of Congress G850.1933.L5
—— Copy 2.
Copyright A 83752 919.9

NL 0411324 DLC NN

The **Little** American: a series of stories and sketches for young folks.
West Point ₍N. Y.₎ 18
v. illus. 25½cm. semimonthly.
Editors: Susan Warner, Anna Warner.

I. Warner, Susan, 1819–1885, ed. II. Warner, Anna Bartlett, 1820–1915, ed.

CA 10—5580 Unrev'd

Library of Congress AP200.L25

NL 0411325 DLC

C 57451

Little American Cinderella to Queen Victoria.
n.p., n.d.
89 p. 23 cm.
Cover-title.

NL 0411326 RPB

LITTLE American Cinderella to Queen Victoria. [Chicago? 1893?] 47 p. 22½cm.

Cover-title.
Poetry and prose.

NL 0411327 NN

The Little American songster, containing **a choice collection** of modern and popular songs, as sung by Jefferson, Cowell, Horn, Miss Fisher, Miss Kelly, &c. &c. &c. New York, Nafis & Cornish; St. Louis, Mo., Nafis, Cornish & co.; ₍etc.₎ ₍184-₎
1 p. l., 125–184, 201–250 p. front. 12½cm.
Without music.
Imperfect: p. 185–200 wanting.

1. American ballads and songs.

30–15361

Library of Congress PS593.L9L56

NL 0411328 DLC

Little and Brown, *publishers, Boston*
see **Little, Brown and Company,** *Boston.*

"The little angel"
see under [Marsh, Charles H.]

Little animal stories, illustrated by Philip B. Parsons. Springfield, Mass., McLoughlin bros., inc. ₍1942₎
₍60₎ p. incl. col. front., illus. (part col.) 17½ x 13½cm. (*On cover:* The Little color classics ... 812)

42–19759

Library of Congress PZ5.L685

NL 0411331 DLC

LITTLE Ann; a true story and other pleasing poetical pieces for children. New York, printed by M.Day,1826.

pp.23.
Front.and other illustr.

NL 0411332 MH

Little Anne, a true story; and other pleasing poetical pieces for children. New York, Printed and sold by Mahlon Day, 1828.
1 p.l., 5-23 p. front., illus. 15 cm.
Frontispiece is printed on p. [2] of cover.

NL 0411333 RPB

Little Ann, a true story; and other pleasing poetical pieces for children ...
New York, Printed by Mahlon Day, 1829.
23 p.

NL 0411334 OClWHi

Little Ann, a true story; and other pleasing poetical pieces, for children. New York: M. Day, 1831. 23 p. front., illus. 24°.

1. Juvenile literature—Poetry, English.
N. Y. P. L. November 30, 1926

NL 0411335 NN CtY

---

xPZ5
L717

Little Ann and her mamma. New York, McLoughlin Bro's ₍18--₎
4ₗ.i.e. 8ₚ. col.illus. 27cm. (Uncle Ned's picture books)

Cover title.

NL 0411336 IaU ICU

VOLUME 336

Little Ann and her mama. London [1871]
see under [Gilbert, Ann (Taylor)] 1782-1866.

Little Ann; or, Every-day lessons on interesting subjects.
see under American Sunday-School Union.

Little Anna
see under Wulff, Margarete.

"Little Anne." A mother's memory. Richmond: Presbyterian committee of publication [1871]
45 p. front. 15½cm.

NL 0411340 ViW DLC

Little Annie's A. B. C. showing the use and sounds of the letters in words of one syllable. Philadelphia, G. S. Appleton; New York, D. Appleton & co., 1851.
[58] p. 14½ x 12cm.

1. Spellers.

CA 17-3011 Unrev'd

Library of Congress PE1144.L7

NL 0411341 DLC

KR372.4 L729 Little Annie's first book; chiefly in words of three letters, by her mother. Philadelphia, G. S. Appleton, 1849.
v, 126 p. illus. 14 1/2 cm.

NL 0411342 MiD NcD

LITTLE Annie's first book: chiefly in words of three letters. By her mother. Philadelphia, G.S.Appleton,etc.,etc.,1850.

Illustr.

NL 0411343 MH

Little Annie's first book, chiefly in words of three letters. By her mother. New York, R.Carter & brothers, 1857.

NL 0411344 MH

Little Annie's first book, chiefly in words of three letters. By her mother. New York, Robert Carter & brothers, 1874.
v, [7]-126 p. front., illus. 14½ x 12cm.
On spine: Annie's first book.

1. Primers—1800-1870. I. Title: Annie's first book.

NL 0411345 ViU

Little Annie's first-[second] book; chiefly in words of three letters. By her mother. New York R.Carter & brothers, 1882.

2 pt, in 1.

NL 0411346 MH

PZ6 .L544 Little Annie's New or third book. By her mother. New York, A.D.F.Randolph, 1859.
177p. illus. 15cm.

NL 0411347 NNU-W

PZ262 .L77 1860 Little Annie's second book, chiefly in words of one syllable. By the author of "Little Annie's first book". New York, R. Carter, 1860.
iv, 5-124 p. front., illus., plates.

NL 0411348 ICU

Little Annie's second book, chiefly in words of one syllable. By the author of "Little Annie's first book." New York, Robert Carter & brothers, 1867.
iv, [5]-124 p. front., illus. 15 x 12cm.
On spine: Annie's second book.

1. Primers—1800-1870. I. Title: Annie's second book.

NL 0411349 ViU MH

Rare Book Room Is94 tl 2 Little Annie's speller. Prettily illustrated. [Published by George S. Appleton,164 Chestnut st.Swaim's buildings,Philadelphia.[c1850]]
66,[16]p. incl.front.(?)illus. 14cm.
"A catalogued of illustrated ... juvenile works. Published by George S. Appleton": p.[67-82]
Imperfect: p.[1-2] (front.?) wanting; t.-p. mutilated,with loss of imprint.

NL 0411350 CtY DLC-P4

Little Annie's speller ... Philadelphia, G. S. Appleton; New York, D. Appleton & co., 1851.
1 p. l., 5-66 p. illus. 14½ x 12cm.

1. Spellers.

CA 17-3012 Unrev'd

Library of Congress PE1144.L75

NL 0411351 DLC

A little anthology of hitherto uncollected poems by modern writers
see under Guthrie, Stuart, ed.

A little anthology of patriotic quotations
see under Heizer, Mrs. Jessie (Harper) comp.

A little anthology of very short poems from the magazines of 1921
see under [Humphries, Rolfe] comp.

BT 3203 .L77 The Little apostle of the mountain province.
v.1- June, 1924-
Baguio [Philippines] Catholic Press, 1924-
v. illus. 22cm. monthly.
"Organ of the Missionaries of the Immaculate Heart of Mary..."
1. Catholic Church - Missions - Period. 1. Missionaries of the Immaculate Heart of Mary.

NL 0411355 DCU

Little apple blossom. [1863]
see under Davis, Caroline E. (Kelly) b. 1831.

Little Arthur's history of France, from the earliest times to the fall of the Second Empire. On the plan of "Little Arthur's England." London. Murray. 1884. x, (1), 294 pp. Illus. Plates. Map. Sm. 8°. 2619.36
Same. New York. Crowell & Co. [1885?] x, 295 pp. 12°. 2619.37

July 28, 1903
E9801 — France. Hist.

NL 0411357 MB CtY

Little Arthur's history of France, from the earliest times to the fall of the Second Empire. London, Murray, 1899.

NL 0411358 MH

Little Arthur's history of France, from the earliest times to the fall of the second empire... London: J. Murray, 1906. x, 294 p. front., map, plates. 16°.

275036A. 1. France—Hist.
N. Y. P. L. April 21, 1927

NL 0411359 NN

Little Arthur's holidays; or, the uncle from India.
= London. Nelson. 1855. 30 pp. Illus. Plate. Vignette. 8°.
Some pages are missing at the end.

G2318

NL 0411360 MB MH

The Little artist. v. 1; Dec. 1899–Nov. 1900. [New York, E. Knaufft, 1899–1900]
[48] p. illus. 30cm. monthly.
No more published.

4-24650

NL 0411361 DLC

Little artist, The: or, the history of Francis Thomas. 3d edition.
London. Westley. 1824. 16 pp. Illus. Plate. Vignette. 10½ cm.

M7610 — Chap-books.

NL 0411362 MB

The little Bach book
see under [Hoelty-Nickel, Theodore] ed.

VOLUME 336

The little barefoot, v.1, Nov.1871- B'klyn,1871-

NL 0411364 NBLiHi

Little barefoot, a domestic drama in five acts
see under Waldauer, Augustus.

Little Barford, Eng. (Parish)
The parish register of Little Barford (1602-1812). (In: Bedfordshire, England. County Records Committee. Bedfordshire parish registers. Bedford, 1933. 34cm. v. 6, B. ii, 179 p.)

Reproduced from typewritten copy.

675840A. 1. Parish registers—Gt. Br. —Eng.—Barford, Little. I. Ser.
N. Y. P. L. November 28, 1933

NL 0411366 NN

Little Barren church, Kentucky.
Minutes... 1841

NL 0411367 KyBgW

Little, The, basket-maker, and other tales. A story book for holiday hours. [Translated from the German.] Philadelphia: R. S. H. George, 1847. 96 p., 4 pl. illus. sq. 16°.

1. Juvenile literature.—Fiction (German).
N. Y. P. L. March 19, 1913.

NL 0411368 NN OKentU

Fiction
RA The little basket-maker, and other tales. A story book for holiday hours. Philadelphia: William G. Wardle, 1848.
96,96p.illus.7col.plates.14cm.

Bound in old black cloth, gold-stamped spine.

1. Children's lit. (RA cat only)

NL 0411369 OC NcD

The little basket maker, and other tales. A sunny book for holiday hours. Philadelphia, 1854.
96 p. illus., front. 15 cm.

NL 0411370 RPB

Epsteen Coll. in RareBooks Room
The little basket-maker, and other tales; a story book for the young. Philadelphia, H. McGrath, 1871.
96 p. illus. 14cm. (The Good child's library, no.4)

"Translated from the German."

NL 0411371 CoU

Beinecke Library Broadsides 4° By6 1728
The Little Beaus petition, to His Ex——y the L. C——t. Against the young ladies of Dublin ... Dublin, Printed for James Nichkelson, opposite Bull's Head in Fleet-street, March 25th, 1728.
broadside. 33 x 11 cm.
The Little Beau was Patrick Walsh; or possibly Thomas Sheridan. - cf. Swift. Works (1814) xv,117, as quoted by Bradshaw no.1281.
In verse.
I. Walsh, Patrick. II. Sheridan, Thomas, 1719-1788.

NL 0411372 CtY

The Little ... bee, a Catholic gatherer of amusing and instructive reading. Under the patronage of the American league of the cross. ser. 1; [Sept.] 1884-[Aug.] 1885. Chicago, J. M. Hayes, s. j., 1885.
2 p. l., 384 p. illus. 23½cm. monthly.
J. M. Hayes, editor.

I. Hayes, James M., ed. II. American league of the cross.

Library of Congress AP2.L645 7-22284

NL 0411373 DLC ICHi

LITTLE Beniamin | Or | Truth Discovering Error: | Being a clear and full Answer unto the | Letter, Subscribed by 47 Ministers of the | Province of London, And presented to | his Excellency, January 18. 1648. | To {Inform the Ignorant | Satisfie the desirous{ of {the concurrent proceedings | the Parliament and Army. | In | Taking away the life of Charles Stuart, late King | of England, together with, &c. | By a reall lover of all those, who love peace and truth. | . . . (5 lines). February 17. 1648. | Imprimatur Gil. Mabbot. |
Printed at London, For George Whittington, at the Blew Anchor | in Cornehill, neer the Royall Exchange, 1648. | Line border. 18.2x14cm. (4),16p.
Preface signed J.R. Ascribed to John Reading, DNB.47:364b, and to John Robothom, DNB.49:60a

NL 0411374 NNUT-Mc

Little Bertram's dream
see The Winter's tale; to which is added Little Bertram's dream

Little Bessie. [Fiction.]
New York. [1854?] 32 pp. Illus. Plate. Illustrated title-page. Decorated cover. [American Tract Society, New York. Publications. Children's tracts, illustrated. Series 4. No. 53.] 15 cm., in 8s.
Bound with the original paper covers.

E888 — S.r.c.

NL 0411376 MB

244 L778be
Little Bessie, and other stories for children and youth. New York, American Tract Society [18--]
1 v. illus. 16 cm.

nos. 53-56.
Each story has separate t. p. and paging.
Contents.-Little Bessie.-Sammy and his father.-Ellen's visit to the shepherd.-Louise Scheppler.

I. American Tract Society. II. Title. III. Title: Sammy and his father. IV. Title: Ellen's visit to the shepherd. V. Title: Louise Scheppler.

NL 0411377 N

Little Bethel Baptist Association
see Baptists. Kentucky. Little Bethel Association.

The little Bible (Oxford University Press)
see under Bible. English. Selections. 1931. (also 1935; also 1944, with added specification: Authorized)

YA .S182
Little Bill at the pump. By a pastor of the Protestant episcopal church. Philadelphia, [c1850] 36p.

(Sunday school books; arr. numerically.)

NL 0411380 DLC

Little Bill's bold risk.
See
Wheeler, Edward L
Denver Doll as detective.

Little Bill's big loss.
See
Wheeler, Edward L
Denver Doll's mine.

A little biographer.
The juvenile biographer; containing the lives of little masters and misses
see under title

Little biographies ... New York, Breitkopf & Hartel, inc. [c1921]-
v. illus. (incl. music) 15½cm.

1. Musicians. I. Humiston, William Henry, 1869-1923. II. Martens, Frederick Herman, 1874-1932.

Library of Congress ML385.L47 22—7627

NL 0411384 DLC OrStbM NN LU KMK OO

A little bird's song on my birthday
see under [Whittier, John Greenleaf] 1807-1892.

Little bits of Judaism... 1907
see under "Amiel", pseud.

Little Black Herman
see
Rucker, Herman.

Little Black Primitive Baptist association
see Primitive Baptists. Mississippi. Little Black Primitive Baptist association.

VOLUME 336

Little Black Sambo.
See under
[Bannerman, Mrs. Helen]

NL 0411389

PN6120 .A5L485 ... Little black Sambo, in three acts, for fold-a-way miniature theatre. [Chicago? c1932]
folder ([6] p.) 16x10½cm. [Fold-a-way play-folder for fold-a-way miniature theatre. no. 3]
Copyrighted by Will Pente.
At head of title: Play.
I. Pente, William, 1873-

NL 0411390 DLC

... The Little Black Sambo story book, a treasury of sunshine stories for children; illustrations by Eunice Stephenson. Philadelphia, The John C. Winston co. [c1930]
1 p. l., 5-95 p. col. illus. 19½cm. (Winston easy-to-read story books)
1. Readers and speakers—1870- I. Stephenson, Eunice, illus.
Library of Congress PE1121.L7 30-30723
Copyright A 29247 [2] 372.4

NL 0411391 DLC

The little blind girl
see under [Griffith, Arabella]

The little blind girl of Normandie ...
see under [Griffith, Arabella]

Little Blossom; her book of stories ... Boston, Lothrop publishing company [c1899]
[37] p. illus., pl. 26½cm. (Lettered on cover: Snowtime series)
Library of Congress PZ7.L73 99-1994 Revised

NL 0411394 DLC

Little blossoms
see under [Gerson, Virginia]

25.7 5240 The little blue book; a register of federal offices and salaries. [anon.] New York, G.A. Whitehorne, 1861.
xii, 9-122 p. 18°.

NL 0411396 DLC

Little blue book.
Girard, Kan., Haldeman-Julius Publications [etc.] 19
no. 13 cm.
Numbering irregular: many no. repeated.
Edited by E. Haldeman-Julius.
Rare Book Division has 1848 Little Blue Books published through 1936
I. Haldeman-Julius, Emanuel, 1889-1951, ed.
AC1.L8 58-22654 ‡

NL 0411397 DLC OFH OU CoU TxU NN

The little blue book and position seekers' guide; containing lists of government jobs not under civil service, and pay, compiled from official documents, U. S. statutes and directories ... Washington, Smith & Kennedy [c1913]
136 p. 13½ x 6½cm. $0.25
1. U. S.—Registers. I. Title: Position seekers' guide.
Library of Congress JK771.L5 1913 13-7567

NL 0411398 DLC

Haldeman Julius BiZ Little Blue Book Company, Girard, Kan.
Big blue books; catalog [of 942 larger books. Girard, Kan., 1951?]
62p. 13cm.
1. Big blue books.

NL 0411399 IEN

Z473 H15 A35 Small Books Little blue books.
Complete catalog of 1,375 Little blue books. Girard, Kansas [193-]
49, [15] p. 13 cm.
Cover-title.
1. Little blue books. 2. Catalogs, Publishers--U.S.

NL 0411400 RPB CtY

808.8 L721Yc 1933 Stark Lib'y Little blue books.
1933-1934 catalog, Little blue books ... Girard, Kan., Haldeman-Julius Publications [1933]
64p. 12½cm.
Cover title.
At head of title: Almost 1750 titles.
1. Little blue books - Catalogs.

NL 0411401 TxU

E83 .L0 The little blue flag. v. 4, no. 9, July, 1909. Dayton, Ohio.
1 no. port. 24cm.
Contains biographical sketch, editorial and other appreciations of Henry Clay Lowe.
1. Lowe, Henry Clay, 1848-1909.

NL 0411402 WHi

Little blue mantle; or The poor man's friend. A true story. New York, Thomas Nelson & sons, [1871].

NL 0411403 OCl

The little blue room; a comedy in four acts. Tr. from the French and adapted by Florence Gerald... New York, Manuscripts universal, soc. of writers [192-?] 71 p. 20cm.
1. Drama, French—Translations into English. I. Gerald, Florence, 1858?-1942.
N. Y. P. L. June 30, 1947

NL 0411404 NN

xPZ5 L7177 Little Bo-Peep. New York, McLoughlin Bros. [18--]
[8]p. col.illus. 15cm. (Susie sunshine's series)
Cover title.

NL 0411405 IaU MH

Little Bo Peep. New York, McLoughlin [186-?]
[8] l. (incl. covers) col.illus. 28cm. (Aunt Jenny's series)
Cover title.

NL 0411406 MiDW

Little Bo Peep. New York, McLoughlin Bros. [187-]
10 p. illus. (Little folks series)
An elaboration, in form of fairy-tale, of the old nursery-rhyme.

NL 0411407 NNC

* PZ7 .L729L 1890 Little bo-peep. New York, E. P. Dutton [ca. 189-?]
[12] p. illus. (part col.) 22 x 19cm.
Cover title, title page wanting.
"Printed in Bavaria, 1271."

NL 0411408 ViU

VM 1497 D 54t LITTLE Bo-Peep, a favorite song, as sung at most of the nobilitys & gentrys private concerts. With an accompaniment for the harp, or piano forte. London, Lavenu [179-?]
2 leaves.
Binder's title: Dibdin. Twelve songs and other music.
Caption title.
Imprint at head of title.

NL 0411409 ICN IEN

Little - Bo-peep: a nursery rhyme picture book
see under Brooke, Leonard Leslie, 1862-1940, illus.

LITTLE Bo-Peep; a pantomine.
The anonymous author of the above has written another work, entitled, "The BUTTERFLY'S BALL". 1855.

NL 0411411 MH

Little Bo-Peep and her foolish sheep.
Broadside. New York. Strong. 1861. Size, 9½ × 14⅜ inches.
[Strong's Dime caricatures. No. 2.]
Little Bo-Peep is the Confederacy.
D7341 — S.r. — Broadsides. — United States. Hist. Civil War. Humor, caricatures, etc.

NL 0411412 MB

VOLUME 336

LITTLE Bo-peep, and other stories. [n.p., 18--?] 8 l. illus. 16x13cm.

Caption-title.
Illustrations colored by hand.

708424A. 1. Juvenile literature--Picture books.

NL 0411413 NN

Little Bo-Peep, and other stories for children ... Boston, Lothrop pub. co. [1900]
[64] p. col. front., illus. 8°.

July 26, 1900–101

Library of Congress

NL 0411414 DLC

Little Bo-Peep, and other good stories; seventy illustrations. Philadelphia, H. Altemus company [°1905]
iv, 5-64 p. col. front., illus., col. pl. 22cm. (Altemus' Bo-Peep series, 1)
p. 63-64, advertising matter.

5-24849

NL 0411415 DLC

LITTLE Bo-Peep,or Queen Butterfly's ball, and King Grasshopper's feast,in Birmingham of the olden time. [Birmingham,James Upton,18-]

pp.24.
At head of title: Swanborough's grand Christmas pantomime.
Imperfect:-title-page wanting and too closely trimmed.

NL 0411416 MH

---

*pFB8 N1627 Z803l The little boasters final determination: or John Bull rather angry!!!
[London] Publish'd at R.Ackermann's gallery, 1803. Nº 101.Strand.
plate. 26.5x33cm.,mounted to 41x54.5cm.
Broadley A-950.
Lithograph (hand-colored), unsigned.
A satire on Napoleon's threatened invasion.

NL 0411417 MH

The little boats
see under [Alcott, Louisa May] 1832-1888.

The Little Bob Logic; or, The Art of Laughing like a Gentleman. Miniature Edition. London, Hodgson, n.d.
2 vols. Red paper covers.
Colored vignettes on engraved titles.

NL 0411419 CSmH

Little Bobo and his blue jacket
see under [Evers, Alf]

Little Bony sneaking into Paris
see under [Elmes, William] fl. 1797-1814.

---

*pFB8 N1627 Z805n Little Boney in the whales. belley.
[London] Pub^{d} by Roberts Middle row.[1803]
plate. 26.5x43cm.,mounted & bd.to 50x40cm.
George 10141; Broadley A-541.
Engraving (hand-colored), unsigned; engraved by P. Roberts.
A satire on Napoleon's intended invasion.
No.103 in a volume lettered on spine: Napoleonic caricatures.

NL 0411422 MH

Little Bonne Femme Baptist Association
see Baptists. Missouri. Little Bonne Femme Association.

A little book about books: how they are made & why they are bought and cherished. London, Printed, bound and published at the Sunday times book exhibition, 1935.
31, [1] p. 13½cm.

1. Books. I. The Sunday times, London.

36-25876

Library of Congress Z116.A2L7
[3] 655

NL 0411424 DLC

A little book about Danvers, Massachusetts
see under Old Berry Tavern, Danvers, Mass.

A little book about roses
see under
Peterson, George Henry, 1868-

The little book (Alpha and Omega)
see under
Taylor, Rollin Marshall

A little book for children, containing a few rules for the regulation of their tho'ts, words, and actions.

This work is available in this library in the Readex Microprint edition of Early American Imprints published by the American Antiquarian Society.
This collection is arranged according to the numbers in Charles Evans' American Bibliography.

NL 0411428 DLC

Little book, A, for children, containing a few rules for the regulation of their tho'ts words and actions.
— Portsmouth. Fowle. 1758. 16 pp. 48°.

NL 0411429 MB

FILM x177 L729 A little book for children, containing a few rules for the regulation of their tho'ts, words and actions. Portsmouth, N.H., Printed by D. Fowle, 1758.

Microfilm copy made in 1954 by Boston Public Library. Negative.
Collation of the original: 16p.

NL 0411430 IU

A Little book for little children. Boston, 1702.
94 p. 24°.

NL 0411431 MWA

The Little book for little children...Nursery rhymes, pictures, stories and games. New York, Amsco music pub. co., [c1935]
cover-title, 96p. illus. 24 cm.

NL 0411432 RPB

A little book for little folks, compiled by H. W. R. Philadelphia, Henry Longstretch [18--]
132 p. illus.

I. R., H. W.

NL 0411433 NNC

A little book for little folks, compiled by H.W.R. ... Philadelphia, 1878.
133 p. illus., front. 18 cm.

NL 0411434 RPB

A little book in memory of Gertrude Goldsmith
see under Goldsmith, Gertrude.

The little book in the hand of the angel
see under Israelite House of David.

The little book o' tricks. 1000 hours of harmless, interesting & innocent fun... Contains tricks with cards. Tricks with matches. Tricks with figures. Tricks with words. Tricks with handkerchiefs. Also a series of puzzles, sketches and other novel experiments. London, E. Smith & co. [18—] 13 l. illus. 18cm.

With bookplate of Milton Arlanden Bridges.

280068B. 1. Legerdemain.
N. Y. P. L. August 28, 1944

NL 0411437 NN

A little book of ballads
see under [Utterson, Edward Vernon] 1776?-1856, comp.

Little book of Bible stories for children.
Worcester, Dorr, H. & co.[n.d.]
24 p. Illus. 32°.

NL 0411439 MB

VOLUME 336

A little book of book-plates containing forty designs
see under [Guthrie, James Joshua] 1874-

A little book of bookly verse
see under The Bookfellows.

A little book of college verse, selected from the undergraduate verse of Mount Holyoke college, chiefly from the pages of the Mount Holyoke; comp., ed. and published by the L N S S a Δεῖνα of the class of nineteen two. [Springfield, Mass.] The Springfield printing and binding co., 1901.
6 p. l., 64 pp. 17½cm.

2-19—M 2

NL 0411442 DLC

The little book of confectionery. London, G. Newnes, [1912].
95 p. 9cm.

NL 0411443 ICJ

A little book of conundrums
see under
[Nelson, Winifred L.] comp.

A little book of dainty dishes
see under Federal Pure Food Company, Chicago.

A Little book of English lyrics; with a frontispiece by W. E. F. Britten. London, Methuen, 1900.
xiv, 461 p. front. (port.) 16 cm.

NL 0411446 PU

A little book of Evansville, announcing a ceremonial session of Hadi temple... Friday, Nov. the 30th, 1917 at the Soldiers' and sailors' memorial coliseum. [Evansville, Ind., Printed and engraved by Keller-Crescent co., 1917.]

NL 0411447 InU

Little, The, book of French cookery. London: G. Newnes. Ltd [1912.] 95(1) p. 48°.

1. Cookery (French).
N. Y. P. L. April 2, 1913.

NL 0411448 NN

A little book of friendly wishes ... Boston, W.A. Wilde co. [c1910]
11 l. 16 cm. (The Canterbury series)
Poetry and prose.

NL 0411449 RPB

M
786.408
L729

A little book of fugues by German masters. Seventeen small fugues by masters of the 17th and 18th centuries. New York, Edwin F. Kalmus, c1950.
16 p.

1. Canons, fugues, etc. 2. Harpsichord music - Collections and selections. 3. Organ music - Collections and selections.

NL 0411450 WaU DLC KEmT TU OkU NcU

The little book of Geneva for visitors
see under [Bradfield, Beatrice]

The little book of Greenwich Village;
see under
[Arens, Egmont]

A little book of heavenly wisdom; selections from some English prose mystics
see under Gregory, Eleanor C ed.

A little book of heroic verse. Decorations by M.W.Hawes. London, etc., Oxford university press [1941]
64 p. illus. 19 cm.
Half-title: Chameleon books, 19.

NL 0411454 MH

Little book of instructions for christian mothers. [1892]
see under Reinhold, Paul.

A little book of Japanese wisdom
see under Hoshino, Ken, d. 1913?, comp.

Little, The, book of Jewish cookery. London: G. Newnes, Ltd. [1912.] 95(1) p. 48°.

1. Cookery (Jewish).
N. Y. P. L. April 10, 1913.

NL 0411457 NN

A little book of Judson verse...
see under Judson, Sarah (Hall) Boardman, 1803-1845.

A little book of life and death
see under Waterhouse, Elizabeth, comp.

A Little book of light verse, with an introduction and notes, by Anthony C. Deane...
see under Deane, Anthony Charles, 1870-1946, ed.

PZ214
.T75
no.2

Little book of natural history. Worcester [Mass.] H. J. Howland [183-?]
8 p. illus. 9cm.
[Toy books, no.2]

NL 0411461 ICU MWA

A little book of necessary ballads
see under Harper, Wilhelmina, comp.

808.8
L721

A Little book of New Year's wishes. Chicago, Canterbury Co. [1910]
[23]p. 16cm.

Alternate pages blank.

1. Gift-books (Annuals, etc.)

NL 0411463 IU

A little book of old time verse
see under Crouch, Gladys Sidney, comp.

A LITTLE book of Oxford movement poetry... London: Society for Promoting Christian Knowledge[, 1932]. ix, 11-56 p. 18½cm.

649026A. 1. Poetry, Religious, English—Collections. I. Title: Oxford movement poetry.

NL 0411465 NN IaU

The little book of pastries and cakelets. London, G. Newnes, [1912].
95 p. 9½cm.

NL 0411466 ICJ

A little book of ping-pong verse; containing also the complete rules for playing the popular game of table-tennis ... Boston, D. Estes & company [1902]
xii, 11-150 p. 17½cm.

1. Ping-pong.

2—19587

Library of Congress GV1005.L5

NL 0411467 DLC NN

A little book of poetry for children ... Pittsfield, Mass., 1847.
cover title, 8 p. illus. 8 cm.

NL 0411468 RPB

... A little book of prayers for those who believe in the communion of saints
see under [Bubb, Charles Clinch] comp.

A little book of prayers from old English sources
see under Gasquet, Francis Aidan, cardinal 1846-1929.

VOLUME 336

A little book of remembrance ...
see under [Myers, Emily Niles (Huyck) i.e. Mrs. David Moffat Myers] 1882-1912.

The little book of preserves and pickles. London, G. Newnes, [1912].
95 p. 9½cm.

NL 0411472 ICJ

398.9 L778
A Little book of proverbs, alphabetically arranged. London, Sands [191?]
96p. 11cm.

1. Proverbs - Dictionaries, indexes, etc.

NL 0411473 CLSU

The little book of puddings. London, G. Newnes, [1912].
95 p. 9½cm.

NL 0411474 ICJ

... A little book of Robinson Crusoe and other good old tales. Springfield, Mass., McLoughlin bros., inc. [c1934]
[252] p. illus. 13½cm. (The little big books)
On cover: My book of good old stories.

I. Defoe, Daniel, 1661?-1731. Robinson Crusoe. II. Title: Robinson Crusoe.

Library of Congress PZ7.L728Li4 no. 13 34-10382

NL 0411475 DLC

The little book of roses
see under Werner, Alfred, 1911-

The little book of salads and savouries. London, G. Newnes, [1912].
95 p. 9cm.

NL 0411477 ICJ

The little book of sandwiches and beverages. London, G. Newnes, [1912].
95 p. 9cm.

NL 0411478 ICJ

A little book of Somerset county verse. Somerset, 1945. 37 p. 22cm. (Somerset county (Pa.) historical society. Sesquicentennial publications no. 3)

1. Poetry, American—U. S.—Pa. —Somerset. I. Ser.
N. Y. P. L. February 7, 1951

NL 0411479 NN PHi MH

821.04 L778
The Little book of songs, being a choice patriotick, Yankee, English and Irish collection ... Watertown, N. Y. Published by Knowlton and Rice. 1832.
72 p. 15 cm.

1. Songs. Collections.

NL 0411480 N

PZ7 L57 t
[Little books, 1-] Racine, Wis., Whitman Publishing Co., 193-?-
v. illus. 10cm

NL 0411481 CSt

A little book of sundial mottoes. With illustrations in colour, by Alfred Rawlings. London, Boston, [etc.], T. N. Foulis, [1914].
37, [1] p. col. front. 3 col. pl. 17cm.

NL 0411482 ICJ PU

A little book of sundial mottoes, with illustrations in colour. London, Boston, [etc.] T.N.Foulis, ltd., [1923] 37[1]p. incl.4 col. plates. 18½x10cm. (On cover: Friendship booklets).

1. Sun-dials. 2. Mottoes.

NL 0411483 MWelC

The little book of superiors, 1889
see under Sylvain, Abbé Charles.

Little book of the twenty-four stones

See
Here begynneth a lytell boke of the xxiii. stones ... 1535?]

A little book on prayer. A contribution from the experience of Quaker retreats. London, Friends' book centre [1946]
32 p. 16½cm.

NL 0411486 PHC

The little book open
see under [Hall, John Bishop] of Cincinnati.

The little book series
see Rice, Wallace de Groot Cecil, 1859-1939, comp.
The little book series.

The LITTLE book of trades; describing some plain things. New Haven [Conn.] Published by S. Babcock [183-?] 8 p. illus. 90mm.

Leaves unopened.
CONTENTS.--Blacksmith.--Paper-maker.--Weaver.

NL 0411489 NN

Is94 t 1 v.1(1
The little book of trades; describing some plain things. New Haven, Published by S.Babcock, 1840.
8p. illus. 7½cm.
Title vignette.
Pamphlet

NL 0411490 CtY

Little book special
see under Chü, Chung-fu.

A little book: to obtain means for placing a memorial stone upon the grave of the poet Henry Timrod
see under [Rivers, William James] 1822-

Little books for Africa.
[no.
London: Sheldon Press[, 192 12°.
nos. illus.

NL 0411493 NN

Little Books on art. Ed. by Cyril J.H. Davenport. Lond., Methuen, 19-
v. il.

NL 0411494 OO OCl OClh

Little books on Asiatic art. v. 1- Calcutta [A. N. Gangoly] 1927-
v. plates (part col.) 19 cm.

NL 0411495 NcD

Little books on missions.
Cincinnati, Jennings and Graham[etc.,etc.]

NL 0411496 CtY

Little books on religion; ...
London, 18-

NL 0411497 DLC

The LITTLE box; a dramatic dialogue in three acts. n.p.,n.d.

Without title-page. Caption title.
Running title: Dramatic dialogues.

NL 0411498 MH

The little boxer. 1895. Official records of the prize ring and of boxing ... Boston, Mass., F. K. Lanpher & co., c1894.
64 p. illus. (ports.) 11cm.

1. Boxing. I. Lanpher, F. K., & co.

Library of Congress GV1137.L75 5-25432†

NL 0411499 DLC

VOLUME 336

The LITTLE boy and his mother. Boston, Seth Bliss, 1833.
18 cm. pp.32. Illustr.
Mutilated: pp.3,4,15-18,21,22 torn - text missing.

NL 0411500 MH

Little Boy Blue. Springfield, Mass., n.d.
[6] p. col. illus. 23 cm.
Cover title, illus. in colors. At head of title: Untearable.

NL 0411501 RPB

Little Boy Blue and other poems for children; illustrated by Priscilla Pointer. Springfield, Mass., McLoughlin bros., inc. [c1941]
[59] p. incl. col. front., illus. (part col.) 17 x 13½cm. (The little color classics)

1. Children's poetry. I. Pointer, Priscilla, illus.
41-22149
Library of Congress PZ8.3.L65

NL 0411502 DLC

35
Little boy Blue, and other stories. Boston, D. Lothrop & co. [1877]
unp., 27 l. 7 pl. 16°.
By Clara A. Goodenow and others.

NL 0411503 DLC

PS3500 .L773 19- Rare bk room
A little boy in grey. [19-?]
1 l., 8 numb. l. 28x21½cm.
Caption title.
Adapted from Wm. Gillette's drama, "Secret service."
An episode of the war of the rebellion in one act.

NL 0411504 ICU

The little boy who found a knife
see under Pardee, Caroline Julia, 1911-

The little boy who minded trifles. Designed for children from six to eight years old. One of a series of stories by the author of 'Fruit and flowers.' Boston, Hilliard, Gray, Little, and Wilkins, 1828. 19 p. 15cm.
In original illustrated gray covers.

54R0728. (I. Fruit and flowers. Author of.

NL 0411506 NN MH

Little boys and girls A B C. New York, [?], McLoughlin, c1884.
cover-title, [8] p. col. illus. 23cm.
Text on pages 2 and 3 of cover.

No Subject

NL 0411507 NNC

Little boys' and girls' own primer
see under Teachem, Mrs., pseud.

The Little boy's English grammar, in easy dialogues; intended as an introduction to facilitate the study of the Latin Grammar, by an experienced teacher. London, Houlston, 1837.
50 p. front. 15 cm.

NL 0411509 PU-Penn

Coll.A LI714
The Little boy's forget-me-not. Philadelphia, American Sunday-School Union [c1843]
109 p. incl. 7 plates. 12 x 10 cm.

I. American Sunday-School Union, pub.

NL 0411510 RPB

The little boy's own book of sports, pastimes, and amusements
see under [Clarke, William] 1800-1838.

Is94 tl v.7
The little boy's question. New-York: Published by T. Mason and G. Lane, for the Sunday school union of the Methodist Episcopal church, 1839.
8p. 10½cm.

I. Methodist Episcopal church. Sunday school union.

NL 0411512 CtY

Little branches. A collection of songs prepared especially for the primary and infant departments of the Sunday school... [c. 1893]
see under Gabriel, Charles Hutchinson, 1856-1932, ed.

Little-Breeches; a Pike County view of special providence
see under Hay, John, 1838-1905.

LITTLE Breeches, and the Cock of Drury-Lane. [London], J. Catnach, [1821].
nar. 8°. Vigns.
Without title-page. Caption title.
A ballad relating to Mrs. Cox and Edmund Kean.

NL 0411515 MH

Little Br'er Rabbit, and other stories, with color plates and half tone drawings. Buffalo, N. Y., Berger publishing company, c1907.
[24] p. incl. col. front., illus. (partly col.) 18 x 14cm.

7-36245

NL 0411516 DLC

The little breviary
see under Catholic Church. Liturgy and ritual. Breviary. English. [Miscellaneous]

Little Britain, Pa. Little Britain Presbyterian church.
Year book of the Little Britain Presbyterian church, Lancaster county, Pa. ... Lancaster, Pa., The New era book and job print,
v. 18cm.

39-5078
Library of Congress BX9211.L52L5

NL 0411518 DLC

Little Britain Presbyterian church, Little Britain, Pa.
see
Little Britain, Pa. Little Britain Presbyterian church.

Little brother & little sister, and other tales, by the Brothers Grimm
see under Grimm, Jakob Ludwig Karl, 1785-1863.

Little brothers of Mary
see
Marist brothers.

Little brothers of the air.
See under
[Miller, Mrs. Harriet (Mann), 1831-1918.]

Little, Brown and Company, *Boston.*
Book publishing at 34 Beacon Street. Boston [1951]
30 p. 19 cm.

I. Title.
Z473.L758 655.5 52-1607 rev

NL 0411523 DLC NN TxU

Epsteen Coll. in RareBooks Room
Little, Brown & co., Boston.
Books for boys and girls, a catalogue in tribute to Louisa May Alcott. With descriptions of our new books and a classified list of all our books for children. Boston, Little, Brown [1932]
24 p. illus. 23cm.
Portrait on cover.
"Books by Louisa May Alcott": p. 5-7.
1. Alcott, Louisa May, 1832-1888 - Bibliography. I. Title.

NL 0411524 CoU

Little, Brown and Company.
Books from Beacon Hill; the story of the Boston publishing house of Little, Brown and Company, 1837-1926... Boston[: Little, Brown and Co., 1926.] 12 p. illus. 12°.

1. Publishers and publishing—U. S.—Mass.—Boston. 2. Title.
N. Y. P. L. June 29, 1927

NL 0411525 NN ICN MiU MH

VOLUME 336

Little, Brown and company, *Boston.*
Books from Beacon Hill, the story of the Boston publishing house of Little, Brown and company, 1837-1926. Boston [1927]
12 p. front., pl. 19 cm.
"Some events in Little, Brown and company's history": p. 11.

1. Little, Brown and company, Boston. I. Title.
Z473.L76 27-18666 rev

NL 0411526 DLC

Little, Brown and Company, Boston.
Stevens and Haynes, *firm, law booksellers, London.*
A catalogue of American law books and reports, imported to order by Stevens and Haynes, law publishers, booksellers & importers ... London, 1869.

LITTLE, BROWN and Company, Boston.
Catalogue of books ancient and modern, lately selected in London and Paris: for sale. [With prices.] Boston, 1842.

NL 0411528 MH

Z 4784 .51 LITTLE, BROWN AND CO., firm publishers, Boston.
A catalogue of books, ancient and modern, comprising useful and valuable works in every class of literature. Boston, Little, Brown and Co., 1857.
224p. 22cm.

NL 0411529 ICN

LITTLE, BROWN and Company, Boston.
Catalogue of books suitable for Christmas and New Year's Presents, recently imported. [B.], 1846.
pp.16.

NL 0411530 MH

Little, Brown and Company, Boston.
Catalogue of [his] choice and valuable collection of rare books of proverbs and emblems, dance of death, etc., ...
see under Bartlett, John, 1820-1905.

Little, Brown, & Co., Boston
(1837. Charles C. Little and James Brown)
A catalogue of law books published and for sale by Charles C. Little and James Brown. Boston, 1837.
viii, 70 p.

NL 0411532 NNC

Little, Brown and company, *Boston.*
A catalogue of law books published and for sale by Charles C. Little and James Brown ... Boston, Printed by Freeman and Bolles, 1843.
1 p. l., ix, 88 p. 17 cm.

1. Law—Bibl.—Catalogs. 2. Law—U. S.—Bibl.
Z6459.Z9L7 1843 5-1368 rev

NL 0411533 DLC MH-L

Little, Brown and company, *Boston.*
A catalogue of law books, published and for sale by Charles C. Little and James Brown. Boston, 1846.
1 p. l., xi, 160 p. 17 cm.

1. Law—Bibl.—Catalogs. 2. Law—U. S.—Bibl.
Z6459.Z9L7 1846 5-1367 rev

NL 0411534 DLC NcD MH

LITTLE, BROWN, & CO.
Catalogue of Law Books. Boston, 1855.
47 p.

NL 0411535 MH-L

Little, Brown and Company.
A catalogue of law books, published and for sale by Little, Brown and Company. Boston, 1856. 44 p. 8°.
In: XA p. v. 1, no. 3.

1. Law.—Bibliography.
N. Y. P. L. October 7, 1912.

NL 0411536 NN

Little, Brown and Company.
A catalogue of law books, published and for sale by Little, Brown and Company. Boston, 1858. 44 p. 8°.
In: XA p. v. 1, no. 4.

1. Law.—Bibliography.
N. Y. P. L. October 7, 1912.

NL 0411537 NN

Little, Brown and Company.
A catalogue of law and miscellaneous books, published by Little, Brown and Company. Boston, 1862. 80 p. 8°.
In: XA p. v. 1, no. 5.

1. Law.—Bibliography.
N. Y. P. L. October 7, 1912.

NL 0411538 NN KPT

LITTLE, BROWN, & CO.
Catalogue of Law and Miscellaneous Books. Boston, 1869.
iv+67 44 p.

NL 0411539 MH-L

LITTLE, BROWN, & CO.
Catalogue of Law Books. Boston, 1882.
xxi+164 p.
Interleaved copy.

NL 0411540 MH-L

Little, Brown & co., firm, booksellers, Boston.
Catalogue of law books.. with a list of ... English law books.. Boston, 1886.
23 cm.

NL 0411541 DLC

Little, Brown and company, *Boston.*
A catalogue of law books published or for sale by Little, Brown, & co., law publishers and booksellers. Boston, 1880.
xxi, 164 p. 17½ cm.

1. Law—Bibl.—Catalogs. 2. Law—U. S.—Bibl.
Z6459.Z9L7 1880 7-17983 rev

NL 0411542 DLC

Little, Brown and company, *Boston.*
Catalogue of law books published by Little, Brown, and company. Boston, 1896.
iv, 140 p. 22½ cm.
—— Subject-list of law books for sale by Little, Brown, & co. March, 1897.
27 p. 22½ cm. [*With its* Catalogue. 1896]

1. Law—Bibl.—Catalogs. 2. Law—U. S.—Bibl.
Z6459.Z9L7 1896 7-17984 rev

NL 0411543 DLC

Little, Brown and company, *Boston.*
A catalogue of law books published by Little, Brown, and company; including treatises, leading cases, reports, digests, legal biography, speeches, etc. Boston, 1900.
2 p. l., 105 p. 22 cm.

1. Law—U. S.—Bibl. 2. Law—Bibl.—Catalogs.
Z6459.Z9L7 1900 0-5766 rev 2

NL 0411544 DLC NN

Little, Brown and company, *Boston.*
A catalogue of the best books in every department of literature; with complete author, subject, and title index. Boston, Mass., Little, Brown & co. [1899]
1 p. l., vii-x, 335, 343-406 p. 24½ cm.
Title edition of catalog comp. for and originally pub. by the Burrows bros. co., Cleveland; the plates, preface, and p. 337-341 ("A partial list of books published by the Burrows brothers company") omitted.

1. Bibliography—Best books. 2. Catalogs, Booksellers'—U. S.
Z1036.L75 0-650 rev 2

NL 0411545 DLC

Little, Brown, & co., Boston.
A complete catalogue of the extensive and valuable collection of ancient and modern books, in several languages, and in every department of literature, for sale by Little, Brown, & co. ‹Charles C. Little, James Brown, Augustus Flagg, & James P. Brown,› 112, Washington street, Boston. January, 1853. Boston, Printed by J. Wilson & son, 1853.
106p. 23cm.
Bound with The theory of the common law. By James M. Walker. 1852.
1. Catalogs. Booksellers'.

Printed by the Wesleyan University Library, 1936

NL 0411546 CtW

LITTLE, BROWN & CO
Edison Marshall, the man and his books. Boston, Author [1925?]
[15] p.

NL 0411547 Or

Little, Brown & Co.
English reports in law and equity. The common law, equity, and criminal reports combined. Boston [187-?]. 8 p. 8°.
In: XA p. v. 1, no. 6.

1. Law.—Bibliography.
N. Y. P. L. October 7, 1912.

NL 0411548 NN

VOLUME 336

E175 .5 .P22 Little, Brown & Co., Boston.
Francis Parkman. Boston, 1897.
cover-title, 15 p. 20cm.

1. Parkman, Francis, 1823-1893.

NL 0411549 MB CU NjP NN RPB MH

Little, Brown and Company, Boston.
A general catalogue of law books published during the present century; and including all the reports from the earliest period. Boston, 1850.
lxvi, 113 p. 17 cm.
1. Law - Bibl. — Catalogs. 2. Law - U.S. - Bibl.

NL 0411550 ViU

Little, Brown and company, *Boston.*
A general catalogue of law books; including all the reports, both English and American, from the earliest period. By Little, Brown, & company (Charles C. Little, James Brown, Augustus Flagg, James P. Brown) ... Boston, 1853.
lxxiv, 148 p. 17 cm.

1. Law—Bibl.—Catalogs. 2. Law—U. S.—Bibl.

Z6459.Z9L7 1853 5-1366 rev

NL 0411551 DLC OU

Little, Brown and company, *Boston.*
A general catalogue of law books; including all the reports, both English and American, from the earliest period. By Little, Brown & company, (Charles C. Little, Augustus Flagg, James P. Brown,) ... Boston, 1856.
lxxii, 149 p. 17½ cm.

1. Law—Bibl.—Catalogs. 2. Law—U. S.—Bibl.

Z6459.Z9L7 1856 016.34 38-38891 rev

NL 0411552 DLC

Little, Brown and company, *Boston.*
A general catalogue of law books; including all the reports, both English and American, from the earliest period. Pub. or for sale by Little, Brown and company ... Boston, 1864.
lii, 128 p. 17 cm.

1. Law—Bibl.—Catalogs. 2. Law—U. S.—Bibl.

Z6459.Z9L7 1864 5-1365 rev ‡

NL 0411553 DLC

Little, Brown and company, *Boston.*
A handbook of editorial rules. Boston, Little, Brown, and company, 1925.
4 p. l., ₍3₎-47 p. 22 cm.

1. Authorship—Handbooks, manuals, etc. 2. Printing, Practical—Style manuals. I. Title.

PN147.L5 25-7931 rev

NL 0411554 DLC OCl

Little, Brown & co., Boston.
Henryk Sienkiewicz. Boston, 1898.

NL 0411555 NjP

LITTLE, BROWN & CO., Boston.
A history of the United States, by George Bancroft. [Prospectus]. containing a letter from M.d la Luzerne to Mgr.de Vergenn published in justification of Bancroft. Boston, n.d.

NL 0411556 MH

Little, Brown and company, Boston.
Law book bulletin. No. 18- . Boston, Mass., Little, Brown & company.
I. Title.

NL 0411557 WaU-L

Little, Brown & Co.
Little, Brown & Co.'s list of law books. Boston, 1852. 16 p. 8°.
In: XA p. v. 1, no. 2.

1. Law.—Bibliography.
N. Y. P. L. October 7, 1912.

NL 0411558 NN

Little, Brown & co., Boston.
Massachusetts decisions reported in North eastern reporter vols. 1 to July, 1885-
Boston, Mass., Little, Brown, and company; St. Paul, Minn., West publishing co. 1937-

---

Law Little, Brown and Company, Boston.
Massachusetts digest annotated, 1761 to date, covering all cases reported in Massachusetts reports and North eastern reporter. By the publishers' editorial staff. Boston, Little, Brown ₍1933-

---

Little, Brown and Company, *Boston.*
... Memorandum to correct the highly misleading summary of Little, Brown's publishing activities which appeared in the August 31st issue of Counterattack. ₍Boston₎ 1951.
₍4₎ p. (on double leaves) 28 cm.
Title from first lines of text.

1. Counterattack. I. Title.

Z473.L762 53-18804 rev ‡

NL 0411561 DLC

Little, Brown, & Company.
Monthly catalogue of rare books, Dec., 1884, 1886, May, Sept., Nov., Dec., 1887, Jan., March-May, Oct.-Dec., 1888, Jan.-May, Nov., 1889, June, Oct., 1890, Oct.-Dec., 1891.
Boston. 1884-91. v. 20½ cm.

The title varies.
Some of the issues have serial numberings.

D2409 — Catalogues. Booksellers'.

NL 0411562 MB

CT99 .F236L5 [Little, Brown & co., Boston]
The novels of Jeffery Farnol, master of romantic fiction. [Boston, Little, Brown & company, 1923?]
15 p. illus. incl. port. 19cm.

1. Farnol, Jeffery, 1878-

NL 0411563 DLC OrU CLSU Or NBuG

Little, Brown and company, *Boston.*
One hundred years of publishing. 1837-1937. Boston, Little, Brown and company ₍1937₎
5 p. l., 3-83 p. front., illus. (incl. ports., facsims.) 19½ cm.
"First edition."
"A few of the famous books published by Little, Brown and company": p. 79-82; "Some famous books published by Roberts brothers until 1898, then by Little, Brown and company": p. 83.

1. Little, Brown and company, Boston. I. Title.

Z473.L763 655.47446 37-3470 rev

CU WaSp MoSW WaE WaT OrP OrU CaBVaU OClCC OCU ViU NcRS NcD ICRL KU-M ScU CoU Or WaS MeB
NL 0411564 DLC PPAmP MH ICJ MiU-C RPB NN MB OO OCl

Little, Brown & co., Boston.
Proposals for publishing by subscription a new and uniform edition of the speeches, forensic arguments, and diplomatic papers of Daniel Webster. [Boston, 1851]
1l. 25x20cm.
Signed at end: Boston, February 1, 1851. Little and Brown.
Caption title. Printed on bluish paper.

Rare Book Room Broadsides 1P Cb4A 1851

NL 0411565 CtY

LITTLE, BROWN & COMPANY, Boston.
[Prospectus of the works of Charles Lever. Boston, 1894] 1 v. (various pagings) illus., plates. 23cm.

Some of the etchings are by H. K. Browne, some by E. L. van Muyden.

1. Lever, Charles James, 1806-1872—Illustrations. I. Browne, Hablot Knight, 1815-1882, engr. II. Muyden Evert Louis van, 1853-1922, engr.

NL 0411566 NN

Little, Brown & co., Boston, pub.
Romances of the reign of Henry II.; the Valois romances; the d'Artagnan romances; the Regency romances; the Marie Antoinette romances: the Count of Monte Cristo, etc., by Alexandre Dumas. Introductory notes and lists of characters. Boston, Little, Brown, and company, 1895.

Little, Brown and Company, *Boston*
see also **Roberts Brothers,** *Boston.*

Little, Brown & Co., firm, booksellers
see **Little, Brown and Company, Boston.**

Little, Brown & Co., firm, publishers.
see **Little, Brown and Company, Boston.**

VOLUME 336

Little brown Bessie, 1877
see under Ware, F E

Little brown church of the air (Radio program)

Holland, John Wesley, 1877-
The great friendship and other sermons of the Little brown church of the air. [By] Dr. John W. Holland, pastor WLS radio station. [Chicago, The Prairie press, 1942]

Little brown jug. By the author of "Better than gold"
see under [Baker, George Melville] 1832-1890.

The Little Budget of Wit, containing choice Bon-Mots, Repartees, Anecdotes, &c. &c. Miniature edition. Edinburgh, Oliver & Boyd, n.d.
Brown paper cover.
Note. Front. and engraved title.

NL 0411574 CSmH

Little buds and blossoms. [Chicago] Baker & Hayes, c1885.
[10] p. illus.

Cover title.
"Compliments of E. W. Gillett, manufacturer magic yeast, Chicago, Ill."
Poems and stories.

I. Gillett, E. W., manufacturer

NL 0411575 MiD

The little bugler
see under [Roger, George Monroe]

LITTLE BUILDING, Boston, Mass. - Trustees.
Little building, corner Boylston and Tremont Streets, Boston, Mass. [A description]. [Boston, Mass., Folsom engraving co., 1917?]

f°. pp.(16). Illustr. and plans.
US 13188.35F

Plans of Little's building, corner of Boylston and Tremont St's, Boston, Mass., 1916. [Boston, 1916].
3 plates, 6 plans 35x 25 3/4 in, in pf.

NL 0411577 MH-BA

Little Bumps gets into trouble; a story of a funny little dog. Racine, Wis., Whitman Publishing Co., c1922.
cover-title, [12] p. col. illus. 20x35½cm.

NL 0411578 ViW

The little burnt girl [1845]
see under Prime, Samuel Irenaeus, 1812-1885.

Little busy bodies; a rare collection of prose, poetry and pictures for the wee toddlers who are never idle ... [New York] The Oriental Pub. Co., 1894.
[128] p. illus., plates. 26cm.

1. Children's literature.

NL 0411580 ViU

The little, but affecting history of Mary Howard. [Sanbornton, N.H.?] Sanbornton press, 1835.
16p. 9½cm.
Cover dated: 1836.
At head of title on cover: No.6.

Is94
t1
v.2

NL 0411581 CtY

Little by little; or, The cruise of the Flyaway; a story for young folks, by...
see under [Adams, William Taylor] 1822-1897.

A little Candlemass garland ...
see under [Bubb, Charles Clinch] comp.

The little captain; a temperance tale
see under [Peebles, Mary Louise (Parmelee)] 1833-1915.

4DC
1330

The little Captive King; a historical episode of the French Revolution. Calcutta, K. C. Singh, 1889.
46 p.

NL 0411585 DLC-P4

Little cares; and what will you do with them. Boston, American Tract Society, n. d.
15 p. 89mm.

NL 0411586 MiD-B

Little Caroline and Jasper. n.p., 1869.
[1] p. 23cm.

Broadside.

NL 0411587 PHC

The Little carpenter. New York, S. Raynor, [185-?]
8 p. illus. nar. 16°. (New books and true books for the young, no. 4)

NL 0411588 NN

---

xPZ5
L7188

The little casket; filled with pleasant stories for the instruction of the young. New York, Kiggins & Kellogg [18--]
24p. illus. 16cm. (Fourth series, no.2)

Cover title: The casket, filled with pleasant stories for the improvement of the young.

I. Title: The casket, filled with pleasant stories for the improvement of the young.

NL 0411589 IaU NNC

The Little casket; filled with pleasant stories for the instruction of the young. [4th ser. no. 2.] N.Y., Redfield, n.d.
24 p. 24°.
Title on cover is The casket.

NL 0411590 MB

YARC
L778

Little catechism and prayers for children. New York, Cincinnati, Chicago, 1896.

NL 0411591 DLC

YARC
L7783

Little catechism of popular devotions. No.1: Devotion of the scapular.
San Francisco, 1872.

NL 0411592 DLC

A little catechism of the Christian doctrine, approved by the Rev. Archbishop of Oregon and Right Rev. Biship of Nesqualy. Portland, Ore., J. F. Atkinson, 1874.
77 p.

NL 0411593 WaSpG

Little catechism on the infallibility of the sovereign pontiff...
see under Catholic church. Catechisms. English.

Little Catherine of the miraculous medal
see under [Wimsey, Josepha, sister] 1893-

Little Catholic catechism. By a Benedictine [1898]
see under [Schmid, Placid, Father] 1856-1932.

The little Catholic hymn book; containing a collection of hymns, anthems, etc., for schools and private use. Selected from approved sources. New York, Edward Dunigan & brother, 1851, [c.1850]
128 p. front., illus. 12 cm.
Pieces unnumbered.
Bound with is: The Catholic choralist... 1851 [c.1850]

NL 0411597 NNUT DLC

VOLUME 336

The Little Catholic hymn-book, for schools and private use. London, Burns and Lambert [n.d.]
32 p. 12 cm.
Published ca. 1850.
Bound with O'Leary, Arthur. The Catholic servant's apology. 1843.

NL 0411598 PLatS

*
PZ7
.L7311
1884
The little cavalier. Cincinnati, Peter G. Thomson, 1884.
1 v. illus. (part col.) 28cm. (The little cavalier series)
Cover title.

1. Children's stories.

NL 0411599 ViU

The Little centre bulletin, vol.1,no.1- vol. ,no. , June, 1947- . Victoria,B.C.The Centre,1947-19 .
no.0.

NL 0411600 CaBViP

YARC
L778.5
The Little chaplet of the immaculate conception. [anon.] [New York, Benziger brothers, 1880]
2 l. unp. 18°.

NL 0411601 DLC

...Little Charles and his dog. New York, Engraved & published by T. W. Strong [1850?]
[16]p. col. illus. 20 cm. (Aunty Jaunty's tales)
At head of title: Strong's edition

NL 0411602 RPB

PZ262
.L78
1857
Little Charley's Christmas amusements. Philadelphia, C. G. Henderson, 1857.
32 l. illus.
Cover date: 1856.

NL 0411603 ICU

PZ262
.L79
1856
Little Charley's games and sports. Philadelphia, C. G. Henderson, 1856.
32 p. front., illus.

1. Games. 2. Sports.

NL 0411604 ICU

Little Charley's picture home book; or, Treasury of amusement and pleasing instruction... Philadelphia: C. G. Henderson & Co., 1857. [178] p. front., illus., plates. 24°.

Various paging.
Some chapters were published as separates in 1852. — *cf. Roorbach, Bibliotheca Americana. Suppl.* New York, 1855.
Contents: The picture alphabet. Little Charley's rhymes and jingles. Little Charley's games and sports. Little Charley's country walk. Charley's stories of great men. Charley's Christmas amusements.

1. Juvenile literature, American.
N. Y. P. L. June 29, 1932

NL 0411605 NN

35
Little Charley's puzzle. [anon.] Philadelphia, American S.S. Union. [1859]
28 p. 18°.

NL 0411606 DLC

1852
Juv. coll.
Little Charley's stories of great men. Philadelphia, C.G. Henderson & Co. 154 Chestnut street, 1852.
[2] 3-32 l. 15 cm.

NL 0411607 DLC

PZ262
.L797
1857
Little Charley's stories of great men. Philadelphia, C. G. Henderson, 1857.
32 l. illus.
Cover date: 1856.

NL 0411608 ICU

PZ262
.L799
1855
Little Charley's visit to the menagerie. Boston, Brown, Bazin, 1855.
128 p. front., illus., plates. (On cover: Young America juvenile library)

1. Animals--Habits and behavior.

NL 0411609 ICU

The Little charmer; a select collection of Scotch & English songs, catches, glees, &c... Glasgow, Printed by J.Mennons [17--?]
1 v. 1 illus.

NL 0411610 NjP

LITTLE CHART, Eng. (Parish)
The parish registers of Little Chart, Kent, 1538-1813. Transcribed by Christopher Hales Wilkie. Canterbury, Priv. print.: Cross and Jackson, 1914. 200 p. 22cm.
One of 25 copies printed.

1. Little Chart, Eng.--Geneal. I. Wilkie, Christopher Hales, ed. t. 1914.

NL 0411611 NN

PZ7
.L7312
1878
Little chatterbox. New York, R. Worthington [1878]
unpaged. illus. 21cm.

1. Children's literature.

NL 0411612 ViU

The Little chief. A magazine for boys and girls. Indianapolis, Ind.
Publisher varies: Dowling and Shortridge, 1867-1868; Shortridge & Alden, Feb.-June, 1869; A.C. Shortridge, July 1869-June 1870; Shortridge, Button, July 1870-May 1871; Shortridge, Button & Hanley, June-July 1871; Button & Hanley, Aug.-Oct. 1871; Button & Hobbs, Jan.-Feb. 1872.
DLC: YA27473

NL 0411613 In DLC

35
The Little chief, and other stories. [anon.] Boston, D. Lothrop & co. [1880]
unp., 22 l. 10 pl. 16°.

NL 0411614 DLC

Little chief library.
v. 1
New York, Nickel library co., 188 v. 23cm.
Weekly.

1. Dime novels—Collections.
N. Y. P. L. December 31, 1947

NL 0411615 NN

BY1996
.G71a
1917
The little child and the heavenly father. Beginners' teacher's textbook. pts.1-8. Prepared by Frances W. Danielson. New York, Graded Press [°1909-1911, °1917-1918]
1v. illus. 20cm. quarterly. (Graded course, international system: Beginners')
"A two-year beginners' course in eight parts (for children four and five years of age)."—Title page.

NL 0411616 IEG

BY1996
.G71a
1928
The little child and the heavenly father. pt.1-8. Teacher's textbook. By Frances W. Danielson and Jessie Eleanor Moore. New York, Graded Press [1928-1930]
1v. illus. 20cm. quarterly. (Graded courses, international system: Beginners'.)
"A two-year beginners' course in 8 parts (for children 4 and 5 years of age)."—Title page.

Also called: Church school closely graded courses.

1. Sunday schools, Methodist Episcopal Church. 2. Sunday schools—Curricula—Methodist Episcopal Church. I. Danielson, Frances W. (Series)

NL 0411618 IEG

VOLUME 336

BT1996 .G71a 1936 The little child and the heavenly father. pt.1-8. Teacher's textbook. By Esther Freivogel. Outline by Frances W. Danielson and Jessie Eleanor Moore. New York, Graded Press [1936-1937] 1v. 20cm. quarterly. (Graded course, international series: Beginners')

"A 2 year beginners' course in 8 parts (for children 4 and 5 years of age)"—Title page.

Also called: Church school closely graded courses.

1. Sunday schools, Methodist Episcopal Church. 2. Sunday schools—Curricula—Methodist Episcopal Church. I. Freivogel, Esther. (Series)

NL 0411620 IEG

BX 2150 .L 5 The little child of Mary. A manual of instruction and prayers adapted to preserve the fruits of first communion. New York, Cincinnati, Chicago, Benziger Brothers, 1897.

NL 0411621 DLC

A little child: the Christmas miracle told in Bible verses chosen by Jessie Orton Jones see under Bible. English. Selections. 1946. Authorized.

"The little children that are gone" see under [Chapin, Mrs. C B] comp.

Little children's book: for schools and families see under General Council of the Evangelical Lutheran Church in North America.

Little Children's Hymns and Songs see under [Lewis, Henry King]

The little child's A B C. Providence, G.P. Daniels, 1845.

NL 0411626 MH

RP PZ 6 1830 L58 The LITTLE child's book; illustrated by emblematic figures. Boston, Munroe & Francis [1830] 64, 64, 64, 64 p. illus.
Each section has separate paging and special t.p.
Contents.- The little child's book.- The little child's present.- The little child's gift.- The little child's pictures.

NL 0411627 CaBVaU

PZ262 .L81 184- [The little child's book. Boston, Munroe & Francis; [etc., etc., 184-?] 64 p. illus.
Imperfect: t.-p. and all preceding p.17 wanting. Title supplied from Roorbach.

NL 0411628 ICU

The Little child's book. New York, Blakeman & Mason [c1830] 64 p. front., illus.

NL 0411629 NNC

The little child's book of divinity see under [Macduff, John Ross] 1818-1895.

... The little child's first reader. Adapted to either mode of teaching; by letters or by words. 1st ed. Philadelphia, T. E. Zell, 1862.
[3]-64 p. illus. 17½cm. (Friends' educational series)

1. Readers and speakers—1800-1870. I. Title.

14-1237

Library of Congress PE1124.F7L6

NL 0411631 DLC ICU

The little child's friend; by the author of "Rose and her lamb," "The two new scholars," &c., &c. Boston, Ticknor, Reed, and Fields, 1851.
iv, [2], [7]-120 p. incl. plates. 15cm.
Prose and verse.

I. Rose and her lamb, Author of.

43-27338

Library of Congress PZ6.L69

NL 0411632 DLC

---

76 L19157 1855 The little child's friend; by the author of "Rose and her lamb," "The two new scholars," etc. etc. 3d ed. Boston, Ticknor and Fields, 1855.
120 p. incl. plates. 16 cm.
Prose and verse.

I. Rose and her lamb, Author of.

NL 0411633 RPB

PZ262 .L81 184- The little child's gift; illustrated by emblematic figures. Boston, Munroe & Francis; [etc., etc., 184-?] 64 p. illus. [With The little child's book. Boston, 184-?]

NL 0411634 ICU

---

j808 L728 The little child's gift; illustrated by emblematic figures. New York, Blakeman & Mason [184-?] 64p. illus.

Title vignette.
Title and text within ornamental borders.
Engraved frontispiece signed: Anderson; illustrations probably engraved by Alexander Anderson.

I. Anderson, Alexander, 1775-1870, illus.

NL 0411635 IU

Little child's home A B C book. New York, McLoughlin bros. [1870?]

NL 0411636 MH

Little childs home ABC book. New York, McLoughlin & Brothers, 1886.
[16]p. col.illus. 27½cm.

NL 0411637 NBu

PZ262 .L81 184- The little child's pictures; illustrated by emblematic figures. Boston, Munroe & Francis; [etc., etc., 184-?] 64 p. illus. [With The little child's book. Boston, 184-?]
Imperfect: p.47 mutilated.

NL 0411638 ICU OClWHi

Little childs scriptural lessons in rhyme see under American Sunday-School Union.

J L778 1845 The little child's tutor; or, First book for children, in words not exceeding two syllables. A new ed. Derby, Mozley [1845] 72p. illus. T.
Educ.

NL 0411640 IaU

The little chimney sweeper ... [London, E. Wallis, 18--?] [2] p. illus. 18 cm.

A poem, from The heart's ease.
Begins: Papa, how I pity that little black boy.
Photostat reproduction (positive) of Dr. S.A. Henry's copy.

NL 0411641 MH-BA

The Little chimney-sweeper, Boston, 1864 see under Urbino, Levina (Buoncore)

The Little Christian. Boston, Mass., Scriptural Tract Repository, 1866-1904?
Vols.1-5, 1866-70; ser.2, vol.1-34, 1871-1904?
Supplement to the Christian.

NL 0411643 NbHi

The Little Christian, a Sunday-school paper for boys and girls. v. 1- 1871- Boston, H. L. Hastings [1871]-
v. 27cm. monthly.

10-26187†

NL 0411644 DLC

VOLUME 336

The little Christian; a play
see under [Clarke, Charles H]

Little Christmas; or, How the toys come; a story of a little boy, far away, long ago, and today, pictures by Zdeněk Guth. New York, The Macmillan company, 1929.
[84] p. col. plates. 19cm.

Library of Congress PZ8.L719 30-24321

NL 0411646 DLC WaS OO OClh NN

Little Christopher Columbus
see under Caryll, Ivan, 1861-1921.

The Little chronicle, a weekly magazine and record of history in the making
see
The World's chronicle.

The Little chronicle, a weekly news-magazine for boys and girls
see The World's chronicle.

Little chronicle company, *Chicago.*
The industries of a great city, by the editorial staff of the Little chronicle company. Chicago, Ill., The Little chronicle company [1912]
[iii]-viii, 9-128 p. illus. 26cm. $0.75

1. Chicago—Indus. I. Title.

Library of Congress HC108.C4L5 12—16094

NL 0411650 DLC NN ICJ

Little chronicle company, Chicago.

Atkinson, *Mrs.* Eleanor (Stackhouse) 1863–
The story of Chicago and national development, 1534–1912. By Eleanor Atkinson. Edited and extended by the editorial staff of the Little chronicle company. 10th ed. Chicago, Ill., The Little chronicle company [1911]

Little chronicle company, *Chicago.*
A treasury of good stories for moral and humane education, by the editorial staff of the Little chronicle company. Chicago, Ill., The Little chronicle company [1912]
[iii]-v, [1], 7-124, [3] p. illus. 26cm. $0.75

1. Animals, Treatment of. 2. Animals, Legends and stories of. I. Title.

Library of Congress HV4711.L5 12-16381

NL 0411652 DLC

The little chronicle of Magdalena Bach
see under [Meynell, Mrs. Esther Hallam (Moorhouse)]

Little Church around the Corner songster, The. Also, all the popular sentimental songs of the day.
— New York. Hilton. [186-?] 64 pp.
The song entitled The Little Church around the Corner was written to show the unfavorable attitude of many people towards actors.

M4439 — Actors. — Songs. Without music. Colls.

NL 0411654 MB

Little Church on the Circle, *Indianapolis*
see
Indianapolis. Christ Church.

A little civilization
see under [Kipling, Rudyard] 1865-1936.

... Little classics. Edited by Rossiter-Johnson ...
see under Johnson, Rossiter, 1840-1931, ed.

786.374M
L 721 Little classics for the piano. v.1. [New York, G. Schirmer [c1893]
82 p. 30cm.

Binder's title.
Includes works by J.S. Bach, L. van Beethoven, M. Clementi, J.L. Dussek, E. Grieg, G.F. Händel, J. Haydn, St. Heller, J.N. Hummel, Fr. Hünten, Th. Kullak, F. Mendelssohn, I. Moscheles, W.A. Mozart, C. Reinecke, F. Schubert, R. Schumann, P. Tschaikowsky, C.M. von Weber.

NL 0411658 OO TU

R.B.R. Little classics of the South. New York, Purdy Press, 1926–
v. in illus., port. 19 cm.

Edited by H. R. Palmer.
Each story has special t.p.
Contents.-[1] South Carolina: A monarch of the sky, by A. Rutledge; Two Gullah tales, by A. E. Gonzales.-[2] Mississippi: Gran'mammy, by S. Bonner; A trip through the piney woods, by J.F.H. Claiborne.
I. Palmer, Henrietta Raymer, 1867- ed.

NL 0411659 NcD NN NBuG OO IU

The little clincher
see under [Winchell, DeForest B]

---

35 The Little cloister ruin. Philadelphia, Lutheran board of publication, 1871.
130 p. 2 pl. 16°. [The fatherland series]

NL 0411661 DLC

A little colored boy, and other stories. New York, Cincinnati, Methodist Book Concern [190-]
64p. incl. front., illus. 17 cm.

Includes original poetry.

NL 0411662 RPB

The little commission. Richmond, Va. 1 Sept. 1945-
[2], 3-

NL 0411663 KyLoS

The Little Commonwealth, Evershot, Eng.
Annual report.
[no.]
[London? 19 8°.
v. illus.

1. Criminals (Juvenile).—Communities (Self-governing), Gt. Br.: Eng.: Evershot.
N. Y. P. L. August 24, 1916.

NL 0411664 NN

Little companions. Illustrated. New York, Cassell, Petter, Galpin [c1881]
96 p. illus.

NL 0411665 NNC

242
597
L72 Little Company of Mary.
The path of Mary; 6th edition. Chicago, Little Company of Mary [1950?]
128p front 14cm (Our Lady's little library of Mary)

At head of title: Convent of the Maternal Heart of Mary.
First published 1878 in England.

NL 0411666 MnCS

HJ9013
.L54 Little Compton, R. I.
Report of the town treasurer.
Providence, 18
v 8°

NL 0411667 DLC RPB

Little Compton, *R. I. Assessors of taxes.*
Little Compton tax book
Fall River, Mass. [etc.] 18
v. 22½-24½cm.
Title varies slightly.

1. Taxation—Little Compton, R. I. I. Title.
CA 10—1686 Unrev'd

Library of Congress HJ9013.L54 g

NL 0411668 DLC

Little Compton, R.I. Superintendent of public schools.
Annual report... 1879, 1883-1884, 1886, 1888-1889, 1891, 1894-1897. Providence, etc., 1879-1897.
10 v. 19-25 cm.

NL 0411669 RPB

MF58.6
L729m Little Compton, R.I. United Congregational church.
Manual of the United Congregational church, Little Compton, R.I. Revised 1903. Church organized November 30, 1704. [n.p., 1903?]
43 p. illus. 19 cm.

NL 0411670 CtY-D

VOLUME 336

MF58.6 L729o Little Compton, R.I. United Congregational church.
The one hundred and seventy-fifth anniversary of the organization of the United Congregational church, Little Compton, R.I. Providence, Providence press co., 1880.
76 p. 24 cm.

"Celebrated June 2d, 1880."

NL 0411671 CtY-D NN MH

Little Compton, R. I. United Congregational church.
The two-hundredth anniversary of the organization of the United Congregational Church, Little Compton, Rhode Island, September 7, 1904. Little Compton, R. I., The United Congregational society ₍1906₎
120 p. front., plates, ports., facsims. 24½cm.
"Historical discourse, by Rev. Wilson R. Buxton": p. ₍11₎–36.
"Historical address. The town of Little Compton. By Roswell B. Burchard": p. 61–108.
1. Little Compton, R. I. I. Buxton, Wilson Riley, 1861– II. Burchard, Roswell Beebe. III. Title.
Library of Congress BX7255.L66U5 19-16932

NL 0411672 DLC NN MH-AH MB

LITTLE COMPTON GARDEN CLUB.
Favorite recipes of Little Compton garden club members. Rev. and enl. [Little Compton, R.I.]1947.
218 p. (p. 216-218 blank for "Memorandum") illus. 21cm.

1. Cookery, American, 1926-

NL 0411673 NN

The Little-Compton scourge; or, The anti-courant. Boston: Printed and sold by J. Franklin, over against Mr. Sheaf's School in Queen-Street. Price 3d. ₍1721₎
(*In* The Magazine of history, with notes and queries. Tarrytown, N. Y., 1923. 26½cm. Extra number. no. 92 (v. 23, no. 4) 2 l. at end)
A satire, originally printed as a broadside.
Attributed to Benjamin Franklin. "Though there is no proof that he was the author of the skit, it is not unlikely that he was connected with its origin; and that he certainly had some connection with its actual printing." *cf.* Pref.
I. Franklin, Benjamin, 1706–1790.
Library of Congress E173.M24 vol. 24 24-3339

NL 0411674 DLC NcD MB

The little conscience, and other stories
see under [Baker, Harriette Newell (Woods)] 1815-1893.

Little Constancy's birthday.
(In Novels and tales reprinted from Household Words, conducted by Charles Dickens. Vol. 8, pp. 79-108. Leipzig, 1858.)

Δ1078

NL 0411676 MB

"A little content"
see under Justin, Jennie, comp. [Supplement]

A little cook book for a little girl
see under [Burrell, Mrs. Caroline Frances (Benedict)]

The Little corporal; an illustrated magazine for boys and girls ... v. 1–19; July 1865–Dec. 1874. Chicago, A. L. Sewell ₍etc.₎ 1865–74.
19 v. in 7. illus., plates, ports. 22½–29cm. monthly.
Editors: July 1865–June 1871, A. L. Sewell (with Edward Eggleston, June 1866–Feb. 1867; Emily H. Miller, Aug. 1867–June 1871).—July 1871–1874, Emily H. Miller.
Absorbed Work and play in Apr. 1872.
Merged into St. Nicholas in 1875.
I. Sewell, Alfred L., ed. II. Eggleston, Edward, 1837–1902, ed. III. Miller, Mrs. Emily Clark (Huntington) 1833–1913, ed.
Library of Congress AP200.L3 10-23463 Revised

PU ICRL ODW OCl OO OClWHi
NL 0411679 DLC MiU IU ICHi ICRL ICN OHi N FTaSU

The little corporal; a comic opera
see under Engländer, Ludwig, 1853-1914.

The Little corporal's school festival; an original magazine devoted to school festivals, entertainments, dialogues, recitations, readings, tableaux, charades, &c., &c., conducted by Alfred L. Sewell ... no. 1-5; Jan. 1870–Jan. 1871. Chicago, A. L. Sewell & co. ₍etc.₎ 1870–71.
cover-title, 160 p. 20½cm. quarterly.
Continued as the National school festival.
I. Sewell, Alfred L., ed.
10-23800
Library of Congress AP200.N4

NL 0411681 DLC

The little cot; a favorite song. New York Printed & sold at G. Gilfert's, piano forte warehouse Nº 177 Broadway. And to be had at P. A. von Hagen's. Nº 3 Cornhill Boston. And G. Willig. Nº 185 Market Street. Philadelphia. ₍ca. 1800₎
₍2₎ l. 33 cm. (₍Collection of early American music, published or manuscript. v. p., 179-?-182-?₎ v. 5, no. 57)
Caption title.
Part for flute at end.
1. Songs (Medium voice) with piano.
M1.A11 vol. 5, no. 57 62-40111/M

NL 0411682 DLC

809.22 F22L7 The Little Country Theater - Yesterday - Today - Tomorrow. ₍35th anniversary. Fargo? N.D. 1949₎
₍32₎ p. illus. (incl.ports.) 28cm.
Thirty-first Legislative Assembly State of North Dakota. Senate concurrent resolution, relating to the Little Country Theater and congratulating Alfred G.Arvold, the founder, on the forthcoming thirty-fifth anniversary of the founding of the Little Country Theater.- ₍4₎ p. tipped in at end.
1.Fargo, N.D. Little Country Theater.

NL 0411683 CSt

The little country visitor. A drama. In two parts. [By the authoress of "The misfortunes of anger"] ... Boston, Printed for [W. Spotswood, 1798?]
38 p. front. 10 cm.
Imp., t.-p. and p. 5-14 mutilated, p. 3-4 missing.

NL 0411684 CtY MH

MICP1 812.08 Little country visitor. Boston, 179-?
(In Three centuries of drama: American)
Microprint.

NL 0411685 MoU

Analyzed The little cousins of long ago series... Boston, 1913-

NL 0411686 DLC

The little cowherd of Slainge...
see under [Campbell, Joseph] 1879-

The Little craft books.
Oxford₍, Eng.₎: Oxford Univ. Press, 1932 19 – 22cm.
v. illus., plates (part col'd).
Editor : F. V. Burridge.
1. No subject. I. Burridge, Frederick Vango, 1869– , editor. N. Y. P. L. June 15, 1933

NL 0411688 NN

The little crib
see under Hirschfeld, Max, arr.

Little crib-curtain stories. [1888]
see under Pratt, Ella (Farman) 1837-1907.

LITTLE cripple, The. 7589a.
Lond. Cooper. n. d. 12 pp. 64°.

NL 0411691 MB

E98 .F61G6 1910 Little Crow, Dakota Chief, d.1863.
Ta-ó-ya-te-dú-ta is not a coward ₍speech₎
(In Gordon, H.L. Indian legends & other poems. Salem, Mass., 1910. 23cm. p.382-383)

NL 0411692 MnHi

---

17 1845a The Little crown of saint Joseph. Compiled and translated from approved sources by a sister of St. Joseph. Permissu superiorum. [anon.] New York, D. & J. Sadlier & co., 1875.
351 p. front. 18°.

NL 0411693 DLC

Little crumbs, Author of.
The child's morning book
see under title

Little crumbs for little mouths; or, Very easy readying lessons. By a mother. Part I. In words not exceeding three letters. Part II. In words not exceeding four letters. New ed. London, Houlston and Co. [ca.1845?]
106 p. illus.

NL 0411695 CLU

"Little Cuba;" or, Circumstantial evidence
see under [Barclay, George Lippard]

VOLUME 336

The little cyclopedia of Mormonism
see under Light on Mormonism.

244
L7782 The little daisy; or, Early piety. New York, General Protestant Episcopal S.S. Union, 1855.
24 p. illus. 15 cm.

1. Sunday-school literature. I. Title.

NL 0411698 N

The Little daisy; or, Early piety. New York, Gen. Prot. Episc. S.S. Union, 1862.
24 p. 24°.

NL 0411699 NN

The little dame and the wild animals
see under [Barry, Margaret N]

... Little Dame Crump, and her little white pig. London, J. L. Marks [n.d.]
cover-title, 8 l. col.illus. 17.7 cm.
"Marks's edition", at head of title.

NL 0411701 MiU-C

962
L778 Little Dame Crump and her white pig. New York, McLoughlin Bro's [1888-?]
15 p. col.illus.

Cover title.

NL 0411702 CU

Little Dame Crump and her little white pig. The adventures of little Dame Crump and her little white pig. Marks' edition. Albany, R. H. Pease [19--]
15 p. illus.

Caption title: The history of little Dame Crump and her little white pig.

NL 0411703 NNC

PZ 112
.L5 Little dame Trot. London, Dean [1866?]
8 l. col. illus.

NL 0411704 ICU

Little Dave. New York, American tract society [18--?]
14 p. illus. 11½cm.

I. American tract society.

NL 0411705 NjP

Little deacon.
The devil unmasked
see under
Cooksey, Nicias Ballard, 1846-

PZ221
.L77 Little delights. New York, McLoughlin bros. [187-?]
9 v. illus.
Contents.--[v.1] Jack and the beanstalk.--[v.2] Diamonds and toads.--[v.3] Hop o' my thumb.--[v.4] Little old woman.--[v.5] Aladdin.--[v.6] Heedless Johnny.--[v.7] Lazy Charlotte.--[v.8] Frog's bride.--[v.9] Inky boys.

NL 0411707 ICU

813.29
L778l The little deserter. New York, McLoughlin Bros. [189-?]
12 p. col. illus. 23 cm. (Aunt Matilda's series)

Cover title.

NL 0411708 N

The little deserter; or, Holiday sports; a tale: dedicated to all good boys. Embellished with engravings ... New Haven, J. Babcock & son; [etc., etc.] 1824.
30 p., 1 l. incl. front., illus. 14½cm.
Frontispiece and last page mounted on inside of covers.
Running title: Holiday sports.

I. Title: Holiday sports.

28-27516

Library of Congress PZ6.L71

NL 0411709 DLC

The Little devil. A fascicle of apostolic asseverations, and other saintly sayings, for everybody but mental mendicants and moral runts. v. 1-4, v. 5, no. 1- [July 1905]- 1908. Los Angeles [Little devil pub. co., etc.] 1905-08.
5 v. 18cm. monthly.
Absorbed the Little classic in Apr. 1908 and continued as the Bystander.

CA 10-4405 Unrev'd

Library of Congress AP2.B95

NL 0411710 DLC InU

Little dialogues for little people
see under [Bates, Mrs. Margaret Holmes (Ernsperger)] 1844-

Little Dimple Cheek's album. New York, T. Nelson [1878]
[26] p. illus. (Dewdrop series)

NL 0411712 NNC ICU

Little ditties for little children
see under [Sproat, Nancy]

Little Doctor Comfort. N[ew] Y[ork], McLoughlin Bros., [18-?]
8 p. illus. 16°.

NL 0411714 NN

The little doctor 'round the corner
see under Frazer, McPherson.

LITTLE dog. New York. The Hobby press. 1919.
7(1) p. illus. 88mm.

1. Dog--Legend and stories.

NL 0411716 NN

The little dog Dash. Fourth edition. London: Printed for Houlston and Co., 1843.
47 p. front., illus. 12cm.

I. Dash.

NL 0411717 ViW

Little Dog Stray. Poem. Broadside. 1100

NL 0411718 ViW

Little dog Trusty
see under [Edgeworth, Maria] 1767-1849.

The Little dog who forgot how to bark ... The little boy who found his fortune, Why the monkey still has a tail. Illustrated by Hildegarde Hopkins. New York, Wonder books [1946]
[40] p. illus. (part col.) 25 x 19 cm.

I. Hopkins, Hildegard L., illus.

Library of Congress PZ10.3.L717 46—21743

NL 0411720 DLC

LITTLE don of Spain. Boston, cop.1878.
4°.

NL 0411721 MH-Mu

... The little Don Quixote: a story for youth. Translated from the German, by Robert R. Raymond. Syracuse: Hall and Hopkins, 1855. 163 p. front., plates. 16°. (The Nutwood library. no. 1.)
Imperfect copy: p. 163 mutilated.

23995A. 1. Juvenile literature.—Fiction (German). 2. Raymond, Robert Raikes, 1817-88, translator.
N. Y. P. L. December 30, 1921.

NL 0411722 NN

VOLUME 336

Little Dora, Author of.
The child's first history of America
see under title

Little Dorrit
see under [Dickens, Charles] 1812-1870.

35 Little Dot's picture gallery. Hundreds of beautiful pictures. [Anon.] Boston, Estes & Lauriat, 1883 [1882]
unp., 56 l. 4°.

NL 0411725 DLC

Little Downy, or The history of a field-mouse; a moral tale. London, Dean and Munday, 1822.
(2), 5-48 p. Hand colored front. and other illustr.

NL 0411726 MH

The little dreamer
see under [Tuttle, George] 1804-1872.

... The little drummer boy, Clarence D. McKenzie
see under [Bingham, Luther Goodyear] 1798-1877.

The little drummer; or, Filial affection. A story of the Russian campaign. [By H. D.] With illustrations by J. Gilbert. London: G. Routledge, & Co., 1856.
viii, 9-192 p., 4 pl. 16°.

NL 0411729 NN

The little duke: a comic opera in three acts
see under Lecocq, Alexandre Charles, 1832-1918.

Little Dumpling's Christmas gift. New York, E. P. Dutton, 1881.
[117] p. illus.

NL 0411731 NNC

Little duties for little people: a story of Katie Lee. Philadelphia [etc.] Amer. Sunday-school union [c1864] 60 p. front., pl. 15½cm.

1. Juvenile literature—Fiction, American. I. American Sunday-school union.
N. Y. P. L. June 20, 1940

NL 0411732 NN

Little Eagle, *Cherokee Indian*
see Cody, Iron Eyes, 1904-

Little Echeconnee association
see Primitive Baptists. Georgia. Little Echeconnee association.

Little Edward; or, lessons in reading for children between four and six years old.
= Boston. Bowles & Dearborn. 1828. 56 pp. Plate. 24°.
Two copies. The original copy lacks the first leaf of the cover; the "A" copy lacks the title-page.

G8167 — English language. Read. —.

NL 0411735 MB MH

"Little Ella," Author of.
Fields and woodlands
see under title

Little Ella, Author of.
Henry's fireside, with peeps at his grandpa's farm
see under title

Little Ellen, and other pleasing poetic stories
see under [Lee, Abby]

Juv. coll. Little Ellen: or, The good girl. Worcester, Published by S.A. Howland, Hancock and Howland, printers [n.d.]
[3] 4-15 p. 9.5 cm.

NL 0411739 DLC

Little Elsie: to which is added, Little Jemmy, the chimney-sweeper ... N.Y. Stanford & swords. 1851.
81 p.

NL 0411740 OClWHi

LITTLE Emery's Sunday lesson. Designed for children four or five years old. By the author of "Fruit and flowers". Boston, Hilliard, Gray, Little, and Wilkins, 1828.
24°. pp.15.

NL 0411741 MH

The Little emigrant;..
see under [Peacock, Lucy] 1786-1815.

Little Emma. 1845
see under [Bradbury, Osgood]

PZ262 .L812 1863 Little Emma. Boston, H. Hoyt, 1863.
64 p. 12cm.

NL 0411744 ICU

Little engravings; classical & contemporary. NY

no.2 (1902): William Blake; being all his woodcuts photographically reproduced in facsimile with an intro. by Laurence Binyon

NL 0411745 MH

"The little entomologist", Author of.
The little marine botanist; or, Guide to the collection and arranging of sea-weed
see under title

The little epicure
see under [Larned, Mrs. Linda (Hull)] 1853-1939.

The little Episcopalian...
see under
Cruse, Mary Anne.

Little Eppie, and other tales. Comp. for the Presbyterian board of publication. Philadelphia, Presbyterian board of publication [1865]
216 p. front., 2 pl. 15½cm.

Library of Congress PZ5.L72 7-16061†

NL 0411749 DLC

35 Little Ernest; or, the land beyond the river. [anon.] Philadelphia, American S.S. Union, [1859]
36 p. 1 pl. 18°.

NL 0411750 DLC

The little Esop
see under Aesopus. English.

Little Eva, the flower of the South. [New York, Philip J. Cozans,] n.d.
8p. illus. 18cm.

NL 0411752 DHU

Little Eva. To her papa. As sung by little Cordelia Howard, in the successful drama of "Uncle Tom's cabin," at Forbes' theatre, Providence ... Little Eva in heaven. As sung by G.C. Howard, at Forbes' theatre... Providence, R.I. A.Crawford Greene, book and job printer, [ca. 1855]
broadside. 12.3 x 20.9cm. (10.2 x 19.3cm.)
Text within engraved border.

1.Stowe, Harriet Beecher. Uncle Tom's cabin. 2.Poetry. 3.Broadsides. 4.Drama - Poetry. I. Howard, G.C. II. Howard, Cordelia. III. Little Eva in heaven.

NL 0411753 MiU-C

VOLUME 336

The little evangel
see under Coleman, Robert Henry, 1869- ed. and comp.

A little eye-salve for the kingdome and armie, that they may see. Wherein is cleerly represented what the supreme power of the kingdome is, and how it may be knowne. By a true friend and lover of those powers and magistrates that be of God. [London, 1647]
8 p. 19cm.
Caption title.

1. Gt. Brit.—Hist.—Civil war, 1642-1649—Pamphlets.
8-7930†
Library of Congress DA412.1647.L55

NL 0411755 DLC InU CtY NNUT-Mc TxU MH ICN

PZ 8 .2 .L57x Little fables for little folks. New York [etc.] Cassell [1869] vi [9]-117 p. illus. 17 cm.

NL 0411756 OKentU

PZ 162 .L7665 1865 Little facts for little people. By S.T.C. With four engravings. New York, T.Y. Crowell [ca. 1865] 184 p. illus. (The Dove series)

I. S.T.C. II. C., S.T.

NL 0411757 ICU

398.4 L778 Little fairy tales. New York, McLoughlin, °1902.
1 v. illus. (part col.) 24 cm.
Cover title.

1. Fairy tales.

NL 0411758 N

Little Falls, Minn. High school.
Lindbergh, the flier of Little Falls ... [St. Cloud, Minn., 1928]

LITTLE FALLS, Minn. Ordinances, etc.
Charter and Ordinances, 1907; compiled by Fred Cary and Donat Trettel. n.p., n.d.
8vo.

NL 0411760 MH-L

JS997 .L7A46 Little Falls, Minn. Ordinances, etc.
Ordinances of the city of Little Falls ... [Little Falls, 19
v. tables. 28½cm.
Loose-leaf.
Compiled under the direction of the City council.
Ordinances of 18

NL 0411761 DLC

Little Falls, Minn. [telephone directory].
Little Falls, Minn.: Northwestern Telephone Exchange Co. [19 8°.
v.
Cover-title.

1. Little Falls, Minn.—Directories.
N. Y. P. L. October 18, 1916.

NL 0411762 NN

Little Falls, N.Y. Academy.
Catalogue of the officers and students, for the year ending Nov. 25, 1846.
Little Falls. 1846. 20 pp. 8°.

NL 0411763 MB

Little Falls, N. Y. Board of education.
Annual report. 1900/01; 1906/09; 12/16
Little Falls, N. Y., 1901-1917
8 v. front., plates. 22½cm.

NL 0411764 DHEW

Little Falls, N. Y. *Board of public works.*
Annual report.
[Little Falls,
v. 21½cm.

1. Little Falls, N. Y.—Public works.
11-31114
Library of Congress TD25.L5A3

NL 0411765 DLC DNLM

W 2 AN6.2 L7B6a LITTLE FALLS, N. Y. Board of Water Commissioners
Annual report.
1st- 1885/88-
Little Falls.
v.

NL 0411766 DNLM RPB

Little Falls, N.Y. Board of water commissioners.
Rules and regulations and schedule of water rates for the introduction and management of water supply... Little Falls, 1889.
16 p. 18 cm.

NL 0411767 RPB

Little Falls (N. Y.). Charters.
Charter of the city of Little Falls, passed May 8, 1895, as amended by subsequent legislation; the city ordinances and the rules of the Common Council. Printed by authority of the Common Council... Little Falls, N. Y.: Press of Stebbins & Burney, 1908. [256] p. 8°.
Various paging.

1. Municipal charters and ordinances, U. S.: N. Y.: Little Falls. 2. Little Falls (N. Y.). Common Council. 3. Little Falls (N. Y.). Ordinances.
N. Y. P. L. May 24, 1921.

NL 0411768 NN N

LITTLE FALLS, N.Y. Charters.
The charter of the city of Little Falls (Laws of 1895, Ch. 565, as amended) [Albany, 1949] 59, 8, 2 p. 29cm. [IN: New York (State). Audit and control dept. Municipal affairs division. Charters of the cities of New York state. Albany, 1949. v.4]
Includes 1949 suppl.

I. Ser. t. 1949.

NL 0411769 NN

Little Falls, New York. Citizens.
Petition, to restore to the village of Little Falls its ancient Indian name. [Little Falls, New York? 1841]
broadside, 31 1/2 x 20 1/2 cm.

NL 0411770 CSmH

Little Falls, N. Y. Committee to celebrate the hundredth year of corporate existence.
Development of Little Falls; a brief account of conditions and happenings which compiled the settlement and development of this city, with some reference to present conditions. Compiled and written for the Committee organized to celebrate the hundredth year of corporate existence following the charter of 1811. [Little Falls, 1911] 96 p. illus. 16 x 25cm.
On cover: Centennial review, Little Falls, N. Y., 1811-1911.

242298B. 1. No subject.
N. Y. P. L. October 8, 1943

NL 0411771 NN MB

Little Falls, N.Y. Farmers' Club
see Farmers' Club of Little Falls, N.Y.

Ib52 900 [Little Falls, N.Y. First presbyterian church]
There's Rosemary that's for remembrance ...
[Little Falls, N.Y., Press of Stebbins & Burney, 19—?]
cover-title, 78p., 1l. 23½x19cm
"Compiled by the ladies of the First presbyterian church, Little Falls, New York."

1. Quotations, English. I. Title.
x First presbyterian church, Little Falls, N.Y.

NL 0411773 CtY

Little Falls, N.Y. Ordinances.
Charter of the city of Little Falls, passed May 8, 1895, as amended by subsequent legislation; the city ordinances
see under Little Falls (N.Y.) Charters.

352.0747 L778 Little Falls, N. Y. Ordinances, etc.
Code of ordinances of the city of Little Falls, New York. Recodified - pursuant to resolution of the Common Council, adopted February 6, 1940. [Little Falls, 1940?]
222 p. 24 cm.
Pocket provided for supplements.

NL 0411775 N

VOLUME 336

Little Falls (N. Y.). Police Department.
Rules and regulations of the Police Department, city of Little Falls, N. Y. 1912... [Little Falls, 1912.] 73 p. 24°.

7218A. 1. Police, U. S.: N. Y.: Little Falls.
N. Y. P. L. May 19, 1921.

NL 0411776 NN

282.08 L776 Little Falls, N. Y. St. Mary's Church.
Addresses at the jubilee celebration of St. Mary's church, May 13-20. Little Falls, N. Y., 1928.
67 p. illus. 24 cm.

1. Catholic Church. Addresses, essays, lectures. I. Title.

NL 0411777 N

HE2791 .L682
Little Falls and Dolgeville Railroad Company.
Report of the board of directors. (1910-)
New York.
v. 30 cm. annual.

HE2791.L682 57-51640 ‡

NL 0411778 DLC

Little Falls and Dolgeville directory
see Williams' Little Falls and Dolgeville directory.

Little Falls high school, Little Falls, Minn.
see
Little Falls, Minn. High school.

*F612 .M79L7 1888ℓ
The Little Falls Water Power Co., Little Falls, Minn.
Unexcelled water power. [St. Paul, Brown, Treacy & co., printers, 1888]
cover-title, 18 [1] p. illus., map. 13 x 20cm.

NL 0411781 MnHi

BX 7971 .F2 A2 1955
Little Family of St. Therese of the Child Jesus.
Constituzioni della "Piccola Famiglia di S. Teresa del B.G." in Ravenna. Cesena (Forli) Scuola tip. Orfanelli dell'Addolorata, 1955.
76 p. 17 cm.

1. Monasticism and religious orders for women - Rules.

NL 0411782 DCU

s808.83 L721
Little Fanny, and other simple stories for very little readers. New York, Nelson & Phillips [188-?]
108p. illus. 16cm.

1. Children's stories.

NL 0411783 IU

LITTLE FARM, A, well till'd, a little cot well fill'd. [Trio. T. T. B.]
Manuscript. (3) pp. F°.

NL 0411784 MB

The little farmer; a companion for the little poulterer. Designed for the instruction of children. By a lady. Philadelphia, Pub. by Morgan & Yeager, at the Juvenile Bookstore, [18--?]
16 p. illus. 13 x 11 cm.

1. Illustrated books, children's.

NL 0411785 NjP

PZ 7 .L777
The little farmer girl, and other stories, illustrated. New York, McLoughlin Bros. [188-?]
32 p. illus.

NL 0411786 MiU

Little faults. Philadelphia, Davis, Porter & Coates [185-?]
cover-title, [8] p. col. illus. 17 cm.
(Aunt Mattie's series)
Imperfect copy.

NL 0411787 RPB

Little ferns for Fanny's little friends.
See under
Parton, Sara Payson (Willis), 1811-1872.

Little Ferritt; or, The Philadelphia detective. [n. p., n. d.]
33 l. 31cm.
Typescript.
Title on cover: The lightning rod agent; or, Little Ferritt.
Produced at the Opera house, Chattanooga, Tenn., March 28, 1898.

1. Drama, American. 2. Drama—Promptbooks and Typescripts.
I. Title: The lightning rod agent. II. Title: The Philadelphia detective.

NL 0411789 NN

Is94 tl v.2
The little field daisy ... New-York: Printed & sold by Mahlon Day [ca. 1829]
16p. illus. 9cm.
Verse.
Title vignette, repeated on front cover; illustrated back cover.

NL 0411790 CtY

The little fire engine. Pictures by Vic Havel. Kenosha, Wis., John Martin's House [1949]
[28] p. col. illus. 21 cm. (A Bonnie book)

I. Havel, Victor, illus.

PZ7.L733 50-23549

NL 0411791 DLC OCl

The little fish-peddler; or, Mackerel Will and his friend Emma. By the author of "Stories for school boys," etc. Richmond, Presbyterian committee of publication, 1867.
134 p. illus. 15.5 cm.
1. Va. Literature.

NL 0411792 NcD

Beinecke Library Is94 Tl v.2
The Little fisherman ... New-York; Baker, Crane & Day, 374 & 158 Pearl Street [1835?]
8 p. illus. 8 cm.

NL 0411793 CtY

Little fishing classics. [N.Y., W. Binner Co., n.d.
see under
[Meisselbach, A. F. & bro.]

Little fistiana, 1895. Comp. and ed. by B. H. Benton (Rob Roy) ... Official records of the prize ring and of boxing ... Boston, Mass., F. K. Lanpher & co., °1895.
182 p. incl. ports. 12°.

1. Boxing. I. Benton, Benjamin H., ed. II. Lanpher, F. K., & co.

Library of Congress GV1137.L77 CA 5—1744 Unrev'd

NL 0411795 DLC

Little fistiana, 1898. Official records of the prize ring and of boxing; all the principal battles from 1719 to 1898. Marquis of Queensberry, and London prize ring rules, etc. Boston, Mass., F. K. Lanpher & co. [°1898]
[128] p. incl. ports. 11½°.

1. Boxing. I. Lanpher, F. K., & co.

Library of Congress GV1137.L77 CA 5—1971 Unrev'd

NL 0411796 DLC

A little flat in the Temple
see under [Scott, Mrs. Winifred Mary (Watson)]

Little Flock association of Regular Baptists
see Primitive Baptists. Kentucky. Little Flock association of Regular Baptists.

VOLUME 336

BX6495 .S58L7 LITTLE FLOCK BAPTIST CHURCH, Harrison Co., Ind.
[Letter of dismission for Elizabeth Smith, issued by the Little Flock Baptist church of Harrison county, Indiana, October 1821]
facsim.: 1 l. 27½cm.
Photostat copy (negative)

1. Manuscripts, English--Facsimiles.

NL 0411799 ICU

Little Flock Primitive Baptist association (Texas) see Primitive Baptists. Texas. Little Flock Primitive Baptist association.

Little Flora. By a lady. New York, General Protestant Episcopal Sunday school union.

NL 0411801 MB

Little Flora. Designed for the instruction and amusement of youth. Brooklyn, E. B. Carter, 1844.
7 l. illus. 11 cm.
Illustrated t.-p.
Text within ornamental borders.

NL 0411802 RPB

"Little Flora," Author of,
Christmas at home, and the ebony box
see under title

Little Flora, Author of.
James Haswell, the ferryman
see under title

Little Flora. Plate.
(In Charley's lessons about animals. Pp. 69–110. New York. [1870.])

NL 0411805 MB

BW 2124 T3 L77 The Little Flower at the Benedictine Convent. Reminiscences of her teachers and class-mates by one of her teachers. Tr. by Odette Duval Lisieux. Huntington, Ind., Our Sunday Visitor Press [c.1930]
95 p. port., illus. 20 cm.

1. Thérèse, Saint, 1873-1897.

NL 0411806 IMunS

The Little flower-gatherer. Philadelphia, American Sunday-School Union [18–]
[64] p. illus. 12 cm.
Cover title: Flower gatherer.
Each tract has special t. p. and separate paging.
CONTENTS: The little flower-gatherer.—The rainy day; or, Be your own Kate.—The story of the dew-drop.—Heels and toes too.—The three handfuls of grain.—James Ferguson; or, What trying will do.

1. Children's stories. I. American Sunday-School Union. II. Title: Flower gatherer.

PZ6.L72 (Rare Bk Coll.) 813'.01 73-170109

NL 0411807 DLC

The Little flower magazine.
[Oklahoma City, The Discalced Carmelite fathers, 19
v. illus. (incl. ports.) 27cm. monthly.
Volume numbers irregular: v. 14, no. 10-12 called v. 15; v. 15, no. 9 called v. 16.

1. Catholic church—Period.

42-46952

Library of Congress BX801.L5
[2] 282.05

NL 0411808 DLC

Little flower monastery messenger
see
Pax; a Catholic monthly.

Little Flower of Jesus
see Thérèse, *Saint*, 1873–1897.

The Little flower prayer book, compiled by a friend of the Little flower, from approved sources. Oklahoma City, The Little flower press, 1923.
3 p. l., [11]–294 p. illus. (port.) 14cm.

1. Catholic church—Prayer-books and devotions. I. Teresa, Sister, originally Marie Françoise Thérèse Martin, 1873–1897. II. A friend of the Little flower.

24-680

Library of Congress BX2110.L76

NL 0411811 DLC

Little flower series.
Chicago, Ill., c1926-

BX4700 .T5L5

NL 0411812 DLC

Little flowers of poetry ...
see under [Leichter, Elsa]

The Little flowers of saint Francis of Assisi
see under Francesco d'Assisi, Saint. Legend. Fioretti. English.

LITTLE folded hands; prayers for children; illustrated by Otto Keisker. St. Louis, Concordia pub. house [194-?] 115 p. illus. 16cm.

1. Prayer-books, Juvenile.

NL 0411815 NN

AP 201 .L78 Little folks; a magazine for the young.
London, Paris [etc.] Cassell, Petter, Galpin & co. [18
v. illus., plates. 24½cm. monthly.
Includes songs with piano accompaniment.

NL 0411816 MiU MB NNC

Little folks: a magazine for the young, v.1-
N.Y., American News Company [187]
v. illus. 22 cm.
Also published in London. Cf. Union List of Serials.

NL 0411817 RPB

Little folks, a magazine for the young.
The Little Folks diary & note book for 1891
see under Skidmore, Mrs. Beatrice (Crane)

Little folks; a magazine for the young.
The little folks' holiday album ...
see under title

Little folks; an illustrated monthly for youngest readers
see Little folks; the children's magazine, Salem, Mass.

Little folks; the children's magazine. v. 1– 29, no. 4; Nov. 1897–Feb. 1926. Salem, Mass. [etc.] S. E. Cassino [1897–1926]
29 v. illus., plates (part col.) 25cm. monthly.
Subtitle varies.
Editors: 1897–May 1909, C. S. Pratt, Ella F. Pratt.—June 1909–Feb. 1926, Margherita O. C. Osborne.
Absorbed Our little ones and the nursery in Apr. 1899; Little men and women—Babyland and the Favorite in Sept. 1900.
Merged into Junior home magazine.
L. C. set incomplete: v. 27, no. 1 wanting.

I. Pratt, Charles Stuart, 1854– ed. II. Pratt, Ella (Farman) 1837–1907, ed. III. Osborne, Margherita Osborn (Cassino) 1878– ed.

10-23464 Revised

Library of Congress AP201.L7

NL 0411821 NcGU DLC MiGr OU OO RPB IU AzTeS MiU MB NNC

Juv. coll. ... Little folk's A B C. New York, McLoughlin Bros. [n.d.]
[15] p. 7 cm.
Linen book.

NL 0411822 DLC

The little folks animal story book
see under Hoopes, Margaret Campbell.

VOLUME 336

40 Little folks' annual [1895] Stories and pictures in abundance for young readers. Boston, Lothrop publishing co., [1895] 4°.

NL 0411824 DLC

Little folks' annual, 1905... New York, Cincinnati, 1904

25.9

NL 0411825 DLC

Little folks annual; for youngest readers, little listeners and lookers at pictures. Boston, Small, Maynard & company [°1921]–

v. mounted col. front., illus., plates. 23½cm.

Cover-title: Little folks illustrated annual.

Library of Congress PZ5.L722 21-19480

NL 0411826 DLC

Little Folks astray
see under [Clarke, Rebecca Sebbia] 1833-1906.

Little folks' book of nursery rhymes. London & New York, F. Warne & co., ltd. [°1936]

63, [1] p. col. front., illus., col. plates. 16cm.

1. Nursery rhymes.

Library of Congress PZ8.3.L66 38-4097

NL 0411828 DLC

Little folks' books... [v.] New York: Leavitt & Allen, 18 v. illus. 12½cm.

Unpaged. Each story preceded by half-title.
edited by Madame de Chatelain.

CONTENTS.

[v. 2] Cinderella. The Princess Rosetta. Fair One and [i. e. with] Golden Locks. Beauty and the beast. Little Red Riding Hood. The sleeping beauty.

1. Fairy tales. I. Chatelain, Clara (de Pontigny) de, 1807-1876, ed.
N. Y. P. L. June 4, 1940

NL 0411829 NN

Little folks' colored picture book. New York, McLoughlin bros. [187-?] 1 v. col. plates. 27cm.

NL 0411830 NN

Little folks everyday book
see under Harris, Amanda Bartlett, 1824-1917.

823.89
L778

The Little folks' holiday album ... Lond., N.Y. [etc.] Cassell Petter & Galpin [n.d.] 192p. front., illus. 25cm.

On cover: Holiday album for little folks.
"Stories reprinted from the 'Little folks' magazine."

1. Children's books. I. Title: Holiday album.

NL 0411832 N CtY

The Little folks' holiday album. London, Cassell, Petter & Galpin [1879] 192 p. illus. 26cm.

"This volume consists of stories reprinted from the "Little folks" magazine."

NL 0411833 MiDW

Little folks' home amusements; a boon to mothers and teachers on rainy days ... [Philadelphia?], 1902.

[198] p. incl. illus., pl. (part col.) 24½cm.

Library of Congress (✱) (PZ7) 2—28730

NL 0411834

The "Little folks" illuminating book; a series of Scripture texts...
see under Bible. English. Selections. 1881.

Little folks, for youngest readers
see Little folks, the children's magazine, Salem, Mass.

Spec.
PZ 5
.L 7

LITTLE FOLKS LIBRARY. ... Chicago, New York, The Werner co. [°1896] 6 v. 2 3/8 by 2 3/13 in. illus.

Russo: A bibl. of George Ade, p. 16-17.
In case. From the F. J. Meine collection.
Each volume has been rebacked.
Contents: v. [1] Circus day. - v. 2. Stories from history. - v. 3-4. Fairy tales from Shakespeare. - v. [5] Rhyme upon rhyme. -v. 6. Little farmers.
Vols. [1-2] were written by George Ade and illustrated by J. T. McCutcheon.

I. Ade, George, 1866-1944. II. McCutcheon, John Tinney, 1870-1949, illus.

NL 0411838 InU

Little Folks Magazine, Salem, Mass.
see Little folks; the children's magazine. Salem, Mass.

Little folks' menagerie. Boston, D. Lothrop & company [1881]

1 p. l., 43 pl. (incl. front.) 32cm.

1. Zoology—Pictorial works.

Library of Congress QL49.L77 4-30029

NL 0411840 DLC

The little folks' model arithmetic...
see under [Belfield, Henry Holmes] 1837-1912.

Little folks natural history. New York, McLoughlin bros., °1904.

[72] p. illus. (partly col.) 23 x 17½cm.

Cover-title: Natural history for little folks.
Published also under title: Natural history for little folks.

1. Natural history—Juvenile and popular literature.

Library of Congress QL49.N3 12-36291

NL 0411842 DLC

Epsteen
Coll.

Little folks' own book of fairy tales. New York, Hurst [1902?] [223] p. illus. 16cm.

1. Fairy tales.

NL 0411843 CoU

The little folks picture album... London [etc.] Cassell, Petter & Galpin [187-?] 168 p. illus. 26cm.

Cover-title: Picture album for little folks.

355593B. 1. Juvenile literature— Picture books.
N. Y. P. L. December 24, 1946

NL 0411844 NN

The little folks picture album in colour. 1904
see under Hamer, Sam Hield, 1869-

The little folks picture gallery. London, Cassell, Petter, Galpin [1880]

175 p. illus.

NL 0411846 MH

Little folks' plays of American heroes. Boston, [c1914-]

Analyzed

NL 0411847 DLC

VOLUME 336

Coll LI91033 Harris Collection
Little folks' prize: illustrated stories and poems for little people. With nearly two hundred original illustrations. New York, George Sully [c1891]
160 p. illus., incl. col. front., col. plates. 26 cm.

1. Children's poetry.

NL 0411848 RPB

Little folks' reader. v. 1- 3 [Jan. 1880?]- Dec 1882. Boston, D. Lothrop & co. [1879-82]
3 v. illus. 23½cm. monthly.
Edited by the editors of Wide awake and Babyland.
Continued as Our little men and women.

1. Readers and speakers.

CA 7-4411 Unrev'd

Library of Congress LB1525.A2L7

NL 0411849 DLC MH

Little folk's stories of great Americans for young Americans, telling in simple language the inspiring stories of the lives of George Washington, Benjamin Franklin, Patrick Henry, Abraham Lincoln, Robert E.Lee, Theodore Roosevelt. Philadelphia, J.C.Winston co. [1910?, c.1898]
136 p. ports., plates, illus. 24.5 cm.

NL 0411850 MH

Little folks; stories for boys and girls. Newark, N. J. [etc.] C. E. Graham & co. [19—?] 96 l. col'd front., illus., col'd pl. 25cm.

160227B. 1. Juvenile literature—Fiction, American—Collections.
N. Y. P. L. April 23, 1942

NL 0411851 NN

The little folks' self-instructing drawing book. Boston, G. F. Bouvé & co., 1865.
22 numb. l. illus. 17½ x 18½cm.

1. Drawing—Instruction.

CA 11-2859 Unrev'd

Library of Congress NC655.L63

NL 0411852 DLC

Little folk's verses. [1892]
see under Parramore, Miss A., compiler.

Little forest warbler, *pseud.*
The duke's chase ... 1871
see
McCormick, M R.

Ts94 t 1 v.1(1
The little forget-me-not. A token of love. Embellished with numerous beautiful engravings. New-Haven, Printed and published by S.Babcock, 1841.
24p. illus. 15cm. (Babcock's moral, instructive and amusing toy books [no.4 or six cent toys, v.4])
Title vignette.

NL 0411855 CtY MH

PZ 5 L5
The little forget-me-not. A token of love. Embellished with numerous beautiful engravings. New Haven, S. Babcock [19--]
24p. illus. 15cm. (Babcock's moral, instructive and amusing toy books)

1. Children's literature (Collections)

NL 0411856 WU

The little forget-me-not. A gift for all seasons. Philadelphia, H. F. Anners, 1842.
iv, 5-167 p. front., plates. 12cm.

Library of Congress PZ10.7.L722 15-17165

NL 0411857 DLC

The little forget me not. Philadelphia, 1842.
see also The boys' and girls' little forget me not. Philadelphia [184-?]

PR 975 L729
The Little foundling; a story. Edinburgh, Waugh & Innes, 1823.
35 p.

NL 0411859 CLU

PZ162 .L767 1865
The little fox: or, the story of Captain Sir F.L. M'Clintock's Arctic Expedition. Written for the young, by S.T.C. ... London, Seeley, Jackson, and Halliday, 1865.
195 p. front., 16 cm.

I. M'Clintock, Sir Francis Leopold, 1819-1907. II. S. T. C. III. C., S. T.

NL 0411860 ICU

The little Fox: or, the story of Captain Sir F. L. M'Clintock's Arctic expedition. Written for the young. By S.T.C.
= New York. Dodd. 1867. (3), 198 pp. Plate. Sm. 8°.

F5375 — Arctic Regions. — MacClintock [M'Clintock], Sir Francis Leopold. — Fox, ship. — T.r.

NL 0411861 MB MH NcD

35
The little foxes; or, small beginnings traced to their consequences: a book for both parents and children. [anon.] Boston, Massachusetts Sabbath school society, [1853]
108 p. 1 pl. 18°.

NL 0411862 DLC

The little foxes story book ... Akron, O., New York, The Saalfield publishing co. [°1941]
[62] p. front., illus. 28 x 20cm.

1. Children's stories.

Library of Congress PZ5.L723 41-11989

NL 0411863 DLC

Little Frank, and other tales. Chiefly in words of one syllable. Philadelphia: G. S. Appleton [etc., etc.] 1850. iv, 5-64 p. front. 15cm.

NL 0411864 NN ViU

Juv. coll.
Little Frank and other tales. Chiefly in words of one syllable. Philadelphia, C. G. Henderson & Co. N. W. Corner Fifth and Arch Street. New York, D. Appleton & Co. 200 Broadway, 1856.
[2] 3-64 p. 14.5 cm.

NL 0411865 DLC

Little Frank's Almanac for 1837. Montpelier, Vt. E.P. Walton & Son. (1836).
1839 on cover.

NL 0411866 MWA

Little Frank's almanack, to show little boys and girls their play days. Concord [N.H.] Fisk & Chase, 1831.
7 [7] p. illus. 9cm.
Cover imprint: Concord, John W. Moore & Co., 1832.

NL 0411867 Nh CtY

1837 Juv. coll.
Little Frank's almanack, to show little boys and girls their play days. Concord, John F. Brown, 1837.
7, [7] p., 1 l. 9 cm.

NL 0411868 DLC

1846 Juv. coll.
Little Frank's almanack to show little boys and girls their play days. Concord, John F. Brown, 1846.
1 p.l., 7, [7] p. 9 cm.

NL 0411869 DLC

LITTLE FRANK'S almanack, to show little boys and girls their play days. Portland [Me.] Bailey & Noyes [186-?] 1 p.l., 7(1) p., 3 l. illus. 93mm.

In original illustrated blue paper covers, with the number "6" at head of title.

NL 0411870 NN CtY

VOLUME 336

Little Frank's almanack, to show little boys and girls their play days. — Portland. Bailey & Noyes. [187-?] (2), 7, (7) pp. Illus. 9½ cm.
No. 6 of the publishers' chap-book series.

H9739 — Almanacs. — S.r.c.

NL 0411871 MB

Little Frank's story book, 1873
see under Sanford, Mrs. D. P.

The "Little fraud" songster
see under De Witt, Robert M., 1827-1877, New York, pub.

The little freeholder
see under [Hailes, Sir David Dalrymple, lord] 1726-1792.

Beinecke Library 1973 S3
The Little freethinker. A freethought journal for the young.
Camden, N.J., F.Wm.E. Cullingford.
24 cm.
Editor: 1900- E.D. Slenker.
Includes advertising matter.

1. Free thought - Period. I. Slenker, Elmina Drake, ed.

NL 0411875 CtY

The little French lawyer. 1778
see under Booth, Mrs. actress of Covent Garden Theatre.

Little French masterpieces; Ed. by Alexander Jessup
New York and London, 1903

, Analyzed

NL 0411877 DLC OClW MiDW OCl

Little French masterpieces; ed. by Alexander Jessup ... N.Y., Putnam, 1905.
6 v.

NL 0411878 NcRS

LITTLE friends of the Christ Child; Christmas playlet for the primary grades, by S.M.A., a sister of Loretto... [Milwaukee, Wis., 1929] 15 p. 17½cm. (Library of Catholic plays.)

757919A. 1. Juvenile literature—Drama, American. 2. Christmas—Drama. I. A., S.M. II. S. M. A., a sister of Loretto. III. Ser.

NL 0411879 NN

The little friend's offering. New York, Turner & Fisher [18—]
[7] l. illus.

NL 0411880 NNC

The little frog and pretty mouse (*Folk-song*)
see
A frog he would a-wooing go (*Folk-song*)

821.89 qL778l
The little frog's lecture, and other stories. [New York? 18—]
[12] p. illus. 27 cm.
Cover title.
Text on p. [2] and illus. on p. [3] of cover.

1. Children's poetry.

NL 0411882 N

n.d. Juv. coll.
The Little frog's lecture and other stories. [New York, McLoughlin Bros.] [n.d.]
[14] p. 27 cm.

NL 0411883 DLC

Little frog's lecture, The, and other stories. *2390.27
= New York. McLoughlin. 1856. (13) pp. Plates. 8°.
Contents. — The frog's lecture. — Peter Little and the lucky sixpence. — The pet lamb.
The title is on the cover.

NL 0411884 MB ICU

Little gallery tours in the Metropolitan museum, New York, N. Y. ... published for teachers, students and visitors by the Brown-Robertson co., inc. New York [°1927-
v. 20cm.
CONTENTS.—no. 1. American paintings and painters, by Edith Very Sherwood.

1. New York. Metropolitan museum of art. I. Sherwood, Edith Very.

Library of Congress N610.A43 27-11681

NL 0412001 DLC

xPZ5 L72 1875
Little games for little players. Otley, W.Walker and Sons [ca.1875]
8p. illus.(part col.) 17cm.
Cover title.
At head of title: Coloured.

NL 0412002 IaU

*
PZ6 .L533 1850
The little gardener ... Philadelphia, Henry F. Anners, 1850.
1 p. l., 175 p. front. 16cm. (Abbott's moral library)

1. Children's stories.

NL 0412003 ViU

SB403 .L5
Little gardens; a quarterly magazine of the Northwest.
[Seattle, The Lake Washington garden club, 19
v. illus. 28cm.
Emma B. Edwards, editor.
1. Gardening—Period.

NL 0412004 DLC WaS OrP

A little garland from Cathay
see under Gaunt, T ed. and tr.

Little garland of Celtic verse.
= Portland. Mosher. 1905. viii, (41), (1), (1) pp. 17½ cm.
No. 29 of an edition of 100 copies printed on Japan vellum.

M8360 — Ireland. Lit. Poetry. Colls.

NL 0412006 MB MoSW CLU-C MH MWA CSmH

A little garland of Celtic verse. [2d ed.] Portland, Me., T. B. Mosher, 1907.
viii, 41, [1] p., 1 l. 17½cm.
"Nine hundred and fifty copies of this book printed on Van Gelder hand-made paper and the type distributed."

1. Irish poetry (English) 2. English poetry—Irish authors.

Library of Congress PR8851.L5 14-1135 rev.

NL 0412007 DLC NcU KU MnU

PR 8851 .L5
A little garland of Celtic verse. [4th ed.] Portland, Me., T. B. Mosher, 1916.
41 p. 18 cm.

1. Irish poetry (English) 2. English poetry - Irish authors.

NL 0412008 WU MH CSmH IU

808.81 L778
A Little garland of Christmas verse... Portland, Me., T. B. Moser, 1905.
viii, 47 p. 18cm.
Half-title.
Printer's device on t.p. and last page.
Issued in slipcase.
"Ten copies of this book printed on pure vellum, numbered and signed by the publisher [of which this is] no. 10"
Bookplate of John Quinn.

1. Christmas - Poetry.

NL 0412010 FU ViU CSmH MH CtY ICU CoU MoSW MnU

VOLUME 336

A little garland of Christmas verse. Portland, Me., T. B. Mosher, 1908.
viii, 49, [1] p., 1 l. 17½cm.
Third edition.
"Nine hundred and fifty copies of this book printed on Van Gelder hand-made paper and the type distributed."

1. Christmas—Poetry.

14-908

Library of Congress PN6110.H4L5

NL 0412011 DLC OrU CSmH MiU N ViU

A little garland of Christmas verse. Portland, Me., T. B. Mosher, 1914.
viii, 52, [2] p., 1 l. 18cm.
"First edition, October, 1905 ... Fourth edition, December, 1914."
"Nine hundred and fifty copies ... printed on Van Gelder hand-made paper and the type distributed."

1. Christmas—Poetry.

33-15059

Library of Congress PN6110.C5L5 1914 808.1

NL 0412012 DLC FU MeB

The Little gem, a Christmas, New Year's, and birth-day present... Hartford, S. Andrus and son, 1846.
2 p. l., [iii]-vi, [7]-144 p. front. 10½ x 7½cm.
Added t.-p., in colors.
"Anecdotes, and short pieces selected principally from some of the late annuals."—Advertisement.

1. Gift books (Annuals, etc.)

43-33668

Library of Congress AY11.L83 1846

NL 0412013 DLC RPB MnHi

The LITTLE gem, a Christmas, New Year's, and birth-day present... Hartford, S. Andrus and son, 1847.
2 p. l., [iii]-vi, [7]-144p. front. 10cm.
Added t.-p. decorated in color.

1. Gift-books (Annuals, etc.)

Printed by Wesleyan University Library

NL 0412014 CtW MB NRU GEU

---

xPZ5
L722
1855
The little gem; a Christmas, New Year's, and birth-day present. Hartford, S.Andrus and Son, 1855.
144p. front. 11cm.
Added t.p. in colors.
"Anecdotes, and short pieces selected principally from some of the late annuals."

1. Gift books (Annuals, etc.)

NL 0412015 IaU

The Little gem, a Christmas, New Year's, and birth-day present... New York, H. Dayton [1857?]
vi, [7]-144 p. front. 10½ x 7½cm.
"Anecdotes, and short pieces selected principally from some of the late annuals."—Advertisement.

1. Gift-books (Annuals, etc.)

43-33669

Library of Congress AY11.L83 1857.

NL 0412016 DLC

Little gem brand book ... (continuation of Big four brand book ...) for the fall work of 1900 ... v. 1, no. 1 ... Kansas City, Mo., Little gem brand book co., 1900.
2 p. l., 2-27, 158 p. illus. 17½cm.
No more published?

1. Cattle brands.

Library of Congress SF103.L78 0-5462 Revised

NL 0412017 DLC ICN TxU

368.3
L274 Little gem life chart; an authoritative analysis of life insurance.

Cincinnati, National Underwriter Co.
v. tables. 17cm. annual.

1. Insurance, Life - Policies. 2. Insurance, Life - U.S. I. National Underwriter Co.

NL 0412018 CaBVa WaS TxU MB TU FU OU KyLoU NNC TxFTC NbU

Little gem life chart of legal reserve life insurance companies... [no.

Cincinnati: National Underwriter Co., 19 nar. 16°.
v. tables.

1. Insurance, Life—Agents' manuals.
N. Y. P. L. April 8, 1929

NL 0412019 NN DLC ViU IaU

PZ8
.3
.L7297
Little gem stories.
New York, c1904

NL 0412020 DLC

The little gem vest pocket chart of regular life insurance companies ...
see under [Dawe, Sampson]

Little gems of literature for memorizing
see under [Gilbert, Josiah Hotchkiss] 1834-

Little gentile, a Deseret romance. 1879
see under Moore, Emily H.

The LITTLE gentleman. no.1-6; Jan. 1-Apr. 29, 1831. New Haven, H. Howe.
174p. 16cm.

All published.

NL 0412024 ICN NNC

A little gentleman
see under [Alcott, Louisa May] 1832-1888.

Little George and His Hatchet, or the Book of Pictures. Greenfield, Mass.: A. Phelps, 1847.
2 p. l., (1) 8-26 p. incl. front., illus.
24 mo.
Stitched.

NL 0412025 CSmH

PZ116
.B804
no.1
... Little George and the apple-tree. New York, American tract society [1830?]
15 p. illus. 9cm.
[Chap-books; religious, no.1]

NL 0412026 ICU

V 613
813.3
L778
Little George and the apple tree. [illustration] New York, American tract society, 150 Nassau Street [Egbert, Hovey & King, printers; 1845?]
15, [1]p. illus. 8.6 cm. [Publications. no.xiv]

1. Children's stories. 2. Bibliography. Miniature editions. I. Series.

NL 0412027 N

BV4510
L5
Little George and the apple tree. New York, The American tract society [1860?]

cover-title,15p. illus. 10cm.in12½cm.

I. American tract society.

NL 0412028 NBuG

Little George; or parental recollections.
London. Westley. 1824. 16 pp. Illus. Vignette. 10½ cm.

M7610 — Chap-books.

NL 0412029 MB

LITTLE George; or, Temptation resisted. New York, Kiggins & Kellogg, 123 & 125 William St. [186-?] 16 p. illus. 12cm.

At head of cover title: Third series. - No. 4.
In original illustrated blue paper covers, with publishers' advertisements on back.
"Schoolboy days," a poem, p. 15-16.

784358. I. Title: Temptation resisted.

NL 0412030 NN RPB

Little Georgie.
A bad boy's diary
see under [Booram, George E.]

VOLUME 336

N 244 L77822 Little Gerald; or, "I've no patience with that wicked Cain." New York, Sunday-School Union [184-?]
15 p. 11 cm.

1. Sunday-school literature.

NL 0412032 N

PZ262 .L814 1850 Little Gerald; or, I've no patience with that wicked Cain." Rev. by D. P. Kidder. New York, Lane & Scott, 1850.
2 v. in 1. 11cm.

Contents: Little Gerald. Fanny's return to school.

NL 0412033 ICU

LITTLE Gertrude; a story for the young. London and Edinburgh, T. Nelson & sons [186-?] 31 p. 1 plate. 12cm.

In original illustrated white paper covers, printed in pink and gold.
Cover title.
Includes "The forbidden fruit," a story, p. 28-31.

625080A.

NL 0412034 NN

Little Giant (*Indian name*)
see
Kelsey, Henry, *ca.* 1670–*ca.* 1724.

The Little Giant: his life, travels, and death. Chicag 1860.
10 p. illus. 12 cm.
Verse.

1. Douglas, Stephen Arnold, 1813-1861—Cartoons, satire, etc.

E415.9.D73L5 56-52188

NL 0412036 DLC RPB NN

TS853 L7 Little Giant Co., Mankato, Minn.
Woodworking equipment. Mankato [192-?]
15 l. p. illus. 29cm.

NL 0412037 MnHi

The little giant detective, by the author of "Old Thunderbolt." New York. Norman L. Munro 1883.
44p

(Old Cap Collier library, no.49.)

(Dime Novel Collection - PZ 2)

NL 0412038 DLC

The little giant fact book and handy standard dictionary containing a chronological record of the great events in the history of the world; based on the Funk & Wagnalls Standard dictionary of the English language. New York and London, Funk & Wagnalls company [c1922]
xxxii, 294 p., 1 l. maps. 15½ x 7cm.

1. English language—Dictionaries. 2. Encyclopedias and dictionaries.

Library of Congress AG105.L75 23-307

NL 0412039 DLC

Little Giant, The, in the character of the gladiator.
— [Philadelphia. 1860.] Broadside, 21⅞ × 13⅞ inches. Lithograph.
Cartoon representing Douglas as champion of popular sovereignty.

G7187 — Caricatures. — Douglas, Stephen Arnold.

NL 0412040 MB

Little Giant of the North (*Indian name*)
see
Kelsey, Henry, *ca.* 1670–*ca.* 1724.

S681 .L77 Little giant stump puller company.
The Little giant improved stump puller and rock extractor...
[Atsion? N.J. 1876?]

NL 0412042 DLC

Little giant Webster dictionary, self pronouncing, based upon the foundation laid by Noah Webster, LL. D., and other recognized lexicographers. Rev. and brought up to date. New York, World Syndicate Co. [c1922]
188 p. 15 x 8 cm.

1. English language—Dictionaries. I. Webster, Noah, 1758-1843.

PE1628.L5 1922 54-47345

NL 0412043 DLC

The Little gift
see under Colman, Pamela (Chandler) ed.

The little gift for 1844
see under Colman, Pamela (Chandler) ed.

---

xPN6071 C5L5 The little gift for little folks.
Philadelphia, B.Walker, 1845.
96p. illus. 10 x 9cm.

1. Children's literature.

NL 0412046 IaU

Little gift, The, for little folks.
— Philadelphia. Simon. 1848. 96 pp. Illus. Plates. 11 cm., in 8.
Prose and verse.

D1920 — Books for the young. Imprints before 1850.

NL 0412047 MB

---

76 L7781g Harris Small Books The little gift; or, Pictures and verses for infant readers. New Haven, S. Babcock, 1850.
7 p. illus. 10 cm.

1. Children's poetry. I. Babcock, S., pub.

NL 0412048 RPB CtY

The little gingerbread man, [pub. by] Royal baking powder co. N. Y., 1923
[16] p. col. illus. & pl. 18 cm.

NL 0412049 RPB

The little gipsy [song]
see under Arne, Thomas Augustine, 1710-177

The Little gipsy; a musical farce
see under Garrick, David, 1717-1779.

The "little girl" series
see under Douglas, Amanda Minnie.

The little girl who should have been a boy
see under [Jones, Frances (Lander)] d. 1947.

The LITTLE girl who was taught by experience. Boston, Bowles and Dearborn, I.R. Butts and co., printers, 1827. 50 p. 15cm.

Back of original buff paper covers, with an engraving of Bowles & Dearborn's store, attached.
Also has continuous paging: [101]-150 and "Vol. II" at foot of many pages.

NL 0412054 NN DLC

The Little girl's forget-me-not. Philadelphia, American Sunday-school union [1843]
110 p. incl. plates. front. 11cm.

1. Gift-books (Annuals etc.) I. American Sunday-school union.

CA 17-1866 Unrev'd

Library of Congress PZ10.7.L723

NL 0412055 DLC

VOLUME 336

The little girl's own story book... New York: F. A. Stokes co., 1929. 176 p. col'd front., col'd plates. 24½cm.
"Formerly published under the title of 'Baby Peggy's own story book'."

187548B. 1. Juvenile literature—Collections.
N. Y. P. L. December 3, 1942

NL 0412056 NN WaSp

A little girl's writings.
See under
Johnson, Florence Kendrick.

PZ6 .L547 The little glass shoe, and other stories for children... New York, J. Miller, n.d.
128p. front.,plates. 15cm.

NL 0412058 NNU-W

YA .S610 The little glass shoe, and other stories for children.
Philadelphia, 1854.
128p.

(Sunday school books; arr. numerically.)

NL 0412059 DLC

Little glass slipper
see under Cinderella.

1b55 te865s The Little gleaner; being a choice collection of popular songs ... London, Printed by J. and C. Evans [ca. 1820?]
8p. 18cm.
No. [31] in a collection of songsters lettered on spine: Song books.

NL 0412061 CtY

The Little gleaners. Published under the direction of the Committee of General Literature and Education, appointed by the Society for Promoting Christian Knowledge. London, Society for Promoting Christian Knowledge, 1849.
16 p.incl.front.,illus.
[No.6] in a collection, Society for Promoting Christian Knowledge, London. [Collection of tracts. London, 1847-49]

NL 0412062 CLU

Little glimpses of the Kiangan mission.
n.p., 1916.

NL 0412063 NjP

Little gold business books.
no.

Stamford, Conn.: J. O. Dahl, 19 15½cm.
nos.

Published by the Hospitality Guild, Stamford, Conn.
Also known as Hospitality library.

1. Food—U. S. 2. Hotels—U. S. I. Dahl, Joseph Oliver, 1893- ed. II. Hospitality Guild, Stamford, Conn. III. Hospitality library.
N. Y. P. L. May 7, 1936

NL 0412064 NN

Little Golden; or, The pride of the family ...
see under [Jones, Mrs. Emma Garrison]

The Little golden book of poetry; illus. by Corinne Malvern. New York, Simon and Schuster [1947]
[42] p. illus. (part col.) 20 cm. (The little golden library [38])

1. Children's poetry. I. Malvern, Corinne, 1905- illus. (Series)
PZ8.3.L72983 47—5528*

NL 0412066 DLC

Little good nights
see under Valentine, Grace.

Little Goody two shoes. [Liverpool? 1878?] 10-58 p. 17cm.
Caption-title.
Prince of Wales theatre, Liverpool, 1878-9. — ms. note, p. [9]

83280B. 1. Pantomimes, English. I. Title: Goody two shoes.
N. Y. P. L. June 25, 1943

NL 0412068 NN

Little grammarian, or An easy guide to the parts of speech
see under [Black, J]

Little Grandfather
see under [Clarke, Rebecca Sophia] 1833-1906.

The little graves ... New-York, Printed and sold by M. Day [182-]
8 p. illus. 8°.
Poems.

22-22298
Library of Congress PZ6.L73

NL 0412071 DLC

Little graves; choice selections of poetry and prose
see under [Wilder, Mrs. N. W.] comp.

"The little gray lady" ...
see under [Pollock, Channing] 1880-

The little great man of T. C. A. new. ed. enl. and corr., Boston, 1851.
39 p. 23 cm.

NL 0412074 RPB

The little green trading stamp. [a poem]
New York, n. d.
[8] p. 14 cm.
Caption title
Cover title: Stamps.

NL 0412075 RPB

PZ167 .L77 1809 The little grey mouse: or, The history of Rosabelle & Paridel ... 2d ed. Wellington [Eng.] Houlston, 1809.
69 p. front., illus.

NL 0412076 ICU

A little guide-book to the royal residence Cracow and its environs
see under Society for the Promotion of Foreign Travel in Poland.

A little guide to Malvern Priory church
see under [Hamand, Louis Arthur] 1873-

A little guide to Niagara Falls, 1890
see under [Gluck, James Fraser] 1852-1897.

Little guides, The.
London. Methuen & Co., Ltd. [1902-16.] 42 v. Plates. Maps. Plans. 15½ cm., in 8s.
Namely: —
Berkshire. By F. G. Brabant. 2469a.255
Brittany. By S. Baring-Gould. 2669.82
Buckinghamshire. By E. S. Roscoe. 2469a.244
Channel Islands, The. By E. E. Bicknell. 2469a.333
Cheshire. By W. M. Gallichan. 2469a.250
Cornwall. By A. L. Salmon. 2469a.238
Derbyshire. By J. C. Cox. 2469a.246

Devon. By S. Baring-Gould. 2469a.334
Dorset. By F. R. Heath. 2469a.252
Durham. By J. E. Hodgkin. 2469a.257
East Riding, The, of Yorkshire. By J. E. Morris. 2469a.248
English lakes, The. By F. G. Brabant. 2469a.240
Essex. By J. C. Cox. 2469a.335
Gloucestershire. By J. C. Cox. 2469a.336
Hampshire. By J. C. Cox. 2469a.249
Hertfordshire. By H. W. Tompkins. 2469a.239
Isle of Wight, The. By G. Clinch. 2469a.242

Continued in next column

VOLUME 336

Continued from preceding column

Kent. By G. Clinch. 2469a.241
Leicestershire and Rutland. By A. Harvey and V. B. Crowther-Beynon. 2469a.337
London. By G. Clinch. 2469a.338
Malvern country, The. By B. C. A. Windle. 2469a.173
Middlesex. By J. B. Firth. 2469a.254
Monmouthshire. By G. W. Wade, and J. H. Wade. 2469a.339
Norfolk. By W. A. Dutt. 2469a.237
Normandy. By C. Scudamore. 2669.80
North Riding, The, of Yorkshire. By J. E. Morris. 2469a.247

North Wales. By A. T. Story. 2469a.340
Northamptonshire. By W. Dry. 2469a.253
Northumberland. By J. E. Morris. 2469a.341
Nottinghamshire. By E. L. Guilford. 2469a.342
Oxfordshire. By F. G. Brabant. 2469a.251
Rome. By C. G. Ellaby. 4769a.88
Saint Paul's Cathedral, London. By G. Clinch. 2469a.232
Shropshire. By J. E. Auden. 2469a.256
Sicily. By F. H. Jackson. 4769a.87
(Continued on the next card.)

Somerset. By G. W. Wade, and J. H. Wade. 2469a.343
Staffordshire. By C. Masefield. 2469a.344
Suffolk. By W. A. Dutt. 2469a.245
Surrey. By F. A. H. Lambert. 2469a.243
Sussex. By F. G. Brabant. 2469a.236
West Riding, The, of Yorkshire. By J. E. Morris. 2469a.345
Wiltshire. By F. R. Heath. 2469a.346

NL 0412084 MB NcU DLC OO NcD

Little Guzzy and other stories
see under [Habberton, John] 1842-1921.

The little gypsy [in a prologue and three acts] [n. p., C. H. Rosskam? 1914?] 1 v. (various pagings) 32cm.

Typescript.

1. Drama. English. 2. Drama —Promptbooks and Typescripts.

NL 0412086 NN

A Little handbook for pilgrims to Chester cathedral, 1933, by F.L.M.B. [Chester, Phillipson]1933.
Illus.sq.T.

NL 0412087 CaBViP

Little handbooks for pilgrims ...
[Chester] 1928.

NL 0412088 PPT-L

Little Harry, and the apples. Northampton, J. Metcalf, 1836.
1 p. l., [5]-18 p. 11cm.
Title vignette; tail-piece.

28-20103

Library of Congress PZ6.L731

NL 0412089 DLC CtY NN

PZ262 .L815 1837 Little Harry, and the apples. Northampton, J. Metcalf, 1837.
18 p. 11cm.

NL 0412090 ICU

Juv. coll. Little Harry's book of stories.
New York, Leavitt & Allen. [n.d.]
[4] 5-64 p. 15 cm.

NL 0412091 DLC

Juv. coll. Little Harry's nursery tales. Containing 86 engravings. New York John McLoughlin, publishers. [n.d.]
[5] 6-64 p. 14.5 cm.

NL 0412092 DLC

The LITTLE haymakers. Boston, printed by Freeman and Bolles, 1839.

Front.

NL 0412093 MH MWA

The little haymakers. New York: S. Raynor, [185-?]
8 p. illus. nar. 16°. (New books and true books for the young, no. 8)
First copy, cream cover.
Second copy, pink cover.
Titles from covers.
In: NAS p.v. 6, no. 12-13.

NL 0412094 NN

Little Hazel, the kings' messenger, Author of.
The crown of glory; or, "Faithful unto death"
see under title

Little Helen; or, A day in the life of a naughty girl. New Haven, S. Babcock [1825?]
16 p. illus. 11cm.
Title vignette.
Inside covers contain illustrations.

21-3863

NL 0412096 DLC NN

The little helper; full of sunshine and gladness ... Boston, Lothrop pub. co. [1899]
[21] p. illus., pl. 4°. (Play room series)

99-1865

Library of Congress

NL 0412097 DLC

Little helpers 1883-1885 (v. 1.-3)
[Boston] n. d.
3 v. in 1 illus. 24 cm.
Publication of the Woman's Baptist Foreign Missionary society for children.

NL 0412098 RPB NRAB

PZ6 .L2225L Little Henri. A German tale. Translated from the French of M. Lambert. New-York, O.A. Roorbach, 1827.
106 p. front. 15 cm.

Imperfect: frontispiece mutilated.

I. Lambert, M tr.

NL 0412099 NjR

Little Henry and his bearer, Author of.

PZ6 .S554 Re 6 [Sherwood, Mary Martha (Butt)] 1775-1851.
The red book, and Mary Anne, by the author of Little Henry and his bearer. 1st American from the 2d London ed. New-York, Pendleton and Hill, 1831.

Little Henry and his bird.
see under [Bolles, John R.] supposed author

Little Henry's holiday at the Great exhibition
see under [Newcombe, Samuel Prout]

Little herder stories ... Na'nízkaadí yázhí baa haní'
see under [Clark, Ann Nolan]

The little hermitage, with other tales: Good and evil, The characters, and The gift of fate. London, R. Philips, 1801.
133 p. illus. 15cm.

"The tales ... have been published ... in ... the Monthly preceptor; or, Juvenile encyclopaedia."

NL 0412104 MiDW

Little histories of North American Indians.
no. 1- 1909- Cedar Rapids, Iowa, The Torch press, 1909-
v. plates, maps, facsims., tables 21 cm.

NL 0412105 MH-P DLC

1845 Juv. coll. The little history of England. Philadelphia: Loomis and Peck. New Haven: Durrie & Peck. 1845.
[3] 4-191 p. 8 cm.

NL 0412106 DLC

VOLUME 336

The little history of England. Philadelphia, Loomis and Peck; New Haven, Durrie & Peck, 1847.
vi,7-191,[1] p.incl.front.,plates. 8cm. [Miniature juveniles]
Page v numbered 5.
Title vignette.

1.Gt.Brit.—History,Juvenile.

NL 0412107 MiU

The little history of the United States. New York, Clark, Austin & Smith [185-?]

"Tom Thumb series."

NL 0412108 MH

The little history of the United States. Philadelphia, Loomis & Peck, 1846.
191 p. incl. front., plates. 8 x 6½cm.

1. U. S.—Hist.

8-27816

Library of Congress E178.L77

NL 0412109 DLC NIC

The little history of the United States. Philadelphia, Loomis & Peck, 1847.
191 p. incl. front., plates. 8½ x 7cm. (Miniature juveniles)
Title vignette.

1. U. S.—Hist.

22-5746

Library of Congress E178.L78

NL 0412110 DLC MB

Little Hodge
see under [Jenkins, Edward] 1838-1910.

LITTLE Holland; comedy in three acts. London, Mrs. Marshall's type writing office, 1908. 29, 31, 26 l. 27cm.

Typescript.

1. Drama, English. 2. Drama--Promptbooks and typescripts.

NL 0412112 NN

Little home histories in our early homes, Belmont county, Ohio, 1942. [Aldan? Pa., 1942]
152 l. 28cm.

Introduction signed: Robert D. McDonald, Beulah Patten McDonald.

1. Belmont county, O.—Hist. 2. Historic houses—U.S.—O.—Belmont county. I. McDonald, Robert D., ed. II. McDonald, Beulah Patten, ed. III.McDonald, Robert D. IV. McDonald, Beulah Patten.

NL 0412113 NN

YA .S893 Little Home missionaries. New York [n.d.]
47p.

(Sunday school books; arr. numerically.)

NL 0412114 DLC

Little Hoover Commission
see
Minnesota. *Efficiency in Government Commission.*
Vermont. *Commission to Study State Government.*

The little house in the hollow.
see under [Robertson, Margaret Murray]

PZ7 .L7551 1880 The little housekeeper, and other stories. New York, T. Y. Crowell [188-?]
124 p. front. 18cm.

1. Children's stories.

NL 0412117 ViU

813.5 L778h The little housekeeper and other stories. New York, McLoughlin Bros., c1904.
unpaged. col. illus. 22 cm. (Playtime series)

1. Children's stories.

NL 0412118 N NNC

Little housewife (The). *New York: Dodd, Mead & Co.*, [1884]. 7-59 pp. 16°.
Bd. with December (A) Story. *New York*, [cop. 1884.] 16°.

NL 0412119 NN

Little Huguenot, The.
(In Novels and tales reprinted from Household Words, conducted by Charles Dickens. Vol. 7, pp. 286-301. Leipzig, 1858.)

Δ1079

NL 0412120 MB

Little Humpy, and other stories...
Phila., 1870

[Snowdrop library]

NL 0412121 DLC

The little hunchback horse
see under [Ershov, Petr Pavlovich] 1815-1869.

Little Hungary, New York.
A night in Little Hungary [February 14th, 1905. New York, 1907?]

35 p. illus. 14 cm.
A vest pocket memorandum book, with pages of miscellaneous information, memorandum calendar for 1907, maps of U.S., etc. inserted between pp.18 and 19.
p.4-10, address by President Roosevelt.

NL 0412123 MH

W827 L778 Little hydrogen; or, The devil on two sticks in London. London, Printed for J.J. Stockdale, 1819.
206p. 20cm.

A satire.

NL 0412124 NcU CSmH MH

Little Hydrogen; or, The Devil on two sticks in London. 2d ed. London, Printed for J. J. Stockdale, 1819.
206 p. col. plates. 20 cm.

PR3991.A1L4 1819 50-49995

NL 0412125 DLC CSmH MH

Little hymn book. Worcester, S.A. Howland, H. J. Howland, printer [184-?]
Coll L7781h a Harris Small Books 16 p. illus. 10 cm.

With this are bound Hymns for infant minds, Worcester, [184-?], and Juvenile songster, Worcester, [184-?]

1. Children's hymns. I. Howland, S.A. pub.

NL 0412126 RPB ICU NNC

The Little Hymn Book. A Selection of Hymns from different authors
see under Funk, George

The little hymn book; compiled for the moral and religious instruction of children
see under Wood, Mrs. S. B., comp.

The Little hymnal, one hundred and one hymns from the hymnal, with morning and evening canticles and versicles pointed for chanting
see under Kimber, Arthur Clifford, comp.
[Supplement]

VOLUME 336

Little hymns and pictures for little readers. Boston, James M. Usher, 1846.
51 p. illus.

NL 0412130 NNC RPB

Little hymns and pictures for little readers, Author of.
A little present for little children
see under title

Ia94 tl v.1
The little idle girl, and the Sunday scholar. New Haven-S.Babcock,Sidney's press,1831.
23p.incl.front.,illus. 14cm.

NL 0412132 CtY

Little Ilford, Eng. City of London Cemetary
see City of London Cemetery, Little Ilford, Eng.

Jt35.122
Little illustrated books on old French furniture. 1-4. London, William Heinemann ltd., 1920-27.
4v. plates. 19cm.

v.1: New impression.
Binder's title: Little books on old French furniture.
No more published.

NL 0412134 CtY

The little image merchants ... Boston, Massachusetts S. S. soc.[n.d.]
64 p.

NL 0412135 OClWHi

---

*pEB65 A100 585l2
The little infant Titus: or Oates exalted above his brethern. Who recieved sentence at the Kings-bench-bar, at Westminster the 16th day of May, 1685.
London,Printed by George Croom,at the sign of the Blue-Ball in [Thames-street,over against Baynard's castle,1685]
broadside. illus. 35.5x30cm.
In verse.
Imperfect: top and bottom edges cropped; last line of imprint cut away.

NL 0412136 MH

Little, The, innocent porcupine hornet's nest... [Also, The slaves. An elegy.] United States of America: Printed for the author [1800?]. 35 p. 12°.

Anti-slavery.
Contains no reference to Cobbett, and may be later than 1800.
Edges untrimmed.

FORD COLLECTION.
1. Slavery, U. S.
N. Y. P. L. February 11, 1915.

NL 0412137 NN

Little innocents; childhood reminiscences by Dame Ethel Smyth, Lord Berners, Harold Nicolson [and others] ... Preface by Alan Pryce-Jones. London, Cobden-Sanderson, 1932.
viii, 124 p. 22^{cm}.

1. Children. I. Pryce-Jones, Alan, 1908- ed.
33-14960
Library of Congress CT776.L5
[3] 920.042

NL 0412138 OCl OkU DLC FTaSU NBC TxU NBuU ICU OrU CU NN NcD

Little Isaac.
Useful hints to single gentlemen, respecting marriage, concubinage, and adultery
see under title

[Little Isaac] pseud.
Vincent and Isabella: or, The reward of virtue
see under title

Little Island and Big Island; or, Children's talk at Runnymede. By the author of the "Canton police". Dublin: Webb & Chapman, 1841.
16 p. 8°.

NL 0412141 NN

The little Italian boy
see under Cousin Mary, pseud.

Little Italy neighborhood association.
Annual report. [B'klyn]

NL 0412143 NB

Little Italy neighborhood association.
____ Twenty five years of service, 1904-1929. [B'klyn,1929] [4]p.illus.

NL 0412144 NBLiHi

Little Jack and his rocking horse [in verse] New York, n. d.
12 numbered l. col. illus. 13 cm.
Illus. cover title
Pub. by T. Illman, N. Y.

NL 0412145 RPB

Little Jack Horner
see Jack Horner.

Little Jack of all trades; or, Mechanical arts described, in prose and verse, suited to the capacities of children... London: Printed for Harvey and Darton, 1823. 66 p. front., plates. 17cm.

Cover-title: Jack of all trades.
Imperfect: frontispiece wanting.

—— —— 1829.

DARTON COLLECTION.
137950B. 1. Industrial arts. I. Title: Jack of all trades.
N. Y. P. L. February 25, 1942

NL 0412147 NN

Little Jack of all trades. With suitable representations. Part 2. — Boston. Munroe & Francis. [18—?] 94 pp. Illus. Vignette. [Juvenile library.] 32°.

G1909 — Industrial arts. — S.r.

NL 0412148 MB MH

---

*H.99D .80
Little Jack of all trades, with suitable representations. London, Printed and sold by Darton & Harvey, 1806.
2 v. illus. 16cm.

[1. Children's literature--Gt. Brit.]

NL 0412149 MB

WE1110 L77
Little Jack of all trades, with suitable representations... London, Darton, Harvey, and Darton, 1812. 2 v. illus. 15 cm.

Running-title: Jack of all trades.
"The glass-blower": p. 31-33.

994. 1. Art industries and trade. I. Title: Jack of all trades.

NL 0412150 NCorniC

Little Jack Rabbit books
see under Cory, David Magie, 1872-

VOLUME 336

... Little Jacob, and how he became fat ...
New York, McLoughlin bros. [n. d.]
cover-title, [10] p. col. illus. 17 cm.
(Little slovenly Peter series)
Printed on linen.
1. Children's poetry.

NL 0412152 RPB

xPZ5
L725
Little James: or, Busy as bees, and other stories. Boston, H.Hoyt ‹18--›
64p. illus. 16cm. (Little peoples' library)
Title on spine: Little Jamie.
Added illus. title page.

I. Title: Busy as bees.

NL 0412153 IaU

Little Jane.
= [New-York. 182-?] 15 pp. Illus. 16°.
The title-page and pp. 1-3 are missing.

G8169 — Chap-books.

NL 0412154 MB

Little Jane. A memoir of Jane E. J. Taylor. Who died in the 14th year of her age. London, Printed for The Religious Tract Society, by J. Nisbet, 1831.
36 p. 13½cm.

Bound (6) with Barbauld, A. L. A. Hymns, in prose, for children. London, 1825.

Religious Tract Society, London.

NL 0412155 CLU

Little Jane. A memoir of Jane E. J. Taylor ...
see also A memoir of Jane E. J. Taylor ...

Little Jane & her favorite little black cat. N. York, Publ by S. King ‹1822?› 16 f. illus. 16cm.
Caption-title and imprint.
In verse.
Illustrations colored by hand.
Imperfect: many folios torn and mended.
With autograph of Huldah H. Taylor, 1824.

554044B.
N. Y. P. L. December 1, 1950

NL 0412157 NN

Little Jane and her mother. Boston, T. H. Carter, 1838.
16 p. Illustr.

NL 0412158 MH

Little Jane E. J. Taylor, and other books for children and youth. New York, American tract society ‹185-?›
1 v.

Contents.--Little Jane.--Angusina, the Greenlander.--Memoir of Margaret Ann Walton. Abridged --Africaner, a Namacqua chief of South Africa.

Taylor, Jane E J 1815?-1829. 2. Angusina, Daniel, d. 1721. 3. Walton, Margaret Ann, 1818- 1825. 4. Africaner.

NL 0412159 NNC

PZ991
A1
L657
185-
Little Jane, or playing with fire. New York, Solomon King [183-?]
8 p. col. illus. 8 cm.

I. Title: Playing with fire.

NL 0412160 RPB

Little Jane Primrose; industrious Maria; and other pretty stories. Providence, 1850.
16 p. illus. 14 cm.
Industrious Maria. -Little Jane Primrose. -Little Laura. -Miss Cecil.

NL 0412161 RPB

Little Jane, the young cottager. A true narrative, by the author of the Dairyman's daughter. Philadelphia, n. d.
2 pt. [Pamphlets no. 9]

NL 0412162 IU

76
L191jp
Harris Collection
Little Jane's pet. ‹N. Y.› Leavitt & Allen ‹1856?›
cover-title, 16 leaves. col. illus. 15 cm.
Printed on one side of leaf only, the printed pages facing each other.
Text & illustrations mounted on p. ‹1›, 2 and ‹4› of cover.

NL 0412163 RPB

JUC-YA
.S295
Little Janie; or, Sunshine in the house...
Philadelphia, 1858.
119 p.

(Sunday school books; arr. numerically.)

NL 0412164 DLC

Little Jennie, the minister's daughter... Boston, American tract soc. ‹1863› 79 p. illus. 14cm.

386750B. I. American tract society. II. Title.
N. Y. P. L. April 19, 1948

NL 0412165 NN DLC

PZ
6
.L736x
Little Jenny, the water-cress seller, and other stories. Boston, Mass. Sabbath School Society [1866]
160 p. illus. 16 cm.

NL 0412166 OKentU

Little Jenny Wrenn and other Mother Goose rhymes with pictures by Blanche Fisher Wright.
Chicago, [c1914]
62 p. col. pl. 17 cm.

NL 0412167 RPB

1860
Juv. coll.
Little Jerry. A story for boys. Boston. Henry Hoyt. No. 9 Cornhill [c. 1860]
[3],4-53 p. 15.5 cm.

NL 0412168 DLC

Little Jerry; a story for boys. Boston, I. Bradley & Co. ‹18--›
53 p. front.

NL 0412169 NNC

Little Jessie's work
see under [Fry, Sarah Maria]

Little Jetts Bible, by Wade C. Smith
see under Bible. English. Selections. 1942-44. Authorized.

[Supersedes DLC a.e.]

Little Jim, the rag merchant. A tale of truth and honesty.
= Philadelphia. American Sunday-School Union. [1850.] 54 pp. Plate. 24°.

NL 0412172 MB

The little Joanna.
See under
Bellamy, Mrs. Elizabeth Whitfield (Croom), 1837-1900.

Little Joe and his strawberry plant, Author of. The bunch of grapes
see under title

Little Joe Ashton; or, Forbidden ground. With other stories. Philadelphia, Presbyterian Publication Committee ‹1866›
125 p. front.

NL 0412175 NNC

VOLUME 336

Little Joe Carter, 1864
see under Finley, Martha, 1828-1909.

Little John.
The history of Little Dick, written by Little John ...
see under title

Little John and Will Scarlett
see under Forest Ranger, pseud.

The LITTLE John story (working title) by Robert J. Gurney, jr. New York [Hart stenographic bureau, 19 --] 143 l. 29cm.

Shooting script.

1. Moving picture plays--Texts and outlines. 2. Robin Hood--Drama. I. Gurney, Robert J. jr.

NL 0412179 NN

470. LITTLE JOHNNIE'S PRAYERS. T. Nelson and Sons London — Edinburgh and New York. n. d. NAS p.v.5, no.8
10.5 x 6.5 cm. 8 p. Pink paper covers; first cover page decorative. Frontispiece.
In prose.

NL 0412180 NN

Little Johnny Bull's pet turkey ..
see under Vex, Trottimus.

Little Johnny Green. Philadelphia, J. B. Keller, 1852.
15 p. col. illus. 19cm.
At head of title: Keller's edition.

CA 17-1697 Unrev'd

Library of Congress PZ8.3.L7299

NL 0412182 DLC RPB MH

LITTLE-JOHN'S answer to Robin-Hood and the duke of Lancaster; a ballad. London, printed by T. White, [1720?]

f°. pp.4.

NL 0412183 MH

The little joker. Especially adapted to shortening long evenings, long journeys and long faces ... New York, A. J. Fisher; Baltimore, T. H. Denison & co. [1873]
1 p. l., [5]-112 p. illus. 12½cm.

1. American wit and humor. I. Fisher, A. J., pub.

CA 19-557 Unrev'd

Library of Congress PN6161.L57

NL 0412184 DLC

The little joker. New York, F. Tousey [1883]
see under [Tousey, Sinclair] 1818-1887, comp.

Little Joseph; or, The young Savoyard, and other tales. N. Y., D. & J. Sadlier & co. 1865.
216 p. (Added t.-p.: Young people's library)

NL 0412186 PV

YA .S585 Little Josephine. Philadelphia, [1848?]
69 p.

NL 0412187 DLC

The Little journal. Boston
see under Little (Arthur D.) inc.

W 1 LI871 The LITTLE journal. v. 1- Nov. 15, 1924-
[Chicago?]
v. illus., ports.
Vol. 1, no. 1 issued without title.
House organ of the American Medical Association.
I. American Medical Association

NL 0412189 DNLM

A little journey around the world ...
see under [Keith, Carl]

A little journey into Asia Minor. n.p. n.d.
15p.
YA.17082.

NL 0412191 DLC

A little journey through the new Toledo public library
see under Toledo. Public Library.

... A little journey to Alaska, for intermediate and upper grades
see under [Kern, Mrs. Edith (Kingman)]

A little journey to Norway and Sweden
see under [Randall, Lida E]

A little journey to Switzerland. London, Cassell & co., 1910.
64p. front., col.plates. 18cm.

NL 0412195 PSt

A Little journey to the Central Manufacturing District of Chicago
see under Central Manufacturing District of Chicago.

A Little journey, vividly narrated by a traveling man to the folks at home
see under American Issue Publishing Company, Westerville, O.

Day-NW Folio F 852 L57 Little journeys; eighteen loop trips throughout the Inland Empire, Spokane, Wash.] Published by Spokane Chamber of Commerce [and] Inland Automobile Association [192-?] [18] p. illus., maps. 32 cm.

Cover title.

NL 0412198 IdU

Little journeys into bookland, prepared by the editorial boards of the University society and the After school club of America, assisted by the following special editors and contributors: John Burroughs, Laura E. Richards ... and many others. New York, The University society, inc., for the After school club of America, Philadelphia [1912]
2 v. fronts. (ports.) illus., col. pl. 24cm. $1.75
Poems on lining-papers within ornamental borders.
Paged continuously.
Title within ornamental border.

I. University society, New York. II. After school club of America.

Library of Congress PZ5.L725 12-16326

NL 0412199 DLC

Little journeys to Alaska and Canada. Chicago, Flanagan [c1901]
see under George, Marian M 1865- ed.

Little journeys to Alaska and Canada; Alaska, by Edith Kingman Kern, Canada, by Marian M. George. Chicago, A. Flanagan company, 1923.
80, [7]-93, [1] p. illus. 19½cm. (*Lettered on cover:* Library of travel)
Published, 1901, under title: Little journeys to Alaska and Canada, for intermediate and upper grades; edited by Marian M. George.
"Canadian boat song" with music (1 p. at end)

1. Alaska—Descr. & trav. 2. Canada—Descr. & trav. I. Kern, Mrs. Edith (Kingman) II. George, Marian M., 1865-

23-13200

Library of Congress F909.L77

NL 0412201 DLC OO

VOLUME 336

Little journeys to Alaska and Canada; Alaska, by Edith Kingman Kern, Canada, by Marian M. George. Chicago, A. Flanagan company, 1926.
80, [7]-93, [1] p. illus. 19½cm. (*Lettered on cover:* Library of travel)
Published, 1901, under title: Little journeys to Alaska and Canada, for intermediate and upper grades; edited by Marian M. George.
"Canadian boat song" with music: [1] p. at end.

1. Alaska—Descr. & trav. 2. Canada—Descr. & trav. I. Kern, Mrs. Edith (Kingman) II. George, Marian M., 1865-
Library of Congress F909.L77 1926 26-7894

NL 0412202 DLC

Little journeys to Alaska and Canada; Alaska, by Edith Kingman Kern, Canada, by Marian M. George. Rev. ed. Chicago, A. Flanagan company, 1928.
167, [1] p. illus. 19½cm. (*Lettered on cover:* Library of travel)
"Canadian boat song" with music (1 p. at end)

1. Alaska—Descr. & trav. 2. Canada—Descr. & trav. I. Kern, Mrs. Edith (Kingman) II. George, Marian M., 1865-
Library of Congress F909.L77 1928 28-22069

NL 0412203 DLC OCIh

Day-NW F 852 L58 Little journeys, to outstanding beauty spots and places of interest along the highways and byways of the Inland Empire/of the Pacific Northwest. Spokane, Wash., Spokane Chamber of Commerce and Inland Automobile Association [194-?]
15 p. illus., maps. 22½ cm.
Cover title.

NL 0412204 IdU

Little journeys to the homes of American authors
see under [Hubbard, Elbert] 1856-1915, ed.

Little journeys with Martin Luther ...
see under [Harley, William Nicholas]

Little journies in the Black Hills...
see under [Chicago, Burlington and Quincy Railroad Company]

Little Kanawha and Elk River Petroleum and Mining Company.
Report of C. S. Richardson ... on the oil, coal, salt and iron lands ...
see under Richardson, Charles Samuel.

813.5 L7785 Little Karl; a story for children, by Uncle Milton. New York, Cupples & Leon, 1908.
unpaged. col. illus. 24 cm.

1. Children's books. I. Title.

NL 0412209 N

PZ6 A1L7757 Little Kate. [New York, P.J. Cozans [18--?]]
8 p. col. illus. 23 cm.
At head of cover: Aunt Mary's picture book.
Hand colored.

I. Title: Aunt Mary's picture book.

NL 0412210 NjR

---

76 L7781k 185-? The Little keepsake. Charlestown, Mass., G. W. Hobbs [185-?]
[62] p. illus., incl. front. 18 cm.
Variant binds.

NL 0412211 RPB

The little keepsake. Charlestown, Mass., Hobbs [186-?]
12 p. col. illus.

NL 0412212 NNC RPB

The Little Keepsake; a poetic gift for children. New York, Kiggins & Kellogg [1857]
8 p. illus. 8cm.
On cover: First series, no. 11.

1. Gift-books (Annuals, etc.)
Library of Congress PZ6.L734 21-3864

NL 0412213 DLC NN CtY

The little keepsake for 1844
see under Colman, Pamela (Chandler)

Is94 t 1 v.1(1 The little keepsake: or, Easy lessons, in words of one syllable. New Haven, Published by S. Babcock [18--?]
16p. illus. 9cm.
Title vignette.
Pamphlet

NL 0412215 CtY

The little keepsake, original and selected
see under Colman, Pamela (Chandler)

Is94 t1 v.1 The little keepsake present; or, Simple tales in easy verse. New Haven, Published by S. Babcock, 1850.
8p. illus. 9½cm.
Title vignette; illustrated covers.

NL 0412217 CtY

The Little keepsake; selected in part from the writings of the celebrated J. C. Lavater, by an American parent. New York, S. Colman, 1843.
96 p. front., plates. 11½cm.
Added t.-p.

1. Gift-books (Annuals, etc.) I. Lavater, Johann Caspar, 1741-1801.
Library of Congress PZ10.7.L725 15-18031

NL 0412218 DLC MHi

The little key of heaven: a selection of approved prayers for the use of Catholics. Philadelphia, H. L. Kilner & co., 1890.
192 p. 10½cm.

1. Catholic church—Prayer-books and devotions—English.
Library of Congress BX2110.K4 1890 a 89-25235
Copyright 1890: 18698 [2] 264.02

NL 0412219 DLC

PZ 9.5 A1L72 Little kings and queens; or, Royal children of English history. Profusely illustrated. Chicago, W. B. Conkey Co., c1903.
128 p. illus.

1. Gt.Brit. - Kings and rulers - Juvenile literature.

NL 0412220 CLU

"Little Kitty's library," Author of.
Harry and his pony
see under title

... The little Klondyke nugget; story of the discovery ... U. S. and Canada mining laws in full. Chicago, Laird & Lee, 1897.
192 p. incl. front., illus., fold. map. 32°.
"From official documents."

1. Klondike gold fields. 2. Mining law—Alaska. 3. Mining law—Canada. I. Laird & Lee, pub.
F931.L77 1—16563-M 1

NL 0412222 DLC MnHi

A little known American poet.
From- Literary Digest, Nov. 21, 1896
16 cm. [4] l. port]

NL 0412223 RPB

... Little known facts... about America at work
see under [National association of manufacturers of the United States of America]

Little known facts about the scheduled air transport industry
see [Air transport Facts and figures]

VOLUME 336

Little known historical spots in New England ...
see under [Arnold, Nason H]

Little known Lincoln episodes
see under [Warren, Louis Austin] 1885-

Little known Lincoln humor
see under [Warren, Louis Austin] 1885-

PZ162 .L78 1869 Little ladders to learning about how things are made, geography and costumes, science and art, city scenes, rural scenes, country employments ... London ˛etc.˛ G. Routledge, 1869.
6 pts. in 1 v. illus.

1. Industry. 2. Science. 3. Art.

NL 0412229 ICU

---

030 L778 Little ladders to learning about things indoors, what we eat and drink, animals and their uses, birds and birds' nests, fishes, butterflies, and frogs, trees, shrubs, and flowers. London, New York, G. Routledge, 1867.
1 v. illus. 19 cm.

I. Children's questions and answers.

NL 0412230 N OrP

Little lads, by George Cary Eggleston, Mary E. Wilkins, Frances A. Humphrey, Margaret Eytinge, Mrs. A. D. T. Whitney, Mary D. Brine, etc. ... Akron, O., New York ˛etc.˛ The Saalfield publishing company, 1904.
˛188˛ p. illus. 24cm.

I. Eggleston, George Cary, 1839- 4-24502

NL 0412231 DLC InU

Little Lady Mildred's inheritance
see under [Draper, Constance]

Little Lake Cemetery, Peterborough
see Peterborough, Ontario. Little Lake cemetery.

PZ216 .R36L7 The little lamb. Rev. by D. P. Kidder. New York, Lane & Scott, 1851.
39 p. illus. 11cm.

NL 0412234 ICU

The LITTLE lamb. New York, Published by the American tract society, 150 Nassau-street [188-?]
16 p. illus. 16 x 13cm.

In original decorative white and blue paper covers.

1. Parables--Bible. N.T.--The lost sheep. I. American tract society.

NL 0412235 NN MB N

The little lame prince and his travelling cloak
see under [Craik, Dinah Maria Mulock 1826-1887.

Sl 66 Little lands in America.
[San Francisco, Cal.]1916-

NL 0412237 DLC

Little lasses and lads; with coloured illustrations by Oscar Pletsch. London, Seeley, Jackson and Halliday; Boston, Roberts Brothers, 1869.
126 p. illus.

Pletsch, Oscar 1830-1888, illus.

NL 0412238 NNC

Little lassies, by Mary E. Wilkins, Mary D. Brine, Kate Upson Clark, Joaquin Miller, Margaret Sidney, Susan Coolidge, author of "John Halifax gentleman," etc. ... Akron, O., New York ˛etc.˛ The Saalfield publishing company, 1904.
˛188˛ p. illus. 24cm.

Freeman, Mrs. Mary Eleanor (Wilkins) 1862- 4-24501

NL 0412239 DLC RPB

Slavery E 441 M46 v.181 no.4 Little Laura, the Kentucky abolitionist. An address to the Young Friends of the Slave. Newcastle, Printed by T. Pigg, 1859.
12 p. 19cm.

May anti-slavery pamphlets, v. 181.

1. Abolitionists. I. Title.

NL 0412240 NIC

Little lays for little lips. ˛Poems˛ With outline illustrations by H. J. A. Miles. 5th ed. Now York, A. D. F. Randolph ˛1879?˛
48 p. illus. 15 x 12cm.

I. Miles, Helen J A illus.

NL 0412241 ViU

Little League
see Little League Baseball, inc.

GV862 .L5 Little League Baseball, inc.
Little Leaguer. v. 1-3; May 1953-Dec. 1955. ˛Williamsport, Pa., etc.˛

GV877 .T78 Little League Baseball, inc.
Turkin, Hy, *ed.*
The official encyclopedia of Little League baseball; edited by Hy Turkin for Little League Baseball, inc. New York, Barnes ˛1954˛

Little League Baseball, inc.
Official rules.
˛Williamsport, Pa.˛
v. illus. 20 cm.

GV877.L47 796.357 53-16709 ‡

NL 0412245 DLC

LITTLE LEAGUE BASEBALL, INC.
This is Little league.
[Williamsport, Pa.] no. illus. 28cm.

1. Baseball--U.S. I. Title.

NL 0412246 NN

Little Leaguer. v. 1-3; May 1953-Dec. 1955. ˛Williamsport, Pa., etc.˛
3 v. in illus., ports. 28 cm. 6 no. a year.
Official publication of Little League Baseball, inc.
L. C. set incomplete: v. 1 wanting.

1. Little League Baseball, inc.—Period. I. Little League Baseball, inc.
GV862.L5 68-43703

NL 0412247 DLC

PZ164 .L77 1875 The little learner's A B C picture book. London, Religious Tract Society ˛1875?˛
˛10˛ l. col. illus.

1. Alphabets.

NL 0412248 ICU

P N 35 L72 Little leather library corp., New York.
Collection of works by standard authors, in minature form. New York, Little leather library corp., n.d.
27 v. 8x10½cm.

NL 0412249 DNC

Little leather sun-books
see
Little sun-books

VOLUME 336

PZ6
.L548 A Little leaven, and what it wrought at Mrs. Blake's school. By the author of "Our little girls." New York, A.D.F. Randolph, 1859.
iv, ,5,-252p. front., plates. 17cm.

NL 0412251 NNU-W

A little leaven in a lump
see under Chamberlain, Parthene Ballard.

Little Lenin library.
[London, Lawrence & Wishart ltd., 19
v. 18½cm.

1. Socialism—Collections. I. Lenin, Vladimir Il'ich, 1870-1924.
44-560
Library of Congress HX311.L5
[2] 335.082

NL 0412253 DLC KU

Little Lenin library. v. 1– New York: Internat. Publishers[, 1929–]. v. 19½cm.

Cover-title.
v. 4, cop. 1929. v. 5–7, printed in Great Britain.
Reprinted in part from "The imperialist war" and "The Iskra period."
v. 1–4, Editor's pref., signed: Alexander Trachtenberg.
"Bibliography of Marxism," v. 1, p. 37–48.
Contents: v. 1. The teachings of Karl Marx. v. 2. The war and the Second International. v. 3. Zinoviev, G., and V. I. Lenin. Socialism and war. v. 4. What is to be done? Burning questions of our movement. v. 5. The Paris Commune. v. 6. The Revolution of 1905. v. 7. Religion.

1. Socialism. 2. Bolshevism. I. Trachtenberg, Alexander, editor. II. Zinov'yev, Grigoriĭ, 1883– III. Title.
N. Y. P. L. November 21, 1932

NL 0412254 NN IdB OCU CU DCU NNC ICU OrU WaS

76
LI91l
2
Harris Collection

Little lessons for little folks. With colored pictures. No. 2. [New York, Hurd and Houghton, 18--]
cover-title, 15p. col. illus. 14cm.
[Illuminated toy books]

NL 0412255 RPB NNC

Little lessons for little housekeepers
see under [Huntington, Emily] 1841-1909.

LITTLE lessons for little learners. New Haven, S.Babcock, 1839.

11.5 x 10 cm. pp.24. Illustr.
Cover: Babcock's no.4. Toys.

NL 0412257 MH

Ia94
tl
v.1

Little lessons for little learners. In words of one syllable. New Haven, Printed and published by S.Babcock [ca.1840]
16p. illus. 11cm. ([Babcock's moral, instructive, and entertaining toy books, no.3, or three cent toys, v.11])
Title and front cover vignettes, illustrated inside covers.

NL 0412258 CtY NN NjP ICU MH

A little lexicon, explaining such words as occur in the first three chapters...
see under [Brown, Charles Philip] 1798-1884.

808
L72

The Little library of liberal arts.
no. 1-
New York, Liberal arts press, 1948-
v. 20cm.

"A series designed to reprint shorter classics in philosophy, religion, political science, education, and literature."
Editor: 1948- Oskar Piest.
1. Literature - Collections. Piest, Oskar ed.

NL 0412260 NNC

Little library of useful information. no. [1]–
Chicago, Popular mechanics press, °1939–
nos. in v. illus. (incl. diagrs.) 24cm.
Nos. 1- 48 issued without title; no. 1- without numbering.

1. Receipts. I. Popular mechanics press, Chicago.
T49.L5 605 47-38604

NL 0412261 DLC

Little lights, and how they shone
see under [Chambers, Talbot Wilson] 1819-1896.

LITTLE Lily's alphabet. With rhymes by S.M.P. and pictures by Oscar Pletsch. London, F.Warne & Co., [1865].

1.8°. pp.(51). Front.and other illustr.
Printed on one side of the leaf only.
Presentation copy from John Ruskin, with his autograph.

I. P., S. M.

NL 0412263 MH

"Little Lily's picture lessons", Author of.
Little Lily's travels; a book for the young
see under title

Little Lily's travels; a book for the young. By the author of "Little Lily's picture lessons". London, New York [etc.] 1873.
163 p. illus.

NL 0412265 NNC

The little linguist, being a compendious introduction to English philology. London, Printed for the author, 1838.
1 p. l., 96, 144, 134 p., 1 l., [44] p. front. 9cm.

Illustrated t.- p.
"The miniature English grammar ... London, W. Mason & son"; 96 p., has special t.-p.
Contents.- The miniature English grammar.- English verbal distinction.- Miscellaneous English examples.- The population of the principal places throughout the world.

1. English language - Grammar - 1800-1870.

NL 0412267 NNC

Little lives. Animal stories in prose and verse.
= Boston. Roberts. 1872. iv, 169 pp. Plates. 17 cm., in 8s.

M7227 — Animals. Stories and anecdotes.

NL 0412268 MB

Little Lizzie. [New York: National Temperance Soc. and Publ. House, 187–.] 4 p. 12°.
Caption-title.
In: VTZ p. v. 52, no. 53.

1. Temperance.—Fiction. 2. Fiction (American). BLACK TEMPERANCE COLL.
N. Y. P. L. October 4, 1918.

NL 0412269 NN

Little Lizzie's letter to a soldier. [N. Y. 1863]

NL 0412270 NjP

DA 679
A132
1863

The little London directory of 1677. The oldest printed list of the merchants and bankers of London. Reprinted from the exceedingly rare original; with an introduction pointing out some of the most eminent merchants of the period. London, J. C. Hotten, 1863.
xxii, [128] p., 1 l. 14½cm.
Added t.-p.: A collection of the names of the merchants living in and about the city of London ... London, Printed for S. Lee [etc.] 1677.

1. London—Direct.
9-6388†
Library of Congress DA679.A13

NL 0412271 DLC ViW FU OU

VOLUME 336

A little looking-glass for the times; or, A brief remembrancer for Pennsylvania.

This work is available in this library in the Readex Microprint edition of Early American Imprints published by the American Antiquarian Society.
This collection is arranged according to the numbers in Charles Evans' American Bibliography.

NL 0412272 DLC

A little looking-glass for the times; or, A brief remembrancer for Pennsylvania. Containing some serious hints, affectionately addressed to people of every rank and station in the province: with an appendix, by way of supplication to Almighty God. By G. C. ... Wilmington [Del.] Printed by J. Adams, 1764.
v, 6-24 p. 16cm.

1. Pennsylvania. I. C., G

10-19539

Library of Congress F152.L75

NL 0412273 DLC PSC-Hi PPRF PPL MHi DeWI

... A little looking-glass for the times or, a brief remembrancer for Pennsylvania. Containing some serious hints, affectionately addressed to people of every rank and station in the province: with an appendix, by way of supplication to Almighty God. By G. C. ... Wilmington, Printed and sold by James Adams, 1764. New York, Reprinted, W. Abbatt, 1913.
(*In* The magazine of history with notes and queries. New York, 1913. 27cm. Extra no. 22, p. [67]-93)
At head of title: As near a fac-simile of the original as possible.
1. Pennsylvania. I. C., G. II. Title.

A 14-3036

Title from Brown Univ. Printed by L. C.

NL 0412274 RPB NN MiU CtY

MANN
TS
1490
L77

Little loomhouse group.
Little loomhouse country fair, contemporary American handwoven textiles, seventh season, 1945-1946. [Louisville, Ky., c1946]
80 p. illus. 28 cm.

Cover title.

1. Hand weaving - U. S. I. Tate, Lou. II. Title. II. Title: Comtemporary American handwoven textiles.

NL 0412275 NIC MiD NcRS KyBgW

TT848
.T3

Little loomhouse group.

Tate, Lou.
Weaving is fun [by] Lou Tate. [Louisville, Ky.] 1946.

PZ7
.C527
Li

Little Lord Fauntleroy.

Claire, Malcolm, 1898-
Little Lord Fauntleroy, as told by Uncle Mal (Malcolm Claire) for today's boys and girls. Illustrated by Marion Kohs Sandusky, O., New York, Prang company [1946]

Little loose-leaf library for boys' workers everywhere ...
see under Cheley, Frank Hobart, 1889- ed.

The little Lord Jesus. London, New York [etc.] Longmans, Green and co., 1924.
[48] p. illus. 22½cm. $1.25
Rhymes for children.

24-29895

Library of Congress PZ8.3.L72995

NL 0412279 DLC

Little Lotta, pseud.
see Crabtree, Lotta, 1847-1924.

The little Lotta joker. Containing very amusing bon mot, jokes, squibs, etc., etc., as perpetrated by the most celebrated wits and humorists of the day. New York, F. A. Brady [1870]
64 p. 15cm.

CA 19-579 Unrev'd

Library of Congress PN6161.L573

NL 0412281 DLC

A little lottery book for children ...

Editions of this work printed in America before 1801 are available in this library in the Readex Microprint edition of Early American Imprints published by the American Antiquarian Society.
This collection is arranged according to the numbers in Charles Evans' American Bibliography.

NL 0412282 DLC

The little Louvre... N.Y., c1855
see under [Abbott, Jacob] 1803-1879.

LITTLE Lucifer; comedy in three acts. London, Mrs. Marshall's typewriting office, 1909 48, 39, 30 l. 26cm.

Typescript.

1. Drama, English. 2. Drama-- Promptbooks and typescripts.

NL 0412284 NN

Little luck at Rough Ranch.

See

[Wheeler, Edward L]
Sierra Sam's sentence.

Little Lucy and her lamb... New-York, Printed and sold by Mahlon Day [183-?] 8 p. illus. 8cm.
In original illustrated green paper covers, with publisher's advertisements.

NL 0412286 NN

---

n. d.
Juv. coll.

Little Lucy Cary. New York: Published by N. B. Holmes, No. 262 Greenwich Street. [n. d.]
[5] 6-108 p. 15 cm.

NL 0412287 DLC

---

*XJ
820
.A10L

Little Lucy: or The careless child reformed. Cambridge: Printed by Hilliard and Metcalf. 1820.
33 p. 14.5cm.
Shaw/Shoemaker (1820) 1981; d'Alté Welch, 714.
Printed buff wrappers.

NL 0412288 MB

Little Lucy: or, The pleasant day. An example for little girls. New Haven, S. Babcock [1825?]
16 p. illus. 10½cm.
Title vignette.
Inside covers contain illustrations.

21-3865

Library of Congress PZ6.L736

NL 0412289 DLC NN

Is94
tl
v.1

Little Lucy: or, The pleasant day. An example for little girls. New Haven, Printed and published by S. Babcock, 1840.
16p. illus. 11cm.
Title and front cover vignettes; inside of covers illustrated.

NL 0412290 CtY NN

Little Lucy, the invalid; or, Nursery dialogues. London: Darton and Harvey, 1835. 121 p. front. 14½cm.

DARTON COLLECTION.

137594B. 1. Juvenile literature—dialogues. Fiction, English. I. Title: Nursery
N. Y. P. L. February 25, 1942

NL 0412291 NN

The little Lychetts, and other stories. New York, R. Carter & Brothers, 1860.
146 p. illus.

NL 0412292 NNC

Little, The, Lychetts, and other stories. New York: R. Carter & Bros., 1866. iv, 5-355 p., 7 pl. 16°. (Fireside library.)

1. Juvenile literature.—Fiction (English.)
N. Y. P. L. November 5, 1913.

NL 0412293 NN

VOLUME 336

Little Mabel. By the author of "Winnie O'Moore." A New Year's tract, for the children of the Warren street chapel, January 1, 1859. [Boston, 1859]
12 p. 16°.
N. t. p.

NL 0412294 MB

Call LI9104 Harris Collection
Little Mabel. Philadelphia, The Charles E. Hires co., [1891?]
[16] p. illus. 15 cm.
Advertising Hires' Root Beer.
Colored illustrations on cover.

NL 0412295 RPB

Little Mac campaign songster ... New-York, E. P. Patten [1864]
14, [1] p. 14½cm.
Title vignette (portrait)
Without music.

1. Campaign songs, 1864—Democratic. I. Patten, E. P., New York, pub.
18-2263
Library of Congress E458.4.L77

NL 0412296 DLC NN CSmH

Little Mac: how he captured Manassas. Boston, Lee and Shepard [186-]
cover-title, 9 pl. 13½cm.
Folder.

1. McClellan, George Brinton, 1826-1885.
Library of Congress E470.L77 4-27759†

NL 0412297 DLC

The little Mac songster. Containing...entirely new and original patriotic, convivial, comic, gay and rollicking camp songs. Interspersed with comic stump speeches, recitations and bits of camp wit... New York, Dick & Fitzgerald [c1862] 72 p. 14cm.
Words only; tunes of most of the songs indicated by title.

295324B. 1. United States—Hist.—Civil war—Poetry.
N. Y. P. L. April 25, 1945

NL 0412298 NN ICN CtY RPB CSmH OC1WHi LNHT

Little Mac's double feat of equitation.
— Providence. Williams. 1864. Broadside, 12½ × 17 inches.
This is a caricature on McClellan's nomination for the presidency.

G1434 — Broadsides. — Caricature. — Presidential elections. 1864. — MacClellan [McClellan], George Brinton. 1826-1885. Caricatures.

NL 0412299 MB

The LITTLE magazine. v. 1, no. 1-5; Dec. 1933-Sept. /Oct. 1934. New York. v. 27cm.
Bimonthly (irregular).
Edited by H. Davis.
Ceased publication?

1. Periodicals—U. S. I. Davis, Harry, ed. II. Davis, Harry.

NL 0412300 NN OU ICN

Little magazine [1145]
see under [Bainbridge, John]
From The New Yorker.

Journalism D050 AL725
Little magazine directory. 2d annual number. 1950.
17-[34] p. 28 x 14cm.

From Galley, v. 2, no. 1, spring 1950.

1. Periodicals - Directories. I. Galley; the little magazine for little magazine publishers.

NL 0412302 NNC

Little Maggie [1868]
see under [Baker, Harriette Newell (Woods) 1815-1893.

YA .S583
Little Maggie's trials and triumphs. Philadelphia, [c1852]
161p.

(Sunday school books; arr. numerically.)

NL 0412304 DLC

The little maid and the gentleman
see under [Wordsworth, William] 1770-1850.

The Little man. Issue 1 (Spring, 1938). (Cincinnati) [Cincinnati] c1938.
48 p. illus. 20cm.
University of Cincinnati student publication, edited by R. J. Lowry.
For later series, privately published, see: A little man book.

1. Colleges and universities—Student publications—U. S.—Cincinnati university. I. Lowry, Robert James, 1919- , ed. II. Cincinnati. University.
April 17, 1945

NL 0412306 NN OCU IEN OU NcU InU

The Little man. Cincinnati.
Murderpie
see under Lowry, Robert James, 1919-

PR6031 .A395P6
Little man.
Panjabi, Lata K
Poetical politics. Introductory paras to the poems, wherever they appear, are written by the "Little man" of the Bombay sentinel. Bombay, Punkul Pub. House [1945]

The little man. [n.p., 191-?]
see under [Galsworthy, John] 1867-1933.

---

*pFB8 N1627 Z805n
A little man alarmed at his own shadow. [London] Pub^d by Roberts middle row.[1803]
plate. 35.5x24.5cm.,mounted & bd.to 50x40cm.
George 9994; Broadley A-543 (ascribed to Woodward).
Engraving (hand-colored), unsigned; engraved by P. Roberts.
A satire on Napoleon.
No.105 in a volume lettered on spine: Napoleonic caricatures.

NL 0412310 MH

The little man and his little gun.
The wonderful adventures of the little man & his little gun. Illustrated by "Morte". Boston, Mayhew and Baker [°1858]
31 p. incl. front., illus. 17½cm. (On cover: Fireside picture books)
Frontispiece and last leaf mounted on inside of covers.
Prose amplification of the nursery rhyme.
"The little man and his little gun", with music: p. 30-31.

I. Title.
28-27517
Library of Congress PZ8.L7364

NL 0412311 DLC

The little man and the little maid. New York, H. Ropes [18--]
[16] p. (incl. cover) illus.

One version of: "There was a little man,/ And he wooed a little maid,/ And he said, Little maid, will you wed, wed, wed?". This version reads: "There was a little man,/ And he had a little mind/ To ask a little maid for to wed, wed, wed."

NL 0412312 NNC

The LITTLE man and the little maid. Providence, Winsor & Perrin, stereotyped and printed by G.C. Rand & co., Boston, 1849. 12 p. illus. 19cm.
In original illustrated blue paper covers, with publishers' advertisements on back.
Cover title.
In verse.

NL 0412313 NN RPB MB

PZ262 .L617 186-
The little man and the little maid. New York, Sheldon [186-]
[12] p. col. illus. (Pleasure books)

NL 0412314 ICU

The Little man and the little maid. [New York] Hurd & Houghton [187-?]
8 l. illus. 12°.
In: NAS p.v. 4, no. 3.

NL 0412315 NN

VOLUME 336

A Little man book. *DY
ser. 1

Cincinnati: The Little man press, 1939- 8½-35cm.
nos. illus.

Ser. 1, part -7, ser. 3, 5 lack series title.
Editor : ser. 1- R. J. Lowry.
Title varies: ser. 1-2, 4, The Little man; ser. 6 A Little man book.

1. No subject. I. Lowry, Robert James, 1919- , ed. II. The Little man.
January 25, 1943

NL 0412316 MH NN

Little man—this now, by X. Y. Z. London, V. Gollancz ltd., 1940.
256 p. 20cm.

I. Z., X. Y. II. X. Y. Z.
41-84
Library of Congress PZ3.L2796

NL 0412317 DLC

A little man's night's comforts, or Boney's visions
see under [Braddyll, Thomas Richmond Gale] 1776-1862.

The Little manual of devotion, to the Sacred heart of Jesus. A. M. D. G. ... Cincinnati, J. P. Walsh, 1867.
171 p. 11½cm.
With this is bound, as issued: Spiritual bouquet, offered by pious souls, to the Sacred heart of Jesus. By a father of the Society of Jesus ... Cincinnati, 1867.

1. Sacred heart, Devotion to. 2. Catholic church—Prayer-books and devotions—English. I. Title: Manual of devotion, to the Sacred heart of Jesus.
Library of Congress BX2158.L6 43-49160

NL 0412319 DLC

Little manual of the Sacred heart. A collection of instructions, prayers, hymns, and various practices of piety. In honor of the Sacred heart of Jesus. Compiled and adapted from approved sources ... New York, Sullivan & Schaefer, 1883.
2 p. l., [iii]-ix, [1], [11]-124 p. front., illus., plates. 12½cm.

1. Sacred heart, Devotion to. 2. Catholic church—Prayer-books and devotions—English.
Library of Congress BX2158.L65 43-49157

NL 0412320 DLC

The little manufacturer, or, The history of Sarah Wright. Boston: Crocker & Brewster, 1825. 72 p. 24°.

245505A. N. Y. P. L. 1. Tracts, Religious, Juvenile.
November 1, 1926

NL 0412321 NN

Little Maplestead, Essex, Eng. Church of St. John.
The Round church of Little Maplestead, Essex, formerly belonging to the Knights Hospitallers of S. John of Jerusalem. A relic of antiquity, chivalry, and Christian faith ... London: Joseph Masters, 1850.
2 p. l., [9]-32 p. front. 16 cm.
Title page and text in borders.
In verse.

NL 0412322 NNUT

LITTLE MARIA. [London] The Religious tract society [Printed by William Clowes and sons, 185-?]
32 p. illus. 16 x 13cm.

In original buff paper covers, decorated in blue and green, with the number "7" on inside of front cover.
Cover title.
Illustrated half-title.

I. Religious tract society, London.

NL 0412323 NN

Little Marian's pilgrimage. Revised by the committee of publication. Philadelphia, New York [etc.] American Sunday-school union [1852]
1 p. l., 5-23 p. front., plates. 17½cm.

I. American Sunday-school union.
16-3073
Library of Congress PZ3.L73

NL 0412324 DLC MB NN

The little marine botanist; or, Guide to the collection and arranging of sea-weed. By the author of "The little entomologist." London: Darton and Clark [1840] xiii, 72 p. 4 pl. (incl. col'd front.) 9½cm.

DARTON COLLECTION.
1. Algae. I. The little entomologist, Author of. II. Title: Guide to the collection and arranging of sea-weed.
N. Y. P. L. March 9, 1942

NL 0412325 NN

The little market woman and her little dog; ...
see under [Burr, William Henry]

942.575
L778e
Ms.
Little Marlowe, Eng. (Parish)
Extracts from Little Marlow register.
[n.p., n.d.]

9 l. 26cm.

1. Registers of births, etc. - Little Marlow, Eng. 2. Manuscripts, English.

NL 0412327 FU

244
L773m
Little Martha; or, The grace of God in leading a child to Christ. [n.p., 182-?]
8 p. 18 cm. (Baptist General Tract Society. Tract no. 33)

1. Sunday-school literature. 2. Seele, Martha Ann, 1813-
Series: American Baptist Publication Society. Tract no. 33.

NL 0412328 N

PZ6
.L7285
Little Mary.
Boston, 1831.

NL 0412329 DLC

Juv. coll.
Little Mary. New York, Published by the American tract society, 150 Nassau Street. [n. d.]
16 p. 11.5 cm.
With Mary Lord and other books for children.

NL 0412330 DLC

LITTLE Mary; a story for children from four to five years old. Pt.I. By a mother. Boston, Cottons and Barnard, 1831.

pp.36. Illustr.

I. A mother.

NL 0412331 MH

Little Mary, an illustration of the power of Jesus to save even the youngest. With an introduction by Baron Stow, D. D. Boston, Gould and Lincoln, 1861.
xii, [13]-106 p. 15½cm.

1. Gilmore, Mary Achsah, 1847-1860.
37-20256
Library of Congress BR1715.G5L5
[2] 922

NL 0412332 DLC NRAB

Little Mary, Author of.
Ellen's visit to the shepherd
see under title

Little Mary grown older. Second edition. London, Published by R.B. Seeley and W. Burnside; and sold by L.B. Seeley and sons, 1835. Pp. viii, 136. 14.6x9.4cm.

NL 0412334 CaOTP

Little Mary's primer, and the house where little Mary lived. [Boston, Munroe and Francis, 18-?]

NL 0412335 MH

HS731
.L5
Little masonic library.
Washington, D. C. [c1924]

NL 0412336 DLC OC1 OC1W

VOLUME 336

Little masonic library ... Kingsport, Tenn., Southern publishers, inc. [1946]
5 v. 2 illus. (incl. facsim.) diagrs. 20½cm.
The works in this collection were published separately in the series Little masonic library.
Includes music.
CONTENTS.—book I. The landmarks of freemasonry, by S. H. Shepherd. Anderson's Constitutions of 1723, by Lionel Vibert. Masonic jurisprudence, by Roscoe Pound.—book II. The Comacines, by W. Ravenscroft. Modern masonry, by J. F. Newton. The Morgan affair and anti-masonry, by J. C. Palmer. Mormonism and masonry, by S. H. Goodwin.—book III. A history of the York and Scottish rites of freemasonry, by H. R. Evans. Freemasonry in the American revolution, by Sidney Morse. The great light in masonry, by J. F. Newton. Masonry and the flag, by J. W. Barry.—book IV. The three degrees and great symbols of masonry. The ethics of freemasonry, by Dudley Wright. Great American masons, by G. W. Baird. A master's wages, by C. H. Claudy.—book V. Masonry and Americanism. The meaning of masonry, by Albert Pike. The old past master, by C. H. Claudy. Masonic poems.

1. Freemasons.

46-5188
Library of Congress HS371.L53
[4] 366.1

NL 0412338 DLC UU CaQML

Little masterpieces of autobiography
see under Iles, George, 1852-1942, ed.

Little masterpieces of English poetry
see under Van Dyke, Henry, 1852-1933, *ed.*

Little masterpieces of science
see under Iles, George, 1852-1942, ed.

LITTLE Master's miscellany, or Divine and moral essays in prose and verse, adapted to the capacities, and design'd for the improvement of the youth of both sexes. To which is added select fables, moral songs and useful maxims. London, J. Robinson, 1746.

nar. 16°. 3 p.l., 124 p. Front. and other illustr.

NL 0412342 MH

BJ 1661
.W 29
1755 R Little master's miscellany: or, Divine and moral essays in prose and verse; adapted to the capacities, and design'd for the improvement of youth, of both sexes. Containing, dialogues on the following subjects, viz. On lying, On prayer ... a ramble thro' the town, in a dialogue between Master Joseph, and Miss Patty. To which is added, select fables, moral songs, and useful maxims ... The 4th ed., illustrated with copper-plates. Birmingham, Printed by T. Warren, 1755.
vi, [2], [9]-96 p. front., plates. 16½cm.

NL 0412343 MdBJ

R.B.R. The little match girl; a poem, by a lady of Charleston, S. C. With illus. by the author. Charleston, S. C., Fogartie's Book Depository [c1870]
20 p. 4 col. plates. 17 cm.

I. A lady of Charleston, S. C.

NL 0412344 NcD

Little May and her lost A. Boston, 1879.
52 p. illus. 21 cm.
Illus. t.p.
Contains poetry.

NL 0412345 PPB

Little May mining co., Salt Lake City, Utah.
Annual stockholders' meeting, financial report. 1922.

NL 0412346 DI-GS

Little May; or, Of what use am I? By the author of "Rosa's childhood," "Bessy Graham," etc. London, The Religious tract society [1859]
173, [1] p. incl. front., plates. 15cm.

I. Religious tract society, London.

43-20230
Library of Congress PZ6.L7368

NL 0412347 DLC

Little May; or, Of what use am I? By the author of "Rosa's childhood", "Bessy Graham", etc. Boston, H. Hoyt [1873]
232 p. illus.

NL 0412348 NNC

---

xPZ5
L728 **Little May-Queen.** New York, T.Nelson & Sons; London, S.W.Partridge & Co. [18--]
50p. illus. 13cm.
Colored illus. mounted on cover.

NL 0412349 IaU

Little Mayflower. Picture Book. Illustrated. New York, 1883.
80 p. 18°

NL 0412350 PBL

The little medicine carrier; or, The boyhood of George Wayland. By the author of "Basil," etc. ... Richmond: Published by E. Thompson Baird [18-?]
113 p. front., illus. 15cm.

NL 0412351 ViW

The little medly
see under [Brunt, Jonathan] b. 1760.

Little Meg
see under [Stretton, Hesba] 1832-1911.

Little Meg's children
see under Stretton, Hesba, 1832-1911.

Little memorial library, *Columbia, Conn.*
see
Saxton B. Little memorial library, *Columbia, Conn.*

Little men and women—Babyland.
Boston, Alpha publishing company, 18
v. illus., plates. 24-25cm. monthly.
Title varies: 1898, Little men and women.
Jan. 1899- 1900, Little men and women—Babyland.
Editors: C. S. Pratt, Ella F. Pratt.
Absorbed Babyland in Jan. 1899.
Merged into Little folks.

I. Pratt, Charles Stuart, 1854- ed. II. Pratt, Mrs. Ella (Farman) 1843-1907, ed.

CA 10—5058 Unrev'd
Library of Congress AP201.L74

NL 0412356 DLC NbHi

Little men and women-Babyland
see also Little folks.

---

*
PZ7
.L735
19— Little men and women stories. Boston, D. Lothrop [19—?]
106-127 p. illus. 23cm.
Cover title.

1. Children's stories.

NL 0412358 ViU

Ib62
tl **The little menagerie; or, Birds, beasts, and fishes.** London: Darton and co. [18--?]
15p. incl. col. front., col. illus. 24cm.
Frontispiece and p.15 mounted on inside of covers.
Pamphlet

NL 0412359 CtY

VOLUME 336

...The LITTLE merchant. Lowell [Mass.] Published by J. Merrill [184-?] 11 p. illus. 16cm. (Cousin Grace's pretty story books. no. 9)

In original illustrated grey paper covers, with last leaf pasted to cover and a list of "Cousin Grace's pretty story books" on back.
Cover title.
Half-title, p. [2]: The little merchant; or, The history of John Harris.

1. Cousin Grace's pretty story books.

NL 0412360 NN

Little Mercy. By a pupil of the Pennsylvania institution for the instruction of the blind... Philadelphia: H. B. Ashmead, 1857. 6 p. front. 15cm.

1. Juvenile literature—Fiction, American. I. A pupil of the Pennsylvania institution for the instruction of the blind.
N. Y. P. L. June 20, 1940

NL 0412361 NN

Little merry hearts; a charming collection of delightful stories ... Chicago and New York, W. B. Conkey co., 1898.
[105] p. illus., pl. 4°.

Library of Congress (PZ7) 98—761
Copyright 1898: 55845 [a33b1]

NL 0412362

Little merry-makers. Illustrated. New York, Cassell, Petter, Galpin & Co. [c1881]
96 p. illus.

NL 0412363 NNC

The Little messenger. v. 1-5; July 1868-Aug. 1, 1873. Philadelphia, 1868-73.
5 v. in 1. illus. 32cm. semimonthly.

Pub. under the auspices of an editorial committee appointed by the General convention of the New Jerusalem church.
W. H. Hinkley, editor, Aug. 1872-Aug. 1873.
No more published?

I. Hinkley, Willard H., ed. II. New Jerusalem church. General convention.

10-23465†

Library of Congress AP200.L5

NL 0412364 DLC

Little Messenger of Mary.(a quarterly devoted to The Blessed Virgin).
1-3,1900 - 1902,Jan-Dec.

NL 0412365 MWH

Little Miami natural history society, Yellow Springs, O.
...Annual report ... 1st-5th 1876-1880. Yellow Springs, O., 1876-80.
5 v. in 1.

Extract from the transations of the Little Miami natural history society. 1876.

NL 0412366 OO

Little Miami Rail Road Company. An act to incorporate the Little Miami Rail Road Company. n.p. [1836.] 12 p. 8°.
Caption-title.
The charter, p. [1]-8, is followed by an estimate of the probable cost and dated, Clifton, Sep. 29th, 1836, and signed, T. G. Bates. — Streeter.
1321

I. Bates, T.G.

NL 0412367 NN DBRE

Little Miami Railroad Company.
Agreement and lease of the Little Miami R. R. and Pittsburgh, Cincinnati & St. Louis railway co. [with] the Pennsylvania railroad. [Phila. ? 1870]
20 p. 8°.

NL 0412368 MB DLC NN

Little Miami Railroad Company.
Annual report of the President to the stockholders of the Little Miami Railroad Company. ... Cincinnati, O., [1846]-1915.
Library has 1845/6, 1848/9, 1856/8, 1859/60, 1914. tables. 23½cm.
Title varies: 1856/7-1859/60, Second-fifth joint annual report of the ... Little Miami and Columbus & Xenia Railroad Companies, being the fifteenth-eighteenth annual report of the L. M. Company, and the eighth-eleventh annual report of the C. & X. Company.

NL 0412369 ICJ OClWHi

Little Miami railroad company.
Charter and by-laws of the Little Miami rail road co. Cincinnati, E. Shepard's steam press, 1850.
cover-title, 23 p. 21½cm.

I. Ohio. Laws, statutes, etc.

A 18-222
Title from Bureau of Railway Economics. Printed by L. C.

NL 0412370 DBRE ICU OClWHi

Little Miami railroad company.
Explanatory letter to the stockholders of the Little Miami rail road company. Cincinnati, C. F. Bradley & co.'s power press, 1854.
16 p. 22cm.
Signed: Jacob Strader, pres't.

I. Strader, Jacob.

A 21-2081
Bur. of railway econ. Libr. for Library of Congress HE2791.L7723 1854
[a44b1]†

NL 0412371 DBRE OHi ICU DLC OClWHi

Little Miami Railroad Company.
... Joint annual report of the Directors to the stockholders of the Little Miami and Columbus & Xenia Railroad Companies, ... Cincinnati, 1858-1861.
No. 2-3, 5: 1856/8, 1859/60. tables. 23½cm.
The 15th-18th report of the Little Miami Co. and the 8th-11th, of the Columbus and Xenia Co.

NL 0412372 ICJ DLC NN NcU

Little Miami railroad company.
Lease of the Little Miami R. R. to the Pittsburgh, Cincinnati & St. Louis railway co., and other contracts of the Little Miami R. R. co. Philadelphia, Review printing house, 1870.
3 p. l., 221 p. 22cm.

I. Pittsburgh, Cincinnati and St. Louis railway company.

A 20-646
Title from Bureau of Railway Economics. Printed by L. C.

NL 0412373 DBRE

Little Miami railroad company.
Mortgage of Little Miami railroad company to Central trust and safe deposit company, New York, trustee. Dated February 1, 1901. Securing $3,000,000 betterment bonds of $1,000 each, dated February 1, 1901, payable February 1, 1951, bearing 3½ per cent. interest. [n. p., 1901?]
23 p. 23cm.

1. [Railroads—Mortgages] I. Central trust and safe deposit company, New York.

A 19-625
Title from Bureau of Railway Economics. Printed by L. C.

NL 0412374 DBRE

Little Miami railroad company.
Report of the engineer to the president and directors of the Little Miami rail road company. Cincinnati, Printed at the Cincinnati gazette office, 1839.
14 p. 21cm.

CA 15-1519 Unrev'd
Library of Congress HE2791.L7723 1839

N 0412375 DLC NN MiU

Little Miami Union Regular Baptist Association
see Baptists. Ohio. Little Miami Union Regular Association.

The Little milkmaid, folk song from Suffolk, collected and arranged by E. J. Moeran. [London] Oxford univ. press [c1925]
4p.

Score for low voice with piano accompaniment.

I. Moeran, Ernest John, 1894-

NL 0412376 IEN

292
L72
Little Mill Creek, Coshocton, Ohio, Infiltration Committee.
Channel storage study. [n.p.] 1939.
17 [54] l.

1. Little Mill Creek Watershed, Ohio.
2. Water-storage.

NL 0412377 DNAL

VOLUME 336

Little mill dam; with other select and original moral tales. New York, Kiggins & Kellogg [186-]
140 p. illus.

Pasted on inside front cover: Reward of merit, Sep. 1861.

NL 0412378 NNC

The Little mine; a Catholic pre-primary magazine. v. 1- Sept. 1948-
[Minneapolis, Youth Associates]
v. in illus. 31 cm. monthly (except July and Aug.)

1. Children—Religious life—Period. 2. Catholic Church—Period.

BV4560.L55 268.432 56-37544

NL 0412379 DLC MnHi

The little minister ...
see under [Barrie, Sir James Matthew] bart. 1860-1937.

Little Minnie; the story of her life, written for her friends, by one who loved her. [New York] Published for private distribution by Anson D. F. Randolph, 1862.
53 p.

"Little Willie": p. [41]-53.

NL 0412381 NNC

Little Miriam's Bible stories for little Jewish readers
see under Magnus, Katie, lady, 1844-

... Little Miss Duck, by A. E. H., with illustrations from original drawings by Bess Goe Willis. Philadelphia, Henry Altemus company [°1930]
56 p., 1 l. incl. col. front., col. illus. 14½cm. (Altemus' wee books for wee folks)

I. H., A. E. II. A. E. H.
Library of Congress PZ10.3.L72 30-19600

NL 0412383 DLC

---

n.d. Juv. coll. Little Miss Giant. New York, McLoughlin Bros. [n.d.]
[2] 3-7 p. 6.5 cm.

NL 0412384 DLC

Little Miss Muffet and other good stories; sixty-nine illustrations. Philadelphia, H. Altemus company [°1905]
iv, 5-64 p. col. front., illus., col. pl. 22cm. (Altemus' Bo-Peep series, 6)
p. 63-64 advertising matter.

5-26826

NL 0412385 DLC

Little Miss Muffet, and other stories. New York McLoughlin bros., °1902.
72 p. illus. (part col.) 20½cm.
Illustrated t.-p. in colors.

Library of Congress PZ8.3.L733 ca 16-499 Unrev'd

NL 0412386 DLC

LITTLE Miss Nobody. [London] Lyric Theatre [1916?]
16 l. illus. 18cm.

Cover-title.
Caption-title: The story retold.
Souvenir designed for the Lyric Theatre by Rudolph B. Birnbaum.

1. No subject. I. Dumont, Frank. Little Miss Nobody. II. London. Lyric Theatre.

NL 0412387 NN

---

sE L721 Little Miss Prim. New York, T. Nelson and sons; [etc., etc., 188-?]
[62]p. front., illus.

1. Readers.

NL 0412388 IU NjR

The little missionary; or, A biographical sketch of Gratia Olive Leonard ... Philadelphia, New York [etc.] American Sunday-school union [1855]
90 p. incl. front., illus. 15½cm.
Preface signed: M. J. P. R.

1. Leonard, Gratia Olive. I. R., M. J. P. II. M. J. P. R. III. American Sunday-school union.
Library of Congress BR1715.L4L5 37-37997
[2] 922

NL 0412389 DLC

LITTLE MISSOURI RIVER STOCKMEN'S ASSOCIATION.
By-laws of the Little Missouri River Stockmen's Association... New York: Press of G.P.Putnam's Sons, 1885. 6 p. 16cm.

Photostat reproduction.

782398A. 1. Cattle—Breeding and raising—Assoc. and org. —U.S.

NL 0412390 NN MiU-C MH

Little Mr. Bouncer and his friend, Verdant Green
see under [Bradley, Edward] 1827-1889.

Little mittens for the little darlings...
see under Barrow, Mrs. Frances Elizabeth (Mease) 1822-1894.

The little modeller
see under Clarke, H.G., & Co., publishers.

The Little Momus: a Collection of Jests, Bon Mots, etc. London: D. Carvalho, n.d.
2 vols. Pink and olive-green paper covers. Folding colored frontispieces, and colored vignettes on engraved titles.
Miniature Edition.
Halsey Library. -From F.T. Sabin, Lond., 1869.

NL 0412394 CSmH

The little monitor, or Good examples for children. Edinburgh, Oliver and Boyd [1820?]

NL 0412395 MH

A little morality
see under [Kipling, Rudyard] 1865-1936.

PZ262 .L818 1864 A little more. New York, American Tract Society [1864]
96 p. illus.

NL 0412397 ICU

A little more cider
see under [Baker, George Melville] 1832-1890.

A little more nonsense
see under [Davies, Randall] 1866-

A Little more of that same; or, A recollection of sundry material passages omitted in a late treatise entituled The devil to pay at St. James's. Particularly the downfall of bumbazeen; the demolition of Figg the prize-fighter; the hurly-burly about a new parliament ... a most surprizing account of the miracles perform'd by the flying ass at Belsize; a proposal for the improvement of musick, by manufacturing eunuchs in England; concluding with England's joy, or the happy type of an union betwixt Whig and Tory, in the reconciliation of Mr. Nathaniel Mist and Mr. Colley Cibber ... Cum multis aliis. London, A Moore 1727.
16 p. 21 cm.
I. The Devil to pay at St. James's.
PR3291.A1L53 66-59840
[1]

NL 0412400 DLC MH ICN

Little mother for youngest readers ... Boston, Lothrop pub. co. [1899]
[37] p. illus., pl. 4°. (Snowtime series)

Library of Congress 99—1995

NL 0412401 DLC

VOLUME 336

Little mothers and their little friends. Boston, De Wolfe, Fiske and co. [c.1886]

NL 0412402 MH

Ix
L716
860l
The little mountain guide; or, How to be happy. Boston, H.Hoyt[1860?] 299p. front., plates. 14cm.

I.Title: How to be happy.

NL 0412403 CtY

The LITTLE mountaineers of Auvergne, or The adventures of James and Georgette. Altered from the French and adopted to the perusal of youth. London, R. and L. Peacock, etc., 1801.

nar.12°. pp.viii,232. Front.and vigns.

NL 0412404 MH

813.39
L778
The little museum, to interest and instruct children. Phil., H.F.Anners, 1847. 95p. front., illus. 12cm.

NL 0412405 N CtY

The little musicians... N.Y., 1860 see under [Baker, Sarah Schoonmaker (Tuthill)] 1824-1906.

Little Nancy, or, The punishment of greediness. A moral tale ... Philadelphia: Pub. by Morgan & Yeager, at the juvenile bookstore, no. 114, Chesnut street [181–]

8 p. front., 3 pl. 13cm.

In verse.

Library of Congress PZ6.L737 21-8355

NL 0412407 DLC NN CSmH

LITTLE Nancy; or, The punishment of greediness. A moral tale. Embellished with superb engravings. London, Dean and Munday, 1815.

16p. front., 3 pl. 12 x 10cm.

Printed on one side of leaf only, printed sides facing each other. Blank sides included in paging.
In verse.

NL 0412408 MnU

Little Nannette, a narrative, by a bereaved mother. N.Y., American tract society, n.d. 1 p.l., [5]-32 p. illus.

Title vignette.

I. American Tract Society.

NL 0412409 PMA

Little Nannette. A narrative of facts... Salem: Whipple and Lawrence, 1825. 36 p. 24°.

"From the 3. English ed."

1. Tracts, Religious, Juvenile.
N. Y. P. L. December 31, 1926

NL 0412410 NN

Little Neck (N. Y.) community association.
The history of Little Neck. [Ida Fowler compiled all the material from all sources] [Little Neck, N. Y., 1952] 88 p. illus., ports. 21cm.

1. Little Neck, N. Y.—Hist. I. Fowler, Ida.

NL 0412411 NN

WB
880
qL778
LITTLE NECK, N. Y. Physico-Biological Research
[Collection of publications]

The library has a collection of miscellaneous publications of this organization kept as received. These publications are not listed nor bound separately.

NL 0412412 DNLM

Little Nell of the Ozarks. [n. p., 1935?] 31 f. 32cm.

Caption-title.
Typewritten, with title, corrections and notes in ms.
Played on Bryant's Show Boat.
Mutilated.

1. Drama, American.
N. Y. P. L. April 23, 1942

NL 0412413 NN

PZ
6
.L776
Little Nellie's velvet carpet. Philadelphia, Presbyterian Board of Publication [1865] 72 p. illus. (Presbyterian Board of Publication. Series for youth)

NL 0412414 MiU

...Little Nelly... [London:] Religious Tract Soc. [, 183–?] 4 p. 16°. (Narrative ser. no. 821.)

Caption-title.

436074A. 1. Simmons, Eleanor, 1816–1830. 2. Tracts, Religious. 3. Religious Tract Society.
N. Y. P. L. March 12, 1930

NL 0412415 NN

Little Nemo in slumberland see under [Levine, Edna Sarah]

Little Nobody, and how God cared for her. Philadelphia: Amer. Baptist Publ. Soc. [186–?] 141 p., 3 pl. (incl. front.) 16°.

BLACK TEMPERANCE COLL.

1. Temperance.—Fiction. 2. Juvenile literature.—Fiction (American).
N. Y. P. L. November 19, 1917.

NL 0412417 NN

LITTLE | Non-Such: | Or, | Certaine new Questions | Moved out of | Ancient Truths. | I. Concerning the words, Let us make | man after our own Image. | II. Whether that was a materiall Apple | which Adam did eate | III. Whether the forbidding of marriage be | not a Popish injunction onely, and not | rightly grounded from the Scripture. | Newly published with intent to finde out the | truth, if it be not here already. | . . . (1 line).
London, Printed for H.P. 1646. | Border. 18.2x14.5cm. 16p.

NL 0412418 NNUT-Mc TxU CtY

"Little Norway" in pictures; R. N. A. F. in Canada. [Toronto? 1943?]
cover-title, 2 p. l., [88] p. of illus. (incl. ports.) 23½ x 31cm.

1. Royal Norwegian air force training camp, Ontario. 2. Norway. Flygevåpnet.
Library of Congress UG635.N6L5 44-26591
[3] 358.4

NL 0412419 DLC IdU WaTC CaBViP IaAS CaOTU MnHi IU

Little Norway in pictures, with supplement, Norway—yesterday and today. Toronto, S. J. R. Saunders [1944?]
[124] p. illus. (incl. ports.) 23½ x 31cm.
On cover: R. N. A. F. in Canada.

1. Royal Norwegian air force training camp, Ontario. 2. Norway. Flygevåpnet.
Library of Congress UG635.N6L5 1944 a 44-6400
[18] 358.4

NL 0412420 DLC MtBC MtBuM NcRS PSt PLF OCl OEac OO OLak OOxM MiHM ViU CaBVa CaBVaU OrU OrCS WaWW WaSpG WaT WaS

... Little Nugget see under [Anderson, J J] major.

The little nun; the diary of one of Belgium's unhappy victims, from her original manuscript. London: Cassell and Co., Ltd. [1916.] vii(i), 119(1) p. 12°.

Preface signed: E. A.

1. European war, 1914– . Atrocities. 2. A., E., translator.
N. Y. P. L. October 27, 1916.

NL 0412422 NN NjP

VOLUME 336

The Little Nut Cracker; or, Bon-Mots Extraordinary. London: T. Hughes, n. d.
Red paper cover.
Colored front, and colored vignette on title.
Miniature Edition.
Halsey Library. -From F. T. Sabin, Lond., 1896.

NL 0412423 CSmH

Little object finders A B C. New York: McLoughlin Bros. [18-- ?] 6 l. illus. 8°.

NL 0412424 NN

Little odes to great folks ... see under Pindar, Minimus, pseud.

A little of everything: or, Short notes for the consideration of the people, before they vote in October next !!! Baltimore, Md. ? 1839? 36 p. 8°.

NL 0412426 NN

Little office of the Most Sacred Heart of Jesus ... see under Catholic Church. Liturgy and ritual. Little office of the Most Sacred Heart of Jesus. English & Latin.

Little Oh-Dear-Me! Four years old. [Poem.] New York. Randolph & Co. 1869. 12 pp. 18 cm.

NL 0412428 MB

Little old New York ... Poughkeepsie, N. Y., Oxford publishing company, °1910.
cover-title, 32 p. illus., fold. plan. 17½cm. $0.10

1. New York (City)—Descr.—Views. I. Oxford publishing co., Poughkeepsie, N. Y.

Library of Congress F128.37.L77 10-22959

NL 0412429 DLC MB

The little old woman. London, Dean and son [ca. 1855]. Ff. [8] 23.6x15.8cm.

NL 0412430 CaOTP

The little old woman. New York, McLoughlin [186-?] [8] p. col. illus. 19cm. (Susie Sunshine series)

NL 0412431 MiDW RPB NN ICU MH

The Little old woman and her silver penny. With numerous engravings. Devonport: Printed by and for Samuel and John Keys [ca. 1820?]
cover-title, 11 p. illus. (woodcuts) 11cm.

Original printed rose wrappers with illustration on p. [1]; pages 2 and 11 pasted down to covers.
No. 2 in a Collection of chapbooks published at Devonport.

NL 0412432 CLU

The little olive leaf put in the mouth... see under [Björck, Tobias Eric] 1668-1740.

The little one's alphabet. Philadelphia, Davis Porter & co. [18--]
Cover-title, [8]p. col. illus. 13½cm.
Title within colored pictorial border.
The woodcut illustrations are by Alexander Anderson.

£94 tl v.2(2

NL 0412434 CtY NN MH

Little ones annual. Stories and poems for little people. With 350 original illustrations. Boston, Estes & Lauriat [c1888]

Lettered on cover: v.7. Little Ones' annual.

NL 0412435 OCl

1890 Juv. coll.

Little ones annual. Stories and poems for little people. With 405 original illustrations. Boston: Estes & Lauriat [c. 1890] [iii] iv-xvi [3] 4-384 p. 23.5 cm.

NL 0412436 DLC

Little ones at play, 1883 [1882] see under Neally, Amy.

The LITTLE one's budget. London [etc.] Blackie & son ltd. [1934?] 64 l. col'd front., illus. 22cm.

72798B. 1. Juvenile literature, English—Collections.

NL 0412438 NN

The little one's first book. Philadelphia, Davis, Porter & co., [18--]
Cover-title, [8]p. col. illus. 13½cm.
Title within colored pictorial border.
The woodcut illustrations are by Alexander Anderson.

£694 tl v.2(2

NL 0412439 CtY MH

Little one's first book, The.
— Philadelphia. Davis, Porter & Coates. [185-?] (4), 19-24, (1) pp. Illus. 24°.

G9758 — Davis, Porter & Coates, publishers. — English language. Read.

NL 0412440 MB NN

... The little one's ladder, or First steps in spelling and reading. Designed for the use of families and schools. Embellished with numerous engravings. New York, G. F. Cooledge, 1858.
61, [2] p. front., illus. 19½cm.
Illus. t.-p.
Ornamental borders.
"The illustrations in this book were engraved by Dr. Alex. Anderson, in the eighty-third year of his age! from designs by Wm. P. Morgan."
At end: The end of the first part of The little one's ladder.

1. Readers and speakers—1800-1870. 2. Spellers.

Library of Congress PE1119.A1L7 12-6795

NL 0412441 DLC NN

The little orange girl and other stories Concord, N. H., Rufus Merrill & Son, n. d. var. paging. illus. 21 cm.
Excerpts from Forrester's Illustrated and Juvenile keepsake.

NL 0412442 RPB

The little orange-sellers; or, The story of Patty White. see under American Sunday-school union.

The Little orator for boys and girls. see under Pearson, Henry Bromfield, comp.

LITTLE ORCHESTRA SOCIETY OF NEW YORK.
Program notes. [1st]-date season; 1947/48-date New York. v. illus. 24cm.

Eight concerts a season. Some years accompanied by unnumbered programs of concerts.

1. Programs. 2. Concerts—Programs.

NL 0412445 NN MB

A LITTLE organ book in memory of Hubert Parry. London, A. & C. Black; Boston, C. C. Birchard [c1924] 45 p. 28cm. (The Year book press music series)

Music by C. Hubert H. Parry, C. V. Stanford, A. Herbert Brewer, Alan Gray, Charles Macpherson, Ivor Atkins, Frank Bridge, Harold E. Darke, Charles Wood, Walter G. Alcock, G. Thalben Ball, H. G. Ley and Walford Davies.

1. Organ—Collections. 2. Parry, Sir Charles Hubert Hastings, bart., 1848-1918. I. The Year book press music series.

NL 0412446 NN IU

VOLUME 336

The little orphan
see under [Church, Mrs. Ella Rodman (MacIlvane)] 1831-

The Little orphan of the House of Chao: a Chinese tragedy. (In: [Percy (T)] Miscellaneous pieces relating to the Chinese. London, 1762. 2 v. 8°. v. 1- p. 101-213)

NL 0412448 NN

The little Osage captive
see under [Cornelius, Elias] 1794-1832.

Juv. coll. The little painter. Philadelphia, Scholz & Janentzky, 112 South 8th Street [n. d.]
7 l. 7 cm.

NL 0412450 DLC ICU

s608.8 L722 Little Pansy picture book; stories and pictures. New York, Worthington Co., 1886.
[109] p. illus. (part col.) music. 25cm.

1. Literature--Collections.

NL 0412451 IU

WA 16323 The little partners; The snow fort; and Little Howard. New York, Sunday-School Union [c1859]
56 p. illus.

I. Sunday-School Union, New York.

NL 0412452 CtY OClWHi

The little patriots
see under [Leathley, Mary Elizabeth Southwell (Dudley)]

Little Patty (Schooner)
Ausführlicher Bericht von Captain Gere welcher den Schooner Little Patty befehligte...
see under Gere, Captain.

LITTLE pavier, The.
Dublin. Tract repository. n. d. 30 pp. Illus. 32°.

NL 0412455 MB

The little peace-maker
see under [Morton, Charles] 1627-1698.

Little pea-nut merchant
see under [Atkins, Mary A] 1819-1882.

Little Peg O'Shaughnessy.
(In Good stories. [Part 4.] Pp. 119-152. [Boston, 1868.])
6259.42

Reprinted from All the Year Round, vol. 15 [Per. Room (*7312.1.15)].

NL 0412458 MB

Little people whom the Lord loved [1871]
see under Flagg, Elizabeth E.

Little people's A B C. New York, Huestis and Cozans [1857?]

NL 0412460 MH

Little people's speaker; composed of recitations, motion songs, holiday exercises, temperance and patriotic pieces
see under Shoemaker, Rachel Walter (Hinkle) "Mrs. J.W. Shoemaker", 1838-1915, comp.

1863 Juv. coll. Little pet primer. The "Hobart Hall" reading without tears, for all good children, by their loving friend, the Rector. New York: Alexander Fleming. No. 657 Sixth Avenue [c. 1863]
[5] 6-24 p. 19.5 cm.

NL 0412462 DLC IaU MH

"A little perfect hour"
see under [McLaughlin, Wendell] comp.

Little Peter, a Christmas morality for children of any age... 1888
see under [Harrison, Mrs. Mary St. Leger (Kingsley)] 1852-1931.

Little Peter and his sister Patty. Philadelphia, American Baptist Publication Society [c1853]
27 p. illus.

NL 0412465 NNC MWA

Am.Lt. PZ6 .L55 Little pet's book. Philadelphia, Lippincott, Grambo & co., 1854.
viii, 9-128p. incl.front., illus. 14cm.
(Added t.-p.: The little ones' library)

NL 0412466 NNU-W

PZ262 .L824 186- Little pet's linen ABC. New York, McLoughlin [186-?]
[12] p. col. illus.

1. Alphabets.

NL 0412467 ICU

PZ262 .L825 186- Little pet's picture alphabet. New York, McLoughlin bros. [186-?]
[14] p. illus.

NL 0412468 ICU

A Little philosopher.
An epistle to the admirers of the Lord Bishop of London's letter ...
see under title

YA .S180 The little philosopher. Philadelphia, [c185-?]
90p.

(Sunday school books; arr. numerically.)

NL 0412470 DLC

Little pictorial lives of the saints
see under Shea, John Dawson Gilmary, 1824-1892.

Ie94 t 1 v.1(1 The little picture Bible, containing interesting stories from the Old and New Testaments. Illustrated with beautiful and appropriate engravings. New-Haven, Printed and published by S.Babcock, 1841.
24p. illus. 15cm. (Babcock's moral, instructive and amusing toy books [no.4, or six cent toys, v.6])

-- --- Another issue, without date. Leaf of title misbound at end.

NL 0412472 CtY IU MH

PZ262 .L826 1845 The little picture book. New York, Baker, Crane & Day [1845]
8 p. illus. 7cm.

NL 0412473 ICU

VOLUME 336

... The little picture book. New York, Cornish, Lamport [n. d.]
64 p. col. illus. 15 cm. (Kriss Kringles library)
T. -p. illustrated in colors.
1. Children's poetry.

NL 0412474 RPB

Juv. coll.
... The little picture book. New York: Sheldon, Lamport, and Blakeman [n. d.]
[2] 3-64 p. 14.5 cm.
Kriss Kringle's library

NL 0412475 DLC

Little picture, The; or, "Little by little."
New York. [1858.] 32 pp. Illus. Plate. [American Tract Society. Publications. Children's tracts. Series 4. No. 58.] 15 cm.
Bound with the original paper covers.

E1703 — S.r.

NL 0412476 MB

Juv. coll.
Little pictures for little boys. [n. p., n. d.]
8 p. 8 cm.

NL 0412477 DLC

Little Pierre, the pedlar of Alsace; or, The reward of filial piety. Tr. from the French, by J. M. C. ... New York, Catholic publication society, 1872.
236 p. front., 26 pl. $18\frac{1}{2}$ cm.
I. C., J. M., tr.

Library of Congress PZ3.L7297 7-16062†

NL 0412478 DLC NN DGU

F 895539 .51
LITTLE PIGEON CREEK, Ind. Baptist Church.
Minute book of Little Pigeon Creek Baptist Church, 1816-1840. Spencer County, Indiana. [n.p., n.d.]
125p. 29cm.

Xerox copy.

NL 0412479 ICN

LITTLE pig's menagerie, The.
Bost. Brown, T. & C. 1858. 31 pp. Illus. Sq. 16°.

NL 0412480 MB

The Little pilgrim.
Jan. 1854-
Philadelphia [L. K. Lippincott, etc.] 1854-
9 v. illus. $24\frac{1}{2}$ cm. monthly.
Editor: Jan. 1854- Grace Greenwood (pseud. of Mrs. S. J. C. Lippincott)

I. Lippincott, Mrs. Sara Jane (Clarke) 1823-1904, ed.

10-23462†

Library of Congress AP200.L6

NL 0412481 DLC MiU-C ViU ICN NN N

A little Pilgrim. Boston, Little, Brown, 1909
see under [Oliphant, Mrs. Margaret Oliphant (Wilson)] 1828-1897.

The little pilgrim. Rev. and illustrated. By Helen Petrie. London, Griffith & Farran; New York, E. P. Dutton & co., 1880.
61 p. incl. front., illus., plates. $22\frac{1}{2}$ cm.
First pub. in 1852, under title: Little Marian's pilgrimage.

I. Petrie, Helen, illus.

16-10112

Library of Congress PZ8.3.L7344

NL 0412483 DLC

The little pilgrim. With illustrations by Emily Cook & E. Heatly. London, E. Nister; New York, E. P. Dutton & co. [1897?]
39, [1] p. incl. col. front., illus., col. plates. 15 cm.
In verse.

NL 0412484 CtY

The little pilgrim. Philadelphia, American Sunday School Union [1879]
see under [Church, Ella Rodman (MacIlvane)] 1831-

YA .8183
The little pilgrim. A simple story.
Philadelphia, [1848?]
36 p.

(Sunday school books; arr. numerically.)

NL 0412486 DLC

The little pilgrim, a true story for children. Macon, Ga, 1867.
3 p. l., [7]-27 p. illus. 15 cm.
Bound with A Mother, pseud. Very little verses for very little folks.

NL 0412487 RPB

... Little pilgrim at Aunt Lou's
see under [Church, Mrs. Ella Rodman (MacIlvane)] 1831-

... Little pilgrim at housekeeping
see under [Church, Mrs. Ella Rodman (MacIlvane)] 1831-

The little pilgrim. Further experiences
see under [Oliphant, Margaret Oliphant (Wilson)] 1828-1897.

A little pilgrim in the unseen
see under [Oliphant, Mrs. Margaret Oliphant (Wilson)] 1828-1897.

Little pilgrims
see under American Tract Society.

Little pilgrim's Christmas
see under [Church, Ella Rodman (MacIlvane)] 1831-

A little pilgrim's peeps at Parnassus. ...
see under [Katzin, Olga] 1896-

The LITTLE Pilgrim's Progress. Philadelphia, Smith and Peck, 1844.

8 cm. Plates and title vign.
A children's version of Bunyan's original.

NL 0412495 MH

Little Pilgrim's progress. Part II. Philadelphia, A.C. Peck & Theo. Bliss, 1856.
95 p. 12 cm.

NL 0412496 NRAB

Little Pine's journal: the appeal of a Christian Chippeway chief on behalf of his people. With an introduction by Edward F. Wilson. Toronto: Copp, Clark and Co., 1872. 29 p. 8°.

1. Indians (N. A.): Chippewa. 2. N. Y. P. L.
EAMES INDIAN COLLECTION. Wilson, Edward Francis. August 27, 1914.

NL 0412497 NN

VOLUME 336

Little pitchers with big ears, by the children of the fifth grade and Nan Hall, their teacher. Garden City, N. Y., Garden City publishing company [1942]
[64] p. illus. 27½cm.
Reproduced from hand-written copy.
Written by twenty-five children of the Pryor street school in Atlanta.

1. Children as authors. I. Hall, Nan. II. Atlanta. Pryor street school.
Library of Congress PZ7.L73 42-8147

NL 0412498 DLC

A little plain English, addressed to the people of the United States
see under [Cobbett, William] 1763-1835.

Little playfellows for happy hours ... Boston, Lothrop pub. co. [1900]
[77] p. front., illus. 4°. (Sunbeam series)

Library of Congress 0—3499

NL 0412500 DLC

Little playmates; happy hours for the little people ... Boston, Lothrop pub. co. [1899]
[20] p. illus., pl. 4°. (Play room series)

Library of Congress 99—1866

NL 0412501 DLC

Little plays and exercises; a collection of bright and charming pieces including drills and music for younger children, by various authors ... Dansville, N. Y., F. A. Owen publishing company [°1909]
[197] p. 18cm. (On cover: Instructor entertainment series) $0.35
"Republished from Normal instructor and Primary plans."
Each play has special t.-p. and pagination.
CONTENTS.—Mother Goose convention, by Mary Mackinlay.—Fairy sunshine, by Laura R. Smith.—The flowers' party, by Louise Dietz.—Harvest time, by Laura R. Smith.—The fairies' revelry, by W. N. Bugbee.—A Japanese reception, by Laura R. Smith.—Little mothers; exercises for mothers' afternoon or for any special occasion, by Grace B. Faxon. Also Miss Columbia's party.—Christmas secrets, by Alice E. Allen and T. B. Weaver.—The real Santa Claus, by Laura R. Smith.—Mother Goose party, by Rosemary Richards.—Red, white and blue; a ribbon drill (with music) by Lettie Sterling.—"Parasol" and "Rainy daisies" exercises; with music, by S. Emily Potter.
1. Amusements.
Library of Congress PN4271.L5 9—30418

NL 0412502 DLC RPB Or

Little plays for Christmas
see under Clark, Ada.

Little plays for little people. A series of favorite tales of childhood arranged in a dramatic form for home performance school exhibition, etc. [by An experienced amateur] N. Y., n. d.
various/paging 19 cm.

NL 0412504 RPB

Little plays of Saint Benedict: [a Pax book] Oxford, B. Blackwell, 1929.
xiv, 137 p. 19 cm.
Contains music.
Foreword signed: F. W. Powicke.

1. Religious drama, English. I. Powicke, Frederick Maurice, 1879-

NL 0412505 CSmH

LITTLE plays to amuse and instruct little folks in the nursery and school-room. New York, A.D.F.Randolph, 1860.
17.5 cm. pp.55. Plates.

NL 0412506 MH

Little pocket looking-glass, intended to exhibit some of the features of different Christian denominations. Chester. Vt. Whipple. 1829.
45 p.

NL 0412507 PPPrHi

Coll L1913p
Little poems. Northampton [Mass.] A. R. Merrifield [182-?]
10 p. illus. 11 cm.
Harris Small Books
Title vignette.

1. Children's poetry.

NL 0412508 RPB MB

Little poems for children.
— Windsor, Vt. Cochran. 1815. 31 pp. Plate. 10½ cm.

D2453 — Children's poems. — Books for the young. Imprints before 1850.

NL 0412509 MB MWA

LITTLE poems for little children. New York, Kiggins & Kellogg, 88 John street [185-] 16 p. illus. 96mm.

At head of cover title: Second series. - No. 12.
In original blue paper covers, with publishers' advertisements on back.
CONTENTS.--The Lord's prayer.--My mother.--My father.--The good-natured girls.--Going to bed at night.--Rising in the morning.--The doll.--The tempest.
784357.

NL 0412510 NN RPB

Little poems for little folks. Philadelphia: Smith & Peck, 1844.
vi, 7-192 p. illus. 48°.

NL 0412511 NN MH

808.81 L722
Little poems for little folks. Philadelphia, Smith and Peck, 1845.
192p. illus., 8cm.

1. Children's poetry.

NL 0412512 IU NNU-W CtY MH

Little poems for little people. Illustrated. Boston, D. Lothrop [18--]
190 p. illus.

NL 0412513 NNC

Little poems for little people. Boston: Brown, Bazin & Co., 1855. 128 p. incl. front., illus., plates. sq. 24°.

84632A. 1. Juvenile literature.— Poetry (American).
N. Y. P. L. May 22, 1923.

NL 0412514 NN

Little poems for little people, London Chapman and Hall
see under Claude, Mary S

Little poems for little readers. New York, Samuel Wood.
see under [Gilbert, Ann (Taylor)] 1782-1866.

I894 tl v.2(6
Little poems for little readers. Northampton, John Metcalf, 1336 [i.e. 1836]
1p.l., [5]-22p. illus. (in this copy; incomplete?) 13½cm.
Cover-title and imprint: Little poems for little folks. Northampton. J.H.Butler.
Numbered 5 at head of cover-title.
Title and front cover vignettes, illustration on back cover.
Frontispiece wanting?

NL 0412517 CtY

1840 Juv. coll.
Little poems for little readers. Northampton, John Metcalf, 1840.
[5] 6-24 p. 13 cm.

NL 0412518 DLC

Little poems, for little readers. Wendell, 1828.
23 p. 24°

NL 0412519 MWA

Little poems for little readers. Worcester: Pub. by J. Grout, jr [183-?] 16 p. illus. 11cm.
In original illustrated pink paper covers.
CONTENTS.—The force of example.—The little girl and the robin.—The cow.—The butterfly.—Mary and her lamb.—My kite.

NL 0412520 NN RPB

VOLUME 336

Little poems, from the German. Part first. Boston, Brown, Taggard & Chase [185?]
cover-title, 16 p. col. illus 18 cm.
At head of title: New colored toys.
Imperfect copy: p 5-8 bound at end out of order.

NL 0412521 RPB

Little poems. From the German. Part I. Boston. Carter & Co. [186-?] v. Colored illus. [The boys' & girls' library. No. 4.] 18 cm.
Ed. by Mrs. Colman.

H3857 — T.r. — Germany. Lit. Poetry. Colls. — Children's poems. — S.r.c.

NL 0412522 MB

Ls94 tl v.1(5

The little post-office; or, My brothers and sisters. A mother's offering. New Haven, S. Babcock, 1835.
24p. illus. 14½cm.
Title vignette, repeated on front-cover; illustrated back-cover.
Front cover mutilated.

NL 0412523 CtY

The LITTLE poulterer. Designed for the instruction of children. By a lady. Embellished with neat copperplate engravings. Philadelphia, Published by Morgan & Yeager, at the Juvenile bookstore [1824?] 16 p. 6 col. plates. 13cm.

Rosenbach: Early American children's books, 641. Weiss: William Charles, p. 9.
In original illustrated tan paper covers, with publishers' advertisements on back.
On cover: The little poultrer. Designed for the instruction of children with plates...
The plates are handcolored.

Lenox. I. A lady.

NL 0412525 NN

The LITTLE poulterer. Embellished with engravings. Philadelphia, Published and sold, wholesale and retail, by Mary Charles, 1821. 16 p. 5 plates. 13cm.

See: Rosenbach: Early American children's books, 641. Weiss: William Charles, p. 9.
In original illustrated reddish brown covers, with publisher's advertisements on back.
On cover: The little poultrer. Designed for the instruction of children with plates...
With autograph of Solomon Morse

NL 0412526 NN

Little prattler: good things for the young.
New York, George Rutledge [
v. illus.

Published in New York and London 1868-1877.
Title varies: 1868-1872, Good words for the young; title varies slightly, 1873-1877.

NL 0412527 NNC

Little prattler: good things for the young.
see also Good words for the young.

---

244 L7783

The Little prayer, by the author of Getting Rich. New York, Sunday-School Union [18--]
52 p. illus. 11 cm.

1. Sunday-school literature.

NL 0412529 N

Little prayer book for the use of Catholics. Staten Isl., N.Y. Mission of the Immaculate Conception, 1894.
1 v.

NL 0412530 DCU-H

Little prayers for little children
see under American Sunday School Union.

Coll. LI913pr Harris Collection

Little prayers for little people. n.p., n.d.
cover-title, [8]p. illus. (port. col.) 13x17cm.

In verse.

NL 0412532 RPB

The little preacher; or, Five short sermons for children
see under Uncle Charles, pseud.

PZ216 .P62L7

A little present. Northampton, J. Metcalf, 1840.
8 p. illus. 8cm.

NL 0412534 ICU

Little present, for a good child. Greenfield, A. Phelps ... 1846.
18 p. illus. 10 cm
Illus. t.p.

NL 0412535 RPB

A LITTLE present, for a good child. Northampton [Mass.] John Metcalf, 1837. 18 p., 1 l. (incl. covers) illus. 11cm.

See: Gilmore: Northampton, 410, 428. See: Rosenbach: Early Amer. children's books, 776.
In original illustrated blue paper covers, with number "9" at head of title.
Cover title and imprint: Little present. Northampton, J. H. Butler.

Continued in next column

Continued from preceding column

Begins: "The squirrel leaps from tree to tree."
Contains 14 couplets, each with two woodcuts.
Includes 2 alphabets, p. [4]

1. Children's rhymes.

NL 0412537 NN RPB

LITTLE present for a good child. Northampton, A.R. Merrifield [184-?] 10 p., 1 l. (incl. covers) illus. 79mm.

In original illustrated buff paper covers.
Begins: "The owl until the evening sleeps."
Contains 6 couplets, each with two woodcuts.
Includes an alphabet, p. [4]
Illustrations colored by hand.

1. Children's rhymes.

NL 0412538 NN MB

A little present for Friends and friendly people, in the form of a miscellaneous discourse
see under [Hicks, Edward] 1780-1849.

A little present for little children. Boston, J. M. Usher, 1846.
4 p. l., 5-28 p. incl. front., illus. 17 cm.
By the compiler of "Little hymns and pictures for little readers"

NL 0412539 RPB

---

*EC7 M3148 714ac

Little Preston: an heroi-comick poem, upon the late action at Holywell. To which is added the Chester lady's congratulation to the hero Ashy ...
London: Printed, and sold by J. Roberts in Warwick-lane. MDCCXVII.
8°. 20p. 19.5cm.
Satire on the Jacobite uprising.
No.8 in a volume labeled on spine: Rivella. Poems &c

NL 0412540 MH CtY PU

A little pretty pocket-book, intended for the instruction and amusement of little Master Tommy, and pretty Miss Polly. With two letters from Jack the giant-killer; as also a ball and pincushion; the use of which will infallibly make Tommy a good boy, and Polly a good girl. To which is added, A little song-book, being a new attempt to teach children the use of the English alphabet, by way of diversion. The 1st Worcester ed. Printed at Worcester, Massachusetts. By Isaiah Thomas, and sold, wholesale and retail, at his bookstore. 1787.
2 p. l., [7]-122 p. front., illus. 10cm.
A reprint of the London edition originally published by John Newbery in 1744.
"Rules for behaviour in children": p. [94]-122.
1. Primers—1500-1800. 2. Games. 3. Etiquette.
Library of Congress PZ6.L7375 22—5880 [a45c1]

00 OEac MB NN MWA RPJCB IdU OrP Or OrU NjP IU ICHi MH NBC CU CtY PSt NcGW NBC NIC NN OCl
NL 0412541 DLC MiU-C Or OrP OrU ICN FTaSU MiU PMA

"Little priest", pseud.
see under Lemoine, George Joseph Guyon- , 1860-

VOLUME 336

Is94 tl v.2 The little primor. A book for children ... Pittsfield,Mass.,Published by E.Werden,1848. 8p. illus. 8cm. ([Toy books] no.8)
Front cover vignette; illustration on back cover.

NL 0412543 CtY

PE 1119 .A1 L5 1844 The Little primer; or, First lessons for children. Newark, N.J., Printed and published by Benjamin Olds, 1844. 24p. illus. 11cm.

1. Primers. 1800-1870. I. Title: First lessons for children.

NL 0412544 OrU MH

The little princess and Gulliver ... see under [Williams, C] fl. 1797-1820 (ca.)

The little Princess Narina and her silver-feathered shoes. Boston, Walker, Wise, and company, 1861.

88 p. illus. 16cm. (On cover: The Silver penny series)

NL 0412546 MnU OKentU

Z 1 L729 The Little printer. v.

New York, New York Institution for the Instruction of the Deaf and Dumb, v. 11cm. weekly (during the school year)

Edited, published and printed by printer apprentices of the New York Institution for the Instruction of the Deaf and Dumb.
Each vol. issued in one paper cover.

NL 0412547 NNC

The little prisoner; or, A visit to the island of Malta. Founded on fact. 2. ed. London, Harvey and Darton, 1825. 245 p. front. 14cm.

275719B. 1. No subject. I. Title: A visit to the island of Malta.
N. Y. P. L. August 15, 1944

NL 0412548 NN CaBVaU

Little Prudy's children see under Clarke, Rebecca Sophia, 1833-1906.

Little Prudy's Flyaway series see under Clarke, Rebecca Sophia, 1833-1906.

Little purr-purr people, and how they tried to be folks. By "Boz" [pseud.] St. Louis, Hamilton-Brown shoe company [1887]
[16] p. illus. 13 x 16cm.

1. Children's poetry. I. Boz, pseud.

Library of Congress PZ8.3.L7346 CA 17-1705 Unrev'd

NL 0412551 DLC

The Little puzzle book. Mount Vernon, N. Y., Peter Pauper Press [1955]
[62] p. 20 cm.

1. Puzzles. I. Peter Pauper Press, Mount Vernon, N. Y.

GV1493.L53 70-6949 MARC

NL 0412552 DLC NN OCl

YA .S442 The little queen: A story for children... Philadelphia, 1850. 34 p.

(Sunday school books; arr. numerically.)

NL 0412553 DLC

YA .S564 The little questioners. Philadelphia, [c1847] 72p.

(Sunday school books; arr. numerically.)

NL 0412554 DLC

The little rambler; and other tales. Embellished with three copper-plate engravings. Philadelphia, J. Johnson, 1808. 34 p. illus. 14cm. (J. Johnson's juvenile library)

Copy imperfect: Front. mutilated; all pages after p. 34 missing.

NL 0412555 NNC

Little Rambler, and other tales. New Haven, 1815. 31 p. 32°. (last page imperfect and frontispiece)

NL 0412556 MWA

Little ramblers, and other stories. By favorite authors. New York [etc.] Cassell [c1885] 16 l. illus. 26cm.

252803B. 1. No subject.
N. Y. P. L. January 25, 1944

NL 0412557 NN

GRAFF 4887 LITTLE RAPID PLACER MINING COMPANY, BLACK HILLS, DAKOTA.
Prospectus. [New York, 1880?]
16p. front. (map) fold. plate. 24cm.
Map: Little Rapid Placer Mining Co's. property, on Little Rapid Creek, Black Hills, Pennington County, Dakota. With inset.
Folded plate at end: 1. The Roy Stone hydraulic excavator. 2. Hydraulic "Giants" at work.

Bookplate: T.W.S. (i.e.Thomas W. Streeter) Streeter Sale IV, 2071.

NL 0412559 ICN CtY

The LITTLE reader;a progressive step to knowledge. London,J.Harris,[183-?].

14 x 10.5 cm. Illustr.

NL 0412560 MH

Little reader: comprising short and easy stories for young children. Boston, n.d. 14 cm.

NL 0412561 RPB

The Little reading-book in words of one syllable. London, Nelson, 1871.

NL 0412562 MH

LITTLE reading lessons, with pictures... New-York, Printed and sold by Mahlon Day, at the new Juvenile book-store, 374 Pearl-street [1833?] 4 l. illus. 80mm.

In original tan wrappers.

784354. 1. Primers, American.

NL 0412563 NN

RARE BOOK COLL. PS991 A1L58 The Little rebel. Boston, J. E. Tilton, 1864. 295 p. 16 cm.

Added title page, illustrated.

NL 0412564 OU CtY

VOLUME 336

The **little** rebels, a drama founded on facts, reprinted from the Juvenile miscellany, issue of September, 1826. Illustration on page five from the Juvenile miscellany; title-page illustration and tailpiece from book of the period; engraved on wood; with introduction by Robert Seaver. Boston, G. S. Howland, 1925.

3 p. l., 5-10 p., 1 l. illus. 22½cm.

"This edition limited to three hundred fifty copies." This copy not numbered.

1. U. S.—Hist.—Revolution—Drama.

25-22406

Library of Congress PZ6.L5

NL 0412565 DLC MB OrU

Little recreations for the piano. (Grades 1 and 2.)
— Boston. Oliver Ditson Co. 1910. 64 pp. [The half dollar music series.] 31 cm.

H4972 — S.r. — Pianoforte. Music. Colls.

NL 0412566 MB

The little red book, 1902-1903
see under Great Lakes red book.

The "Little red book"; Spalding's official base ball record
see Little red book of major league baseball.

The **Little** red book of major league baseball. 1926–
New York, N. Y., A. M. Elias baseball bureau, inc.; [etc., etc., 1926–

v. illus. (ports.) 17-19cm.

1933 not published.
Issues for 1926-32 published as Spalding's athletic library.
Title varies: 1926-32, The "Little red book"; Spalding's official base ball record.
1934-37, Charlie White's "Little red book" of base ball (varies)
1938, The Pocket cyclopedia of major league baseball.
1939- The Little red book of major league baseball.

Issues for 1926-37 compiled by C. D. White.
Editors: 1926-32, J. B. Foster.—1938- F. C. Lane.
Imprint varies: 1926-32, New York, American sports publishing company.—1934-37, Cortland, N. Y., C. White.

1. Base-ball—Year-books. I. White, Charles D., d. 1937, comp. II. Foster, John Buckingham, 1863-1941, ed. III. Lane, F. C., ed.

26-4174 Revised 2

Library of Congress GV877.L5
[r46g2] 796.357058

NL 0412570 DLC WaS NcC PP MB PSt

Little Redcap. A tale for boys.
Boston. Lothrop Co. [187-?] Illus. 16°.

NL 0412571 MB

Little Red Cloak
see under [McKeever, Harriet Burn] 1807-1886.

Little red hen.
The cock, the mouse and the little red hen; illustrated by Fern Bisel Peat. Akron, O., New York, The Saalfield publishing company, ©1932.

[20] p. illus. (part col.) 22½cm. (*Lettered on cover:* Calico classics)
Illustrated t.-p. and lining-papers in colors.

I. Peat, Mrs. Fern Bisel, illus. II. Title.

CA 33-1 Unrev'd

Library of Congress PZ10.3.L724Co

NL 0412573 DLC

Little red hen.

Juv. coll. The little red hen. New York, McLoughlin Bros [n. d.]
8 p. 16.5 cm.

NL 0412574 DLC

PZ264 .L75 188- LITTLE RED HEN.
The little red hen. New York, McLoughlin bros. [188-?]
7 p. col. illus.

NL 0412575 ICU

Little red hen.
The little red hen. Illustrated by Berta & Elmer Hader. [New York] Macmillan, 1928.

[42] p. col. illus. 15 cm. (The Happy hour books)

I. Hader, Berta (Hoerner) illus. II. Hader, Elmer, 1889- illus.

PZ10.3.L724Had 28-21040 rev*

NL 0412576 DLC MB OCl OO OClh OrAshS OrMonO

Little red hen.
The little red hen, illustrated by Rudolf. New York city, Simon and Schuster, inc., 1942.

[42] p. illus. (part col.) 20½ x 17½cm. (*On cover:* The Little golden library, 6)

I. Freund, Rudolf, 1915- illus.

42-50765

Library of Congress PZ10.3.L724Li

NL 0412577 DLC Or OrP WaS OO OOxM

Little red hen.
Little red hen; illustrated by Beth Wilson. Racine, Wis., Whitman Pub. Co., ©1953.

unpaged. illus. 17 cm. (Tell-a-tale books, 930)

I. Wilson, Beth, illus.

PZ10.3.L724Wi 54-22398 ‡

NL 0412578 DLC

Little red hen.
The little red hen, a favorite folk-tale. Pictures by J. P. Miller. [New ed.] New York, Simon and Schuster [1954]

unpaged. illus. 21 cm. (A Little golden book, 209)

I. Miller, J. P., 1913- illus.

PZ10.3.L724Mi 54-14959 ‡

NL 0412579 DLC OO

---

sE L724w Little Red Hen.
The little red hen and other nursery tales, illustrated by Erika Weihs. Chicago, Wilcox & Follett [1945]
[28]p. col.illus. 24cm.

I. Weihs, Erika, illus. II. Title.

NL 0412580 IU PP

Little red hen.
The little red hen and the wheat, and other stories. With pictures by Miriam Rodier. [Kenosha, Wis., John Martin's House, 1948]

[36] p. col. illus. 25 cm.

PZ10.3.L724Ro 49-1162*‡

NL 0412581 DLC

Little red hen.
The little red hen, Black Sambo [and] Peter Rabbit, illustrated by Hilda Miloche and Wilma Kane. Racine, Wis., Whitman publishing company, ©1944.

[64] p. col. illus. 28½cm.

I. *Bannerman, Helen. The story of Little Black Sambo. II. Potter, Beatrix, 1865 or 6-1943. Peter Rabbit. III. Miloche, Hilda, illus. IV. Kane, Wilma, joint illus.

45-1079

Library of Congress ° PZ5.L726Li

NL 0412582 DLC

Little red hen.
The little red hen; the old nursery tale retold by Helen Dean Fish, from the version of Nurse Befabbycash. Pictures by Katharine R. Bernard. Boston, Houghton Mifflin company, 1945.

[20] p. col. illus. 21cm.

I. Fish, Helen Dean.

45-4581

Library of Congress ° PZ10.3.L724Fi

NL 0412583 DLC Or WaS OCl

Little red hen.

PZ8 .O 582 One more story, please! Illus. by Hilda Miloche and Wilma Kane. Racine, Wis., Whitman Pub. Co., ©1947.

Little red hen.

The Stories of Chicken Little, Henny Penny and The little red hen, illustrated by Charles Clement. New York, Pied Piper books [1946]

Little red hen.
The story of the little red hen; with illustrations by Keith Ward. Racine, Wis., Whitman publishing co. [©1935]

[16] p. illus. 33½cm.

I. Ward, Keith, illus. II. Title.

35-20107

Library of Congress PZ10.3.L7248t

NL 0412586 DLC

VOLUME 336

Little red hen.
The story of the little red hen; illustrated by Ruth Easthill. Racine, Wis., Whitman publishing co. [©1937]
[34] p. illus. (part col.) 17cm.
Lining-papers illustrated in colors.

I. Easthill, Ruth, illus. II. Title.
37-21958
Library of Congress PZ10.3.L7248t 3

NL 0412587 DLC

The Little red hen.
The story of the little small red hen
see under Byron, May Clarissa Gillington, d. 1936.

Little red hen story book, The: a treasury of sunshine stories for children. Illustrations by Frederick Richardson.
— Philadelphia. The John C. Winston Co. [1920.] (2), 89 pp. Colored illus. [Winston Easy-to-read story books.] 19 cm., in 8s.
Several copies.

M525 — S.r. — Richardson, Frederick, illus., 1862–

NL 0412589 MB

The Little red library.
Chicago, Daily Worker Pub. Co. [n. d.]
no. 16 cm.
No. 3 is a photocopy (negative) (16 x 22 cm)
Published for the Communist Party of the United States of America (no. for the party under an earlier name: Workers Party of America)

1. Communism—Collections. I. Communist Party of the United States of America.
HX15.L5 52-64913 ‡

NL 0412590 DLC ICU

LITTLE RED RIDINGHOOD.
The adventures of little Red Riding Hood. London, Dean & Munday, [18-].
32°. pp.15. Illustr.
Cover: The history of little Red Riding Hood.
Each page mounted on a 12° leaf.
I. Title. 25276.32.3*

NL 0412591 MH

Little Red Riding-Hood.
... Adventures of Little Red Riding Hood.
Albany: Published by R.H.Pease[ca.1850]
Is94 cover-title,8p. illus. 17½cm.
tl At head of title: Marks' edition.
v.2 Caption title: History of Little Red Riding hood.
In verse.
Wood engravings by R.H.Pease.

NL 0412592 CtY MWA

Little Red Riding-Hood.
Caiḋpín Dearg, agus scéalta eile. [Baile Áṫa Cliaṫ, C. S. Ó Fallaṁain, teo. [1941?]
cover-title, 48 p. illus. 17cm. (Scéalta do leanḃaí)
Free translations from the brothers Grimm and Hans Christian Andersen.
CONTENTS.—Caiḋpín Dearg.—An t-iascaire agus a ḃean.—Cailín na lasán.—An t-éan órḋa.

1. Fairy tales. 2. Irish language—Chrestomathies and readers. I. Grimm, Jakob Ludwig Karl, 1785–1863. II. Grimm, Wilhelm Karl, 1786–1859. III. Andersen, Hans Christian, 1805–1875. Den lille pige med svovlstikkerne. IV. Title. *Title transliterated:* Caidhpín dearg.
43-42062
Library of Congress PZ90.I 7L5

NL 0412593 DLC

PZ74 Little Red Riding Hood.
.P56 FOR OTHER EDITIONS SEE MAIN ENTRY
1943 **Perrault, Charles,** 1628–1703.
Caperucita roja, cuento "ilustración sorpresa," por Carlos Perrault; versión española de José María Huertas, ilustraciones de J. Juez. Buenos Aires, Editorial Molino [1943]

Little Red Riding Hood.
Clóicín Dearg. Pádraic MacDiarmada a rinne an leagan Gaeḋilge. [2. cló] Baile Áṫa Cliaṫ. Oifig an tSoláṫair, 1940.
82 p. 19 cm. (Cluiċí gearra, 46)
Irish adaptation of the play (London, W. & G. Foyle)

I. MacDiarmada, Pádraic, tr. II. Title. (Series: Cluichí gearra, 46) *Title transliterated:* Clóicín Dearg.
PZ90.I 7L5 1940 54-48863

NL 0412595 DLC

Little Red Riding-Hood.

Cinderella.
Les deux plus beaux contes de fées: Cendrillon, Le Petit Chaperon Rouge, avec 5 compositions de David et Daniel Burnand et 7 dessins en silhouettes de Félicien Philipp. Lausanne, Spes [1921]

Little Red Riding Hood.
The entertaining story of Little Red Riding Hood, and Tom Thumb's toy ... York, J. Kendrew, printer [ca. 1820]
31 p. illus. 9½cm.
The illustrations to Little Red Riding-Hood are after cuts by Bewick.

I. Bewick, Thomas, 1753–1828, illus. II. Title. III. Title: Tom Thumb's toy.
26-24415
Library of Congress PZ6.L738Eh 1820

NL 0412597 DLC

Little Red Riding Hood.
The history of little Red Riding Hood; in verse, with the moral of the tale. London, G. B. Pim [18-]
12 p.
Another copy.
With variation in the illustr. on the cover.

NL 0412598 MH

Little Red Riding Hood.
The history of Little Red Riding Hood. Devonport: Printed by S. & J. Keys [ca.1820?]
cover-title, 11, [1] p. illus. (woodcuts) 11cm.

Original printed green wrappers with illustrations on pages [1] and [12]; pages 2 and 11 pasted down to covers.
No. 6 in a Collection of chapbooks published at Devonport.

NL 0412599 CLU

Little Red Riding-Hood.
The history of Little Red Riding-Hood. In verse ... 2nd American ed. Philadelphia, M. Charles, 1821.
12 p. 12 (*i. e.* 11) col. pl. 13cm.
Plates colored by hand.
Cover-title: The renowned history of Little Red Riding-Hood.
Based on an earlier prose translation of Perrault's Le Petit Chaperon Rouge.

I. Perrault, Charles, 1628–1703. II. Title.
21-3047
Library of Congress PZ6.L738Hi

NL 0412600 DLC

Little Red Riding-Hood.
...The history of Little Red Riding Hood. New York, Edward Dunigan & brother [185-?] 1 p.l., 8 p., 1 l. illus. 20cm.
At head of title: Dunigan's edition.
In verse.
Title-page and two illustrations colored by hand.
Publishers' advertisements, p. [10]

53R0230.

NL 0412601 NN MiU

Little Red Riding Hood.
... The history of Little Red Riding Hood. Philadelphia, Fisher & brother [1868?]
8 p. illus. 15cm. (Fisher's toy books)
Illustrated t.-p., in colors.

I. Fisher & brother, Philadelphia, pub. II. Title.
Library of Congress PZ6.L738Hi

NL 0412602 DLC

Little Red Riding Hood.
Little Red Riding Hood
For editions illustrated by Walter Crane, see under Crane, Walter, 1845-1915.

Juv. Little Red Riding hood.
coll. ... Little Red Riding Hood. [n. p., n. e.]
[3] 4-23 p. 16.5 cm.
The Home treasury.

NL 0412604 DLC

398.8 Little Red Riding Hood.
L778 Little Red Riding Hood. New York, John McLoughlin, n.d.
cover-title, 12p. illus. 15cm.

NL 0412605 LNHT

VOLUME 336

Rare Books Dept. Little Red Riding Hood.
Little Red Riding-Hood. Derby, Printed by and for Henry Mozley and Sons [182-?]
ll, [1] p. incl. covers. illus. 11cm. [A collection of nineteenth-century children's books, including chapbooks, published in Great Britain and the United States, 36]

NL 0412606 CU

Little Red Riding Hood.
... Little Red Riding Hood. Baltimore. Bayly & Burns, 1837.
8 l. col. illus. 18 cm.
At head of title: Bayly & Burns' edition.
Imperfect copy: pages wanting

NL 0412607 RPB

Little Red Riding-Hood.
Das kleine Rothkäppchen. Ein Kinder-Märchen mit 16 Bildern. Frei nach dem Französischen, von Gustav Holting. Berlin: Winckelmann und Söhne[, 1840]. 24 p. col'd illus. 17½cm.

Schatzki Coll. of Children's Books.
651860A. 1. Fairy tales, German. I. Holting, Gustav, translator. II. Title.
February 6, 1934

NL 0412608 NN

Little Red Riding Hood.
— Glasgow. Gibb & Co. [185-?] 8 pp. Illus. [Gibb's Good child's picture library. No. 3.] Sm. 8°.
The title is on the cover.

G0748 — Gibb, James, & Company, publishers. — S.r.

NL 0412609 MB NN

PZ111 .C47 no.7 LITTLE RED RIDING-HOOD.
Little Red Riding Hood. [Otley, J. S. publishi[ng] and stationery co., 1850?]
8 p. illus. (part col.)
[Chap-books, 1850?, no.7]

NL 0412610 ICU OCl

Little Red Riding Hood.
Little Red Riding Hood. [New York, McLoughlin [186-?]
[15] p. col.illus. 28cm. (Big picture books for little children.)
Cover title. Caption title: Red Riding Hood.
In verse.

I. T.: Red Riding Hood.

NL 0412611 MiDW

LITTLE RED RIDING—HOOD.
...Little Red Riding Hood. Glasgow: J. Gibb & Co.[, 187-?] 8 p. illus. (part col'd.) 16cm. (Gibb's good child's picture library. [no.3.])

Cover-title.

Nas p.v. 6, no.24——— ——— Second copy.

493026. 1. Fairy tales, French.

NL 0412612 NN

Little Red Riding Hood.
Little Red Riding Hood. New York, McLoughlin [187-?]
[11] p. col.illus. 17cm. (Uncle Dick's series)
Cover title.

NL 0412613 MiDW N ICU

PZ264 .L76 1875 LITTLE RED RIDING HOOD.
Little Red Riding Hood. New York, McLoughlin [1875?]
[10] p. col. illus. (Aunt Friendly's colored picture books)

NL 0412614 ICU

76-01 M1658L Little Red Riding Hood
Little Red Riding Hood. New York, McLoughlin Bro's [188-?]
cover-title, [8] p. col. illus. 19 cm.

Caption title: History of Little Red Riding Hood.
In verse.

I. McLoughlin Brothers, pub. II. Title: History of Little Red Riding Hood.

NL 0412615 RPB

Little Red Riding-Hood.
Little Red Riding Hood. New York, McLoughlin brothers [19-?]

19 x 15 cm.
Paper cover serves as title-page.
Aunt Friendly's colored picture books.

NL 0412616 MH

Little Red Riding-Hood.
Little Red Riding Hood. New York: McLoughlin Bros., 1901. 6 l. illus. (part col'd.) 28 x 21½cm. (Red rose series.)
Cover-title.
Text also on inside of covers.

829850. 1. Juvenile literature—Picture books. 2. Fairy tales, French.
N. Y. P. L. Revised February 28, 1934

NL 0412617 NN

xE L723a Little Red Riding-Hood.
Little Red Riding Hood. Pictured by John R. Neill. Chicago, Reilly and Britton [c1908]
57p. col.illus. 18cm. (The Children's red books, v.7)

NL 0412618 IU

Little Red Riding Hood.
Little Red Riding Hood; illustrated by Susan Jordan. Racine, Wis., Whitman publishing co. [c1934]
[48] p. illus. 19½ x 21½cm.
Pages 2 and 3 of cover illustrated in colors.
On cover: Story and pictures by Susan Jordan.

I. Jordan, Susan, illus.

Library of Congress PZ8.L733L814 34-31808

NL 0412619 DLC

Little Red Riding-Hood.
Little Red Ridinghood; illustrations by C. Carey Cloud and Harold B. Lentz; the illustrated pop-up edition. New York, Blue ribbon press [c1934]
[18] p. incl. front., illus. (part col.) 23½cm.
Colored pop-up illustrations on lining-papers and one in text.

I. Cloud, Claude Carey, 1899- illus. II. Lentz, Harold B., illus.
CA 35-2 Unrev'd
Library of Congress PZ8.L733Cl

NL 0412620 DLC

Little Red Riding Hood.
Little Red Riding Hood, illustrated by Elizabeth Tedder. New York, Grosset & Dunlap, c1938.
[16] p. illus. (part col.) 26½ x 24½cm.
Illustrated lining-papers.

I. Tedder, Elizabeth, illus.
38-18602
Library of Congress PZ8.L733 1938

NL 0412621 DLC

Little Red Riding Hood.
Little Red Riding-Hood; illustrated by Sari [pseud.] Springfield, Mass., McLoughlin bros., inc. [c1941]
[58] p. incl. col. front., illus. (part col.) 17 x 13½cm. (The little color classics)

I. Fleur, Anne Elizabeth, 1901- illus.
41-22145
Library of Congress PZ8.L733F1

NL 0412622 DLC

Little Red Riding Hood.
... Little Red Riding Hood; illustrations by Emma C. McKean. Springfield, Mass., McLoughlin bros., inc., c1943.
[14] p. col. illus. 22½ x 29½cm. (Magic fairy tales)

I. McKean, Emma C., illus.
44-21952
Library of Congress PZ8.L733Mac

NL 0412623 DLC

Little Red Riding Hood.
Little Red Riding Hood, animated by Julian Wehr. New York, Duenewald printing corporation [c1944]
[18] p. col. illus. 21½ x 17cm.

I. Wehr, Julian, illus.
45-1392
Library of Congress PZ8.L733We

NL 0412624 DLC

Little Red Riding Hood.
Little Red Riding Hood, retold by Eileen Ritchie; dolls designed by Amalia Serkin. New York, Chanticleer Press [c1948]
[21] p. col. illus. 27 cm. (A Chanticleer junior book)

I. Ritchie, Eileen. II. Serkin, Amalia.

PZ8.L733Ri 49-2005*‡

NL 0412625 DLC

VOLUME 336

Little Red Riding Hood.
Little Red Riding Hood, told and illus. by Elizabeth Orton Jones. New York, Simon & Schuster [1948]
[42] p. illus. (part col.) 21 cm. (The Little golden library, 42)

I. Jones, Elizabeth Orton, 1910- illus. II. Series.

PZ8.L732Jo 48-1942*

NL 0412626 DLC OCISA WaS Or

Little Red Riding Hood.
Little Red Ridinghood. Illustrated by Primrose. Kenosha, Wis., John Martin's House [1949]
[28] p. col. illus. 22 cm. (A Bonnie book)

I. Robertson, Primrose McPherson, illus.

PZ8.L733Ro 50-23550

NL 0412627 DLC

Little Red Riding Hood.
Little Red Riding-Hood; illustrated by Esther Friend. Chicago, Rand McNally °1950.
[33] p. col. illus. 17 cm. (A Rand McNally book-elf junior, 608)

I. Friend, Esther, illus.

PZ8.L733Fr 51-21210

NL 0412628 DLC

Little Red Riding Hood.
Little Red Ridinghood. Illustrated by Primrose. Kenosha, Wis., John Martin's House [1950, °1949]
[24] p. col. illus. 20 cm. (The Television Bonnie books)
A Bonnie book.

I. Robertson, Primrose McPherson, illus.

PZ8.L733Ro 2 50-23551

NL 0412629 DLC

Little Red Riding Hood.
Little Red Riding Hood; illustrated by Stella [pseud.] Racine, Wis., Whitman Pub. Co., °1953.
unpaged. illus. 17 cm. (Tell-a-tale books, 937)

I. Stella, pseud., illus.

PZ8.L733St 54-22399 ‡

Library of Congress

NL 0412630 DLC

Little Red Riding Hood.
Little Red Riding Hood. Pictures by Jean Tamburine. New York, Wonder Books [1954]
unpaged. illus. 21 cm. (A Two-in-one wonder book, 609)
Bound with Three little pigs. The three little pigs. New York, °1954.

I. Tamburine, Jean, illus.

PZ10.3.T413Pel 54-19835 ‡

NL 0412631 DLC

Music HE553 Harris Collection
Little Red Riding-Hood
Little Red Riding-Hood, a musical play, arranged by Eloise Hemphill. Philadelphia. The Penn publishing company [c1908]
cover-title, 14 p. 18 cm.

With musical themes

I. Hemphill, Eloise, arr. 1. Children's plays.

NL 0412632 RPB

Little Red Riding-Hood.
Little Red Riding Hood; a terror tale of the nursery
see under Weiss, Harry Bischoff, 1883-

Little Red Riding-Hood.
Little Red Riding-Hood, also The little red hen, and The three wishes. Chicago, Rand, McNally & company [°1933]
64 p. col. illus. 17cm.

I. Title: The little red hen. II. Title: The three wishes.

33-38003

Library of Congress PZ8.L733Li 11

NL 0412634 DLC WaS Or

---

sL7292ℓ Little Red Riding Hood.
Little Red Riding Hood, and other stories ... Philadelphia, H. Altemus company [190-?]
96p. col.front., illus., col.plates.

Title vignette.

NL 0412635 IU

PZ121 .B21 v.10
LITTLE RED RIDING HOOD.
Little Red Riding Hood, & The history of Tom Thumb; illustrated by H. Isabel Adams. London, J. M. Dent, 1895.
57, [1] p. front., illus. (The Banbury cross series, v.10)

NL 0412636 ICU

Little Red Riding-Hood.
Little Red Riding-Hood, The fairy, and Blue Beard; with morals. Philadelphia: Printed and sold by John M'Culloch. 1797. 31 p. 100mm.

Photostat of the original owned by d'Alté A. Welch.
Pages [1-2] blank.

55R0521. I. Title: The fairy. II. Title: Bluebeard.

NL 0412637 NN

---

* PZ8 .L736L 18—
Little Red Riding Hood.

Little Red Riding Hood, fairy tales.
[n. p., 18—?]
4 p. 14cm.
Cover title.

NL 0412638 ViU

Little Red Reding Hood.
Le Petit Chaperon Rouge
see under Perrault, Charles, 1628-1703.

Little Red Riding Hood.
Red Riding Hood: the pictures by R. André. New York, McLoughlin bro's., °1888.
[16] p. col. illus. 20½cm. (Little folks series)

I. Title.

44-35885

Library of Congress PZ8.L733An

NL 0412640 DLC

Rare Book Coll. PZ8 .L738Re 1891
Little Red Riding Hood.
Red Riding Hood. New York, McLoughlin Bros. c1891.
[8] ℓ. illus. (pt. col.) 29.6cm.

Wrapper title; pictorial wrappers included in collation.
Pages open from center like French doors.

NL 0412641 ViU

Little Red Riding-Hood.
Rotkäppchen. Bilder von Beatrice Braun Fock. Mainz: J. Scholz [19—?] 7 l. illus. (part col'd.) 22cm.
Illustrated t.-p.

1. Fairy tales, French. I. Title.
N. Y. P. L. May 9, 1941

NL 0412642 NN

Little Red Riding-Hood

PZ37 .B36
Beintker, Käte.
Rotkäppchen, ein Spiel in zwei Teilen nach dem Märchen von Gebr. Grimm, in Versen. [Fürth i. Bay., K. Bernheim, 194-]

Little Red Riding Hood.
The story of Little Red Riding Hood, and other stories. Racine, Wis., Whitman publishing co. [189-?]
[45] p. front., illus. 25 cm.
Prose and poetry.
Frontispiece and p. [45] mounted on covers.
I. Title

NL 0412644 RPB

PZ111 .C44 v.8
LITTLE RED RIDING HOOD.
The story of Little Red Riding Hood. London, T. Goode [1854?]
8 p. illus. (part col.)
[Chap-books, v.8]

NL 0412645 ICU

VOLUME 336

Little Red Riding Hood.
The story of Little Red Riding Hood, and other stories. ‹Racine, Wis., Whitman Publishing Co., c1928›
‹44› p. illus.

NL 0412646 NNC

Little Red Riding Hood.
The story of Little Red Riding Hood, retold from Perrault. Illustrations by Primrose ‹pseud.› Chicago, Wilcox & Follett co., °1946.
‹27› p. col. front., col. illus. 24 x 20ᶜᵐ.

I. Perrault, Charles, 1628-1703. II. Robertson, Primrose McPherson, illus.
PZ8.L733Ro 47-804

NL 0412647 DLC

Little Red Riding Hood.
The story of little Red Riding Hood, rhymed and retold by Kenneth Graham Duffield. ‹N.Y.› Altemus, c1921.
62 p. illus.

NL 0412648 Or

1864 Juv. coll. Little Red Riding-Hood.
The story of Little Red Riding Hood, told in verse by Richard Henry Stoddard. Illustrated by Alfred Fredericks. Engraved in colours by Bobbett and Hooper. New York. James C. Gregory, publishers. [c. 1864]
[7] p. 4 illus. 26.5 cm.

I. Stoddard, Richard Henry, 1825-1903.

NL 0412649 DLC NNC

NAC p.v.601
Little Red Riding-Hood.
The story of Little Red Riding Hood, told in verse by Richard Henry Stoddard. Illustrated by Alfred Fredericks. Engraved in colours by Bobbett and Hooper. New York: J. G. Gregory ‹1864› 8 p. col'd plates. 26 x 21cm.

1. Juvenile literature—Poetry, American. I. Little Red Riding Hood.
N. Y. P. L. March 19, 1942

NL 0412650 NN

Little Red Riding-Hood.
The story of Little Red Riding Hood told in verse by Richard Henry Stoddard. Illus. by Alfred Fredericks. Engraved in colors by Bobbett and Hooper. New York, Hurd, 1865.
8 p. col. front., col. plates. Q.
Illustrated cover has date 1866.
Presentation copy from Clara Blades Hauberg to Iowa university.

NL 0412651 IaU CtY

LITTLE RED RIDING-HOOD.
Words of the pantomime of Little Red Riding-Hood, and the house that Jack built, or Old Mother Hubbard and her wonderful dog. Edinburgh J.Brydone, [187-.]

pp.32.
Cover serves as title-page.

NL 0412652 MH

Little Red Riding Hood, and other fairy tales, pictured by Lillian Causey. Philadelphia, The Penn publishing company, 1918.
88 p. col. front., illus., col. pl. 23½ᶜᵐ.

I. Causey, Lillian, illus.
18-21889
Library of Congress PZ8.L733Cau
‹a45b1›

NL 0412653 DLC

Little Red Riding Hood and the fairies... [18--]
AW 10 E545: E:21: B41 ENGLISH and American drama of the 19th century; American plays, 1831-1900, English plays, 1801-1900. Edited by George Freedley and Allardyce Nicoll. New York, Readex Microprint Corp. [1965?-
cards. 23 x 15 cm.
Micro-opaque

NL 0412653-1 CaBVaU

Little Red Riding-Hood and the wolf, and other stories for children ... Boston, Lothrop publishing company ‹1899›
‹80› p. col. front., illus. 24 x 19ᶜᵐ.

99-1996
Library of Congress PZ8.L733Lo

NL 0412654 DLC

PN6120 .A5L487
... Little Red Riding Hood, in three acts, for fold-a-way miniature theatre. [Chicago? c1932]
folder ([6] p.) 16x10½cm. [Fold-a-way play-folder for fold-a-way miniature theatre. no. 1]
Copyrighted by Will Pente.
At head of title: Play.

I. Pente, William, 1873-

NL 0412655 DLC

... Little Red Riding Hood; or, Harlequin
see under [Glover, Edmund] 1813?-1860.

Little Red Riding Hood. The grand annual comic pantomime, 1893
see under Locke, Fred.

Little Red river missionary Baptist association
see Baptist. Arkansas. Little Red river missionary Baptist association.

L11 .L5
The little red schoolhouse. v. 1-
Nov. 1927-
‹Akron› New York State Rural School Improvement Society.
v. in illus., ports. 31 cm.
Frequency varies.

1. Education—Period. 2. Rural schools—New York (State) I. New York State Rural School Improvement Society.

L11.L5 379.173

NL 0412658 DLC

Little red shoes, Author of.
Fairy tales told again
see under title

The little red wagon
see under [Roszelle, Mary Helene]

The little republic. Original articles, by various hands
see under Smith, Mrs. Eliza T P , ed.

The Little review; literature, drama, music, art. v. 1-
Mar. 1914-
Chicago, Margaret C. Anderson, 1914-
v. mounted illus., mounted plates. 25½ cm. monthly.
Editor: Mar. 1914- Margaret C. Anderson.

I. Anderson, Margaret C., ed.

AP2.L647 17-30435

CtNIC KPT DAU MiU OrU OrPP CaBVaU
NL 0412662 DLC ICN IC NcU MNS KU CoU NcU AzTeS AAP

---

*AP2 .L647
The Little review. v. 1-12. Mar. 1914-May 1929. New York [etc.] Margaret C. Anderson, 1914-1929.
12 v. in 11. illus. 24-26 cm.
Volume numbering irregular.
Editor: 1914-1929, Margaret C. Anderson.
Some volumes are photographic reprints made in 1967 by Kraus Reprint Corporation, New York.

1. Periodicals, English. I. Anderson, Margaret C., ed.

PPT CLSU
NL 0412663 MB MtU OkS GU ICN FU N MiU IaAS NcRS

VOLUME 336

AP 2 L647 The Little review; literature, drama, music, art. v.1-12, no. 2; Mar. 1914-May 19, 1929.
New York, Kraus Reprint, 1967.
12 v. in 9. illus. 25 1/2cm.
Indexes:
General index.
Vols. 1-12, Mar. 1914-May 19, 1929.
1 v.
Photoreproduction.
"As originally published by Margaret C. Anderson."

NL 0412664 CU-I

FM 792 L778 The Little Review.
The International Theatre Exposition, New York, 1926. [New York, 1926]
Collation of the original: 122 p. illus.
Microfilm copy, made in 1946 by Photographic Laboratory, Brown University. Positive.
At head of title: Special theatre number.
On same film: [Catalog, Machine-Age exposition New York [1927]
1. Theatre. Exhibitions. I. Title.

NL 0412665 N

The Little review.
The Little review anthology, edited by Margaret Anderson. New York, Hermitage House, 1953.
383 p. 22 cm.

1. American literature—20th cent. 2. Literature—Hist. & crit. I. Anderson, Margaret C., ed. II. Title.
PS536.L57 810.82 53—6005 ‡

WaT CaBViP OrPS WaE CaOTP FTaSU CtY OC1W OU PLFM NcRS PU MB NcD CoU OrP Or OrU Wa WaS
NL 0412666 DLC CaBVaU OrCS OCU OC1 TxU NN ViU OOxM

The Little Review.
Machine-age Exposition [architecture, engineering, industry. New York, May 16-28, 1927] Catalog
see under Machine Age Exposition, New York, 1927.

PS625 .L74 Atkinson Coll. The Little review.
Plays, synopses, etc. from the Little review. Atkinson collection.
2 nos. 26cm.
For individual entries see the Atkinson card catalog.

NL 0412668 ICU

Little reviews anthology. [1943]–
London, Eyre and Spottiswoode [etc., 1943–
v. 19 cm.
Editor: 1943– D. V. Baker.

1. English literature—20th cent. Baker, Denys Val, ed.
PR1149.L53 820.82 A 44—1320
Harvard Univ. Library for Library of Congress [58r46l½]†

MtU DLC OrU UU TU CaOTP ICN PPT KMK FTaSU MH OrCS CaBVaU IU WaTC
NL 0412669 MH IdPI CU TxU MiU MoSW IaAS KMK WU NBuU

A little revolution
see under [Browne, John Hutton Balfour] 1845-1921.

---

76 T5932 a Harris Small Books The little reward [and] The little present. Charlestown [Mass.] G.W. Hobbs [n.d.] [32] p. col. illus., incl. front. 9 cm.
Poems.
Cover-title: The tiny picture book.
1. Children's poetry. The little present. (title anal) The tiny picture book (title anal).

NL 0412671 RPB

Is94 tl v.2(6 Little rhymes. Greenfield [Mass.] A. Phelps, [18--]
1p.l.,5-18p. illus. 10½cm.
Title and front cover vignettes, illustration on back cover.
Numbered 2 at head of cover-title.

NL 0412672 CtY NNC

... Little rhymes for little folk. Springfield, Mass., McLoughlin brothers inc. [°1928]
60 p. illus. (1 col. mounted) 15cm. (The little big books)

Library of Congress PZ7.L728Li ca 30-283 Unrev'd

NL 0412673 DLC

PZ111 .J93 Little rhymes for little folks ... New York, M. Day, 1834.
23 p. front., illus. [The juvenile library, no.11]

NL 0412674 ICU

LITTLE rhymes for little folks, or A present for Fanny's library. By a lady, author of "Cato", "Infants' Friend", &c. London, J. Harris and Son, 1823.
17.5 cm. ff.17+. Colored illustr.
Printed on one side of the leaf only.
"Harris's cabinet of amusement and instruction.

NL 0412675 MH

LITTLE rhymes for little folks, or Poetry for Fanny's library. New ed. London, J. Harris [185-?].
18 cm. ff.2-17. Hand colored illustr.
Printed on one side of the leaf only, with a verse and illustration on each leaf.
Imperfect: lacks title-page. Title taken from cover.

NL 0412676 MH

Little rhymes for little readers.
— London. Dean. N. d. 11 pp. Illus. [Nurse Rockbaby's Pretty Story Books.] 16°.

Aug. 13, 1900
*D6292 — Chap-books. — S.r.

NL 0412677 MB

Box 1830-1839

Little rhymes for little readers. Wendell, Mass., J. Metcalf, 1832.
18 p. illus. 10cm.
Title vignette.
Copy imperfect: p. 15-18 mutilated.

NL 0412678 NNC

PZ 212 .L65 Little rhymes for little readers. Northampton, J. Metcalf, 1837.
18 p. illus. 11 cm.

NL 0412679 ICU

PZ262 .L827 185- Little rhymes, for merry times, with the little folks of all climes. Dexter, Me., Leviathan [185-?]
[8] p. illus. 12cm.

NL 0412680 ICU

PZ 6 .L78 Little Richard: a story for little boys. Northampton, E. Turner [18--]
1 p. l., [5]-18 p. illus. 12cm.
Illustrated t.-p.
Signed: Schoolmaster.

I. Schoolmaster.

NL 0412681 MiU

---

*XLJ .817 .A10L Little Richard; a story for little boys. New York: Published by Samuel Wood & Sons, no.261 Pearl Street. [ca.1817?]
20 p. illus. 12.5cm.
Title vignette.
Printed orange wrappers.

NL 0412682 MB

LITTLE Richard; a story for little boys. New York, Published by Samuel Wood & sons, 261 Pearl street [182-?] 20 p. illus. 14cm.
In verse.

NL 0412683 NN CSmH

Little Richard; a story for little boys. New York, S. Wood [1853?]
20 p. illus.
1853 penciled on title-page.

NL 0412684 NNC

VOLUME 336

Juv. coll. The little riddle book. Dexter, Me. Leviathan printing establishment [n. d.]
[14] p. 11.5 cm.

NL 0412685 DLC

The little riddle-book, compiled for the use of good boys and girls, in England, Scotland, Ireland, & America. By John-the-giant-killer. Boston, S. Hall, 1798.
29 p. front., illus. 10 cm.
Book somewhat mutilaged.
I. John-the-giant-killer.

NL 0412686 RPB

The Little riddle book; illustrated by Eva Geiringer. Mount Vernon, N. Y., Peter Pauper Press [1954]
unpaged. illus. 19 cm.

1. Riddles. I. Geiringer, Eva, illus. II. Peter Pauper Press, Mount Vernon, N. Y.
PN6371.L55 793.73 54-31978 ‡

NL 0412687 DLC

The Little riddler. Worcester [Mass.] J. Grout, Jr. [18—]
24 p. illus. 15 cm.

1. Riddles.
PN6371.L56 66-58789

NL 0412688 DLC RPB MWA CtY

Little River Baptist Association
see Baptists. Arkansas. Little River Baptist Association. [Supplement]

627.5 L72f Little River Drainage District.
Final report of Board of Engineers of the Little River Drainage District of Missouri. [Exhibit III: Plan for drainage. Cape Girardeau? 1909]
111p. 23cm.
"Exhibit VIII. Railroad crossings over the diversion channel and floodway, and the estimated cost of same": p.95-110.
1. Drainage—Missouri.

NL 0412690 IU

Little Robert's first day at the Sunday School. Revised by the Committee of publication of the American S. S. Union. Philadelphia, New-York, Boston, American Sunday-School Union, [n.d.]
72 p. incl. front. illus. 14.3 cm.

NL 0412691 MiU-C

Little Robin Red Breast.

Editions of this work printed in America before 1801 are available in this library in the Readex Microprint edition of Early American Imprints published by the American Antiquarian Society.
This collection is arranged according to the numbers in Charles Evans' American Bibliography.

NL 0412692 DLC

In Ed37 848e The little Robinson and other tales. London and Edinburgh, W. and R. Chambers [1853?]
4p.l., 166p. front. 15cm. (Chambers's library for young people)
Issued with Edgeworth, Maria. Orlandino. Edinburgh, 1853.
Contents. - The little Robinson (from the French). - Michael the miner. - Ellen and her bird.

NL 0412693 CtY

[Little Rock, Arkansas]
Lincoln centenary banquet, Hotel Marion, Friday, February 12, 1909. [Little Rock, Arkansas, Democrat printing and lithographing company, 1909]
[8] p. illus. (incl. facsim.) 22 cm.

NL 0412694 MiU

Little Rock, Ark.
Mayor's message and report of city officers... Little Rock, Ark.

JS13 .L745

NL 0412695 DLC DNLM MB CtY NN

Little Rock, Ark.
Report.

TH9505 .L5O1

NL 0412696 DLC

Little Rock, Ark. Arkansas Baptist college
see
Arkansas Baptist college, Little Rock, Ark

Little Rock, Ark. Arkansas deaf mute institute
see Arkansas. School for the deaf, Little Rock.

Little Rock, Ark. Arkansas female college
see Arkansas female college, Little Rock.

Little Rock, Ark. Arkansas gazette
see
Arkansas gazette, *Little Rock.*

Little Rock, Ark. Bank of the State of Arkansas
see Bank of the State of Arkansas.

Little Rock, Ark. Bar
Proceedings at Little Rock, Arkansas, on "John Marshall day," with the orations delivered on that occasion by Judges John McClure and U. M. Rose. [Little Rock? 1901]
1 p. l., 42 p. 2 port. 23½cm. (*In* Dillon, J. F., comp. Centenary and memorial addresses and proceedings ... on Marshall day, 1901. [New York, 190-] 27½cm. v. 5)
The portraits are mounted and inserted.
1. Marshall, John, 1755-1835. 2. John Marshall day. I. McClure, John, 1834-1915. II. Rose, Uriah M., 1834-1913. III. Title.
CA 15-1081 Unrev'd
Library of Congress E302.6.M4D57 vol. 5

NL 0412702 DLC

Little Rock, Ark. Bar
see also Little Rock bar association.

Little Rock, Ark. Board of commerce.
Correspondence between Board of commerc and Allied shop crafts in the state of Arkansas, bearing on the recent strike of those crafts. (Little Rock, 1919)
15 p. 23 cm.

NL 0412704 DL

Little Rock. *Board of Health.* Cleanliness, health, happiness. Report on domestic sanitation. The most important element in this connection. Adopted July 31, 1879. 11 pp., 1 diag. 8°. *Little Rock, Blocher & Mitchell,* 1879.

NL 0412705 DNLM

Little Rock, Ark. Board of trade.
Annual cotton statement.
[Little Rock,
v. 28cm.
Report year ends August 31.
1. Cotton trade—Stat. 2. Cotton trade—Little Rock, Ark.
CA 17-81 Unrev'd
Library of Congress HD9078.L67L5

NL 0412706 DLC

Little Rock, Ark. Board of trade.
Annual report. 1st-
1886-
Little Rock, 1886-1913.
v. illus., plates. 22½-24cm.
Title varies: 1886 ... Annual statement of the trade and commerce of Little Rock.
18 -1912/13 ... Annual report of the Little Rock Board of trade.
7-33240 Revised
Library of Congress HF296.L77

NL 0412707 DLC ICJ MB

Little Rock, Ark. Board of trade.

Purdue, Albert Homer, 1861-
Compendium of the mineral resources of Arkansas ... by A. H. Purdue ... [Little Rock, Ark., Democrat print. & litho. company, 1912]

VOLUME 336

Little Rock. Board of trade.
Hand book to the city of Little Rock, state of Arkansas. Popularly styled "the City of the roses." Eighteen hundred and ninety-seven. Being a faithful account of Arkansas' capital city from the standpoint of a manufacturing center ... [Little Rock, Press of Gazette publishing company, 1897]
cover-title, 63 p. 28½ x 11½cm.
"From the Arkansas gazette, January 15, 1897. Reported and copyrighted by Col. M. L. De Malher, staff member."
Published under the auspices of the Little Rock board of trade.
1. Little Rock.
Library of Congress F419.L7L8 6-1145

NL 0412709 DLC

Little Rock, Ark. Board of trade.
...List of members, November 1, 1901
[Little Rock, Ark., 1901]
F419 .L7L82

NL 0412710 DLC

GGF-Z L779 1944 Little Rock, Ark. Chamber of commerce.
Map of Little Rock and N. Little Rock, Arkansas. Issued by Little Rock Chamber of commerce. [Little Rock, Ark., 1944?]
map. 33½x53cm.
No scale.
Index to streets and data about Little Rock in margins.
Inset: Ward map of Little Rock and North Little Rock.
1. Little Rock, Ark.--1944? 2. North Little Rock, Ark.--1944?

NL 0412711 IU

4K U.S. 311 Little Rock, Ark. Charters.
Charter of the city of Little Rock; being that portion of an Act of the General Assembly of the State of Arkansas entitled "An act for the incorpration, organization and government of municipal corporations", approved March 9, 1875, that relates to cities of the first class, and amendments thereto. [Little Rock,]
343 p.

NL 0412712 DLC-P4

Little Rock, Ark. City Health Department.
Annual report.
[Little Rock, 22cm.
Report for 1924 includes summary from 1917 to 1924.
A report is also included annually in the Little Rock year book, -1928.
1. Hygiene, Public—U. S.—Ark.—Little Rock.
N. Y. P. L. August 24, 1934

NL 0412713 NN

W 2 AA8. 2 L7C5m LITTLE ROCK, Ark. City Health Dept.
Monthly bulletin.
v. [1]- Feb. 1920-
Little Rock.
v.

NL 0412714 DNLM

Little Rock, Ark. City Planning Commission
see Little Rock, Ark. Planning Commission,

LITTLE ROCK, Ark. Clerk.
Statement of receipts and disbursements.
[Little Rock, 24½cm.
Annual.
1. Finance—U.S.—Ark.—Little Rock.

NL 0412716 NN IU

Little Rock, Ark. College of physicians and surgeons
see
College of physicians and surgeons of the city of Little Rock.

Little Rock, Ark.- Congregation B'nai Israel.
Constitution and by-laws. Revised 1897... n.p. [Little Rock,Ark.,] 1935. 10 p., 1 L. 12.

NL 0412718 OCH

Little Rock, Arkansas.-Congregation B'nai Israel.
1867-1920. Installation of Rabbi J. G. Heller, Friday, January 30, Saturday. January 31, Sunday, Februaryl, Nineteen hundred twenty. [Program.] [Little Rock, 1920.]
2 L.

NL 0412719 OCH

Little Rock, Arkansas.-Congregation B'nai Israel.
Seventieth anniversary services and dedication of the new altar, Congregation B'nai Israel, Little Rock, Arkansas. Friday, March fifth...Saturday, March sixth... nineteen hundred thirty-seven. [Little Rock, Arkansas, 1937.]
6 L., 1 pl., 1 port. illus. 8.

NL 0412720 OCH

Little Rock, Ark. Convention of colored citiznes
see Arkansas. Convention of colored citizens.

375.47 L73c Little Rock, Ark.--Dept. of education.
Course of study monograph (tentative form) First and second year Latin for junior high schools, grades 8 and 9. Little Rock, Arkansas, 1930-1931. Little Rock, 1930.
cover-title, 195 numb.l. 21½x36cm.
Mimeographed.
Contains bibliographies.

NL 0412722 IU

375.6 L73c Little Rock, Ark.--Dept. of education.
Course of study monograph (tentative form) Practical arts courses for boys, junior high schools, grades 7, 8, 9. Little Rock, Arkansas 1930-1931. Little Rock, 1930.
cover-title, 162 numb.l. 21½x36cm.
Mimeographed.
Contains bibliographies.

NL 0412723 IU

Little Rock (Ark.). Dept. of Education.
Suggestive lessons in reading and writing. Designed for use during moonlight schools in Arkansas... Little Rock [191-?].
4 l. 8°.
1. Reading.—Teaching. 2. Handwriting.—Study, etc., U. S.: Ark.: Little Rock.
N. Y. P. L. March 5, 1919.

NL 0412724 NN

Little Rock, Ark. Eclectic society
see
Eclectic society of Little Rock, Ark.

Little Rock, Ark. Exposition of the resources of Arkansas, 1887.
Exposition of the resources of Arkansas at Little Rock. Opens October 25, and closes November 17, 1887. Little Rock, Press printing company, 1887.
12 p. 22cm.
Four leaves of advertising matter inserted between p. 8 and 9.
1. Arkansas.
Library of Congress F411.L7 45-46485

NL 0412726 DLC

Little Rock, Ark. Federal Home Loan Bank
see Federal home loan bank of Little Rock.

LITTLE ROCK, ARK. Finance dept.
Financial report.
Little Rock. 28cm.
Annual.
For earlier file, see: Little Rock, Ark. Clerk. Statement of receipts and disbursements.
1. Finance--U. S.--Ark.--Little Rock.

NL 0412728 NN

Little Rock, Ark. Fort Worth loan and life association
see
Fort Worth loan and life association of Little Rock, Arkansas, and Fort Worth, Texas

---

Little Rock, Ark. Health Dept.
see Little Rock, Ark. City Health Dept.

VOLUME 336

Little Rock, Ark. --High school.
Fragments, by members of 12A Literature, Little Rock high school ... [Little Rock, Ark., Senior high school print shop] 1929.
51 p. 21 cm.
Illustrated t.-p.
1. School verse--Little Rock, Ark.--High school. I. Title.

NL 0412731 RPB

331.83 L78r Little Rock, Ark. Housing Authority.
A redevelopment plan for the Dunbar High School area of Little Rock, Arkansas. [Little Rock, Ark., 1951?]
16p. illus. 23x29cm.
Cover title.
1. Housing—Little Rock, Ark.

NL 0412732 IU

Little Rock, Ark. Institute for the education of the blind
see
Arkansas. School for the blind, Little Rock.

Little Rock, Ark. Mayor.
Mayor's message and report of city officers ...
see under Little Rock, Ark.

Little Rock, Ark. Mayor.
Mayor's message to the City Council.
Little Rock 4°.
Title varies slightly.
1. Municipal government—U. S. —Ark.—Little Rock.
N. Y. P. L. August 11, 1927

NL 0412736 NN

Little Rock, Ark. Mayor.
A workable program for the city of Little Rock, Arkansas. [Little Rock, Ark.] 1955.
1v. (various pagings) plans tables (part fold.) 28cm.
1. Cities and towns - Planning - Little Rock, Arkansas. I. Title.

NL 0412737 NcU

Little Rock, Ark. Museum of fine arts.
Catalog. Little Rock, Museum of fine arts [194-?] 87 p. plates. 18cm.

NL 0412738 NN

Little Rock, *Ark. Ordinances, etc.*
Digest of the city of Little Rock, Arkansas. Embracing the provisions of the statutes of Arkansas applicable to said city up to and inclusive of the acts of the General assembly of 1903, and the ordinances and resolutions of a general character passed by the City council of said city up to and including the session of September 12, 1904. Comp. and digested by authority of the City council, under resolution of September 22, 1902, by Roy D. Campbell, and Jas. H. Stevenson ... Little Rock, Ark., Thompson lithograph and printing co., 1904.
3 p. l., [5]-408, xci p. 23cm
I. Arkansas. Laws, statutes, etc. II. Campbell, Roy Davies, 1872- III. Stevenson, James Herbert, 1876-
11-10486
Library of Congress JS998.A3 1904

NL 0412739 DLC

Little Rock, *Ark. Ordinances, etc.*
Digest of the city of Little Rock, Arkansas. Embracing the ordinances and resolutions of a general character passed by the City council of said city up to and including the session of September 21, 1914. Comp. and digested by authority of the City council by Harry C. Hale ... Little Rock, Ark., Democrat printing & lithographing co., 1915.
3 p. l., 459, cxxiii p. 23½cm.
I. Hale, Harry C., of Little Rock, Ark., comp. II. Title.
17-17028
Library of Congress JS998.A3 1914

NL 0412740 DLC MH-L

Little Rock, *Ark. Ordinances, etc.*
A digest of the laws and ordinances of the city of Little Rock, with the constitution of state of Arkansas, general incorporation laws, and all acts of the General assembly relating to the city. Digested, comp. and pub. by authority of the Common council, by Geo. E. Dodge and P. C. Dooley. Little Rock, Ark., Republican steam press print, 1871.
383 p. 22½cm.
I. Arkansas. Laws, statutes, etc. II. Dodge, George E. III. Dooley, P. C.
11-13790
Library of Congress JS998.A3 1871

NL 0412741 DLC PU MH-L

Little Rock, *Ark. Ordinances, etc.*
Digest of the laws and ordinances of the city of Little Rock, with the constitution of the state of Arkansas; general incorporation laws; and all acts of the General assembly relating to the city; in force March 10, 1882. Digested, comp. and pub. by authority of the Common council, by John H. Cherry. Little Rock, Union printing and publishing company, 1882.
88 p., 1 l., 95 p., 1 l., 379 p. 23½cm.
I. Arkansas. Laws, statutes, etc. II. Cherry, John H., ed.
11-13196
Library of Congress JS998.A3 1882

NL 0412742 DLC

Little Rock, Ark. Ordinances.
Digest of the ordinances of the city of Little Rock, Arkansas, containing the ordinances and resolutions of a general and permanent nature passed by the City Council to and including April 25, 1932. Compiled and published by direction of Little Rock City Council by Linwood L. Brickhouse and John T. Castle. [Little Rock, Ark.: Central Prtg. Co., 1932] 510, lxxxvii p. 23½cm.
853358A. I. No subject. I. Brickhouse, Linwood Leonard, 1897- II. Castle, John Thomas, 1872-
N. Y. P. L. April 15, 1937

NL 0412743 NN

LB1629 .L5 Little Rock, Ark. Paul Laurence Dunbar high school.
...Course of study monograph (tentative form) ... Special edition. Little Rock, Ark., 1932-
2 v. 34x21cm.
Mimeographed.
Contents. - [no.1] Boys practical arts. - [no.2] Home economics.
1. Education - Curricula - High schools. 2. Junior high schools. 3. Education - Arkansas - Curricula.

NL 0412744 OCU

Little Rock, Ark. Philander Smith college
see
Philander Smith college, Little Rock, Ark.

Little Rock, Ark. Planning Commission.
Land subdivision regulations, adopted July 20, 1950.
11p.

NL 0412746 PPCPC

711.40973 L727l Little Rock, Ark. Planning Commission.
Report.
Little Rock, Ark.
v. illus., diagrs. 28cm. annual.
Vols. for -1960 include also report of the Traffic Engineering Dept.

NL 0412747 IU

Little Rock, Ark. Public library.
Annual report.
[Little Rock,
v. 23½cm.
Report year ends December 31.
Library of Congress Z733.L752 CA 15-975 Unrev'd

NL 0412748 DLC OCl Or

Little Rock, Ark. Pulaski county child welfare exhibit, 1916.
Handbook of the Pulaski county child welfare exhibit, from April 24 to April 29, 1916 (inclusive) Old State Capital... Little Rock, Ark. Little Rock Ark. H. G. Pugh printing co. 1916.
18 p. illus. 23 cm.

NL 0412749 DL

Little Rock, *Ark. School board.*
Annual report. 1871/72-
Little Rock, Ark. [1872-
v. in front., illus., plates. 19-22cm.
Reports for 1872/73-1874/75 pub. in 1 v.
No reports pub. for the years 1889/90, 1892/93, 1895/96, 1897/98-1901/02.
E 12-895
Library, U. S. Bur. of Education L123.L7A2

NL 0412750 DHEW OFH OO Nh CtY PHi MoS

VOLUME 336

Little Rock, Ark. School board.
Directory of the Little Rock public schools. Little Rock, Ark.
v. 21 cm.

NL 0412751 DHEW

Little Rock, Ark. School for the blind
see
Arkansas. School for the blind, Little Rock.

Little Rock, Ark. State bank
see Bank of the state of Arkansas.

Little Rock, Ark. State Hospital
see
Arkansas. State Hospital, *Little Rock and Benton.*

Little Rock, Ark. State Hospital for Nervous Diseases
see
Arkansas. State Hospital, *Little Rock and Benton.*

Little Rock, Ark. State Map Library
see Arkansas. *Office of the State Geologist. State Map Library.*

Little Rock, Ark. Superintendent of Schools
see Little Rock, Ark. School Board.

388.312 Little Rock, Ark. Traffic Engineering Dept.
L72r Report.
Little Rock.
v. illus. 28cm.
Vols. for are combined reports of the Traffic and Planning Depts.

NL 0412758 IU

Little Rock, *Ark. Vice commission.*
Report of the Little Rock Vice commission, May 20, 1913, and the order of Mayor Chas. E. Taylor to close all resorts in Little Rock by August 25, 1913. [Little Rock, Ark., 1913]
29 p. 22½cm.
John E. Martineau, chairman. Report prepared by Rev. Hay Watson Smith, secretary.
Includes "Report of the Little Rock colored vice commission," Joseph A. Booker, chairman.
1. Prostitution—Little Rock, Ark. I. Martineau, John E. II. Smith, Hay Watson. III. Booker, Joseph A. IV. Title.
13-26040
Library of Congress HQ146.L67A5 1913

NL 0412759 DLC NN

Little Rock, Ark. Water department.
...Annual report of the...Municipal water works...1st- 1936-
[Little Rock, 1937- 23½cm
1. Water supply—Little Rock, Ark.
N. Y. P. L. January 28, 1942

NL 0412760 NN

The history of Catholicity in Arkansas from the earliest missionaries down to the present time. Published under the auscpices of the Historical Commission of the Diocese of Little Rock. Little Rock, Ark., The Guardian, 1925.

1. Arkansas - Church history. 2. Little Rock (diocese) - History.

NL 0412761 IMunS NcD

Little Rock (U.S. cruiser)
The "Arkansas traveler" U.S.S. Little Rock, 1945-1947
see under title

Little Rock and Fort Smith Railroad Company.
Homes in Arkansas. 1,000,000 acres of choice river bottom and upland for sale, on credit or for cash at low rates, by the Little Rock and Fort Smith R. R. Co... Little Rock, Ark.: Gazette Pub. Co., 1871. 32 p. fold. maps. 8°.
Cover-title.
52708A. 1. Arkansas.
N. Y. P. L. April 7, 1923.

NL 0412763 NN PHi OCHP

Little Rock and Fort Smith railroad company.
Report of J. W. Washburn [sic] and W. P. Denckla, upon the natural resources of the Arkansas valley, from Little Rock, Ark., to Fort Gibson, C. N., made to the Little Rock and Fort Smith railroad company. New York, D. Taylor, printer, 1867.
1 p. l., iii, [4]-71 p. front. (fold. map) 23cm.
1. Arkansas—Descr. & trav. 2. Mines and mineral resources—Arkansas. I. Washbourn, J. W. II. Denckla, William P.
Rc-1255 Revised
Library of Congress F411.L77

NL 0412764 DLC

Little Rock and Fort Smith railroad company.
... Report of the president & chief engineer of the Little Rock and Ft. Smith R.R. co., 1860. [Little Rock] Johnson & Yerkes [1869]
19 [1] (Senate doc.)

NL 0412765 GEU ArU

HE2791
.L786
Little Rock and Fort Smith Railroad Company.
Report of the president made to the Governor, includin the report of the special agent.
Little Rock, Arkansas Gazette Print.
v. 22 cm. annual.
HE2791.L786 57-5360

NL 0412766 DLC TxU MoSM CSt Ar-Hi

Little Rock and Fort Smith railway company.
Thyfault, I M.
Fondation d'une colonie française, sous la direction des Pères du St. Esprit, sol, climat, ressources de cette magnifique contrée et avantages immenses offerts aux immigrants par la compagnie Little Rock & Fort Smith R. R. Lettres du Dr. I. M. Thyfault sur l'ouest de la vallée de l'Arkansas ... Kankakee, Ill., Impr. du Courrier de l'Illinois, 1878.

Little Rock and Fort Smith railway company.
Heimstætten in Arkansas. Man kaufe eisenbahn-land für welches die Vereinigten Staaten besitztitel ausstellen. 1,000,000 acker des auserlesendsten fluss-, thal- und hochlandes sind zu verkaufen, auf kredit oder für baar, zu den niedrigsten preisen durch die Little Rock & Fort Smith eisenbahn-gesellschaft... St. Louis, Woodward, Tiernan & Hale, printers [1876?]
cover-title, 23 p. 2 maps (1 fold.) 23½cm.
Library of Congress, no. F411.L76.

——— St. Louis, Woodward, Tiernan & Hale, printers [1876?]
cover-title, 23 p. 2 maps (1 fold.) 22cm.
Differs from the preceding in the color and ornamentation of the cover.
Subject entries: Arkansas—Descr. & trav.
4-1943-4
Library of Congress, no. F411.L761.

NL 0412769 DLC NjP

Little Rock and Fort Smith railway company.
Homes in Arkansas! Buy railway lands where the title comes from the United States. 1,000,000 acres of choice river bottom and upland for sale on credit or for cash at low rates, by the Little Rock & Fort Smith railway co. ... St. Louis, Woodward, Tiernan & Hale, printers [1876]
cover-title, 24 p. 2 maps (1 fold.) 23½cm.
1. Arkansas—Descr. & trav.
4—1150
Library of Congress F411.L75

NL 0412770 DLC InU NN

Little Rock and Fort Smith railway company.
St. Louis, Iron Mountain & Southern railway company.
Manufacturing opportunities in Arkansas ... 3d ed. By S. L. Kay. Issued by Land department of the St. Louis, Iron Mountain & Southern and Little Rock & Fort Smith railways ... Little Rock, Ark. [190-?]

Litle Rock and Fort Smith railway company.
Kay, S L.
Mineral wealth of Arkansas. World's fair industrial series—no. 5, by S. L. Kay. Issued by Land department of the St. Louis, Iron Mountain & Southern and Little Rock & Fort Smith railways... Little Rock, Ark. [1904?]

HE2791
.L78632
Little Rock and Fort Smith Railway Company.
Report to the stockholders.
Boston, A. Mudge & Son, printers.
v. 23 cm. annual.
HE2791.L78632 57-5358

NL 0412773 DLC

VOLUME 336

Little Rock and Pulaski County Medical Association. Constitution, by-laws, and code of medical ethics. 26 pp. 8°. Little Rock, J. D. Butler, 1866.

NL 0412774 DNLM

Little Rock and Pulaski county medical association. Transactions. Defense against charges made public by act of the committee on publications of the state medical association; and in justification of the action in the matter of controversy between drs. Lawrence, Hobson, and Brooks, of Hot Springs Little Rock, Office of the Arkansas gazette, 1873. 70, iv p. 8°. George W. Lawrence, Orlando A. Hobson, and Almon Brooks.

NL 0412775 DLC DNLM Nh

Little Rock, Arkansas. [1920] see under [Brooks, Robert H]

Little Rock Baptists Association see Baptists. Arkansas. Little Rock Association.

Little Rock bar association. ... Constitution, membership, code of ethics, officers and committees, 1911. Organized May fifth, 1910. [Little Rock? 1910] cover-title, 21 [1] p. 23 cm. At head of title: Little Rock bar association.

NL 0412778 CtY

[Little Rock bar association] In memoriam U. M. Rose. [Little Rock? Ark., 1913?] cover-title, 1 l., 30 p. port. 25½cm.
"Address of Wilson E. Hemingway on presenting to the Supreme court of Arkansas the resolutions of the Little Rock bar association."

1. Rose, Uriah M., 1834-1913. I. Hemingway, Wilson Edwin, 1854-1922. II. Title.
Library of Congress CT275.R783L5 24—20905

NL 0412779 DLC ViU-L

Little Rock city directory see Polk's Little Rock and North Little Rock directory.

Little Rock conference of the Methodist Episcopal church see Methodist Episcopal church. Conferences. Little Rock.

Little Rock Cotton Exchange, Little Rock, Ark. Annual cotton statistics. 19
[Little Rock, Ark., 19 4°. nos. illus.
Cover-title.

1. Cotton—Exchanges—U. S.—Ark. —Little Rock.
N. Y. P. L. April 2, 1926

NL 0412782 NN

Little Rock daily gazette see Arkansas gazette.

Case 4A 3175 1858
LITTLE ROCK MINING CO. A statement of the operations of the Little Rock Mining Co. in the La Salle Coal Basin. Cheap fuel for Chicago and the North-west. Chicago, C. Scott, 1858. 14p. 22cm.
In: Reports of Railroad companies, 1858, v.1.

NL 0412784 ICN ICHi

Little Rock, Mississippi River and Texas railroad see Mississippi Onachita and Red River railroad company.

Little Rock Parkways Association. Report on a park system for Little Rock Arkansas see under Nolen, John, 1869-

HE2791 L6
Little Rock, Pine Bluff and New Orleans railroad company. Annual report.
Little Rock, Ark., Price and Barton, 1870- vols. 21cm.
1. Railroads.-Arkansas.

NL 0412787 NBuG MdHi CSt

Little Rock sketch book see Arkansas sketch book.

The Little rooster and ugly duckling. New York, McLoughlin Bros., c1900. 8 l. illus. f°.

NL 0412789 NN

LITTLE rose bud. New York, Phillips & Hunt, etc., etc., 1879.
Illustr.
A collection of prose and poetry for children.

NL 0412790 MH

Little Rose; or, Stories on the Lord's prayer and other scriptures ... see under Kidder, Daniel Parish, 1815-1891, ed.

The "Little rosebud" songster see under De Witt, Robert M., 1827-1877.

M 1628 L5 I 2
Little Rosebud's I'm little but you bet I can dance songster. New York, New York Popular Publishing Co. [1879] 64 p. 17cm.
1. Songs, American.

NL 0412793 CoU DLC

Little Rossie ... Written for the Mass. Sabbath school society see under [Perry, Thomas W]

Little Rosy's pets see under Miller, Thomas, 1807-1874.

Little Rosy's travels [by Thomas Miller and others] New York, Sheldon, 1869. 6 v. front. illus., plates. 12 cm.

NL 0412796 ICN

Little Rosy's travels. A sad adventure. Illustrated. N.Y., Publ. Sheldon & co., 1872. 55 p.

NL 0412797 OCX

Little Rosy's travels; or, Country scenes in the south of France. With twenty-four illustrations by L. Frölich. London, Seeley, Jackson, and Halliday, 1867. iv, 238 p. illus.

NL 0412798 NNC

VOLUME 336

Little Rosy's travels: or, Country scenes in the south of France. With twenty-four illustrations by L. Frölich. New York, D. Appleton, 1872.
iv, 300 p. illus.

I. Title: Country scenes in the south of France. II. Fröhlich, Lorens, 1820-1908, illus.

NL 0412799 NNC

Little Rosy's voyage of discovery undertaken in company with her cousin Charley
see under [Hetzel, Pierre Jules] 1814-1886.

The Little Sailor Boy [1800?]
see under Rowson, Susanna (Haswell) 1762-1824.

PZ262 .L83 1856 ... Little sailor boy. New York, McLoughlin bros., 1856.
cover-title, [13] p. col. illus. (Aunt Mary's series)

NL 0412802 ICU

The little Sailor Boy, a Ballad.
Philadelphia, Baltimore, and New York, [c.1798] sheet music.

NL 0412803 RPJCB

Rare Books Dept.

The little saint; or, The life and death of Mary Grant, of York: a pious Sunday scholar. Designed for the rising generation. York, Printed by Richard Burdekin [182-?]
15 p. incl. front. 11cm. (Burdekin's reward books)

[A collection of nineteenth-century children's books, includin chapbooks, published in Great Britain and the United States, 37]

1. Didactic literature.

NL 0412804 CU

Little Sally of the Sabbath school. New York, American tract society [182-?]
16 p. illus., plates. 10cm.

NL 0412805 NNC DLC MB

PZ262 .L83F 183- Little Sally of the Sabbath school. Portland, Bailey & Noyes [183-?]
16 p. illus. 11cm.

NL 0412806 ICU NNC

PZ262 .L835 1834 Little Sally of the Sabbath school. [Concord M. Atwood, 1834]
16 p. illus. 10cm.
Imperfect: t.-p. and p. 15-16 wanting. Title supplied from Pegasus book shop catalog.

NL 0412807 ICU

Is94 tl v.2(2 Little Sally of the Sabbath school ... Portland[Maine]Bailey & Noyes[ca.1840?]
16p.incl.illus. 10½cm. ([Toy books] 7th ser. no.11)
Title vignette; illustrated covers.

NL 0412808 CtY

Is94 tl v.2(6 Little Sally of the Sabbath school ... Concord:Published by Atwood & Brown,1847.
16p. illus. 9½cm. ([Atwood and Brown's toy books] Seventh series, no.11)
Imprint on front cover: Portland:S.H. Colesworthy.1847.
Title and front cover vignettes, two illustrations on back cover.

NL 0412809 CtY ICU

PZ111 .B72 Little Sally of the Sabbath school. New York, American Tract Society [1848?]
16 p. 11cm.
[Books for children, v.2]

NL 0412810 ICU MB

PZ111 .C43 Little Sally of the Sunday school. [New York] New-York religious tract society [1820?]
16 p. illus., plates. 11cm. [Chap-books, 1820-1845?]

NL 0412811 ICU

PZ211 .C46 v.7 Little Sally; or, The good girl. Philadelphia, American Sunday school union, 1827.
7 p. illus. 11cm.
[Chap-books, 1827-185-?, v.7]

NL 0412812 ICU

PZ260 .L815 18— Little Samaritan. Philadelphia, Bible and Publication Society [18--]
64 p. illus.

NL 0412813 ICU

Little Samuel, and Dangerous sport
see under [Jones, Joseph Huntington] 1797-1868.

The little savage
see under [Marryat, Frederick] 1792-1848.

Little Saxham, Eng.
see Saxham, Little, Eng. (Parish)

The little scholar's pretty pocket companion, or Youth's first step on the ladder of learning, in rhyme and prose ... By a friend to the youth of Columbia. Bennington [Vt.], Printed by Anthony Haswell.[ca.1795?]
[36]p. illus. 10cm.
Signatures: one quire of 18 leaves, signed [A]-F4.2, the signatures being placed inside each other, in this order:[A]1-2, B1, C1-2, D1, E1-2, F1-2, E3-4, D2, C3-4, B2, [A]3-4.

NL 0412817 CtY

Little school mate series, ...
New York, [c1913-

NL 0412818 DLC

The little schoolmaster
see under Uncle Charles, pseud.

Little Schuylkill and Susquehanna railroad company
see
Catawissa, Williamsport and Erie railroad company.

Little Schuylkill navigation railroad and coal company.
Abstract of a report on the coal and iron estate ...
see under Roberts, William F.

Little Schuylkill Navigation, Rail Road and Coal Company. The act, and supplements thereto, authorising the incorporation of the Little Schuylkill Navigation, Rail Road and Coal Company. Reading: Douglass W. Hyde, 1830. 33 p. 24°.
Acts of the state of Pennsylvania.

NL 0412822 NN

Little Schuylkill navigation railroad and coal company.
The act incorporating the Little Schuylkill navigation rail road and coal company, and supplements thereto. Philadelphia, J. & W. Kite, 1835.
48 p. 18cm.

I. Pennsylvania. Laws, statutes, etc.

A 15—2280

Bur. of railway econ. Libr. for Library of Congress [a41b1]

NL 0412823 DBRE MWA

VOLUME 336

Little Schuylkill navigation, railroad and coal company. Report of the president and managers.

Philadelphia, 18

v. 23rd. annual.

45-50003

Library of Congress HE2791.L7972

NL 0412824 DLC

AP2
.L6475 Little scissors. v. 1– Feb. 1856– New York, Nesbitt & co., 1856–

v. in illus. 24cm. irregular.

Caption title.

I. Nesbitt (George F.) and company, New York.

43-21407

Library of Congress AP2.L6475

NL 0412825 DLC

The little scrap book: for little readers. New Haven, S. Babcock, 1850.

8 p. illus. 10cm.

1. Readers and speakers—1800-1870.

36-12918

Library of Congress PE1119.A1L72 428.6

NL 0412826 DLC

The little sea-bird. By the author of "Mackerel Will," etc. New York, American tract soc. [186-?] 192 p. illus. 16cm.

DLC: YA 5920

519417B. I. Mackerel Will, Author of.

NL 0412827 NN DLC

The little seed
see under Alcott, Louisa May, 1832-1888.

YA
.S561 The little seed and how it grew. Philadelphia, c1846.
24p.

(Sunday school books; arr. numerically.)

NL 0412829 DLC

Little sergeant.

[Bryson, Joseph H]

Pray without ceasing. An adaptation from Joaquin Miller's poem, "The port of ships." By "The Little sergeant." [Hampton, Va.] 1896.

The little sermon book; sixty-four short sermons for the Sundays and chief holy days of the Christian year with blank leaves for Ms. additions, by an Oxford M.A. London, Skeffington, 1906.
191 p. 19 cm.
1. Church of England. Sermons. I. An Oxford M.A.

NL 0412831 IEG NjP

A little sheaf of sonnets of the spirit in time of war
see under [Denison, Robert Charles] 1868-

The LITTLE ship. v.24-date; 1957-date
London. v. illus. 25cm

Quarterly.

For earlier file, whose numbering it continues, see: Little ship club. Journal. (vol. 24, 1957 is bound with earlier file.)

Journal of the Little ship club.

1. Yachts and yachting--Per. and soc. publ. I. Little ship club.

NL 0412833 NN MH

LITTLE SHIP CLUB.

Journal. v.1-2, no.3, 6-v.3, no.3, v.4-5, no.5, v.6-21, 22, no.2-v.23; 1927-Feb., Nov.1928-Mar., Nov.1929-Mar., Nov.1931-1954, Apr./June, 1955-1956
London. v. illus. 24cm.

Monthly (irregular) during the winter months, 1927-May, 1939; quarterly, June, 1946-1956.

Suspended publication between v.13, no.6, Apr./May, 1939 and v.15, no.1, June, 1946. During the suspension, its War-time pamphlet was issued.

With v. 23, 1956 is bound: The Little ship; journal of the Little ship club. For later file, issued with this title and continuing this numbering, see entry under the Little ship.

1. Yachts and yachting--Per. and soc. publ.

NL 0412835 NN

Little ships of the Royal navy. [n. p., 194-?]

15, [1] p. col. illus. 26½cm.

1. Gt. Brit. Navy—Illustrations.

45-43696

Library of Congress VA458.A1L5 [2] 85

NL 0412836 DLC MH

---

*pFB8
N1627
Z805n Little!! ships!! or Iohn Bull very inquisitive.
[London] Pubd by P Robetrts[!] 28 Middle row [1803]

plate. 26.5x33.5cm.,mounted & bd.to 50x40cm.
George 9995; Broadley A-547.
Engraving (hand-colored), unsigned.
A satire on Napoleon's intended invasion.
No.108 in a volume lettered on spine: Napoleonic caricatures.

NL 0412837 MH

Little ships' war; a tribute to the coastal forces of India's fighting Navy. [n. p., 1944]

[20] p. illus., ports., maps. 25 cm.

"Published as a special supplement to Bin log, the monthly magazine of the Royal Indian Navy."

1. World War, 1939-1945—Naval operations, Indian. I. Bin log. Supplement.

D784.I 4L5 940.545 50-43166

NL 0412838 DLC

...Little Silver-Hair and the three bears, a pastoral drama. By an experienced amateur. New York: Happy Hours Co. [187–] 7 p. 12°. (Parlor plays for home performance.)

1. Amateur theatricals.
N. Y. P. L. April 24, 1920.

NL 0412839 NN MH

The little singing girl; a new favorite song. [1799]
see under [Hook, James] 1746-1827.

Little sins, a dialogue. To which is added, an abstract of an interesting conversation. Philadelphia: To be had of Benjamin & Thomas Kite, 1825.
8 p. 19cm. (With: Friends, Society of. Tract association. A series of essays...1826)

NL 0412841 NcD OClWHi

...The little siren (La resalada); alborada asturiana. English version by Mary Ellis Opdycke. After Baldomero Fernández by Kurt Schindler. [Boston] O. Ditson Co., cop. 1922. Publ. pl. no. 73998. 6 p. 31cm. (Songs of the Spanish provinces. 2.)

For medium voice with piano acc. English and Spanish words.
Caption-title.

1. Folk songs, Spanish—Asturias. I. Fernandez, Baldomero. II. Schindler, Kurt, 1882-1935, ed.
N. Y. P. L. April 12, 1937

NL 0412842 NN

... Little Sister. 1882.
see under [Yardley, Mrs. Jane Woolsey]

A little sister missionary, by her Benedictine sister; translated from the French by Ida Mary Smalley; with foreword by His Eminence, Patrick Cardinal Hayes ... New York, Cincinnati [etc.] Benziger brothers, 1932.

xvii, 229, [1] p. incl. front., illus., ports. 19cm.

1. Marie-Mercédès, soeur, 1862-1925. 2. Little sisters of the assumption. I. Une petite-soeur missionnaire. II. Her Benedictine sister. III. Smalley, Ida Mary, tr.

32-35178

Library of Congress BX4705.M39L5

——— Copy 2.

Copyright A 58096 [3] 922.2

NL 0412844 DLC OCl

The little sister; or, The child from the cradle to the school
see under [Hoffmann-Donner, Heinrich] 1809-1894.

VOLUME 336

Little Sister Snow
see under [Macaulay, Mrs. Fannie Caldwell] 1863-

Little sisters' infant shelter, San Francisco.
Annual report. 1887 San Francisco, 1887.
1 v. 23 cm. [1887, Pamphlets on charities. v. 2]

NL 0412847 CU

Little sisters of the Assumption.
Fifty years in the harvest field; golden jubilee of the Little sisters of the Assumption in England... 1880–1930. London, Burns, Oates & Washbourne, 1930. x, 88 p. illus. 25cm.

NL 0412848 NN

Little sisters of the poor.
... A century in the service of the aged poor, 1839–1939. Congregation of the Little sisters of the poor. [Lyon, Héliogravure M. Lescuyer, 1939?]
60 p. illus. (incl. ports.) 19 x 14½cm.

I. Title.

Library of Congress BX4402.L5 46-38653
[2] 271.95

NL 0412849 DLC WaSpG

Little Sisters of the Poor.
...Congrégation des Petites sœurs des pauvres. Paris: Letouzey et Ané, 1924. 255 p. plates. 15. ed. 12°. (Les ordres religieux.)

NL 0412850 NN MH

Little Sisters of the Poor.
Congregation of the Little Sisters of the Poor. From the French. Paris, Librairie Letouzey et Ané [1899]
12-288 p. front. (ports.) illus., port, plates, 18 cm.
1. Little Sisters of the Poor.

NL 0412851 PLatS OrStbM

Little Sisters of the Poor.
Congregation of the Little Sisters of the Poor. From the French. Paris, Librairie Letouzey et ané [1927]
288 p. front., plates, ports. 19 cm.
1. Little Sisters of the Poor.

NL 0412852 MoSU InStme

Little Sisters of the Poor.
History of the Little Sisters of the Poor
see under Leroy, A.

The LITTLE sisters; or, Emma and Caroline. New Haven [Conn.] Published by S. Babcock [183-?] 16 p. illus. 92mm.

In original decorated green paper covers, with publisher's advertisement on back.
Imprint on cover: New Haven, Sidney Babcock.
"Every day not play-day," a poem, p. 16.

----Second copy.
Without covers.
Imperfect: t.p. mutilated, p. 15-16 wanting.

NL 0412855 NN MNS CtY DLC

PZ262 .L837 1838
The little sisters; or, Emma and Caroline. New Haven, S. Babcock, 1838.
16 p. illus. 9cm.

NL 0412856 ICU

The LITTLE sketch-book; or Useful objects illustrated. New York, Kiggins & Kellogg [186-?] 8 p. illus. 80mm.

On cover: First series. no. 8.
Imperfect: covers wanting.

1. Juvenile literature--Picture books.

NL 0412857 NN

A little sketch of my life
see under [Gillis, James D.] 1870-

Little sketches of big folks, Minnesota, 1907; an alphabetical list of representative men of Minnesota, with biographical sketches. St. Paul, Minneapolis [etc.] R. L. Polk & co., °1907.
441 p. 24cm.

1. Minnesota—Biog. I. Polk, R. L., & co., pub.

Library of Congress F605.L77 7-21375

NL 0412859 DLC NN

Little sketches of some contemporary authors... New York: G. P. Putnam's Sons [1917]. 1 p.l., 58 p. port. 16°.

Consists of sketches of: Florence L. Barclay; James B. Hendryx; Cynthia Stockley; Anna Katharine Green; Cyrus Townsend Brady; A. H. Fitch; John Reed Scott; Ethel M. Dell; Amy McLaren; Maud Diver; Leslie Moore; F. W. Bain; Hilda M. Sharp; Richard Marsh; Paul Bourget; Rose Pastor Stokes; Ellen Key; Norman Angell; Frederick S. Dellenbaugh; Arthur Christopher Benson; James M. Beck; André Maurel; Ananda K. Coomaraswamy, and Gustav Kobbé.

NL 0412860 NN OO Vi

The little small red hen
see under Byron, May Clarissa (Gillington) d. 1936.

The little Smith barn; a story of the triangular plot now called Pritchard Park, Asheville, North Carolina. [Asheville? The Bank of Asheville?] n.d.
[12] p. illus., ports. D.

NL 0412862 NcU

LITTLE Snow-White and other fairy stories. Illustrated by H.Robinson, E.Stuart Hardy, and others. London, E.Nister, etc., etc., [1916?]

pp.64. Plates, (colored) and other illustr. (The FAIRY gold series.)

NL 0412863 MH

Little Snow-White, and other Grimm fairy tales
see under Grimm, Jakob Ludwig Karl, 1785-1863.

Little Snow White, and other stories; with 127 illustrations and a frontispiece in colors. New York, A. L. Burt company [°1906]
iv, 123 p. col. front., illus. 22cm.

6-16509

Library of Congress PZ5.L727 (Copyright A 140984)

NL 0412865 DLC

Little Snow-white and the seven dwarfs, as exhibited by the Park street Sunday school, at City Hall, April 30 and May 1, 1869. Portland, 1869.
12 p. 18 cm.

NL 0412866 RPB PU

Rare Book Coll.
PZ8 .3 .L58 1903
Little Snowdrop ... New York, McLoughlin Bros., c1903.
[4] l. illus. (pt. col.) 18.8cm. (Pretty linen series)

Printed on linen.
Wrapper title; pictorial wrappers included in collation.

NL 0412867 ViU

Little Snowdrop, the unbaptised one
see under Caddell, Cecilia Mary, d. 1877.

Little soldier
see The Young soldier.

The little soldier, a plea for peace
see under [Tuttle, Sarah]

VOLUME 336

Little soldier boys. New York, McLoughlin Bros., c1896.
8 l. illus. 4°.

NL 0412871 NN

Little soldier boys. New York, McLoughlin bros., °1899.
cover-title, [12] p. col. illus. 27 x 23½cm.
Text on p. [3] of cover.

44-25679

Library of Congress PZ8.3.L7347

NL 0412872 DLC

The little soldier of the cross
see under [Cox, Edward]

The little soldier of the revolution. New York, Philip J. Cozans [185-?]
16p. illus. 23 cm.

Caption title: Harry Brave, or, The little soldier of the revolution.
Includes song (to the tune of Marble halls)

I. Title: Harry Brave.

NL 0412874 RPB

Is94 tl 1 The little soldiers; or, Holidays sports. Dedicated to all good boys. Embellished with plates. Sidney's press:New Haven--S.Babcock, 1833.
24p.incl.front.,illus. 14cm.
Original green printed wrappers.

NL 0412875 CtY MBC PP

Is94 tl v.1 The little soldiers; or, Holiday sports; dedicated to all good boys. Embellished with engravings. New Haven:S.Babcock,1839.
24p. illus. 11½x9½cm. (Babcock's [moral, instructive and amusing toy books] no.4 [or six cent] toys)
Title vignette.

I.Babcock, Sidney, publisher, New Haven.

NL 0412876 CtY PP

A little song and other stories. N.Y., n.d.
64 p. front. illus. pl. 17 cm.
Illus. t.p.

NL 0412877 RPB

A little song book of the nations ...
see under [Thomas, Alan Ernest Wentworth] ed.

Little songs by great composers. Boston, A. P. Schmidt and company [°1883]
[53] p. front., illus. 24½ x 19½cm.
Piano accompaniment.
A statement that the music was written for "Wide awake" accompanies most of the songs.

1. Children's songs. I. Wide awake.

40-15415

Library of Congress M1997.L698
[2] 784.624

NL 0412879 DLC OCl MB

Little songs, by M. R. L. C.
see under
Chapin, Mary R L

Little songs, for little boys and girls ...
see under [Follen, Eliza Lee (Cabot)] "Mrs. C. T. C. Follen," 1787-1860.

Za Zal 859l Little songs for little people. New-York, A.D.F.Randolph,1859.
405p.incl.front.,illus. 16cm.
Poems.

NL 0412882 CtY DLC PMA

LITTLE songs for little people. New-York, A. D. F. Randolph, 1859.
2 p. l., [7]-384p. illus. 15½cm.
Illustrated t.-p.

1. Children's poetry.

Printed by Wesleyan University Library

NL 0412883 CtW

Little songs for little people; with numerous illustrations. 254p. N.Y.Carlton & Porter, [c1860]

NL 0412884 OCl

PZ8.3 L73 Little songs for little people. New York, Anson D. F. Randolph & co., 1880.
405p.incl.front.,illus. 17cm.

1. Children's poetry.

NL 0412885 NBuG

Little songs for little readers. With numerous illustrations. New York, Carlton & Lanahan; Cincinnati, Hitchcock & Walden [c1860]
2 p.l. [7]-256 p. illus. 17 cm.
In borders.
Editor's note signed: D.W.

NL 0412886 NNUT

Little songs for little singers
see under Mason, Lowell, 1792-1872.

M1988 .L76 LITTLE songs of long ago. "More old nursery rhymes." The original tunes harmonized by Alfred Moffat; illustrated by H.Willebeek Le Mair. London,Augener; [etc.,etc.,c1912]
63,[1]p. col.illus. 23x29½cm.
Contains music.
"Uniform with this volume Our old nursery rhymes."

1.Children's songs. 2.Nursery rhymes.

NL 0412888 ICU OClW OO IU MB

Little songs of long ago. "More old nursery rhymes." The original tunes harmonized by Alfred Moffat; illustrated by H. Willebeek Le Mair. Philadelphia, D. McKay; London, Augener, ltd. [1913?]
[64] p. col. illus. 22 x 29½cm.
Printed in England.
"Uniform with this volume Our old nursery rhymes."

I. Moffat, Alfred Edward, 1866- II. Le Mair, Henriette Willebeek illus.

A 14-1396

New York. State library for Library of Congress [a37g1]

NL 0412889 N NN ViU GU OClh OCl WaS Or OrMonO

Little songs of love and memory by H. F. F. Rutland, Vt., 1924.
24 p. 20 cm.
Cover title: Forget-me-nots.

NL 0412890 RPB

Little songs of shade and sunshine; by G.J. Illustrated by Kwasson & Shoso. Tokyo, Hasegawa [1900?]
[20] p. (on double leaves) illus.
Cover title: Shade & sunshine

NL 0412891 MH

Coll LI913sg The little songster for good children. Bouckville [N.Y.] Stationer's Company [183-?]
16 p. illus. 11 cm.

Title vignette.
Poems.

1. Children's poetry.

NL 0412892 RPB

LITTLE Sophy, a true story for children. N. Y. Gen. prot. episc. union. n. d. 52 pp. 24°.

NL 0412893 MB

Little Sophy, Author of.
Recollections of a beloved sister
see under title

VOLUME 336

The little Southern pilgrim gone to rest. By L. M. 2d thousand. Edinburgh, J. Menzies, 1865.
31 p. col. front. 13 x 10.5 cm.

Lettered on cover: The little Southern pilgrim.
Story of a boy from Petersburg, Virginia.
Biblical references in foot-notes.

1. Christian life. I. M., L. II. L. M.

NL 0412895 ViU CSmH

The Little Spaniard
see under [Nowell, Mrs. Harriet]

A little spasm at the home of Wolfgang Mozart
see under [Richmond, Clifford]

The little speaker, and juvenile reader
see under Northend, Charles, 1814-1895, comp.

Little speeches for little people
see under [Bates, Charles Austin] 1866-

The LITTLE sportsman's alphabet. Illustrated by Fred Grey. London, F. Warne & co., [188-?

4°. [22] p. Illustr.
Cover-title.
(Aunt Louisa's London toy books, 95)

NL 0412900 MH

Little Stalin library.
no.

London: Lawrence & Wishart ltd., 1941- 18½cm
nos.

NL 0412901 NN CU

(The) Little star. semi-m.
Sabbath-school paper. 35 per year
Freewill Baptist register & yearbook 1382 p. 87

NL 0412902 NHC

Little stories. National Reference Library, c1951.
43 p.

NL 0412903 WaE

PS 1336 L77 Little stories about Mark Twain. [New York Harper, 1911?]
[32]p. port.(on cover) 14cm.
cover title.
Probably pub. as an advertisement for Harper's "New National edition" of Mark Twain's collected work.

1. Clemens, Samuel Langhorne. I. Harper, firm, publishers, New York.

NL 0412904 NRU FU WU PPFr MiU NN

... Little stories about the cat, dog, and pig, in words of one syllable. Newark (N. J.) Benjamin Olds, 1835.
8 p. illus. 9cm. (At head of title: Cobb's toys, first series, no. 2)
Cover-title with vignette has imprint date: 1842.

I. Cobb's toys. 1st series, no. 2.

NL 0412905 ViW

PZ262 .L84 1835 ... Little stories about the hen, duck, goose, and hawk, in words of one syllable. Newark, B. Olds [1835]
8 p. illus. 9cm. (One cent toys. First series, no.4)

NL 0412906 ICU

Little stories along the line of the Western Pacific railroad...
see under [Brown, Thomas Pollok] 1879-

Little stories for good little people
see under American Tract Society.

Little stories for little children ... New-York: Printed & sold by Mahlon Day [ca.1830]
Is94 tl v.2 16p. illus. 9½cm.
Title vignette.

NL 0412909 CtY CaBVaU OClWHi

PZ262 .L66 1839 Little stories for little children. Portland, S. H. Colesworthy, 1839.
16 p. illus. 10cm.

NL 0412910 ICU

1847 Juv. coll. Little stories for little children...
New York: S. M. Crane, 374 Pearl Street.
Egbert, Hovey & King, printers 1847
16 p. 9½ cm

NL 0412911 DLC

Little stories for little children.
[Chicago] Baker & Hayes, c1885.
[10] p.

Cover title.
"Compliments of E. W. Gillett, manufacturer magic yeast, Chicago, Ill."
Poems.

I. Gillett, E. W., manufacturer

NL 0412912 MiD

Little stories for little folks. N.Y. Pub. by McLoughlin Bros., n.d.
unp. illus., pl., col., front. 25 cm.

NL 0412913 RPB

Little stories for little folks. Boston: Massachusetts Sabbath school soc. [183-?] 64 p. illus. 11½cm. (On cover: Aunt Susie's library.)

1. Juvenile literature—Fiction, American. I. Massachusetts Sabbath school society.
N. Y. P. L. September 27, 1939

NL 0412914 NN

YA .8497 Little stories for little folks...Philadelphia [c1847].
35p. (Sunday school books; arr. numerically)

NL 0412915 DLC

Little stories for little folks, in easy lessons...

Editions of this work printed in America before 1801 are available in this library in the Readex Microprint edition of Early American Imprints published by the American Antiquarian Society.
This collection is arranged according to the numbers in Charles Evans' American Bibliography.

NL 0412916 DLC

Little stories for little folks, in easy lessons of one, two, and three syllables.
— Boston: Printed and sold by Samuel Hall . . . [1795?] 70 pp. Illus. 10½ cm.

K5400 — Chap-books.

NL 0412917 MB

... Little stories for little people. Springfield, Mass., McLoughlin brothers inc. [1928]
56 p. illus. (1 col. mounted) 15cm. (The little big books)

Library of Congress PZ7.L728Li ca 30-284 Unrev'd

NL 0412918 DLC

VOLUME 336

Ip
L73
868
Little stories for little people, in words of one and two syllables. London, New York[etc.] T.Nelson and sons,1868.
32p.incl.front.,illus. 15½cm.

NL 0412919 CtY

LITTLE stories, of one and two syllables, for little children. London, J.Masters, 1849.
40 p. col. illus. 13x11 cm.

NL 0412920 CaBVaU

Little stories of pretty little birds
see under [Kendall, Edward Augustus] 1776?-1842.

A little story about S. M. S. feeder calves
see under S. M. S. Ranch, Swenson Bros.

1834
Juv. coll.
The little story book. Written for the American Sunday-School union, and revised by the Committee of publication. Philadelphia, American Sunday-School Union. No. 146 Chesnut Street [c. 1834]
[3] 4-54 p. 14.5 cm.

NL 0412923 DLC

The little story book. Boston, American Tract Society ₍186-?₎
64 p. front.
"Reprinted from the London Religious Tract Society."
Religious Tract Society edition published in 1867; original edition published by American Sunday School Union ca. 1830.
Contents.--The magician fish.--A gathered blossom.--Jan Harmsen, the Dutch orphan.

NL 0412924 NNC

PZ
6
.L738x
Little story book for little folks. New York, Howe & Ferry [1844]
88 p. illus. 13 cm.

NL 0412925 OKentU

Little story book for little folks. New York, S. Raynor, 1852.
88 p. front., illus., plates. 13 cm.
On front cover: Little Lu Lu tales; on back cover: Lu-Lu books.
Illustrated title-page.
Copyrighted, 1844 by B. Walker.
Prose and verse by various authors.

NL 0412926 RPB

Little story book for little folks. New York, S.Raynor, 1853.
88 p. front.,illus.,plates. 13 x 10½cm.
Illustrated t.-p.
On front cover: Lu Lu tales; on back cover: Lu-Lu books.
Copyrighted 1844 by B.Walker.
Prose and verse by various authors,whose names or initials are usually given.

1.Children's stories.

NL 0412927 MiU NjR

The little story book. Full of pretty pictures. New Haven,Published by S.Babcock, 1842.
16p. illus. 9cm.
Title vignette.
Pamphlet
Another issue, without date on t.-p. and cover.

NL 0412928 CtY DLC

Little story for a little boy.
— Northampton. Merrifield. [18—?] 10 pp. Illus. 48°.

E8384 — Chap-books. Apr. 9, 1903

NL 0412929 MB NNC

A little story of a little life, or, The sunbeam ...
see under [Jones, Cecilia Anne]

A little story of the Boston & Providence railroad company
see under [Fisher, Charles Eben] 1889-

Little studies in Judaism
see under Jewish Publication Society of America.

The little sunbeam; a collection of music
see under Doane, William Howard, 1831-1915, comp.

Little sunbeam stories, comprising: Little schoolmates, Little playfellows [and] Little chatterer [by] Uncle Ned. New York, London, and Paris, Cassell, Petter Galpin & Co. [c1880]
95, 96, 94 p. illus., incl. fronts., plates. 22 cm.
Each part has individual t.-p.

Uncle Ned--Little chatterer.

NL 0412934 RPB DLC

Little sunbeams [Stories and poems for children] N.Y., Pub. by McLoughlin Bros., n.d.
unp. illus. pl. 26 cm.
Illus. t.p.

NL 0412935 RPB

Little sunbeams. 1871-72
see under Mathews, Joanna Hooe, 1849-1901.

Little Sunshine's holiday: a picture from life
see under [Craik, Mrs. Dinah Maria (Mulock)] 1826-1887.

PZ116
.R38C4
no.7
Little Susan. New York, American tract society ₍184-?₎
16 p. illus. 11cm.
₍Chap-books; religious, no.7₎

NL 0412938 ICU DLC

n. d.
Juv. coll.
Little Susan and her lamb. a story for children. Boston: Wait, Green and Co. [n. d.
[3] 4-6 p. 13½ cm

NL 0412939 MB DLC

Little Susan and her lamb. New-York: Printed and sold by M. Day, 1829. 16 p. incl. plates. illus. 11cm.

NL 0412940 NN

Little Susan and her lamb. [Fiction.]
Boston. Christ Church Sunday School. [184-?] 6 pp. Illustrated covers. 14.5 cm.
The title is on the cover.

NL 0412941 MB

LITTLE Susan. Designed for children two or three years old. By the author of "Fruit and Flowers'. Boston,Hilliard,Gray,Little,and Wilkins,1828.
24°. pp.15.

NL 0412942 MH

VOLUME 336

BV4531
.L7
1892 Little Susan; or, A memoir of Susan Kollock, daughter of Rev. Shepard K. Kollock, of Norfolk, Va. Written for the American S. S. Union, and revised by the Committee of Publication. New ed. Philadelphia, American Sunday School Union [1892]
107 p. illus. 15cm.
This title listed in the American catalogue ... books in print, July 1, 1876.
"The affectionate daughter", p. 101-107, is an advertisement, giving a brief sketch of the story.
Rev. Shepard K. Kollock was Pastor of the First Presbyterian Church in Norfolk, Va., from 1825 to 1834. cf. Norfolk, Va. First Presbyterian Church. The church on the Elizabeth river ... 1892?

1. Sunday-school literature. 2. Christian life. I. American Sunday School Union. II. Kollock, Shepard Kosciuszko, 1795-1865. III. Title: Susan Kollock, A memoir of.

NL 0412944 ViU Vi ViW MWA

244
L729 Little Susan, or, The young Christian, written for the American S.S. Union, and revised by the Committee of Publication. Philadelphia, American Sunday-School Union, 1830.
72p. 15cm.

NL 0412945 OrU

Little Switzerland, N.C. Committee of Mass Meeting.
What citizens think about Attorney Chas. Ross' attack on the Switzerland Co. and its stockholders. Charlotte, Huneycutt Printing Co. [1938]
20 p. illus., map. 16 cm.
1. Little Switzerland, N.C. 2. N.C.-Reads.

NL 0412946 NcU

Little Switzerland. N.p., 1916.

NL 0412947 NcU

Little Switzerland on the Mississippi
see under
Wis-O-Wa Scenic Association, Prairie du Chien, Wis.

Little Sylvia of Hartford... 1890
see under Aunt Martha, pseud.

Little syndicate, *New York.*
Gentle Bermuda. New York, The Little syndicate [©1938]
3 p. l., 6a, 4b, 6c, 4d p., 2 l. plates. 28½cm.
Includes selections from the Royal gazette and colonist daily and "A guide book to the islands, by the staff correspondent of the Little syndicate".

1. Bermuda islands—Descr. & trav.—Guide-books. 2. Bermuda islands—Soc. life & cust. I. Royal gazette and colonist daily, Hamilton, Bermuda islands. II. Title.

Library of Congress F1631.L58 38-5841
——— Copy 2.
Copyright A 114702 [3] 917.299

NL 0412950 DLC

---

x823
L725 Little tales for boys. An amusing book for the moral improvement of children. Guben, Printed by F. Fechner [18--]
12 l. col.plates. 18cm.

Cover title: Stories for little boys.

1. Children's stories. I. Title: Stories for little boys.

NL 0412951 IU ICU

A little talk with patients and superintendents of sanatoria
see under [Colby, Charles De Witt] 1865-

YA
.S174 Little talks for little folks... Philadelphia, [c1857]
72p.
(Sunday school books; arr. numerically)

NL 0412953 DLC

Pequot
L75 The little teacher, for reading and spelling well. By a parent. Second edition. Philadelphia:Published by Jacob Johnson, no.147,Market-street.1806.(Price 18 cents.)
[36]p. illus. 14cm.

NL 0412954 CtY

Pn
371.3E
L723 THE LITTLE TEACHER; the word method. Cincinnati, Van Antwerp,Bragg & co.,1855
illus. 17cm.

NL 0412955 PU RPB

Little teachers
see under [Logie, Sarah E Chester]

LITTLE technical library. Photographic series. Chicago,Ziff-Davis Publishing Co.,1939.

17 cm. 10 vol.
Contents:- 1.Your camera and how it works by W.E.Dobbs and Charles A.Savage. 2.Developing, printing and enlarging by Al and Devera Bernsohn 3.Filters and their use by W.Bradford Shank. 4. Composition for the amateur by Kenneth Heilbron 5.Movie making for the beginner by Herbert C. McKay. 6.Color in photography by Ivan Dmitri. 7 Child photography by Harold Lambert. 8.Home portraiture and make-up by Maurice Seymour and Syd Simons. 9.Tricks for camera owners,reprinted from Popular Photography. 10.A glossary for photography compiled by Frank Fenner,jr.

NL 0412958 MH OLak

Shea
BX
2149
.L5 The little testament of Jesus in the Holy Eucharist, containing an admonition, pious aspiration, and practice for each day of the month, by a Catholic priest. From the latest Dublin ed. Philadelphia, E. Cummiskey [183-]
32 p. (Catholic tracts, small size, no. 1)

NL 0412959 DGU

The little te-totaller; or, True liberty. Written for the American Sunday-School Union, and revised by the Committee of Publication. Philadelphia: Amer. Sunday-School Union [cop. 1844].
1 p.l., 5-24 p. 24°.

1. Temperance.—Fiction. 2. Juvenile literature.—Fiction (American). 3. American Sunday-School Union.
N. Y. P. L. June 25, 1917.

NL 0412960 NN ICU

Little Theatre, New York
see New York (City) Little Theatre.

Little theatre arts. v. 1-
Feb. 1937-
St. Louis, Mo.
v. illus. 10 nos. a year.
1. Theater-Period.

NL 0412962 CU-Riv

Little theatre classics
see under Eliot, Samuel Atkins, 1893- ed.

---

*BROAD-
SIDE
1921
.L47 Little Theatre League of Richmond. Richmond, Va.

Programme [for] February 22 and 23, 1921. Richmond, Va., Virginia Stationery Co., Engravers, Stationers and Printers, 1921.
broadside([3] p.) 18 x 13 cm.

1. Richmond, Va.—Theaters. I. Title.

NL 0412964 ViU

VOLUME 336

Little theatre magazine. San Francisco, May-June 1917
see Little theatre monthly. San Francisco.

PN2000 .L5 The Little theatre magazine; a complete digest of the amateur theatrical world. - v. 2, no. 3; - Mar. 1922. San Francisco, Calif., Red Star Producing Co., etc.
v.

NL 0412966 DLC

The Little theatre monthly.
The college builds its theatre; February sees the opening of theatres in Princeton, Ohio Wesleyan, Allegheny college and Wesleyan (Conn.) n.p., 1930.
Extract from The Little theatre monthly, April, 1930, v. 20, no. 7.

NL 0412967 ODW

808.205 L721 Little theatre monthly. v.1,no.1- ; May 1917- San Francisco.
v. illus. 24cm.

Title varies: May-June,1917, Little theatre magazine.
Ceased publication with v.1,no.5,Nov.1917.

1. Theater. Little theater movement. Per soc etc. I. Title: Little theatre magazine.

NL 0412968 OrU

The Little Theatre of Dallas magazine.
v. 1-

Dallas, Tex., 1927- 23cm.
v. illus.

"Published with each production at the Little Theatre of Dallas."
Editor : Oct., 1927- O. Hinsdell.
Includes various special programmes.

1. Stage—U. S.—Tex.—Dallas. 2. Stage—Little theatre movement—U. S.—Tex.—Dallas. 3. Stage—Playbills and programmes—U. S. I. Hinsdell, Oliver, editor. II. Little Theatre of Dallas.
N. Y. P. L. September 6, 1937

NL 0412969 NN

Little theatre society of Indiana.

Indiana prize plays, as presented by the Little theatre society of Indiana during the season of 1922-23; preface by William O. Bates. Indianapolis, The Bobbs-Merrill company [c1924]

Little theatres;...
[New York] 192-

Pn2267 .A1L5

NL 0412971 DLC

Little Theodore. Written for the American Sunday-school union, and revised by the committee of publication. Philadelphia, Amer. Sunday-school union [1836] 90 p. front. 15cm.

335440B. 1. No subject. I. American Sunday school union.
N. Y. P. L. December 11, 1946

NL 0412972 NN DLC

Little things
see under Wilson, Henrietta, d. 1862.

Little things-great things. A New Year's gift, from the children of the Warren Street Chapel January, 1842. Boston, Tuttle and Dennett, Printers. 1842.
sm. 12 mo.

NL 0412974 CSmH

DO71 L729 The Little Times.
vol. (no.

New York, The New York Times,
v. illus., ports. 34cm. monthly.

No. 52-54 repeated in numbering.
Dec. 15, 1928 issue bound in before Oct. 15 1928; Sept. 15, 1928 issue bound in following Nov. 15, 1928.

NL 0412975 NNC

---

xfF629 I46L5 Little tin god on wheels. v.1- Jan.1, 1881-
Iowa City, Ia.
v. 32cm.

"The Little tin god on wheels devoted to music, art, the drama, and society in general.' Horace L.Wood, editor and proprietor.

1. Iowa City, Ia. I. Wood, Horace L.

NL 0412976 IaU

The Little tin gods-on-wheels; or, Society in our modern Athens
see under Grant, Robert, 1852-1940.

Little tips on near by trips along the Pocahontas trail. 1929.
unp.

NL 0412978 OClWHi

The little token, or Child's handbook of instruction and amusement. Boston, T.H.Carter [18-]

96 p. illus.

NL 0412979 MH RPB

Little Tom Tell-Truth's pretty stories. London:Religious tract society ... [ca.1850?]
15,[1]p. illus. 9cm. ([Religious tract society, London. Children's tracts] 8) [Short stories, 1]

NL 0412980 CtY

Little Tom, the huntsman's boy
see under American Sunday-School Union.

Is94 tl v.1 Little Tom, the ploughman's boy. An interesting story. New Haven,S.Babcock.Sidney's press. 1829.
[2],4-17p. illus. 10½cm. (New Haven toy books - no.1's ... New series, Book 6)
"First edition."

NL 0412982 CtY

Little Tom the sailor
see under [Hayley, William] 1745-1820.

LITTLE TOM TUCKER. London, Printed and published at W. S. Fortey's wholesale juvenile book warehouse, 2 & 3 Monmouth Court, Bloomsbury, W. C. [1859?] 4 l. col. illus. 18cm.

Cover title.
On back cover: The Catnach press... William S. Fortey (sole successor to the late J. Catnach), printer, publisher, and wholesale stationer, 2 & 3, Monmouth Court, Seven Dials, London, W. C.

Illustrations are hand colored.
In original printed and illustrated yellow paper covers, with publisher's advertisement.
In verse.

1. Juvenile literature--Picture books.

NL 0412985 NN

Little tot's A B C and animal book; ringing A B C jingles appropriate for children ... Chicago and New York, W. B. Conkey co., 1898.
[41] p. illus., pl. 8°.

Library of Congress (✱) (PZ7) 98—1338

NL 0412986

Little tots' delight, containing a picture alphabet; nursery stories; jingles and rhymes ... n.p. n.d.
unp. illus. pl. 26 cm.

NL 0412987 RPB

4PZ 158 Little tots' ten minute stories. New York, Platt & Peck Co. [c1913]
1 v. unpaged

NL 0412988 DLC-P4

VOLUME 336

N
398.4
L778t Little Totty. New York, McLoughlin Bros. ₍187-?₎
₍12₎ p. coll. illus. 14 cm. (Uncle Toby's series)

NL 0412989 N

PZ124
.L77 Little Totty, and other nursery tales. London F. Warne ₍186-?₎
4 v. in 1. col. illus. ("Now and then" juvenile series)

Contents.--1. Little Totty.--2. Red Riding Hood.--3. Cinderella.--4. Dame Trot and her cat

NL 0412990 ICU

The Little town on the hill. Kenosha, Wis., John Martin's House ₍°1948₎
₍28₎ p. col. illus. 21 cm. (A Bonnie book)

PZ7.L736 49-1574*

NL 0412991 DLC

821.08
L721 The little track and other verses [by Capel Boake and others] Melbourne, Robertson & Mullens, 1922.
32p. 19cm.

I. Kerr, Doris Boake, 1893-

NL 0412992 TxU

MINIATURE
PR
3991
.A1
L5 The little trapper boy, and other stories. Boston, H.A. Young ₍c1875₎
63p. illus. 12cm.

NL 0412993 OrU DLC

Little traveller.
Boston. Bowles & Dearborn. 1828. 32 pp. Vignette. [Original moral tales. Vol. 6, no. 4.] 24°.
Pp. 29, 30 are missing from the copy on shelf-number No. 4 in *4509a.343.
In the copy on shelf-number **H.99c.162, pp. 9 and 10 are badly mutilated

G2060 — S.r. — Chap-books.

NL 0412994 MB

The LITTLE traveler. Providence, G.P.Daniels, 1836.

15 cm. pp.(16). Colored illustr.
Cover serves as title-page.
Printed on one side of the leaf only.

NL 0412995 MH

... The little traveller. New York, E. Dunigan [185-?]
cover-title, 6 l. col., illus. 18 cm.
(Dame Wonder's transformations)
With curious cut-out face.

NL 0412996 RPB

The little traveller, Author of.
The juvenile English grammar
see under title

M917.7488
L77 Little Traverse Bay resorts. ₍Petoskey? Mich., ca.1902₎
₍36₎p. illus. 18x27cm.

On covers: Where to spend the summer.- Michigan resorts on Little Traverse Bay...

1.Emmet Co., Mich.-Descr. & trav. 2.Petoskey, Mich.-Descr. 3.Little Traverse Bay.

NL 0412998 Mi

Little treasure of the devout clients of St. Anthony of Padua [1891]
see under Schaefer, Joseph.

4BV
-5018 A little treasury of daily prayers. Grand Rapids, W. B. Eerdmans Pub. Co., 1949.
86 p.

NL 0413000 DLC-P4

The Little treasury of Saint Anthony. A manual of devotions in honor of Saint Anthony, compiled from approved sources. Paterson, N.J., St. Anthony's guild, Franciscan monastery, c 1928.
74 p.

NL 0413001 DHN

A Little Treatise of Baile and Maineprize
see under [Coke, Sir Edward] 1552-1634.

Little-Tree Landscaping and Forestry Service, Framingham Centre, Mass.
The landscape art.
— Framingham Centre, Mass. [1929.] 39, (1) pp. Illus. Plates. Plans. 31 cm.
Relates to the United States.

D4863 — Landscape gardening. — United States. F.a. Landscape gardening.

NL 0413003 MB MH-A

The Little Trib.
Chicago.

NL 0413004 NN

Za
M686
798t The little trifler. A drama. In three parts. [By the authoress of "The misfortunes of anger"] ... Boston:Printed for W.Spotswood, 1798.
95p. 10cm.

NL 0413005 CtY MH

Little trifler. Boston, 1798.
(In Three centuries of drama: American)

Microprint.

NL 0413006 MoU

The LITTLE truant boys; or, The dangers of disobedience. New Haven [Conn.] S. Babcock, 1838. 8 p. illus. 76mm.

In original illustrated blue paper covers.

NL 0413007 NN

A little true forraine newes: better than a great deale of domestick spurious false newes, published daily without feare or wit, to the shame of the nation, and beyond the liberty of Paris pasquils. Vnto which is added a letter written by the lievtenant of the Tower, to the Parliament, in defence of himselfe, and may give satisfaction to all men. London: Printed for N. Butter, 1641. 11 ₍i. e. 12₎ p. 18cm. (4°.)

JCB, 1919, II, 290. Union theological seminary: McAlpin collection, v. 2, p. 54. Pages 3, 12 wrongly numbered 1, 11.

Printed in 1641/42.— *cf. Thomason, v. 1, p. 61.*
Comprises: An extract out of divers letters written in Brazeil, concerning the glorious victory of the taking of the great and populous citie of Loando do S. Paulo in Angola: by the fleet of the Generall West-India company, under the command of the Admirall Houtebeene or Wooden legge ₍Cornelis Jol₎, which was done the 26 of August, 1641. Imprinted at Middelburgh, by the widow and heirs of Simon Mowlers, ordinarie printer to the High and Mighty Lords, States of Zealand...1642 (p. ₍3₎-8). A copy of John Coulombels letter sent from Pernambuck, to Philip Bishop, bearing date the 14. of October, 1641 (p. 9-10). An extract of an other letter sent from N. N. in Brazeil bearing date the 1. of November. 1641. to his friend dwelling in Rochel... (p. 10-11). ₍Letter, dated and signed: 12. Ianuary, 1641. J. Byron₎ (p. 11-₍12₎).

1. Brazil—Hist.—Dutch conquest, 1624-1654. I. Byron, John Byron, 1st baron, d. 1652.
N. Y. P. L. *Revised* October 4, 1937

NL 0413009 NN InU RPJCB NNUT-Mc

Little truths better than great fables
see under [Darton, William] 1747-1819.

Little truths; containing information on divers subjects
see under Darton, William, 1747-1819.

Little truths, for the instruction of children
see under [Darton, William] 1747- 1819.

PZ262
.L87
1835 Little truths; or The juvenile tell-tale. New Haven, S. Babcock, 1835.
16 p. illus. 10cm.

NL 0413013 ICU

VOLUME 336

Little tunes for little folks ... New York, N. Y., F. B. Haviland pub. co. [190–?
v. 31 x 23½cm.
For piano solo.
CONTENTS.—
no. 2. Arranged by Hermann Lichner.

1. Piano music, Juvenile—Teaching pieces. I. Lichner, Hermann, arr.
Library of Congress MT758.L575 46-32832

NL 0413014 DLC

A **little** Turk, and other interesting boys and girls. By S. S. Cox, James Steele [and others] Boston, D. Lothrop company [1892]
225 p. incl. illus., plates. front. 18½cm.
CONTENTS.—L'enfant terrible turk [by] S. S. Cox.—Three little Indians [by] James Steele.—Some Indian children [by] M. B. Norton.—Japanese boys and girls [by] E. S. Morse.—A grand peace meet [by] W. P. Hooper.—Boy shepherds in the African mountains [by] David Ker.—Underground homes [by] David Ker.—How the Boojums went down the crater [by] ten of the Boojums.—Camping among the sunflowers [by] Alice C. Fletcher.—The Carlisle Indian pupils at home [by] Alice C. Fletcher.—Some little Shakers [by] Amanda B. Harris.—Snow spectacles [by] Ernest Ingersoll.

1. Children.
Library of Congress HQ785.L77 9-8175†

NL 0413015 DLC

Little Turtle, Miami chief, d. 1812.

Friends, Society of. *Baltimore Yearly meeting. Committee for Indian affairs.*
Memorial of Evan Thomas, and others, a committee appointed for Indian affairs, by the Yearly meeting of the people called Friends, held in Baltimore. 7th January, 1802 ... [Baltimore, 1802?]

The little turtle that could not stop talking and How Brother Rabbit fooled the whale and the elephant. [New York] The Platt & Munk co., inc. [c1933]
cover-title, [10] p. illus. (part col.) 27cm.

I. Title: How Brother Rabbit fooled the whale and the elephant.
Library of Congress PZ10.3.L726 CA 33-993 Unrev'd

NL 0413017 DLC

"Little unknown."
Colonel Thompson's Principle of "new Protestantism"...
see under title

LD7501 Little Valley, N. Y. Academy.
L5C2 Catalogue of the officers and students
Little Falls, N. Y., 18-
vols. 20cm.

NL 0413019 NBuG

Little verse for a little clan
see under [Woollen, F D]

Little verses and big names. New York, George H. Doran company, 1915.
xix, 305 p. col. front., plates. 23½cm. $2.00

Library of Congress PZ8.3.L735 15-20399

NL 0413021 DLC MWA ViW MiD TxU OKentU

Little verses for good children. [New York] Published by the New-York Religious Tract Society; D. Fanshaw, printer [1824?]
15 p. illus. 9 cm. ([New York Religious Tract Society. Children's tracts; ser. 1, no. 2)
Leaf paged 3-4, wrongly folded, follows p. 14 in L. C. copy.

I. New York Religious Tract Society. II. Series.
PZ8.3.L737 1824 73-153424 MARC

NL 0413022 DLC N

Little verses for good children. New York 144 Nassau St. [1828?]
15 p. illus. (part col.) 9 cm. (American Tract Society. Series I, no. 2)

Title vignette.
Issued by the American Tract Society.

NL 0413023 RPB

P201 Little verses, for good children. Wendell,
.T75 Mass., J. Metcalf, printer, 1831.
no.2 8 p. illus. 9cm.
[Toy books, no.2]

NL 0413024 ICU

Little verses for good children. Northampton [Mass.] A. R. Merrifield [184-?]
1 p. l., 5-10 p. illus. 7½cm.

1. Bibliography—Microscopic and miniature editions—Specimens.
Library of Congress PZ8.3.L737 45-22317

NL 0413025 DLC MB

Little verses for good children. [New York] American Tract Society [not before 1848]
15 p. illus. 11 cm. ([American Tract Society. Children's tracts, ser. 1, no.] 2)

I. American Tract Society. II. Series.
PZ8.3.L737 1848 73-153413 MARC

NL 0413026 DLC

Little verses for good children. [New York] American Tract Society [ca. 1850]
15 p. illus. 11 cm. ([American Tract Society. Children's tracts, ser. 1, no.] 2)
Bound with History of Ann Lively and her Bible. [New York, ca. 1850]

I. American Tract Society. II. Series.
PZ6.H6244 73-153425 MARC

NL 0413027 DLC

Little verses for good children.
= [New York.] American Tract Society. [186-?] 16 pp. Illus. [Little children's library.] 32°.

NL 0413028 MB

The Little Vespers book, for the use of churches and chapels in which Vespers are chanted. London, Thomas Richardson and Son [n.d.].
48 p. music. 12 cm.
Latin and English on opposite pages.
Published ca. 1850.
Bound with O'Leary, Arthur. The Catholic servant's apology. 1843.

NL 0413029 PLatS

The little villager's verse book; consisting of short verses, for children to learn by heart.. 1826
see under Bowles, William Lisle, 1762-1850.

Ax
A100
878L
Rare
Books
Col

Little Violet's picture-album. New York: Thomas Nelson & sons; London: S.W. Partridge & co. [1878?] [26]p. illus. 12½cm. in envelope in folder 23cm. [The "Dewdrop" series. Picture book, no.12]

Title-page and illustrations have been colored by hand.

NL 0413031 TxU ICU

Little visitors; in words composed chiefly of one and two syllables. Lond. Darton, 1819.
101 p.
By M. H.

NL 0413032 PP

Little visits to historical points in Westchester county ... v. 1, no. 1-5; Jan.-May 1902. Mamaroneck, N. Y., The Richbell press, 1902.
1 p. l., 149 (i. e. 157) p. front., 4 pl. 19½cm. monthly.
Each number is preceded by an unpaged t.-p.
No more published.
CONTENTS.—no. 1. White Plains.—no. 2. New Rochelle.—no. 3. Tarrytown.—no. 4. The manors of Westchester co.—no. 5. Ossining and Croton.

1. White Plains, N. Y. 2. New Rochelle, N. Y. 3. Tarrytown, N. Y. 4. Westchester co., N. Y. 5. Manors—Westchester co., N. Y. 6. Ossining, N. Y. 7. Croton acqueduct.
Library of Congress F127.W5L7 7-20575

NL 0413033 DLC

The little voice within
see under American Sunday-School Union.

Little Wabash Baptist Association
see Baptists. Illinois. Little Wabash Association.

The little waif, 1871
see under Cullen, Henry Francis.

VOLUME 336

The little waist defended; a favorite new song. New-york Printed & sor [i. e. sold] by G. Gilfert & Co No 209 Broadway near St Pauls [1795?]

[2] l. 34 cm. (In [Collection of early American music, published or manuscript. v. p., 179-?-182-?] v. 3, no. 58)

Caption title.

1. Songs (Medium voice) with piano—To 1800.

M1.A11 vol. 3, no. 58 M 61-1247

NL 0413037 DLC

Little Walla irrigation union.

Oregon. State engineer.

... Little Walla irrigation union, a corporation, and about 40 others, plaintiffs, appellants and cross-respondents, vs. Finis irrigation company, a corporation, and about 400 others, defendants and respondents, of which about 50 are also cross-appellants. Brief prepared by state engineer and submitted by attorney general as to the state's interests in the unappropriated waters of the streams in controversy. John H. Lewis, state engineer, A. M. Crawford, attorney general. [n. p., 1911?]

Little Walla irrigation union, and about 40 others, plaintiffs, appelants and cross-respondents.

Finis irrigation company, a corporation, and about 400 others, defendants and respondents.

(Little Walla irrigation union, a corporation, and about 40 others, plaintiffs, appellants and cross-respondents)

Water-rights case.

244
L778 Little Walter of Wyalusing. By a guest in "The old castle." N.Y., R. Carter & brothers, 1863.

105 p. front. 16 cm. (Carter's fireside library)

NL 0413040 N NNUT

Little wanderers. [17--?]
69 p. illus. 9cm.

Copy imperfect: Title page missing; title from caption title.

NL 0413041 NNC

The little wanderers. Founded upon fact. By the author of "The gold thimble," "Jane Courtney," "The Contrast," "The adventures of a bodkin," "The flower girl," "Edwin," "Contentment," &c. Boston: Cottons and Barnard, 184 Washington Street. M DCCC XXXII [1832]

16 p. front. 15cm.

Publisher's advertisement on back wrapper.

1. Children's literature.

NL 0413042 MiU-C MB

The Little wanderers' friend.
[New York]

no. 24 cm.

Issued by Howard Mission and Home for Little Wanderers; numbers for include an account of the mission's work.
Includes music.

1. Hymns, English. I. Howard Mission and Home for Little Wanderers, New York.

M2198.L785 52-52687 ‡

NL 0413043 DLC DNLM OFH

-VM
2198
L 77 The LITTLE wanderers' friend. Extra... New York, Howard mission & home for little wanderers [1864]
cover-title, 64p.

Advertising matter included in paging.
An account of the work of the mission and a selection of hymns with music.

NL 0413044 ICN

The little wanderers' friend. [1865?]
see under Howard Mission and Home for Little Wanderers, New York.

-VM
2198
L 77
1872 ...The LITTLE wanderer's friend. (Extra)... Rev. W.C.Van Meter, editor... New York, Howard mission and home for little wanderers, 1872.
cover-title, 130p. 19cm.

Imperfect: p.41-42 wanting.
An account of the work of the mission and a selection of hymns with music.
"Church and Sunday-school directory [of New York city]": p.43-69.

NL 0413046 ICN

Is94
tl
v.2(6 The little wanderers; or, The surprising history and miraculous adventures of two pretty orphans. Embellished with cuts. Published for all good children. Hartford: Printed by Lincoln & Gleason, 1805.
vi, [7]-63p. incl. front., illus. 10½cm.
Frontispiece and p.63 mounted on inside covers.

NL 0413047 CtY MWA

Is94
tl
v.2 The little wanderers; or, The surprising history, and miraculous adventures of two pretty orphans ... New-York: Printed by J. Swaine, 1805.
58p. front. 12cm.
Vignette on p.27.

NL 0413048 CtY

The little wanderers: or the surprising history and miraculous adventure of two pretty orphans. Embellished with pictures. Concord, N.H. Published by George Hough.... Sold wholesale and retail at his bookstore. 1812.

69 p. illus. 9.7cm.

1. Children's lit. I. Ptr. II.-III. Assn.

NL 0413049 MiU-C

The little warbler. v. ... Providence, Hutchens & Shepard,
v. front. 11 cm.
Contents.-v. 6. Naval songs.

NL 0413050 RPB

The Little Warbler. Irish Songs. London, R. Mills, n.d.
Miniature Edition.
Red paper cover.
Note. Halsey Library.-From F. T. Sabin, London, 1896.

NL 0413051 CSmH

The LITTLE warbler of the cottage and her dog Constant. By a lover of children. With engravings. Boston, Munroe and Francis, etc., etc., 1827.

15 x 9.5 cm. pp.(2), [5]-68. Plate.
Imperfect: 1 plate wanting.

NL 0413052 MH

The Little warbler; or, The vocal gleaner. Edinburgh, Printed by T. Oliver for G. Miller, Dunbar [1803]-05.
2 v. in 1. 68 mm.

L.S.U. copy imperfect: t.p. and p. 1-8 of v.1 wanting.
Vol. 1 contains Scottish ballads and songs; v.2, English and Irish songs.

1. Scottish ballads and songs. 2. English ballads and songs. 3. Irish ballads and songs. 4. Bibliography--Microscopic and minature editions--Specimens. I. Title: The vocal gleaner.

NL 0413053 LU

The little water-cress sellers
see under [Fry, Mrs. Sarah Maria]

The little Weaver family. A Congleton sketch, by the author of "Little Ned," "Gabriel Fletcher," &c. Leeds: J. Kershaw and Son [18—?]. 4 p. 12°.

Caption-title.
In: VTZ p. v. 189, no. 17.

1. Temperance.—Fiction. 2. Fiction (English).
N. Y. P. L. April 22, 1919.

NL 0413055 NN

LITTLE Wentworth's morning lesson. Designed for children two or three years old. By the author of 'Fruit and Flowers'. Boston, Hilliard Grey, Little and Wilkins, 1828.

24°. pp.9.

NL 0413056 MH

The little Western against the Great Eastern: or, Brother Jonathan vs. John Bull: being a review by a plebeian of the Western hemisphere of abolitionism, as exposed by Doctor Sleigh. Philadelphia, 1838. 12 p. 23½cm.

Signed: The Little Western.

1. Slavery—U. S.—Controversial literature, 1838. 2. Sleigh, William Willcocks, b. 1796. Abolitionism exposed! I. A plebeian of the Western hemisphere of abolitionism.
N. Y. P. L. February 11, 1941

NL 0413057 NN

Little wheel a-turnin' in my heart: American negro folksong, arr. by W. A. Fisher.
Ditson, c 1919.
(American negro melodies)
Medium.

NL 0413058 OrP

VOLUME 336

Little Whelnetham Parish, Eng.
see Whelnetham, Little, Eng. (Parish)

The little while, and other poems... [1865]
see under Crewdson, Mrs. Jane (Fox) 1808-1863.

The Little White Gnome, a fairy tale for children and grown-ups who still believe in fairies
see under Henley, Mrs. Bessie Stella (Jones) 1888-

Little White House Conference
see
Governor's Conference on Children and Youth (*Maryland*)

A little white shadow
see under [Morgan, Emily Malbone] 1862-1937.

LB 1573 .5 .L 79

Little wide awake; an illustrated magazine for good children. Edited by Mrs. Sale Barker ... London, G. Routledge and sons, 18 -
v. col. front., illus. 25cm.

NL 0413064 MdBJ MiD

The little Wild Girl
New York, [c.1804-1814] sheet music

NL 0413065 RPJCB

PS3500 f.L81 19- Rare bk room

Little wildflower. [19-?]
2 l.,27 numb.l. 32cm.
Caption title.
Typewritten.
On cover:Wildflower.

NL 0413066 ICU

Little Will, The Alpine cross, and Jesus' seat
see under American Tract Society.

LITTLE William; or, The true way to be happy. New-York, Published by the American tract society, 150 Nassau-street [183-?] 16 p. illus. 11cm.

At head of title: No. 39. On cover: Series II. No. XXXIX.
In original illustrated blue paper covers, with publishers' advertisements on back.
Also has continuous paging: p. [97]-112.

Continued in next column

Continued from preceding column

Titles of no. 17-32 of the series listed on back cover.

---- Second copy.
Titles of no. 25-37 of the series listed on back cover.

I. American tract society.

NL 0413069 NN ICU

PZ 6 L7378

Little Willie. By the Author of "Uncle Jack the fault-killer", "Unica", etc. New York, General Protestant Episcopal Sunday School Union, and Church Book Society, 1860.
134p. illus. 15cm.
On cover: St. Michael's Church, Litchfield, Sunday School Library, No. 605.

1. Sunday-school literature--Early to 1870.

NL 0413070 CtU

Little Willie [1895]
see under [Field, Eugene] 1850-1895.

LITTLE Willies. Boston: The Carol Press[, cop. 1911]. 9 l. 32°.

Humorous verses.
Printed at the Stetson Press, Boston.

583268A. 1. Wit and humor, American.

NL 0413072 NN RPB MH OO

Little Willie's holiday, or A visit to Cowslip farm. London, Ward & Lock [1858]
16 p. illus.

NL 0413073 MH

Little Willy: a story for little children. New York, S. Wood & sons [1833?]
19 p. illus. 13 cm.
Illustrated t.-p.
1. Children's poetry.

NL 0413074 RPB

Little Willy; a story for little children. Northampton, E. Turner [1833?]
1 p.l., [5]-16 [1] p. illus. 12 cm.

NL 0413075 RPB DLC

Little Willy; a story for little children. Northampton, E. Turner [1840?]
16 p. illus. 14 cm.

In verse.
In slipcase.

NL 0413076 NjP

PZ260 .L83 18—

Little Willy, the good boy. Cincinnati, W. T. Truman [18—]
16 p. illus. (Truman's entertaining toy book)

NL 0413077 ICU

Mhc8 1642 L73

Little-wits protestation, to defend popery: since the decease of his sister svperstition. Anno dom.1642. By I. G. gent. London,F.Coules, 1642.
1p.l.,4p. 18½cm.
Signed on p.4: Little-wit.

NL 0413078 CtY

Little woman and the pedlar, The
N.Y., 1810.
15 engravings 18°

NL 0413079 MWA

The LITTLE woman and the pedlar [with the strange destraction that seized her,and the undutiful behaviour of her little dog on that occasion]. London,printed for M.J.Godwin and Co.,1822.

16 cm. pp.xxxi. Colored illustr.
Printed on one side of the leaf only.
Imperfect: title-page worm-eaten.

NL 0413080 MH

Little women
see under Alcott, Louisa May, 1822-1888.

Little wonder book.
[Columbus, O., C. E. Merrill Co., 19
no. illus. 21 cm.

AC8.L66 372.4 47-879 rev*‡

NL 0413082 DLC

Little Woolstone, Parish, Buckinghamshire, England
see Woolstone, Little, England (Parish)

Juv. coll.

Little words and little pictures [n.p.,n.d.]
8 p. 8 cm.

NL 0413084 DLC

The little worker for helpful little folks ... Boston, Lothrop pub. co. [1899]
[61] p. illus., pl. 4°. (Childhood series)

99—1997

NL 0413085 DLC

VOLUME 336

PZ
7
.L778

Little workers. New York, McLoughlin Bros. [1883?]
32,32,32 p. illus.

NL 0413086 MiU

The little workers; or, How Frank, Charley, and Lilly helped their sick father. A story for little ones. New York, Sunday-School Union [182-?]
56 p. illus. 11 cm.

I. Sunday School Union of the Methodist Episcopal Church.

NL 0413087 N

The little world; or, A liuely description of all the partes and properties of man
see under [Underwood, Robert] fl. 1600.

The little writer: designed as an aid to children in acquiring an easy and familiar epistolary style ... Boston, J. Dowe, 1836.
108 p. 15cm.

1. Letter-writing.

11-7683

Library of Congress PE1495.L6

NL 0413089 DLC

A little yet true rehearsall of severall passages of affairs, collected by a friend of Doctor Alexander's at Aberdeen, 1635–1645. (*In* Rogers, Charles. Historical notices of St. Anthony's monastery. Leith . . . London. 1877. 22½cm. p. 41–62)

Caption title.
Ed. from a contemporary ms.

2-7285

NL 0413090 DLC

Little York Gold Washing and Water Company, defendant.
James H. Keyes vs. Little York Gold Washing and Water Company
see under James H plaintiff.

PZ 6
1830
L58

LITTLE Zoe, and The spoiled children. Concord, N.H., R. H. Sherburne, 1830.
16? p. illus. 10 cm.
Library's copy imperfect: all after p. 10 lacking.
Title vignette.

I. Title: The spoiled children.

NL 0413092 CaBVaU

Littleboy, Anna L.
The Bible and social reform; a series of study outlines prepared for the use of adult schools. By Anna L. Littleboy and Frank W. Metcalfe and with a section by Effie Ryle ... and G. Currie Martin ... London, National adult school union [1929]
68 p. 18½cm.

1. Sociology, Christian. I. Metcalfe, Frank W., joint author. II. Ryle, Effie. III. Martin, George Currie, 1865- IV. Title.

NL 0413093 MiU

Littleboy, Anna L.
A history of Jordans. Lond., 1909.

NL 0413094 PHC PHi NcGuG

Littleboy, Anna L.
A history of Jordans... New ed...London, Headly, 1911.
26 p.

NL 0413095 PPF

H
289.642
L72j

Littleboy, Anna L
A history of Jordans. 5th ed. London, Friends' Bookshop, 1925.
32p. illus., map. 18 1/2cm.

1. Friends, Society of. England. 2. Jordans Meeting-house. I. Title.

NL 0413096 ViHarEM PSC-Hi MB

Mnm69
1927
L27

Littleboy, Anna I
A history of Jordans. London, Friends' Book Centre, 1927.
32p. plates, fold. map. 18cm.

NL 0413097 CtY

Littleboy, Anna L
A history of Jordans, by Anna L. Littleboy ... London, Friends' book centre, 1934.
32 p. plates, fold. map. 18½cm.

1. Beaconsfield, Eng. Jordans meeting-house. 2. Friends, Society of. Beaconsfield, Eng.

NL 0413098 NNC

Littleboy, Anna L
A history of Jordans. L, Friends' Book Centre, 1938

NL 0413099 MH

Littleboy, Anna L
A history of Jordans, by Anna L. Littleboy. London, Friends home service committee [1949].
28p. plates. 18½cm.

NL 0413100 PSC-Hi

Littleboy, Anna L.
A history of Jordans. [10th revised edition] London, Friends Home Service Committee [1953]
20 p. illus. O.

NL 0413101 PPAmP

Littleboy, Anna L.
A history of the Friends' reference library with notes on early printers and printing in the Society of Friends, being the presidential address of the Friends historical society for the year 1920, by Anna L. Littleboy. London, Society of Friends, 1921.
cover-title, 31, [1] p. facsim. 23cm.
Running title: Devonshire house reference library.

1. London. Friends' reference library. I. Friends' historical society.

22-2324

Library of Congress Z792.L583L

NL 0413102 DLC PPFr ICJ PHC

Littleboy, Anna L.
"Period" in English history teaching. Friends Guild of teachers, 1899.

NL 0413103 PSC-Hi

FILM
9279
PQ

[Littleboy, Anna L]
Relations between French and English literature in the 16th and 17th centuries. [London, H.K. Lewis, 1895]
41 p. On film (Negative) (The Quain essay, 1895)

Microfilm. Original in British Museum.
Caption title.

1. Literature, Comparative - French and English. 2. Literature, Comparative - English and French. I. Title.

NL 0413104 CU

Littleboy, Sarah, supposed author.
A visit to the grave of William Penn, at Jordans, in Buckinghamshire ... London, W. & F. G. Cash, 1853.

Littleboy, Wilfrid E.
With Christ as leader ... London, Friends' book centre, 1940.
cover-title. 12 p. 23 cm.

NL 0413106 PHC

Littleboy, William.
The appeal of Quakerism to the non-mystic. [London], Published by R.Davis for the "1905 committee of Yorkshire Quarterly meeting of the Society of Friends" [19- ?]

16 p. 21.5 cm.

NL 0413107 MH PHC

VOLUME 336

Littleboy, William.
The appeal of Quakerism to the non-mystic. [A Quaker view] London, Friends' Book Centre [1945]
15 p. 22 cm.

1. Friends, Society of.

A 49-6895*

Harvard Univ. Library for Library of Congress [1]

NL 0413108 MH PHC

Littleboy, William.
The day of our visitation, by William Littleboy. [London:] Published for the Woodbrooke Extension Committee by Headley Bros., Ltd., 1917. 62 p. 12°. (Swarthmore lectures, 1917.)

1. Jesus Christ.—Advent (Second). 2. Friends (Society of).—Doctrine. 3. Series.
N. Y. P. L. October 17, 1917.

NL 0413109 NN InRE PSC PU NcD MH ICN ICU PHC

Littleboy, William.
... Friends and peace ... London, Pub. for the Friends' Home mission and extension committee by the Friends' tract association, 1915.
cover-title. 11 p. 20.5 cm. (The "Woolman" series. no. 2)

NL 0413110 PHC

Littleboy, William
The meaning and practice of prayer, by William Littleboy. [Philadelphia,The Tract Association of Friends,1947]
16p. 13cm.

NL 0413111 PSC-Hi

Littleboy, William and others.
Methods of propaganda, being the report of Commission and issued by the committee of the Peace conference of all Friends. n.d.
37 p.

NL 0413112 PSC-Hi

Littlebury, Isaac, tr.

Fénelon, François de Salignac de La Mothe-, *abp.*, 1651-1715.
The adventures of Telemachus, the son of Ulysses. In twenty-four books. Written by the Archbishop of Cambray. To which are added, The adventures of Aristonous. Done into English by Mr. Litterbury [!] and Mr. Boyer. The 19th ed., carefully rev. and cor. ... London, Printed for J. Buckland [etc.] 1778.

Littlebury, Isaac, tr.

Herodotus.
The history of Herodotus. Tr. from the Greek. By Isaac Littlebury. London, E. Castle [etc.] 1709.

LITTLEBURY,Robert.
Catalogus bibliothecae illustrissimi Domini Gulielmi Ducie vicecomitis duni,equitis aurati, ordinis balnei. Londini,1680.

23 x 17 cm. pp.40. pp.(2),40.

NL 0413115 MH

TH12
.B6
Littlebury and company, ltd., Worcester, Eng.
Builders', architects' and civil engineers' manual. Worcester [Eng.] Littlebury & company ltd. [1946]

Littlebury and company, ltd., Worcester, Eng.
Littlebury's guide to Worcester and its neighbourhood
see under title

Littlebury and company, ltd., Worcester, Eng.
Littlebury's Illustrated guide to Worcester and district
see under title

HF3503
.M3
1948
Littlebury and Company, ltd., Worcester. Eng.
FOR OTHER EDITIONS SEE MAIN ENTRY
Manufacturers, bankers and exporters manual; the ABC of British exports. Worcester, Littlebury [1948]

GV1025
.G7M65
Littlebury and Company, ltd., Worcester, Eng.
Motorists and cyclists road guide. Worcester [Eng.] Littlebury [1947]

HD9731
.3
.T7
Littlebury and Company, ltd., Worcester, Eng.
The Trades directory of British manufacturers and buyers guide, with register of British manufactures. Worcester [Eng.] Littlebury [n. d.]

1468
.985
.59
Littlebury's directory & gazetteer of the County of Worcester (with an Appendix). London, J. Littlebury (1873)
1046 p. illus.,map (folded) 23 cm

1. WORCESTERSHIRE, ENG. - DIRECT. I. Littlebury, J

NL 0413122 NjP

Littlebury's guide to Worcester and its neighbourhood, containing a description of the city.. Worcester, Eng. J.Littlebury [1880]

NL 0413123 MH

---

ar V
3907
Littlebury's guide to Worcester and its neighbourhood, containing a description of the city--its cathedral, churches, chapels, public schools, hospitals, buildings, places of amusement, manufactories, etc.; also a list of the streets, roads, etc., in the city; followed by a brief description of places of interest in the neighbourhood... 2d ed. Worcester [Eng., 1882?]
142 p. illus. 20cm.

NL 0413124 NIC

Littlebury's guide to Worcester and its neighbourhood. Containing a description of the city — its cathedral, churches, chapels, public schools, hospitals, buildings, places of amusement, manufactories, etc.; also a list of the streets, roads, etc., in the city; followed by a brief description of places of interest in the neighbourhood ... Worcester [Eng.] Littlebury and co. [etc., 1883] 148 p. incl. tables. front. (plan), illus., map. 20cm.
At head of title: Third edition.
Advertising matter interspersed.

968526A. 1. Worcester, Eng.—Guidebooks, 1883. I. Title.
N. Y. P. L. May 5, 1939

NL 0413125 NN

Littlebury's illustrated guide to Worcester, containing a description of the city: its cathedral, churches, chapels, public schools, historical buildings, etc. Worcester, [Eng.] Littlebury [1889]

"6th ed."

NL 0413126 MH

Littlebury's Illustrated guide to Worcester and district, ... 10th edition.
= Worcester. [1907.] 188 pp. Illus. Plates. Plan. 18½ cm., in 16s.

K309 — Worcester, England. Descr. Guide-books.

NL 0413127 MB

HV7914
L5
Littlechild, John George
The reminiscences of Chief-Inspector Littlechild. 2d ed. London, Leadenhall Pr., 1894
238 p. 20 cm

NL 0413128 NjP MH-L

LITTLECHILD, Mary J,
Think on these Things. New York, Vantage Press, c1951. 5-80 p. 21 cm.

1.Bible-Interpretations of. 2. Title.

NL 0413129 NNJ

Littlechild, Walter Poole.
A short account of King's College Chapel.
— Cambridge. W. Heffer & Sons, Ltd. 1920. (5), 25, (1) pp. Diagram. 16½ cm.

M1053 — University of Cambridge. King's College Chapel.

NL 0413130 MB CtY

VOLUME 336

Littlechild, Walter Poole.
A short account of King's college chapel, by W. P. Littlechild ... 2d ed. ... Cambridge [Eng.] W. Heffer & sons, ltd., 1921.
vi p., 1 l., 47, [1] p. front., 1 illus., plates. 18cm.

1. Cambridge. University. King's college. Chapel.
35-20197
Library of Congress DA690.C2L5 1921 914.259

NL 0413131 DLC NN

DA 690 .L75L5 1897
Littlecote. London, Print. for private circulation, 1897.
63 p. illus. 21 cm.
First published in 1897.
Much of the information regarding Littlecote house, Wiltshire, the home of the Calston, Darrell and Popham families, has been compiled from Mr. Hubert Hall's "Society in the Elizabethan age," and other sources.

1. Littlecote house, Wiltshire, England. 2. Calston family. 3. Darrell family. 4. Popham family. 5. Leybourne-Popham family.

NL 0413132 OKentU

Littlecote. [2d ed.] London, Print. for private circulation, 1900.
6 p. l., 130 p., 1 l., xii p. front., plates, 4 geneal. tab. (2 fold.) 30cm.
First published in 1897.
Much of the information regarding Littlecote house, Wiltshire, the home of the Calston, Darrell and Popham families, has been compiled from Mr. Hubert Hall's "Society in the Elizabethan age," and other sources.

1. Littlecote house, Wiltshire, Eng. 2. Calston family. 3. Darrell family. 4. Popham family. 5. Leyborne-Popham family.
20-10928
Library of Congress DA690.L75L5 1900

NL 0413133 DLC IU

[Littledale, Anthony]
A catalogue of the elegant library of an eminent collector, deceased, removed from his residence in the country. [Sold at auction by Sotheby, 5 June & 4 following days, 1820.] [London, 1820]
34p.
Priced, with buyers' names.

NL 0413134 MH

HQ750 .A2M2
Littledale, Clara (Savage) 1891- ed.
The Metropolitan mothers' guide; devoted to the welfare of children in New York private schools and selected suburban schools. v. 1-2, no. 2; Nov. 1932-Feb. 1933. [New York, The Parents' publishing association, inc., etc., 1932-33]

PZ3 .H318 Sc 80
Littledale, Clara (Savage) 1891- ed.
Hawthorne, Nathaniel, 1804-1864.
The scarlet letter, by Nathaniel Hawthorne, with condenser's comment by Clara Savage Littledale ... New York, N. Y., The Parents' institute, inc. [1945]

PN44 .T76
Littledale, Clara (Savage) 1891-
Twelve of the world's famous adventure books, condensed to about 20 minutes reading time each ... New York, N. Y., Keep-worthy books, inc. [1946]

PN44 .T8
Littledale, Clara (Savage) 1891-
Twelve of the world's famous books, condensed to about 20 minutes reading time each ... New York, N. Y., Keep-worthy books, inc. [1945]

PN44 .T82
Littledale, Clara (Savage) 1891-
Twelve of the world's famous love stories, condensed to about 20 minutes reading time each ... New York, N. Y., Keep-worthy books, inc. [1946]

D741 L72
Littledale, Clara Savage, 1891-
What to do about the "comics"; because substitution is better than prohibition, the publishers of "Parents' magazine" are launching "True comics" and so enabling you to offer your children a magazine that is worthwhile, by Clara Savage Littledale ... [New York, The Parents' institute, inc., c1941]
[4] p. illus., ports. 28cm.
Caption title.

NL 0413140 NNC

Littledale, Edward, 1779-1837.
Catalogue of the library of the late Edward Littledale ... also his paintings and prints ... which will be sold by auction by Mr. Evans ... July 14 ... 1837. [London, W. Nicol, 1837]
124 p. 22cm.

1. Bibliography - Rare books.

NL 0413141 NNC

Littledale, Edward, 1779-1837.
[Constable, Henry] 1562-1613.
Diana. Or, The excellent conceitful Sonnets of H. C. Augmented with diuers Quatorzains of honorable and lerned personages. Deuided into viij. Decads ... At London, Printed by James Roberts for Richard Smith. 1584 [i. e. 1594] [London, Reprinted for the Roxburghe club, 1818]

Littledale, Harold, 1853-1930.
Cymbeline, in a Hindoo playhouse. [London and New York, The Macmillan and co., etc., etc., 1880]
p.65-68
Extract from Macmillan's magazine, vol. 42, May, 1880.

NL 0413143 PU-F

PR5560 L5 1893
Littledale, Harold, 1853-1930
Essays on Lord Tennyson's Idylls of the king. London, New York, Macmillan, 1893.
x, 308 p. 19 cm.
Bibliographical footnotes.

1. Tennyson, Alfred Tennyson, baron, 1809-1892. Idylls of the king

NL 0413144 OOxM OCl OU ODW CtY TxU NjP ViU FTaSU MeB MH CLSU MoU PPFr PPL PHC MB FMU

Littledale, Harold, 1853-1930.
Essays on Lord Tennyson's Idylls of the king, by Harold Littledale, M. A. London, Macmillan and co., limited, 1907.
x, 331, [1] p. 19cm.
"First edition 1893; reprinted 1907."

1. Tennyson, Alfred Tennyson, 1st baron. Idylls of the king. 2. Arthur, King.
8-37744
Library of Congress PR5560.L5

NL 0413145 DLC OOxM MsU ICU NcD OCl OClW MtU

Littledale, Harold, 1853-
Essays on Lord Tennyson's Idylls of the king. London: Macmillan and Co., 1912. x, 331(1) p. 12°.

1. Tennyson (1. baron), Alfred Tennyson: Idylls of the king.
N. Y. P. L. April 20, 1914.

NL 0413146 NN CaBVaU WaT PPGi

Littledale, Harold, 1853-
Essays on Lord Tennyson's Idylls of the king, by ..., M. A. London, Macmillandand co., limited, 1913.
x, 331, 1 p.

NL 0413147 OO

Littledale, Harold, 1853-1930, ed.
Dyce, Alexander, 1798-1869.
A glossary to the works of William Shakespeare, by the Rev. Alexander Dyce. The references made applicable to any edition of Shakespeare, the explanations revised and new notes added by Harold Littledale ... London, S. Sonnenschein & co., lim.; New York, E. P. Dutton & co., 1902.

Littledale, Harold, 1853-1930.
... The good-natured man
see under Goldsmith, Oliver, 1728-1774.

Littledale, Harold, 1853-1930, ed.
Wordsworth, William, 1770-1850.
... Lyrical ballads, 1798, edited by H. Littledale ... London, Oxford university press, H. Milford [1931]

Littledale, Harold, 1853-1930, ed.
Wordsworth, William, 1770-1850, *comp.*
Poems and extracts chosen by William Wordsworth for an album presented to Lady Mary Lowther, Christmas, 1819. Printed literally from the original album with facsimiles. London, H. Frowde, 1905.

Littledale, Harold, 1853-1930, ed.
Fletcher, John, 1579-1625.
The two noble kinsmen. By William Shakspere and John Fletcher. Ed. from the quarto of 1634 by Harold Littledale ... London, Pub. for the New Shakspere society, by N. Trübner & co., 1876-85.

VOLUME 336

Littledale, Harold, 1853-1930.
The two noble kinsmen. By William Shakspere and John Fletcher. Edited from the quarto of 1634 by Harold Littledale. Part 2. General introduction and list of words. London, The New Shakspere Society, 1881.
82, 145-150 p. 21 cm., in 8s.
Proof. - To be read at the 66th meeting of the New Shakespere Society, January 21, 1881.

NL 0413153 MB

PR2411 .W4 1920

Littledale, Harold, 1853-1930, ed.

The **Welsh** embassador ... [London, Printed for the Malone society by F. Hall at the Oxford university press, 1921]

Littledale, Harold A
Mastering your disability. New York, Rinehart [1952]
224 p. illus. 20 cm.

1. Disabled—Rehabilitation, etc. I. Title.

RD795.L5 *362.43 52—8734 ‡

WaS WaE CaBVa
PJA MB NN TU NcC DNLM KEmT Or IdB OrU-M OrP WaT Wa
NL 0413155 DLC IdPI WaTC OkU NBuC LU ViU OC1W PSt

Bon. Y 682 .L 72

[Littledale, Henry Anthony] d.1859.
Boltonæ laudes. Bolton juxta Bowland. [Manchester]1858. sq.Q.

Latin poem.
Author's autograph presentation copy.

NL 0413156 ICN

Littledale, Henry Anthony, *d.* 1859.
King Henry's well, and Pudsay's leap. Ballads, founded on Craven legends. Printed for private circulation. Bolton by Bowland. [Manchester, Printed by G. Falkner] 1856.
35 p. 3 pl. (incl. front.; 1 pl. fold.) 25½cm.
Dedication signed: H. A. Littledale.
Errata slip inserted at end.

1. Craven, Eng. I. Title. II. Title: Pudsay's leap.

16-12140

Library of Congress PR4890.L4K5

NL 0413157 DLC CtY

Littledale, Henry Anthony, d. 1859.
The Song of Solomon in the dialect of Craven in the West riding of Yorkshire... London, 1859
see under Bible. O. T. Song of Solomon. English (Yorkshire) 1859. Littledale.

Littledale , Horace A
Chart of government duplication of activities. New York, National budget committee, c1921.

Copyright by New York Evening post, inc.

NL 0413159 OC1FRB MH-BA

Littledale, Isaac.
... A catalogue of the entire, select, and valuable library, of the late Isaac Littledale. [Sold at auction by T. Winstanley & son, 4 Aug. & 4 following days, 1828.] [Liverpool, 1828]

32,2,4p.
Interleaved with prices & buyers' names.

NL 0413160 MH

Littledale, Sir Joseph, 1767-1842.
Catalogue of the greater portion of the valuable law library of the late Right Honourable Sir Joseph Littledale. [Sold at auction by Sotheby, 14 Jan. 1843.] [London, 1842]

14p.
Interleaved with prices & buyers' names.

NL 0413161 MH

Littledale, *Sir* **Joseph,** 1767–1842.
Catalogue of the ... library of the Right Honourable Sir Joseph Littledale, one of the judges of the Court of Queen's bench, deceased. Which ... will be sold by auction, by Mr. S. Leigh Sotheby ... January 23d, 1843, and six following days (Sunday excepted) ... [London, 1843?]
79 p. 21½cm.
No. 1 in a vol. of pamphlets lettered: Sale catalogues.
1,739 lots.

13-7048

Library of Congress Z997.L78 no. 1

NL 0413162 DLC MH

Littledale, Sir Joseph, 1767-1842, ed.

Skelton, John, 1460?-1529.
Magnyfycence; an interlude. By John Skelton, poet laureat to Henry VIII. [n. p., n. d.] London, Re-printed by G. Woodfall, 1821.

Littledale, Ralph Pudsay, 1856- *ed.*
... The Pudsay deeds. The Pudsays of Bolton and Barforth, and their predecessors in those manors. Edited by Colonel Ralph Pudsay Littledale ... [London] The Society, 1916.
v p., 1 l., 434 p., 1 l. plates, facsims., geneal. tables (part fold.) 23cm. (The Yorkshire archæological society ... Record series. v. 56)

1. Deeds—Yorkshire, Eng. 2. Yorkshire, Eng.—Geneal. I. Title.

35-10911

Library of Congress DA670.Y59Y6 vol. 56
[3] (942.74) 333.3094274

NL 0413164 DLC CU PPL PU-L MB MH NN

BR759 .A1P13 no. 9

Littledale, Richard Frederick, 1833-1890.
Additional services. A second letter to Charles Thomas, Lord Archbishop of Canterbury, President of the Royal Commission on Ritual. London, G. J. Palmer, 1868.
32p. 21cm. (Pamphlets [no. 9])

1. Church of England. Liturgy and ritual. I. Longley, Charles Thomas, Abp. of Canterbury, 1794-1868. II. Title.

NL 0413165 IEG

Littledale, Richard Frederick, 1833-1890.
Catholic ritual in the Church of England scriptural, reasonable, lawful. ... 8th thous. London, n.d.
21 p. 16°. [In v. 711, College Pamphlets]

NL 0413166 CtY

2479

Littledale, Richard Frederick, 1833-1890.
The Christian priesthood. [London, G. J. Palmer, 1867]
4 p.
Caption title.
Bound with pamp. 2450.

1. Priests. I. Title.

NL 0413167 TxDaM-P

2478

Littledale, Richard Frederick, 1833-1890.
The Christian sacrifice. [London, G. J. Palmer, 1867?]
4 p.
Caption title.
Bound with pamp. 2450.

1. Sacrifice. 2. Lord's Supper. I. Title.

NL 0413168 TxDaM-P

Littledale, Richard Frederick, *1833–1890.*
Church principles tested by their results.
(*In* Lectures in defence of Church principles. Pp. 75-93. Oxford. 1871.)
A defense of the High Church Party of the Church of England.

M7714 — England, Church of. Doc[trin]al and controversial works. — Anglo-Catholic Movement.

NL 0413169 MB

Littledale, Richard Frederick, 1833-1890.
A commentary on the Psalms from primitive and medieval writers... London, 1860-74
see under Bible. O. T. Psalms. English. 1860-74. Coverdale.

and with later dates (frequently of mixed editions) beginning 1860-74, 1868-74, 1868-83, 1869-74, 1872-74, 1873-74, 1874, 1879-84, 1879-86, 1879-87, 1883-1889, and 1884.

Littledale, Richard Frederick, 1833–1890.
A commentary on the Song of songs. From ancient and mediæval sources. By Richard Frederick Littledale ... London, J. Masters; New York, Pott and Amery, 1869.
xl, 382 p. 18cm.

NL 0413171 DLC CtY NNUT

Littledale, Richard Frederick, 1833-1890
Controversy on the constitutions of the Jesuits between Dr. Littledale and Fr. Drummond. Winnipeg, Manitoba Free Press Print., 1889.
25 p.

Cover title.

NL 0413172 CaOTU

VOLUME 336

BR83
.841 Littledale, Richard Frederick, 1833-1880.
The crisis of disestablishment; a lecture delivered at the Mechanics' Institute, Bradford, May 16th, 1870. London, G. J. Palmer, 1870.
36 p. 18 cm.
"Reprinted by request."

NL 0413173 MB

LITTLEDALE, Richard Frederick, 1833-1890.
Early Christian ritual. A lecture, read before the guild of S. Alban the Martyr. 2d ed. London, C. Cull, [1867].

pp.16. C 6475.11

NL 0413174 MH

Littledale, Richard Frederick, 1833-1890. The elevation of the Host. A liturgical essay. 2nd ed. London, Palmer, 1866. 23 p.

NL 0413175 PPPD

281.9
L779 Littledale, Richard Frederick, 1833-1870.
The Holy Eastern Church; a popular outline of its history, doctrines, liturgies, and vestments. By a priest of the English Church. The preface by the Rev. Dr. Littledale. 2d ed. London, J.T. Hayes, 1873.
xi, 102 p. illus. 19 cm.

1. Orthodox Eastern Church. Hist. I. Title.

NL 0413176 N OCISA

Littledale, Richard Frederick, 1833-1890.
—— Incense. A liturgical essay. 2nd ed. London, Palmer, 1866. 33 p.

NL 0413177 PPPD CtY

BX5123
.L78
1868 Littledale, Richard Frederick, 1833-1890.
Innovations. A lecture delivered in the assembly rooms, Liverpool, April 23rd, 1868.
SWTS Oxford, A.R. Mowbray; London, Simpkin, Marshall, 1868.
62 p. 17cm.
Cover-title.

1. Ritualism. I. Title

NL 0413178 IEG WaPS PPL PPPD MH

LITTLEDALE, Richard Frederick, 1833-1890.
The law of ritual. [London], n.d.

1 pam.

NL 0413179 MH

BV825.52
.L78
1866 Littledale, Richard Frederick, 1833-1890.
The mixed chalice. A letter to Henry, Lord Bishop of Exeter. 3d ed. London, G. J. Palmer, 1866.
20p. 21cm.

1. Lord's Supper--Bread and wine. I. Title. II. Phillpotts, Henry, Bp. of Exeter, 1778-1869.

NL 0413180 IEG PPPD

Littledale, Richard Frederick, 1833-1890.
The North-side of the Altar. A liturgical essay ... 3d ed. London, 1865.
32 p. 8°. [In v. 689, College Pamphlets]

NL 0413181 CtY PPLT PPPD

Littledale, Richard Frederick, 1833-1890.
Offices from the service-books of the Holy Eastern church
see under Orthodox Eastern church. Liturgy and ritual.

LITTLEDALE, Richard Frederick, 1833-1890.
The ornaments, rubric, and the eastward position. Strictures on Dean Howson's pamphlet, in a letter to J.M. Gladstone. Liverpool, 1875.

pp.15.

NL 0413183 MH

X
O
.507
v.1 [Littledale, Richard Frederick] 1883-1890.
The Oxford solar myth, a contribution to comparative mythology... [Dublin, McGee, 1870] p.145-154.

Caption title.
Satire on Max Müller.
Extract from Kottabos, Trinity college, Dublin. 1870.
Binder's title: Linguistic pamphlets.

NL 0413184 ICN

[Littledale, Richard Frederick] 1833-1890, ed. & comp.
The people's hymnal ... London, Joseph Masters, 1867.
2 p.l., 227 [1] p. 13.5 cm.
600 hymns
Hymns 592-600 are "metrical litanies", each of which is followed by short excerpt from the Book of common prayer.
Copies are badly mutilated, - hymns cut out.
Julian in his dictionary attributes this work to Littledale.
Hymns assigned in index to A. L. P. (i.e. A London priest) are by Littledale.

NL 0413185 NNUT MBU-T

---

ar U
1596 [Littledale, Rev. Richard Frederick] 1833-1890, comp.
The people's hymnal. London, J. Masters: New York, Pott and Amery, 1868.
iv, 552 p. 15cm.

Without music.

1. Hymns, English. I. Title.

NL 0413186 NIC NNUT

[Littledale, Richard Frederick] 1833-1890, ed. & comp.
The people's hymnal ... Fourth edition. London, Joseph Masters, 1871 [pref. 1867]
2 p.l., 227 [1] p., 13.5 cm.
600 hymns.
Hymns 592-600 are "metrical litanies", each of which is followed by short excerpt from the Book of common prayer.
Jesus, lover of my soul, given on p. 222 as a varient hymns for number 507.
Julian in his Dictionary of hymnology attributes this work to Littledale.

Hymns assigned in index to A. L. P. (i. e. A London priest) are by Littledale.

NL 0413188 NNUT

BX
1765
.L78 Littledale, Richard Frederick, 1833-1890.
The Petrine claims. A critical inquiry by Richard Frederick Littledale ... Published under the direction of the Tract committee. London, Society for promoting Christian knowledge; New York, E.& J.B. Young & co., 1889.
3 p.l., [v]-xvi, 363 p. 17½cm.
"A corrected reissue of ... articles which appeared in the Church quarterly review in 1878-1884."--Preface.

1. Papacy. 2. Catholic church--Doctrinal works--Protestant authors. I. Title.

MH
NL 0413189 MiU CU RPB NjNbS NcD PPLT PPRETS PPPD

Littledale, Richard Frederick, 1833-1890.
Pharisaic proselytism: a forgotten chapter of early church history. London, J. T. Hayes, 1870.
31 p.
Bound with pamp. 2450.

NL 0413190 TxDaM-P

Littledale, Richard Frederick, 1833-1890.
Plain reasons against joining the church of Rome, by Richard Frederick Littledale ... 20th thousand, further revised and enlarged ... London, Society for promoting Christian knowledge; New York, Pott, Young & co., 1880.
224 p. 17½cm.

1. Catholic church—Doctrinal and controversial works—Protestant authors. I. Title.
Library of Congress BX1765.L5 31—2752
[43b1] 239.9

NNUT PPEB NcD
NL 0413191 DLC IEG ICU MH NN MiU DCU PV PU PPPD

Littledale, Richard Frederick, 1833-1890.
Plain reasons against joining the Church of Rome...London, 1881.
225 p.

NL 0413192 PPPD

BX
1765
L77
1884 Littledale, Richard Frederick, 1833-1890.
Plain reasons against joining the Church of Rome. Rev. and much enl. London, Society for Promoting Christian Knowledge, 1884.
252 p. 18cm.

1. Catholic Church--Doctrinal and controversial works--Protestant authors. I. Title.

NL 0413193 NIC IaU NRCR

VOLUME 336

Littledale, Richard Frederick, 1833-1890.
Plain reasons against joining the Church of Rome... London, 1886.
252 p.

NL 0413194 PPPD

Littledale, Richard Frederick, 1833-1890.
Plain reasons against joining the Church of Rome. London, Society for Promoting Christian Knowledge, 1890.
252 p. 16°.

NL 0413195 NN NjP DNC

Mnj95 L7293 Littledale, Richard Frederick, 1833-1890.
Plain reasons against joining the Church of Rome, by the late Richard Frederick Littledale ... Last ed. pub. in the author's life-time, carefully rev. and much enl. 47th thous. Pub. under the direction of the Tract committee.
London[etc.]Society for promoting Christian knowledge,1892. 17cm.

NL 0413196 CtY DNC NN

Littledale, Richard Frederick, 1833-1890.
Plain reasons against joining the Church of Rome. Fifty Second Thousand. London, S.P.C.K. 1905.

NL 0413197 PV KyWA

Littledale, Richard Frederick, 1833-1890.

Plain reasons against joining the church of Rome. Last ed. pub. in the author's life-time, carefully rev. and much enl. London, Society for Promoting Christian Knowledge; New York, E. S. Gorham, 1909.
252 p. 18cm.
"Books on the Roman controversy": p. 7-8.

1. Catholic church—Doctrinal and controversial works—Protestant authors. Title.

NL 0413198 ViU

Littledale, Richard Frederick, 1833-1890.
Plain reasons against joining the Church of Rome. Last ed...rev. & enl. London, S.P.C.K. 1924.
252 p.

NL 0413199 PPPD

Littledale, Richard Frederick, 1833-1890.

The prayer-gauge debate. By Prof. Tyndall, Francis Galton, and others, against Dr. Littledale, President McCosh, the Duke of Argyll, Canon Liddon, and "The Spectator." Boston, Congregational publishing society, 1876.

2475
Littledale, Richard Frederick, 1833-1890.
Prayers for the dead. [London, G. J. Palmer, 1867]
4 p.
Caption title.
Bound with pamp. 2450.

NL 0413201 TxDaM-P MH PPPD

Littledale, Richard Frederick, 1833-1890.
The priest's prayer book
see under title

Coxe Collection BX1765 L52 Littledale, Richard Frederick, 1833-1890.
Ragioni chiare contro il congiungersi alla chiesa romana, per Riccardo Federigo Littledale ... Londra, Società per la promozione della scienza cristiana; New York, Pott, Young & co., 1881.
235 l. p. 17½cm.

x. Littledale, Riccardo Federigo.
1. Catholic church.-Doctrinal and controversial works.

NL 0413203 NBuG

Littledale, Richard Frederick, 1833-1890.
Razones sencillas contra los errores y las innovaciones del Romanismo. New York, Sociedad Americana de Tratados [189-?]
330 p. 12°.

NL 0413204 NN

BR759 .A1P12 no. 7 Littledale, Richard Frederick, 1833-1890.
The Real Presence. [London, Palmer, 18__?]
4p. 21cm. (Pamphlets. no. 7)

1. Lord's Supper—Real Presence. I. Title.

NL 0413205 IEG PPPD

BX5149 .C5L77 1879 Littledale, Richard Frederick, 1833-1890.
The Real Presence. New York, Church League Press, 1879.
4p. 24cm. (The Church League Series. No. 1)

1. Lord's Supper--Real Presence. I. Title. (Series)

NL 0413206 IEG

BR759 .A1P12 no. 11 Littledale, Richard Frederick, 1833-1890.
Religious communities of women in the early and mediaeval church. 2d. ed. London, Joseph Masters, 1864.
42p. 21cm. (Pamphlets. no. 11)

1. Monasticism and religious orders for women. I. Title.

NL 0413207 IEG

2476
Littledale, Richard Frederick, 1833-1890.
Ritualists not romanists. [London, G. J. Palmer, 1876]
8 p.
Caption title.
Bound with pamp. 2450.

1. Ritualism. I. Title.

NL 0413208 TxDaM-P

Littledale, Richard Frederick, *1833-1880.*
Secessions to Rome.
(*In* Lectures in defence of Church principles. Pp. 145-160. Oxford. 1871.)
A defence of the Tractarian Movement as satisfying, within the Church of England, the desires of those who might otherwise be moved to join the Roman Catholic Church.
It combats the belief that the High Church school is an ally of Roman Catholicism.

N3165 — England, Church of. Doctrinal and controversial works. — Tractarian Movement, 1833-1841.

NL 0413209 MB

Littledale, Richard Frederick, 1833- ed.
Sequences, hymns, and other ecclesiastical verses
see under Neale, John Mason, 1818-1866.

BX830 1545 .L75 Littledale, Richard Frederick, 1833-1890.
A short history of the Council of Trent, by Richard Frederick Littledale ... Pub. under the direction of the Tract committee. London, Society for promoting Christian knowledge; [etc., etc.] 1888.
viii, 120 p. 17cm.

1. Trent, Council of, 1545-1563.

NL 0413211 ICU KyLxCB PCC PHC PPC CtY NN DNC

BX830 1545 L5 Littledale, Richard Frederick, 1833-1890
A short history of the Council of Trent ... London, Society for Promoting Christian Knowledge, 1890.
viii, 120p. 18 cm.

NL 0413212 RPB

Littledale, Richard Frederick, 1833-1890.
A short history of the council of Trent. London, S.P.C.K.,1898.
120 p.

NL 0413213 PPPD

2477
Littledale, Richard Frederick, 1833-1890.
What is ritualism? and why ought it to be supported? [London, G. J. Palmer, 1867]
4 p.
Caption title.

1. Ritualism.

NL 0413214 TxDaM-P PPPD

Littledale, Richard Frederick, 1833-1890. Words for truth: replies to Roman cavils against the Church of England. London, Kent, 1888.
80 p.

NL 0413215 PPPD

VOLUME 336

BX5136
.L77 Littledale, Richard Frederick, 1833-1890.
1888a Words for truth: replies to Roman cavils against the Church of England. Rev. and enl. London, Church Defence Institution; New York, Pott, 1888.
86, vp. 21cm. (With this is bound: Montagu, Robert. Right Honourable Lord Robert Montagu's reasons for leaving the Church of Rome [n.d.] Fuller, Morris. "The Roman sect and cult" 1887; Ingle, John. The Roman meeting house in the mint. 2d ed. 1873.)
1. Church of England--Doctrinal and controversial works. I. Title.

NL 0413216 IEG

Littledale, Saint George R.
Caucasian aurochs; Ovis argali of Mongolia; The Ovis poli of the Pamir. Illus. Plates.
(In Phillipps-Wolley, Edward. Big game shooting. Vol. 2, pp. 65-76, 363-376. London. 1903.)

G2329 — Aurochs. — Sheep. Wild.

NL 0413217 MB

LITTLEDALE,WILLIAM F.
The Society of King's inns, Dublin: its origin and progress, and the present results of its assumed control over the legal profession in Ireland, with some suggestions for its future government. By William F. Littledale... Dublin,T.Connolly,1859.
1 p.l.,54 p. 21cm.

1.Lawyers--Ireland. 2.King's inns,Dublin.

NL 0413218 ICU IU ICN FU

Littledale, William Harry Perceval.
Catholic, not Roman Catholic.
(*In* Lectures in defence of Church principles. Pp. 94-123. Oxford. 1871.)
"I am to set before you, . . . the Catholic Church, both in its fulness and its exclusiveness." — *Page 94.*

M7717 — T.r. — Anglo-Catholic Movement.

NL 0413219 MB

Littledale, Willoughby Aston, *ed.*
A collection of miscellaneous grants, crests, confirmations, augmentations and exemplifications of arms in the mss. preserved in the British museum, Ashmolean library, Queen's college, Oxford, and elsewhere. Edited by Willoughby A. Littledale. London [Printed by J. Whitehead and son, ltd.] 1925-26.
2 v. 2 facsim. (1 double) 27cm. (*Half-title:* The publications of the Harleian society ... vol. LXXVI-LXXVII)

1. Heraldry—Gt. Brit. I. Title.

27-19955

Library of Congress CS410.H3 vol. 76-77

NL 0413220 DLC TxU ViU PSt CU OCl OU MiU PPL MB

Littledale, Willoughby Aston, ed.

London. Christ church, *Newgate.* FOR OTHER EDITIONS SEE MAIN ENTRY
The registers of Christ church, Newgate, 1538 to 1754. Ed. by Willoughby A. Littledale ... London [Mitchell & Hughes, printers] 1895.

Littledale, Willoughby Aston, ed.

London. St. Bene't, *Paul's wharf (Parish)*
The registers of St. Bene't and St. Peter, Paul's wharf, London. Edited by Willoughby A. Littledale ... London, 1909-12.

Littledale, Willoughby Aston, ed.

London. St. Vedast church.
The registers of St. Vedast, Foster Lane, and of St. Michael le Quern, London. Ed. by Willoughby A. Littledale ... London [Mitchell and Hughes] 1902-03.

Littlefair, Duncan Elliot, 1912-
... Logical analysis of concepts in selected systems of theology ... by Duncan Elliot Littlefair. [Chicago] 1942.
1 p. l., 242-253 p. 23cm.
Part of thesis (PH. D.)—University of Chicago, 1940.
Lithoprinted.
Bibliographical foot-notes.

1. God (Theory of knowledge) I. Title: Concepts in selected systems of theology.

A 42-3051

Chicago. Univ. Library for Library of Congress BT101.L55

NL 0413224 ICU NcD NcU OrU DLC

BT101 Littlefair, Duncan Elliot, 1912-
.L75 The nature of God. Grand Rapids, Mich. [1945]
10 pts. in 1 v.
A series of 8 sermons, with two additional sermons, "Was it God or Jesus" and "How can we find God", at end.

1. God.

NL 0413225 ICU

Pamph. LITTLEFAIR, Duncan Elliot, 1912-
v.413 The principle of non-intrusion. Grand Rapids, Mich., Fountain Street Baptist Church, [1952]
76p. 19.5cm.

NL 0413226 MH-AH

---

882 Littlefair, Duncan Elliott, 1912-
L779ri Religious issues. Grand Rapids, Mich., Fountain Street Baptist Church [1949]
88p. 21.7cm.

NL 0413227 MH-AH

Littlefair, Duncan Elliot, 1912-
A religious primer for modern man; with an introd. by Henry Nelson Wieman. Boston, Starr King Press; distributed by the Beacon Press [1955]
28 p. 19 cm.

1. Theology, Doctrinal—Popular works. I. Title.

BT77.L57 202 55-5758 ‡

NL 0413228 DLC

---

882 LITTLEFAIR, Duncan Elliot, 1912-
L779ru Rules for living. [Grand Rapids, Mich., Fountain Street Baptist Church, 1948]
93p. 23cm.

NL 0413229 MH-AH

---

882 LITTLEFAIR, Duncan Elliot, 1912-
L779s Sermons series on: world problems, world religions, one world. Grand Rapids, Mich., Fountain Street Baptist Church [1953]
82p. 19.5cm.

NL 0413230 MH-AH

---

882 LITTLEFAIR, Duncan Elliot, 1912-
L779w World religions. [Grand Rapids, Mich., Fountain Street Baptist Church, 1947]
148p. 23cm.

NL 0413231 MH-AH CMIG

Littlefair, Mary.
An English girl's adventures in hostile Germany, by Mary Littlefair. London, J. Long, limited, 1915.
3 p. l., 9-128 p. 19cm.

1. European war, 1914- —Personal narratives. I. Title.

17-13836

Library of Congress D640.L54

NL 0413232 DLC NcU NN NjP PPL

Littlefellow, A.
Another day in another way, by A. Littlefellow; illustrated by Carmen R. Carnevale. Pittsburgh, Pa., D. D. Mangone [©1934]
3 p. l., 226 p. front., plates. 19cm.

I. Title.

Library of Congress PZ3.L7299An 34-40875

NL 0413233 DLC

Littlefield, Ada Douglas.
An old river town, by Ada Douglas Littlefield; being a history of Winterport, (old Frankfort), Maine, illustrated from photographs. New York, Calkins and company, 1907.
xiii p., 1 l., 249 p. front., illus., plates, fold. plan. 21cm.

Winterport, Me.—Hist.

8-3505

Library of Congress F29.W83L7

NL 0413234 DLC CU MB NN OClWHi MeB CoU

Littlefield, Alfred Henry, 1829-1893.
A review of the public debt, with a few thoughts upon the financial panic of 1857, the tariff and our civil war. A paper read before the Pawtucket business men's association, Monday evening, May 19, 1884, by Ex-Gov. Alfred H. Littlefield. [Pawtucket, Printed by Sibley & Lee, 1884?]
29 p. 23½cm.

1. Debts, Public—U. S. 2. Finance—U. S. 3. Currency question—U. S. 4. Panics—1857. I. Title.

CA 14-311 Unrev'd

Library of Congress HJ8101.L7

NL 0413235 DLC

Pam. Littlefield, Arthur Warner.
Coll.
A mountain shrine. Middleboro, Mass.,
29247 Printed by the Namaskett Press [1927]
[12] p. illus. 18 cm.

1. New Hampshire. Description and travel. 2. Cannon Mountain, N. H.

NL 0413236 NcD RPB

VOLUME 336

LITTLEFIELD, Arthur Warner.
The value of unitarian fellowship. [Boston], n.d.

1 pam.
(AMER.UNIT.ASSOC [Tracts] 9th series, 9.)

NL 0413237 MH

Littlefield, Arthur Wesley, 1905- joint author.

Smith, Samuel, 1904-
Best methods of study; a practical guide for the student [by] Samuel Smith ... [and] Arthur W. Littlefield ... with special sections by Louis Shores ... [and] A. C. Jordan ... New York, Barnes & Noble, inc. [°1938]

Littlefield, Arthur Wesley, 1905-
Essential tools for good citizenship, by A. W. Littlefield, Jay Adams [and] Chevalier Adams, Jr. Ames, Iowa, Littlefield, Adams [1950]
95 p. illus. (part col.) 21 cm.

1. U. S.—Constitutional history—Sources. I. Title.

JK11 1950.L5 342.7382 50-13829

NL 0413239 DLC PCM Or

Littlefield, Arthur Wesley, 1905- joint ed.

Barnes, William Robbins, 1866- ed.
The Supreme court issue and the Constitution; comments pro and con by distinguished men, edited by William R. Barnes and A. W. Littlefield. New York, Barnes & Noble, inc. [°1937]

BX7149
.W4L5 [Littlefield, Beatrice B.]
History of the First Parish and the First Congregational Church of West Springfield, Massachusetts; including the Park Street church records, comp. for the two hundred fiftieth anniversary of the church. [West Springfield, Mass., 1948]
21 p. 18cm.
1. West Springfield, Mass. First Parish. 2. West Springfield, Mass. First Congregational Church.

NL 0413241 MB

Littlefield, C.

New York (*State*) *Legislature. Assembly. Select committee to investigate water rights on Black River.*
Report of Select committee appointed to investigate grievances of owners of water rights on Black River. Transmitted to the Legislature, February 29, 1856. Albany, C. Van Benthuysen, printer to the Legislature, 1856.

Littlefield, Charles Alvin, 1856-
William Rice Newhall, by two of his friends, Charles A. Littlefield and John W. Maynard; with ... introduction, addresses, resolutions, editorials, press notices and interviews, extracts from communications ... [Lynn? Mass.] 1914. 97 p. incl. facsim. front. (port.) 24½cm.

822323A. 1. Newhall, William Rice, 1859- 1860-1913. I. Maynard, John Walter, jt. ed.
N. Y. P. L. April 21, 1937

NL 0413243 NN CtW MBNMHi

Littlefield, Charles Edgar, 1851-1915.

U. S. *Congress. House. Committee on the judiciary.*
... Bill requiring returns from corporations ... Report. <To accompany H. R. 2.> [Washington, Govt. print. off., 1906]

Littlefield, Charles Edgar. 1851-

U. S. *Congress. House. Special committee on case of Brigham H. Roberts.*
... Case of Brigham H. Roberts, of Utah ... Report <to accompany H. res. 107.> [Washington, Govt. print. off., 1900]

Littlefield, Charles E[dgar], 1851-1915.
Class legislation. [Address delivered March 18, 1908. New York, 1910?] 26 p. nar. 8°. (National Association of Manufacturers of U. S. A. [Educational literature.] no. 12.)

1. Injunctions, U. S.
N. Y. P. L. October 18, 1912.

NL 0413246 NN

Littlefield, Charles Edgar, 1851-1915.
... Class legislation, by Hon. Charles E. Littlefield ... New York [1911?]
26 p. 22 cm. (National association of manufacturers of the United States of America. [Educational literature] no. 11)
Address delivered March 18, 1908.
1. Injunctions.

NL 0413247 CU OrU

Littlefield, Charles Edgar, 1851-

Virginia, *plaintiff.*
... Commonwealth of Virginia *vs.* state of West Virginia. Record. [Richmond] Richmond press, inc., law printers [1909]

Littlefield, Charles Edgar, 1851-

U. S. *Congress. House. Committee on merchant marine and fisheries.*
... Discrimination against sailing vessels in coasting trade ... Report. <To accompany H. R. 5281.> [Washington, Govt. print. off., 1906]

LITTLEFIELD, Charles Edgar, 1851-1915.
Fisheries within the territorial limits of the states are not subject to congressional control. A reply on behalf of the State of Maine to the arguments submitted to sustain the Lapham bill, prepared for Charles E. Littlefield and submitted by Charles F. Chamberlayne. Boston, Rockwell & Churchill, 1892.

NL 0413250 MH PHi

Littlefield, Charles Edgar, 1851-1915.
... The insular cases. The annual address by Charles E. Littlefield, ... at Denver, Colorado, on August 22, 1901. [1901?]
cover-title, 53 p. 24½cm.
At head of title: The American Bar Association.
An address on the civil and political status of the inhabitants of the territories of the United States under the Constitution.

NL 0413251 ICJ PU-L MH NjP

Littlefield, Charles E[dgar], 1851-1915.
Puerto Rico, the pearl of the Antilles, "The ever-faithful isle." Speech of Hon. Charles E. Littlefield, of Maine, in the House ... February 23, 1900. Washington [Gov't print. off.] 1900. 45 pp. 8°.
—— Copy 2. 1-3654

NL 0413252 DLC NIC MH

Littlefield, Charles Edgar, 1851-1915.
Railroad rate bill ... Speech of Hon. Charles E. Littlefield, of Maine, in the House of representatives, Monday, February 5, 1906. Washington, 1906.
30 p.

1. Railroads - U. S. - Rates.

NL 0413253 NNC

Littlefield, Charles Edgar.
... Regulating interstate commerce in certain cases ... Report
see under U.S. Congress. House. Committee on the Judiciary.

Littlefield, Charles Edgar, 1851-1915.

U. S. *Dept. of justice.*
Reply of the attorney-general, dated January 3, 1903, to a communication, dated December 22, 1902, from the Honorable Charles E. Littlefield, chairman of a sub-committee of the Committee on the judiciary of the House of representatives. Washington, Govt. print. off., 1903.

Littlefield, Charles Edgar, 1851-1915.

U. S. *Congress. House. Committee on expenditures in the Department of agriculture.*
... Report of the Committee on expenditures in the Department of agriculture, House of representatives. Fifty-ninth Congress, second session. Washington, Govt. print. off., 1907.

Littlefield, Charles Edgar, 1851-
Representative-elect from Utah ... Speech of Hon. Charles E. Littlefield, of Maine, in the House of representatives ... January 23, 1900. Washington [Govt. print. off.] 1900.
52 p. 23cm.

1. Roberts, Brigham Henry, 1857-

CA 11-1938 Unrev'd

Library of Congress JK1359.56th.U8L

NL 0413257 DLC CU-B MB

Littlefield, Charles Edgar.
Sherman anti-trust law and the proposed amendments thereto. Annual address Illinois state bar association proceedings, 1908. Springfield, 1908. 8°

NL 0413258 I

VOLUME 336

HF1756 Littlefield,Charles Edgar,1851-1915.
.L77 ...Speech of Hon.Charles E.Littlefield of Maine, in the House of representatives...April 27,1904. [Philadelphia,Pa.,1904]
16 p. 21½cm.

At head of title:No.10.
In favor of protection.
DLC: YA 12679
1.Free trade and protection-Protection.

NL 0413259 ICU DLC

Littlefield, Charles Edgar, 1851-1915.
The three departments of government and their relation to each other. An address delivered in the Assembly chamber of the Capitol, Albany, N. Y., before the New York state bar association, at its twenty-ninth annual meeting, January 16, 1906, and reprinted from the twenty-ninth annual report of the proceedings of the Association. By Charles E. Littlefield ... [Albany? 1906]
36 p. 23cm.

1. Separation of powers—U. S.

8-10080 Revised
Library of Congress JK305.L5

NL 0413260 DLC ICJ

Littlefield, Charles Edgar, 1851-1915.

League for industrial rights.
To Daniel Davenport, esq., from members of the American anti-boycott association and friends ... Davenport testimonial. [New York, Cameron & Bulkley, 1915]

Littlefield, Charles Wentworth, 1859-
The beginning and way of life ... Illustrated with one hundred twenty-four half-tone copper plates ... By Charles Wentworth Littlefield ... [1st ed.] [Seattle] The Rainbow temple association [c1919]
3 p. l., xi-xxxvi, 632, xxxvii-lix p. front. (port.) illus. 24cm.
CONTENTS.—pt. 1. The new biology.—pt. 2. The new psychology.—pt. 3. The new healing.

1. Life. 2. Medicine, Biochemic. I. Title.

20-10602
Library of Congress QH325.L7

NL 0413262 DLC PPC

Littlefield, Charles Wentworth, 1859-
Man, minerals and masters, by Charles W. Littlefield ... Los Angeles, De Vorss & co. [c1937]
3 p. l., xi-xxvi p., 2 l., 140 p. front., illus. 23½cm.

1. Cabala. 2. Symbolism of numbers. I. Title.

37-15736
Library of Congress BF1611.L5
Copyright A 106990 [3] [159.961] 133

NL 0413263 DLC MB

Littlefield, Charles Wentworth, 1859-
The twelve vitalized tissue remedies for private and domestic use, constituting a new science in the work of health and healing. By Charles Wentworth Littlefield ... 1st ed. [Seattle, Metropolitan press, printers, c1910]
xxxvii, 392 p. 23½cm. (*On cover:* The companion life series, vol. II)

1. Medicine, Biochemic.

10-15175
Library of Congress RM130.L6

NL 0413264 DLC ICJ

Littlefield, Charles Winsor, 1874-
The makers of America and their Land of Promise; 101 sonnets and an epic poem. [1st ed.] New York, Exposition Press [1952]
187 p. 21 cm.

1. U. S.—Hist.—Poetry. 2. Poetry of places—U. S. I. Title.

PS3523.I 84M3 811.5 52-9821 ‡

NL 0413265 DLC

Littlefield, Cleatice Louis, 1917-
An approach to improved utilization of personnel during peak loads in office work volume ... 1950.
205 numb. l.

Thesis (PH.D.) - Ohio state university, 1950

NL 0413266 OU

Littlefield, Clyde.
Track and field athletics for coaches, contestants and others interested in athletics, by Clyde Littlefield ... Austin, Tex., Von Boeckmann-Jones co. [c1933]
94 p. incl. illus., diagrs., forms. 23½cm.
"Books helpful to the coach and contestant": p. 94.

1. Track-athletics. 2. Coaching (Athletics) I. Title.

33-22424
Library of Congress GV701.L5
——— Copy 2.
Copyright A 65041 [2] 796.4

NL 0413267 DLC PPGi OCl OClh OO OOxM

Littlefield, Cyril O.
History of Company E, 332nd Infantry, from departure overseas to return and discharge. An active "ring" in Wallace's "circus" during the World War.
— [Whitman, Mass. 1919.] Unpaged. Portraits. Plates. Autograph facsimile. 23 cm., in 8s.
The introduction is by Harold Chamberlain.
The author's name is signed to a preface.

M1441 — United States. A. & n. Army. American Expeditionary Forces. European War. 332d Regiment. Infantry. Company E. — Chamberlain, Harold, pref.

NL 0413268 MB

[Littlefield, Dennis G.]
A history of the improvements applicable to the base burning or horizontal draught stove, from the original invention by M. Delesme [sic] in 1680, to the present time, and the base burning stove as an engine of combustion, compared with other stoves, by the inventor of the railway coal burner, parlor furnace, &c. Erastus Corning & co., agents, Albany, N. Y. Albany: C. Van Benthuysen, printer, 1859. 63 p. illus. 21cm.

Cover-title.
Introduction signed: D. G. Littlefield.

1. Stoves.
N. Y. P. L. December 31, 1942

NL 0413269 NN N

[Littlefield, Dennis G]
A history of the improvements applicable to the base burning or horizontal draught stove, from the original invention by M. Delesme, in 1680, to the present time, and the base burning stove as an engine of combustion... Erastus Corning & co., agents... Albany, Printed by C. Van Benthuysen, 1860.
cover-title,80 p. incl. illus.,diagrs. 21cm.
"Second edition."
Imperfect: p.33-36 missing, illus. clipped from p.24.
1. Stoves. I. Title: The base burning or horizontal draught stove.

NL 0413270 DP MB

Littlefield, Dennis G.
Theory of the base-burning stove and the origin of the "Morning glory"...by D. G. Littlefield... Albany, N. Y.: Littlefield stove manufacturing co., 1871. 55 p. illus. 19cm.

"Second edition."
"Base-burner days. By Wm. H. Coleman," p. [53]-55. Reprinted from the Independent.

1. Stoves. I. Littlefield stove manufacturing company, Albany, N. Y.
N. Y. P. L. May 20, 1940

NL 0413271 NN DLC

Littlefield, Dennis G
Theory of the base-burning stove and the origin of the "Morning Glory." [3d ed.] Albany, N.Y., Littlefield Stove Mfg. Co., 1872.

NL 0413272 MH

Littlefield, Dennis G
Theory of the base-burning stove and the origin of the "Morning Glory". Albany, N.Y., 1873, c1870.
51 p. illus. 20 cm.
On cover: Fourth edition.

NL 0413273 ICHi

SD409 Littlefield, Edward Winchester, 1897-
L5 ... Forest planting in New York; instructions on obtaining nursery stock, methods of planting, and care of forest plantations ... by E. W. Littlefield ... [Albany, 1941]

33p. illus. 22½cm. (New York (State) Conservation dept. Bulletin 2)

"This publication takes the place of the bulletin 'Reforesting,' prepared by the late Clifford R. Pettis .. "

NL 0413274 NBuG

SD409
.L5 Littlefield, Edward Winchester, 1897-
Forest planting in New York; instructions on obtaining nursery stock, methods of planting, and care of forest plantations. Albany, 1942.
33 p. illus. 23 cm. (State of New York. Conservation Dept. Bulletin 2)

Cover title.
1. Afforestation - New York (State) 2. Reforestation - New York (State) 3. Tree planting - New York (State) i.t. ii.s: Bulletin. State of New York. Conservation Department. 2.

NL 0413275 NNBG

Littlefield, Ethel F.
My progress book in French ... by Ethel F. Littlefield ... New York, N. Y., Columbus, O., Looseleaf education, inc. [c1929]
v. illus. 28cm. [The progress book series]
On cover: Individual work book, drill material, ability tests.

1. French language—Composition and exercises. I. Title.

29-2449
Library of Congress PC2111.L725

NL 0413276 DLC MH ODW PPT CaBVaU

Littlefield, Ethel F
My progress book in French. No. 2. New York, etc., American education press, inc. [c.1930]

NL 0413277 MH ODW

VOLUME 336

TX1
.E8
Littlefield, Eunice B., ed.

Everyday housekeeping. a magazine for practical housekeepers and mothers. v. 1-24: Apr. 1894-Mar. 1908. Boston, Clark-Clary Pub. Co. ₍etc.₎

NL 0413279 MeBa MiU

Littlefield, Francis L.
The capture of the Chesapeake ... Read before the ... society, April 17, 1901.
(*In* Collections of the Maine historical society. Portland, 1906. 23½cm. 3d ser., v. 2, p. 285-309)
The passenger steamer "Chesapeake" in regular service between New York and Portland, Me., captured by a group of men in the interest of the Confederate States Dec. 7, 1863. She was taken to Nova Scotia, and quickly recovered by U. S. authorities.

1. Chesapeake (Steamer) Capture of the, 1863.

A 15-1324

Title from Bangor Pub. Libr. Library of Congress F16.M33

NL 0413279 MeBa MiU

TA439
.P86
1954
Littlefield, Garnett, ed.

Prestressed Concrete Conference. *1st, University of Utah, 1954.*
Proceedings. Compiled and edited by Garnett Littlefield. ₍Salt Lake City₎ University of Utah, College of Engineering, Dept. of Civil Engineering, 1955.

LITTLEFIELD, George E
Open secrets. And other sermons.
= Boston. Unity press. [1899.] 48 pp. 16°.

NL 0413281 MB

Nx73
1
1911
[Littlefield, George Elmer]
The Fellowship farm plan: how one fellow makes an honest living on the land and is a free man. Westwood,Mass.,Ariel press on Fellowship farm[n.d.]

Caption title: On the land, edited by a Fellowship farm settler.
Signed, George Elmer Littlefield.

NL 0413282 CtY

Littlefield, George Elmer.
Illumination and love, by Ariel, George Elmer Littlefield. Santa Barbara, Calif., The Red rose press ₍1928₎
3 p. l., iv p., 1 l., ₍13₎-96 p. illus. 20½cm.

1. Rosicrucians. I. Title.

38-10410

Library of Congress BF1623.R7L5
₍2₎ 212

NL 0413283 DLC

[LITTLEFIELD, GEORGE EMERY,] 1844-1915.
...Catalogue of books and pamphlets relating to the American Indians. Boston: G.E. Littlefield [,1883?]. 24 p. 8°.

Cover-title.
Cover mutilated; imprint partly wanting.
"no. 10, Nov., 1883."

20503. 1. Indians, N.A.— Bibl.

NL 0413284 NN PHi DNLM

Littlefield, George Emery, *1844-1915.*
A catalogue of old, rare, and curious books, comprising early American history, genealogy, travels, etc. No. 1-21, 23-44. [1878-1897.]
[Boston. 1878-97.] 1 v. 22½ cm.
The binder's title is Bibliotheca Americana.
The title of the individual numbers vary.
Included are several unnumbered issues.

N3204 — T.r. (in note). — America. Bibl. — Catalogues. Booksellers'.

NL 0413285 MB CSmH

Littlefield, George Emery, 1844-1915.
Catalogue of the valuable private library of the late George Emery Littlefield, including rare & curious books selected from his stock ... Boston, C.F. Libbie & co. [1915]
2 v. front. (port., v. 1) 24 cm.
Pt. 1: A-L; pt. 2: M-Z.
Includes many rare American books, especially those of New England.

NL 0413286 Mi MWA

Z1207
Z9L7
Littlefield, George Emery, 1844-1915.
Catalogues of historical and genealogical books relating to America. Issued by George Littlefield. Nos. I.-[LXXXI] Boston, 1899. [1878-1915]
81 nos. in 2 v. 23cm. Tan buckram.
Nos. 1-81, 1878-1915, all published.

1. America--Bibl.--Catalogs. 2. Catalogs, Book sellers'--U. S.

NL 0413287 CSmH MiU-C

Littlefield, George Emery, *1844-1915.*
[Clog-almanac.]
= [Boston. 190-?] Mounted on a block of wood, size 7½ × 1 × 1 inches.
Two copies of an edition of 53 copies lithographed and mounted on wood, representing an original in the possession of the editor, and illustrating a paper read by him before the Club of Odd Volumes.
The "A" copy bears manuscript notes.
The calendar of the prayer-book [5455.40] and The every-day book, by William Hone [B.H.Ref.634.10(6227.7)] contain descriptions and illustrations of clog-almanacs.

H9167 — Clog-almanac.

NL 0413288 MB

Littlefield, George Emery, 1844-1915.
A descriptive catalogue of the Massachusetts exhibit of colonial books at the Jamestown Ter-Centennial Exposition
see Massachusetts. Board of Jamestown Exposition Managers. 1607-1907.
A descriptive catalogue ...

Littlefield, George Emery, 1844-1915.
Early Boston booksellers 1642-1711; by George Emery Littlefield. Boston, The Club of odd volumes, 1900.
1 p. l., 256 p. front., plates, facsims. (part fold.) 24½cm.
"Limited to on hundred and fifty copies, of which this is no. 5."

1. Booksellers and bookselling—Boston. 2. Printing—Hist.—Boston. 3. Boston—Biog. I. Club of odd volumes, Boston. II. Title.

3-16855

Library of Congress Z473.L77

NL 0413290 Nh NjP MiU MB ViU RPJCB DLC OrU MoU NBu NcD NIC PU OCl MiU-C MWA

Littlefield, George Emery, 1844-1915.
The early Massachusetts press, 1638-1711, by George Emery Littlefield ... Boston, Mass., The Club of odd volumes, 1907.
2 v. front., plans, facsims. 24½cm.
"Limited to one hundred and seventy-five copies, of which this is no. 175."
CONTENTS.—I. Richard Steere. James Cowse. Reverend Jose Glover. The beginnings of the college. The first printing office. Stephen Day. Matthew Day. The second printing office. Reverend John Eliot. The third printing house. Samuel Green. Marmaduke Johnson.—II. John Foster. Samuel Sewall. Samuel Green, jr. James Glen. Richard Pierce. Bartholomew Green. John Allen. Timothy Green. James Printer. Envoy.
1. Printing—Hist.—Massachusetts. 2. American literature—Massachusetts—Bibl. I. Club of odd volumes, Boston.

7-17901

Library of Congress Z209.M4L7
Copyright A 176316. 176317

NL 0413291 MiU-C OCl NcD MH GU NSyU PPRF NcGU DLC ICJ ViU DFo RPJCB MH-L MB PU MWA OO

Littlefield, George Emery, 1844-1915.
Early schools and school-books of New England, by George Emery Littlefield. Boston, Mass., The Club of odd volumes, 1904.
1 p. l., viii p., 1 l., 11-354 p. incl. illus., pl., facsims. front. 24½cm.
"Limited to one hundred and sixty-seven copies, of which this is no. 166."

1. Text-books—Bibl. 2. Education—New England. I. Club of odd volumes, Boston.

4-6887

Library of Congress LA206.L77

NL 0413292 NN NjP RPJCB MiU-C ViU PU DLC MWA CU NBu ICarbS ViW OClW OU MB

Littlefield, George Emery, 1844-1915.
Elijah Corlet and the "faire grammar schoole" at Cambridge.
(In Colonial Society of Massachusetts. Publications. Vol. 17, pp. 131-140. Boston. 1915.)
Supplementary remarks by Julius H. Tuttle. pp. 140-142.

K8041 — Cambridge, Mass. Public schools. — Corlet, Elijah, 1610-1687. — Massachusetts. Education.

NL 0413293 MB OO

Z5817
.L75
Mss
room
Littlefield, George Emery, 1844-1915.
Littlefield's notes on early text-books.
₍Boston, 1915₎
98 l. 24cm.
Manuscript.
A catalog of a collection purchased by the University of Chicago Library.

1. Text-books—Bibl. I. Chicago. University Library. 2. Manuscripts, English.

NL 0413294 ICU

Littlefield, George Emery, 1844-1915.
Notes on the calendar and the almanac, by George Emery Littlefield.
(*In* American antiquarian society, Worcester, Mass. Proceedings. Worcester, Mass., 1914. 25cm. n. s., v. 24, p. 11-64)

1. Calendar. 2. Almanacs.

A 35-1314

Title from Newberry Libr.
Library of Congress [E172.A35 vol. 24]

NL 0413295 ICN RPJCB PPF NNC CtY OClWHi MB NBuG

Littlefield, George Emery, 1844-1915.
Notes on the "Faire grammar school" in Cambridge, Massachusetts, and its master, Elijah Corlett.
... *Typewritten manuscript.* Boston. 1907. (1), 12 ff. 28 cm.
Printed in Publications of the Colonial Society of Massachusetts, vol. 17, pp. 131-140 [*4353.148.17].

L0751 — Cambridge, Mass. Public schools. — Corlet, Elijah, 1610-1687. — Massachusetts. Educ. — Manuscripts. English.

NL 0413296 MB

VOLUME 336

Littlefield, George Emery, 1844–1915.
Notes on the first Bible printed in America in the English language, by George Emery Littlefield. Boston, 1910. 30 p. 28cm.

Clipping mounted on t.-p. and on verso of p. 19.
One of four typewritten copies.

105294B. 1. Bible. English. 1752. 2. Bible—Printing—U. S.
N. Y. P. L. May 22, 1941

NL 0413297 NN MB

Littlefield, George Emery, 1844-
On almanacs;...
Boston, 1912

CE73
.L6

NL 0413298 DLC

Littlefield, George Sherman.

Winchester, *Mass.*
July 4th, 1890. 250th anniversary of the first white settlement within the territory of Winchester ... ⌊Boston, The Barta press, 1890⌋

Littlefield, Harold.
The actor's roadway, a psychology for the player, by Harold Littlefield. ⌊Newark, N. J., J. James, °1934⌋
4 p. l., 11–75 p. 15½cm.

1. Acting. I. Title. 35-37837
Library of Congress PN2065.L5
——— Copy 2.
Copyright A 85266 ⌊2⌋ 792

NL 0413300 DLC

Littlefield, Harold J
The problems of public scepticism and fear as related to air travel advertising. ⌊New York, Flight Safety Foundation, Inc.⌋ 1949.
iii, 49 p.

Bibliographical footnotes.
Adapted from thesis - Graduate School of Business Administration, New York University.

NL 0413301 MH-BA

Littlefield, Hazel
see Smith, Hazel Littlefield.

Littlefield, Henrietta, joint ed.

Sapper, *Frau* Agnes (Brater) 1852–1929.
Die familie Pfäffling; eine deutsche wintergeschichte, von Agnes Sapper; edited with notes, exercises and vocabulary by Bertha Reed Coffman and Henrietta Littlefield ... New York, F. S. Crofts & co., 1934.

Littlefield, Henry Wilson, comp.

D359
.2
.H5

History of Europe since 1815. ⌊1st⌋– ed.; 1932–
New York, Barnes & Noble.

Littlefield, Ivory.
Public opinion.
7 p. 27 cm.
Typewritten mss.
Commencement oration, 1909.

NL 0413305 RPB

Littlefield, J., ed.

AP2
.H667

The Home library. v. 1–2, no. 1; June 13–Dec. 12, 1857.
Foxboro', Mass., W. H. Thomas, 1857.

Littlefield, James Bancroft.
The quieter life.
5 p. 27 cm.
Typewritten mss.
Commencement oration, 1902.
Caption-title.

NL 0413307 RPB

Littlefield, James Drake.
Notes for forge shop practice; a course for high schools, by James Drake Littlefield ... Springfield, Mass., The Taylor-Holden company, 1910.
68, ⌊4⌋ p. incl. illus., plates. 20½cm. (The Haytol series of textbooks for industrial education, ed. by F. E. Mathewson)
Three blank pages for notes at end of volume.

1. Forging. I. Title: Forge shop practice. 10—24274
Library of Congress TT215.L7

NL 0413308 DLC OrP PU OCl ICJ

Littlefield, James Drake
Notes for forge shop practice; a course for high schools....Springfield, Mass. Taylor-Holden Co., 1913. 84 p.
(Haytol series of textbooks for industrial education, ed. by F.E. Mathewson)

NL 0413309 OU OCl MtU

Littlefield, James Drake
Notes for forge shop practice; a course for high schools, by James Drake Littlefield... 3d ed. Springfield, Mass., The Taylor-Holden co., 1918.
84 ⌊1⌋ p. incl. illus., plates (The Haytol series of textbooks for industrial education, ed. by F. E. Mathewson)

7 blank pages for notes at end of volume.

NL 0413310 MiD TU

Littlefield, James Edwin.
The Littlefield system of eye and nerve measurements, invented by Dr. J. E. Littlefield ... ⌊Saco? Me., °1905⌋
108 l. illus., col. plates, diagrs. 30 x 21 cm.
Printed on one side of leaf only.

I. Title. 5—14980
Library of Congress RE925.L55

NL 0413311 DLC

Littlefield, James Edwin.
Optometry; the Littlefield system of eye and nerve measurements ... by Dr. J. E. Littlefield ... ⌊Biddeford, Me., Press of the Biddeford journal, °1905⌋
240 p. illus., col. plates, port., diagrs. 23½cm.
"Fifth edition of the Littlefield system of eye and nerve measurements."—Introductory.

I. Title: Littlefield system of eye and nerve measurements.
43-29513
Library of Congress RE925.L55 1905 b

NL 0413312 DLC

Littlefield, Jimmy.
The barnyard band. Words and music by Jimmy Littlefield, Harry Filler ⌊and⌋ Johnny Fortis. ⌊New York⌋ E. B. Marks music corp., c1944.
First line: I love a real jam session.
Chorus: There's a crow in the garden.

1. Farms. 2. Bands. I. Filler, Harry. II. Fortis, Johnny. III. Song index (3).
N. Y. P. L. April 16, 1947

NL 0413313 NN

F862
.1
L5

Littlefield, John W plaintiff.
John W. Littlefield, plaintiff, vs. John Nichols and Richard Roe, defendants. Transcript on appeal. B. S. Brooks, attorney for plaintiff. J. M. Seawell, attorney for defendants. San Francisco, J. Thompson, law printer, 1870.
116 p. 26cm.

Cover title.
At head of title: No.___ in the Supreme Court of the state of California.

NL 0413314 CU-B

Littlefield, Jubal K pseud.
see Klinefelter, Walter, 1899-

Littlefield, Ken, ed.

U408
.3
.C7

Crampton, Charles Ward, 1877–
Fighting fitness, a premilitary training guide, by C. Ward Crampton, M. D., with the editorial assistance of Ken Littlefield. New York, London, Whittlesey house, McGraw-Hill book company, inc. ⌊1944⌋

Littlefield, L. Arthur.
Fitting out a whaler. Illus. Plates.
(In Old Dartmouth Historical Society. Old Dartmouth historical sketches. No. 14, pp. 4-13. [New Bedford. 1906.])

K6631 — T.r. — Whale fishery.

NL 0413317 MB

TL586
.C58

Littlefield, Lawrence, joint author.

Collier, Kent.
Naval air navigation for C. A. A. war training service schools ⌊by⌋ Kent Collier, Lawrence Littlefield, and Charles R. Shields ... ⌊Lawrence, Kan., The University of Kansas, Dept. of aeronautical engineering⌋ °1944.

VOLUME 336

Littlefield, Louis.
High points of auction bridge; brief suggestions for beginners and others, by Louis Littlefield, ed. by Bramwell Davis. Charleston, Miss., The Mississippi sun, 1921.
52 p. illus. 17cm.

1. Auction bridge. I. Davis, Bramwell, ed. II. Title.
Library of Congress GV1282.L5 21-9989

NL 0413318 DLC

Littlefield, Louis.
High points of auction bridge; brief suggestions for beginners and others, by Louis Littlefield, edited by Bramwell Davis. Charleston, Miss., The Mississippi sun, 1923.
2 p. l., [3]-128 p. diagrs. 17cm.
"The New York laws": p. 83-128.

1. Auction bridge. I. Davis, Bramwell, ed. II. Title.
Library of Congress GV1282.L5 1923 23-8253

NL 0413319 DLC ICRL OCl ICJ

Littlefield, *Mrs.* Louise (Hall) 1889- *comp.*
The triad anthology of New England verse, compiled by Louise Hall Littlefield; with foreword by Angela Morgan. Portland, Me., Falmouth book house, 1938.
166, [5] p., 1 l. 24½cm.
"Of this special edition one hundred copies only have been printed."

1. New England—Descr. & trav.—Poetry. 2. Poetry of places—New England. 3. American poetry—20th cent. 4. American literature—New England. I. Title. II. Title: Anthology of New England verse. III. Title: New England verse.
Library of Congress PS541.L5 39-1300
——— Copy 2.
Copyright A 124279 [5] 811.50822

NL 0413320 DLC OU

Littlefield, Lucille Jane, 1900-
Suggestions toward improving the fine arts collection in a library of a teachers college training special art teachers. 1936.
31 l.

Paper prepared for LS s330, School of library service, Columbia university.
"Sources of information": l.30-31.

NL 0413321 NNC

Littlefield, Luella Gardner, joint ed.

Littlefield, Milton Smith, 1864- *ed.* FOR OTHER EDITIONS SEE MAIN ENTRY
The school hymnal; a book of worship for young people, ed. by Milton S. Littlefield, with the collaboration of Luella Gardner Littlefield. New York, The A. S. Barnes company, 1920.

B 995 .512 LITTLEFIELD, LYMAN Omer.
The martyrs; a sketch of the lives and a full account of the martyrdom of Joseph and Hyrum Smith, together with a concise review of the most prominent incidents connected with the persecutions of the saints, from the time the church was organized up to the year 1846... Salt Lake city, Juvenile instructor office, 1882.
120p.

NL 0413323 NNC WHi CU NIC NjP CoD ICN NcD CStbS CU MH RPB DLC NcD OO CtY

Littlefield, Lyman Omer.
Reminiscences of Latter-day Saints, giving an account of much individual suffering endured for religious conscience. Logan, Utah, Utah Journal Co., printers, 1888.
208 p. port. 22 cm.
Errata slip inserted.

1. Mormons and Mormonism—Hist. 2. Persecution. I. Title.
BX8611.L62 49-43780*

NL 0413324 DLC CU-B NjP CtY ViU ICN ICU MH IHi

LC3981 .S6 **Littlefield, Lynell, comp.**
Special education personnel in State education departments. 1955-
Washington, U. S. Office of Education.

Littlefield, Max Sylvan, 1900-
An investigation of the molding sand resources of Illinois, by M. S. Littlefield ... [Urbana, Ill., 1925]
3 p. l., 5-183 p. illus. (incl. maps) diagrs. 25cm.
Thesis (PH. D.)—University of Iowa, 1925.
Bulletin no. 50 of the Illinois State geological survey, with a special thesis t.-p. added. The bulletin has title: Natural-bonded molding sand resources of Illinois.

1. Sand.
Library of Congress TN939.L52 1925 26-22021
Univ. of Iowa Libr.

NL 0413326 IaU DLC UU NIC PU-El CtY OO

Littlefield, Max Sylvan, 1900-
... Natural-bonded molding sand resources of Illinois, by M. S. Littlefield. Laboratory tests in cooperation with the Engineering experiment station, University of Illinois. Urbana, 1925.
183 p. illus., maps, tables, diagrs. 26cm. (Illinois. State geological survey. Bulletin no. 50)
At head of title: State of Illinois. Department of registration and education. Division of the state geological survey.

1. Sand. I. Title. G S 26—253
U. S. Geol. survey. Library for Library of Congress (253) I1 5b no. 50 [a41g1]

NL 0413327 ICJ PPAN PSt MtBuM WaS DI-GS MoU CU OU MiU OCl OO OClMN DBS

Littlefield, Max Sylvan, 1900-
... Preliminary report of an investigation of the molding sand resources of Illinois, by M. S. Littlefield. In cooperation with the Engineering experiment station of the University of Illinois. Urbana, 1925.
37 p. tables. 25½ cm. (Illinois. State geological survey. Report of investigations, no. 3)
At head of title: State of Illinois. Dept. of registration and education. Division of State geological survey.

1. Sand, Molding.
TN939.L53 G S 25-88 rev 2
U. S. Geol. Survey Libr. for Library of Congress [r56j2]†

NL 0413328 MtBuM DI-GS CU MoU PP OO OU OClMN NN DLC

Littlefield, Max Sylvan, 1900-
A reservoir study of the West Edmond Hunton pool, Oklahoma, by Max Littlefield, L. L. Gray, and A. C. Godbold.
(*In* Petroleum technology. York, Pa., 1938-48. 23 cm. v. 10, no. 6, Nov. 1947. 34 p. diagrs.)
American Institute of Mining and Metallurgical Engineers. Technical publication no. 2203 (Class G, Petroleum technology, Nov. 1947)
Bibliography: p. 25.

1. Petroleum—Geology—Oklahoma. 2. Petroleum—Oklahoma. I. Title. II. Title: West Edmond Hunton pool, Oklahoma.
[TN860.P55 vol. 10, no. 6] P O 52-212
U. S. Patent Office. Library for Library of Congress [½]

NL 0413329 DP

VR60 1908H 1910 Littlefield, Milton Smith, 1864- , ed.
Forms and services for Sunday school worship prepared by Milton S. Littlefield and H. Augustine Smith.
New York, The Century co., 1910.
37 p. 21.5 cm.

(in Hymns of worship and service...1910.[c.1908 publishers note 1908.)

NL 0413330 NNUT OO

R60 908H 913 Littlefield, Milton Smith, 1864- ed.
Forms and services for Sunday school worship, prepared by Milton S. Littlefield and H. Augustine Smith.
New York, The Century co., 1913, [1908]
iv, 5-37 p. 21.5 cm.

(in Hymns of worship and service. For the Sunday school. 1913.)

NL 0413331 NNUT

Littlefield, Milton Smith, 1864-
Forms and services for Sunday School worship prepared by Milton S. Littlefield and H. Augustine Smith. New York, Century Co., 1916.
37p.

Bound with Hymns of worship and service for the Sunday School. New York, 1916.

NL 0413332 ICRL

Littlefield, Milton Smith, 1864-
Forms and services for Sunday school worship. Prepared by Milton S. Littlefield and H. Augustine Smith.
New York, The Century co., 1920, [c1908].
37 p. 21.5 cm.

Bound with: Hymns of worship and service, for the Sunday school. 1920, [c1908].

NL 0413333 NNUT

Littlefield, Milton Smith, 1864- ed.
Forms and services for Sunday school worship, prepared by Milton S. Littlefield and H. Augustine Smith. New York, Century co., 1924.
37 p. 22 cm.
Includes music.
With Century company. Hymns of worship and service for the Sunday school 1924.

NL 0413334 RPB

Littlefield, Milton Smith, 1864-
Hand-work in the Sunday-school, by Milton S. Littlefield, with an introduction by Patterson Du Bois. Philadelphia, The Sunday school times company [1908]
xvii, 162 p. incl. illus., maps. front., plates. 18cm.

1. Sunday-schools. I. Title.
Library of Congress BV1536.L5 8-19114

NL 0413335 OOxM MB NN Wa OrP WaSp DLC ICRL Or PU PHC PPC OCl OO ODW OCH

VOLUME 336

BV520 LITTLEFIELD, MILTON SMITH, 1864- ed.
.L744 The hymnal for young people. Ed. by Milton S. Littlefield and Margaret Slattery. New York, A.S. Barnes and company, 1928.
xxii, 326 p. 22cm.
"Services and readings for worship": p.[279]-326.

1. Hymns, English.

NL 0413336 ICU IEN PPEB PPC OO

Littlefield, Milton Smith, 1864- ed.
The hymnal for young people, edited by Milton S. Littlefield and Margaret Slattery. New York, A.S. Barnes, 1930.
xxii, 326 p. music. 22 cm.
"Services and readings for worship": p. [279]-326.

NL 0413337 KKcB NNUT

Littlefield, Milton Smith, 1864- comp.
Hymns and services for use in conferences. Selected from the hymnal for young people. Compiled and prepared by Milton S. Littlefield and Margaret Slattery. New York, A. S. Barnes and company, c1927.
cover-title, 64 p. 22 cm.
61 hymns with music; other pieces numbered 62-69.

NL 0413338 NNUT

Littlefield, Milton Smith, 1864- ed.
Hymns of the Christian life. Ed. by Milton S. Littlefield. New York, A.S. Barnes and company, 1925.
xxx, 429 p. 23 cm.
Hunnewell, Frank S ed. Scripture selections ... [c1911] (bd. with)

NL 0413339 RPB OLak NNUT OCl OO OOxM NcD OrU

M2121 Littlefield, Milton Smith, 1864-1934, ed.
L58 Hymns of the Christian life. New York, A.S. Barnes, 1927 [c1925]
430, 60p. 23cm.

1. Hymns, English. I. Title.

NL 0413340 IaU MH OrU

Littlefield, Milton Smith, 1864- ed.
bMusic
L7993h Hymns of the Christian life. Ed. by
1928 Milton S. Littlefield. New York, A. S. Barnes and Co. [c1928]
xxxiv, 446 p. 22 cm.
Hunnewell, Frank S ed. Scripture selections... [c1911] (bd. with)

NL 0413341 RPB OrP

VP40 Littlefield, Milton Smith, 1864- ed.
1925L
1931 Hymns of the Christian life. Edited by Milton S. Littlefield.
New York, A.S. Barnes and company, 1931, [c1925, 1928 pref. 1925]
xxxiv, 430 p. 22 cm.
543 hymns, chants, etc.; nos. 544-548 readings and prayers, no.549 amens. Hymns preceded by Call to worship.
With music.
Bound with this is: Hunnewell, Frank S ed. Scripture selections for use in the responsive service ... [c1911]

NL 0413342 NNUT OBlC PPC

M Littlefield, Milton Smith, 1864-
2121 Hymns of the Christian life. New York,
L5 A.S. Barnes & Co., 1934.
430 p.

With this is bound Hunnewell, Frank S. & Shepard Benjamin, Scripture selections for use in the responsive service. New York, A.S. Barnes and Co. [n.d.]

HYMNS, ENGLISH

NL 0413343 KMK MB

783.9
L73h Littlefield, Milton Smith, 1864-
Music Hymns of the Christian life. New York,
Lib'y A.S. Barnes, 1937 [c1928]
xxxiv, 446p. 23cm.

1. Hymns, English. I. Title.

NL 0413344 TxU

Littlefield, Milton Smith, 1864- ed.
Hymns of worship and service
see under title

Littlefield, Milton Smith, 1864-
Intermediate teacher's manual. year 1-4
see under title

Littlefield, Milton Smith, 1864-
Intermediate textbook
see under title

Littlefield, Milton Smith, 1864–
The Littlefield O. T. historical maps. New York, Wm. W. Smith & Bureau of education, Jewish community, 1911. 16 maps. 21cm.
Title at foot of each plate.

I. Palestine—Maps. I. Smith, William Walter, 1868–
N. Y. P. L. August 22, 1944

NL 0413348 NN

Littlefield, Milton Smith, 1864– ed.
The school hymnal; a book of worship for young people, ed. by Milton S. Littlefield, with the collaboration of Luella Gardner Littlefield. New York, The A. S. Barnes company, 1920.
x, 310 p. 22 cm.
With the music.

1. Hymns, English. I. Littlefield, Luella Gardner, joint ed. II. Title.

M2193.L79S3 20--11682

NL 0413349 DLC MiU MH-AH WaE Or OrU

1920L Littlefield, Milton Smith, 1864– ed.
1921 The school hymnal; a book of worship for young people, ed. by Milton S. Littlefield, with the collaboration of Luella Gardner Littlefield. New York, A. S. Barnes company, 1921 [c.1920, Editor's note 1920].
x, 310 p. 22cm.
With the music.
307 hymns; Readings and services numbered 308-33
Bound with is: Cooper, Charles Hermance, 1855- Responsive readings for schools. 1921.

NL 0413350 NNUT ODW OrU MnSL

VR60 Littlefield, Milton Smith, 1864- ed.
1920L
1928 The school hymnal, a book of worship for young people. Edited by Milton S. Littlefield with the collaboration of Luella Gardner Littlefield.
New York, A.S.Barnes and company, 1928, [c1920, Editor's note 1920].
x, 290 p. 22 cm.
307 hymns, etc.; nos. 308-315, readings, services etc. (without music), followed by Prayers.
With music.

NL 0413351 NNUT

VR60 Littlefield, Milton Smith, 1864- ed.
1908H
Topical services for Sunday school worship prepared by Milton S. Littlefield and H. Augustine Smith.
New York, The Century co., 1908.
37 p. 21.5 cm.

(in Hymns of worship and service. 1908)

NL 0413352 NNUT

Littlefield, Myra.
Christian perfection. A letter to the Church in North Bridgewater. = Boston. Ela. 1831. 12 pp. 12°.

F4794 — Perfection.

NL 0413353 MB MH

Littlefield, Nathan Whitman, 1846–
Governor Marcus Morton. An address . . . Portrait. Autograph facsimile.
(In Old Colony Historical Society. Vol. 7, pp. 75-93. Taunton. 1909.)

K797 — Morton, Marcus. 1784–1864.

NL 0413354 MB MWA

VOLUME 336

Littlefield, Nathan Whitman, 1846–
... James C. Hunter vs. Mabel B. Conrad, et al. Brief for the complainant on motion to remand to state court ... [Providence] n.d.
3 p. 27 cm.
I. U.S. Circuit court, District of R.I.
II. N.W. Littlefield, solicitor for complainant.

NL 0413355 RPB

Littlefield, Nathan Whitman, 1846–
... John Shepard v. Gustavus Taylor et al. Brief. [Providence, 1887]
8 p. 26 cm.
Caption-title.
N.W. Littlefield, solicitor ...
At head of title: Supreme court, Providence, Oct. term 1887.

NL 0413356 RPB

Littlefield, Nathaniel Swett, 1804–1882.
Speech of Hon. N. S. Littlefield, of Maine, on the bill making appropriations for fortifications. Delivered in the House of representatives, July 19, 1841. [Washington? 1841]
7 p. 22½cm.
Caption title.

1. Fortification—U. S.

17-30654

Library of Congress UG410.L7

NL 0413357 DLC ViU MeB

Littlefield, Walter, 1867–1948.
Bismarck's letters to his wife
see under Bismarck, Otto, fürst von, 1815–1898.

Littlefield, Walter, 1867–1948.
Czechoslovaks, a new belligerent nation, by Walter Littlefield. The Czechoslovaks and Alsace-Lorraine, by Charles Downer Hazen. [New York? 1918?]. 4 l. illus. (map.) 23cm.
Cover-title.
"Reprinted from the New York Times, August 18, 1918."

1. Czecho-Slovak expeditionary force. I. Hazen, Charles Downer, 1868– The Czecho-Slovaks and Alsace-Lorraine.
N. Y. P. L. September 22, 1939

NL 0413359 NN

LITTLEFIELD, Walter.
Dante; [an interpretation of Inferno v.100-102].

Cutting from the New York times, Saturday review, April 1, 1905.

NL 0413360 MH

Littlefield, Walter, 1867– tr.

Noussanne, Henri de, 1865–
The kaiser as he is: or, The real William II. (Le véritable Guillaume II) by Henri de Noussanne: tr. into English by Walter Littlefield ... New York and London, G. P. Putnam's sons, 1905.

Littlefield, Walter, 1867–

Strachey, Lionel, 1864– ed.
Love letters of famous poets and novelists, selected by Lionel Strachey and prefaced with descriptive sketches by Walter Littlefield. New York, The J. McBride co., 1909.

Littlefield, Walter, 1867–1948.

Strachey, Lionel, 1864– ed.
Love letters of famous royalties and commanders, selected by Lionel Strachey, and prefaced with descriptive sketches by Walter Littlefield. New York, The J. McBride co., 1909.

Littlefield, Walter, 1867–1948

Forgione, Louis.
The men of silence, by Louis Forgione ... with an introduction by Walter Littlefield. New York, E. P. Dutton & co., inc. [°1928]

Littlefield, Walter, 1867–1948, ed.

PS716 .B6P6 1894 Rare Bk Coll

[Brown, William Hill] 1766–1793.
The power of sympathy; or, The triumph of nature, founded in truth. By Mrs. Perez Morton (Sarah Wentworth Apthorp) Edited by Walter Littlefield. Boston, Cupples & Patterson [1894]

Littlefield, Walter, 1867–1948 comp.
Byron, George Gordon Noël Byron, *6th baron*, 1788–1824.
With Byron in love, compiled by Walter Littlefield with introduction and notes ... New York, J. H. Sears & company, inc. [°1926]

Littlefield, William Lord.

U. S. *Hydrographic office.*
... Table of distances in nautical and statute miles via the shortest navigable routes as determined by the United States Hydrographic office, Bureau of navigation. Pub. by the Hydrographic office under the authority of the secretary of the navy. Washington, Govt. print. off., 1912.

[Littlefield & Gladding, Bristol, R.I.]
Gladding combination suit [a descriptive leaflet]
[Providence, 1890?]
8 p. 24 cm.

NL 0413368 RPB

Littlefield & Littlefield, New York
...Brief for the defendant [the American anti-boycott association]
[New York? 1912]

HD5461 .L6

NL 0413369 DLC

★★
cHD 9958 M2 L5

Littlefield and Shaffer.
Ledger, traders, June 1852-Oct. 1853.
Marysville, Calif., 1853.
[25] 182 [i.e. 364, 12] p. 33cm.

Title from label inside front cover.
In manuscript.

1. Account books. 2. Manuscripts. I. Shaffer, William C. II. Littlefield, J. D.

NL 0413370 C

Littlefield directory publishing co., Boston, pub.
... The Bangor, Brewer and Penobscot county directory ... 1851, 1864/5, 1869/70, 1871/2, 1873/4, 1875/6, 1877/8, 1879/80, 1882, 1884, 1885, 1887/8, 1890, 1892/3. [v. 1–14] Boston, Littlefield directory publishing co., 1851–'92.

Littlefield directory publishing co., Boston, pub.
... The Boston business directory ... 18

v.
Boston, Mass., Littlefield directory publishing co., 18

Littlefield Directory Publishing Co., Boston.
Dover, Great Falls, and Strafford county directory
see under title

Littlefield directory publishing co., Boston, pub.
... The Melrose directory ...
see under title

Littlefield Stove Manufacturing Co., Albany, N.Y.
Theory of the base-burning stove and the origin of the "Morning Glory"
see under Littlefield, Dennis G.

Littleford, Mrs.
God will defend the right
see under title [supplement]

---

*
PS586 .Z92 .L566W7 1820

Littleford, Mrs.
The wreath: or, Verses on various subjects. By a Lady of Lexington. Lexington, Kentucky, Printed by D. Bradford, 1820.
viii, [9]–118 p. 15cm.

NL 0413377 ViU KyLx

[Littleford, *Mrs.*
The wreath; or, Verses on various subjects. By a lady of Richmond. 2d ed., enl. ... Richmond, Printed by Samuel Shepherd & co., 1828.
5 p. l., [7]–132 p. 19½cm.
Author's name given in copyright notice, and commendatory letter prefixed.
Copyrighted in Kentucky in 1820, as "By a lady of Lexington". *cf.* Copyright notice.
List of subscribers' names: p. [128]–132.

I. Title.

28-7942

Library of Congress PS2248.L38

NL 0413378 DLC ViW TU PU Vi ViU PHi CSmH

VOLUME 336

Littleford, Robert Anthony, 1910–
A study of the life history of *Dactylometra quinquecirrha*, L. Agassiz, and the taxonomic validity of this species, by Robert A. Littleford ... ₍College Park, Md., 1938₎
3 p. l., 47 numb. l. 29½ x 24ᶜᵐ.
Thesis (PH. D.)—University of Maryland, 1938.
Type-written (carbon copy)
Bibliography: leaves ₍43₎–47.
1. Dactylometra quinquecirrha.
42-39125
Library of Congress QL377.S4L5

NL 0413379 DLC

LITTLEFORK, Minn. - Commercial Club.
Facts about Littlefork, Koochiching Co., Minnesota. [Littlefork?, 18- ?].
24°. pp. (4).
Without title-page. Caption title.

NL 0413380 MH

370.954 Littlehailes, R
L73p ... Progress of education in India 1922-27 ... Calcutta, 1929.
2v. tables, diagrs. (part fold.) (9th quinquennial review).
At head of title: Education, India.

NL 0413381 IU CtY

Littlehale, Ednah Dow, 1824-1904
See
Cheney, Mrs. Ednah Dow (Littlehale), 1824-1904.

Littlehale, Frederick Henry, 1849– *comp.*
A complete history and genealogy of the Littlehale family in America from 1633 to 1889. Collated and compiled by Frederick H. Littlehale, of Boston, Mass. ... Boston, Mass., A. W. & F. H. Littlehale, 1889.
vi, 128 p. plates, ports., coat of arms, geneal. tables. 24ᶜᵐ.
1. Littlehale family (Richard Littlehale, d. 1663) 2. Littlehale, Richard, d. 1663. I. Title.
A 25-568
Title from Harvard Univ. Printed by L. C.

NL 0413383 MH MWA

E
7
.L 7322
LITTLEHALE, FREDERICK HENRY, 1849- comp.
A genealogy of the Littlehale family in America, from 1633 to 1880. Collated and compiled by F.H.Littlehale...from original records... Dallas, Tex., Bolles, 1880.
10p.

NL 0413384 ICN RHi MWA

Littlehale, Nellie M.
Dainty desserts for dainty diners.
Springfield, Mass. Bryan & Co. [1887.] 74 pp. 16½ cm.
Two copies.
H3600 — T.r. — Desserts.

NL 0413385 MB

Pamphlet
FL
Canada
51
Littlehales, Edward Baker
Journal of an exploratory tour partly in sleighs but chiefly on foot, from Navy Hall, Niagara, to Detroit, made in the months of February and March, A. D. 1793, by His Excellency Lieut.-Gov. Simcoe. With introd. and notes by Henry Scadding. Toronto, Copp, Clark, 1889.
23 p. 22cm.

NL 0413386 NIC NBu NN ICN CaOTP MiDW

Littlehales, George Washington, 1860–
Altitude, azimuth and geographical position; comprising graphical tables for finding the altitude and azimuth, the position-line, and the variation of the compass; and for identifying observed celestial bodies, and finding the course and distance in great circle sailing, by G. W. Littlehales ... Philadelphia, Press of J. B. Lippincott company, 1906.
3 p. l., 5-11 p. illus., 3 tab. on 6 p., 1 l., 368 charts on 184 p., fold. chart. 60 x 36½ᶜᵐ.
1. Navigation—Tables. 2. Azimuth.
6—24890
Library of Congress VK563.L77

NL 0413387 DLC DN-Ob WU ICJ

LITTLEHALES, George Washington.
The average form of isolated submarine peaks, and the interval which should obtain between deep-sea soundings taken to disclose the character of the bottom of the ocean. Washington, 1890.
pp.7. Charts.
(United States-Bureau of navig.-Hydrog. office. [Publ.] 95.)

NL 0413388 MH CtY NjP DLC OCl PU

Littlehales, George Washington, 1860–
U. S. *Hydrographic office.*
... The azimuths of celestial bodies whose declinations range from 24° to 70°, for parallels of latitude extending to 70° from the equator. Prepared by G. W. Littlehales ... with the assistance of G. G. Radelfinger, J. W. Froley, and C. C. Ennis ... Washington, Govt. print. off., 1902.

Littlehales, George Washington, 1860–
U. S. *Hydrographic office.*
... Azimuths of the sun and other celestial bodies of declination 0° to 23° for latitudes extending 70° from the equator. 13th ed. Published by the Hydrographic office under the authority of the secretary of the navy. Washington, U. S. Govt. print. off., 1930.

Littlehales, George Washington, 1860–
U. S. *Hydrographic office.* FOR OTHER EDITIONS SEE MAIN ENTRY
... Azimuths of the sun for latitudes extending to 70 degrees from the equator. 12th ed. Pub. by the Hydrographic office under the authority of the secretary of the navy ... Washington, U. S. Govt. print. off., 1927.

VK
563
.L78
Littlehales, George Washington, 1860–
The chart as a means of finding geographical position by observations of celestial bodies in aerial and marine navigation.
(In United States naval institute proceedings, v. 44, no. 181, March 1918, p. ₍567₎-583.
Detached copy.

NL 0413392 MiU

Littlehales, George Washington, 1860–
The configuration of the oceanic basins. Madrid, 1930.
42 p. 2 charts. 4°.

NL 0413393 MH

Littlehales, George Washington, 1860–
... Contributions to terrestrial magnetism, the magnetic dip or inclination. As observed at thirty important maritime stations, together with an investigation of the secular change in the direction of a freely suspended magnetic needle at twenty-nine of the stations. By G. W. Littlehales ... Washington, Govt. print. off., 1897.
45 p. fold. chart. 22½ᶜᵐ. (₍U. S.₎ Hydrographic office. ₍Publications₎ no. 114)
1. Magnetism, Terrestrial—Secular variation.
7—1002
Library of Congress QC828.L78

NL 0413394 DLC OrP PP DAS OO MiU MB ICJ Nh

Littlehales, George Washington, 1860–
U. S. *Hydrographic office.*
... The development of great circle sailing, by G. W. Littlehales ... Under the direction of George L. Dyer ... Washington, Govt. print. off., 1889.

Littlehales, George Washington, 1860–
U. S. *Hydrographic office.*
... The methods and results of the survey of the west coast of Lower California by the officers of the U. S. S. "Ranger" during the season of 1889 and 1890. Washington, Govt. print. off., 1892.

Littlehales, George Washington, 1860–
Progress of science ... in terrestrial magnetism. n.p. [1900]

NL 0413397 NjP

Littlehales, George Washington, 1860–
... The progress of science as exemplified in terrestrial magnetism. Annual presidential address by G.W.Littlehales ... Washington, Philosophical society of Washington, 1905.
cover-title, 327-337 p. 25½ᶜᵐ.
At head of title: Philosophical society of Washington. Bulletin, vol. XIV, pp. 327-336 ₍i.e. 337₎
1. Magnetism, Terrestrial.

NL 0413398 MiU NN

Littlehales, George Washington, 1860– joint author.
Bauer, Louis Agricola, 1865–
Proposed magnetic survey of the North Pacific Ocean, by L. A. Bauer and G. W. Littlehales ... Washington, D. C., Press of Judd & Detweiler, 1905.

Littlehales, G₍eorge₎ W₍ashington₎, 1860-1943.
The south magnetic pole. The magnetic inclination and declination in the approaches to it, as deduced from observations made in 1840 by the U. S. expedition commanded by Lieut. Charles Wilkes, U. S. N. ₍New York, 1910.₎ 8 p., 1 map. 8°.
Repr.: Bull. Amer. Geograph. Soc., v. 42, no. 1.
1. Pole (Magnetic) South.
N. Y. P. L. January 18, 1911.

NL 0413400 NN

VOLUME 336

Littlehales, George Washington, 1860-1943.
Secular change in the direction of the terrestrial magnetic field at the earth's surface. Washington, 1899
7 pl. 1 tab. (69) p. 24cm.

Washington, Phil. Soc. Bull., 13, 1895-99, p. 269-336.

NL 0413401 DN-Ob

Littlehales, George Washington, 1860-1943.

TK5661 .U6

U. S. *Hydrographic Office.*
Submarine cables. Instruments and implements employed in cable surveys. Theory of cable laying. Specifications and costs. Submarine cable systems of the world. ⌊By G. W. Littlehales⌋ Washington, Govt. Print. Off., 1892.

Littlehales, George Washington, 1860-1943.

VK569 .U62 1933

U. S. *Hydrographic office.*
... The Sumner line of position furnished ready to lay down upon the chart by means of tables of simultaneous hour angle and azimuth of celestial bodies. Between 27° and 63° of declination, latitude 60° N. to 60° S. ⌊2d ed.⌋ Published by the Hydrographic office under the authority of the secretary of the navy ... Washington, U. S. Govt. print. off., 1933.

LITTLEHALES, George Washington, 1860-1943.
Table of meridional parts, for the terrestrial spheroid, compression 1/293.465. Washington, 1889.

pp.23.
(United States - Bureau of navig.-Hydrog. office. [Publ.] 91.)
By George Washington Littlehales and John Selmar Siebert.

NL 0413404 MH DNLM DLC

Littlehales, G⌊eorge⌋ W⌊ashington⌋, 1860-1943.
The uncertainties of geographical position in polar exploration. ⌊Annapolis, 1909.⌋ p. 1043-1054. 8°.
Repr.: United States Naval Institute Proceedings, v. 35, no. 4, whole no. 132.

1. Arctic exploration.
N. Y. P. L. January 18, 1911.

NL 0413405 NN

Littlehales, Henry, 1859- *ed.*
English fragments from Latin medieval service-books; with two coloured facsimiles from medieval prymers. Ed. by Henry Littlehales. London, For the Early English text-society by K. Paul, Trench, Trübner & co., limited, 1903.
9 p. 2 facsim. in colors. $22\frac{1}{2}$cm. (*Half-title:* Early English text society; extra series, XC)

1. Catholic church. Liturgy and ritual.

4—37093

Library of Congress PR1119.E5 no.90

PBm PP PU NjP OrU CaBVaU
NL 0413406 DLC KEmT NN OU ODW OCU OO OCl ViU MB MH

Littlehales, Henry, 1859- ed.
English fragments from Latin medieval service-books; with two coloured facsimiles from medieval prymers. Edited by Henry Littlehales. London, Published for the Early English Text Society by K. Paul, Trench, Trübner & Co., 1903.
9 p. 2 col. facsims. 23cm. (Early English Text Society. Extra series, XC)

Micro-opaque. ⌊Washington, Microcard Editions, 1952⌋ 1 card. 7.5 x 12.5 cm. (Fo-52: 216)

NL 0413407 NNC MU

Littlehales, Henry, 1859-
A list of parish churches retaining special mediaeval features, glass vestments, plate, etc. London, Rivingtons, 1839.
43 p. Plate. Sm. 8°.

NL 0413408 MB

Littlehales, Henry, 1859- ed.
The medieval records of a London city church (St. Mary at Hill) A. D. 1420-1559
see under London. St. Mary at Hill (Church)

Littlehales, Henry, 1859- joint author.

BV193 .G7W66

Wordsworth, Christopher, 1848-1938.
The old service-books of the English church, by Christopher Wordsworth ... and Henry Littlehales. London, Methuen & co. ⌊1904⌋

Littlehales, Henry, 1859- ed.
Pages in facsimile from a layman's prayer-book in English about 1400 A.D.
see under Catholic church. Liturgy and ritual. Hours. [Salisbury] English. [1890]

Littlehales, Henry, 1859- ed.
The Prymer; or, Lay folks' prayer book (1895-97)
see under Catholic Church. Liturgy and ritual. Hours. [Salisbury] English.

Littlehales, Henry, 1859- ed.
The Prymer; or, Prayer-book of the lay people in the Middle Ages (1891-92)
see under Catholic Church. Liturgy and ritual. Hours. English.

Littlehales, Henry, 1859-
... Some notes on the road from London to Canterbury in the middle ages; ed. by Henry Littlehales. London, Pub. for the Chaucer society by N. Trübner & co., 1898.
56 p. 2 fold. maps. 23cm. (Chaucer society. ⌊Publications. Second series. 30⌋)
CONTENTS.—section I. The route or routes.—section II. Dr. Furnivall's table of allusions, &c. Appearance of the country in the middle ages. Of pilgrimages. Of pilgrims' signs. Ogilby's map of the road in 1675.

1. Chaucer, Geoffrey. Canterbury tales. 2. Roads—England. 3. Pilgrims and pilgrimages—Canterbury, Eng. I. Ogilby, John, 1600-1675.

19-19010

Library of Congress PR1901.A3 no. 30

ViU MB PSC PHC OrU CaBVaU NjP
NL 0413414 DLC MdBP NjP PU OCl OCU OU MiU OClW

Littlehales, Henry, 1859- ed.
Some notes on the road from London to Canterbury in the Middle Ages. London, Trübner, 1898
56 p. maps (Chaucer Society. [Publications. 2d ser. 30]
Microfilm, master copy, of Harvard College Library copy

NL 0413415 MH OOxM

LITTLEHALES, HENRY, 1859-
Tewkesbury abbey; or, An account of the Benedictine abbey of St. Mary, founded at Tewkesbury in Gloucestershire, A.D. 715. By H.Littlehales. New edition... Tewkesbury: W. North [189-] 59 p. front., plan, plates. 19cm.

1. Tewkesbury abbey.

NL 0413416 NN

Littlehales, Lillian.
... Pablo Casals. New York, W. W. Norton & co., incorporated ⌊©1929⌋
216, ⌊1⌋ p. front., illus. (incl. music) pl., ports. 22 cm.

1. Casals, Pablo, 1876- 2. Casals, Pablo, 1876- —Discography.
ML418.C4L5 29—29563

WaU WaT CSt IdU NcU WaSp OrP Or WaS CaBVa Wa MtU
NL 0413417 DLC ViU OCU OO OCl OU PPCI PSt PP NN MB

Littlehales, Lillian.
Pablo Casals. ⌊Rev. and enl. ed.⌋ New York, W. W. Norton ⌊1948⌋
232 p. plates (incl. ports.) facsims., music. 22 cm.
"A list of Casals' recordings": p. 225-228.

1. Casals, Pablo, 1876-
ML418.C4L5 1948 927.8 48-9125*

CaBViP WaE WaS MtBC WaTC OrP OrU Or
NL 0413418 DLC PSt KyBB KyMdC OU NIC MB PP WU

Littlehales, Lillian.
Pablo Casals, una vida. Versión española de Baltasar Samper. Con un apéndice sobre el Festival Bach-Casals celebrado en Prades. México, 1951.
305 p. illus. 22 cm. (Biografías Gandesa, 2)

1. Casals, Pablo, 1876- 2. Casals, Pablo, 1876- —Discography.
ML418.C4L516 52-57 ‡

NL 0413419 DLC

Littlehales, Thomas.
How can the Church evangelise the world? A sermon preached ... Sept. 19, 1844. London, 1844.
15 p. 8°. [In v. 647, College Pamphlets]

NL 0413420 CtY

YA 16526

Littlehales, William L.
An address on the mission of the common schools in the U.S... Washington, 1893.
15p.

NL 0413421 DLC MH

VOLUME 336

LITTLEHAMPTON, ENG. GLASSHOUSE CROPS RESEARCH INSTITUTE.
Report. 1954-55.

NL 0413422 IU

Littleheart, Oleta, pseud.
see
Abbott, Aaron, 1867-

[Littlejohn, Abram Newkirk] bp., 1824-1901.
Address by the bishop of Long Island [i.e.: A.N. Littlejohn] on the twenty-fifth anniversary of the Church Charity Foundation in the Church of the Holy Trinity, Brooklyn. Quinquagesima Sunday, 1877. Brooklyn, Church Charity Foundation-Orphans' Pr., 1877.
16 p. 12°.

NL 0413424 NN NJQ

[Littlejohn, Abram Newkirk] bp. Address delivered at the annual matriculation of students of the General theological seminary, Nov.29, 1876, by the bishop of Long Island. N.Y. Cadmus pr.[1876] 12p.

NL 0413425 NBLiHi

041 F144 v.36 no.11 Littlejohn, Abram Newkirk, bp., 1824-1901.
Address delivered at the dedication of the new grounds of the Evergreen cemetery, of New Haven, July 29th, 1856 ... New Haven, Printed by S. Babcock, 1856.
15p.
[Fahnestock pamphlets, v.36,no.11]

I. Evergreen cemetery, New Haven.

NL 0413426 IU DNLM

40 Littlejohn, A[bram] N[ewkirk] bp. 1824-1901.
Address ... The ecclesiastical system best adapted to meet the religious wants of our country. [n.p., 1866]
[8] p. 8°. [Slavery pamphlets, 53:14]
[Protestant Episcopal church in the United States. Board of missions. Missionary tracts. no. 2]

NL 0413427 DLC CtY

[Littlejohn, Abram Newkirk] bp. 1824-1901.
Address to the clergy of the Diocese of Long Island, assembled in convocation, at St. George's church, Flushing, on Wednesday and Thursday, Nov.16th and 17th,1870. n.p. [1870] 15p. Caption title.

NL 0413428 NBLiHi

041 F144 v.36 no.10 Littlejohn, Abram Newkirk, bp., 1824-1901.
The American character: its faults and its wants. An address pronounced before the Belles lettres society of St. James' college, Md., June 5th,1855 ... New Haven, T. J. Stafford, printer, 1855.
24p.
[Fahnestock pamphlets, v.36,no.10]
Published by request of the Belles lettres society.
I. St. James school, St. James school, Md. Belles lettres society. II. Title.

NL 0413429 IU NcD DLC ICN PHi OClWHi MH NN

Littlejohn, Abram Newkirk, Bp., 1824-1901.
Annual address of the Bishop to the clergy and laity in convention assembled. 1888, 1889, 1890.
Brooklyn. Orphan's Press. [1888-1890] 3 v. in 1. 22 cm.

H7046 — Protestant Episcopal Church in the United States. Diocese of Long Island.

NL 0413430 MB NBuC

R 250 L77 a Littlejohn, Abram Newkirk, bp., 1824-1901.
Bishop Littlejohn's address to the clergy of the Diocese of Long Island, assembled in convocation, at St. George's church, Flushing, on Wednesday and Thursday, Nov.25th and 26th,1869.
10p. n.p.[1869?]

Caption title.

NL 0413431 NJQ NB MH

[Littlejohn, Abram Newkirk] bp., 1824-1901. Brooklyn, its growth and needs. From address to the Diocesan convention, May 19,1885, by the Bishop of Long Island. n.p.[1885] 8p.map. Caption title.

NL 0413432 NN

Littlejohn, A[bram] N[ewkirk], bp., 1824-1901.
Catholic dogma: its nature and obligations. (In Catholic dogma. 1892. p.3-34)

NL 0413433 NNUT

Littlejohn, Abram Newkirk, bp., 1824-1901.
... The Christian ministry at the close of the nineteenth century, by Rt. Rev. A. N. Littlejohn ... New York, T. Whittaker, 1884.
xiii, 422 p. 24cm. (The Paddock lectures, 1884)

I. Title.

Library of Congress BV660.L5 24-8243

NL 0413434 DLC IEG NjNbS TNJ-R NBLiHi PPEB PPLT OO

Littlejohn, Abram Newkirk, bp., 1824-1901.
The church's duty to the family. The triennial charge of the Rt. Rev. A. N. Littlejohn ... to the clergy and laity in convention assembled, in the Church of the Holy Trinity, Brooklyn, May 27th, 1884. Brooklyn, N. Y., 1884.
36 p. 23cm. [With Protestant Episcopal church in the U. S. A. Long Island (Diocese) Journal of the 17th convention, 1884. Brooklyn, N. Y., 1884]

1. Family—Religious life. 2. Protestant Episcopal church in the U. S. A.—Pastoral letters and charges. I. Title.

Library of Congress BX5918.L6A3 17th, 1884 38-12489

NL 0413435 DLC RPB

Littlejohn, Abram Newkirk, bp., 1824-1901.
The comparative dependence of human progress on tradition and invention. An address pronounced before the House of convocation of Trinity college, July 16th, 1856. By the Rev. A. N. Littlejohn ... Hartford, Case, Tiffany and company, 1856.
31 p. 23cm.

1. Civilization.

Library of Congress CB155.L7 16-10642

NL 0413436 DLC Nh NcD PHi NN

250 L779 Littlejohn, Abram Newkirk, bp., 1824-1901.
Conciones ad clerum, 1879-1880 ... 3d ed. N. Y., T. Whittaker, 1881.
339 p. 20 cm.

1. Clergy. 2. Theology. Pastoral. I. Title.

NL 0413437 N NjNbS DNC MH-AH NJQ OO

Littlejohn, Abram Newkirk, bp., 1824-1901.
God's maintenance of His own cause; a sermon preached at the consecration of St. James' Church, Chicago, May 19th, 1864. Published by the vestry of St. James Church, with a short historical sketch of the parish, and of the consecration service. Chicago, J.W. Middleton & co., 1864.
19 p. 22 cm.

NL 0413438 ICHi

Littlejohn, Abram Newkirk, bp., 1824-1901.

Brooklyn. St. Ann's church (Protestant Episcopal)
Inaugural sermons, preached at the opening services of St. Ann's on the heights. Brooklyn, N. Y. Published by the vestry. Brooklyn, Printed by H. M. Gardner, jr., 1869.

Littlejohn, Abram Newkirk, bp., 1824-1901.
Individualism: its growth and tendencies: with some suggestions as to the remedy for its evils. Sermons preached before the University of Cambridge in November, 1880. By the Right Reverend A. N. Littlejohn ... Cambridge, Deighton, Bell and co.; London, G. Bell and sons [etc.] 1881.
viii, 206 p. 19cm.

NL 0413440 NcD IEdS NjNbS NbHi MH PPPD

Littlejohn, Abram Newkirk, bp. 1824-1901.
The ministerial gift: a sermon preached before the convention of the Protestant Episcopal church of the diocese of Connecticut, June 12, 1855 in Christ church, Norwich. New Haven, 1855.
25 p. 22 cm.

NL 0413441 RPB MB Nh

[Littlejohn, Abram Newkirk] bp., 1824-1901.
More laborers needed; a sermon preached before the annual meeting of the Society for the increase of the ministry, in the Church of the Holy Trinity, Brooklyn, on the Sunday after Ascension day, May 12th,1861. N.Y. 1861. 24p.

NL 0413442 NBLiHi Nh MH

VOLUME 336

⁌Littlejohn, Abram Newkirk⁍ bp., 1824-1901.
The nature of dogma and its obligation. N.Y.Young,1891. 34p. (Church Club lectures)

NL 0413443 NBLiHi

⁌Littlejohn, Abram Newkirk⁍ bp., 1824-1901.
The nature of dogma and its obligation. N.Y.Young,1892. 34p.(Church club lectures)

NL 0413444 MWA

Littlejohn, Abram Newkirk, bp. 1824-1901.
The necessity, uses, &c. of a church literature. A sermon, in behalf of the General Protestant Episcopal S.S. union and church book society, at its thirty-first anniversary, preached in the Church of the Holy Communion, New York ... June 21, 1857 ... New Haven, Printed by T.J. Stafford, 1858.
27 p. 23cm.
"Published by the Society."
1 Sermons, English. I. Protestant Episcopal church in the U.S.A. Sunday school union and church book society.

NL 0413445 MnU NcD Nh MB

233.085
L779o ⁅Littlejohn, Abram Newkirk⁆ bp., 1824-1901.
The office of the laying on of hands; its witness to the growing life of the church and to the surest grounds of Christian nurture. The charge of the Bishop of Long Island. Delivered at the Diocesan convention, in the Cathedral of the Incarnation, Garden City, on the nineteenth day of May, 1891. ⁅n.p., 1891?⁆
22p. 24cm.
1. Confirmation--Anglican communion. 2. Protestant Episcopal church in the U.S.A.--Pastoral letters and charges. I. Title. II. Title: The laying on of hands.

NL 0413446 TxDaM

Littlejohn,Abram Newkirk, bp., 1824-1901.
Our martyr President, Abraham Lincoln. Voices from the pulpit of New York and Brooklyn. Oration by Hon. Geo. Bancroft. Oration at the burial, by Bishop Simpson. New York, Tibbals & Whiting ⁅1865⁆

BX5968
.L732 Littlejohn, Abram Newkirk, bp., 1824-1901.
The position of the laity in the Protestant Episcopal Church in the United States. Reprinted from the National Review (of England) October, 1886. Brooklyn, N. Y. ⁅n.p.⁆ 1886.
35 p.
1. Laity - Protestant Episcopal Church. I. Title.

NL 0413448 CtHC MH NBHi TxDaM

Littlejohn, Abram Newkirk, bp., 1824-1901.
The present outlook of the church as indicated by the facts of the hour. The annual sermon before the fourteenth convention of the diocese of Long island, preached in St. Ann's church, Brooklyn, May 17th, 1881, by the Rt. Rev. A. N. Littlejohn ... Brooklyn, N. Y., Orphans' press—Church charity foundation, 1881.
22 p 23cm
With Protestant Episcopal church in the U.S.A. Long island (Diocese) Journal Brooklyn, N.Y., 1875-1881 (v.2)
1 Church work 2 Protestant Episcopal church in the U.S.A.—Sermons I. Title

NL 0413449 ViU

LITTLEJOHN,Abram Newkirk,bp.,1824-1901.
The present popular estimate of the Christian ministry and its causes;the sermon preached at the fourth annual ordination of the Berkeley Divinity School in the Church of the Holy Trinity,Middletown,Wednesday,May 26,1858. Hartford, Case,Lockwood and Company,1858.
23 cm. pp.18.

NL 0413450 MH RPB CtHT-W NN

Littlejohn, Abram Newkirk, bp., 1824-1901.
The primary charge and the primary address of the Rt. Rev. A.N. Littlejohn, bishop of Long Island. Delivered before the second convention of the diocese, in the Church of the Holy Trinity, Brooklyn, September 29th and 30th, 1869. ⁅New York, 1869?⁆
29p. 23cm.
1. Protestant Episcopal church in the U.S.A.--Pastoral letters and charges.

NL 0413451 TxDaM N NbHi MB

Littlejohn, Abram Newkirk, bp., 1824-1901.
Sermon [on the death of President Lincoln]. By A. N. Littlejohn. (*In* Our martyr president. Pp. 145-158. New York. 1865.].)

D7641 — Lincoln, Abraham. Addresses, sermons, etc., about.

NL 0413452 MB

⁌Littlejohn, Abram Newkirk⁍ bp., 1824-1901.
Some alleged faults of the ministry considered. A sermon preached at the consecration of the Right Rev.Thos.Alfred Starkey, D.D. Bishop of northern New Jersey, in Grace church, Newark, by the Bishop of Long Island, Jan.8th,1880. n.p.Standing com.of the Diocese of northern New Jersey,1880. 31p.
YA 11567.

NL 0413453 MWA NBLiHi NN NSM DLC

Littlejohn, Abram Newkirk, bp. 1824-1901.
Some of the ethical faults of modern knowledge. Baccalaureate sermon, Columbia college in the city of New York. By Rt. Rev. A. N. Littlejohn ... in St. Thomas' church, New York, second Sunday after Trinity, 1891. ⁅New York, 1891⁆
31 p. 22½cm.

I. Title.

E 17-447

Library, U. S. Bur. of Education LD1263.1891.L73

NL 0413454 DHEW NbHi

⁌Littlejohn, Abram Newkirk⁍ bp., 1824-1901.
The Sunday school. Extract from the annual address, delivered at the convention at Garden City, May 20,1890. B'klyn,Church charity foundation,1890. 11p.

NL 0413455 MWA NN NBuG Nh

⁅Littlejohn, Abram Newkirk⁆ bp., 1824-1901.
Theology and practical religion as affected by the humanitarian tendencies of the day. The triennial charge of the bishop of Long island. Delivered before the eleventh convention of the diocese, in the Church of the Holy Trinity, Brooklyn, May 21, 1878. Brooklyn, N. Y., Orphans' press—Church charity foundation, 1878.
40 p. 23cm. ⁅With Protestant Episcopal church in the U. S. A. Long island (Diocese) Journal of the 11th convention, 1878. Brooklyn, N. Y., 1878⁆
1. Christianity—19th cent. 2. Protestant Episcopal church in the U. S. A.—Pastoral letters and charges. I. Title.

38-12487

Library of Congress BX5918.L6A3 11th, 1878

NL 0413456 DLC ViU NN MB

Littlejohn, Agnes.
Drowsy hours, and other poems. Sydney, Edwards Dunlop, 1936.
78 p. 20 cm.

I. Title.
PR6023.I 69D7 72-255109 MARC

NL 0413457 DLC NN

Littlejohn, Agnes.
The guardian of the gate, and other poems. Rev. ed. Sydney, Edwards Dunlop, 1934.
122 p. 20 cm.

I. Title.
PR6023.I 69G8 1934 71-256146 MARC

NL 0413458 DLC NN

Littlejohn, Agnes.
The lady of the doves, and other poems. Sydney, Edwards Dunlop, 1929.
66 p. illus. 20 cm.

I. Title.
PR6023.I 69L3 71-234280 MARC

NL 0413459 DLC NN

PR
9598
L77
L3 Littlejohn, Agnes.
A lapse of memory, and other stories. Sydney, J. A. Packer, 1909.
239 p. illus. 22cm.
Contents.--A lapse of memory (Part I).--A lapse of memory (Part II).--Reported killed. --On ocean wave.--Saddanath's legacy.--Wasted years.

NL 0413460 NIC ViU

VOLUME 336

Littlejohn, Agnes.
Lighthouse keepers, and other poems. Sydney, Edwards Dunlop, 1938.
105 p. 20 cm.

I. Title.
PR6023.I 69L5 821 70-262516 MARC

NL 0413461 DLC

Littlejohn, Agnes.
Lyrics and lyrical prose. Illustrated by Albert Collins and H. M. Burton. Sydney, Edwards Dunlop [1927]
63 p. illus. 20 cm.

I. Title.
PR6023.I 69L9 77-234279 MARC

NL 0413462 DLC

Littlejohn, Agnes.
Lyrics and Mystic sketches, by Agnes Littlejohn. Illustrations and designs by J. Muir Auld. Sydney, Edwards Dunlop and co. [1928?] 155 p. illus. 23cm.

NL 0413463 NN

Littlejohn, Agnes.
Poems. [2d edition]
Sydney. Gorton. 1915. 31 pp. 21 cm.
The cover-title is Lyrical poems.
This is a second edition of the volume entitled Verses, published in 1914, which is on shelf-number 2569a.403.

NL 0413464 MB

PR 6023 L732r Littlejohn, Agnes.
Rainbow dreams. Illustrated by Alek Sass. Frontispiece by Albert Collins. Sydney, Edwards, Dunlop, 1919.
78 p. illus.

NL 0413465 CLU

823 L732s 1924 **Littlejohn, Agnes.**
The sleeping sea-nymph. Illustrated by Albert Collins & Olive Crane. Sydney, E. Dunlop [1924]
56p. illus.(part mounted col.) 23cm.

NL 0413466 TxU

PR 6023 .I78 U5 Littlejohn, Agnes.
The unforgotten watch, and other poems. Sydney, E. Dunlop, 1935.
58 p. 20cm.

NL 0413467 WU NcD NN

Littlejohn, Agnes.
The unforgotten watch, and other poems. Rev. ed. Sydney, Edwards Dunlop, 1936.
113 p. 20 cm.

I. Title.
PR6023.I 69U5 1936 78-256145 MARC

NL 0413468 DLC

Littlejohn, Agnes.
Verses.
= Sydney. Gorton. 1914. 24 pp. 22 cm.
A second edition, entitled Poems, is on shelf-number 2569a.401.

NL 0413469 MB

LITTLEJOHN, Alexander, vs. Strattoh, Arthur.
The appellant's case. [London?, 1759?]

f°. pp.4.
Relates to salmon fishing in the river Northesk.

NL 0413470 MH

LITTLEJOHN, Alexander, vs. Stratton, Arthur.
The respondent's case. [London?, 1759?]

f°. pp.4.
Relates to salmon fishing in the river Northesk.
Judgment given in ms. at end.

NL 0413471 MH

Littlejohn, C E S
Short communion service for chorus of mixed voices, with organ accompaniment. 24 p.
N.Y. Schrimer, [c1910]

NL 0413472 OCl

Littlejohn, Charles Edward, 1918–
Effect of operating variables on composition of overhead vapors and residue from a continuous flash distillation for the system methanol-water at atmospheric and sub-atmospheric pressures. Ann Arbor, University Microfilms [1952]
([University Microfilms, Ann Arbor, Mich.] Publication no. 4329)
Microfilm copy of typescript. Positive.
Collation of the original: 141 l. diagrs. (part fold.) tables (part fold.)
Thesis—Virginia Polytechnic Institute.
Abstracted in Dissertation abstracts, v. 12 (1952) no. 6, p. 823–824.
Vita.
Bibliography: leaves 131–138.
1. Distillation. I. Title.
Microfilm AC-1 no. 4329 Mic A 54-1029
Virginia Poly. Inst. for Library of Congress Library [1]†

NL 0413473 ViBlbV DLC

Littlejohn, Charles Edward, 1918–
A literature review of the utilization of fly ash. Clemson, S. C., Engineering Experiment Station, Clemson A. & M. College, 1954.
42 p. illus. 23 cm. ([Clemson Agricultural College of South Carolina] Engineering Experiment Station. Bulletin no. 6)
Bibliography: p. 38–42.

1. Fly ash. I. Title. II. Title: Utilization of fly ash. (Series)
S111.E5 no. 6 660.288 54-62808

NL 0413474 DLC ViU DI TxU

Littlejohn, David, 1841-
New Spalding club, *Aberdeen.*
The miscellany of the New Spalding club ... Aberdeen, Printed for the Club, 1890–1908.

Littlejohn, David, 1841- **ed.** FOR OTHER EDITIONS SEE MAIN ENTRY
Aberdeenshire, *Scotland. Sheriff court.*
Records of the Sheriff court of Aberdeenshire, ed. by David Littlejohn ... Aberdeen, Printed for the University, 1904–07.

Littlejohn, David, 1841- Some general observations on Aberdeenshire fiars courts and prices . . . New Spalding Club, 1906. 75 p. 8°.

NL 0413477 PPPD

Littlejohn, David Stewart.
A sketch of the law of Scotland; an address to the Dundee law apprentices. 2d ed. Edinburgh, Bell & Bradfute, 1890.
89 p. 23 cm.

1. Law—Scotland—Addresses, essays, lectures. I. Title.
52-57690 ‡

NL 0413478 DLC

ar W 15382 Littlejohn, DeWitt Clinton, plaintiff.
The Littlejohn libel suit; the case of DeWitt C. Littlejohn against Horace Greeley, tried at the Oswego term of the Supreme Court of the State of New York, at Pulaski, Sept. 10-13, 1861, before his Honor, William J. Bacon; phonographically reported by James L. Crosby. New York, Tribune Association, 1861.
56 p. 22cm.
I. Greeley, Horace, 1811-1872, defendant. II. New York (State) Supreme Court. III. Crosby, James L reporter.

NL 0413479 ICN NIC ICU MH CtY MnU NbU NBuG MnU OClWHi MnBedf NIC DLC DI NNU-W NcD-L NcD PHi PPL PP

Littlejohn, Elbridge Gerry, 1862-1935.
The geography of Texas, by E. G. Littlejohn ... and P. A. Knowlton...New York, The Macmillan company, 1921.
1 p.l., 62 p. illus. (incl. maps) 24 cm.

NL 0413480 DHEW

920 L4791i Littlejohn, Elbridge Gerry, 1862-1935.
Robert E. Lee. In Texas History Stories, Richmond, Johnson, 1901.

NL 0413481 ViLxW

Littlejohn, Elbridge Gerry, 1862–1935 comp.
Selections for the observance of San Jacinto day and other days, comp. by E. G. Littlejohn ... Dallas, Tex., C. A. Bryant & company [1907]
96 p. $18\frac{1}{2}$cm.
Cover-title: The days we celebrate, state and national.

1. Special days.
E 13-1164
Library, U. S. Bur. of Education LB3525.T4L7

NL 0413482 DHEW

VOLUME 336

T371
L732s

Littlejohn, Elbridge Gerry, 1862-1935.
Spices, an essay on the practice of teaching. Galveston, Tex., 1934.
19p. 16cm.

1. Teaching.

NL 0413483 TxU

Littlejohn, Elbridge Gerry, 1862-1935.
... Texas, by E. G. Littlejohn ... New York, The Macmillan company; London, Macmillan & co., ltd., 1903.
xi, 94 p. illus. (incl. maps) 19 x 15cm. (Tarr and McMurry geographies, supplementary volume)
"Sources": p. ix.

1. Texas. 3-14974

Library of Congress F391.L77

NL 0413484 DLC TxH DHEW OCl OOxM NN PPD

Littlejohn, Elbridge Gerry, 1862-1935.
Texas history stories. Houston, Austin, Crockett, La Salle. (For supplementary reading in primary grades) Galveston, Tex., E. G. Littlejohn [°1897]
65 p. 15½ x 12cm.

1. La Salle, Robert Cavelier, sieur de, 1643-1687? 2. Houston, Samuel, 1793-1863. 3. Crockett, David, 1786-1836. 4. Austin, Stephen F., 1793?-1836. 5. Texas—Hist.—To 1846. I. Title.

Library of Congress F387.L76 Rc-2495 Revised

NL 0413485 DLC TxU

308
Z
Box 890

Littlejohn, Elbridge Gerry, 1862-1935.
Texas history stories; Houston, Austin, Crockett, La Salle. 2d ed. Galveston, Tex., E. G. Littlejohn [c1898]
64 p.

1. Texas - Hist. - To 1846. I. Title.

NL 0413486 NNC TxU

Littlejohn, Elbridge Gerry, 1862-1935.
Texas history stories, by E. G. Littlejohn ... Richmond, B. F. Johnson publishing company, 1901.
6 pt. in 1 v. illus. (incl. ports.) 18 x 13½cm.

1. Texas—Hist.—To 1846.

Library of Congress F387.L77 1-24819

NL 0413487 DLC OkU KMK OCl MB MH NN

T371
L732w

Littlejohn, Elbridge Gerry, 1862-1935, comp.
What shall I do? Suggestions and simplified directions for class management and teaching for young teachers entering the profession and for older ones who still retain the desire to improve themselves. Galveston, Tex., Oscar Springer Print [c1934]
38p. 22cm.

1. Teaching. 2. School management and organization. I. Title.

NL 0413488 TxU CtY

Littlejohn, Elbridge Gerry, 1862-1935.

Tarr, Ralph Stockman, 1864-1912.
World geographies ... by Ralph S. Tarr ... and Frank M. McMurry ... with many colored maps and numerous illustrations chiefly photographs of actual scenes. New York, The Macmillan company, 1918.

M1990
.S66F5

Littlejohn, Fini R., 1914- illus.

Smith, Leonore Rose, *arr.*
First nursery songs, illus. by Fini. Garden City, N. Y., Garden City Pub. Co., °1945.

PZ7
.H152
Se

Littlejohn, Fini R., 1914- illus.

Hall, William Norman, 1915-
The seven little elephants. Pictures by Fini [*pseud.*] [New York] T. Y. Crowell Co., °1947.

Littlejohn, Flavius Josephus, 1804-1880.
Legends of Michigan and the old North West; or, A cluster of unpublished waifs, gleaned along the uncertain, misty line, dividing traditional from historic times. By F. J. Littlejohn. Allegan, Mich., Northwestern Bible and publishing co., 1875.
614 p. incl. front. (port.) pl. 22½cm.

1. Indians of North America—Michigan. 2. Indians of North America—Legends. I. Title. 2-14197

Library of Congress E78.M6L7

MiU OOxM MnU OU InU GU CoU OC MH MiAlbC ViU
NL 0413492 DLC OCl OHi MiKW N ICJ OClWHi MiU-C

TK2851
.W27

Littlejohn, Harry Fendley, 1920-

Ward Leonard Electric Company, *Mount Vernon, N. Y.*
Handbook of power resistors, compiled by H. F. Littlejohn, Jr.; edited by Christian E. Burckel and associates. 1st ed. Mount Vernon [1951]

Littlejohn, Harvey, 1861-1927.
Forensic medicine, illustrated by photographs and descriptive cases, by Harvey Littlejohn ... with 183 illustrations. London, J. & A. Churchill, 1925.
xv, 285, [1] p. incl. plates. 25½cm.

1. Medical jurisprudence. I. Title.
[*Full name:* Henry Harvey Littlejohn]
31-11135

Library of Congress RA1051.L6 340.6

NL 0413494 DLC DNLM MH-L PU-L PPC

Littlejohn, Harvey, 1861-1927.

Scotland. *Local government board.*
... Report on complaints of overcrowding and understaffing of Ruchill fever hospital, Glasgow, and on its administration and management, by Donald Crawford ... Harvey Littlejohn ... and A. Murray ... Edinburgh, Printed for H. M. Stationery off., by Neill & co., limited, 1908.

Littlejohn, *Sir* Henry Duncan, 1828-1914. Case of criminal poisoning with oxalic acid in which perforation of the stomach took place. 8 pp., 1 pl. 8°. [*Edinburgh, Murray & Gibb,* 1862.] [P., v. 1497.]
Repr. from: Edinb. M. J., 1861-2, vii.

NL 0413496 DNLM

Littlejohn, Sir Henry Duncan, 1828-1914.
Health of the city. Weekly report on mortality
see under Edinburgh. Public Health Dept.

RA
1054
L77

Littlejohn, Sir Henry Duncan, 1828-1914.
Lectures on medical jurisprudence, by Sir Henry Littlejohn, summer session 1897 [at the] University of Edinburgh. [Manuscript notes of Sutherland Simpson, Edinburgh, 1897]
326 l. illus. 23cm.

Includes also Simpson's notes on Littlejohn's Lectures on toxicology and Lectures on public health, all delivered during the same session.

1. Medical jurisprudence. 2. Toxicology. 3. Hygiene, Public. I. Simpson, Sutherland, 1863-1926.

NL 0413499 NIC

Littlejohn, Sir Henry Duncan, 1828-1914. On the cleansing operations of Edinburgh, as compared with other towns. Read before the Social Science Association, 1863. 12 pp. 8°. *Edinburgh, Colston & Son,* 1865.

NL 0413500 DNLM

Littlejohn, Sir Henry Duncan, 1828-1914.
Report on the sanitary condition of the city of Edinburgh
see under Edinburgh. Public Health Department.

Littlejohn, Sir Henry Duncan, 1828-1914.

——. Report to the board of supervision as to outbreak of typhoid fever at Crosshill, parish of Cathcart, and county of Renfrew. 12 pp. 8°. *Edinburgh, Murray & Gibb,* 1875.

NL 0413502 DNLM

Littlejohn, Henry Harvey
see Littlejohn, Harvey, 1861-1927.

VOLUME 336

Littlejohn, J. P., ed.
History of the quartermaster, Peninsular base section, Mediterranean theater of operations, in the Italian campaign, October 1943-May 1945
see under U.S. Army. Mediterranean Theater of Operations.

Littlejohn, James B.
Notes on histology, by James B. Littlejohn ... Kirksville, Mo., Weekly advocate print, 1899.
cover-title, 53 p. 25cm.

1. Histology.
Library of Congress QM553.L7 Mar. 16, 99-41

NL 0413505 DLC

QSA L779n 1899
LITTLEJOHN, James B
Notes on histology. St. Louis, Becktold, 1899.
66 l.
Course of lectures presented at the American School of Osteopathy.

NL 0413506 DNLM

Littlejohn, James B.
Outlines of pathology, by James B. Littlejohn ... Kirksville, Mo., Weekly advocate print, 1899.
2 p. l., 124, [4] p. 24½cm.
"A series of lectures, with additions, delivered to the class in pathology during the fall term, 1898, and published for the use of the students of the American school of osteopathy."—Pref.

1. Pathology.
Library of Congress RB119.L77 Mar. 16, 99-42

NL 0413507 DLC

Littlejohn, John Martin, 1867- ed.
The Journal of the science of osteopathy, scientific. A bi-monthly magazine devoted to the demonstration and exposition of the principles of osteopathy and surgery.
v. 1-
Feb. 1900-
Kirksville, Mo., 1900-

Littlejohn, J[ohn] M[artin] 1867-
Lecture notes on physiology, delivered before the January and April classes of the American school of osteopathy, by Dr. J. M. Littlejohn. Kirksville, Mo., Advocate book and job print, 1898.
4 p. l., [1], 19-277 p. 24½cm.

1. Physiology.
Library of Congress QP34.L78 Copyright Sept. 7, 98-51

NL 0413509 DLC

Littlejohn, John Martin, 1867-
Lectures on psycho-physiology. Kirksville, Mo., American school of osteopathy, 1899.
12 p. 8°.

QP359.L75 99—1706

NL 0413510 DLC DNLM

Littlejohn, John Martin, 1867 -
The Osteopathic world, a magazine of osteopathic medicine and surgery.
Minneapolis, W. R. Dobbyn & sons,

Littlejohn, J[ohn] Martin, 1867-
Physiology, exhaustive and practical. A series of practical lectures delivered ... by J. Martin Littlejohn ... in the American school of osteopathy at Kirksville, Missouri. Especially adapted for students of osteopathy. Kirksville, Journal printing company, 1898.
285, iv p., 1 l., [286]-832, iv p. 25½cm.

1. Physiology. 2. Osteopathy.
Library of Congress QP34.L77 Copyright Apr. 13, 99-79

NL 0413512 DLC ICJ

Littlejohn, John Martin, 1867-
The political theory of the schoolmen and Grotius [by] J. Martin Littlejohn. [College Springs, Current-press, 1894]
2 p. l., iv, 296 p. 20cm.

1. Political science—Hist. 2. Scholasticism.
Library of Congress JA82.L6 9—19982

NL 0413513 DLC

Littlejohn, J[ohn] Martin, 1867-
The political theory of the schoolmen and Grotius, parts I, II and III ... [n. p.] 1896.
2 p. l., iv, 296 p., 1 l. 24½cm.
Thesis (PH. D.)—Columbia university.
College degrees and honors.

1. Political science—Hist. 2. Scholasticism.
Title from Columbia Univ. Printed by L. C. A 10-2303

NL 0413514 NcD NNC NIC OrU NcU ViU PU OCl CtY PHC MB

Littlejohn, John Martin, 1867-
[The prophylactic and curative value of the science of osteopathy, by J. Martin Littlejohn] In memoriam ... transactions. Presented to the fellows of the Society of science, London ... Ipswich, East Anglian daily news printing works, 1900.
24 p. 23 cm. [Pamphlets on medicine. v. 9, no. 9]
Caption title.
1. Osteopathy.

NL 0413515 CU

Littlejohn, John Martin, 1867-
The science of osteopathy; its value in preventing and in curing disease. By J. Martin Littlejohn... [Cambridge, Mass.: The Cooperative Press, 1900] 30 p. 23cm.
Caption-title.
Cover-title: Osteopathy explained.
"Address, delivered in London before the Royal Society... is reproduced... from the Journal of the science of osteopathy (scientific) of February, 1900."

850731A. 1. Osteopathy.
N. Y. P. L. November 10, 1936

NL 0413516 NN MB

Littlejohn, John W.
Skiing for Beginners.
3 p.
From: St. Nicholas Magazine, v.30.

NL 0413517 PPAmSwM

Littlejohn, Lewis John Shanks, 1914-
Save the soil, by L. J. S. Littlejohn ... illustrated by Capt. D. L. Izod. [Nicosia] Cyprus, Dept. of agriculture [194-?]
20 p. illus. 30cm.
Text continued on p. [3] of cover.
English, modern Greek and Turkish.

1. Soil conservation—Cyprus. 2. Erosion. I. Title.
S623.L5 631.45 46-45088

NL 0413518 DLC DNAL

Littlejohn, Lewis John Shanks, 1914-
Soil conservation in Cyprus. [Lake Success] 1949.
8 p. (United Nations. [Document] E/CONF. 7/SEC/W.256)

1. Soil conservation. Cyprus. 2. Soil erosion. Prevention and control. Cyprus. I. United Nations. Economic and Social Council. II. United Nations Scientific Conference on the Conservation, and Utilization of Resources, Lake Success, 1949.

NL 0413519 DNAL

Littlejohn, Neil, pseud.
see
Prenter, Neilson Hancock, 1878-

Littlejohn, P.
Cypher; or, the world as it goes. London (?) 1791.
3 v.

NL 0413521 MnU

---

*EC75 L7326 800m
Littlejohn, P
The mistake: or, Something beyond a joke. In three volumes. By P. Littlejohn, author of Henry and The cipher ...
London: Printed for the author, by J. Bonsor, Salisbury square. And sold by T. Hurst, Paternoster-row, Kerbys, Bond street, and Dutton, Birchin lane. 1800.
12°. 3v. 19.5cm.

NL 0413522 MH

Littlejohn, P B
Letter from Waiilatpu, Dec. 6, 1840, to Alvin T. Smith, at Clearwater, describing life at the Whitman mission.
Manuscript.
To be used by permission only.

NL 0413523 WaSp

VOLUME 336

D570.34 332d L779 ⌈Littlejohn, Robert M⌉ comp.
History of the 332d machine gun battalion, 86th division, 171st brigade. ⌈Chicago, Ill., Printed by R.R. Donnelley and sons company, 1919?⌉
29 p., 1 l. incl.col.front.,illus. fold. ports. 27½cm
Front. is embossed seal of battalion.
"Introduction" signed: R.M. Littlejohn.
"Rosters": p.15-29.
1.European war,1914-1918 - Regimental histories U.S. - 332d machine gun battalion. 2. U.S. - Army - Machine gun battalions - 332d, 1917-1919.

NL 0413524 CSt-H CSt

Littlejohn, W
German carbon industry
see under Gt. Brit. British Intelligence Objectives Sub-committee.

Littlejohn, W W
... Making income tax returns ... State College, Miss., Mississippi state college ⌈1945⌉
cover-title, 3-17 p. (Mississippi state college. School of business and industry. Business research station. Bulletin, vol. VI, no. 7)
"Supplement of Mississippi business review."

NL 0413526 MH-BA

Littlejohn, W W
... Making income tax returns. Differences in federal and Mississippi requirements ... State College, Miss., Mississippi state college ⌈1940⌉
13 p. (Mississippi state college. School of business. Business research station. Bulletin, v.1, no.1)

NL 0413527 MH-BA

Littlejohn, W W
... Making income tax returns. Difference in federal and Mississippi requirements ... State College, Miss., Mississippi state college ⌈1943⌉
cover-title, 3-14 p.incl.tab. (Mississippi state college. School of business and industry. Business research station. Bulletin, v.2, no. 2)
"Supplement of Mississippi business review."

NL 0413528 MH-BA

Littlejohn, W W
... Making income tax returns. Major provisions of the 1943 income tax amendment ... State College, Miss., Mississippi state college ⌈1944⌉
cover-title, 3-6 p. (Mississippi state college. School of business and industry. Business research station. Bulletin, vol. V, no.7)
"Supplement of Mississippi business review."

NL 0413529 MH-BA

Littlejohn, William.
Stories of the Buchan cottars before the year "one"; being sketches of life and character in a Buchan parish in Aberdeenshire in the olden times. by William Littlejohn. Aberdeen: Milne and Hutchison, 1929. iv, 50 p. front. (port.) 12°.

455624A. 1. Buchan, Scotland—Social life.
N. Y. P. L. February 3, 1930

NL 0413530 NN MH

⌈Littlejohn, William Harris⌉ 1883-
Wm. Littlejohn descendants. ⌈Shreveport? La., 1949?⌉
iv, 561 p. pl., ports. 23 cm.
"A revision of the 'Family circle' compiled by Roger P. Atkinson (of the Thomas Blount line) in the 1860s." - Preface, signed: W. H. Littlejohn, F. S. Littlejohn.
With authors' autographs.
"William Harris Littlejohn, by his daughter, Mrs. Elizabeth L. Leavell": slip mounted on p. 287.
1. Littlejohn family (William Littlejohn, 1740-1817) I. Littlejohn, Frank Starr, 1883- joint author. II. Atkinson, Roger Pleasants, 1828-1889.

NL 0413532 Vi TxU

UG91 L779 Littlejohn, Wolcott H
The coming conflict: or, The United States to become a persecuting power. A series of papers on the present Sunday agitation. By W.H.Littlejohn. Battle Creek,Mich.,Review and Herald publishing house⌈c1883⌉
L,⌈3⌉-384p. 18cm.
Page ⌈3⌉ numbered iii.

NL 0413533 NNUT NcD OFH MnHi WHi

Littlejohn, Wolcott H
The constitutional amendment: or, The Sunday, the Sabbath, the change, and restitution, by W. H. Littlejohn. Battle Creek, Mich., Steam press of the Seventh day Adventist publishing association, 1873.
iii, 4-79 p. 17½cm.
1. Sabbath. 2. Sunday. 3. Seventh-day Adventists—Doctrinal and controversial works. 4. Sunday legislation—U. S. I. Title.
45-40601
Library of Congress BV125.L5

NL 0413534 DLC

Littlejohn, Wolcott H
The constitutional amendment: or, The Sunday, the Sabbath, the change, and restitution. A discussion between W. H. Littlejohn ... and the editor of the Christian statesman. Battle Creek, Mich., Steam press of the Seventh day Adventist publishing association, 1873.
384 p. 18cm.
1. Sabbath. 2. Sunday. 3. Seventh-day Adventists — Doctrinal and controversial works. 4. Sunday legislation—U. S. I. Christian statesman. II. Title.
45-40597
Library of Congress BV125.L53

NL 0413535 MiU OO OClWHi ICU CU MH Nh DLC GEU CtY IU CU OrU MiD-B NjNbS MiD

Littlejohn, Wolcott H
Position and work of the true people of God under the third angel's message. Battle Creek Seventh-day adventist pub. Assoc. 1870.
80 p.

NL 0413536 OO

Littlejohn, Wolcott H.
Rome in prophecy. Complete spiritual and temporal power to be restored to the papacy in the near future ... by Elder Wolcott H. Littlejohn. Battle Creek, Mich., Review and herald publishing co. ⌈1898⌉
cover-title, 64 p. pl. 19cm.
1. Bible. N. T. Revelation—Criticism, interpretation, etc. I. Title.
Library of Congress BS649.R7L5 0-4339 Revised

NL 0413537 DLC

LITTLEJOHN, Wolcott H.
"The Seventh part of time": a sermon on the Sabbath. [Battle Creek,Mich.,Seventh-Day Adventist Publishing Association,1870]
sm.16°. pp.31.

NL 0413538 MH

---

17 1064 a Littlejohn, Wolcott H.
The seventh part of time. Oakland, Pacific press publishing co., 1889.
32 p. 16°. [Bible students library, no. 21]

NL 0413539 DLC CtY RPB MB PU

Littlejohn College and Hospital, *Chicago*
see Chicago. College of Osteopathy.

Littlejohns, Idalia Blanche (Hewett)
Beadcraft, by Idalia B. Littlejohns ... London, New York ⌈etc.⌉ Sir I. Pitman & sons, ltd., 1930.
xii, 101 p. col. front., illus. 19cm. (*Lettered on cover:* Pitman's craft for all series)
1. Beadwork. I. Title.
Library of Congress TT860.L5 30-20621
⌈3⌉ 746

NL 0413541 DLC AAP Or OCl OEac PP MB NN

Littlejohns, Idalia Blanche (Hewett)
Gesso, by Idalia B. Littlejohns ... London, New York ⌈etc.⌉ Sir I. Pitman & sons, ltd., 1929.
x, 86 p. col. front., illus. 19cm. (*On cover:* Pitman's craft for all series)
1. Gesso.
Library of Congress NK5080.L5 31-20637
⌈a43d1⌉ 731

NL 0413542 DLC OCl MtU OrP CaBVa

Littlejohns, Idalia Blanche (Hewett)
Ornamental homecrafts, a practical description of various methods of ornamenting by means of dyeing, gesso, bleaching, batik, lacquer, enamelling, etc., by Idalia B. Littlejohns ... London, New York ⌈etc.⌉ Sir I. Pitman & sons, ltd., 1927.
xv, 160 p. incl. illus., plates. col. front., col. plates. 21 x 16½cm.
1. Handicraft. 2. Decoration and ornament. 3. Dyes and dyeing. I. Title. II. Title: Homecrafts.
Library of Congress NK1130.L5 28-4224

NL 0413543 WaT CaBViP DLC ICRL OCl OClh OU OClW MB ICJ NN

VOLUME 336

Littlejohns, Idalia Blanche (Hewett)
Painted fabrics, by Idalia B. Littlejohns ... London, New York [etc.] Sir I. Pitman & sons, ltd., 1930.
x, 104 p. col. front., illus. 19cm. (On cover: Pitman's craft for all series)

1. Painting. 2. Art, Decorative. I. Title.
31—11885
Library of Congress ND1625.L5
[a44g1] 751

NL 0413544 DLC OCl NN MB WaS CaBVaU

Littlejohns, Idalia Blanche (Hewett)
Prints and patterns, ornamental patterns, printed with hand-made tools, by Idalia B. Littlejohns ... London, New York [etc.] Sir I. Pitman & sons, ltd., 1929.
xi, 90 p. col. front., illus. 19cm. (On cover: Pitman's craft for all series)

1. Design, Decorative. I. Title.
29-19636
Library of Congress NK8560.L5

NL 0413545 DLC WaS CaBVaU OCl OClh OLak NN MB

---

*EC9 L7325 911ℓ Littlejohns, John.
Lovat Fraser. By John Littlejohns.
1911. Pontypridd[Wales]:Glamorgan county times office.
389p. 19cm.
Much of the story is set in the United States.

NL 0413546 MH

Littlejohns, John, 1874–
Allied arts and crafts, junior course, first[–fourth] year ... by J. Littlejohns ... and A. C. Horth ... London, Sir I. Pitman & sons, ltd. [1934]
4 v. illus. (part col.) diagrs. 28 x 22cm.
Cover-title.

1. Handicraft. I. Horth, Arthur Cawdron, 1874– joint author. II. Title.
35-7690
Library of Congress LB1542.L55
[5] 745

NL 0413547 DLC NN WaS

NC730 .L58 1926 Littlejohns, John, 1874–
Art for all; a course of drawing, composition and design, by J. Littlejohns. London, I. Pitman [1926?]
v. illus. 23 x 28cm.
v.2. Bridges. Spring flowers. The willow.—
1. Drawing. 2. Composition (Art). I. Title.

NL 0413548 ViU

Littlejohns, John, *1874–*
"Art for all" drawing series. [An edition of the author's constructive drawing series, specially prepared for the private student.] Vol. 2 (no. 1); 3 (no. 1); 8 (no. 1); 9 (no. 1)
London. Sir Isaac Pitman & Sons, Ltd. [193–?] 4 v. Illus. Plates. Illustrated title-page. 22 × 28 cm.
Contents. — 2. Figure: 1. Faces and expressions. 3. Animals: 1. The horse. 8. Flowers: 1. Spring, flowers. 9. Birds: 1. Ducks and hens.

D9041 — T.r. — Drawing.

NL 0413549 MB

Littlejohns, John, 1874–
The art for all pastel series [by] J. Littlejohns ... New York, Pitman publishing corporation [1930]
3 v. illus. (part col.) plates (part col.) diagrs. 28 x 22cm.
Cover title.
CONTENTS.—[v. 1] Common objects.—[v. 2] Flowers.—[v. 3] Landscape. buildings.

1. Pastel drawing. I. Title.
37-31762
Library of Congress NC880.L5
[3] 741

NL 0413550 DLC Or

ND 2135 L53 Littlejohns, John, 1874-
The art for all water colour series; trees. London,Pitman[n.d.]
24p. col.illus. 28cm.
Cover title.
1. Water-color painting - Technique. I. Title.

NL 0413551 MH PPPL

---

751 L73a Littlejohns, John, 1874-
The art for all water colour series.
[London, Pitman, 1927-
v. col.illus. 28cm.
Cover title.

NL 0413552 IU MH

Littlejohns, John, 1874-
The art for all: Water colour series. vol. 1, pt. 1
London, Pitman [1928]
__vols. illus. (part. col.) 28cm.
Contents: v.1: Landscape: pt.1: An English village.- v.2: Flowers.- v.3: Fruit.-v.4: Trees.- v.5: Boats and ships.

NL 0413553 NBuG MH

Littlejohns, John, 1874-
The art for all water colour series. New York, Pitman Pub. Corp. [193-?]
v. illus. 28cm.
Imprint varies.
CONTENTS.—v. 1. Landscape.— v. 3. Fruit.— v. 5. Boats and ships.—v. 6. Mountains and valleys.
1. Water-color painting. I. Title.

NL 0413554 MB MH CtY

Littlejohns, John, *1874–*
The Art for all water colour series. Mountains & valleys.
London. Sir Isaac Pitman & Sons Ltd. [1932] 24 pp. Illus. Colored plates. 28 cm.
The title is on the cover.

D2153 — T.r. — Water-color painting.

NL 0413555 MB

Littlejohns, John, 1874–
The art for all water colour series [by] J. Littlejohns ... London [etc.] Sir I. Pitman & sons ltd. [1936?] 6 nos. in 1 v. col'd illus. 27½cm.
Cover-title.
Mounted colored illus. on covers.
CONTENTS.—1. Landscape.—2. Flowers.—3. Fruit.—4. Trees.—5. Boats & ships.—6. Mountains & valleys.

895799A. 1. Water color painting— Technique. I. Title.
N. Y. P. L. August 19, 1937

NL 0413556 NN

Littlejohns, John, 1874–
The art for all water colour series. [London] Pitman [194
v. col. illus. 28 cm.
Cover title.
CONTENTS.— [2] Flowers.

1. Water-color painting—Technique. I. Title.
ND2135.L53 751.42 49-1990*

NL 0413557 DLC NNBG Or WaE CaBVa CaBViP

Littlejohns, John, 1874–
Art in schools, by J. Littlejohns ... With an introduction and additional notes, by R. R. Tomlinson ... London, University of London press, ltd., 1928.
170 p. incl. illus., plates (part col.) col. front., plates (1 col.) 22½cm.
"The art library": p. 146-152.
"An important supplement is included consisting of a number of drawings, some in colour, by children in London elementary schools."

1. Art—[Study and] teaching. 2. Art—[Study and] teaching—Gt. Brit. I. Title.
E 28-630
Library, U. S. Bur. of Education N350.L73

NL 0413558 DHEW CaBVa CaBViP PPPL OCl MB NN

FOR OTHER EDITIONS SEE MAIN ENTRY
Littlejohns, John, 1874- joint author.
Richmond, Leonard.
The art of painting in pastel, by L. Richmond ... and J. Littlejohns ... with frontispiece and introduction by Frank Brangwyn, R. A. London, New York [etc.] Sir I. Pitman & sons, ltd., 1927.

Littlejohns, John, 1874–
British water-colour painting & painters of to-day, by J. Littlejohns ... New York, London [etc.] I. Pitman & sons [1931]
xii, 105, [1] p. illus., plates (part col. mounted) 28cm.

1. Water-color painting—Gt. Brit. 2. Water-colors, British. I. Title.
31-11826
Library of Congress ND1928.L5
[3]

NL 0413560 DLC GU NIC MB NN PP OCl OClW ViU CaBVa IdU-SB CaBViP WaS

Littlejohns, John, *1874–*
The composition of a landscape. A sequel to 'Sketching from nature in line and tone.'
London. Winsor & Newton, Ltd. [1931.] 31 pp. Plates, some colored. 21½ cm.

D484 — T.r. — Landscape painting. — Composition. In art.

NL 0413561 MB

VOLUME 336

Littlejohns, John, 1874–
The "essential" colour system; its use and value, by J. Littlejohns... London: Winsor & Newton, Ltd.[, 1928.] 23 p. diagrs., illus. 8°.

426055A. 1. Color in art.
N. Y. P. L. August 20, 1929

NL 0413562 NN OCl

Littlejohns, John, 1874–
Examples of lettering and design, by J. Littlejohns ... London, New York [etc.] Sir I. Pitman & sons, ltd., 1928.
58, [1] p. illus. 23½cm.

1. Lettering. I. Title.

Library of Congress NK3600.L5 29-2371

NL 0413563 DLC PP OU OClh OCl NN MB

Littlejohns, John, 1874–
How to enjoy pictures, by J. Littlejohns ... New York, The Macmillan company; London, A. & C. Black, limited, 1927.
vii, 81, [1] p. incl. illus. (1 mounted) col. mounted plates. 26cm.

1. Painting—Study and teaching. I. Title.

Library of Congress ND1143.L5 27-27516

NL 0413564 IU WaE CaBVa OrP Or IdU-SB DLC MiDW AAP OKentU OCl ODW OClh NN MB

Littlejohns, John, 1874–
An introduction to the study of colour, by J. Littlejohns... London: Winsor & Newton, Ltd.[, 1928.] 62 p. illus., col'd pl. 8°.

409084A. 1. Color in art.
N. Y. P. L. May 20, 1929

NL 0413565 NN

Littlejohns, John, 1874–
Landscape sketching and composition, by J. Littlejohns ... London, Sir I. Pitman & sons, ltd., 1933.
ix, 114, [1] p. illus. (part col. mounted) 28cm.

1. Landscape drawing. 2. Landscape painting. 3. Pastel drawing. I. Title.

Library of Congress NC795.L5 33-16590
[3] [741] 758

NL 0413566 DLC OrCS WaS CaBVa MB NN OCl CtY

Littlejohns, John, 1874–
Leaves from my sketchbooks, by J. Littlejohns ... London, Sir I. Pitman & sons, ltd., 1932.
27 l. incl. plates. 18½ x 26cm.
Cover has imprint: London, New York [etc.] Sir I. Pitman & sons, ltd.

I. Title.

Library of Congress NC1115.L5 33-34128
[3] 741

NL 0413567 DLC CaBVa ViU NN RPB MS

Littlejohns, John, 1874-
Sketching from nature in line and tone. Wealdstone,Harrow,Middx.,Winsor & Newton. [n.d.] 23p.illus. (Winsor & Newton's art manuals)

NL 0413568 CaBVa

Littlejohns, John, *1874–*
Sketching from nature in line and tone. 4th thousand.
London. Winsor & Newton, Ltd. [193–?] 36 pp. Plates. 21½ cm., in 8s.

D78 — T.r. — Sketching.

NL 0413569 MB MH-FA OCl OClh

Littlejohns, John, 1274- joint author.
Richmond, Leonard.
The technique of pastel painting, by L. Richmond ... and J. Littlejohns ... London, New York [etc.] Sir I. Pitman & sons, ltd., 1931.

Littlejohns, John, 1874- joint author.
FOR OTHER EDITIONS SEE MAIN ENTRY
Richmond, Leonard.
The technique of water-colour painting, by L. Richmond ... and J. Littlejohns ... New York, Chicago, Pitman publishing corporation, 1936.

Littlejohns, John, 1874–
Training of taste in the arts and crafts, by J. Littlejohns ... with an account of investigations on children's preferences by A. Needham ... London, Sir I. Pitman & sons, ltd., 1933.
viii, 152 p. incl. illus. (part col. mounted) plates. 23cm.

1. Art—Study and teaching. 2. Art—Psychology. 3. Esthetics—Study and teaching. I. Needham, A. II. Title.

Library of Congress N350.L5 33-32354
[3] [159.922747] [136.747] 707.61

NL 0413572 IdU-SB DLC OClW PP PPPL MB NN OCU OCl OClMA

Littlejohns, Raymond *Trewolla, 1893–*
Birds of our bush, or Photography for nature-lovers, by R. T. Littlejohns and S. A. Lawrence, ... With an introduction by J. A. Leach, ... Illustrated from photographs by the authors. Melbourne and London, [etc.], Whitcombe & Tombs, [192–]
207, [1] p. incl. front., illus. 23cm.

NL 0413573 ICJ

598.2 L73b Littlejohns, Raymond Trewolla, 1893-
Birds of our bush; or, Photography for nature-lovers, by R. T. Littlejohns and S. A. Lawrence ... With an introduction by J. A. Leach ... Melbourne [etc.] Whitcombe & Tombs limited [1921]
207p. front., illus.

1. Birds--Australia. I. Lawrence, S. A., joint author. II. Title.

NL 0413574 IU WaU CtY

LITTLEJOHNS, RAYMOND TREWOLLA, 1893-
Birds of our bush; or photography for nature-lovers. Melbourne, Whitcombe & Tombs, [1925?].
207 p. illus.
(70) 1. Birds. Australia. I. Lawrence, S A. II. Title.

NL 0413575 DNAL

Littlejohns, Raymond Trewolla, 1893–
The lyre-bird, Australia's wonder-songster, by R. T. Littlejohns, R. A. O. U. Illustrated with photographs by the author. Sydney and London, Angus & Robertson, limited, 1938.
12 p. xxx pl. on 20 l. 27½cm.

1. Lyre-birds. 2. Birds—Australia.

A 40-2970

Minnesota. Univ. Libr.
for Library of Congress [2]

NL 0413576 MnU CU DLC NcD CtY

QL696 P2L52 Biol. Lib. Littlejohns, Raymond Trewolla, 1893-
Lyrebirds calling from Australia [by] R.T. Littlejohns ... Foreword by Charles Barrett ... Melbourne, Robertson & Mullens [1943]
40 p. front.,plates. 21cm.

"First edition."

NL 0413577 CU

Littlejohns, Raymond Trewolla, 1893–
Lyrebirds calling from Australia. With 24 illus. from photos. by the author. Foreword by Charles Barrett. [2d ed.] Melbourne, Robertson & Mullens [1947]
40 p. plates. 21 cm.

1. Lyre-birds.
QL696.P2L74 1947 598.81 49-14824*

NL 0413578 DLC MiU TxU MH

Littlejohns, Raymond Trewolla, 1893–
The magic voice; a story of the Australian lyre-bird. Illus. from photos. by the author. With a foreword by A. H. Chisholm. Melbourne, Ramsay Pub. Pty. [©1933]
40 p. plates. 25 cm.
"Intended to be complementary to a sound-film and to ... [the lyre-bird] gramophone record with the production of which ... [the author] has been associated."

1. Lyre-birds. I. Title.

QL696.P2L75 598.81 49-41137*

NL 0413579 DLC

Littlemore, F., pseud.
see Moore, Frank Frankfort, 1855-1931.

821 L732s Littlemore, Gilbert I
Songs of a hermit. With an introd. by J. Le Gay Brereton. [1st ed.] London, Epworth Press [1927]
128p. 20cm.

Poems.

NL 0413581 TxU NN

VOLUME 336

Littlemore, S
A poem on the death of the celebrated Mrs. Oldfield, who dy'd October 23. 1730... By S. Littlemore... London, A. Moore, 1730. 2 p.l., 4 p. 38cm.

1. Oldfield, Anne, 1683-1730— Poetry.
N. Y. P. L. August 13, 1947

NL 0413582 NN MH

WX 2 FE5 L7A8r
LITTLEMORE, Eng. Littlemore Asylum.
Report.
1846-
[Littlemore?]
v. in

NL 0413583 DNLM

Littleover, Eng.
Mickleover, Eng.
The registers of Mickleover (1607-1812) and of Littleover (1680-1812), co. Derby. Transcribed by Llewellyn Lloyd Simpson ... ₍Exeter, Eng.₎ Issued by the Parish register society ₍1909₎

HD9536 L7794
Littlepage, John D.
À la recherche des mines d'or de Sibérie, 1928-1937 ₍par₎ John D. Littlepage en collaboration avec Demaree Bess. Paris, Payot, 1948.
255 p. map. 23cm. (Collection de documents et de témoignages pour servir à l'histoire de notre temps)
Translation of In search of soviet gold.

1. Gold mines and mining - Russia. 2. Russia - Soc. condit. 3. Russia - Descr. - 1917- I. Bess, Demaree. II. Title.

NL 0413585 CSt-H InU ViU IU OU

Littlepage, John D.
In search of soviet gold, by John D. Littlepage and Demaree Bess. New York, Harcourt, Brace and company ₍°1938₎
xv, 310 p. 21cm.
Map on lining-papers.
"This entire book is essentially the story of Littlepage's ten years in the service of the Soviet gold trust, and is told in the first person. But some of the deductions and conclusions from these experiences were worked out in conversations and correspondence between Littlepage and myself, and he has therefore requested that I also should append my signature to the book."—Collaborator's foreword.
"First edition."

1. Gold mines and mining—Russia. 2. Russia—Soc. condit. I. Bess, Demaree. II. Title.
Library of Congress TN415.R9L5. 1938 38-27739
——— Copy 2.
Copyright A 123068 ₍10-10₎

PPL PU WaS OO OU OCl OEac MiU NN WaSp TU NcU Or CoU OrPR WaE NcD PPA OrU PBm Wa PP
NL 0413586 DLC ScU OKentU OrP CU CaBVaU AAP IdB

Littlepage, Lewis, 1762-1802.
Works by this author printed in America before 1801 are available in this library in the Readex Microprint edition of Early American Imprints published by the American Antiquarian Society.
This collection is arranged according to the numbers in Charles Evans' American Bibliography.

NL 0413587 DLC

Littlepage, Lewis, 1762-1802.
Answer to a pamphlet, containing the correspondence between the Honorable John Jay, secretary for foreign affairs; and Lewis Littlepage, esquire, of Virginia; at present chamberlain and secretary of the cabinet of his Majesty the King of Poland ... New-York, Printed and sold by Francis Childs, at the corner of Wall and Water-streets ₍1786₎
1 p. l., 29 p. 20cm.
Imperfect: p. 29 wanting.
1. Jay, John, 1745-1829. Letters, being the whole of the correspondence ... 1786.
Library of Congress E302.6.J4L71 11-21130

NL 0413588 DLC NHi CtY NN

Littlepage, Lewis, 1762-1802.
Answer to a pamphlet, containing the correspondence between the Honorable John Jay, secretary for foreign affairs; and Lewis Littlepage, esquire, of Virginia; at present chamberlain and secretary of the cabinet of His Majesty the King of Poland ... Philadelphia, Printed and sold by Enoch Story, corner of Walnut & Second streets ₍1786₎
35 p. 18½cm.
Verso of p. 35 contains publisher's advertisement.
1. Jay, John, 1745-1829. Letters, being the whole of the correspondence ... 1786.
Library of Congress E302.J4L7 11-21282

NL 0413589 DLC ICN MdHi

Littlepage, Lewis, 1762-1802.
Answer to a pamphlet, containing the correspondence between the Honorable John Jay, Secretary for foreign affairs; and Lewis Littlepage, Esquire, of Virginia; at present chamberlain and secretary of the cabinet of his Majesty the King of Poland... New-York: Printed and sold by Francis Childs ₍1787₎ 1 p.l., 29 p. 4°.
Evans 20462. Sabin 41549.
Biographical matter inserted.

1. Jay, John, 1745-1829.
September 15, 1919.

NL 0413590 NN RPJCB

Littlepage, Lewis, 1762-1802.
Answer to a pamphlet, containing the correspondence between the Honorable John Jay, Secretary for Foreign Affairs; and Lewis Littlepage, esquire, of Virginia; at present chamberlain and secretary of the cabinet of His Majesty the King of Poland... Philadelphia: Printed and sold by Enoch Story ₍1787₎ 35(1) p. 4°.
See: Evans 20463.

1. Jay, John, 1745-1829.
N. Y. P. L. December 31, 1918.

NL 0413591 NN

Littlepage, Lewis, 1762-1802.
FOR OTHER EDITIONS SEE MAIN ENTRY
Jay, John, 1745-1829.
Letters, being the whole of the correspondence between the Honorable John Jay, esq. and Mr. Lewis Littlepage; a young man whom Mr. Jay, when in Spain, patronized and took into his family. A new and correct ed. To which is added an appendix, not before published. New-York, Printed by Eleazer Oswald, at the printing-office, no. 25, Water-street, 1786.

Littlepage, Samuel Carpenter, 1833-1915.
The analysis of the body of death, or Campbellism dissected. ₍n.p.₎ McGregor News print ₍1895?₎
51 p.
Cover title.

1. Harrison, M D I. Title.

NL 0413593 TxDaM TxU

Littlepage, T. P. Extending the pecan area. Read at meeting of National nut-growers' association, held at Mobile, Oct. 5-7, 1911. [Mobile, Ala. 1911.] 8°. pp. 8.

NL 0413594 MH-A

Littlepage, T. P.
——— The Indiana pecan. Read at a meeting of the Northern nut-growers association, held at Cornell university, Dec. 14-15, 1911. [Ithaca. 1911.] 8°. pp. 15.

NL 0413595 MH-A

J75 1925 .C9j Serial 22
Littlepage, Thomas Price, 1873-*1942.*
U. S. *Congress. House. Committee on the judiciary.*
Charges of impeachment against Frederick A. Fenning. Hearing₍s₎ before the Committee on the judiciary, House of representatives, Sixty-ninth Congress, first session on House Resolution 228. May 20, 21, 24, 26, 27, 28, 29, June 1, 2, 3, 4, 5, and 7, 1926. ₍And₎ Brief₍s₎ ... Washington, Govt. print. off., 1926.

The Littlepage manuscripts
see [Cooper, James Fenimore] 1789-1851.
The chainbearer; or, The littlepage manuscripts.

Littleport manor.
... The court baron ... 1891
see under Maitland, Frederic William, 1850-1906, ed.

Littleproud, J Roy, 1889-1941.
The Christian assembly. [3d ed.] Calif., Ralph E. Welch Foundation, n.d.

200 p.

1. Church--Biblical teaching. 2. Plymouth Brethren--Doctrinal and controversial works.

NL 0413599 CLamB

Littler, Clarence Arthur, 1909-
Potentials at metal-solution interfaces. ₍n. p., 1950₎
₍1016₎-1027 p. diagrs. 26 cm.
Cover title.
C. A. Littler's thesis—Johns Hopkins University.
Reprint of an article by W. A. Patrick and C. A. Littler, published in the Journal of physical and colloid chemistry, v. 54, no. 7, Oct. 1950, under title: Method of measuring the absolute potential of aqueous half-cells.
Vita.
"References": p. 1027.
1. Potential, Theory of. I. Patrick, Walter Albert, 1888- joint author. II. Title. III. Title: Metal-solution interfaces.
QA825.L56 A 51-3964
Johns Hopkins Univ. for Library of Congress Library ₍1₎†

NL 0413600 MdBJ DLC

Littler, D J
An introduction to reactor physics, by D. J. Littler and J. F. Raffle. London, Published for the United Kingdom Atomic Energy Authority ₍by₎ Pergamon Press, 1955.
196 p. illus. 23 cm.

1. Nuclear physics. 2. Nuclear reactors. I. Raffle, J. F., joint author. II. Title: Reactor physics.
QC776.L5 1955a *539.7 539.1 56-1400 ‡

NL 0413601 DLC MiU OU PP PSt

VOLUME 336

Littler, D J
An introduction to reactor physics, by D. J. Littler and J. F. Raffle. Published for the United Kingdom Atomic Energy Authority. New York, McGraw-Hill, 1955.
196 p. illus. 21 cm.

1. Nuclear physics. 2. Nuclear reactors. I. Raffle, J. F., joint author. II. Title: Reactor physics.
QC776.L5 *539.7 539.1 55-4896 ‡
Library of Congress [30]

IdPI MtBC OrCS OrPR WaS
KEmT TxU PBL PSC PPLas NcRS ICJ OClW OClU MiU OO NN
NL 0413602 DLC OCU OCl NcD PPF CU IU TU DI MB ViU

Littler, Émile, 1903- joint author.

Rouverol, *Mrs.* Aurania (Ellerbeck) 1885–
Love isn't everything; a comedy in three acts, by Aurania Rouverol and Émile Littler. London, S. French [1937]

Littler, Émile, 1903-

Flavin, Martin, 1883–
Too young to marry, a comedy in three acts, by Martin Flavin, adapted by Emile Littler. London, S. French [1937]

Littler, Frank Mervyn.
A handbook of the birds of Tasmania and its dependencies. By Frank Mervyn Littler ... Launceston, Tasmania, The author, 1910.
2 p. l., [iii]-xviii, 242 p. plates. 24½cm.

1. Birds—Tasmania. [1. Tasmania—Ornithology]
Agr 16-1097
Library, U. S. Dept. of Agriculture 413L73

NL 0413605 DNAL NIC CtY CU ICJ PPAN IU

Littler, Henry Lawrence, *comp.*
... Dear old friend; muster zu englischen privatbriefen, mit deutscher übersetzung, von Henry L. Littler und dr. S. D. Stirk. Deutsche übersetzung und bearbeitung von dr. Hans Marcus. 1. aufl. Berlin-Schöneberg, Langenscheidt [1937]
x, 102 p. 19cm. (Langenscheidts musterbriefe)
The letters themselves are from the pens of cultured Englishmen; some are the work of Dr. S. D. Stirk. cf. p. iv.

1. Letter-writing, English. 2. Letter-writing, German. I. Stirk, Samuel Dickinson. II. Marcus, Hans, 1892- tr. III. Title.
42-1863
Library of Congress PE1497.L5
[2] 808.6

NL 0413606 DLC NcD MH N MoU CtY

641.5 L73o
Littler, Nora Delany, compiler.
Our favourite dish: the theatre recipe book; 250 recipes contributed by members of the British theatrical profession. Compiled by Mrs. Prince Littler. Edited by Naomi Waters. [London] Putnam [1952]
xvi, 282 p. illus. 20cm.

At head of title: For the Actors' Orphanage.
1. Cookery. I. Waters, Naomi, ed. II. Title.

NL 0413607 LU N NN MB OCU CaBVa

Littler, Mrs. Prince,
see
Littler, Nora Delany.

Littler, Sir Ralph Daniel Makinson, 1835-1908
Compensation in licensing; the Licensing bill, 1908, with a historical and legal retrospect. 4th ed., almost entirely rewritten. London, Butterworth, 1908. 106p. 21cm.

NL 0413609 MWelC

Littler, Sir Ralph Daniel Makinson, 1835-1908, joint author.

Tidswell, Richard Thomas, *b.* 1830.
The practice and evidence in cases of divorce and other matrimonial causes: together with the acts, rules, forms, &c. By Richard Thomas Tidswell, M. A., and Ralph Daniel Makinson Littler ... London, W. Benning & son [etc.] 1860.

4K 7959
Littler, Sir Ralph Daniel Makinson, 1835-1908.
The rights and duties of justices, by R.D.M. Littler and Arthur Hutton. London, Butterworth, 1899.
122 p.

NL 0413611 DLC-P4

Littler, Sir Ralph Daniel Makinson, 1835-1908.

Fawcett, *Sir* John Henry, 1831–1898.
A treatise on the Court of referees in Parliament, containing chapters on the practice and jurisdiction of the court, on the locus standi of petitioners in the House of commons, and reports of the cases decided in that court during last session, reprinted by permission (with additions, from "The Law times." By John Henry Fawcett ... Together with a chapter on engineering and estimates, and a digest of the reports made by the referees to Parliament. By R. D. M. Littler ... London, H. Cox [1866]

Littler, Robert M., comp.
Directory of creameries, cheese factories, dairymen
see under title

Littler, Robert M., comp.
... Directory of producers, dealers and shippers of butter, cheese, eggs and poultry, in the north-western, western and middle states, and Canada West. Also a register of produce commission houses and dealers in the principal cities of the United States. Essays and reports on butter and cheese making, egg and poultry shipping, etc. Comp. and pub. ... by Robt. M. Littler, secretary of the National butter, cheese and egg association. Davenport, Gazette company, printers, 1878.

Littler, Robert McDonald Charles, 1904– *comp.*
Cases and materials on labor law, selected by Robert Littler ... [Stanford University, Calif.] School of law, Stanford university, 1939.
1 p. l., 493 (*i. e.* 506) numb. l. 29cm.
Reproduced from type-written copy.
Extra numbered leaves inserted.

1. Labor laws and legislation—California—Cases. 2. Labor laws and legislation—U. S.—Cases. 3. U. S. National labor relations board. 4. Labor contract—California. 5. Labor contract—U. S. I. Title.
41-6132
Library of Congress

NL 0413615 DLC

Littler, Robert McDonald Charles, 1904–
The governance of Hawaii; a study of territorial administration, by Robert M. C. Littler. Stanford University, Calif., Stanford university press, 1929.
xvii, 281 p. front. (map) diagrs. 20 cm. [Stanford books in world politics]
Bibliography at end of each chapter.

1. Hawaii—Pol. & govt.—1900-1959. I. Title.
JQ6115 1929.L5 29—12601
Library of Congress [a66q1]

WaS MtU CaBViP
MU MB WaT OrCS Or OClW OCl OO OCU NcRS NcD OrSaW
NL 0413616 DLC OU PU ViU WaU NjN IdU MH-L ICRL MiU

Pam. Coll. 10744
Littler, Robert McDonald Charles.
The government of the city and county of Honolulu ... [Honolulu, 1926?]
57 p. illus., ports. 23cm.
"In this pamphlet is published the series of twenty articles by ... [the author] on the city and county government which appeared in the Honolulu Star-Bulletin daily beginning June 12, 1926."

NL 0413617 NcD

Littler, Robert McDonald Charles.
The government of the city and county of Honolulu. [Honolulu:] Printed for the Univ. of Hawaii by the Honolulu Star-Bulletin, 1927. 64 p. 8°.
The material in this pamphlet was prepared in 1925 by Mr. Robert Littler; in order to bring it up to date Dr. K. D. Lum and K. C. Leebrick of the University of Hawaii have gone over the articles and added necessary facts. — *cf. Introd.*

555252A. 1. Municipal government—Hawaii—Honolulu. I. Leebrick, Karl Clayton, 1885- . II. Lum, Kalfred Dip. III. Hawaii (territory). University. IV. Honolulu Star-Bulletin.
N. Y. P. L. December 16, 1931

NL 0413618 NN IU

Littler, Walter.
Elementary chemistry, by W. Littler ... Book II. 2d ed. Toronto, Clarke, Irwin & company limited, 1942.
x, 334 p. illus., diagrs. 19cm.
Table on lining-paper.
"Second edition, July, 1934. Reprinted ... April, 1942."
An edition for use in Canadian schools of an English work of the same title (published 1931) arbitrarily called "book II" by the publisher.
"Answers to numerical examples": p. 333-334.

1. Chemistry.
44-137
Library of Congress QD33.L77 1942
[3] 540

NL 0413619 DLC

Pamphlet C 21
Littles, Sarah E
The Falls Field tragedy! The confession of Sarah E. Littles, being an authentic narrative of the facts connected with the murder of her husband, Charles W. Littles, at Rochester, N. Y., on the night of the 19th of December, 1857. Rochester, N. Y., Curtis Butts & Co., 1858.
24 p. 19cm.

NL 0413620 NIC PHi

The littlest Christmas tree and other Christmas stories
see under Worman, Theresa, 1907-

VOLUME 336

B 1827 Littleton, Adam, 1627-1694.
525* Bibliotheca Littletoniana. The library of the reverend and learned Adam Littleton ... will be sold by auction, on Monday April 15th, 1695. and the following days, at three in the afternoon, at Tom's coffee house adjoyning to Ludgate. By John Bvllord ...
[London,1695]

4°. 1p.ℓ.,20,4,13-41(i.e.14)p. 23cm.
Page 14 (2d count) misnumbered 41.

NL 0413622 MH

Littleton, Adam, 1627-1694.
1669 **The/ Churches Peace/ ASSERTED/ UPON A/ CIVIL ACCOUNT./ As it was (great part of it) deliver'd in a Ser-/mon before the Right Honourable the Lord/Mayor,in Guild-Hall-Chappel,July 4./ By AD. LITTLETON, Presbyter./...LONDON, Printed for Philip Chetwind, MDCLXIX./**
[10] 38 p. 20 x 15 cm.

Wing: L2560.

NL 0413623 NNG TxU NNUT-Mc CtY MnU

Littleton, Adam, 1627-1694, ed.
Dissertatio epistolaris de juramento medicorum ...
see under Hamey, Baldwin, 1600-1676.

---

252 [Littleton, Adam] 1627-1694.
L734h Hezekiah's return of praise for his recovery. By A. L. ... London, Printed by E. Cotes, for Samuel Tomson at the Bishops-Head in Duck-lane, 1668.
2 p.l., 43p. 18½cm.

1. Sermons. I. Title.

NL 0413625 IU NNUT-Mc

Aj
L734
678lf
Rare
Books
Col

LITTLETON, ADAM, 1627-1694.
Dr. Adam Littleton's Latin dictionary, in four parts: I. An English-Latin. II. A Latin-classical. III. A Latin-proper. IV. A Latin-berbarous. I. The English before the Latin ... II. The Latin-classical before the English ... III. The Latin-proper names ... IV. The Latin-barbarous ... The law-Latin, as used in the common law, and very necessary for the understanding of charters, &c. are in this, and in no other dictionary, of the kind, laboriously collected and explained. The sixth edition. With large amendments and improvements, comprising all that is valuable in former

dictionaries: and two maps, one of Italy, the other of old Rome.
London: Printed for J. Walthoe, J.J. and P. Knapton, R. Wilkin, D. Midwinter, T. Osborne, A. Bettesworth and C. Hitch, R. Gosling, J. and A. Bonwicke, W. Innys and R. Manby, B. Sprint, B. Motte, J. Brotherton, R. Ford, R. Robinson, A. Ward, T. Longman, D. Browne, S. Birt, T. Ward

and E. Wicksteed, J. Clarke, S. Austen, H. Lintot, J. King, B. Cowse. M.DCC.XXXV. [1430]p. 2 maps. 25cm.
Signatures: 1 leaf unsigned, A², a⁴, a-z⁴, aa-ff⁴, Gg-Zz⁴, 3A-3L⁴, Mmm-Zzz⁴, Aaaa-Gggg⁴, 4H-4R⁴, Ssss-Zzzz⁴, 5A-5Z⁴, 6A-6Z⁴, 7A-7Z⁴, 8A-8Q⁴ (dd2, 7M2, 8Q2 incorrectly signed Dd2, M2, Q2, respectively)

First published, 1678, with title Linguae latinae.
—— Another copy. 24cm.
Imperfect copy: maps and p.[1340-1430] (sig.8E4, 8F-8Q⁴) wanting.
1. Latin language - Dictionaries - English. 2. English language - Dictionaries - Latin. I. Title: Latin dictionary.

NL 0413629 TxU MH PU OC1 ViU OC KyLx CLL RPB CU

[LITTLETON, Adam] 1627-1694.
[Latine Dictionary, in four parts: I. An English-Latin. II. A Latine-Classical. III. A Latine-Proper. IV A Latine-Barbarous. London, 17-.]

4°. 2 maps.
Title-page wanting and otherwise imperfect.
Without pagination.

NL 0413630 MH

Aj LITTLETON, ADAM, 1627-1694.
L734 Linguae latinae liber dictionarius
678l quadripartitus. A Latine dictionary, in four parts. I. An English-Latine. II. A Latine-classical. III. A latine-proper. IV. A Latine-barbarous. Therein the Latine and English are adjusted, with what care might be, both as to stock of words and proprieties of speech. Particularly, 1. In the English-latine, more words and proprieties of our language, as now spoken, are set down, by several thousands,

than in any other dictionary yet extant. 2. In the Latine-classick, the etymologies, significations, and phrases are fully and plainly, yet briefly, discoursed; together with the several kinds and constructions of the verbs; a thing hitherto not much regarded. 3. In the Latine-proper, the expressions of story, which

were taken mostly out of Cooper, are much amended; and many useful things are now added, which were formerly omitted; with two mapps, one of Italy, another of old Rome. 4. In the Latine-barbarous, those words which through mistake of writing have been corrupted from the Latine, or by ignorance or boldness of later authors have crept into the Latine, are

exposed and expounded. And in all four parts, many things that were utterly impertinent and cumbersom to school-institution and to the true uses of learning, are laid aside. Of all which several performances, together with considerable additions of new matter by way of appendage to the main work, a fuller account is given in the prefaces. Opera & studio Adami Littleton ...

London,Printed,for T.Basset at the George in Fleet-street,J.Wright at the Crown on Ludgate-Hill,and R.Chiswell at the Rose and Crown in St. Paul's Church-yard.1678. [1346]p. 2 maps. 21½cm.
Bound in two volumes.
"Dictionarium latino-barbarium" has special t.-p. dated 1677.

TxDaM-P MoSU-D MdBP RPB NN CtY
NL 0413635 TxU MH WU ICN CSt IEN NjP OClW MnU IU

Littleton, Adam, 1627-1694.

Linguae latinae liber dictionarius quadripartitus. A Latine dictionary, in four parts. I. An English-Latine. II. A Latine-classical. III. A Latine-proper. IV. A Latine-barbarous. Wherein the Latine and English are adjusted, with what care might be, both as to stock of words and proprieties of speech.... Opera & studio Adami Littleton ... London, Printed, for T. Basset ... J. Wright ... and R. Chiswell ... 1678.
2 v. fronts., 2 maps. 26½cm.

First edition.
Signatures: [v.1] 1 leaf unsigned, A⁴, A-Z⁴, Aa-Zz⁴, Aaa-Iii⁴, Aaa-Zzz⁴ (Hhh1 incorrectly signed Hh), Aaaa-Zzzz⁴ (Hhhh3 incorrectly signed Hhhh2), Aaaaa-Ddddd⁴; [v.2] 1 leaf unsigned, A-Z⁴, Aa-Cc⁴, Dd², Ee-Ll⁴, A-U⁴, X³, 1 leaf unsigned, Aaaaaa-Eeeeee⁴, *-², Ffffff⁴.**
Unpaged.

NL 0413637 CLU-C OC PPL DFo

[Littleton, Adam, 1627-1694]
[Lingvae latinae liber dictionarius quadripartitus. 2d ed. London, 1678]
8 p.l., [1652] p. map, plan.
Title-page lacking; above title, etc. taken from Dictionary of National Biography.
Contents: The English-Latin dictionary. - English proper names of most of the chief places in the world rendred into Latine. - The most usual Christian names of men and women rendred into Latine. - Lingvae latinae dictionarium classicum. - Dictionarium poeticum, historicum, & geographicum. - Dictionarium Latino-Barbarum.

NL 0413638 PMA

---

473 **Littleton, Adam,** 1627-1694.
L731 **Linguæ latinæ liber dictionarius quad-**
1723 **ripartitus. Dr. Adam Littleton's Latin dictionary, in four parts: I. An English-Latin. II. A Latin-classical. III. A Latin-proper. IV. A Latin-barbarous ... The 5th ed. Improved from the several works of Stephens, Cooper, Holyoke, and a large ms. in three volumes of John Milton &c ... With two maps; one of Italy, another of old Rome. London,**

Chiswell, 1678.
2v. front.(v.1.) maps.

The "Dictionarium latino-barbarum" has special t.-p. with vignette with imprint: Londini, typis J. C., impensis J. Wright & R. Chiswel, 1677.

The arrangement of material does not follow that indicated on the t.-p. of vol.I.

NL 0413641 IU

RARE
BOOKS
DEPT.

Littleton, Adam, 1627-1694.
Linguae latinae liber dictionarius quadripartitus. A Latine dictionary, in four parts. I. An English-Latine. II. A Latine-classical. III. A Latine-proper. IV. A Latine-barbarous. Wherein the Latine and English are adjusted, with what care might be, both as to stock of words and properties of speech ... London, Printed for T. Basset, J. Wright, and R. Chiswell, 1684.
[1328] p. front., maps. 25cm.

Fourth ed.
Title within double line border; text within line borders.
English-Latin in quadruple columns; remainder of text in triple columns.
Wing L-2564.

NL 0413642 CU ViLxW ICN MdBP CtY IaU

Littleton, Adam, 1627-94
Linguae Latinae liber dictionarius quadripartus. **Dr.Adam Littleton's** Latine dictionary. **[3d ed.? London, 1695?]**

1 v. illus.
Imperfect: t.p. and other pages lacking

NL 0413643 MH

Littleton, Adam, 1627–1694.

Lingvæ latinæ liber dictionarius quadripartitus. Dr. Adam Littleton's Latine dictionary, in four parts: I. An English-Latine. II. A Latine-classical. III. A Latine-proper. IV. A Latine-barbarous ... 4th ed., improved from the several works of Stephens, Cooper, Holyoke ... John Milton ... With two maps, one of Italy, another of old Rome. London, Printed for W. Rawlins [etc.] 1703.

[1443] p. front., 2 maps. 24½cm.

Unpaged.

1. Latin language — Dictionaries — English. 2. English language — Dictionaries—Latin.

10-23293

Library of Congress PA2365.E5L76 1703

NL 0413644 DLC WaU InU NNNAM OU NcD ViW TxU

VOLUME 336

LITTLETON, Adam, 1627-1694.
Lingvae latinae liber dictionarius quadripartitus. Dr. Adam Littleton's Latine dictionary, in four parts: I. An English-Latine. II. A Latine-classical. III. A Latine-proper. IV. A Latine-barbarous ... 4th ed., improved from the several works of Stephens, Cooper, Holyoke ... John Milton ... With two maps, one of Italy, another of old Rome. London, Printed for W. Rawlins [etc.] 1703.
[1446] p. front., 2 maps.

Unpaged.

473 L734L4 Signatures: title-page unsigned, A^4, a^4, $a\text{-}z^4$, $aa\text{-}tt^4$; $A\text{-}Z^4$, $Aa\text{-}Zz^4$, $Aaa\text{-}Zzz^4$, $Aaaa\text{-}Zzzz^4$, $6A\text{-}6S^4$; $A\text{-}Z^4$, $Aa\text{-}Cc^4$, Dd^2.
Unpaged.
Errors in register: sig. Ssss-Zzzz lettered Sssss-Zzzzz.
Imperfect: frontispiece wanting.
"English proper names of ... the chief places in the world rendred into Latine": sig.ss^5-tt^2.

NL 0413646 WaU

870.3 L78 1715 Littleton, Adam, 1627-1694.
Linguae latinae liber dictionarius quadripartitus. Dr. Adam Littleton's Latin dictionary, in four parts: I. An English-Latin. II. A Latin-classical. III. An Latin-proper. IV. A Latin-barbarous ... The 4th ed. Improved from the several works of Stephens, Cooper, Holyoke ... John Milton ... With two maps; one of Italy, another of old Rome. London, Printed for D. Brown [etc.] 1715.
[1446] p. front., map, plan. 25^{cm}.
Unpaged.
1. Latin language—Dictionaries—English.

NL 0413647 MiU PU ICU PPC ODaStL

X 672 .512 **LITTLETON, ADAM, 1627-1694.**
Linguæ latinæ liber dictionarius quadripartitus. Dr. Adam Littleton's Latin dictionary, in four parts: I. An English-Latin. II. A Latin-classical. III. A Latin-proper. IV. A Latin-barbarous. The 5th edition. Improved from the several works of Stephens, Cooper, Holyoke, and a large ms. in three volumes of John Milton, &c. With two maps; one of Italy, another of old Rome. London, Brown, 1722.
unpaged.

NL 0413648 ICN

473.2 L781l 1723 LIMITED CIRCULATION Littleton, Adam, 1627-1694.
Linguae Latinae liber dictionarius quadripartitus. Dr. Adam Littleton's Latin dictionary in four parts: I. An English-Latin. II. A Latin-Classical. III. A Latin-Proper. IV. A Latin-Barbarous. [Eighteen lines] The fifth edition. Improved from the several works of Stephens, Cooper, Holyoke, and a large MS. in three volumes of John Milton, &c. In the use of all which, for greater exactness, recourse has always been had to the authors themselves. With two maps; one of Italy, another of Old Rome. London, Printed for D. Brown, [etc.], 1723.
1 v. (unpaged) front., 2 maps. 25cm.

Title within double line border.
Note in ms. on title: Thomas Jenings his booke cost 16 shillings 1724. Repeated verso frontispiece. Preliminary blank leaf contains list of titles.
Bound in contemporary calf, first board broken apart, raised spine, red edges.
Brit. Mus. gen. cat. v.138, col.791.

1. Latin language - Dictionaries - English. 2. English language - Dictionaries - Latin. I. Title.

NL 0413651 FU NNUT NN ICN NjR PBa IU DCU

Aj L734 678Le Rare Books Col LITTLETON, ADAM, 1627-1694.
Linguae latinae liber dictionarius quadripartitus. Dr. Adam Littleton's Latin dictionary, in four parts: I. An English-Latin. II. A Latin-classical. III. A Latin-proper. IV. A Latin-barbarous. Representing I. The English words and phrases before the Latin; among which latter, no word or expression is to be admitted, but what is classic, and of an approv'd authority. II. The Latin classic before the English; wherein care is taken, that the proper and original signification of each word is first set down, which is followed by those that are derivative, metaphorical or remote. III. The Latin-proper names of those persons, people or countries that frequently occur, or are any way remarkable in classic authors, with explications from their several languages, and a short account of them historical and geographical. IV. 1. The Latin barbarous, explaining as well such technical words or terms of art, as are made necessary to us by the many inventions and discoveries not known to the ancients, as those which crept into the Latin tongue during the ignorance and darkness of the Middle Ages. 2. The law-Latin, comprehending those words, which are made use of by the common lawyers in their particular profession; very necessary for the understanding of charters, &c. The fifth edition. Improved from the several works of Stephens, Cooper, Holyoke, and a large MS. in three volumes of John Milton, &c. In the use of all which, for greater exactness, recourse has always been had to the authors themselves. With two maps; one of Italy, another of old Rome.
London: Printed for D. Brown, M. Laurence, R. Bonwicke, J. Walthoe, J. Knapton, J. Wyat, R. Wilkin, J. and B. Sprint, B. and S. Tooke, D. Midwinter, T. Osborn, B. Cowse, R. Gosling, W. Taylor, J. Osborne, R. Robinson, T. Ward, and J. Bateman. M, DCC, XXIII.
[1446]p. front., 2 maps. 25cm.
Signatures: 1 leaf unsigned, A^4, a^4, $a\text{-}z^4$, $aa\text{-}tt^4$, $A\text{-}Z^4$, $Aa\text{-}Zz^4$, $Aaa\text{-}Zzz^4$, $Aaaa\text{-}Uuuu^4$ (Tttt1-2 signed TTTT, TTTTT2), $XXXX\text{-}ZZZZ^4$, $AAAAA^4$, $5BBBBB\text{-}5FFFFF^4$, $GGGGG^4$, $5HHHHH\text{-}5IIIII^4$, $Kkkkk\text{-}Lllll^4$, $6M\text{-}6Q^4$, $5R\text{-}5S^4$, $A\text{-}Z^4$, $Aa\text{-}Cc^4$, Dd^2.
1. Latin language - Dictionaries - English. 2. English language - Dictionaries - Latin. I. Title.

NL 0413656 TxU

Littleton, Adam, 1627-1694.
Linguae romanae dictionarium luculentum novum
see under title

Littleton, Adam, 1627-1694, tr.

Selden, John, 1584-1654.
The reverse or back-face of the English Janus. To-wit, all that is met with in story concerning the common and statute-law of English Britanny, from the first memoirs of the two nations, to the decease of King Henry II. set down and tackt together succinctly by way of narrative ... Written in Latin by John Selden ... and rendred into English by Redman Westcot, gent. [pseud.] London, Printed for Thomas Basset, and Richard Chiswell, MDCLXXXII.

---

252 Se662 v.3 Littleton, Adam, 1627-1694.
A sermon at a solemn meeting of the natives of the city and county of Worcester, in the church of St. Mary le Bow, June 24.1680. By Adam Littleton, D.D. chaplain in ordinary to His Majesty. London, Printed for William Birch, and are to be sold by John Crump at the Three Bibles in St. Paul's church-yard, 1680.
2 p.l., 36p. 21cm.
[Sermons on various subjects, 1637-1706. v.3, no.8]
1. Sermons. 2. Bible--N.T.--2 Peter I, 7.

NL 0413659 IU NjPT CtY

Mhc8 1680 L73 **Littleton, Adam, 1627-1694.**
A sermon before the Right Honourable the Lord Mayor and the Right Worshipful the Aldermen of the City of London, preached on Febr. 28 $16\frac{79}{80}$, at Guildhall-Chappel ... London, Printed by S.Roycroft, for R.Marriott, 1680.
4p.l., 31p. 22cm.

NL 0413660 CtY NNUT-Mc CSmH

Wing L2572 Littleton, Adam, 1627-1694.
Sixty one sermons... five formerly printed... With a table. London, Printed by S. Roycroft, 1680.
352, 328, 102 p.

In 3 pts. with 5 sep. t.p.

I. Roycroft, Samuel (Printer) II. 1680.

NL 0413661 TxDaM

LITTLETON, Adam, 1627-1694.
Sixty one sermons preached mostly upon publick occasions, where of five formerly printed. With a table. London, printed by S. Roycroft for R. Marriott, 1680.

f°. pp. (867.)
Various paging.
Each part has special title-page dated 1679.

NL 0413662 MH

Beinecke Library Mhc9 L734 S6 [Littleton, Adam] 1627-1694.
Solomon's gate, or An entrance into the church, being a familiar explanation of the grounds of religion conteined in the fowr heads of catechism ... By A.L. ... London Printed by R.Daniel, 1662.
15p.l., 476, [2]p. 15cm.
Signatures: $*\text{-}**^8$($*_1$ blank)A-Gg^8(Gg_8 blank)
Dedication signed: Adam Littleton.

NL 0413663 CtY

Littleton, Adam, 1627-1694, tr.

Selden, John, 1584-1654.
Tracts written by John Selden of the Inner-Temple, esquire. The first entituled, Jani Anglorvm facies altera, rendred into English, with large notes thereupon, by Redman Westcot, gent. [pseud.] The second, England's epinomis. The third, Of the original of ecclesiastical jurisdictions of testaments. The fourth, Of the disposition or administration of intestates goods. The three last never before extant. London, Printed for Thomas Basset and Richard Chiswell, and are to be sold by Robert Clavell, MDCLXXXIII.

---

x875.1 L73t [Littleton, Adam] 1627-1694, supposed author.
Tragi-comoedia Oxoniensis. [Oxford, H. Hall, 1648]
8p. 19cm.
Error in paging: p.2 numbered 1.
A satire in Latin verse on the proceedings of the University visitors. The author is believed to be Adam Littleton, expelled in this year by the visitors; but Thomas Barlow attributed it to John Carrick. Cf. Madan. Oxford books, v.2, p.468.
Wing L-2574.

NL 0413665 IU NjP ICN CLU-C CSmH CtY MH

VOLUME 336

Littleton, Alfred Henry, 1845-1914.
A catalogue of one hundred works illustrating the history of music printing from the fifteenth to the end of the seventeenth century, in the library of Alfred Henry Littleton ... London, Printed by Novello and co., ltd., 1911.
38 p., 1 l. illus. (incl. facsims.) 26 x 20cm.

1. Music—Bibl.—Catalogs. 2. Music printing.
11—27736
Library of Congress ML138.L4

NL 0413666 DLC NcRS MH NcU ICU MiU OC1MA MB CtY

Littleton, Alfred Henry, 1845-1914.
Some notes on early printed music. Facsimiles.
(In Company of Musicians. English music [1604-1904]. . . . Pp. 478-496. London. 1906.)

G3575 — Music. Bibl.

NL 0413667 MB

Littleton, Alfred Henry, 1845-1914.
Te Deum laudamus. In E flat. [Accomp. for organ.]
(In Novello's Parish Choir Book. Pp. 139-142. London. [186-?]) No. 27 in **M.157.30
Same. (In Parish Choir, The. No. 218, pp. 869-872. Medford, 1883.) *8042.142.218

May 7, 1902
E4014 — T.r. — Church music. Anthems, &c.

NL 0413668 MB

Littleton, Algernon Charles.
Vocabulary of sea words in English, French, German, Spanish, & Italian. For the use of officers of the royal and mercantile navies, yachtsmen, travellers, etc. By Commander the Hon. A. C. Littleton. Portsmouth: Griffin & co. [etc., etc.] 1879. 81 p. 17cm.

252204B. 1. Nautical dictionaries, Polyglot, 1879.
N. Y. P. L. December 10, 1943

NL 0413669 NN OC DNW DN

Littleton, Ananias Charles, 1886-
Accounting evolution to 1900, by A. C. Littleton ... New York, N. Y., American institute publishing co., inc. [c1933]
xi p., 2 l., 3-368 p. diagr. 24cm.
Bibliography: p. 23-24. "References" at end of most of the chapters.

1. Accounting—Hist. I. Title.
33-24511
Library of Congress HF5605.L5
—— Copy 2.
Copyright A 66057 [3] 657.09

NL 0413670 DLC IU FMU CoU PP PU PPD OOxM OU ODW OC1 ViU MB TU CU OrP NcD IdU WaS MtU OrU

Littleton, Ananias Charles, 1886-
... Directory of early American public accountants, by A. C. Littleton ... Urbana, The University of Illinois, 1942.
39 p. incl. tables, diagr. 23cm. (University of Illinois. Bureau of economic and business research. Bulletin no. 62)
On cover: University of Illinois bulletin, vol. 40, no. 8.
At head of title: University of Illinois, College of commerce and business administration, Charles M. Thompson ... dean. Bureau of economic and business research, H. K. Allen, PH. D., director.

1. Accountants—Direct.
A 42-4984
Illinois. Univ. Library for Library of Congress HF5011.I 5 no. 62
[8]†

NL 0413671 IU CaBViPA IEdS NIC OC1CC OCU OU OO DLC PPT PU

Littleton, Ananias Charles, 1886-
The historical foundations of modern accounting, by Ananias Charles Littleton ... Urbana, Ill., 1931.
1 p. l., 11, [1] p. 23cm.
Abstract of thesis (PH. D.)—University of Illinois, 1931.
Vita.

1. Accounting—Hist.
31-7996
Library of Congress HF5606.L5 1931
Univ. of Illinois Libr.
—— Copy 2. [2] 657.09

NL 0413672 IU DLC NIC PU OU MH

Littleton, Ananias Charles, 1886-

Paton, William Andrew, 1889-
An introduction to corporate accounting standards, by W. A. Paton ... [and] A. C. Littleton ... [Chicago] American accounting association, 1940.

Littleton, Ananias Charles, 1886-
An introduction to elementary accounting, with a program of study and practice assignments, by A. C. Littleton ... [Champaign, Ill., Flannigan Pearson co.] c1919.
64 p. 23½cm.

1. Accounting. I. Title.
19-16056
Library of Congress HF5625.L65

NL 0413674 DLC

Littleton, Ananias Charles, 1886-
An introduction to elementary accounting.
Cincinnati, O., South-Western Pub. Co., 1920.
64 p. 24 cm.
1. Accounting - 1901-

NL 0413675 CU

658 L7341 Littleton, Ananias Charles, 1886- ed.
Lectures on retail merchandising; a short course in business for retail merchants given at the University of Illinois by the College of commerce and business administration, February 23, 24, 25, 26, 1920. Champaign, Ill., 1920.
143p.

NL 0413676 IU

Littleton, Ananias Charles, 1886-
Structure of accounting theory. [Urbana, Ill.] American Accounting Association, 1953.
234 p. 23 cm. (American Accounting Association. Monograph no. 5)

1. Accounting. I. Title.
HF5635.L75 657 53-35974 ‡

NL 0413677 DLC CaBVaU MtBC IdU OrCS OrU WaTC C ScU IEdS MoU ICarbS MU UU NcD DAU MsSM OOxM PSt PU-W ViU OCU PHC TxU FTaSU OU NNC CoU OC1

LITTLETON, C M
The enchanted ring, a tale, by C. M. Littleton, L.L.D. ...
London. Printed for Thomas Tegg, June 1 - 1810.
1p.l.,[5]-28p. col.front. 17cm.
Title-page engraved, with colored vignette.
Signatures: [-]^2,A-B^6 ([-]1,front.; [-]2, t.-p.)
Unbound.

NL 0413678 PPRF NjP

Littleton, Cecil J.
The work and influence of the Holy Spirit; letters written for confirmation candidates.
London, Mowbray, 1909.
135 p.
(The English churchman's library)

NL 0413679 PPPD

Littleon, Cecil J.
The Handmaid of the Lord. London, Gardner, [1911]
123 p.

NL 0413680 PPPD

Littleton, Cecil J.
Office & Work of a Priest.
Lond. 1894 Skeffington & Son.

NL 0413681 DNC

Littleton, Charles T 1901-
Industrial piping. Special chapter on estimating, by R. A. Dickson. 1st ed. New York, McGraw-Hill, 1951.
394 p. illus. 24 cm.

1. Pipe lines. 2. Pipe. I. Title.
TP159.P5L5 621.8672 51-12385 ‡

NL 0413682 DLC ICJ OrCS IU CU MiHM MB NN TxU ViU NcRS TU CaBVa CaBVaU IdU MtBC OrP WaS WaT

Littleton, Covington H S.
Money and prosperity, by C. H. S. Littleton. Philadelphia, The Eastern bimetallic league, 1898.
124 p. front. (port.) 19cm.

1. Bimetallism. I. Title.
98-377 Revised
Library of Congress HG562.L78

NL 0413683 DLC ViU

STC 15365 Littleton, Edmund, fl.1596-1616.
A briefe catechisme, containing the summe of the Gospell of Iesus Christ, and his life, declared more at large by the foure euangelists, Mathew, Marke, Luke and Iohn. Written by Edmund Littleton, of Sittingborne in Kent, preacher ...
London, Printed by George Pvrslovve for Simon Stafford, 1616.
[13]p. 14cm., in case 15cm.
Not in first ed. of STC.
No.2 in a volume labeled on spine: Catechisms; in green morocco case.

NL 0413684 MH

FILM
Littleton, Edmund, fl. 1596-1616.
A briefe catechisme, containing the summe of the Gospels. With two godly and deuout prayers, to be said before and after the receiuing of the Lords Supper. London, Printed by I. Haviland for H. Bell, 1631.
The "prayers" are lacking.
Short-title catalogue no.15718 (carton 808)

1. Theology, Doctrinal.

NL 0413685 MiU

VOLUME 336

Littleton, Edward, b. 1626.
De Juventute. Oratio habita in Comitijs Oxoniensibus Ab Eduardo Litletono... Londini, Typis Abrahami Miller apud Gulielmum Lee, 1664.
[6], 73 p. 20 cm.

Bound with Lloyd, William. A Sermon Preached before the King. London, 1668.

NL 0413686 PPiPT

Beinecke Library Lmd77 A664 664b
Littleton, Edward, b.1626
De juventute. Oratio habita in Comitiis oxoniensibus. Ab Edvardo Litletono ... Londini, prostant apud Tho.Newborough ... 1689.
2 p.l., 72 p. 22 x 16 cm.
Signatures: [*]^{2}B-K^4.
Wing: L 2576.
First published in 1664.
1. Tollet, George - Bookplate. I. Oxford. University. Encaenia, 1664. II. Title (1)

NL 0413687 CtY CLU-C

British Tracts 1693 D45
Littleton, Edward, b. 1626.
The descent upon France considered; in a letter to a member of Parliament. [Colophon:London,R.Baldwin,1693]
8p. 21cm.
Caption title.
Signed: E.L.
A commentary upon A project of a descent upon France, attributed to Edward Littleton: cf. Wing Short-title cat.

1. A project of a descent upon France. I. L., E. II. [Lit]tleton, Edward, fl.1690, supposed author. [...]a chronology card

NL 0413688 CtY

[Littleton, Edward] b. 1626.
The groans of the plantations: or, A true account of their grievous and extreme sufferings by the heavy impositions upon sugar, and other hardships. Relating more particularly to the island of Barbadoes. London, Printed by M. Clark in the year 1689.
1 p. l., 35 p. 19½ x 15 cm.

1. Tariff on sugar—Gt. Brit. 2. Sugar trade—Gt. Brit. 3. Gt. Brit.—Colonies. 4. Sugar refining—Barbados. I. Title.

HF2651.S8G76 6—8101

NL 0413689 RPJCB InU OCl LU MB DLC NN PPAmP NjP CtY PPL MnU CSmH MiU-C

382.70942 L781g RARE BOOK COLLECTION
Littleton, Edward, b. 1626.
The / groans of the / plantations: / or / A True account / of their / Grievous and Extreme Sufferings / By the Heavy / impositions / upon sugar, / And other hardships. / Relating more particularly to the / island of Barbados. / London, / Printed by M. Clark in the Year MDCLXXXIX. /
[]^1, A - D^4, E^2 ; [2], 35, [1] p. ; 4°

Head margins trimmed.
Tail margins trimmed, affecting text.
Ornamental initial.
Published anonymously.
1. Tariff - Gt. Brit. 2. Sugar trade - Gt. Brit. 3. Gt. Brit. - Colonies. 4. Sugar - Manufacture and refining - Barbados. I. Title.

NL 0413691 FU

[Littleton, Edward] b. 1626.
The groans of the plantations: or, A true account of their grievous and extreme sufferings by the heavy impositions upon sugar, and other hardships. Relating more particularly to the Island of Barbados. London, Printed by M. Clark, in the year 1689, and reprinted 1698.
31 p. 20½cm.

1. Gt. Brit.—Tariff. 2. Sugar trade—Gt. Brit. 3. Gt. Brit.—Colonies. 4. Sugar refining—Barbados.

Library of Congress HF2651.S843L7 6-8100†

NL 0413692 DLC ICN NcD MB MiU-C

---

*Defoe 30 .690 .L73M
[Littleton, Edward] b. 1626.
The management of the present war against France consider'd. In a letter to a noble lord. By a person of quality.
London, Printed for R. Clavel, C. Wilkinson and J. Hindmarsh, and are to be sold by Randal Taylor near Stationers-Hall, 1690.

1 p.l., 30 p. 20cm.
Wing L2579.

NL 0413693 CtY DFo MiU-C MB ICU MH OU NNUT-Mc CSmH PU ICN MB In

---

[Littleton, Edward] b. 1626.
Observations upon the warre of Hungary. London, Printed and are to be sold by R. Taylor, 1689.
47 p. 24 cm.

1. Hungary—History, Military. I. Title.

DB925.5.L5 56-51516

NL 0413694 DLC MH CSmH

---

*EC65 L7344 691p
[Littleton, Edward, b.1626]
A project of a descent upon France. By a person of quality.
London.Printed;and are to be sold by Rich. Baldwin.M DC XCI.
2p.l.,28p. 22.5cm.
Narcissus Luttrell's copy, with his annotation and priced & dated by him: 4d [&] 27. May.

NL 0413695 MH DLC InU MnU CLU-C

Littleton, E[dward] b. 1626.
A proposal for maintaining and repairing the highways. By E. Littleton. London, Printed and are to be sold by R. Taylor, 1692.
23 p. 21½cm.
3-14072

NL 0413696 DLC CtY

Littleton, Edward, b. 1626.
A short discourse about our keeping our money
see under title

AC911 Y5 L57 RARE BOOK COLLECTION
Littleton, Edward, d. 1733.
A sermon preach'd before the honourable House of Commons, at St. Margaret's Westminster, on Saturday, January XXX. 1730. By Edward Littleton, LL.D. Fellow of Eton College, and Chaplain in Ordinary to His Majesty. London: Printed for R. Williamson. 1731.
24 p. 22 cm.

In envelope.

NL 0413698 CU-A RPB CtY CLU-C

252.03 L781s
Littleton, Edward, d. 1733.
Sermons upon several practical subjects. [Five lines] Published by subscription, for the benefit of his widow and children. London, J. Tonson and J. Watts, 1735.
2 v. 20cm.

Titles within double line borders.
Head and tail pieces. Initials. Catchwords.
Bound in calf with goffered edges.

Sprinkled edges.
First edition.

1. Church of England - Sermons. 2. Sermons, English.

NL 0413700 FU CLU-C

Littleton, Edward John Walhouse, *1st baron Hatherton*
see
Hatherton, Edward John Walhouse Littleton, *1st baron*, 1791-1863.

Littleton, Edward Littleton, lord, 1589-1645.
Letter to the Lords of the Privy-Councell and the conservators of the peace of the kingdom of Scotland. Oxford, 1643. sm. 4°. (*Tracts rel. to Scotl.*) 2594

NL 0413702 MdBP

---

pDA412 1642 L58L6
Littleton, Sir Edward Littleton, lord, 1589-1645.
The Lord Keepers speech to the House of Commons, at the passing of two bills. Togeter [!] with the Kings Majesties message to both Houses, concerning the raising of men for Ireland, the taking away of the bishops votes out of the House of Peeres, the banishing of popish priests, and the setling of the government and liturgie of the church. London, Printed for Iohn Burroughes and Iohn Franke. 1641.
1 p.l., 6 p. 19cm.

Not in Wing.
Provenance: Isaac Foot.
1. Ireland (Country) - Hist. - 1641 (Rebellion) - Sources. 2. Church of England - Bishops - Temporal power. I. Gt. Brit. Sovereigns, etc., 1625-1649 (Charles I) II. 1641.

NL 0413703 CU-B ICN NN CU

Littleton, Edward Littleton, lord, 1589-1645, reporter.
Gt. Brit. *Court of common pleas.*
Les reports des tres honorable Edw. seigneur Littleton, baron de Mounslow ... en le courts del Common banck & Exchequer, en le 2, 3, 4, 5, 6, 7 ans del reign de roy Charles le I. [1627-1631] London, Printed by W. Rawlins, S. Roycroft, and H. Sawbridge, assigns of Richard and Edward Atkins, for Thomas Bassett, Samuel Heyrick, William Crooke, and William Hensman, MDCLXXXIII.

1642 L73
Littleton, Edward Littleton, lord, 1589-1645
A svbmissive and petitionary letter subscribed. To the right honourable the lords of Parliament, in the upper House of Parliament assembled. And intituled The humble submission and supplication of the Lord Littleton, lord keeper of the great seale of England.
[n.p.,1642]
7p. 17½cm.
Caption titlo.

NL 0413705 CtY DFo

VOLUME 336

British Tracts 1641 L73 [Littleton, Edward Littleton] 1st Baron, 1589-1645
A trve and fvll relation of the horrible and hellish plot of the Iesuites, popish priests and other papists in Ireland, for the massacring of the two chiefe justices, ... As it was related by My Lord Keeper in the House of Commons November the first, 1641. London, Printed for T. Bankes, 1641.
1 p.ℓ., 5 p. 18 cm.

NL 0413706 CtY MnU

---

x248 L734d ₑLittleton, G ₃
A discourse on Providence: being an essay to prove that this doctrine, as delivered in the Gospel, is a demonstration of the divine original of the Christian dispensation. London, Printed for R. Dodsley and sold by M. Cooper, 1747.
viii, 46p. 19cm.

Attributed to G. Littleton by Halkett and Laing and in the British Museum Catalog.
Attributed by Straus in his biography of Dodsley to George Lyttelton, 1st baron Lyttelton.

NL 0413707 IU CtY CLU-C

Mhc8 1748 L73 [Littleton, G]
A discourse on providence: being an essay to prove that this doctrine, as it is delivered in the Gospel, is a demonstration of the divine original of the Christian dispensation. The 2d ed. London, Printed for R.Dodsley, and sold by M.Cooper, 1748.
1p.ℓ.,[v]-viii,46p. 19cm.

NL 0413708 CtY IEN

Littleton, George Littleton, 1st baron
see Lyttelton, George Lyttelton, 1st baron, 1709-1773.

Littleton, Henry A.
Digest of fire insurance decisions in the courts of Great Britain and North America. By H. A. Littleton and J. S. Blatchley. 2d ed., rev. and enl. By Stephen G. Clarke ... Dubuque, Daily Times Book and Job Printing Establishment, 1862.
515 p. 24cm.

NL 0413710 FU WaU-L NjP CtY

Littleton, Henry A.
Digest of fire insurance decisions in the courts of Great Britain and North America. By H. A. Littleton and J. S. Blatchley. 2d ed., rev. and enl. By Stephen G. Clarke ... New York, Baker, Voorhis & co., 1868.
723 p. 23½cm.

1. Insurance law—Cases. 2. Insurance, Fire—U. S. 3. Insurance, Fire—Gt. Brit. 4. Insurance, Fire—Canada. I. Blatchley, Joel Sherland, joint author. II. Clarke, Stephen G., ed. III. Title.

Library of Congress 31-34341

NL 0413711 DLC CtY MnU PPT ViU-L NjP NN

Littleton, Henry A.
Digest of fire insurance decisions in the courts of Great Britain and North America. By H. A. Littleton and J. S. Blatchley. With the additional notes to the second edition, by Stephen G. Clarke. 3d ed., rev. and enl. By Clement Bates ... New York, Baker, Voorhis & co., 1873.
1 p. l., 32 p., 1 l., [33]-795 p. 24cm.

1. Insurance law—Cases. 2. Insurance, Fire—U. S. 3. Insurance, Fire—Gt. Brit. 4. Insurance, Fire—Canada. I. Blatchley, Joel Sherland, joint author. II. Clarke, Stephen G., ed. III. Bates, Clement, 1845- ed. IV. Title.

Library of Congress 31-34342

NL 0413712 DLC CtY MnU-L PPB PU-L MH NN PP NcD

Littleton, Henry A. Digest of fire insurance decisions.
Clement, George Ansel, 1851-1919.
Digest of fire insurance decisions in the courts of the United States, Great Britain and Canada. Being a supplement or continuation of the 3d and last edition of Littleton & Blatchley, Clarke, and Bates' Digest. From 1872 to 1882. By George A. Clement ... New York, Baker, Voorhis & co., 1882.

353.82 L73c Littleton, Isaac Thomas, 1921-
Clearinghouse for Federal, Scientific and Technical Information: its history and publications. ₑn.p., n.d.₃
11p. 28cm.

Title corrected in manuscript; original title: The office of Technical Services: its history and publications.
Bibliography: p.10-11.

NL 0413714 IU

Littleton, Jesse Talbot, 1887-
The electrical properties of glass, by J. T. Littleton ... and G. W. Morey ... New York, J. Wiley & sons, inc.; London, Chapman & Hall, limited, 1933.
x, 184 p. illus., diagrs. 23½cm. (*Half-title:* Monograph no. III. National research council. Committee on electrical insulation) $3.00

1. Glass. 2. Electric conductivity. 3. Dielectrics. I. Morey, George Washington, 1888- joint author. II. Title.

Library of Congress QC611.L5 33-23800
——— Copy 2.
Copyright A 65092 [5] 537.5

NL 0413715 ICJ PPD PP OClW MiHM IdU OrPR WaS OrCS OrU NCorniC DLC CU FMU NcD NcRS OU ODW MiU OCl MB

Littleton, Jesse Talbot, 1856-
The story of Captain Smith and Pocahontas; a souvenir of the Jamestown exposition, by J. T. Littleton ... Nashville, Tenn., Dallas, Tex., Publishing house of the M. E. church, South, Smith & Lamar, agents, 1907.
94 p. 19cm.

7-25232
Library of Congress (Copyright 1907 A 177610)

NL 0413716 DLC NcD ViW ViU

BS647 .L49 Littleton, John
Two world wars, by a man without a home, J. Littleton ... St. Louis [Frederick printing & stationery co., c1926]
v. 17½cm.

1. Bible—Prophecies. 2. War and religion—Biblical teaching. I. Title.

NL 0413717 DLC

BS647 .L5 [Littleton, John]
Two worlds in prophecy, by a man without a home. [n. p. 1925]
v. 20cm.

Volume 2 has cover-title only.

1. Bible—Prophecies. I. Title.

NL 0413718 DLC

---

976 L781f Littleton, John O
Frontier military posts of the Southwest [by] John O. Littleton. Santa Fe, N. Mex., National Park Service, Region Three Office, 1953.
23 ℓ. plates. 27cm.

Cover title.
Bibliography: ℓ. 22-23.

1. Military posts - Southwest, Old. 2. Military posts - Southwest New. 3. Southwest, Old - Hist. 4. Southwest, New - Hist. I. U. S. National Park Service. II. Title.

NL 0413719 FU

Littleton, John O
A survey of history in the Arkansas-White-Red River Basins
see under
U.S. National Park Service.
A survey of archaeology and history in the Arkansas-White-Red River Basins.

Littleton, Leonidas Rosser.
Molecular rearrangements in the camphor series. Derivatives of isocamphoric acid; isoaminocamphonanic acid and its decomposition products, by Leonidas R. Littleton ... Easton, Pa., Eschenbach printing company, 1913.
9, [1] p. 24½cm.
Thesis (PH. D.)—University of Illinois, 1912.
Biographical.

1. Camphor.

13-17447
Library of Congress QD416.L5
Univ. of Illinois Libr.

NL 0413721 IU DLC NIC OU MiU IU

Littleton, Mark, pseud.
see Kennedy, John Pendleton, 1795-1870.

Littleton, Martin Wilie, 1872-1934.
Address. (In, Lincoln centennial association. Addresses ... Feb. 11, 1911, p. 29-35)

NL 0413723 RPB

Littleton, Martin Wilie, 1872-1934.
Address of Hon. Martin W. Littleton, at the dinner of the Real Estate Board of New York, held on Saturday evening, February 3... [New York? 1917.] 2 l. port. 8°.
Caption-title: Present-day events inspire patriotism.
Repr.: Record and guide. Feb. 10, 1917.

1. European war, 1914- —Addresses, sermons, etc.
N. Y. P. L. October 30, 1917.

NL 0413724 NN

VOLUME 336

Littleton, Martin Wilie, 1872-1934.
Are radical activities weakening American institutions? Addresses by Hon. Martin W. Littleton and Hon. O.L. Smith. New York, The American defense society, inc. [1925]
26 p. [Pamphlets on socialism, communism, bolshevism, etc., v. 7, no. 28]
"Speeches ... at a meeting held February 7, 1925 by the Non-partisan Saturday discussion committee of the National Republican club, Inc., New York city."

NL 0413725 DLC DNW NN

Littleton, Martin Wilie, 1872-1934.

McGuire, James K 1868- ed.
The Democratic party of the state of New York; a history of the origin, growth and achievements of the Democratic party of the state of New York, including a history of Tammany Hall in its relation to state politics; ed. by James K. McGuire. An historical chapter on Kings county Democracy, by Martin W. Littleton. Biographical sketches of the leading Democratic politicians in the state of New York ... [New York] United States history company, 1905.

Littleton, Martin Wilie, 1872-1934.
The excise-tax bill ... Speech of Hon. Martin W. Littleton of New York in the House of representatives, March 18, 1912. Washington, [Govt. print. off.] 1912.
57 p. (In Legal pamphlets. v. 3)

NL 0413727 WaU-L NN

Littleton, Martin Wilie, 1872-1934.
The fiddler of the Tennessee mountains; address at the Apollo Club dinner, April 21st, 1902. [n.p., 1902?]
6l. 18cm.

NL 0413728 TxU

Littleton, Martin Wilie, 1872-1934.
The greatest American ... [Buffalo? 1906?]
[4]p. 30½cm.
Newspaper clippings, mounted.
1. Washington, George, 1732-1799.- Addresses, sermons, etc.
I. Title.

NL 0413729 NBuG

Littleton, Martin Wilie, 1872-1934.
In re proposed ports and railroad legislation pending in Cuban congress, by Martin W. Littleton, counsel, Cuba N.R.C. [New York, 1923]

NL 0413730 DPU

Littleton, Martin Wilie, 1872-1934.
The independent judge. A paper presented at the twenty-sixth annual meeting of the New York state bar association, held at the city of Albany, N. Y., on the 20th and 21st days of January, 1903, and reprinted from the twenty-sixth annual report of the proceedings of the association. By Martin W. Littleton ... [Albany? 1903]
22 p. 23½cm.

I. New York state bar association.

6-11785

NL 0413731 DLC NN

Littleton, Martin W[ilie], 1872-1934.
Industrial and corporate problems; address, at Chattanooga, Tenn., January 19, 1912. [Washington, D. C.: Gov. Prtg. Off., 1912.] 50 p. 8°.
Title from cover.

1. Trusts, U. S., 1912.
N. Y. P. L. September 20, 1912.

NL 0413732 NN OO OClWHi

Littleton, Martin Wilie, 1872-1934.
Industrial liberty; address by Martin W. Littleton, Chamber of commerce, Pittsburgh, Pa., October 31, 1911. [n.p., 1911]
23 p. 22½cm.

1. Sherman Antitrust Law, 1890- . 2. Trusts, Industrial. I. Title

NL 0413733 NcD

Littleton, Martin Wilie, 1872-1934.
"Law and economics"; an address by Hon. Martin W. Littleton before the Law academy of Philadelphia, May 5, 1911. [Philadelphia] The Law academy of Philadelphia, 1911.
27 p. 27cm.

1. Economics.
I. Title.
II. Law academy of Philadelphia.

NL 0413734 NNC WaU-L

[Littleton, Martin Wilie] 1872-1934.
Memorandum respecting jurisdiction of Committee on public lands and surveys. [New York, Printed in the U. S. by Pandick press, inc., 1924]
cover-title, 27, [1] p. 23cm.
Signed: Martin W. Littleton, J. W. Zevely, counsel.
"Reference to authorities and precedents": p. 27.

1. U. S. Congress. Senate. Committee on public lands. I. Zevely, James W., joint author. II. Title.

24-12712

Library of Congress HD242.5.L5

NL 0413735 DLC

Littleton, Martin Wilie, 1872-1934
Monticello
see under Littleton, Maud (Wilson) "Mrs. M.W. Littleton."

Littleton, Martin Wilie, 1872-1934.
Oral argument of Martin W. Littleton, Esq., for Plaintiff-in-Error, and Supplemental Brief for Plaintiff-in-Error [in the] United States Circuit Court of Appeals for the Second Circuit. Charles W. Morse, Plaintiff-in-Error, against United States of America, Defendant-in-Error. [New York] U. S. Court of Appeals for the Second Circuit [191-]
136 p. 23 cm.
Cover title.

NL 0413737 MeB NjP

Littleton, Martin Wilie, 1872-1934.
Protection and privilege. Address delivered at the dinner of the National democratic club, April 13, 1907, by Martin W. Littleton. [n. p., 1907]
cover-title, 8 p. 23½cm.

1. Industry and state—U. S. I. Title.

45-29850

Library of Congress HD3616.U46L5

NL 0413738 DLC

Littleton, Martin Wilie, 1872-1934.
Radicalism in Washington: a notable address of national importance delivered by Hon. Martin W. Littleton at the first annual conference dinner of Patriotic Societies under the auspices of Key Men of America at the Hotel Roosevelt, New York, April 18, 1927. [New York, Key Men of America, 1927?]
31 p. illus.
"The proof, a postscript by Fred R. Marvin" - p. 11-29.

I. Socialism in the U.S. I. Marvin, Fred Richard, 1868-

NL 0413739 MiEM DLC

Littleton, Martin Wilie, 1872-1934.
The reign of democracy, its blessings and its dangers. Address delivered...at Charlottesville, Virginia ...1909.
27 p.

NL 0413740 ViU

[Littleton, Martin Wilie,] 1872-1934.
The revolution against American government. New York City: American Defense Soc., 1924. 27 p. facsims., illus. (ports.) 23cm.
"Address delivered by Hon. Martin W. Littleton before the American Defense Society, October 22, 1924."

734111A. 1. United States—Politics, 1924. 2. Bolshevism—U. S. I. American Defense Society.
N. Y. P. L. October 30, 1934

NL 0413741 NN MiEM OO MiU

Littleton, Martin Wilie, 1872-1934.

U. S. *Congress. Senate. Committee on privileges and elections.*
Senator from Michigan. Hearings before the subcommittee on privileges and elections, United States Senate, Sixty-sixth Congress, second session[-Sixty-seventh Congress, first session] pursuant to Senate Res. 11, a resolution authorizing the investigation of alleged unlawful practices in the election of a senator from the state of Michigan ... Printed for the use of the Committee on privileges and elections. Washington, Govt. print. off., 1920-21.

Littleton, Martin Wilie, 1872-1934.

New York (City) Anti-communist mass meeting, 1931.
Souvenir booklet. Anti-communist mass meeting under the combined auspices of national patriotic, civic, church and labor organizations, at Carnegie hall, January 9, 1931 at 8:30 P. M. ... containing the complete text of the addresses, resolutions, names of participating organizations and their representatives. New York city, Committee to combat socialism [1931]

Littleton, Martin Wilie, 1872-1934.
Tribute to Lincoln: Excerpts from address delivered by Congressman Martin W. Littleton at Lincoln Banquet, Springfield, Ill., February 11, 1911. [Springfield? Ill., 1911]
folder[4]p. 23cm.

NL 0413744 IHi

VOLUME 336

K272
A186 Littleton, Martin Wilie, 1872-1934.
United States vs. Harry F. Sinclair. Argument of Martin W. Littleton on behalf of defendant. [New York, Pandick Press, n.d.]
51 p. 25 cm.
Cover title.
At head of title: In the Supreme Court of the District of Columbia.

1. Sinclair, Harry Ford, 1876- . 2. Petroleum - U.S. I. District of Columbia. Supreme Court.

NL 0413745 DI ICJ

Littleton, Martin Wilie, 1897-1966.
... Opening to the court or jury, by Martin W. Littleton ... [New York] Practicing law institute, c1946.
1 p.l., 17-31 p. (Trial practice Series I, no. 11. 1946)

NL 0413746 WaU-L PU

Littleton, Martin Wilie, 1897-1966.
...Opening to the court or jury, by Martin W. Littleton...December 1953 ed. [N.Y.] Practising Law Institute, c1953.
p.[15]-31. (Trial practice, 11-R-4)

At head of title: Trial practice. Roscoe Pound, general editor, General and Trial practice series.
Bound with as issued: Bodin, H.S. Opening the trial. [N.Y.] c1953.

NL 0413747 NcD-L NNC

Littleton, Mary Brabson.
By the king's command, a romance of Ferdinand De Soto, by Mary Brabson Littleton. New York, P. J. Kenedy & sons, 1928.
viii p., 1 l., 309 p. 21 cm.

1. Soto, Hernando de, 1500 (ca.)-1542—Fiction. I. Title.

PZ3.L737By 28—25550

NL 0413748 DLC PPCCH

Littleton, *Mrs.* Mary Brabson.
Whence cometh victory? By Mary Brabson Littleton. 2d ed. [Baltimore, John Murphy company, printers, °1918]
109 p. 18cm.

I. Title.

Library of Congress BT135.L5 19-15930

NL 0413749 DLC NN

Littleton, Mary Brabson.
Whence victory? By Mary Brabson Littleton. Sea Isle City, N. J., New York [etc.] Scapular press [1943]
11 p. l., 19-181 p. front., plates, ports. 21cm.
A new and enlarged edition of the author's Whence cometh victory?

1. Providence and government of God. 2. World war, 1939- —Religious aspects. I. Title.

43-13442
Library of Congress BT135.L5 1943
[3] 264.1

NL 0413750 DLC WaSpG OrStbM

Littleton, *Mrs.* Mary L.
Christopher Columbus, an historical spectacle, presenting the most magnificent scenes and dramatic events in connection with the discovery of America, arranged for presentation during the World's fair at Chicago. By M. L. Littleton, Nashville, Tenn. [Nashville] 1891.
10 p., 1 l. 23½cm.

1. Colombo, Cristoforo—Drama. I. Title.

12-34283
Library of Congress E120.L78

NL 0413751 DLC CaBVaU

---

34 Littleton, Mary L.
De Soto or the fall of the Incas. By Mary L. Littleton and Frank C. Drake. In 4 acts. [n.p., 1895]
23 l. unp. 4°.
1. Drake, Frank C.

NL 0413752 DLC

Littleton, Maud (Wilson) "*Mrs.* M. W. Littleton."
Monticello, by Mrs. Martin W. Littleton. [n. p., 1912?]
cover-title, [59] p. illus., plates, ports. 23½ x 18cm.

1. Monticello. 2. Jefferson, Thomas, pres. U. S., 1743-1826.

17-21240
Library of Congress F234.M7L78

NL 0413753 DLC NN NIC TxU OClWHi OO

Littleton, Maud (Wilson) "Mrs. M.W. Littleton."
One wish. [An appeal for the purchase by the United States of the home of Thomas Jefferson at Monticello.] By Mrs. Martin W. Littleton. [New York, 1912.] 8 l., 4 pl., 1 port. sq. 8°.
Title from cover. With autograph of author.

1. Jefferson, Thomas, 3. president of the United States.
N. Y. P. L. September 14, 1912.

NL 0413754 NN NJQ ViU OClWHi Vi NRvS

Littleton, Maud (Wilson) "Mrs. M.W.Littleton."
One wish.... [n.p.,1912?]
cover-title, [18]p. front. (port.) 4 pl.
One wish and a will: [2] p. at end.

NL 0413755 ViU

---

ar W
14854 Littleton, Maud (Wilson) "*Mrs.* M. W. Littleton."
... One wish, by Mrs. Martin W. Littleton ... Washington [D. C.] 1912.
16 p. 24½cm.
A proposal to purchase and preserve Monticello as a monument to Thomas Jefferson.
"Printed in the Congressional record at the request of Hon. Richard W. Austin, of Tennessee, April 13, 1912."

1. Monticello. 2. Jefferson, Thomas, pres. U. S., 1743-1826. I. Title.

38-20406
Library of Congress F234.M7L783
[2] 923.173

NL 0413756 DLC ViN NIC

Littleton, Maud (Wilson) "Mrs. M. W. Littleton".

U. S. *Congress. Senate. Committee on the Library.*
Public ownership of Monticello. Hearing before the Committee on the Library, United States Senate, Sixty-second Congress, second session, on S. J. res. 92, a joint resolution providing for the purchase of the home of Thomas Jefferson, at Monticello, Virginia ... Washington, Govt. print. off., 1912.

Littleton, Maud (Wilson) "Mrs. M.W. Littleton."
U. S. *Congress. House. Committee on rules.*
Public ownership of Monticello. Hearings before the Committee on rules of the House of representatives on S. Con. res. 24, Wednesday, July 24, 1912 ... Washington, Govt. print. off., 1912.

F234
.M7L785 [Littleton, Maude (Wilson) "Mrs. M.W. Littleton"]
To those who have read this little story of Monticello. [Washington? 1912]
8 p. 22 cm.
Signed: Mrs. Martin B[!] Littleton.

NL 0413759 DLC

Littleton, Osborn.
Tragi-comoedia oxoniensis ... 1648.
see Littleton, Adam, 1627-1694.

Littleton, R. H.
The biography of William C. Macready, tragedian.
= London. Vickers. [1851?] 24 pp. Portrait. 17½ cm., in 8s.
The title is on the cover.

J362 — Macready, William Charles. 1793-1873.

NL 0413761 MB MH

Littleton, Robert.
An era of infamy; a factual and outstanding recital of the events which have brought America down the road of destruction during the past 20 years. [Cleveland? 1952]
128 p. 21 cm.

1. U. S.—Pol. & govt.—1933- 2. Campaign literature, 1952—Republican. I. Title.

E816.L58 329.01 52-3284 ‡

NL 0413762 DLC OrU

Littleton, Robert Thomas, 1916-
Geology and ground-water hydrology of the Angostura irrigation project, South Dakota, by Robert T. Littleton, with a section on the mineral quality of waters, by Herbert A. Swenson. [Washington] 1949.
v, 96 p. illus., 2 fold. maps (in pocket) 27 cm. (U. S. Geological Survey. Circular 54)

1. Geology—South Dakota. 2. Water, Underground—South Dakota. 3. Water-supply—South Dakota. 4. Angostura irrigation project. I. Swenson, Herbert Alfred, 1911- (Series)

[QE75.C5 no. 54] (557.3) G S 50-27
U. S. Geol. Survey. Libr.
for Library of Congress [5]

NL 0413763 DI-GS

Littleton, Robert Thomas, 1916-
Ground-water conditions in the vicinity of Gillette, Wyoming. With a section on the quality of ground waters, by Herbert A. Swenson. [Washington] 1950.
iii, 43 p. map, diagr., tables. 27 cm. (U. S. Geological Survey. Circular 76)
"References": p. 43.

1. Water, Underground—Wyoming—Gillette. 2. Water-supply—Wyoming—Gillette. 3. Water—Composition. I. Swenson, Herbert Alfred, 1911- II. Title: Quality of ground waters. (Series)

[QE75.C5 no. 76] G S 57-355
U. S. Geol. Survey. Libr.
for Library of Congress [3]

NL 0413764 DI-GS

VOLUME 336

QE75
.C5
no. 80
Littleton, Robert Thomas, 1916–
Reconnaissance of the geology and groundwater hydrology of the Laramie Basin, Wyoming. With special reference to the Laramie and Little Laramie River Valleys. Compiled as part of program of Interior Department for development of the Missouri River Basin. ⌜Washington⌝ 1950.
iv, 37 p. 2 maps (1 fold. in pocket) diagrs., tables. 27 cm. (⌜U. S.⌝ Geological Survey. Circular 80)
Cover title.
"References": p. 37.
1. Water, Underground—Wyoming—Laramie Basin. 2. Geology—Wyoming—Laramie Basin. 3. Water-supply—Wyoming—Laramie Basin. I. Title: Laramie Basin, Wyoming. (Series)
QE182
.L3L5 [QE75.C5 no. 80] (557.3) G S 51-63
Copy 2
U. S. Geol. Survey. Libr.
for Library of Congress ⌜3⌝

NL 0413765 DI-GS DLC

Littleton, Robert Thomas, 1916–
Reconnaissance of the ground-water resources of the Wheatland Flats area, Wyoming. Compiled as part of program of Interior Dept. for development of the Missouri River Basin. ⌜Washington⌝ 1950.
32 p. maps (1 fold., in pocket) diagrs. 27 cm. (⌜U. S.⌝ Geological Survey. Circular 70)
"References": p. 32.
1. Water, Underground—Wyoming—Platte Co. 2. Water-supply—Wyoming—Platte Co. I. Title. II. Title: Wheatland Flats area, Wyoming. (Series)
[QE75.C5 no. 70] (557.3) G S 50-239
U. S. Geol. Survey. Libr.
for Library of Congress ⌜3⌝

NL 0413766 DI-GS

Littleton, Sir Thomas, d. 1481.
Coke, *Sir* **Edward,** 1552–1634.
An abridgment, containing the substance, of Coke upon Littleton; with considerable additions, explaining the difficulties of the text, by references to the statutes and decided cases; and a copious index. By William Hawkins ... The 8th ed., with notes, corrections, and references, by John Rudall ... London, S. Sweet; ⌜etc., etc.⌝ 1822.

Littleton, Sir Thomas, d. 1481.
FOR OTHER EDITIONS
SEE MAIN ENTRY
Coke, *Sir* **Edward,** 1552–1634.
An abridgment of the first part of My L^d. Coke's Institutes: with some additions explaining many of the difficult cases, and shewing in what points the law has been altered by late resolutions and acts of Parliament. By William Hawkins ... The 4th ed. To which is now added, a large index in the nature of an analysis of the most general heads. ⌜London⌝ In the Savoy, Printed by E. and R. Nutt and R. Gosling, (assigns of E. Sayer) for J. Walthoe, 1725.

Littleton, Sir Thomas, d. 1481.
Coke, *Sir* **Edward,** 1552–1634.
An abridgment of the Lord Coke's Commentaries upon Littleton: being a brief explanation of the grounds of the common law. Composed by that famous and learned lawyer, Sir Humphrey Davenport, knight ... With a table of the most remarkable things therein contained. London, Printed by the assigns of Richard Atkyns and Edward Atkyns, 1685.

Littleton, Sir Thomas, d. 1481.
Fisk, George.
An analysis of Coke on Littleton, comprised in a series of questions, to be answered by the student in the course of his study of that work. By George Fisk ... London, Printed for S. Sweet ⌜etc.⌝ 1824.

Littleton, *Sir* **Thomas,** *d.* 1481.
Anciennes loix des François, conservées dans les coutumes angloises, recueilles par Littleton; avec des observations historiques & critiques, où l'on fait voir que les coutumes & les usages suivis anciennement en Normandie, sont les mêmes que ceux qui étoient en viguer dans toute la France sous les deux premieres races de nos rois. Ouvrage également utile pour l'étude de notre ancienne histoire & pour l'intelligence du droit coutumier de chaque province. Par M. David Hoüard ... Rouen, Impr. de R. Lallement, 1766.
2 v. 25½ x 20^cm.
Vol. 2 has title: Anciennes loix des François, ou Additions aux remarques sur les coutumes angloises. Recueillies par Littleton ...
I. Hoüard, David, 1725–1802, ed. and tr.
Library of Congress ⌜a23c1⌝ 10—33935

CaBVaU
NL 0413771 DLC NN MdBP ICU DFo InNd PU PU-L CtY

K
47
.506
LITTLETON, Sir THOMAS, 1402-1481.
Anciennes loix des françois, conservées dans les coutumes angloises, recueillies par Littleton; avec des observations historiques & critiques, ou l'on fait voir que les coutumes & les usages suivis anciennement en Normandie, sont les mêmes que ceux qui étoient en vigueur dans toute la France sous les deux premieres races de nos rois. Par M. Houard. Nouvelle édition. Rouen, chez Le Boucher, 1779.
2v. 27cm.
Vol. 2 has title: Anciennes loix des françois, ou Additions aux remarques sur les coutumes angloises- recueillies par Littleton.

NL 0413772 ICN MnU-L NhM PU-L

Littleton, Sir Thomas, d. 1841.
FOR OTHER EDITIONS
SEE MAIN ENTRY
Coke, *Sir* **Edward,** 1552–1634.
The first part of the Institutes of the laws of England; or, A commentary upon Littleton. Not the name of the author only, but of the law itself ... Hæc ego grandævus posui tibi, candide lector, authore Edwardo Coke, milite. Rev. and cor., with additions of notes, references, and proper tables, by Francis Hargrave and Charles Butler ... including also the notes of Lord Chief Justice Hale and Lord Chancellor Nottingham; and an analysis of Littleton, written by an unknown hand in 1658-9. By Charles Butler ... 1st American, from the 19th London ed., cor. ... Philadelphia, R. H. Small, 1853.

Littleton, Sir Thomas, 1402-1481.
Coke, *Sir* **Edward,** 1552–1634.
A readable edition of Coke upon Littleton. By Thomas Coventry ... London, Saunders and Benning, 1830.

Littleton, Sir Thomas, 1402-1481.
Coke, *Sir* **Edward,** 1552–1634.
Synopsis or, An exact abridgement of the Lord Cokes Commentaries upon Littleton: being a briefe explanation of the grounds of the common law. Composed by that famous and learned lawyer, Sir Humphrey Davenport ... with a perfect table poynting out the most remarkeable things therein contained ... London, Printed by E. G. for M. Walbancke and H. Twyford, 1652.

Littleton, Sir Thomas, d. 1481.
FOR OTHER EDITIONS
SEE MAIN ENTRY
Coke, *Sir* **Edward,** 1552–1634.
A systematic arrangement of Lord Coke's First Institute of the laws of England, on the plan of Sir Matthew Hale's analysis; with the annotations of M^r. Hargrave, Lord Chief Justice Hale, and Lord Chancellor Nottingham; and a new series of notes and references to the present time: including tables of parallel reference, analytical tables of contents, and a copious digested index ... By J. H. Thomas ... London, Printed by S. Brooke, and sold by Messrs. Butterworth and son ⌜etc.⌝ 1818.

FILM
Littleton, Sir Thomas, 1402-1481.
Leteltun teners newe correcte. ⌜London, R. Pynson, 1510?⌝
Film reproduction, position 3.
Pynson's device with his name appears on verso of last leaf.
University microfilms no.484 (case 13, carton 77)
Short-title catalogue no.15723.
1. Land tenure--Gt.Brit. 2. Real property--Gt.Brit.

NL 0413777 MiU

Littleton, *Sir* **Thomas,** 1402–1481.
Tenores nouelli. Londini, Johannes Lettou et Wilhelmus de Machlinia ⌜1482?⌝
70 l. 2° (29½^cm)
Proctor 9759 (3 London 2—1, 2); Duff 273; Morgan 711. Goff: L-232.
Signatures: a–h⁸, i⁶.
From the collection of Henry Newnham Davis. Bound by Hering; dark green morocco, inside border. Capitals supplied in red.
First edition.
L. C. copy agrees with Duff's description; L. C. and Duff differ from Morgan, f. 70^b, colophon, line 1 ends, L. C. and Duff "Wilħʒ" (Morgan "wilħʒ") L. C., Duff and Morgan differ from Hain 10126 in the division of the lines of the colophon.
1. Land tenure—Gt. Brit. 2. Real property—Gt. Brit.
CA 18-1474 Unrev'd
Library of Congress Incun.X.L7

NL 0413778 DLC

FILM
Littleton, Sir Thomas, d. 1481.
Tenores novelli. London, John Lettou and William de Machlinia ⌜1482?⌝
Colophon: Explicitt Tenores nouelli. Jmpssi p nos Johēȝ Lettou & Willȝ de Machlinia ī citate Londoniaȝ...
Leaf ⌜2^a⌝: Tenant en fee simple ...
Duff 273. Goff: L-232.
University microfilms no.1850 (case 81, carton 481)
Short-title catalogue no.15719.
1. Land tenure--Gt.Brit. 2. Real property--Gt.Brit.

NL 0413779 MiU DLC

Littleton, *Sir* **Thomas,** 1402–1481.
Tenores nouelli. Londini, Wilhelmus de Machlinia ⌜1483?⌝
68 l. 2° (27½^cm)
Hain 10127; Proctor 9766 (3 London 4—1, 2); Duff 274. Goff: L-233.
Signatures: a–g⁸, h–i⁶.
Book-plate: Victor Albert George Child Villiers, earl of Jersey. Osterley park. Bound in old red morocco, gilt. Capitals, line borders, and initial strokes supplied in red.
Imperfect: f. 1 (recto, blank; verso, table) wanting, supplied in facsimile.
1. Land tenure—Gt. Brit. 2. Real property—Gt. Brit.
CA 18-1475 Unrev'd
Library of Congress Incun.X.L73

NL 0413780 DLC

FILM
Littleton, Sir Thomas, 1402-1481.
⌜Tenores nouelli. Rouen, 1490⌝
Film reproduction, position 3.
Colophon: ... Impressi per me vvilhelmū (!) le tailleur in opulentissima ciuitate rothomagensi ... ad instantiam Richardi pynson.
Device of Pynson mounted on recto of first leaf.
Title supplied from Duff, Fifteenth century English books.
Date of publication given as 1490 by Beale, A bibliography of early English law books; as 1495? by Brit.mus. Catalogue. Goff: L-234.
University microfilms no.483 (case 17, carton 97)
Short-title catalogue no.15721.
1. Land tenure--Gt.Brit. 2. Real property--Gt.Brit.

NL 0413781 MiU

Littleton, *Sir* **Thomas,** *d.* 1481.
⌜Tenores novelli⌝ ⌜London, R. Pynson, 1496⌝
124 l. 28 x 22½^cm.
Binder's title.
Signatures: AB⁸, C–D⁶, E–F⁸, G–I⁶.
"Photostat facsimile ⌜positive⌝ reproduced from the copy in the Henry E. Huntington library."—Label on inside of front cover.
Collation of original on the basis of the facsimile: 1 p. l., ⌜122⌝ p. The photostat includes a fly leaf with manuscript notes ("Bibliographie")
Woodcut of Henry VII & his court on first leaf; printer's device (Richard Pynson) on last leaf.
Goff: L-235.
1. Land tenure—Gt. Brit.—Law. 2. Real property—Gt. Brit. I. Title.
42-39215
⌜2⌝

NL 0413782 DLC CLL CSmH CtY

VOLUME 336

FILM
Littleton, Sir Thomas, 1402-1481.
[Tenores nouelli. London, R. Pynson, 1496]
Film reproduction, position 3.
Colophon: Expliciunt Tenores Lytylton.
Device of Richard Pynson on verso of last leaf.
Title supplied from Duff, Fifteenth century English books.
University microfilms no.2497 (case 23, carton 134)
Short-title catalogue no.15722.
Goff: L-235.
1. Land tenure--Gt.Brit. 2. Real property--Gt.Brit.

NL 0413783 MiU

FILM
Littleton, Sir Thomas, d.1481.
[Tenorum Lytylton. London, 1518?]
Film reproduction, position 3.
Colophon: Tenorum Lytylton Lector iam cernito finem.
Device of Pynson on verso of last leaf
Begin: Tenaunt en fe symple.
University microfilms no.486 (case 17, carton 97)
Short-title catalogue no.15725.
1. Land tenure--Gt.Brit.--Law. 2. Real property--Gt. Brit.

NL 0413784 MiU

FILM
Littleton, Sir Thomas, 1402-1481.
[Tenorum Lytylton. London, R.Pynson, 1528?]
Film reproduction, position 3.
Colophon: Tenorum Lytylton lector iam cernito finem.
Begin: TEnant en fee simple.
University microfilms no.488 (case 17, carton 97)
Short-title catalogue no.15729.
1. Land tenure--Gt.Brit. 2. Real property--Gt.Brit.

NL 0413785 MiU

Littleton, Sir Thomas, d.1481.
Les Tenures. London, R.Pynson, [1502]
folio

NL 0413786 CSmH

Littleton, Sir Thomas, d.1481.
Tenures. [London, Pynson, 1504]
(French)

NL 0413787 MH

Littleton, Sir Thomas, d.1481.
Tenures. [London, Pynson, 1516]
(French)

NL 0413788 MH

FILM
Littleton, Sir Thomas, 1402-1481.
[Tenures. London, R. Pynson, 1516]
Film reproduction, position 3.
Colophon: Impressum per me Richardū Pynson. Anno dñi. M.CCCCC.xvi.
University microfilms no.485 (case 13, carton 77)
Short-title catalogue no.15724.
In French.
1. Land tenure--Gt.Brit. 2. Real property--Gt.Brit.

NL 0413789 MiU

Littleton, *Sir* **Thomas,** 1402–1481.
Tenures. [London, R. Pynson, 1518?]
58 (?) l. 30cm.
f. 1a title: ℭ Leteltun tenuris new correcte. ‖ [woodcut: royal arms (Henry VII or VIII) surmounted by the Tudor rose partly encompassed by scroll supported by angels, bearing the motto: "Hęc rosa uirtutis de cælo missa sereno. Aeternū florens regia sceptra feret"]
f. 1b: woodcut of the king and his court.
f. 2a (sig.: Lit. tenures. A.ii.) line 1: TEnaunt en fee simple ...
Without paging or catchwords. 58? leaves, sig. A in eight, B–H in sixes, I in eight? Imperfect: wanting all after f. 51 (sig. I[i]) 43 lines to the full page. Paper 28.6 x 20.2cm, printed page 19.8 x 13.4cm. Gothic type. Initials. Ms. notes.
Probably the edition listed by the British museum as printed by Pynson [1518?] (Brit. mus. G2191)
1. Land tenure—Gt. Brit. 2. Real property—Gt. Brit.
18-4445

NL 0413790 DLC

Littleton, Sir Thomas, d.1481.
Tenures. [Londini, in edibus Pynsoni, 1525]
(French)

NL 0413791 MH

FILM
Littleton, Sir Thomas, 1402-1481.
Lytylton tenures newly and moost truly correctyd & amendyd. [Londini, 1525]
Colophon: Londini in ędibus Richardi Pynsoni regij impressoris. Anno a Christi natu. 1525.quarto idus Octobris.
In French.
University microfilms no.1851 (case 27, carton 161)
Short-title catalogue no.15726.
1. Land tenure--Gt.Brit. 2. Real property--Gt.Brit.

NL 0413792 MiU PPT

Littleton, Sir Thomas, d.1481.
Tenures. [Londini, in edibus Pynsoni, 1528]
(French)
Dunn 110

NL 0413793 MH

FILM
Littleton, Sir Thomas, 1402-1481.
Lytylton tenures newly and most truly corrected & amended. [London, 1528]
Film reproduction, position 2.
Colophon: ... Lōdini in edibus Richardi Pynsonis. Anno.dñi.M.CCCCC.xxviii ...
In French.
Printer's device on t.-p. and verso of last leaf.
University microfilms.no.2498 (case 21, carton 123)
Short-title catalogue no.15728.
1. Land tenure--Gt.Brit. 2. Real property--Gt.Brit.

NL 0413794 MiU

Littleton, Sir Thomas, d.1481.
Tenures. [London, Redman, 1528]
(French)
Dunn 111

NL 0413795 MH

FILM
Littleton, Sir Thomas, 1402-1481.
Lytylton tenures newly and most truly correctyd & amendyd. [London, 1528]
Film reproduction, position 3.
Colophon: Expliciūt Tenores Litiltoni cum alterationibus eorundem et additionib' nouis ... Londini in edibus Roberti Redman anno salut' nostre M.ccccc.xxviii ...
With this is Natura breuium newly and moost trewly corrected. 1529.
University microfilms no.487 (case 17, carton 97)
Short-title catalogue no.15727.
1. Land tenure--Gt.Brit. 2. Real property--Gt.Brit.

NL 0413796 MiU

Littleton, *Sir* **Thomas,** *d.* 1481.
Lyttyltō te= ‖ nures uew= [!] ‖ ly impzin= ‖ ted. ‖ ∴ ‖ [*Colophon:* ℭ Londini in edibus Thome Berthe= ‖ lett Reg. impzessozis / in Fletestrete ‖ pzope aquagium sitis / sub signo ‖ Lucrecie Romane. Anno ‖ domini. M.D.XXX.]
[272] p. 13½cm.
Signatures: A–R8.
1. Land tenure—Gt. Brit. 2. Real property—Gt. Brit.
28-23594

NL 0413797 DLC MiU

FILM
Littleton, Sir Thomas, 1402-1481.
Lyttyltō [tenures newly imprinted. [London, 1530]
Film reproduction, position 3.
Colophon: Londini in edibus Thome Bertheleti ... Anno domini.M.D.xxx.
University microfilms no.490 (case 17, carton 98)
Short-title catalogue no.15731.
1. Land tenure--Gt.Brit. 2. Real property--Gt.Brit.

NL 0413798 MiU

FILM
Littleton, Sir Thomas, d.1481.
Lyttyltō tenures uewly [!] imprinted. [Colophon: Londini in edibus Thome Bertheleti ... M.D.xxx]
University microfilms no.10083 (case 51, carton 303).
Also University microfilms no.490 (case 17, carton 98)
Short-title catalogue no.23881 [i.e.15731]
1. Land tenure--Gt.Brit. 2. Real property--Gt.Brit.

NL 0413799 MiU

Littleton, *Sir* **Thomas,** 1402–1481.
ℭ Lyttylton ‖ tenures newly imprin- ‖ ted. ‖ [*Royal arms*] ‖ [*Colophon:* ℭ Imprynted at London ‖ by me Robert ‖ Redman. ‖ ℭ Cum gratia et priuilegio ‖ Regali. ‖ [n. d., 1530?]]
203 (*i. e.* 201) numb. l., [4] p., 1 l. 12½cm.
Signatures: A–Z8, AA–BB8, CC4.
Numbers 32–33 omitted in foliation.
Redman's device on verso of leaf at end.
1. Land tenure—Gt. Brit. 2. Real property—Gt. Brit.
19-8701

NL 0413800 DLC

FILM
Littleton, Sir Thomas, 1402-1481.
Lyttylton [tenures newly imprinted. [London, 1530?]
Film reproduction, position 3.
Colophon: Imprinted at London by me Robert Redman ...
University microfilms no.489 (case 17, carton 98)
Short-title catalogue no.15730.
1. Land tenure--Gt.Brit. 2. Real property--Gt.Brit.

NL 0413801 MiU

Littleton, Sir Thomas, d. 1481.
Les Tenures de Lyttleton novelment imprimes et ovesqz. toute diligence revises, coriges et amendes; et ensement ove plusours authoriteis annotes et marques en le marge de cest lyver, etc. Colophon: Imprynted at London by me Robert Redman, cum gratia et Privilegio Regali. [1536?]
Printed in neat roman type, double columns, 54 lines; royal arms on title, and woodcut border on reverse; wide margins with numerous contemporary manuscript notes; russia leather binding.

Continued in next column

VOLUME 336

Continued from preceding column

There is no imprint on the title. The title bears several signatures of "Henry Mordaunt" and mottoes: "Maners makes or marres quothe Mordaunt," etc. This Mordaunt may have been related to John Mordaunt, first Baron Mordaunt (1490?-1562).

NL 0413803 N

Littleton, Sir Thomas, d. 1481.
Tenures. ₍London, Redman, 1539.
(French)

NL 0413804 MH

Littleton, *Sir* **Thomas,** 1402–1481.
❦ Les Tenvres ‖ De Lyttelton Novelment Impri- ‖ mes, et ouesq; toute diligence reuises, coriges, et amendes: ‖ et ensement oue plusours authoriteis annotes ‖ et marques en le marge de cest lyuer, ou ‖ mesme les cases sount ouerte- ‖ ment debatus et purpar- ‖ les pluis a ‖ large. ‖ ❦ ‖ ₍*Royal arms*₎ ‖ [*Colophon:* ℂ Imprynted at London ‖ by me Robert ‖ Redman. ‖ ℂ Cum gratia et priuilegio ‖ Regali. ‖ ₍n. d., 1540?₎]
1 p. l., 50 numb. l., 1 l. 26cm.
Signatures: 1 leaf unsigned (title), A–M⁴, N³.
In double columns; manuscript notes.
1. Land tenure—Gt. Brit. 2. Real property—Gt. Brit.

19-8702

NL 0413805 DLC N

FILM

Littleton, Sir Thomas, 1402-1481.
Les tenvres de Lyttelton novelment impriñes, et ouesq toute diligence reuises, coriges, et amendes: et ensement oue plusours authoriteis annotes et marques en le marge de cest lyuer, ou mesme les cases sount ouertment debatus et purparles pluis a large. ₍London, 1540?₎
Film reproduction, position 3.
Colophon: Imprynted at London by me Robert Redman ...
University microfilms no.491 (case 13, carton 77)
Short-title catalogue no.15732.
1. Land tenure--Gt.Brit. 2. Real property--Gt.Brit.

NL 0413806 MiU

Littleton, *Sir* **Thomas,** 1402–1481.
❧ Lytyl- ‖ ton ‖ Tenvres ‖ Nevvly ‖ Impryn- ‖ ted. ‖ ❦ ‖ Anno. M.D.XLI. ‖ ₍*Colophon:* ❧ Londini in ędibus Thome ‖ Bertheleti Regii impressoris. ‖ Cvm priuilegio ad imprimen- ‖ dum solum. ‖ Anno. M.D.XLI.₎ ‖
138 numb. l., ₍2₎ p. 15cm.
Signatures: A–R⁸, S².
Title within ornamental border, with date 1534 in lower part of border.
1. Land tenure—Gt. Brit. 2. Real property—Gt. Brit.

19-8703

NL 0413807 DLC

Littleton, *Sir* **Thomas,** *d.* 1481.
❧ Lytylton Tenvres nevvly revised, and truly corrected vvith a table (after the alphabete to fynde out brefely the cases desyred in the same) therto added very necessary to the reders. ✠ ℂ Cvm privilegio ad imprimendvm solum per septennium. ✠ ₍*Colophon:* ❧ Imprinted at London in Fletestrete at the sygne of the George by VVyllyam Myddylton. In the yere of our Lorde M.CCCCC.XLV. The XXVI. day of Marche ...₎
15 p. l., 151 numb. l., ₍2₎ p. 14½cm.
Signatures: 8 leaves unsigned, ✠⁸ (last leaf blank), A–T⁸.
1. Land tenure—Gt. Brit.—Law. 2. Real property—Gt. Brit.

38-33645

NL 0413808 DLC MH

FILM

Littleton, Sir Thomas, 1402-1481.
Lytylton tenvres neulye imprynted. ₍London₎ An.M.D.XLV.
Film reproduction, position 3.
Colophon: Imprinted at London ... by VVyllyam Myddylton. In the yere of our Lorde M.CCCCC.XLV.
University microfilms no.492 (case 13, carton 77)
Short-title catalogue no.15733.
In French.
1. Land tenure--Gt.Brit. 2. Real property--Gt.Brit.

NL 0413809 MiU

Littleton, Sir Thomas, d.1481.
Tenures. ₍London, Smyth, 1545.
₍15₎, 151, ₍1₎ p.
(French)
Dunn 115

NL 0413810 MH

FILM

Littleton, Sir Thomas, 1402-1481.
Lytylton Tenvres neulye imprynted. ₍London₎ An.M.D.XLV.
Film reproduction, position 2.
Colophon: Prynted at London by Henry Smyth ...
In French.
University microfilms no.2499 (case 21, carton 123)
Short-title catalogue no.15734.
1. Land tenure--Gt.Brit. 2. Real property--Gt.Brit.

NL 0413811 MiU

LITTLETON, Sir Thomas, d. 1551.
Tenures.
[London, Powel, 1553].
24mo. (13) cli (1) fol.
In French.

NL 0413812 MH-L

FILM

Littleton, Sir Thomas, d.1481.
Lytylton tenvres nevvly revised, and truly corrected ... ₍London, 1553₎
Colophon: Imprinted at London ... by Wyllyam Powel ... 1553 ...
In French.
University microfilms no.16354 (case 74, carton 443)
Short-title catalogue no.15736.
1. Land tenure--Gt.Brit. 2. Real property--Gt.Brit.

NL 0413813 MiU

FILM

Littleton, Sir Thomas, 1402-1481.
Lyttylton tenvres nevvly revised, and truly corrected ... Jmprinted at London ... by Richard Tottel ... 1554 ...
University microfilms no.16355 (case 80, carton 475)
Short-title catalogue no.15737.
In French.
1. Land tenure--Gt.Brit. 2. Real property--Gt.Brit.

NL 0413814 MiU

Littleton, *Sir* **Thomas,** 1402–1481.
¶Litletons ‖ Tenures. ‖ Apud Richardum Tottele ‖ Cum priuilegio. ‖ 1557. ‖ ₍*Colophon:* ℂ Imprin- ‖ ted at London in Flete stret ‖ within Temple barre, at the ‖ sygne of the hand and ‖ starre, by Rychard ‖ Tottil, ẏ. xxviii. ‖ daie of Octo- ‖ ber. ‖ Anno domini. 1557, ‖ (·:) ‖ Cum priuilegio ad impri- ‖ mendum solum.₎ ‖
1 p. l., 173 numb. l., ₍2₎ p. 14cm.
Signatures: A–X⁸, Y⁷.
1. Land tenure—Gt. Brit. 2. Real property—Gt. Brit.

—— —— Copy 2. 14½cm.
Manuscript notes. "Index To the Doctor & Student" (24½ p.) and "Abstract Of the Preface to the 1721 edition" (1½ p.) in manuscript at beginning of volume.
With this are bound: ₍A Profitable ‖ booke of Maister Iohn ‖ Perkins ... trea- ‖ ting of the law- ‖ es of Eng- ‖ lande. ‖ ₍Londini₎ apud Richardum Tottell ₍1567₎ *and* ℂ The Dyaloges ‖ in Englishe, betwene ‖ a Doctour of diui- ‖ nitie, and a Stu- ‖ dent ‖ in the lawes of Englande, ‖ ... ₍*Colophon:* ¶Londini in ædibvs Richardi ‖ Totteli. An. 1554.₎ ‖

19-8705

NL 0413816 DLC CLL NN CtY-L CSmH PU-L

FILM

Littleton, Sir Thomas, 1402-1481.
Litletons tenures ... ₍London₎ Apud Richardum Tottel ... 1557.
Colophon: Jmprinted at London ... by Richard Tottil ... 1557.
University microfilms no.15908 (case 44, carton 264)
Short-title catalogue no.15738.
In French.
1. Land tenure--Gt.Brit. 2. Real property--Gt.Brit.

NL 0413817 MiU

FILM

Littleton, Sir Thomas, d.1481.
Les tenures du monsieur Littelton, ouesque certein cases addes p auters de puisne temps ... ₍London, 1567.
Colophon: Jmprinted at London ... by Rychard Tottil ... 1567 ...
University microfilms no.16356 (case 74, carton 443)
Short-title catalogue no.15739.
1. Land tenure--Gt.Brit. 2. Real property--Gt.Brit.

NL 0413818 MiU

Littleton, Sir Thomas, d. 1481.
Les Tenures du Monsieur Littletõ, ouesque certein cases addes p auters de puisne temps, queux cases troueres signes oueso cest signe al commencement al fine de chescun deux, au fine que ne poyes eux misprender pour les cases de monsieur Littletõ; pur q̃l inconuenience, ils fuerent derniermen tolles de cest liuer et cy vn foitz plus admotes al request des gentilhomes students en le ley dẽgleterre. ... 1569. Colophon: Imprinted at London ... by Rycharde Tottill. 1569.

sm. 8 vo. Black roan & maroon cloth.
Brandreth copy from C.S.B., March 1921.

NL 0413820 CSmH MH

FILM

Littleton, Sir Thomas, 1402-1481.
Les tenures du monsieur Litteltõ, ouesque certein cases addes p auters de puisne temps ... ₍London₎ 1569.
Colophon: Jmprinted at London ... by Rycharde Tottill. 1569 ...
University microfilms no.15909 (case 44, carton 264)
Short-title catalogue no.15740.
1. Land tenure--Gt.Brit. 2. Real property--Gt.Brit.

NL 0413821 MiU

Littleton, Sir Thomas, d. 1481.
¶Les tenures du monsieur Littelton ₍!₎, ouesque certein cases addes per auters de puisne temps, queux cases troueres signes ouesque cest signe ⁓❦ al commencement & al fine de chescun deux, au fine que ne poyes eux misprender pour les cases de monsieur Littleton: pur quel inconuenience, ils fuerent desnierment tolles de cest liuer, & cy vn foytz plus admotes al requeste des gentil homes students en le ley dengleterre. (·:·) Cum priuilegio. 1572. ₍Colophon: Imprinted at London in Fletestrete within Temple barre, at the signe of the hand and starre by Richard Tottill. 1572. Cum priuilegio.₎
1 p. l., 170 l., ₍2₎ p. 15cm.

Signatures: A-X⁸, Y⁴.
Interleaved, with manuscript notes on blank leaves and on margins in French in fine cursive writing.
Contemporary vellum.
Bookplate of Edwd Dyneley Esqre and Ex-libris de la Germonière.
In slip case.

NL 0413823 NNC DFo MH

VOLUME 336

FILM

Littleton, Sir Thomas, d. 1481.
Les tenures du monsieur Littelton, ouesque certein cases addes per auters de puisne temps ... ‹London› 1572.
Colophon: Jmprinted at London ... by Rychard Tottill. 1572 ...
University microfilms no. 16357 (case 74, carton 444)
Short-title catalogue no. 15741.

1. Land tenure—Gt. Brit. 2. Real property—Gt. Brit.

NL 0413824 MiU

FILM

Littleton, Sir Thomas, 1402-1481.
Les tenures du monsier Littleton, ouesq̄ certein cases addes p̄ auters de puisne temps ... ‹London› 1572.
Colophon: Imprinted at London ... by Richard Tottyl. 1574 ...
University microfilms no. 15910 (case 44, carton 264)
Short-title catalogue no. 15742.

1. Land tenure—Gt. Brit. 2. Real property—Gt. Brit.

NL 0413825 MiU

Littleton, *Sir* **Thomas,** 1402–1481.
¶Les || Tenures du mon- || sier Littleton, oues- || q̄ certein cases addes p au || ters de puisne temps, queux cases tro- || ueres signes ouesque cest signe al || cōmencement ⁊ al fiñ de chescun deux, || au fine que ne poies eux mispren- || der pour les cases de monsieur || Littleton: pur quel incon- || uenience, ils fuerent || der- nierment tol- || les de cest || liuer, || ⁊ cy vn foytz plus admotes || al requeste des gentil || homes students || en le ley den- || gleterre. || (.:.) ¶Cum priuilegio. || 1572 ||

‹Colophon: Imprinted at Lon- || don in Fletestre ‹!› with- || in Temple barre, at the signe || of the hand and starre || by Richard Tottyl. || 1574. || Cum priuilegio.› ||
1 p. l., 170 numb. l., ‹2› p. 14cm.
Signatures: A–X^8, Y^4.
Manuscript notes.

1. Land tenure—Gt. Brit. 2. Real property—Gt. Brit.

19-8706

NL 0413827 DLC DFo NNC IaU PU-L CtY

Littleton, Sir Thomas, d. 1481.
Tenures. ‹London, Tottyl, 1577.
‹1›, 170, ‹1› p.
(French)

NL 0413828 MH

FILM

Littleton, Sir Thomas, d. 1481.
Les tenures du monsier Littleton, ouesq̄ certen cases addes p̄ auters de puisne tēps ... ‹London› 1577.
Colophon: Imprinted at London ... by Rychard Tottyl. 1577 ...
University microfilms no. 16358 (case 74, carton 444)
Short-title catalogue no. 15743.

1. Land tenure—Gt. Brit. 2. Real property—Gt. Brit.

NL 0413829 MiU

Littleton, *Sir* **Thomas,** 1402–1481.
¶Les || Tenures du mon- || sieur Littleton, oues- || que certein cases addes p || auters de puisne temps, queux cases || vous troueres signes ouesque cē signe || al cōmencement ⁊ al fine de ches- || cun deux, au fine que ne poies eux mis- || prender pur les cases de monsieur || Littleton: pur quel incon- || uenience, ils fuerent || dernier- ment tol- || les de cest || liuer. || Et cy vn foits plus admotes || al request des gentil || home studentes || en le ley den- || gleterre. || (.˙.) || ¶Cum priuilegio. || 1579. ||

Continued in next column

Continued from preceding column

‹Colophon: ¶Imprinted at Lon- || don in Fletestrete with- || in Temple barre, at the sygne || of the hande and starre || by Rychard Tottyl, || 1579. || Cum Priuilegio.› ||
1 p. l., 170 numb. l., ‹2› p. 16½cm.
Signatures: A–X^8, Y^4.
Large paper; interleaved; manuscript annotations.

1. Land tenure—Gt. Brit. 2. Real property—Gt. Brit. 19-8709

NL 0413831 DLC MH

FILM

Littleton, Sir Thomas, d. 1481.
Les tenures du monsieur Littleton, ouesque certein cases addes p̄ auters de puisne temps ... ‹London› 1579.
Colophon: Imprinted at London ... by Rychard Tottyl, 1579 ...
University microfilms no. 16359 (case 74, carton 444)
Short-title catalogue no. 15744.

1. Land tenure—Gt. Brit. 2. Real property—Gt. Brit.

NL 0413832 MiU

Littleton, *Sir* **Thomas,** *d.* 1481.
Les tenures du monsieur Littleton, ouesque certein cases addes p auters de puisne temps, queux cases vous troueres signes ouesque cē signe al cōmencement ⁊ al fine de chescun deux, au fine que ne poies eux misprender pur les cases de monsieur Littleton: pur quel inconuenience, ils fuerent dernierment tolies de cest lieur. Et cy vn foits pluis admotes al request des gentill homes studentes en le ley dengleterre. Cum priuilegio. ‹London› 1581.
1 p. l., 170 numb. l., ‹48› p., 1 l. 15cm.
Colophon: Imprinted at London in Fletestrete within Temple Barre, at the signe of the Hande and starre by Rychard Tottel. 1581.

Signatures: A–Z^8, A^8, B^4.
Edited by William West.
Manuscript notes.

1. Land tenure—Gt. Brit.—Law. 2. Real property—Gt. Brit. I. West, William, fl. 1568–1594, ed.

42-33486

NL 0413834 DLC CtY CSmH

Rare Book Room
P75
L734
481e

Littleton, Sir Thomas, 1402-1481.
[Les tenures du monsieur Littleton ... London, R. Tottell, 1581]
1p.ℓ., 170 numb.ℓ., [2]p. 10½cm.
Colophon: Imprinted at London in Fletestrete within Temple barre, at the signe of the Hande and Starre by Rychard Tottel. 1581.
First edition edited by W. West.
Sections numbered consecutively through the text.
Signatures: A-X^{8}Y^4.

T.-p. wanting; title supplied from J.H. Beale, A bibliography of early English law books, p.114. The Y copy is without the 24ℓ index found issued with some copies (cf. Beale, p.118 and Huntington check-list)

NL 0413836 CtY MH

FILM

Littleton, Sir Thomas, 1402-1481.
Les tenures du monsieur Littleton, ouesque certein cases addes p̄ auters de puisne temps ... ‹London› 1581.
Colophon: Imprinted at London ... by Rychard Tottel. 1581.
Edited by William West.
University microfilms no. 15911 (case 44, carton 264)
Short-title catalogue no. 15745.

1. Land tenure—Gt. Brit. 2. Real property—Gt. Brit. I. West, William, fl. 1568-1594, ed.

NL 0413837 MiU

Littleton, *Sir* **Thomas,** *d.* 1481.
¶ Les tenures du monsieur Littleton, ouesque certein cases addes per auters de puisne temps, queux cases vous troueres signes ouesque cest sigñ al cōmencement ⁊ al fine de chescun deux, au fine que ne poies eux misprender pur les cases de monsieur Littleton: pur quel inconuenience, ils fueront dernierment tolles de cest liuer. Et cy vn foits pluis admotes al request des gentill homes students en le ley dengleterre. (.˙.) ¶ Cum priuilegio. ‹*Colophon:* Imprinted at London in Fleestrete ‹!› within Temple Barre, at the signe of the Hand and Starre, by Rychard Tottill› 1583.
1 p. l., 171 (*i. e.* 170) numb. l., ‹2› p. 16½cm.

Signatures: A–X^8, Y^4.
Edited by W. West.
Irregularities in foliation: numbers 67–70 are given in the following order: 67, 70, 69, 68; number 104 is omitted.
Sections numbered consecutively through the text.

1. Land tenure—Gt. Brit.—Law. 2. Real property—Gt. Brit. I. West. William, fl. 1568–1594, ed.

33-21010

NL 0413839 DLC MH CtY N

STC 15746

Littleton, Sir Thomas, 1402-1481.
Les tenures du Monsieur Littleton, ouesque certein cases addes per auters de puisne temps ... 1583.
Colophon: Imprinted at London by Rychard Tottill, 1583.
A-X^8, Y^4, ‹2d›A-‹2d›C^8. 8vo.
Edited by William West with index.
Manuscript notes.
Beale, Bibl. of early English law books, p. 114, no. T31 and Supplement, p. 44, T31.

NL 0413840 DFo

Littleton, *Sir* **Thomas,** 1402–1481.
¶ Les Tenures de Monsieur Littleton, ouesque certeine Cases addes per auters de puisne temps, queux cases vous troueres signes ouesque cest Signe al commencement, ⁊ al fine de chescū de eux, au fine que ne poies eux misprender pur les cases de Monsieur Littleton: Pur quel inconuenience, ils fueront dernierment tolles de cest Lieur. Et cy vn foits pluis admotes al request des Gentlehomes, Students en le ley Dengleterre. (****) ¶ Cum Priuilegio. ‹*Colophon:* Imprinted at London in Fletestrete within Temple Barre, at the signe of the Hand and Starre, by Rychard Tottill› 1585.
1 p. l., 171 (*i. e.* 170) numb. l., ‹48› p., 1 l. 14cm.
Signatures: A–X^8, Y^4, A–C^8.
Irregularities in numbering the leaves: numbers 67–70 are given in the following order: 67, 70, 69, 68; number 104 is omitted.
Edited by W. West.
First edition of the Tenures with the sections numbered.—Lowndes, Bibliographer's manual.
Manuscript marginal notes in French.
1. Land tenure—Gt. Brit. 2. Real property—Gt. Brit. I. West, William, fl. 1568–1594, ed.

18-18986

NL 0413842 DLC MH CtY PU

FILM

Littleton, Sir Thomas, 1402-1481.
Les tenures de monsieur Littleton, ouesque certeine cases addes per auters de puisne temps ... ‹London› 1585.
Colophon: Imprinted at London ... by Rychard Tottill. 1585 ...
Edited by William West.
University microfilms no. 15912 (case 44, carton 264)
Short-title catalogue no. 15747.

1. Land tenure—Gt. Brit. 2. Real property—Gt. Brit. I. West, William, fl. 1568-1594, ed.

NL 0413843 MiU

Littleton, *Sir* **Thomas,** *d.* 1481.
¶ Les Tenures de Monsieur Littleton, ouesque certeine Cases addes per auters de puisne temps, queux cases vous troueres signes ouesque cest Signe al commencement, & al fine de chescū de eux: au fine que ne poies eux misp̄nder pur les cases d'Monsieur Littleton: Pur quel inconuenience, ils fueront dernierment tolles de cest Lieur, Et cy vn foits pluis admotes al request des Gentlehomes, Students en le ley Dengleterre. (.˙.) Cum Priuilegio. ‹*Colophon:* ¶ Imprinted at London, in Fleete-strete within Temple Barre, at the Signe of the Hand and Starre by Richarde Tottell.› 1588.
1 p. l., 171 (*i. e.* 170) numb. l., ‹48› p., 1 l. 12½ x 7cm.

Continued in next column

VOLUME 336

Continued from preceding column

Signatures: A–X⁸, Y⁴, A–C⁸.
In numbering the leaves number 104 is omitted.
Edited by W. West.

1. Land tenure—Gt. Brit. 2. Real property—Gt. Brit. I. West, William, fl. 1568–1594, ed.

7-29863 rev. 2

NL 0413845 DLC MH MiU-L NNC-L DFo CtY

FILM

Littleton, Sir Thomas, 1402-1481.
Les tenures de monsieur Littleton, ouesque certeine cases addes per auters de puisne temps ... ‹London› 1588.

Colophon: Imprinted at London ... by Richarde Tottell ...
Edited by William West.
University microfilms no.15913 (case 44, carton 264)
Short-title catalogue no.15748.

1. Land tenure—Gt.Brit. 2. Real property—Gt.Brit. I. West, William, fl.1568-1594, ed.

NL 0413846 MiU

Littleton, *Sir* Thomas, 1402–1481.
Les ‖ Tenures de Monsieur ‖ Littleton ‖ Ouesque certaine Cases addes per ‖ Auters de puisne temps: Queux ‖ Cases vous troueres signes oues- ‖ que cest Signe ✠ al com- ‖ mencement & fine ‖ de chescun de ‖ eux: ‖ Au fine que ne poies eux mis- ‖ prender pur les Cases de ‖ Monsieur Littleton, ‖ pur quel inconueniens, ils fue- ‖ ront dernierment celles ‖ de cest Lieur: ‖ Et cy vn foits pluis admotes al request ‖ des Gentlehomes Studentes en ‖ le Ley Dangliterre. ‖ Cum Priuilegio Regiæ ‖ Maiestatis. ‖ 1591. ‖

1 p. l., 171 (*i. e.* 170) numb. l., ‹6› p. 10½cm.

Signatures: A–R¹².
Number 104 omitted in foliation.
The sections are numbered consecutively through the text.
Edited by W. West.

1. Land tenure—Gt. Brit. 2. Real property—Gt. Brit. I. West, William, fl. 1568–1594, ed.

19-8713

NL 0413848 DLC CLL

Littleton, *Sir* Thomas, 1402–1481.
¶Les ‖ Tenures de Mon- ‖ sieur Littleton, ouesque ‖ certain Cases addes per auters ‖ de puisne temps, queux cases vous ‖ troueres signes ouesque cest Signe ☙ al ‖ commencement, & al fine de chescun ‖ de eux: au fine que ne poies eux ‖ misprender pur les cases d'Mon- ‖ sieur Littleton: Pur quel in- ‖ conuenience, ils fue- ‖ ront dernierment ‖ tolles de cest ‖ Lieur. ‖ Et cy vn foits pluis admotes ‖ al request des Gentle- ‖ homes, Students ‖ en le ley Den- ‖ gleterre. ‖ (∴) ‖ Cum Priuilegio. ‖ 1591. ‖

‹*Colophon:* ¶Imprinted at Lon- ‖ don, in Fleetestrete within ‖ Temple Barre, at the Signe of ‖ the Hand and Starre ‖ by Richarde ‖ Tottell. ‖ ¶Cum priuilegio.› ‖

1 p. l., 171 (i. e. 170) numb. l., ‹48› p., 1 l. 2 port. (incl. front.) 21cm.

Signatures: A–X⁸, Y⁴, A–C⁸.
Number 104 omitted in foliation.
Large paper; sections numbered consecutively through the text.
Edited by W. West.

1. Land tenure—Gt. Brit. 2. Real property—Gt. Brit. I. West, William, fl. 1568–1594, ed.

19-8712

NL 0413850 DLC

STC 15749

Littleton, Sir Thomas, 1402-1481.
Les tenures de Monsieur Littleton, ouesque certain cases addes per auters de puisne temps ... 1591.
Colophon: Imprinted at London by Richarde Tottell

A-X⁸, Y⁴, ‹2d›A-‹2d›C⁸. 4to.
Edited by William West, with index.
Interleaved except for index. Text printed only on the upper and inner quarter of each leaf.
Beale, Bibl. of early English law books, p. 115, no. T35 and Supplement, p. 44, T35.

---- ---- Another issue.
Differs from STC 15749 in that this issue is printed on an octavo format.
Manuscript notes.
Shirley family library copy.

NL 0413852 DFo CtY

FILM

Littleton, Sir Thomas, 1402-1481.
Les tenures de monsieur Littleton, ouesque certain cases addes per auters de puisne temps ... ‹London› 1591.

Colophon: Imprinted at London ... by Richarde Tottell ...
University microfilms no.15914 (case 44, carton 264)
Short-title catalogue no.15749.

1. Land tenure—Gt.Brit. 2. Real property—Gt.Brit.

NL 0413853 MiU

Littleton, Sir Thomas, 1402-1481.
Les tenures, ouesque certaine cases addes per auters de puisne temps.
‹n.p.› 1591.
12°.

STC No. 15750.

NL 0413854 CSmH

FILM

Littleton, Sir Thomas, 1402-1481.
Les tenures de monsieur Littleton ouesque certaine cases addes per auters de puisne temps ... ‹London, R. Tottell› 1591.
Edited by William West.
University microfilms no.12353 (case 40, carton 240)
Short-title catalogue no.15750.

1. Land tenure—Gt.Brit. 2. Real property—Gt.Brit. I. West, William, fl.1568-1594, ed.

NL 0413855 MiU

Littleton, *Sir* Thomas, 1402–1481.
Les ‖ Tenures de Monsieur ‖ Littleton, Ouesque certaine Cases addes per Auters de ‖ puisne temps: Queux Cases vous troue- ‖ res signes ouesque cest Signe ✲ al ‖ commencement & fine de ‖ chescun de eux. ‖ Au fine que ne poies eux mispren- ‖ der pur les Cases de Mounsieur ‖ Littleton, pur quel incon- ‖ uenience, ils fueront dernier- ‖ ment tolles de cest Lieur: Et cy ‖ vn foites plus admotes al re- ‖ quest des Gentlehomes Students ‖ en le Ley Dengleterre. ‖ Reuieu & change en lordre des ‖ sections, oue vn nouel Index ou ‖ Table pursuant lordre des dits ‖ sections. ‖ Londini ‖ In ædibus Caroli Yetsvverti ‖ Armigeri. 1594. ‖ Cvm Privilegio. ‖

1 p. l., 170 numb. l., ‹54› p. 11cm.

Signatures: A–Q¹², R⁴.
The sections of each chapter are numbered separately.

1. Land tenure—Gt. Brit. 2. Real property—Gt. Brit.

19-8715

NL 0413857 DLC CtY

FILM

Littleton, Sir Thomas, d.1481.
Les tenures de monsieur Littleton, ouesque certaine cases addes per auters de puisne temps ... Reuieu & change ... Londini in aedibus Caroli Yetsvverti ... 1594 ...
University microfilms no.16361 (case 74, carton 444)
Short-title catalogue no.15751.

1. Land tenure—Gt.Brit. 2. Real property—Gt.Brit.

NL 0413858 MiU

STC 15752

Littleton, Sir Thomas, 1402-1481.
Les tenures de Monsieur Littleton, ouesque certaine cases addes per auters de puisne temps ... Reuieu & corrige en diuers lieux ... Londini, In aedibus Ianae Yetsweirt relictae Caroli Yetsweirt AF nuper defuncti. ‹1595?›

A-Q¹². 12mo.
Dated ‹1597› in Beale, Bibl. of early English law books, p. 115, no. T37 and p. 300.
John Wrenford-Harmsworth copy.

NL 0413859 DFo MH

FILM

Littleton, Sir Thomas, 1402-1481.
Les tenures de monsieur Littleton, ouesque certaine cases addes per auters de puisne temps ... Reuieu & corrige ... Londini in aedibus Ianae Yetsvveirt relictae Caroli Yetsvveirt ... ‹1595?›

University microfilms no.15915 (case 56, carton 335)
Short-title catalogue no.15752.

1. Land tenure—Gt.Brit. 2. Real property—Gt.Brit.

NL 0413860 MiU

Littleton, *Sir* Thomas, *d.* 1481.
Les tenvres de monsievr Littleton, ouesque certaine cases addes per auters de puisne temps: queux cases vous troueres signes ouesque cest signe § al commencement & fine de chescun de eux, au fine que ne poies eux misprender pur les cases de mounsieur Littleton, pur quel inconuenience, ils fueront dernierment tolles de cest lieur: et cy vn foits plus admotes al request des gentle-homes students en le ley dengleterre. Reuieu & cor. en diuers lieux queux vous troueres signes ouesque ceux signes. * * Londini, in ædibus Thomæ Wight, & Bonhami Norton, 1599.

1 p. l., 170 numb. l., ‹41› p. 10½ x 6cm.

Signatures: A–Q¹².
The sections of each chapter are numbered separately.

1. Land tenure—Gt. Brit.—Law. 2. Real property—Gt. Brit.

42-42497

NL 0413862 DLC N ICN

FILM

Littleton, Sir Thomas, d.1481.
Les tenvres de monsievr Littleton, ouesque certaine cases addes per auters de puisne temps ... Reuieu & corrige ... Londini in aedibus Thomae Wight & Bonhami Norton ... 1599.
University microfilms no.16362 (case 74, carton 444)
Short-title catalogue no.15753.

1. Land tenure—Gt.Brit. 2. Real property—Gt.Brit.

NL 0413863 MiU

Littleton, Sir Thomas, d. 1481.
Les tenures de monsieur Littleton: ouesque certeine cases addes p auters de puisne temps, queux cases vous troueres signes ouesque cest signe ✲ al commencement, & al fine de chescun de eux: au fine que ne poies eux misprender pur les cases de mounsieur Littleton; pur ql inconuenience, ils fueront dernierm̃t tolles de cest liuer; et cy vn foits pluis admotes al request des gentlehomes, students en le ley dengleterre. Londini, In aedibus Tho. Wight. Cum priuilegio. 1604.
1 p. l., 171 (i. e. 170) numb. l., 1 l. 15cm.

NL 0413864 NNC CLL

VOLUME 336

*EC65 Ev226 Zz604l

Littleton, Sir Thomas, 1402-1481.
Les tenures de monsieur Littleton: ouesque certeine cases addes p auters de puisne temps ...
Londini, in aedibus Tho. Wight. Cum priuilegio. 1604.
1p.ℓ., 171(i.e.170) numb.ℓ., [48]p. 14.5cm., in case 15.5cm.
STC 15754.
Leaves 116, 140 misnumbered 119, 132; 104 omitted in numbering.

This copy contains the autograph & numerous ms. annotations of John Evelyn, the diarist; it also contains the autograph of Richard Evelyn, his father.

NL 0413866 MH MiU

---

le L734 Eh604t Rare Books Col

Littleton, Sir Thomas, d. 1481.
Les tenures de monsieur Littleton: ouesque certeine cases addes p auters de puisne temps: queux cases vous troueres signes ouesque cest signe ★ al commencement & al fine de chescun de eux: au fine que ne poies eux misprender pur les cases de mopnsieur Littleton; pur ql inconuenience, ils fueront derniermnt tolles de cest lieur: et cy vn foits plus admotes al request des gentle-homes, students en ley dengleterre.
Londini, In aedibus Tho. Wight. Cum Priuilegio. 1604. 1p.ℓ., 171 [i.e. 170] numb.ℓ., [49]p. 20cm.

Signatures: A-X^8, Y^4, A-C^8.
In numbering of leaves 104 was omitted and 116 incorrectly numbered 119.
The sections of each chapter are numbered separately.

1. Land tenure - Gt. Brit. 2. Real property - Gt. Brit.

NL 0413868 TxU DLC NNC DFo

FILM

Littleton, Sir Thomas, d. 1481.
Les tenures de Monsieur Littleton: ouesque certeine cases addes p auters de puisne temps ... Londini, In aedibus Tho. Wight ... 1604.
University microfilms no.17446 (carton 558)
Short-title catalogue no.15754a; i.e. Bishop Checklist no.15754.1;

1. Land tenure—Gt. Brit. 2. Real property—Gt. Brit.

NL 0413869 MiU

Littleton, *Sir* Thomas, 1402-1481.
Les Tenures de Monsieur Littleton: Ouesque certeine Cases addes per auters de puisne temps, queux Cases vous troueres signes ouesque cest Signe ⁜ al commencement, & al fine de chescun de eux: au fine que ne poies eux misprender pur les cases de Mounsieur Littleton; Pur quel inconuenience, ils fueront derniermemt tolles de cest Lieur; Et cy vn foits pluis admotes al request des Gentlehomes, Students en le ley Dengleterre. London, Imprinted for the Companie of Stationers. cum priuilegio. 1608.
1 p. l., 170 numb. l., [48] p., 1 l. 14½cm.
Edited by William West, of the Inner Temple. *cf.* last leaf.
1. Land tenure—Gt. Brit. 2. Real property—Gt. Brit. West, William, fl. 1568-1594, ed.
19-11851

NL 0413870 DLC GU-L CSmH

FILM

Littleton, Sir Thomas, d. 1481.
Les tenures: ouesque certeine cases addes per auters de puisne temps, queux cases vous troueres signes ouesque cest signe ★ al commencement, & al fine de chescun de eux: au fine que ne poies eux misprender pur les cases de Mounsieur Littleton; pur quel inconvenience, ils fueront derniermemt tolles de cest lieur; et cy vn foits pluis admotes al request de gentlehomes, students en le ley dEngleterre. London, Imprinted for the Companie of Stationers, 1608.

Edited by William West.
Short-title catalogue no.15755 (carton 808)

1. Land tenure--Gt. Brit. 2. Real property--Gt. Brit. I. West, William, fl. 1568-1594, ed.

NL 0413872 MiU

STC 15755

Littleton, Sir Thomas, 1402-1481.
Les tenures de Monsieur Littleton: ouesque certeine cases addes per auters de puisne temps ... London, Imprinted for the Companie of Stationers, 1608.
A-Q^{12}, R^6. (R9-11 lacking.) 12mo.
Edited by William West, with index.
Harmsworth copy.

NL 0413873 DFo

Littleton, Sir Thomas, d. 1481.
Les Tenures de Monsieur Littleton: Ouesque certaine Cases addes per auters de puisne temps, queux Cases vous troueres signes ouesque cest Signe al commencement, & al fine de chescun de eux: au fine que ne poies eux misprender pur les cases de Monsieur Littleton; Pur quel enconuenience, ils fueront derniermemt tolles de cest Lieur; Et cy vn foits pluis admotes al request des Gentlehomes, Students en le ley Dengleterre. London, Imprinted for the Companie of Stationers, 1612.
[1], 168 numb. ℓ. 12 cm.
1. Land tenure. Gt. Brit. 2. Real property. Brit. Lw. 1. Land tenures. Gt. Gt. Brit.

NL 0413874 N-L

Littleton, *Sir* Thomas, 1402-1481.
Les Tenures de Monsieur Littleton: Ouesque certaine Cases addes per auters de puisne temps, queux Cases vous troueres signes ouesque cest Signe ⁜ al commencement, & al fine de chescun de eux: au fine que ne poies eux misprender pur les cases de Monsieur Littleton; Pur quel enconuenience, ils fueront derniermemt tolles de cest Lieur; Et cy vn foits pluis admotes al request des Gentlehomes, Students en le ley Dengleterre. London, Imprinted for the Companie of Stationers, Cum priuilegio. 1612.
1 p. l., 170 numb. l., [48] p., 1 l. 14cm.
Signatures: A-Q^{12}, R^4.

Interleaved; manuscript notes; sections numbered consecutively through the text.
Edited by W. West.
1. Land tenure—Gt. Brit. 2. Real property—Gt. Brit. I. West, William, fl. 1568-1594, ed.
Library of Congress
—— —— [Another issue] Large paper. 22½cm.
Title-page wanting.
Signatures A^{2*}, B-Z^8, Aa^8, Bb^4.
Full page portrait of Littleton precedes folio 1; the same portrait in a smaller size is mounted on recto of fly-leaf preceding full sized potrait. An abridgment of Doctor & Student in manuscript at end of volume ([16] p.) and fourteen lines on p. [17]; at head of p. [17] is written Perkins. Sect.
—— —— [Another issue] Large paper. 23cm.
Signatures A-Z^8, Aa^8, Bb^4.
Interleaved.
19-8718

NL 0413876 DLC CLL NN GU-L

Littleton, *Sir* Thomas, 1402-1481.
Les Tenures de Monsieur Littleton: Ouesque certaine Cases addes per auters de puisne temps, queux Cases vous troueres signes ouesque cest Signe ⁜ al commencement, & al fine de chescun de eux: au fine que ne poies eux misprender pur les cases de Monsieur Littleton; Pur quel enconuenience, ils fueront derniermemt tolles de cest Lieur; Et cy vn foits pluis admotes al request des Gentlehomes, Students en la ley Dengleterre. London. Imprinted for the Companie of Stationers. Cum priuilegio. 1617.
1 p. l., 170 numb. l., [48] p., 1 l. 14½cm.

Signatures: A-Q^{12}, R^4.
The sections are numbered consecutively through the text.
Edited by W. West.

1. Land tenure—Gt. Brit. 2. Real property—Gt. Brit. I. West, William, fl. 1568-1594, ed.
19-8719
Library of Congress

NL 0413878 DLC NjP DFo NIC PU-L NjP

FILM

Littleton, Sir Thomas, d. 1481.
Les tenures: ouesque certaine cases addes per auters de puisne temps, queux cases voux troueres signes ouesque cest signe ★ al commencement, & al fine de chescun de eux: au fine que ne poies eux misprender pur les cases de Monsieur Littleton; pur quel encouuenience, ils fueront derniermemt tolles de cest lieur; et cy vn foits pluis admotes al request des gentlehomes, students en la ley dEngleterre. London, Imprinted for the Companie of Stationers, 1617.

Edited by William West.
Short-title catalogue no.15757 (carton 808)
Microfilm.

1. Land tenure--Gt. Brit. 2. Real property--Gt. Brit. I. West, William, fl. 1568-1594, ed.

NL 0413880 MiU

WILLIAM ANDREWS CLARK MEMORIAL LIBRARY

Littleton, Sir Thomas, d. 1481.
Les Tenures de Monsieur Littleton: Ouesque certaine Cases addes per auters de puisne temps, queux Cases vous troueres signes ouesque cest Signe * al commencement, & al fine de chescun de eux: au fine que ne poies eux misprender pur les cases de Monsieur Littleton; Pur quel enconuenience, ils fueront derniermemt tolles de cest Lieur; Et cy vn foits pluis admotes al request des Gentlehomes, Students en la ley Dengleterre. London. Imprinted for the Companie of Stationers. Cum priuilegio, 1617.

[1], 170, [25] l. 22x16½cm.
Edited by W. West.
Signatures: A-Z^8, Aa^8, Bb^4.
Leaves 87, 111 incorrectly numbered 78, 112, respectively.
The sections are numbered consecutively through the text.
Large paper copy.
Copious manuscript notes in a contemporary hand in the margins of th first three leaves.
Bound in old ca

NL 0413882 CLU-C CtY

Littleton, *Sir* Thomas, 1402-1481.
Les Tenures de Monsieur Littleton: Ouesque certain Cases addes per auters de puisne temps q̃ux cases vo9 troueres signes ouesq; cest signe ⁜ al commenceṁt, & al fine de chescun de eux: au fine que ne poies eux misprender pur les cases de Monsieur Littleton; Pur quel enconuenience, ils fueront derniermeṁt tolles de cest Lieur. Et cy vn foits pluis admonetes al request des Gentlehomes, Students en la ley Dengleterre. London, Imprinted for the Companie of Stationers. Cum priuilegio. 1621.
1 p. l., 170 numb. l., [39] p. 11cm.

Continued in next column

VOLUME 336

Continued from preceding column

Signatures: A–Z⁸, Aa⁷.
The sections are numbered consecutively through the text.
Title-page somewhat mutilated.

1. Land tenure—Gt. Brit. 2. Real property—Gt. Brit.

Library of Congress 19-8720

NL 0413884 DLC CLL

Littleton, *Sir* **Thomas,** 1402–1481.

Les Tenures de Monsieur Littleton: Ouesque certaine Cases addes per auters de puisne temps, queux cases vous troueres signes ouesq; cest signe ✛ al commencem̃t, & al fine de chescun de eux: au fine que ne poies eux misprender pur les cases de Monsieur Littleton; Pur quel enconuenience, ils fueront dernierm̃t tolles de cest Lieur; Et cy vn foits pluis admonetes al request des Gentle homes, Students en le ley Dengleterre. London, Printed by the Assignes of John More Esquire. Cum priuilegio. 1639.

1 p. l., 170 (*i. e.* 169) numb. l., [39] p. 10½cm.

Signatures: A⁷, B–Z⁸, Aa⁷.
Title-page slightly mutilated.
Leaf 7 (sig. A⁵) wanting.
The sections are numbered consecutively through the text.

1. Land tenure—Gt. Brit. 2. Real property—Gt. Brit.

19-8723

NL 0413886 DLC CtY CLL

FILM

Littleton, Sir Thomas, d.1481.

Les tenures: ouesque certaine cases addes per auters de puisne temps, queux cases vous troueres signes ouesq; cest signe ✚ al commencemt, & al fine de chescun de eux; au fine que ne poies eux misprender pur les cases de Monsieur Littleton; pur quel enconuenience, ils fueront dernierm̃t tolles de cest lieur; et cy vn foits pluis admonetes al request des gentle homes, students en la ley dEngleterre. London, Printed by the assignes of J.More, 1639. Microfilm

Short-title catalogue no.15759 (carton 809)

1.Land tenure--Gt.Brit. 2.Real property--Gt.Brit.

NL 0413887 MiU

Littleton, *Sir* **Thomas,** 1402–1481.

Littleton's Tenures, In French and English. With an alphabetical table of the principal matters therein contained. London, Printed by John Streater, James Flesher, and Henry Twyford, Assigns of Richard Atkins, and Edward Atkins, Esquires, 1671.

11 p. l., 436 (*i. e.* 426), [2] p. 13½cm.

Signatures: a–b⁸, A–Z⁸, Aa–Mm⁸, Nn⁴.
First leaf blank; second leaf unsigned (title)
Irregularities in paging.
French and English in parallel columns

1. Land tenure—Gt. Brit. 2. Real property—Gt. Brit.

19-8725

NL 0413888 DLC WaU DGU N CSt-Law IaU NcU CtY PPL CLL

LITTLETON, Sir Thomas, d.1581.

Tenures in Englysshe. (1) cc[205] (1) fol. Device No.1. [col.London,Petyt],n.d. 24mo. Petyt 1536-1554.

[Same]. Tenures truely translated into englysshe. (1) 162[161] (1) fol. Device No.5. [Berthelet],1545. 24mo.

Another issue variations as follows:-fol.41 reverse,line 15: alsoo and Also,if and yf,vyllayne and villayne,be and bee,etc.,etc. Dunn 130.

Continued in next column

Continued from preceding column

[Same]. Tenures truely translated into englyshe. clxxx (2) fol. Devices No.102(N) and 106(M). [col.Lodon,Powell],1548. 24mo. Dunn 132.

[Same]. Tenures truely translated into Englyshe. clxxx (2) fol. Device No.106(M). [Col.Lodon,Powell],1551. 24mo. Imperfect. One leaf lacking.

[Same]. Tenures truelye translated into Englishe. clxxx (2) fol. [col.Londo,Marshe], 1556. 24mo.

Same. 145 (1) fol. [col.London,Tottle,1556. 24mo.

Same. 142 (2) fol. [col.London,Tottell, 1556]. 24mo.

Same. 142 (2) fol. [col. London,Tottill, 1568]. 24mo.

Same. 142 (2) fol. [col.London,Tottel,1581] 24mo. Dunn 138.

Same. 142 (2) fol. [col.London,Tottill, 1586]. 24mo.

"In English" in Roman. Last page in manuscript.

Same. 142 (2) fol. [col.London,Tottill, 1586]. 24mo.

"In English" in Italics. Three last leaves pasted in at H.L.L. Found loose in book. Dunn 141.

Same. Amended. 142 (2) fol. London, Charles Yetsweirt,1594. 24mo.

Same. Amended. 142 (2) fol. London,Iane Yetsweirt,1597. 24m

NL 0413892 MH

FILM Littleton,Sir Thomas,1402-1481.

Lytelton tenures in Englysshe. [London, R. Redman, n.d.]

University microfilms no.17718 (carton 673)

Short-title catalogue no.15760a[i.e.Bishop Checklist no.15760.1]

1.Land tenure--Gt.Brit. 2.Real property--Gt.Brit.

NL 0413893 MiU

FILM

Littleton,Sir Thomas,1402-1481.

Lyttelton tenures in Englysshe. [London, J.Rastell, 1525?]

Film reproduction,position 3.
Edwards brothers no.493 (case 2,carton 12)
Short-title catalogue no.15760.

1.Land tenure--Gt.Brit. 2. Real property--Gt.Brit.

NL 0413894 MiU

Case 3A 621

LITTLETON, Sir THOMAS, 1402-1481.

Lytelton Tenures in Englysshe. [London, R.Redman, 153-]

[1],CCiiii,[1]l. 16cm.

Signatures: A-X⁸,Aa-Ff⁸,Ee⁶.

Colophon: Imprynted at London in Fletestrete, by me Robert Redman dwellynge at the sygne of the George nexte to Saynt Dunstones Church cum priuilegio.

Many errors in foliation.

Ownership signature on t.-p. with date 1656; 4 leaves with contemporary ms. bound in as flyleaves.

In contemporary binding (rebacked in modern times)

Bookplate of Louis H. Silver.

Not in STC.

NL 0413896 ICN

Law Case

Littleton, Sir Thomas, 1402-1481. Lytylton tenures.

Natura breuium. ‖ The olde tenures. ‖ Lyttylton tenures. ‖ The new talys. ‖ The articles vppon ‖ the new talys. ‖ Diuersyte of courtes. ‖ Justyce of peace. ‖ The chartuary. ‖ Court baron. ‖ Court of hundrede. ‖ Returna breuium. ‖ The ordynaunce for ‖ takynge of fees in ‖ the escheker. ‖ And fyrste a table to ‖ all these .xii. bokes. ‖ Cum priuilegio. ‖ [*Colophon:* ... Prentyd ‖ by W. Rastell ‖ in Fletestreete in ‖ saynt Brydys chyrche ‖ yarde, the yere of ‖ oure lorde ‖ 1534 ‖ ⁖ ‖]

STC 15760.2

Littleton, Sir Thomas, 1402-1481.

Lytelton tenures in Englysshe. [ca. 1537]

Colophon: Imprynted at London by me Robert Redman.

A-X⁸, 2A-2E⁸. (2E7, probably blank, lacking.)

8vo.

Harmsworth copy.

NL 0413898 DFo

FILM

Littleton,Sir Thomas,1402-1481.

Lyttilton Tenvres truely translated into Englysshe. Londini, in aedibus Tho.Berthelet, an.M.D.XXXVIII.

Film reproduction,position 3.
Edwards brothers no.494 (case 2,carton 12)
Short-title catalogue no.15761.

1.Land tenure--Gt.Brit. 2.Real property--Gt.Brit.

NL 0413899 MiU PPT

Littleton, *Sir* **Thomas,** 1402–1481.

❧ Lyttelton ‖ tenures in En ‖ glysshe. ‖ [*Royal arms*] ‖ [*Colophon:* ℂ Prynted at london in ‖ paules churche yearde at ‖ the sygne of the may- ‖ dens heed, by Tho- ‖ mas Petyt. ‖ [n. d., 1544?]]

1 p. l., cc (*i. e.* 204) numb. l., [2] p. 14cm.

Signatures: A–X⁸, AA–DD⁸, EE⁴.
Folio cciiii numbered cc.

1. Land tenure—Gt. Brit. 2. Real property—Gt. Brit.

19-8700

NL 0413900 DLC NIC N NNC PPT

FILM

Littleton,Sir Thomas,1402-1481.

Lyttelton tenures in Englysshe. [London, T.Petyt, 1544?]

Film reproduction,position 3.
Edwards brothers no.495 (case 2,carton 12)
Short-title catalogue no.15762.

1.Land tenure--Gt.Brit. 2.Real property--Gt.Brit.

NL 0413901 MiU

Littleton, *Sir* **Thomas,** 1402–1481.

❧ : Lyttelton ‖ tenures in ‖ Englysshe ‖ ❧ * ❧ ‖ [*Royal arms*] ‖ [*Colophon:* ℂ : Imprynted ‖ at London in Fletstrete ‖ at the sygne of the George ‖ next to saynt Dũstones church ‖ by Wyllyam Myddylton. ‖ In the yere of our Lorde ‖ 1544. The fourth ‖ day of May. ‖ ☞ * ☜ ‖]

1 p. l., clxii numb. l., [2] p. 15cm.
Signatures: A–W⁸, X⁴.
Number lxxxv duplicated and clxi omitted in foliation.
A very few manuscript notes; initials; printer's ornaments on lower half of t.-p.
1. Land tenure—Gt. Brit. 2. Real property—Gt. Brit.

20-10455

NL 0413902 DLC DFo MnU-L

VOLUME 336

FILM
Littleton, Sir Thomas, 1402-1481.
Lyttilton tenvres truely translated in to englysshe. [London] An.M.D.XL.V.
Film reproduction, position 2.
Title within woodcut border, dated 1534, used by Thomas Berthelet. cf. Beale, A bibliography of early English law books.
University microfilms no.2500 (case 21, carton 126)
Short-title catalogue no.15735.

1. Land tenure--Gt.Brit. 2. Real property--Gt.Brit.

NL 0413903 MiU

FILM
Littleton, Sir Thomas, 1402-1481.
Lyttilton Tenvres truely translated in to englyshe. [London, W.Powell] an.M.D.XLVIII.
Film reproduction, position 3.
Edwards brothers no.496 (case 2, carton 12)
Short-title catalogue no.15765.

1. Land tenure--Gt.Brit. 2. Real property--Gt.Brit.

NL 0413904 MiU

Littleton, *Sir* Thomas, 1402-1481.
Lyt- ‖ tilton Te- ‖ nvres. ‖ truly translated into ‖ Englishe. ‖ (?) ‖ Anno domini. ‖ M.D.L.VI. ‖
180 numb. l., [2] p. 14cm.
Signatures: A-Y⁸, Z⁴.
Title within ornamental border.

1. Land tenure—Gt. Brit. 2. Real property—Gt. Brit.
19-8704

NL 0413905 DLC N CLL MnU

FILM
Littleton, Sir Thomas, d.1481.
Lyttilton Tenvres. Trulye translated into Englishe. [London] ... M.D.L.VI.
Colophon: Jmprinted at Londō ... by Thomas Marshe ... M.D.LVI.
University microfilms no.16364 (case 74, carton 444)
Short-title catalogue no.15768.

1. Land tenure--Gt.Brit. 2. Real property--Gt.Brit.

NL 0413906 MiU

Littleton, *Sir* Thomas, *d.* 1481.
Littleton Tenvres in Englishe. Cum priuilegio ad imprimendum solum. [*Colophon:* Imprinted at London in Flete strete within Temple Barre at the sygne of the Hande and starre by Richard Tottell the .xvi. daye of Aprill. Anno. Do. 1556]
142 numb. l., [3] p. 14½cm.
Signatures: A-S⁸.
Imperfect: lower part of leaf 137 mutilated.
Gothic type.
1. Land tenure—Gt. Brit.—Law. 2. Real property—Gt. Brit.
41-39193

NL 0413907 DLC CtY-L CSmH

FILM
Littleton, Sir Thomas, 1402-1481.
Littleton tenvres in Englishe ... [London, 1556]
Colophon: Jmprinted at London ... by Richard Tottell ... 1556.
University microfilms no.15916 (case 56, carton 335)
Short-title catalogue no.15767.

1. Land tenure--Gt.Brit. 2. Real property--Gt.Brit.

NL 0413908 MiU

FILM
Littleton, Sir Thomas, d.1481.
Littleton Tenvres in Englishe ... [London?, 1560?]
University microfilms no.16365 (case 74, carton 444)
Short-title catalogue no.15769.

1. Land tenure--Gt.Brit. 2. Real property--Gt.Brit.

NL 0413909 MiU

Littleton, *Sir* Thomas, *d.* 1481.
Littleton Tenvres in Englishe. Cum priuilegio. [*Colophon:* Imprinted at London in Fletestrete within Temple Barre, at the Signe of the Hand and starre, by Rychard Tottill, 1568]
142 numb. l., 1 l. 15cm.
Signatures: A-S⁸ (S₈, probably blank, wanting)
Gothic type.
L. C. copy imperfect: leaf 9 wanting.

1. Land tenure—Gt. Brit.—Law. 2. Real property—Gt. Brit.
47-36465

NL 0413910 DLC

Littleton, *Sir* Thomas, 1402-1481.
¶Little- ‖ ton Tenvres ‖ in Englishe. ‖ ¶Cum priuilegio. ‖ [*Colophon:* Imprinted at London ‖ in Fletestrete within Temple ‖ Barre at the signe of the hand ‖ and Starre by Ry- ‖ chard Tottyl. ‖ 1574. ‖ Cum priuilegio.] ‖
142 numb. l., [3] p. 14cm.
Signatures: A-S⁸.
Manuscript notes.

1. Land tenure—Gt. Brit. 2. Real property—Gt. Brit.
19-8707

NL 0413911 DLC CSt-Law PU-L

STC 15770
Littleton, Sir Thomas, 1402-1481.
Littleton tenures in Englishe ...
Colophon: Imprinted at London by Rychard Tottyl, 1574.

A-S⁸. 8vo.
Beale, Bibl. of early English law books, p. 117, no. T53.

NL 0413912 DFo

FILM
Littleton, Sir Thomas, 1402-1481.
Littleton tenvres in Englishe ... [London, 1574]
Colophon: Imprinted at London ... by Rychard Tottyl. 1574 ...
University microfilms no.15917 (case 56, carton 335)
Short-title catalogue no.15770.

1. Land tenure--Gt.Brit. 2. Real property--Gt.Brit.

NL 0413913 MiU

Littleton, *Sir* Thomas, 1402-1481.
¶Little- ‖ ton Tenvres ‖ in Englishe. ‖ ¶Cum priuilegio. ‖ [*Colophon:* Imprinted at London ‖ in Fleetstreete within Temple ‖ Barre at the signe of the Hand ‖ and Starre by Ry- ‖ chard Tottyl. ‖ 1576. ‖ ¶Cum priuilegio.] ‖
3, 6-120, 129-142 numb. l., [3] p. 15cm.
Signatures: A⁴, A*⁴, B-P, R-S⁸.
Folios 4-5 (sig. A*⁴) and 121-128 (sig. Q⁸) wanting.
Manuscript notes.

1. Land tenure—Gt. Brit. 2. Real property—Gt. Brit.
19-8708

NL 0413914 DLC N MH

LITTLETON, Sir Thomas, 1402-1481.
Tenures in English. Quesq certen cases addes. [London, Tottyl], 1577.

32mo. (1) 170+(1) fol.

NL 0413915 MH-L

Littleton, *Sir* Thomas, 1402-1481.
¶Little ‖ tons Tenvres ‖ in English. ‖ Cum priuilegio. ‖ [*Colophon:* Imprnted [!] at Lon- ‖ don in Fleestrete [!] within ‖ Temple Barre, at the signe of ‖ the Hand and Starre, by ‖ Rychard Tottill. ‖ 1583. ‖ Cum priuilegio.] ‖
142 numb. l., [3] p. 14cm.
Signatures: A-S⁸.
Manuscript notes.

1. Land tenure—Gt. Brit. 2. Real property—Gt. Brit.
19-8710

NL 0413916 DLC CLL PU-L CSmH

FILM
Littleton, Sir Thomas, 1402-1481.
Littletons tenvres in English ... [London, 1583]
Colophon: Imprnted [!] at London ... by Rychard Tottill, 1583 ...
University microfilms no.16367 (case 80, carton 475)
Short-title catalogue no.15772.

1. Land tenure--Gt.Brit. 2. Real property--Gt.Brit.

NL 0413917 MiU

Littleton, *Sir* Thomas, 1402-1481.
¶Little- ‖ tons Tenvres ‖ in English. ‖ Cum priuilegio. ‖ [*Colophon:* Imprinted at London ‖ in Fletestrete within Temple ‖ Barre, at the signe of the Hand ‖ and Starre by Ryvharde ‖ Tottill. ‖ 1586. ‖ Cum Priuilegio.] ‖
142 numb. l., [3] p. front. (port.) 13½cm.
Signatures: A-S⁸.

1. Land tenure—Gt. Brit. 2. Real property—Gt. Brit.
19-8711

NL 0413918 DLC N CLL DFo MnU MnU-L

FILM
Littleton, Sir Thomas, 1402-1481.
Littletons tenvres in English ... [London, 1586]
Colophon: Imprinted at London ... by Rycharde Tottill. 1586 ...
University microfilms no.15918 (case 56, carton 335)
Short-title catalogue no.15773.

1. Land tenure--Gt.Brit. 2. Real property--Gt.Brit.

NL 0413919 MiU

Littleton, *Sir* Thomas, 1402-1481.
Little- ‖ tons Tenvres ‖ in English. ‖ [*Conventional design*] ‖ Imprinted at London within Tem- ‖ ple Barre, at the Signe of the Hand ‖ and Starre, by Richard ‖ Tottell. ‖ 1592. ‖ ¶Cum Priuilegio. ‖ T. H. ‖ [*Colophon:* ¶Imprinted at London ‖ in Fleetestreete within Temple ‖ Barre, at the signe of the Hand ‖ and Starre by Richard ‖ Tottill. ‖ 1593. ‖ ¶Cum Priuilegio. ‖ T. H.] ‖
142 numb. l., [3] p. 15½cm.
Signatures: A-S⁸.
1. Land tenure—Gt. Brit. 2. Real property—Gt. Brit.
19-8714

NL 0413920 DLC N CtY MnU-L

VOLUME 336

FILM

Littleton, Sir Thomas, 1402-1481.
Littletons tenvres in English. Imprinted at London ... by Richard Tottell. 1592 i.e. 1593, ...
Colophon dated 1593.
University microfilms no.16368 (case 80, carton 475)
Short-title catalogue no.15774.

1. Land tenure--Gt.Brit. 2. Real property--Gt.Brit.

NL 0413921 MiU

Littleton, Sir Thomas, d. 1481.
Littletons tenvres in English. Lately perused and amended. London, Imprinted at London by Charles Yetsweirt, Temple Bar, 1594.
142 numb. ℓ. 15 cm.

1. Land tenure. Gt. Brit. Lw. I. Land tenures. Gt. Brit. 2. Real property. Gt. Brit.

NL 0413922 N MiU-L

STC 15775

Littleton, Sir Thomas, 1402-1481.
Littletons tenures in English. Lately perused and amended. Imprinted at London by Charles Yetsweirt Esq., 1594.
Colophon.

A-S⁸. (I4-5 and S7-8 lacking.) 8vo.
Some leaves frayed affecting text.
Beale, Bibl. of early English law books, pp. 117-118, no. T59.

NL 0413923 DFo

FILM

Littleton, Sir Thomas, 1402-1481.
Littletons tenvres in English. Lately perused and amended. Imprinted at London by Charles Yetsweirt ... 1594 ...
University microfilms no.16369 (case 80, carton 475)
Short-title catalogue no.15775.

1. Land tenure--Gt.Brit. 2. Real property--Gt.Brit.

NL 0413924 MiU

Littleton, [Sir] Thomas, 1402-1481.
Tenures in Englisne. London, Yetsweirt, 1597.

NL 0413925 CSmH

FILM

Littleton, Sir Thomas, 1402-1481.
Tenvres in English. Lately perused and amended. London, Imprinted by I.Yetsweirt, 1597.
Short-title catalogue no.15776 (carton 995)
Microfilm.

1. Land tenure--Gt.Brit. 2. Real property--Gt.Brit.

NL 0413926 MiU

Littleton, *Sir* Thomas, 1402-1481.
Little- ‖ tons Te- ‖ nures in English. ‖ Lately perused and ‖ amended. [*Conventional design*] ‖ ¶Imprinted at London by ‖ Thomas Wight. ‖ 1600. ‖ Cum Priuilegio Regiæ ‖ Maiestatis. ‖
142 numb. l., [3] p. 13½ᶜᵐ.
Signatures: A-S⁸.

1. Land tenure—Gt. Brit. 2. Real property—Gt. Brit.

19-8716

NL 0413927 DLC N DFo MnU-L

FILM

Littleton, Sir Thomas, 1402-1481.
Littletons tenures in English. Lately perused and amended. Imprinted at London by Thomas Wight. 1600 ...
University microfilms no.16371 (case 80, carton 475)
Short-title catalogue no.15777.

1. Land tenure--Gt.Brit. 2. Real property--Gt.Brit.

NL 0413928 MiU

Littleton, *Sir* Thomas, *d.* 1481.
Tenvres in English, lately perused and amended. London, Imprinted by T. Wight, 1604.
142 l. 15 cm.

1. Land tenure—Gt. Brit.—Law. 2. Real property—Gt. Brit.

52-47863

NL 0413929 DLC CLL PU-L NNC CSmH MH

STC 15778

Littleton, Sir Thomas, 1402-1481.
Littletons tenures in English. Lately perused and amended. Imprinted at London by Thomas Wight, 1604.

A-S⁸. 8vo.
Harmsworth copy.

NL 0413930 DFo

FILM

Littleton, Sir Thomas, d.1481.
Tenvres in English. Lately perused and amended. London, Imprinted by T.Wight, 1604.
Short-title catalogue no.15778 (carton 809)
Microfilm.

1. Land tenure--Gt.Brit. 2. Real property--Gt.Brit.

NL 0413931 MiU

Littleton, *Sir* Thomas, *d.* 1481.
Tenvres in English, lately perused and amended. London, Imprinted for the Companie of Stationers, 1608.
142 l. 15 cm.

1. Land tenure—Gt. Brit.—Law. 2. Real property—Gt. Brit.

51-46607

NL 0413932 DLC CtY

STC 15779

Littleton, Sir Thomas, 1402-1481.
Littletons tenures in English. Lately perused and amended. Imprinted at London for the Companie of Stationers, 1608.

A-S⁸. 8vo.

NL 0413933 DFo MiU-L

FILM

Littleton, Sir Thomas, d.1481.
Tenvres in English. Lately perused and amended. London, Imprinted for the Companie of Stationers, 1608.
Short-title catalogue no.15779 (carton 844)
Microfilm.

1. Land tenure--Gt.Brit.--Law. 2. Real property --Gt.Brit.

NL 0413934 MiU

Littleton, *Sir* Thomas, 1402-1481.
Littletons Tenvres In English, Lately perused and amended. London, Printed for the Companie of Stationers. 1612.
141 (*i. e.* 142) numb. l., [3] p. 13ᶜᵐ.
Signatures: A-S⁸.
Number 142 omitted and 141 duplicated in foliation.

1. Land tenure—Gt. Brit. 2. Real property—Gt. Brit.

19-8717

NL 0413935 DLC NBuU-L PU-L CtY MH CSmH

Littleton, *Sir* Thomas, *d.* 1481.
Littletons Tenvres in English, lately perused and amended. London, Printed for the Companie of stationers, 1616.
142 numb. l., [3] p. 14½ᶜᵐ.
Signatures: A-S⁸ (last verso blank)

1. Land tenure—Gt. Brit.—Law. 2. Real property—Gt. Brit.

32-21954

NL 0413936 DLC NjP CSmH

Littleton, *Sir* Thomas, 1402-1481.
Littletons Tenvres In English, Lately perused and amended. London, Printed for the Companie of Stationers. 1621.
142 numb. l., [3] p. 14½ᶜᵐ.
Signatures: A-S⁸.

1. Land tenure—Gt. Brit. 2. Real property—Gt. Brit.

19-8721

NL 0413937 DLC CtY PU-L

Littleton, *Sir* Thomas, 1402-1481.
Littletons Tenvres In English, Lately perused and amended. London, Printed for the Companie of Stationers. 1627.
142 numb. l., [3] p. 15ᶜᵐ.
Signatures: A-S⁸.

1. Land tenure—Gt. Brit. 2. Real property—Gt. Brit.

19-8722

NL 0413938 DLC DFo TxU CSt WU CLL N PU CtY

VOLUME 336

FILM
Littleton, Sir Thomas, 1402-1481.
Tenvres in English, lately perused and amended. London, Printed for the Companie of Stationers, 1627.
University Microfilms no.20591 (carton 770)
Short-title catalogue no.15783.

1. Land tenure--Gt.Brit. 2. Real property--Gt.Brit.

NL 0413939 MiU

Littleton, *Sir* Thomas, *d.* 1481.
Littletons Tenures in English, Lately perused and amended. London, Printed for the Company of Stationers, 1656.
1 p. l., 257, [3] p. 14½cm.
Signatures: A–Q⁸, R⁴ (last verso blank)

1. Land tenure—Gt. Brit. 2. Real property—Gt. Brit.

28-23595

NL 0413940 DLC N PU-L

Littleton, *Sir* Thomas, 1402–1481.
Littletons Tenures In English, Lately perused and amended. London, Printed for the Company of Stationers, 1661.
1 p. l., 257, [3] p. 14½cm.
Signatures: A–Q⁸, R⁴.
Imprint slightly mutilated.

1. Land tenure—Gt. Brit. 2. Real property—Gt. Brit.

19-8724

NL 0413941 DLC CLL

Littleton, *Sir* Thomas, 1402–1481.
Littleton's Tenures, in English. Printed from the 2d ed. of the Commentary of Sir Edward Coke. London, W. Clarke and sons, 1813.
xx, 319 p. tab. 18cm.

1. Land tenure—Gt. Brit. 2. Real property—Gt. Brit. I. Coke, Sir Edward, 1552–1634. The first part of the Institutes of the laws of England; or, A commentary upon Littleton.

19-8726

NL 0413942 DLC GU CU-AL NcD CtY MH PU-L

Littleton, *Sir* Thomas, 1402–1481.
Littleton's Tenures, in English ... London, H. Butterworth, 1825.
xviii, 290 p. tab. 20cm.

1. Land tenure—Gt. Brit. 2. Real property—Gt. Brit.

19-8727

NL 0413943 DLC CtY

Littleton, Sir Thomas, d. 1481.
Littleton's Tenures in English. A new ed., corr. London, J. & W. T. Clarke, 1825.
viii (i. e. xviii), 341 p. 15cm.

Interleaved.
Manuscript notes on some blank leaves and on margins.

NL 0413944 NNC PU-L MH NN

Littleton, Sir Thomas, 1402–1481. Tenures.

Cary, Henry, 1804–1870.
A commentary on the tenures of Littleton; written prior to the publication of Coke upon Littleton: edited from a copy in the Harleian collection of manuscripts, by Henry Cary ... London, Saunders and Benning, 1829.

Littleton, *Sir* Thomas, *d.* 1481.
Littleton's Tenures in English. A new ed., cor. London, J. & W. T. Clarke, 1831.
xiii, [1], 261, [1] p. 12½cm.

1. Land tenure—Gt. Brit.—Law. 2. Real property—Gt. Brit.

32-24321

NL 0413946 DLC GU-L CtY PU-L

Littleton, *Sir* Thomas, 1402–1481.
Littleton's Tenures in English. A new ed., cor. London, V. & R. Stevens and G. S. Norton, 1845.
xv, 323 p. tab. 14cm.

1. Land tenure—Gt. Brit. 2. Real property—Gt. Brit.

19-8728

NL 0413947 DLC CLL CtY

Littleton, *Sir* Thomas, *d.* 1481.
Littleton's Tenures; with notes explanatory of the text of Littleton, and showing the recent alterations in the law. By the editors of "The Law students' magazine." London, R. Hastings, 1846.
1 p. l., ii, 254, vi p. 21½cm.
Issued in monthly parts, from Sept. 15, 1845, to Feb. 21, 1846, as the Library division of the Law students' magazine.

1. Land tenure—Gt. Brit.—Law. 2. Real property—Gt. Brit.

6-19171

NL 0413948 DLC CtY PPB

Littleton, *Sir* Thomas, *d.* 1481.
Littleton's tenures in English; edited by Eugene Wambaugh ... Washington, D. C., J. Byrne & co., 1903.
3 p. l., 5-6, v-vii, xi-lxxxiv, 341 p. tab. 22½cm. (*Half-title: Legal classic series*)
Bibliography: p. lxvii-lxxxiv.

1. Land tenure—Gt. Brit.—Law. 2. Real property—Gt. Brit. I. Wambaugh, Eugene, 1856-1940, ed.

3—18321

Library of Congress

[a42g1]

NL 0413949 TU N NcD PU-L OU ViU-L CLL DLC NBuU-L PPHirL WaU-L CaBVaU PPB

Littleton, *Sir* Thomas, 1402–1481.
Lyttleton, his treatise of tenures, in French and English. A new ed., printed from the most ancient copies, and collated with the various readings of the Cambridge mss. To which are added the ancient treatise of the Olde tenures, and the Customs of Kent. By T. E. Tomlins ... London, S. Sweet, 1841.
2 p. l., [vii]-lv, 727 p. tab. 22cm.
Does not contain Olde tenures and Customs of Kent.
1. Land tenure—Gt. Brit. 2. Real property—Gt. Brit. I. Tomlins, Thomas Edlyne, 1804-1872, ed.

15-17358

NL 0413950 DLC NN CtY PPB PU-L MH

Littleton, Tommy, pseud.
Juvenile trials for robbing orchards, telling fibs, and other heinous offences. By Master Tommy Littleton, secretary to the court; with a sequel by Dr. Aikin... Boston: Printed for F. Nichols, 1797. 1 p.l., xvi, (1)18–118 p. 24°.
"Phaeton junior, or, The gig demolished," a poem by Dr. Aikin; p. 112-118.
Lenox copy.

DUYCKINCK COLLECTION.
1. Juvenile literature. 2. Aikin, John, 1747-1822.
N. Y. P. L. August 4, 1915.

NL 0413951 NN DLC-P4 MB

[**Littleton, Tommy,** pseud.]
Juvenile trials, for telling fibs, robbing orchards, and other offences. Recommended by the author of Evenings at home. London: Printed by Darton and Harvey, 1806. v, 7–108 p. col'd front., col'd illus. 12½cm.

SCHATZKI COLL. OF CHILDREN'S BOOKS.
646665A. 1. Children—Management and discipline. I. Title.
N. Y. P. L. October 9, 1933

NL 0413952 NN

J [Littleton, Tommy] pseud.
J97 Juvenile trials, for telling fibs,
1811 robbing orchards, and other offences. Recommended by the author of Evenings at home. London, Printed for Darton, 1811.
Educ. 83p. illus. T.

NL 0413953 IaU

Littleton, W ed.
British The prophecie of Thomas Becket, arch-bishop
Tracts of Canterbury in the reign of King Henry the
1666 Second; concerning the wars betwixt England,
L73 France, and Holland; lately found in an ancient manuscript at Abington, by Dr. Ailsworth; and by him sent as a rarity to the University of Oxford. With the interpretation and judgment of divers of the learned masters ... London, G. Freeman, 1666.
1p.ℓ., 6p. 18cm.
I. Thomas à Becket, Saint, Abp. of Canterbury, 1118-1170, supposed author.

NL 0413954 CtY MH

Littleton, William Graham, 1868-
The battle between the Alabama and the Kearsarge off Cherbourg, France, Sunday June 19, 1864. (Being an address delivered at the meeting of the Pennsylvania Commandery, Military Order of the Loyal Legion of the United States, held Oct.15, 1932. at the Union League of Philadelphia. Ph., 1932.

NL 0413955 PPL

Littleton, William Graham, 1868–
The battle between the Alabama and the Kearsarge, off Cherbourg, France, Sunday, June 19, 1864; being an address delivered at the meeting of the Pennsylvania commandery, Military order of the loyal legion of the United States, held October 5, 1932, at the Union league of Philadelphia ... By William G. Littleton ... [Philadelphia, ©1933]
1 p. l., 9 p. 23cm.
"Upon this occasion ... presentation of the portrait of Rear Admiral John A. Winslow, commander of the Kearsarge, was made to the representatives of the Council of state of the republic and canton of Geneva, Switzerland."

1. Alabama (Confederate cruiser) 2. Kearsarge (U. S. corvette) 3. U. S. Hist.—Civil war—Naval operations. I. Military order of the loyal legion of the United States. Pennsylvania commandery. II. Title.

Library of Congress E599.A3L5 33-17131
—— —— Copy 2.
Copyright AA 123964 [3] 973.754

NL 0413957 DLC PHi

VOLUME 336

LITTLETON, William Graham, 1868-
Constitutional Inquiry into the reason for Tax Free Bonds; being an address delivered before the Constitutional Club of Philadelphia Oct.30,1923. Philadelphia,n.d.
16 p.

NL 0413958 MH-L

Littleton, William Graham, 1868-
A Constitutional inquiry into the reason for tax free bonds... Phila., Fidelity Trust Co., 1923.
16 p.

NL 0413959 PPFRB

Littleton, William Graham, 1868–
The Cumberland, the Monitor and the Virginia (popularly called the Merrimac) being an address delivered at the meeting of the Pennsylvania commandery, Military order of the loyal legion of the United States, held May 10, 1933, at the Union league of Philadelphia. By William G. Littleton ... [Philadelphia, ©1933]
1 p. l., 19 p. 22½cm.
1. Hampton roads, Battle of, 1862. 2. Cumberland (Frigate) 3. Monitor (Ironclad) 4. Merrimac (Frigate) I. Military order of the loyal legion of the United States. Pennsylvania commandery.
33-17132
Library of Congress E473.2.L57
—— —— Copy 2.
Copyright AA 123965 [3] 973.752

NL 0413960 DLC PHi PPL

Littleton, William Graham, 1868-
An essay of eviction in Pennsylvania. Phila., n.d.
24 p.

NL 0413961 PU-L

Littleton, William Graham, 1868-
The general functions of a trust company doing business in Philadephia; being an address delivered before the Phila. chapter American institute of banking Feb. 7, 1921. Ph., 1921.

NL 0413962 PPL

Littleton, William Graham, 1868-
Shall the sovereignty of the states be destroyed in order that their bonds may be taxed; being an address delivered before the Pennsylvania Institute of certified accountants, Jan. 21, 1924. Ph., 1924.

NL 0413963 PPL

LITTLETON, William Graham, 1868-
United States Bonds should not be subject to State Taxation. Philadelphia, 1924.
fol.
The Manufacturer, vol.6, no.3, Mar.1924, p.3-7.

NL 0413964 MH-L

Littleton, William S.
Trumpeter's hand-book and instructor. By William S. Littleton ... Published by authority of the secretary of war, Adjutant-General's office, May 9, 1901. Kansas City, Mo., Hudson-Kimberly publishing co. [1902]
71 p. 12½cm.
1. Trumpet—Instruction and study. 2. U. S.—Army—Signaling.
2-15889
Library of Congress UH43.L78

NL 0413965 DLC ICRL ICJ

Littleton, William S.
... Trumpeter's hand-book and instructor. By William S. Littleton ... Published by authority of the secretary of war, Adjutant-General's office, May 9, 1901. [3d ed.] Kansas City, Mo., F. Hudson publishing co. [©1905]
3 p. l., 5-71 p. 12½cm.
1. Trumpet—Instruction and study. 2. Military calls and signals—U. S.
6-13223
Library of Congress UH43.L8

NL 0413966 DLC DNW

C352.0788
L734 Li
1894
Littleton, Colo. Ordinances, etc.
The general ordinances of the town of Littleton, printed and published by authority of the town of Littleton, rev. by M.J. Bartley. Littleton, Independent Print., 1894.
54p. 23cm.
"Errata" slip inserted.

NL 0413967 CoD

Littleton, *Me.*
Annual report of the selectmen, treasurer, and other officers of the town ...
[Houlton,
v. tables. 23cm.
Report year ends March 11.
CA 34-1574 Unrev'd
Library of Congress JS13.L784 352.07411

NL 0413968 DLC

Littleton, Me. Superintendent of schools.
Report. 1909/10
Houlton, Me., 1916)
1 v.

NL 0413969 DHEW

Littleton, *Mass.*
Records of Littleton, Massachusetts. Printed by order of the town. First installment. Births and deaths from the earliest records in the town books begun in 1715 ... Littleton, Mass. [Patriot press, Concord, Mass.] 1900.
4 p. l., [5]-542, 178 p. 23 cm.
Compiled by J. A. Harwood.
Index to places: 178 p. at end.
Genealogical notes of Samuel Smith from manuscript in the Reuben Hoar library: p. 398-534.
1. Registers of births, etc.—Littleton, Mass. 2. Epitaphs—Littleton, Mass. 3. Littleton, Mass.—Genealogy. I. Harwood, Joseph Alfred, b. 1827. II. Smith, Samuel.
F74.L77L7 A 10-1747 rev
Haverhill, Mass. Public Library for Library of Congress [r48c1]†

00 DLC
NL 0413970 MHa WaSp WaS CaBVa MB ViU PHi OClWHi

Littleton, Mass.
Records of Littleton, Massachusetts. First installment.
— Littleton, Mass. 1900, [1909]. 1 v. Tables. 22 cm.
Contents. — 1. Births and deaths, from the earliest records in the town books begun in 1715.
"Compiled by Joseph Alfred Harwood. This work completed 1909. Pages 49 to the end of this book were printed by Huntley S. Turner, Ayer, Mass."—*Vol. 1, page 2.*
No more appears to have been published.

E2715 — Harwood, Joseph Alfred, c. — Littleton, Mass. Biog. & geneal. — Genealogy. Littleton, Mass.

NL 0413971 MB NN

LITTLETON, *Mass.*
Report of the selectmen, highway surveyors . . . for 1867/68–74
Bost. 1868–75. v. 8°.

NL 0413972 MB

JS13
.L785
Littleton, Mass.
Reports of the town officers ... 1922-
Ayer, The news printing co., 1923-
1 v.

NL 0413973 DLC

Littleton, Mass. Assessors.
Assessors' report of the valuation and taxes of the town for the year 1870, 90, 1900.
Boston, 1870–1901. v. 8°.

NL 0413974 MB

Littleton, Mass. Hoar library.
see
Reuben Hoar library. Littleton, Mass.

Littleton, Mass. Lyceum.
Semi-centennial. Proceedings on the fiftieth anniversary of the organization of the Littleton Lyceum, Tuesday, Dec. 23, 1879, consisting of historical address by Miss H.P. Hodge of Littleton ... Boston, Mass., 1881.
36 p. 23 cm.

NL 0413976 RPB DLC OClWHi Nh

Littleton, Mass. Reuben Hoar library.
see
Reuben Hoar library, Littleton, Mass.

Littleton, Mass. School committee.
Report. 1853/54 54/55; 78/79 89/90 94/95 97/98 1903/04 04/05
Croton Junction, Boston, Mass., (etc.) 1854-1905.
10 v.

NL 0413978 DHEW

Jul
la
L734
Littleton, Mass. Zoning committee.
Proposed zoning by-law for the town of Littleton, Massachusetts; report of the Zoning committe [!], February 1, 1928. ...
[n.p., 1928?]

NL 0413979 CtY

VOLUME 336

Littleton(N.H.)
Annual municipal reports for the town and district for the year ending Feb.15,1860- Littlejohn,1859-1902.

NL 0413980 Nh

Littleton, *N. H.*
Chiswick, 1764. Apthorp, 1770. Littleton, 1784. Exercises at the centennial celebration of the incorporation of the town of Littleton, July 4th, 1884. Pub. by the town. Concord, N. H., N. H. Democratic press co., 1887.
328 p. incl. map. 23½cm.

1. Littleton, N. H.—Hist. 2. Littleton, N. H.—Centennial celebrations, etc. I. Title. II. Title: Exercises at the centennial celebration of the incorporation of ... Littleton ...

Library of Congress F44.L7L7 1-8025

MnHi
NL 0413981 DLC ICN NBuG MeB NIC ICN MH Nh NhDo

Littleton, N.H.
Report of agent to audit the accounts of J. J. Barrett Town treasurer
see under Felton, Nathan B.

Littleton(N.H.) Auditors.
Report of auditors appointed to investigate the accounts of liquor agents for the years 1856- n.p.1897.

NL 0413983 Nh

Little(N.H.).Fire department.
Annual report, 1892. Littleton,1892.

NL 0413984 Nh

Littleton(N.H.) First Congregational church.
Catalogue of the Sunday school library. Littleton,n.d.

NL 0413985 Nh

285.8742
L781F Littleton, N.H. First Congregational church.
Manual of the First Congregational church, Littleton, N.H. issued in 1896. ⌜Littleton, N.H., Printed by White Mountain Republic Journal, 1896⌝
74p. illus. 19cm.

NL 0413986 TxDaM ICN MH MB Nh

Littleton(N.H.).Graded School.
Catalogue for 1871- Conc.,1871-95.

NL 0413987 Nh

Littleton, N. H. High school.
A general catalogue of the pupils and graduates of the high school, Littleton, N. H., with lists of the officers and teachers since the establishment of the school. 1868–1891. Littleton, E. B. Wallace, printer, 1891.
2 p. l., ⌜7⌝-49 p. front., fold. tab. 21½cm.

Library of Congress LD7501.L68H3 7-12484†

NL 0413988 DLC Nh

Littleton(N.H.).High school.
Handbook for school year,1900-1. Littleton, 1900.

NL 0413989 Nh

Littleton(N.H.) Highway precinct, commissioners and auditor.
Report, 1892-3. Littleton, 1892-3.

NL 0413990 Nh

Littleton(N.H.).Public library.
Catalogue. Littleton, 1893.

NL 0413991 Nh

Littleton(N.H.).Selectmen.
Checklist of all the legal voters in the town. Littleton,n.d.

NL 0413992 Nh

Littleton(N.H.).Superintending school committee.
Annual report for the year ending March 1, 1875- Littleton, 1880-5.

NL 0413993 Nh

Littleton, N. H. Village library.
Founded Feb. 6, 1867. Merged into the Public library in 188–?

Littleton, N. H. Village library.
Catalogue of the Littleton village library. Concord, Printed by McFarland & Jenks, 1867.
16 p. 19½cm.
—— Supplement ... Concord, McFarland & Jenks, printers, 1871.
8 p. 19cm.

Library of Congress Z881.L741 8-24485-6†

NL 0413995 DLC

Littleton(N.H.).Union school district treasurer.
Annual report for the year ending January, 1887-93. Littleton, 1887-93.

NL 0413996 Nh

Littleton, N. H. Woman's Christian temperance union
see
Woman's Christian temperance union. Littleton, N. H.

Littleton, N.C. Methodist Episcopal Church, South.
Membership, showing assessments for 1915. ⌜Littleton, 1915?⌝
12 p. 17cm.

1. N.C.--Church history--Methodist Episcopal

NL 0413998 NcU

The Littleton ⌜N. H.⌝ directory, 1903; containing the general and business directory of the citizens ... Comp. ... by Edward E. Stockbridge & co. Manchester, N. H., E. E. Stockbridge & co., 1903.
v. 23½cm.

NL 0414001 DLC

Littleton historical society, *Littleton, Mass.*
Proceedings. no. 1-3; 1894/95-1908. Littleton, Mass., 1896-1908.
3 v. in 2. 24cm.
No more published.

1. Littleton, Mass.—Hist.—Societies.

Library of Congress F74.L77L87 44-31890

NL 0414002 DLC Nh NBuHi IU NN MB OClWHi

---

q978.811
L734s
Journ
Lib'y
LITTLETON INDEPENDENT.
60th anniversary edition 1888-1948. Littleton, Colorado, 1948.
[90]p. illus. 40cm.

Issued as a special number of the Littleton Independent, vol.61, no.3, section 2. Cover title.

1. Littleton, Colo.

NL 0414003 TxU

Oversize
F
784
L45L4
Littleton Independent.
The story of Littleton, Denver's best suburb, 1888-1938. Golden jubilee number. ⌜Littleton, Colo.⌝ 1938.
1 v. (unpaged) illus., ports. 40cm.

Cover title.
Vol. 51, no. 1, section 2, July 22, 1938.

1. Littleton, Colo. I. Title.

NL 0414004 CoU CoD

Littleton lyceum
see Littleton, Mass. Lyceum.

VOLUME 336

Littlewood, Dudley Ernest.
The skeleton key of mathematics; a simple account of complex algebraic theories. London, New York, Hutchinson's University Library, 1949.
138 p. 19 cm. (Hutchinson's university library: Mathematical and physical sciences, no. 18)

1. Algebra. I. Title.

QA155.L5 512 50—2475

MB LU ViU TxU OrSaW
NcU ICN MU OrCS OrPR CaBVaU OrU IdPI WaTC TU OCU
NL 0414006 DLC KEmT PU PSC NcRS NcD MiU MsSM MoU

Littlewood, Dudley Ernest.
The theory of group characters and matrix representations of groups, by Dudley E. Littlewood. Oxford, The Clarendon press, 1940.
viii, 292 p. incl. tables. 25ᶜᵐ.
Bibliography: p. [285]–290.

1. Groups, Theory of. 2. Matrices. I. Title: Group characters and matrix representations of groups.

Library of Congress QA171.L77 41-15984

OrSaW
ICJ PU-Math PHC NcD NcRS OCIW OrU CaBVaU OrCS MtU
NL [illegible] DLC NBuU CU MoU MH TU OU OCU NN OO CtY

Littlewood, Dudley Ernest.
The theory of group characters and matrix representations of groups. 2d ed. Oxford, Clarendon Press, 1950.
viii, 310 p. 24 cm.
Bibliography: p. [301]–307.

1. Groups, Theory of. 2. Matrices. I. Title: Group characters and matrix representations of groups.

QA171.L77 1950 512.86 50-10155

MsU NBuC NNC AAP TxU ViU
NL 0414008 DLC CaBVaU OrU OrCS OrPR MiU FMU LU FU

Littlewood, Dudley Ernest.
A university algebra. London, Heinemann [1950]
viii, 292 p. 22 cm.

1. Algebra.

A 52-5255

Rochester. Univ. Libr. for Library of Congress QA154.L5 [1]

NL 0414009 NRU MtBC OrU OrPR OrCS TNJ IU TxU NcRS

Littlewood, E T
Graphical representation of some of the simpler analytical function of a complex variable. Read Oct. 19, 1910.
(See Royal soc. of S.Africa, Trans. v. 2. p. 173-182.)

NL 0414010 OO

Littlewood, Francis Desmond.
The law of municipal and public entertainment. London, Shaw, 1951.
xxiii, 288 p. 23 cm.
Corrigendum slip inserted.
Bibliography: p. 274.

1. Amusements—Gt. Brit.—Laws and regulations.

790 52-16037

NL 0414011 DLC

Littlewood (H[arry]). An address delivered before the Yorkshire College Medical Society on October 18, 1893. 15 pp. 8°. *Leeds, J. Whitehead & Son*, 1893.

NL 0414012 DNLM

Littlewood, John Edensor, 1885–
The elements of the theory of real functions; being notes of lectures delivered in the University of Cambridge, 1925. 2d (rev.) ed. by J. E. Littlewood ... Cambridge [Eng.] W. Heffer & sons ltd., 1926.
vii, 60 p. 22ᶜᵐ.

1. Aggregates. 2. Functions of a real variable.

28-13178 Revised

Library of Congress QA248.L6 1926

IU NjP NcD PBm PHC MtBC NNC OrPR CaBVaU OrU ODW
NL 0414013 DLC NcRS TxU AU CU OU OO OCU OCIW ICU

Littlewood, John Edensor, 1885–
The elements of the theory of real functions; being notes of lectures delivered in the University of Cambridge. 3d ed., completely rev. New York, Dover Publications [1954]
71 p. 22 cm.

1. Aggregates. 2. Functions of real variables.

QA248.L6 1954 55—14847 ‡

OrU-W WaSpG WaS WaTC CoU FMU CLSU PSt KEmT DAU
PPT PP OCIW PHC PPF TU WaWW IdU MtU OrCS OrU
NL 0414014 DLC WU OU PPLas OOxM NN IU MB ViU NNC

Littlewood, John Edensor, 1885- joint author.
Francis, Edward Carey.
Examples in infinite series, with solutions, by E. C. Francis ... and J. E. Littlewood ... Cambridge [Eng.] Deighton, Bell & co., ltd., 1928.

Littlewood, John Edensor, 1885- joint author
Hardy, Godfrey Harold, 1877–
Inequalities, by G. H. Hardy, J. E. Littlewood [and] G. Pólya. Cambridge [Eng.] The University press, 1934.

Littlewood, John Edensor, 1885–
Lectures on the theory of functions, by J. E. Littlewood ... [London] Oxford university press, 1944.
4 p. l., 243 p. diagrs. 26ᶜᵐ.
"The introduction and chapter I were printed off in 1931."—Pref.
"Erratum" slip inserted.

1. Functions.

A 45-2922

New York. Public library for Library of Congress QA331.L77

OrCS OrPR OrU
OrPS NBuU TxU NN MU CU MoU TNJ CaBVaU MtBC OCIJC
NL 0414017 NN DLC PSt PBm OCU OU PHC CtY TU NcRS

514.3
L735l
1944r
LITTLEWOOD, JOHN EDENSOR, 1885-
Lectures on the theory of functions, by J.E. Littlewood ... [London] Oxford university press [1947]
4p.ℓ.,243,[1]p. diagrs. 26cm.
"First edition 1944. Reprinted photographically in Great Britain at the University Press, Oxford, 1947, from sheets of the first edition."
"The introduction and chapter I were printed off in 1931."—Pref.

1. Functions.

NL 0414018 TxU DLC ViU

Littlewood, John Edensor, 1885–
A mathematician's miscellany. London, Methuen [1953]
vii, 136 p. diagrs., tables. 21 cm.
CONTENTS.—Mathematics with minimum raw material.—From the mathematical tripos.—Cross-purposes, unconscious assumptions, howlers, misprints, etc.—The zoo.—Ballistics.—The dilemma of probability theory.—From Fermat's last theorem to the abolition of capital punishment.—A mathematical education.—Review of Ramanujan's collected papers.—Three reviews.—Newton and the attraction of a sphere.—Large numbers.—The discovery of Neptune.—The Adams-Airy affair.—'Lion and man.'

1. Mathematics—Addresses, essays, lectures. I. Title.

A54-1866

Rochester. Univ. Libr. for Library of Congress QA7 [a55f3]

NN NcD NcU DCU ICU IEN TxU
NL 0414019 NRU MoU MU CLSU FU OCU OU PHC PSC PLF

J808.1
L73
Littlewood, Letty, ed.
The bower book of simple poems for boys & girls, ed. by Letty and Ursula Littlewood; illus. by H. C. Appleton. London, Warne, 1922.
267 p. illus.

1. Poetry - Collections I. Littlewood, Ursula, ed. I. Title.

NL 0414020 MiD MH

Littlewood, Letty, and Frank Littlewood.
Our nursery rhyme book; edited by Letty and Frank Littlewood, illustrated by Honor C. Appleton. Boston: Dana Estes & Co. [1912?] iii-xiv, 181(1) p., 12 col'd pl. illus. 8°.

1. Nursery rhymes. 2. Littlewood, Frank, jt. au. 3. Title.
N. Y. P. L. CENTRAL CIRCULATION. February 10, 1913.

NL 0414021 NN MH

Littlewood, Margaret.
Bamum and Bamileke

see under

International African Institute.
Peoples of the Central Cameroons: Tikar.

Littlewood, Rowland Whitelaw, 1888–
... Livestock of southern India, by Captain R. W. Littlewood ... Madras, Printed by the superintendent, Government press, 1936.
viii p., 2 l., 239 p. front., illus. 25ᶜᵐ.
At head of title: Government of Madras.
Introduction signed: R. W. Littlewood, deputy director of agriculture, livestock.

1. Stock and stock-breeding—India—Madras (Presidency) [1. India—Domestic animals] 2. [Cattle—India—Madras (Presidency)] I. Madras (Presidency) Dept. of agriculture. II. Title.

Agr 38-78 †

U. S. Dept. of agr. Library for Library of Congress 40L73 SF55.I 4L5 [a46d1]† 636.08

NL 0414023 DNAL NcU IU DLC

Littlewood, S C T
Legal aid. Third International Conference of the legal profession, International Bar Association, London, July, 1950. The Hague, M. Nijhoff [1950]
9 p. 24 cm.
Cover title.

1. Legal aid—Addresses, essays, lectures. I. International Bar Association.

361.4 51-19749

NL 0414024 DLC

VOLUME 336

Littlewood, Samuel Robinson, 1875- *ed.*
An anthology of modern drama, edited by S. R. Littlewood. London, New York [etc.] T. Nelson and sons, ltd. [1936]
viii, 295 p. 18cm. (*Half-title:* Modern anthologies; general editor—Richard Wilson ... no. 3)

1. English drama (Selections: Extracts, etc.) I. Title.

Library of Congress PR1272.L5 38-5252
[3] 822.910822

NL 0414025 DLC WaU

Littlewood, Samuel Robinson, 1875-
The art of dramatic criticism. With a foreword by Sir Barry Jackson. London, Pitman [1952]
182 p. 22 cm. (Theatre and stage series)

1. Criticism—Hist. 2. Drama—Hist. & crit. I. Title.

PN1707.L48 808.2 53—260 ‡

NL 0414026 TxU PU MH MP OO NBuG OClW OOxM KMK LU NIC UU WaU DLC OrU CaBVa CaBVaU IdPI MtBC WaS CoU

Littlewood, Samuel Robinson, 1875-
... Dramatic criticism, by S. R. Littlewood; with a foreword by Sir Barry Jackson. London, Sir I. Pitman & sons, ltd., 1939.
viii, 323 p. front. (port.) 22cm. (Theatre and stage series)
"References" at end of each chapter.

1. Criticism—Hist. 2. Drama—Hist. & crit. I. Title.

Library of Congress PN1707.L5 39-10092
[3] 808.2

NL 0414027 TU OCl OU DLC WaWW OrU WaU GU WU MsSM KU CU NIC

Littlewood, Samuel Robinson, 1875-
Elizabeth Inchbald and her circle; the life story of a charming woman (1753-1821) By S. R. Littlewood. London, D. O'Connor, 1921.
vii, [1], 135, [1] p. front., ports. 22cm.
"Mrs. Inchbald's books and plays": p. 133-135.

1. Inchbald, Elizabeth (Simpson) 1753-1821.

Library of Congress PR3518.L5 22—2540

NL 0414028 NIC Vi TU GU NcRS CtY MH ViU NN OOxM DLC MiU OClW OO OU PU PPL LU MiU NcD WaU

Littlewood, Samuel Robinson, 1875- ed.
Essays in criticism
see under Arnold, Matthew, 1822-1888.

4GR 155 Littlewood, Samuel Robinson, 1875-
The fairies, here and now. London, Methuen [1913]
147 p.

NL 0414030 DLC-P4

Littlewood, Samuel Robinson, 1875-
The fairies—here and now, by S. R. Littlewood ... New York, McBride, Nast & co., 1914.
vii, 147, [1] p. 17½cm.

1. Fairies. I. Title.

A 14-2528

Title from Chicago Pub. Libr. Printed by L. C.

NL 0414031 IC OrU OKentU OCl MB NN

PR 2888 L5 Littlewood, Samuel Robinson, 1875-
The London Shakespeare Commemoration League; its purposes and its story. London, Printed for the London Shakespeare League, to be obtained from W.J. Bryce, 1928.
16 p. 21 cm.

1. London Shakespeare League.

NL 0414032 LU MH NN

Littlewood, Samuel Robinson, 1875- tr.

Perrault, Charles, 1628-1703.
Perrault's Fairy tales, newly tr. by S. R. Littlewood, with twelve coloured illustrations by Honor C. Appleton. Boston, D. Estes & co.; [etc., etc., 1911]

792.0942 L73s Littlewood, Samuel Robinson, 1875-
Somerset and the drama, by S.R. Littlewood, and others. London, Somerset Folk Press, 1922.
108 p. illus. 19 cm. (Somerset folk series, no. 7)

1. Theater--Gt. Brit.--Hist. 2. Theater--Somersetshire, Eng.--Hist. I. Title.

NL 0414034 LU MH NN NcD InU IaU

Littlewood, Samuel Robinson, 1875-
The story of Santa Claus, by S. R. Littlewood. With illustrations by Sidney Filmore and Gerald Leake. London, Herbert & Daniel, 1912.
vi, [2], 103, [1] p. col. front., col. plates. 19cm. (World-stories illustrated)

1. Santa Claus. 2. Christmas. I. Title.

A 13-2323

Title from Enoch Pratt Free Libr. Printed by L. C.

NL 0414035 MdBE PPL

Littlewood, Thomas, 1752-1817.

Baptists. *England. Yorkshire and Lancaster association.*
The necessity and importance of observing the positive institutions of the gospel. The ministers of the several Baptist churches, assembled in association at Ackrington, on the 28th and 29th of May 1806, send Christian salutation, to the several communities over which they preside, meeting for divine worship at Ackrington, Bacup, Barnoldswick ... Rochdale, Printed at the office of J. Hartley, 1806.

Littlewood, W. N., ed.

American bureau of engineering, *Chicago.*
... Home study course in automotive electricity ... W. N. Littlewood, editor-in-chief. Chicago, Ill., The American bureau of engineering, inc., 1922.

Littlewood, Walter, and Kate Littlewood.
Cane and rush weaving on sloyd principles; for infant and junior classes, and specially adapted for backward children. London: George Philip & Son [18—?]. 30 p. diagr., illus. 8°.
Music in text.

CENTRAL RESERVE.
1. Chair caning. 2. Title. 3. Littlewood, Kate, jt. au. 4. Weaving
N. Y. P. L. August 17, 1914.

NL 0414038 NN

Littlewood, Walter, *&* **Littlewood, Kate.**
Cane and rush weaving on sloyd principles. For infant and junior classes, and specially adapted for backward children (standard O). 29.[3] p. il. sq.O. London: G Philip & Son. [1897].

NL 0414039 ICJ

Littlewood, William, 1898-
Technical trends in air transport, the sixteenth Wright Brothers lecture. [New York] Institute of Aeronautical Sciences, 1953.
p.225-279. illus., charts, tables.

Reprinted from the Journal of the Aeronautical Sciences, v.20, no.4, April, 1953.
Discussions of the lecture, and reply: p.268-279.

NL 0414040 MH-BA

Littlewood, William Edensor, 1831-1886.
Bible biographies; or, Stories from the Old Testament... London, M. Ward, 1878.
214 p. illus. 20cm.

NL 0414041 MB NjPT

Littlewood, William Edensor, 1831-1886.
Essentials of English history, containing a consise history of England...3rd ed. London, Longsman, 1868. 165 p.

NL 0414042 OO

Littlewood, William Edensor, 1831-1886.
The essentials of English history containing a concise history of England,... by Rev, W.E. Littlewood,...London, Longmans, Green, and Co.,1878.
4p.l. 158p. tables, 17cm.
YA 26772.

NL 0414043 DLC

Littlewood, William Edensor, 1831-1886.
Essentials of New Testament study . . . embracing an introductory account of the New Testament; a resumé and harmony of Gospel history; tables . . .
London. Longmans, Green & Co. 1872. viii, 541, (1) pp. Maps. Plans. Sm. 8°.

G5570 — Bible. N. T. Study and teaching.

NL 0414044 MB NRCR

VOLUME 336

Littlewood, William Edensor, 1831-1886.
Essentials of New Testament study: intended as a companion to the New Testament, and embracing an introductory account of the New Testament; a resumé and harmony of Gospel history... a dictionary of hard words and phrases... a biographical and geographical dictionary... N.Y., A.D.F. Randolph, 1872.
viii, 541 p. maps, plans, tables. 18cm.

NL 0414045 NjPT MH-AH ODW

PR4889 .L865 G3 1887 Littlewood, William Edensor, 1831-1886.
A garland from the parables. With portrait. 2d ed., with corrections and additional poems. London, Wm. Mack [1887]
144p. 19cm.

First edition published in 1858.
Portrait missing.

NL 0414046 NcU

3829 .534 .342 Littlewood, William Edensor, 1831-1886.
Gustavus Adolphus; a poem, which obtained the chancellor's medal at the Cambridge commencement, M.D.CCC.LI. [Cantabrigiae, Smith, 1851]
12 p. 21 cm.

Forms part of Prolusiones academicae praemiis annuis dignatae et in curia Cantabrigiensi recitatae comitiis maximis, M.D.CCC.LI.

NL 0414047 NjP

Littlewood, William Edensor, 1831-1886.
Lovely in their lives. A book for earnest boys.
London. Church of England Sunday School Institute. [1875.]
205 pp. Plate. Sm. 8°.

NL 0414048 MB

Littleworth, *Dr., pseud.*
see Davol, Ralph, 1874-

Littlington, Nicholas
see Litlington, Nicholas, 1316?-1386.

1951 L736 Littman, Armand.
Intragastric beta radiation in the dog. Chicago [1951]
85, 9 l. diagrs., fold. tables. 28cm.

Thesis--University of Illinois.
Typewritten.
Bibliography: leaves 1-9 at end.

1. Beta rays. 2. Stomach--Ulcers. I. Title.

NL 0414051 IU

614.7 L781f Littman, F E
The formation of ozone in the Los Angeles atmosphere, by F.E. Littman, H.W. Ford, and N. Endow; a paper presented at the 128th national ACS meeting, Minneapolis, Minn., September 11 to 16, 1955. [n.p., 1955?]
[24] l. illus. 28cm.

1. Air - Pollution - Los Angeles. 2. Ozone. I. Ford, H W joint author. II. Endow, N joint author. III. Title.

NL 0414052 CLSU

Littman, Frederic H., joint author.

Exton, Everard Nelson, 1897-
Modern furniture, by E. Nelson Exton and Frederic H. Littman. London, Boriswood [1936]

Littman, Joseph Benjamin, 1904-
The preparation and resolution of asymmetric amines; a study of the Knoevenagel's condensation. [Columbus] Ohio state university. 1930.
73 p.
Thesis (Ph.D.) Ohio state univer sity.

NL 0414054 OU

Littman, Lydia, joint ed.

Shurter, Edwin DuBois, 1863- *ed.*
... School savings banks. (The University department of extension and the Texas Bankers' association co-operating) Ed. by E. D. Shurter ... and Lydia Littman ... Austin, Tex., The University [1917]

Littman, Richard Anton, 1919-
Latent learning in a T maze after two degrees of training ... 1948.

Thesis (Ph.D.) - Ohio state university, 1948.

NL 0414056 OU

Littman, Richard Anton, 1919-
Student guide and workbook for Ernest R. Hilgard's Introduction to psychology. Prepared by Richard A. Littman ... and Richard C. Teevan ... New York, Harcourt, Brace [1953]

viii, 163 p. illus., diagrs., forms. 28cm.

NL 0414057 NcD

Littman, Sidney, tr.

Bergson, Henri Louis, 1859-
The introduction to a new philosophy; introduction à la métaphysique, by Henri Bergson ... Boston, J. W. Luce and company, 1912.

Littmann, Adolf, 1882-
Sicht- und Zeitsichtwechsel in der gerichtlichen Praxis ... von Adolf Littmann ... Oldenburg i.Gr., A. Littmann, 1910.
viii, 80 p., 1 l. 22cm.

Inaug.-Diss. -Heidelberg.
"Lebenslauf": leaf at end.
"Literaturverzeichnis": p.[vi]-viii.

NL 0414059 MH-L ICRL

Littmann, Arnold.

DD247 .N6M68 Mondt, Gerhard.
Herbert Norkus und die Hitlerjungen vom Beusselkietz; nach dem Tagebuch des Kameradschaftsführers Gerd Mondt und nach Mitteilungen der Familie, von Arnold Littmann. Vorwort von Baldur von Schirach. Berlin, Kolk [°1934]

Littmann, Arnold, ed.

DK267 .C5532 Churchill, Winston Leonard Spencer, 1874-
Mein Bundesgenosse; Aussprüche aus zwei Jahrzehnten, illustriert von englischen und amerikanischen Pressezeichnern. Berlin, Nibelungen-Verlag, 1944.

DK267 .C553 Littmann, Arnold. ed.

Churchill, Winston Leonard Spencer, 1874-
Mon allié Staline, de Winston Churchill. [n. p., 194-?]

PT 2492 .L782 LITTMANN, ARNOLD.
Schillers Geschichtsphilosophie. Langensalza, H. Beyer, 1926.
128 p.

Lebenslauf.
Thesis: Friedrich-Wilhelm-Universität zu Berlin, 1926.

1. Schiller, Johann Cristoph Friedrich von, 1759-1805.

NL 0414063 InU PU ICRL CLSU NN NNC OCU CtY MH

Littmann, Bettina, 1930-
Die kollisionsrechtliche bedeutung von art. 418, lit b., Abs. 2 OR ... von Bettina Littmann ... Winterthur, P.G. Keller, 1955.
viii, 111, [1] p. 21cm.
Diss. - Zürich.
"Curriculum vitae": p. [112]
Bibliography: p. vi-viii.

NL 0414064 MH-L IU ICU NNC-L

Littmann, Bettina, 1930-
Die kollisionsrechtliche Bedeutung von Art. 418, lit. b, Abs. 2 OR. Winterthur, P. G. Keller, 1955.
viii, 111 p. 21 cm.
Issued also as thesis, Zürich.
Bibliography: p. vi-viii.

1. Conflict of laws—Commercial agents—Switzerland.

59-18283

NL 0414065 DLC CU-L

VOLUME 336

Littmann, Carl Christian.
Littmann's gebet buch. Leipzig, Weidmannische buchhandlung, 1815.

NL 0414066 PPeSchw

Littmann, Dieter.
Die Kostengünstigkeit industrieller Anschaffungen. Stuttgart, W. Kohlhammer, 1954.

139 p. 21 cm.

Inauguraldiss.—Bern.
Bibliography: p. 139.

1. Costs, Industrial. I. Title.

HD47.L5 56-21582

NL 0414067 DLC CtY MH-L NNC

Littmann, Eberhard, 1909 -
Bewertungsfreiheiten, Gewerbesteuer. Freiburg/Br. [Ullstein-Verlag] 1951.

128 p. 21 cm. (Der Steuerzahler, 1951, 4)

Die Ullstein-Steuer-Reihe.

1. Income tax—Germany (Federal Republic, 1949-)—Law. 2. Business tax—Germany (Federal Republic, 1949-) I. Title.

52-34285 ‡

NL 0414068 DLC

Littmann, Eberhard, 1909-
Die D-mark-eröffnungsbilanz in der praxis (Gesetz vom 21. August 1949) von dr. jur. Eberhard Littmann ... [Düsseldorf, Rhenus, 1949]

120 p. forms. 20½cm. (Rhenus-reihe über steuer und wirtschaft, bd. 7)

NL 0414069 MH-L

Littmann, Eberhard, 1909 -
Das Einkommensteuerrecht; eine Darstellung des seit 21. 6. 1948 geltenden Rechtes mit 550 Beispielen für die Praxis. [Düsseldorf, Rhenus-Verlagsgesellschaft, 1950]

viii, 487 p. 21 cm. (Rhenus-Reihe über Steuer und Wirtschaft, Bd. 9)

1. Income tax—Germany (Federal Republic, 1949-)—Law. I. Title.

52-26129

NL 0414070 DLC

Littmann, Eberhard, 1909 -
Das Einkommensteuerrecht; eine Darstellung des seit 21. 6. 1948 geltenden Rechtes mit 600 Beispielen für die Praxis, von Eberhard Littmann. 3. ergänzte Aufl. [Düsseldorf, Rhenus-Verlagsgesellschaft, 1952]

xix, 614 p. 22 cm. (Rhenus-Reihe über Steuer und Wirtschaft, Bd. 9)

1. Income tax—Germany (Federal Republic, 1949-)—Law. I. Germany (Federal Republic, 1949-) Laws, statutes, etc. Einkommensteuergesetz. 1952.

53-32349

NL 0414071 DLC

Littmann, Eberhard, 1909-
Das einkommensteuerrecht; kommentar zum einkommensteuergesetz nach dem stand vom 1. Juni 1954 ... erläutert von dr. Eberhard Littmann ... 4. erweiterte aufl. Stuttgart, Schäffer, 1954.

xx, 790, 66, 78 p. 21cm.

Includes legislation.
Includes bibliographies.

NL 0414072 MH-L

Littmann, Eberhard, 1909 -
Das Einkommensteuerrecht; Kommentar zum Einkommensteuergesetz nach dem Stand vom 1. Juni 1954 mit 590 Beispielen für die Praxis; erläutert von Eberhard Littmann. 4. erweiterte Aufl. Stuttgart, Fachverlag für Wirtschaftsund Steuerrecht, Schäffer, 1954.
xx, 790, 78 p. 22 cm.
—— Nachtrag. Stand 1. Januar 1955. Stuttgart, Fachverlag für Wirtschafts- und Steuerrecht, Schäffer, 1955.
37 p. 22 cm.
1. Income tax—Germany (Federal Republic, 1949-)—Law. I. Germany (Federal Republic, 1949-) Laws, statutes, etc. Einkommensteuergesetz. 1954. II. Title.

54-35528

NL 0414073 DLC

Littmann, Eberhard, 1909-
... Gewerbesteuer bearb. von ... dr. Littmann. Straubing, Wurm, 1952.

2 p.l., [2], 72 p. 21cm. (Das steuerrecht in frage und antwort, bd. 5)

NL 0414074 MH-L

Littmann, Eberhard, 1909-
Gewerbesteuer bearb. von dr. Eberhard Littmann ... 2. erweiterte aufl. Stuttgart, Schäffer, 1953.

xvi, 215 p. 21½cm. (Buchreihe finanz und steuern, bd. 16)

NL 0414075 MH-L

Littmann, Eberhard, 1909 -
Lexikon der abzugsfähigen und nichtabzugsfähigen Ausgaben bei der Einkommensteuer. Die Betriebsausgaben in der Einkommensteuer; bearb. und zusammengestellt nach dem neuesten Stand. [Freiburg i. Br.] Ullstein-Verlag [1951]

127 p. 21 cm. (Die Ullstein-Steuer-Reihe)

1. Income tax—Germany (Federal Republic, 1949-)—Deductions.

52-20342 rev ‡

NL 0414076 DLC

Littmann, Eberhard, 1909-
Die Rechtsstellung des Sicherungseigentümers im Konkurs des Sicherungsgebers und in der Einzelvollstreckung ... von Eberhard Littmann ... Borna-Leipzig, Robert Noske, 1937.

xi, 89 p., 1 l. 21cm.

Inaug.-Diss. - Jena.
"Lebenslauf": leaf at end.
"Schriftennachweis": p. ix-xi.

NL 0414077 MH-L ICRL

Littmann, Eberhard, 1909-
... Richtig und vorteilhaft abschreiben ... von ... dr. Eberhard Littmann. Ludwigshafen Rh., F. Kiehl [1955]

1 p.l., 99 p. tables. 21cm. (Bücherei für wirtschafts- und steuerrecht, bd. 56)

"Beilage ...": [4] p. inserted.

NL 0414078 MH-L

Law

Littmann, Eberhard, 1909 - ed.

Germany (*Federal Republic, 1949-*) *Laws, statutes, etc.*
Was zahle ich für den Lastenausgleich? Vermögensabgabe, Hypothekengewinnabgabe, Kreditgewinnabgabe; mit Gesetztexten. [von] E. Littmann. Freiburg i. Br., Vereinigte Verlage und Vertriebe für Wirtschafts- und Steuerliteratur [1952]

Littmann, Edwin Robert, 1899-
The formation of cyclic quaternary ammonium salts from halogenated aliphatic tertiary amines, by Edwin Robert Littmann ... Urbana, Ill., 1929.

[7] p. 23½cm.

Abstract of thesis (PH. D.)—University of Illinois, 1929.
Vita.
Bibliography: p. [6]

1. Ammonium salts. 2. Amines.

Library of Congress QD341.A8L77 1929 29-22671
Univ. of Illinois Libr.

NL 0414080 IU OU MH DLC

TP690 .L6

Littmann, Edwin Robert, 1899- joint author.

Lochte, Harry Louis, 1892-
The petroleum acids and bases [by] H. L. Lochte and E. R. Littmann. New York, Chemical Pub. Co., 1955.

---

296 L73s

Littmann, Ellen, 1900-
Studien zur Wiederaufnahme der Juden durch die deutschen Städte nach dem schwarzen Tode. Ein Beitrag zur Geschichte der Judenpolitik der deutschen Städte im späten Mittelalter. Breslau, Druck von T. Schatzky, 1928.
54p. 23cm.
Inaug.-Diss.--Cologne.
Lebenslauf.
"Literatur-Verzeichnis": p.52-54.

1. Jews in Germany. 2. Jews--Political and social conditions.

NL 0414082 IU CU

Littmann, Emmy.
Durch das Tor des Ostens; Erzählungen aus morgenländischer Vergangenheit. Strassburg i. E.: Schlesier & Schweikhardt, 1910. 4 p.l., (1)12-175 p. 12°.

1. Fiction (German). 2. Title.
N. Y. P. L. April 11, 1911.

NL 0414083 NN

Littmann, Enno, 1875- 1958.
... Abessinien. Hamburg, Hanseatische verlagsanstalt [©1935]

114, [1] p. illus. (map) 20½cm.

1. Ethiopia. I. Title.

[*Full name:* Ludwig Richard Enno Littmann]

36-2372

Library of Congress DT373.L58
Copyright A—Foreign 29898
[2] 916.3

NL 0414084 DLC ICU NN CtY

VOLUME 336

Littmann, Enno, 1875-1958.
Abessinische Klagelieder; alte Weisen in neuer Gewandung. Tübingen, J. C. B. Mohr, 1949.
75 p. 25 cm.

1. Tigré ballads and songs—Hist. & crit. I. Title.
Full name: Ludwig Richard Enno Littmann.

PJ9131.L5 52-67577

NL 0414085 DLC IEN ICU MH NNC PPDrop OCl NN

Littmann, Enno, 1875-1958.
Abessinische miszellen. Strassb. [1911]

NL 0414086 NjP

Littmann, Enno, 1875–
Abessinische Parallelen zu einigen altarabischen Gebräuchen und Vorstellungen.
(In Beiträge zur Kenntnis des Orients. Band 6, pp. 52-58. Halle. 1908.)

K5883 — Abyssinia. Manners.

NL 0414087 MB

Littmann, Enno, 1875–
Die abessinischen handschriften der sammlung Littmann in Tübingen, von Murad Kamil. Leipzig, Deutsche morgenländische gesellschaft, in kommission bei F. A. Brockhaus, 1936.
46, [1] p. $23\frac{1}{2}$cm. (*Half-title:* Abhandlungen für die kunde des Morgenlandes; mit unterstützung der Deutschen forschungsgemeinschaft hrsg. von der Deutschen morgenländischen gesellschaft. XXI, 8)

1. Manuscripts, Ethiopic—Catalogs. I. Kamil, Murad. II. Title.
[*Full name:* Ludwig Richard Enno Littmann]
A 42-1128

Newberry library for Library of Congress [PJ5.D5 bd. 21, nr. 8] [3] (490.6243)

NL 0414088 ICN CU PU IU ICarbS OCl

Littmann, Enno, 1875– ed.
Ägyptische nationallieder und königslieder der gegenwart, in umschrift herausgegeben und übersetzt von Enno Littmann. Leipzig, Deutsche morgenländische gesellschaft, Kommissionsverlag F. A. Brockhaus, 1938.
2 p. l., 39, [1] p. 23cm. (*Half-title:* Abhandlungen für die kunde des Morgenlandes, mit unterstützung der Deutschen forschungsgemeinschaft, hrsg. von der Deutschen morgenländischen gesellschaft. XXIII, 6 [i. e. 4])
Transliterated Arabic text with German translation on opposite pages. Without music.
1. Arabic ballads and songs. 2. National songs, Egyptian. 3. Folk-songs, Egyptian. 4. Folk-songs, Arabic. I. Title.
[*Full name:* Ludwig Richard Enno Littmann]
A C 30-1386

Newberry library for Library of Congress [PJ5.D5 bd. 23, nr. 4] [3] (490.6243)

NL 0414089 ICN UU CU OCl PU DLC IU ICarbS CLU

4CN 40 Littmann, Enno, 1875–
Äthiopische Inschriften. [Berlin, Akademie-Verlag, 1950]
98-127 p.

NL 0414090 DLC-P4

Littmann, Enno, 1875-1958.
Die äthiopischen handschriften im griechischen kloster zu Jerusalem. n.p., n.d.

NL 0414091 NjP

Littmann, Enno, 1875-1958, ed. and tr.

AS182 .M232 Nr. 3 Aḥmed il-Bedawi, ein Lied auf den ägyptischen Nationalheiligen, aufgezeichnet, hrsg. und übers. von Enno Littmann. Mainz, Verlag der Akademie der Wissenschaften und der Literatur; in Kommission bei F. Steiner, Wiesbaden [1950]

Littmann, Enno, 1875–
Die altamharischen kaiserlieder ... Strassburg, Universitätsbuchdr. von J. H. E. Heitz, 1914.
36 p. $23\frac{1}{2}$cm.
Rede—Univ. Strassburg.

1. Amharic poetry. I. Title.
[*Full name:* Ludwig Richard Enno Littmann]
24-8196

Library of Congress PJ9262.L5

NL 0414093 DLC ICRL DDO CtY PPDrop OCl NN

Littmann, Enno, 1875-1958.
Arabian nights
for translations see under Arabian nights. German. 1921 and later.

Littmann, Enno, 1875-1958.
Arabic humor. [n.p., 190-]

NL 0414095 NjP

Littmann, Enno, 1875-1958, ed.

PN6519 .A7S55 Singer, Mrs. A P comp.
Arabic proverbs, collected by Mrs. A. P. Singer. Edited by Enno Littmann. Cairo, F. Diemer, 1913.

PJ7737 Z67 Near Eastern Lang. Littmann, Enno, 1875-
Arabische Beduinenerzählungen. I. Arabischer Text. Strassburg, K.J. Trübner, 1908.
vii,58 p. (Schriften der Wissenschaftlichen Gesellschaft in Strassburg, 2)

Bound with: Zotenberg, Hermann. Notice sur quelques manuscrits des Mille et une nuits et la traduction de Galland. [1887]

1. Tales, Arabic. 2. Bedouins. I. Title.

NL 0414097 CU OCl OCH ICU PU-Mu PPDrop NN MB NIC MH

Littmann, Enno, 1875- ed.and tr.

Arabische geisterbeschwörungen aus Ägypten. Leipzig, Harrassowitz, 1950.
114 p. $23\frac{1}{2}$ cm. (Sammlung orientalistischer arbeiten. 19.hft.)

1.Arabic language - Dialects - Egypt. 2.Exorcism.

NL 0414098 IEN CU DLC-P4 MH ICU NNC NIC NjP CU OCl CtY NcD PU RPB IU InU OCH

PJ 7680 .L782 G4 LITTMANN,ENO,1875-1958,comp. and tr.
Arabische Märchen, aus mündlicher Überlieferung gesammelt und übertragen. Leipzig, Insel-Verlag [1935]
479 p.

Translation of his Modern Arabic tales.

1. Tales--Arabic. 2. Arabic literature--Translations into German. I. Title.

NL 0414099 InU ICU CtY

Littmann, Enno, 1875-1958, *comp. and tr.*
Arabische Märchen und Schwänke aus Ägypten nach mündlicher Überlieferung gesammelt. Mainz, Verlag der Akademie der Wissenschaften und der Literatur; in Kommission bei F. Steiner, Wiesbaden [1955]
174 p. 25 cm. (Akademie der Wissenschaften und der Literatur. Abhandlungen der Klasse der Literatur, Jahrg. 1955, Nr. 2)
Pages also numbered 24-187.
Bibliography: p. 119-121.
1. Tales, Arabian. 2. Arabic wit and humor. 3. German literature—Translations from Arabic. 4. Arabian literature—Translations into German. I. Title. (Series: Akademie der Wissenschaften und der Literatur, Mainz. Klasse der Literatur. Abhandlungen, Jahrg. 1955, Nr. 2)
Full name: Ludwig Richard Enno Littmann.
A 60-5924

Illinois. Univ. Library for Library of Congress [2]

NL 0414100 IU MH MiU ICU CtY OCl NIC OU RPB TxU

Littmann, Enno, 1875–
Arabische Schattenspiele. Mit Anhängen von Dr. Georg Jacob. Berlin. Mayer & Miller. 1901. (5), 84 pp. $22\frac{1}{2}$ cm., in 8s.
The Anhängen, by Georg Jacob, are catalogued separately.

K9141 — Drama. Arabian. — Shadow pantomimes.

NL 0414101 MB NjP NNUT OCl NN MH OCl CtY

Littmann, Enno, 1875–
Ein arabisches Karagöz-Spiel. Von Enno Littmann... (In: Deutsche morgenländische Gesellschaft. Zeitschrift. Leipzig, 1900. Bd. 54, p. 661-680.)
Arabic text, with Latin transliteration and German translation.

263521. 1. Shadow plays, Arabic. 2. Arabic literature—Drama—Translations into German. 3. Drama, German—Translations from Arabic.

NL 0414102 NN

Littmann, Enno, 1875-
Arde'et...
see under title

Littmann, Enno, 1875-1958.
Aus den abessinischen Klöstern in Jerusalem. [Strassburg, 1902]

NL 0414104 NjP

Littmann, Enno, 1875- ed.

PJ9096 .B5 Bibliotheca Abessinica; studies concerning the languages, literature and history of Abyssinia. v. 1-4. Leyden, Brill; Princeton, N. J., University Library, 1904-11.

Littmann, Enno, 1875-1958.
Bemerkung über den Islam in Nordabessinien. [Strassburg, 1910]

NL 0414106 NjP

VOLUME 336

Littmann, Enno, 1875 –
The British government is responsible for the present war... n. p., n. d.
15 p. 24 cm.

NL 0414107 DNW

Littmann, Enno, 1875-
Das Buch der Jubiläen... Tübingen, 1900
see under Bible. O. T. Apocryphal books. Book of Jubilees. German. 1900. Littmann.

Littmann, Enno, 1875-
Le chant de la belle-mère arabe moderne. Paris, 1903.

NL 0414109 NjP OCl

Littmann, Enno, 1875-1958.
Catalogue et monks and mss. in the Abyssinian convents in Jerusalem. [n.p., 1902]

NL 0414110 NjP

Littmann, Enno, 1875- ed.
PJ9025 .D5 1941
Dillmann, August, 1823-1894.
Chrestomathia aethiopica, edita et glossario explanata ab Augusto Dillmann. Editio stereotypa; addenda et corrigenda adiecit Enno Littmann. Lipsiae, W. Keller, 1941.

Littmann, Enno, 1875- and tr.
The chronicle of King Theodore of Abyssinia...
see under [Zaneb]

Littmann, Enno, 1875-
... Der deutsche beitrag zur wissenschaft vom Vorderen Orient. Stuttgart und Berlin, W. Kohlhammer, 1942.
2 p. l., 43 p. 23cm. (Der Deutsche beitrag zur gestaltung und erforschung der englischen kultur, hrsg. von Wilhelm Horn)

1. Oriental philology—Hist. 2. Learning and scholarship—Germany.
[Full name: Ludwig Richard Enno Littmann]
44-33698
Library of Congress PJ60.G5L5
[2] 490.9

NL 0414113 DLC PU CU NN CtY MH ICU

Littmann, Enno, 1875-
Deux inscriptions religieuses de Palmyra, Paris, 1901.

NL 0414114 NjP

PJ7723 .L5
Littmann, Enno, 1875- tr.
Arabian nights.
Die Erzählungen aus den tausendundein Nächten. Vollständige deutsche Ausg. zum ersten Mal nach dem arabischen Urtext der Calcuttaer Ausg. aus dem Jahre 1839 übertragen von Enno Littmann. [Wiesbaden] Insel-Verlag [1953]

Littmann, Enno, 1875-
Friesische erzählungen aus Alt-Wangerooge; letzte klänge einer verschollenen sprache... Oldenburg i.O., Littmann, 1922.
32 p. 22 cm.

1. Friesian literature - Collections. 2. Friesian language - Dialects - Wangeroog.

NL 0414116 NjP MH IU CU

Littmann, Enno, 1875-
Galla-Verskunst; ein Beitrag zur allgemeinen Verskunst nebst metrischen Übersetzungen, von Enno Littmann. Tübingen: J. C. B. Mohr, 1925. vi, 55 p. 8°.

1. Prosody, African. 2. African tribes—Galla.
N. Y. P. L. July 31, 1926

NL 0414117 NN CSt CtY OCl MH NjP WU ICU

Littmann, Enno. 1875-
Geschichte der äthiopischen Litteratur.
(In Brockelmann, Carl, and others. Geschichte der christlichen Litteraturen des Orients. Pp. 185-270. Leipzig. 1909.)

H2511 — Ethiopia. Lit. Hist.

NL 0414118 MB PU-Hyg

Littmann, Enno, 1875- FOR OTHER EDITIONS SEE MAIN ENTRY
Geschichte der christlichen litteraturen des Orients, von C. Brockelmann, Franz Nikolaus Finck, Johannes Leipoldt, Enno Littmann. 2. ausg., mit berichtigungen. Leipzig, C. F. Amelang, 1909.

*Littmann, Enno, 1875- ed.
Schulthess, Friedrich, 1868-1922.
Grammatik des christlich-palästinischen aramäisch, von Friedrich Schulthess; hrsg. von Enno Littmann mit nachträgen von Theodor Nöldeke und dem herausgeber. Tübingen, J. C. B. Mohr, 1924.

F/ BR36 L781
Littmann, Enno, 1875-
... Greek and Latin inscriptions ... Southern Syria, by Enno Littmann ... Leyden, Late E.J.Brill, 1907-21.
7pt.in lv. illus., facsims. 32cm.
(Syria; publications of the Princeton university archaeological expeditions to Syria in 1904-5 and 1909, Division III, Section A)
Pt.2-5 by Enno Littmann, David Magie, jr., and Duane Reed Stuart; pt.6-7 by Enno Littmann and David Magie, jr.
Paged continuously

NL 0414121 NNUT InU MnU PU MWelC PBm RPB NN

DS211 .N5
Littmann, Enno, 1875-1958.
Nielsen, Ditlef, 1874-1942.
Handbuch der altarabischen Altertumskunde, in Verbindung mit Fr. Hommel und Nik. Rhodokanakis hrsg. von Ditlef Nielsen. Mit Beiträgen von Adolf Grohmann und Enno Littmann. 1. Band: Die altarabische Kultur. Kopenhagen, A. Busck, 1927.

*Littmann, Enno, 1875- tr.
Castanhoso, Miguel de, d. 1565?
Die heldentaten des dom Christoph da Gama in Abessinien; nach dem portugiesischen berichte des Miguel de Castanhoso übers. und hrsg. von Enno Littman ... Berlin, K. Curtius, 1907.

[Littmann, Enno] 1875-
I accuse England. n. p. [1914.] 12 p. 8°.
Signed: Enno Littmann.
Title from cover.
In: BTZE p. v. 3, no. 1.

1. European war, 1914- . 2. Title.
N. Y. P. L. November 4, 1914

NL 0414124 NN MH NjP

Littmann, Enno, 1875-1958.
Iets over de betrekkingen tusschen Nederland en Abessinie. [n.p., 1902]

NL 0414125 NjP

Littmann, Enno, 1875-
Indien und Abessinien, von Enno Littmann... (In: Beitraege zur Literaturwissenschaft und Geistesgeschichte Indiens. Bonn, 1926. 8°. p. [406]-417.)
Caption-title.

306131A. 1. Abyssinia.
N. Y. P. L. November 22, 1927

NL 0414126 NN

Littmann, Enno. 1875-
Die Inschriften des Königs Kalumu.
(In Koeniglich preussische Akademie der Wissenschaften, Berlin. Sitzungsberichte. Jahrgang 1911, Halbband 2, pp. 976-895. Berlin. 1911.)
Phoenician inscriptions excavated at Sinjirli, Syria.

K4195 — Inscriptions. Phoenician. — Sinjirli, Syria. Antiq.

NL 0414127 MB

BK64 L7361
Littmann, Enno, 1875-1958, ed and tr.
Islamisch-arabische Heiligenlieder aufgezeichnet, hrsg. und übers. von Enno Littmann. Mainz, Verlag der Akademie der Wissenschaften und der Literatur; in Kommission bei F. Steiner, Wiesbaden [1951]
74 p. 26 cm. (Akademie der Wissenschaften und der literatur. Abhandlungen der Geistes- und Sozialwissenschaftlichen Klasse, Jahrg. 1952, nr. 2)
Also paged [101]-168.
Bibliographical footnotes.

NL 0414128 CtY-D NcU MU NIC DDO CtY OCl

VOLUME 336

Littmann, Enno, 1875–
...Jaeger und Prinzessin; ein neuarabisches Märchen aus Jerusalem, von Enno Littmann. Bonn: A. Marcus und E. Weber, 1922. 32 p. 12°. (Kleine Texte für Vorlesungen und Übungen. [Heft] 150.)
"Dies Marchen wurde mir...von Bšāra Sāra aus Jerusalem erzählt."
Arabic text with transliteration.

1. Fairy tales, Arabic. 2. Arabic language—Dialects—Syria. 3. Ser.
N. Y. P. L. July 1, 1927

NL 0414129 NN CtY PPDrop OCH OCU OCl CtY

Littmann, Enno, 1875–1958.
Ein Jahrhundert Orientalistik; Lebensbilder aus der Feder von Enno Littmann und Verzeichnis seiner Schriften. Zum achtzigsten Geburtstage am 16. September 1955 zusammengestellt von Rudi Paret und Anton Schall. Wiesbaden, O. Harrassowitz, 1955.
ix, 194, [1] p. port. 25 cm.
CONTENTS.—Lebensbilder von Orientalisten, von E. Littmann.—Verzeichnis der Schriften von Enno Littmann, von A. Schall (p. [139]–[195])
1. Oriental philology—Addresses, essays, lectures. 2. Scholars. I. Paret, Rudi, 1901– ed. II. Schall, Anton. III. Title.
Full name: Ludwig Richard Enno Littmann.
PJ63.L5 A 56—3082
Harvard Univ. Library for Library of Congress [a60d1]†

CSaT CSt-H UU CtY NNC
NL 0414130 MH NcD CU DLC ICU PPDrop NIC NN DLC

Littmann, Enno, 1875– ed. and tr.
Kairiner sprichwörter und rätsel, herausgegeben und übersetzt von Enno Littmann. Leipzig, Deutsche morgenländische gesellschaft, in kommission bei F. A. Brockhaus, 1937.
xv, 71 p. 23½cm. (Half-title: Abhandlungen für die kunde des Morgenlandes, mit unterstützung der Deutschen forschungsgemeinschaft, hrsg. von der Deutschen morgenländischen gesellschaft. XXII, 5)
Arabic original followed in each case by German translation.

1. Proverbs, Arabic. 2. Riddles, Arabic. I. Title.
[Full name: Ludwig Richard Enno Littmann]
A C 38-2357
Newberry library for Library of Congress [PJ5.D5 bd. 22, nr. 5]
[2] (490.6248)

NL 0414131 ICN IU ICarbS UU CU PU OCl

Littmann, Enno, 1875– ed. and tr.
Kairiner Volksleben. Arabische Texte. Leipzig, F. A. Brockhaus, 1941.
81 p. 24 cm. (Abhandlungen für die Kunde des Morgenlandes, XXVI, 2)
Arabic and German on opposite pages.
Bibliography included in "Vorwort."

1. Cairo—Soc. life & cust. I. Title. (Series: Deutsche Morgenländische Gesellschaft. Abhandlungen für die Kunde des Morgenlandes, XXVI, 2)
Full name: Ludwig Richard Enno Littmann.
[PJ5.D5 XXVI, 2] A 51-7657
New York. Public Libr. for Library of Congress [2]

NL 0414132 NN IU ICarbS ICU

892.06
D49a
v.26
no.2
Littmann, Enno, 1875- ed. and tr.
Kairiner Volksleben, Arabische Texte. Leipzig, Kommissionsverlag F.A.Brockhaus, 1941. [Ann Arbor, Mich., 1961]
81 p.(on double leaves) (Abhandlungen für die Kunde des Morgenlandes, XXVI, 2)
Photocopy (positive) made by University Microfilms.
Arabic and German.

1.Cairo--Soc.life & cust. I.Title.
Full name: Ludwig Richard Enno Littmann.

NL 0414133 MiU

Littmann, Enno, 1875-1958.
Ein koptisch-arabischer bauernkalender. [Riga, 1938]
From In piam memoriam Alexander von Bulmerincq. 1938 (Abhandlungen der Herder-gesellschaft und des Herder-instituts zu Riga. 6. bd., nr. 3)
[Full name: Ludwig Richard Enno Littmann]

NL 0414134 MiU

Littmann, Enno, 1875-
Koptischer einfluss im Ägyptisch-Arabischen. n.p. 19-

NL 0414135 NjP

Littmann, Enno, 1875-1958 ed.

Sheba, Queen of. Legend.
... The legend of the Queen of Sheba in the tradition of Axum, by the editor [E. Littmann] Leyden, E. J. Brill; Princeton, N. J., The University library, 1904.

Littmann, Enno, 1875– ed. and tr.
Lieder der Tigrē-Stämme: deutsche Übersetzung und Commentar. Leyden: E. J. Brill, Ltd., 1913–15. 2 v. 8°. (Princeton University. Publ. of the Princeton expedition to Abyssinia. v. 4 A–B.)
Contents: A. Lieder der Mānsa', Bēt-Gūk und Māryā. B. Lieder der 'Ad-Temāryām, 'Ad-Hebtēs (Habāb), 'Ad-Taklēs, und kleinerer Stämme.

1. African languages: Tigré. 2. Series.
N. Y. P. L. April 27, 1916

NL 0414137 NN ICN

Littmann, Enno, 1875-

[Garrett, Robert] 1875–
A list of Arabic manuscripts in Princeton university library. By Enno Littmann, PH. D. Princeton, University library; Leipzig, O. Harrassowitz, 1904.

*Littmann, Enno, 1875-
... Lydian inscriptions ... Leyden, E. J. Brill, 1916–

Littmann, Enno, 1875 - 1958 ed. and tr.
Märchen und Legenden aus der syrisch-arabischen Wüste. (In Koenigliche Gesellschaft der Wissenschaften, Göttingen. Nachrichten. Philologisch-historische Klasse, 1915, pp. 1–27. Berlin. 1915.)

L7699 — Arabia. Lang. Works in Arabic. — Syria. Folk-lore. — Fables.

NL 0414140 MB NjP

*Littmann, Enno, 1875- ed.

Suratci oyuni.
... Das malerspiel: ein schattenspiel aus Aleppo nach einer armenisch-türkischen handschrift herausgegeben von Enno Littmann ... Heidelberg. C. Winter. 1918.

Littmann, Enno, 1875– ed.
... Modern Arabic tales, by Enno Littmann, PH. D. vol. I. Arabic text. Leyden, Late E. J. Brill, 1905.
vii, [272] p. 23½cm. (Publications of an American archaeological expedition to Syria in 1899–1900 ... pt. VI)
Text paged with Arabic numerals.
No more published.

1. Tales, Arabic. I. Title.
[Full name: Ludwig Richard Enno Littmann]
19-5912 Revised
Library of Congress PJ7825.A1L5
[r35b2] 892.73

NL 0414143 DLC ICarbS NIC LU CU PPDrop OCl MB

Littmann, Enno, 1875– 1958
Morgenländische spruchweisheit; arabische sprichwörter und rätsel, aus mündlicher überlieferung gesammelt und übertragen, von Enno Littmann. Leipzig, J. C. Hinrichs, 1937.
x p., 1 l., 64 p. 24½cm. (On cover: Morgenland; darstellungen aus geschichte und kultur des Ostens, hft. 29)

1. Proverbs, Arabic. 2. Riddles, Arabic. I. Title.
[Full name: Ludwig Richard Enno Littmann]
38-2535
Library of Congress PN6519.A7L5
[3] 398.90953

NL 0414144 DLC PPiPT TNJ NIC CU OO PU NBB MB

PF
3582
O6L7
1920
Littmann, Enno, 1875-
Morgenländische Wörter im Deutschen. Berlin, Karl Curtius, 1920.
vii, 51 p.

1. German language - Foreign words and phrases. I. Title.

NL 0414145 CLU MiDW CU OCH

Littmann, Enno, 1875–
Morgenländische wörter im deutschen, von Enno Littmann. 2., verm. und verb. aufl., nebst einem anhang über die amerikanischen wörter. Tübingen, Mohr, 1924.
xii, 161 p., 1 l. 18½cm.
"Schriften": p. xii.

1. German language—Foreign words and phrases. I. Title.
46-33182
Library of Congress PF3582.A3L5 1924

NBuU GU TNJ NcU FTaSU
MiU NjP ICU IU MH OCl OO OCU OCH WaU TxU ICN IaU
NL 0414146 DLC CaBVaU WaU MoU PSt NcD OU CU CtY NN

Littmann, Enno, 1875-1958.
Nabataean inscriptions from Egypt by Enno Littmann; with an introduction and classical notes by David Meredith.
Reprinted from the BSOAS., 1953, xv/1 and 1954, xvi/2 Pt. I and II.

NL 0414147 DDO

Littmann, Enno, 1875-
Nabataean inscriptions from the southern Haurân... xxviii, 93p. il., maps. Leyden, E. J. Brill, 1914. (Princeton university - Archaeological expeditions to Syria in 1904-1905 and 1909. Publications, division 4, section A)

NL 0414148 OCl PU-Mu

VOLUME 336

*Littmann, Enno, 1875-

Preisigke, Friedrich, 1856-1924.
Namenbuch enthaltend alle griechischen, lateinischen, ägyptischen, hebräischen, arabischen und sonstigen semitischen und nichtsemitischen menschennamen, soweit sie in griechischen urkunden (papyri, ostraka, inschriften, mumienschildern usw) Ägyptens sich vorfinden, bearb. und hrsg. von dr. Friedrich Preisigke ... Mit einem anhange von professor dr. Enno Littmann, enthaltend die in diesem Namenbuche vorkommenden abessinischen, arabischen, kanaanäischen und persischen namen. Heidelberg, Selbstverlag des herausgebers, 1922.

Littmann, Enno, 1875-1958.
Eine neuarabische Posse aus Damascus. [n.p., 190-]

NL 0414150 NjP

Littmann, Enno, 1875- *comp.*
... Neuarabische volkspoesie, gesammelt und übersetzt von Enno Littmann. Berlin, Weidmannsche buchhandlung, 1902.
1 p. l., 157, [1] p., 1 l. 27 cm. (Abhandlungen der Königlichen gesellschaft der wissenschaften zu Göttingen. Philologisch-historische klasse. n. f., bd. v, nro. 3)
Much of the Arabic text is given in roman transliteration only; the rest appears in Arabic characters accompanied by transliteration on opposite page.
CONTENTS.—Arabische texte: Einleitung. A. Texte aus Palästina. B. Texte aus Syrien.—Uebersetzung: Einleitung. A. Texte aus Palästina. B. Texte aus Syrien.—Schlussbemerkung.
1. Arabic poetry—Translations into German. 2. German poetry—Translations from Arabic. 3. Folk-literature—Syria. I. Title.
Full name: Ludwig Richard Enno Littmann.
AS182.G812 n. f., bd. 5, nr. 3 A C 38-4058
Newberry Library for Library of Congress [a54c½]†

NL 0414151 ICN DLC MiU PPDrop MB NN PU NcD CU

---

*Littmann, Enno, 1875- ed. and tr.

[**Giusto da Urbino,** *padre*], 1814-1856.
... Philosophi abessini ... Parisiis, e Typographeo reipublicae; [etc., etc.] 1904.

Littmann, Enno, 1875-1958.
Die pronomina im Tigrē; ein Beitrag zur aethiopischen Dialektkunde. München [1897?]

NL 0414153 NjP

Littmann, Enno, 1875-
Publications of the Princeton Expedition to Abyssinia. Leyden, Late E. J. Brill, 1910-15.
4 v. in 5. plates. 24 cm.
L. C. set incomplete: v. 1 and 3 wanting.
CONTENTS.—v. 1. Tales, customs, names and dirges of the Tigrē tribes: Tigrē text.—v. 2. Tales, customs, names and dirges of the Tigrē tribes: English translation.—v. 3. Lieder der Tigrē-Stämme: Tigrē text.—v. 4. Lieder der Tigrē-Stämme: Deutsche Übersetzung und Commentar. A. Lieder der Mänsa', Bēt-Ǵuk und Māryā. B. Lieder der 'Ad-Temāryām, 'Ad-Hebtēs (Ḥabāk), 'Ad-Taklēs und kleinerer Stämme.
1. Folk-lore — Ethiopia. 2. Folk-songs — Ethiopia. I. Princeton Expedition to Abyssinia, 1905-1906.
Full name: Ludwig Richard Enno Littmann.
GR360.E55L5 48-32153*

MiU WaU ICU InU CU OCH
NL 0414154 DLC CSt MU ICarbS IU LU NIC MoU ICJ

Littmann, Enno, 1875-1958.
R. Dussand,"Les Arabes en Syrie avant l'Islam [Review] [n.p., 1908]

NL 0414155 NjP

DT390 **Littmann, Enno** , 1875 - 1958.
f.A9B5 Reisebericht der expedition, topographie und geschichte
v. 1 Aksums von Enno Littmann, unter mitwirkung von Theodor von Lüpke ... Berlin, G. Reimer, 1913.
vi, [1], 64 p. illus., 2 pl. (1 double) fold. map, double plan. 38cm. (*Added t.-p.:* Deutsche Aksum-expedition hrsg. von der generalverwaltung der Königlichen museen zu Berlin. bd. I)
1. Aksum, Abyssinia.

NL 0414156 ICU MH NN NjP CtY IEG

Littmann, Enno, 1875-
Ruinenstätten und Schriftdenkmäler Syriens. Leipzig, E. Gaeblers Geographisches Institut, 1916.
42 p. map. 24 cm. (Länder und Völker der Türkei; Schriften der Deutschen Vorderasien-Gesellschaft, n. F., Heft 2)
1. Syria—Hist.—Outlines, syllabi, etc. I. Title. (Series: Länder und Völker der Türkei, n. F., Heft 2)
DS95.L5 58-50418

NL 0414157 DLC MH CU CtY NN DDO NIC

DT390 **Littmann, Enno**, 1875 - 1958.
f.A9B5 Sabaische, griechische und altabessinische inschriften, von
v. 4 Enno Littmann ... Berlin, G. Reimer, 1913.
viii, [1], 94, [2] p. illus., VI pl. (part double) fold. map. 37cm. (*Added t.-p.:* Deutsche Aksum-expedition, hrsg. von der generalverwaltung der Königlichen museen zu Berlin. bd. IV)
1. Inscriptions, Sabaean. 2. Inscriptions, Greek. 3. Inscriptions, Abyssinian.

NL 0414158 ICU OCl MH NN CtY IEG

Littmann, Enno, 1875-
Ṣafā — Inschriften, von Enno Littmann. (Extrait des Mélanges syriens offerts à M. R. Dussaud.) Gembloux (Belgique) J. Duculot [1939?] p. 661-671. illus. 27cm.
1. Safa inscriptions.
N. Y. P. L. March 24, 1950

NL 0414159 NN

Littmann, Enno, 1875-1958.
Sardis. Leiden, 1916.

NL 0414160 NjNbS

Littmann, Enno, 1875-1958, ed.
Die schönsten Geschichten aus 1001 Nacht
see under Arabian nights. German.

Littmann, Enno, 1875-
... Semitic inscriptions, by Enno Littmann, PH. D. New York, The Century co., 1904.
xiii, 230 p. illus. 37 x 29½cm. (*Half-title:* Publications of an American archæological expedition to Syria in 1899-1900 ... pt. IV)
Series title also at head of t.-p.
Caption title: Semitic inscriptions from northern central Syria, Palmyra, and the region of the Ḥaurân.
CONTENTS.—Syriac inscriptions.—Palmyrene inscriptions.—Nabatæan inscriptions. — Hebrew inscriptions. — Safaïtic inscriptions. — Arabic inscriptions.
1. Inscriptions, Semitic. 2. Inscriptions, Syriac. 3. Syria—Antiq.
[*Full name:* Richard Ludwig Enno Littmann]
Library of Congress PJ3081.L6 4-28428 Revised

PHC PBm MiU OCl OClW MB MH NN
NL 0414162 DLC CU NjP KyWAT NIC DDO OCH NcD PU

Littmann,Enno, 1875-
Semitic inscriptions. Leyden, Brill, 1914-49.

4 v. illus. (Publications of the Princeton University Archaeological Expeditions to Syria in 1904-1905 and 1909, IV)
Contents:-Sect.A. Nabataean inscriptions from the southern Haurân.- Sect.B. Syriac inscriptions.- Sect.C. Safaftic inscriptions.- Sect.D. Arabic inscriptions.

NL 0414163 MH PU-Mu InU RPB

Littmann, Enno, 1875-
...Semitische Philologie. (In: Abb, G., editor. Aus fuenfzig Jahren deutscher Wissenschaft. Berlin, 1930. 4°. p. [250-] 261.)
501674A. 1. Semitic languages.
N. Y. P. L. January 5, 1931

NL 0414164 NN

Littmann, Enno, 1875-1958, ed. and tr.
Semitische Stammes-sagen der Gegenwart. Aus dem Tigrē übersetzt. Von Enno Littmann.
(In Orientalische Studien Theodor Nöldeke . . . gewidmet. Vol. 2, pp. 941-958. Giessen. 1906.)
G5629 — T.r. — Tigre. Folk-lore. — Folk-lore.

NL 0414165 MB

Littmann, Enno, 1875-1958.
Semitische Volkspoesie in Abessinien. [n.p., 1902]

NL 0414166 NjP

Littmann, Enno, 1875-1958.

DS94
.5
.P7
Princeton University Archaeological Expeditions to Syria in 1904-1905 and 1909.
Syria; publications of the Princeton University Archaeological Expeditions to Syria in 1904-5 and 1909. Leyden, E. J. Brill, 1907-49 [v. 1, 1930]

Littmann, Enno, 1875-
Syriac inscriptions... Leyden, E. J. Brill, 1934.
[4],xi,[1],70p. plates, fold.maps. (Princeton university - Archaeological expeditions to Syria in 1904-1905 and 1909. Publications, Division IV, section B)

NL 0414168 OCl

---

*Littmann, Enno, 1875-

Euting, Julius, 1839-1913.
Tagbuch einer reise in Inner-Arabien, von Julius Euting ... Leiden, E. J. Brill, 1896-1914.

Y LITTMANN, ENNO, 1875-
497 ..Tales, customs, names and dirges of the Tigrē
.71 tribes.. Leyden,E.J.Brill,ltd.,1910.
2v. (Princeton expedition to Abyssinia.
v.1-2 Publications. v.1-2)

Contents.—v.1. Tigrē text.—v.2. English translation.

NL 0414170 ICN PPDrop NN

VOLUME 336

Littmann, Enno, 1875–
... Tausendundeine nacht in der arabischen literatur, von E. Littmann ... Tübingen, J. C. B. Mohr (P. Siebeck) 1923.
37 p. 22cm. (Philosophie und geschichte ... 2)
"Der hiermit veröffentlichte vortrag ... wurde in ungefähr der gleichen form am 19. juli 1923 ... als akademische antrittsrede gehalten."—p. 3.

1. Arabian nights. 2. Arabic literature—History and criticism. I. Title.
[Full name: Ludwig Richard Enno Littmann]
A C 35-2416
Title from Yale Univ. Printed by L. C.

NL 0414171 CtY NN OCl PPDrop OCH

Littmann, Enno, 1875–
Thamūd und Ṣafā, studien zur altnordarabischen inschriftenkunde, von Enno Littmann ... Leipzig, Kommissionsverlag F. A. Brockhaus, 1940.
xii, 164 p. 23½cm. (*Half-title:* Abhandlungen für die kunde des Morgenlandes; mit unterstützung der Deutschen forschungsgemeinschaft hrsg. von der Deutschen morgenländischen gesellschaft. xxv, 1)
"Abkürzungen" (bibliography): p. [xi]–xii.

1. Inscriptions, Thamudic. 2. Inscriptions, Safaitic. I. Title.
[Full name: Ludwig Richard Enno Littmann]
A 41-2740
Newberry library for Library of Congress [PJ5.D5 bd. 25, nr. 1]
[2] (490.6243)

NL 0414172 ICN CU-S ICarbS IU PU CU

Littmann, Enno, 1875–
Tschakydschy; ein türkischer Räuberhauptmann der Gegenwart, von Enno Littmann... Berlin: K. Curtius, 1915. 53 p. 8°.
"Volkslieder auf Tschakydschy" p. 29-53.
Turkish text 20 p. at end.

1. Tshakidshaly Mehmet, 1864?-1911. 2. Robbers and robberies—Turkey.
N. Y. P. L. December 13, 1927

NL 0414173 NN NNC WaU NjP MH

Littmann, Enno, 1875-1958, ed. and tr.
Ein türkisches Märchen aus Nordassyrien. [n.p., 1900?]

NL 0414174 NjP PU

BS 1520.5 L5 Littmann, Enno, 1875-1958.
Über die Abfassungszeit des Tritojesaia. Freiburg i.B., J.C.B. Mohr, 1899.
vii,52p.

1. Bible. O.T. Isaiah XLVI-LXVI--Commentaries. I. Title: Die Abfassungszeit des Tritojesaia.

NL 0414175 UU NjPT NNUT MH OCH

492.8 L781v **Littmann, Enno, 1875-**
Das Verbum der Tigresprache in Abessinien. Teil I. Halle, F.Straub, 1898.
35p. 22cm.
Inaug.-Diss. - Halle.
Vita.
No more published?
Bibliographical footnotes.

1.Tigré language - Verb.

NL 0414176 CLSU CtY MH IU ICRL

Typ 920 25.5250 Littmann, Enno, 1875-
Vom morgenländischen Floh; Dichtung und Wahrheit über den Floh bei Hebräern, Syriern, Arabern, Abessiniern und Türken von Enno Littmann. Mit Radierungen von Marcus Behmer. Im Insel-Verlag, Leipzig, 1925.
2p.l.,[7]-68p.,1l.incl.front.,illus. 20cm., in box 20.5cm.
Title-page, front. and illus. printed from etched plates.
'Hier endet das Büchlein "Vom morgenländischen

Floh" von Enno Littmann, mit Radierungen von Marcus Behmer.-Gedruckt für den Insel=Verlag zu Leipzig bei Otto von Holten, Berlin, in 330 Exemplaren, davon 300 mit Nr.1 bis 300 und 30 nicht für den Handel bestimmte Exemplare mit Nr.i bis xxx handschriftlich numeriert.-Kupferdruck vom bibliographischen Institut in Leipzig.-Dies ist Nr.245.'
Original half vellum, paper label on front cover; top edges gilt; in publisher's box.

NL 0414178 MH OCH NcU OCl MiU NN

AS 182 B51A31+ 1906 no.11 Littmann, Enno, 1875-
Vorbericht der deutschen Aksumexpedition, von E. Littmann und D. Krencker.
(In Akademie der Wissenschaften, Berlin. Abhandlungen. Berlin. 27cm. [v.90] (1906) Anhang. Philosophische und historische Abhandlungen, 2)

NL 0414179 NIC MB NjP DDO MBU

Littmann, Enno, 1875- tr.
Zar'a-Jacob, ein einsamer Denker in Abessinien see under [Giusto da Urbino, padre] 1814-1856.

Littmann, Enno, 1875-1958.
Zigeuner-arabisch, wortschatz und grammatik der arabischen bestandteile in den morgenländischen zigeunersprachen, nebst einer einleitung über das arabische rotwälsch und die namen der morgenländischen zigeuner, von dr. Enno Littmann ... Bonn-Leipzig, K. Schroeder, 1920.
2 p. l., 147 p. 25cm.

1. Gipsies—Language. 2. Gipsies—Levant. 3. Arabic language—Dialects—Glossaries, vocabularies, etc. I. Title.
[Full name: Ludwig Richard Enno Littmann]
43-37892
Library of Congress DX161.L5

NL 0414181 DLC CU CtY OCl MH ICU OCl NN PU PPDrop

Littmann, Enno, 1875-1958.
Zur Bedeutung von miskîn. [n.p., 19-]

NL 0414182 NjP

Littmann, Enno, 1875-1958.
Zur entzifferung der Safâ-inschriften, von Enno Littmann. Mit 7 autographierten tafeln. Leipzig, O. Harrassowitz, 1901.
1 p. l., ix, 76 p. facsim. 23½cm.
"Abkürzungen": p. ix.
CONTENTS.—I. Ueber die von Halévy's alphabet abweichenden buchstabenwerte.—II. Transscription einzelner inschriften und beiträge zu ihrer erklärung.

1. Inscriptions, Safaitic. I. Title.
Full name: Ludwig Richard Enno Littmann]
2-4038 Revised
Library of Congress PJ6690.L5

NL 0414183 DLC PU OCl MiU NN NjP CtY MB NNUT

DS41 .V9 v.9 Littmann, Enno, 1875-1958.
Zur Entzifferung der thamudenischen Inschriften. Eine Untersuchung des Alphabets und des Inhalts der thamudenischen Inschriften auf Grund der Kopieen von Professor J. Euting und unter Benutzung der Vorarbeiten von Professor D. H. Müller, nebst einem Anhange über die arabischen Stammeszeichen. Berlin, W. Peiser [1904]
viii, 112 p. 12 plates. (Mitteilungen der Vorderasiatischen Gesellschaft, 9.Jahrg., 1)
Bibliographical footnotes.

NL 0414184 ICU MB PU NIC MB OCH NNUT OCl CU

Littmann, Erich, 1900-
Versuche zur Synthese von verbindungen des typus der triaryl-hydrazine in der phosphor- und arsenreihe.
Inaug. diss. Berlin, 1930.

NL 0414185 ICRL OU CtY

Littmann, Ernst, 1905-
Versuche zur synthese von nitro- und aminoindolen
Inaug. Diss. Braunschweig, 1932.

NL 0414186 ICRL

Littmann, Friedrich.
Unterspannungsseitige anstelle von oberspannungsseitigen messungen bei transformatoren. ...
Inaug. Diss. - Techn. Hochschule München, [1935]

NL 0414187 ICRL

KD1334 .I9B2 1931 Littmann, Georg.
Das Bankguthaben. Tübingen, J. C. B. Mohr (P. Siebeck) 1931.
92 p. (Beiträge zur Kenntnis des Rechtslebens, Heft 7)

1. Banking law--Germany. 2. Accounting--Law--Germany. I. Title. Series.

NL 0414188 ICU MiU-L

Littmann, Gustav Adolf Otto
see Littmann, Otto, 1860-

Littmann, Hildegard, 1907–
Das dichterische bild in der lyrik George Merediths und Thomas Hardys im zusammenhang mit ihrer weltanschauung ... von Hildegard Littmann ... Bern, 1938.
487 p. 22½cm.
Inaug.-diss.—Bern.
Vita.
Published also as Schweizer anglistische arbeiten, bd. 6, under title: Die metapher in Merediths und Hardys lyrik.
"Bibliographie": p. 477–481.

1. Meredith, George, 1828–1909. 2. Hardy, Thomas, 1840–1928. 3. Metaphor. 4. Figures of speech. I. Title.
40-16822
Library of Congress PR5018.L5 1938
[2] 821.89

NL 0414190 DLC NN IU ICRL PU CtY

VOLUME 336

Littmann, Hildegard, 1907–
... Die metapher in Merediths und Hardys lyrik. Zürich und Leipzig, M. Niehans [1938]
485 p. 24½cm. (Added t.-p.: Schweizer anglistische arbeiten; Swiss studies in English ... 6. bd.)
Imprint covered by label: Bern, A. Francke, a.-g.
Issued also as inaugural dissertation, Bern, under title: Das dichterische bild in der lyrik George Merediths und Thomas Hardys.
"Bibliographie": p. 477–481.
1. Meredith, George, 1828–1909. 2. Hardy, Thomas, 1840–1928. 3. Metaphor. 4. Figures of speech. I. Title.
Library of Congress PR5018.L5 1938 39-25845
[3] 821.89
NcD CaBVaU MB GEU ScU MoU NNC OClW TxU ICU PU ICN NcU
NL 0414191 DLC CoU OrU OCU GU FTaSU IdPI PSt OOxM

WO 500 L781s 1953 LITTMANN, Imre.
Sebészeti műtéttan. Budapest, Egészségügyi Kiadó, 1953.
370 p. illus. (Egyetemi tankönyv)
1. Surgery - Operative
NL 0414192 DNLM

LITTMANN, Ismar.
Das gesetzliche rücktrittsrecht etc. Inaug. diss, Rostock. Berlin, 1902.
NL 0414193 MH-L ICRL

Littmann, Johann August Heinrich, ed.
Die Protestation der evangelischen Stände auf dem Reichstage zu Speyer im Jahre 1529
see under Protest of Spires, 1529.

Littmann, Joseph.
Experimenteller beitrag zur lehre von der athetose.
Inaug. diss. Zuerich, 1927.
Bibl.
NL 0414195 ICRL CtY

W 4 R83 1937 LITTMANN, Konrad, 1910-
Zur Frühdiagnose endocarditischer Veränderungen besonders an der Mitralis. [n. p.] 1937.
26 p.
Inaug. -Diss. - Rostock.
1. Endocarditis
NL 0414196 DNLM CtY

HD5706 .E6 Littmann, Leo.
Epting, Karl, ed.
Arbeitslager und freiwilliger arbeitsdienst in Deutschland, Schweiz, Holland, Wales; herausgegeben von dr. Karl Epting. Genf, Schweiz [1933]

Littmann, Leo.
Das europäische Friedensproblem und der Balkan; ein orientierender Überblick der weltpolitischen Lage. München: Hans Sachs-Verlag, 1913. 1 p.l., ii, 2-65 p. 8°.
1. Balkan war, 1912-13.
N. Y. P. L. October 3, 1913.
NL 0414198 NN MH

Littmann, Ludwig Richard Enno
See
Littmann, Enno, 1875-1958.

Littmann, Martin.
Getterstoffe und ihre anwendung in der hochvakuumtechnik (gasaufzehrung durch metalldämpfe) von Martin Littmann. Mit 45 textfiguren, 4 tabellen und einem patentschriftenverzeichnis. Leipzig, C. F. Winter, 1938.
vii, 103 p. illus., diagrs. 21½cm.
"Literaturverzeichnis": p. [87]–88.
1. Gases—Absorption and adsorption. 2. Vacuum-tubes. I. Title.
Library of Congress QC544.V3L53 41-695
[2] 542.77
NL 0414200 DLC CtY NNE

---

*ZP-11
Film Reproduction
LITTMANN, Martin, 1864-1925.
Betrachtungen zu den Schriftabschnitten des Jahres. Zürich, G. v. Ostheim, 1907. 86 p. 23cm.
Film reproduction. Positive.
"Separatabdruck aus dem Israel. Wochenblatt für die Schweiz."
Schiff Collection
1. Sermons, German.
NL 0414201 NN

Littmann, Martin, 1864-1925
Josef ben Simeon Kara als Schrifterklärer... von M. Littmann. Breslau: S. Schottlaender, 1887. 32 p. 8°.
Dissertation, Leipzig, 1886.
Vita.
SCHIFF COLLECTION.
1. Kara, Joseph b. Simeon, ca. 1060-ca. 1130.
N. Y. P. L. July 1, 1927
NL 0414202 NN ICRL OCH DLC MH PP

LITTMANN, Martin, 1864-1925
Worte der Erinnerung gesprochen am Grabe des Herrn Louis Liebmann... Gest. 11. Juni 1901...8p 20.5cm
1. Funeral Sermons. 2. History-Switzerland-Zürich.
NL 0414203 NNJ

LITTMANN, MAX, 1862-1931.
Das Charlottenburger Schiller-Theater, von Max Littmann; mit einer Einleitung von Raphael Loewenfeld. [München: A. Bruckmann, 190-] 57 p. illus. (incl. plans), plates. 24½cm.
Plates printed on both sides.
788713A. 1. Theatres—Germany—Charlottenburg. I. Title.
NL 0414204 NN

NA 6840 G39L78++ Littmann, Max, 1862-1931
Das grossherzogliche Hoftheater in Weimar. Denkschrift zur Feier der Eröffnung. München, L. Werner, 1908.
49 p. illus. 35 x 24cm.
1. Weimar. Hoftheater. 2. Theaters—Construction.
NL 0414205 NIC NNC MH CU NN

Littmann, Max, 1862-1931.
Die Königlichen hoftheater in Stuttgart, von professor Max Littmann. Darmstadt, A. Koch, 1912.
4 p.l., 79, [6] p. incl. illus., plates (1 double) plans. 41cm.
Three plates not included in paging.
Autographed by author.
1. Stuttgart. Hoftheather. 2. Theaters—Construction.
WaU OkU OrU
NL 0414206 ViU PP WU CLSU CLU MB ICN MiU NN MH UU

Littmann, Max, 1862-1931.
Das Landestheater in Neustrelitz in Mecklenburg. München, F. Bruckmann, 1928.
23 p. illus. 25 cm.
1. Theaters - Construction. 2. Theaters - Germany. I. Title.
NL 0414207 OU

Littmann, Max, 1862-1931.
Max Littmann, 1862-1931
see under Wolf, Georg Jacob, 1881-1936.

Littmann, Max, 1862-1931.
Das Münchner Künstlertheater. Von Prof. Max Littmann. München, L. Werner, 1908.
38, [2] p. incl. front., illus. 25cm.
NL 0414209 ICJ DLC-P4 CU NN CtY ViU NNC CLSU

Littmann, Max, 1862-1931.
Das Prinzregenten-theater in München, erbaut vom baugeschäft Heilmann & Littmann, g.m.b.h. Denkschrift zur feier der eröffnung, herausgegeben von architekt M. Littmann. München, L. Werner, architektur-buchhandlung, 1901.
4 p.l., [3]-18, [6] p. illus. (incl. port.) XVII pl. (2 double) plans. 48 x 33cm.
Plates loose in portfolio attached to inside back cover.
1. Munich. Prinzregenten theater. 2. Theaters—Construction. I. Title.
NL 0414210 ViU CU ICU CLSU CtY DCU NIC

4NA 504 Littmann, Max, 1862-1931.
Das Stadttheater in Hildesheim. München, L. Werner, 1909.
23 p.
NL 0414211 DLC-P4 NIC NNC ViU CU

725.8 L781v Littmann, Max, 1862-1931.
Das variable Proszenium für Oper, Tondrama und Schauspiel. [n.p., n.d.]
[7]p. illus. 25cm.
1. Theaters - Construction. I. Title.
NL 0414212 CLSU

Littmann, Minna.
Walton Ricketson, sculptor and gentleman. New Bedford, Mass., 1923.
1. Ricketson, Walton, 1839-1923
NL 0414213 PHC

VOLUME 336

Littmann, Otto, 1860-
Ueber das verhältniss von längsdilatation und querkontraktion elastischer metallcylinder ... Breslau, Breslauer Genossenschafts-buchdruckerei, 1885.
2 p.l., 48 [2] p. incl. tables 1 fold. pl. 22 cm. (German mathematical dissertations. Breslau. v. 4)
Inaug.-diss. - Breslau.
Lebenslauf.
Bibliographical foot-notes.

NL 0414214 RPB PU NjP ICRL

MANN SF 275 Y5 L7
Littmann, Otto Karl Ernst, 1902-
Beiträge zur kenntnis der joghurtbereitung. Plieningen-Stuttgart, Fr. Find söhne, 1934.
46 p. tables, diagrs. 23 cm.
Inaug.-diss. - Hohenheim.
"Literaturverzeichnis": p. 45.
Lebenslauf.
1. Yogurt. I. Title.

NL 0414215 NIC ICRL

Littmann, Otto von, 1903-
Ueber ein verfahren zur bestimmung der α oder β-struktur von disacchariden.
Inaug. diss. Berlin, 1929.

NL 0414216 ICRL OU CtY

LITTMANN, Richard Ludwig Enno
See LITTMANN, Enno, 1875-1958.

Littmann, Wilheln Heinrich Arnold.
see Littmann, Arnold.

Littmarck, Robert.
Malerdalens nomeder ... Stockholm (1930)
84 p. 20 cm.

NL 0414219 DL

Littner, Alexandre S 1909-
... La fièvre du neuvième jour sans éruption au cours du traitement par les arsenicaux ... Paris, 1935.
Thèse - Univ. de Paris.
"Bibliographie": p. [31]-32.

NL 0414220 CtY

DS135 G33L78
Littner, Jakob.
Aufzeichnungen aus einem Erdloch. München, H. Kluger, 1948.
147 p. 20cm.
1. Jews in Germany. 2. National socialism. 3. Jews - Persecutions. 4. World War, 1939-1945 - Personal narratives, German. I. Title.

NL 0414221 CSt-H MiU CoU WU

Litto, Victor del.
Bibliographie stendhalienne. Grenoble, Arthaud, 1945-
v. 26cm.
Continues Bibliographie stendhalienne, 1928-1935, by L. Royer.
Vol. 4- published by Éditions du Grand-Chêne (Lausanne, 1958-) in Collection stendhalienne.
Contents.-[1] 1938-1943.-[2] 1944-1946 [et] Suppléments, 1938-1943.-[3] 1947-1952.-[4] 1953-1956.
1. Beyle, Marie Henri, 1783-1842 - Bibl.

NL 0414222 CSt MH NIC NN WU DCU CU

Litto, Victor del.
Bibliographie stendhalienne, 1938-1943. Grenoble, Arthaud, 1945.
30 p. 26 cm.
"Tiré à 220 exemplaires numérotés. No. 46."
Continues Bibliographie stendhalienne, 1928-1935, by L. Royer.
—— —— 1944-1946. Suppléments, 1938-1943. Grenoble, Arthaud, 1948.
70 p. 25 cm.
"Tiré à 220 exemplaires numérotés."
Z8092.8.L55 Suppl.
1. Beyle, Marie Henri, 1783-1842—Bibl.
Z8092.8.L55 012 A 47-4308 rev*
Rochester. Univ. Libr. for Library of Congress [r50c2]†

NL 0414223 PU IU NIC CLSU TxU ViU NRU OrU NN CoU CU NRU DLC OU ICU RPB CLU ICN NcD PPT CtY

Litto, Victor del.
Bibliographie Stendhalienne, 1947-1952. Grenoble, B. Arthand, 1955.
120p. 25½cm.
Tiré à 300 exemplaires numérotés, no. 85.
1. Beyle, Marie Henri, 1947-1952-Bibl.

NL 0414224 DHU NN NcD ICU RPB OClW IaU CU

Litto, Victor del.
...Un Dauphinois méconnu, Louis-Joseph Jay, fondateur du musée de Grenoble. Grenoble, Impr. Allier, 1946. p. 125-146. 25cm.
1. Jay, Louis Joseph, 1755-1836.
N. Y. P. L. December 12, 1949

NL 0414225 NN ICU CU PU

Litto, Victor del.
En marge des manuscrits de Stendhal; compléments et fragments inédits (1803-1820) suivis en appendice d'un courrier italien. Paris, Presses universitaires de France, 1955.
434 p. facsims. 22 cm. (Université de Grenoble. Publications de la Faculté des lettres, 13)
"Ouvrage publié avec le concours du Centre national de la recherche scientifique."
1. Beyle, Marie Henri, 1783-1842—Bibl. I. Title. (Series: Grenoble. Université. Faculté des lettres. Publications, 13)
A 56-4692
Kentucky. Univ. Libr. for Library of Congress [2]

NL 0414226 CtY NIC ViU CU IaU OU IEN InU NcD LU GEU FTaSU TNJ MiU NN CU-S NBuU IaU PPT MeB MiU OCU KyU CLSU WaU ICU ICN LNHT FU MoU MiEM

LITTO, Victor del.
In memoriam: les travaux Stendhaliens de Henri Jacoubet (+ 4 décembre 1943) [Paris?, 1944?]
14 p. 26cm.
Film reproduction. Negative.
Bibliography, p. 12-14.
1. Beyle, Marie Henri, 1783-1842. 2. Jacoubet, Henri, 1877-1943.

NL 0414227 NN

Litto, Victor del.
... Lettres à Stendhal...
see under [Beyle, Marie Henri] 1783-1842.

Litto, Victor del.
Manuel d'italien commercial. Grenoble, B. Arthaud [1944]
323 p. fold. maps. 20 cm.
1. Italian language—Business Italian. 2. Italian language—Text-books for foreigners—French.
PC1120.C7L5 458.244 50-50996 rev

NL 0414229 DLC MH NjP ICU

843.71 L781D
Litto, Victor del.
...Quelques nouveaux documents sur l'abbé Raillane. Le Divan, 1943.
cover-title, 25 p. 19 cm.
Bibliographical references included in footnotes.

NL 0414230 NcD CU

Litto, Victor del.
Scholies stendhaliennes; notes inédites
see under [Beyle, Marie Henri] 1783-1842.

Litto, Vittorio del
see Litto, Victor del.

LITTOLFF, Denise.
Étude des acides naphtalène-monosulfoniques. [Thèse], Strasbourg. Mulhouse, Société alsacienne d'édition "Alsatia", 1927.
pp.69 Diagrs.

NL 0414233 MH-C CtY

Litton, Abram, 1814-
An address to the graduates of the medical department of the St. Louis University. 14 pp., 1 l. 8°. St. Louis, Missouri Republican, 1851.

NL 0414234 DNLM PU

Litton, Abram, 1814-
An introductory lecture, to the course of chemistry and pharmacy, in the Medical department of the St. Louis university. By A. Litton ... Saint Louis, Printed by Chambers & Knapp, 1844.
23 p. 22cm.
1. Chemistry—Addresses, essays, lectures. 2. Pharmacy—Addresses, essays, lectures.
Library of Congress RS99.L73 7-29925†

NL 0414235 DLC

VOLUME 336

Litton, Abram, 1814-
A preliminary report on some of the principal mines in Franklin, Jefferson, Washington, St. François and Madison counties, Missouri. 239,[1] p. il. 6 pl. 4 maps, 1 table. [*In* MISSOURI. STATE GEOLOGIST. First and second annual reports. Jefferson City 1855.]

NL 0414236 ICJ PPL MH OO

Litton, Alexander H
A short and comprehensive introduction to arithmetic and book-keeping, designed for the use of young ladies and junior classes in academies. By Alexander H. Litton ... Dublin, Printed by Charles Downes, 1808.
v, [1], 108, 24 p. 19cm.

1. Arithmetic. 2. Bookkeeping.

NL 0414237 NNC

Litton, E L.
Selections of French handwriting; exercises for the use of students, by E. L. Litton. London, Gee & co., ltd., 1929.
[48] p. incl. facsims. 21½cm. (*Half-title:* London school of economics & political science (University of London) Studies in commerce ... vol. III)
Includes blank pages for "Notes and vocabulary" ([3] at end)
"Selected to familiarise the student with French handwriting."—Pref.

1. French language—Writing. I. Title.
39-9099
Library of Congress Z43.L78
[2] 652

NL 0414238 DLC NN

Hist.
18th c.
WZ
260
L782P
1747
Litton, Edmund.
Philosophical conjectures on aereal influences, the probable origin of diseases: with an unusual cure in the scurvy... London, Printed for T. Trye, 1747.
57 p. 21 1/2 cm.

1. Diseases Outbreaks. 2. Scurvy. I. Title.

NL 0414239 WU-M DNLM NNE

Litton, Edmund.
Philosophical conjectures on aereal influences, the probable origin of diseases, addressed to Peter Shaw. 2nd.ed. London, Trye, 1750.
57 p.

NL 0414240 PPC

Litton, Edmund.
The Theory of the distemper among the horned cattle. London, 1750.
23 p. O.

NL 0414241 RPB

BV600 .L77 Litton, Edward Arthur, 1813-1897.
The church of Christ, in its idea, attributes, and ministry: with a particular reference to the controversy on the subject between Romanists and Protestants. By Edward Arthur Litton ... London, Longman, Brown, Green, and Longmans, 1851.
xxxi, 707, [1] p. 23cm.

1. Church. 2. Catholic church—Doctrinal and controversial works—Protestant authors.

NL 0414242 ICU CtW CtY

BV600 .L78 Litton, Edward Arthur, 1813-1897.
The church of Christ, in its idea, attributes, and ministry: with a particular reference to the controversy on the subject between Romanists and Protestants... 1st American ed. Rev. by the author. Published by a lay member of the Protestant Episcopal church. Philadelphia[etc.] 1856.
xxiv, [25]-468p. 24cm.

NL 0414243 ICU PPL PP NN OCl NjNbS CLSU

Litton, Edward Arthur, 1813–1897.
The church of Christ, in its idea, attributes, and ministry: with a particular reference to the controversy on the subject between Romanists and Protestants. By Edward Arthur Litton ... 2d American ed. rev. by the author. Philadelphia, Smith & English; New York, A. D. F. Randolph, 1859.
xxiv, [25]-468 p. 24cm.

1. Church. 2. Church—Marks. 3. Clergy—Office. I. Title.
45-46424
Library of Congress BV600.L55 1859

NL 0414244 DLC WaTC CtY PPPD OO ViU

Litton, Edward Arthur, 1813-1897.
The church of Christ, in its idea, attributes, and ministry: with a particular reference to the controversy on the subject between Romanists and Protestants. 3d American ed., rev. by Charles W. Quick. Philadelphia, Smith & English, 1863.
468 p. 24 cm.

"Published by a lay member of the Protestant Episcopal Churcy."
Bibliographical footnotes.

NL 0414245 KKcB PPRETS PPPrHi NRCR

Litton, Edward Arthur, 1813-1897
The Church of Christ, in its idea, attributes and ministry, with a particular reference to the controversy on the subject between Romanists and Protestants. 4th. Amer. ed. rev. by C.W. Quick... Philade phia, Smith, etc.,1869.
468 p.

NL 0414246 PPLT PPRETS CtY

---

ar W
9139
Litton, Edward Arthur, 1813-1897.
The gospel not a ceremonial law; a sermon preached before the University of Oxford, at St. Mary's, on Monday, January 30, 1854, being the anniversary of the martyrdom of King Charles I. Oxford, W. Graham, 1854.
22 p. 22cm.

No. 21 in vol. lettered: Charles I. Sermons.

NL 0414247 NIC

Litton, Edward Arthur, 1813-1897.
A guide to the study of Holy Scripture... 4th thousand. London, Seeley, Jackson, and Halliday, 1866.
xii, 402 p. maps. 18cm.

NL 0414248 NjPT

Litton, Edward Arthur, 1813-1897.
Intellectual religionism pourtrayed. A sermon preached before the University of Oxford ... March 28, 1852. ... Oxford, 1853.
22 p. 21 cm.

NL 0414249 RPB

BX
5131
L781i
Litton, Edward Arthur, 1813-1897.
Introducation to dogmatic theology, on the basis of the XXXIX Articles of the Church of England. London, E. Stock, 1882.
viii, 295p. 20cm.

Contains only the first part of the work.

1. Church of England--Doctrinal and controversial works.
2. Theology, Doctrinal --Introductions.

NL 0414250 ICMcC PPPD NNUT NRCR KyWA IEG

230
L73i
1912
Litton, Edward Arthur, 1813-1897.
Introduction to dogmatic theology on the basis of the thirty-nine articles, by the Rev. E. A. Litton ... 3d ed., edited by the Rev. H. G. Grey ... Introduction by the very Rev. Henry Wace ... London, R. Scott, 1912.
603p.

1. Theology, Doctrinal. 2. Church of England--Doctrinal and controversial works. 3. Church of England--Articles of religion. I. Grey, Harry George, 1851-1925, ed.

NL 0414251 IU

Litton, Edward Arthur, 1813–1897.
Miracles. By the Rev. E. A. Litton ... Pub. under the direction of the Tract committee. London, Society for promoting Christian knowledge [1868?]
191 p. 17½ cm.

1. Miracles.
BT97.L5 20—17713

NL 0414252 DLC PPL NNUT NcD MiU NN

Litton, Edward Arthur, 1813–1897.
The Mosaic dispensation considered as introductory to Christianity. Eight sermons preached before the University of Oxford at the Bampton lecture for the year MDCCCLVI. By the Rev. Edward Arthur Litton ... London, T. Hatchard; [etc., etc.] 1856.
xix, 387 p. 22cm.
Binder's title: Bampton lectures. 1856.

1. Covenants (Theology) 2. Typology (Theology) 3. Christianity and other religions—Judaism. 4. Jews—Religion—Relations—Christianity. I. Title.
38-16202
Library of Congress BR45.B3 1856
[3] (230.082) 220.6

NL 0414253 DLC MH RPB NN NjNbS PP PPPD PBm CtY PBL NNUT

VOLUME 336

Litton, Edward Arthur, 1813-1897.
A sermon on John III 5, preached in reference to the recent legislative decision in the case of Gorham v. Bishop of Exeter London, 1850.
47 p. 8°. [In College Pamphlets, v. 1766]

NL 0414254 CtY

Litton, Edward Arthur, 1813-1897.
Lmd21 University reform. A letter to the Right Hon.
850k Lord John Russell ... London, T.Hatchard, etc., etc., 1850.
2p.l., 59p. 20½cm.

-- A postscript to a letter to the Right Hon. Lord John Russell ... containing additional suggestions ... London, T.Hatchard, etc., etc., 1850.
1p.l., 61-84p. 20½cm. Bound with the above.

NL 0414255 CtY MH

Litton, Edward Arthur, 1813-1897.
University reform. A letter to the Right Hon. Lord John Russell ... 2d ed., with a postscript. London [etc.] 1850.
1 p.l., 84 p. 22.5 cm. [Binder's title: Oxford Univ. Reform, 1850]
1. Oxford. University - Administration.
2. Russell, John Russell, 1st earl, 1792-1878.

NL 0414256 CtY

Litton, Edward Falconer, 1827-1891.
Life or death; the destiny of the soul in the future state. London, Longmans, Green, 1886.
viii, 263 p. 23cm.

1. Future life. 2. Immortality. 3. Soul. I. Title. II. Title: Destiny of the soul in the future state.

NL 0414257 ViU

Litton, Gaston L., joint ed.

Dale, Edward Everett, 1879– ed.
Cherokee cavaliers; forty years of Cherokee history as told in the correspondence of the Ridge-Watie-Boudinot family, by Edward Everett Dale & Gaston Litton. Norman, University of Oklahoma press, 1939.

Litton, G[eorge] J[ohn] L[etablère].
China. Report of a journey to North Ssu-Ch'uan. London: Harrison and Sons, 1898. 48 p., 4 maps. 8°. (Great Britain. Foreign Office. Diplomatic and consular reports. Miscellaneous series. no. 457.)

1. China.—Description, 1898.
N. Y. P. L. January 3, 1913.

NL 0414259 NN NcU WaU

Litton, George John Letablere.
China. Notes of a journey to Tachienlu. London: Harrison and Sons, 1898. 15(1) p., 1 map. 8°. (Great Britain. Foreign Office. Diplomatic and consular reports. Miscellaneous series. no. 475.)

1. China.—Description, 1898.
N. Y. P. L. January 3, 1913.

NL 0414260 NN NcU

Wason [Litton, George John Letablère]
DS703 Report on a journey in north and north-
Z143 west Yunnan, season 1902-1903. Shanghai, Printed at the Shanghai Mercury, 1903.
27 p. 25cm.

In vol. lettered: China and the Chinese. Pamphlets. Vol. 43.

1. Yünnan, China (Province)--Descr. & trav.

NL 0414261 NIC MH MSaE NN

Litton, George John Letablère.
Report of a journey to North Szechuen. Shanghai. Printed at the Shanghai Mercury office 1898.
32 p.

NL 0414262 OCl MSaE

Litton, George Washington, 1910–
Feeding lambs on pasture and phenothiazine at breeding time [by George W. Litton and others] Blacksburg, Agricultural Experiment Station, V. P. I., 1954.
14 p. illus., tables. 23 cm. (Virginia. Agricultural Experiment Station, Blacksburg. Bulletin 468)
Cover title.
"Literature cited": p. 14.

1. Phenothiazine. 2. Sheep—Feeding and feeding stuffs. 3. Stock and stock-breeding. I. Title. (Series)
[S123.E2 no. 468] A 54-9803
Virginia Poly. Inst. Library
for Library of Congress [1]

NL 0414263 ViBlbV

[Litton, J.N.]
Appellant's Statement. [Atlantic & Pacific R.R. vs. James Freeman] [An answer to the grounds of objection of the defendants in their demurrer, in the case of The Atlantic & Pacific Railroad Company, Plaintiff, vs. James Freeman and Zenas Freeman, Defendants] n.p., n.d. [1873?]
8 p. Octavo.
From Anderson Galleries, 10-11 Mar. '19, lot 350 (part)
Signed at end, "J.N. Litton, Appellant."

Latest date in text, April, 1872.
Bound (11) with: South Pacific Railroad Company. Memorial ... 1871. Bound in 3/4 green calf, gilt, with red label, lettered "Pacific Railroad - Memorial and Briefs of Cases".

NL 0414265 CSmH

[Litton, J.N.]
... Buffington vs. The Atlantic & Pacific Railroad Co. Appellant's Statement. [caption-title]. n.p., n.d. [1874]
11 p. Octavo.
From Anderson Galleries, 10-11 Mar. '19, lot 350 (part)
At head of title: "In the April General Term, 1874."
Signed at end, "J.N. Litton, For appellant."
Bound (22) with: South Pacific Railroad Company. Memorial ... 1871. Bound in 3/4 green calf, gilt,

red label lettered "Pacific Railroad - Memorial and Briefs of Cases".

NL 0414267 CSmH

[Litton, J.N.]
... Emma G. Gavisk vs. Pacific Railroad. Appellant's Statement. [caption-title] n.p., n.d. [1872]
22 p., 1 blank leaf. Octavo.
From Anderson Galleries, 10-11 Mar '19, lot 350 (part).
At head of title: "In the Supreme Court, January Term, 1872."
Signed at end by "J.N. Litton, for Appellant."
Imperfect: The leaf containing pages 13-14 has been cut and the lower half is lacking.

Bound (5) with: South Pacific Railroad Company. Memorial ... 1871. Bound in 3/4 green calf, gilt, w. red label lettered "Pacific Railroad. - Memorial and Briefs of Cases."

NL 0414269 CSmH

[Litton, J.N.]
... H.N. Ells, Respondent, vs. Pacific Railroad, Appellant. The Appellant's Statement. [caption-title] n.p., n.d. [1874]
15 p. Octavo.
From Anderson Galleries, 10-11 Mar. '19, lot 350 (part)
At head of title: "No. 24. In Supreme Court, January Term, 1874".
Signed at end, "J.N. Litton, Attorney for Appellant."

Bound (20) with: South Pacific Railroad Company. Memorial ... 1871. Bound in 3/4 green calf, gilt; red label, lettered "Pacific Railroad - Memorial and Briefs of Cases."

NL 0414271 CSmH

[Litton, J.N.]
Henry Cunningham and Laura Cunningham, Respondents, vs. The Pacific Railroad Appellant. No. 52. In the Supreme Court Jefferson City. October Term, 1875. Appellant's Statement. [caption-title] n.p., n.d. [1875]
25 p. Octavo.
From Anderson Galleries, 10-11 Mar. '19, lot 350 (part)
Signed at end, "J.N. Litton, for Appellant."

Bound (30) with: South Pacific Railroad Company. Memorial ... 1871. Bound in 3/4 green calf, gilt; red label lettered "Pacific Railroad - Memorial and Briefs of Cases."

NL 0414273 CSmH

[Litton, J.N.]
... James A. Spurlock, Appellant, vs. The Pacific Railroad, Respondent. Respondent's Statement. [caption-title] n.p., n.d. [1874]
31 p. Octavo.
From Anderson Galleries, 10-11 Mar. '19, lot 350 (part).
At head of title; "No. 38. In the Supreme Court. July Term, A.D. 1874."
Signed at end, "J.N. Litton, Attorney for Deft. in error."
"Appendix", p. 23-31.

Bound (24) with: South Pacific Railroad Company. Memorial ... 1871. Bound in 3/4 green calf, gilt; red label lettered "Pacific Railroad - Memorial and Briefs of Cases".

NL 0414275 CSmH

VOLUME 336

[Litton, J.N.]
James D. White, Respondent, vs. The Pacific Railroad, Appellant. Appeal from Circuit Court of St. Louis Co. Room No. 3. Appellant's Statement. [caption-title] n.p., n.d. [1873?]
20 p. Octavo.
From Anderson Galleries, 10-11 Mar, '19 lot 350 (part).
Signed at end, "J.N. Litton, For Defendant."
Latest date in text, Aug. 7, 1872.
Bound (10) with: South Pacific Railroad Company. Memorial ... 1871. Bound in 3/4 green calf, gilt, with red label, lettered "Pacific Railroad - Memorial and Briefs of Cases".

NL 0414277 CSmH

[Litton, J.N.]
... John Miller, by Guardian, Respondent, vs. The Atlantic & Pacific Railroad Company, Appellant. Statement of Appellant. [caption-title] n.p., n.d. [1873?]
31 p. Octavo.
From Anderson Galleries, 10-11 Mar. '19, lot no. 350 (part).
At head of title: "In Circuit Court of Saint Louis County. General Term." Signed, p. 24, "J.N. Litton, Attorney for Appellant."
Latest date used in text is Nov. 4th, 1872.
Bound (2) with: South Pacific Railroad Company. Memorial ... 1871. In 3/4 green calf, gilt, w. red label, lettered "Pacific Railroad - Memorial and Briefs of Cases".

NL 0414279 CSmH

[Litton, J.N.]
Joseph H. Page, Respondent, vs. Atlantic and Pacific Railroad Company, Appellant. No. 95. Supreme Court, Jefferson City, October Term, 1875. Appellant's Statement [caption-title] n.p., n.d. [1875]
19 p. Octavo.
From Anderson Galleries, 10-11 Mar '19, lot 350 (part)
Signed at end, "J.N. Litton, for Appellant."
Bound (31) with: South Pacific Railroad Company. Memorial ... 1871. Bound in 3/4 green calf, gilt; red label lettered "Pacific Railroad - Memorial and Briefs of Cases".

NL 0414281 CSmH

[Litton, J.N.]
... Mary Devitt, Respondent, vs. Pacific Railroad, Appellant. Statement by Appellant. [caption-title] n.p., n.d. [1872]
16 p. Octavo.
From Anderson Galleries, 10-11 Mar. '19, lot no. 350 (part)
At head of title: "In the Supreme Court at Jefferson City. July Term, 1872." Signed at end, "J.N. Litton, for Appellant."
Bound (7) with: South Pacific Railroad Company. Memorial ... 1871. Bound in 3/4 green calf, gilt, w. red label lettered "Pacific Railroad - Memorial and Briefs of Cases."

NL 0414283 CSmH

[Litton, J.N.]
... Pacific Railroad, Appellant, vs. Cass County, Respondent. Appellant's Statement. [caption-title] n.p., n.d. [1873]
23 p. Octavo.
From Anderson Galleries, 10-11 Mar. '19, lot 350 (part)
Signed at end, "J.N. Litton, Attorney for Appellant."
Bound (12) with: South Pacific Railroad Company. Memorial ... 1871. Bound in 3/4 green calf, gilt; red label lettered "Pacific Railroad - Memorial and Briefs of Cases."

NL 0414285 CSmH

[Litton, J.N.]
... Pacific Railroad vs. Timmermann. Appellant's Statement. [caption-title] n.p., n.d. [1874]
8 p. Octavo.
From Anderson Galleries, 10-11 Mar. '19, lot 350 (part)
At head of title: "No. - In General Term. - June, 1874."
Signed at end, "J.N. Litton, For Appellant."
Bound (23) with: South Pacific Railroad Company. Memorial ... 1871. Bound in 3/4 green calf, gilt; red label, lettered "Pacific Railroad - Memorial and Briefs of Cases."

NL 0414287 CSmH

[Litton, J.N.]
Respondents Statement [in the case of Emma Smith Smith] N.p., n.d. [1874?]
11 p. Octavo.
From Anderson Galleries, 10-11 Mar '19, lot 350 (part)
Note: Statement of the amended petition of the plaintiff in the case of Emma Smith, Plaintiff, vs. Pacific Railroad, Defendant. In the Circuit Court of Cole County, Missouri, November Term, A.D. 1873, with the demurrer of the defendant, and Litton's points on the question whether the demurred was properly sustained. Signed at end, "J.N. Litton for Respondent."
Bound (18) with: South Pacific Railroad Company, Memorial ... 1871. Bound in 3/4 green calf, gilt; red label lettered "Pacific Railroad - Memorial and Briefs of Cases".

NL 0414289 CSmH

[Litton, J.N.]
W.W. Southgate, Respondent. vs. The Atlantic and Pacific Railroad Company, Appellant. No. 134. In the Supreme Court of Missouri. October Term 1875. Appellant's Statement. [caption-title] n.p., n.d. [1875]
7 p. Octavo.
From Anderson Galleries, 10-11 Mar. '19, lot 350 (part)
Signed at end, "J.N. Litton, for Appellant."
Bound (38) with: South Pacific Railroad Company. Memorial ... 1871. Bound in 3/4 green calf, gilt; red label lettered "Pacific Railroad - Memorial and Briefs and Cases".

NL 0414291 CSmH

[Litton, J.N.]
William Long, Respondent, vs. Pacific Railroad, Appellant. No. 75, Supreme Court of Missouri, October Term 1875. Appellant's Statement. [caption-title] n.p., n.d. [1875]
27 p. Octavo.
From Anderson Galleries, 10-11 Mar. '19, lot 350 (part)
Signed at end, "J.N. Litton, for Appellant."
Bound (33) with: South Pacific Railroad Company. Memoral ... 1871. Bound in 3/4 green calf, gilt; red label lettered "Pacific Railroad - Memorial and Briefs of Cases".

NL 0414292 CSmH

LITTON, John.
Thoughts on education, to which is added reflections on the life of Richard Brinsley Sheridan. Contained in the inaugural address, delivered before the Sheridan literary society, of Rotonto, 12th of Nov., 1859. Toronto, Roswell & Ellis, [1859].

Pamphlet.

NL 0414293 MH

TD1953
L736

Litton, Maurice Lovell, 1917-
A study of selected aspects of the pre-service preparation of two groups of junior college teachers. Austin, Tex., 1953.
372, [2] ℓ. tables. 28cm.

Thesis (D.Ed.) - University of Texas, 1953.
Vita.
Bibliography: ℓ. [291]-296.

1. Teachers, Training of. 2. Junior colleges - U.S.

NL 0414294 TxU

Litton, Richard.
Save the American way ...
see under Goldman, Edwin Franko, 1878-

Litton, Robert Tuthill.

Geological society of Australasia, *Melbourne.*
List of members of the Geological society of Australasia ...
Melbourne, Geological society of Australasia; London, Dulau & co., 18

Litton, Robert Tuthill, ed.
Transactions ...
see under Geological society of Australasia, Melbourne.

Litton (Samuel). *De calculo. 13 pp. 8°.
Edinburgi, A. Neill et soc., 1807.

NL 0414298 DNLM

Litton, Samuel George.
Christ and the Church. A sermon preached at the opening of the eleventh annual convention of the diocese of Tennessee... Tennessee, 1839.
10 p.

NL 0414299 PPiPT

VOLUME 336

Litton, Rev. Samuel George
The examiner examined; a review of a sermon [by R.D. Thomason] purporting to be an examination of the claims of episcopacy. Memphis, Tenn., 1839. 8°

NL 0414300 NN

DA 670 .L75 L5 Littondale: past and present. Pt. I. Fifty years in Arncliffe, by the Venerable Archdeacon Boyd. Pt. II. Halton Gill in the olden time, by the Rev. W. A. Shuffrey. Leeds, R. Jackson, 1893.
155 p. illus. 23cm.
Errata slip laid in.
1. Littondale, Eng. - Antiq. 2. Arncliffe, Eng. - Antiq. 3. Halton Gill, Eng. - Antiq. I. Boyd, William, Vicar of Arncliffe. II. Shuffrey, William Arthur, 1851- III. Title: Fifty years in Arncliffe. IV. Title: Halton Gill in the olden time.

NL 0414301 WU

Littooy, G J
Canada; aspecten van het land en zijn economische ontplooiïng. Eindhoven, Uitg. Mij. "De Pelgrim," 1949.
158 p. illus., fold. map. 20 cm.
"Literatuuropgave": p. 158.
1. Canada. 2. Canada—Econ. condit.—1918-
F1008.L74 50-16152

NL 0414302 DLC NhD NN

LITTOOY, J. F.
New raspberry and blackberry culture. n.d. Everett, (Wash.) Pub. by author.

NL 0414303 Or

The littoral fauna of Krusadai Island
see under Madras. Government Museum.

Le littoral yougoslave de l'Adriatique
see under Rojc, Milan, 1855-

LITTORIA; documenti della ricostruzione fascista. v. 1-
Roma: Libreria del Littorio, 1928- 22cm.
v.

NL 0414306 NN

Littoria e la sua provincia.
see under [Camillacci, S]

Bml4a Is7m IV.6 I Littoriali dell'anno XVI ... Roma, Istituto nazionale di cultura fascista, 1938.
38p., 1l. plates. 24cm. (Studi di "Civiltà fascista". Serie IV, 6)
"Estratto dalla rivista 'Civiltà fascista', anno V, n.5, del maggio 1938."
Contents. - A.Starace. Prefazione. - G.A. Longo. Orientamenti della gioventù fascista. - N.Tripodi. Il convegno di dottrina del fascismo. - G.Calendoli. Il convegno di politica estera. - N.Galdo. Il convegno di politica educativa. - S.Zaccagnini. Il convegno di organizzazione del lavoro. - V. Buonassisi. Il convegno di studi militari. - R.Jacobbi. Il convegno di letteratura. - P.E.Gennarini. Il convegno d'arti figurativo. - G.Ballo. Il convegno di critica teatrale. - G.Bardi. Il convegno di critica cinematografica. - R.Assunto. Il convegno di critica radiofonica. - E.Saini. Il convegno di critica musicale.

NL 0414309 CtY

Littoriali dell'arte, Trieste.
Catalogo della mostra d'arte ai littoriali dell'anno XVII... 30 marzo - 6 aprile. Trieste [1939]
1 v.(unpaged) plates 19 cm.
Cover title

NL 0414310 MH

Littorin, Frank T 1900–
How to preach the Word with variety. Grand Rapids, Baker Book House, 1953.
157 p. 21 cm.
1. Preaching. I. Title.
BV4211.L55 251.8 53-3411 ‡

NL 0414311 DLC

Il Littorio; giornale di propaganda fascista... Anno 1
New York: Adria Printing & Pub. Co. [1933– 56cm.
v. illus.
Irregular.
Subtitle varies slightly.
Text in English or Italian.
1. Italians in the U. S.—Per. and soc. publ. 2. Fascism—Per. and soc. publ.—U. S.
N. Y. P. L. March 19, 1936

NL 0414312 NN

Littré, Freemason, .
Loge française et ecossaise de la Clémente Amitié. Fête anniversaire de la réception du F. Littré
see under Freemasons. Paris. Loge de la Clémente Amitié.

Littré [Alexis] [1658-1726]. Observations sur une espèce d'enfleure appellée emphysème. pp. 4-14. 8°. Paris, 1715.
Cutting from: Mém. Acad. roy. d. sc., Par., 1713.

NL 0414314 DNLM

Littré, Émile, 1801-1881. 3915-53
Ampère et l'électro-magnétisme.
(In his La science au point de vue philosophique. Pp. 85-109. Paris, 1873.)
Aug.4, 1902
E5231 — Electro-magnetism. — Ampère, André Marie. — No main card.

NL 0414315 MB

Littré, Émile, 1801-1881.
Analyse raisonnée du cours de philosophie positive de m. Auguste Comte. Par m. E. Littré ... Utrecht, Kemink & zoon, 1845.
1 p. l., 106 p. 23½cm.
1. Comte, Auguste, 1798-1857.

NL 0414316 MiU

---

*Littré, Émile, 1801-1881, tr.
Hippocrates.
Aphorismes d'Hippocrate, traduits en français, avec le texte en regard; accompagnés d'un argument et de notes, par É. Littré ... Paris, Chez J. B. Baillière; [etc., etc.] 1844.

Littré, Émile, 1801-1881.
Application de la philosophie positive au gouvernement des sociétés et en particulier à la crise actuelle, par É. Littré ... Paris, Librairie philosophique de Ladrange, 1850.
vii, 158 p., 1 l. 22cm.
1. Positivism.

NL 0414318 MiU MH InU PU

Littre, Émile, 1801-1881.
Atlas populaire de médecine de chirurgie, de pharmacie, de l'art vétérinaire
see his Dictionnaire de médecine. Atlas populaire

194.8 L782A Littré, Émile, 1801-1881.
Auguste Comte et la philosophie positive ... Paris, L. Hachette, 1863
687 p. 21½cm.
"Ouvrages de m. Comte": p. [683]-684.
1. Comte, Auguste, 1798-1857

NL 0414320 NcD InU PPT MiU NN MdBP WU

Littré, Émile, 1801-1881.
Auguste Comte et la philosophie positive, par É. Littré. 2. éd. Paris, L. Hachette et cie, 1864.
2 p. l., xi, 687, [1] p. 22½cm.
"Ouvrages de m. Comte": p. [683]-684.
1. *Comte, Auguste, 1798-1857.
[Full name: Maximilien Paul Émile Littré]
6-24765 rev.
Library of Congress B2247.L7

NL 0414321 DLC NjP OCIW ViU NIC PU OCl CtY

VOLUME 336

194 Littré, Émile, 1801-1881.
C74 Auguste Comte et la philosophie positive.
XL12 Paris, Aux Bureaux de la Philosophie Positive, 1877.
1877 xi,675p. 22cm.

Bibliography: p.[699]-671.

1.Comte, Auguste, 1798-1857. 2.Positivism.

NL 0414322 CLSU OrCS OCU

B2247 Littré, Émile, 1801-1881.
L5 Auguste Comte et Stuart Mill; suivi de Stuart Mill et la philosophie positive, par G. Wyrouboff. New York, German Baillière [1-
86 p. 23cm.

1.Comte, Auguste, 1798-1857. 2.Mill, John Stuart 1806-1873. I.Wyrouboff, G. Stuart Mill et la philosophie positive. II.Title.

NL 0414323 OrCS

B2247 Littré, Émile, 1801-1881.
.M648 Auguste Comte et Stuart Mill, réimprimé de la Revue des deux mondes; suivi de Stuart Mill et la philosophie positive, par G. Wyrouboff. [Paris, G. Baillière [1867]
iv, 86 p.
A reply to J. S. Mill's Auguste Comte and positivism.

1. Mill, John Stuart, 1806-1873. Auguste Comte and positivism.

NL 0414324 ICU DLC-P4 ICJ CU NjP MH-AH MH

LITTRÉ, Émile, 1801-1881.
Comment dans deux situations historiques les sémites entrèrent en compétition avec les aryens pour l'hégémonie du monde et comment ils y faillirent. Leipzig,etc.,[1879].

pp.52.

NL 0414325 MH OCH DLC NcD

Littré, Émile *i. e.* Maximilien Paul Émile, 1801-1881.
... Comment les mots changent de sens, par É. Littré, avec un avant-propos et des notes, par Michel Bréal. Paris, C. Delagrave [etc.] 1888.
60 p. 22cm. (Mémoires et documents scolaires, pub. par le Musée pédagogique. [fasc. no. 45])

I. French language.

E 14-1884

Library, U. S. Bur. of Education

NL 0414326 DHEW NcD MH CtY OCl MiU

PC2625 Littré, Émile, 1801-1881.
L52 Comment j'ai fait mon dictionnaire de la langue française; causerie. Für den Schulgebrauch erklärt[;] von J. Imelmann. Leipzig, Rengersche Buchhandlung, 1895.
viii,55 p. (Französische und englische Schulbibliothek. Reihe A: Prosa. Bd.91. Französische)

NL 0414327 CU

Littré, Émile, 1801-1881.
Comment j'ai fait mon dictionnaire de la langue française. Nouvelle édition, précédée d'un avant-propos par Michel Bréal.
— Paris. Delagrave. 1897. viii, 47 pp. 16°.

Nov. 28, 1900
*D7555 — Bréal, Michel Jules Alfred, ed. — Dictionaries. Construction.

NL 0414328 MB

Littré, Émile, 1801-1881.
Conservation, révolution, et positivisme, par É. Littré ... Paris, Ladrange, 1852.
xxxii, 331, [1] p. 18½cm.

1. Socialism. 2. Positivism. 3. France—Soc. condit.
[Full name: Maximilien Paul Émile Littré]

Library of Congress HN429.L8 9-5822 Revised

NL 0414329 PU PPL DLC GEU MU MdBP ScU PBm ICJ NN ViU PHC

194.9 Littré, Émile, 1801-1881.
L782C Conservation, révolution et positivisme, par É. Littré. 2. éd. Paris, Bureau de la philosophie positive, 1879.
2 p.l., viii, 499 p. 17½cm.
"La première édition ... 1852." --Préf., p. [i]

NL 0414330 NcD RPB CLU

F146
L73
Littré, Émile, 1801-1881.
Conservation, révolution,et positivisme, par É. Littré. 2. éd., aug. de remarques courantes. Paris, Aux Bureaux de la philosophie positive, 1879.
2 p. l., viii, 499 p.
Microfilm of a copy in the Brown University Library.
1. Positivism. 2. Socialism. 3. France - Social conditions.

NL 0414331 NNC

Littré, Émile, 1801-1881.
Cuvier, et les ossements fossiles.
(In his La science au point de vue philosophique. Pp. 129-148. Paris, 1873.)

Aug.4, 1902
E5231 — Cuvier, Georges Léopold Chrétien Frédéric Dagobert, Baron. — Bones. — No main card.

NL 0414332 MB

Littré, Emile, 1801-1881.
Cosmos: essai d'une description physique du monde, par Alexandre de Humboldt.
(In his La science au point de vue philosophique. Pp. 1-43. Paris, 1873.)

Aug.4, 1902
E5135 — Humboldt, Friedrich Heinrich Alexander, Freiherr von. — Universe. — No main card.

NL 0414333 MB

Littré, Émile, 1801-1881.
De l'ancien Orient.
(In his La science au point de vue philosophique. Pp. 376-409. Paris, 1873.)

NL 0414334 MB

Littré, Émile, 1801-1881.
De l'établissement de la troisième république, par É. Littré ... Paris, Bureaux de la Philosophie positive, 1880.
2 p. l., x, 595 p. 20½cm.

1. France—Pol. & govt.—1870-
[Full name: Maximilien Paul Émile Littré]

Library of Congress JN2562.L78 9-33508 Revised

NL 0414335 DLC NcD NcU MdBP NIC OCl PPL MH NN

Littré, Émile, 1801-1881.
De l'histoire de la civilisation en Angleterre, par Buckle.
(In his La science au point de vue philosophique. Pp. 478-521. Paris, 1873.)

Aug.4, 1902
E5231 — Civilization. — Buckle, Henry Thomas. — No main card.

NL 0414336 MB

Littré, Émile, 1801-1881.
De la condition essentielle qui sépare la sociologie de la biologie.
(In his La science au point de vue philosophique. Pp. 348-375. Paris, 1873.)

Aug.4, 1902
E5231 — Sociology. — Biology. — No main card.

NL 0414337 MB

B2249 LITTRÉ, ÉMILE, 1801-1881.
.P8L81 De la philosophie positive, par É. Littré... Paris, Librairie philosophique de Ladrange, 1845.
[3], 103 p. 21½cm.

1.Comte, Auguste, 1798-1857. 2.Positivism.

NL 0414338 ICU DNLM MH CLSU NIC NNC

Littré, Emile, 1801-1881.
"De La Poésie Epique dans la Société Féodale [from Revue Des Deux Mondes] [n.p., ca. 1854]
[Bound with Alvin, Louis Joseph, Le Divine]

NL 0414339 PU

Littré, Émile, 1801-1881.
De la science de la vie dans ses rapports avec la chimie.
(In his La science au point de vue philosophique. Pp. 191-244. Paris, 1873.)

Aug.4, 1902
E5231 — Chemistry. — Biology. — No main card.

NL 0414340 MB

VOLUME 336

Littré, Émile, 1801-1881.
De quelque points de physiologie psychique.
(In his La science au point de vue philosophique. Pp. 306-330. Paris, 1873.)

NL 0414341 MB

F443 L78 1863 Littré, Émile, 1801-1881.
Dictionnaire de la langue Francaise contenant ... la nomenclature... la grammaire... la signification des mots... La partie historique... l'étymologie. Paris, Hachette, 1863-69.
4 v. 33 cm.

F443 L78 1863 Supp. -- ---Supplément...Ce supplément est suivi d'un dictionnaire étymologique de tous les mots d'origine orientale, par Marcel Devic. Paris, Hachette, 1877.
iv, 375, vii, 84 p. 33 cm.

NL 0414342 MdBP MH NcU PPD PU MB CU MnHi CtY RPB ICJ

LITTRÉ, Émile, 1801-1881.
Dictionnaire de la langue française. Paris, L.Hachette et cie, etc., etc., 1863-72.

2 vol. 33 cm.

6225.17.2

-- Supplement. Suivi d'un dictionnaire étymologique de tous les mots d'origine orientale par Marcel Devic. Paris, Hachette et cie, etc., etc., 1879.

33 cm.

NL 0414343 MH MdBP ICN NjP MH-A MiU-C CtY PU-F

Littre, Émile, 1801-1881

Dictionnaire de la langue française contenant...la nomenclature...la grammaire...la signification des mots... la partie historique...l'etymologie... Paris, Hachette, 1863-1872.

4 v.

Supplement...Ce supplement est suivi d'un dictionnaire etymologique de tous les mots d'origine orientale par Marcel Devic.

NL 0414344 WaSpG

LITTRÉ, EMILE, 1801-1881.
Dictionnaire de la langue française. Paris, Librairie Hachette, 1863-77 [v.1, 1873] 5 v. 33cm.

Vol. 5 comprises a supplement and a dictionary of words of Oriental origin by M. Devic.

1. French language--Dictionaries.

NL 0414345 NN DLC PU MdBP MB

Littre, Emile, 1801-1881.
Dictionnaire de la langue française... et supplément; ce supplément est suivi d'un dictionnaire etymologique de tous les mots d'origine orientale par Marcel Devic. Paris, Hachette, 1863-78.
5v.

NL 0414346 PPULC

Littré, Émile, 1801-1881.
Dictionnaire de la langue française. Supplément renfermant un grand nombre de termes d'art, de science, d'agriculture, etc., et de néologismes de tous genres appuyés d'exemples et contenant la rectification de quelques définitions du dictionnaire... ce supplément est suivi d'un dictionnaire étymologique de tous les mote d'origine orientale, par Marcel Devic. Paris, Hachette, 1863-1897.
4v. & sup.

NL 0414347 ScU

Littré, Émile, 1801-1881.
Dictionnaire de la langue française... Supplement, 1870-78.

NL 0414348 PPL

Littré, Émile, 1801-1881.
Dictionnaire de la langue française contenant ... la nomenclature ... la grammaire ... la signification des mots ... la partie historique ... l'étymologie ... par É. Littré. Paris [etc.] Hachette et c^ie, 1873.
4 v. 32^cm.
Vols. 1-2, 3-4 paged continuously.
Originally issued in 30 parts, 1863-72.

1. French language—Dictionaries.

26-6894

Library of Congress PC2625.L6 1873

NL 0414349 DLC OrCS IdU NN CtY OCICC

Littré, Émile, 1801-1881.
Dictionnaire de la langue française contenant ... la nomenclature ... la grammaire ... la signification des mots ... la partie historique ... l'étymologie ... par É. Littré ... Paris [etc.] Hachette et c^ie, 1873-74.
4 v. 33^cm.
Vols. 1-2, 3-4 paged continuously.
PC2625.L6 1883
——— Supplément ... Ce supplément est suivi d'un dictionnaire étymologique de tous les mots d'origine orientale, par Marcel Devic. Paris [etc.] Hachette et c^ie, 1892.
2 p. l., iv, 375 p., 1 l., vii, 84 p., 1 l. 33^cm.
1. French language—Dictionaries. 2. French language—Foreign words and phrases—Oriental. I. Devic, L. Marcel.
[Full name: Maximilien Paul Émile Littré]

NL 0414350 ViU NcU DNLM NjNbS PPAN PPFr PBa OU

PC 2625* L78 1873 Littré, Emile, 1801-1881.
Dictionnaire de la langue francaise, contenant la nomenclature, la grammaire, la signification des mots, la partie historique [etc.] l'étymologie, par É. Littré. Paris, Hachette, 1873-79.
5 v. 32 cm.

Vols. 1-2, 3-4 paged continuously.
Originally issued in 30 parts, 1863-72.
Contents. - v.1. A-C. - v.2. D-H. - v.3. I-P. - v.4. Q-Z. - v.5 Supplement.

NL 0414351 OU DI

Littre, Emile, 1801-1881.
Dictionnaire de la langue Française ... & supplement. 5 v. Paris. 1873-1882.

NL 0414352 ODW

PC2625 .L6 1874 Littré, Emile, 1801-1881.
Dictionnaire de la langue française contenant ... la nomenclature ... la grammaire ... la signification des mots ... la partie historique ... l'étymologie. Paris, Hachette, 1874.
4 v. 31 cm.

1. French language--Dictionaries.

NL 0414353 TU

Ref. PC2625 L6 Littré, Émile, 1801-1881.
Dictionnaire de la langue française contenant ... la nomenclature ... la grammaire ... la signification des mots ... la partie historique ... l'étymologie. Paris, Hachette, 1874-75.
4 v.
v. 1-2, 3-4 paged continuously.
____ Supplément ... ce supplément est suivi d'un dictionnaire étymologique de tous les mots d'origine orientale, par Marcel Devic. Paris, 1879.

NL 0414354 NBuU

LITTRÉ, Émile, 1801-1881.
Dictionnaire de la langue française contenant 1.Pour la nomenclature... 2.Pour la grammaire... 3.Pour la signification des mots... 4. Pour la partie historique... 5.Pour l'étymologie... Paris; Londres, Librairie Hachette et Cie, 1875.
4 v. 32.5cm.

NL 0414355 MH-AH NjP MH

Littré, Émile, 1801-1881.
Dictionnaire de la langue française contenant ... la nomenclature ... la grammaire ... la signification des mots ... la partie historique ... l'étymologie ... par É. Littré ... Paris [etc.] Hachette et c^ie, 1875-76.
4 v. 33^cm.
Vols. 1-2, 3-4 paged continuously.
PC2625.L6 1882
——— Supplement ... Ce supplément est suivi d'un dictionnaire étymologique de tous les mots d'origine orientale, par Marcel Devic. Paris [etc.] Hachette et c^ie, 18—?
2 p. l., iv, 375 p., 1 l., 84 p., 1 l. 33^cm.
1. French language — Dictionaries. 2. French language — Foreign words and phrases—Oriental. I. Devic, L. Marcel.
[Full name: Maximilien Paul Émile Littré]

NL 0414356 ViU

LS AG66 .L5 LITTRÉ, ÉMILE, 1801-1881.
Dictionnaire de la langue française contenant... la nomenclature...la grammaire...la signification des mots...la partie historique...l'étymologie... Paris [etc.] Hachette et cie., 1875-79.

4 v. and suppl.

NL 0414357 DDO

Littre, Emile, 1801-1881.
Dictionnaire de la langue française.. Paris, [etc.] Hachetteret cie, 1876-77.
4v.

NL 0414358 PSC

VOLUME 336

Littré, Emile, 1801-1881
Dictionnaire de la langue française ... par E.Littré. Paris, Hachette, 1876-85 (v.1,1885)

4 v.
Vols. 1-2, 3-4 paged continuously
6225.18.6F

——Supplément. Suivi d'un Dictionnaire etymologique de tous les mots d'origine orientale, par Marcel Devic. Paris, Hachette, 1886
iv, 375, vii,84 p.

NL 0414359 MH

Littré, Émile, 1801–1881.
Dictionnaire de la langue française, par E. Littré ... Supplément renfermant un grand nombre de termes d'art, de science, d'agriculture, etc. et de néologismes de tous genres appuyés d'exemples; et contenant la rectification de quelques définitions du dictionnaire ... ce supplément est suivi d'un dictionnaire étymologique de tous les mots d'origine orientale par Marcel Devic. Paris, Londres, Hachette & c^ie, 1877.
2 p. l., iv, 375 p., 1 l., vii, 84 p., 1 l. 33½cm.
1. French language—Dictionaries. I. Devic, L. Marcel.
[Full name: Maximilien Paul Émile Littré]
F-3614 Revised
Library of Congress PC2625.L6 1873 Suppl. 1

DCU-H
NL 0414360 DLC CaBVa NjNbS PPLas MB OClND PPA

Littré, Emile
Dictionnaire de la langue française... Paris, Hachette, 1877-1878.
5 v.

Vol.5, Supplément...suivi d'un Dictionnaire étymologique de tous les mots d'origine orientale par Marcel Devic.

NL 0414361 MiD

LANG-R PC 2625 .L6 1878
Littré, Émile, 1801-1881.
Dictionnaire de la langue francaise contenant ... la nomenclature ... la grammaire ... la signification des mots ... la partie historique ... l'étymologie ... Paris [etc.] Hachette & cie., 1878.
4 v.

---- ------Supplement. 1877.

375 p.

#French language--Dictionaries.

NL 0414363 MoU OClW MH I

Littre, Emile, 1801-1881
Dictionaire de la langue Français. 1878 4 v.
----Same. Sup. 1882.

NL 0414364 DN

Littré, Emile, 1801-1881
Dictionnaire de la langue francaise avec supplement. ... Paris, Hachette & cie., 1878-97.
5 vols. 32 1/2 cm.

Library has: 3 copies, various eds. (acc. nos.)

NL 0414365 DNW PPF OClCC

PC 2625 L6 1881 OVERSIZE
Littré, Émile, 1801–1881.
Dictionnaire de la langue française contenant ... la nomenclature ... la grammaire ... la signification des mots ... la partie historique ... l'étymologie ... par É. Littré ... Paris [etc.] Hachette et c^ie, 1881.
4 v. 33 cm.
Vols. 1–2, 3–4 paged continuously.

PC 2625 L6 1881 Supp. OVERSIZE
—— ——Supplément ... Ce supplément est suivi d'un dictionnaire étymologique de tous les mots d'origine orientale, par Marcel Devic. Paris [etc.] Hachette et c^ie, 1881.
2 p. l., iv, 375 p., 1 l., 84 p., 1 l. 33 cm.
PC2625.L6 1882 Suppl.
1. French language—Dictionaries. 2. French language—Foreign words and phrases—Oriental. I. Devic, L. Marcel.

NL 0414366 CU-I

Littré, Émile, 1801–1881.
Dictionnaire de la langue française, par É. Littré ... Supplément renfermant un grand nombre de termes d'art, de science, d'agriculture, etc., et de néologismes de tous genres appuyés d'exemples et contenant la rectification de quelques définitions du dictionnaire ... ce supplément est suivi d'un dictionnaire étymologique de tous les mots d'origine orientale, par Marcel Devic. Paris [etc.] Hachette et c^ie, 1881.
2 p. l., iv, 375 p., 1 l., vii, 84 p., 1 l. 33cm.
1. French language—Dictionaries. I. Devic, L. Marcel.
[Full name: Maximilien Paul Émile Littré]
F-3615 Revised 2
Library of Congress PC2625.L6 1873 Suppl. 2 ~~1881~~

NL 0414367 DLC CaBVa MH PSt PHC PU PV

Littré, Émile, 1801-81
Dictionnaire de la langue française. Paris, Hachette, 1881-83

4 v.
RR 2241.7

________Supplément. Suivi d'un dictionnaire étymologique de tous les mots d'origine orientale, par Marcel Devic. Paris, Hachette, 1883

375, 84 p.

NL 0414368 MH

Littré, Émile, 1801–1881.
Dictionnaire de la langue française contenant ... la nomenclature ... la grammaire ... la signification des mots ... la partie historique ... l'étymologie ... par É. Littré ... Paris [etc.] Hachette et c^ie, 1881-85.
4 v. 33 cm.
Vols. 1–2, 3–4 paged continuously.
—— ——Supplément ... Ce supplément est suivi d'un dictionnaire étymologique de tous les mots d'origine orientale, par Marcel Devic. Paris [etc.] Hachette et c^ie, 1884.
2 p. l., iv, 375 p., 1 l., 84 p., 1 l. 33 cm.
PC2625.L6 1882 Suppl.
1. French language—Dictionaries. 2. French language—Foreign words and phrases—Oriental. I. Devic, L. Marcel.

NL 0414369 MeB PPWa PP

Littré, Émile, 1801–1881.
Dictionnaire de la langue française contenant ... la nomenclature ... la grammaire ... la signification des mots ... la partie historique ... l'étymologie ... par É Littré ... Paris [etc.] Hachette et c^ie, 1882.
4 v. 33cm.
Vols. 1–2, 3–4 paged continuously.
PC2625.L6 1882
—— ——Supplement ... Ce supplément est suivi d'un dictionnaire étymologique de tous les mots d'origine orientale, par Marcel Devic. Paris [etc.] Hachette et c^ie, 1883.
2 p. l., iv, 375 p., 1 l., 84 p., 1 l. 33cm.
1. French language — Dictionaries. 2. French language — Foreign words and phrases—Oriental. I. Devic, L. Marcel.
[Full name: Maximilien Paul Émile Littré]
F—3613
Library of Congress PC2625.L6 1882 Suppl.

TU NcU NcD PU ICJ
NL 0414370 DLC WaTC OrP MtU WaS CaBVaU OrCS OrPR

Littré, Émile, 1801–1881.
Dictionnaire de la langue française contenant ... la nomenclature ... la grammaire ... la signification des mots ... la partie historique ... l'étymologie ... par É. Littré ... Paris [etc.] Hachette et c^ie, 1883.
4 v. 33 cm.
Vols. 1–2, 3–4 paged continuously.
—— ——Supplément ... Ce supplément est suivi d'un dictionnaire étymologique de tous les mots d'origine orientale, par Marcel Devic. Paris [etc.] Hachette et c^ie, 1883.
1 p. l., iv, 375 p., 1 l., vii, 84 p., 1 l. 33 cm.
PC2625.L6 1883 Suppl.
1. French language—Dictionaries. 2. French language—Foreign words and phrases—Oriental. I. Devic, L. Marcel.
Full name: Maximilien Paul Émile Littré.
PC2625.L6 1883 443 38—37128

NL 0414371 DLC NjP MB MBtS PPDrop PBL OCU OClW CtY

LITTRÉ, MAXIMILIEN PAUL ÉMILE, 1801-1881.
Dictionnaire de la langue française... par É.Littré. Paris,Londres,Hachette et cie,1885.
4v. 32cm.

—— ——— Supplement... suivi d'un dictionnaire étymologique de tous les mots d'origine orientale, par Marcel Devic. Paris,Londres, Hachette et cie,1884.
[iii,iv],375,vii.84p. 32cm.

NL 0414372 PU MH

PC2625 .L6 1885
Littré, Émile, 1801–1881.
Dictionnaire de la langue française contenant ... la nomenclature ... la grammaire ... la signification des mots ... la partie historique ... l'étymologie ... par É. Littré ... Paris [etc.] Hachette et c^ie, 1885.
4 v. 33cm.
Vols. 1–2, 3–4 paged continuously.
PC2625.L6 ~~1882~~ Suppl.
—— ——— Supplément ... Ce supplément est suivi d'un dictionnaire étymologique de tous les mots d'origine orientale, par Marcel Devic. Paris [etc.] Hachette et c^ie, 1886.
2 p. l., iv, 375 p., 1 l., vii, 84 p., 1 l. 33cm.
1. French language—Dictionaries. 2. French language—Foreign words and phrases—Oriental. I. Devic, L. Marcel.
[Full name: Maximilien Paul Émile Littré]

NL 0414373 ViU FMU MoU MH ICN OU OCU CtY INS

PC 2625 L6 1889
Littré, Émile, 1801-1881.
Dictionnaire de la langue française contenant ... la nomenclature ... la grammaire ... la signification des mots ... la partie historique ... l'étymologie. Paris, Hachette, 1889.
4 v. 33 cm.

Vols. 1-2, 3-4 paged continuously.

PC 2625 L6 1889 supp.
________ Supplement ... Ce supplément est suivi d'un dictionnaire étymologique de tous les mots d'origine orientale, par Marcel Devic. Paris, Hachette, 1892.
375 p., 84 p. 33 cm.

1. French language - Dictionaries. 2. French language - Foreign words and phrases - Oriental. I. Devic, L. Marcel. II. Title.

NL 0414375 CU-S CtY NjP PPT ICN MB NN

Littré, Emile, 1801-1881.
Dictionnaire de la langue française contenant ... la nomenclature ... la grammaire ... la signification des mots ... la partie historique ... l'étymologie ... par E. Littré ... Paris [etc.] Hachette et cie, 1889-1897.
4 v. 33 cm.
Vols. 1-2, 3-4 paged continuously.
------ Supplement ... Ce supplément est suivi d'un dictionnaire étymologique de tous les mots d'origine orientale, par Marcel Devic. Paris [etc.] Hachette et cie, 1897.

2 p.l., iv., 375 p., 1 l., 84 p., 1 l. 33 cm.
1. French Language - Dictionnaires.
2. French language - Foreign words and phrases - Oriental. I. Devic, L. Marcel.

NL 0414377 NcD

Littré, Émile, 1801-1881. Dictionnaire de la langue française.
Beaujean, Amédée, 1821-1888.
Dictionnaire de la langue française; abrégé du Dictionnaire de É. Littré ... par A. Beaujean ... 17. éd. Paris, Hachette, 1932.

VOLUME 336

*Littré, Émile, 1801-1881. Dictionnaire de la langue francaise.
Beaujean, Amédée, 1821–1888.
Petit dictionnaire universel, ou Abrégé du Dictionnaire français de É. Littré ... Augmenté d'une partie mythologique, historique, biographique et géographique par A. Beaujean ... 9. éd., conforme pour l'orthographe à la 7. et dernière éd. du Dictionnaire de l'Académie française. Paris, Hachette et cie, 1889.

W
13
L782di
1885
LITTRÉ, Émile, 1801-1881
Dictionnaire de médecine: Atlas populaire de médecine, de chirurgie, de pharmacie, de l'art vétérinaire, et des sciences qui s'y rapportent, pouvant servir de complément à tous les dictionnaires de médecine. Paris, Baillière, 1885.
xii p., 48 plates.

NL 0414380 DNLM KyU

Littre, Émile, 1801-1881.
Dictionnaire de médecine, de chirurgie, de pharmacie
For first through ninth edition see under Nysten, Pierre Hubert, 1771-1818.

W
L782d
LITTRÉ, Émile, 1801-1881
Dictionnaire de médecine, de chirurgie, de pharmacie et des sciences qui s'y rapportent. [10]- éd. Paris, Baillière, 1855-
v. illus.
Title varies slightly.
Revision of Nysten's Dictionnaire de médecine, de chirurgie, de pharmacie, des sciences accessoires et de l'art vétérinaire.

1. Medicine - Dict. - French
I. Nysten, Pierre Hubert, 1771-1818

NL 0414383 DNLM

Littré, Émile, 1801-1881.
Dictionnaire de médecine, de chirurgie, de pharmacie, des sciences accessoires et de l'art vétérinaire, de P. H. Nysten. 10. éd, entirérement refondue par E. Littré ... Ch. Robin ... Ouvrage augmenté de la synonymie grecque, latine, allemande, anglaise, espagnole, et italienne, et suivi d'un glossaire de ces diverses langues. Illustré de 500 figures intercalées dans le texte. Paris, J.-B. Baillière, 1855.
4 p. l., 1485 p. illus. (incl. diagrs.) 26cm.
1. Medicine—Dict. 2. Veterinary medicine—Dict. I. Littré, Émile, 1801-1881, ed. II. Robin, Charles Philippe, 1821-1885, joint ed

NL 0414384 MiU MH Nh PP PPC DNLM

R121
N99
1858
Littré, Émile, 1801-1881.
Dictionnaire de médecine, de chirurgie, de pharmacie, des sciences accessoires et de l'art vétérinaire, de P.-H. Nysten. 11. éd. rev. et corr. par É. Littré ... [et] Ch. Robin ... Ouvrage augmenté de la synonymie latine, grecque, allemande, anglaise, italienne, et espagnole et suivi d'un glossaire de ces diverses langues ... Paris, J.-B. Baillière, 1858.
4 p. l., 1671 p. illus., diagrs.

NL 0414385 NNC WaU PU-D PPWI PPC DNLM MBCo

NON-
CIRC.
HISTORY
Littré, Émile, 1801-1881.
Dictionnaire de médicine, de chirurgie, de pharmacie, des sciences accessoires et de l'art vétérinaire. Ouvrage contenant la synonymie latine, grecque, allemande, anglaise, italienne et espagnole et le glossaire de ces diverses langues. 12. éd. entièrement refondue par É. Littré [et] Ch. Robin. Paris, J. B. Baillière, 1865.
viii, 1800 p. illus. 26 cm.

Last 5 p. publisher's catalog.

1. Medicine--Dictionaries--French. 2. Surgery--Dictionaries--French. 3. Pharmacy--Dictionaries--French. 4. Veterinary medicine--Dictionaries--French. I. Robin, Charles Philippe, 1821-1885, joint editor. II. Title.

NL 0414386 DNLM PPC NNC PPL MnU ViU OCIW-H CU-M

R121
L73
1873
Littré, Émile, 1801-1881.
Dictionnaire de médecine, de chirurgie, de pharmacie, de l'art vétérinaire et des sciences qui s'y rapportent, publié par J.-B. Baillière et fils. 13. éd. entièrement refondue par É. Littré ... [et] Ch. Robin ... Ouvrage contenant la synonymie latine, grecque, allemande, anglaise, italienne et espagnole et le glossaire de ces diverses langues ... Paris, Baillière, 1873.
xiv, 1836 p. illus. 28cm.

NL 0414387 NNC PPC NIC

610.3
L73d
1878
Littré, Émile, 1801-1881.
Dictionnaire de médecine, de chirurgie, de pharmacie, de l'art vétérinaire et des sciences qui s'y rapportent; ouvrage contenant la synonymie latine, grecque, allemande, anglaise, italienne et espagnole et le glossaire de ces diverses langues. 14. éd. entièrement refondue par É. Littré [et] Ch. Robin. Paris, J.-B. Baillière, 1878.
2v. (viii, 1896p.) illus. 26cm.
YA10288

PPC ICJ ICRL NN
NL 0414388 IU PPC PU KU-M CaBVaU WU NNC OU DLC

Littré, Émile, 1801-1881.
Dictionnaire de médecine, de chirurgie, de pharmacie, de l'art vétérinaire et des sciences qui s'y rapportent, ouvrage contenant la synonymie grecque, latine, allemande, anglaise, italienne et espagnole et le glossaire de ces diverses langues 15. éd. viii, 1880 pp. 8°. *Paris, J.-B. Baillière & fils*, 1883.

NL 0414389 DNLM

Littré, Émile, 1801–1881.
... Dictionnaire de médecine, de chirurgie, de pharmacie, de l'art vétérinaire et des sciences qui s'y rapportent. Ouvrage contenant la synonymie grecque, latine, allemande, anglaise, italienne et espagnole et le glossaire de ces diverses langues. 15. éd. ... Paris, J.-B. Baillière et fils, 1884.
2 v. illus. 26cm.
Paged continuously.
1. Medicine—Dictionaries. 2. Veterinary medicine--Dictionaries.
[*Full name:* Maximilien Paul Émile Littré]
Agr 7–2138 Revised
U. S. Dept. of agr. Library for Library of Congress 41L73 [r38b2]

NL 0414390 DNAL ICRL DNLM OU NN

Littré, Emile, 1801-1881.
... Dictionnaire de médecine, de chirurgie, de pharmacie, de l'art vétérinaire et des sciences qui s'y rapportent ... Seizième édition ... Paris, 1886.
1876 p.

NL 0414391 KyU

610.3
L782d17
Littré, Émile, 1801-1881.
... Dictionnaire de médecine, de chirurgie, de pharmacie, de l'art vétérinaire et des sciences qui s'y rapportent ... 17. éd ... Paris, J.-B. Baillière & fils, 1893.
1894p. illus.

1. Dictionaries, Medical. 2. Dictionaries, Pharmaceutical. 3. Dictionaries, Veterinary.

NL 0414392 IU-M DNLM ICRL PPC

610.3
L73d18
Littré, Emile, 1801-1881.
...Dictionnaire de médecine, de chirurgie, de pharmacie, de l'art vétérinaire et des sciences qui s'y rapportent. Ouvrage contenant la synonymie grecque, latine, allemande, anglaise, italienne et espagnole, et le glossaire de ces diverses langues. 18. éd., mise au courant des progrès des sciences médicales et biologiques et de la pratique journalière... Paris, J.B. Baillière et fils, 1898.
1910p. illus. 26cm.

At head of title: E. Littré.

NL 0414393 LU IU-M MiU

Littre, Emile, 1801-1881.
...Dictionnaire de medecine, de chirurgie, de pharmacie, de l'art veterninarie et des sciences qui s'y rapportent. Ouvrage contenant grecque, latine, allemande, etc. 20 ed. Paris, Bailliere 1903. 1910 p.

NL 0414394 MiU

Littré, Émile, 1801-1881.
Dictionnaire de médecine, de chirurgie, de pharmacie et des sciences qui s'y rapportent, par É. Littré .... Vingt et unième édition entièrement refondue par A. Gilbert, ... Paris, J.-B. Baillière et fils, 1905.
viii, 1842 p. 866 illus. incl. diagrs. 26½cm.

NL 0414395 ICJ DNLM ICRL

Littré, Émile, 1801–1881.
Dictionnaire de médecine, de chirurgie, de pharmacie, et des sciences qui s'y rapportent par E. Littré ... 21. éd., entièrement refondue par A. Gilbert ... Paris, J.-B. Baillière et fils, 1908.
vi, [2], 1842 p. illus., diagrs. 26 cm.

1. Medicine—Dictionaries. 2. Veterinary medicine—Dictionaries. I. Gilbert, Augustin Nicolas, 1858–1927, ed.
Agr 17–320
U. S. Dept. of Agr. Libr. for Library of Congress 41L73 [a48b1]

NL 0414396 DNAL CtY PPJ

Littré, Emile
Discours prononcés... 5 juin 1873...
see under
Académie française, Paris.

VOLUME 336

Littré, Émile, 1801-1881. 3915-53
Discours sur l'étude de la philosophie naturelle [par J. F. W. Herschel].
(In his La science au point de vue philosophique. Pp. 44-54. Paris, 1873.)

NL 0414398 MB

W 13 L782d 1879
LITTRÉ, Émile, 1801-1881
Dizionario di medicina e chirurgia, di terapeutica medico-chirurgica, farmacia, arte veterinaria e scienze affini, per E. Littré e Ch. Robin. 1. ed. italiana sulla 14. ed. originale, con aggiunte relative ai più recenti progressi delle scienze mediche. Napoli, Detken [1879]-92.
1653 p. illus.
Cover title.

Issued in fascicles.
1. Medicine - Dict. - Italian I. Robin, Charles Philippe, 1821-1885

NL 0414400 DNLM

RC126 L5 Public Health Library
Littré, Émile, 1801-1881
Du choléra oriental. Paris, Germer-Baillière, 1832.
164 p. tables.

1. Cholera, Asiatic.

NL 0414401 CU PPC

Littré, Émile, 1801-1881.

Dante Alighieri, 1265-1321.
... L'Enfer, mis en vieux langage françois et en vers, accompagné du texte italien et contenant des notes et un glossaire, par É. Littré ... 2. éd. Paris. Hachette et c^ie^, 1879.

Littré, Emile, 1801-1881.
Essai sur la philosophie des sciences ... see under Ampère, André Marie, 1775-1836.

Littré, Émile, 1801-1881.
Études et glanures pour faire suite à l'Histoire de la langue française, par E. Littré ... Paris, Didier et c^ie^, 1880.
2 p. l., xiv, 452 p. 22½cm.
CONTENTS.—Préface. Pathologie verbale, ou Lésions de certains mots dans le cours de l'usage.—Ethnologie gauloise ... par Roget, baron de Belloguet.—Chronique de la Pucelle, ou chronique de Cousinot, suivie de la Chronique normande de P. Cochon ... pub. par M. Vallet de Viriville.—Histoire et glossaire du normand, de l'anglais et de la langue française, par E. Le Héricher ...—Lives of Edward the Confessor ... ed. by H. R. Luard.—Hugues Capet, chanson de geste, pub. par M. le marquis de la Grange.—Li livres dou Tresor, par B. Latini, pub. ... par Chabaille.—Noms de lieux de France: 1. Étude sur la signification des noms de lieux en France, par Houzé. 2. De la formation française des anciens noms de lieux, par J. Quicherat.—Addenda aux lexiques latins, par L. Quicherat.—Baudouin et Jean de Condé, Dits et contes.—Conjugaison française: Histoire et théorie de la conjugaison française, par C. Chabaneau.—Latin mérovingien: la déclinaison latine en Gaule, à l'époque mérovingienne par M. H. d'Arbois de Jubainville.—Méraugis chevalier de la Table ronde.—Méraugis de Portlesguez, roman de la Table ronde, par R. de Houdenc, pub. par H. Michelant, Paris, 1869.—Comparaisons épiques avec nos chansons de geste.—Comment j'ai fait mon dictionnaire de la langue française; causerie.—Petit glossaire pour les textes anciens cités.
1. French language—History. 2. French philology—Collected works.
[Full name: Maximilien Paul Émile Littré]
1-12967 Revised
Library of Congress PC2075.L6

NL 0414405 DLC NjP LU MdBP WaU CU CLSU CtY NN MiU PPL PSC

Littré, Émile, 1801-1881.
Études sur les barbares et le moyen âge, par É. Littré ... Paris, Didier et c^ie^. 1867.
2 p. l., xxxii, 456 p. 23cm.

1. Middle ages—Hist. 2. French literature—Old French—Hist. & crit. 3. Literature, Medieval—Hist. & crit. I. Title.
[Full name: Maximilien Paul Émile Littré]
18-15561 Revised
Library of Congress D119.L5 1867

NL 0414406 DLC DCU-IA OCIW OU CtY NN NjP PSt NSyU

D 119 .L5 1869
Littré, Émile, 1801-1881.
Études sur les barbares et le moyen âge. 2.éd. Paris, Didier, 1869.
456 p. 23 cm.
A collection of the author's reviews previously published in the Journal des savants; National: Histoire littéraire de la France, v. 22, and Revue de deux mondes.

1. Middle ages - Hist. 2. French literature - Old French - Hist. & crit. 3. Literature, Medieval. I. Title.
D119.L5 1874

NL 0414407 NBuU NIC CLSU OCl OCIW DNLM MH

Littré, Émile, 1801-1881.
Études sur les barbares et le moyen âge, par É. Littré ... 3. éd. Paris, Didier et c^ie^, 1874.
2 p. l., xxxii, 456 p. 18cm.
A collection of the author's reviews previously published in the Journal des savants; National; Histoire littéraire de la France, v. 22, and Revue de deux mondes.

1. Middle ages—Hist. 2. French literature—Old French—Hist. & crit. 3. Literature, Medieval. I. Title.
[Full name: Maximilien Paul Émile Littré]
15-6526 Revised
Library of Congress D119.L5 1874

NL 0414408 DLC NcD DDO CaBVaU PU

Littré, Emile, 1801-1881.
Études sur les barbares et le moyen age. Paris, Didier et Cie., 1883.
2 p.l., xxxii, 456 p. 12°.
4. éd.

NL 0414409 NN RP PPL MiU

Littré, Émile, 1801-1881.
Fragments de philosophie positive et de sociologie contemporaine, par É. Littré. Paris, Aux Bureaux de la philosophie positive, 1876.
xv, 606 p. 25cm.
Reprinted essays and book reviews, mostly from various French periodicals.

1. Positivism—Addresses, essays, lectures.

NL 0414410 MiU MH NN NcD MdBP

---

*Littré, Émile, 1801-1881.

Brachet, Auguste, 1844-1898.
... Grammaire historique de la langue française; avec une préface par É. Littré ... 7. éd. ... Paris, J. Hetzel et c^e^ [1873?]

Littré, Émile i.e. Maximilien Paul Émile, 1801-1888, tr.
Hippocrates.
Hippocrates on airs, waters, and places. The received Greek text of Littré, with Latin, French, and English translations by eminent scholars ... London, Printed—not for sale—by Wyman & sons, 1881.

Littre, Émile, 1801-1881.
Histoire de la langue française; etudes sur les origines, l'etymologie, la grammaire, les dialectes. la versification and les lettres au moyen âge. Ed. 2. Par., Didier, 1863.
2v

NL 0414413 PU ICN NjP OU

LITTRÉ, Émile, 1801-1881.
Histoire de la langue française, étude des sur les origines, l'étymologie la grammaire, les dialectes, la versification, et les lettres au moyen âge. Nouvelle éd. Paris, 1863.

2 tom.
For a continuation of this work, see his "Études et glanures", etc., 1880."

NL 0414414 MH CtY PPAmP

Littré, Émile, 1801-1881.
Historie de la langue française. Études sur les origines, l'étymologie, la grammaire, les dialectes, la versification, et les lettres au moyen âge. Paris, Didier et Cie., 1867.
2 v. 8°.
4. ed.

N. 0414415 PPDrop NN

PC2075 .L7 1869
Littré, Émile, 1801-1881.
Histoire de la langue française. Études sur les origines, l'étymologie, la grammaire, les dialectes, la versification et les lettres au moyen âge, par É. Littré. 5. éd. Paris, Didier et c^ie^, 1869.
2 v. 18½cm.
"Ceci est un recueil d'articles écrits à des temps différents, insérés dans des publications diverses, le Journal des savants, la Revue des deux mondes, le Journal des débats."

CONTENTS.—[t.] 1. Introduction. De l'étymologie de la langue française, de la grammaire française et de la correction des vieux textes. De la poésie épique dans la société féodale. La poésie homérique et l'ancienne poésie française. Étude sur Dante.—[t.] 2. Étude sur Patelin. Étude sur Adam (Mystère). Des patois. Légende sur le pape Grégoire le Grand. Le chant d'Eulalie et le fragment de Valenciennes. Dictionnaire français-latin. Girart de Rossillon. Grammaires provençales. Le Livre des psaumes, texte du douzième siècle. Lettres de Marguerite, reine de Navarre, sœur de François Ier. Table analytique.
1. French language—Hist. 2. French philology—Collected works. 3. French literature—Old French—Hist. & crit.
[Full name: Maximilien Paul Émile Littré]

NL 0414417 ViU NjP ICIU CU PU PV PSC

Littré, Émile, 1801-1881.
Histoire de la langue française. Études sur les origines, l'étymologie, la grammaire, les dialectes, la versification et les lettres au moyen âge, par É. Littré. 6. éd. Paris, Didier et c^ie^, 1873.
2 v. 18½cm.
"Ceci est un recueil d'articles écrits à des temps différents, insérés dans des publications diverses, le Journal des savants, la Revue des deux mondes, le Journal des débats."

CONTENTS.—[t.] 1. Introduction. De l'étymologie de la langue française, de la grammaire française et de la correction des vieux textes. De la poésie épique dans la société féodale. La poésie homérique et l'ancienne poésie française. Étude sur Dante.—[t.] 2. Étude sur Patelin. Étude sur Adam (Mystère). Des patois. Légende sur le pape Grégoire le Grand. Le chant d'Eulalie et le fragment de Valenciennes. Dictionnaire français-latin. Girart de Rossillon. Grammaires provençales. Le Livre des psaumes, texte du douzième siècle. Lettres de Marguerite, reine de Navarre, sœur de François Ier. Table analytique.
1. French language — Hist. 2. French philology — Collected works. 3. French literature—Old French—Hist. & crit.
[Full name: Maximilien Paul Émile Littré]
11-2857 Revised
Library of Congress PC2075.L7

NL 0414419 DLC CaBVaU MtU IaU NcD PV OO MiU

VOLUME 336

Littré, Émile, 1801-1881.
Histoire de la langue française; études sur les origines, l'étymologie, la grammaire, les dialectes, la versification, et les lettres au moyen age. 8. éd. Paris, Didier et cie., 1878.
2 v.

NL 0414420 MH WaSpG

PC 2075 L7 Littré, Émile, 1801-1881
Histoire de la langue française; études sur les origines, l'étymologie, la grammaire, les dialectes, la versification et les lettres au moyen âge. 8. éd. Paris, Librairie académique, 1882.
2v. 19cm.
"Ceci est un recueil d'articles écrits à des temps différents, insérés dans des publications diverses, le Journal des savants, la Revue des deux mondes, le Journal des débats."
Bibliographical footnotes..

1. French language - Hist. 2. French philology - Collected works 3. French literature - Old French - Hist. & crit. I. Title

NL 0414422 WU PP DCU-H MiU MH

Littre, Emile, 1801-1881.
Histoire de la langue francaise; etudes sur les origines, l'etymologie, ...London, 1882-86.
2v.

NL 0414423 PPL

440.9 L782H9 Littré, Émile, 1801-1881.
Histoire de la langue française. Études sur les origines, l'étymologie, la grammaire, les dialectes, la versification et les lettres au moyen âge; 9. éd. Paris, Perrin, 1886.
2v. 18cm.

1. French language - Hist. 2. French philology - Collected works 3. French literature - Old French - Hist. & crit.

NL 0414424 NBC OC1W OU MdBP ICN

Littré, Émile, 1801-1881.
Histoire de la langue française: etudes sur les origines, l'étymologie, la grammaire, les dialectes, la versification, et les lettres au moyen âge. Nouv. éd. Paris, 1886. 2 v. 12°.
—2157

NL 0414425 MdBP

Littré, Émile, 1801-1881.
Les hypothèses positives de cosmogonie.
(In his La science au point de vue philosophique. Pp. 522-562. Paris, 1873.)

NL 0414426 MB

Littré, Émile, 1801-1881.
J. Kramers Jz. Nouveau dictionnaire ...
see under Kramers, Jacob, 1802-1869.

Littré, Émile, 1801-1881.

Maury, Max, pseud.?
Laird & Lee's vest-pocket Littré-Webster English-French, anglais-français; and French-English, français-anglais dictionary, by Max Maury ... Chicago, Laird & Lee, 1920.

Littré, Émile, 1801-1881.
Littérature et histoire, par É. Littré ... Paris, Didier et cie, 1875.
[4], viii, 460 p. 22½cm.

1. Literature — Addresses, essays, lectures. 2. History — Addresses, essays, lectures.
[Full name: Maximilien Paul Émile Littré]
A 14-2907 Revised
Title from Univ. of Chicago PN37.L8 Printed by L. C.

NL 0414429 ICU MH MdBP

ar V 4376 Littré, Émile, 1801-1881.
Littérature et histoire. 2. éd.
Paris, Didier et Cie, 1877.
viii, 460 p. 18cm.

1. Literature--Hist. & crit.

NL 0414430 NIC OrPR NN MWelC PPD CtY

W 9 L782m 1872 LITTRÉ, Émile, 1801-1881
Médecine et médecins. Paris, Didier, 1872.
viii, 512 p.
Reprinted from various periodicals.

NL 0414431 DNLM PPC IU CU WaU MiU IU-M

LITTRÉ, Émile, 1801-1881.
Médecine et médecins, 2e éd. Paris, 1872.

NL 0414432 MBCo NcD-MC KyU PPC PU NjP NN

R 131 L78 1875 Littré, Émile, 1801-1881.
Médecine et médecins. 3. éd. Paris, Didier, 1875.
viii, 512 p. 18cm.

1. Medicine--Hist.--Addresses, essays, lectures. 2. Medicine--France--Hist.

NL 0414433 NIC PSt

Littré, Émile, 1801-1881.
Notice biographique [d'Armand Carrel].
(In Carrel, Jean Baptiste Nicolas Armand. Œuvres littéraires et économiques . . . Pp. 5-66. Paris. 1854.)

NL 0414434 MB PU

R126 .H55 1839 Littré, Émile, 1801-1881, ed. and tr.

Hippocrates.
Œuvres complètes. Traduction nouvelle avec le texte grec en regard, collationné sur les manuscrits et toutes les éditions; accompagnée d'une introduction, de commentaires médicaux, de variantes et de notes philologiques; suivie d'une table générale des matières. Par É. Littré. Paris, J. B. Baillière, 1839-61.

Littre, Emile, 1801-1881.

Carrel, Armand, 1800-1836.
Œuvres littéraires et économiques d'Armand Carrel, recueillies et annotées, par m. Charles Romey; précédées d'une notice biographique par m. Émile Littré. Paris, Guillaumin et cie [etc.] 1854.

Littré, Emile, 1801-1881.

Carrel, Armand i. e. Jean Baptiste Nicolas Armand, 1800-1836.
Œuvres politiques et littéraires d'Armand Carrel; mises en ordre, annotées et précédées d'une notice biographique sur l'auteur, par M. Littré ... et M. Paulin ... Paris, F. Chamerot, 1857-59.

Littré, Émile, 1801-1881.
Origine de l' idée de justice.
(In his La science au point de vue philosophique. Pp. 331-347. Paris, 1873.)

NL 0414438 MB

Littré, Émile, 1801-1881.
Opusculos de filosofía positiva. Vertidos en castellano por Valentín Letelier. Copiapó, imprenta de el Constituyente, 1878.
pp. 118.

NL 0414439 MH

Littré, Émile, 1801-1881.
Par quelle conduite la République française peut-elle consolider le succès qu'elle a obtenu? Question de sociologie pratique. Paris, Charavay, 1879.
15 p. 26cm.

1. France--Social conditions.

NL 0414440 NIC

Littré, É[mile], 1801-1881.
Paroles de philosophie positive. Paris, A. Delahays, 1859.
pp. 62.

NL 0414441 MH CtY CLSU DNLM

146 L78 Littré, Émile, 1801-1881.
Paroles de philosophie positive, par É. Littré. 2e. éd. Paris, Librairie philosophique de Ladrange, 1863.
102 p. 18½ cm.

NL 0414442 MH CU MdBP

VOLUME 336

Littré, Émile, 1801-1881.
Petit dictionnaire universel; ou, Abrégé du dictionnaire français de E. Littré; augmenté d'une partie mythologique, historique, biographique etgéographique, par A. Beaujean. Paris, Hachette et Cie, 1876.
2 p.l., 908 p. 16°.

NL 0414443 NN PPL

---

*Littré, Émile, 1801-1881, ed.

La Philosophie positive; revue dirigée par É. Littré & G. Wyrouboff ...

Paris, Bureau de la Philosophie positive [18

Littré, Émile, 1801-1881.
Première leçon d'un cours d'histoire fait à l'École polytechnique.
(In his La science au point de vue philosophique. Pp. 410-436. Paris, 1873.)

June 4, 1902
E4688

NL 0414445 MB

Littré, Émile, 1801-1881.
Résumé des nouvelles recherches des géomètres sur la chaleur de la terre.
(In his La science au point de vue philosophique. Pp. 110-128. Paris, 1873.)

June 4, 1902
E4688

NL 0414446 MB

Littré, Émile, 1801-1881.
Restauration de la légitimité et de ses alliés, par E. Littré ... Paris, E. Dentu, 1873.
32 p. 26 cm.

1. France--Politics and government--1870-1940. I. Title.

NL 0414447 NSchU

---

504 Littré, Émile, 1801-1881.
L737s La science au point de vue philosophique. Paris, Didier, 1873.
viii, 562 p.

NL 0414448 WaU MdBP MH CtY

Littre, Emile, 1801-1881
La science au point de vue philosophique... 1873. 3.ed.

NL 0414449 MiU

Littré, Émile, 1801-1881.
La science au point de vue philosophique, par É. Littré ... 4. éd. ... Paris, Didier et c^{ie}, 1876.
2 p. l., viii, 562 p., 1 l. 18½cm.
CONTENTS.—Le Cosmos d'Alex. de Humboldt.—La philosophie naturelle d'Herschel.—Les étoiles filantes.—Ampère et l'électro-magnétisme.—La chaleur de la terre d'après les géomètres.—Cuvier et les ossements fossiles.—Les hommes fossiles.—La science de la vie et la chimie.—La physiologie.—Études de physiologie psychique.—Origine de l'idée de justice.—La sociologie et la biologie.—L'ancien Orient.—Leçon d'histoire faite à l'École polytechnique en 1870.—Les peuples sémitiques d'après M. Renan.—La civilisation d'après Buckle.—Les hypothèses positives de cosmogonie.
1. Science—Addresses, essays, lectures.
[Full name: Maximilien Paul Émile Littré]
Library of Congress Q171.L8 1876 11-23489 Revised

NL 0414450 DLC NIC CU

Littré, Émile, 1801-1881.
La science au point de vue philosphique, par É. Littré ... 5. éd. ... Paris, É. Perrin, 1884.
2 p. l., viii, 562 p., 1 l. 19cm.
Preface dated 1873.
CONTENTS.—Le Cosmos d'Alex. de Humboldt.—La philosophie naturelle d'Herschel.—Les étoiles filantes.—Ampère et l'électro-magnétisme.—La chaleur de la terre d'après les géomètres.—Cuvier et les ossements fossiles.—Les hommes fossiles.—La science de la vie et la chimie.—La physiologie.—Études de physiologie psychique.—Origine de l'idée de justice.—La sociologie et la biologie.—L'ancien Orient.—Leçon d'histoire faite à l'Ecole polytechnique en 1870.—Les peuples sémitiques d'apres M. Renan.—La civilisation d'après Buckle.—Les hypothèses positives de cosmogonie.
1. Science—Addresses, essays, lectures.
Full name: Maximilien Paul Émile Littré]
3—11036
Library of Congress Q171.L8 1884

NL 0414451 DLC DNLM PPL MiU

WC 262 L782t 1832 LITTRÉ, Émile, 1801-1881
Traité du choléra oriental, rédigé principalement d'après les documens publiés par les médecins allemands. Paris, Germer-Baillière, 1832.
164 p.

WC 264 S432r 1832 -- --- Another copy. [With Scoutetten, H. Relation historique et médicale de l'épidémie de choléra qui a régné à Berlin en 1831. Paris, 1832]

NL 0414452 DNLM

Littré, Emile, 1801-1881.
... La vérité sur la mort d'Alexandre le Grand, par E. Littré. La mort de Jules César, par Nicolas de Damas. Frontispice avec portraits à l'eau-forte de Ulm. Paris, R. Pincebourde, 1865.
2 p. l., 120 p., 1 l. front. 15½ x 12cm. (Bibliothèque originale)
The translation of the "Mort de Jules Cesar" was made by Alfred Didot. cf. British museum. Catalogue.
"La vérité sur la mort d'Alexandre est extrait d'un travail publié, par M. Littré sur La science des poisons considérée dans l'histoire". Avertissement.
1. Alexander the Great, B.C. 356-323. 2. Caesar, C. Julius. I. Nicolaus Damascenus. II. Didot, Alfred Firmin, 1828-1913, tr.

NL 0414453 MiU DNLM NhU NjN MB ICU NNC WU

LITTRÉ, ÉMILE, 1801-1881.
Wie ich mein Wörterbuch der französischen Sprache zu Stande gebracht habe. (Comment j'ai fait mon Dictionnaire de la langue française.) Eine Plauderei von É. Littré... Autorisirte Uebersetzung... Leipzig, W. Friedrich, 1881. 100 p. port. 16cm.

1. French language—Lexicography.

NL 0414454 NN ODW CtY

Littré, Émile, 1801-1881.
Y-a-t-il eu des hommes sur la terre avant la dernière époque géologique?
(In his La science au point de vue philosophique. Pp. 149-190. Paris, 1873.)

June 18, 1902
E4563

NL 0414455 MB

Littré, Florence.
... L'adolescente émerveillée. Paris, B. Grasset [1946]
3 p. l., [9]-275 p., 2 l. 18½cm.

I. Title.
PQ2623.I 74A7 47-19666

NL 0414456 DLC

LA 2375 F72 L5 Littré, Florence
La mauvaise herbe; souvenirs et confidences. Issy-les-Moulineaux (France), La Fenêtre Ouverte [c1946]
251p. 19cm.

1. Teachers - France - Correspondence, reminiscences, etc. I. Title

NL 0414457 WU DLC-P4

Littré, Maximilien Paul Émile

see

Littré, Émile, 1801-1881.

Littrell, Anita, 1912–
Home, ham, and hominy. Caldwell, Idaho, Caxton Printers, 1953.
224 p. 24 cm.

I. Title.
PZ7.L737Ho 52-5208 ‡

NL 0414459 DLC Or NN IdU PU

591.1 L737s Littroll, Jae Luis, 1908-
Some cytological characteristics of brown fat, with special reference to the interscapular lobes in the Syrian hamster and albino rat. Urbana [1947]
53 l. illus. 28cm.

Thesis--University of Illinois.
Typewritten (carbon copy)
Vita.
Bibliography: leaves 55-58.
1947 L737 ---- ---- Thesis copy.

NL 0414460 IU

Littrell, Jae Luis, 1908–
Some cytological characteristics of brown fat, with special reference to the interscapular lobes in the Syrian hamster and albino rat. Urbana [1947]
6 p. 23 cm.
Abstract of thesis—University of Illinois.
Vita.

1. Anatomy, Comparative. 2. Fat. I. Title: Brown fat.
QL950.3.L5 A 53-3138
Illinois. Univ. Librar. for Library of Congress [2]†

NL 0414461 IU DLC CtY DNAL

VOLUME 336

Littrell, John Harvey, 1912–
Mathematics needed for the in-school experiences of students in selected semi-professional curricula. Ann Arbor, University Microfilms, 1950.
(University Microfilms, Ann Arbor, Mich. Publication no. 1675)
Microfilm copy of typewritten ms. Positive.
Collation of the original: ix, 268 l.
Thesis—University of Missouri.
Abstracted in Microfilm abstracts, v. 10 (1950) no. 2, p. 48-50.
Vita.
Bibliography: leaves 249–253; "References analyzed for the study": leaves 254–259.
1. Mathematics—Study and teaching.
Microfilm AC-1 no. 1675 Mic A 50-189
Michigan. Univ. Libr. for Library of Congress (1)†

NL 0414462 MiU DLC

Littrow, A. von
Über die relative Wärmeleitungsfähigheit verschiedener Bodenarten und den betreffenden Einfluss des Wassers.

NL 0414463 DAS

Littrow, Auguste (Bischoff) von, 1819–1890.
Aus dem persönlichen verkehre mit Franz Grillparzer, von Auguste von Littrow-Bischoff. Wien, L. Rosner, 1873.
4 p. l., 220 p. 19cm.
1. Grillparzer, Franz, 1791–1872.
42-34371
Library of Congress PT2264.A9L5

NL 0414464 DLC CaBVaU IaU PU NcU MU IU NIC OClW MH

Littrow, C von
see Littrow, Karl Ludwig, edler von, 1811-1877.

Littrow, Carl Ludwig von
see Littrow, Karl Ludwig, edler von, 1811-1877.

Littrow, Charles de
see
Littrow, Karl Ludwig, edler von, 1811-1877

LITTROW, Heinrich.
Uiber serbische poesie und ihre parallelen. [Prag, J. Nestler, 1880.]
pp. 29+.
Without title-page. Caption title.

NL 0414468 MH

Littrow, Heinrich von, 1820-1895.
Aus der See; Gedichte... Triest, F. H. Schimpff 1876.
387 [6] p.

NL 0414469 MiD

Littrow, Heinrich von, 1820-1895.
Carl Weyprecht, der österreichische nordpolfahrer. Erinnerungen und briefe gesammelt und zusammengestellt von Heinrich v. Littrow. Mit dem porträt von Carl Weyprecht und abbildung des "Tegetthoff." Wien [etc.] A. Hartleben, 1881.
96 p. incl. front. (port.) illus. 24cm.
1. Weyprecht, Karl, 1838-1881.
1-G-2796
Library of Congress G585.W4L5

NL 0414470 DLC

Littrow, Heinrich von, 1820-1895.
Die Marine
see under Brommy, Karl Rudolf, 1809-1860.

[**Littrow, Heinrich von.**] 1820-1895. 50558.41
Von Wien nach Triest. Reisebilder als eisenbahnlektüre in gemüthlichen reimen von H. L. Wien, etc., L. C. Zamarski & C. Dittmarsch, 1863.
pp. (8), 287 +.

NL 0414472 MH

Littrow, Hermann von. L070.160 A938
Das Eisenbahnwesen auf der Weltausstellung in Chicago 1893. 147, [1] p. 16 pl. 3 tables. [*In* AUSTRIA. K. K. CENTRAL-COMMISSION FÜR DIE WELTAUSSTELLUNG IN CHICAGO 1893. Officieller Bericht, no. 8. Wien 1895.]

NL 0414473 ICJ

KE 15865
Littrow, Joseph Johann, Edler von, 1781-1840.
Analytische Geometrie. Wien, C. Schaumberg und Comp., 1823.

NL 0414474 MH NN

Littrow, Joseph Johann, *edler* **von,** 1781–1840.
Anfangsgründe der gesammten mathematik. Von J. J. v. Littrow. Mit fünf kupfertafeln. Wien, C. Gerold, 1838.
xvi, 460 p. fold. tab. 22½cm.
1. Mathematics.
3—20750
Library of Congress QA37.L78

NL 0414475 DLC PBL

Littrow, Joseph Johann, edler von, 1781-1840.
Anleitung zur Berechnung der Lebensrenten und Wittwenpensionen ohne Hülfe der Algebra. Von J. J. Littrow... Wien: J. G. Heubner, 1829. x, 145 p. tables. 20½cm.
Bound with his: Die Wahrscheinlichkeitsrechnung. Wien, 1833.
1. Annuities—Tables.
N. Y. P. L. Revised July 26, 1934

NL 0414476 NN

Littrow, Joseph Johann, edler von, 1781-1840.
Anleitung zur höheren Mathematik. Von J. J. Littrow... Wien: C. Gerold, 1836. viii, 515 p. diagrs. 8°.
Bibliography, p. 511–515.
1. Calculus—Textbooks, 1836.
N. Y. P. L. June 28, 1926

NL 0414477 NN

Littrow, Joseph Johann, edler von, 1781-1840.
Annalen der K.K. Sternwarte in Wien
see under Vienna. Universität. Sternwarte.

Littrow, Joseph Johann, *edler* **von,** 1781–1840.
Atlas des gestirnten himmels. Für freunde der astronomie hrsg. von J. J. v. Littrow ... Stuttgart, Hoffmann, 1839.
2 p. l., xxxvi p. 18 double pl. 24 x 20cm.
1. Stars—Atlases.
5-37097
Library of Congress QB65.L7

NL 0414479 DLC NjP WaS OkU PU MiU

Littrow, Joseph Johann, *edler* **von,** 1781-1840.
J. J. von Littrow's Atlas des gestirnten himmels für freunde der astronomie. 2., vielfach verbesserte und vermehrte aufl., hrsg. von Karl von Littrow ... Stuttgart, Hoffmann, 1854.
x p., 1 l., 47, [1] p. 19 double pl. 22cm.
1. Stars—Atlases. I. Littrow, Karl Ludwig von, 1811-1877, ed.

NL 0414480 MiU WU ViU MH PPF ICU

4QB-76 **Littrow, Joseph Johann, edler von, 1781-1840.**
Atlas des gestirnten Himmels für Freunde des Astronomie. 3., vielfach verb. und verm. Aufl., hrsg. von Karl von Littrow. Stuttgart, G. Weise, 1866.
64 p.

NL 0414481 DLC-P4 NBuG NN CtY

23.89 Littrow, Joseph Johann, edler von, 1781-1840.
.73a4 ... Atlas des gestirnten himmels für freunde der astronomie. 4. vielfach umgearb. und verm. aufl. hrsg. von Edmund Weiss. Berlin, 1886.
91p. plates, diagr.

NL 0414482 IU DN-Ob

Littrow, Joseph Johann, *edler* **von,** 1781-1840.
Littrows Atlas des gestirnten himmels für freunde der astronomie. Taschenausgabe. Mit einer einleitung von professor dr. J. Plassmann. 2., unveränderte aufl. Berlin, F. Dümmler, 1920.
iv, 48 p. 17 diagrs. (5 double) 17cm.
1. Stars—Atlases. I. Plassmann, Joseph, 1859-

NL 0414483 MiU ICU PSt

VOLUME 336

CE 73 .L78 LITTROW,JOSEPH JOHANN,Edler VON,1781-1840
Calendariographie, oder, Anleitung alle Arten Kalender zu verfertigen. Wien, Im Verlage von I.G. Heubner, 1828.
532 p.

1. Calendar.

NL 0414484 InU MH DN-Ob

Littrow, Joseph Johann, *edler* **von, 1781-1840.**
Chorographie; oder, Anleitung alle arten von land-, see- und himmelskarten zu verfertigen. Von J. J. Littrow ... mit 5 lithographirten tafeln. Wien, F. Beck, 1833.
2 p. l., 208 p. v fold. pl. 19½cm.
Bibliography: p. 6-8.

1. Cartography. I. Title.

16-24870

Library of Congress GA105.L5

NL 0414485 DLC DN-Ob NN NNC

QB 543 1820 .L78 (Rare) Littrow, Joseph Johann, Edler von, 1781-1840.
Darstellung der grossen und merkwürdigen Sonnenfinsterniss des 7. Septembers 1820, für die vorzüglichsten Städte Deutschlands. Pesth, Hartlebens Verlag, 1820.
48 p. maps.

1. Eclipses, Solar--1820. I. Title.

NL 0414486 ICU DN-Ob NN MdBP MH

QC 385 .L78 Littrow,Joseph Johann,edler von,1781-1840.
Dioptrik,oder,Anleitung zur verfertigung der fernröhre. Von J.J.Littrow ... Wien, J.B.Wallishausser, 1830.
xviii,494 p. 22½ cm.
"Vorzügliche optische werke": p.485-494.

NL 04144 7 MiU ViU MH NN DN-Ob NRU NNC MnU

Littrow, J[oseph] J[ohann, *edler von, 1781-1840.*
Die doppelsterne. Gemeinfasslich dargestellt von J. J. Littrow ... (Mit 1 tafel) Wien, F. Beck's universitäts-buchhandlung, 1835.
2 p. l., 174 p. incl. tables. 1 fold. pl. 21½cm. [With his Geschichte der entdeckung der allgemeinen gravitation durch Newton. Wien, 1835]

1. Stars, Double.

6-16250†

Library of Congress QB3.L78

NL 0414488 DLC OkU

Littrow, Joseph Johann, Edler von, 1781-1840.
Elemente der Algebra und Geometrie. Wien, J. G. Heubner, 1827.
xii, 456 p. fold. plates. 22cm.

1. Algebra. 2. Geometry.

NL 0414489 NNC CtY MdBP NN PBL

Kress Room Littrow, *Joseph Johann, edler von, 1781-1840.*
Gedrängter abriss der münz-, maass- und gewichtkunde der neueren zeiten und des alterthumes. In tabellen zur vergleichung mit dem neuen französischen und dem österreichischen systeme ... Güns, Reichard, 1834.
87 p. 22.5 cm.

Bibliography included in "Vorwort," p.[3]-5.

1.Weights and measures - Tables. 2.Money - Tables. I.Title.

NL 0414490 MH-BA

Littrow, Joseph Johann, *edler von, 1781-1840.*
Geschichte der entdeckung der allgemeinen gravitation durch Newton. Gemeinfasslich dargestellt von J. J. Littrow. Wien, In der F. Beck'schen universitäts-buchhandlung, 1835.
2 p. l., 100 p. diagr. 21½cm.
CONTENTS.—1. abth. Geschichts-erzählung der entdeckung der allgemeinen schwere.—2. abth. Erläuterungen zu der vorhergehenden geschichtserzählung.

1. Gravitation. 2. Newton, Sir Isaac, 1642-1727.

6—16252

Library of Congress QB3.L78

NL 0414491 DLC OkU CSt ICJ

OYK p.v.1

LITTROW, JOSEPH JOHANN, *edler von, 1781-1840.*
Gnomonik; oder, Anleitung zur Verfertigung aller Arten von Sonnenuhren. Von I.I.Littrow... Mit einer lithographirten Tafel. Wien: C.Gerold, 1831. 58 p. incl. tables. diagr. 24cm.

585280. 1. Sun dial, 1831.

Revised
January 13, 1937

NL 0414492 NN PLH

OYO

Littrow, Joseph Johann, *edler von, 1781-1840.*
Gnomonik; oder, Anleitung zur Verfertigung aller Arten von Sonnenuhren. Von I. I. von Littrow... Zweite, gänzlich umgearbeitete Auflage. Mit zwei Kupfertafeln. Wien: C. Gerold, 1838. iv, 108 p. incl. tables. diagrs. 21cm.

FORD COLLECTION.

172897. 1. Sun dial, 1838.
N. Y. P. L.

Revised
February 26, 1937

NL 0414493 NN NNC MH ICJ DN-Ob

Littrow, Joseph Johann, edler von, 1781-1840.
Kurze anleitung zur gesammten mathematik, von J.J.v. Littrow... Wien, C. Gerold, 1838.
xxiv, 384 p. 3 fold.diagrs. 14½cm.

NL 0414494 WU NNC CtY

Littrow, Joseph Johann, Edler von, 1781-1840, ed.
Johann Samuel Traugott Gehler's Physikalisches wörterbuch, neu bearb,von Brandes
see under Gehler, Johann Samuel Traugott, 1751-1795.

Littrow, Joseph Johann, *edler von, 1781-1840.*
Populäre Astronomie. Von J. J. Littrow... Wien: J. G. Heubner, 1825. 2 v. diagrs., maps, plates, tables. 21½cm.
Vol. 2 issued in 2 parts.

1. Astronomy—Elementary and popular works, 1825.
N. Y. P. L.

Revised
April 30, 1936

NL 0414496 NN PBL MH

Littrow, Joseph Johann, *edler* **von, 1781-1840.**
Sternatlas, nach der 4. aufl. von Littrows Atlas des gestirnten himmels vollständig neubearb. von Friedrich Becker. Mit einer einleitung von professor dr. J. Plassmann. Berlin, F. Dümmlers verlagsbuchhandlung, 1923.
2 p. l., 20, [4] p. illus., 16 pl. (2 double) tables. 29 x 22cm.

1. Stars—Atlases. I. Becker, Friedrich, 1900- ed. II. Plassmann, Joseph, 1859-

NL 0414497 MiU

Littrow, J[oseph] J[ohann, *edler von] 1781-1840.*
Sterngruppen und nebelmassen des himmels. Gemeinfasslich dargestellt von J. J. Littrow ... (Mit 3 kupferplatten) Wien, F. Beck's universitäts-buchhandlung, 1835.
87 p. 3 fold. pl. 21½cm. [With his Geschichte der entdeckung der allgemeinen gravitation durch Newton. Wien, 1835]

1. Stars—Clusters. 2. Nebulae.

6-16251†

Library of Congress QB3.L78

NL 0414498 DLC NN

B520 L735 Littrow, Joseph Johann, edler von, 1781-1840.
Theoretische und practische Astronomie, von J. J. Littrow ... Wien, J. B. Wallishausser, 1821-1827.
3 v. plates, tables. 23cm.

Vol. 3 has added t.-p.: Elemente der physischen Astronomie.

1. Astronomy.

DN-Ob CtY PU DSI MiU
NL 0414499 NNC CU WU MH ViU NjP PU MiU MdBP NN

QB723 .B6L7 (A) **Littrow, Joseph Johann,** *edler von, 1781-1840.*
Über den gefürchteten kometen des gegenwärtigen jahres 1832 und über kometen überhaupt. Von J. J. Littrow ... Wien, C. Gerold, 1832.
xvi, 175 p. fold. pl. 21cm.

1. Comet, Biela's. 2. Comets.

NL 0414500 ICU OU WU NNC

Littrow, Joseph Johann *Edler* **von, 1781-1840.**
Ueber Kometen. Mit einem Anhange über den im Jahre 1835 erscheinenden Halley'schen Kometen von Karl Ludwig Littrow. Neue Aufl. Mit zwey lithographirten Tafeln. Wien, C. Gerold, 1835.
xvi, 223 p. 2 plates. 21 cm.

1. Comets. 2. Halley's comet. I. Littrow, Karl Ludwig, Edler von, 1811-1877.

QB721.L78 5-7702 rev*

NL 0414501 DLC NN CU MdBP

Littrow, Joseph Johann, *edler von, 1781-1840.*
Ueber lebensversicherungen und andere versorgungsanstalten. Wien, 1832. 8° pppx-163.

NL 0414502 PBL OClW MiU NjP CtY

VOLUME 336

Littrow, Joseph Johann, edler von, 1781-1840.
Uebersicht des Planeten-Systemes. Verzeichniss der berechneten Kometen.
(Wien, 1835)
38 p. 23 cm.

Author's Wunder des Himmels, 5 Aufl., p. 987-1024.

NL 0414503 DN-Ob

Egleston
D620.71
Z
v.1
Littrow, Joseph Johann, edler von, 1781-1840.
Über ⌈:⌉ den erweiterten gebrauch der multiplikationskreise. Prag, G. Haase, 1820.
78 p.

"Für die Abhandlungen der k. böhm. Gesellschaft der wissenschaften."
Vol. of pamphlets.

NL 0414504 NNC

Kress Room
Littrow, Joseph Johann, edler von, 1781-1840.
Vergleichung der vorzüglichsten masse, gewichte und münzen mit den im Oesterreichischen Kaiserstaate gebräuchlichen ... Wien, F.Beck, 1832.
x, 132 p. 22.5 cm.

1.Foreign exchange - Tables. 2.Weights and measures - Tables. 3.Money - Austria. 4.Weights and measures - Austria. I.Title.

NL 0414505 MH-BA

Q
113
L5
Littrow, Joseph Johann, edler von, 1781-1840
Vermischte Schriften, hrsg. von C. L. v. Littrow. Stuttgart, Hoffmann, 1846.
3v. illus. 23cm.

1. Science I. Littrow, Karl Ludwig, Edler von, 1811-1877 II. Title

NL 0414506 WU DN-Ob NNC ICJ MH CtY

8407
.591
Littrow, Joseph Johann, edler von, 1781-1840.
Vorlesungen über astronomie.. Wien, Heubner, 1830.
2 v.in 1. fold.diagrs. 21 cm.

I.Main cd.(SO)

NL 0414507 NjP PBL DN-Ob NN NNC

Littrow, Joseph Johann, edler von, 1781-1840.
Die Wahrscheinlichkeitsrechnung in ihrer Anwendung auf das wissenschaftliche und practische Leben. Von J. J. Littrow... Wien: F. Beck's Universitätsbuchh., 1833. 102 p. 20½cm.

With this is bound his: Anleitung zur Berechnung der Lebensrenten und Wittwenpensionen. Wien, 1829.

1. Probability.
N. Y. P. L.
Revised July 26, 1934

NL 0414508 NN GAT PHC MH NjP DN-Ob CtY

Littrow, Joseph Johann, *edler* **von, 1781–1840.**
Die wunder des himmels; oder Gemeinfassliche darstellung des weltsystems. Von J. J. Littrow ... Mit dem bildnisse des verfassers und astronomischen tafeln ... Stuttgart, C. Hoffmann, 1834–36.
3 v. front. (port.) 17 fold. pl. 21cm.

Each volume has also special t.-p.
CONTENTS.—1. th. Theorische astronomie.—2. th. Beschreibende astronomie.—3. th. Physische astronomie. Beschreibung und lehre vom gebrauch der astronomischen instrumente.

1. Astronomy. I. Title.

Library of Congress QB43.L5 1834 4-13092

NL 0414509 DLC CU PPG NjP

Littrow, Joseph Johann, edler von, 1781-1840.
Die wunder des himmels, oder gemeinfassliche darstellung des welt-systems.
Stuttgart, 1834-41.
4 vols. 8vo.

NL 0414510 NN

Littrow, Joseph Johann, *edler* **von, 1781–1840.**
Die wunder des himmels; oder Gemeinfassliche darstellung des weltsystems. Von J. J. von Littrow ... 2. verb. aufl. in einem bande. Mit dem portrait des verfassers und 117 figuren ... Stuttgart, Hoffmann, 1837.
3 p. l., [v]-x p., 1 l., 814 p. front. (port.) 23 pl. (part fold.) 23cm.

1. Astronomy. I. Title.

Library of Congress QB43.L5 1837 4-13093

NL 0414511 DLC PU PHC PSC

Littrow, Joseph Johann, edler von, 1781-1840.
Die Wunder des Himmels; oder, Gemeinfassliche Darstellung des Weltsystems. Von J. J. von Littrow... Stuttgart: Hoffmann, 1842. xii, 814 p. incl. tables. diagrs., front. (port.), plates. 2. rev. ed. 8°.

14780A. 1. Astronomy.—Elementary and popular works, 1842. 2. Title.
N. Y. P. L. August 20, 1921.

NL 0414512 NN MH OkU NjP DN-Ob

QB43
.L81
(A)
Littrow, Joseph Johann, edler von, 1781-1840.
Die wunder des himmels; oder, Gemeinfassliche darstellung des weltsystems. Von J. J. von Littrow. 4. aufl. Nach den neuesten fortschritten der wissenschaft bearb. von Karl v. Littrow ... Stuttgart, Hoffmann, 1854.
xx, [1], 833, [1] p. incl. illus., tables, diagrs. 8 pl. (part double) 22½cm.

1. Astronomy.

NL 0414513 ICU CtY ViU ICJ NN MiU TxU OkU

Littrow, ⌈Joseph Johann⌉, edler von, 1781-1840.
Die Wunder des Himmels. Eine gemeinfassliche Darstellung des Weltsystemes. Von J. J. von Littrow. Fünfte Auflage. Nach den neuesten Fortschritten der Wissenschaft bearbeitet von K. von Littrow. Berlin: G. Hempel [1866]. xviii p., 1 l., 1033(1) p., 10 pl., 1 port. illus. 8°.

1. Astronomy.—Elementary and popular works, 1866. 2. Littrow, Karl von, editor.
N. Y. P. L. September 30, 1911.

NL 0414514 NN MH ViU MoU OkU DLC-P4

Littrow, Joseph Johann, edler von, 1781-1840.
Die wunder des himmels oder Gemeinfassliche darstellung des weltsystemes. Von J. J. von Littrow. 6. aufl. Nach den neuesten fortschritten der wissenschaft bearb. von Karl von Littrow... 3. ausg. derselben redaction. Mit 14 lithographirten tafeln und 133 holzschnitt-illustrationen. Berlin, G. Hempel, 1878.
xxxi, 1177 p. illus., XII pl. (part col., part double) tables, diagrs. 23½ cm.

NL 0414515 DN-Ob NN NBuG

QB
43
.L78
1886
Littrow, Joseph Johann, edler von, 1781-1840.
... Wunder des himmels, oder gemeinfassliche darstellung des weltsystemes. Siebente auflage. Nach den neuesten fortschritten der wissenschaften bearb. von dr. Edmund Weiss ... Berlin, G. Hempel, 1886.
xxiii, 1278, [2] p. incl. illus., tables, diagrs. XV pl. (part col., 5 double) 23½cm.

NL 0414516 MiU ICarbS MB

Littrow, Joseph Johann, Edler von, 1781-1840.
... Wunder des himmels; oder, Gemeinfassliche darstellung des weltsystems. 8. aufl. Nach den neuesten fortschritten der wissenschaft bearbeitet von dr. Edmund Weiss ... Berlin, F. Dümmler, 1897.
xxiii, 1099, [1] p. illus. (part col.) XIV pl. (part col., incl. double charts) diagrs. 23 cm.
At head of title: Littrow.
1. Astronomy - 1801-1900. I. Weiss, Edmund, 1837-1917.

NL 0414517 CU IU

Littrow, Joseph Johann, edler von, 1781-1840.
...Die Wunder des Himmels; gemeinverständliche Darstellung des astronomischen Weltbildes. Zehnte Auflage, zugleich Jubiläumsausgabe, vollständig neu bearbeitet von Professor Dr. Friedrich Becker... Bonn [etc.] F. Dümmlers Verlag [1939] viii, 579 p. incl. diagrs., tables. col'd front., illus. (incl. charts, ports.) 23½cm.

5453B. 1. Astronomy—Elementary and popular works, 1939. I. Becker, Friedrich, 1900– , ed. II. Title.
N. Y. P. L. August 3, 1939

NL 0414518 NN NNC DLC-P4

Littrow, Joseph Johann, edler von, 1781-1840.
Zusaetze zur ersten auflage von L's wunder des himmels. [Stuttgart, 1837?]
8°

NL 0414519 NN

Littrow, Karl Ludwig, Edler von, 1811-1877.
Andeutungen für Seeleute über den Gebrauch und die Genauigkeit der Methoden, Länge und Missweisung durch Circummeridianhöhen zu bestimmen. Wien, 1868.

NL 0414520 DN

Littrow, Karl Ludwig, *edler* **von, 1811–1877.**
Andeutungen über astronomische beobachtungen bei totalen sonnenfinsternissen. Von Karl von Littrow ... Wien, K. K. Hof- und staatsdruckerei, In commission bei K. Gerold's sohn, 1860.
12 p. 24cm.
Aus dem xxxix, bande, s. 625, des jahrganges 1860 der Sitzungsberichte der Mathem.-naturw. classe der Kaiserlichen akademie der wissenschaften besonders abgedruckt.

1. Eclipses, Solar.

Library of Congress QB541.L7 CA 6—2343 Unrev'd

NL 0414521 DLC DN-Ob

VOLUME 336

Littrow, Karl Ludwig, edler von, 1811-1877.

Vienna. Universität. *Sternwarte.*
Annalen der K. K. Sternwarte in Wien. Nach dem befehl Seiner Majestät auf öffentliche kosten herausgegeben ... Wien, 1821-40.

Littrow, Karl Ludwig, Edler von, 1811-1877, ed.
Atlas des gestirnten Himmels für Freunde der Astronomie
see under Littrow, Joseph Johann, Edler von, 1781-1840.

Littrow, Karl Ludwig, edler von, 1811-1877.
Bahnnähen zwischen den periodischen Gestirnen des Sonnensystemes. Wien Sitz. Ber. XII, 1854.
p. 44-76.

NL 0414524 OClW

13545 Littrow, Karl Ludwig, Edler von, 1811-1877.
Y Beitrag zur Kenntnis der Grundlagen von
v.9 Piazzi's Sternkatalog. ₍Wien, K.K. Hof- und Staatsdruckerei, 1855₎
67-140 p. tables. 29cm. (Akademie der Wissenschaften, Vienna. Mathematisch-naturwissenschaftliche Klasse. Denkschriften, Bd. 9, 1. Abth.)

1. Stars—Catalogs. 2. Piazzi, Giuseppe, 1746-1826.

NL 0414525 NIC DN-Ob

Littrow, Karl Ludwig, edler von, 1811-1877.
Bemerkungen über das von M. Eble überreichte "Neue Zeitbestimmungswerk".
Wien, 1854
5 p. 22 cm.

Wien Sitz. Ber., 14, 1854, p. 125-127.

NL 0414526 DN-Ob

13545 Littrow, Karl Ludwig, Edler von, 1811-1877.
Y Bericht über die in den Jahren 1847-
v.5 1851 ausgeführte Verbindung der österreichischen und russischen Landesvermessung. ₍Wien, K.K. Hof- und Staatsdruckerei, 1853₎
111-128 p. plates. 29cm. (Akademie der Wissenschaften, Vienna. Mathematisch-naturwissenschaftliche Klasse. Denkschriften, Bd. 5)

1. Surveying—Public lands.

NL 0414527 NIC

4GA Littrow, Karl Ludwig, Edler von, 1811-
114 1877.
Bericht über die von den Herren: Dir. C. Bruhns, Dir. W. Förster und Prof. E. Weiss ausgeführten Bestimmungen der Meridiandifferenzen Berlin -Wien-Leipzig. Vorgelegt in der Sitzung am 11. April 1872. Wien, Aus der Kaiserlich-Königlichen Hof- und Staatsdruckerei; in Commission bei K. Gerold's Sohn, 1872.
Library of Congress 62 p.

NL 0414528 DLC-P4 DN-Ob NIC

Littrow, Karl Ludwig, Edler von, 1811-1877.
Bestimmung der Meridiandifferenz Leipzig-Dablitz für die von
15951 Herrn Generallieutenant J. J. Baeyer vorgeschlagene mitteleuropäische Gradmessung. Von C. von Littrow, ... ₍Wien, 1868.₎
128 p. incl. tables. v pl. 31½ x 24½cm.
Caption title.
Extracted from "Denkschriften der K. Akad. d. Wissensch. Mathem. Naturw. Cl. xxviii. Bd. 1868."

NL 0414529 ICJ DN-Ob MB NIC

Littrow, Karl Ludwig, Edler von, 1811-1877.
Beyträge zu einer Monographie des Halley'schen Cometen. Bey
14079 Gelegenheit seiner Erscheinung im Jahre 1835 gemeinfasslich dargestellt von Carl Ludwig Littrow, ... Mit mehreren Abbildungen. Wien, H. F. Müller, 1834.
[4], 72 p. fold. front., 1 fold. pl. 18½cm.
Bibliography, p. [71]-72.

NL 0414530 ICJ NN CtY OCl WU MdBP

Littrow, Karl Ludwig, edler von, 1811-1877.
Die Culminationspunkte der östlichen Central-alpen.
Wien, 1853
4 p. 21cm.

Wien, Sitz. Ber., 11, 1854, p. 742-744.

NL 0414531 DN-Ob

Littrow, Karl Ludwig, Edler von, 1811-1877.
Deutschlands vorzüglichste sternwarten.
Wien, 1848.

NL 0414532 NjP

---

40 Littrow, Karl Ludwig, Edler von, 1811-1877.
Drei quellen ueber den kometen von 1556.
[Wien, 1856]
15 p. 8°. [Astronomical pamphlets, v. 7:12]
Aus dem aprilhefte des jahrganges 1856 der sitzungsberichte der mathem.-naturw. classe der kais. akademie der wissenschaften besonders abgedruckt.

NL 0414533 DLC

QB43 Littrow, Karl Ludwig, edler von, 1811-1877.
L53 Erläuterungen zu J. J. v. Littrow's Vorlesungen über Astronomie (Wien, 1830, bei J. G. Heubner) Wien, In Commission der C. Gerold, 1842.
x, 203 p. 5 plates.

1. Astronomy - 1801-1900. I. Littrow, Joseph Johann von, 1781-1840.

NL 0414534 CU

SPECIAL COLLECTIONS
B526.62
Z2
Littrow, Karl Ludwig, edler von, 1811-1877.
Instructions sur l'usage et la précision des méthodes pour trouver la longitude et la variation du compas par des hauteurs circum-méridiennes. Vienne, G. Gerold fils, 1868.
14 p. 23cm.

Published also in German and English.
Volume of pamphlets.

NL 0414535 NNC

QB9 Littrow, Karl Ludwig, edler von, 1811-1877.
.L75 Kalender für alle stände. Beilage. 1863-64, 1866, 1869. Wien, 1863-69.
4 v. 22-22.5 cm. S
Caption title.

NL 0414536 DLC

Littrow, Karl [Ludwig, edler von] 1811-1877.
Ein merkwürdiger Regenbogen.
QC976 Wien, 1862
.R2L8 2 p. 21cm.

Wien, Sitz. Ber., 45 (Abth. 2), 1862, p. 155-156.

NL 0414537 DN-Ob DLC

Littrow, Karl Ludwig, edler von, 1811-1877.

Vienna. Universität. *Sternwarte.*
Meteorologische beobachtungen an der K. K. Sternwarte in Wien von 1775 bis 1855. Auf öffentliche kosten hrsg. von Carl von Littrow, director, und Carl Hornstein. Wien, In commission bei J. B. Wallishausser, 1860-66.

Littrow, Karl Ludwig, edler von, 1811-1877.
Method of finding the time at sea. 1864.

NL 0414539 DN-Ob

Littrow, Karl Ludwig, edler von, 1811-1877.
Åstrand, Johan Julius, 1819-1900.
Neue einfache methode für zeit- und längenbestimmung. Von J. J. Åstrand ... Mit vorbemerkungen von Karl v. Littrow ... ₍Wien, 1867₎

Littrow, Karl Ludwig, edler von, 1811-1877.
Johann Samuel Traugott Gehler's Physikalisches wörterbuch, neu bearb, von Brandes
see under Gehler, Johann Samuel Traugott, 1751-1795.

Littrow, Karl ₍Ludwig₎ edler von, 1811-1877.
Physische zusammenkünfte der planeten (1) bis (42) während der nächsten jahre. Von Karl v. Littrow ... Wien, K. K. Hof- und staatsdruckerei, In commission bei K. Gerold's sohn, 1859.
64 p. 5 fold. pl. 31 x 24½cm.
Aus dem XVI. bande der Denkschriften der Mathematisch-naturwissenschaftlichen classe der Kaiserlichen akademie der wissenschaften besonders abgedruckt.

1. Planets, Minor.

Library of Congress QB377.L7 6-6577†

NL 0414542 DLC OClW NIC

13545 Littrow, Karl Ludwig, Edler von, 1811-
Y 1877.
v.31 Physische Zusammenkünfte der Planeten. (1)-(82) während der nächsten Jahre. ₍Wien, K.K. Hof- und Staatsdruckerei, 1872₎
157-186 p. tables. 29cm. (Akademie der Wissenschaften, Vienna. Mathematisch-naturwissenschaftliche Klasse. Denkschriften, Bd. 31, 1. Abth.)

1. Mechanics, Celestial.

NL 0414543 NIC

VOLUME 336

Littrow, Karl Ludwig, *edler* **von,** 1811-1877.
... Physische zusammenkünfte von asteroiden im jahre ... Von Karl v. Littrow ...
[Wien, K. K. Hof- und staatsdruckerei, 1861-
v. 23½cm.
Caption title.
"Sonderabdruck aus de[n] Sitzungsberichte[n] der Kais. Akademie der wissenschaften."

1. Planets, Minor.
6-20053 rev.
Library of Congress QB651.L78

NL 0414544 DLC OC1W

Littrow, Karl [Ludwig], edler von, 1811-1877.
Physische Zusammenkunft der Planeten Amphitrite und Melpomene im November 1857.
Wien, 1857
2 p. 21cm.

Wien, Sitz. Ber., 25, 1857, p. 251-252.

NL 0414545 DN-Ob OC1W

Littrow, Karl Ludwig, edler von, 1811-1877.
Physische Zusammenkünfte der Planeten ①-㊷ während der nächsten Jahre.
Wien, 1871.
Astr. Nachr. 77, 1871, col. 151-154.

NL 0414546 NjP

Littrow, Karl Ludwig, edler von, 1811-1877.
Populäre geometrie ... Stuttgart, 1839.
12°.

NL 0414547 NN PPL

Littrow, Karl Ludwig, edler von, 1811-1877, tr.
G.B. Airy's ... Populäre physiche astronomie
see under Airy, Sir G[eorge] B[iddell] 1801-1892.

Littrow, Karl Ludwig, edler von, 1811-1877.
P. Hell's Reise nach Wardoe bei Lappland ...
see under Hell, Maximilian, 1720-1792.

[Littrow, Karl Ludwig, edler von, 1811-1877
...Die sonne.
[Wien, 1864]

QB521
.L77

NL 0414550 DLC

Littrow, Karl Ludwig, edler von, 1811-1877.
Sternschnuppen und Kometen. - Anzahl der wahrnehmbaren Sterne, geschlossen aus dem Bonner Verzeichnisse. Neue Planeten und Kometen. Astronomische Preisaufgabe. Uebersicht des Planetensystenes.
Uebersicht der meteorologischen Beobachtungen an der K.K. Sternwarte zu Wien im Jahre 1868.
Wien,
5 p. 23cm.

Kalender für alle Stände.

NL 0414551 DN-Ob

Littrow, Karl Ludwig, *edler* **von,** 1811-1877.
Suggestions for mariners about the use and the exactness of the methods for determining the longitude and the variation of compass by circummeridian altitudes. By Charles de Littrow ... Vienna, C. Gerold's son, 1868.
14 p. 22½cm.

1. Longitude. 2. Compass.
13-14224
Library of Congress VK567.L82

NL 0414552 DLC NjP NNC DN-Ob DSI CtY

Littrow, Karl Ludwig, *edler* **von,** 1811-1877.
Sur une nouvelle méthode pour déterminer en mer l'heure et la longitude par les différences de hauteurs circumméridiennes; par M. Charles de Littrow ... Vienne, C. Gerold fils, 1868.
30 p. 22½cm.
"Mémoire présenté dans la séance du 8 janvier 1863 et inséré dans les Comptes rendus de l'Académie imp. de Vienne, vol. XLVII; traduit de l'allemand et annoté par l'auteur."

1. Longitude.
13-14225
Library of Congress VK567.L83

NL 0414553 DLC DN-Ob NNC DSI

509
L782u
Littrow, Karl Ludwig, Edler von, 1811-1877.
Ueber das Zurückbleiben der Alten in den Naturwissenschaften; Rectorsrede.
Wien, C.Gerold's Sohn, 1869.
28p. 21cm.

1.Science - History. I.Title. IC

NL 0414554 CLSU NjP CSdS MB

Littrow, Karl Ludwig, edler von, 1811-1877.
Über die Methode der Längenbestimmung durch Differenzen von Circummeridianhöhen und deren Anwendung während der Weltumsegelung S. M. Fregatte Novara.
Wien, 1863
26 p. 24cm.

Wien, Sitz. Ber., 47, (Abth. 2), 1863, p. 394-419.

NL 0414555 DN-Ob

Lomb
Q311
.L65
v.18,
no.13
Littrow, Karl Ludwig, edler von, 1811-1877.
Über eine Modification des Hansen'schen Registrirapparates. Von Karl v. Littrow.
[Wien, Aus der k. k. Hof- und Staatsdruckerei, 1865?]
3 p. plate. 33cm. (Lomb miscellaneous pamphlets, v. 18, no. 13)
Cover title.
"Sonder-Abdruck aus dem LII. Bde. der Sitzungsber. der kais. Akad. d. Wissenschaften."
Original paper wrappers.
1. Optics, Physical. I. Title.

NL 0414556 ViU

522.4
Z
Littrow, Karl Ludwig, edler von, 1811-1877.
Über eine Modification des Hansen'schen Registrirapparates. (Vorgelegt in der Sitzung vom 30. November 1865) [1866]
3 p. plate.

Reprinted from Sitzungsberichte der Mathem.-naturwissensch. Klasse der K. Akademie der Wissenschaften, Vienna, 52. Bd., 1866.
Volume of pamphlets.

NL 0414557 NNC

Littrow, Karl Ludwig, edler von, 1811-1877.

Littrow, J[oseph] J[ohann] von, 1781-1840.
Ueber kometen. Von J. J. Littrow ... Mit einem anhange über den im jahre 1835 erscheinenden Halley'schen kometen von Karl Ludwig Littrow ... Neue aufl. Mit zwey lithographirten tafeln. Wien, C. Gerold, 1835.

Littrow, Karl [Ludwig], edler von, 1811-1877.
Über lichte Faden im dunkeln Felde bei Meridian-Instrumenten.
Wien, 1856.
1 pl. 10 p. 22cm

Wien, Sitz. Ber., 20, 1856, p. 253-260.

NL 0414559 DN-Ob DLC

G105
.L78
Littrow, Karl Ludwig, Edler von, 1811-1877.
Verzeichniss geographischer Ortsbestimmungen nach den neuesten Quellen und mit Angabe derselben. Aus dem neuen physikalischen Wörterbuche besonders abgedruckt. Leipzig, E. B. Schwickert, 1844.
526, 36 p.
"Nachträge": 36 p.

1. Names, Geographical.

NL 0414560 ICU

[Littrow, Karl Ludwig, edler von, 1811-1877
...Uebersicht des planetensystemes.
[Wien, 1863]

QB601
.L77

NL 0414561 DLC

Littrow, Karl (Ludwig), edler von, 1811-1877.
Die Wunder des Himmels
see under Littrow, Joseph Johann Edler von, 1781-1840.

40
Littrow, Karl Ludwig, edler von, 1811-1877.
Der zonen-apparat am mittagsrohre der Wiener sternwarte. Wien, k.k. hof-und staatsdruckerei, 1858.
10 p., 1 pl. 8°. [Astronomical pamphlets, v. 6:15]
Aus dem dec.-hefte des jahrganges 1857 der sitzungsberichte der mathem.-naturw. classe der kais. akad. der wissenschaften besonders abgedruckt.

NL 0414563 DLC

523.3
Z
Littrow, Karl Ludwig, edler von, 1811-1877.
Zur Kenntniss der kleinsten sichtbaren Mondphasen. [1872]
22 p.

"Aus dem LXVI. Bande der Sitzb. der k. Akad. der Wissensch. II. Abth. Dec.-Heft. Jahrg. 1872."
Volume of pamphlets.

1. Moon.

NL 0414564 NNC DN-Ob

VOLUME 336

Littrow, Otto von
Über eine neue Einrichtung des Spectralapparates.
Wien, 1863
1 pl. 7 p. 23cm.

Wien, Sitz. Ber., 47, (Abth. 2), 1863, p. 26-32.

NL 0414565 DN-Ob

Littrow, Otto von
Über einen Heliostaten nach August's Princip.
Wien, 1863
2 pl. 12 p. 22cm.
Wien, Sitz. Ber., 48 (Abth. 2), 1863, p. 337-348.

NL 0414566 DN-Ob

Littrow-Bischoff, Auguste von
see
Littrow, Auguste (Bischoff) von, 1819-1890.

Kress Room

Littry, France. Propriétaires des mines de houille.
Observations des propriétaires des mines de houille de Littry (Calvados), sur la demande en réduction des droits de douane sur les charbons étrangers. Paris, Imprimerie de madame Huzard, 1822
20 p. 24.5 cm.

Signed: le marquis De Briqueville, président.

NL 0414568 MH-BA

Littschwager, Felix, 1890-
Alexandriner in den dramen Shakespeares. 1. teil: Scheinbare Alexandriner ... Berlin, E. Felber, 1912.
2 p. l., 47, [1] p. 20½cm.
Inaug.-diss.—Königsberg.
Lebenslauf.
Published in full as no. 2 in vol. II of "Normannia," 1912 (viii, 77 p.)
"Literatur": 2d prelim. leaf.

1. Shakespeare, William—Versification. 2. Alexandrine verse.

18-5079

Library of Congress PR3085.L5

NL 0414569 DLC NcU PBm PU CtY MiU NN IU MH

Littschwager, Gerhard, 1907-
Eigentumserwerb des erstehers bei der versteigerung an einer gepfändeten, aber dem schuldner nicht gehörigen beweglichen sache. (Nach geltendem recht und nach dem entwurf einer neuen ZPO.) ...
Inaug. Diss. -Freiburg, 1933.
Lebenslauf.
Bibliography.

NL 0414570 ICRL

Littwack, Bernhard, 1902-
... Ueber Scharlachpsychosen ... Bonn, 1930.
Inaug.-Diss. - Bonn.
Lebenslauf.
"Literaturverzeichnis": p. 35-36.

NL 0414571 CtY

LB1063
.L77

Littwin, Maxwell F.
Literature memorization in the light of experimental pedagogy, by Maxwell F. Littwin... [Worcester,Mass.,Pedagogical seminary,1916.
cover-title, p.[502]-527. tables. 23cm.
Reprinted from the Pedagogical seminary December,1916, Vol.XXIII,pp.502-527.
Bibliography:p.527.
1.Memory. 2.Educational psychology. 3.Literature - Study and teaching. I.Title.

NL 0414572 NNU-W

Littwin, Maxwell F., joint author.
Colligan, Eugene Aloysius.
United States history ... Colligan—Littwin. [New York, W. H. Sadlier, inc., °1931-32]

Littwin, Walter, 1902-
Die energie trocken-und feuchtlabiler schichtungen. ... Danzig, 1935.
Inaug. Diss. - Techn. Hochschule Danzig, 1935.
Lebenslauf.

NL 0414573 ICRL

Littwin, Walter, 1902-
Die energie trocken- und feuchtlabiler schichtungen ... Danzig, A.W. Kafemann, 1935.
20 p., 1 l. diagrs. 27 cm.
Film copy of the original in the library of the American mathematical society. Negative.
Thesis - Technische hochschule, Danzig.
Lebenslauf.
"Erscheint gleichzeitig als heft 4 der 'Forshcungsarbeiten des Staatlichen observatoriums Danzig.'"

NL 0414574 RPB

M(055)
K86d

Littwin, Walter, 1902-
Die Energie trocken- und feuchtlabiler Schichtungen. Leipzig, Akademische Verlagsgesellschaft M.B.F., 1935.
26 p. illus., diagrs., tables. 27 cm.
(Danziger meteorologische Forschungsarbeiten Heft 4)
"Literaturnachweis": p. 26.
Translation of title: The energy of dry and moist unstable stratification.

NL 0414575 DAS

Littwitz (Georg) [1877-]. *Nasolabioskopie beim Rind. [Leipzig.] 35 pp., 5 pl. 8°. Breslau. G. Schenkalowsky. 1924.

NL 0414576 DNLM CtY ICRL

Littwitz, Walter: Die syphilitischen Geburten der letzten 10 Jahre. [Maschinenschrift.] °. — Auszug: Berlin (1922): Ebering. 2 Bl. 8°
Berlin, Med. Diss. v. 1. Sept. 1922 [U 22. 500

NL 0414577 ICRL

Litty, Albert, 1877-
Beitraege zur kenntnis der normalen und pathologischen anatomie der glandula thyreoidea und parathyreoidea des pferdes.
Inaug. Diss. Leipzig, 1907
Bibl.

NL 0414578 ICRL CtY OCU MBCo

Litty, Friedrich Albert, 1877-
see Litty, Albert, 1877-

Litty, Heinz, 1910-
... Die Behandlungsergebnisse mit Cumasina-Präparaten bei chronischen Mittelohreiterungen ... Gütersloh i. Westf., 1937.
Inaug.-Diss. - Königsberg.
Lebenslauf.
"Literatur": p. 16.

NL 0414580 CtY

Lituanica, Lietuvių skautų tuntas, *Chicago.*
101 [i. e. Šimtas viena] daina. Chicago, 1955.
122 p. illus. 17 cm.
Lithuanian song-book.

1. Song-books, Lithuanian. I. Title.

M1766.L4L5 M 56-1341

NL 0414581 DLC

La Lituanie et la guerre Européenne: revue trimestrielle. ... Lausanne, Bureau d'informations de Lituanie, 1918-
v. 25cm.

NL 0414582 DNW

La Lituanie et la paix de Versailles. Lausanne: Librairie centrale des nationalités [1919]. 22 p. 12°.
Repr.: Lituanie indépendante. Sept. 1, 1919.

1. Lithuania. 2. European war, 1914-18.—Territorial questions, Lithuania. 3. Versailles (Treaty of), 1919.
N. Y. P. L. November 1, 1923.

NL 0414583 NN

Lituanistikos institutas, *Kaunas*
see
Kaunas. Antano Smetonos lituanistikos institutas.

LITUANUS, ____ [pseud].
La vérité polonaise sur les Lithuaniens. Lausanne,Bureau d'information de Lithuanie, 1917.

pp.16.
Cover-title:-"Extrait de Pro Lithuania,N°, 10,1916".

NL 0414585 MH

VOLUME 336

Lituanus. v. [1]– Nov. 1954–
[Brooklyn, N. Y., etc.]
v. in illus., ports. 28 cm. quarterly.
Issues for 1954-57 have no vol. numbering but constitute v. 1-3 and are called also no. 1-13.
Issues for June and Sept. 1960 published in combined form and called v. 6, no. 2.
Vols. for 1954– published by the Lithuanian Student Association (1954-56 by its Secretariate for External Relations)

1. Lithuanians—Period. I. Lithuanian Student Association.

DK511.L2A265 63-38829

NL 0414586 DLC OU ICU CaOTP KU MnCS

Lituma, Luis.
...Crítica de la tesis neopagana "La religion está sujeta a la raza y a esta misma ley debe adaptarse." [Lima? 1938] 72 p. 21cm.

"Bibliografía," p. [71]-72.

1. Religion—Germany. 2. Church and state—Germany, 1934–
N. Y. P. L. May 6, 1943

NL 0414587 NN MH

Lituma, Luis.
Primer curso de educación moral y religiosa, acomodado al plan de estudios de instrucción media, por el pbro. Luis Lituma ... Lima (Perú) C. Larrabure, 1937.

97 p. 21½cm.

1. Religious education—Text-books for young people—Catholic. 2. Moral education. I. Title: Educación moral y religiosa.

41-31871

Library of Congress BX930.L5
[2] 377

NL 0414588 DLC

Liturgarion
see
Orthodox Eastern Church. *Liturgy and ritual. Leitourgikon. Church Slavic.*

Liturgia.
Negrelos, Edições "Ora & Labora."
v. in illus. 23 cm. monthly.
"Boletim ... de vulgarização litúrgica e questões paroquiais editada pelos Monges Beneditinos de Singeverga."

1. Catholic Church. Liturgy and ritual—Period. 2. Theology, Pastoral—Catholic Church. 3. Catholic Church—Period. I. Negrelos, Portugal. Mosteiro de Singeverga.

BX1970.A1L5 52-38038 ‡

NL 0414590 DLC MnCS KAS

Liturgia; revista benedictina.
Año 1- 1946-
Burgos, Abadía de Santo Domingo de Silos, 1946-
v. 25cm. monthly.

1. Liturgy - Periodicals. I. Burgos, Spain. Abadía de Santo Domingo de Silos.

NL 0414591 KAS

Liturgia; ossia, Preghiere ed agende perle Chiese Evangeliche Riformate Italiane nell' Alta-Rezia
see under Chiese evangeliche riformate italiane. Liturgy and ritual.

G282.05
L737 Litúrgia e vida.

Rio de Janeiro.
v. 24cm. bimonthly.

Began 1954? Cf. New serial titles, 1961-65.
Title varies: 1954?- Revista gregoriana.
"Órgão do Instituto Pio X do Rio de Janeiro."

1. Catholic Church - Period. I. Instituto Pio X do Rio de Janeiro. II. Title: Revista gregoriana.

NL 0414593 TxU

Liturgia Judaica. London, 1740
see under Jews. Liturgy and ritual.

C
866
.87 Liturgia missae Orthodoxo-catholicae occidentalis. The liturgy of the Western orthodox-Catholic mass. [London,Taylor and co.,187-?]
24p. 22cm.

Follows closely, with an occasional interpolation and some omissions, the Ordo missae and Canon missae of the Missale romanum, including rubrics. English translation on opposite pages. Apparently intended for the use of Anglo-Catholics.

NL 0414595 ICN

Liturgia Mozarabica secundum regulam beati Isidori
see under Catholic Church. Liturgy and ritual. Mozarabic rite. [NC 0213500,-01,-02]

Liturgia per il culto publico raccomandata alle chiese dal venerabile sinodo
see under Église évangélique vaudoise. Liturgy and ritual.

Liturgia Romana vetus, tria Sacramentaria complectens
see under Catholic church. Liturgy and ritual. Sacramentary.

Liturgia sacra, sev ritus ministerij in ecclesia peregrinorum Francofordiae ad Moenum
see under Frankfurt am Main. Église reformée française. [Supplement]

Liturgia S[ancti] Clementis
see Clementine liturgy.

Liturgia sancti Dionysii [ascribed to the Areopagita]

In: Migne, J. P. Patrologiae cursus completus. Series graeca. Paris, 1857-1886. 165 v. (t.3)
BR60. M5

PBMC PU RP RPB CaOTU
MdBP NIC NN NNC NNUT NhD NjMD NjNbS NjP NjPT OC OO
NL 0414601 DLC CU CtHC CtY DCU ICN ICU MB MH MH-AH

Liturgia sancti Gregorii Naz. duplex.

In: Migne, J. P. Patrologiae cursus completus. Series graeca. Paris, 1857-1886. 165 v. (t.36)
BR60. M5

PBMC PU RP RPB CaOTU
MdBP NIC NN NNC NNUT NhD NjMD NjNbS NjP NjPT OC OO
NL 0414602 DLC CU CtHC CtY DCU ICU ICN MB MH MH-AH

Liturgia sancti Ignatii [Antiochensis]

In: Migne, J. P. Patrologiae cursus completus. Series graeca. Paris, 1857-1886. 165 v. (t. 5)
BR60. M5

PBMC PU RP RPB CaOTU
MdBP NIC NN NNC NNUT NhD NjMD NjNbS NjP NjPT OC OO
NL 0414603 DLC CU CtHC CtY DCU ICN ICU MB MH MH-AH

Liturgia sanctorum apostolorum Adaei et Maris; cui accedunt duae aliae ... Urmiae, 1890
see under Nestorian Church. Liturgy and ritual.

Liturgia, seu liber precum communium ... juxta usum ecclesiae anglicanae ...
see under Church of England. Book of common prayer. Latin.

Liturgia; seu, Liber precum communium ... Amharice versus
see under Church of England. Book of common prayer. Amharic. [supplement]

Liturgia svecanae ecclesiae catholicae & orthodoxae conformis ...
see under Svenska Kyrkan. Liturgy and ritual.

Liturgia tigurina: or, The book of common prayers
see under Evangelisch-Reformierte Kirche des Kantons Zürich.

La Liturgia ynglesa, O, El libro de oracion commun y administration de los sacramentos,...
see under Church of England. Book of Common Prayer. Spanish.

VOLUME 336

Liturgiae Ibericae antiquiores
see under Tarchnisvili, Michael, ed.

Liturgiae S[ancti] Basilii Magni, S. Gregorii theologi, S. Cyrilli Alexandrini, ex Arabico conuerse, a Victorio Scialach, accurensi Maronita è monte Libano. Augustae Vindelicorum [Augsburg] Apud Christophrum Mangum, 1604.
[vi], 78 p. 4°.

NL 0414611 PPPD DCU-H PPLT

264.019
G811

Liturgiæ, sive Missæ sanctorvm patrvm: Iacobi apostoli & fratris Domini: Basilij Magni, è vetusto codice latinæ tralationis: Ioannis Chrysostomi, interprete Leone Thusco. De ritv missæ et Evcharistia: ex libris B. Dionisij Areopagitæ: Iustini Martyris: Gregorij Nysseni: Ioannis Damasceni: Nicolai Methonensis: Samonæ Gazæ archiepiscopi: Germani archiepiscopi Constantinopolitani: Nicolai Cabasilæ, Gentiano Herueto interprete: Maximi monachi B. Dionisij interpretis: Bessarionis cardinalis. Proclus archiepiscopus Constantinopolitanus præfatur. Qvibvs accessit ad calcem e libris d. Ioannis Chrysostomi, locorum annotatio, & initio aliquot capita, vnde litvrgica comprobantur: avctore F. Clavdio de Sainctes, theologo Parisiensi. Antverpiæ, ex officina Christophori Plantini, 1560.
210 numb.l., 1 l. 17cm.
Signatures: A-Z[8], Aa-Cc[8], Dd[4](last leaf blank)
Device of printer on t.-p. and on verso of last leaf.

Dedicatory letter by Joannes a Sancto Andrea.
With this is bound: Garet, Jean. Omnivm ætatvm, nationvm ac provinciarvm in veritatem corporis Christi in Eucharistia, consensvs. Antverpiae, 1569.

1. Mass. 2. Christian literature, Early. I. Sainctes, Claude de, 1525-1591. II. Joannes a Sancto Andrea. I. Tuscus, Leo, 12th cent., tr.

NL 0414614 IU NNUT

Lit
+400
1560

.LITVRGIAE SIVE MISSAE SANCTO-/ RVM PATRVM:/ Iacobi apostoli & fratris Domini./ Basilij magni,e vestusto codice Latinae tralationis./ Ioannis Chrysostomi, interprete Leone Thusco./ DE RITV MISSAE ET/ EVCHARISTIA: Ex libris B. Dionysij Areopagitae./ Justini martyris. Gregorij Nysseni./ Ioannis Damasceni. Nicolai Mathonensis./ Samonae Gazae archiepiscopi Constantinopolitani./ Nicolai Cabasilae, Gentiano Herueto interprete./ Maximi Monachi B.Dionysij interpretis./Bessarionis Cardinalis./ Proclus archiepiscopus Constantinopolitanus praefatur./ QVIBVS ACCESSIT AD CALCEM E LIBRIS/ D.Ioan.Chrysostomi, locorum annotatio, & initio aliquot Capita, vnde Liturgica com-/ probantur, auctore F. Claudio De Sainctes, Theologo Parisiensi./, PARISIIS, M.D.LX./ Apud Guil Morelium, in Graecis typographum Regium./PRIVILEGIO REGIS
[16] 212 p. 30 x 20 cm.
Bound with O.E.Church Lit. & rit.Leitourgikon. Greek.1560.
Provenance: Bp. Whittingham, Maryland Diocesan Library.
1. O.E.Church --Lit. & rit. I. Sainctes, Claude de, Bp, 1525-1591.

NL 0414617 NNG MH

Liturgiae, siue Missae sanctorum patrum: Iacobi Apostoli & fratris Domini: Basilij Magni ... Ioannis Chrysostomi, interprete Leone Thusco. De ritu Missae et eucharistia... praefatur. Quibus accessit ... annotatio ... auctore F. Claudio de Sainctes... Antuerpiae, Ex officina Christophori Plantini, 1562.
210, [3] p., 17 cm.
Title-page and first leaves wanting. Title supplied from the British Museum catalogue.

NL 0414618 NNUT

Liturgiae sive missae sanctorum patrum;Jacobi apostoli & fratris Domini[etc.], Quibus accessit ad calcem e libris Joannis Chrysostomi locorum annotatio & initio aliquot capita,unde liturgica comprobantur,auctore [Claudio de Sainctes. Antverpiae,in aedibus J. Stelsii,1562.

NL 0414619 MH

Liturgiae Syriacae septimanae passionis Domini nostri Jesu Christi excerptum ...
Lipsiae... 1720
see under Catholic Church. Syrian rite. Liturgy and ritual. Holy Week offices.
[NC 0228360]

Liturgiarum orientalium collectio, in qua continentur liturgiae Copititarum tres, Basilii, Gregorii theologi & Cyrilli Alexandrini, Latine conversae ...
see under Renaudot, Eusèbe, 1646-1720, comp. & tr.

Liturgic hymns of the United Brethren
see under Moravian Church. Liturgy and Ritual.

Liturgic Psalmody and hymnal... (Roehampton, 1862)
see under [Biber, Edward] 1801-1874, ed. and comp.

Liturgic worship; sermons in the Book of Common Prayers
see under New York Bible and Common Prayer Book Society.

Liturgica opuscula aetatis incertae.

In: Migne, J. P. Patrologiae cursus completus. Series graeca. Paris, 1857-1886. 165 v. (t. 106)
BR60. M5

PBMC PU RP RPB CaOTU
MdBP NIC NN NNC NNUT NhD NjMD NjNbS NjP NjPT OC OO
NL 0414625 DLC CU CtHC CtY DCU ICN ICU MH MB MH-AH

BX9853
.316

Liturgical and extemporaneous worship.
[n.p.,n.d.]
caption-title.

NL 0414626 DLC

Liturgical arts; a quarterly devoted to the arts of the Catholic church. v. 1- fall 1931-
New York, The Liturgical arts society, 1932-
v. illus., plates (part col., part mount.) port., facsims. 30½cm.
Published in Concord, N. H. (editorial office, New York) spring 1932-

1. Christian art and symbolism — Period. 2. Church architecture — Period. 3. Church decoration and ornament—Period. I. Liturgical arts society, New York.

Library of Congress N7810.L5 38-9921
246.05

CStclU PCaD TxLT KyLxCB N LU CtY-D CU-Riv
CaOTP PSt IEG OrPS CBGTU GU KyLoU NjPT ICN OU
MoSW OC CSt MWH MoSC PPiD ODaStL MoSC MWH DS MNS
IC MB KU LNL OrP TxU MdBWA OClJC OU INS MBtS ILS
NL 0414627 DLC OCl NN PPLT PBm MWelC MoS MoCA

---

q709.54
L737R

LITURGICAL arts.
[The religious art and architecture of India]
N.Y. 1953. 40p. illus. plans.
(Liturgical arts. v.22, no.1, Nov. 1953)

(On cover: Around the world in ninety days. 4. India)
"A partial, annotated bibliography of Indian art and culture": p.32-40.

NL 0414628 WaS

Liturgical Arts Society, New York.
Art sacré, an exhibition of French modern religious art and architecture...
see under title

BQT5937
L58
1933

Liturgical arts society, New York, comp.
Catalogue of a small church exhibition With forewords by the Rev. John La Farge, S.J. [and] Charles D. Maginnis, F.A.I.A. New York, Published bor the Liturgical Arts Society by Sheed& Ward, 1933
30p illus , 29 plates. 20cm

NL 0414630 InStme

Liturgical arts society, *New York, comp.*
The Eastern branches of the Catholic church; six studies on the Oriental rites, compiled by the Liturgical arts society, with an introduction by Donald Attwater. New York, Toronto, Longmans, Green and co., 1938.
xi p., 1 l., 110 p. front., illus. (map) tab. 21 cm.
"This book is a reprint of a series of articles that first appeared in Liturgical arts in 1935."—p. x.
"First edition."
"List of books, periodicals and pamphlets introductory to a study of the Eastern rites": p. 95-110.

CONTENTS.—The Eastern branches of the tree of life, by F. J. McGarrigle.—A new branch of the tree of life: the Syro-Malankara church, by Mar Ivanios.—The Ethiopic church, by Eugène cardinal Tisserant.—The code of canon law and the Catholics of Eastern rites, by J. M. O'Hara.—Liturgy and asceticism in the Eastern church, by John La Farge.—The spiritual and aesthetic value of icons, by Ildefonse Dirks.

1. Catholic church—Oriental rites. I. McGarrigle, Frances Joseph, 1888- II. Panikervirtis, Givergis Thomas, abp., 1882- III. *Tisserant, Eugène, cardinal, 1884- IV. O'Hara, Joseph Michael, 1884- V. La Farge, John, 1880- VI. Dirks, Ildefonse, 1874- VII. Attwater, Donald, 1892- ed. VIII. Title.

BX4710.L5 281.9 38—33931

NcD ICU DDO
NL 0414632 DLC OrStbM OWorP MBtS PPLT WaU OClJC

VOLUME 336

Liturgical arts society, New York.

Liturgical arts; a quarterly devoted to the arts of the Catholic church. v. 1- fall 1931-
New York, The Liturgical arts society, 1932-

NL 0414635 DLC

Liturgical Arts Society, New York.
Religious sculpture, 1950
see under Dayton Art Institute, Dayton, Ohio.

Liturgical arts society, inc., *New York.*
A spiritual practice for members of the Liturgical arts society. New York [The Harbor press] 1933.
[14] p. 9½cm.

1. Catholic church—Prayer-books and devotions. 2. Devotional exercises. I. Title.

33-17446

Library of Congress BX2182.L55 242

NL 0414635 DLC

LITURGICAL ARTS SOCIETY, INC., New York.
The work of the Liturgical arts society. New York, N.Y.: Liturgical arts soc., inc. [1935] 32 p. illus. 13½cm.

NL 0414636 NN

Liturgical catechism, a catechism on the divine liturgy of the Byzantine-Slavonic rite. [Chicago, Paluch, 1954]
110 p., illus., 23 cm,

NL 0414637 OrStbM

BX1970 .A1N3
Liturgical Conference, inc.

North American Liturgical Week.
North American Liturgical Week. [Proceedings] 1st- 1940-
Washington [etc.]

Liturgical conference, INC.
[What is the liturgical movement? [Highland Park, Ill.] The Liturgical Conference [1947]
32p. 23cm.
"Designed and printed by the Pio Decimo Press."

1. Liturgical movement.

NL 0414639 KAS

Liturgical Conference, Inc.
What is the liturgical movement? Published by the Liturgical Conference. 1948.
32 p. 23 cm.

Copies 2-3: 2 ed. [1948]

NL 0414640 PLatS

Liturgical Conference, inc.
see also
North American Liturgical Week.

The liturgical considerator considered: ... (London, 1661)
see under [Firmin, Giles] 1614-1697.

SPEC COLL 1669 2
A liturgical discourse of the holy sacrifice of the Mass wherein is contained a summary explication of the several parts...collected faithfully by A.F. the least of Friar Minours. [n.p.], 1669.
1 v. [various pagings] 17 1/2 cm.

I. A.F., the least of Friar Minors.
II. F., A., the least of Friar Minors.

NL 0414643 NNF

Liturgical Institute. *1st, Valparaiso University, 1949.*
Essays presented at the First Liturgical Institute, held under the auspices of Valparaiso University at Valparaiso, Indiana, June 7th, 8th, and 9th, 1949. Valparaiso, Valparaiso University Press [1950]
108 p. 24 cm.
Addendum slip inserted.
Includes bibliographies.
CONTENTS.—Address delivered by President O. P. Kretzmann.—Form and tradition in worship, a theological interpretation, by J. J. Pelikan.—The pastor's part of the liturgy, by C. Bergen.—The liturgy of the Eucharist, by A. Wismar.—Music of the liturgy, by M. A. Bichsel.
1. Lutheran Church. Liturgy and ritual.
BX8067.A1L5 1949 264.041 50-28566

NL 0414644 DLC PPLT

Liturgical law; a handbook of the Roman liturgy
see under Bachofen, Charles Augustine, 1872-

... The **Liturgical** movement. Collegeville, Minn., The Liturgical press, 1930.
29 p. 18cm. (Popular liturgical library, series IV, no. 3)
CONTENTS.—The liturgical movement, its general purpose and its influence on priestly piety.—The significance of the liturgical movement.—A survey of the liturgical movement.

1. Catholic church. Liturgy and ritual.

Library of Congress BX1975.L5 31-22134
Copyright A 20786 [2] 264.02

NL 0414646 DLC OrStbM

[Liturgical music] [sc. medieval, Catholic]
[Used sometimes as a supplied title for untitled manuscript collections, not more specifically identified as an Antiphonary, Gradual, Processional, or otherwise.
see under Catholic Church. Liturgy and ritual.
NB. Meant to be limited to chants (plain, Georgian, etc.)

Liturgical reform. London, 1858.
24 p. 21 cm. (Progressionist church tracts, no. 1.)

NL 0414648 RPB

Liturgical rules for organists, singers, and composers, from rubrical and other authentic sources. London, 1868.

NL 0414649 PPL

RARE BOOK BV 175 L7
Liturgical Society of St. James, New York (City).
Bulletin. no.1- 1936-
New York, 1936-
v.
Xerox copy, 1971.

NL 0414650 MoSCS

M 2173 L5I 52
Liturgical society of St. James, New York.
Introits for Advent and Christmas. New York, Liturgical society of Saint James [c1936]
[8] p. 27 cm.

1. Introits (Music) 2. Advent. 3. Christmas. I. Lutheran church. Liturgy and ritual. II. Title.

NL 0414651 NRCR MoSCS

M 2173 L5I 5
Liturgical society of Saint James, New York.
Introits for Lent and Easter. New York, Liturgical society of Saint James [c1937]
10 p. 27 cm.

1. Introits (Music) 2. Lent. I. Lutheran church. Liturgy and ritual. II. Title.

NL 0414652 NRCR MoSCS

M 2173 L5M8
Liturgical society of Saint James, New York
Music of the ordinary. New York, Liturgical society of Saint James [c1936]
10 p. 27 cm.

1. Church music. 2. Responsive worship. I. Lutheran church. Liturgy and ritual. II. Title.

NL 0414653 NRCR MB

VOLUME 336

RARE BOOK M 2173 L6 Liturgical Society of St. James, New York.
The music of the ordinary. New York [c1936]
10 leaves. music.
Xerox copy.

NL 0414654 MoSCS

Liturgical society of Saint James, New York.
Pro Ecclesia lutherana. v. 1- ; Dec. 1933-
[Hoboken, N. J., etc., Published by the Liturgical society of Saint James] 1933-

---

[Liturgical pamphlets. n.p.,n.p.,1865-1884]

NL 0414656 NRCR

Liturgical Press, Collegeville, Minn.
Liturgical symbols
see under title

Liturgical symbols...Collegeville, Minn. Liturgical press. [19-]
50 col.plates in each series.

NL 0414658 OClND

The liturgical poetry of Adam of St. Victor
see under Adam de Saint Victor, d. 1192.

Liturgical prayers and services... New York, Wagner, [1932]
see under Catholic Church. Liturgy and ritual. Ritual. [Miscellaneous] [supplement]

The liturgical question answered; reply to an attack upon the Common Service... Gettysburg (Pa.) Wible, n.d.
77 p.
From the Lutheran quarterly, April, 1890.

NL 0414661 PPLT

BX9573 .L5 The liturgical question with reference to the provisional liturgy of the German Reformed church.
Philadelphia,1862.
72 p]

NL 0414662 DLC PPeSchw

USC9 L737 Liturgical services containing prayers, ancient and modern for use in the churches. Boston, Pilgrim Press [c1903]
78 p. 19 cm.

"Among Congregational churches there has been an increasing demand for a simple liturgical service book. At the request of the publishers the effort to meet that demand was undertaken by Reuen Thomas."

1. Congregational churches in the U.S.A. Liturgy and ritual. 2. Orders of worship. 3. Prayers - Collections. I. Thomas, Reuen, 1840-1907 (2)

NL 0414663 CtY-D NN OCl

Liturgical services: Liturgies and occasional forms of prayer set forth in the reign of Queen Elizabeth
see under Church of England. Liturgy and ritual.

Liturgical tracts. 1547-1675.

NL 0414665 IaU

Liturgical Week
see
North American Liturgical Week.

Liturgical worship... by a member of the Presbyterian Church. Belfast, Aitchison, 1858.
12 p.

NL 0414667 PPPrHi

Liturgie; publiée sous la direction de Fernand Cabrol. Par., Bloud, 1907-
v.1-

NL 0414668 PU

La Liturgie Angloise. Ov Le Livre des Prieres Publiques, ...
see under Church of England. Book of Common Prayer, French.

Liturgie bei dem öffentlichen Gottesdienste der Evangelisch-Christlichen Kirche in dem Herzogthum Nassau ... Wiesbaden, 1843
see under Evangelische Landeskirche in Nassau. Liturgy and ritual. [Supplement]

La Liturgie, c'est à dire, Le Formulaire des Prières Publiques, ...
see under Church of England. Book of Common Prayer, French.

Liturgie de l'Église catholique gallicane, suivie d'un abrégé du catéchisme ...
see under Loyson, Charles Jean Marie, known as Père Hyacinthe, 1827-1912.

Liturgie de Prémontré; le Liber ordinarius...
see under Catholic Church. Liturgy and ritual. Ordines. [Premonstratensian]

La liturgie de Saint Jacques
see Liturgy of St. James [with specification: (Greek) or (Syrian)]
and/or the references found under that heading.

Die Liturgie der Brandenburg-Nürnbergischen Kirchenordnung von 1533. Mit Ergänzungen aus andern fränkischen Liturgieen. [Nördlingen, Beck, 1853]
52 p.
I. Evangelisch-Lutherische Kirche in Ansbach (Principality) Kirchenordnung. 1533.

NL 0414675 MoSCS

Die Liturgie der neuen christlichen Kirche, in der Offenbarung genannt Das Neue Jerusalem
see under New Jerusalem Church. Liturgy and ritual.

Liturgie des Églises reformées de France
see under Églises reformées evangeliques de France. Liturgy and ritual.

Liturgie des Malades
see under [Communauté de Taizé]

Liturgie du Baptême.
see under [Communauté de Taizé]

Die Liturgie im evangelische Gottesdienste
see under Haupt-verein fuer christliche Erbauungsschriften in den preussischen staaten.

Liturgie Lutherischer gemeinde-gottesdienste, Nördlingen, Beck, 1851.
83 p.

NL 0414681 PPLT

VOLUME 336

Die Liturgie, nebst andern gottesdienstlichen Handlungen der Kirche
see under Catholic Apostolic Church. Liturgy and ritual.

La Liturgie ou formulaire des prières publiques, selon l'usage de l' Église anglicane
see under Church of England. Book of Common Prayer. French.

La liturgie; ou, la manière de célébrer le service divin dans l'église de Genève
see under Geneva. Église de Genève. Liturgy and ritual.

BT 4139.5 .N48 A2
La liturgie, ou la manière de célébrer le service divin, qui est établie dans les églises de la principauté de Neufchâtel & Vallangin. Basle, Jean Pistorius, 1713.
123 p. 27 cm.
Compiled by Jean Frédéric Osterwald? Cf. Brit. Mus. Cat.

1 Liturgy - History - Switzerland - Neuchâtel. 2. Neuchâtel. 3. Valangin

NL 0414685 DCU PPAN

T.R. BX9427 .A1 1714 SWTS
La Liturgie ou la manière de célébrer le service Divin; qui est établie dans les églises de la principauté de Neufchatel & Vallangin. Basle, Jean Pistorius, 1714.
[11] l., 124p. [1] l. 26cm.
"Epître dedicatoire" signed: Charles Tribolet

I. Reformed Chruch of Neuchâtel. Liturgy and ritual. II. Tribolet, Charles.

NL 0414686 IEG

La liturgie;ou, La manière de célébrer le service divin... comme elle est établie dans les Églises de la principauté de Neuchâtel & Valengin. Nouvelle éd. Neuchâtel, De l'Imprimerie de la Société typog., 1772.
221 p.

NL 0414687 PPLT

Liturgie; ou, Manière de célébrer le service divin dans l'église réformée. Précédée de prières. Valence, J. Marc Aurel, 1844.
96 p. 48°.

NL 0414688 NN

... Liturgie pour les paroisses de langue française.. see under Evangelisch-reformierte Kirche des Kantons Bern. Liturgy and ritual.

BV182 .142 .L782l
Liturgie pour les Protestans de France, ou prieres pour les familles des fidéles privés de l'exercice public de leur religion. A'usage des Protestants de ce Royaume, avec un discours preliminaire sur quelques matiéres intéressantes.
3rd. ed. Amsterdam, Marc-Michel Rey, 1745.
380p.

NL 0414690 TNJ-R

Liturgie pour les Protestans de France, ou, prières ...
see also Liturgies pour les Protestans de France, ou, prières ... (1758)

Liturgie und frauenseele; hrsg. von der abtei Maria Laach
see under [Wintersig, Athanasius]

Liturgie und gesangbuch für die neue kirche, bezeichnet als das neue Jerusalem in der offenbarung Johannis. Baltimore, 1855.
12°

NL 0414693 NN RPB

Liturgie und Mönchtum. Laacher Hefte. Heft 1-
1948-
Maria Laach, Verlag Ars Liturgica.
v. in illus. 22 cm. irregular.
Vols. 1-5 published in Freiburg by Herder.
Editor: 1948- T. Bogler.

1. Catholic Church—Period. 2. Catholic Church. Liturgy and ritual—Period. 3. Liturgical movement—Period. 4. Monasticism and religious orders—Period. 5. Benedictines—Period. I. Bogler, Theodor, 1897- ed. II. Maria Laach (Benedictine monastery)

BX803.L57 54-34859 rev

NL 0414694 DLC MH DCU NcD PLatS MnCS

Liturgie und Seelsorge; zur religiösen Formung des Christen von heute
see under Österreichisches Seelsorge-Institut. 6 Weihnachts-Seelsorgertugung, 1936.

La liturgie vaudoise
see under Église nationale vaudoise. Liturgy and ritual. [supplement]

BX8C .A2A4 1851
Liturgieen für den evangelisch-lutherischen gottesdienst. Bevorwortet von dr. G. C. A. Harless. Hrsg. von Julius Leopold Pasig ... Leipzig, B. G. Teubner, 1851.
xii, 136 p. 24cm.

NL 0414697 ICU PPLT

Liturgiegeschichtliche Forschungen. Heft 1-10. Münster in Westf., Aschendorff, 1918-27.
10 v. in 8. 26 cm.
No. 6-10 (1923-27) issued by the Verein zur Pflege der Liturgiewissenschaft.
Edited by F. J. Dölger, K. Mohlberg and A. Rücker.
Superseded by Liturgiegeschichtliche Quellen und Forschungen (later Liturgiewissenschaftliche Quellen und Forschungen)

I. Dölger, Franz, 1891- ed. II. Mohlberg, Cunibert, 1878- ed. III. Verein zur Pflege der Liturgiewissenschaft.

BV170.L5512 58-51489

NL 0414698 DLC InStme

BV170 .L55
Liturgiegeschichtliche Quellen. Heft 1/2-11/12. Münster in Westf., Aschendorff, 1918-27.
12 v. in 8. 25 cm.
No. 4-11/12 (1923-27) issued by Verein zur Pflege der Liturgiewissenschaft.
Edited by K. Mohlberg and A. Rücker.
Superseded by Liturgiegeschichtliche Quellen und Forschungen (later Liturgiewissenschaftliche Quellen und Forschungen)

1. Liturgics. I. Mohlberg, Cunibert, 1878- ed. II. Rücker, Adolf, 1880- ed. III. Verein zur Pflege der Liturgiewissenschaft.

BV170.L55 58-51490

NL 0414699 DLC TxDaM-P InStme NjPT NN NcD MoSC

Liturgiegeschichtliche Quellen und Forschungen
see Liturgiewissenschaftliche Quellen und Forschungen.

Liturgien für evangelisch-lutherische sonn- und festtagsgottesdienste nebst musikalischem anhange ... Greiz, 1853
see under Evangelisch-Lutherische Landeskirche in Reuss. Liturgy and ritual.

Liturgies and other documents of the ante-Nicene period. Edinburgh, T. & T. Clark, 1872.
viii, 186 p. 23 cm. (Ante-Nicene Christian library ... v. 24)
Contents.—Early liturgies: The divine liturgy of James, tr. by William Macdonald. The divine liturgy of the holy apostle and evangelist Mark, tr. by G. R. Merry. Liturgy of the holy apostles; or, Order of the sacraments, tr. by Dr. Donaldson.—Syriac documents of the ante-Nicene period: Ambrose and A letter of Mara, son of Serapion, tr. by B. P. Pratten.—Selections from the prophetic Scriptures, and Fragments of Clemens Alexandrinus, tr. by William Wilson.

1. Liturgies, Early Christian. (Series)

BR60.A4 vol. 24 50-48287

MH NN ICN MB CBBD
NL 0414702 DLC OrStbM MdBP MH-AH ICN DCU OCl MiU

Liturgies of S. Mark, S. James, S. Clement, S. Chrysostom and the church of Malabar; tr...by J.M.Neale. London, Hayes, 1859.
224 p.

NL 0414703 PPLT

The liturgies of S. Mark, S. James, S. Clement, S. Chrysostom, S. Basil: or according to the use of the churches of Alexandria, Jerusalem, Constantinople, and the formula of the apostolic constitutions. Edited by the Rev. J. M. Neale ... London: J. T. Hayes, 1859. vi, [7]-174 p. 17cm.
Each liturgy has special t.-p., dated 1858.
Text in Greek.

NL 0414704 NN NRCR MH

VOLUME 336

PR 10
M8 N4
1859
The LITURGIES of St. Mark, St. James, St. Clement, St. Chrysostom, St. Basil ... 1859.

I. Neale, John Mason, 1818-1866, ed.

NL 0414705 CaBVaU

The liturgies of S. Mark, S. James, S. Clement, S. Chrysostom, S. Basil: or, according to the use of the churches of Alexandria, Jerusalem, Constantinople, and the formula of the Apostolic constitutions... Second edition... London, J. T. Hayes, 1868. xii, 172p., 17 cm.

NL 0414706 MBC NN NjNbS PPPD MH

PR 10
M8 N4
1868
The LITURGIES of St. Mark, St. James, St. Clement, St. Chrysostom, St. Basil ... 1868.

I. Neale, John Mason, 1818-1866, ed.

NL 0414707 CaBVaU

C
85
.86
The liturgies of SS. Mark, James, Clement, Chrysostom, and Basil, and the Church of Malabar. Translated, with introduction and appendices, by the Rev. J.M.Neale...and the Rev. R.F.Littledale... 2d edition. London,J.T.Hayes,1869.
xl,256p. 17cm.

NL 0414708 ICN NBuG CtY PPPD PPPrHi NjNbS MH NN

PR 10
M8 N4
1869
L5
The LITURGIES of St. Mark, St. James, St. Clement, St. Chrysostom, St. Basil ... [1869]

I. Neale, John Mason, 1818-1866, tr.

NL 0414709 CaBVaU

The liturgies of SS. Mark, James, Clement, Chrysostom, and Basil, and the church of Malabar; tr., with introd. and appendices, by J.M. Neale and R.F. Littledale. 4th ed. London, J.T. Hayes, [1883]
xl, 256 p. illus. 17 cm.
1. Liturgies, Early Christian. I. Neale, John Mason, 1818-1866, tr. I. Littledale, Richard Frederick, 1833-1890, joint tr.

NL 0414710 MdBP NN

245
003
N2C
3ed
The liturgies of S. Mark, S. James, S. Clement, S. Chrysostom, S. Basil: or, according to the use of the churches of Alexandria, Jerusalem, Cosstantinople, and the formula of the Apostolic constitutions... With preface by Dr. Littledale. 3d ed. London, J.T. Hayes, 1875.
172p 17cm

PPL MdBP
NL 0414711 MnCS DDO CtY NN OCl ICU PP PPPrHi PPPD

BX350
A2N4
1896
The liturgies of S. Mark, S. James, S. Clement, S. Chrysostom, S. Basil: or, according to the use of the churches of Alexandria, Jerusalem, Constantinople, and the formula of the apostolic constitutions. Ed. by the Rev. J.M. Neale. 4th ed., with pref. by Dr. Littledale. London, R.D. Dickinson, 1896.
xii,172 p.

Text in Greek, with introductions and notes in English.

NL 0414712 CU MiU DNC MWelC

The liturgies of SS. Mark, James, Clement, Chrysostom, and Basil, and the church of Malabar. Translated, with introduction and appendices, by J. M. Neale and R. F. Littledale. 7th ed. London, Griffith Farran [189-?]
xl, 256 p. illus. 17cm.
I. Orthodox Eastern Church. Liturgy and ritual. English. II. Neale, John Mason, 1818-1866, tr. III. Littledale, Richard Frederick, 1833-1890, ed. IV. Title.

PPPD PPStC NcD MWelC
NL 0414713 ViU CtY NjP DCU-H PBm PP ICU IU MBC

Les liturgies populaires.

GR160
.N63
Nourry, Émile Dominique, 1870-1935.
Rondes enfantines et quêtes saisonnières; les liturgies populaires [par] P. Saintyves. Paris, Édition du Livre mensuel, 1919.

Liturgies pour les protestans de France, ou prieres pour les familles ... 2d ed. Amsterdam, 1758. 293 p. YA 232

NL 0414715 DLC

Liturgies pour les Protestans de France, ou, prières ...
see also Liturgie pour les Protestans de France; ou, prières ... (1745)

BV170
.L5513
Liturgiewissenschaftliche Quellen und Forschungen. Heft 23-
Münster Westfalen, Aschendorff, 1928-
v. 26 cm.

Publication suspended 1940-56.
Supersedes Liturgiegeschichtliche Quellen (no. 1/2-11/12) and Liturgiegeschichtliche Forschungen (no. 1-10) and continues their combined numbering.
Title varies: no. 23-31 (1928-39) Liturgiegeschichtliche Quellen und Forschungen.
No. 23-31 (1928-39) issued by the Verein zur Pflege der Liturgiewissenschaft; no. 32- (1957-) by the Abt-Herwegen-Institut, Maria-Laach.

Editors: 1928-39, K. Mohlberg and A. Rücker.—1957- O. Heiming.

1. Liturgics. I. Mohlberg, Cunibert, 1878- ed. II. Rücker, Adolf, 1880- ed. III. Heiming, Odilo, 1898- ed. IV. Verein zur Pflege der Liturgiewissenschaft. V. Maria Laach (Benedictine Monastery)

BV170.L5513 58-23822

NL 0414718 DLC TxDaM-P NN InStme NN CaBVaU MiU NcD

4BX
Luth.
41
Liturgikus rend; lelkészi szolgálat. 3. kiad. Budapest, Evangélikus Egyetemes Sajtóosztály, 1955.
46 p.

NL 0414719 DLC-P4

Liturgisch tijdschrift. 1.-5., no.1 jaarg. Dec. 1910-Dec. 1919. Leuven [Belgique] Abdij van den Keizerberg. 5 v. illus. (music) 23-24cm. monthly.

Suspended 1915-Nov 1919.--cf. Union list of serials.
Superseded by Tijdschrift voor liturgie.--cf. Union list of serials.

1. Catholic Church. Liturgy and ritual--Period.

NL 0414720 CU CBGTU

Liturgische Bibliothek. Sammlung gottesdienstlicher Bücher aus dem deutschen Mittelalter
see under Schönfelder, Albert, ed.

Period
1109
LITURGISCHE Blaetter; Handreichungen fuer den evangelischen Gottesdienst. Hrsg. von "Arbeitskreis fuer Liturgie" im Auftrage des Prot. Landeskirchenrates der Pfalz. Speyer, Klambt, 1952-
v. 22cm.

NL 0414722 MH-AH

Liturgische Blätter für Mecklenburg; redigirt von Theodor Kliefoth... Rostock Etc....
v. 1-2 in 1.

NL 0414723 PPLT

Liturgische dichtungen der Juden; Genizafragmente aus Babylonien ...
see under Jews. Liturgy and ritual.

Liturgische Gesänge der evangelischen Brüdergemeinen...
see under Moravian church. Liturgy and Ritual.

Liturgische Gesänge über biblische Texte ... 1853
see under Moravian church. Liturgy and ritual.

Period.
1109.3
LITURGISCHE Monatschrift; Formulare fuer etliche kirchliche Handlungen und liturgische Akte. [Beardstown, Illinois, J.C. Ross & Sohn, 1884-1886.]
2v. 21.3cm.

Appeared in twenty issues.
Edited by Friedrich Johann Carl Lochner.

NL 0414727 MH-AH PPLT

Liturgische passions-andachten; das leiden und sterben unseres Herrn Jesu Christi mit liederversen. Leipzig, Bredt,1858.
35 p.

NL 0414728 PPLT

VOLUME 336

Liturgische Prosen erster [-zweiter] Epoche ... (Analecta hymnica medii aevi 53-55)
see
Blume, Clemens, 1862-1932, ed.
Thesauri hymnologici Prosarium ...
Leipzig, Reisland, 1911-22.

... Liturgische Prosen zweiter Epoche auf Feste der Heiligen, nebst einem Anhange: Hymnodie des Gelderlandes und des Haarlemer Gebietes ... 1922. (Analecta hymnica medii aevi. Bd. 55) [separately cataloged]
see under Blume, Clemens, 1862-1932, ed. [supplement]

... **Liturgische** texte ... Bonn, A. Marcus und E. Weber, 1903–
v. 19cm. (Kleine texte für vorlesungen und übungen, 5, 19. 35-37, 61, 70, 75, 125, 141, 144

CONTENTS.—I. Zur geschichte der orientalischen taufe und messe im II und IV jahrhundert, ausgewählt von lic. Hans Lietzmann.—II. Ordo missae secundum Missale romanum, hrsg. von lic. Hans Lietzmann.—III. Die konstantinopolitanische messliturgie vor dem IX jahrhundert. Übersichtliché zusammenstellung des wichtigsten quellenmaterials, von dr. Anton Baumstark.—IV. Martin Luthers Von ordnung Gottesdiensts, Taufbuechlein, Formula missae et communionis, 1523, hrsg. von d. Hans Lietzmann.—V. Martin Luthers Deutsche messe, 1526, hrsg. von d. Hans Lietzmann.—VI. Die klementinische liturgie aus den Constitutiones apostolorum VIII, nebst anhängen, hrsg. von d. Hans Lietzmann.—VII. Die preussische agende im auszug, hrsg. von Hans Lietzmann.—VIII. Die sächsische agende im auszug, hrsg. von Hans Lietzmann.—IX. Die hannoversche agende im auszug, hrsg. von d. Johannes Meyer.—X. Einführung in das römische brevier von Hans Lietzmann.—XI. Taufe und firmung nach dem römischen missale, rituale und pontificale, hrsg. von Ildefons Herwegen.

1. Liturgies. I. Luther, Martin, 1483-1546. II. *Lietzmann, Hans, 1875– ed. III. Baumstark, Anton, 1872– ed. IV. Meyer, Johannes, 1869– ed. V. Herwegen, Ildefons, 1874– ed.

A C 34-2541

Title from Univ. of Mich. Printed by L. C.
[2]

NL 0414732 MiU ICU OCU OC1 NcD DDO MH NN CLSU

Liturgische texte und studien.
[Paderborn?], 1920-

NL 0414733 DLC

Liturgische Vespern zum Wochenschluss, den Sonn- und Festtagen auf Grund der lutherischen Vesperordnung zusammengestellt... (1844)
see under Hoffmann, H.

Liturgische Zeitschrift. 1.-5. Jahrg. Regensburg, F. Pustet, 1929-32/33.
5 v. 25 cm. bimonthly
Superseded by Liturgisches Leben. Cf. Union list of serials.
Library has: v. 1-4, in 3 v.

1. Liturgy--Periodicals.
BT4002.L487

NL 0414735 KAS DCU

Liturgische Zeitschrift zur veredelung des Synagogengesangs mit Berücksichtigung des ganzen Synagogenwesens, Hrsg. in Gemeinschaft mit vielen israel. Gelehrten, Schullehrern und Cantoren von H. Ehrlich.
Meiningen, 1848-1862.

I. Ehrlich, Hermann, musician, ed.

NL 0414736 OCH

Die liturgischen reimofficien auf die heiligen Franciscus und Antonius
see under Catholic Church. Liturgy and ritual. Office, Saint Francesco d'Assisi. [Historia rhythmata]

[Liturgisches handbuch zum gebrauche fuer superintendenten, pastoren, ... 2...verm...aufl.
Berlin, Deck, 1871.
272 p.
[Lutheran? or Evangelische Kirche der Altpreussischen Union?]

NL 0414738 PPLT

Liturgisches Jahrbuch. 1951–
Münster Westf., Aschendorff.
v. 25 cm.
"Im Auftrage des Liturgischen Instituts in Trier hrsg. von Joseph Pascher."
Includes sections "Berichte" and "Liturgische Bibliographie."

1. Catholic Church. Liturgy and ritual—Yearbooks. [1. Liturgy—Period] 2. Catholic Church. Liturgy and ritual—Bibl. [2. Liturgy—Bibl.] I. Pascher, Josef, 1893– ed.

A 52-7376

Catholic Univ. of America. Library
for Library of Congress [1]

MoSU-D
NL 0414739 DCU CU NjPT ICU DDO MnCS NIC IEG

Liturgisches kirchengebetbüchlein; ... Allentown, Pa., Brobst, 1864
see under Evangelical Lutheran Ministerium of Pennsylvania and Adjacent States. Liturgy and ritual.

Liturgisches leben. v.1-6. 1934-1939.
Berlin, 1934-1939.
v. irregular.
Supersedes Liturgische zeitschrift.
[1]-5 [6]

NL 0414741 DCU

Liturgisches Liederbuch für den Gebrauch der Religionsschulen ... Berlin, Poppelauer, 1912
see under Jews. Liturgy and ritual. [supplement]

Liturgy. [quarterly] St. Gregory's Society
see Life and worship.

Liturgy and agenda. St. Louis, Concordia Publishing House (1917) (1918) (1921) (1936)
see under Lutheran Church--Missouri Synod.

Liturgy and hymns for Sunday-schools
see under Protestant Episcopal society for the promotion of evangelical knowledge.

Liturgy and hymns for use of the Protestant church of the United Brethren, or Unitas Fratrum
see under Moravian church. Liturgy and Ritual.

Liturgy and sociology. v.1-3, no.1, Feb. 1936-Jan. 1938.
New York

1. Liturgy - periodicals. 2. Sociology - Periodicals.
BT4002.L54

NL 0414747 KAS

... The **liturgy** and the layman: I. The liturgy and the laity, by Dr. K. F. McMurtrie ... II. Catholic action and the liturgy, by Dom Joseph Kreuter ... III. The liturgy and Catholic women, by Dom Virgil Michel ... Collegeville, Minn., The Liturgical press, 1930.
28 p. 18cm. (Popular liturgical library, series IV, no. 4)
Reprinted from Orate fratres, vol. III.

1. Catholic church. Liturgy and ritual. I. McMurtrie, Kenneth Francis. II. Kreuter, Joseph. III. Michel, Virgil G., 1890–

31-6619

Library of Congress BX1970.L5
Copyright A 22116 [3] 264.02

NL 0414748 DLC

Liturgy collected for the use of the church at King's Chapel, Boston
see under Boston. King's Chapel.

A Liturgy compiled from the Book of common prayer reformed according to the plan of the late Dr. Samuel Clarke together with a collection of Psalms and hymns for public worship. Plymouth, M. Haydon, 1791 [i.e. 1790-91 ?]
106+213 p. 18 cm.
Cf. Brit. Mus. Cat. v. 139 col. 838.
Edited by Thomas Porter for the Plymouth [Eng.] Unitarian Congregation (and used by it)
The Book of common prayer reformed according to the plan of the late Dr. Samuel Clarke (1774) was an adaptation by Theophilus Lindsey, a Church of England minister.
Cf. A.E. Peaston. The Prayer book reform movement in the XVIIIth century. 1940.

NL 0414751 CBPac

A liturgy, containing forms of devotion for each Sunday
see under [Carpenter, Benjamin] 1752-1816.

VOLUME 336

Liturgy for Christian congregations of the Lutheran faith ... Newport, Ky., n.p., 1902.
157 p.

NL 0414753 PPLT

A liturgy for church Sunday schools ... [1867 or earlier
see under Church of England Sunday school institute.

A liturgy for Sunday-schools. Published by the Executive committee of the "Protestant Episcopal society for the promotion of evangelical knowledge." [c. 1849]
see under Protestant Episcopal society for the promotion of evangelical knowledge.

Liturgy for the school-room, containing daily, morning, evening and mid-day offices, ... London, Whitaker, 1852.
40 p.

NL 0414756 PPLT

BX5947 .C4L5 Liturgy for the use of church schools. New York, James Pott, 1863.
64 p.

NL 0414757 DLC

Liturgy for the use of Evangelical Lutheran pastors; ... Columbus, O., Luth. Book Con., 1912.
186 p.
[Authorized by the Evangelical Lutheran Joint Synod of Ohio and Other States? Cf. A. R. Wentz. A basic history of Lutheranism in America. 1964. p. 228]

NL 0414758 PPLT

A liturgy for the use of the church at King's chapel in Boston; ...
see under Boston. King's chapel.

A liturgy for the use of the Evangelical Lutheran church. By authority of the ministerium of Pennsylvania and adjacent states
see under Evangelical Lutheran Ministerium of Pennsylvania and Adjacent States. Liturgy and ritual.

The liturgy, Gospels and Epistles of the English Evangelical Lutheran church in New-York. ... 1806
see under Williston, Ralph, comp.

The liturgy, Gospels and Epistles of the Lutheran Church, Luther's Catechism ...
see under Strebeck, George.

LS77.1 P97 The liturgy in no danger. A letter to the author of an article in the "New-Englander," for October, 1843, entitled "The liturgy of the Protestant Episcopal Church in America." New York, James A. Sparks, 1843.
20p.
Bound with Pusey, Edward Bouverie. "The holy eucharist a comfort to the penitent." New York, 1843.
1. Protestant Episcopal Church in the U.S.A. Liturgy and ritual - Addresses, essays, and lectures.

NL 0414763 CSaT NcU NN PPL MB

BX1970 L58 Liturgy in the classroom [by Betty Ricker, and others] Conception, Mo., Conception Abbey Press, c1955]
32 p.

1. Catholic Church. Liturgy and ritual - Addresses, essays, lectures. 2. Religious education - U. S. I. Ricker, Betty.

NL 0414764 ODaU

Liturgy in the parish. London, Mowbray, n.d.
50 p.

NL 0414765 PPPD

Liturgy of funeral offerings.
... The liturgy of funerary offerings, the Egyptian texts with English translations, by E. A. Wallis Budge ... London, K. Paul, Trench, Trübner & co., ltd., 1909.
xviii, 268 p. illus. 19cm. (Books on Egypt and Chaldaea. [vol. xxv])

1. Funeral rites and ceremonies—Egypt. I. Budge, Ernest Alfred Thompson Wallis, ed.

10-13900

Library of Congress PJ1559.L6 1909

LU InU FTaSU KU-M WaSp MiD
MBrZ PPStC MB OCH OCl OCU MiU OClMA OO OCH NcD PSt
NL 0414766 DLC KU PPPD PU PPDrop PPL NN CU ICN

Liturgy of funeral offerings.

AS222 .R645 ser. 3, vol. 8, etc.

Bock of opening the mouth.
Il Libro dei funerali degli antichi egiziani. Memoria del dott. Ernesto Schiaparelli ...
(*In* Atti della R. Accademia dei Lincei. Memorie della Classe di scienze morali, storiche e filologiche. Roma, 1883-90. 28½-29½ cm. ser. 3, vol. VIII, p. [1]-166; ser. 4, vol. VII, pt. 1)

A liturgy of hope, cantata for solo soprano, male choir and organ. [c1928]
see under Sowerby, Leo, 1895-1968.

Liturgy of St. James (Greek) English and Greek.
Ἡ τοῦ ἁγίου Ἰακώβου λειτουργία. The Greek liturgy of St. James, edited with an English introduction and notes; together with a Latin version of the Syriac copy, and the Greek text restored to its original purity and accompanied by a literal English translation. By the Rev. W. Trollope ... Edinburgh, T. & T. Clark; [etc., etc.] 1848.
xi, 164 p. 23½cm.

I. Trollope, William, 1798-1863, ed. II. Title: The Greek liturgy of St. James.

41-30945

Library of Congress BX350.A2 1848

NL 0414769 DLC ICU MH PPPD NRU RP RPB MnCS

Liturgy of St. James (Greek) Latin and Greek.
La liturgie de saint Jacques; édition critique du texte grec avec traduction latine par B.-Ch. Mercier. Paris, Firmin-Didot, 1946.
142 p. illus. 29 cm. (Patrologia orientalis, t. 26, fasc. 2)
Cover title.
Pages also numbered [119]-256, continuing the paging of the preceding number of the series.
I. Mercier, B. Ch., ed. and tr. (Series)
BR60.P25 t. 26, fasc. 2 A 52-7436

New York. Public Libr.
for Library of Congress [½]†

NL 0414770 NN DLC NjPT

Liturgy of Saint James (Syrian)
[Ascribed to St. James "Brother of the Lord"; formed perhaps in 4th century. While its origins precede the schism and its use is not limited to the Monophysite Syrian Jacobite Church, some editions or translations will be found, because of its close association with that church, under the heading: Jacobite Church. Liturgy and ritual.

The liturgy of Saint Peter
see under Catholic Church. Liturgy and ritual. Liturgy of Saint Peter.

The Liturgy of the French protestant church, arranged for the use of the congregation in Charleston
see under Charleston, S.C. French Protestant Church.

Liturgy, or Book of worship, for the use of the New Church signified by the New Jerusalem
see under New Jerusalem Church. Liturgy and Ritual.

Liturgy; or, Formulary for the use of Evangelical Lutheran churches. Lancaster, O. Herman, 1830.
120 p.

NL 0414775 PPLT

The Liturgy used in the churches of the Principality of Neufchatel: with a letter from the learned Dr. Jablonski, concering the nature of liturgies; to which is added, the Form of prayer lately introduced into the Church of Geneva. London, J. Downing, 1712.
xii, 116 p. 4°.
The part pertaining to Neuchâtel compiled originally by J.F. Osterwald. -- Cf. Brit. Mus. Cat. v. 139 col. 1144.

NL 0414776 PPL

VOLUME 336

A liturgy with a collection of hymns and chants for the use of Sunday schools...
see under Lombard, James.

Liturgy's vindicated by the dissenters: or, the lawfulness of forms of prayer and liturgies ...
see under [Leslie, Charles] 1650-1722.

BXZ
480
.B93
Z6
L7

Litva, A S.J.
La "Sophia" dans la création selon la doctrine de S. Boulgakof. Romae, 1951.
48 p. [i.e., p.1-11, 39-74] 24cm.
Part of diss. - Pontificia Università Gregoriana, Rome.
"Bibliographie": p. [9]-11.
1. Bulgakov, Sergiei Nikolaevich, 1871-1944.
2. God - Wisdom. I. Title.

NL 0414779 DCU

Litva
see **Lithuania.**

Litvac, A.
Propriétés et structure des substances intercellulaires formées en culture in vitro ... Par A. Litvac ...
(*In* Archives d'anatomie microscopique ... Paris [1937] 25cm. t. 33, p. [151]-166. 1 illus., pl. XIX-XXII)
"Institut de biologie physico-chimique et Laborat. d'embryogénie comparée de Collège de France."
"Bibliographie": p. 165-166.

1. Connective tissues. 2. Tissues—Culture.
A C 40-1203
Rochester. Univ. Library
for Library of Congress [2]

NL 0414781 NRU

Litvak, Arkadiĭ Moiseevich.
Giants arise. Translated by H.P.Marshall and J.A.Shestakov. Moscow, Centrizdat, 1931.

NL 0414782 MH

Litvak, Arkadiĭ Moiseevich.
... Neue punkte auf der landkarte; was im lande der sowjets im jahre 1931 gebaut wurde. Moskau, Verlagsgenossenschaft ausländischer arbeiter in der UdSSR, 1932.
31, [1] p. illus. 22cm.
At head of title: A. Litwak.
Map on p. [1] and [4] of cover.
Title on p. [3] of cover: Новые точки на карте (*transliterated:* Novye tochki na karte)

1. Russia—Indus. 2. Building—Russia. I. Title. *Translation of* Огни на новой карте (*transliterated:* Ogni na novoĭ karte)
43-48626
Library of Congress HC335.L57
[2] 330.947

NL 0414783 DLC NcD

Litvak, Arkadiĭ Moiseevich.
New points on the map. What has been built in the land of the Soviets during 1931, by A. Litvak. Moscow, Co-operative publishing society of foreign workers in the U. S. S. R., 1932.
32 p. front., plates. 18½cm.

1. Russia—Industries. 2. Building—Russia. I. Title.
A 34-3093
Title from Carnegie Endow. Int. Peace. Printed by L. C.
[2]

NL 0414784 NNCE NcD MdBJ DL NN

HD9506
.R87Z3

Litvak, Arkadiĭ Moiseevich.
Строка пятилетки; повесть о битве за стальной лист. [Москва] Профиздат, 1948.
114 p. 17 cm.

1. Zaporozhstal' Zavod. I. Title.
Title transliterated: Stroka piatiletki.
HD9506.R87Z3 49-24968*

NL 0414785 DLC

TN734
L5

Litvak, D V
Газовое цианирование стали. Москва, 1943.
39, [1] p. illus. 21 cm. (Стахановская библиотека, № 14)
At head of title: Госплан СССР. Институт технико-экономической информации.
Errata slip inserted.
Bibliography: p. [40]

1. ~~Cementation (Metallurgy)~~ 2. Steel—Metallurgy. I. Title.
Title transliterated: Gazovoe tsianirovanie stali.
TN734.L5 54-46752

NL 0414786 DLC

PG3476
.L64B3

Litvak, Grigoriĭ N
Барыня. Пьеса в 4 действиях по А. П. Чехову. Москва, Искусство, 1940.
73 p. 21 cm.

I. Chekhov, Anton Pavlovich, 1860-1904. Barynia. II. Title.
Title transliterated: Barynia.
PG3476.L64B3 52-58323 ‡

NL 0414787 DLC

PG3986
.R3L5

Litvak, Grigoriĭ N *ed. and tr.*
Песни и думы советской Украины. В переводах с украинского Г. Литвака, предисл. М. Рыльского. Москва, Гос. изд-во худож. лит-ры, 1951.
334 p. 21 cm.

1. Ukrainian poetry—Translations into Russian. 2. Russian poetry—Translations from Ukrainian. 3. Folk-songs, Ukrainian. I. Title. *Title transliterated:* Pesni i dumy sovetskoĭ Ukrainy.
PG3986.R3L5 51-35222 rev 2 ‡

NL 0414788 DLC

Litvak, Jerome Bernard, 1907- joint author.

Bartholomew, William J.
Handbook of Newark ordinances, by William J. Bartholomew ... [and] Jerome B. Litvak ... [Newark, N. J., °1940]

T58
.L54

Litvak, L V
Вопросы повышения cosφ промышленных предприятий. Москва, Гос. энерг. изд-во, 1950.
114 p. illus. 23 cm.
Bibliographical footnotes.
Second ed. published in 1957 under title: Повышение коэффициента мощности на промышленных предприятиях (romanized: Povyshenie koéf-

1. Efficiency, Industrial. 2. Machinery in industry.
Title transliterated: Voprosy povyshenii͡a cosφ promyshlennykh predprii͡atiĭ.
T58.L54 50-55275

NL 0414790 DLC

Litvak, Zelman
see Litwak, Selmann.

Litvak, Z. L. Raschet martenovskoi pechi.

TN740
.O4

Oĭks, Grigoriĭ Naumovich.
Расчеты мартеновских печей; под ред. К. Г. Трубина. Допущено в качестве учеб. пособия для металлургических техникумов. Москва, Гос. науч.-техн. изд-во лит-ры по черной и цветной металлургии, 1949.

Litvak Recepter, Isidoro, 1909-
Administración y realización de bienes en las quiebras. Santiago de Chile, 1933.
94 l. 27 cm.
Typescript (carbon copy)
Tesis (licenciatura en ciencias jurídicas y sociales)—Universidad de Chile.
Bibliography: leaf 91.

1. Bankruptcy—Chile. I. Title.
54-46317

NL 0414793 DLC

J5140
5
ebr

Litvakov, Moses, 1875 (*ca.*)-
אף צוויי פראנטן, זאמלונג ארטיקלען. מאסקווע, צענטראלער פעלקער־פארלאג פון פ. ס. ס. ר.
[Москва] 1931.
174 p. 22 cm.

1. Yiddish literature—Hist. & crit. I. Title.
Title transliterated: Af tsvey frontn.
PJ5140.L5 58-52858 ‡

NL 0414794 DLC

PN3035
.L5
Hebraic
Sect.

Litvakov, Moses, 1875 (*ca.*)-
פינף יאר מלוכישער אידישער קאמער־טעאטער (1924–1919)
מאסקווע, פארלאג "שול און בוך," 1924 [Москва]
138 p. illus., ports. 22 cm.

1. Moscow. Gosudarstvennyĭ evreĭskiĭ teatr.
Title transliterated: Finf yor Mlukhisher idisher kamer-teater.
PN3035.L5 52-52769

NL 0414795 DLC

VOLUME 336

PJ5129 .L583 I 6 Hebraic Sect.

Litvakov, Moses, 1875 (*ca.*)-
אין אימרוה. קיעווער פארלאג ‚Kiev, 1918/19‚
120 p. 20 cm.
Critical essays.

1. Yiddish literature—Addresses, essays, lectures.
Title transliterated: In umruh.

PJ5129.L583 I 6 52-59094

NL 0414796 DLC

Litvakov, U. M.

TK275 .R8 1949

Russia (*1923- U. S. S. R.) Ministerstvo ėlektropromyshlennosti. T͡Sentral'noe bi͡uro tekhnicheskoĭ informat͡sii.*
Справочник по стандартам, ведомственным техническим условиям и ведомственным нормалям на продукцию Министерства электропромышленности; составил У. М. Литваков. Москва, 1949.

TP858 .L57

Litvakovskiĭ, A A
Электроплавленые литые высокоглиноземистые огнеупоры для стеклоделия. Москва, Гос. изд-во легкой промышл., 1941.
107 p. illus. 22 cm.
At head of title: А. А. Литваковский и М. В. Осипов.
Errata slip inserted.

1. Refractory materials. 2. Glass manufacture. I. Osipov, M. V., joint author.
Title transliterated: Ėlektroplavlenye litye vysokoglinozemistye ogneupory.

TP858.L57 50-40619

NL 0414798 DLC

LITVAKOVSKI, A. A.
Fused cast refractories. [Translated by I. Morgenstern Jerusalem, Israel Program for Scientific Translations, 1961; [available from the Office of Technical Services, U.S. Dept. of Commerce, Washington] 273 p. illus., diagrs., tables. 25cm.

"Published... pursuant to an agreement with the National science foundation, Washington, D. C. and the Department of the interior.

Includes bibliographies.

1. Refractory materials. I. United States. National science foundation. II. United States. Interior dept. t. 1961

NL 0414800 NN

Litvan, Franz Josef, 1909-
Neue methoden zum abbau aliphatischer ketten. ... Zürich, 1935. 34 p.
Inaug. Diss. - Zürich, 1935.
Vitae.

NL 0414801 ICRL CtY

TN840 .R9L5

Litvi͡akov, Ivan Ignat'evich.
Добыча фрезерного торфа укрупненными колоннами машин; опыт работы Оричевского торфопредприятия. Москва, Гос. энерг. изд-во, 1955.
29 p. illus. 21 cm. (Новаторы производства в торфяной промышленности)
At head of title: И. И. Литвяков и С. М. Яковлев.

1. Peat *[machinery]* I. I͡Akovlev, Sergeĭ Malakhievich, *[water in peat]* joint author. II. Title.
Title transliterated: Dobycha frezernogo torfa.

TN840.R9L5 56-27019

NL 0414802 DLC

TN808 .R92 D6214

Litvin, A Z
Скоростное проведение горизонтальных и наклонных выработок на шахтах Донбасса. ‚Москва, Углетехиздат, 1948‚
51 p. diagrs. 22 cm.
At head of title: Министерство угольной промышленности западных районов СССР. А. З. Литвин, Р. Г. Парунакян, М. Г. Розенбаум.
Errata slip inserted.

1. Coal mines and mining—Russia—Donets Basin. 2. Shaft sinking.
Title transliterated: Skorostnoe provedenie ... vyrabotok na shakhtakh Donbassa.

TN808.R92D6214 50-25549

NL 0414803 DLC

Litvin, Aleksandr
see
Litwin, Aleksander.

…J265 …56 …949

Litvin, Aleksandr Moiseevich.
Основы теплоэнергетики. Утверждено в качестве учеб. пособия для подготовки рабочих кадров и средне-техн. персонала. Изд. 4., перер. и доп. Москва, Гос. энерг. изд-во, 1949.
223 p. diagrs. 21 cm.

1. Thermodynamics. I. Title.
Title transliterated: Osnovy teploėnergetiki.

TJ265.L56 1949 50-32142 rev

NL 0414805 DLC

Litvin, Aleksandr Moiseevich.
Основы теплоэнергетики. Изд. 5., перер. и доп. Рекомендовано в качестве учеб. пособия для курсов техн. обучения рабочих кадров и мастеров. Москва, Гос. энерг. изд-во, 1954.
344 p. diagrs. 20 cm.

1. Thermodynamics. I. Title.
Title transliterated: Osnovy teploėnergetiki.

TJ265.L56 1954 55-38837 rev

NL 0414806 DLC

…J265 …568 …947

Litvin, Aleksandr Moiseevich.
Техническая термодинамика. Изд. 2., перер. и доп. Допущено в качестве учебника для теплотехн. специальностей энерг. втузов. Москва, Гос. энерг. изд-во, 1947.
388 p. diagrs. (part in pocket) tables. 27 cm.
Bibliography: p. 371.

1. Thermodynamics. I. Title
Title transliterated: Tekhnicheskai͡a termodinamika.

TJ265.L568 1947 60-44914

NL 0414807 DLC

TJ265 .L57 1944

Litvin, Aleksandr Moiseevich.
Теоретические основы теплотехники; техническая термодинамика и теория теплопередачи. Под ред. Я. М. Рубинштейна. Изд. 2., перер. и доп. Допущено в качестве учебника для нетеплотехн. специальностей ВТУЗов и теплотехн. специальностей техникумов. Москва, Гос. энерг. изд-во, 1944.
368 p. diagrs., tables. 23 cm.
2. Heat—Transmission.

1. Thermodynamics. I. Title.
Title transliterated: Teoreticheskie osnovy teplotekhniki.

TJ265.L57 1944 51-53733 rev*

NL 0414808 DLC

TJ265 .L57 1950

Litvin, Aleksandr Moiseevich.
Теоретические основы теплотехники; техническая термодинамика и теория теплопередачи. Изд. 3., перер. Рекомендовано в качестве учеб. пособия для энерг. техникумов. Москва, Гос. энерг. изд-во, 1950.
855 p. diagrs., tables. 23 cm.
2. Heat—Transmission.

1. Thermodynamics. I. Title
Title transliterated: Teoreticheskie osnovy teplotekhniki.

TJ265.L57 1950 51-25001 rev

NL 0414809 DLC

…G3476 75Z69

Litvin, Ėsfir' Solomonovna.
Поэзия Исаковского и народное творчество. ‚Смоленск‚ Смоленское книжное изд-во, 1955.
201 p. 21 cm.

1. Isakovskiĭ, Mikhail Vasil'evich, 1900- I. Title.
Title transliterated: Poėzii͡a Isakovskogo i narodnoe tvorchestvo.

PG3476.I 75Z69 57-22435 ‡

NL 0414810 DLC

…T3150 …5A3 (Hebr)

Litvin, F
וואס וועט זיין נאכדעם? אדער, דער צוריקקער פון די בושלם. פאריז. ‚Paris‚ 1949.
66 p. 22 cm.

I. Title. *Title transliterated:* Vos vet zayn nokhdem?

CT3150.L5A3 58-53369

NL 0414811 DLC

Litvin, *Faĭdor L'vovich.*

Microfilm Slavic …110 …AC

Kolchin, N I
Методы расчета при изготовлении и контроле зубчатых изделий; приложение аналитической теории и геометрии зацеплений. Ленинград, Гос. научно-техн. изд-во машиностроит. лит-ры‚ Ленинградское отд-ние‚ 1952.

Litvin, Faĭdor L'vovich.
Некруглые зубчатые колеса; конструирование, теория зацепления и производство. Москва, Гос. научно-техн. изд-во машиностроит. лит-ры, 1950.
218, ‚2‚ p. illus. 23 cm.
Bibliography: p. 218-‚219‚

1. Gearing. I. Title.
Title romanized: Nekruglye zubchatye kolesa.

TJ184.L5 50-37375

NL 0414813 DLC

Litvin, Faĭdor L'vovich.
Производство многозаходных червячных передач с новой геометрией. Под общей ред. Н. И. Колчина. Ленинград, Гос. научно-техн. изд-во машиностроит. и судостроит. лит-ры ‚Ленинградское отд-ние‚ 1953.
50, ‚2‚ p. illus. 22 cm. (Новаторы производства)
At head of title: Ф. Л. Литвин, С. Г. Принценталь, Г. Ф. Шигорин.
Bibliography: p. ‚51‚

1. Gearing, Worm. I. Print͡sental', S. G. II. Shigorin, G. F. III. Title.
Title romanized: Proizvodstvo mnogozakhodnykh chervi͡achnykh peredach s novoĭ geometrieĭ.

TJ200.L5 54-35324

NL 0414814 DLC

VOLUME 336

Litvin, Félii͡a Vasil'evna
see Litvinne, Mme. Félia, 1863-

Litvin, G
see
Litvin-Molotov, Georgiĭ Zakharovich.

TH7121
.L5

Litvin, G E
Пламенные печи. Москва, Гос. научно-техн. изд-во машиностроит. лит-ры, 1945.
71 p. illus. 22 cm. (Рационализация энергоиспользования на машиностроительных заводах, вып. 3)
At head of title: НКСМ СССР. Главное управление автомобильными заводами им. Сталина. Г. Е. Литвин и А. И. Ващенко.
Erratum slip inserted.
1. Furnaces. I. Vashchenko, A. I., joint author. II. Title. (Series: Rat͡sionalizat͡sii͡a ėnergoispol'zovanii͡a na mashinostroitel'nykh zavodakh, vyp. 3) Title transliterated: Plamennye pechi.
TH7121.L5 51-26260

NL 0414817 DLC

Litvin, Józef
see Litwin, Józef.

Litvin, K
see
Lytvyn, K

TC547
.L5

Litvin, M G
Комплексная механизация опалубочных и бетонных работ на строительстве бетонной плотины. Москва, Гос. изд-во лит-ры по строительству и архитектуре, 1952.
24 p. illus. 20 cm. (Стахановцы строительной индустрии)
1. Dams. I. Title. Title transliterated: Kompleksnai͡a mekhanizat͡sii͡a opalubochnykh i betonnykh rabot.
TC547.L5 53-25644

NL 0414820 DLC

TG375
.L5

Litvin, N I
Содержание и ремонт деревянных мостов с фермами Гау. Москва, Дориздат, 1948.
98 p. illus. 20 cm.
Errata slip inserted.
Bibliography: p. 97.
1. Bridges, Wooden. I. Title. Title transliterated: Soderzhanie i remont derevi͡annykh mostov.
TG375.L5 52-20479

NL 0414821 DLC

LA131
.L5

Litvin-Molotov, Georgiĭ Zakharovich.
Париж—Оксфорд; на международных слетах просвещенцев. Москва, Профиздат, 1936.
69 p. 18 cm.
At head of title: Г. Литвин.
1. Education—Aims and objectives. I. Title: Na mezhdunarodnykh sletakh prosveshchent͡sev. Title transliterated: Parizh—Oksford.
LA131.L5 66-33537 ‡

NL 0414822 DLC

Litvin-Sedoi, Mikhail Zinov'evich.

TJ213
.C577
1951b

Conference on Automatic Control, Cranfield, Eng., 1951.
Автоматическое регулирование; сборник материалов конференции. Перевод с английского, под ред. М. З. Литвина-Седого. Москва, Изд-во иностранной лит-ры, 1954.

Litvin-Sedoĭ, Mikhail Zinov'evich.
Корректирующие цепи в автоматике; сборник переводов статей. Москва, Изд-во иностранной лит-ры, 1954.
519 p. diagrs. 23 cm.
Includes bibliographies.
1. Automatic control. 2. Electric circuits. I. Title. Title transliterated: Korrektirui͡ushchie t͡sepi v avtomatike.
TJ213.L513 55-29883

NL 0414824 DLC

Litvina, Li͡udmila Markovna.
Моделирование одежды из клетчатых тканей. Москва, Гос. научно-техн. изд-во, 1954.
61 p. illus. 23 cm.
1. Tailoring (Women's) I. Title. Title transliterated: Modelirovanie odezhdy iz kletchatykh tkaneĭ.
TT560.L56 63-48064 ‡

NL 0414825 DLC

Litvine, G.
The education and educational workers of the U. S. S. R. By G. Litvine. [n. p., 1937] 21 f. 30cm.
1. Education — Russia, 20th cent.
N. Y. P. L. September 10, 1941

NL 0414826 NN

Litvine, Max, ed.

Law

Belgium. Laws, statutes, etc.
Code du droit aérien belge [par] Max Litvine, Préf. de G. Périer. Bruxelles, F. Larcier, 1946.

Litvine, Max.
Précis élémentaire de droit aérien. Bruxelles, É. Bruylant, 1953.
259 p. 22 cm.
"Extrait du Répertoire pratique du droit belge, tome XIV."
1. Aeronautics—Belgium—Laws and regulations. 2. Aeronautics—Laws and regulations.
54-23479 ‡

NL 0414828 DLC OU MH-L CtY-L NBuU-L

Litvinenko, A. N., historian, ed.

DK264
.2
.K78A5

Russia (1923- U. S. S. R.) Ministerstvo vnutrennikh del. Upravlenie po Kurskoĭ oblasti. Arkhivnyĭ otdel.
Революционные события 1905–1907 гг. в Курской губернии; сборник документов и материалов. [Редакционная коллегия: А. Н. Литвиненко (председатель) и др. Курск] Курское книжное изд-во, 1955.

Litvinenko, Aleksandr Nikolaevich.
Высокие урожаи озимой ржи; опыт В. Н. Королевой. Москва, Гос. изд-во с.-х. лит-ры, 1952.
44 p. illus., ports. 20 cm. (Передовой опыт в сельском хозяйстве)
At head of title: А. Н. Литвиненко.
1. Rye. I. Title. Title romanized: Vysokie urozhai ozimoĭ rzhi.
SB191.R9L73 58-41052

NL 0414830 DLC

Litvinenko, Alekseĭ Semenovich.
... Dictionary of radio terminology in the English, German, French and Russian languages, by A. S. Litvinenko, edited by Prof. V. I. Bashenoff ... Moscow, USSR, 1937.
xii, [1] p., 1 l., 558, [2] p. 26½ cm.
At head of title: Editorial office of technical encyclopaedias and dictionaries.
Added title-pages in Russian, German and French; table of contents and prefatory matter in Russian, English, German and French.
On cover: Радио-словарь; on back of cover: Словарь радиотехнической терминологии ...
Errata (1 leaf) inserted.
Bibliography: p. xli-[xlii]
1. Radio—Dictionaries—Polyglot. 2. English language—Dictionaries—Polyglot. I. Title: Radio-slovar'. II. Title: Slovar' radiotekhnicheskoĭ terminologii.
TK6544.L5 621.38403 38-13280 rev

NL 0414831 DLC OrP MB ViU NIC CU MtU PP CtY OU OCl OO ICJ NN

LB1025
.N2

Litvinenko, E. P.
На путях к новой школе; 14-я опытная школа МОНО (Центросоюза) [Сборник ... составлен Е. П. Литвиненко и А. В. Янковской] Москва, Гос. учебно-педагог. изд-во, 1949.

TA404
.R9L5

Litvinenko, Evgeniĭ Evstaf'evich.
Производство местных строительных материалов для сельского строительства. Киев. Гос. изд-во лит-ры по строительству и архитектуре УССР, 1955.
177, [3] p. illus. 22 cm. (Сельскому строительству)
Errata slip inserted.
Bibliography: p. 177-[178]
1. Building materials industry—Russia. I. Title. Title transliterated: Proizvodstvo mestnykh stroitel'nykh materialov.
TA404.R9L5 57-21034

NL 0414833 DLC

Litvinenko, L. B., joint author.

S695
.P57

Poli͡akova, M V
Механизированная уборка кукурузы. [Харьков] Харьковское книжно-газетное изд-во, 1954.

P336
.58

Litvinenko, Mikhail Semenovich.
Коксохимическая промышленность США. Харьков, Гос. научно-техн. изд-во лит-ры по черной и цветной металлургии, 1947.
288 p. illus. 22 cm.
Includes bibliography.
1. Coke industry—U. S. 2. Coke. I. Title. Title transliterated: Koksokhimicheskai͡a promyshlennost' SShA.
TP336.L58 54-42136 rev ‡

NL 0414835 DLC

VOLUME 336

E205
A4L6

Litvinenko, P M
Орошение семенной люцерны. Ташкент, 1941.
44 p. illus. 21 cm.
At head of title: Наркомзем СССР. Всесоюзный научно-исследовательский институт по хлопководству.

1. Alfalfa. I. Title.
Title transliterated: Oroshenie semennoi liutserny.

SB205.A4L6 57-51154 ‡

NL 0414836 DLC NIC

Litvinne, *Mme.* **Félia,** 1863–
... Ma vie et mon art (souvenirs) Préface de Charles Widor ... Avec 13 gravures hors texte. Paris, Plon [°1933]
4 p. l., iv, 292 p. ports. 19cm.
At head of title: Félia Litvinne.

1. Musicians—Correspondence, reminiscences, etc. I. Title.
34-11997
Library of Congress ML420.L78A2
Copyright A—Foreign 23469
[2] 927.8

NL 0414837 DLC OrU CoU

Litvinne, *Mme Félia, 1863-* 8055.598
School of singing: exercises & counsels.
— Paris. Au Ménestrel. [1924.] (1), iii, 33 pp. Illus. Portrait. Music. 28½ cm.

M9118 — T.r. — Singing. Instruction books.

NL 0414838 MB

Litvinof, Dmitri (Ivanovitch)
see Litvinov, Dimitriĭ Ivanovich.

Litvinoff, Barnet.
Ben-Gurion of Israel. London, Weidenfeld and Nicolson [1954]
273 p. illus. 22 cm.

1. Ben-Gurion, David, 1887–
DS125.3.B37L5 1954a 923.2569 55-25850 ‡

PPDrop OrCS WaTC
NL 0414840 DLC MU ScU CaBViP OCH MH NN TxU IEN

Litvinoff, Barnet.
Ben-Gurion of Israel. New York, Praeger [1954]
xii, 273 p. ports., maps. 22 cm.

1. Ben-Gurion, David, 1887–
DS125.3.B37L5 923.2569 54-9526

CaBVaU IdB Or Wa WaS WaSp
OOxM OClTem NcC PBL PLF CaBVa OrP WaT PU PPT PJA NNJ
NL 0414841 DLC MeB ViU MU OU PP PSt MB TU NcD OClW

Litvinoff, Emanuel.
Conscripts; a symphonic declaration. [London, Favil press ltd., 194-?]
[6] p. 25 cm. ("Resurgam" younger poets, 6)
Caption-title.

NL 0414842 MH

Litvinoff, Emanuel.
A crown for Cain. [Poems] London, Falcon Press [1948]
81 p. 23 cm.

I. Title.
PR6023.I 7C7 821.91 49-24730*

NL 0414843 DLC WU MH

Litvinoff, Emanuel.
... The untried soldier. [London] Routledge [1942]
40 p. 18½cm. (*On cover:* Routledge new poets)
"First published 1942."

I. Title.
43-2050
Library of Congress PR6023.I 7U5

NL 0414844 DLC IEN CU FTaSU TxU

Litvinoff, Ivy (Low)
see
Litvinova, Ivy (Low)

Litvinoff, Maxim Maksimovich
see **Litvinov, Maksim Maksimovich,** 1876–1951.

Litvinoff, terrioist, conspirator, jail bird and smuggler, now soviet commissar of foreign affairs in Moscow
see under [Andersen, Hanns]

Microfilm
Slavic
587
AC

Litvinov, *Andreĭ Sergeevich.*
Russia *(1923– U. S. S. R.) Ministerstvo Vooruzhennykh Sil. Avtomobil'noe upravlenie.*
Автомобиль М-20 "Победа." [Книга написана А. С. Литвиновым] Москва, Воен. изд-во, 1949.

Litvinov, Dmitriĭ Ivanovich, 1854-1929.
——— Florae turkestanicae fragmenta. i, ii. С.-Петербургъ. 1902–09. l. 8°.
"Extrait des *Travaux du Musée botanique de l'Académie impériale des sciences de St. Pétersbourg,* 1902"–09. i. 12–22; vii. 71–101

NL 0414849 MH-A

Litvinov, Dmitriĭ Ivanovich, 1854-1929.
——— Die pflanzen der küsten des Aralsees gesammelt von L. Berg. С.-Петербургъ. 1905. l. 8°. pp. [2], 41. 2 plates, and other illustr.
"Оттискъ изъ Извѣстій Турк. отд. Импер. русск. геогр. общ., т. iv, вып. 5, 1905, стр. 1—41."
In Russian.

NL 0414850 MH-A

Litvinov, Dimitrii Ivanovich.
... О реликтовомъ характерѣ флоры каменистыхъ склоновъ въ Европейской Россіи. Санктпетербургъ, Типографія императорской академіи наукъ, 1902.
cover-title, 34 p. 25cm.
"Оттискъ изъ 'Трудовъ Ботаническаго музея императорской академіи наукъ' вып. I, 1902."
Concerning the relict character of the flora of stony slopes in European Russia.

1. Russia. Botany. 2. Relict plants.
Agr 8-597
Library, U. S. Dept. of Agriculture 459L71

NL 0414851 DNAL

Litvinov, Felia
see Litvinne, Mme. Félia, 1863-

Litvinov, F.
Ou se trouvait la chambre mortuaire de l'empereur Pierre la Grand? Par Th. Litvinov... St.-Pétersbourg, 1913. 19 p. illus. 30cm. (Akademiya nauk. Muzeĭ antropologii i etnografii. Сборникъ. Томъ 1 [часть] 14.)
Text and added t.-p. in Russian: Къ вопросу въ какой палатѣ скончался императоръ Петръ Великій... С.-Петербургъ, 1913.
Bibliographical footnotes.

1. Peter I, the Great, emperor of Russia, 1672–1725. I. Ser.
N. Y. P. L. April 4, 1944

NL 0414853 NN

Litvinov, Gleb Andreevich, joint author.
Brodskiĭ, Vladimir Isakovich.
Организация работы автотранспортного хозяйства; опыт Рижской автотранспортной конторы № 1 Министерства автомобильного транспорта и шоссейных дорог Латвийской ССР. Изд. 2. Москва, Научно-техн. изд-во автотрансп. лит-ры, 1955.

Litvinov, I. I., joint ed.

S469
.R9L22

Lācis, Mārtiņš, 1888– *ed.*
Пути подъема и социалистической реконструкции сельского хозяйства; сборник статей под ред. М. И. Лациса и И. И. Литвинова. Москва, Гос. изд-во, 1929.

Litvinov, Ivan Mykhaĭlovych, 1907 –
see Lytvynov, Ivan Mykhailovych, 1907-

Litvinov, Ivy (Low)
see Litvinova, Ivy (Low)

VOLUME 336

RS161 qL5 pam
Litvinov, M A
Antibiotic lenzitin, by M.A. Litvinov and E.N. Moiseeva. East Orange, N.J., Associated Technical Services [1951]
4 numb. l. illus. 29cm. (Translation RJ-53)
Translated from the Russian.
Article appeared originally in Priroda, No.1, 60-62 (1951)
1. Antibiotics. I. Title: Lenzitin, Antibiotic.

NL 0414858 OrCS

T807 58
Litvinov, M A
... Исторія крѣпостного права въ Россіи. Съ тремя портретами ... Москва, Изданіе М. В. Клюкина, 1897.
1 p. l., 367, [1] p. ports. 18½ cm. (Общеполезная библіотека для самообразованія ... no. 5-7)
1. Serfdom—Russia. 2. Russia—Hist.—Alexander II, 1855-1881.
Title transliterated: Istorīfā krēpostnogo prava.
HT807.L58 28-29029 rev

NL 0414859 DLC

Lītvīnov, Maksīm Maksīmovīch, 1876-1951.
Against aggression; speeches by Maxim Litvinov, together with texts of treaties and of the Covenant of the League of nations. London, Lawrence & Wishart ltd. [1939]
208 p. 22 cm.
"Texts of treaties and the Covenant of the League of nations": p. [133]-208.

NL 0414860 CtY

Litvinov, Maksim Maksimovich, 1876-1951.
Against aggression; speeches by Maxim Litvinov, together with texts of treaties and of the Covenant of the League of nations. New York, International publisher co. inc. [1939]
208 p. 22 cm.
Printed in Great Britain.
"First published 1939."
1. Russia—For. rel.—1917-1945. 2. Russia—For. rel.—Treaties. I. Title.
Name originally: Meer Genokh Moiseevich Vallakh.
DK268.L5A35 327.47 40-3773

NL 0414861 DLC MU CoU DAU GU FTaSU NSyU ViU PBm OU OrPR OrU CtY OCU OCl PU PSt NcD NNC OrSaW WaS WaU-L WaTC OrCS

Litvinov, Maksim Maksimovich, 1876-1951.
Against aggression; speeches by Maxim Litvinov, together with texts of treaties and of the Covenant of the League of nations. New York, International publisher co. inc. [1939]
208 p. 22 cm.
Printed in Great Britain.
"First published 1939."
DK268 .L5A35 1939a
——— Photocopy. Ann Arbor, Mich., University Microfilms, 1970.
1. Russia—For. rel.—1917-1945. 2. Russia—For. rel.—Treaties. I. Title.
Name originally: Meer Genokh Moiseevich Vallakh.

NL 0414862 OrPS

Litvinov, Maksim Maksimovich, 1876-1951.
The Bolshevik revolution: its rise and meaning, by Maxim Litvinoff ... with foreword by E. C. Fairchild. London, British Socialist party, 1918.
54 p. 18cm.
On cover: Second edition.
1. Russia—Hist.—Revolution, 1917- 2. Bolshevism—Russia.
[*Name originally:* Meer Genokh Moiseevich Vallakh]
18-17931 Revised
Library of Congress DK265.L5 1918
[r32d2] 947.084

NL 0414863 DLC MiU ICU MU ViU

Litvinov, Maksim Maksimovich, 1876-1951.
The Bolshevik revolution: its rise and meaning, by Maxim Litvinoff. London, British Socialist party [1919]
54 p. 19cm.
On cover: Third and enlarged edition, with additional chapter, compiled by Ivy Litvinoff from notes left by her husband, bringing the record down to the end of 1918.
1. Russia—Hist.—Revolution, 1917- 2. Bolshevism—Russia. I. Litvinova, Mrs. Ivy, ed.
[*Name originally:* Meer Genokh Moiseevich Vallakh]
20-9935 Revised
Library of Congress DK265.L5 1919
[r32d2] 947.084

NL 0414864 DLC NIC IU IaU TxU MH-BA NjP NN CtY

LITVINOV, MAKSIM MAKSIMOVICH, 1876-
The Bolshevik revolution; its rise and meaning, by Maxim Litvinoff...with supplementary chapters by Ivy Litvinoff. Chicago: Socialist party of the United States, 1920. 79 p. 19cm.
1. Russia—Hist.—November revolution, 1917. 2. Bolshevism—Russia. English. I. Litvinov, Ivy (Low).

NL 0414865 NN CSt-H LU CU MiU NNC MH OU

Litvinov, Maksim Maksimovich, 1876-1951.
Hague. Conference on Russia, 1922.
Conférence de la Haye. I. Commission non-russe. II. Commission russe. 26 juin-20 juillet 1922. Actes et documents. Ministère des affaires étrangères. La Haye, Imprimerie nationale, 1922.

Litvinov, Maksim Maksimovich, 1876-1951.
Hague. Conference on Russia, 1922.
Conference at The Hague. I. Non-Russian commission. II. Russian commission. June 26-July 20, 1922. Minutes and documents. Department of foreign affairs. The Hague, Government printing office, 1922.

Litvinov, Maksim Maksimovich, 1876-
Contra la agresión; discursos de Maxim Litvinoff, seguidos de un apéndice con los textos de algunos tratados y el pacto de la Liga de las naciones. La Habana, Cuba, Editorial "Páginas" [1942]
160 p. front. (port.) 20cm.
On cover: La política exterior de la Unión soviética.
"Primera edición en castellano, 1942."
1. Russia—For. rel.—1917- I. Title.
[*Name originally:* Meer Genokh Moiseevich Wallach]
42-19296
Library of Congress DK267.L54
[2] 327.47

NL 0414868 DLC DPU NN

CPA VF 935
Litvinov, Maksim Maksimovich, 1876-1951.
Czechoslovakia and the world crisis, by Maxim Litvinov ... [New York] International publishers [1938 ?]
15 p. 20½cm.
Published in Russian under title: За мир—против войны.
"Complete text of the speech ... before the League of Nations Assembly in Geneva on September 21, 1938.
1. League of nations. 2. Security, International. I. Title.
[*Name originally:* Meer Genokh Moiseevich Wallach]
Library of Congress JX1975.L75
[2] 341.1

NL 0414869 DLC MiEM NcU

Litvinov, Maksim Maksimovich, 1876-
Czechoslovakia and the world crisis, by Maxim Litvinov ... [New York] International publishers [1938]
14, [1] p. 20½cm.
Published in Russian under title: За мир—против войны.
1. League of nations. 2. Security, International. I. Title.
[*Name originally:* Meer Genokh Moiseevich Wallach]
44-52746
Library of Congress JX1975.L75
[2] 341.1

NL 0414870 DLC CSt-H MH NN

Litvinov, Maksim Maksimovich, 1876-
Disarmament; an address at a luncheon given under the auspices of the American committee and the International club, Geneva, Feb.20th, 1932. (Reproduced from typewritten copy.) n.p., n.d.
(1), 6 fol. 4°.
"Printed by the American committee."

NL 0414871 MH-L

Litvinov, Maksim Maksimovich, 1876-
Preparatory Commission for the Disarmament Conference. *Delegation from Russia.*
Draft convention for the reduction of armaments submitted by the Delegation of the Union of Socialist Soviet Republics. Geneva, 1928.

Litvinov, Maksim Maksimovich, 1876-
Stalin, Iosif, 1879-
The draft new constitution; speeches by J. V. Stalin and M. M. Litvinov, delivered at the special Soviet congress November 25, 1936. London, The Anglo-Russian parliamentary committee, 1936.

JX1953 L587 (Hebr)
Litvinov, Maksim Maksimovich, 1876-1951.
פאר שאלעם—קעגן מילכאמע; רעדע אפן פלענום פון דער פעלקער-ליגע, דעם 21 סענטיאבער 1938 י. מאסקווע, מעלוכע-פארלאג "עמעס." [Москва] 1938.
27 p. 21 cm.
1. Security, International. 2. Russia—For. rel.—1917-1945. I. Title.
Title transliterated: Far sholem—kegn milkhome.
Name originally: Meer Genokh Moiseevich Wallach.
JX1953.L587 59-59179 ‡

NL 0414874 DLC

D809 .R9R8
Litvinov, Maksim Maksimovich, 1876-
Russian war relief, inc.
Financial and operations report of Russian war relief, for the period from September 12, 1941 to December 31, 1942, together with a statement of Ambassador Maxim Litvinov to the Board of directors of Russian war relief, inc., January 12, 1943. [New York, 1943]

VOLUME 336

FILM 12655 JX
Litvinov, Maksim Maksimovich, 1876-1951.
The foreign policy of the Soviet Union. London, Friend. of Soviet Russia [192-?]
31 p. On film (Negative)

Microfilm. Original in Univ. of California Library.

1. Russia - For. rel. - 1917-1945. I. Title.

NL 0414876 CU

Pamphlet D 1176
Litvinov, Maksim Maksimovich, 1876-1951.
The foreign policy of the Soviet Union. [London] FOSR [1930?]
31 p. 22cm.

1. Russia--For. rel.--1917-1945. I. Title.

NL 0414877 NIC

D764 .M6
Litvinov, Maksim Maksimovich, 1876-

Molotov, Vfácheslav Mikhaĭlovich, 1890-
The German attack on the U. S. S. R. Speeches by Mm. Molotov, Stalin and Litvinov, foreword by Neil Maclean ... London, The Anglo-Russian parliamentary committee, 1941.

D443 .L524
Litvinov, Maksim Maksimovich, 1876-1951.
К современному международному положению. [Москва] Гос. изд-во полит. лит-ры, 1938.
31 p. port. 17 cm.

1. World politics. I. Title.
Title transliterated: K sovremennomu mezhdunarodnomu polozhenifù.
Name originally: Meer Genokh Moiseevich Wallach.

D443.L524 52-46539

NL 0414879 DLC

Litvinov, Maksim Maksimovich, 1876-

Preparatory Commission for the Disarmament Conference. *Delegation from Russia.*
Letter from M. Litvinoff (delegate of the U. S. S. R.) to M. Loudon, president of the Commission, dated 26th March, 1928; letter from M. Loudon, dated 2nd April, 1928, to M. Litvinoff. Geneva, 1928.

DK267 .S679
Litvinov, Maksim Maksimovich, 1876-

Stalin, Iosif, 1879-
... La lutte de l'U. R. S. S. pour la paix mondiale. Paris, Bureau d'éditions, 1934.

Litvinov, Maksim Maksimovich, 1876-1951.
... Против агрессии. [Москва] Огиз, Государственное издательство политической литературы, 1938.
111, [1] p. 23cm.

At head of title: М. Литвинов.
"Основные выступления т. Литвинова и документы, характеризующие борьбу Советского союза против агрессии."—p. 5.

1. Russia—For. rel.—1917-1945. 2. Russia—For. rel.—Treaties. I. Title.
[*Name originally:* Meer Genokh Moiseevich Wallach]

41-27081

Library of Congress DK268.L5A34

NL 0414882 DLC

Litvinov, Maksim Maksimovich, 1876-1951.
... Против войн. За всеобщее разоружение. Советские предложения о полном и частичном разоружении. Москва-Ленинград, Государственное издательство, 1928.
151, [1] p. port. 16½cm.

At head of title: М. М. Литвинов.

1. Disarmament. I. ~~Russia (1923- U. S. S. R.) Delegatsiia v Podgotovitel'noĭ komissii Konferentsii po razoruzheniiu.~~ II. League of nations. III. Title.
(L. of N. author file Brv; topic file C: Disarmament)
[*Name originally:* Meer Genokh Moiseevich ~~Vallakh~~ Wallach]

40-19162

Library of Congress JX1974.L57
[2] 341.6

NL 0414883 DLC

Litvinov, Maksim Maksimovich, 1876-1951.
Notes for a journal. Introd. by E. H. Carr. [London] A. Deutsch [1955]
303 p. 22 cm.

1. Russia—For. rel.—1917-1945. I. Title.
Name originally: Meer Genokh Moiseevich Wallach.

DK268.L5A213 1955 55-3613

Or OrP OrPR OrStbM OrU Wa WaE WaS WaSpG ViU IaU NcD IEN PP PPFr PBm CaBViP CaBVa CaBVaU
NL 0414884 DLC WaT WaWW MCM NSyU OU PPT PPLas

Litvinov, Maksim Maksimovich, 1876-1951.
Notes for a journal. Introd. by E. H. Carr and a prefatory note by Walter Bedell Smith. New York, Morrow, 1955.
347 p. 22 cm.

1. Russia—Hist.—1917- —Sources. I. Title.
Name originally: Meer Genokh Moiseevich Wallach.

DK267.L542 55-10264 ‡
*947.083 947.084

MB NN CU TxU FMU NcU
NL 0414885 DLC NBuT ViU MeB GU AAP OOxM PPD PPDrop

Litvinov, Maksim Maksimovich, 1876-1951.
...On Soviet Russia. [London: People's Russian Information Bureau, 1919.] 2 l. 8°.

"Extracts from two letters...to an American correspondent..."

1. Russia.—Social conditions. 2. Bolshevism.
N. Y. P. L. February 17, 1922.

NL 0414886 NN

LITVINOV, MAKSIM MAKSIMOVICH, 1876-
Relations between the U.S.S.R. and Uruguay; speeches by M.Litvinov... London: Anglo-Russian Parliamentary Committee, 1936. 32 p. 21½cm.

Speeches delivered before the Council of the League of Nations.

859682A. 1. Russia—For.rel.—Uruguay, 1936. 2. Uruguay—For.rel.—Russia, 1936. I. Anglo-Russian Parliamentary Committee, London.

NL 0414887 NN MH

LITVINOV, MAKSIM MAKSIMOVICH, 1876-
"Soviet dumping" fable; speech of soviet commissar of foreign affairs, Litvinov, in European commission, May 18, 1931... New York: Published for Daily Worker...by Workers Library Publishers [1931] 31 p. illus. (port.) 14½x11cm.

778314A. 1. Economic history—Russia, 1917- . 2. Dumping (Commercial policy)—Russia.

NL 0414888 NN CU CSt-H MH Or

DK 267 .L544
Litvinov, Maksim Maksimovich, 1876-1951
The Soviet Union stands for peace. [New York, Workers Library Publishers, 1932]
16 p. 17 cm.

Cover title.

1. Russia - For. rel. - 1917-1945
2. Peace 3. Disarmament I. Title

NL 0414889 WU MiEM MH NcD NIC

Pamphlet D 1165
Litvinov, Maksim Maksimovich, 1876-1951.
The Soviet's fight for disarmament. Containing speeches by M. Litvinov at Geneva, 1932, and other documents in sequel to The Soviet Union and peace. With an introd. by M. Lunacharsky. London, M. Lawrence [1932]
iii, 44p. 22cm.

NL 0414890 NIC NN

Litvinov, Maksim Maksimovich, 1876-
The Soviet's fight for disarmament, containing speeches by M. Litvinov at Geneva, 1932, and other documents in sequel to "The Soviet union and peace", with an introduction by m. Lunacharsky. New York, International publishers [1932]
iii, 44 p. 21½cm.

1. Russia—Foreign relations—1917- 2. Peace. 3. Disarmament. I. Lunacharskiĭ, Anatoliĭ Vasil'evich, 1875-1933. II. Title.
[*Name originally:* Meer Genokh Moiseevich Vallakh]

A 32-2205 Revised

Title from Carnegie Endow. Int. Peace. Printed by L. C.

NL 0414891 NNCE InU OCl

Litvinov, Maksim Maksimovich, 1876-

Stalin, Iosif, 1879-
... Die Sowjetunion im kampf für den frieden. Moskau-Leningrad, Verlagsgenossenschaft ausländischer arbeiter in der UdSSR, 1934.

DK267 .3 1936 .L5
Litvinov, Maksim Maksimovich, 1876-1951.
СССР—могучий оплот всеобщего мира; речь на Чрезвычайном VIII Всесоюзном Съезде Советов 28 ноября 1936 г. [Москва] Партиздат, 1936.
31 p. illus. 19 cm.

On cover: Чрезвычайный VIII Всесоюзный Съезд Советов.

1. Russia—For. rel.—1917-1945. 2. Peace. I. Title.
Title transliterated: SSSR—moguchiĭ oplot vseobshchego mira.
Name originally: Meer Genokh Moiseevich Wallach.

DK267.3 1936.L5 54-46458 ‡

NL 0414893 DLC

DK267 L543
Litvinov, Maksim Maksimovich, 1876-1951.
СССР в борьбе за мир; речь на IV сессии ЦИК Союза ССР 29 декабря 1933 г. Москва, Партийное изд-во, 1934.
31 p. port. 18 cm.

1. Russia—For. rel.—1917-1945. 2. Security, International. I. Title.
Title transliterated: SSSR v bor'be za mir.
Name originally: Meer Genokh Moiseevich Wallach.

DK267.L543 52-46416

NL 0414894 DLC

VOLUME 336

Litvinov, Maksim Maksimovich, 1876-
Testimonial dinner tendered to the Honorable Maxim M. Litvinoff...
see under American Russian Chamber of Commerce, New York.

Litvinov, Maksim Maksimovich, 1876–
... L'U. R. S. S. et la paix. Paris, Bureau d'éditions, 1939.
200 p. 21½cm.
At head of title: Maxime Litvinov.
CONTENTS.—Discours.—Documents. I. Traités de non-agression et de règlement pacifique des conflits. II. Définition de l'agression. III. Pactes d'assistance mutuelle.
1. Russia—For. rel.—1917– 2. Russia—For. rel.—Treaties. 3. Security, International. 4. Peace. I. Title.
[Name originally: Meer Genokh Moiseevich Vallakh]
40-1217
Library of Congress DK268.L5A4
[2] 327.47

NL 0414896 DLC NNC

Litvinov, Maksim Maksimovich, 1876–
... The U. S. S. R., a powerful bulwark of universal peace, speech delivered at the extraordinary eighth Congress of soviets of the U. S. S. R., November 28, 1936. Moscow, Co-operative publishing society of foreign workers in the U. S. S. R., 1937.
23, [1] p. front. (port.) 23½cm.
At head of title: M. M. Litvinov ...
On p. [4] of cover: М. М. Литвинов. СССР, могучий оплот всеобщего мира.
1. Russia—For. rel.—1917– 2. Peace. 3. Fascism. I. Russia (1923– U. S. S. R.) S"ezd sovetov. II. Title.
[Name originally: Meer Genokh Moiseevich Vallakh]
42-12242
Library of Congress DK268.L5A38
[2] 947.084

NL 0414897 DLC

LITVINOV, MAKSIM MAKSIMOVICH, 1876–
...The USSR and the League of Nations. [New York city: Workers Library Publishers, 1934] 31 p. 15cm.

868241A. 1. League of Nations—Relations with Russia. 2. Russia—For.rel., 1917–

N. Y. P. L. January 4, 1937

NL 0414898 NN TxFTC NcD CtY NNC MiEM CSt-H NIC MH

Litvinov, Maksim Maksimovich, 1876–

JX1974
.R85
1928b
Preparatory commission for the Disarmament conference. *Delegation from Russia.*
В борьбе за мир. Советская делегация на v сессии Комиссии по разоружению. Речи тов. М. М. Литвинова. Москва, Издание Литиздата Н. К. И. Д., 1928.

JX1953
.L57
Litvinov, Maksim Maksimovich, 1876–1951.
В борьбе за мир [речи. Москва] Партиздат, 1938.
192 p. port. 23 cm.
1. Security, International. 2. Russia—For. rel.—1917–1945. I. Title.
Title transliterated: V bor'be za mir.
Name originally: Meer Genokh Moiseevich Wallach.
JX1953.L57 52-47238

NL 0414900 DLC

DK63
.L53
1935
Litvinov, Maksim Maksimovich, 1876–1951.
Внешняя политика СССР; речи и заявления, 1927–1935. Москва, Гос. социально-экон. изд-во, 1935.
iv, 363 p. group port. 23 cm.
Microfilm Slavic 686 AC
— — Microfilm copy (negative) made in 1955 by H. M. Stationery Office.
1. Russia—For. rel.—1917–1945. I. Title.
Title transliterated: Vneshni͡ai͡a politika SSSR.
Name originally: Meer Genokh Moiseevich Wallach.
DK63.L53 1935 51-49718

NL 0414901 DLC

Litvinov, Maksim Maksimovich, 1876–
Внешняя политика СССР; речи и заявления, 1927–1937. 2. доп. изд. Москва, Гос. социально-экон. изд-во, 1937.
431 p. ports. 23 cm.
1. Russia—For. rel.—1917–1945. I. Title.
Title transliterated: Vneshni͡ai͡a politika SSSR.
Name originally: Meer Genokh Moiseevich Wallach.
DK63.L53 1937 51-49717

NL 0414902 DLC

JX1953
.L58
Litvinov, Maksim Maksimovich, 1876–
За мир—против войны; речь на пленуме Лиги Наций 21 сентября 1938 г. [Москва] Гос. изд-во полит. лит-ры, 1938.
22 p. 19 cm.
1. Security, International. 2. Russia—For. rel.—1917–1945. I. Title.
Title transliterated: Za mir—protiv voĭny.
Name originally: Meer Genokh Moiseevich Vallakh.
JX1953.L58 54-50138 ‡

NL 0414903 DLC

D450
.L5
Litvinov, Maksim Maksimovich, 1876–1951.
За создание подлинной безопасности в Европе; речь на сессии Совета Лиги Наций в Лондоне 17 марта 1936 года. [Ленинград] Леноблиздат, 1936.
15 p. 17 cm.
1. World politics—Addresses, essays, lectures. 2. Security, International. I. Title.
Title transliterated: Za sozdanie podlinnoĭ bezopasnosti v Evrope.
Name originally: Meer Genokh Moiseevich Wallach.
D450.L5 54-45480 ‡

NL 0414904 DLC

JX1974
.L58
Litvinov, Maksim Maksimovich, 1876–1951.
За всеобщее разоружение; речи М. М. Литвинова и советские предложения о полном и частичном разоружении. Москва, Московский рабочий [1928]
185 p. port. 17 cm.
1. Disarmament. I. Title.
Title transliterated: Za vseobshchee razoruzhenie.
Name originally: Meer Genokh Moiseevich Wallach.
JX1974.L58 52-47237

NL 0414905 DLC

Litvinov, Maksim Maksimovich, 1876-1951.
see also Rusia (1923- U.S.S.R.) Narodny komissariat po inostrannym delam.

W 1
ZD862
sv. 42
1953
LITVINOV, N N
Přednášky o organisaci zdravotnictví, o problémech hygienicko-epidemické služby v SSSR a o organisaci zdravotnictví v ČSR. [1. vyd.] Praha, Státní zdravotnické nakl., 1953.
145 p. port. (Zdravotnické aktuality, sv. 42)
1. Public health - Czechoslovak Republic 2. Public health - Russia

NL 0414907 DNLM

Litvinov, Nikolaĭ Nikolaevich.
Двигатели внутреннего сгорания, применяемые на геолого-разведочных работах. Москва, Гос. научно-техн. изд-во лит-ры по геологии и охране недр, 1954.
382 p. illus. 27 cm.
Bibliography: p. 380–[381]
1. Gas and oil engines. 2. Prospecting. I. Title.
Title transliterated: Dvigateli vnutrennego sgoranii͡a, primeni͡aemye na geologo-razvedochnykh rabotakh.
TJ785.L55 54-43441 rev

NL 0414908 DLC

Litvinov, O. O., ed.
Akademii͡a arkhitektury URSR, *Kiev. Instytut budivel'nykh materialiv.*
Строительные материалы: сборник. Под общей ред. О. О. Литвинова. Киев, Изд-во Академии архитектуры УССР, 1949.

TN871
.35
.L5
Litvinov, S Ӏ͡A
Промысловая геофизика. Допущено в качестве учеб. пособия для студентов нефтяных вузов. Москва, Гос. научно-техн. изд-во нефтяной и горно-топливной лит-ры, 1954.
184 p. illus. 23 cm.
At head of title: С. Я. Литвинов, Л. В. Архаров.
Bibliography: p. [182]
1. Oil well logging. 2. Petroleum—Geology. I. Arkharov, L. V., joint author. II. Title. *Title transliterated:* Promyslovai͡a geofizika.
TN871.35.L5 55-23322

NL 0414910 DLC

TK6548
.R9L5
Litvinov, Sergeĭ Vladimirovich.
Сельский радиокружок; в помощь организатору и руководителю сельского радиокружка. Москва, Гос. изд-во культурно-просветительной лит-ры, 1950.
53, [3] p. illus. 22 cm.
Bibliography: p. 53–[54]
1. Radio—Russia. I. Title.
Title transliterated: Sel'skiĭ radiokruzhok.
TK6548.R9L5 51-22368 rev

NL 0414911 DLC

TH9151
.L54
Litvinov, V D
Пожарно-прикладной спорт; пособие для начальствующего состава пожарной охраны. Москва, Изд-во Министерства коммунального хозяйства РСФСР, 1953.
155 p. illus. 22 cm.
Errata slip inserted.
1. Fire extinction. 2. Sports. I. Title.
Title transliterated: Pozharno-prikladnoĭ sport.
TH9151.L54 53-39937

NL 0414912 DLC

VOLUME 336

Litvinov, Vladimir Vladimirovich.
Сочинение в старших классах как самостоятельная работа. Москва, Гос. учебно-педагог. изд-во, 1953.
87 p. 20 cm. (Опыт передового учителя)

1. Russian language—Composition and exercises. I. Title.
Title romanized: Sochinenie v starshikh klassakh.

PG2420.L5 54-24434 ‡

NL 0414913 DLC

Law

Litvinov-Falinskiĭ, Vladimir Petrovich, 1868–
... Фабричное законодательство и фабричная инспекція въ Россіи. С.-Петербургъ, Тип. А. С. Суворина, 1900.
xix, 305 p. 24 cm.
At head of title: В. П. Литвиновъ-Фалинскій.
Bibliographical notes in preface.

1. Labor laws and legislation—Russia. 2. Factory inspection—Russia. I. Title. *Title transliterated:* Fabrichnoe zakonodatel'stvo.

19-14583 rev

NL 0414914 DLC NN

Litvinov-Falinskiĭ, Vladimir Petrovich, 1868– ed.

Russia. *Laws, statutes, etc.*
Какъ и для чего страхуются рабочіе; полный текстъ новыхъ законовъ о страхованіи рабочихъ, съ объясненіями. С.-Петербургъ, 1912.

HC335
.L58

Litvinov-Falinskiĭ, Vladimir Petrovich, 1868–
Наше экономическое положеніе и задачи будущаго. С.-Петербургъ, Тип. В. Ф. Киршбаума, 1908.
x, 149 p. 27 cm.
"Литературные источники": p. [v]–vi.

1. Russia—Econ. condit. 2. Russia—Economic policy. I. Title.
Title transliterated: Nashe ėkonomicheskoe polozhenie.

HC335.L58 48-32896*

NL 0414916 DLC KU

Litvinov-Falinskiĭ, Vladimir Petrovich, 1868–
... Новый законъ о вознагражденіи увѣчныхъ рабочихъ. Текстъ закона 2-го іюня 1903 года съ объясненіями. С.-Петербургъ, Тип. А. С. Суворина, 1903.
vii, 196 p. 23½ cm.
At head of title: В. П. Литвиновъ-Фалинскій.

1. Employers' liability—Russia. 2. Insurance, Industrial—Russia.

18-11480

Library of Congress HD7816.R7 L5

NL 0414917 DLC

Law

Litvinov-Falinskiĭ, Vladimir Petrovich, 1868– ed.

Russia. *Laws, statutes, etc.*
Новые законы о страхованіи рабочихъ. Текстъ законовъ съ мотивами и подробными разъясненіями. С.-Петербургъ, Тип. А. С. Суворина, 1912.

HD7179
.L58

Litvinov-Falinskiĭ, Vladimir Petrovich, 1868–
... Организація и практика страхованія рабочихъ въ Германіи и условія возможнаго обезпеченія рабочихъ въ Россіи. С.-Петербургъ, Тип. А. С. Суворина, 1903.
1 p. l., viii, 275 p. 23½ cm.
At head of title: В. П. Литвиновъ-Фалинскій.

1. Insurance, Social—Germany. 2. Insurance, Social—Russia.
3. Insurance—Russia. I. Title.
Title transliterated: Organizat͡sii͡a i praktika strakhovanii͡a rabochikh v Germanii.

HD7179.L58 19-14581 rev

NL 0414919 DLC

HD7816
R9L58
1900

Litvinov-Falinskiĭ, Vladimir Petrovich, 1868–
Отвѣтственность предпринимателей за увѣчья и смерть рабочихъ по дѣйствующимъ въ Россіи законамъ. Изд. 2., доп. и испр. С.-Петербургъ, Типо-лит. И. Г. Гершуна, 1900.
394 p. plate, form. 24 cm.
Bibliographical footnotes.

1. Workmen's compensation—Russia. I. Title.
Title transliterated: Otvi͡etstvennost' predprinimateleĭ za uvi͡ech'i͡a i smert' rabochikh.

19-14582 rev*

NL 0414920 DLC CU

Litvinov-Falinskiĭ, Vladimir Petrovich, 1868–
Отвѣтственность предпринимателей за увѣчья и смерть рабочихъ по дѣйствующимъ въ Россіи законамъ. Изд. 3., доп. и испр. С.-Петербургъ, Тип. А. С. Суворина, 1903.
x, 272, 95 p. plate, form, tables. 23 cm.
Bibliographical footnotes.

1. Workmen's compensation—Russia. I. Title.
Title transliterated: Otvi͡etstvennost' predprinimateleĭ za uvi͡ech'i͡a i smert' rabochikh.

64-58190

NL 0414921 DLC

Litvinova, A. V., ed.

PG2640
.Z27
1950

Zaĭmovskiĭ, Semen Grigor'evich.
Краткий русско-английский и англо-русский словарь. Под ред. А. В. Литвиновой. Около 16 000 слов. Москва, Гос. изд-во иностранных и национальных словарей, 1950.

B481
L55

Litvinova, Elizaveta Fedorovna, 1845?–1919.
Аристотель; его жизнь, научная и философская дѣятельность. Біографическій очеркъ. С.-Петербургъ, Тип. И. Г. Салова, 1892.
78 p. illus. 19 cm. (Жизнь замѣчательныхъ людей; біографическая библіотека Ф. Павленкова)
Includes bibliography.

1. Aristoteles. *Title transliterated:* Aristotel'.

B481.L55 60-58130 ‡

NL 0414923 DLC

Litvinova, Elizaveta Fedorovna, 1845?–1919.
Даламберъ, его жизнь и научная дѣятельность. Біографическій очеркъ. С.-Петербургъ, Тип. Ю. Н. Эрлихъ, 1891.
80 p. port. 19 cm. (Жизнь замѣчательныхъ людей; біографическая библіотека Ф. Павленкова)

1. Alembert, Jean Lerond d', 1717–1783.
Title transliterated: Dalamber.

B1936.L5 58-54900

NL 0414924 DLC OU

Litvinova, Elizaveta Fedorovna, 1845?–1919.
Джонъ Локкъ; его жизнь и философская дѣятельность. Біографическій очеркъ. С.-Петербургъ [Изд.] Ф. Павленкова, 1892.
77 p. illus. 19 cm. (Жизнь замѣчательныхъ людей)

1. Locke, John, 1632–1704. *Title transliterated:* Dzhon Lokk.

B1297.L5 55-46375 ‡

NL 0414925 DLC

B1197
.L57

Litvinova, Elizaveta Fedorovna, 1845?–1919.
Ф. Бэконъ; его жизнь, научные труды и общ. дѣятельность. Біографическій очеркъ. С.-Петербургъ, Тип. Товарищ. "Общественная польза," 1891.
79 p. illus. 19 cm. (Жизнь замѣчательныхъ людей; біографическая библіотека Ф. Павленкова)
Includes bibliography.

1. Bacon, Francis, viscount St. Albans, 1561–1626.
Title transliterated: F. Bėkon.

B1197.L57 60-58132 ‡

NL 0414926 DLC

CT1018
.C58L5

Litvinova, Elizaveta Fedorovna, 1845?–1919.
Кондорсэ; его жизнь и дѣятельность, научная и политическая. Біографическій очеркъ Е. Ѳ. Литвиновой. С.-Петербургъ, Тип. Т-ва "Общественная польза," 1894.
80 p. port. 19 cm. (Жизнь замѣчательных людей, біографическая библіотека Ф. Павленкова)

1. Condorcet, Marie Jean Antoine Nicolas Caritat, marquis de, 1743–1794.
Title transliterated: Kondorsė.

CT1018.C58L5 66-46493

NL 0414927 DLC

QA29
E8L5

Litvinova, Elizaveta Fedorovna, 1845?–1919.
Лапласъ и Эйлеръ, ихъ жизнь и научная дѣятельность; біографическіе очерки. С.-Петербургъ, Тип. Товар. "Общественная польза," 1892.
79 p. illus. 19 cm. (Жизнь замѣчательныхъ людей; біографическая библіотека Ф. Павленкова)

1. Euler, Leonhard, 1707–1783. 2. Laplace, Pierre Simon, marquis de, 1749–1827. *Title transliterated:* Laplas i Ėĭler.

QA29.E8L5 61-57745 ‡

NL 0414928 DLC

Litvinova, Elizaveta Fedorovna, 1845?–1919.
Lösung einer abbildungsaufgabe ... St. Petersburg, Buchdruckerei der K. Akademie der wissenschaften, 1879.
28 p. 26½ cm.
Inaug.-diss.—Bern.

1. Conformal mapping.

QA646.L78 4-12396 rev

NL 0414929 DLC NjP

VOLUME 336

CT 194 L78 Litvincva, Elizaveta Fedorovna.

Правители и мыслители. Біографическіе очерки Е. Ѳ. Литвиновой. Съ 16 портретами. Изданіе Ф. Павленкова. С.-Петербургъ, Тип. С. Н. Худекова, 1897.

2 p. l., 302 p. 16 port. 21cm.

CONTENTS.—Платонъ и тиранъ сиракузскій.—Фридрихъ II и философы.—Наполеонъ и Карно.—Александръ Благословенный и Лагарпъ.—Жуковскій и его августѣйшіе друзья.—Петръ Великій и Лейбницъ.—Королева Христина и Декартъ.—Екатерина Великая и философы.—Лейбницъ въ Ганноверѣ и Берлинѣ.

1. Biography. I. Title.

Title transliterated: Praviteli i mysliteli.

NL 0414930 NIC

QA29 K67L5 Litvinova, Elizaveta Fedorovna, 1845?–1919.

С. В. Ковалевская, женщина-математикъ; ея жизнь и ученая дѣятельность. Біографическій очеркъ. С.-Петербургъ ‹Изд.› Ф. Павленкова, 1894.

92 p. port. 20 cm. (Жизнь замѣчательныхъ людей)

1. Kovalevskaia, Sof'ia Vasil'evna (Korvin-Krukovskaia) 1850–1891. Title transliterated: S. V. Kovalevskaia.

QA29.K67L5 55–45266

NL 0414931 DLC

QB36 .S75L5 Litvinova, Elizaveta Fedorovna, 1845?–1919.

В. Я. Струве; его жизнь и научная дѣятельность. С.-Петербургъ ‹Изд. Ф. Павленкова› 1893.

78 p. port. 19 cm. (Жизнь замѣчательныхъ людей)

1. Struve, Wilhelm, 1793–1864.

Title transliterated: V. IA. Struve.

QB36.S75L5 54–51982 ‡

NL 0414932 DLC

Litvinova, Ivy (Low) tr.

Rozanov, Sergeĭ Grigor'evich.

The adventures of Misha, by Sergei Rosanov; translated from the Russian by Ivy Low, drawings by Alexander Mogilevsky. New York, Frederick A. Stokes company, 1938.

Litvinova, Ivy (Low), ed.

Litvinov, Maksim, 1876–

The Bolshevik revolution: its rise and meaning, by Maxim Litvinoff. London, British Socialist party ‹1919›

Litvinova, Ivy (Low) tr.

DK267 .K432 Kerzhenfsev, Platon Mikhaĭlovich, 1881–1940.

... Bolshevism for beginners, a handbook for new members of the Communist party and for self-education. Translated from the Russian by Ivy Low. Moscow, Pub. by Centrizdat, 1931.

Litvinova, Ivy (Low)

823.912 L782G Growing pains; a novel, by Ivy Low. London, W. Heinemann, 1913.

viii, 300 p. 20 cm.

I. Title.

NL 0414936 NcD

Litvinova, Ivy, (Low)

Growing pains; a novel, by Ivy Low... New York: G. H. Doran co., 1913. viii, 300 p. 19½cm.

116212B. 1. Fiction, English. I. Title.

NL 0414937 NN

Litvinova, Ivy (Low)

Moscow mystery, a novel by Ivy Litvinoff. New York, Coward-McCann, inc. ‹1943›

xiv, 268 p. 21cm.

I. Title.

43–4860

Library of Congress PZ3.L738Mo

OrU PP PU PPL OEac OClW OU OLak CaBVaU
NL 0414938 DLC GU NcD NIC WaT WaS IdU MtU OrCS

Litvinskiĭ, Boris Anatol'evich.

Древнейшие страницы истории горного дела Таджикистана и других республик Средней Азии. Сталинабад, Изд-во Академии наук Таджикской ССР, 1954.

45, ‹1› p. illus. 23 cm. (Академия наук Таджикской ССР. Институт истории, археологии и этнографии. Научно-популярная библиотека, вып. 19)

At head of title: Б. А. Литвинский.
Added t. p. in Tajik.
Bibliographical references included in "Примечания" (p. 42–‹46›)

1. Mineral industries—Tajikistan—Hist. I. Title.
Title transliterated: Drevneĭshie stranifsy istorii gornogo dela Tadzhikistana.

DK921.L5 67–58083

NL 0414939 DLC

Litvinsky, Volo, 1898–

Tout le métier de coiffeur; pour les candidats au C. A. P. et au B. P. Paris, Société d'éditions modernes parisienne ‹1955›

280 p. illus. 25 cm.

1. Hairdressing. I. Title.

TT957.L5 56–28991 ‡

NL 0414940 DLC

TN740 .L5 Litvishko, V N

Опыт сталеваров-скоростников Н.-Салдинского металлургического завода. Свердловск, Гос. научно-техн. изд-во лит-ры по черной и цветной металлургии, 1954.

49, ‹3› p. illus. 22 cm. (Передовые методы труда)

Errata slip inserted.
Bibliography: p. ‹51›

1. Nizhne-Saldinskiĭ metallurgicheskiĭ zavod. 2. Open-hearth process. I. Title. Title transliterated: Opyt stalevarov-skorostnikov.

TN740.L5 55–15046

NL 0414941 DLC

LITVOMANAI. Drama 4-tuose veikimuose. Parašė Dvi Moteri. Tilže, M. Saunus, 1905. 58 p. 15cm.

'Atspauzdinta iš "Varpo"'

1. Drama, Lithuanian.

NL 0414942 NN

Litwa
see
Lithuania.

Litwa do Unii Lubelskiej
see under ‹Ślizień, A ›

DK 511 .L2L876 Litwa i Ruś. stycz.1912- Wilno.

"Miesięcznik ilustrowany, poświęcony kulturze, dziejom, krajoznawstwu i ludoznawstwu."

‹Holdings under main entry in ‹serial record.

1. Lithuania. 2. Periodicals (Polish)

NL 0414945 ICU

Litwa pod względem prześkladowania w niej rzymakokatolickiego kościola, szczególniej w dyecezyi wileńskiej od roku 1863 do 1872. Wydanie Biblioteki polskiej w Paryzu. Poznań, Nakl. J.K. Zupańskiego, 1872.

107 p. 24 cm.

[illegible]

NL 0414946 PU

DK511 L26L78 ... Litwa podczas wojny. Zbiór dokumentów, uchwał, odezw i t.p. Zebrał i do druku przygotował L.A. Warszawa ‹Wyd. Departamentu spraw politycznych› 1918.

143 p. 24cm

At head of title: Drukowano na prawach rękopisu.
On cover: Problem Litwy podczas wojny ...

1. Lithuania. 2. European war, 1914-1918- Lithuania. 3. Poles in Lithuania. I. L.A. II. A., L.

NL 0414947 CSt-H CU

DK 511 L26 L5 Litwa za rządów ks. Isenburga. Kraków, Nakł. Krakowskiego Oddziału Zjednoczenia Narodowego, 1919.

157 p. 20 cm.

1. Lithuania - Hist.

NL 0414948 WU NN PU MH CU

Litwak, A.
see
Helfand, Jacob, 1874–1932.
Litvak, Arkadiĭ Moiseevich.

VOLUME 336

MF301.152
L737 **Litwak, Eugene.**
Primary group instruments for social control in industrialized society: the extended family and the neighborhood. [New York] 1958.
x, 335 l.

Microfilm (positive)
Thesis- Columbia University.
Bibliography: l.329-335.

NL 0414950 OrU

Litwak, Mordko, 1876-
... Ein Fall von primaerem papillaeren Adeno-Karzinom des Corpus uteri mit Matastasen [!] am Ovarium. Berlin (1914): Blanke. 2
25 p. 8°. S.

NL 0414951 CtY DNLM

LITWAK, Selmann, 1891-
Ueber die beteiligung des uvealtractus bei der keratitis parenchymatosa. Inaug.-diss. Basel, buchdruckerei Brin & cie., 1914.

pp.28.

NL 0414952 MBCo DNLM CtY MiU

Litwiller, Earl. 8130.01-102
An appraisal and abstract of available literature on landscape architecture as an occupation.
— [New York. 1936.] 8, (1) pp. [National Occupational Conference.] 25 cm.
Bibliography, pp. 6-8.

E2990 — S.r. Pubs. — Landscape gardening. Bibl. — Occupation.

NL 0414953 MB OrU OU IU

Litwiller, Earl Milo, 1893–
Manufacture of jellies and preserves. Corvallis, Agricultural Experiment Station, Oregon State College, 1950.
[4] p. 23 cm. (Oregon. Agricultural Experiment Station. Corvallis. Station bulletin 490)

1. Canning and preserving. 2. Jelly. I. Title: Jellies and preserves.
[S105.E32 no. 490] (630.72) A 50-8938

Oregon. State College. for Library of Congress Library [2]

NL 0414954 Or

Litwiller, Earl Milo, 1893 -
Nitrogen deficiency in relation to spoilage of the blueberry, Vaccinium ovatum, by Earl Milo Litwiller ... (Corvallis, Ore.) 1944.
53 numb.l. incl. plates, tables. 28cm.

NL 0414955 OrCS

Litwiller, Raymond, 1910–
... Quantitative studies on nerve regeneration in *Amphibia.* I. Factors controlling nerve regeneration in adult limbs. II. Factors controlling nerve regeneration in regenerating limbs ... By Raymond Litwiller ... [Chicago, 1938]
1 p. l., p. 427–447, 377–397 incl. tables, diagrs. 25½cm.
Part of thesis (PH. D.)—University of Chicago, 1937.
"Private edition, distributed by the University of Chicago libraries, Chicago, Illinois."
"Reprinted from the Journal of comparative neurology, vol. 69, no. 3, December, 1938 and the Journal of experimental zoology, vol. 79, no. 3, November, 1938."
"Literature cited": p. 447, 396–397.
1. Nerves. 2. Regeneration (Biology) 3. Extremities (Anatomy) 4. Batrachia—Anatomy.
39-11702
Library of Congress QP331.L5 1937
Univ. of Chicago Libr.
—— —— Copy 2. [2] 612.8226

NL 0414956 ICU NcD OCU DLC

[Litwin,]
[Kilka słów z powodu listu z kraju pod tytułem: Sprawa polska w 1861 r. Paryż, Martinet, 1862.
40 p.

Signed: Litwin.

1. Poland - History - 1795-1864. 2. Poland - History - Revolution,, 1863-1864. I. Title.

NL 0414957 NNC

Litwin, A., pseud.
see Hurwitz, Samuel, 1862-1943.

Litwin, Aleksander.
JN6769
.A5P68
Polska Zjednoczona Partia Robotnicza. *Komitet Centralny. Wydział Historii Partii.*
Pod rządami bezprawia i terroru; konstytucje, sejmy i wybory w Polsce przedwrześniowej. Materiały i dokumenty. [Opracowali: A. Litwin, F. Kalicka i M. Minkowski] Warszawa, Książka i Wiedza, 1952.

Litwin, Aleksander.
HD8039 Powszechny strajk włókniarzy łódzkich w 1936
T42P7L782 roku. [Warszawa] Książka i Wiedza, 1953.
133 p. 21cm.
At head of title: Wydział Historii Partii KC PZRR.

1. Textile Workers Strike, Łódź, Poland, 1936. 2. Strikes and lockouts - Łódź, Poland. I. Polska Zjednoczona Partia Robotnicza. Komitet Centralny. Wydział Historii Partii. II.Title.

NL 0414960 CSt-H MH

Litwin, Aleksander, ed.
DK440
.T93
Tymczasowy Komitet Rewolucyjny Polski.
[Tymczasowy Komitet Rewolucyjny Polski. [Opracował i wstępem opatrzył Aleksander Litwin. Wyd. 1. Warszawa] Książka i Wiedza, 1955.

Litwin, Harry.
The green kingdom, by Harry Woodbourne [pseud.] Drawings by Louise E. Jefferson. [Portland, Me.] Bond Wheelwright Co. [1955]
310 p. illus. 21 cm. [American saga series]
Verse and prose.

1. Gardening. I. Title.
SB453.L58 635.9 55-6262 ‡

NL 0414962 DLC IU TU DNAL

Litwin, Jacob Henry
Electrolytic Safronine, a thesis submitted to the faculty of the College of Engineering of the University of Cincinnati in part requirement for the degree of Chemical Engineer...
[Cin.] 1919.
33 l.

NL 0414963 OCU

Litwin, Janusz.
ABC planu sześcioletniego. [Redaktor: Tadeusz Wójcik. Warszawa] Czytelnik, 1951.
242 p. illus. 20 cm.

1. Poland—Economic policy. I. Title.
HC337.P7L58 52-42744 ‡

NL 0414964 DLC NN OU

Litwin, Józef.
O potrzebie republikacji obowiązujących przepisów prawnych zaborczycvch w polskich tekstach autentycznych. Warszawa, 1937.
19 p. 25 cm.
Bibliographical footnotes.

1. Law—Translating. 2. Law—Poland—Sources. I. Title.
66-49442

NL 0414965 DLC MH-L

Law Litwin, Józef.
Poland. *Laws, statutes, etc.*
Prawo o aktach stanu cywilnego 1945 r. Wraz z przepisami wprowadzającymi, wstępem objaśniającym poprzedził Józef Litwin. [Warszawa?] Czytelnik, 1945.

Litwin, Józef.
Prawo o aktach stanu cywilnego, z komentarzem
see under Poland. Laws, statutes, etc.

Law Litwin, Józef, ed.
Poland. *Laws, statutes, etc.*
Prawo szkól wyższych. [Ustawa o szkolnictwie wyższym i o pracownikach nauki, z dnia 15 grud. 1951 r.] Teksty i komentarze. [Wyd. 1.] Warszawa, Państwowe Wydawn. Naukowe, 1955.

347.9(438)
L4 Litwin, Józef
Postępowanie administracyjne, postępowanie karno- administracyjne, postępowanie przymusowe w administracji, objaśnione orzecznictwem sądów najwyzszych i okólnikami ministerialnymi. 2. wyd. Łódź, Ginter, 1948
250 p.

NL 0414969 NNUN

VOLUME 336

Litwin, Józef
352.0438
L782U Uchwały rad narodowych; wzory i przykłady. Warszawa, Wydawnictwo Prawnicze, 1955.
318 p. 25 cm.

1. Local government. Poland. 2. Administrative law. Poland. I. Title.

NL 0414970 NcD MH-L

Litwin, Sophie, 1887– Über Geburtsblutungen am kindlichen Schaedel. Freiburg i. B.: Hammerschlag & Kahle 1910. 31 S. 8°
Freiburg i. B., Med. Diss. v. 1910, Ref. Krönig
[Geb. 3. Jan. 87 Akkerman; Wohnort: Freiburg i. B.; Staatsangeh.: Rußland; Vorbildung: Gymn. Akkerman Reife 02; Studium: Bern 7, Freiburg i. B. 4 S.; Rig. 10. Mai 10.] [U 10. 984

NL 0414971 ICRL DNLM

Litwinow, M
see Litvinov, Maksim Maksimovich, 1876–1951.

Litwinowicz, Michael.
Die Hypothekarverschuldung des Grossgrundbesitzes physischer Personen in der Bukowina, des Grundbesitzes in der Landeshauptstadt Czernowitz und des Kleingrundbesitzes physischer Personen im Gerichtsbezirke Czernowitz. Czernowitz: [H. Pardini,] 1907. 93 p. half lea. 4°. (Bukowina, province, Austria. Statistisches Landesamt. Mittheilungen. Heft 12.)

1. Mortgages, Austria: Bukowina.
N. Y. P. L. October 11, 1913.

NL 0414973 NN

Litwinowicz, Wacław.
... Motores de aviação; potências e utilização económica. Lisboa, Parceria A. M. Pereira, 1946.
xxiv, 335, [1] p. incl. front. (port.) illus. (incl. diagrs.) tables. fold. plates (1 col.) 25½ᶜᵐ.
"Adaptação em língua portuguesa por José Avelino Faria de Fonseca Santos."
"Erratas": slip tipped in.

1. Aeroplanes—Motors. I. Faria de Fonseca Santos, José Avelino, tr. II. Title.
A 47-739
Yale univ. Library for Library of Congress [a47d2]

NL 0414974 CtY

LITWIŃSKI, JAN.
Album pieniędzy papierowych polskich z roku 1794 z podaniem historycznem, Wyd. 2. Kraków, Nakł. H. Kowarzyka, 1908. 16 p. facsims. 23cm.

1. Money, Paper—Poland.

NL 0414975 NN

PG
6635
L5 Litwiński, Jan, teacher in Lublin
Słownik polsko-łacińsko-francuzki, na zasadach słowników Knapskiego, Danneta i Troca. W Warszawie, Nakł. Zawadzkiego i Węckiego, 1815.
2 v. 21 cm.

1. Polish language - Dictionaries - Polyglot I. Title

NL 0414976 WU

Litwinski, Léon.
Intellectual Poland; a lecture delivered at Cambridge on May 19, 1916, with a pref. by the Rt. Hon. Viscount Bryce. London, Published for the Polish Information Committee by G. Allen & Unwin [1916]
61 p. 22 cm. (Polish Information Committee, London. Publications. Ser. A, 8)
"First published in 1916."

1. Poland—Intellectual life. I. Title. (Series)
DK402.5.P7 no. 8 16-22449 rev*

NL 0414977 DLC CaBVaU CSt-H CLSU OO OCl MB MiD

Litwinski, Léon.
Intellectual Poland; a lecture delivered at Cambridge on May 19, 1916, with a pref. by the Rt. Hon. Viscount Bryce. New York, The Polish Book Importing Co. [1916]
61 p. 22 cm. (Polish Information Committee, London. Publications. Ser. A, 8)
"First published in 1916."

1. Poland—Intellectual life. I. Title. (Series)
DK411.L5 1916 30-6375 rev*

NL 0414978 DLC

Litwinski, Léon.
Polish currency problems. By Dr. L. Litwinski... [London, 1918.] 7(1) p. 8°.
Cover-title.
"Reprinted from The economist, Oct. 26, 1918."

1. Money, Poland. 2. European war, 1914– .—Economic aspects, Poland. 3. Title.
N. Y. P. L. May 20, 1919.

NL 0414979 NN

MANN
HB
172
L78 Litwinski, Léon.
Le problème des débouchés et l'internationalisme économique; considerations sur les conditions de l'equilibre entre la production et la consommation dans l'economie mondiale. Bruxelles, Goemaere, 1927.
22 p. 24 cm.

1. Economics. 2. Supply and demand. 3. Commerce.

NL 0414980 NIC MH CSt CSt-H

Litwinski, Léon.
La question de la situation financière des Chemins de fer de l'État belge. Bruxelles, Goemaere, 1911.
118 p. 24 cm.
Bibliography: p. [5]-7.

1. Société nationale des chemins de fer belges. I. Title.
HE3120.S63L5 11-28315 rev*

NL 0414981 DLC NNC CtY NN CU

Litwinski, Léon.
The surrender of Dantzig to Poland. By Dr. Leon Litwinski ... [London: The Avenue Press, 1918.] 4 p. 12°.
Cover-title.
"Reprinted from The Shipping world of October 23, 1918."

1. Dantzig. 2. Polish question, 1914– . 3. European war, 1914– .—Peace terms. 4. Title.
N. Y. P. L. May 20, 1919.

NL 0414982 NN

DS 145
L7 Litwinski, Leon, 1887–
Anti semitismo [por] Leon Litwinski [e] Samuel Schwarz. Conferências realizadas em 27 de junho de 1944 sob os auspicios da Associação dos Cidadãos Polacos em Lisboa; na presença de Gustaw Potworowski, Ministro Plenipotenciário da Polónia em Portugal. Ilustrações de João Carlos. Lisboa, 1944.
76 p. illus. 25 cm.

Text in French or Portuguese.

NL 0414983 OU NN OCH

KF 3405
Litwinski, Léon, 1887–
Les aspects stheniques et astheniques dans les conduites et les sentiments complexes. Coimbra [Composto e impresso nas oficinas da Gráfica de Coimbra (Portugal)] 1943.
149 p. 23.5 cm.

NL 0414984 MH

Litwinski, Léon, 1887–
...La psychologie américaine et les problèmes de rééducation et de psychopathologie d'après-guerre. Conférence faite à la Faculté de médecine de l'Université de Lisbonne. [Coimbra] 1945. 23 p. 23cm.

1. World war, 1939–1945—Psychological aspects. 2. World war, 1939–1945—Post-war problems. 3. World war, 1939–1945—U. S.
N. Y. P. L. December 29, 1947

NL 0414985 NN

PQ145
.L7 Litwinski, Léon, 1887–
... La psychologie et la littérature. Coimbra [Oficinas da gráfica] 1944.
29 p.
"Leçon faite à l'Institut des hautes études de l'Académie des sciences de Lisbonne, le 21 avril 1944."

NL 0414986 ICU

4BF-
260 Litwinsky, Léon, 1887-
La psychologie et la littérature; lição proferida em 21 de abril de 1944. Lisboa, Academia das Ciências de Lisboa, 1944.
49 p. (Biblioteca de altos estudos)

NL 0414987 DLC-P4 MB CU NjP NcU MH

[Litwinski, Léon] 1887–
Le sens des choses: evocations [par] Noël Till [pseud.] Lisboa, A. M. Pereira, 1943.
[2] l., [7]-192, [1] p. 19ᶜᵐ.
Author's autographed presentation copy to Mr. J. L. Newcombe signed: Leon Litwinski (Noel Till).

NL 0414988 ViU

VOLUME 336

Litwinski, Léon, 1887-
Le spatial et le psychique dans la hiérarchie des états. Coimbra, 1943.
15 p. 24 cm.

1. States, Small. I. Title.
JC365.L58 50-40352

NL 0414989 DLC

Litwinski, Leon, 1887-
La timidité constitutionnelle et ses formes passive et active. De l'intimidé à l'intimidant. Lisbonne [Imp. na Sociedade industrial de tipografia, limitada] 1944.
32 p. 18 cm.

NL 0414990 MH

91.56 L73
Lityński, Adam.
Groch. Warszawa, Państwowe Wydawnictwo Rolnicze i Leśne, 1953.
40 p. (Biblioteka rolnicza gromady)

1. Peas.

NL 0414991 DNAL

QK731 .L5
Lityński, K.
Jak żyje roślina. Warszawa, Państwowe Wydawn. Rolnicze i Leśne, 1953.
34 p. illus. (Upowszechnienie wiedzy rolniczej. Agrotechnika) Biblioteczka spółdzielni produkcyjnych. (11) 1. Plant growth. I. Title.

NL 0414992 DNAL

91.58 L73
Lityński, M
Uprawa pomidorów. Warszawa, Państwowe Wydawnictwo Rolnicze i Leśne, 1952.
46 p. (Biblioteka rolnicza gromady)

1. Tomatoes. I. Skapski, T joint author.

NL 0414993 DNAL

---

91 L73
Lityński, M ed.
Warzywnictwo. Warszawa, Państwowe Wydawn. Rolnicze i Leśne, 1955.
1116 p.

1. Vegetable gardening. Poland.

NL 0414994 DNAL

Lityński, Michał.
Wiek XIX; obrazy historyczne. Lwów, Nakł. autora, 1900.
174 p. illus., ports. 28 cm.

1. Nineteenth century. I. Title.
D358.L5 50-53107

NL 0414995 DLC

Lityński, Tadeusz.
O związku pomiędzy zdolnością rośliny wydzielania fosforu a odpornością jej na zatrucie wysoką dawką tego pokarmu. The relation in a plant of its phosphorussecreting capacity to its immunity from poisoning by an excessive dose of this nutrient. Kraków, Nakł. Polskiej Akademii Umiejętności; skł. gł. w księg. Gebethnera i Wolffa, 1939.
43 p. illus. 24 cm. (Polska Akademia Umiejętności. Prace rolniczo-leśne, nr. 36)
Summary in English.
Bibliography: p. 39.
[1. Plants, Effect of phosphorus on. I. Title. (Series: Polska Akademia Umiejętności, Krakow. Prace rolniczo-leśne, nr. 36)
QK898.P6L5 67-118528

NL 0414996 DLC

Lityński, Tadeusz N
Grobowce w kościele Alexandronewskim w S. Petersburgu zebrane w roku 1804. Z dodatkiem wiersza na pamiątkę obchodu stoletniego założenia tey stolicy. W Wilnie, J. Zawadzki, 1808.
48 p. illus. 22 cm.
Bound with Malecki, Klemens. Wiersz o nieśmiertelności duszy. W Warszawie, 1818; Kalendarz polski, ruski, astronomiczny i gospodarski. W Warszawie, 1828, and Gołuchowski, Józef. Głos żałobny nad grobem ś. p. JW. z xiążąt Sanguszków ... Zielonkowej. W Warszawie. [1827]
1. Leningrad. Svíàto-Troïtskaíà Aleksandro-Nevskaíà lavra. 2. Leningrad—Sepulchral monuments. I. Title.
DK579.L5 58-51053

NL 0414997 DLC

Lityński, Zygmunt.
I was one of them, by Zygmunt Litynski; translated from the French by Anna Maclaren. London, J. Cape [1941]
272 p. 20½ cm.
"In writing this book I have had only one object: to describe what I saw in this war and to say what I thought about it."—Pref.
"First published 1941."

1. World war, 1939- —Personal narratives, Polish. I. Maclaren, Anna, tr. II. Title.
41-15684 Revised
Library of Congress D811.L52 1941
[r43d3] 940.5481438

NL 0414998 DLC OO OCl CtY

Lityński, Zygmunt.
... Warsaw, a warning, by Zygmunt Litynski. [London, MaxLove publishing company limited, 1944]
1 p.l., 23, [1] p. illus. (incl. map) 21½ cm.

1. World war, 1939- —Poland—Warsaw. I. Title.
44-47039
Library of Congress D765.L57
[4] 940.53438

NL 0414999 DLC CtY NN

Film 823 J89zLi
Litz, Arthur Walton.
The evolution of James Joyce's style and technique from 1918 to 1932.
[ll., x, 300 p.
Negative microfilm by Oxford University Press.
Thesis (Ph.D.) - Merton College [1955?]
Bibliography: p. 270-300.

1. Joyce, James, 1882-1941. I. Title.

NL 0415000 NcU

Litz, D., tr.

The little altar boy's manual. Instructions for serving at mass, vespers, benediction, etc., with the proper responses. With prayers at mass, vespers, morning and evening prayers, etc. New York, Cincinnati [etc.] Benziger brothers, 1898.

Litz, Francis Edwards Aloysius, 1892- tr.

Mencke, Johann Burkhard, 1674-1732.
The charlatanry of the learned (De charlataneria eruditorum, 1715) by Johann Burkhard Mencken (1674-1732) translated from the German by Francis E. Litz, with notes and an introduction by H. L. Mencken. New York, London, A. A. Knopf, 1937.

Litz, Francis Edwards Aloysius, 1892-

English as you like it ... by Angela M. Broening ... William J. Flagg ... Benjamin E. Fleagle ... Ethel Howard ... Francis E. Litz ... [and] Katharine E. Moog ... New York and London, Harper & brothers, 19

Litz, Francis Edwards Aloysius, 1892-
Father Tabb; a study of his life and works, with uncollected and unpublished poems, by Francis A. Litz ... Baltimore, The Johns Hopkins press, 1923.
4 p. l., 303 p. front. (2 port.) 21 cm.
Bibliography: p. 289-291.

1. Tabb, John Bannister, 1845-1909.
23-11247 Revised
Library of Congress PS2968.L5 1923

NL 0415004 OOxM OCX MH-AH ViU NcD PPFr PV PU DLC OrCS Or MtU OrP ViU MB OU OO OCl MiU

Litz, Francis Edwards Aloysius, 1892-
Father Tabb; a study of his poetry, by Francis A. Litz ... Baltimore, Litz printing company, 1924.
2 p. l., 123-193, 284-288 p., 1 l. 20 cm.
Thesis (PH. D.)—Johns Hopkins university, 1921.
Life.

1. Tabb, John Bannister, 1845-1909.
Library of Congress PS2968.L55 1923 24-18672

NL 0415005 DLC NIC PPT MB MiU

PS2968 .A4 1950
Litz, Francis Edwards Aloysius, 1892- ed.
Tabb, John Banister, 1845-1909.
Letters—grave and gay, and other prose. Edited with introd. and notes by Francis E. Litz. Washington, Catholic University of America Press, 1950.

Litz, Francis Edwards Aloysius, 1892- ed.
Tabb, John Banister, 1845-1909.
The poetry of Father Tabb, John Banister Tabb, edited by Francis A. Litz ... New York, Dodd, Mead & company, 1928.

VOLUME 336

Litz, Karl
Die selbstaendigen gutsbezirke des preussischen rechts.
Inaug. Diss. Greifswald, 1913.
Bibl.

NL 0415008 ICRL

Litz, Karl Theodor, 1921–
Die historischen Grundbegriffe bei Heinrich Friedjung. Zürich, Dissertations-Druckerei Gebr. Leemann, 1948.
95, [2] p. 23 cm.
Thesis—Zürich.
Lebenslauf.
"Quellen und Literaturverzeichnis": 2 p. at end.

1. Friedjung, Heinrich, 1851–1920. I. Title.
DD86.7.F75L5 49-27771*

NL 0415009 DLC CtY

Litz, Leo Meredith, 1897–
Report from the Pacific, by Leo M. Litz ... Illustrations by J. Hugh O'Donnell ... [Indianapolis, The Indianapolis news, 1946]
4 p. l., 427 p. illus., plates, ports. 21cm.

1. World war, 1939–1945—Personal narratives, American. 2. World war, 1939–1945—Pacific ocean. 3. World war, 1939–1945—Indiana. I. Title.
D811.5.L56 940.542 46-23167

NL 0415010 DLC GU MoU

Litz, Valentin.
...Sozialpolitische Reiseeindrücke in den Vereinigten Staaten; Vortrag gehalten vor den Mitgliedern des Verbandes Berliner Metallindustrieller, von Direktor Dr. ing. Valentin Litz... Berlin: F. Zillessen (H. Beenken) [, 1925]. 30 p. 8°. (Vereinigung der deutschen Arbeitgeberverbände. Schriften. Heft 11.)

1. Labor—U. S., 1924. 2. Ser.
N. Y. P. L. July 30, 1926

NL 0415011 NN DLC-P4

Litz, Valentin, *ed.*
... Spanlose formung; schmieden, stanzen, pressen, prägen, ziehen, bearbeitet von dipl.-ing. M. Evers, dipl.-ing. F. Grossmann, dir. M. Lebeis, dir. dr.-ing. V. Litz [und] dr.-ing. A. Peter, hrsg. von dr.-ing. V. Litz ... Mit 163 textabbildungen und 4 zahlentafeln. Berlin, J. Springer, 1926.
v, 151, [1] p. illus., diagrs. 23½cm. (Schriften der Arbeitsgemeinschaft deutscher betriebsingenieure. bd. IV)

1. Metal-work. 2. Forging. I. Title.
Library of Congress TS205.L6 27-7421

NL 0415012 DLC NN MiU

Litz, Val[entin]: Die Vorteile der Massenherstellung von Maschinenteilen gegenüber ihrer Einzelherstellung im allgemeinen Maschinenbau. [Maschinenschrift.] 27 S. m. Abb. 4°. — Auszug: (Berlin 1921: Hermann). 14 S. m. Tab. 8° ¶In: Werkstattstechnik. Berlin TeH., Diss. v. 1921 [1922] [U 22. 10000]

NL 0415013 ICRL PU DBS

---

*
PS3511
.A86Z99 Litz, Walton.
.L58W5
1952 William Faulkner's moral vision. [n. p.] 1952.
p. 200–209. 28cm. [Faulkner miscellaneous material]
Reproduced from Southwest review, vol. XXXVII, no. 3 (Summer, 1952)

1. Faulkner, William, 1897– —Philosophy.

NL 0415014 ViU

ZM
795.4
L738h Litzau, Edward A
How it's done; a complete exposé of tested formulas for card men. Colon, Mich., Abbott Magic Novelty Co. [192-?]
34p. 18cm.

NL 0415015 TxU

Litzau, Edward A.
How it's done; a complete expose for tested formulas for card men. How they are made and how they are applied, by Edward A. Litzau. Milwaukee, Midwest specialty co., 1938. 36 p. 19cm.

HOOKER COLLECTION.
280066B. 1. Cards—Tricks.
N. Y. P. L. August 28, 1944

NL 0415016 NN CU

Litzau, Johann Barend, 1822–1893.
Einleitung, Fuge und Variationen über "Christ ist erstanden von der Marter alle" aus dem 12ten Jahrhundert für die Orgel, componirt von J. B. Litzau... Op. 15... Rotterdam: G. Alsbach & Co. [ca. 1884.] Publ. pl. no. G. A. & Co. 99. 15 p. f°.
Dedication at head of title.

1. Organ.
N. Y. P. L. April 20, 1918.

NL 0415017 NN

Litzau, Johannes Barend. No. 7 in **M.414.37
Einleitung und Doppelfuge (D moll) im freien Styl zum Concertvortrag für die Orgel. Op. 14.
= Rotterdam. Alsbach. 1879. 11 pp. F°.

G531 — Fugues. — Organ. Music.

NL 0415018 MB

Litzau, Johannes Barend. No. 6 in **M.414.37
Einleitung, Variazionen und Choral mit Fuge über ein Sterbelied aus dem 16ten Jahrhundert für die Orgel. Op. 12.
= Rotterdam. Alsbach. 1877. 15 pp. F°.

G531 — Organ. Music. — Variations. Organ.

NL 0415019 MB

Litzau, Johann Barend, 1822–1893.
Sonate (A moll) für die Orgel, componirt von J. B. Litzau. Op. 19... Rotterdam: G. Alsbach & Co. 1886. Publ. pl. no. G. A. & Co. 130. 19 p. f°.
Dedication at head of title.

1. Organ.—Sonatas.
N. Y. P. L. April 20, 1918.

NL 0415020 NN

Litzel, Georg
see Lizel, Georg, 1694-1761.

Litzell, Karl Emil
Kristus se hywä paimen, jonka hywyydestä ja uskollisuudesta lyhykäisesti ja yksinkertaisesti 23 Dawidin psalmin johdosta. 2.painos. Turussa, Granlund, 1860
96 p.

NL 0415022 MH

LITZELMANN, Erwin.
Heimische Orchideen. Mit Aufnahmen von G. Eberle, H. Herschel, E. Litzelmann und H. Schurhammer Berlin, Brehm Verlag, [1931].
pp.30,(2). 21 cm. Illustr.
"Die Brehm-Bücher, 10."

NL 0415023 MH

Litzelmann, Erwin.
Heimische Orchideen; mit 24 Aufnahmen von G. Eberle [et al. Die Neuaufl. wurde von Friedrich Böhme bearb. und durch den Anhang erweitert] Leipzig, Geest & Portig, 1950.
42 p. illus. 21 cm. (Die Neue Brehm-Bücherei; das Leben der Tiere und Pflanzen in Einzeldarstellungen)

1. Orchids—Germany. I. Title.
QK495.O64L85 1950 51-41006 ‡

NL 0415024 DLC DNAL

Litzelmann, Erwin.
...Pflanzenwanderungen im klimawechsel der nacheiszeit... Oehringen, Rau, 1938.
48 p. illus.(maps)plates,table. 25 cm. ([Aus der heimat] Schriften des Deutschen naturkundevereins. Neue folge. bd.7)

1.Botany of Europe.

NL 0415025 NjP MoU

LITZELMANN, LÉON.
...'S muess andersch wäre! Schwank in am Akt, vun Léon Litzelmann. Strasbourg: F.-X. Le Roux & Cie. s.a., 1932. 30 p. 20½cm. (Le Roux, elsässisches Vereinstheater. No. 92.)
On cover: Schwank in eim Akt.

1. Drama, Alsatian. 2. German language—Dialects—Alsace. I. Title. II. Ser.

NL 0415026 NN

Litzelmann, J., joint comp.

N5068
.D8 Dupont, Jacques, *comp.*
Peintures méconnues des églises de Paris; retour d'évacuation. Préf. de Y. Bizardel, introd. de Jean Verrier. [Paris] Musée Galliera, 1946.

VOLUME 336

Litzenberg, Jennings Crawford, 1870–
... Contributions to the pathology of pregnancy, by Jennings C. Litzenberg ... Lawrence, University extension division, University of Kansas, 1937.
5 p. l., [3]–72 p. illus. 22½cm. (Porter lectures series. VI)
Delivered at the University of Kansas school of medicine, Lawrence, Kansas City, March, 1936.
"References" at end of first two lectures.
CONTENTS.—The pathology of ectopic pregnancy.—Missed abortion.—A physician who became a god.

1. Pregnancy, Complications of. 2. Imhotep. I. Title.
38-28045
Library of Congress RG571.L55
——— Copy 2.
Copyright A 114913 [3] 618.3

NL 0415028 DLC OCIW-H OrU-M KU-M KMK PPT DNLM NcD PPJ ViU OU

Litzenberg, Jennings Crawford, 1870–
Synopsis of obstetrics, by Jennings C. Litzenberg ... with 157 illustrations including 5 in color. St. Louis, The C. V. Mosby company, 1940.
394 p. illus. (part col.) 20cm.

1. Obstetrics. I. Title.
40-11896
Library of Congress RG531.L57
——— Copy 2.
Copyright 618.2

NL 0415029 DLC OrU-M DNLM OU PPC PPJ

Litzenberg, Jennings Crawford, 1870–
Synopsis of obstetrics, by Jennings C. Litzenberg ... with 157 illustrations including 5 in color. 2d ed. St. Louis, The C. V. Mosby company, 1943.
405 p. illus. (part col.) 20 cm.

1. Obstetrics. I. Title.
RG531.L57 1943 618.2 SG 44—3
U. S. Armed Forces for Library of Congress Medical Libr. [a54d½]†

NL 0415030 DNLM NcD OU DLC ICRL OrU-M

Litzenberg, Jennings Crawford, 1870–
Synopsis of obstetrics ... 3d ed. St. Louis, Mosby, 1947.
416 p. illus. 20 cm.

1. Obstetrics. I. Title.
RG531.L57 1944 618.2 Med 47—2440
U. S. Armed Forces for Library of Congress Medical Library [WP1200L782s 1947] [a53c½]†

NL 0415031 DNLM DLC CU Wa OrU-M PPHa ICU OCIW CtY-M

Litzenberg, Jennings Crawford, 1870–
Synopsis of obstetrics. 4th ed., revised by Chas. E. McLennan. St. Louis, Mosby, 1952.
378 p. illus. 20 cm.

1. Obstetrics. I. Title.
RG531.L57 1952 618.2 52-4235 ‡

NL 0415032 DLC NcU-H DNLM PPT CaBVaU ViU OCIW-H OrU-M

Litzenberg, John Elmer, 1865–
The Litzenbergs in America; a biographical record of George Litzenberg and his wife, Grace Coates, with a preview of their ancestors and a genealogical and biographical record of their descendants. Centerberg, Ohio, 1948.
xvii, 629 p. port., map. 23 cm.

1. Litzenburg, George, 1758-1841. 2. Litzenburg family (Simon Litzenberger, 1718-1798) 3. Pennington family. 4. Bottenfield family. 5. Mahannah family. 6. Denny family (John Denny, 1762-1847) I. Title.
CS71.L782 1948 49-377*

NL 0415033 DLC N PHi KyHi

FILM 5069 Litzenberg,Karl,1905-
Contributions of the Old Norse language and literature to the style and substance of the writings of William Morris,1858-1876. [Ann Arbor? Mich.] 1933.
400 l.
Thesis--University of Michigan.
Includes bibliography.
Microfilm (negative) of typescript. Ann Arbor, University of Michigan Library Photoduplication Service, 1963. 1 reel. 35 mm.
1.Morris,William,1834-1896. 2.Literature, Comparative--English and Icelandic and Old Norse. 3.Literature,Comparative--Icelandic and Old Norse and English.

NL 0415034 MiU

Litzenberg, Karl, 1905- *2255.40.10
The social philosophy of William Morris and the Doom of the Gods. (*In* University of Michigan. Publications. Language and literature. Vol. 10. Essays and studies in English and comparative literature. Pp. 183-203. Ann Arbor. 1933.)

D1460 — Morris, William, 1834-1896. — Sociology.

NL 0415035 MB NIC

Litzenberg, Karl, 1905–
The Victorians and the Vikings: a bibliographical essay on Anglo-Norse literary relations. [Ann Arbor] Univ. of Michigan Press, 1947.
27 p. 23 cm. (The University of Michigan contributions in modern philology, no. 3)
Cover title.
Bibliographical footnotes.

1. Literature, Comparative—English and Icelandic and Old Norse. 2. Literature, Comparative — Icelandic and Old Norse and English. I. Title. (Series: Michigan. University. The University of Michigan contributions in modern philology, no. 3)
PB13.M5 no. 3 820.9 A 48-189*
Michigan. Univ. Libr. for Library of Congress [3]†

NL 0415036 MiU CaBVaU TxU PHC ViU OCIJC PBm PU MoU DLC

Litzenberg, Karl, 1905–
William Morris and Scandinavian literature; a bibliographical essay.
(*In* Scandinavian studies and notes. Menasha, Wis. 1935 24 cm. v. 13, no. 7, p. 93-105)
Thesis—Univ. of Michigan.
Without thesis statement.
Bibliographical footnotes.
——— Detached copy.
Thesis statement on label mounted on p. [2] of cover.
PR5086.L5
1. Morris, William, 1834-1896. 2. Literature, Comparative—English and Icelandic and Old Norse. 3. Literature, Comparative—Icelandic and Old Norse and English. 4. Morris, William, 1834-1896—Bibl.
PD1505.S6 vol. 13, no. 7 A 49-1565*
Michigan. Univ. Libr. for Library of Congress [2]†

NL 0415037 MiU DLC

Litzenberg, Rudolf, 1909-
Der grundsatz "ne bis idem" und seine anwendung auf dem gebiete des fortgesetzten und kollektivdelikts. Hamburg [Paul Evert druck und verlag] 1936.
69,[1] p. 24cm.

Dissertation: Hamburg, 1936.
Bibliography: p.7-8.

NL 0415038 OrU

Litzenberger,Erich,1904-
Ueber die strahlung der kohlenstaubflamme und die punktweise bestimmung der belastung der strahlungsheizflaeche.
Inaug. diss. Tech.hochs.,Darmstadt,1928. (Braunschweig,1930.)
Bibl.

NL 0415039 ICRL

Litzenberger, Erich, 1904-
Unfreiwilliges und freiwilliges Ausscheiden von Aktionären. Ein Beitrag zur Lehre der Aktiengesellschaft, Nebenleistungsaktiengesellschaft und individualistischen Aktiengesellschaft ... Gelnhausen, 1932.
Inaug.-Diss. - Frankfurt am Main.

NL 0415040 CtY

Litzenberger, Rudi, 1905-
Die volkswirtschaftlichen Auswirkungen der deutschen technischen Rationalisierung auf die Produktionsfaktoren Arbeit und Kapital in der Nachkriegszeit ... Siegen, 1933.
Inaug.-Diss. - Köln.

NL 0415041 CtY

S33 E22 no.16 **Litzenberger, Samuel Cameron, 1914-**
Edda barley for Alaska. [By S.C. Litzenberger and B.M. Bensin]. Palmer, Alaska, 1951.
10 p. illus., tables. 24 cm. (Alaska. Agricultural Experiment Stations. Circular 16)
Alaska Agricultural Experiment Station, Palmer, Alaska, in cooperation with the United States Agricultural Research Administration.

1. Barley. I. Bensin, B.M., jt. auth. II. U.S. Agricultural Research Administration. III. Title. (Series)

NL 0415042 DI

S33 E22 no.15 **Litzenberger, Samuel Cameron, 1914-**
Golden rain oats for Alaska. [By S.C. Litzenberger and B.M. Bensin]. Palmer, Alaska, 1951.
9 p. illus., tables. 24 cm. (Alaska. Agricultural Experiment Stations. Circular 15)
Agricultural Experiment Station, Palmer, Alaska, in cooperation with the U.S. Agricultural Research Administration.

1. Oats. I. Bensin, B. M., jt. auth. II. U.S. Agricultural Research Administration. III. Title. (Series)

NL 0415043 DI

VOLUME 336

Litzenberger, Samuel Cameron, 1914–
Inheritance of resistance to specific races of crown and stem rust, to *Helminthosporium* blight, and of certain agronomic characters of oats. [n. p., 1949]
[453]–496 p. illus. 23 cm.
Cover title.
From thesis—Iowa State College of Agriculture and Mechanic Arts. Doctoral thesis no. 895.
"Contribution from the Botany and Plant Pathology Section and Farm Crops Subsection, Agronomy Section, of the Iowa Agricultural Experiment Station in cooperation with the Bureau of Plant Industry, Soils and Agricultural Engineering, United States Department of Agriculture, Projects 72 and 654."

"Reprinted from Iowa Agricultural Experiment Station Research bulletin 370, December, 1949."
Bibliography: p. 494–496.

1. Oats—Disease and pest resistance. 2. Puccinia coronata. 3. Helminthosporium victoriae.
SB608.O2L55 633.13 A 51-6933
Iowa. State Coll. Libr. for Library of Congress [1]†

NL 0415045 IaAS DLC

Litzenberger, *Samuel Cameron, 1914-*
Selective sprays for the control of lawn weeds. Bozeman, Mont. 1943.
23 p.
(Montana. Agricultural experiment station (Bozeman) Bulletin 411)
cover-title.
By S.C. Litzenberger and A. H. Post.

NL 0415046 PP

Litzenburger, Ludwig, 1907–
Die Wirtschaftsgeschichte des Klosters Werschweiler. [Heidelberg, 1945]
79, 27, v l. 30 cm.
Typewritten (carbon copy)
Inaug.-Diss.—Heidelberg.
Vita.
Bibliography: leaves [i]–v.

1. Werschweiler (Cistercian abbey) I. Title.
BX2618.W4L5 50-30645

NL 0415047 DLC

QD319 .L78 Litzendorff, Jakob, 1881-
Ueber die spaltung des dijodkohlenstoff's (dijodacetylen) in kohlenstoff und tetrajodaethylen Marburg, 1904
Dissert.

NL 0415048 DLC MH PU CtY

---

4 K Greece 424 Litzeropoulos, Alexandros.
'Υποθήκη καί έπιφύλαξις κυριότητος έπί κινητῶν ὡς συμβαδίζοντες νομικοί τρόποι άναπτύξεως τῆς έμποροβιομηχανικῆς πίστεως. 'Αθῆναι, I. N. Ζαχαρόπουλος, 1930.
38 p.
Title transliterated; Hypothēkē kai epiphylaxis kyriotētos epi kinētōn.

NL 0415049 DLC-P4

4K 1322 Litzeropoulos, Alexandros G
Hē idiaitera physis tou nomologikou dikaiou. Ischyousa nomothesia kai nomothetikē politikē. Thessalonikē, 1935.
41 p.
In Greek letters.

NL 0415050 DLC-P4

---

4 K Greece 324 Litzeropoulos, Alexandros G
'Η καταγγελία τῆς συμβάσεως έργασίας μετά τό νομοθετικόν διάταγμα 424/1951. 'Ερμηνεία τῶν νέων περιοριζουσῶν τήν άπόλυσιν έργατοϋπαλληλικοῦ προσωπικοῦ διατάξεων. 'Αθῆναι, Ν. Α. Σάκκουλας, 1942.
180 p.
Title transliterated: Hē katangelia tēs symbaseos ergasias.

NL 0415051 DLC-P4

---

4 K Gr. 57 Litzeropoulos, Alexandros G
Κληρονομικὸν δίκαιον τοῦ 'Αστικοῦ κώδικος. [Αθῆναι] 'Εκδοτικὸν Βιβλιοπωλεῖον "Τὸ Νομικὸν" Ν.Α.Σάκκουλα, 1947-
pt. (1)
Issued in parts.
Cover title.
Title transliterated: Klēronomikon dikaion tou Astikou kōdikos.

NL 0415052 DLC-P4

GRE 906 LIT Litzeropoulos, Alexandros G
'Η Νομολογία ὡς παράγων διαπλάσεως τοῦ ἰδιωτικοῦ δικαίου, σύγχρονος έπιστήμη καί 'Ελληνική δικαστηριακή πρακτική. Θεσσαλονίκη, 1932.
295 p. 24cm.
Title transliterated: Nomologia hos paragōn..

NL 0415053 MH-L

4K Greece 225 Litzeropoulos, Alexandros G
Zētēmata ek tou arthrou 670 tou Emporikounomou. Athēnai, 1934.
54 p.
In Greek letters.

NL 0415054 DLC-P4

4HD 1042 Litzeropoulos, Alexandros L
Hē ex ergatikōn atychēmatōn euthynē Epi ergasiōn kai epicheirēseōn kath' as mesolaboun hypergodotai e hypergolaboi (arthron 8, n. 551) Athēnai, I.N. Zacharopoulos, 1937.
66 p.
In Greek letters.

NL 0415055 DLC-P4

Litzica, Constantin.

Academia română, *Bukharest. Biblioteca.*
... Catalogul manuscriptelor grecești intocmit de Constantin Litzica ... Ediţiunea Academiei române. Cu 15 stampe facsimile. București, C. Göbl, s-r I. St. Rasidescu, 1909.

LITZICA, CONSTANTIN.
Das Meyersche satzschlussgesetz in der byzantinischen prosa, mit einem anhang über Prokop von Käsarea... München, A. Buchholz, 1898.
52 p.
"Inaugural-Dissertation..."

NL 0415057 DDO CtY NjP CU

Litzica (Jean). *Du varicocèle et de son diagnostic différentiel. 50 pp. 4°. *Paris*, 1850, No. 47. [P., v. 498.]

NL 0415058 DNLM

Litzinger, Anne Elizabeth.
... Researches on pyrimidines. CLIV[–CLV] ... By Anne Litzinger and Treat B. Johnson. [Easton, Pa., 1936]
2 pt. 26½ x 20cm.
Cover-title.
Thesis (PH. D.)—Yale university, 1936.
Part 2: By Treat B. Johnson and Anne Litzinger.
"Reprint from the Journal of the American chemical society, 58 ... (1936)."
Bibliographical foot-notes.
CONTENTS.—Pyrimidine side chain reactions useful for the synthesis of 1, 3-diazines related structurally to vitamin B_1.—The synthesis of thyminylamine and its conversion into uracil.
1. Pyrimidines. I. Johnson, Treat Baldwin, 1875– joint author. II. Title.
42-31231
Library of Congress QD401.L792

NL 0415059 DLC

Litzinger, H.J.
... De antiquorum populorum mercatura, quatenus ex Homeri carminibus cognoscitur. Partic. I. Essen, 1866.
1 p. l., 20 p. 26 cm. [Homerica. v. 1]
Programm - K. Gymnasium zu Essen (with Schulnachrichten)

NL 0415060 CtY PU NjP

Litzinger, H.J.
De Thaleta poeta. n.p. 1851.

NL 0415061 NjP

Litzinger, H J
Entstehung und Zweckbeziehung des Lucasevangeliums und der Apostelgeschichte. Essen, F.J. Halbeisen, 1883.
128 p. 24cm.

NL 0415062 NjPT MH

Litzinger, Heinrich, 1890–
Achtung!-Fallstricke! Die unterschiedliche Schreibweise gleichklingender Wörter Zahlreiche Beispiele in Abc-Form. Hildesheim, F. M. Hörhold [1953]
75 p. 12 cm. (Miniatur-Bibliothek, Nr. 1656 a–e)

1. German language—Orthography and spelling. I. Title.
Full name: Karl Heinrich Litzinger.
PF3145.L55 54-22189 ‡

NL 0415063 DLC

Litzinger, Karl Heinrich
see
Litzinger, Heinrich, 1890–

Litzinger, Marie, 1899–
... A basis for residual polynomials in *n* variables ... by Marie Litzinger ... [New York, 1935]
1 p. l., [1], 216–225 p., 1 l. 27½cm.
Thesis (PH. D.)—University of Chicago, 1934.
Vita.
"Private edition, distributed by the University of Chicago libraries, Chicago, Illinois."
"Reprinted from Transactions of the American mathematical society, vol. XXXVII, no. 2, March, 1935."
1. Polynomials. 2. Congruences and residues. I. Title: Residual polynomials in *n* variables.
35-19081
Library of Congress QA244.L5 1934
Univ. of Chicago Libr.
——— Copy 2. [2] 512.81

NL 0415065 ICU DLC NcD OCU OU

VOLUME 336

AC 831 Litzka, Erich, 1906-
Ist eintritt in den streik ein grund zur fristlosen entlassung? ... 1933. 54 p.
Inaug. Diss. -Halle-Wittenberg, 1933.
Lebenslauf.
Bibliography.

NL 0415066 ICRL MiU

T113 L5 1933 Litzka, Georg, 1905-
... Experimentelle Untersuchungen über den Einfluss der Schwangerschaftshormone auf den Organismus des Foetus und Neugeborenen ... [n.p.,1933].
Inaug.- Diss. - Leipzig.
Lebenslauf.
"Literaturverzeichnis": p.756-757.

NL 0415067 CtY

Litzkau, Heinrich, fl. 17th cent.
[Sonatas. 2 violins & bass. B♭ maj.]
...Sonate für zwei Violinen und Generalbass (Violoncello ad libitum); herausgegeben von Peter Epstein. Münster in Westfalen: E. Bisping[, 1930]. Publ. pl. no. E. B. 3037. 4 parts in 1 v. 30½cm. (Haus- und Kammermusik aus dem XVI.–XVIII. Jahrhundert.)

Violin I and II with harpsichord or piano (realized from basso continuo), in score. The violoncello, used to double the harpsichord bass, is optional with piano. Three string parts.

His: Sonata a 2 violinin [sic] cum basso generali. Breslauer Stadtbibliothek ms. At head of title: Nr. 59. Edition Bisping...

JUILLIARD FOUNDATION FUND.
1. Chamber music, 17th cent.—Trios. 2. Violin—Trios—Two violins and basso continuo (harpsichord or piano). I. Epstein, Peter, 1901-1932, editor. II. Ser.
N. Y. P. L. September 29, 1933

NL 0415068 NN

LD3907 .E3 1947 .L5 Litzky, Leo, 1912-
Censorship of motion pictures in the United States; a history of motion picture censorship and an analysis of its most important aspects... New York, 1947.
vi,380 typewritten leaves. tables (1 fold.) 29cm.
Thesis (Ph.D.) - New York university, School of education, 1947.
"Selected bibliography": p.[347]-352.

NL 0415069 NNU-W

FILM 792.5 L78c Litzky, Leo, 1912-
Censorship of motion pictures in the United States. A history of motion picture censorship and an analysis of its most important aspects. [New York] New York University, 1947.

Microfilm copy of typescript. Negative.
Collation of the original, as determined from the film: vi, 380 l. tables.
Thesis—New York University.

Leaves 138 and 139 transposed.
Bibliography: leaves [347]-352.

1. Moving-pictures—Censorship. I. Title.

NL 0415071 IU

Litzman, C., respondent.
... De amore
see under Bechmann, Johann Volkmar, 1624-1689, praeses.

Litzmann, Anna Behrens
see Behrens-Litzmann, Anna.

792.0943 L782a Litzmann, Berthold, 1857-1926.
Aus den Lehr- und Wanderjahren des deutschen Theaters. Berlin, Paetel, 1912.
[116]-130p. 25cm.
"Sonderabdruck. Deutsche Rundschau, herausgegeben von Julius Rodenberg, 38. Jahrgang, Heft 7, April 1912."
Author's autograph presentation copy to Max Reinhardt.

1.Theater - Germany. I.Title.

NL 0415074 CLSU

PT 2482 L73a Litzmann, Berthold, 1857-1926.
... Aus Schillers dramatischen lehrjahren. Vortrag, gehalten am 8. november 1891 im "Freien deutschen hochstift zu Frankfurt am Main" zur feier von Schillers geburtstag, von prof. dr. B. Litzmann ... [Frankfurt a.M., Druck von gebrüder Knauer, 1892]
p. [25*]-41*.

"Sonderabdruck aus 'Berichte des Freien deutschen hochstiftes'. Jahrg. 1892, heft 2."

Caption title.

1. Schiller, Johann Christoph Friedrich von, 1759-1805.

NL 0415076 CLSU

Litzmann, Berthold, 1857-1926.
Bismarck und wir. Rede bei der Bismarckfeier des liberalen Bürgervereins in Bonn am 31. März 1915. Bonn, 1915.
16 p. 23.5 cm. [Bismarck pamphlets]

NL 0415077 CtY

Litzmann, Berthold, 1857-1926, ed.
Bonner forschungen, hrsg. von Berthold Litzmann..
see under title

PT2424 L55L5 Litzmann, Berthold, 1857-1926.
Christian Ludwig Liscow in seiner litterarischen Laufbahn. Hamburg und Leipzig, L. Voss, 1883.
xii, 155 p. 22cm.

Reproduced by Duopage process by Micro Photo Division, Bell & Howell.

1. Liscow, Christian Ludwig, 1701-1760.

NL 0415079 GU CU OO WaU OClW NjP PBm MWelC

Litzmann, Berthold, 1857-1926.
Clara Schumann; an artist's life based on material found in diaries and letters, by Berthold Litzmann. Tr. and abridged from the 4th ed. by Grace E. Hadow, with a preface by W. H. Hadow ... London, Macmillan & co., ltd.; [etc., etc.] 1913.
2 v. 7 port. (incl. fronts.) 24cm.
"List of compositions by (a) Clara Wieck: (b) Clara Schumann": v. 2, p. [440]-441.
"Works studies, and repertoire, 1824-1891": v. 2, p. [442]-452.
1. Schumann, Clara Josephine (Wieck) 1819-1896. I. Hadow, Grace Eleanor, 1875- tr.
A 13—1756
Springfield, Mass. City Library for Library of Congress ML417.S4L72 [a40d1]

OCl OO CtY

NL 0415080 MS NIC OU OrP PPL NN CU MB DLC OOxM

Litzmann, Berthold, 1857-1926.
Clara Schumann, ein künstlerleben, nach tagebüchern und briefen, von Berthold Litzmann ... Leipzig, Breitkopf und Härtel, 1902-10.
3 v. 7 port. (incl. front.) 22½cm.
"Verzeichnis der kompositionen von Clara Wieck": v. 3, p. [613]-614.
CONTENTS.—1. bd. Mädchenjahre, 1819-1840. 1902.—2. bd. Ehejahre, 1840-1856. 3. durchgesehene aufl. 1907.—3. bd. Clara Schumann und ihre freunde, 1856-1896. 3. durchgesehene aufl. 1910.
1. Schumann, Clara Josephine (Wieck) 1819-1896. I. Schumann, Clara Josephine (Wieck) 1819-1896.
13—7486
Library of Congress ML417.S4L7

PU-FA ViU

NL 0415081 DLC NSyU OKentU NN CU IU ICN MH MB PBL

780.92 Sch81l 1910 Litzmann, Berthold, 1857-1926.
Clara Schumann, ein Künstlerleben nach Tagebüchern und Briefen. Leipzig, Breitkopf & Härtel, 1910-12 (v.1, 1912)
3v. 7 port. (incl. fronts.) 23cm.

"Verzeichnis der Kompositionen von Clara Wieck": v.3, p.[613]-614.

1. Schumann, Clara Josephine (Wieck) 1819-1896. I. Schumann, Clara Josephine (Wieck) 1819-1896.

L 0415082 KU MH PP IEN

Litzmann, Berthold, 1857-
Clara Schumann, ein künstlerleben nach tagebüchern und briefen, von Berthold Litzmann ... Leipzig, Breitkopf & Härtel, 1920.
3 v. 7 port. (incl. fronts.) 22½cm.
"Verzeichnis der kompositionen von Clara Wieck": v. 3, p. [613]-614.
CONTENTS.—1. bd. Mädchenjahre, 1819-1840. 7. aufl.—2. bd. Ehejahre, 1840-1856. 6. aufl.—3. bd. Clara Schumann und ihre freunde, 1856-1896. 4. unveränderte aufl.
1. Schumann, Clara Josephine (Wieck) 1819-1896. I. Schumann, Clara Josephine (Wieck) 1819-1896.
Library of Congress ML417.S4L7 1920 23-8686

NL 0415083 DLC CU OCU TU MiU OrP

ML 417 S388 L78 1920 Litzmann, Berthold, 1857-1926.
Clara Schumann, ein künstlerleben nach tagebüchern und briefen, von Berthold Litzmann ... Leipzig, Breitkopf & Härtel, 1920-23.
3 v. 7 port. (incl. fronts.) 22½cm.
"Verzeichnis der kompositionen von Clara Wieck": v. 3, p. [613]-614.
CONTENTS.—1. bd. Mädchenjahre, 1819-1840. 7. aufl.—2. bd. Ehejahre, 1840-1856. 6. aufl.—3. bd. Clara Schumann und ihre freunde, 1856-1896.
5. und 6. Aufl. 1923.

NL 0415084 NIC

Litzmann, Berthold, 1857-1926.
Clara Schumann, ein künstlerleben, nach tagebüchern und briefen, von Berthold Litzmann ... Leipzig, Breitkopf & Härtel, 1923-25.
3v. fronts., ports. 22½cm.

"Verzeichnis der kompositionen von Clara Wieck": v.3, p.[613]-614.
Contents.- 1.bd. Mädchenjahre, 1819-1840. 8.aufl. 1925.- 2.bd. Ehejahre, 1840-1856. 7.aufl. 1925.- 3.bd. Clara Schumann und ihre freunde, 1856-1896. 5.und 6.aufl. 1923.

NL 0415085 PSt CaBVaU

VOLUME 336

Litzmann, Berthold, 1857-1926, ed.

Schumann, Clara Josephine (Wieck) 1819-1896.
Clara Schumann, Johannes Brahms: briefe aus den jahren 1853-1896, im auftrage von Marie Schumann hrsg. von Berthold Litzmann ... Leipzig, Breitkopf & Härtel, 1927.

NL 0415086

Litzmann, Berthold, 1857-1926.
Das deutsche drama in den litterarischen bewegungen der gegenwart. Vorlesungen, gehalten an der Universität Bonn, von Berthold Litzmann ... Hamburg und Leipzig, L. Voss, 1894.
vi p., 1 l., 216 p. 24½cm.
CONTENTS.—Überblick über die deutsche litteratur im ersten jahrzehnt nach dem grossen kriege.—Das drama der gegenwart: Ernst von Wildenbruch. Die litterarische revolution. Ibsen. Gerhart Hauptmann. Hermann Sudermann.—Schluss. Die zukunft der deutschen litteratur.—

NL 0415087 ViU CU OrU CaBVaU CtY PU MB NjP

Litzmann, Berthold.
Das deutsche drama in den litterarischen bewegungen der gegenwart; vorlesungen gehalten an der Universitat Bonn. Ed.3. enl., Hamburg. 1896.
240 p.

NL 0415088 PBm

Litzmann, Berthold, 1857-
Das deutsche drama in den litterarischen bewegungen der gegenwart. Vorlesungen, gehalten an der Universität Bonn, von Berthold Litzmann ... 4. aufl. Hamburg und Leipzig, L. Voss, 1897.
xii, 240 p. 23½cm.
CONTENTS.—Überblick über die deutsche litteratur im ersten jahrzehnt nach grossen kriege.—Das drama der gegenwart: Ernst von Wildenbruch. Die litterarische revolution. Ibsen. Gerhart Hauptmann. Hermann Sudermann. — Schluss. Die zukunft der deutschen litteratur.—Rückblick und ausblick, 1896.
1. German drama—19th cent.—Hist. & crit. I. Title.
1-22243
Library of Congress PT661.L5

MB NjP OC1W
NL 0415089 DLC OU TU GU MU MiU OCU OC1 OO OU PSC

PT661
.L5
1912
Litzmann, Berthold, 1857-1926.
Das deutsche Drama in den litterarischen Bewegungen der Gegenwart. Vorlesungen, gehalten an der Universität Bonn ... 5. Aufl. Leipzig, L. Voss, 1912.
viii, 240 p.

1. German drama - 19th cent. - Hist. & crit.

NL 0415090 CU ODW OC1W CU-S IEN

Litzmann, Berthold, 1857-1926.
Die entstehungszeit des ersten deutschen Hamlet... Berlin, A. Haack, 1887.
13 p.

NL 0415091 PU

Litzmann, Berthold, 1857-
Ernst von Wildenbruch, von Berthold Litzmann ... Berlin, G. Grote, 1913.
v. front., ports., facsim. 24½cm.

1. Wildenbruch, Ernst i. e. Adam Ernst von, 1845-1909.
14-5468
Library of Congress PT2647.I 43Z95

NL 0415092 DLC NcD PPT NN

PT 2580 LITZMANN,BERTHOLD,1857-1926
.W15 Z68
Ernst von Wildenbruch. Berlin, G. Grote, 1913-16.
2 v. illus., ports.

Contents: v. 1. 1845-1885. v. 2. 1885-1909.

1. Wildenbruch, Ernst von, 1845-1909.

ViU TNJ GU CaBVaU
NL 0415093 InU WaU NIC CU OCU MiU OC1W PU CtY NcU

Litzmann, Berthold, 1857-
... Ernst von Wildenbruch und der nationale gedanke; rede am 26. november 1914 gehalten von dr. Berthold Litzmann ... Hrsg. von der Zentralstelle für volkswohlfahrt und dem Verein für volkstümliche kurse von Berliner hochschullehrern. Berlin, C. Heymann, 1914.
30 p. 20cm. (Deutsche reden in schwerer zeit. [12])
1. Wildenbruch, Ernst von, 1845-1909. I. Zentralstelle für volkswohlfahrt. II. Verein für volkstümliche kurse von Berliner hochschullehrern. III. Ser.

NL 0415094 ViU NjP

Litzmann, Berthold, 1857-1926.
Festschrift für Berthold Litzmann zum 60. Geburtstag
see under title

Litzmann, Berthold, 1857-1926.
Friedrich Ludwig Schröder. Ein beitrag zur deutschen litteratur- und theater geschichte von Berthold Litzmann ... Hamburg und Leipzig, L. Voss, 1890-94.
2 v. front. (v. 2) ports. 22cm.

1. Schröder, Friedrich Ludwig, 1744-1816.
4-11020
Library of Congress PN2658.S5L4

MiU OC1W MB
NL 0415096 DLC CU MH CLSU CU NIC CtY MB PBm PU

Litzmann, Berthold, 1857-1926, ed.

Günther, Johann Christian, 1695-1723.
Gedichte von Johann Christian Günther. Herausgegeben von Berthold Litzmann. Mit Günthers bildniss. Leipzig, P. Reclam jun. [1880]

NL 0415097

Litzmann,Berthold,1857-1926.
Goethes Faust,eine einführung von Berthold Litzmann. Berlin, E.Fleischel & co., 1904.
4 p.l.,399,[1] p. 21½cm.
CONTENTS.—Einleitung.—I.Faust vor Goethe.—II.Der tragödie erster teil.—III.Der tragödie zweiter teil.

1.Goethe,Johann Wolfgang von. Faust. 2.Faust.

PSC MA CtY MWelC MB IU
NL 0415098 MiU NIC PU TNJ TxU OrU PSt PBm MH NcD

Litzmann, Berthold, 1857-
Goethes Faust; eine einführung. 2.aufl.
Ber.1904. 399p. 22cm.

NL 0415099 CU

Litzmann, Berthold, 1857-
Goethes lyrik; erläuterungen nach künstlerischen gesichtspunkten ... Berlin, 1903.
21 cm.

NL 0415100 CU

PT1904 Litzmann,Berthold,1857-
.L78
Goethes lyrik;erläuterungen nach künstlerischen gesichtspunkten. Ein versuch von Berthold Litzmann. 2.aufl. Berlin,E.Fleischel & co.,1903.
[7],257,[1] p. 22½cm.

1.Goethe,Johann Wolfgang von-Criticism and interpretation.

PU MH NcU NIC TU
NL 0415101 IU MWelC MiU OO OCU OU MB MH IaU PBm

832.622
L738g
1912
Litzmann, Berthold, 1857-1926.
Goethes Lyrik; Erläuterungen nach künstlerischen Gesichtspunkten; ein Versuch. 3. Aufl. Berlin, Egon Fleischel, 1912.
257p. 22cm.

1. Goethe, Johann Wolfgang von, 1749-1832. I. Title.

NL 0415102 TxU OCU NcD

Litzmann, Berthold, 1857-1926
Goethes lyrik; erlauterungen nach kunstlerischen gesichtspunkten; ein versuch; 4. verm. aufl. Berlin, 1921.

NL 0415103 ODW MA

LITZMANN, BERTHOLD, 1857-
Das grosse Schröder. Berlin,Schuster & Loeffler,[1904]
75p. ports.,2 fold.facsims. 17cm. (Das theater, bd.1)

NL 0415104 PU

Litzmann, Berthold, 1857-
Der grosse Schröder, von Berthold Litzmann. 2. tausend. Berlin und Leipzig, Schuster & Loeffler [1904]
75, [1] p. pl., 5 port. on 4 l. (incl. front.) 2 fold. facsim. 16½cm. (Half-title: Das theater, bd. I)

8-17224
Library of Congress

NL 0415105 DLC OCU CLSU ViU NN

PT 2510 LITZMANN,BERTHOLD,1857-1926
.S2 Z73
Der grosse Schröder. Berlin, Schuster & Loeffler [1905]
75 p. illus., ports. (Das Theater, v.1)

1. Schröder, Friedrich Ludwig, 1744-1816.

NL 0415106 InU

VOLUME 336

PR 2807 .L78 Litzmann,Berthold,1857-1926.
... Hamlet in Hamburg,1625. Von Berthold Litzmann. Berlin, Gebrüder Paetel [1892]
cover-title,[427]-434 p. 23½cm.
"Separatabdruck. Deutsche rundschau ... Heft 6. märz 1892."
A discussion of Johannes Rist's report of the performance of "Der bestrafte brudermord".
Author's inscribed presentation copy to Julius Zupitza.

1.Shakespeare,William. Hamlet—Sources. 2.Rist, Johannes,1607-1667. 3.Der bestrafte brudermord.

NL 0415107 MiU

Litzmann, Berthold, 1857-1926.
Ibsens dramen, 1877-1900. Ein beitrag zur geschichte des deutschen dramas im 19. jahrhundert; von Berthold Litzmann ... Hamburg und Leipzig, L. Voss, 1901.
4 p. l., 176 p. 20½cm.

1. Ibsen, Henrik, 1828-1906.

Library of Congress PT8895.L5 2—26970

NL 0415108 OO DLC CU OOxM PU PGP CU MH NN ViU OU MiU

4CT 338 Litzmann, Berthold, 1857-1926.
Im alten Deutschland; Erinnerungen eines Sechzigjährigen. Berlin, G. Grote, 1923.
400 p.

NL 0415109 OU MdBJ NcU CU ScU NjP TU MiU DLC-P4 CSt MH NN PPG CtY IU NRU RPB MA

---

92 V445L Litzmann, Berthold, 1857-1926.
Johannes Velten; Legende und Geschichte. Berlin, E.Fleischel [n.d.]
[56]-71p. plate. 21cm.

"Separatabdruck aus dem Archiv für Theatergeschichte im Auftrag der Gesellschaft für Theatergeschichte herausgegeben von Hans Devrient."

1.Velten, Johannes, 1640-1692.

NL 0415110 CLSU

Litzmann, Berthold. 1857- *6907.12.2
Johannes Velten. Legende und Geschichte.
(In Archiv für Theatergeschichte. Vol. 2, pp. 56-71. Berlin. 1905.)

G17c2 — Velten. Johannes. 1640-169-?

NL 0415111 MB

Litzmann, Berthold, 1857-1926, ed.
Letters of Clara Schumann and Johannes Brahms
see under Schumann, Clara Josephine (Wieck) 1819-1896.

Litzmann, Berthold, 1857-1926.
Meine Ziele im akademischen Lehramt; eine Antwort an Herrn Professor Erich Schmidt, von Berthold Litzmann ... Dortmund, F. W. Ruhfus, 1905. 15 p. 23cm.

1. Schmidt, Erich, 1853-1913. 2. German literature—Study and teaching—Germany.
N. Y. P. L. March 4, 1949

NL 0415113 NN CU MH IU

Litzmann, Berthold, 1857-1926.
Mittelungen der Literarhistorischen Gesellschaft Bonn ...
see under Literarhistorische Gesellschaft, Bonn.

Litzmann, Berthold, 1857-1926.
Rede, gehalten bei der Schillerfeier der Rheinischen Friedrich-Wilhelms-Universität am 9. Mai 1905
see his Schiller und das deutsche drama der vergangenheit und zukunft.

Litzmann, Berthold, 1857-1926, ed.

Jena. Universität. *Deutsches seminar.*
Schiller in Jena. Eine festgabe zum 26. mai 1889 aus dem Deutschen seminar. Herausgegeben von Berthold Litzmann ... Mit vier abbildungen und einem grundriss. Jena, F. Mauke (A. Schenk) 1889.

PT2492 .L78 Litzmann,Berthold,1857-1926.
Schiller und das deutsche drama der vergangenheit und zukunft. [Rede,gehalten bei der Schillerfrier der Rheinischen Friedrich-Wilhelms-universität am 9.mai 1905,von Berthold Litzmann] Bonn,Röhrscheid & Ebbecke,1905.
cover-title,24 p. 23cm.

1.Schiller,Johann Christoph Friedrich von,1759-1805. 2.German drama-Hist.& crit.

NL 0415117 CU CLSU MiU PU

Litzmann, Berthold, 1857-1926, ed.
Schröder, Friedrich Ludwig, 1744-1816.
Schröder und Gotter. Eine episode aus der deutschen theatergeschichte. Briefe Friedrich Ludwig Schröders an Friedrich Wilhelm Gotter. 1777 und 1778. Eingeleitet und herausgegeben von dr. Berthold Litzmann ... Hamburg und Leipzig, L. Voss, 1887.

Litzmann, Berthold, 1857-1926. 2871.114
Schillers Balladendichtung. Portrait. Coat of arms.
(In Marbacher Schillerbuch. Pp. 181-188. Stuttgart. 1905.)

F7501

NL 0415119 MB

Litzmann, Berthold, 1857- ed.
Theatergeschichtliche forschungen.
Hamburg, 1891-1910.
v. 1-21.

NL 0415120 IU

Litzmann, Berthold, 1857-1926.
...Theodor Storm, zwei aufsätze von Berthold Litzmann. Bonn, F. Cohen, 1917-18.
3 p. l., p. 35-75. 23½cm. (*On cover:* Mitteilungen der Literarhistorischen gesellschaft Bonn unter dem vorsitz von professor B. Litzmann. 11. jahrgang, 1917/18, hft. 2/3)

1. Storm, Theodor, 1817-1888.

Printed by Wesleyan University Library

NL 0415121 CtW InU NN MiU NjP OCU

Litzmann, Berthold, 1857-1926.
Von neuer Erzählkunst. (Literarhistorische Gesellschaft Bonn. Bonn, 1912. 8°. Jahrg. 7, p. 153-178.)

1. Fiction (German).—History.
N. Y. P. L. August 29, 1913.

NL 0415122 NN

PT2281 .G9Z8L7 Litzmann,Berthold,1857-1926.
Zur textkritik und biographie Johann Christian Günther's,von Berthold Litzmann. Frankfurt a/M., Rütten & Loening,1880.
viii,[1],157 p. 21½cm.

1.Günther,Johann Christian,1695-1723.

NL 0415123 ICU MWelC CU OClW CU PSt

WQ L782g 1889 LITZMANN, Carl Conrad Theodor, 1815-1890
L'accouchement dans les rétrécissements du bassin d'après des observations et des recherches personnelles. Tr. par A. Thomasset et publié sous la direction de A. Fochier. Lyon, Mégret, 1889.
xiii, 265 p.
Translation od Die Geburt bei engem Becken.

NL 0415124 DNLM PPC

WE L782c 1862 LITZMANN, Carl Conrad Theodor, 1815-1890
Contributions to the knowledge of osteomalacia, tr. from the German by J. Matthews Duncan. Edinburgh, Oliver & Boyd, 1862.
41 p.
Translation of Beiträge zur Kenntniss der Osteomalacie, which supplements Die Formen des Beckens.
Also published in the Edinburgh medical journal.

NL 0415125 DNLM

Litzmann (Carl Conrad Theodor) [1815-].
*De arteriitide. 29 pp., 1 l. 8°. Hala, ex off. C. Grunerti, [1838].

NL 0415126 DNLM PPC

VOLUME 336

B610.24
H15D632
1839-1842
v.2
Litzmann, Carl Conrad Theodor, 1815-1890, respondent.
De causa partum efficiente. Halis Sax, formis Gebaueriis, 1840.
38 p. 20 cm. (In Dissertationes Halensis, 1839-1842)
Thesis - Halle, 1840.

NL 0415127 MnU-B

Litzmann, Carl C[onrad] T[heodor], 1815-1890. Ger. Lib.
Emanuel Geibel, aus erinnerungen, briefen, und tagebüchern. Berlin, W. Hertz, 1887.
pp. vii, 254 +.

NL 0415128 CaBVaU CtY PU MiU OClW OU MH KU ICarbS TNJ GU NcU NIC InU NjP

C-1418
Cat.B
Litzmann, Carl Conrad Theodor, 1815-1890.
Erkenntnis und Behandlung der Frauenkrankheiten im Allgemeinen. Vier Vorträge, in der gynäkologischen Klinik zu Kiel im Sommer-Semester 1885. Berlin, A. Hirschwald, 1886.
82p.

NL 0415129 ICRL DNLM IU-M

B611.96
qL739f
Litzmann, Carl Conrad Theodor, 1815-1890.
Die Formen des Beckens, insbesondere des engen weiblichen Beckens, nach eigenen Beobachtungen und Untersuchungen, nebst einem Anhange über die Osteomalacie. Berlin, G. Reimer, 1861.
vi, 152, [1] p. 6 col. plates. 30cm.
1. Pelvis. 2. Osteomalacia.

NL 0415130 MnU WU ICJ WU-M NNU DNLM NNC-M CtY-M

AV-RC946
L73
1861
Litzmann, Carl Conrad Theodor, 1815-1890.
Die Formen des Beckens, insbesondere des engen weiblichen Beckens, nach eigenen Beobachtungen und Untersuchungen, nebst einem Anhange über die Osteomalacie. Berlin, G. Reimer, 1861.
vi, 152 p. 6 plates, tables.
~~Microfilm~~ copy.
Bibliography: p. [115]-118.

NL 0415131 NNC-M

Litzmann, Carl Conrad Theodor, 1815-1890, ed.

Hölderlin, Friedrich, 1770-1843.
Friedrich Hölderlins leben. In briefen von und an Hölderlin. Bearbeitet und herausgegeben von Carl C. T. Litzmann. Mit einem bilde der Diotima nach einem relief von Ohmacht. Berlin, W. Hertz, 1890.

Litzmann, Carl Conrad Theodor, 1815-1890. 618.52 O400
Die Geburt bei engem Becken. Nach eigenen Beobachtungen und Untersuchungen von Dr. Carl Conrad Theodor Litzmann, ... Leipzig, Breitkopf & Härtel, 1884.
x, [2], 738, [2] p. 23½cm.

NL 0415133 ICJ PPC ViU OClW-H

WQ
L782k
1844
LITZMANN, Carl Conrad Theodor, 1815-1890
Das Kindbettfieber in nosologischer, geschichtlicher, und therapeutischer Beziehung. Halle, Anton, 1844.
viii. 346 p.

NL 0415134 DNLM MiU ICJ PPC ICU ICRL

Litzmann, Carl Conrad Theodor, 1815-
——. Die Reform der Medicinal-Verfassung Preussens. Ein Votum. iv, 52 pp. 8°. *Greifswald. C. A. Koch*, 1847.

NL 0415135 DNLM

RD772
+853l
Litzmann, Carl Conrad Theodor, 1815-1890.
Das schräg-ovale Becken, mit besonderer Berücksichtigung seiner Entstehung im Gefolge einseitiger Coxalgie. Kiel, Akademische Buchhandlung, 1853.
33p. illus. 41cm.
26049
1. Hip joint - Diseases. 2. Pelvis - Abnormities & deformities. I. Title.

NL 0415136 CtY-M MnU ICJ PPC DNLM NNNAM

Litzmann, E.
Aus dem Lande der Märchen und Wunder. Indische Skizzen. Berlin: D. Reimer, 1914. 3 p.l., 74 p., 1 l., 26 pl. 8°.

1. India.—Description, etc., 191–.
N. Y. P. L. June 2, 1914.

NL 0415137 NN MH OCl

Litzmann, Elisabeth, 1883– Klinischer Beitrag zur Lehre von der diffusen Sklerodermie. Heidelberg 1911: Hörning. 40 S. 8°
Heidelberg, Med. Diss. v. 12. Febr. 1912, Ref. Hoffmann
[Geb. 23. Febr. 83 Kosel O.-S.; Wohnort: Karlsruhe i. B.; Staatsangeh.: Preußen; Vorbildung: Mädchengymn. Karlsruhe Reife Juli 03; Studium: Berlin 3, Heidelberg 1, Berlin 1, Halle 2, Berlin 1, Heidelberg 2 S.; Coll. 7. Juni 10; Approb. 11. Juli 11.] [U 12. 2259

NL 0415138 ICRL DNLM MBCo

Litzmann, *Frau* Grete (Herzberg) 1875–
Das erbe von Redentin; novelle von Grete Litzmann. Leipzig, P. Reclam jun. [°1921]
124 p. 16cm. (*On cover:* Reclams universal bibliothek, nr. 6271, 6272)

I. Title.
Library of Congress PT2623.I 88E7 1921 23-3377

NL 0415139 DLC MB

Litzmann, Grete, (Herzberg) 1875–
Gerhart Hauptmanns Festpiel in deutschen reimen, referat von Grete Litzmann. Ein französischer farbenstich von 1791 zu Hauptmanns Festpiel, von Bernhard Köhler. Bonn, Verlag F. Cohen, 1913.
[64]-114 p. 22½cm. (Mitteilungen der literarhistorischen gesellschaft, Bonn ... 8. jahrg., 1913, heft. 3/4)

NL 0415140 NcD

809.2
L739n
Litzmann, Grete (Herzberg)
Das naturalistische Drama; von seiner Entstehung und Technik. Dortmund, F.W. Ruhfus, 1907.
312-336p. 24cm. (Mitteilungen der literarhistorischen Gesellschaft Bonn. 2. Jahrg., 8. Sitzung, Nr.8)

828943 1. Drama - 19th cent. - Hist. & crit. 2. Naturalism in literature. I. Series: Literarhistorische Gesellschaft, Bonn. Mitteilungen. 2. Jahrg., Nr.8.

NL 0415141 TxU InU

Litzmann, Frau Grete (Herzberg) 1875– ed.

Heyking, Elisabeth (von Flemming) *baronin* von, 1861-1925.
... Tagebücher aus vier weltteilen 1886/1904, hrsg. von Grete Litzmann. Leipzig, Koehler & Amelang [1926]

Litzmann, Hans, 1875-1942
see Lietzmann, Hans, 1875-1942.

Litzmann (Henr. Car. Frid.) * De scarlatina. 54 pp. 8°. *Halæ, in off. Batheana*, 1803.

NL 0415144 DNLM PPC

Litzmann (Heinrich Carl Wilhelm). Ueber Dammrisse. 17 pp. 4°. *Kiel, Schmidt u. Klaunig*, 1873.
In: SCHRIFT. d. Univ. zu Kiel, ix, 1873, med., x.

NL 0415145 DNLM

Litzmann, Jakob Dieterich, respondent.
De discrimine revelationis et inspirationis
see under Baumgarten, Siegmund Jakob, 1707-1757, praeses.

Litzmann, Johann, respondent.
... De materia injuriarum ...
see under Brunnemann, Johann, 1608-1672, praeses.

Litzmann, Karl, 1850– 355.42 P800
Beiträge zur taktischen Ausbildung unserer Offiziere. .... Von Litzmann, Generalleutnant und Direktor der Kriegsakademie. .... Berlin, R. Eisenschmidt, 1898-1905.
4 vol. in 2. 22cm.
Maps to vol. 1 in pocket.
Contents. — 1. Offizier-Felddienstübungen. Vierte, verbesserte Auflage. 1904. viii, 142, 8* p. 1 fold. pl., 3 fold. maps. — 2. Gefechtsübungen mit kriegstarken Zügen, Kompagnien und Bataillonen, zur Schulung der Unterführer für den Kampf im grösseren Rahmen. Dritte, umgearbeitete Auflage. 1903. viii, 115 p. 3 fold. maps. — 3. Taktische Uebungsritte. Zweite, verbesserte Auflage. 1898. vii, [1], 154 p. 3 fold. maps. — 4. Stellen und Lösen taktischer Aufgaben. Einführung in den Betrieb des Kriegsspiels. 1905. vii, [1], 156 p 3 fold. maps, 1 chart.

NL 0415148 ICJ DNW

Litzmann, Karl, 1850–
Contributions to the tactical training of officer.

NL 0415149 DNW

VOLUME 336

4DC-686 Litzmann, Karl, 1850-
Ernstes und Heiteres aus den Kriegsjahren 1870/71; nach eigenen Erlebnissen. Mit Kartenskizzen, Abbildungen und einer Kunstdruckbeilage, nach Orginalzeichnungen des Verfassers. Berlin, Vaterländische Verlags- und Kunstanstalt, 1911.
90 p.

NL 0415150 DLC-P4

Litzmann, Karl, 1850–
...Excursiones tácticas, por Litzman... Buenos Aires: Ferrari hnos., 1920. 160 p. map, plans. 12°. (Biblioteca del oficial. v. 23.)
"Revisado por el capitán Carlos von der Becke."

507683A. 1. Military reconnoitering. I. Becke, Carlos von der. II. Ser.
N. Y. P. L. January 19, 1931

NL 0415151 NN

Litzmann, Karl, 1850-
Exercises de Combat exécutés par des sections, compagnies et bataillons à l'effectif de guerre, contribution à l'instruction tactique de nos officiers: dressage des sous-ordres en vue du combat encadré ... 4e. édition allemande ... Traduit de l'allemand, par le capitaine Corteys ... Paris, H. Charles Lavauzelle, 1908.

NL 0415152 DNW

Litzmann, Karl, 1850-
Exercises de Service en Campagne poor Officiers: préparation et direction, critique par le directeur, compterendu par les chefs der parti, par le général Litzmann, ... Traduit de l'allemand par A.G. Paris, H. Charles-Lavauzelle, 1906.

NL 0415153 DNW

Litzmann, Karl, 1850-
Geländeübungen zur Förderung der Wehrkraft. Dem Bunde ... Jungdeutschland gewidm. 2. Aufl. Berlin, C.S. Mittler & Sohn, 1914.

NL 0415154 DNW

Litzmann, Karl, 1850–
Lebenserinnerungen. Berlin, R. Eisenschmidt, 1927 [1925]–
v. illus., port., maps (part fold. in pocket) 24 cm.

1. Generals—Correspondence, reminiscences, etc. 2. European War, 1914–1918—Germany. 3. European War, 1914–1918—Campaigns—Eastern. I. Title.
DD231.L57A3 52-51783

NL 0415155 DLC DNW OU MnU NN TNJ MH

Litzmann, Karl, 1850–
Das neue deutsche Volksheer, von Karl Litzmann... Berlin: Die Tägliche Rundschau, 1919. 24 p. 8°.

1. Army (German), 1919.
N. Y. P. L. April 1, 1924.

NL 0415156 NN MH

Litzmann, Karl, 1850-
Preparation for tactical ride.

NL 0415157 DNW

LITZMANN, Karl, 1850-
La ruptura hacia Brzeziny.-La batalla de invierno en Masuria.-El ataque á la plaza fuerte de Kowno.-Servicio de Estado Mayor. Buenos Aires, librería "Cervantes," 1921.
Port.,maps,plans and table.
H 861.150.5

NL 0415158 MH

Litzmann, Karl, 1850– 355.42 Q901
.... Thèmes tactiques et jeu de la guerre. Contribution à 119334 l'instruction tactique de nos officiers. Comment poser et résoudre des thèmes tactiques, introduction à la pratique du jeu de la guerre. Traduit de l'allemand et annoté par le capitaine Corteys, ... Avec trois cartes hors texte. 2e édition, d'après la 2e édition allemande. Paris, H. Charles-Lavauzelle, [1909].
216 p. 3 fold. maps, 2 diagr., 1 table. 22½cm.
At head of title: Général Litzmann, ...
"Compas de marche" in pocket.

NL 0415159 ICJ DNW

Litzmann, Karl, 1850-
The Winter in Masuria (n.p., 1932)
1 p. 28 cm.
typewritten translation from his LEBENSERINNERUNGEN, vol. 1, pages 317-330, by Maj. Harm

NL 0415160 DNW

4UE-4 Litzmann, Karl, 1850-
Wir von der Kavallerie, die Geschichte des Preussischen Kavallieristen für ihn geschrieben von Generalleutnant z. D. Litzmann. Berlin, Verlagsanstalt Bundruck [c1913]
220 p.

NL 0415161 DLC-P4

Litzmann, Karl Konrad Theodor
see Litzmann, Carl Conrad Theodor, 1815-1890.

Litzmannstadt
see
Łódź, *Poland.*

Litzner (Max) [1879-]. *Der Sternalwinkel (Angulus Ludovici) am phthisischen Thorax. 20 pp., 1 l. 8°. Leipzig. A. Edelmann 1904.

NL 0415164 DNW CtY ICRL

Litzner, Stillfried, 1897-
... Experimentelle und klinische Untersuchungen über das Verhalten der Blutmenge bei Nierenerkrankungen ... Berlin, 1929.
Habilitationsschrift - Halle-Wittenberg.
Published also in Zeitschrift für klinische Medizin, Bd, 112.
"Literatur": p. 123.

NL 0415165 CtY ICRL

Litzner, Stillfried, 1897–
Gutartige albuminurien ... Nephritis, nephrosklerose, nephrose. 2., verb. aufl. Von Stillfried Litzner ... Leipzig, G. Thieme, 1941.
85 p. 24½cm. (*Added t.-p.:* Die Urologie in einzeldarstellungen, hrsg. von professor dr. H. Boeminghaus)
At head of title: Aus der Inneren abteilung des Heinrich-Braun-krankenhauses (Staatliches-krankenstift in Zwickau i. Sa.

1. Albuminuria. 2. Kidneys—Diseases.
43-48908
Library of Congress RC902.L54 1941
616.61

NL 0415166 DLC

Litzsinger, Louisa E
One link in the golden chain; an essay, by Miss Louisa E. Litzsinger ... Clayton, Mo., Printed at the office of the People's advocate, 1897.
viii p. illus. (port.) 16 cm.

1. Blind—Education. I. Title.
HV1626.L7 CA 10—3794 Unrev'd

NL 0415167 DLC

Litzsinger, Louisa E.
Violets under the snow; a collection of short poems, by Louisa E. Litzsinger ... Clayton, Mo., The People's advocate press, 1898.
73 p. incl. port. 19½cm.

I. Title.
Nov. 23, 98–135
Library of Congress PS3523.I 86V4 1898

NL 0415168 DLC

Liu, An
see
Huai-nan tzŭ, *d.* 122 *B. C.*

Liu, An-ch'ang.
生理學講話 柳安昌著 台北 中華文化出版事業委員會 民國43 [1954]
241 p. illus. 19 cm. (現代國民基本知識叢書第1輯)

1. Physiology. I. Title.
Title romanized: Shêng li hsüeh chiang hua.
QP33.L5 C 58-5851 ‡

NL 0415170 DLC CLU-C

VOLUME 336

Lŭ, Bai-ŭi
see
Liu, Pai-yü.

Liu, Bangnee Alfred, 1901–
Educational research in major American cities, by Bangnee Alfred Liu ... New York, King's crown press, 1945.
2 p. l., [vii]–xi, 168 p., 1 l. incl. tables, diagrs. 22cm.
Thesis (PH. D.)—Columbia university, 1944.
Published also without thesis note.
Vita.
Includes bibliographies.

1. Educational research. 2. Public schools—U. S.
A 46-3649
Columbia univ. Libraries for Library of Congress LB1028.L5 1945 a
[3]† 370.78

NL 0415172 NNC ICU OCIU DLC CaBVaU

Liu, Bangnee Alfred, 1901–
Educational research in major American cities, by Bangnee Alfred Liu. New York, King's crown press, 1945.
2 p. l., [vii]–xi, 168 p. incl. tables, diagrs. 21½cm.
Reproduced from type-written copy.
Includes bibliographies.

1. Educational research. 2. Public schools—U. S. I. Title.
A 46-595
Columbia univ. Libraries for Library of Congress LB1028.L5
[6]† 370.78

NL 0415173 NNC OrU MtU OCU OCl TxU ICJ PP PPT DLC

Liu, Beatrice.
Little Wu and the watermelons. Illus. by Graham Peck. Chicago, Follett Pub. Co. [1954]
96 p. illus. 25 cm.

I. Title.
PZ7.L739Li 54-10099 ‡

OrLgE OrPS OrU WaS WaSp
NL 0415174 DLC MiU IU PP PPT OCl FU Or OrAshS OrP

Liu, Bejü
see
Liu, Pai-yü.

Liu, Chai-jên.
海港工程學　劉宅仁著　上海　中國科學圖書儀器公司 1951.
4, 6, 295, [1] p. illus., map, diagrs., plans. 26 cm.
Bibliography: p. [296]

1. Harbors. 2. Hydraulic engineering. I. Title.
Title romanized: Hai kang kung chêng hsüeh.
TC205.L56 C 59-1455

NL 0415176 DLC

Liu Chai-lien
see Liu, Chieh-lien, fl. 1670-1724.

Liu, Chan-ên
see
Liu, Herman Chan-En, 1896–1938.

Liu, Ch'ang.
續墨子閒詁　劉載賡[劉昶]著　上海　掃葉山房　民國 14 [1925]
4 v. (double leaves) in case. 20 cm.
Lithoprinted.

I. Mo, Ti, fl. 400 B. C. Mo-tzŭ. II. Sun, I-jang, 1848–1908. Mo-tzŭ hsien ku. III. Title.
Title romanized: Hsü Mo-tzŭ hsien ku.
B128.M8L55 C 66-326

NL 0415179 DLC

Liu, Ch'ang, *ed.*
續墨子閒詁　劉載賡[劉昶]著　[臺北　藝文印書館 195–]
238 p. 19 cm.
Facsimile reproduction of 民國 14 (1925)上海掃葉山房石印本

I. Mo, Ti, fl. 400 B. C. Mo-tzŭ. II. Sun, I-jang, 1848–1908. Mo-tzŭ hsien ku. III. Title.
Title romanized: Hsü Mo-tzŭ hsien ku.
B128.M8S84 C 66-554

NL 0415180 DLC OU

Liu, Ch'ang-hsün.
黎明日本　柳長勛著　臺北　中華文化出版事業委員會　民國 44 [1955]
1, 2, 196 p. map. 19 cm. (現代國民基本知識叢書第8輯)

1. Japan—Descr. & trav.—1945– I. Title.
Title romanized: Li ming Jih-pên.
DS811.L5 C58-1592
Indiana. Univ. Libr. for Library of Congress [1]†

NL 0415181 InU DLC CaBVaU RPB OO CLU-O WU WaU

620.1125 L74s
Liu, Chang-keng, 1922-
Stresses and deformations due to tangential and normal loads on an elastic solid with applications to contact stresses. Urbana [1950]
ix, 128 l. illus. 28cm.

Thesis--University of Illinois.
Typewritten (carbon copy)
Vita.
Bibliography: leaves 127-128.

NL 0415182 IU

Liu, Chang-keng, 1922–
Stresses and deformations due to tangential and normal loads on an elastic solid with applications to contact stresses. Urbana, 1950.
3 p. 23 cm.
Abstract of thesis—University of Illinois.
Vita.

1. Strains and stresses. 2. Deformations (Mechanics)
TA405.L55 A 53-3020
Illinois. Univ. Library for Library of Congress [1]†

NL 0415183 IU NIC DLC

Liu, Ch'ang-ning.
物價統制論　劉長寧著　重慶　財政評論社 1943.
6, 136 p. 23 cm. (財政評論社叢書)

1. Price regulation. I. Title.
Title romanized: Wu chia t'ung chih lun.
HB236.A3L5 C 66-4

NL 0415184 DLC

Liu, Ch'ang-shêng, 1903-
Chung-kuo kung ch'an tang yü Shang-hai kung jên
see under title

Liu, Ch'ang-shêng, 1903–
抗美援朝保家衛國運動中的上海人民　劉長勝著　上海　勞動出版社 1951.
99 p. 19 cm.

1. Shanghai—Hist.—Anecdotes. I. Title.
Title romanized: K'ang Mei yüan Ch'ao pao chia wei kuo yün tung.
DS796.S2L46 C 65-201.

NL 0415186 DLC ViU

Liu, Chao-chi, *ed.*
西南采風錄　劉兆吉編　上海　商務印書館　民國 35 [1946]
[11], 194 p. 19 cm.

1. Folk-songs—China. I. Title.
Title romanized: Hsi-nan ts'ai fêng lu.
PL2519.F6L5 C 67-1

NL 0415187 DLC WaU

Wason DS701+ B93m ser.B no.2
Liu Ch'ao-yang.
Calendar of the early Chou period. Chengtu, China, Pub. by the Chinese Cultural Studies Research Institute, West China Union University, 1944.
2,1,viii,112 p. 26cm. (Studia serica. Monographs. Ser. B, no. 2)

In Chinese, with added title and introduction in English.

NL 0415188 NIC MH

BJ12a +St92 3
Liu, Ch'ao-yang
Chronology of the late Yin period. Chengtu, Chinese Cultural Studies Research Institute, West China Union University, 1945.
vii, 136p. (Studia serica monographs ser. B, no.3)
Cover title.
Text and added t.-p. in Chinese; introd. in English.
Chinese title: 晚殷長曆 (Wan yin ch'ang li)

NL 0415189 CtY NIC MH

VOLUME 336

Liu, Chên.
俄帝研究 劉珍著 臺北 中央文物供應社 民國 44 [1955]
100 p. illus. 19 cm. (敵情叢書)

1. Russia—Descr. & trav.—1945- I. Title.
Title romanized: O ti yen chiu.

DK28.L53 C 58-5617 ‡

NL 0415190 DLC MiU

Liu, Chên, *lawyer.*
律師道德論 劉震著作 上海 商務印書館 民國 23 [1934]
1, 2, 98, 40 p. 20 cm.
Colophon title.

1. Lawyers—China—Discipline. I. Title.
Title romanized: Lü shih tao tê lun.

C 66-577

NL 0415191 DLC

Liu, Ch'ên, writer on pottery
see
Ch'ên, Liu.

Liu, Chên, 1912-
教育行政 劉真 錢卓升合著 臺北 中華文化出版事業委員會 民國 43 [1954]
2, 4, 2, 200 p. 19 cm. (現代國民基本知識叢書第2輯)
Bibliography: p. 197-200.

1. Education and state. I. Ch'ien, Cho-shêng, joint author. II. Title.
Title romanized: Chiao yü hsing chêng.

LC71.L57 C 66-2669

NL 0415193 DLC CLU-C

Liu, Chên, 1912-
旅美書簡 劉真著 [臺北] 台灣商務 民國 43 [1954]
129 p. 19 cm.

1. U. S.—Descr. & trav.—1940- I. Title.
Title romanized: Lü Mei shu chien.

E169.L77 C 58-5933 ‡

NL 0415194 DLC MiU

Liu, Chên-chung.
民法債編通則講義 劉鎮中著 上海 羣益書社 [民國 22 (1933) 序]
330 p. 19 cm.

1. Debtor and creditor—China. 2. Contracts—China. I. Title.
Title romanized: Min fa chai pien t'ung tsê chiang i.

C 60-2786 ‡

NL 0415195 DLC

Liu, Chên-chung, ed.
Min fa shih yung chai pien ko lun
see under China. Laws, statutes, etc.

Liu, Chên-chung.
民法物權編講義 劉鎮中著 上海 羣益書社 [民國 22 (1933) 序]
240 p. 19 cm.

1. Property—China. I. Title.
Title romanized: Min fa wu ch'üan pien chiang i.

C 60-2767 ‡

NL 0415197 DLC

Liu, Chên-hsiang.
王文玉投親 豫剧 刘振祥整理 西安 長安書店 1955.
57 p. 18 cm.
Cover title.
Play.

I. Title.
Title romanized: Wang Wên-yü t'ou ch'in.

PL2879.C37W3 C 68-1735

NL 0415198 DLC

Liu, Chên, hua, 1883-
開發西北計畫書 [劉鎮華著 n. p. 民國20 (1931) 識]
2, 4, 74 p. fold. map. 26 cm.

1. China, Northwest—Economic policy. I. Title.
Title romanized: K'ai fa Hsi-pei chi hua shu.

HC428.N6L5 C 67-713

NL 0415199 DLC

595.78
L74e
1934

Liu, Chên-hua (Chang)
Étude du développement des races univoltines et polyvoltines du Bombyx mori dans les conditions normales et expérimentales, par Liou Tchang Tcheng-Houa. Paris, Hermann, 1934.
129p. 10 plates. 26cm.

Title also in Chinese; preface in Chinese.
Errata: p. [131]
Bibliography: p. [111]-126.
1. Silkworms. 2. Bombyx mori.

NL 0415200 KU CtY

Liu, Chên-mo.
船舶常用物料中英文名稱統一對照表 劉鎮謨編 [臺北] 招商局訓練委員會 民國 41 [1952]
22 p. 19 cm. (訓練教材乙種)

1. Ships—Equipment and supplies. I. Title.
Title romanized: Ch'uan po ch'ang yung wu liao Chung Ying wên ming ch'êng t'ung i tui chao piao.

VM781.L57 C 61-2423 ‡

NL 0415201 DLC

Liu, Chên-mo.
船上油漆調配法 劉鎮謨編 [台北] 招商調練委員會 民國 41 [1952]
8 p. 19 cm. (訓練教材乙種)

1. Ships—Painting. I. Title.
Title romanized: Ch'uan shang yu ch'i t'iao p'ei fa.

VM961.L5 C 61-2667

NL 0415202 DLC

Liu, Chên-mo.
大圈駕駛法 劉鎮謨編 [臺北] 招商局訓練委員會 民國 41 [1952]
13 p. illus. 19 cm. (訓練教材甲種)

1. Great-circle sailing. I. Title.
Title romanized: Ta ch'üan chia shih fa.

VK571.L73 C 61-2424 ‡

NL 0415203 DLC

Liu, Chên-tung, 1901?-
中國幣制改造問題與有限銀本位制 劉振東著 上海 商務印書館 民國 23 [1934]
[12], 178 p. 23 cm. (中國經濟學社叢書)

1. Currency question—China. 2. Silver. I. Title.
Title romanized: Chung-kuo pi chih kai tsao wên t'i.

HG1224.L49 C 67-968

NL 0415204 DLC WU

Liu, Chên-tung, 1901?-
Hsien chêng tzŭ liao hui pien
see under Chiao, Ju-ch'iao, ed.

Liu, Ch'eng-chao, 1902-
Amphibians of western China. [Chicago] Chicago Natural History Museum, 1950.
400 p. illus. (part col.) maps. 31 cm. (Fieldiana: zoology memoirs, v. 2)
"References": p. 392-396.

1. Batrachia—China. I. Title. (Series: Chicago. Natural History Museum. Fieldiana: zoology memoirs, v. 2)

QL3.C47 vol. 2 597.6 50-13279

FMU TxU
NL 0415206 DLC PSt GU FU MB NNC ViU DI PPAN UU NbU

Microfilm
1191
AC

Liu, Ch'eng-chao, 1902-
Natural history studies of West China amphibia. [Ann Arbor, University Microfilms, n. d.]
Microfilm copy (positive)
Collation of the original, as determined from the film: 39-78 p. plates.
Caption title.
From the Journal of the West China Border Research Society, 1943, v. 14, ser. B.
Bibliography: p. 49-50.

1. Batrachia—China.

Mic 62-7130

NL 0415207 DLC

Liu, Ch'eng Chao, 1902-
... Natural history studies of West China amphibia. V. Life history of staurois chunganensis ... [Peking, 1941]
[291]-295 p. illus. 26 cm.

Reprinted from the Peking natural history bulletin, 1940-41, vol. 15, part 4.

1. Staurois chunganensis. 2. Batrachia. China

NL 0415208 NcD

VOLUME 336

Liu, Ch'eng-chao, 1902- joint author.

Schmidt, Karl Patterson, 1890–
... A new toad from western China, by Karl P. Schmidt ... and Ch'eng-chao Liu ... ⌈Chicago, 1940⌉

Liu, Ch'eng-chao, 1902–
Secondary sex characters of Chinese frogs and toads. Chicago, 1936.
115–156 p. 12 plates. 25 cm. (Chicago. Field Museum of Natural History. Publication 368. Zoological series, v. 22, no. 2)
Bibliography: p. 152.
1. Frogs. 2. Toads. 3. Batrachia—China. 4. Sex. I. Title. II. Title: Chinese frogs and toads. (Series: Chicago. Natural History Museum. Publication 368. Series: Chicago. Natural History Museum. Fieldiana: zoology, v. 22, no. 2)
QL1.F4 vol. 22, no. 2 37–12127 rev*
——— Copy 2. QL668.E2L63

NL 0415210 DLC OrCS IdU MU OO OU OCU ViU

Liu, Ch'eng-chao, 1902-
Secondary sex characters of Chinese Salientia. Ithaca, N. Y., 1934.
174 l. illus.,(plates) 28 cm.
Thesis (Ph. D.) - Cornell Univ., Feb. 1934.
1. Anura. 2. Amphibians - China. 3. Gynandromorphism. I. Title. II. Title: Chinese salientia.

NL 0415211 NIC

Liu, Ch'eng-chao, 1902–
Secondary sex characters of Chinese *Salientia* ... by Ch'eng-chao Liu. Ithaca, N. Y., 1934.
1 p. l., 6 p. 23cm.
Abstract of thesis (PH. D.)—Cornell university, 1934.
1. Frogs. 2. Toads. 3. Batrachia—China. 4. Sex. I. Title: Salientia, Secondary sex characters of Chinese.
35–4511
Library of Congress QL668.E2L65 1934
Cornell Univ. Libr.
——— Copy 2. ⌈3⌉ 597.8

NL 0415212 NIC PSt DLC

Liu, Ch'êng-chao, 1902–
Two new scutigers from Chao-chiao-hsien, Sikang. ⌈Ann Arbor, University Microfilms, n. d.⌉
Microfilm copy (positive)
Collation of the original, as determined from the film: 35-38 p. plate.
Caption title.
From the Journal of the West China Border Research Society, 1943, v. 14, ser. B.
1. Scutigeridae.
Microfilm 1191AC Mic 62–7126

NL 0415213 DLC

Liu, Ch'êng-ch'ing.
中國童子軍訓練法 劉澄清著 重慶 商務印書館 民國31 ⌈1942⌉
3, 4, 151 p. 18 cm.
Bibliography: p. 149–151.
1. Chung-kuo t'ung tzŭ chün.
Title romanized: Chung-kuo t'ung tzŭ chün hsün lien fa.
HS3313.B9C6 C 66–891

NL 0415214 DLC

Liu, Ch'êng-han, 1903–
民用航空法論 劉承漢 蔡喆生合著 ⌈臺北⌉ 中國交通建設學會 ⌈1954⌉
4, 8, 498 p. 21 cm. (交通叢書)
1. Aeronautics, Commercial—Law and legislation. I. Ts'ai, Chê-shêng, 1910– joint author. II. Title.
Title romanized: Min yung hang k'ung fa lun.
71–835688

NL 0415215 DLC

Liu, Ch'êng-han, 1903–
郵政法總論 劉承漢著 長沙 商務印書館 民國 29 ⌈1940⌉
2, 5, 299 p. tables. 21 cm.
1. Postal service—China—Laws and regulations. I. Title.
Title romanized: Yu chêng fa tsung lun.
C 62–282

NL 0415216 DLC

Liu, Chêng-ming.
南洋華僑問題 劉徵明著 國立中山大學社會研究所編輯 坪石 金門出版社 民國33 ⌈1944⌉
2, 4, 246 p. 21 cm. (國立中山大學社會研究所叢刊之 2)
Includes bibliographical references.
1. Chinese in Southeastern Asia. 2. China—Emig. & immig. I. Title. (Series: Chung-shan ta hsüeh, Canton, China. Shê hui yen chiu so. Kuo li Chung-shan ta hsüeh shê hui yen chiu so ts'ung k'an chih 2)
Title romanized: Nan-yang Hua ch'iao wên t'i.
JX8701.Z29S65 C 66–916

NL 0415217 DLC

LD3921 Tex. mfg. L58
Liu, Chester F T
The manufacturing and testing of 40's yarn under specified conditions. Raleigh, N. C. [1925]
81 l. illus., tables. 28cm.
Thesis - North Carolina State University at Raleigh.
1.North Carolina. State University at Raleigh - Theses - Textile manufacturing. I.Title.

NL 0415218 NcRS

U101 .C48 1853 Orien China
Liu, Chi, 1311-1375, ed.
Liu Po-wên hsien shêng ch'ung tsuan Chu-ko Chung-wu hou ping fa hsin yao.
Chu-ko, Liang, 181–234.
劉伯溫先生重纂諸葛忠武侯兵法心要 ⌈諸葛亮著 劉基重纂 n. p. 咸豐癸丑(1853)序⌉

Liu, Chi, 1311–1375.
太師劉文成公集 ⌈20卷⌉ 劉基撰 南田 果育堂藏板 ⌈乾隆 11 (1746) 跋⌉
10 v. (double leaves) in 2 cases. 29 cm.
Caption title: 誠意伯文集
I. Title. II. Title: Ch'êng i po wên chi.
Title romanized: T'ai shih Liu Wên-ch'êng kung chi.
C 64–784
Michigan. Univ. Asia Library PL2698
for Library of Congress ⌈3⌉

NL 0415220 MiU CaBVaU

F1868 C5C44 Orien China
Liu, Chi, 1311-1375.
Ti t'ien sui
Ching, T'u.
滴天髓 ⌈京圖撰 劉基註 程芝雲校訂⌉ 窮通寶鑑 ⌈上下卷 余春臺編輯⌉ 秦慎安校勘 上海 文明書局 民國 15 ⌈1926⌉

Liu, Ch'i, *fl.* 1711.
助字辨略 ⌈5 卷⌉ 劉淇著 章錫琛校注 北京 中華書局 1954.
8, 10, 316, 12 p. 19 cm.
1. Chinese language—Particles. I. Chang, Hsi-ch'ên, 1889– ed. II. Title.
Title romanized: Chu tzŭ pien lüeh.
PL1237.L5 C 58–5169

NL 0415222 DLC ViU

Liu, Chi-ch'ên.
江蘇地質誌 劉季辰 趙汝鈞原著 ⌈北京⌉ 農商部地質調查所 ⌈鎮江⌉ 江蘇實業廳 民國 13 ⌈1924⌉
2, 6, 82, 34 p. 26 cm. (⌈中央地質調查所⌉地質專報 甲種第 4 號 Memoirs of the Geological Survey of China. Ser. A, no. 4)
Summary in English; added t. p.: A preliminary report on the geology and the mineral resources of Kiangsu, by C. C. Liu & J. C. Chao. Peking, The Commercial Press ltd.
Accompanied by a general map and four separate maps.
1. Geology—China—Kiansu (Province) 2. Mines and mineral resources—China—Kiangsu (Province) I. Chao, Ju-chün, joint author. II. Title. III. Title: A preliminary report on the geology and the mineral resources of Kiangsu. (Series: China. Chung yang ti chih tiao ch'a so. Ti chih chuan pao. Chia chung ti 4 hao)
Title romanized: Chiang-su ti chih chih.
QE294.A4 ser. A, no. 4 G S 25–445
——— Copy 2. TN102.K5L5
U. S. Geol. Survey. Libr.
for Library of Congress ⌈r70i1⌉† rev 3 O

NL 0415224 DI-GS DLC MiU PPAN IU OKentU ViU

Liu, Chi-ch'ên.
Preliminary report on the geology and the mineral resources of Kiangsu. Topographic & geologic map of Kiangsu. 1,5000,000 n.d.,c1927.

NL 0415225 PPAN

Liu, Chi-ch'ên.
... Report on the Shui Kou Shan lead and zinc mine, Hunan, by C. C. Liu, C. C. Tien, and C. Y. Ou Yang. Changsha, Hunan, 1927.
1 p. l., 13 p.; 1 p. l., 2, 5, 59 p. incl. illus., tables, diagrs. v pl. (incl. fold. map) on 3 l., 3 fold. plans. 26½cm. (Hunan, China. Geological survey. Bulletin 1. Economic geology 1)
Added t.-p. and text in Chinese; summary in English.
1. Lead mines and mining—China—Hunan. 2. Zinc mines and mining—China—Hunan. I. T'ien, Ch'i-ch'iung, joint author. II. Ou Yang, Ch'ao-yüan, joint author. III. Title: Shui Kou Shan lead and zinc mine, Hunan.
G S 28–118 Revised
U. S. Geol. survey. Library
for Library of Congress QE294.A42 no. 1
⌈r44d2⌉† (555.11) 622.344

NL 0415226 DI-GS DLC

Liu, Chi-ch'ên, comp.
Ti chih tiao ch'a so t'u shu kuan
see under China. Chung yang ti chih tiao ch'a so. T'u shu kuan.

VOLUME 336

Liu, Chi-ch'ên, *economist.*
近代資本主義經濟思潮批判　劉及辰編著　上海生活書店　民國 37 [1948]
6, 1, 338 p. 22 cm.

1. Economics—Hist. I. Title.
Title romanized: Chin tai tzŭ pên chu i ching chi ssŭ ch'ac
HB75.L58 C 67-68

NL 0415228 DLC

Liu, Chi-ch'ên, *economist.*
如何認識我國危機　劉及辰著　北平　時代知識社　民國 26 [1937]
130 p. 19 cm.
Colophon title.

1. China—Econ. condit. I. Title.
Title romanized: Ju ho jên shih wo kuo wei chi.
HC427.L487 C 66-926

NL 0415229 DLC

Liu, Ch'i-ching.
最新內科治療學　劉棨敬編　增訂 5 版　九龍新醫書局 1950 [i. e. 1952]
413 p. illus. 21 cm. (新醫叢書之一)
Previous editions published under title: 新撰內科治療法集成

1. Medicine—Practice. I. Title.
Title romanized: Tsui hsin nei k'o chih liao hsüeh.
RC46.L66 1952 C 63-2074 ‡

NL 0415230 DLC

Liu, Chi-han, 1909–
Die Verkehrswirtschaft der deutschen Gemeinden. [Berlin-Lichterfelde, 1941]
56 p. 21 cm.
Inaug.-Diss.—Berlin.
Vita.
Bibliography: p. 56.

1. Local transit—Germany. I. Title.
HE4774.A3L5 57-50494

NL 0415231 DLC NIC CtY NjP

Liu, Chi-hsüan, 1895–
History of Chinese family colonization in the South seas, by Liu Chi-hsuan and Shu Shi-cheng. 2d ed. Shanghai, Commercial press, 1935.

NL 0415232 WaU-L

Liu, Chi-hsüan, 1895–
國民守則釋證　劉繼宣著 [重慶] 正中書局　民國 34 [1945]
1, 43 p. 19 cm.
Cover title.

1. Civics, Chinese. 2. Conduct of life. I. Title.
Title romanized: Kuo min shou tsê shih chêng.
JQ1517.A2L58 C 67-804

NL 0415233 DLC

Liu, Ch'i-huan, joint author.
Piao tien fu hao shih yung shou ts'ê
see under Chang, Shou-k'ang.

Liu, Chi-pan, 1898–
... General statement on the antimony industry of Hunan, by C. P. Liu. Changsha, Hunan, 1928.
cover-title, [42] p. incl. tables, diagrs. 3 fold. pl. (map and 2 tab.) 26cm. (Hunan. Geological survey. Bulletin 3; special report 1)
Text in Chinese.

1. Antimony. I. Title.
G S 28-452 Revised
Library, U. S. Geological Survey (610.3) B no. 3

NL 0415235 DI-GS

Liu, Chi-pan, 1898–
... General statement on the mining industry of Hunan, by C. P. Liu, S. Y. Kuo and H. C. Hsiu. Changsha, Hunan, 1927.
1 p. l., iv, [168] p., 2 l. incl. tables. fold. map, 9 fold. tab. 26½cm. (Hunan, China. Geological survey. Bulletin 6; special report 2)
At head of title: Geological survey of Hunan. C. P. Liu, director.
Text in Chinese.

1. Mines and mineral resources—China—Hunan. 2. Mineral industries—China—Hunan. I. Kuo. S. Y. II. Hsiu, H. C. III. Title.
G S 30-36 Revised
Library, U. S. Geological Survey (610.3) B no. 6

NL 0415236 DI-GS

Liu, Ch'i-shang.
養魚法　劉祁尙編著　上海　新農出版社 1953.
99 p. illus. 19 cm.

1. Fisheries—China. I. Title. *Title romanized:* Yang yü fa.
SH297.L5 C 59-2467 ‡

NL 0415237 DLC

Liu, Ch'i-wei, 1913–
工場管理概要　劉其偉編著 [基隆] 國是日報基隆分社　民國 36 [1947]
6, 126 p. 18 cm.
Colophon title.

1. Factory management. I. Title.
Title romanized: Kung ch'ang kuan li kai yao.
TS155.L63 C 67-1989

NL 0415238 DLC

QL 503 S6 L78
Liu, Chi-ying.
The fleas of China, order Siphonaptera. [Manila, Bureau of printing] 1939.
122 p. tables, diagrs. 26 cm. (The Philippine journal of science, v. 70, no. 1)

Bibliography: p. 112-117.
Caption title.

1. Fleas - China. I. Title.

NL 0415239 NIC MU

DS777 53 H87
Liu, Chi-yu.

Hua, Shan.
The shepherd's message. Drawings by Liu Chi-yu. [1st ed.] Peking, Foreign Languages Press, 1954.

Liu, Chi-yu, illus.
Tung kuo hsien shêng
see under Tung, Chü-hsien.

Liu, Chia-chi, *ed.*
語文選讀　劉家驥編選　鄭州　河南人民出版社 1955.
114 p. 18 cm.

1. Chinese literature—20th cent. I. Title.
Title romanized: Yü wên hsüan tu.
PL2455.L55 C 60-390 ‡

NL 0415242 DLC

Liu, Chia-chü, *of Sikang.*
西藏政教史略　劉家駒著 [n. p.] 中國邊疆學會 1948.
2, 25 p. 21 cm.
Cover title.

1. Tibet—Hist. I. Title.
Title romanized: Hsi-tsang chêng chiao shih lüeh.
DS785.L58 C 66-2616

NL 0415243 DLC CaBVaU WaU

Liu, Chia-chü, *of Sikang.*
康藏　劉家駒著　上海　新亞細亞月刊社　民國 21 [1932]
110 p. illus. 19 cm.

1. Sikang, China. 2. Tibet. I. Title.
Title romanized: K'ang Tsang.
DS793.S55L58 C 67-1317

NL 0415244 DLC

Liu, Chia-mou, *fl.* 1849–1853.
校註海音詩全卷　劉家謀撰　吳守禮校 [臺北] 臺灣省文獻委員會 [1953]
[3], 29, 6, 30, [3] double l. 25 cm. (臺灣叢書　學藝門第2種)

I. Wu, Shou-li, ed. II. Title. III. Title: Hai yin shih.
Title romanized: Chiao chu hai yin shih.
PL2718.I 77H3 1953 C 68-2915

NL 0415245 DLC CaBVaU

Liu, Chia-tsê.
怎樣開展增產節約勞動競賽　劉家澤編著　廣州華南人民出版社 1953.
34 p. 19 cm.

1. Labor productivity. I. Title.
Title romanized: Tsên yang k'ai chan tsêng ch'an chieh yüeh lao tung ching sai.
HD57.L58 C 60-662 ‡

NL 0415246 DLC NIC

Liu, Ch'iang.
内科鑑别診斷法　劉強編　北京　人民衛生出版社 1953.
86 p. illus. 18 cm.

1. Diagnosis. I. Title.
Title romanized: Nei k'o chien pieh chên tuan fa.
RC71.L69 C 58-6157 ‡

NL 0415247 DLC

VOLUME 336

Liu, Chiang, 1895–
Isolation and contact as factors in the cultural evolution of China, Korea, and Japan prior to 1842, by Chiang Liu. [n. p., 1925?]
cover-title, 1 p. l., 22 p. 21cm.
Abstract of thesis (PH. D.)—University of Iowa, 1923.
Bibliography: p. 20–22.

1. Civilization, Oriental. I. Title.

Library of Congress CB251.L5 1923 26–21718
Univ. of Iowa Libr.

NL 0415248 IaU DLC OU MiU OO

Liu, Chieh.
K'ên chih pien huang pan fa ni i
see Lao tzŭ ho i ti k'ên chih pien huang pan fa.

Liu, Chieh.
物產證券與按勞分配學說體系 劉杰著 [n. p.] 抗戰復興出版社 民國29 [1940]
6, 14, 414, 20 p. 19 cm.

1. Yen, Hsi-shan, 1883–1960. Wu ch'an chêng ch'üan yü an lao fên p'ei. 2. Economics. I. Title.
Title romanized: Wu ch'an chêng ch'üan yü an lao fên p'ei.

HB771.L55 C 66–2383

NL 0415250 DLC ICU MH ICU-FE

Liu, Chieh, 1901–
楚器圖釋 劉節著 北平 國立北平圖書館 民國 24 [1935]
9, 21 double l., 2 p. (on double leaf) illus., plates, maps. 43 cm.
Caption title: 壽縣所出楚器考釋
Colophon inserted.
壽縣所出銅器考略 唐蘭: p. 1–2 (3d group)

1. Shou-hsien, China—Antiq. 2. Bronzes, Chinese. I. T'ang, Lan, 1900– II. Title.
Title romanized: Ch'u ch'i t'u shih.

NK7983.L5 C 61–4468
California. Univ. East Asiatic Library
for Library of Congress [2]†

NL 0415251 CU-E DLC

Liu, Chieh, 1901–
中國古代宗族移殖史論 劉節編著 [上海] 正中書局 民國 37 [1948]
1, 1, 256 p. 21 cm.

1. Clans and clan system. I. Title.
Title romanized: Chung-kuo ku tai tsung tsu i chih shih lun.

GN492.L56 C 64–143

NL 0415252 DLC

Liu, Ch'ieh, 1906–
China. *Laws, statutes, etc.*
The Civil code of the republic of China ... Translated into English by Ching-Lin Hsia ... James L. E. Chow ... Liu Chieh ... [and] Yukon Chang, B. SC. Introduction by the Hon. Foo Ping-Sheung ... Shanghai [etc.] Kelly & Walsh, limited, 1931.

Liu, Ch'ieh, 1906–
JX1907 .A8 no. 448 **Carnegie Endowment for International Peace.**
International trusteeship system [by] Liu Chieh. Visiting missions. Reports on Ruanda-Urundi and Tanganyika. New York [1949]

Liu, Chieh-ao.
比例代表法概說 劉絜敖編 上海 商務印書館 民國 20 [1931]
60 p. 19 cm. (社會科學叢書)

1. Proportional representation. I. Title.
Title romanized: Pi li tai piao fa kai shuo.

JF1071.L5 C 61–354 ‡

NL 0415255 DLC WU

Liu, Chieh-lien, fl. 1670–1724.
The Arabian prophet; a life of Mohammed from Chinese and Arabic sources. A Chinese-Moslem work, by Liu Chai-lien, translated by Isaac Mason ... With appendices on Chinese Mohammedanism. Foreword by Rev. Samuel M. Zwemer ... Shanghai [Printed by the Commercial press, limited] 1921.
2 p. l., xvii, 313 p. front., 1 illus., plates, fold. map, fold. plan, facsims. 19½cm.
Abridged from the original work, finished in 1724, and first published in 1779 in 20 small volumes. cf. p. vii–viii, xii.

1. Muhammad, the prophet. 2. Mohammedans in China. I. Mason, Isaac, tr. II. Title.

Library of Congress BP75.L4 24–1459

NL 0415256 DLC Or OCl WaS CtY-D CSt MiU PU CU NIC

Liu Chieh-lien, fl. 1670–1724.
The Arabian prophet; a life of Mohammed from Chinese and Arabic sources. A Chinese-Moslem work, by Liu Chai-lien, translated by Isaac Mason ... With appendices on Chinese Mohammedanism. Foreword by Rev. Samuel M. Zwemer... Shanghai Printed by the Commerical press, limited 1927.

NL 0415257 Mi

Liu, Chieh-lien, fl. 1670–1724.
(T'ien fang chih shêng shih lu nien p'u)
天方至聖實錄年譜 [20 卷 劉介廉著述 錦城(廣西) 寶真堂重鐫 同治壬申 i. e. 1872]
10 v. (double leaves) in case. 24 cm.
Block print.
L. C. copy imperfect: All leaves after 17 in 卷 6 wanting.

1. Muḥammad, the prophet. I. Title.

BP75.29.C5L54 1872 72–835980

NL 0415258 DLC

Liu, Chieh-p'ing, ed.
Mu-p'i-san-k'o ku tz'ŭ
see under Chia, Ying-ch'ung, ca. 1589–ca. 1671.

Liu, Chieh-p'ing.
蒲留仙遺著考略與志異遺稿 劉階平玫輯 [臺北] 正中書局 民國 39 [1950]
50 p. (on double leaves) port., facsims. 18 cm.

1. P'u, Sung-ling, 1640–1715. Liao chai chih i.
Title romanized: P'u Liu-hsien i chu k'ao lüeh yü chih i i kao.

C 59–5141
Indiana. Univ. Libr. PL2695
for Library of Congress [2]

NL 0415260 InU WU OU

Liu, Chieh-p'ing.
從白陽傳疏論晚明軍政 劉階平著 臺北 華國出版社 民國 40 [1951]
1 v. (various pagings) 18 cm.

1. Pi, Tzŭ-yen, 1569–1638. 2. China—History, Military. I. Title.
Title romanized: Ts'ung Pai-yang chuan su lun wan Ming chün chêng.

DS753.L548 C 58–6010

NL 0415261 DLC

Liu, Ch'ien.
孔雀東南飛—京劇 柳倩改編 北京 北京大衆出版社 1955.
36 p. 19 cm.
Play.

I. Title.
Title romanized: K'ung ch'üeh tung nan fei.

PL2879.C42K8 C 64–1136 ‡

NL 0415262 DLC

Liu, Chien, *fl.* 1720.
庭聞錄 [6卷] 劉健述 [n. p. 庚子(1720)序]
4 v. (double leaves) in case. 18 cm.
Block print.
附錄 平定緬甸: at end of v. 4.

1. China—Hist.—Shun-chih, 1644–1661. 2. China—Hist.—K'ang-hsi, 1662–1722. I. Title.
Title romanized: T'ing wên lu.

DS754.2.L58 C 66–1334

NL 0415263 DLC

Liu, Ch'ien-chün.
歷代名賢經武粹語 劉千俊編 臺北 正中書局 民國 42 [1953]
272 p. 19 cm.

1. Military art and science. 2. Maxims. I. Title.
Title romanized: Li tai ming hsien ching wu ts'ui yü.

U19.L75 C 58–5714 ‡

NL 0415264 DLC CaBVaU NIC CtY WU

Liu, Ch'ien-chün.
鄂政紀要 劉千俊編着 [n. p.] 民國 34 [1945]
2 v. in 1. tables. 22 cm.
Appendices (v. 2): 陳誠先生重要計劃與言論—湖北省重要單行法令—重慶各報有關鄂政紀載

1. Hupeh, China (Province)—Pol. & govt. I. Title.
Title romanized: O chêng chi yao.

C 58–7529
Hoover Institution
for Library of Congress [2]

NL 0415265 CSt-H

VOLUME 336

Liu, Chien-hêng.
達爾文主義　劉劍横著　[上海　北新書局 1929]
4, 2, 98 p. 18 cm. (社學科學小叢書之)

1. Evolution. I. Title.
Title romanized: Ta-êrh-wên chu i.

QH367.L57　C 67-2661

NL 0415266 DLC

W 4 Liu, Chien-Tau, 1905-
B51 Beobachtungen an 600 autoptisch
1939 kontrollierten Fällen von doppelseitigen Nephropathien. Charlottenburg, Hoffmann, 1939.
49, [2] p.

Inaug.-Diss. - Berlin.
Bibliography: p. [50]

NL 0415267 DNLM

Liu, Ch'ien-tu.
富二嫂的風情　劉前度著　檳城　馬來亞出版社 1953.
88 p. 18 cm. (馬來亞出版社叢書)
Short stories.

I. Title.
Title romanized: Fu êrh sao ti fêng ch'ing.

PL2879.C43F8　C 62-2001 ‡

NL 0415268 DLC

Liu, Chien-wêng.
雍正謀皇秘史　劉建翁編輯　上海　中國第一書局　民國 11 [1922]
1, 2, 136 p. 19 cm.
Colophon title.

1. Ching Shih-tsung, Emperor of China, 1677-1735—Fiction.
Title romanized: Yung-chêng mou huang pi shih.

C 61-4182

Harvard Univ. Chinese-Japanese Library 5776 for Library of Congress [2]

NL 0415269 MH-HY

Liu, Chih, of Ch'ing dynasty.
The Arabian prophet ...
see under Liu, Chieh-lien, fl. 1670-1724.

Liu, Chih-chi, 661-721.
史通　劉知幾撰　浦起龍註釋　曹聚仁校　上海　梁溪圖書館　民國 15 [1926]
[66], 477 p. 19 cm.

1. China — Hist. — Historiography. I. P'u, Ch'i-lung, 1679-ca. 1762, ed. II. Title.
Title romanized: Shih t'ung.

C 63-780

Harvard Univ. Chinese-Japanese Library 2460 for Library of Congress [2]

NL 0415270 MH-HY

Liu, Chih-chi, 661-721.
史通　[劉知幾撰]　選註者劉虎如　上海　商務印書館　民國 17 [1928]
164 p. 19 cm. (學生國學叢書)

1. China—Hist.—Historiography. I. Liu, Hu-ju, ed. II. Title.
Title romanized: Shih t'ung.

DS734.7.L58 1928　C 61-977 ‡

NL 0415271 DLC

Liu, Chih-chi, 661-721.
史通　劉知幾撰　劉虎如選註　上海　商務印書館　民國 18 [1929]
21, 10, 2, 164 p. table. 18 cm. (學生國學叢書)
萬有文庫
In colophon: Selections from Liu Tsu Chi's discourse on history.

1. China—Hist.—Historiography. I. Liu, Hu-ju, ed.
Title romanized: Shih t'ung.

C 61-4158

Harvard Univ. Chinese-Japanese Library 2460 for Library of Congress [2]

NL 0415272 MH-HY

Liu, Chih-chien, joint author.
Chung-kuo li shih ku shih chi
see under Yang, Yeh.

Liu, Chih-chien.
義和团　柳志堅編寫　孫翰春插畫　北京　通俗讀物出版社 1955.
23 p. illus. 18 cm.

1. Boxers. I. Title.
Title romanized: I ho t'uan.

DS771.L58　C 60-2700 rev ‡

NL 0415274 DLC

Liu, Chih-hsiang
see
Liu, K'un, *chin shih* 1903.

Fv Liu, Chih-hsien
5736 Au temps des palanquins de jade. 12 planches
7286 hors-texte dues au pinceau de Dao-Van-Minh.
H1950 Paris, Des Presses du Temps Present 1950
162 p. illus. 19 cm. (Collection:"Connaissance des peuples des quatre-mers")
At head of title: Lao Chi-Hien.
Title in Chinese: [illegible]

1. Short stories, Chinese.
cdu Chin. shelf.

NL 0415276 CtY

Liu, Chih-ming, 1906-
清算蕭軍的反動思想　劉芝明著　香港　新民主出版社 1949.
69 p. 19 cm.

1. Hsiao, Chün, 1908- I. Title.
Title romanized: Ch'ing suan Hsiao Chün ti fan tung ssŭ hsiang.

PL2303.H7L5　C 62-631 ‡

NL 0415277 DLC WaU

Liu, Chih-ming, 1906-
資本主義　劉芝明著　[上海]　生活讀書新知上海聯合發行所 1949.
33 p. 17 cm. (新中國百科小叢書)

1. Capitalism. I. Title.
Title romanized: Tzŭ pên chu i.

HB501.L55　C63-34 ‡

NL 0415278 DLC

Liu, Chih-p'ing, 1909- joint author.
Chien chu shê chi ts'an k'ao t'u chi
see under Liang, Ssŭ-ch'ên, 1901-

Liu, Chih-pu
see
Liu, Frederick Fu, 1919-

Liu, Chih-t'ien.
華僑與菲律濱　劉芝田著　[n. p.]　菲律濱公理報社　民國44 [1955]
159 p. 19 cm.
Bibliography: p. 152-159.

1. Chinese in the Philippine Islands. I. Title.
Title romanized: Hua ch'iao yü Fei-lü-pin.

C 60-5042

Cornell Univ. Library DS666 for Library of Congress [2]

NL 0415281 NIC

Liu, Chin Hsu, 1917-
Studies of the calcium metabolism on dogs. [Ithaca, N.Y.,] 1952.
66 l. illus. 28cm.

Thesis (Ph.D.)—Cornell Univ., Sept., 1952.

NL 0415282 NIC

Liu, Chin-ling
see Liou, Kin-ling.

Liu, Chin-ming, joint author.
Chêng chih ch'ang shih Chung-kuo li shih wên ta
see under Ch'ien, Yeh.

LIU, Chin-Nien.
Contributions to the restricted problem of three bodies. Thesis, Harvard University, 1930.

Typewritten. 1.8°. ff.(2),108.

NL 0415285 MH

VOLUME 336

Liu, Chin-t'ao.
Egg industry in Tientsin. By Liu Chin T'ao. [Tientsin, Hautes études, etc., etc.] 1941. 46 p. 26cm. (Institut des hautes études industrielles et commerciales, Tientsin. Commerce, Faculté de. Economic studies. no. 18.)

Cover-title also in Chinese.
"References," p. 46.

1. Eggs—Trade and stat.—China —Tientsin. I. Ser.
N. Y. P. L. January 7, 1949

NL 0415286 NN

Liu, Chin-tsao, *chin shih* 1894– *comp.*
清朝續文獻通考 [400卷] 劉錦藻撰 上海 商務印書館 民國 25 [1936]

4 v. (7491-11525 p.) 27 cm. (十通第10種)
萬有文庫第 2 集

Caption title: 皇朝續文獻通考
Reprint ed.

1. China—Hist.—Ch'ing dynasty, 1644-1912. I. Title. II. Title: Huang ch'ao hsü wên hsien t'ung k'ao. (Series: Shih t'ung ti 10 chung)
Title romanized: Ch'ing ch'ao hsü wên hsien t'ung k'ao.

DS735.S483 vol. 10 C66-760

NL 0415287 DLC CLU-C

Liu, Ch'ing.
Hsien fa ch'ang shih chiang hua
see under title

Liu, Ch'ing.
普選常識講話 劉青編著 北京 工人出版社 1953.

85 p. 19 cm.

1. Elections—China (People's Republic of China, 1949–) I. Title. *Title romanized:* P'u hsüan ch'ang shih chiang hua.

JQ1518.L5 C 59-2400 ‡

NL 0415289 DLC MiU-L

PL2652 .H78 Orien China

Liu, Ch'ing, 1916–
Hsi shih.
喜事 茅盾等著 [n. p.] 燎原書屋 1946.

Liu, Ch'ing, 1916–
銅牆鐵壁 柳青著 文藝建設叢書編輯委員會編輯 編委丁玲 [等] 北京 人民文学出版社 1951.

347 p. illus. 19 cm. (文藝建設叢書)

1. China—Hist.—1937-1945—Fiction. I. Title.
Title romanized: T'ung ch'iang t'ieh pi.

PL2879.C5T8 C 59-2364 ‡

NL 0415291 DLC MH-HY NIC

Liu, Ch'ing, 1916–
銅牆鐵壁 柳青著 北京 人民文學出版社 1954.

2, 348 p. map. 19 cm.

1. China—Hist.—1937-1945—Fiction. I. Title.
Title romanized: T'ung ch'iang t'ieh pi.

C 59-5294

Cornell Univ. Library for Library of Congress PL3000 [2]

NL 0415292 NIC

Liu, Ching, 1916–
Wall of bronze. [1st ed. Translated by Sidney Shapiro] Peking, Foreign Languages Press, 1954.

283 p. illus. 22 cm.

1. China—Hist.—1937-1945—Fiction. I. Title.

PZ4.L783Wal 55—38605 ‡

NL 0415293 DLC CaOTP WaU KU ICU NcD NNC MH NN CtY CU IaU NjP NIC IEdS CaBVaU OrU

Liu, Ching-an.
中國純文學史綱— 新編分類 劉經菴編著 北平 北平著者書店 民國 24 [1935]

8, 4, 4, 484, 4 p. 20 cm.

Appendices (p. 463-484): 1. 中國歷代文學家籍貫生卒年表— 2. 中國純文學書目舉要

1. Chinese literature—Hist. & crit. I. Title.
Title romanized: Chung-kuo ch'un wên hsüeh shih kang.

PL2264.L53 C 61-4011

Harvard Univ. Chinese-Japanese Library 5220 for Library of Congress [2]†

NL 0415294 MH-HY DLC

Liu, Ching-an.
歌謠與婦女 劉經菴編 上海 商務 民國 17 [1928]

280 p. 20 cm.

1. Folk-lore, Chinese. 2. Folk-lore of woman. I. Title.
Title romanized: Ko yao yü fu nü.

GR470.L46 1928 C 59-2086 ‡

NL 0415295 DLC CaBVaU

Liu, Ching-an.
歌謠與婦女 劉經菴編 上海 商務印書館 民國 23 [1934]

3, 1, 8, 233 p. 19 cm.

1. Folk-lore, Chinese. 2. Folk-lore of woman. I. Title.
Title romanized: Ko yao yü fu nü.

GR470.L46 1934 C59-5256

Chicago. Univ. Far Eastern Library for Library of Congress [3]†

NL 0415296 ICU NIC

Liu Ching Fu
see Fu, Liu Ching.

Liu, Ching-hêng
see
Liu, Hêng-ching.

Liu, Ching-Ho, 1914-
The influence of cultural background on the moral judgment of children. 1950.
101 l. tables. 28½cm.

Thesis, Columbia university.
Typewritten manuscript.
Bibliography: l. 100-101.

NL 0415299 NNC

Liu, Ching-ho, 1914–
The influence of cultural background on the moral judgment of children. Ann Arbor, University Microfilms, 1950.

([University Microfilms, Ann Arbor, Mich.] Publication no. 1869)

Microfilm copy of typewritten ms. Positive.
Collation of the original: 101 l. tables.
Thesis—Columbia University.
Abstracted in Microfilm abstracts, v. 10 (1950) no. 4, p. 319-321.
Bibliography: leaves 100-101.

1. Child study. 2. Character tests. 3. Moral education. 4. Chinese in the U. S. I. Title.

Microfilm AC-1 no. 1869 Mic A 50-138

Michigan. Univ. Libr. for Library of Congress [1]†

NL 0415300 MiU NBuU FMU DLC

Liu, Ch'ing-i, 1881-1932.
see
Liu, Ta-pai, 1881-1932.

547.8 L74s

Liu, Ching-i, 1925-
The structure and properties of some metallic derivatives of dyes. I. Azo dyes. II. Substituted 8-hydroxyquinolines. Urbana [1951]
ii, 87l. diagrs. 28cm.

Thesis--University of Illinois.
Typewritten (carbon copy)
Vita.
Bibliography: leaves 57-58, 86-87.

NL 0415302 IU

Liu, Ching-i, 1925–
The structure and properties of some metallic derivatives of dyes. I. Azo dyes. II. Substituted 8-hydroxyquinolines. Urbana, 1951.

8 p. 23 cm.

Abstract of thesis—University of Illinois.
Vita.
Bibliography: p. 2, 3.

1. Azo compounds. 2. Hydroxyquinoline. 3. Dyes and dyeing—Chemistry.

TP914.L5 A 52-613

Illinois. Univ. Library for Library of Congress [1]†

NL 0415303 IU NIC DLC

Liu, Ch'ing T'i.

SEE

Liu, T'i ch'ing.

Liu, Ching-wên.
政府制度的比較研究 劉靜文著 台北 帕米爾書店 民國 40 [1951]

74 p. 18 cm.

1. China—Constitutional law. 2. Comparative governments. I. Title.
Title romanized: Chêng fu chih tu ti pi chiao yen chiu.

C 62-1005 ‡

NL 0415305 DLC

VOLUME 336

Liu, Ching-wên.
中國憲政原理 劉靜文著 ⌈重慶⌉ 正中書局 民國 31 ⌈1942⌉
106 p. 22 cm. (社會科學叢刊)

1. China—Constitutional law. I. Title.
Title romanized: Chung-kuo hsien chêng yüan li.

C 61-2520 ‡

NL 0415306 DLC

Liu, Ching-wên.
中國憲政原理 劉靜文編著 增訂本 ⌈重慶⌉ 正中書局 民國 33 ⌈1944⌉
171 p. 22 cm.

1. China—Constitutional law. I. Title.
Title romanized: Chung-kuo hsien chêng yüan li.

C62-2503 ‡

NL 0415307 DLC

Liu, Ching-wên.
中國新憲法論 劉靜文著 南京 獨立出版社 民國 35 ⌈1946⌉
3, 131 p. 19 cm.

1. China—Constitutional law. I. Title.
Title romanized: Chung-kuo hsin hsien fa lun.

C 67-564

NL 0415308 DLC

Liu, Ching-wên.
憲法中政府制的比較研究 劉靜文著 南京 帕米爾書店 民國 37 ⌈1948⌉
74 p. 18 cm.
In colophon: 憲法中各國政府的制度比較

1. China—Pol. & govt.—1912-1949. I. Title.
Title romanized: Hsien fa chung chêng fu chih tu ti pi chiao yen chiu.

JQ1510.L5 C 62-2108 ‡

NL 0415309 DLC

Liu, Chiung-shih.
中國憲法論 劉炯時著 ⌈n. p.⌉ 廣東文化事業公司總經售 民國 35 ⌈1946⌉
74 p. 23 cm.
附錄 中華民國憲法草案 (五五憲草): p. 60-74.

I. China. Constitution. II. Title.
Title romanized: Chung-kuo hsien fa lun.

C 64-1977

NL 0415310 DLC

Liu, Chou-fêng
see Liu, Mrs. Dolly.

Liu, Ch'u-ch'iang.
Introversive centripetal contraction physiotherapy. 1st ed. Taipei, 1953.
51 p. illus.
Corrections slip inserted.

NL 0415312 ICJ OC1W-H

Liu, Chü-ho.
工廠檢查概論 劉巨壑著 上海 商務印書館 民國 23 ⌈1934⌉
306 p. illus. 23 cm.

1. Factory inspection. I. Title.
Title romanized: Kung ch'ang chien ch'a kai lun.

HD3656.L5 C 62-643 ‡

NL 0415313 DLC

Liu, Chüeh.
中國歷史上之民族英雄 劉覺編著 重慶 商務印書館 民國 32-33 ⌈1943-44⌉
2 v. in 1. 18 cm.

1. China—Biog. 2. China—History, Military. I. Title.
Title romanized: Chung-kuo li shih shang chih min tsu ying hsiung.

DS734.L527 C 67-26

NL 0415314 DLC

Liu, Ch'ün.
中國在統一中 劉羣著 ⌈n. p.⌉ 新生出版社 民國 26 ⌈1937⌉
3, 2, 208 p. 19 cm.

1. China—Hist.—1937-1945. I. Title.
Title romanized: Chung-kuo tsai t'ung i chung.

DS777.53.L577 C 66-1422

NL 0415315 DLC NIC

Liu, Ch'ün.
現代學生的根本問題 劉羣著 上海 現代出版社 民國 25 ⌈1936⌉
2, 2, 98 p. tables. 19 cm.
Appendix (p. 83-98): 學生運動統計

1. Students—China. I. Title.
Title romanized: Hsien tai hsüeh shêng ti kên pên wên t'i.

C 58-7470

Hoover Institution 4180.1
for Library of Congress ⌈2⌉

NL 0415316 CSt-H

Liu, Chün, joint author.
Kang t'ieh ti huo hua chien pieh fa
see under Chang, Yin-lang.

Liu, Chün-jên.
中國地名大辭典 劉鈞仁著 北平 國立北平研究院出版部 民國19 ⌈1930⌉
4, 8, 1118, 232, 5 p. 26 cm.
At head of title: 國立北平研究院

1. China—Gazetteers. I. Pei-p'ing yên chiu yüan. II. Title.
Title romanized: Chung-kuo ti ming ta tz'ŭ tien.

DS705.L5 C 66-1268

NL 0415318 DLC

PL2384 Liu, Chun-jo, 1922-
L57 A study of the Tsa-chü of the thirteenth century in China. ⌈Madison, University of Wisconsin, 1952⌉
iii, 184, 54, 38, 44 l. 28 cm.

Xerographic reproduction.
Thesis (Ph.D.) - University of Wisconsin, 1952.
Bibliography: leaves 173-185.

1. Chinese drama - Yüan dynasty, 1279-1368 - Hist. & crit. I. Ti[...]

NL 0415319 NjR

Liu, Ch'un-pai.
國際貿易 劉純白著 臺北 國際經濟研究社 民國 44 ⌈1955⌉
227 p. illus. 19 cm. (國際經濟叢書)

1. Commerce. I. Title. *Title romanized:* Kuo chi mao i.

HF1007.L82 C 60-1383 ‡

NL 0415320 DLC

Liu, Chung.
模範縣政 ⌈劉鐘編 上海 三民公司⌉ 民國18 ⌈1929⌉
11, 8, 240 p. 18 cm.
On spine: 訓政時期模範縣政 三民圖書公司

1. County government—China. I. Title.
Title romanized: Mo fan hsien chêng.

JS7353.A8L57 C 67-2321

NL 0415321 DLC

Liu, Ch'ung-chieh, 1880- tr.
Hsin i Jih-pên fa kuei ta ch'üan
see under Japan. Laws, statutes, etc.

Liu, Chung-ch'ien, *ed.*
物品名目彙編—中英文對照 劉仲謙 姚元綸合編 Names of commodities and other appellatives in Chinese and English, by Lau Chung Him & Yao Yuan Lun. 1st ed. 香港 劉仲謙會計師事務所 Lau Chung Him & Co., 1955.
479 p. 19 cm.
1. Commercial products—Dictionaries—Chinese. 2. Chinese language—Dictionaries—English. I. Yao, Yüan-lun, joint ed. II. Title. III. Title: Names of commodities and other appellatives in Chinese and English.
Title romanized: Wu p'in ming mu hui pien.

HF1002.L5 C 58-5390 rev ‡

NL 0415323 DLC DNAL

VOLUME 336

Liu, Ch'ung-hêng, joint author.
Wu li hsüeh.

Wu, Yu-jên.
物理學 吳友仁 劉崇恒編著 臺北 正中書局 民國 44 [1955]

Liu, Chung-ho.
青年先鋒 劉中和著 臺北 幼獅出版社 民國 44 [1955]
30 p. illus. 16 cm. (幼獅通訊叢書之 7)

1. Youth—Formosa. I. Title.
Title romanized: Ch'ing nien hsien fêng.

HQ799.F6L5 C 58-7218

Hoover Institution for Library of Congress 4788.561 [2]†

NL 0415325 CSt-H DLC CLSU OCU WaU-FE

Liu, Ch'ung-hsi
see
Liu, Hans, 1901–

Liu, Chung-jui.
陝西灌溉事業之實際問題 陝南新興水利事業概況 漢江上游農田水利事業之概況 劉鍾瑞著 [西安] 陝西省政府水利局 [1941?]
36 p. (on double leaves) 26 cm.

1. Irrigation—China—Shensi. I. Title.
Title romanized: Shan-hsi kuan kai shih yeh chih shih chi wên t'i.

TC702.S4L5 C 62-2111 ‡

NL 0415327 DLC

Thesis 1926 L783

Liu, Ch'ung-lo, 1901-
On some factors of natural control of the eastern tent caterpillar (Malacosoma americana Harris), with notes on the biology of the host. Ithaca, N. Y., 1926.
212 l. illus. 27 cm.

Thesis (Ph.D.) - Cornell Univ., May 1926.

1. Eastern tent caterpillar. 2. Insect control - Biological control. [I. Title]

NL 0415328 NIC

Film N1240

Liu, Ch'ung-lo, 1901-
On some factors of natural control of the eastern tent caterpillar (Malacosoma americana Harris), with notes on the biology of the host. Ithaca, N. Y., 1926.
212 l. plates. 27cm.

Thesis (Ph. D.)--Cornell University, June, 1926.
Microfilm (negative) Ithaca, N. Y., Photo Science, Cornell University, 1965. 1 reel. 35mm.

NL 0415329 NIC

Liu, Ch'ung-lo, 1901–
On some factors of natural control of the eastern tent caterpillar (*Malacosoma americana* Harris), with notes on the biology of the host ... by Chung lo Liu. Ithaca, N. Y. [1926]
[3] p. 23cm.

Abstract of thesis (PH. D.)—Cornell university, 1926.

1. Tent-caterpillars. 2. Parasites—Larvae.

34-22041

Library of Congress SB945.T36L5 1926
Cornell Univ. Libr.
——— Copy 2. [2] [632.96] 632.787

NL 0415330 NIC DLC OU

JQ1519 .A52L46 LLFE

Liu, Chung-nung.
黨務政治工作指南 劉重農編著 [北平] 北平聯興印務局 民國18 [1929]
2, 18, 420 p. illus. (part col.) forms. 26 cm.
Cover title.

1. Chuhg-kuo kuo min tang—Party work. I. Title.
Title romanized: Tang wu chêng chih kung tso chih nan.

JQ1519.A52L46 74-836876

NL 0415331 DLC

Liu, Ch'ung-wu.
新中國的農業生產 劉崇武編著 [北京] 生活•讀書•新知三聯書店 [1953]
54 p. 18 cm.

1. Agriculture—China (People's Republic of China, 1949-) I. Title.
Title romanized: Hsin Chung-kuo ti nung yeh shêng ch'an.

S471.C6L49 C 67-2702

NL 0415332 DLC

Liu, Chung-ying, 1876- ed.
Min fa chi ch'êng shih i
see under China. Laws, statutes, etc.

Liu, Chungshee H.
see
Liu, Hans, 1901–

Liu, D.K., 1890-1962
see Liu, Ta-chün, 1890-1962.

Liû, Da-nìan
see Liu, Ta-nien.

Liu, *Mrs.* Dolly.
"Chow"; secrets of Chinese cooking, with selected recipes, by Dolly Liu; illustrated by Henry Liu. Shanghai [etc.] Kelly & Walsh, limited, 1939.
vi, viii, 183 p. front. (ports.) illus. (1 col.) plates (part col.) 20cm.
Title also in Chinese on cover.
"Errata" slips mounted on p. 161 and p. 163.

1. Cookery, Chinese. I. Title.

39-21344

Library of Congress TX725.L5 1939
Copyright A ad int. 25132 [2] 641.5951

NL 0415337 DLC

LIU, DOLLY.
"Chow;" secrets of Chinese cooking with selected recipes, by Dolly Chow (Mrs. C. T. Wang) [with notes on table etiquette] Illustrated by Henry Liu. Rutland, Vt., C. E. Tuttle, 1952. ix, 174 p. illus. 19cm.

On cover: By Dolly Liu (Miss C. T. Wang).

Cookery, Chinese. 2. Etiquette, Table—China.

NL 0415338 NN MiD OCl ViU MB WaE NIC AU

TX725 L5 1953

Liu, Dolly.
Chow! Secrets of Chinese cooking, with selected recipes by Dolly Chow (Mrs. C.T. Wang) Illustrated by Henry Liu. [New and completely rev. ed.] Rutland, Vt., C.E. Tuttle Co., 1953.
ix, 174 p. illus. 19cm.

1. Cookery, Chinese. I. Title.

NL 0415339 CoU

Liu, Ê, 1857–1909.
老殘遊記 繡像繪圖—通俗小說 [劉鶚著] 香港 五桂堂書局 [1934 序]
95 p. illus. 19 cm.

I. Title.
Title romanized: Lao-ts'an yu chi.

PL2718.I 8L3 1934 C 63-318 ‡

NL 0415340 DLC

Liu, Ê, 1857–1909.
老殘遊記 劉鶚著 正續集合訂本 香港 廣智書局 [195-]
2, 324 p. illus. 19 cm.

I. Title.
Title romanized: Lao-ts'an yu chi.

C 61-4218

Cornell Univ. Library for Library of Congress PL3000 [2]

NL 0415341 NIC

Liu, Ê, 1857-1909. Lao-ts'an yu chi êrh chi.

PZ3 .L6367 Nu

Lin, Yutang, 1895- tr.
A nun of Taishan (a novelette) and other translations; translated by Lin Yutang. Shanghai, China, The Commercial press, limited, 1936.

Wason PL3000 L78 1947

Liu, Ê, 1857-1909.
"Mr. Decadent" Tr. by H. Y. Yang and G. M. Taylor. [Nanking, Tu li ch'u pan shê, 1947]
319 p. 19cm.

In Chinese and English. Title in Chinese: Lao ts'an yu chi.

I. Title. II. Lao ts'an yu chi. III. Yang, Hsien-i, tr. IV. Taylor, G. M., jt. tr.

NL 0415343 NIC

VOLUME 336

PL 2718 LIU, Ê, 1857-1909
.I8 L22 Mr. Derelict. Translated by H. Y. Yang
1948 and G.M. Tayler. London, Allen & Unwin
[1948]
167 p.

NL 0415344 InU NN CLSU ICU MH CaOTP

Liu, Ê, 1857-1909.
Putování Starého Chromce. [Z čínského originálu přeložil a úvod napsal Jaroslav Průšek. Básnické vložky přebásnil Bohumil Mathesius. 1. vyd. V Praze] Melantrich [1947]
403 p. illus. 20 cm. (Země a světla východu. Řada druhá, svazek 2)
I. Průšek, Jaroslav, tr. II. Mathesius, Bohumil. 1. Chinese language - Texts and translations.

NL 0415345 CtY

[Liu, Ê] 1857-1909.
Tramp doctor's travelogue, English version by Lin Yi-chin ... and Ko Te-shun ... with a foreword by Professor G. N. Ling ... [Shanghai] China, The commercial press, ltd., 1939.
vi p., 1 l., 263 p., 1 l. 19 cm.
By Liu Eh. cf. Translators' note.

I. Lin, I-chin, tr. II. Ko, Tê-shun, joint tr. III. Title.

PZ3.L74Tr 43-28877 rev

NL 0415346 DLC NIC ICU

Liu, Ê, 1857-1909.
The travels of Lao Ts'an, by Liu T'ieh-yün (Liu E); translated from the Chinese and annotated by Harold Shadick. Ithaca, Cornell University Press [1952]
xxiii, 277 p. illus. 24 cm.
A novel.
Bibliographical references included in "Notes" (p. 232-266)

I. Title.

PL2999.L5A74 895.13 52—14772

CaBVa WaT OrU CaBVaU Wa MoU
OU PU PPL NN DS IU OO AU NcU NIC MU RPB ViU ScU
NL 0415347 DLC KEmT DAU NIC NBuU OC1MA MB NcD NcGU

Liu, Eh
see Liu, Ê, 1857-1909.

Liu, En-Lan
Rainfall variations in China: their nature, causes and effects. [n.p., 1940?]
292p. illus.
Thesis (D.Phil.) - St. Hilda's College.
Contains bibliography.

1. Rain and rainfall - China. I. Title

NL 0415349 MBdAF

SH319 Liu, Fah-hsuen.
F7A3 Review on the trawling ground of South China Sea.
no. 1 (1. Region between Penhu and Hainan Island) By Liu Fah-Hsuen [and] Chen Gin-Chen. [n.p.] 1952.
5, 3, 34 p. maps. 26 cm. (Formosa Fishery Rehabilitation Administration. Research Laboratory. Report no. 1)
Cover title.
In Chinese; added titles and summary in English.
1. Fisheries - Formosa. 2. Traws and trawling. 3. Fishing grounds - South China Sea. I. Chen, Gin-chen, jt. author. (Series)

NL 0415350 DI

Liu, Fan-ju.
書畫人物 劉芃如著 香港 集文出版社 1955.
101 p. illus. 19 cm.

1. Authors. I. Title. *Title romanized:* Shu, hua, jên wu.

PN500.L5 C 59-91 ‡

NL 0415351 DLC

Liu, Fang-hsün, joint author.
T'ien chien ti tsa ts'ao
see under Sun, Tai-yang.

Liu, Fêng.
鄉下丫頭 柳風著 [北平 海音書局] 1929.
2, 140 p. illus. 21 cm. (海音社文藝叢書之 8)
Short stories.

I. Title.
Title romanized: Hsiang hsia ya t'ou.

PL2782.F4H75 C 68-745

NL 0415353 DLC

Mic Liu, Frederick Fu, 1919-
The Nationalist army of China; an administrative study of the period 1924-1946, by Frederick Fu Liu. [Princeton, N.J.] 1951.
381 l.
Thesis (Ph.D.) - Princeton University.
Includes bibliographical references.
Microfilm of typescript. Ann Arbor, Mich., University Microfilms [n.d.] 1 reel. 35 mm.

1. China - History, Military. 2. China. Army - Hist. I. Title. nuc

NL 0415354 MoSW WU

Liu, Fu, 1891-1934.
中國文法講話 劉復著 [上海] 北新書局 [1932]
2, 10, 176 p. 21 cm.

1. Chinese language—Grammar. I. Title.
Title romanized: Chung-kuo wên fa chiang hua.

PL1103.L55 C 67-3220

NL 0415355 DLC

Liu, Fu, 1891-1934.
中國文法通論 [劉復著 上海 中華書局 1939]
viii, 136 p. 23 cm.

1. Chinese language—Grammar. I. Title.
Title romanized: Chung-kuo wên fa t'ung lun.

PL1103.L57 1939 C 67-3231

NL 0415356 DLC WU

Liu, Fu, 1891-1934.
... Étude expérimentale sur les tons du chinois, par Fu Liu ... Paris, Société d'édition "Les Belles lettres"; [etc., etc.] 1925.
viii, 121 p., 1 l. illus., fold. tab., fold. diagrs. and atlas of XXVIII fold. pl. on 14 l. 25½ cm. (Collection de l'Institut de phonétique et des Archives de la parole, fasc. I)
Half-title in Chinese.

1. Chinese language—Intonation.

PL1213.L5 495.115 34-29967 rev

NL 0415357 DLC FMU NjP NIC NN TxU

4PL Liu, Fu, 1891-1934.
184 Les mouvements de la langue nationale en Chine. Paris, Société d'édition "Les Belles Lettres", 1925.
56 p.

WaU CtY CaBVaU
NL 0415358 DLC -P4 DLC MH CSt-H NN InU NjP IU NIC

Liu, Fu, 1891-1934.

Liu, T'ien-hua, 1895-1932.
[Works]

The musical compositions of the late Liu T'ien-hwa. Edited by his brother, Liu Fu. With a biographical note on the lamented deceased and a selection of dedicatory compositions by his bereft friends. Peiping, 1933.

Liu, Fu, 1891-1934, ed.
Sai-chin-hua pên shih
see under Sai-chin-hua, 1874-1936.

Liu, Fu, 1891-1934, comp.
宋元以來俗字譜 劉復 李家瑞編 北平 國立中央研究院歷史語言研究所 [民國19 (1930)]
6, 8, 137, 2 p. facsims. 28 cm. (國立中央研究院歷史語言研究所單刊之 3)

1. Chinese characters—Hist. I. Li, Chia-jui, joint comp. II. Title. (Series: Chung yang yen chiu yüan. Li shih yü yen yen chiu so, Nan-kang, Formosa. Chung yang yen chiu yüan li shih yü yen yen chiu so tan k'an chih 3)
Title romanized: Sung Yüan i lai su tzŭ p'u.

PL1171.L47 C 67-23

NL 0415361 DLC

Liu, Fu, 1891-1934, ed.
Tun-huang to so.
Tun-huang manuscripts.
燉煌掇瑣 [上中輯 劉復編 n.p., 195-]

Liu, Fu, 1919-
see
Liu, Frederick Fu, 1919-

VOLUME 336

Liu, Fu-hua.
少年創作 劉復華編 香港 少年出版社 民國 43 [1954]
85 p. 18 cm. (少年叢書)

I. Title. *Title romanized:* Shao nien ch'uang tso.

PZ90.C5L47 C 60-1574 ‡

NL 0415364 DLC

Microfilm Soc. Sci. 62-9
Liu, Fu-ju.
A comparative demographic study of native-born and foreign-born Chinese populations in the United States. Ann Arbor, University Microfilms [1953]
Microfilm copy (positive) of typescript. Collation of the original: 254 l. tables.
Thesis - Michigan State College.
Bibliography: leaves 209-213.
1. Chinese in the U. S. I. Title.

NL 0415365 NBC

QL 1 H331 v.87 no.2
Liu, Gaines Kan-chih.
New Oriental Cicadidae in the Museum of Comparative Zoölogy. Cambridge, The Museum, 1940.
[73]-117 p. 7 plates. 25cm. (Bulletin of the Museum of Comparative Zoölogy, at Harvard College, v. 87, no. 2)
1. Cicadidae. I. Harvard University. Museum of Comparative Zoology.

NL 0415366 NIC NjP MU

Liü, Go-tszün'
see
Liu, Kuo-chün.

Liu, Hai-ch'ing.
測量儀器的使用檢修與保養法 劉海清編著 上海 中國科學圖書儀器公司 1954.
888 p. illus. 21 cm.

1. Surveying—Instruments. I. Title.
Title romanized: Ts'ê liang i ch'i ti shih yung chien hsiu yü pao yang fa.

TA562.L5 C 58-5129 ‡

NL 0415368 DLC

Liu, Hai-p'êng.
中國的土壤 劉海蓬編著 上海 商務 1953.
74 p. illus. 19 cm. (中國富源小叢書)

1. Soils—China. I. Title. *Title romanized:* Chung-kuo ti t'u jang.

S599.C5L5 C 59-702 ‡

NL 0415369 DLC KU

SD221 .L4
Liu, Hai-p'êng. Chung-kuo ti t'u jang.
Леса и почвы Китая; географический сборник. Перевод с китайского Б. А. Митбрейта и Я. М. Бергера. Ред. и предисл. Н. П. Ремезова. Москва, Изд-во иностранной лит-ры, 1955.

Liu, Hai-p'êng.
... Soils of Chengtu and Hwayang area, Szechuan, by H. P. Liu ... Pehpei, Chungking, China [1941]
1 p. l., 34, 3 p., 1 l. fold. map, tables, fold. diagr. 26½cm. (China. Geological survey. Soil bulletin, no. 23)
Text in Chinese; summary in English.
Published by the National geological survey of China (under the Ministry of economic affairs) with the support of the China foundation for the promotion of education and culture.

1. Soils—China—Szechuan. I. National academy of Peiping. Institute of geology. II. China foundation for the promotion of education and culture.
[S599.C5A3 no. 23] (631.470951) G S 47-77
U. S. Geol. survey. Library for Library of Congress [3]

NL 0415371 DI-GS

Liu, Hai-shêng.
中國之現狀及其前途 劉海生著 [n. p. 1950]
78 p. 19 cm.
Cover title.

1. China—Pol. & govt.—1949- I. Title.
Title romanized: Chung-kuo chih hsien chuang chi ch'i ch'ien t'u.
C 61-4399
Yale Univ. Library for Library of Congress [3]

NL 0415372 CtY

ND 1040 .L78
Liu, Hai-su, 1895-
Chinesische Malerei der Gegenwart. [Berlin, C.Koch, Lichtdruckerei, 193-?]
12 p. 51 plates. 32 cm.
Cover title.
"Die heutige Richtung der chinesischen Malerei und ihr Ursprung, von Professor Liu Hai-su": p.1-12.
Plates no.1-11 are reproductions of the author's paintings.
1.Paintings,Chinese. 2.Painting,Chinese--Hist. I.Title.

NL 0415373 MiU MH NIC

Liu Han.
... Étude sur la réforme de l'éducation contemporaine en Chine ... Paris, E. Muller, 1933.
129, [10] p. 25 cm.
Thèse - Univ. de Paris.
"Bibliographie": p. [136-137]
1. Education - China.

NL 0415374 CtY NIC

Law
Liu, Han-chang, ed.
Chi ch'êng fa.
China. *Laws, statutes, etc.*
繼承法 劉含章著 司法院法官訓練所主編 重慶 商務印書館 民國 33 [1944]

Liu, Hans, 1901-
Hainan, the island and the people, by Hans Liu. [Shanghai, China Journal Pub. Co., 1939?]
30 p. illus. 25 cm.
"Reprinted from the China journal, vol. XXIX, nos. 5-6, pp. 236-246, 302-314."
Includes bibliography.

1. Hainan.
DS793.H3L5 915.1278 57-55979 ‡

NL 0415376 DLC

Liu, Hans, 1901- ...
Sur un instrument musical à anches libres en usage chez les Miao dans la Chine du Sud-Ouest. (IN: L'Ethnographie. Paris. 29cm. Nouv. sér., no.28-29 (15 avril-15 déc. 1934) p.[27]-34. illus.)

Bibliography, p. 34.

1. Lu-sheng. 2. Instruments, Chinese.

NL 0415377 NN

Liu, Hêng-ching.
寡婦的心 劉靜衡(衡靜)著 [n. p.] 言行社 民國 30 [1941]
197 p. 18 cm.
Short stories.

I. Title.
Title romanized: Kua fu ti hsin.

PL2879.H4K8 C 62-2949 ‡

NL 0415378 DLC

Liu, Herman Chan-En, 1896-1938.
和平運動討論大綱 劉湛恩 陳伯華 孫祖基編輯 Peace program for China; a syllabus of questions with reference material for use by civic clubs and discussion groups, by Herman C. E. Liu, T. N. Chan & T. C. Sun. 上海 青年協會書報部 1926.
2, 130 p. 19 cm. (公民教育叢刊第15種 Citizenship training series, no. 15)
Colophon title.
Cover title: 和平運動
In Chinese.
1. China — Pol. & govt. — 1912-1949. I. Ch'ên, Po-hua, joint author. II. Sun, Tsu-chi, joint author. III. Title.
Title romanized: Ho p'ing yün tung t'ao lun ta kang.
DS775.L53 C 68-2216

NL 0415379 DLC

Liu, Herman Chan-En, 1896-
Non-verbal intelligence tests for use in China, by Herman Chan-En Liu ... New York city, Teachers college, Columbia university, 1922.
viii, [2], 84 p., 1 l. incl. illus., tables, diagrs. 25cm.
Thesis (PH. D.)—Columbia university, 1922.
Vita.
Published also as Teachers college, Columbia university, Contributions to education, no. 126.
Bibliography: p. [83]-84.

1. Mental tests. I. Title.

Library of Congress LB1131.L5 1922 a 22-23343

NL 0415380 DLC

Liu, Herman Chan-En, 1896-
Non-verbal intelligence tests for use in China, by Herman Chan-En Liu ... New York city, Teachers college, Columbia university, 1922.
viii, [2], 84 p. incl. illus., tables, diagrs. 23½cm. (Teachers college, Columbia university. Contributions to education, no. 126)
Bibliography: p. [83]-84.

1. Mental tests. I. Title.
Library of Congress LB1131.L5 22-14979
——— Copy 2. LB5.C8

ViU PBm OCU OU ODW MiU OO OCl MB
NL 0415381 DLC OKentU PSt MtU ICJ OrCS OrU WaTC

Liu, Hiang
see
Liu, Hsiang, 77?-6? B. C.

VOLUME 336

Liu, Ho.
Aperçu bibliographique sur les anciens traités chinois de botanique, d'agriculture, de sériciculture et de fungiculture ... par Liou-Ho ... et Claudius Roux ... avec 2 planches hors texte. Lyon, Imprimerie Bosc frères & Riou, 1927.
cover-title, 39 p. II pl. on 1 l. 25cm.
"Index des sources et références": p. 30-37.
"Titres chinois de quelques uns des ouvrages cités": p. 37-38.

1. Botany—China—Bibl. 2. Agriculture—China—Bibl. 3. Sericulture—China — Bibl. 4. Fungi — China — Bibl. 5. Chinese literature — Bibl. I. Roux, Claudius, 1872- joint author. II. Title.
28-5015
Library of Congress Z5358.C5L7

NL 0415383 DLC NN MH-A

S185is
405
Liu, Ho.
... Contribution à l'étude systématique et phytogéographique des lauracées de Chine et d'Indochine ... Paris, Jouve & c^ie, 1932.
2p.l.,207p.,2l.incl.illus.,diagrs. 3pl., map. 24cm.
Thèse - Univ. de Paris.

1.Lauraceae - China. 2.Lauraceae - Indo-China. x.Ho, Liou

NL 0415384 CtY

Liu, Ho.
Lauracées de Chine et d'Indochine; contribution à l'étude systématique et phytogéographique, par Liou Ho ... Paris, Hermann & c^ie, 1934.
xii, 226, [2] p. illus., plates, map, diagr. 25½cm.
Added t.-p. in Chinese.
"Postface de l'auteur" [in Chinese]: p. 219-220; "Postface de m. le professeur Lo Che Yi [in Chinese]: p. 221-226.

1. Botany—China. [1. China—Botany] 2. Botany—Indo-China. 2. Indo-China—Botany] 3. Lauraceae.
Agr 36-159
Library, U. S. Dept. of Agriculture 452.3L74 [QK495.L]

NL 0415385 DNAL NNBG CtY WaU NIC MiU NcD NN CU

Liu, Ho, 1898-
... The salt requirement of tobacco grown in sand cultures, by Ho Liu. College Park, Md., The University of Maryland, Agricultural experiment station, 1926.
1 p. l., [132]-153, [2] p. illus., diagr. 23cm. ([Maryland: Agricultural experiment station] Bulletin no. 288)
"Portion of a thesis submitted to the graduate faculty of the University of Maryland in partial fulfillment of the requirement for the degree of doctor of philosophy [1925]."
"Literature cited": p. 152-153.

1. Tobacco. 2. Plants, Effect of salt on. I. Title.
28-15685
Library of Congress S71.E3 no. 288
Univ. of Maryland Libr. [2]

NL 0415386 MdU DLC

Liu, Ho-tung
see
Liu, Tsung-yüan, 773-819.

633.74 L741g
Liu, Hou-lee, 1915-
Genetic studies on soybeans. Urbana c1948.
1Cl, vi l. illus., diagrs., tables. 28cm.
Thesis--University of Illinois.
Typewritten (carbon copy)
Vita.
Bibliography: leaves i-vi.

1. Soy-bean. 2. Heredity.

NL 0415388 IU

Liu, Hou-lee, 1915-
Genetic studies on soybeans. Urbana, 1948.
13 p. 23 cm.
Abstract of thesis—Univ. of Illinois.
Vita.

1. Soy-bean. 2. Heredity.
SB205.S7L58 A 48-10131 rev*
Illinois. Univ. Library for Library of Congress [r48b1]†

NL 0415389 IU DLC

Liu, Hsi-fan.
嶺表紀蠻 劉錫蕃著 上海 商務印書館 民國 24 [1935]
[30], 307 p. illus., maps, ports. 23 cm.

1. Minorities—Kwangsi, China (Province) 2. Ethnology—China. I. Title.
Title romanized: Ling piao chi man.
DS730.L57 C 66-2545

NL 0415390 DLC WU

Liu, Hsi-fan.
苗荒小紀 劉介[錫蕃]著 上海 商務印書館 民國 23 [1934]
2, 3, 39 p. illus. 19 cm. (史地小叢書)

1. Miao people. 2. Ethnology—China—Kwangsi (Province) I. Title.
Title romanized: Miao huang hsiao chi.
DS731.M5L58 C 67-10

NL 0415391 DLC

PL2718
.I 83C5
1838
Orien
China
Liu, Hsi-hai, *d.* 1853.
嘉蔭簃論泉絕句 [2卷 劉喜海著 n. p.] 道光戊戌 [1838]
2 v. (double leaves) in case. 27 cm.
Caption title: 嘉蔭簃論泉截句
Running title: 論泉絕句
1. Money in literature. I. Title. II. Title: Lun ch'üan chüeh chü.
Title romanized: Chia yin i lun ch'üan chüeh chü.
PL2718.I 83C5 1838 C 63-1568

NL 0415392 DLC

Liu, Hsi-wei, *pseud.*
see
Li, Chien-wu, 1908?-

Liu, Hsi-wu.
黨治與立法 劉錫五著 臺北 中央文物供應社 民國 42 [1953]
57 p. 19 cm. (三民主義叢書)

1. China—Constitutional history. I. Title.
Title romanized: Tang chih yü li fa.
JQ1503 1953.L5 C 61-1139 ‡

NL 0415394 DLC

Liu, Hsi-wu.
顏習齋學傳 劉錫五著 臺北 中央文物供應社 民國 43 [1954]
68 p. 19 cm. (中國文化叢書)

1. Yen, Yüan, 1635-1704.
Title romanized: Yen Hsi-chai hsüeh chuan.
B128.Y42L5 C 59-249 ‡

NL 0415395 DLC CaBVaU MnU

Liu, Hsia.
十八年來之中國青年黨 柳下編 成都 國魂書店 民國30 [1941]
70 p. 19 cm.

1. Chung-kuo ch'ing nien tang. I. Title.
Title romanized: Shih pa nien lai chih Chung-kuo ch'ing nien tang.
JQ1519.A55L5 C 64-2240

NL 0415396 DLC CtY CLU-O

Liu, Hsia.
十八年來之中國青年黨 柳下編 [成都 國魂書店 民國30 i. e. 1941]
70 p.
Xerox copy. Washington, D. C., Center for Chinese Research Materials, Association of Research Libraries, 1970? [40] l. 28 cm. 3.50
1. Chung-kuo ch'ing nien tang. I. Title.
Title romanized: Shih pa nien lai chih Chung-kuo ch'ing nien tang.
JQ1519.A55L5 1941a 78-839572

NL 0415397 DLC ICRL

Liu, Hsia-Ling.
The theory of the state in Dr. Sun Yat-sen's political philosophy. [Cincinnati] 1949.
72 p.
Thesis.

NL 0415398 OCU

Liu, Hsiang, 77?-6? B. C.
PL2521
C53
1950z
Orien
China
Ch'u tz'ŭ
Ch'u tz'ŭ. *Selections.*
楚辭 沈雁冰選註 香港 丁酉印書社 [195-]

Liu, Hsiang, 77?-6? B.C.
Hsin hsü t'ung chien
see under Chung Fa Han hsüeh yen chiu so.

Liu, Hsiang, 77?-6? *B. C.*
顧虎頭畫列女傳 [8卷 劉向編撰 顧愷之圖畫] 南宋余氏本 [n. p.] 揚州阮氏影橅重刊 道光5 [1825 跋]
2 v. (double leaves) in 1. illus. 27 cm.
Caption title: 新編古列女傳
Block print.

1. Women in China. 2. China — Soc. life & cust. I. Ku, K'ai-chih, ca. 350-ca. 410, illus. II. Title: Lieh nü chuan.
Title romanized: Ku Hu-t'ou hua Lieh nü chuan.
DS725.L49 1825 C 63-2095

NL 0415401 DLC

VOLUME 336

Liu, Hsiang, 77?–6? *B. C., supposed author.*
Le Lie-sien tchouan: biographies légendaires de immortels taoïstes de l'antiquité. Traduit et annoté par Max Kaltenmark. Pékin [Centre d'études sinologiques de Pékin] 1953.
iii, 204 p. 26 cm.
At head of title: Université de Paris. Publications du Centre d'études sinologiques de Pékin.
Title and imprint also in Chinese.
"Différentes éditions donnent, comme nom d'auteur, Lieou Hiang."
"Complément aux Addenda et corrigenda" inserted.
Bibliography: p. [27]–29.
1. Legends, Chinese. I. Kaltenmark, Max, ed. and tr. II. Title.
PL2663.L5A35 66-46252
NIC MiU InU
NL 0415402 DLC NPurMC MH RPB CtY OCl CSt NNC NN

Liu, Hsiang, 77?–6? *B. C.*
列仙傳 [4卷 劉向選 還初道人輯 n. p.] 在兹堂藏板 道光癸巳[1833]鐫
4 v. (double leaves) in case. ports. 27 cm.
Block print.
I. Hung, Ying-ming, fl. 1596, ed. II. Title.
Title romanized: Lieh hsien chuan.
PL2663.L5A6 1833 C 66-2864
NL 0415403 DLC NIC

Liu, Hsiang, 77? -6? B.C. Lieh nü chuan.
HQ1737 .O5
O'Hara, Albert Richard, 1907–
... The position of woman in early China according to the Lieh nü chuan, "The biographies of eminent Chinese women," by Albert Richard O'Hara ... Washington, D. C., The Catholic university of America press, 1945.

[**Liu, Hsiang,**] 77?–6? *B. C.*
Typical women of China. (Abridged from the Chinese work "Records of virtuous women of ancient and modern times.") By Miss A. C. Safford. Shanghai [etc.] Kelly and Walsh, limited, 1891.
3 p. l., [v]–x, 192 p., 1 l. plates. 16½ x 16½ cm.
1. Women in China. 2. China—Soc. life & cust. I. Safford, Miss A. C., tr. II. Title.
DS725.L5 1891 396.0951 34-35571 rev
NL 0415405 DLC

[**Liu, Hsiang,**] 77?–6? *B. C.*
Typical women of China. Translated from a popular native work on the virtues, words, deportment, and employment of the women of China, by the late Miss A. C. Safford ... Edited by John Fryer ... 2d ed. Shanghai [etc.] Kelly & Walsh, limited, 1899.
3 p. l., [v]–x, 192 p., 1 l. plates. 16½ x 16½ cm.
1. Women in China. 2. China—Soc. life & cust. I. Safford, Miss A. C., tr. II. Title.
DS725.L5 1899 396.0951 13-11117 rev 2
OCl
NL 0415406 DLC NIC IaU CU ICJ OrU CtY MSaE PP ICJ

Liu, Hsiang, 77? -6? B.C., supposed comp.
Yakuchū So ji
see under Ch'u tz'ŭ.

Liu, Hsiang-yin.
馮玉梅團圓 柳湘吟編 [n. p.] 崇文書社 1955.
94 p. illus. 19 cm. (宋代小說精選)
1. Chinese fiction (Selections: Extracts, etc.) I. Title.
Title romanized: Fêng Yü-mei t'uan yüan.
PL2643.L5 C 60-3311 ‡
NL 0415408 DLC

Liu, Hsiang-yin, ed.
San ku mao lu.
PL2690 .S3155 1955 Orien China
Lo, Kuan-chung, *ca.* 1330–*ca.* 1400, *supposed author.*
三顧茅廬 三國演義新編 羅貫中原著 柳湘吟改編 [香港] 崇文書社 1955.

Law
Liu, Hsiao-liang.
我国公民的基本权利和义务 刘孝良編 [n. p.] 安徽人民出版社 [195–]
56 l. 21 cm.
Photocopy.
Collation of original as determined from the photocopy: 56 p.
1. Civil rights—China (People's Republic of China, 1949–) I. Title.
Title romanized: Wo kuo kung min ti chi pên ch'üan li.
C 66-2125
NL 0415410 DLC

Liu, Hsiao-tung.
常見樹木利用誌略 劉曉東編 重慶 商務印書館 民國34 [1945]
1, 2, 178 p. 18 cm.
1. Trees—China. I. Title.
Title romanized: Ch'ang chien shu mu li yung chih lüeh.
QK490.C6L58 C 67-574
NL 0415411 DLC

Liu, Hsieh, *ca.* 465–*ca.* 522.
文心雕龍范注補正 斯波六郎著 [廣島] 廣島大學文學部中國文學研究室 昭和27 [1952]
51 p. 27 cm. ([中文研究叢刊 第1])
Cover title.
[本書は]范[文瀾]注を参考しながら[劉勰選]文心雕龍を講讀した際の備忘錄を整理した...もの
1. Chinese literature—Hist. & crit. I. Fan, Wên-lan, 1891– II. Shiba, Rokurō, 1894– (Series: Chūbun kenkyū sōkan, dai 1)
Title romanized: Bunshin chōryō Han chū hosei.
PL2254.C55 vol. 1 J 66-111
NL 0415412 DLC

Liu, Hsien, 1901–
see
Liu, Hans, 1901–

Liu, Hsien-ching
The scenic Peking-Suiyuan Railway; photographs and descriptions. Peking, 1925
Chinese and English.
NL 0415414 MH

Liu, Hsien-chou, 1891–
機械工程名詞–英漢對照 劉仙洲編訂 中國機械學工程學會主編 上海 商務印書館 民國36 [1947]
2, 2, 471 p. 18 cm.
1. Mechanical engineering—Dictionaries—Chinese. 2. English language—Dictionaries—Chinese. I. Title.
Title romanized: Chi hsieh kung ch'êng ming tz'ŭ.
TJ9.L57 C 63-53
NL 0415415 DLC

Liu, Hsien-chou, 1891–
機械原理 劉仙洲著 [上海] 商務印書館 [1934?–
v. illus. 21 cm. (國立清華大學叢書之3)
大學叢書
1. Machinery. I. Title. (Series: Ch'ing hua ta hsüeh, Peking. Kuo li ch'ing hua ta hsüeh ts'ung shu chih 3)
Title romanized: Chi hsieh yüan li.
TJ170.L58 74-839433
NL 0415416 DLC

Liu, Hsien-chou, 1891–
(Jo kung hsüeh) 熱工學 劉仙洲編著 [臺北] 國立編譯館 [民國39– i. e. 1950–
v. illus. 21 cm.
At head of title: 部定大學用書
1. Heat engineering. I. Title.
TJ260.L49 77-841174
NL 0415417 DLC

Liu, Hsien-chou, 1891–
(Jo kung hsüeh) 熱工學 劉仙洲編著 北京 新華書店 1950–
v. illus. 21 cm. (大學叢書)
1. Heat engineering. I. Title.
TJ260.L5 C 50-321 ‡
NL 0415418 DLC

---

560 C441p ser.C n.s. no.14 Geol Lib'y
Liu, Hsien-T'ing.
Fossil fishes from locality 14 of Choukoutien. [Shanghai?] Academia Sinica, 1954.
21p. illus. 31cm. (Palaeontologia sinica, new ser. C, no.14, whole no.137)
"Edited by Institute of Palaeontology, Laboratory of Vertebrate Palaeontology, Academia Sinica."
1. Fishes, Fossil. 2. Fishes - China. Series (contents)
NL 0415419 TxU

Liu, Hsien-t'ing.
地球發展的證據–化石 劉憲亭著 上海 商務 1951.
59 p. illus. 18 cm.
1. Paleontology—Juvenile literature. I. Title.
Title romanized: Ti ch'iu fa chan ti chêng chü.
QE714.5.L55 C 60-449 ‡
NL 0415420 DLC

VOLUME 336

Liu, Hsin-huang.
赤魔羣像 劉心煌[i. e. 皇]編著 [臺北] 民主自由出版社 民國40 [1951]
69 p. 19 cm.
Colophon title.

1. China (People's Republic of China, 1949-)—Biography. I. Title.
Title romanized: Ch'ih mo ch'ün hsiang.

DS778.A1L49 74-839417

NL 0415421 DLC

Liu, Hsin-huang.
蘭娜 劉心皇著 臺北 中央文物供應社 民國43 [1954]
84 p. 19 cm. (文藝叢書)
Short stories.

I. Title.
Title romanized: Lan-na.

PL2879.H7L3 C 62-594 ‡

NL 0415422 DLC

Liu, Hsin-huang.
在烽火裡 劉心皇著 臺北 中央文物供應社 民國43 [1954]
196 p. 19 cm. (文藝叢書)
Short stories.

I. Title.
Title romanized: Tsai fêng huo li.

PL2879.H7T75 C 62-1063 ‡

NL 0415423 DLC WU

Liu, Hsing-min, illus.
Chung-kuo chien chu ts'ai hua t'u an
see under China (People's Republic of China, 1949-) Pei-ching wên wu chêng li wei yüan hui.

Liu, Hsing-san, joint author.
Chi kung shu hsüeh
see under Liu, Li-shih.

Liu, Hsiu-ju.
三民主義革命論 劉脩如編著 [重慶] 正中書局 民國31 [1942]
2, 8, 230 p. 21 cm.

1. Sun, Yat-sen, 1866-1925. San min chu i. I. Title.
Title romanized: San min chu i ko ming lun.

DS777.L57 C 59-5072
Hoover Institution for Library of Congress 4788.15 [½]†

NL 0415426 CSt-H DLC

Liu, Hsiu-ju.
社會行政 劉修如編著 臺灣省政府社會處主編 [臺北] 民國43 [1954]
2, 38 p. 19 cm. (社會工作幹部訓練教材)

1. Public welfare—China. 2. Social service—China. I. Title.
Title romanized: Shê hui hsing chêng.

HV386.L5 C 58-7153
Hoover Institution for Library of Congress 4210 [½]†

NL 0415427 CSt-H DLC

Z3101 .P4 Orien China

Liu, Hsiu-yeh, comp.
Kuo hsüeh lun wên so yin.
Pei-ching t'u shu kuan.
國學論文索引 北平北海圖書館編目科編輯 北平 中華圖書館協會 民國18 [1929.

Z3108 .L5W4 Orien China

Liu, Hsiu-yeh, comp.
Wên hsüeh lun wên so yin.
文學論文索引 張陳卿 陳璧如 李維垿編輯 [北平] 中華圖書館協會出版 國立北平圖書館發行 民國21 [1932]

R121 .L57 Orien China

Liu, Hsiung-hua.
實用俄華醫學辭典 劉雄華編 Практический русско-китайский медицинский словарь. Составил Лю Сюн-Хуа. [上海] 西南醫學書社 [1953]
697 p. 18 cm.

1. Medicine—Dictionaries—Russian. I. Title. II. Title: O Hua i hsüeh tz'ŭ tien. III. Title: Prakticheskiĭ russko-kitaĭskiĭ meditsinskiĭ slovar'.
Title romanized: Shih yung O Hua i hsüeh tz'ŭ tien.

R121.L57 C 58-5838

NL 0415430 DLC

DS 703 .C15 no.1

Liu, Hsü, 887-946.
Biographies of Meng Hao-jan. Translated and annotated by Hans H. Frankel. Berkeley, University of California Press, 1952.
25 p. 23 cm. (University of California. Institute of East Asiatic Studies. Chinese dynastic histories translations, no.1)
CONTENTS.--First version of the official biography of Meng Hao-jan (Chiu T'ang-shu 190C.2b)--Second version of the official biography of Meng Hao-jan (Hsin T'ang-shu 203.3a-b)--Bibliography (p.17-25)
1. Meng, Hao-jan, 689-740. I. Ou-yang, Hsiu, 1007-1072. Hsin T'ang shu. II. Frankel, Hans Hermann, 1916- tr. III. Title: Chiu T'ang shu. IV. Title: Hsin T'ang shu.

NL 0415431 MiU

PL2722 .U2L52 Orien China

Liu, Hsü-chih, ed. and tr.
Liao chai.
P'u, Sung-ling, 1640-1715.
聊齋 [蒲松齡原著] 柳栩之編選 香港 廣智書局 [1955?]

Liu Hsüeh-an.
...Four songs, voice and piano... Tokyo: Ryuginsha [etc., etc., c1936] 11 p. 30cm. (Collection Alexandre Tcherepnine. no. 19.)
For 1 voice with piano acc. Chinese and English words.
Title in English, Chinese and Russian.
"English version by Louisine P. Tcherepnine."
CONTENTS.—Song of the lotus time.—The song of youth.—The fallen flowers.—Chrysanthemums.

1. China. I. Ser.
N. Y. P. L. January 17, 1939

NL 0415433 NN

Liu, Hsüeh-hai.
一年來陝北共黨之動態 劉學海著 [n. p.] 民國31 [1942]
8, 120 p. fold. map.
Cover title.
Photo-offset. 香港 1970? 19 cm.

1. China—Politics and government—1912-1949. 2. Communism—China—Shensi. I. Title.
Title romanized: I nien lai Shan pei kung tang.

DS777.47.L57 1970 70-839704

NL 0415434 DLC

Liu, Hsüeh-p'o.
常用藥物學 劉學坡編著 上海 華東醫務生活社 1951.
-, 68 p. 18 cm.

1. Pharmacology. I. Title.
Title romanized: Ch'ang yung yao wu hsüeh.

RM300.L55 C 67-752

NL 0415435 DLC

Liu, Hsün-yü.
實用微積分學 劉薰宇著 上海 商務 1955.
247 p. illus. 21 cm.

1. Calculus. I. Title.
Title romanized: Shih yung wei chi fên hsüeh.

QA303.L66 C 59-320 ‡

NL 0415436 DLC

Liu, Hu, joint comp.
Ho, K'ai, *comp.*
Bibliography on tung tree and tung oil, compiled by K. Ho ... and H. Liu ... With a foreword by Chung-Yu Wang ... [Hankow] The Government testing bureau of Hankow, 1937.

DS734 .7 .L58 1928 Orien China

Liu, Hu-ju, ed.
Shih t'ung.
Liu, Chih-chi, 661-721.
史通 [劉知幾撰] 選註者劉虎如 上海 商務印書館 民國17 [1928]

Liu, Hu-Ju, ed.
Shih t'ung.
Liu, Chih-chi, 661-721.
史通 劉知幾撰 劉虎如選註 上海 商務印書館 民國18 [1929]

VOLUME 336

Liu, Hui.
大陸農村經濟 柳惠著 Rural economics on the China Mainland, by Liu Wai. 九龍 自由出版社 Freedom Press, 民國 42 [1953]
2, 2, 108 p. 19 cm.
In Chinese.
Includes bibliographical references.
1. Agriculture—Economic aspects—China (People's Republic of China, 1949-) I. Title. II. Title: Rural economics on the China Mainland.
Title romanized: Ta lu nung ts'un ching chi.
HD2067.L58 C 68-1943
NL 0415440 DLC

Liu, Hui Sien, 1912-
Analysis of continuous rectangular slabs. [Ithaca, N. Y.] 1937.
169 l. illus. 28cm.
Thesis (Ph.D.)--Cornell University, June, 1937.
1. Elastic plates and shells. 2. Strains and stresses. I. Title: Continuous rectangular slabs, Analysis of.
NL 0415441 NIC

Liu, Hung-chien, 1885-
中華民國物權法論 劉鴻漸著 佟朝珍校 北平 北平朝陽學院出版部 民國 22 [1933]
2, 24, 401 p. 23 cm.
Colophon title.
Errata slip inserted.
Bibliography: p. 390-401.
1. Property—China. I. Title.
Title romanized: Chung-hua min kuo wu ch'üan fa lun.
C 61-2606
NL 0415442 DLC

Liu, Hung-wan.
工業化與中國人口問題 劉鴻萬著 [重慶 商務印書館 1945]
2, 1, 58 p. 18 cm. (國民經濟研究所丙種叢書 第6編)
Bibliography: p. 58-58.
1. China—Population. I. Title. (Series: Kuo min ching chi yen chiu so. Kuo min ching chi yen chiu so: Ping chung ts'ung shu, ti 6 pien)
Title romanized: Kung yeh hua yü Chung-kuo jên k'ou wên t'i.
HB3637.L48 77-835511
NL 0415443 DLC

Liu, Hung-wan.
物價與工業資本 劉鴻萬著 [重慶] 正中書局 民國 33 [1944]
2, 1, 86 p. 19 cm. (戰時與戰後經濟問題叢書)
Cover title.
1. Capital investments—China. 2. Prices—China. I. Title.
Title romanized: Wu chia yü kung yeh tzŭ pên.
HG4237.L5 C 67-604
NL 0415444 DLC

Liu, Hung-yün.
中國古地理圖 劉鴻允編著 中國科學院地質古生物研究所編輯 北京 科學出版社 1955.
50 p. 21 col. maps. 34 x 39 cm.
Scale of maps 1:16,000,000.
Bibliography: p. 45-50.
Errata slip inserted.
1. Paleogeography—China—Maps. I. Chung-kuo k'o hsüeh yüan. Ti chih ku shêng wu yen chiu so, Peking. II. Title.
Title romanized: Chung-kuo ku ti li t'u.
G2306.C5L5 1955 C 65-1874
NL 0415445 DLC CaBVaU

Liu, Hyungki J
see Yu, Hyong-gi, 1897-

Liu, I, joint author.
Chung-kuo ko ming chi pên wên t'i
see under Wang, Hsiang-shêng.

Liu, I-chêng, 1879-
中國文化史 柳詒徵編著 [上海] 正中書局 民國 36 [1947]
3 v. 21 cm. (大學叢書)
1. China—Civilization—Hist. I. Title.
Title romanized: Chung-kuo wên hua shih.
DS721.L67 C 58-6041 ‡
NL 0415448 DLC

DS721
.L672
Orien
China
Liu, I-chêng, 1879-
中國文化史 柳詒徵編著 臺北 正中書局 民國 43 [1954]
3 v. tables. 21 cm. (大學用書)
1. China—Civilization—Hist. I. Title.
Title romanized: Chung-kuo wên hua shih.
C 58-7508
Indiana. Univ. Libr. for Library of Congress [8]
NL 0415449 InU DLC

Liu, I-chêng, 1879-
國史要義 柳詒徵著 [上海] 中華書局 [1948]
2, 239 p. 22 cm.
1. China—Historiography. I. Title.
Title romanized: Kuo shih yao i.
DS734.7.L585 C 67-2916
NL 0415450 DLC

Liu, I-chêng, 1879-
盋山牘存 [柳詒徵著 南京 民國] 37 [1948]
2, 92 p. 18 cm. (江蘇省立國學圖書館叢刊第1輯)
Cover title.
I. Title.
Title romanized: Po-shan tu ts'un.
AC150.L545 71-838517
NL 0415451 DLC

Liu, I-chêng, 1879- ed.
Shou tu chih
see under Wang, Huan-piao, comp.

ML336
.L5
Orien
China
Liu, I-chih.
國樂津梁 劉毅志著 [臺北 臺北市中國民族音樂學會
v. illus. 27 cm. (臺北市中國民族音樂學會中國女子國樂團叢書) 50.00 (v. 3)
1. Music, Chinese—History and criticism. 2. Musical instruments, Chinese. I. Title.
Title romanized: Kuo yüeh ching liang.
ML336.L5 71-837997
NL 0415453 DLC

Liu, I-ch'ing.
西藏現勢 劉挹青著 台北 中央文物供應社 民國 43 [1954]
2, 4, 98 p. illus. 19 cm. (邊疆叢書)
1. Tibet. I. Title. *Title romanized:* Hsi-tsang hsien shih.
C 58-7469
Hoover Institution for Library of Congress 8079.5 [2]
NL 0415454 CSt-H ICU MiU

Liu, I-ch'ing, school teacher, joint author.
Yü wên chiao shih kung tso ts'an k'ao tzŭ liao
see under Ch'u, Chih-k'un.

Liu, I-ch'ing, 403-444.
Ch'ung k'o Shih shuo hsin yü pu
see under Ho, Liang-chün, d. 1573.

Liu, I-ch'ing, 403-444.
世說新語 [劉義慶撰 劉孝標注 臺北] 藝文印書館 [195-]
2 v. (886 p.) in 1. 19 cm.
Text reproduced from 日本影印宋本
I. Liu, Hsiao-piao, 462-521, ed. II. Title.
Title romanized: Shih shuo hsin yü.
PL2666.L55A6 C 62-2184 rev
NL 0415457 DLC WU

Liu, I-fei.
抗日英雄特寫 劉一飛編選 漢口 大時代書店 民國 27 [1938]
2, 4, 250 p. 19 cm.
Colophon title.
1. Sino-Japanese Conflict, 1937-1945—Biography. 2. Generals—China. I. Title.
Title romanized: K'ang Jih ying hsiung t'ê hsieh.
DS777.53.L578 75-842606
NL 0415458 DLC

VOLUME 336

Liu, I-fu.
Chung-kuo ch'ing nien ti chün hsün shêng huo
see under title

Liu, I-jan
see
Liu, Ju-ch'iang, 1895-

Liu, I-Lin, 1907-
... Untersuchungen über vorkommen von bakteriophagen für Brucella-bakterien und für sprosspilze (Monilia) ... Hamburg, 1933.
17p.
Hamburg diss. 1933.

NL 0415461 MiU

Liu, I-t'ing.
八月家書 劉藝亭著 收穫文藝叢書編輯委員會編 北京 工人出版社 1951.
71 p. 19 cm. (收穫文藝叢書)
Poems.

I. Title.
Title romanized: Pa yüeh chia shu.

PL2879.I 23P3 C 62-947 ‡

NL 0415462 DLC

Liu, IUan'-na
see
Liu, Yüan-na.

Liu, J. Heng
see Liu, Jui-hêng, 1890-

QL1 N515 v.5:1 Biology Library

Liu, J Y
On some species of Squilla (Crustacea Stomatopoda) from China coasts. ⌜Peiping, National Academy of Peiping, 1949⌝
⌜27⌝-47 p. illus., plates. (Contributions from the Institute of Zoology, National Academy of Peiping. v.5, no.1)

Caption title.
Title also in Chinese.
Bibliography: p.45-46.

NL 0415465 CU

Liu, James J Y
Elizabethan and Yuan, a brief comparison of some conventions in poetic drama by James Liu. London, China Society, 1955.
12 p. illus. 22 cm. (China Society occasional papers, no. 8)
"Based on a lecture delivered before the China Society on the 19th January, 1954."

1. English drama—Early modern and Elizabethan—History and criticism. 2. Chinese drama—History and criticism. 3. Literature, Comparative—English and Chinese. 4. Literature, Comparative—Chinese and English. I. Title. (Series: China Society, London. China Society occasional papers. New series, no. 8)

PR654.L5 65-56199

NL 0415466 ScU MCM CoU NcU CtY InU NIC NNC HU IaU DLC MH NN LU IU CU MU DLC WU MiU ICU

WY 11 L783o 1947

LIU, James K C
An outline of the history of nursing, prepared by James K. C. Liu and Gladys E. Stephenson. 5th ed. Shanghai, Kwang Hsüeh Pub. House, 1947.
182, 4, 2 p.
Added title page and text in Chinese.
1. Chinese language - Texts
2. Nursing - Hist. I. Stephenson, Gladys E

NL 0415467 DNLM

327.510952 L74s 1950

Liu, James T. C., 1919-
Sino-Japanese diplomacy during the appeasement period 1933-1937. Pittsburgh, Pennsylvania, 1950.
242l. 28cm.

Thesis. - University of Pittsburgh.
Includes bibliographies.
Photocopy.

1. China. Foreign relations. Japan.
2. Japan. Foreign relations. China.
I. Title.

NL 0415468 KU NIC

Liu, Jan-huai, 1908-
Studien über Klima und Witterung des südchinesischen Küstengebietes. ... Ohlau i. Schl. 74 p.
Inaug. Diss. - Berlin, [1934]
Lebenslauf.

NL 0415469 ICRL

Liu, Jên, 1909-
日寇開發華北的陰謀 劉仁著 漢口 黎明書局 民國 27 ⌜1938⌝
2, 68 p. 18 cm.

1. Japanese in China. 2. China—Hist.—1912-1937. I. Title.
Title romanized: Jih k'ou k'ai fa Hua-pei ti yin mou.

DS774.L56 C 67-1356

NL 0415470 DLC

Liu, Jên-fu.
(Chiao yu kai lun)
教育概論 編者劉仁甫 北平 著者書店 民國 22 ⌜1933⌝
4, 2, 308 p. 23 cm.
Colophon title.

1. Education—History. I. Title.

LA126.L58 76-842999

NL 0415471 DLC

Liu, Jên-tê.
中華民國訓政時期約法論釋 劉仁德編著 ⌜重慶⌝ 正中書局 民國33 ⌜1944⌝
4, 126 p. 19 cm.
Cover title.
Bibliography: p. 126.

1. China—Constitutional law. I. Title.
Title romanized: Chung-hua min kuo hsün chêng shih ch'i yüeh fa.

C 66-2819

NL 0415472 DLC

Liu, Jennie Ching-i
see **Liu, Ching-i,** 1925-

Liu, Jo-yü
see
Liu, James J Y

Liu, Ju-ch'iang, 1895- joint comp.

RS180 .C5R4 1936

Read, Bernard Emms, 1887- *comp.*
Chinese medicinal plants from Pen ts'ao kang mu ... A. D. 1596. 3rd. edition of a Botanical, chemical and pharmacological reference list compiled by Bernard E. Read ... ⌜Peiping, China⌝ Peking natural history bulletin, 1936.

Liu, Ju-ch'iang, 1895-
Enumeration of plants collected by the late Mr. Nathaniel Harrington Cowdry in Chihli province. ⌜Peking⌝ Peking Society of Natural History, 1927-28.
194p. (Peking Natural History Bulletin v.2, part 3)

NL 0415476 ICRL NIC MH-A PU ICU

Liu, Ju-ch'iang, 1895-
Enumeration of plants collected by the late Mr. Nathaniel Harrington Cowdry in Chihli Province (and Chefoo) Peking Society of Natural History, 1928.
vii, 47-194 p. illus. 26 cm. (Bulletin of the Peking Society of Natural History, 1927-28, v.2, pt.3)
Cover title: Cowdry collection of Chihli flora (and plants from Chefoo)
Bibliography: p.vii.
Copy 1 inscribed: To Dr. E. D. Merrill, with compliments & gratitude from J. C. Liu.

NL 0415477 NNBG

Liu, Ju-Ch'iang, 1895-
—— The number of vascular bundles in Ephedra sinica and E. equisetina. Diagrs. (In *Lingnan science journal,* 1929, vii, 167-175.)
"References." p. 169.

NL 0415478 MH-A

Liu, Ju-Ch'iang, 1895-
Plantae medicinalis sinensis
see under Read, Bernard Emons, 1887-

Liu, Ju-ch'iang, 1895-
... Systematic botany of the flowering families in North China, by J. C. Liu ... 124 illustrations of common Hopei plants. Peiping, H. Vetch, 1931.
1 p. l., xxxiii, ⌜1⌝, 212 p., 1 l. illus. 19½cm.
Title and author's name also in Chinese on t.-p.

1. Botany—China. I. Title. II. Title: Flowering families in North China.

Library of Congress QK355.L5 1931 32-25806 Revised
⌜r38c2⌝ 581.951

NL 0415480 DLC NcD MtBC NIC CU MH-A NjP ICU PPAN

VOLUME 336

Liu, Ju-ch'iang, 1895–
Systematic botany of the flowering families in North China, by J. C. Liu ... 130 illustrations of common native plants, 170 figures on descriptive terms. (2d ed.) Peiping, China, H. Vetch, 1934.
xvi, 218 p. illus. 20cm.
Half-title gives author's name and title in Chinese.
First edition 1931.

1. Botany—China. I. Title. II. Title: Flowering families in North China.
37-11586
Library of Congress QK355.L5 1934
[2] 581.951

NL 0415481 DLC PPAmP

Liu, Ju-lin, 1905–
漢晉學術編年 劉汝霖編輯 [北平] 國立北平師範大學研究所 民國22 [1933]
2 v. in 1. 19 cm. (師大研究所叢書之一)
Colophon title.

1. Learning and scholarship—China. 2. China—Hist.—Chronology. 3. China—Biog. I. Title. (Series: Shih ta yen chiu so ts'ung shu)
Title romanized: Han Chin hsüeh shu pien nien.
AZ791.L57 C 68-534

NL 0415482 DLC

Liu, Ju-lin, 1905–
崔東壁年譜 劉汝霖著 北平 文化學社 民國17 [1928]
4, 104 p. tables, diagr. 18 cm.

1. Ts'ui, Shu, 1740-1816. *Title romanized:* Ts'ui Tung-pi nien p'u.
C 58-7038
Hoover Library
for Library of Congress

NL 0415483 CSt-H

Liu, Ju-lin, 1905–
東晉南北朝學術編年 劉汝霖著 上海 商務印書館 民國 25 [1936]
7, 492, 51 p. tables. 23 cm.

1. Philosophy—Hist.—China. 2. Learning and scholarship—China. I. Title.
Title romanized: Tung Chin nan pei ch'ao hsüeh shu pien nien.
B126.L57 C 61-4366
Harvard Univ. Chinese-Japanese Library 1017
for Library of Congress [¾]†

NL 0415484 MH-HY DLC

Liu, Jui hêng, 1890-
The Chinese ministry of health. [N.p. n.pub] 1929.
pp.135-148,0.

NL 0415485 CaBViP

Liu, Jui-heng, 1890-

League of nations.
... Health organisation. Intergovernmental conference of Far-Eastern countries on rural hygiene. Preparatory papers: Report of China. [Geneva, 1937]

Liu, Jui-yü.
中國北部的經濟蝦類 劉瑞玉著 中國科學院海洋生物研究室編輯 北京 科學出版社 1955.
iii, 73 p. illus., tables. 26 cm.
Bibliography: p. 70-73.

1. Shrimps. I. Chung-kuo k'o hsüeh yüan. Hai yang shêng wu yen chiu shih, Tsingtao. II. Title.
Title romanized: Chung-kuo pei pu ti ching chi hsia lei.
QL444.D3L53 C 58-5330

NL 0415487 DLC HU

Liu, K. C., joint author.

Wang, Hsiao-ching.
... The antimony ores of Hunan, by H. C. Wang, Y. T. Hsu and K. C. Liu. Changsha, Hunan, 1938.

Liu, K S
see
Kung-sun, Liu.

Liu, K'ai-ch'ü.
中國古代彫塑集 劉開渠編 北京 人民美術出版社 1955.
[15] p., 48 plates. 26 cm.

1. Sculpture, Chinese. I. Title.
Title romanized: Chung-kuo ku tai tiao su chi.
NB1043.L47 C 68-3013

NL 0415490 DLC PBm

Liu, K'ai-jung.
唐代小說研究 劉開榮著 上海 商務印書館 民國 36 [1947]
5, 9, 220 p. 18 cm.
Bibliography: p. 215-220.

1. Chinese fiction—Hist. & crit. I. Title.
Title romanized: T'ang tai hsiao shuo yen chiu.
PL2431.L5 1947 C 66-441

NL 0415491 DLC

Liu, K'ai-shên.
動物畫資料集 劉開申 王端合編 上海 四聯出版社 1955.
108 p. (chiefly illus.) 15 x 19 cm.

1. Animal pictures. I. Wang, Tuan, joint author. II. Title.
Title romanized: Tung wu hua tzŭ liao chi.
SF76.L5 C 59-1870 ‡

NL 0415492 DLC

Liu, Kang.
中共政權解剖 劉剛著 九龍 自由出版社 民國 41 [1952]
99 p. 18 cm.

1. China (People's Republic of China, 1949–)—Pol. & govt. I. Title. *Title romanized:* Chung kung chêng ch'üan chieh p'ou.
DS777.55.L497 C 59-3092 ‡

NL 0415493 DLC NIC

Liu Ke Shu, 1906-
see Liu, K'o-shu, 1906-

Liu, Keetsin.
Der begriff der identität der tat im geltenden deutschen strafprozessrecht. Von dr. jur. Keetsin Liu ... Breslau, Schletter, 1927.
3 p. l., [v]-vii, 96 p. 24cm. (*Added t.-p.:* Strafrechtliche abhandlungen ... hft. 221)
"Verzeichnis der benützten schriften": p. [v]-vii.

1. Pleading—Germany. 2. Criminal procedure—Germany. I. Title. II. Title: Identität der tat.
28-2872

NL 0415495 DLC

Liu Keh Shu, 1906-
see Liu, K'o-shu, 1906-

Lîû, Khaï-pén
see
Liu, Hai-p'êng.

Lîû, Khun-îûn
see
Liu, Hung-yün.

Liu, K'o-ming.
工會是共產主義的學校 劉克明著 瀋陽 東北人民出版社 1952.
30 p. 18 cm.

1. Trade unions—China (People's Republic of China, 1949–) I. Title.
Title romanized: Kung hui shih kung ch'an chu i ti hsüeh hsiao
HD6808.L5 C 60-2689 ‡

NL 0415499 DLC

Liu, K'o-shu, 1906–
交通政策概論 柳克述著 臺北 中國交通建設學會 民國 42 [1953]
266 p. illus. 21 cm. (交通叢書)

1. Transportation—Formosa. I. Title.
Title romanized: Chiao t'ung chêng ts'ê kai lun.
HE277.Z7F66 C 59-1642 ‡

NL 0415500 DLC CtY

Liu, K'o-shu, 1906–
近百年世界外交史 柳克述著 上海 商務 民國 20 [1931]
[11], 262, 1 p. 23 cm.

1. World politics. I. Title.
Title romanized: Chin pai nien shih chieh wai chiao shih
C 58-7239
Hoover Institution
for Library of Congress [2]

NL 0415501 CSt-H

VOLUME 336

Liu, K'o-shu, 1906– *ed.*
中國交通 柳克述主編 臺北 中華文化出版事業委員會 民國 43 [1954]
2 v. (1, 6, 318 p.) in 1. maps (part fold.) 19 cm. (現代國民基本知識叢書第2輯)

1. Communication and traffic—China. 2. Communication and traffic—Formosa. I. Title.
Title romanized: Chung-kuo chiao t'ung.

HE270.L49 C 66-2628

NL 0415502 DLC OO WU CLU-O MoSW

Liu, K'o-shu, 1906–
新土耳其 柳克述編 [上海] 商務印書館 [1929]
[19], 410, 30, 2 p. illus., fold. col. map. 24 cm.
Added colophon title: New Turkey, by Liu Keh Shu.
Bibliography: p. 1–2 (last group)

1. Turkey—Hist. I. Title.
Title romanized: Hsin T'u-êrh-ch'i.

DR440.L5 C 67-2118

NL 0415503 DLC

DS740
.4
.L47
Orien
China

Liu, K'o-shu, 1906–
不平等條約概論 柳克述著 上海 泰東圖書局 民國 15 [26]
1, 3, 6, 4, 235 p. 21 cm.
Colophon title.
Bibliography: p. 1 (4th group)

1. China—For. rel. I. Title.
Title romanized: Pu p'ing têng t'iao yüeh kai lun.

DS740.4.L47 C 64-1377

NL 0415504 DLC

Liu, K'o-shu, 1906–
土耳其革命史 撰述者柳克述 校閱者潘公展 [上海] 商務印書館 [1928]
1, 5, 146 p. 19 cm. (新時代史地叢書)
Added colophon title: History of the Turkish revolution, by Liu Ke Shu.

1. Turkey—Pol. & govt.—1909– I. Title.
Title romanized: T'u-êrh-ch'i ko ming shih.

DR584.L5 C 67-1829

NL 0415505 DLC

Liu, K'o-ts'ung.
汽車保養與檢修 柳克聰著 [重慶] 中華書局 [1945]
2, 88 p. 17 cm.

1. Automobiles—Maintenance and repair. I. Title.
Title romanized: Ch'i ch'ê pao yang yü chien hsiu.

TL152.L55 C 67-2858

NL 0415506 DLC

Liu, Ku-sun.
實用診療要覽 劉穀孫著 增訂本 上海 文通書局 1951.
116 p. 19 cm.

1. Medicine—Practice. I. Title.
Title romanized: Shih yung chên liao yao lan.

RC46.L67 C 60-3145 ‡

NL 0415507 DLC

Liu, Kuan-i.
(K'ang chan wai shih) 抗戰外史 劉貫一輯著 [濟南 膠東通訊社 民國 36 i. e. 1947]
2, 1, 6, 213 p. 19 cm.
Photo-offset. 香港 1970?

1. Sino-Japanese Conflict, 1937–1945—Personal narratives. I. Title.

DS777.53.L5783 1970 76-841025

NL 0415508 DLC

Liu, Kuan-ying.
新體寫版印刷法 劉冠英著 [修訂本] 北京 新中國書店 1952.
79 p. illus. 19 cm.

1. Copying processes. I. Title.
Title romanized: Hsin t'êng hsieh pan yin shua fa.

Z48.L5 C 62-2330 ‡

NL 0415509 DLC

Liu, Kuan-ying, *of Hu-pei.*
現代銀行制度 劉冠英著 上海 商務印書館 民國 26 [1937]
1, 1, 2, 2, 20, 342 p. 23 cm. (現代商業叢書)
Bibliography: p. 336–342.

1. Banks and banking. I. Title.
Title romanized: Hsien tai yin hang chih tu.

HG1607.L5 C 67-883

NL 0415510 DLC

Liu, Kuang-chieh.
初級俄語讀本 劉光傑編 北京 北京市中蘇友好協會俄文夜校 1953.
254 p. 19 cm.

1. Russian language—Text-books for foreigners—Chinese. I. Title.
Title romanized: Ch'u chi O yü tu pên.

PG2129.C5L48 71-840091

NL 0415511 DLC

Liu, Kuang-ching
see
Liu, Kwang-Ching, 1921–

Liu, Kuang-hua, 1891–
殖民政策 劉光華撰述 上海 商務 民國 19 [1930]
5, 168 p. 20 cm. (新時代史地叢書)

1. Colonies. 2. Colonization. I. Title.
Title romanized: Chih min chêng ts'ê.

C 58-7471

Hoover Institution
for Library of Congress [2]

NL 0415513 CSt-H HU

Liu, Kuang-hua, 1891–
農業政策 劉光華著 上海 南京書店 民國 21 [1932]
6, 256 p. 21 cm.

1. Agriculture and state—China. I. Title.
Title romanized: Nung yeh chêng ts'ê.

HD2068.L55 1932 C 66-369

NL 0415514 DLC

Liu, Kuang-yen, 1904–
(Hsin Chung-kuo ti tui wai chêng ts'ê)
新中國的對外政策 (一名國父與蔣總統的外交思想) 劉光炎著 [台北] 帕米爾書店 [民國 42 i. e. 1953]
3, 199 p. 18 cm.
Cover title.

1. China—Foreign relations. 2. Sun, Yat-sen, 1866–1925. 3. Chiang, Kai-shek, 1886– I. Title.

DS740.4.L473 72-841801

NL 0415515 DLC MH-HY

Liu, Kuang-yen, 1904–
新聞學 劉光炎著 [臺北] 臺灣聯合出版社 民國 40 [1951]
4, 169 p. 19 cm.

1. Journalism. I. Title.
Title romanized: Hsin wên hsüeh.

PN4775.L48 C 67-1074

NL 0415516 DLC

Liu, Kuang-yen, 1904–
新聞學講話 劉光炎著 臺北 中華文化出版事業委員會 民國 41 [1952]
8, 228 p. 19 cm. (現代國民基本知識叢書 [第1輯])

1. Journalism. I. Title.
Title romanized: Hsin wên hsüeh chiang hua.

PN4775.L5 C 66-2674

NL 0415517 DLC CLU-O

Liu, Kuang-yen, 1904–
各國政治家 劉光炎編 臺北 中華文化出版事業委員會 民國 43 [1954]
3, 9, 167 p. 19 cm. (現代國民基本知識叢書第2輯)

1. Statesmen. I. Title.
Title romanized: Ko kuo chêng chih chia.

D108.L5 C 66-2464

NL 0415518 DLC CaBVaU CLU-O WU

VOLUME 336

Liu, Kuang-yen, 1904–
歐洲現勢 劉光炎著 臺北 中華文化出版事業委員會 民國42 [1953]
8, 286 p. maps (part fold.) 19 cm. (現代國民基本知識叢書 [第1輯])

1. Europe. I. Title.
Title romanized: Ou-chou hsien shih.

D1051.L55 C 66-2466

NL 0415519 DLC InU CLU-O NRU MnU

DS778 .H85L5 1929 Orien China

Liu, K'uei-i, 1877–
黃興傳記 劉揆一述 [n.p. 民國18 (1929) 序]
2, 78, 2 p. illus. 26 cm.
Cover title.

1. Huang, Hsing, 1874–1916.
Title romanized: Huang Hsing chuan chi.

C 59-5245

Indiana. Univ. Libr. for Library of Congress DS773 [2]

NL 0415520 InU DLC

Liu, Kuei-i, 1877–
黃興傳記 劉揆一著 台北 帕米爾書店 民國41 [1952]
43 p. 19 cm.

1. Huang, Hsing, 1874–1916.
Title romanized: Huang Hsing chuan chi.

DS778.H85L5 C 59-1804 ‡

NL 0415521 DLC NIC

Liu, K'un, chin shih, 1903.

DS763 .T8W8

Wu, Yung, 1865–1936.
The flight of an empress, told by Wu Yung, whose other name is Yü-ch'uan; transcribed by Liu K'un; translated and edited by Ida Pruitt; introduction by Kenneth Scott Latourette. New Haven, Yale university press, 1936.

Liu, K'un, *chin shih* 1903.
辟園史學四種 [劉焜撰 n.p., 192–?]
19 v. (double leaves) in 4. 28 cm.
Running title.
In caption, as stamped: 劉體仁撰
Lithoprinted.
CONTENTS.—[1–4] 十七史說 4卷—[5–10] 通鑑劄記 16卷—[11–15] 續歷代紀事年表 10卷—[16–19] 異辭錄 4卷
1. China—Hist.—Addresses, essays, lectures. I. Liu, T'i-jên. II. Title. III. Title: Shih ch'i shih shuo. IV. Title: T'ung chien cha chi. V. Title: Hsü li tai chi shih nien piao. VI. Title: I tz'ŭ lu.
Title romanized: P'i yüan shih hsüeh ssŭ chung.

DS735.A2L5 C 61-2725 rev

NL 0415523 DLC

Liu, Kung-jên, 1905–
中國歷代徵兵制度考 劉公任著 [長沙] 商務印書館 民國30 [1941]
110 p. 18 cm.

1. Military service, Compulsory—China. I. Title.
Title romanized: Chung-kuo li tai chêng ping chih tu k'ao.

C 62-485 ‡

NL 0415524 DLC CtY InU

Liu, Kung-jên, 1905–
三國新志 劉公任著 [上海] 世界書局 民國36 [1947]
6, 4, 2, 240 p. 18 cm.
Colophon title.

1. China—Hist.—Three Kingdoms, 220–265. I. Title.
Title romanized: San-kuo hsin chih.

DS748.2.L5 C 61-4145

Harvard Univ. Chinese-Japanese Library for Library of Congress 2560 [2]†

NL 0415525 MH-HU CaBVaU DLC

Liu, Kuo-chün.
A system of book classification for Chinese libraries. Nanking, China, 1929.
1 v. (various pagings) 24cm. (Nanking University. Library. Publication No. 2)

In Chinese. Added title in English.

1. Classification—Books—Chinese literature. I. Series.

NL 0415526 NIC ViU

Z845 .N3 no.2 1936

Liu, Kuo-chün
A system of book classification for Chinese libraries. 2d ed. Nanking, China, Univ. of Nanking Library, 1936.
xi, 147 p. 23cm. (University of Nanking Library. Publications. no. 2)
Text in Chinese.
Errata slip inserted.

1. Classification—Books—China. 2. Libraries—China. I. Title.

NL 0415527 ViU NNC

Liu, Kuo-chün.
圖書館學要旨 劉國鈞編 上海 中華書局 1934.
162 p. illus. 19 cm. (中華百科叢書)

1. Library science. I. Title.
Title romanized: T'u shu kuan hsüeh yao chih.

Z665.L77 1934 C 62-2333 ‡

NL 0415528 DLC

Liu, Kuo-chün.
圖書怎樣分類 劉國鈞著 北京 開明書店 1953.
viii, 145 p. 19 cm.

1. Classification—Books. I. Title.
Title romanized: T'u shu tsên yang fên lei.

Z696.L6 C 63-2520

NL 0415529 DLC

Liu, Kuo-shih.
政治常識 劉國士 龐俊 王弗合著 天津 知識書店 1950.
53 p. 17 cm. (大衆方向叢書)

1. China (People's Republic of China, 1949–) I. Title.
Title romanized: Chêng chih ch'ang chih.

DS777.55.L498 C 62-2837 ‡

NL 0415530 DLC

Liu, Kuang-ching, joint author.

Z3108 .A5F3

Fairbank, John King, 1907–
Modern China; a bibliographical guide to Chinese works, 1898–1937, by John King Fairbank and Kwang-ching Liu. Cambridge, Harvard University Press, 1950.

W 4 Z96 1951

LIU, Kwei Teh, 1921–
Die Beeinflussung der Convallatoxinwirkung am isolierten Froschherzen durch vorausgehende oder gleichzeitige Applikation von Cocarboxylase, Ribonuklease, Brenztraubensäure. Bruxelles, Office international de librairie, 1951.
p. 439–458. illus.
Inaug.-Diss. - Zürich.
Reprinted from Archives internationales de pharmacodynamie, t. 87, no. 4, 1951.

1. Enzymes 2. Glycosides - Cardiac 3. Pyruvic acid

NL 0415533 DNLM

Liu, Kwoh-chuin
see
Liu, Kuo-chün.

Liu, Lan-shan.
和英雄們相處的日子 劉嵐山著 北京 自強書局 1953.
68 p. 18 cm.

1. Korean War, 1950–1953—Personal narratives, Chinese. I. Title.
Title romanized: Ho ying hsiung mên hsiang ch'u ti jih tzŭ.

DS919.5.L55 C 60-1298 ‡

NL 0415535 DLC KU

Liu, Lan-sun, joint author.
Hu-nan chih t'uan fang
see under Fu, Chüeh-chin.

Liu, Lang-ch'uan.
中國商事法 劉朗泉著 長沙 商務印書館 民國30 [1941]
2 v. ([11], 581 p.) in 1. 22 cm. (南開大學經濟研究所叢書) 大學叢書

1. Commercial law—China. I. Title. (Series: Nan-k'ai ta hsüeh, Tientsin. Ching chi yen chiu so. Nan k'ai ta hsüeh ching chi yen chiu so ts'ung shu)
Title romanized: Chung-kuo shang shih fa.

C 67-1149

NL 0415537 DLC

Liu, Li-ch'ien, comp.
A history of Hindu-Tibetan Buddhism. [Chengtu] The West China Frontier Research Institute [1946]
2, 102 p. 25cm.

In Chinese, with added title in English.

1. Lamaism. 2. Tibet--Religion. I. Title. II. Title: Yin tsang fo chiao shih.

NL 0415538 NIC

VOLUME 336

Wason
DS785+
L78
Liu, Li-ch'ien, tr.
Tibetan history after Lañdarma.
Translated by Liu Li-ch'ien. [Chengtu]
West China Frontier Research Institute
[1945?]
8, 74 p. 26cm.

In Chinese, with added title in English.

1. Tibet--Hist. I. Title. II. Title:
Hsü tsang shih chien.

NL 0415539 NIC

Liu, Li-k'ai.
一九一九至一九二七年的中國工人運動 劉立凱 王眞著 北京 工人出版社 1953.
59 p. 18 cm.

1. Labor and laboring classes—China. I. Wang, Chên, writer on labor movement, joint author. II. Title.
Title romanized: I chiu i chiu chih i chiu êrh ch'i nien ti Chung-kuo kung jên yün tung.

HD8676.L55 C 63-2168

NL 0415540 DLC CaBVaU

Liu, Li-shih.
技工數學 編者劉立十 劉行三 北京 工學書店 1952-53 [v. 1, 1953]
2 v. illus. 19 cm.

1. Mathematics. I. Liu, Hsing-san, joint author. II. Title.
Title romanized: Chi kung shu hsüeh.

QA39.L57 C 61-442 rev ‡

NL 0415541 DLC

Liu, Li-wêng.
民國政史拾遺 劉荔翁著 [台北] 劉幼衙 民國43- [1954-
v. 19 cm.

1. China—Pol. & govt.—1912-1949. I. Title.
Title romanized: Min kuo chêng shih shih i.

DS774.L58 C 58-7493 rev

Indiana. Univ. Libr.
for Library of Congress [r62b½]†

NL 0415542 InU DLC

Liu, Liang-mo, *comp.*
China sings; folk-songs and fighting songs of China collected by Liu Liang-mo, arranged and translated by Evelyn Modoi ... New York, Boston [etc.] C. Fischer, inc., °1945.
28 p. 26cm.

Publisher's plate no.: 29977.
With piano accompaniment; words in English, Chinese, and Chinese transliterated.

1. Folk-songs, Chinese. 2. War-songs, Chinese. 3. National songs, Chinese. I. Modoi, Evelyn, arr. II. Title.

46-1612

Library of Congre M1804.L78C5

PWcS
NL 0415543 DLC CLU N FTaSU OOxM OU NcGU OCl PP

Liu, Liang-Mo.
A collection of books and pamphlets in Chinese language brought in by Mr. Liu, 1941.
Some written by Liu Liang-Mo and some edited by his wife Chen Wei Giang and some written by other authors.

NL 0415544 NRCR

Liu, Liang-pi, chin shih 1724, ed.
Ch'ung hsiu Fu-chien T'ai-wan fu chih
see under title

Liu, Liao-i, ed.
A Q chêng chuan
see under Chou, Shu-jên, 1881-1936.

PL2862
.I 176
1953
Orien
China
Liu, Lien-ch'ih, joint author.
Liu Hu-lan.
Hsi-pei chan tou chü shê.
劉胡蘭 西北戰鬥劇社集體創作 魏風[等]編劇 羅宗賢等作曲 劉蓮池修訂 北京 人民文學出版社 1953.

Liu, Lin, *writer on hygiene.*
常見疾病手册 劉林編著 增訂本 濟南 華東醫務生活社 1953.
291 p. 18 cm.

1. Medicine—Handbooks, manuals, etc. I. Title.
Title romanized: Ch'ang chien chi ping shou ts'ê.

RC58.L5 C 58-5601 rev ‡

NL 0415548 DLC

Liu, Lin-shêng, 1894-
(Chūgoku bungaku nyūmon) 中國文學入門 劉麟生原著 魚返善雄譯補 [東京] 東京大學出版部 [1951]
3, 195, 26 p. 19 cm.

Translation of 中國文學 ABC (romanized: Chung-kuo wên hsüeh ABC)
Includes bibliographical references.

1. Chinese literature—History and criticism. I. Title.

PL2268.L5 74-821256

NL 0415549 DLC

Liu, Lin-shêng, 1894-
中國政治理想 編者劉麟生 [上海] 商務印書館 [1929]
2, 110 p. 19 cm. (國學小叢書)
Added colophon title: Political thought in China.

1. Political science—Hist.—China. I. Title.
Title romanized: Chung-kuo chêng chih li hsiang.

JA84.C6L565 1929 C 67-1443

NL 0415550 DLC

Liu, Lin-shêng, 1894-
中國政治理想 著作者劉麟生 上海 商務印書館 民國23 [1934]
2, 99 p. 19 cm. (國學小叢書)
Includes bibliographical references.

1. Political science—Hist.—China. I. Title.
Title romanized: Chung-kuo chêng chih li hsiang.

JA84.C6L5 C 65-613

NL 0415551 DLC ICU

Liu, Lin-shêng, 1894-
中國騈文史 劉麟生著 主編者王雲五 傅緯平 [上海] 商務印書館 [1937]
6, 2, 165 p. 19 cm. (中國文化史叢書第1輯)

1. Chinese prose literature—Hist. & crit. I. Title. (Series: Chung-kuo wên hua shih ts'ung shu, ti 1 chi)
Title romanized: Chung-kuo p'ien wên shih.

PL2398.H5L5 1937 C 68-1404

NL 0415552 DLC

Liu, Lin-shêng, 1894-
(Chung-kuo shih tz'ŭ kai lun)
中國詩詞概論 劉麟生編述 [上海] 世界書局 [民國22 i. e. 1934]
6, 195 p. 19 cm. (中國文學叢書)

1. Chinese poetry—History and criticism. 2. Tz'ŭ—History and criticism. I. Title.

PL2307.L573 1934 72-835361

NL 0415553 DLC

Liu, Lin-shêng, 1894-
(Chung-kuo wên hsüeh kai lun)
中國文學概論 劉麟生編著 [上海] 世界書局 [民國 23 i. e. 1934]
2, 102 p. 19 cm. (中國文學叢書)

1. Chinese literature—History and criticism. I. Title.

PL2264.L533 70-841791

NL 0415554 DLC

Liu, Lin-shêng, 1894-
中國沿革地理淺說 劉麟生編 [上海] 商務印書館 [1933]
1, 115 p. 19 cm. (史地小叢書)

1. China—Historical geography. I. Title.
Title romanized: Chung-kuo yen ko ti li ch'ien shuo

DS706.5.L56 70-840490

NL 0415555 DLC

Liu, Ling, 1893-
The Chinese in North America, a guide to their life and progress. Los Angeles, East-West Culture Pub. Assn. [1949]
308 p. illus., ports., maps. 23 cm.
Title pages and captions for illus. in Chinese and English; text in Chinese.

——— Another issue.

Bound with the author's The Chinese in the Americas. Los Angeles [1951]
E29.C5L52

1. Chinese in North America.

E29.C5L5 325.251097 49-4640 rev*

NL 0415556 DLC PU

Liu, Ling, 1893-
The Chinese in the Americas, a guide to their life and progress. Los Angeles, East-West Culture Pub. Association [1951]
[80] p. illus., ports., maps. 24 cm.
Title page and captions for illus. in Chinese and English; text in Chinese.
Bound with the author's The Chinese in North America. Los Angeles [1949]

1. Chinese in America. I. Title.

E29.C5L52 325.251097 51-3248

NL 0415557 DLC CtY IU NIC MnU CCC

VOLUME 336

Liu, Ling-chiu, joint comp.
T'ien chia tu chê tzŭ chuan
see under Chang, Hsüeh-yen, comp.

Liu, Lo-fu
see
Liu, Yüeh-fu.

Liu, Man-ch'ing.
邊疆教育 劉曼卿著 上海 商務 民國 26 [1937]
1, 2, 4, 286 p. tables. 24 cm.

1. Education—China. 2. Minorities—China. I. Title.
Title romanized: Pien chiang chiao yü.

LA1131.L54 C 58-7351

Hoover Institution for Library of Congress 4992.3 [2.]†

NL 0415560 CSt-H DLC WU

Liu, Mao-Yin, 1902-
Die Konstitution des Irisins. Hamburg, 1934.
47 p.
Diss. - Hamburg.

NL 0415561 MiU

Liu, Max Chiwai
see
Liu, Ch'i-wei, 1913-

Liu, Mien-chih.
新中國的婦女在前進 柳勉之編著 北京 生活·讀書·新知三聯書店 1953.
51 p. 18 cm.

1. Women in China. I. Title.
Title romanized: Hsin Chung-kuo ti fu nü tsai ch'ien chin.

HQ1737.L56 C 63-548 ‡

NL 0415563 DLC CaBVaU FTaSU

Liu, Mien-chih, 1870-
中國幣制及生計問題 劉冕執著 [北京] 生計研究社 民國 3 [1914]
2, 2, 160 p. 25 cm.

1. Currency question—China. I. Title.
Title romanized: Chung-kuo pi chih.

HG1224.L493 C 67-1314

NL 0415564 DLC

378.797 Liu, Min Chang
W5l Experiences of a Chinese student in an American college. Pullman, Wash., State college of Wash. [1924?]
12 p. illus.

c.1 is PNC.

NL 0415565 WaPS

Liu, Ming-chih
see
Liu, P'an-sui, 1899-

Liu, Mo-kêng.
自然教學經驗點滴 北京育才小學各科教材教法經驗第三集 劉默耕著 [上海] 中華書局 [1953]
102 p. illus. 18 cm.

1. Nature study. I. Title. II. Title: Pei-ching yü ts'ai hsiao hsüeh ko k'o chiao ts'ai.
Title romanized: Tzŭ jan chiao hsüeh ching yen tien ti.

LB1532.L5 C 68-372

NL 0415567 DLC

Liu Mou-cho.
...De la condition internationale de l'Égypte depuis la déclaration anglaise de 1922...par Liu Mou-Cho. Lyon: Bosc frères & Riou, 1925. 148 p. incl. tables. 4°.

Dissertation, Lyon, 1925.
Bibliography, p. 9-12.

1. Egypt—For. and political rel., 1922- 2. Egypt—Govt., 1922-
N. Y. P. L. November 21, 1927

NL 0415568 NN CtY

Liu, Nai-chen, 1902-
DS703 .4 .M2
MacNair, Harley Farnsworth, 1891- *ed.*
Voices from unoccupied China, by Liu Nai-chen [and others] ... Edited by Harley Farnsworth MacNair. Chicago, Ill., The University of Chicago press [1944]

Liu, Nai-ch'êng.
新縣制綱要淺說 (又名地方自治概要) 劉迺誠著 [重慶?] 國民圖書出版社 民國31 [1942]
6, 4, 250 p. 19 cm.

1. County government—China. I. Title. II. Title: Ti fang tzŭ chih kai yao.
Title romanized: Hsin hsien chih kang yao ch'ien shuo.

JS7353.A8L58 C 67-779

NL 0415570 DLC

Liu, Nai-ch'êng.
比較政治制度 劉迺誠著 [上海] 商務印書館 [民國24- i. e. 1935-
v. 23 cm. (國立武漢大學叢書)

1. Comparative government. I. Title.
Title romanized: Pi chiao chêng chih chih tu.

JF56.C45L56 75-839330

NL 0415571 DLC

Liu, Nai-ch'êng.
比較政治制度—英國政治制度 劉迺誠著 [重慶] 商務印書館 [1946]
2, 3, 2, 172 p. 21 cm. (國立武漢大學叢書)
Includes bibliographies.

1. Gt. Brit.—Pol. & govt. I. Title. II. Title: Ying-kuo chêng chih chih tu.
Title romanized: Pi chiao chêng chih chih tu.

JN321.L54 C 67-1745

NL 0415572 DLC

Liu, Nai-ch'êng.
比較政治制度—美國政治制度 劉迺誠著 [重慶] 商務印書館 [1946]
2, 2, 212 p. 20 cm. (國立武漢大學叢書)
Includes bibliographies.

—— —— Another issue. [上海 1947]
21 cm.
JK274.L577 1947

1. U. S.—Pol. & govt. I. Title. II. Title: Mei-kuo chêng chih chih tu.
Title romanized: Pi chiao chêng chih chih tu.

JK274.L577 1946 C 67-2003

NL 0415573 DLC

Liu, Nanming.
Contribution à l'étude de la population chinoise ... par Nanming I Liu. Genève [Imprimerie et éditions Union, 1935]
1 p. l., 252 p., 1 l. incl. tables. 27cm.
Thèse—Univ. de Paris.
"Corrigenda" leaf inserted.
"Bibliographie": p. [240]-244.

1. China—Population. I. Title.
42-42255 Provisional
Library of Congress HB3637.L5

NL 0415574 DLC ICU PU NNC OU CtY

Liu, Newton Y C
Opium; an avoidable evil! ... Wuchang [1933]
Cover-title.
Pamphlet.

NL 0415575 CtY

Liu Ngo
see Liu, Ê, 1857-1909.

Liu, Ni.
正負數的四則運算 劉尼著 北京 中國青年出版社 1955.
iii, 63 p. illus. 19 cm.

1. Equations, Quadratic. I. Title.
Title romanized: Chêng fu shu ti ssŭ tsê yün suan.

QA161.L58 C 67-371

NL 0415577 DLC

Liu, Nien-chên.
歷史廿二人 劉念真著 香港 亞洲出版社 民國 44 [1955]
282 p. 19 cm.

1. Biography. I. Title. *Title romanized:* Li shih nien êrh jên.

CT203.C5L5 C 58-6436 ‡

NL 0415578 DLC HU

Liu, Nien-ch'ü.
幸福天堂 劉念渠著 重慶 商務印書館 民國 34 [1945]
1, 150 p. 18 cm.

I. Title.
Title romanized: Hsing fu t'ien t'ang.

PL2782.N5H75 C 68-617

NL 0415579 DLC

VOLUME 336

Liu, O
see
Liu, Ê, 1857–1909.

Liu, Pai-ch'uan.
一個小學校長的日記 劉百川著 上海 開華書局 民國 22 [1933]
2, 7, 266 p. port. 19 cm.

1. School management and organization—China. 2. Education—China. I. Title.
Title romanized: I ko hsiao hsüeh hsiao chang ti jih chi.

C 58-7411

Hoover Institution for Library of Congress 4940 [3]

NL 0415581 CSt-H

Liu, Pai-min, 1900–
Chung Jih wên hua lun chi
see under title

Liu, Pai-min, 1900– ed.

PL2455 .D72 Orien China

Drake, Frederick Seguier, 1892– ed.
(Chung-kuo wên hsüan)
中國文選 [林仰山主編 劉百閔等編輯 4版 香港] 香港大學出版社

Liu, Pai-yü.
朝鮮在戰火中前進 劉白羽著 [上海] 新文藝出版社 1951.
140 p. 19 cm.

1. Korean War, 1950–1953—Personal narratives, Chinese. I. Title.
Title romanized: Ch'ao-hsien tsai chan huo chung ch'ien chin.

DS921.6.L6 C 67-2050

NL 0415584 DLC

4DS China 178

Liu, Pai-yü
Fajrolumo en la fronto. El la ĉina lingvo tradukis, S. J. Sü. Sanhajo, Sanhaja Esperantista Ligo, 1951.
148 p.

NL 0415585 DLC-P4

Liu, Pai-yü.
Flames ahead. [1st ed.] Peking, Foreign Languages Press, 1954.
166 p. map (on lining papers) 18 cm.

1. China—Hist.—1945– —Fiction. I. Title.

PZ3.L75Fl 57-34675

CLSU TU CtY NNC NcD MH
NL 0415586 DLC CaBVaU MeB MShM MiU WaU KU CU NjR

Liu, Pai-yü.
幸福 劉白羽著 增訂 3 版 上海 新羣出版社 1952.
137 p. 18 cm. (新羣文藝叢書)

I. Title. *Title romanized:* Hsing fu.

PL2879.P3H75 1952 C 60-1287 ‡

NL 0415587 DLC

Liu, Pai-yü.
Jên min ti chan chêng
see Hsüeh jou hsiang lien.

Liu, Pai-yü.
人民與戰爭 劉白羽等著 [佳木斯] 東北書店 [1947]
88 p. 19 cm.
At head of title: 東北解放區通訊報告選集
A collection of works by various authors.

1. China—History—Civil War, 1945–1949—Personal narratives. I. Title.
Title romanized: Jên min yü chan chêng.

DS777.54.L53 75-835839

NL 0415589 DLC

Liu, Pai-yü.
莫斯科訪問記 劉白羽著 [修訂] 北京 人民文學出版社 1955.
206 p. 19 cm.

1. Moscow—Descr. *Title romanized:* Mo-ssŭ-k'o fang wên chi.

DK601.2.L5 C 62-1584 ‡

NL 0415590 DLC MnU

Liu, Pai-yü.
Six a. m., and other stories. [1st ed.] Peking, Foreign Languages Press, 1953.
149 p. 19 cm.

I. Title.

PL3000.L55T74 57-35388 ‡

OU MeB TU NcD MiU NN CtY
NL 0415591 DLC CaBVaU NIC CLSU WaU CU IaU InU KU

Liu, Pai-yü.
Six heures du matin; nouvelles par Lieou Pai-yu. [1. éd.] Pekin, Editions en Langues Etrangeres, 1953.
164 p. 17 cm.

I. Title.

PL3000.L55T75 57-35393 ‡

NL 0415592 DLC CtY

Liu, Pai-yü.
Tung-pei chieh fang ch'ü tuan p'ien ch'uang tso hsüan
see under title

Liu, Pai-yü.
偉大的戰鬥 劉白羽著 [上海] 海燕書店 1950.
100 p. 18 cm.

1. China—Hist.—Civil War, 1945–1949—Fiction. I. Title.
Title romanized: Wei ta ti chan t'ou.

PL2879.P3W38 C 68-3038

NL 0415594 DLC

Liu, Pai-yü.
爲祖國而戰 劉白羽著 北京 天下出版社 1951.
140 p. 17 cm. (大衆文藝叢書)

I. Title. *Title romanized:* Wei tsu kuo êrh chan.

PL2879.P3W4 C 60-1295 ‡

NL 0415595 DLC

Liu, Pai-yü.
爲祖國而戰 劉白羽[著] 上海 新文藝出版社 1953.
viii, 223 p. 18 cm.

I. Title.
Title romanized: Wei tsu kuo êrh chan.

PL2879.P3W4 1953 C 68-3036

NL 0415596 DLC CaBVaU

Liu, Pai-yü.
無敵三勇士 劉白羽著 西野畫 [佳木斯] 東北書店 [1948]
81 p. illus. 15 cm.
CONTENTS.—無敵三勇士—百戰百勝—政治委員

I. Title.
Title romanized: Wu ti san yung shih.

PL2782.P3W8 C 68-1868

NL 0415597 DLC

PL2653 .W82 1949b Orien China

Liu, Pai-yü. FOR OTHER EDITIONS SEE MAIN ENTRY
Wu ti san yung shih.
無敵三勇士 短篇小說選 [劉白羽等著 n.p. 新華書店 1949]

Liu, Pai-yü.
延安生活 劉白羽著 [n.p.] 現實出版社 1946.
1, 47 p. illus. 17 cm. (現實文叢之一)

I. Title.
Title romanized: Yen-an shêng huo.
C63-232

Harvard Univ. Chinese-Japanese Library 4292.67 for Library of Congress [3]

NL 0415599 MH-HY ICU

VOLUME 336

Liu, Pai-yü.
英雄的記錄 劉白羽著 ⌈佳木斯 東北書店 1947⌉
3, 2, 134 p. 19 cm. (東北文藝叢書 3)

1. China—History—Civil War, 1945-1949—Personal narratives. I. Title.
Title romanized: Ying hsiung ti chi lu.

DS777.54.L54 74-835521

NL 0415600 DLC

Liu, Pai-yü.
永遠前進 1949 短篇選集 劉白羽 生木等著 ⌈北京⌉ 新華書店 ⌈1950⌉
2, 328 p. 18 cm. (中國人民文藝叢書)
A collection of works by various authors.

1. Short stories, Chinese. I. Shêng, Mu. II. Title.
Title romanized: Yung yüan ch'ien chin.

PL2652.L5 C 67-2773

NL 0415601 DLC WaU-FE

Liu, Pai-yü.
Заря впереди. Перевод с китайского С. Иванько и В. Панасюка. Предисл. Н. Пахомова. Редактор Ю. Карасев. Москва, Изд-во иностранной лит-ры, 1951.
113 p. 20 cm.
Translation of Huo kuang tsai ch'ien.

1. China—Hist.—1945- —Fiction. I. Title.
Title transliterated: Zarâ vperedi.

PL3000.L55H87 53-31660

NL 0415602 DLC

Liu, P'an-sui, 1899-
段王學五種 ⌈劉盼遂著 北平 來薰閣書店 1936⌉
4 v. (double leaves) in case. 27 cm. (百鶴樓叢書)
CONTENTS.—⌈1⌉ 經韵樓集補編 上下卷 段玉裁撰 劉盼遂輯校—⌈2⌉ 段玉裁先生年譜 劉盼遂學—⌈3⌉ 王石臞文集補編 王念孫撰 劉盼遂輯校 王伯申文集補編 上下卷 王引之撰 劉盼遂輯校—⌈4⌉ 高郵王氏父子年譜 劉盼遂學
I. Tuan, Yü-ts'ai, 1735-1815. II. Wang, Nien-sun, 1744-1832. III. Wang, Yin-chih, 1766-1834. IV. Title.
Title romanized: Tuan Wang hsüeh wu chung.

PL2729.U3Z77 C 68-1973

NL 0415603 DLC CaBVaU

633.74 L742i Liu, Pao-hua, 1917-
Inheritance of chlorophyll and cotyledon color in soybeans. Urbana ⌈1950⌉
46 l. illus. 28cm.

Thesis--University of Illinois.
Typewritten (carbon copy)
Vita.
Bibliography: leaves 45-46.

1. Soy-bean. 2. Heredity.

NL 0415604 IU

Liu, Pao-hua, 1917-
Inheritance of chlorophyll and cotyledon color in soybeans. Urbana, 1950.
5 p. 23 cm.
Abstract of thesis—University of Illinois.
Vita.

1. Soy-bean. 2. Heredity

SB205.S7L59 A 50-7521

Illinois. Univ. Library for Library of Congress ⌈1⌉†

NL 0415605 IU DNAL NIC DLC

Liu, Pao-shu, 1890-
平均地權 劉寶書著 上海 太平洋書店 民國 17 ⌈1928⌉
90 p. 19 cm.

1. Land tenure. 2. Sun, Yat-sen, 1866-1925. San min chu i. I. Title.
Title romanized: P'ing chün ti ch'üan.

HD111.L5 C 66-1908

NL 0415606 DLC

Liu, P'ei-hêng, joint author.

Q181 .C417 Orien China
Chiang, Tzŭ-hao.
(K'o hsüeh ti hsüeh hsi hsiao tsu) 科學的學習小組 江子豪 劉佩衡合編 ⌈上海⌉ 中國科學圖書儀器公司 ⌈1950⌉

Liu, P'ei-hua.
中國近代簡史 劉培華編 北京 益昌書局 1953.
10, 258, 16 p. maps (7 fold.) 19 cm.

1. China—Hist.—19th cent. 2. China—Hist.—1900- I. Title.
Title romanized: Chung-kuo chin tai chien shih.

DS755.L5 C 58-7491 rev

Indiana. Univ. Libr. for Library of Congress DS740 ⌈r66b2⌉†

NL 0415608 InU DLC NIC CLU-O

Liu, P'ei-jan.
保甲的理論與實施 劉沛然編著 漢口 華中圖書公司 民國 25 ⌈1936⌉
10, 6, 216 p. port. 19 cm. (縣區鄉政叢著之一)
Colophon title.
Bibliography: p. 216.

I. Title.
Title romanized: Pao chia ti li lun.

JS7352.L54 C 67-1179

NL 0415609 DLC

Liu, Pei-ssŭ.
拿紅旗的人 劉北汜著 ⌈上海⌉ 文光書店 ⌈1952⌉
3, 2, 71 p. illus. 17 cm. (和平戰綫文叢)

1. Korean War, 1950-1953—Personal narratives, Chinese. I. Title.
Title romanized: Na hung ch'i ti jên.

DS921.6.L63 70-835520

NL 0415610 DLC

Liu, Pên-li.
產科鎮痛麻醉學 劉本立編著 上海 廣協書局 1952.
136 p. illus. 19 cm.

1. Anesthesia in obstetrics. I. Title.
Title romanized: Ch'an k'o chên t'ung ma tsui hsüeh.

RG732.L5 C 58-5777 ‡

NL 0415611 DLC

Liu, Pên-li.
生育與不育 劉本立著 上海 家出版社 1953.
66 p. illus. 18 cm. (婦產科叢書)

1. Sterility. 2. Pregnancy. I. Title.
Title romanized: Shêng yü yü pu yü.

RG201.L55 C 58-6202 †

NL 0415612 DLC

Liu, P'ing, 1908 *or* 9-
(Hsien fa chih shih tu pên) 憲法知識讀本 劉平著 上海 憲政常識叢書社 ⌈民國 26 i. e. 1937⌉
4, 2, 104 p. 19 cm. (憲政常識叢書之3)
附錄 中華民國憲法草案: p. 79-104.

1. China—Constitutional law. I. China. Constitution. 1937. II. Title.

78-840922

NL 0415613 DLC

Liu, Ping-i.
機械工作計算手册 劉秉彝編 北京 首都出版社 1953.
574 p. illus. 19 cm.

1. Mechanical engineering—Handbooks, manuals, etc. I. Title.
Title romanized: Chi hsieh kung tso chi suan shou ts'ê.

TJ151.L48 C 60-1114 ‡

NL 0415614 DLC

Liu, Ping-kun.
... Résistance à la traction à chaud des matériaux réfractaires ... Nancy, Imprimerie G. Thomas, 1938.
60 p., 1 l. incl. illus., tables, diagrs. 24cm.
Thèse—Nancy.

1. Refractory materials. I. Title.

42-48259

Library of Congress TN677.L52

NL 0415615 DLC

Liu, Ping-li, *ed.*
蔣介石先生思想研究集 劉炳藜編 南京 前途書局 民國 26 ⌈1937⌉
4, 4, 294 p. illus., ports. 22 cm. (前途叢書第2種)

1. Chiang, Kai-shek, 1886- I. Title.
Title romanized: Chiang Chieh-shih hsien shêng ssŭ hsiang yen chiu chi.

DS778.C55L48 C 66-1159

NL 0415616 DLC

Liu, Ping-li.
教育史大綱 劉炳藜著 上海 北新書局 民國 20 ⌈1931⌉
4, 9, 454 p. 19 cm.

1. Education—Hist. 2. Education—China—Hist. I. Title.
Title romanized: Chiao yü shih ta kang.

LA13.L7 C 58-7355

Hoover Institution for Library of Congress 4909 ⌈2⌉†

NL 0415617 CSt-H DLC

VOLUME 336

Liu, Ping-li, ed.
Chung wai jên ming tz'ŭ tien
see under title

Liu, Ping-li.
三民主義之哲學體系一心物綜合論之研究 劉炳藜著 ⌈泰和⌉ 江西省三民主義文化運動委員會 民國 31 ⌈1942⌉
4, 2, 106 p. 20 cm.
Caption title.

1. Sun, Yat-sen, 1866–1925. San min chu i. I. Title.
Title romanized: San min chu i chih chê hsüeh t'i hsi.

C 59–5309

Hoover Institution for Library of Congress 4788.15 ⌈4⌉

NL 0415619 CSt-H

Liu, Ping-li.
三民主義與中國革命 劉炳藜著 重慶 中央週刊社 民國29 ⌈1940⌉
2, 1, 182 p. 18 cm.
Cover title.

1. Sun, Yat-sen, 1866–1925. San min chu i. I. Title.
Title romanized: San min chu i yü Chung-kuo ko ming.

DS777.A567L5 C 66–1220

NL 0415620 DLC

Liu, Ping-lin, 1889–
經濟學 劉秉麟編 ⌈上海⌉ 商務印書館 ⌈1929⌉
12, 385 p. 19 cm.
Bibliography: p. 365–385.

1. Economics. I. Title.
Title romanized: Ching chi hsüeh.

HB180.C5L57 C 68–2765

NL 0415621 DLC

Liu, Ping-lin, 1889–
世界傾銷問題 劉秉麟 潘源來著 上海 商務印書館 民國24 ⌈1935⌉
8, 200 p. 19 cm. (現代問題叢書)

1. Dumping (commercial policy) I. P'an, Yüan-lai, joint author. II. Title.
Title romanized: Shih chieh ch'ing hsiao wên t'i.

HF1425.L5 C 66–40

NL 0415622 DLC MiU

Liu, Ping-lin, 1889–
世界各國無產政黨史 撰述者劉秉麟 校閱者吳敬恆 上海 商務印書館 1928.
4, 171, 2 p. 19 cm. (新時代史地叢書)

1. Socialist parties—Hist. I. Title.
Title romanized: Shih chieh ko kuo wu ch'an chêng tang shih.

HX40.L53 C 66–2022

NL 0415623 DLC

Liu, Pinghou C.
Chinese foreign affairs—organization and control, by Pinghou C. Liu ... ⌈New York⌉ Pub. under the auspices of the Graduate school of New York university ⌈°1937⌉
v, ⌈1⌉, 27 p. diagrs. 23cm.
Abridgment of thesis (PH. D.)—New York university, 1936.
Bibliography: p. iii.

1. China. Ministry of foreign affairs. 2. China—For. rel. I. Title.

38—1636

Library of Congress JX1838.A4L5 1936
——— Copy 2.
Copyright A 112479 ⌈38c2⌉ 327.51

NL 0415624 DLC OC1W OC1 NN NIC PPT

Liu, Po-chou.
海外華僑發展史概論 劉伯周編著 上海 華僑圖書印刷公司 民國24 ⌈1935⌉
1, 1, 104 p. 19 cm.
Colophon title.
Bibliography: p. 103–104.

1. Chinese in foreign countries. I. Title.
Title romanized: Hai wai Hua ch'iao fa chan shih.

DS732.L59 C 67–1061

NL 0415625 DLC

Liu, Po-kang.
經濟史概要 ⌈劉伯剛編 上海 樂華圖書公司 1929⌉
3, 6, 134 p. 18 cm.

1. Economic history. I. Title.
Title romanized: Ching chi shih kai yao.

HC25.L48 C 68–2391

NL 0415626 DLC

Liu, Po-k'uei.
馬來人及其文化 劉伯奎著 ⌈重慶⌉ 商務印書館 ⌈民國33 i. e. 1944⌉
1, 1, 138 p. 18 cm.
Includes bibliographical references.

1. Malaya—Civilization. I. Title.
Title romanized: Ma-lai jên chi ch'i wên hua.

DS594.L58 73–840350

NL 0415627 DLC

Liu, Po-min
see
Liu, Pai-min, 1900–

Liu, Po-wên
see
Liu, Chi, 1311–1375.

Liu, Po-yü
see
Liu, Pai-yü.

Liu, Po-yüan.
(Kuang-tung shêng ts'an yeh tiao ch'a) 廣東省蠶業調查報告書 ⌈劉伯淵調查編輯 廣州⌉ 廣東省地方農林試驗場 民國 11 ⌈1922⌉
91 p. 26 cm.
Cover title.

1. Sericulture—China—Kwangtung (Province) I. Kuang-tung shêng ti fang nung lin shih yen ch'ang. II. Title.

SF553.C6L48 74–841011

NL 0415631 DLC

Liu, Qing
see
Liu, Ch'ing, 1916–

Liu, S. Francis
see Liu, Shih-fang Francis, 1901–

Liu, S I
The flow and fracture characteristics of the aluminum alloy 24ST after alternating tension and compression, by S. I. Liu and G. Sachs.
(*In* Metals technology. New York. 23 cm. v. 15, no. 4, June 1948. 12 p. diagrs.)
American Institute of Mining and Metallurgical Engineers. Technical publication no. 2392 (Class E, Metals technology, June 1948)
"References": p. 12.

1. Aluminum alloys. 2. Metals—Fatigue. I. Sachs, George, 1896– joint author.

[TN1.A5255 vol. 15, no. 4] P O 50–176

U. S. Patent Office. for Library of Congress Library ⌈2⌉

NL 0415634 DP

Liu, S I
Low cycle fatigue of the aluminum alloy 24ST in direct stress, by S. I. Liu ⌈and others⌉
(*In* Metals technology. New York. 23 cm. v. 15, no. 2, Feb. 1948. 22 p. diagrs.)
American Institute of Mining and Metallurgical Engineers. Technical publication no. 2338 (Class E, Metals technology, Feb. 1948)
"References": p. 22.

1. Aluminum alloys. 2. Metals—Fatigue.

[TN1.A5255 vol. 15, no. 2] P O 50–106

U. S. Patent Office. for Library of Congress Library ⌈2⌉

NL 0415635 DP

Liu, San-lang
see
Hsiao, Chün, 1908–

Liu, Schao-tschi
see
Liu, Shao-ch'i, 1900–

Liu, Shan.
中國文法 劉珊著 ⌈台北⌉ 華國出版社 ⌈1951⌉
2, 149 p. 19 cm.

1. Chinese language—Grammar. I. Title.
Title romanized: Chung-kuo wên fa.

PL1109.L5 C 68–2176

NL 0415638 DP CaBVaU

VOLUME 336

Liu, Shao, *3d cent.*
人物志 [3 卷] 劉邵撰 任繼愈斷句 北京 文學古籍刊行社 1955.
1 v. (various pagings) 21 cm.

1. Ability. 2. Leadership. 3. Characters and characteristics. I. Title.
Title romanized: Jên wu chih.

BF118.C5L5 1955 C 60-1022 rev

NL 0415639 DLC HU

Liu, Shao, *3d cent.*
The study of human abilities; the Jen wu chih of Liu Shao, with an introductory study by J. K. Shryock ... New Haven, Conn., American Oriental society, 1937.
x, 168 p. 26cm. (*Added t.-p.:* American Oriental series, v. 11)
Errata slip inserted.
The author "is concerned only with the psychology of public life." cf. p. 5.
"Editions of the Jen wu chih": p. 160-161.
1. Ability. 2. Leadership. 3. Characters and characteristics. 4. Psychology—Early works to 1850. I. Shryock, John Knight, 1890- ed. II. Title. III. Title: Jen wu chih.
37-1835
Library of Congress PL2997.L54J42
[a43b2] 895.18

NL 0415640 PHC PU OO OU OCl OCU DLC NjP PPT PU WaU-L OrU ScU CtY PBm

---

Liu, Shao-ch'i, 1900–
Adresse du premier mai. Pekin, Éditions en langues étrangères, 1950.
38 p. 18 cm.

1. China—Pol. & govt.—1949–

DS777.55.L5 *951.05 951.04 52-41605

NL 0415641 DLC CSt-H NNC

Law
Liu, Shao-ch'i, 1900– FOR OTHER EDITIONS SEE MAIN ENTRY
China (*People's Republic of China, 1949–*) *Laws, statutes, etc.*
The Agrarian reform law of the People's Republic of China and other relevant documents. [4th ed.] Peking, Foreign Languages Press [1952]

Liu, Shao-ch'i, 1900–
Bericht über den Verfassungsentwurf der Volksrepublik China. Die Verfassung der Volksrepublik China. [Von] Liu Schao-tschi. Peking, Verlag für Fremdsprachige Literatur, 1954.
121 p. port. 22 cm.

1. China (People's Republic of China, 1949–)—Constitutional law. I. China (People's Republic of China, 1949–) Constitution. II. Title.
57-36060

NL 0415643 DLC MH-L

Liu, Shao-ch'i, 1900–
Chung-kuo ching chi ti kai tsao
see under title

JQ1519 .A5 K34384
Liu, Shao-ch'i, 1900–
The Communist Party, leader of the Chinese revolution. Peking, Foreign Languages Press, 1951.

HX389 .Z7L486
Liu, Shao-ch'i, 1900–
Cómo ser un buen comunista. [Trabajo, Comisión de Propaganda del Comité Municipal del P. S. P., 195–]
50 p. 19 cm.
"Este material apareció publicado en la revista Fundamentos, en junio de 1953."

1. Communism. I. Title.

HX389.Z7L486 60-33934 ‡

NL 0415646 DLC

LIU, SHAO-CHI, 1900–
Hoe een goed communist te zijn een serie voordrachten in juli 1939 gehouden aan het Instituut voor Marxisme-Leninisme te Jenan. Amsterdam, Pegasus, 1955. 113 p. 20cm.

1. Kung ch'an tang.

NL 0415647 NN

Liu, Shao-ch'i, 1900–
How to be a good communist. [1st ed.] Peking, Foreign Languages Press [1951]
122 p. illus. 19 cm.

1. Communism. I. Title.

HX389.Z7L482 335.4 52-2532 ‡

NL 0415648 DLC NN TxU NcU ICN NBuU N NN MH PSC

Liu, Shao-ch'i, 1900–
How to be a good Communist. New York, New Century Publishers [1952]
64 p. 20 cm.

1. Communism. I. Title.

HX389.Z7L482 1952 335.4 55-19836 ‡

NL 0415649 DLC MiU NBuC CU-B MH OrCS NcD NNC

Liu, Shao-ch'i, 1900–
How to be a good Communist. New York, New Century Publishers [1952]
64 p. 20 cm.
Photocopy. 1970.

NL 0415650 FU

Liu, Shao-ch'i, 1900–
How to be a good Communist. [2d rev. ed.] Peking, Foreign Languages Press [1952]
118 p. illus. 19 cm.

1. Communism. I. Title.

HX389.Z7L482 1952a 335.4 55-20000 ‡

NL 0415651 DLC CaBViP IaU IU MiU

HX389 .Z7L482 1952
Liu, Shao-chi, 1900–
How to be a good Communist. [3d ed.] Peking, Foreign Language Press [1952]
118 p. port. 19cm.

1. Communism.

NL 0415652 ViU

HC427 .9 .H748 1970 Orien
Liu, Shao-ch'i, 1900–
(Hsin min chu chu i ch'êng shih chêng ts'ê) 新民主主義城市政策 劉少奇等著 [香港] 新民主出版社 [1949]

HX389 .H788 Orien China
Liu, Shao-ch'i, 1900–
Hsüeh hsi.
學習 第 1 輯 香港 大公報 [1951?]

Pam. Coll. 24429
Liu, Shao-chi, 1900–
Hur bli en bra kommunist; föredrag hållna i juli 1939 i Marxistisk-leninistiska institutet i Yenan. [Stockholm, Arbetarkultur [1952] 86 p. 19 cm. (Kultur och politik)

Translated, by Sven Johansson, from the English translation of the original Chinese.
1. Communism. I. Johansson, Sven tr. II. Title.

NL 0415655 NcD

---

4 JC 340
Liu, Shao-ch'i, 1900–
Internacionalizmus és nacionalizmus. [Fordította S. Nyirő József] Budapest, Szikra, 1949.
47 p.

(Marxista ismeretek kis könyvtára, 62)

NL 0415656 DLC-P4

Soc JC 311 L682
Liu, Shao-ch'i, 1900–
Internationalism and nationalism. Peking, Foreign Languages Press [n.d.]
50p. illus.

1. Nationalism. I. Title.

NL 0415657 FTaSU

---

q320.15 L74i
LIU, SHAO-CH'I, 1900–
Internationalism and nationalism. New York, N.Y., Committee for a Democratic Far Eastern Policy [1948]
1l.,13 [1]p. 29cm.

1. Nationalism and nationality. 2. Imperialism. I. Title.

NL 0415658 TxU DLC CSt-H NcD NcU NNC NjP

VOLUME 336

Wason DS777.7+ M29 Liu Shao-ch'i, 1900-
Internationalism and nationalism.
New York, Distributed by: Committee for a Democratic Far Eastern Policy [1950?]
13, [1] p. 28cm.

No. 3 in vol. lettered: Mao Tsê-tung. The Chinese revolution.

1. Internationalism. 2. Nationalism and nationality. 3. Communism—China. I. Title.

NL 0415659 NIC NN

Liu, Shao-ch'i, 1900-
Internationalism and nationalism. Peking, Foreign Languages Press [1951?]
54 p. port. 19 cm.

1. Nationalism. I. Title.

JC311.L682 320.15 51—35665

NL 0415660 WaU DLC CaBVaU CLSU FMU CtY MH NcU TU NN

Liu, Shao-ch'i, 1900-
Internationalism and nationalism. [2d ed.] Peking, Foreign Languages Press [1951]
44 p. port.

NL 0415661 MH PU PHC CLSU

Wason JC311 L78 Liu, Shao-ch'i, 1900-
Internationalism and nationalism.
Peking, Foreign Language Press [1952?]
54 p. 19cm.

1. Internationalism. 2. Nationalism and nationality. 3. Communism--China.

NL 0415662 NIC

Liu, Shao-ch'i, 1900-
Internationalism and nationalism [2d ed.]
Peking, Foreign Languages Press c1952
53p.

Photostat of 2d ed. including contents page of 3d ed. (Dec. 1952)

NL 0415663 NNCFR

Liu, Shao-ch'i, 1900-
Internationalism and nationalism. [3d ed.]
Peking, Foreign languages press [1952]
44 p. port.

1. Nationalism. 2. Communism. I. Title.

NL 0415664 NNC IU NN ViU MH-L DLC-P4 N CU-B

Liu, Shao-ch'i, 1900-
Internationalism and nationalism. [4th ed.] Peking, Foreign Languages Press, 1954.
50 p. illus. 19 cm.

1. Nationalism. I. Title.

JC311.L682 1954 320.15 57-34396 ‡

NL 0415665 DLC ICU CSt

Liu, Shao-ch'i, 1900-
L'internationalisme et le nationalisme [par] Liou Chao-chi. [1. ed.] Pékin, Éditions en langues étrangères [1951]
56 p. illus. 19 cm.

1. Nationalism. I. Title.

JC311.L684 1951 55-20019 ‡

NL 0415666 DLC MH

Liu, Shao-ch'i, 1900-
Internationalismus und Nationalismus. Berlin, Dietz, 1952
39 p. (Internationale Schriftenreihe, 12)

NL 0415667 MH

Law Liu, Shao-ch'i, 1900- Kuan yü Chung-hua jên min kung ho kuo hsien fa ts'ao an.
Chung-hua jên min kung ho kuo hsien fa.
China (*People's Republic of China, 1949-*) *Constitution.*
中華人民共和國憲法 [1954年9月20日第一屆全國人民代表大會第一次會議通過] 中共中央馬克思恩格斯列寧斯大林著作編譯局編譯 北京 中華書局 1955.

Liu, Shao-ch'i, 1900-
關於修改黨章的報告 一九四五年五月十四日在中國共產黨第七次全國代表大會上 劉少奇著 大連 大衆書店 民國37 [1948]
90 p. 19 cm.

1. Chung-kuo kung ch'an tang. I. Title.
Title romanized: Kuan yü hsiu kai tang chang ti pao kao.

JQ1519.A5L495 C 67-653

NL 0415669 DLC

Liu, Shao-ch'i, 1900- Kuan yu hsiu kai tang chang ti pao kao.
Chung-kuo kung ch'an tang.
中國共產黨黨章 關於修改黨章的報告 [劉少奇撰 北京] 新華書店 1949.

Liu, Shao-ch'i, 1900-
關於土地改革問題的報告 劉少奇[講] 中華人民共和國土地改革法 新華時事叢刊社編輯 廣州 新華書店 1950.
36 p. 18 cm.

Cover title.

1. Land tenure—China (People's Republic of China, 1949-)—Law. 2. Agricultural laws and legislation—China (People's Republic of China, 1949-) I. China (People's Republic of China, 1949-) Laws, statutes, etc. Chung-hua jên min kung ho kuo t'u ti kai ko fa. II. Hsin hua shih shih ts'ung k'an shê. III. Title.
Title romanized: Kuan yü t'u ti kai ko wên t'i ti pao kao.

C62-2-2998

NL 0415671 DLC

HD865 .L58 Orien China Liu, Shao-ch'i, 1900-
關於土地改革問題的報告 劉少奇[撰] 中華人民共和國土地改革法 人民出版社編輯 四版 北京 1951.
36 p. 19 cm.

1. Land tenure—China (People's Republic of China, 1949-)—Law. 2. Agricultural laws and legislation—China (People's Republic of China, 1949-) I. China (People's Republic of China, 1949-) Laws, statutes, etc. II. Jên min ch'u pan shê, Peking. III. Title.
Title romanized: Kuan yü t'u ti kai ko wên t'i ti pao kao.

C 61-4047

Cornell Univ. Library for Library of Congress [3]

NL 0415672 NIC DLC

Liu, Shao-ch'i, 1900-
... Laporan tentang rentjana undang² dasar republik rakjat Tiongkok.
Undang² dasar republik rakjat Tiongkok.
Peking, Pustaka bahasa asing, 1954.
114 p. front. (port.) 21cm.

"Dibuat pada tanggal 15 september 1954 dalam sidang pertama kongres rakjat nasional ke-I republik, rakjat Tiongkok."

NL 0415673 MH-L

DS777 .55 .M28 Liu, Shao-ch'i, 1900-

Mao, Tsê-tung, 1893-
Lessons of the Chinese Revolution [by] Mao Tse-tung & Liu Shao-chi. [1st Indian ed. Bombay, Published by J. Bhatt for People's Pub. House, 1950]

Liu, Shao-ch'i, 1900-
Lun ch'ün chung lu hsien
see under title

Liu, Shao-ch'i, 1900-
論革命家的修養 劉少奇著 大連 大衆書店 民國37 [1948]
2, 68 p. 18 cm.

1. Communism. I. Title.
Title romanized: Lun ko ming chia ti hsiu yang.

HX389.Z7L49 1948 C 68-1179

NL 0415676 DLC WaU-FE

Liu, Shao-ch'i, 1900-
論共產黨員 劉少奇著 [哈爾濱] 東北書店 [1948]
150 p. 19 cm.

CONTENTS.— 人的階級姓 [sic]—論共產黨員的修養—作一個好黨員建設一個好的黨—黨的群衆路綫問題—論黨內鬥爭—清算黨內的孟塞維主義思想

1. Chung-kuo kung ch'an tang—Discipline. I. Title.
Title romanized: Lun kung ch'an tang yüan.

JQ1519.A52L5 C 67-1991

NL 0415677 DLC

VOLUME 336

Liu, Shao-ch'i, 1900–
論共產黨黨員的修養 1939年7月8日在延安馬列學院的演講 劉少奇[講] 天津 解放社 1949.
111 p. 18 cm.
Bound with Chung-kuo kung ch'an tang. 中國共產黨黨章 [北京] 1949.

1. Communism. I. Title.
Title romanized: Lun kung ch'an tang yüan ti hsiu yang.
C 68-2871
Cornell Univ. Library for Library of Congress [1⅓]

NL 0415678 NIC

Liu, Shao-ch'i, 1900–
論共產黨員的修養 一九三九年七月八日在延安馬列學院的演講 劉少奇著 北京 人民出版社 1952
96 p. 19 cm.

1. Communism. I. Title.
Title romanized: Lun kung ch'an tang yüan ti hsiu yang.
HX389.Z7L49 C 59-1280 ‡

NL 0415679 DLC NhD

Liu, Shao-ch'i, 1900–
論國際主義与民族主義 劉少奇著 [香港] 新民主出版社 [1949]
31 p. 19 cm.

1. Nationalism and socialism. I. Title.
Title romanized: Lun kuo chi chu i yü min tsu chu i.
HX550.N3L55 1949 C 67-1751

NL 0415680 DLC WaU-FE

JC359 .M28 Orien China
Liu, Shao-ch'i, 1900– Lun kuo chi chu i yü min tsu chu i.
Mao, Tsê-tung, 1893–
全世界革命力量團結起來反對帝國主義的侵略 毛澤東[著] 論國際主義與民族主義 劉少奇[著 n.p.] 華東新華書店 1949.

Liu, Shao-ch'i, 1900–
論國際主義與民族主義 劉少奇著 修訂本 [北京] 人民出版社 [1951]
40 p. 18 cm.

1. Nationalism and socialism. I. Title.
Title romanized: Lun kuo chi chu i yü min tsu chu i.
HX550.N3L55 1951 C 67-1750

NL 0415682 DLC

Liu, Shao-ch'i, 1900–
論黨 劉少奇著 大連 大衆書店 1947.
2, 346 p. port. 17 cm.

1. Chung-kuo kung ch'an tang. I. Title.
Title romanized: Lun tang.
JQ1519.A5L497 1947 C 65-1412

NL 0415683 DLC

Liu, Shao-ch'i, 1900–
論黨 劉少奇著 北京 人民出版社 1953.
154 p. 19 cm.

1. Chung-kuo kung ch'an tang. I. Title.
Title romanized: Lun tang.
JQ1519.A5C53385 C 59-1278 ‡

NL 0415684 DLC

Liu, Shao-ch'i, 1900–
論黨內鬥爭 劉少奇著 [香港] 正報社 [民國 36 [1947]
48 p. 18 cm.

1. Chung-kuo kung ch'an tang—Discipline. I. Title.
Title romanized: Lun tang nei tou chêng.
JQ1519.A5L5 C 61-110 ‡

NL 0415685 DLC HU

HD6802 T763 1949L7
Liu, Shao-chi, 1900-
Manifesto & opening speech. [Bombay] People's Publishing House [1950?]
18 p. 18cm.
At head of title: Trade Union Conference of Asian and Australasian Countries, Peking, 1949. [sponsored by World Federation of Trade Unions. - cf. p.1]

1. Trade unions - Australasia. 2. Labor and laboring classes - Australasia. I. Trade Union Conference of Asian and Australasian Countries, Peking, 1949. II. Title.

NL 0415686 CSt-H

Liu, Shao-ch'i, 1900–
О проекте Конституции Китайской Народной Республики; доклад на первой сессии Всекитайского Собрания народных представителей в Пекине 15 сентября 1954 года. Москва, Гос. изд-во полит. лит-ры, 1954.
54 p. 20 cm.

1. China—Constitutional law. I. Title.
Title transliterated: O proekte Konstitut͡sii Kitaĭskoĭ Narodnoĭ Respubliki.
55-30655 ‡

NL 0415687 DLC

JC311 .L7
Liu, Shao-ch'i, 1900–
Об интернационализме и национализме. [Москва] Гос. изд-во полит. лит-ры, 1949.
86 p. 20 cm.

1. Nationalism and nationality.
Title transliterated: Ob internat͡sionalizme i nat͡sionalizme.
50-31079 rev

NL 0415688 DLC

329.951 L783
Liu, Shao-ch'i, 1900-
On inner-party struggle. [New York] New Century Publishers, 1952.
48 p. 21 cm.

1. Kung-ch'an-tang. Discipline. I. Title.

NL 0415689 N NNC CU-B NBuT MiEM

Liu, Shao-ch'i, 1900-
On inner-party struggle. [New York] New Century Publishers, 1952.
48p. 18cm.
"A lecture delivered on July 2, 1941 at the Party School for Central China."

HX389 .Z7L52 1952a
—— —— Photocopy. Ann Arbor, Mich., University Microfilms, 1970.

1. Chung-kuo kung ch'an tang—Discipline. I. t.

NL 0415690 OrPS

Liu, Shao-ch'i, 1900–
On inner-party struggle. A lecture delivered on July 2, 1941 at the party school for Central China. Peking, Foreign Languages Press [1950?]
92 p. port. 19 cm.

1. Kung-ch'an-tang—Discipline. I. Title.
HX389.Z7L52 329.951 52-16293 ‡

NL 0415691 NjP IU DLC ICU NcU MH CSt-H CtY MU CLSU PHC

HX389 Z7L57 1951
Liu, Shao-ch'i, 1900-
On inner-party struggle. A lecture delivered on July 2, 1941, at the Party School for Central China. [1st Indian ed.] Bombay, People's Pub. House [1951]
64 p.

1. Kung-ch'an-tang - Discipline. I. Title.

NL 0415692 CU NNC TxU IEN

HX 389 Z7L52
Liu, Shao-ch'i, 1900-
On inner-party struggle. A series of lectures delivered in July, 1941 at the party school for Central China. Peking, Foreign Languages Press [1950?]
90p. port. 19cm.

1.Chung-kuo kung ch'an tang - Discipline. I.Title.

NL 0415693 CLSU CtY NNC

HX389 .Z7L53 1952
Liu, Shao-ch'i, 1900-
On inner-party struggle. A series of lectures delivered in July 1941 at the party school for Central China. [3d ed.] Peking, Foreign Languages Press [1952]
90 p. port. 19cm.

1. Kung-ch'an-tang—Discipline. I. Title.

NL 0415694 ViU FU

Liu, Shao-ch'i, 1900–
On the party. [2d ed.] Peking, Foreign Languages Press, 1950.
206 p. port. 19 cm.
"The Constitution of the Communist Party of China": p. 155–204.

1. Kung-ch'an-tung. I. Title.
JQ1519.A5K846 1950 329.951 51-22020

NL 0415695 CLSU NcU CU-S DLC CSt-H NNC TxU CtY PSC CaBVaU MShM

VOLUME 336

JQ1519 Liu, Shao-ch'i, 1900-
A5533852 On the party. Peking, Foreign Languages Press, 1951.
190p. front. 18cm.

1. Chung-kuo kung ch'an tang. I. Title.

NL 0415696 IaU

Liu, Shao-ch'i, 1900-
On the party. [3d ed.] Peking, Foreign Languages Press, 1951.
190 p. port. 19 cm.
"The Constitution of the Communist Party of China": p. 141-186.

1. Kung-ch'an-tung. I. Title.
JQ1519.A5K846 1951 329.951 56-18004

NIC CaBVaU IaU NIC NN NcD OU PHC
NL 0415697 DLC OrCS FTaSU ViU MH CU NNC PU ICU

329.951 Liu, Shao-ch'i, 1900-
L490E On the party. Peking, Foreign Languages
1952 Press, 1952.
190p. port. 19cm.

1. Kung-ch'an-tung.

NL 0415698 IU NN KyU OU

JQ Liu, Shao-ch'i, 1900-
1519 On the party. [4th ed.] Peking,
A5K846 Foreign Languages Press, 1952.
1952 190p. port. 19cm.
"The Constitution of the Communist Party of China": p.141-186.

NL 0415699 CLSU LU NSyU ViU

Liu, Shao-ch'i, 1900-
On the party. [5th ed.] Peking, Foreign Languages Press, 1954.
188 p. illus. 19 cm.

1. Chung-Kuo kung ch'an tang. I. Title.
JQ1519.A5L513 1954 342.51 61-21196 ‡

NL 0415700 DLC OrU TxU MiEM CaBVaU FU

Liu, Shao-ch'i, 1900-
On the party. [5th ed.] Peking, Foreign Languages Press, 1954.
188p. port. 19 cm.
"The Constitution of the Communist Party of China": p. [153]-185.
——— ——— Photocopy. Ann Arbor, Mich., University Microfilms, 1969.

NL 0415701 OrPS NcU

Liu, Shao-ch'i, 1900-
HX389 Pour être un bon communiste. Traduit
Z7 par Paul Jamati. Paris, Editions sociales,
L483 1955.
115 p. 19 cm.

NL 0415702 RPB NN

264cr Liu, Shao-ch'i, 1900-
L788 Rapport sur le projet de Constitution de la Republique Populaire
ra de Chine. Constitution de la Republique Populaire de Chine.
Law [Adoptée le 20 septembre 1954 à la première session de la pre-
Library mière Assemblée populaire nationale de la République populaire de Chine] Pekin, Éditions en langues étrangères, 1954.
137 p. port.

At head of title: Liou Chao-chi.

1. China (People's Republic of China, 1949-) - Constitutional law. I. China (People's Republic of China, 1949-) Constitution.

NL 0415703 CU N MiU-L MH-L

Liu, Shao-ch'i, 1900-
Речь на торжественном заседании пекинского актива, посвященном празднику трудящихся 1-го мая, 29 апреля 1950 г. Пекин, Изд-во на иностранных языках, 1950.
36 p. 18 cm.
At head of title: Лю Шао-ци.
On cover: Речь на первомайском собрании.
Translation of 在北京慶祝五一勞動節幹部大會上的演說 (romanized: Tsai Pei-ching ch'ing chu wu i lao tung chieh kan pu ta hui shang ti yen shuo)
1. China (People's Republic of China, 1949-)—Politics and government. 2. China (People's Republic of China, 1949-)—Economic conditions.
Title romanized: Rech' na torzhestvennom zasedanii pekinskogo aktiva.
DS777.55.L517 79-259726

NL 0415704 DLC

Liu, Shao-ch'i, 1900-
Report on the draft constitution of the People's Republic of China. Constitution of the People's Republic of China. [Adopted on September 20, 1954 by the First National People's Congress at its first session] Peking, Foreign Languages Press, 1954.
101 p. port. 22 cm.

1. China (People's Republic of China, 1949-)—Constitutional law. I. China. (People's Republic of China, 1949-) Constitution.
342.5101 56-657

ICRL MiU MB CaBVaU
NL 0415705 DLC MH NNC CtY TxU NN OU AAP IaU NcD

Liu, Shao-ch'i, 1900-
HD865
M315 Mao, Tsê-tung, 1893-
Significance of agrarian reforms in China, by Mao Tse-tung and Liu Shao-chi. [Bombay, Published by J. Bhatt for People's Pub. House, 1950]

Wason Liu, Shao-chi, 1900
HX402 Tentang garis massa. Djakarta, Jajasan
L78 "Pembaruan" [1952]
32 p. illus. 18cm.

1. Communism--Indonesia. 2. Partai Komunis Indonesia. I. Title.

NL 0415707 NIC

Liu, Shao-ch'i, 1900-
在北京慶祝五一勞動節幹部大會上的演說 劉少奇[著] 新華時事叢刊社編 北京] 新華書店 [1950]
30 p. 19 cm.
Cover title.

1. China (People's Republic of China, 1949-)—Politics and government. I. Title.
Title romanized: Tsai Pei-ching ch'ing chu wu i lao tung chieh.
DS777.55.L5 74-830389

NL 0415708 DLC

Liu, Shao-ch'i, 1900-
Über die Partei; Referat über die Abänderung des Parteistatuts auf dem VII. Parteitag der Kommunistischen Partei Chinas im Mai 1945, [von] Liu Schau-tschi. [1. Aufl.] Berlin, Dietz, 1954.
176 p. 21 cm.

1. Chung-kuo kung ch'an tang.
JQ1519.A5K84614 57-58596

NL 0415709 DLC

Liu, Shao-t'ang.
青枝綠葉 劉紹棠著 上海 新文藝出版社 1953.
80 p. 18 cm.

I. Title. *Title romanized:* Ch'ing chih lü yeh.
PL2879.S45C4 C 61-40 ‡

NL 0415710 DLC

951 Liu, Shao t'ang, 1921-
L74G Ich komme aus Rot-China, von Liu Shaw-tong. Kitzingen/Main, Holzner c1953.
289p. 21cm.

Translated from Out of Red China.

1. Communism. China. I. Title.
xLiu, Shaw-tong.

NL 0415711 OrU

Liu, Shao-t'ang, 1921-
Out of Red China; by Liu Shaw-tong. Translated from the Chinese by Jack Chia and Henry Walter. Introd. by Hu Shih. [1st ed.] New York, Duell, Sloan and Pearce [1953]
269 p. 21 cm.

1. Communism—China. I. Title.
DS777.55.L53 52-12620 rev ‡
*951.05 951.042

OrPS
ViU NN OU NcD PSt NcU Or OrP OrU Wa WaS WaT OrMonO
NL 0415712 DLC KyLxCB WU MoSW OCIJC ICU IU TU TxU

Liu, Shao-tsi
see Liu, Shao-ch'i, 1900-

629.13237
L74l
Engin Liu, Shao-Wen.
Lib'y The laminar boundary layer of yawed cylinders with variable section. [Ithaca, N.Y., Graduate School of Aeronautical Engineering, Cornell University, 1955]
5p.l.,2-44 numb.l.,26l. charts, tables. 28cm.

Includes bibliography.

1. Boundary layer. I. Title.

NL 0415714 TxU

VOLUME 336

Liu, Shao-yu.
The relation of age to the learning ability of the white rat. 1927.
ii, 18 l. illus. 29 cm.
Typescript (carbon copy)
Thesis—University of Chicago.
Bibliography: leaf 18.
1. Animal intelligence. 2. Age and intelligence. 3. Learning, Psychology of. 4. Maze tests. I. Title.
QL785.L78 74-298861 MARC

NL 0415715 DLC ICU

Liu, Shaw-tong
see Liu, Shao-t'ang.

Liu, Shaw-tong, 1921-
see
Liu, Shao-t'ang, 1921-

Liu, Shen-chi
see Liu, Shêng-chi.

Liu, Shên-o, 1898-
Collection de lichens recoltes en France [par] Liou Tchen-Ngo.
(In Contributions from the Institute of Botany, National Academy of Peiping. Peiping, 1935. 27 cm. v.3, no.6, p.323-346)
XC .0668 v.3 no.6
Caption title.
Title also in Chinese.
1. Lichenes - France. i.t. ii.s: Contributions from the Institute of Botany, National Academy of Peiping, v.3, no.6.

NL 0415719 NNBG

Liu, Shên-o, 1898-
Convolvulaceae, par Liou Tchen-Ngo et Ling Yong. Peiping, Chine, Academie nationale de Peiping, 1931.
fQK355 .P5 fasc.1
59 p. 22 plates. 36 cm. (Flore illustrée du nord de la Chine, fasc.1)
Added title in Chinese.
French and Chinese.
1. Convolvulaceae - China. i. Ling, Yong. ii.s.

NL 0415720 NNBG CtY

Bot. lib. QK1 .A573 t.3 no.1
Liu, Shên-o, 1898-
Études sur la géographie botanique des Causses. Caen, Pub. par René Viguier, 1929.
220p. illus., plates. (Archives de botanique, t.3, no.1)
1. Botany - France. I. Title.

NL 0415721 NcU NNBG MH-A CtY MH

Liu, Shên-o, 1898-
Les Euphorbiacées chinoises des Laboratoires de botanique de l'Université nationale de Pékin et de l'Académie nationale de Peiping, par Liou Tchen-Ngo.
XC .0668 v.1 no.1
(In Contributions from the Laboratory of Botany, National Academy of Peiping. Peiping, 1931. 27 cm. v.1, no.1, p.1-13)
Title also in Chinese.
1. Euphorbiaceae - China. i.t. ii.s: Contributions from the Institute of Botany, National Academy of Peiping. v.1, no.1.

NL 0415722 NNBG

Liu, Shên-o, 1898-
Pei-p'ing yen chiu yüan. *Chih wu hsüeh yen chiu so.*
Flore illustrée du nord de la Chine: Hopei (Chihli) et ses provinces voisines. Publiée sous la direction de m. Liou Tchen-Ngo, directeur du Laboratoire de botanique de l'Académie nationale de Peiping ... Peiping, Chine, Académie nationale de Peiping, 1931-

---

Liu, Shên-o, 1898-
Materials for study on rusts of China, I-V. [By] Liou Tchen-ngo et Wang Yun-chang.
(In Contributions from the Institute of Botany, National Academy of Peiping. Peiping, 1934-35. v.2, no.6; v.3, no.1, 7-9. plates)
XC .0668 v.2 no.6 etc.
Title also in Chinese.
1. Uredinales - China. i.t. ii. Wang, Yün-chang iii.s: Contributions from the Institute of Botany, National Academy of Peiping, v.2,no.6. iv.s:(v.3, no.1) v.s: (v.3, no.7-9)

NL 0415724 NNBG

Liu, Shên-o, 1898-
Note sur les Lysurus de Chine [par] Liou Tchen-Ngo et Hwang Fung-yuan.
(In Contributions from the Institute of Botany, National Academy of Peiping. Peiping, 1935. 27 cm. v.3, no.8, p.397-402. plate)
XC .0668 v.3 no.8
Caption title.
Title also in Chinese.
1. Lysurus - China. 2. Phallaceae. i.t. ii. Huang, Fêng-yüan iii.s: Contributions from the Institute of Botany, National Academy of Peiping, v.3, no.8.

NL 0415725 NNBG

Liu, Shên-o, 1898-
Note sur les Quercus à feuilles marcescentes de Chine [par] Liou Tchen-Ngo. Peiping, 1936.
23 p. 10 plates. 27 cm. (Contributions from the Institute of Botany, National Academy of Peiping, v.4, no.1)
XC .0668 v.4 no.1
Cover title.
Title also in Chinese.
1. Quercus - China. 2. Fagaceae. i.t. ii.s.

NL 0415726 NNBG

Liu, Shên-o, 1898-
Note sur un Fagus nouveau [par] Liou Tchen-Ngo.
(In Contributions from the Institute of Botany, National Academy of Peiping. Peiping, 1935. 27 cm. v.3, no.10, p.451-452. plate)
XC .0668 v.3 no.10
Caption title.
Title also in Chinese.
1. Fagus tientaiensis - China. 2. Fagaceae. i.t. ii.s: Contributions from the Institute of Botany, National Academy of Peiping, v.3, no.10.

NL 0415727 NNBG

Liu, Shên-o, 1898-
Note sur un Microsphaera du Quercus, par Liou Tchen-Ngo.
(In Contributions from the Laboratory of Botany, National Academy of Peiping. Peiping, 1931. 27 cm. v.1, no.2, p.[19]-22. illus., 3 plates)
XC .0668 v.1 no.2
In French and Chinese.
1. Microsphaera. 2. Microsphaera dentatae. 3. Quercus dentata. i.t. ii.s: Contributions from the Institute of Botany, National Academy of Peiping, v.1, no.2.

NL 0415728 NNBG

Liu, Shên-o, 1898-
Sur la presence de Cuscuta major Choisy dans la Chine proprement dite, par Liou Tchen-Ngo et Ling Yong.
XC .0668 v.1 no.1
(In Contributions from the Laboratory of Botany, National Academy of Peiping. Peiping, 1931. 27 cm. v.1, no.1, p.15-17)
In French and Chinese.
1. Cuscuta - China. 2. Cuscuta major - China. 3. Cuscutaceae. i. Lin, Jung ii.t. iii.s: Contributions from the Institute of Botany, National Academy of Peiping, v.1, no.1.

NL 0415729 NNBG

Liu, Shên-o, 1898-
Sur le groupe de Solanum nigrum L. [par] Liou Tchen-Ngo.
(In Contributions from the Institute of Botany, National Academy of Peiping. Peiping, 1935. 27 cm. v.3, no.10, p.453-458. 2 plates)
XC .0668 v.3 no.10
Caption title.
In French and Chinese.
1. Solanum nigrum - China. 2. Solanum nigrum var. pauciflorum - China. 3. Solanum merrillianum - China. 4. Solanaceae. i.t. ii.s.

NL 0415730 NNBG

Liu, Shên-o, 1898-
Sur les variations foliaires de quelques genres de Convolvulacées, par Liou Tchen-Ngo et Ling Yong.
XC .0668 v.1 no.2
(In Contributions from the Laboratory of Botany, National Academy of Peiping. Peiping, 1931. 27 cm. v.1, no.2, p.23-33. 4 plates)
In French and Chinese.
1. Convolvulaceae - Leaves. 2. Convolvulaceae - China. 3. Leaves. i. Lin, Jung ii.t. iii.s: Contributions from the Institute of Botany, National Academy of Peiping, v.1. no.2.

NL 0415731 NNBG

Liu, Shên-o, 1898-
東北木本植物圖誌 (附新種拉丁文記載) 主編劉慎諤 編者王戰[等], 中國科學院林業土壤研究所編輯 北京 科學出版社 1955.
4, ii, 568, clxx p. illus., maps, tables. 26 cm.
1. Botany—Manchuria. 2. Trees—Manchuria. I. Wang, Chan, ed. II. Chung-kuo k'o hsüeh yüan. Lin yeh t'u jang yen chiu so, Mukden.
Title romanized: Tung-pei mu pên chih wu t'u chih.
QK355.L53 C 59-526 rev

NL 0415732 DLC CaBVaU

VOLUME 336

Liu, Shên--o, 1898-
La Végétation des marais salés du Golfe de Pétchili [par] Liou Tchen-Ngo.
(In Contributions from the Institute of Botany, National Academy of Peiping, Peiping, 1935. 27 cm. v.3, no.9, p.413-431)

XC
.0668
v.3
no.9

Caption title.
In French and Chinese.
1. Phytogeography - China - Hopei. 2. Phytogeography - China - Po Hai Wan. i.t. ii.s: Contributions from the Institute of Botany, National Academy of Peiping, v.3, no.9.

NL 0415733 NNBG

Liu, Shêng-chi, joint author.

DS785
.S47

Shên, Tsung-lien.
Tibet and the Tibetans, by Tsung-lien Shên and Shên-chi Liu. Foreword by George E. Taylor. Stanford, Calif., Stanford University Press [1953]

Liu, Shêng-o, 1898-
see Liu, Shên-o, 1898-

Liu, Shêng-pin, 1910-
印度與世界大戰 劉聖斌著 重慶 時與潮社 民國33 [1944]
2, 2, 2, 223 p. 18 cm. (國際問題叢書之一)

1. World War, 1939-1945—India. I. Title.
Title romanized: Yin-tu yü shih chieh ta chan.

D767.6.L5 C 65-421

NL 0415736 DLC

Liu, Shêng-ts'ai
see
Ts'ai, Liu-sheng.

Liu, Shia Ling
see Liu, Hsia-ling.

Liu, Shih.
樹立新的勞動態度 劉實著 漢口 中南青年出版社 1952.
33 p. 17 cm. (怎樣做一個青年團員小叢書)

1. Youth—China (People's Republic of China, 1949-) I. Title.
Title romanized: Shu li hsin ti lao tung t'ai tu.

HQ799.C55L5 C 61-338 ‡

NL 0415739 DLC

Liu, Shih, *writer on sociology.*
社會學常識 柳湜編 上海 中華書局 民國38 [1949]
108 p. 17 cm. (大衆文化叢書)

1. Sociology—Juvenile literature. I. Title.
Title romanized: Shê hui hsüeh ch'ang shih.

H95.L5 C63-1401 ‡

NL 0415740 DLC

Liu, Shih-ch'ang, *writer on local government.*
縣自治法要義 劉世長編輯 上海 商務 民國13 [1924]
3, 1, 3, 1, 116 p. 19 cm.
Errata slip inserted.
Added title: Principles of district local government.

1. Local government. I. Title.
Title romanized: Hsien tzŭ chih fa yao i.

C 59-5240

Hoover Institution
for Library of Congress [2]

NL 0415741 CSt-H

Liu, Shih-fang Francis, 1901-
Chinese law. [1947]
10 numb. l. 28 cm.
Reproduced from typewritten copy.
This is an outline of 11 lectures given by Dr. S. Francis Liu at the Yale Law School in the fall of 1947.
Contains author's autograph.

NL 0415742 CtY-L

Liu, Shih-fang Francis, 1901-
The civil code of the republic of China. Book iii, law of things (in force from 5th May, 1930). By S. Francis Liu, Boyer P.H. Chu and Lin-chong Chen. n.p., n.d.
4°.
(Chinese and English)

NL 0415743 MH-L

Liu, Shih-fang Francis, 1901- *tr.*
... The Negotiable instrument law of the republic of China; translation by S. Francis Liu ... Boyer P. H. Chu, L. L. B., and Lin-chong Chen, L. L. B. [Shanghai? 1930?]
1 p. l., vii, [2], 40, 40 p. 25½cm.
Chinese title at head of t.-p.
Paged in duplicate, English and Chinese on opposite pages.

1. Negotiable instruments—China. I. China. Laws, statutes, etc. II. Chu, Boyer P. H., joint tr. III. Chên, Lin-chung, joint tr.

32-20588

NL 0415744 DLC PU-L MH-L NNC

Liu, Shih-hêng, 1875-1926.
An tui ta yüan chiu kung tz'ŭ p'u ko chêng ch'üan pên Huan hun chi
see under T'ang, Hsien-tsu, 1550-1616.

Liu, Shih-hêng, 1875-1926.

PL2448
.C48
1896
Orien
China

Ch'u, Chün, 18th cent.
(Chin shih t'u shuo)
金石圖說 [褚峻摹圖 牛運震集說 劉世珩編補 揚州 聚文齋刻 丙申 i. e. 1896]

Liu, Shih-hêng, 1875-1926, ed.
Tung Chieh-yüan hsüan so hsi hsiang chi
see under Tung Chieh-yüan, fl. 1189-1208.

Liu, Shih-jên, 1903-
中國田賦問題 劉世仁著 長沙 商務 民國24 [1935]
2, 19, 347 p. tables. 19 cm. (學藝叢書 23)

1. Land—Taxation—China. I. Title.
Title romanized: Chung-kuo t'ien fu wên t'i.

HJ4398.L58 C 59-411

NL 0415748 DLC WU

Liu, Shih-ju, joint author.
Chung-kuo yü fa chiao ts'ai
see under Li, Chin-hsi, 1890-

Liu, Shih-mu, joint author.
Nan-yang ti li.

DS508
.S517
Orien
China

Shên, Chüeh-ch'êng.
南洋地理 沈厥成 劉士木編著 趙愼一校 [上海] 商務印書館 [1937]

Liu, Shih-nung
see
Liu, Chün-jên.

B128
.H7L53
Orien
China

Liu, Shih-p'ei, 1884-1919.
荀子詞例舉要 [劉師培著 n. p.] 寧武南氏校印 [1936 臺北 藝文印書館 195-]
24 p. 19 cm.

1. Hsün-tzŭ, 340-245 B. C. I. Title.
Title romanized: Hsün-tzŭ tz'ŭ li chü yao.

B128.H7L53 C 66-737

NL 0415751 DLC

Liu, Shih-p'ei, 1884-1919.
毛詩詞例舉要 [劉師培著 臺北? 藝文印書館 195-]
160 p. 19 cm.
Facsimile reproduction.

1. Shih ching.
Title romanized: Mao shih tz'ŭ li chü yao.

PL2466.Z6L5 C 61-452

NL 0415752 DLC

Liu, Shih-p'ei, 1884-1919.
墨子拾補 [劉師培補 臺北 藝文印書館 195-]
62 p. 19 cm.
Facsim. ed.

1. Mo, Ti, fl. 400 B. C. I. Title.
Title romanized: Mo-tzŭ shih pu.

B128.M8L58 C 66-1093

NL 0415753 DLC WU CtY MiEM

VOLUME 336

Liu, Shih Shun, 1900–
Extraterritoriality: its rise and its decline, by Shih Shun Liu ... New York, 1925.
2 p. l., 7–237 p. 22½cm.
Thesis (PH. D.)—Columbia university, 1925.
Vita.
Published also as Studies in history, economics and public law, ed. by the Faculty of political science of Columbia university, vol. CXVIII, no. 2; whole no. 263.
1. Exterritoriality.
25-15774
Library of Congress JX4175.L5 1925 a
Columbia Univ. Libr. [2]
NL 0415754 PPT DLC NNC OrCS CaBVaU NcU NBuU-L NjN NIC

Liu, Shih Shun, 1900–
... Extraterritoriality: its rise and its decline, by Shih Shun Liu, PH. D. New York, Columbia university; [etc., etc.] 1925.
235 p. 22cm. (Studies in history, economics and public law, ed. by the Faculty of political science of Columbia university, vol. CXVIII, no. 2; whole no. 263)
1. Exterritoriality.
25—11423
Library of Congress H31.C7 vol. CXVIII, no. 2
——— Copy 2. JX4175.L5
NL 0415755 PU ViU-L ICJ MB MiU OU ODW OCU OO PV DLC WaTC OrU WaS OrP DAU NcD PSC PBm

Liu, Shih-wei.
Tung-pei hsing
see under Li, Tsung-ying.

Liu, Shou-shên.
剪剪拼拼 劉守身著 北京 中國青年出版社 1955.
131 p. illus. 19 cm.
1. Triangle. I. Title.
Title romanized: Chien chien p'in p'in.
QA557.L5 C 62-2126 ‡
NL 0415757 DLC

Liu, Shu-ch'in.
生活進化史 ABC 劉叔琴[著 上海 ABC叢書社 1929]
86 p. 19 cm. (ABC叢書)
1. Economic history. I. Title.
Title romanized: Shêng huo chin hua shih ABC.
HC25.L5 C 67-1619
NL 0415758 DLC

Liu, Shu-I.
The flow and fracturing characteristics of the aluminum alloy 24st as affected by strain-thermal histories. 1949.
PhD - Metallurgy.
NL 0415759 OClW

Liu, Shu-shih, ed.
Lu hai k'ung chün hsing fa ch'üan chieh
see under China. Laws, statutes, etc.

Liu, Sien-wei.
... Les problèmes monétaires et financiers de la Chine avant et depuis les hostilités sino-japonaises ... Par Liu Sien-wei ... Paris, Domat-Montchrestien, 1940.
200 p. 24½cm.
Thèse—Univ. de Paris.
"Bibliographie": p. [194]–197.
1. Currency question—China. 2. Finance—China. I. Title.
46-42413
Library of Congress HG1224.L496
NL 0415761 DLC CtY MH

Liu, Sing-chen.
... La dépréciation actuelle de l'argent en Chine et ses remèdes ... Nancy, Poncelet, 1931.
cover-title, 1 l., 146 p., 1 l. 25cm.
Thèse—Univ. de Nancy.
"Bibliographie": p. [141]–143.
1. Currency question—China. I. Title.
32-16804
Library of Congress HG1224.L5 1931
[2] 332.40951
NL 0415762 DLC MH CtY NIC

Liu, Ssŭ, *pseud.*
see
Yang, Ts'un-jên.

Liu, Ssŭ-hsün.
中國美術發達史 劉思訓著 [上海] 商務印書館 [1946]
1, 2, 123 p. 18 cm. (藝術研究叢書)
Bibliography: p. 122–123.
1. Art, Chinese—Hist. I. Title.
Title romanized: Chung-kuo mei shu fa ta shih.
N7340.L55 1946 C 67-2156
NL 0415764 DLC

Liu, Ssŭ-hsün.
中國美術發達史 劉思訓著 [上海] 商務印書館 [1950]
1, 2, 123 p. 18 cm. (美術叢書)
Bibliography: p. 122–123.
1. Art, Chinese—Hist. I. Title.
Title romanized: Chung-kuo mei shu fa ta shih.
N7340.L55 1950 C 67-2158
NL 0415765 DLC MoSW

Liu, Ssŭ-mu.
戰前與戰後的日本 [劉]思慕著 [香港] 新中國書局 1949.
104 p. 18 cm. (新中國百科小叢書)
1. Japan—Pol. & govt.—1945– I. Title.
Title romanized: Chan ch'ien yü chan hou ti Jih-pên.
DS889.L48 1949 C 68-1186
NL 0415766 DLC

Liu, Ssŭ-mu.
戰前與戰後的日本 [劉]思慕著 北京 生活讀書新知三聯書店 1950.
3, 104 p. 16 cm. (新中國百科小叢書)
1. Japan—Pol. & govt.—1945– I. Title.
Title romanized: Chan ch'ien yü chan hou ti Jih-pên.
DS889.L48 C 65-198
NL 0415767 DLC

Liu, Ssŭ-mu.
戰後日本問題 [劉]思慕著 上海 士林書店 37 [1948]
3, 2, 172 p. 17 cm.
1. Japan—Pol. & govt.—1945– I. Title.
Title romanized: Chan hou Jih-pên wên t'i.
DS889.L5 1948 C 65-182
NL 0415768 DLC WaU-FE

Liu, Ssŭ-mu.
戰後日本問題 [劉]思慕著 北京 生活讀書新知三聯書店 1949.
172 p. 18 cm. (新中國青年文庫)
. Japan—Pol. & govt.—1945– I. Title.
Title romanized: Chan hou Jih-pên wên t'i.
DS889.L5 C 60-3269 ‡
NL 0415769 DLC

Liu, Ssŭ-mu.
戰後世界政治地理講話 劉思慕著 九龍 南僑編譯社 1947.
3, 102 p. maps (part fold.) 17 cm. (民主文庫 時代知識類 1)
1. Geopolitics. I. Title.
Title romanized: Chan hou shih chieh chêng chih ti li chiang hua.
JC319.L5 C 64-1961
NL 0415770 DLC WU

Liu, Ssŭ-mu, joint author.
Chan shih Jih-pên ch'üan mao
see under Wu, Fei-tan.

VOLUME 336

Liu, Ssŭ-mu.
中國邊疆問題講話 [劉]思慕著 上海 生活書店 民國26 [1937]
4, 4, 174 p. maps. 18 cm. (青年自學叢書第2輯)
Includes bibliographies.

1. China—Bound. I. Title.
Title romanized: Chung-kuo pien chiang wên t'i chiang hua.

DS737.L55 C 68-2662

NL 0415772 DLC MH-HY

Liu, Ssŭ-mu.
Fan tui Mei-kuo wu chuang Jih-pên
see under Hua-tung Shang-hai jên min kuang po tien t'ai.

Liu, Ssŭ-mu.
怎樣學習國際時事 劉思慕著 北京 世界知識出版社 1951.
4, 118 p. 18 cm. (世界知識叢書之 69)

1. History, Modern—Study and teaching. I. Title.
Title romanized: Tsên yang hsüeh hsi kuo chi shih shih.

D16.4.C5L5 1951 C 64-2058

NL 0415774 DLC

Liu, Ssŭ-mu.
櫻花和梅雨 劉思慕著 [重慶] 大時代書局 [1942]
2, 108 p. 19 cm. (文藝叢書)

1. Chinese students in Japan. I. Title.
Title romanized: Ying hua ho mei yü.

LC3089.J3L5 C 67-1800

NL 0415775 DLC

Wason DS731 H3L78

Liu, Su-ying, 1916-
Hakka girl's path to botany. Ann Arbor Mich., Gray Memorial Botanical Association, 1953.
235-266 p. illus. 23cm.

Cover title.
Offprint from Asa Gray bulletin, new series, v.2, no. 3.

1. Hakkas. I. Asa Gray bulletin. II. Title.

NL 0415776 NIC

Liu, Su-ying, 1916-
Studies of *Litchi chinensis* Sonn. Ann Arbor, University Microfilms [1954]
([University Microfilms, Ann Arbor, Mich.] Publication no. 8332)
Microfilm copy of typescript. Positive.
Collation of the original: ix, 261 l. illus., maps, diagrs., tables.
Thesis—University of Michigan.
Abstracted in Dissertation abstracts, v. 14 (1954) no. 7, p. 1018-1019.
Bibliography: leaves 215-223.
1. Litchi.

Microfilm AC-1 no. 8332 Mic A 55-3331

Michigan. Univ. Libr. for Library of Congress [1]†

NL 0415777 MiU DLC

Liu, Sui-shêng.
化學娛樂與實驗—科學娛樂與實驗的姊妹篇 劉遂生編著 上海 商務 1953.
98 p. illus. 18 cm.

1. Chemistry—Experiments. I. Title.
Title romanized: Hua hsüeh yü lo yü shih yen.

QD43.L5 C 59-371 ‡

NL 0415778 DLC

Liu, Sung-fu.
Catalogue of Chinese paintings, ancient & modern, by famous masters, the property of Mr. Liu Sung Fu, compiled by Florence Wheelock Ayscough; exhibited at the China pavilion, Panama-Pacific international exposition, San Francisco. [Shanghai, China, The Oriental press, 1915?]
1 p. l., 112, v p. plates. $23\frac{1}{2}$cm.

1. Paintings, Chinese — Exhibitions. 2. Paintings — Private collections. I. Ayscough, Florence (Wheelock) 1878-1942. II. San Francisco. Panama-Pacific international exposition, 1915. III. Title.

Library of Congress ND1042.L5 42-45407

00
MdBWA CU-B PPPM RPD IEN CtY CSt-H MnU NN MH NBuG
NL 0415779 DLC OCl DSI MSaE OrU Or OrP PU-Mu CU

Liu, Sung-t'ao.
蔣介石禍國史話 劉松濤著 河南文教廳編審科編 [開封] 文教出版社 1951.
42 p. 18 cm. (通俗讀物)

1. Chiang, Kai-shek, 1886-
Title romanized: Chiang Chieh-shih huo kuo shih hua.

DS778.C55L5 C 63-1955 ‡

NL 0415780 DLC

Liu, Szu-Chih
The effect of the position of substitution on the ionization constants of some aromatic ammono-acids in liquid ammonia, by Szu-Chih Liu ... [Lawrence, Kan.] 1929.
Microfilm copy of typewritten ms. Made in 1941 by University Microfilms (Publication no. 223) Positive.
Collation of the original: 6 p.l., 78 numb. l. incl. tables. diagrs.

Thesis-University of Kansas.
Abstracted in Microfilm abstracts, v. 3 (1941) no. 1, p. 5.
Bibliography: numb. l. 77-78.

NL 0415782 NcD

Liu, T. Y., joint author.
Tien, Chi-tsen, 1899-
... Geological reconnaissance along the projected line between Changsha and Pingshih stations of the Canton-Hankow railway, by C. C. Tien, H. C. Wang & T. Y. Liu. Changsha, Hunan, 1933.

Liu, T. Y., joint author.
Wang, Hsiao-ching.
... The geology of Changsha-Changteh district, Hunan, by H. C. Wang & T. Y. Liu. Changsha, Hunan. 1936.

Liu, T. Y., joint author.
Tien, Chi-tsen, 1899-
... The iron ores of Hunan (no. 1), by C. C. Tien, H. C. Wang and T. Y. Liu. Changsha, Hunan, 1934.

Liu, T. Y.
Tien, Chi-tsen, 1899-
... The manganese ores of Hunan, by C. C. Tien, H. C. Wang, Y. T. Hsu & T. Y. Liu. Changsha, Hunan. 1935.

Liu, Ta-chieh, 1904-
中國古代大詩人 劉大杰 王運熙著 上海 少年兒童出版社 1954.
55 p. ports. 19 cm.
CONTENTS.—屈原—李白—杜甫—白居易—陸游

1. Poets, Chinese—Juvenile literature. I. Wang, Yün-hsi, joint author. II. Title.
Title romanized: Chung-kuo ku tai ta shih jên.

PL2277.L58 C 66-305

NL 0415787 DLC MH-HY

Liu, Ta-chieh, 1904-
(Piao hsien chu i ti wên hsüeh)
表現主義的文學 劉大杰著 [上海 北新書局 1928]
vi, 192 p. illus. 20 cm.

1. German literature—20th century—History and criticism. 2. Expressionism. I. Title.

PT405.L55 70-842074

NL 0415788 DLC

Liu, Ta-chieh, 1904-
魏晉思想論 劉大杰著 [上海] 中華書局 [1939]
2, 4, 220 p. 23 cm.

1. Learning and scholarship—China. 2. Philosophy, Chinese. I. Title.
Title romanized: Wei Chin ssŭ hsiang lun.

AZ791.L58 C 67-2418

NL 0415789 DLC WaU-FE MoSW

Liu, Ta-chieh, 1904- ed.
Yüan Chung-lang ch'üan chi
see under Yüan, Hung-tao, 1568-1610.

Liu, Ta-chün, 1890-1962.
King, *Miss* S T.
China's cotton industry. A statistical study of ownership of capital, output, and labor conditions, by Miss S. T. King and D. K. Lieu. [Shanghai? 1929.

VOLUME 336

Liu, Ta-chün, 1890–
China's economic stabilization and reconstruction, by D. K. Lieu. Pub. under the auspices of the Sino-International Economic Research Center, New York, and the China Institute of Pacific Relations, Shanghai. New Brunswick, Rutgers Univ. Press, 1948.
x, 159 p. map. 24 cm.
Includes bibliographical footnotes.

1. China—Econ. condit.—1918– 2. Reconstruction (1919– —China. I. Title.

HC427.L49 338.951 48–6207*

MiEM OClJC CoU
ICU NcU TxU MB ViU MiU MH DNAL NcD PPT NNUN Mi MiU
NL 0415792 DLC CaBVa Or OrP OrU WaS CaBVaU OrCS

Liu, Ta-chün, 1890–
China's industries and finance, being a series of studies in Chinese industrial & financial questions, by D. K. Lieu ... Peking [etc.] The Chinese government bureau of economic information [1927]
xiv, 238 p. incl. tables. port., diagr. 21½cm.

1. China—Econ. condit. 2. China—Indus. 3. Finance—China. I. Title.

28–12985
Library of Congress HC427.L5

DL MH NjP MiU ODW
NL 0415793 DLC CSt-H CaBVaU WaS NIC NcRSA TxU CtY

Liu, Ta-chün, 1890–1962.
經濟動員與統制經濟 劉大鈞著 長沙 商務印書館 民國28 [1939]
172 p. 22 cm. (國民經濟研究所叢書之3)

1. Industrial mobilization. 2. Industrial mobilization—China. I. Title.
Title romanized: Ching chi tung yüan yü t'ung chih ching chi.

UA18.A2L5 C 66–2702

NL 0415794 DLC

Liu, Ta-chün, 1890–
Foreign investments in China. A cooperative research study made under the joint auspices of the Institute of Pacific relations (Honolulu, H. I.), Social science research council (New York), Brookings institute of economics (Washington, D. C.), and Chinese government Bureau of statistics (Nanking). By D. K. Lieu ... [Shanghai?] 1929.
cover-title, 2 p. l., 131 p. incl. tables. 23cm.
Errata (slip and folded leaf) inserted at end.
In vol. XXII of "Documents of the third conference, Institute of Pacific relations, Kyoto, Japan, 1929," a made up set of independent papers, reports, etc., with type-written collective title-pages and contents.
Bibliography: p. 128–131.
1. Investments, Foreign—China. I. Title.
30–24986
Library of Congress DU1.I 5 1929 a vol. 22
[a44d1] 332.670951

NL 0415795 DLC RPB MoSW IU CtY

Pam. Coll. 40195
Liu, Ta-chün, 1890-1962.
Foreign investments in China, by D. K. Lieu. Shanghai, China Institute of Pacific Relations [1931?]
53 p. 22 cm.
"Preliminary paper prepared for the fourth biennial conference of the Institute of Pacific Relations ... Hangchow ... 1931."
Continuation of an earlier paper with the same title.
1. Investments. 2. Investments. China. I. Title.

NL 0415796 NcD IU

Liu. Ta-chun. 1890-
Foreign investments in China, by D. K. Lieu... Shanghai, China: China Institute of Pacific Relations[, 1931]. 38 f. incl. tables. 28cm.
Reproduced from typewritten copy.
"Preliminary paper prepared for the fourth biennial conference of the Institute of Pacific Relations to be held in Hangchow, from October 21st to November 4th, 1931."

642377A. 1. Investments, Foreign—China. I. China Institute of Pacific Relations, Shanghai.
N. Y. P. L. June 1, 1933

NL 0415797 NN

Asia HC428 .S47L5
Liu, Ta-chün, 1890-
The growth and industrialization of Shanghai, by D. K. Lieu. Shanghai, China Institute of Pacific Relations, 1936.
466 p. tables (part folded)
Paper prepared for presentation at the 6th conference of the Institute of Pacific relations, Yosemite national park, 1936.
Bibliographical footnotes.

NL 0415798 HU CU CSt CSt-H NN

Liu, Ta-chün, 1890–
The growth and industrialization of Shanghai, by D. K. Lieu ... Shanghai, China institute of Pacific relations, 1936.
ix, 473 p. incl. tables (part fold.) diagrs. 23cm.

1. Shanghai—Indus. 2. Shanghai—Stat. I. China institute of Pacific relations. II. Title.
38–1718
Library of Congress HC428.S47L5
[3] 330.9511

ICU
NL 0415799 DLC OClW TxU NNUN CaBVaU CtY NjP NNC

HC 427 L515 1955
Liu, Ta-chün, 1890-
Industrial development in Communist China, by D.K. Lieu. New York, Sino-American Amity, 1955.
37 l. 28cm.
"Second printing, May, 1955."

1.China - Indus. I.Title.

NL 0415800 CLSU NN

Liu, Ta-chün, 1890–
Industrial development in Communist China, by D. K. Lieu. [New York, Sino-American Amity] °1955.
33 l. 29 cm.

1. China—Indus. I. Title.

HC427.L515 338 55–2104 ‡

NL 0415801 DLC PBL OCl WaU MH CaBVaU

330.951 L74i
Liu, Ta-chün, 1890-
International aspects of China's economic reconstruction, by D. K. Lieu. Shanghai, China Institute of Pacific Relations, 1947.
32 l. 28cm. (Institute of Pacific Relations. 10th conference, Stratford-upon-Avon, 1947. China paper no.2)
"Based on sections of a larger study, 'Problems of China's economic stabilization and reconstruction'."
"Submitted as a document for the tenth conference of the Institute of Pacific Relations."
Bibliographical foot-notes.

NL 0415802 IU NIC MnU ViU CaBVaU

Liu, Ta-chün, 1890-
The 1912 census of China. Shanghai, 1931.
27 p. diagrs., tables.
At head of title: XXe session de l'Institut international de statistique, Madrid, 1931.

1. China - Census, 1912. I. Institut international de statistique. 20th, Madrid, 1931.

NL 0415803 NNC-EA

Liu, Ta-chün, 1890–
Notes on China's foreign trade and trade policy, by D. K. Lieu. New York, International Secretariat, Institute of Pacific Relations [1945]
34 l. 28 cm. (Secretariat paper no. 5)
"Two chapters from the author's ... 'China and international economic cooperation' ... submitted by the International Secretariat of the I. P. R. [Ninth Conference, January, 1945] ... as a substitute for an expected China Council paper on a similar topic."
Bibliographical footnotes.
1. China—Comm. 2. China—Indus. I. Institute of Pacific Relations. 9th conference, Hot Springs, Va., 1945. II. Title. (Series: Institute of Pacific Relations. Secretariat paper, 1945, no. 5)

HF3776.L5 58–33898

NL 0415804 DLC ViU CCC CtY CSt-H

Liu, Ta-chün, 1890–
... A preliminary report on Shanghai industrialization, by D. K. Lieu ... Shanghai, 1933.
cover-title, 3 p. l., 68 p. incl. tables (part fold.) 23cm. (The China institute of economic and statistical research, ser. 1, no. 1)
Errata sheet mounted on inside back cover.
"Being the first of a series of reports on the Shanghai industrialization study financed by the Institute of Pacific relations."—1st prelim. leaf.

1. Shanghai—Industries. I. Institute of Pacific relations.

A 37–191
Yale univ. Library for Library of Congress [2]

NL 0415805 CtY CaBVaU HU NIC NN OU OCl

Liu, Ta-chün, 1890–1962.
上海工業化研究 劉大鈞著 長沙 商務印書館 民國29 [1940]
2, 2, 366, 2 p. 21 cm. (中山文化教育館研究叢書)

1. Shanghai — Indus. I. Title. (Series: Chung-shan wên hua chiao yü kuan. Chung-shan wên hua chiao yü kuan yen chiu ts'ung shu)
Title romanized: Shang-hai kung yeh hua yen chiu.

HC428.S47L53 C 67–8

NL 0415806 DLC IEN

Liu, Ta-chün, 1890–
The silk industry of China, by D. K. Lieu. Issued under the auspices of the China institute of Pacific relations and the China institute of economic and statistical research. Shanghai, Kelly and Walsh, limited, 1940.
xviii p., 1 l., 266 p. incl. tables (part fold.) diagr. 23cm.
Edited by Dr. Kan Lee.
"Mr. Eugene Lee has done all the translation ... for those of the reports that have not been published in English before."—p. vi.
"Three separate studies of the sericultural districts of Wuhsin, the silk reeling industry of Shanghai and the silk weaving industry of Shanghai ... These three studies are now combined into one book."—p. v.
1. Silk manufacture and trade—China. 2. Sericulture—China. I. Lee, Kan, ed. II. Lee, Eugene, tr. III. China institute of Pacific relations. IV. China institute of economic and statistical research, Shanghai. V. Title.
Library of Congress HD9926.C62L5 41–24786
[3] 338.4

NL 0415807 DLC CaBVaU OrU WaS MH CU OCl CtY WaU

VOLUME 336

Wason
HD9926
C5L78
Liu, Ta-chün, 1890-1962.
The silk industry of China, by D. K. Lieu. Issued under the auspices of the China Institute of Pacific Relations and the China Institute of Economic and Statistical Research. Shanghai, Kelly and Walsh, 1941.
xviii, 266 p. illus. 23cm.
Edited by Dr. Kan Lee.
"Three separate studies of the sericultural districts of Wuhsin, the silk reeling industry of Shanghai and the silk weaving industry of Shanghai ... These three studies are now combined into one book."—p. v.

1. Silk manufacture and trade--China. 2. Sericulture--China. I. Lee, Kan, ed. II. China Institute of Pacific Relations. III. China Institute of Economic and Statistical Research, Shanghai.

NL 0415809 NIC NcU NcD OU

Liu, Ta-chün, 1890–
... The silk reeling industry in Shanghai, by D. K. Lieu ... Shanghai, 1933.
cover-title, viii, 142 p. incl. tables (part fold.) diagrs. 23cm. (The China institute of economic and statistical research. [Publications] ser. 1, no. 2)
"The second of a series of reports on the Shanghai industrialization study financed by the Institute of Pacific relations."
"Errata": leaf inserted at end.

1. Silk manufacture and trade—Shanghai. I. Title.
37-10150
Library of Congress HD9926.C63S6
——— Copy 2. [3]

NL 0415810 DLC CaBVaU NIC IU TxU PPD NN OU CtY

Liu, Ta-chün, 1890–
... Statistical work in China [by] D. K. Lieu. Shanghai, 1930.
1 p. l., 41 p. $26\frac{1}{2}$cm.
At head of title: xix^e session de l'Institut international de statistique, Tokio, 1930.

1. China—Stat. I. Institut international de statistique. 19. session, Tokio, 1930.
43-42869
Library of Congress HA37.C75L5
[2] 315.1

NL 0415811 DLC NGrnUN

Liu, Ta-chün, 1890–1962.
(Wo kuo tien nung ching chi chuang k'uang)
我國佃農經濟狀況 劉大鈞著 上海 太平洋書店 [18 i. e. 1929]
2, 2, 194 p. 17 cm. (建設文庫 經濟類)

1. Farm tenancy—Economic aspects—China. I. Title.
HD1511.C5L53 70-841743

NL 0415812 DLC

Liu, Ta-chung.
China's national income, 1931–36, an exploratory study, by Ta-chung Liu. Washington, D. C., The Brookings institution, 1946.
xii, 91 p. $20\frac{1}{2}$ cm.

1. Income—China. I. Brookings institution, Washington, D. C. II. Title.
HC427.L52 339.351 47-859 rev

NL 0415813 NNUN MiU NN ICRL CoU CU Or OrU OrCS WaS IdPI DLC CaBViP TxU PPT PU MH MB DNAL TxU

339.32
L4
Liu, Ta-chung
Problems of international comparisons of national income [by] Ta-Chung Liu [and] Shan-Kwei Fong. [n.p.- 1944]
83 p.

1. Income I. Fong, Shan-Kwei

NL 0415814 NNUN

Liu, Ta-hai.
Chan tou ti pien chiang
see under Chieh fang chün wên i ts'ung shu pien chi pu.

Liu, Ta-jên.
國際法發達史 劉達人 袁國欽著 [上海] 商務印書館 [1936?]
373 p. illus. 21 cm. (大學叢書)
L. C. copy imperfect.

1. International law. I. Yüan, Kuo-ch'in, joint author. II. Title.
Title romanized: Kuo chi fa fa ta shih.
JX3695.C5L5 C 62-582 ‡

NL 0415816 DLC

QC
437
.L78
Liu, Ta-kong.
Absorption spectra of ethylene oxide and of sulfur hexafluoride in the vacuum ultra-violet region. Notes on spectra of cyclopropane, dimethyl carbonate, and acetylacetone, by Ta-kong Liu ... Rochester, N.Y., Dept. of chemistry, the University of Rochester, 1948.
5 p.l., 58 (i.e.61) numb.l. diagrs. 28 x $21\frac{1}{2}$ cm.
Thesis (Ph.D.)--University of Rochester, 1948.
Each part preceded by half-title not included in the foliation (3 leaves)
Reproduced from type-written copy.
"References": leaves 56-58.
1. Absorption spectra. 2. Spectrum, Ultra-violet.

NL 0415817 MiU

Liu, Ta-nien.
История американской агрессии в Китае; краткий очерк. Перевод с китайского Д. Н. Зильберг; под ред. и с предисл. Д. Н. Никифорова. Москва, Изд-во иностранной лит-ры, 1951.
154 p. 20 cm.
Author's name and title in Chinese on verso of t. p.

1. U. S.—For. rel.—China. 2. China—For. rel.—U. S. I. Title.
Title transliterated: Istorii͡a amerikanskoĭ agressii v Kitae.
E183.8.C5L518 52-43052

NL 0415818 DLC OU

Liu, Ta-nien.
История американской агрессии в Китае. Перевод с китайского Д. Н. Зильберг и К. А. Крутикова. Ред. и предисл. В. Н. Никифорова. Москва, Изд-во иностранной лит-ры, 1953.
332 p. 21 cm.

1. U. S.—For. rel.—China. 2. China—For. rel.—U. S. I. Title.
Title transliterated: Istorii͡a amerikanskoĭ agressii v Kitae.
E183.8.C5L518 1953 54-35433 ‡

NL 0415819 DLC

Liu, Ta-nien.
美國侵華簡史 劉大年著 北京 新華書店 1950.
90 p. 18 cm. (新華時事叢刊)

1. U. S.—For. rel.—China. 2. China—For. rel.—U. S. I. Title.
Title romanized: Mei-kuo ch'in Hua chien shih.
E183.8.C5L5 C 58-6141 ‡

NL 0415820 DLC

Liu, Ta-nien.
美國侵華史 [劉大年著 北平] 工商週報社 [1949]
70 p. 19 cm. (工商必讀文件之4)

1. U. S.—For. rel.—China. 2. China—For. rel.—U. S. I. Title.
Title romanized: Mei-kuo ch'in Hua shih.
E183.8.C5L53 C 60-1545 ‡

NL 0415821 DLC

Liu, Ta-nien.
美國侵華史 劉大年著 [北京] 華北大学 1949.
174 p. 19 cm.

1. U. S.—For. rel.—China. 2. China—For. rel.—U. S. I. Title.
Title romanized: Mei-kuo ch'in Hua shih.
E183.8.C5L52 C 58-6142 ‡

NL 0415822 DLC

Liu, Ta-nien.
美國侵華史 劉大年著 北京 人民出版社 1951.
2, 5, 252 p. 21 cm.

1. U. S.—For. rel.—China. 2. China—For. rel.—U. S. I. Title.
Title romanized: Mei-kuo ch'in Hua shih.
C 59-5296
Cornell Univ. Library for Library of Congress E183.8 [1]

NL 0415823 NIC

Liu, Ta-pai, 1881–1932, *ed.*
五十世紀中國歷年表 劉大白編 上海 商務印書館 民國 18 [1929]
257 p. 39 cm.
——— Another issue. 縮本 民國 22 [1933]
28 cm.
DS733.L46 1933

1. China—Hist.—Chronology. I. Title. II. Title: Chung-kuo li nien piao.
Title romanised: Wu shih shih chi Chung-kuo li nien piao.
DS733.L46 1929 C 66-1537

NL 0415824 DLC CaBVaU

Liu, Ta-wei.
南進路上 劉大為著 [北京] 生活·讀書·新知聯書店 [1950]
101 p. 17 cm.

1. China—History—Civil War, 1945–1949—Personal narratives. I. Title.
Title romanized: Nan chin lu shang.
DS777.54.L55 70-836406

NL 0415825 DLC CaBVaU

VOLUME 336

Liu, Tai Pe
see
Liu, Ta-pai, 1881-1932.

Liu, T'an.
論星歲紀年　劉坦著　歷史研究編輯委員會編輯　北京　科學出版社 1955.
45 p. 26 cm.

1. Chronology, Chinese. 2. China—Hist.—Chronology. I. Title.
Title romanized: Lun hsing sui chi nien.

DS733.L48 C 58-5635 ‡

NL 0415827 DLC CtY

Liu, T'an.
[Shih chi chi nien k'ao]
史記紀年考 [3卷] 劉坦著 長沙 商務印書館 民國27 [1938]
1 v. (various double leaves) 27 cm.
Colophon title.

1. Ssu-ma, Ch'ien, ca. 145-ca. 86 B. C. Shih chi. I. Title.

DS735.A2S675 72-837037

NL 0415828 DLC

Liu, Tan-chai, *illus.*
木蘭從軍　劉旦宅繪　上海　上海人民美術出版社 1955.
44 p. (chiefly illus.) 20 x 26 cm.

1. Mu-lan, 5th cent. *Title romanized:* Mu-lan ts'ung chün.

PZ90.C5L515 C 61-1897 ‡

NL 0415829 DLC NIC MiU

Liu, T'ang-jui.
臺灣經濟植物名錄　劉棠瑞 [台北] 民國41 [1952]
163, 2 p. 26 cm.
Latin, Chinese, and Japanese; added title: List of economic plants in Taiwan, by Tang-Shui Liu.

1. Botany—Formosa. I. Title. II. Title: List of economic plants in Taiwan. *Title romanized:* Tai-wan ching chi chih wu ming lu.

QK369.L5 C 59-2692

NL 0415830 DLC

SB 108 F7 L78

Liu, Tang-Shui.
List of economic plants in Taiwan.
[T'eipei, Formosa, Taiwan Museum, 1952]
163, 2 p. 26 cm.

1. Botany, Economic - Formosa. I. Title.

NL 0415831 NIC

Liu, Tao-yüan.
中國中古時期的田賦制度　劉道元著　陶希聖校 [上海] 新生命書局 [1934]
3, 8, 362 p. 19 cm. (中國社會史叢書第2種)
Includes bibliographical references.

1. Land value taxation—China. 2. Land tenure—China. I. Title.
Title romanized: Chung-kuo chung ku shih ch'i ti t'ien fu chih tu.

HJ4398.L59 70-835126

NL 0415832 DLC

HQ801 .L5 1950z Orien China

Liu, Tê.
愛的奇蹟　劉德　朱美玲合著　星洲　星洲世界書局 [195-]
84 p. 19 cm.

1. Courtship. 2. Love. I. Chu, Mei-ling. II. Title.
Title romanized: Ai ti ch'i chi.

HQ801.L5 1950z C 62-982 ‡

NL 0415833 DLC

Liu, Tê-chih.
史太林死後對俄毛關係的認識　劉德智編著　台北　中山出版社　民國42 [1953]
101 p. 19 cm. (反共叢書之一)

1. China (People's Republic of China, 1949-)—For. rel.—Russia. 2. Russia—For. rel.—China (People's Republic of China, 1949-) I. Title.
Title romanized: Shih-ta-lin ssŭ hou tui O Mao kuan hsi ti jên shih.

DS740.5.R8L5 C 60-637 ‡

NL 0415834 DLC

Liu, Tê-i.
車工操作法　劉德懿編　北京　首都出版社 1953.
342 p. illus. 19 cm.

1. Machinery—Design. I. Title.
Title romanized: Ch'ê kung ts'ao tso fa.

TJ230.L77 C 62-969 ‡

NL 0415835 DLC

Liu, Tê-i.
機械應用手册　劉德懿編譯　北京　民智書店 1953.
13, 503 p. illus., tables. 18 cm.

1. Mechanical engineering—Handbooks, manuals, etc. I. Title.
Title romanized: Chi hsieh ying yung shou ts'ê.

TJ151.L5 C 58-5127

NL 0415836 DLC

Liu, Tê-i.
鍛工操作法　劉德懿編　北京　首都出版社 1952.
208 p. illus. 18 cm.

1. Machine-tools. 2. Tools. I. Title.
Title romanized: Tuan kung ts'ao tso fa.

TJ1180.L55 C 58-5116 ‡

NL 0415837 DLC

Liu, Tê-ming.
空軍儀器飛行教程　劉德明著 [臺北] 空軍總司令部手册法規技術令整理委員會　民國39- [1950-
1 v. (loose-leaf) illus. 19 cm.
Colophon title.
At head of cover title: II—C4—2.

1. Instrument flying. I. Title.
Title romanized: K'ung chün i ch'i fei hsing chiao ch'êng.

TL711.B6L58 C 68-2628

NL 0415838 DLC

Liu, Tê-shu.
快樂的教師　劉德樞著　臺北　民國44 [1955]
120 p. illus. 19 cm.

1. Teachers, Training of. I. Title.
Title romanized: K'uai lo ti chiao shih.

LB1727.C5L5 C 59-565 ‡

NL 0415839 DLC

Liu, Te-yun.

Mavis, Frederic Theodore, 1901-
... The transportation of detritus by flowing water ... by F. Theodore Mavis ... Chitty Ho ... and Yun-cheng Tu ... Iowa City, Ia., The University, 1935-37.

Gest 2077 .591

Liu, Theodore J K
Chinese-English medical dictionary / Rev. and enl. by the Tsinan Translation Bureau. Shanghai, Council on Publication, China Medical Association, 1931.
331 p. 22 cm.

Added t.p. in Chinese.

1. Chinese language - Dictionaries- English. I. Tsinan Translation Bureau.

NL 0415841 NjP

Liu, T'i-ch'ien.
電話外線裝置法　劉體乾著　上海　商務 1952.
92 p. illus. 18 cm. (現代工程小叢書)

1. Telephone lines—Construction. I. Title.
Title romanized: Tien hua wai hsien chuang chih fa.

TK6351.L5 C 60-3009 ‡

NL 0415842 DLC

Liu, T'i-chih.
小校經閣金文拓本 [18卷　劉體智輯 n.p. 乙亥(1935)序]
18 v. (double leaves) in 4 cases. 46 cm. (*His* 小校經閣金石文字之1)
Caption title.
Running title: 金文拓本

1. Inscriptions, Chinese. 2. Chinese language—Writing. I. Title. II. Title: Chin wên t'a pên.
Title romanized: Hsiao chiao ching ko chin wên t'a pên.

PL2448.L53 C 68-1995

NL 0415843 DLC

VOLUME 336

Liu, T'i-ch'ing.
Ancient Chinese jade; explanatory notes on Mr. T. C. Liu's unique collection of examples of Chinese art. U. S. A. representative: Mr. Henry H. Wu. Shanghai, H. H. Wu ₍1933₎
85, ₍1₎ p. incl. illus. (incl. ports.) plates. 37½cm.
Text of inscriptions in Chinese and English; commentary in Chinese, abridged commentary in English
1. Jade. 2. Sculpture, Chinese. 3. Inscriptions, Chinese. I. Wu, Henry H. II. Title.
A 34-288 Revised
New York univ. Wash. sq. library for Library of Congress NK5750.L47
₍r41b3₎
ViU OClWHi OCl MiU
OU WaS CaBVaU OO MtU MB OClMA NN PP ICU CtY DSI
NL 0415844 NNU-W MdBWA CSmH MA OCl MiD WU CU MiU

Liu, T'i-jên.
P'i yüan shih hsüeh ssŭ chung
see under Liu, K'un, chin shih 1903.

Liu, T'i-jên, *chin shih* 1655.
七頌堂詩集 ₍10卷 劉體仁著 n.p. 同治戊辰 (1868) 跋₎
v. 1-2 (double leaves) in case. 27 cm.
In case, as issued, with the author's 七頌堂文集 同治 7 (1868) 記
I. Title.
Title romanized: Ch'i-sung t'ang shih chi.
PL2718.I 9C5 1868 C 65-586
NL 0415846 DLC

Liu, T'i-jên, *chin shih* 1655.
七頌堂文集 ₍2 卷 劉體仁著 n.p. 同治 7 (1868) 記₎
v. 3-4 (double leaves) in case. 27 cm.
In case, as issued, with the author's 七頌堂詩集 n.p. 同治戊辰 (1868) 跋
I. Titl
Title romanized: Ch'i-sung t'ang wên chi.
PL2718.I 9C5 1868 C 65-585
NL 0415847 DLC

Liu, Ti-shêng.
地形模型 劉迪生編著 北京 開明書店 1953.
37 p. illus. 18 cm. (開明青年叢書)
1. Relief maps. I. Title.
Title romanized: Ti hsing mo hsing.
GA140.L5 C 64-1290 ‡
NL 0415848 DLC

Liu, Ti-yüan.
戰時節約儲蓄 劉滌源著 重慶 獨立出版社 民國 31 ₍1942₎
2, 88 p. 18 cm. (公民知識叢書)
1. Saving and thrift. 2. Sino-Japanese Conflict, 1937-1945—Finance—China. I. Title.
Title romanized: Chan shih chieh yüeh ch'u hsü.
HG7920.L5 C 67-609
NL 0415849 DLC

Liu, T'ieh-yün
see
Liu, Ê, 1857-1909.

Thesis 1939 L783
Liu, Tien.
The relation between the solubility of calcium carbonate and the rate of nitrification in soil. ₍Ithaca, N.Y.₎ 1939.
48 l. illus. 27 cm.
Thesis (Ph. D.) - Cornell Univ., June 1939.
1. Nitrification. 2. Calcium carbonate. I. Title.
NL 0415851 NIC

Liu, Tien-chên, 1903–
A study of Hobson's welfare economics, by William Tien-Chen Liu ... Peiping, Kwang Yuen press, 1934.
x, 228 p. 24cm.
Thesis (PH. D.)—Northwestern university, 1930.
Thesis note stamped on t.-p.
Bibliography: p. 211-223.
1. Hobson, John Atkinson, 1858– 2. Economics. I. Title: Welfare economics.
35-1348
Library of Congress HB103.H55L5 1930
Northwestern Univ. Libr.
₍2₎ 330.1
OU CtY ICJ NjP DLC
NL 0415852 IEN ViU WaU FMU CU NIC NcU NcD PU MiU

Liu, Tien-chên, 1903–
A study of Hobson's welfare economics, by William Tien-Chen Liu ... Peiping, Kwang Yuen press, 1934.
x, 228 p. 24cm.
Issued also as thesis (PH. D.) Northwestern university, 1930.
Bibliography: p. 211-223.
1. Hobson, John Atkinson, 1858– 2. Economics. I. Title: Welfare economics.
35-12954
Library of Congress HB103.H55L5 1934
₍3₎ 330.1
NL 0415853 DLC CaBVaU OrU PU NN

Liu, T'ien-hsi.
最新田徑運動 劉天錫 許漢文合編 上海 北新書局 1953.
294 p. illus. 19 cm.
1. Track-athletics. 2. Sports. I. Hsü, Han-wên, joint author. II. Title.
Title romanized: Tsui hsin t'ien ching yün tung.
GV705.L5 C 60-2687 ‡
NL 0415854 DLC

Liu, T'ien-hua, 1894-1932, comp.
Selections from the repertoire of operatic songs and Terpsichorean melodies of Mei Lan-fang, recorded in both Chinese and European notation. [Peiping?, 1929?]
2 v. mainly music. ports.
v.1. Text in English; European notation.
v.2. Text in Chinese; Chinese notation.
1. Operas Chinese—Excerpts. I. Mei, Lan- ang, 1894-1961.
NL 0415855 CSf NIC MB NN MH CLSU OkU CSt

Liu T'ien-Hua, 1894-1932.
Selections from the repertoire of operatic songs and terpsichorean melodies of Mei Lanfang, recorded in both Chinese and European notation by Professor Liu T'ien-Hua, assisted by Prof. Ch'i Ju-Shan, Mr. Hsü Lan-Yuan [and others] [Peping, China, National library of Peping, 1930]
2 v. (in portfolio) 30.5 cm.
[v. 1] European notation, [v. 2] Chinese notation.
"The first edition of this book is limited to one thousand and fifty copies ... No. 206."
NL 0415856 CtY-Mus

Liu, Tien-shih, 1925–
The indium-antimony and indium-arsenic systems. Ann Arbor, University Microfilms, 1953.
(₍University Microfilms, Ann Arbor, Mich.₎ Publication 5273)
Microfilm copy of typescript. Positive.
Collation of the original: vii, 55 l. illus., 22 plates.
Thesis—University of Notre Dame.
Vita.
Bibliography: leaves 53-54.
1. Indium. 2. Antimony. 3. Arsenic. I. Title.
Microfilm AC-1 no. 5273 Mic 55-3987
NL 0415857 DLC

Microcard QP 321 L55
Liu, Tien-si.
Muscular strength in relation to body types. [Iowa City] 1952
v,73ℓ. illus.,forms 28cm.
Bibliography: ℓ.57-60.
Thesis (Ed. D)--University of Iowa.
Micro-opaque. Eugene, Ore., University of Oregon, 1953. 2 cards. 7.5 x 12.5cm.
1. Muscle strength.
NL 0415858 UU LU N MsU CaBVaU OrCS OrU

Liu, T'ien-tz'ŭ.
臺灣最近の經濟界 附 臺灣の產業組合·臺灣經濟重要誌 劉天賜著 ₍臺北₎ 臺灣經濟界社 ₍1933₎
10, 171, 80 p. 19 cm.
1. Formosa—Economic conditions. I. Title.
Title romanized: Taiwan saikin no keizaikai.
HC430.5.L58 76-81271
NL 0415859 DLC

Liu, Timothy Tingfang, 1891-1947
see Liu, T'ing-fang, 1891-1947.

Liu, T'ing-fang, 1891-1947.
China in American school text-books, a problem of education in international understanding and worldwide brotherhood, by Timothy Tingfang Lew. Peking, Chinese Social and Political Science Association ₍1923–
154 p. 22 cm.
"Special supplement of the Chinese social and political science review, July 1923."
Bibliography: p. 150-154.
1. China—Hist.—Study and teaching. 2. Text-books—U. S. I. Title.
DS734.95.L5 56-48377
NNU-W OCl
NL 0415861 DLC WaS CtY ICU DHEW DS MH MnU NN PPT

VOLUME 336

Liu, T'ing-fang, 1891-1947 FOR OTHER EDITIONS SEE MAIN ENTRY

China to-day through Chinese eyes, by Dr. T. T. Lew, Prof. Hu Shih, Prof. Y. Y. Tsu, Dr. Chenk Ching Yi. London, Student Christian movement, 1922.

BV 3415 L49 1924 Liu, T'ing-fang, 1891-1947.
The contribution of Christian colleges and universities to the church in China [by] Timothy Tingfang Lew. Shanghai, China Christian Educational Association, 1924.
13 p. 23 cm. (China Christian Educational Association./Bulletin, no. 4)

1. Christianity - China. 2. Universities and colleges - China. I. Title. II. Series.

NL 0415863 CaBVaU

Liu, T'ing-fang, 1891-1947.

Teng, Tsui Yang, 1885- *ed.*
Education in China; papers contributed by the members of committees of the Society for the study of international education, ed. by T. Y. Teng and T. T. Lew ... Peking, China, The Society for the study of international education, 1923.

Pam. Coll. 1084 Liu, T'ing-fang, 1891-1947.
The new culture movement and Christian education in China ... Shanghai, China Christian Educational Association, 1926.
cover-title, 15 p. 23cm.

"An address delivered at the Second Biennial Conference of the China Association for Christian Higher Education, Shanghai College, February 5, 1926."

NL 0415865 NcD

Liu, T'ing-Fang, 1891-1947.
The psychology of learning Chinese. A preliminary analysis by means of experimental psychology of some of the factors involved in the process of learning Chinese characters, by Timothy Ting-Fang Lew ... [Peking, China? 1923?]
cover-title, 1 p.l., 377 p. illus., tables (part. fold.), diagrs. (part. fold.) 21 cm.

NL 0415866 CU

Liu, T'ing-fang, 1891-1947.
The psychology of learning Chinese; a preliminary analysis by means of experimental psychology of some of the factors involved in the process of learning Chinese characters. By Timothy Ting-fang Lew. [Peking, 1924?]
377, ii p. illus., diagrs., facsim., tables. 22 cm.
Cover title.
Thesis—Columbia University.
Vita.

1. Chinese language—Study and teaching. I. Title.

PL1065.L5 27-7493 rev*

NL 0415867 DLC OrU ViU NIC

Liu, T'ing-fang, 1891-1947.
... Regarding registration of Christian schools with the government ... [Peking, 1925]
11 p. 22.5 cm.
Caption title.
At head of title: Message no. 2.

NL 0415868 CtY

Liu, T'ing-fang, 1891-1947.
司徒雷登博士年譜 劉廷芳初稿 [北平 建國 25 (1936) 序]
1, 21 double l. 20 cm.
Caption title.

1. Stuart, John Leighton, 1876-1962. I. Title.
Title romanized: Ssŭ-t'u Lei-têng po shih nien p'u.

E840.8.S7L5 C 68-887

NL 0415869 DLC

Liu, T'ing-fang, 1891-1947.
Why study China? By T. T. Lew... being a lecture prepared for presentation under the George Goetz Wolfe foundation lectureship. Portland, Ore.: Reed college [1927] 29 p. 19½cm. (On cover: Reed college, Portland, Ore. Bulletin. v. 6, no. 4.)

1. China—Civilization. I. Reed college, Portland, Ore. George Goetz Wolfe foundation lectureship.
N. Y. P. L. November 8, 1937

NL 0415870 NN NIC MH

Liu, T'ing-mien, 1897-
Modern tariff policies with special reference to China, by Ting Mien Liu ... New York, Alliance printing corporation, 1924.
ix, 140 p. 23½cm.
Thesis (PH. D.)—Columbia university.
Bibliography: p. 133-140.

1. Tariff. 2. Tariff—China. I. Title.
24-12912 Revised
Library of Congress HF1711.L5 1924

NL 0415871 DLC NNUN

Wason HF1711 L78 Liu, Ting-Mien, 1897-
Modern tariff policies with special reference to China, by Ting Mien Liu... Peking, Hua Mei Printing Office, 1925.
ix, 140 p. 24cm.

Errata slip inserted.

1. Tariff. 2. Tariff--China. I. Title.

NL 0415872 NIC

Liu, Ting-shêng.
四川歷史 柳定生編 成都 鍾山書局 民國 33 [1944]
1, 2, 78, 6 p. 23 cm. (史地教育叢書)

1. Szechwan, China. I. Title.
Title romanized: Ssŭ-ch'uan li shih.

DS793.S8L5 C 67-1365

NL 0415873 DLC

Liu, Ting-yüeh.
機械用語新字典 英·中·日文對譯 New technical dictionary of mechnical [sic] terms; English, Chinese, Japanese. 劉鼎嶽著 臺北 東方出版社 民國 36 [1947]
191 p. 19 cm.
Cover title.

1. Mechanical engineering — Dictionaries. 2. English language — Dictionaries—Polyglot. I. Title. II. Title: New technical dictionary of mechanical terms.
Title romanized: Chi hsieh yung yü hsin tzŭ tien.

TJ9.L58 C 68-100

NL 0415874 DLC

Liu, T'o.
新中國速記學 劉拓著 [北京] 新中國速記學校 1951.
74 p. 18 cm.

1. Shorthand, Chinese. I. Title.
Title romanized: Hsin Chung-kuo su chi hsüeh.

Z59.5.L55 C 68-459

NL 0415875 DLC

Liu, Toh, 1899-
Investigation of some properties of starches ... by Toh Liu ...
[Columbus] The Ohio state university, 1926.
110 numb. l.
Thesis (Ph.D.) - The Ohio state university.

NL 0415876 OU

Liu, Toh, 1899-
Investigation of some properties of starches ... by Toh Liu ...
[Columbus] The Ohio state university, 1929.
13 p.
Abstract of thesis (Ph.D.) - Ohio state university, 1926.

NL 0415877 OU

Liu, Tsê-jung.
俄文文法 Русская грамматика на русском и китайском языках. 劉澤榮編 第6版 北京 時代出版社 1955-
v. 21 cm.
At head of title: 中俄文講述
CONTENTS.— 上冊 詞法

1. Russian language—Text-books for foreigners—Chinese. I. Title.
Title romanized: O wên wên fa.

PG2129.C5L5 72-839726

NL 0415878 DLC

Liu, Tsê-min
see
Liu, Ju-lin, 1905-

Liu, Tsêng-fu, joint author.
Chieh p'ou shêng li hsüeh
see under Wang, Mao-wei.

VOLUME 336

Liu, Tsing-li, 1903–
The changes of ash and nitrogen in the germinating mung bean. ₍Columbia, Mo.₎ 1936.

Microfilm copy of typewritten ms. Made in 1948 by University Microfilms (Publication no. 927) Positive.
Collation of the original: 72 l. diagrs., photos.
Thesis—Univ. of Missouri.
Abstracted in Microfilm abstracts, v. 8 (1948) no. 1, p. ₍1₎
Vita.
Bibliography: leaves 67–72.

1. Mung bean. 2. Germination. 3. Nitrogen.
Microfilm AC–1 no. 927 Mic A 48–57*

Michigan. Univ. Libr.
for Library of Congress ₍1₎†

NL 0415881 MiU DLC

Liu, Tso-jên.
省地方銀行泛論 劉佐人著 廣州 廣東省銀行 民國 35 ₍1946₎
3, 69 p. 21 cm. (廣東省銀行叢書)

1. Banks and banking—China. I. Title.
Title romanized: Shêng ti fang yin hang fan lun.
C 61–4306

Harvard Univ. Chinese-Japanese Library 4565
for Library of Congress ₍3₎

NL 0415882 MH-HY

Liu, Tsu-ch'un.
中蘇兩國的眞正友誼 劉祖春著 漢口 中南新華書店 1950.
48 p. 18 cm.

1. China—Relations (general) with Russia. 2. Russia—Relations (general) with China. I. Title.
Title romanized: Chung Su liang kuo ti chên chêng yu i.

DS740.5.R8L53 C 61–117 ‡

NL 0415883 DLC

Liu, Tsu-hsiang.
寧波專區農業生產經驗介紹 劉祖香著 ₍上海₎ 新華書店華東總分店 ₍1950₎
78 p. 16 cm.

1. Agriculture—China—Yin-hsien. I. Title.
Title romanized: Ning-po chuan ch'ü nung yeh shêng ch'an.

SB99.C5L5 C 68–1036

NL 0415884 DLC

QH431 Liu, Tsu-tung, 1916–
A1M5
no.59 **The measurement of fertility and its use as an index of reproductive isolation among certain laboratory stocks of Peromyscus. Ann Arbor, Mich., 1953.**
12 p. tables, 26 cm. (Michigan. University. Laboratory of Vertebrate Biology. Contributions, no. 59)
Bibliography: p. 12.

1. Mice. 2. Hybridization. I. Title: Fertility, Measurement. (Series)

NL 0415885 DI

Liu, Tsu-tung, 1916–
Prenatal mortality in *Peromyscus* with special reference to its bearing on reduced fertility in some interspecific and intersubspecific crosses. Ann Arbor ₍University of Michigan Press₎ 1953.

32 p. illus., tables. 26 cm. (Contributions from the Laboratory of Vertebrate Biology, University of Michigan, no. 60)

Caption title.
Thesis—University of Michigan.
Bibliography: p. 30–32.

1. Mice. 2. Sterility. 3. Hybridization. I. Title. (Series: Michigan. University. Laboratory of Vertebrate Biology. Contributions, no. 60)

QH431.A1M5 no. 60 599.32 53–62801

NL 0415886 DLC DI

Liu, Tsu-tung, 1916–
Prenatal mortality in the deer mouse, *Peromyscus*, with special reference to its bearing on reduced fertility in some interspecific and intersubspecific crosses. Ann Arbor, University Microfilms, 1953.
(₍University Microfilms, Ann Arbor, Mich.₎ Publication no. 5067)
Microfilm copy of typescript. Positive.
Collation of the original: vi, 56 l. illus., diagrs., tables.
Thesis—University of Michigan.
Abstracted in Dissertation abstracts, v. 13 (1953) no. 3, p. 455–456.
Published also as no. 60 of Contributions from the Laboratory of Vertebrate Biology, University of Michigan.
Bibliography: leaves 51–56.
1. Mice. 2. Sterility. 3. Hybridization. I. Title.
Microfilm AC–1 no. 5067 Mic A 53–771
Michigan. Univ. Libr.
for Library of Congress ₍1₎†

NL 0415887 MiU DLC

Liu, Tsui-Chieh.
Physiology of Rhizoctonia and its relation to Botryobasidium, by Liu, Tsui-Chieh ... «Corvallis, Ore.» 1940.
5 p.ℓ.,141 numb.ℓ. incl. plates, tables, diagrs. 28cm.
Typewritten.
Thesis (PH.D.) - Oregon state college, 1940.
"Literature cited": ℓ.116-123.

1.Rhizoctonia.

NL 0415888 OrCS

Liu, Tsun-ch'i.
美國 劉尊棋著 香港 新中國書局 1949.
97 p. 18 cm. (新中國百科小叢書)

1. U. S.—Descr. & trav.—1940– I. Title.
Title romanized: Mei-kuo.

E169.L773 1949 C 63–2148 ‡

NL 0415889 DLC

Liu, Tsun-ch'i.
美國 劉尊棋著 ₍北京₎ 生活讀書新知三聯書店 1950.
97 p. illus. 17 cm. (新中國百科小叢書)

1. U. S.—Descr. & trav.—1940– I. Title.
Title romanized: Mei-kuo.

E169.L773 1950 C 63–2139 ‡

NL 0415890 DLC

Liu, Tsun-ch'i.
(Mei-kuo ts'é mien hsiang) 美國側面像 劉尊棋著 ₍上海₎ 士林書店 ₍38 i. e. 1949₎
4, 152 p. illus. 18 cm.

1. U. S.—Description and travel—1940–1960. I. Title.

E169.02.L55 75–840581

NL 0415891 DLC

Liu, Tsun-hsien, 1904– joint author.

McBain, James William, 1882–
... Diffusion of electrolytes, non-electrolytes and colloidal electrolytes, by James W. McBain and Tsun hsien Liu. ₍Easton, Pa., 1931₎

Liu, Ts'un-jên
see Liu, Ts'un-yan.

Liu, Ts'un-liang.
中國人民鹽稅之負担 劉存良著 南京 中國經濟研究會 民國23 ₍1934₎
2, 82 p. 23 cm.
Colophon title.
Includes bibliographical references.

1. Salt—Taxation—China. I. Title.
Title romanized: Chung-kuo jên min yen shui chih fu tan.

HD9213.C42L55 C 66–2380

NL 0415894 DLC

Liu, Ts'un-yan.
人物譚 柳存仁著 香港 大公書局 1952.
3, 205 p. illus. 19 cm.

1. Authors, Chinese. 2. Authors. I. Title.
Title romanized: Jên wu t'an.

PL2277.L59 C 63–1209

NL 0415895 DLC NIC OU CaBVaU WU

Liu, Ts'un-yan.
庚辛—青春之一 柳存仁著 香港 大公書局 ₍195–₎
268 p. 19 cm
Fiction.

I. Title.
Title romanized: Kêng hsin.

PL2879.T7K4 C 65–903

NL 0415896 DLC ViU

Liu, Ts'un-yan.
上古秦漢文學史 柳存仁著 上海 商務印書館 民國 37 ₍1948₎
6, 1, 1, 171 p. 18 cm. (國學小叢書)
Includes bibliographical references.

1. Chinese literature—Hist. & crit. I. Title.
Title romanized: Shang ku Ch'in Han wên hsüeh shih.

PL2284.L5 C 60–5438
Harvard Univ. Chinese-Japanese Library 5221
for Library of Congress ₍r69b1₎† rev

NL 0415897 MH-HY DLC

VOLUME 336

Liu, Tsung-hao.
書籍雜誌報紙處理法 柳宗浩著 上海 長城書局 民國28 [1939]
[16], 170 p. 19 cm.
Colophon title.

1. Processing (Libraries) I. Title.
Title romanized: Shu chi tsa chih pao chih ch'u li fa.

Z688.5.L55 C 67-3399

NL 0415898 DLC

Liu, Tsung-lu.
中國憲法論 劉宗祿著 台北 正中書局 民國37 [1948]
2, 1, 4, 260 p. 21 cm.
附錄 中華民國憲法: p. 239-260.

1. China—Constitutional law. I. China. Constitution. II. Title.
Title romanized: Chung-kuo hsien fa lun.

C 61-1762

NL 0415899 DLC WaU-L CtY

Liu, Tsung-yüan, 773-819.
柳河東全集 [45卷外集 2 卷補遺 1 卷附錄 2 卷] 柳宗元著 上海 世界書局 民國24 [1935]
1, 2, 2, 21, 572 p. 19 cm.

Title romanized: Liu Ho-tung ch'üan chi.
C 61-4120

Harvard Univ. Chinese-Japanese Library 5309 for Library of Congress [2]

NL 0415900 MH-HY OrU CtY

Liu, Tsung Yuan, 1919-
A study of the changes in responsiveness of the uterus of the castrated rat to estrogenic hormone in relation to age. 1954.
75 l.
Thesis - Ohio State University.
1. Rats. 2. Uterus. 3. Hormones.

NL 0415901 OU

Liû, T͡Sze-zhun
see
Liu, Tsê-jung.

AC149 .S75W45 1935 Orien China
Liu, Tun-chên, 1896- Ch'ing Wên Yüan ko shih ts'ê t'u shuo. 1935.
(Wên yüan ko ts'ang shu ch'üan ching)
文淵閣藏書全景 [北京 中國營造學社編輯兼發行 民國24 i. e. 1935]

Liu, Tun-chên, 1896-
河北省西部古建築調査紀略 劉敦楨著 中國營造學社編輯 北平 中國營造學社 民國24 [1935]
55 p. illus., 32 plates. 26 cm.
Cover title.

1. Architecture — Hopei, China (Province) I. Chung-kuo ying tsao hsüeh shê, Peking. II. Title.
Title romanized: Ho-pei shêng hsi pu ku chien chu tiao ch'a chi lüeh.

NA1546.H6L5 C 68-511

NL 0415904 DLC

Liu, Tun-chên, 1896-
牌樓算例 [劉敦楨編訂 北平 中國營造學社 民國22 (1933) 記]
44 p. illus. 26 cm.
Cover title.

1. Arches. 2. Architecture, Chinese. I. Title.
Title romanized: P'ai lou suan li.

NA2880.L5 C 67-2982

NL 0415905 DLC

Liu, Tun-chên, 1896-
蘇州古建築調査記 著作者劉敦楨 北平 中國營造學社 來薰閣寄售 民國25 [1936]
52 p. illus., plates. 26 cm.
Colophon title.
Includes bibliographical references.

1. Architecture—Soochow, China. 2. Architecture, Chinese. I. Chung-kuo ying tsao hsüeh shê, Peking. II. Title.
Title romanized: Su-chou ku chien chu tiao ch'a chi.

NA1547.S6L5 C 67-2458

NL 0415906 DLC NjP

Liu Tung, 1905-
... Ueber das Vorkommen von Leukocyten mit sudanophilem Inhalt im gonorrhoischen Eiter ... München, 1936.
21 p.
Inaug.-Diss. - München.
Lebenslauf.

NL 0415907 CtY

FILM 548 L74e
Liu, Tung, 1926-
The effect of pressure on diffusion in single crystals. Ann Arbor, University Microfilms, 1953.
([University Microfilms, Ann Arbor, Mich.] Publication no.6960)
Microfilm copy of typescript. Positive.
Collation of the original: 81 l. diagrs., tables.
Thesis—University of Illinois.
Vita.
Bibliography: leaves 75-76.

NL 0415908 IU

Liu, T'ung-hsin.
機械工人常識 劉同炘編 北京 首都出版社 1952.
76 p. illus. 19 cm.

1. Mechanical engineering—Tables, calculations, etc. I. Title.
Title romanized: Chi hsieh kung jên ch'ang shih.

TJ151.L58 C 60-2746 ‡

NL 0415909 DLC

Liu, T'ung-k'ang.
鋼線磁帶錄音機原理及實驗 磁性錄音機與磁性錄音術 劉同康編著 上海 無線電科學社 1953.
194 p. illus. 21 cm.

1. Recording instruments. I. Title.
Title romanized: Kang hsien tz'ŭ tai lu yin chi yüan li chi shih yen.

TK393.L54 C 63-1979 ‡

NL 0415910 DLC

Liu, T'ung-k'ang.
世界眞空管大全一世界眞空管特性表 劉同康編 [新編增訂版] 上海 無線電科學社 1953.
64, 16, 432 p. illus., diagrs., tables. 17 cm.

1. Vacuum-tubes. I. Title.
Title romanized: Shih chieh chên k'ung kuan ta ch'üan.

QC544.V3L54 C 59-2971

NL 0415911 DLC

Liu, T'ung-k'ang, *ed.*
世界眞空管大全 The world radio tube handbook. 劉同康編 Hong Kong, 現代無線電出版社 The Wen Kwong Book Store, 1955.
482 p. illus. 18 cm.
At head of title: 世界無線電眞空管手册

1. Vacuum-tubes. I. Title. II. Title: The world radio tube handbook.
Title romanized: Shih chieh chên k'ung kuan ta ch'üan.

TK6565.V3L5 C 62-1493 ‡

NL 0415912 DLC

Liu, T'ung-lun, ed.
Chieh ho ping fang chih fa
see under Su-chia-t'un chieh ho fang chih yüan.

Liu, T'ung-shên.
水產養殖學 劉桐身著 上海 中華書局 1953.
243 p. illus. 21 cm.

1. Marine biology. I. Title.
Title romanized: Shui ch'an yang chih hsüeh.

QH96.L57 C 59-2636 ‡

NL 0415914 DLC

Liu, Tung-yen, 1903- ed.
Chung-kuo li tz'ŭ yüeh fa hsien fa ts'ao an hui tsuan
see under China. Constitution.

Liu, Tzu-chien
see Liu, James T.C., 1919-

Liu, Tzŭ-chiu, 1901-
Chiao shih ti hsin fang hsiang
see under title

Liu, Tzŭ-hua.
... La cosmologie des pa Koua et l'astronomie moderne. Prévision d'une nouvelle planète ... par Liou Tse Houa. Paris, Jouve & c[ie], 1940.
4 p. l., [5]-154 p., 1 l. incl. tables, diagrs. front. (port.) 25cm.
Thèse—Univ. de Paris.
"Bibliographie": p. [142]-151.

1. I ching. 2. Cosmology. I. Title.

46-41615
Library of Congress PL2997.I 29L5 1940 a
[2] 113

NL 0415918 DLC PPAmP

VOLUME 336

Liu, Tzŭ-hua.
... La cosmologie des pa Koua et l'astronomie moderne. Situation embryonnaire du soleil et de la lune. Prévision d'une nouvelle planète; exposé du système scientifique universel concernant la genèse et l'évolution des mondes. Avec 24 tableaux, 29 figures et une photo. Paris, Jouve & c[ie], 1940.
4 p. l., [5]-163, [1] p. front. (port.) tables (1 fold.) diagrs. 24[cm].
At head of title: ... Liou Tse Houa.
Author's name also in Chinese at head of title.
"Bibliographie": p. [142]-151.
1. I ching. 2. Cosmology. I. Title.
44-10667
Library of Congress PL2997.I 29L5
[2] 113

NL 0415919 DLC

Liu Tzu-Hui,
"Halfway up the mountain" ... [San Francisco, Grabhorn press, 1938]
2 l. col. pl. 32.8cm.
Marginal title, from 2d leaf.
A poem.
"Season's greetings from Ruth & Charles De Y. Elkus, 1938-1939."
I. Hart, Henry Hersch. , tr.

NL 0415920 CSmH

Liu, Tzŭ-sung.
法學通論 劉子崧 李景禧編 [上海] 商務印書館 [1934]
3, 2, 16, 266 p. 19 cm.
1. Law—Philosophy. 2. Law—History and criticism. I. Li, Ching-hsi, joint author. II. Title.
Title romanized: Fa hsüeh t'ung lun.
70-835650

NL 0415921 DLC

Liu, Tzŭ-ya.
辦理農村圖書館的經驗 劉子亞編 北京 來薰閣書店 1951.
50 p. 19 cm.
Cover title.
1. Rural libraries. I. Title.
Title romanized: Pan li nung ts'un t'u shu kuan.
Z675.V7L55 C 68-105

NL 0415922 DLC

Liu, Vi-cheng
see **Liu, Wei-chêng,** 1917-

Liu, Wai
see
Liu, Hui.

Liu, Wan-chang.
(Kuang-chou êrh ko chia chi) 廣州兒歌甲集 劉萬章編纂 [廣州] 國立中山大學語言歷史研究所 [民國17 i. e. 1928]
[28], 170 p. 19 cm. (民俗學會叢書)
Added colophon title: A collection of Cantonese child songs.
1. Children's songs, Chinese. I. Chung-shan ta hsüeh, Canton, China. Yü yen li shih hsüeh yen chiu so. II. Title. (Series: Min su hsüeh hui. Min su hsüeh hui ts'ung shu)
GR335.L62 1928 76-839944

NL 0415925 DLC OrU

Liu, Wan-chang.
Su Yüeh ti hun sang
see under Min su hsüeh hui.

Liu, Wei-chêng, 1917-
On compressible laminar boundary layer with suction. Ann Arbor, University Microfilms, 1950 [i. e. 1951]
([University Microfilms, Ann Arbor, Mich.] Publication no. 2419)
Microfilm copy of typewritten ms. Positive.
Collation of the original: viii, 128 l. diagrs., tables.
Thesis—University of Michigan.
Abstracted in Microfilm abstracts, v. 11 (1951) no. 2, p. 209-210.
Bibliography: leaves 123-128.
1. Boundary layer.
Microfilm AC-1 no. 2419 Mic A 51-163
Michigan. Univ. Libr.
for Library of Congress [1]†

NL 0415927 MiU DLC

Liu, Wei-chin, 1916-
A further study of chloromethyl intermediates in preparation of substances of pharmacologic interest. [Baltimore] 1952.
29 l. diagrs. 28 cm.
Typescript (carbon copy)
Thesis—University of Maryland.
Vita.
"Literature cited": leaves 27-28.
1. Chloromethyl.
QD305.E7L5 A 56-253
Maryland. Univ. Libr.
for Library of Congress [3]†

NL 0415928 MdU DLC

Liu, Wei-sên.
反共抗俄基本論問答 劉偉森編著 臺北 正中書局 民國 42 [1953]
50 p. illus. 19 cm.
1. Chiang, Kai-shek, 1886- Fan kung k'ang O chi pên lun. 2. Anti-communist movements—China. I. Title.
Title romanized: Fan kung k'ang O chi pên lun wên ta.
DS777.55.L535 C 60-1634 ‡

NL 0415929 DLC

Liu, Wei-tê, joint author.
T'iao tsao yü shu i
see under Wang, Fêng-chên.

Liu, Weiling, ed.
Ssŭ fa yüan chieh shih yao chih fên lei hui pien
see under China. Ssŭ fa yüan.

Liu, Wên-ch'êng kung
see
Liu, Chi, 1311-1375.

Liu, Wên-ch'ing, 1869-
see Lim, Boon Keng, 1869-

Liu, Wên-ch'üan, joint author.
HJ9927
.C6W34
Orien
China
Wang, Fêng-hsin.
(Chêng fu yü suan k'uai chi chiao ch'êng)
政府預算會計教程 王逢辛 劉文泉編著 [上海] 立信會計圖書用品社 1952.

Liu, Wên-ch'üan, joint author.
Hsin k'uai chi hsüeh chiao ch'êng
see under Wang, Fêng-hsin.

Liu, Wên-hai.
西行見聞記 劉文海著 南京 南京書店 民國22 [1933]
2, 4, 270 p. illus. 22 cm.
1. China—Descr. & trav. I. Title.
Title romanized: Hsi hsing chien wên chi.
DS710.L72 C 65-1729

NL 0415936 DLC

Liu, Wên-t'ai, fl. 1505, ed.
Pên ts'ao p'in hui ching yao
see under title

Liu, Wên-tao, 1893-
行政組合論 劉文島著 [重慶] 正中書局 民國 32 [1943]
2, 2, 4, 212 p. 22 cm. (社會科學叢刊)
Colophon title.
1. Corporate state. I. Title.
Title romanized: Hang yeh tsu ho lun.
JC478.L5 C 66-1692

NL 0415938 DLC

Liu, Wên-tao, 1893-
行業組合與近代思潮 劉文島著 [重慶] 商務印書館 [1943]
7, 161 p. 18 cm.
1. Trade-unions. 2. Political science. I. Title.
Title romanized: Hang yeh tsu ho yü chin tai ssŭ ch'ao.
HD6451.L5 C 67-1744

NL 0415939 DLC

VOLUME 336

Liu, Wên-tao, 1893–
意大利史地 劉文島著 ［重慶］ 商務印書館 ［1944］
5, 307 p. 18 cm. (復興叢書)

1. Italy. I. Title.
Title romanized: I-ta-li shih ti.

DG467.L59 C 67-1879

NL 0415940 DLC

Liu, Wên-tien, 1893- ed.
Chuang-tzŭ pu chêng
see under Chuang-tzŭ.

Liu, Wên-tien, 1893- ed.

BL1920 .H82 1926 Orien China **Huai-nan tzŭ,** *d.* 122 B. C.
(Huai-nan hung lieh chi chieh) 淮南鴻烈集解 ［21卷 淮南子撰］ 劉文典集解 上海 商務印書館 民國 15 ［1926］

Liu, Wên-ying.
水的知識 劉文英編著 上海 中華書局 1951.
28 p. 17 cm. (工農生產知識便覽)

1. Water—Analysis. I. Title.
Title romanized: Shui ti chih shih.

QD142.L6 C 64-2040 ‡

NL 0415943 DLC

Liu, William Tien-Chen
see
Liu, Tien-chên, 1903–

Liu, Wu-chi, 1907–
Confucius, his life and time. New York, Philosophical Library ［°1955］
189 p. 23 cm.

1. Confucius and Confucianism.

B128.C8L56 921.9 56—1686 ‡

OU WaU KEmT
MiU FMU NjPT IU PCC CU OCl NcD NN PPD DCU InU MoU
NL 0415945 DLC LU NcU FU FTaSU OO KyLoU GU DAU

PL 2694 .C5 Z68 LIU,WU-CHI,1907-
The original Orphan of China ［by Chi Chün-hsiang. n.p., n. pub., n.d.］
［193-］212 p.

Chinese title: Chao shih ku êrh.
Reprinted from Comparative Literature, v. 5, no. 3. Summer 1953.

1. Chi, Chün-hsiang--Chao shih ku êrh. I. Title: Orphan of China

NL 0415946 InU

Liu, Wu-chi, 1907- *ed.*
Readings in contemporary Chinese literature, edited by Wu-chi Liu and Tien-yi Li. New Haven, Institute of Far Eastern Languages, Yale University, 1953.
3 v. 24 cm. (Mirror series C, no. 7-9)
Introductory matter in English; added t. p. and text in Chinese.
CONTENTS.—v. 1. Plays and poems.—v. 2. Stories.—v. 3. Essays.
—— Notes. Prepared by Wu-chi Liu, Tien-yi Li, and Grace Wan. New Haven, Institute of Far Eastern Languages, Yale University, 195
v. 24 cm. (Mirror series C, no.
PL2947.L5 Notes
1. Chinese literature—20th cent. I. Li, T'ien-i, joint ed. II. Title. (Series)

PL2947.L5 *495.1864 53-2380 rev

NcU OrU NjP OU InU NN MB NIC
NL 0415947 DLC OO CaBVaU OrPR FMU OrU IU ViU MiU

Liu, Wu-chi, 1907- ed. & tr.
WB 57548 Selected lyrics from Shakespeare and others. [Shanghai, Tashih-tai shu chü] 1947.
11, 114 p. 19 cm.
Title in Chinese: 莎士比亞時代抒情詩
English and Chinese.

1. English poetry - Translations into Chinese. 2. Chinese poetry - Translations from English. I. Title.

NL 0415948 CtY

Liu, Wu-chi, 1907–
A short history of Confucian philosophy. ［Harmondsworth, Middlesex］ Penguin Books ［1955］
229 p. 18 cm. (Pelican books, A333)
Bibliography: p. 209-219.

1. Confucius and Confucianism.

A 56-2312

Rochester. Univ. Libr. for Library of Congress B128 ［2］

WaSpG OrCS
NNC NN IaU TxU MiU NIC LU WaU CaBVaU OrStbM OrU
NL 0415949 NRU IU KAS NBC FMU PSt PPT OCl CU CtY

Liu, Ya-tzŭ, 1887-1958.
懷舊集 柳亞子著 上海 耕耘出版社 1946.
2, 253 p. 18 cm

I. Title.
Title romanized: Huai chiu chi.

C 60-5494

Harvard Univ. Chinese-Japanese Library 5558 for Library of Congress ［1］

NL 0415950 MH-HY CaBVaU

Liu, Yao-shên.
貨幣導論 劉燿燊著 坪石 大學出版社 民國 32 ［1943］
2, 4, 232 p. 19 cm.

1. Money. I. Title.
Title romanized: Huo pi tao lun.

HG221.L58 C 67-788

NL 0415951 DLC

Liu, Yee Jing.
Servomechanisms, charts for verifying their stability and for finding the roots of their third and fourth degree characteristic equations ［by］ Y. J. Liu. Cambridge, Mass., The Massachusetts institute of technology, °1941.
［20］ p. diagrs. (1 fold.) 28 x 21½cm.
Reproduced from type-written copy.
Various pagings.
"Taken from the thesis entitled—Stability and transient analysis of controlled longitudinal motion of aircraft with non-ideal automatic controls as submitted by Dr. Y. J. Liu to the Department of aeronautical engineering at the Massachusetts institute of technology in May, 1941, in partial fulfillment of the requirements for the degree of doctor of science."—Foreword.
1. Stability of aeroplanes. I. Title.

42-2006

Library of Congress TL574.S7L5 ［2］ 629.13236

NL 0415952 DLC PU

Liu, Yen, *ed.*
中華民國二十年來大事記 劉衍編 上海 五洲書局 民國 21 ［1932］
2 v. in 1. 23 cm.
Colophon title.

1. China—Hist.—Chronology. 2. China—Hist.—1912-1937. I. Title.
Title romanized: Chung-hua min kuo êrh shih nien lai ta shih chi.

DS733.L5 C 66-1598

NL 0415953 DLC

Liu, Yen, 1880–
政治學 ［劉彥編述］ 陳世炎藏書 ［北平］ 北平民國大學 1935.
6, 228 p. 26 cm.
Cover title.
北平民國學院講義

1. Political science. I. Title.
Title romanized: Chêng chih hsüeh.

JA69.C5L5 75-836430

NL 0415954 DLC

Liu, Yen, 1880–
中國近時外交史 劉彥著 訂正增補 3 版 上海 太平洋印刷公司印 民國 10 ［1921］
636 p. 22 cm.

1. China—For. rel. I. Title.
Title romanized: Chung-kuo chin shih wai chiao shih.

DS740.4.L48 C 61-565 ‡

NL 0415955 DLC CaBVaU

Liu, Yen, 1880–
被侵害之中國 (即中國最低限度應取消之不平等條約) 劉彥著 上海 太平洋書店 ［民國］ 18 ［1929］
2, 2, 20, 294 p. 21 cm.

1. China—For. rel.—To 1912. 2. China—For. rel.—1912-1949. I. Title.
Title romanized: Pei ch'in hai chih Chung-kuo.

DS740.L57 C 59 5079

Indiana. Univ. Libr. for Library of Congress ［2］†

NL 0415956 InU DLC NIC

Liu, Yen, 1880–
帝國主義壓迫中國史 劉彥著 上海 太平洋書店 民國 19 ［1930］
2 v. 21 cm.
Previous editions published under title: 中國近時外交史

1. China—For. rel. I. Title.
Title romanized: Ti kuo chui ya p'o Chung-kuo shih.

C 61-4067

Chicago. Univ. Far Eastern Library for Library of Congress ［2］

NL 0415957 ICU-FE

Liu, Yen, 1880–
最近三十年中國外交史 劉彥著 上海 太平洋書店 民國 20 ［1931］
6, 194, 58 p. 20 cm.
特錄 1. 中國國民黨第三次全國代表大會外交報告 2. 中國國民黨第三次全國代表大會外交決議案: p. 1-58 (3d group)

1. China—For. rel. 2. Eastern question (Far East) I. Title.
Title romanized: Tsui chin san shih nien Chung-kuo wai chiao shih.

DS740.4.L5 C 60-5257

Indiana. Univ. Libr. for Library of Congress ［2］†

NL 0415958 InU DLC ViU

VOLUME 336

Liu, Yen-ling, *ed.*
明淸散文選 劉延陵編著 胡倫淸校訂 臺北 正中書局 民國42 [1953]
14, 1, 7, 238 p. 18 cm. (正中文庫第1輯)

1. Chinese essays (Selections: Extracts, etc.) I. Title.
Title romanized: Ming Ch'ing san wên hsüan.

PL2607.L5 C 66-275

NL 0415959 DLC

Liu, Yen-shêng.
京劇故事攷 劉雁聲 沈正元編 北京 自強書局 1954.
4, 2, 70 p. illus. 18 cm.

1. Chinese drama (Selections: Extracts, etc.) I. Shên, Chêng-yüan, joint author. II. Title.
Title romanized: Ching chü ku shih k'ao.

PL2568.L49 C 67-189

NL 0415960 DLC NIC InU

Liu, Yi-cheng
see
Liu, I-chêng, 1879–

Liu, Yih-ling, tr.

PL2997 .L39E5 1948

Li, Yü, 937–978.
Poems of Lee Hou-chu; rendered into English from the Chinese by Liu Yih-ling and Shahid Suhrawardy. With Chinese text. Bombay, Orient Longmans [1948]

Liu, Yin, 1904–1942.
中國古代政治哲學批判 李麥麥[劉胤]著 [上海] 新生命書局 [1933]
16, 2, 360 p. 22 cm.

1. Political science—Hist.—China. I. Title.
Title romanized: Chung-kuo ku tai chêng chih chê hsüeh.

JA84.C6L57 C 67-2316

NL 0415963 DLC

Liu, Yin, 1904–1942.
各國民族統一運動史 李建芳[劉胤]遺著 重慶 大道出版社 民國34 [1945]
1, 286 p. 18 cm.
Cover title.
Colophon title: 各國民族統一運動史論

1. Nationalism. I. Title.
Title romanized: Ko kuo min tsu t'ung i yün tung shih.

JC311.L72 C 67-1331

NL 0415964 DLC

Liu, Yin, 1904–1942.
論中國共產黨 李建芳[劉胤]著 上海 眞理出版社 1937.
2, 68 p. 19 cm. (中國近代社會文化運動叢書)

1. Chung-kuo kung ch'an tang. I. Title.
Title romanized: Lun Chung-kuo kung ch'an tang.

JQ1519.A5L53 C 64-909

NL 0415965 DLC

Liu, Yin-fu.
中國工業現狀及其振興方法 劉蔭茀[著 n. p., 1937?]
1 v. (various pagings) maps (1 fold.) plan. 26 cm.
Caption title.
CONTENTS.—中國工業現狀及其振興方法 劉蔭茀—我國如何實施工業統制 歐陽崙—中國勞工問題講演綱要 唐健飛—中國水利概況 鄭肇經—揚子江水利問題 孫輔世—黃河水利問題 鄭肇經—導淮問題 須愷—整理運河問題 汪胡楨—中國蠶絲業概況 譚熙鴻—中國農業推廣問題—中國麥作改進問題演講綱要 沈宗瀚—中國稻作改進問題演講綱要 濇簡良—我國農事試驗概況 張宗成—中國之林業演講綱要 皮作瓊—中國墾殖問題 安漢—中國墾殖問題中之全國總面積問題 安漢—治虫問題 傅勝發—中國農業金融問題—中國經濟問題 羅敦偉—合作問題講議綱要 章元善

1. China—Econ. condit.—1912–1949. I. Title.
Title romanized: Chung-kuo kung yeh hsien chuang chi ch'i chên hsing fang fa.

HC427.8.L58 C 68-1

NL 0415967 DLC

Liu, Ying, ed.
Shih shih kêng chê yu ch'i t'ien li hsiang chieh
see under China. Laws, statutes, etc.

Liu, Yu-Chen.
Interactions within Chinese-American families of Portland, Oregon, resulting from cultural differences. [Corvalis, Ore.] 1951.
9 p.l., 516 numb. l. maps., charts (part fold.), form, photos., tables (part fold.) 28 cm.
Typewritten.
Thesis (Ph.D.) - Oregon State College, 1951.
Bibliography: l. 387-391.
1. Chinese in the U.S. 2. Portland, Ore. - Foreign population.

NL 0415969 OrCS

BF1148 .C5L5 Houd. Coll.

Liu, Yü-ch'ih.
Ts'u i-mien shih-yung hsüch. [n.p.] The Chinese hypnotic association, 1916.
[158] p. plates. 24 cm.
Photograph of "Hwerly the great," mounted on inside of front cover.

NL 0415970 DLC

Liu, Yü-ch'ing.
中華民國憲法概論及條文釋義 劉毓卿編著 修訂版 臺中 瑞成書局 民國43 [1954]
6, 4, 346 p. 21 cm.
附綱要表及高等普通考試憲法試題

1. China. Constitution. I. Title.
Title romanized: Chung-hua min kuo hsien fa kai lun.

C 66-74

NL 0415971 DLC CtY MH-HY

Liu, Yü-lüeh.
中共怎樣對待少數民族? 劉裕略著 九龍 友聯出版社 1953.
66 p. 18 cm. (中共問題問答叢書)

1. Minorities—China. I. Title.
Title romanized: Chung kung tsên yang tui tai shao shu min tsu.

DS777.55.L54 C 58-5645 *

NL 0415972 DLC CtY MiU HU

Liu, Yü-lüeh.
韓玉花 劉裕略著 [香港] 亞洲出版社有限公司 [1955]
202 p. 19 cm.
Fiction.

I. Title.
Title romanized: Han Yü-hua.

PL2782.Y8H3 72-840279

NL 0415973 DLC

Liu, Yü-p'an, 1867–1927.
(Tz'u shih)
詞史 劉毓盤遺著 查猛濟 曹聚仁校 上海 羣衆圖書公司 [1931]
2, 2, 216, 2 p. 19 cm.

1. Tz'u—History and criticism. I. Title.

PL2336.L55 · 1931 73-835382

NL 0415974 DLC

Liu, Yü-shêng, *writer on ethics, ed.*
新國民運動論文選 柳雨生編 上海 太平書局 民國31 [1942]
209 p. 19 cm.

1. Sino-Japanese Conflict, 1937–1945. I. Title.
Title romanized: Hsin kuo min yün tung lun wên hsüan.

DS777.53.L579 C 66-2518

NL 0415975 DLC

Liu, Yü-t'ang.
A history of the selective training and service act of 1940: prolegomena to the place of the military in the United States.

Typewritten. 29 x 21 cm.
Thesis,Ph.D. - Harvard University,1941.

NL 0415976 MH

Liu, Yü-t'ang.
Manchurian booty and international law, by Daniel H. Lew.
(*In* American journal of international law. Concord, N. H., 1946. 26cm. v. 40, p. 584–591)
Bibliographical foot-notes.

1. Enemy property. 2. World war, 1939–1945—Confiscations and contributions—Russia. 3. [World war, 1939–1945—Manchuria] I. Title.

JX1.A6 vol. 40 A 46-6020
Carnegie endow. int. peace. for Library of Congress Library [3]†

NL 0415977 NNCE CaBVaU DLC

VOLUME 336

D899.63
L747
Liu, Yü-t'ang.
Southwest China, a survey of a great potential, ₍by₎ Daniel Hong Lew. 1939.
82 l.

Bibliography: l. ₍83-85₎

1. China - Pol. & govt. - 1937-1945.
I. Title: Southwest China.

NL 0415978 NNC-EA

Liu, Yüan.
(Ling yen ko) 凌煙閣 劉源敬繪 ₍n. p., 涉園重印 庚午 i. e. 1930₎
1 v. (double leaves; chiefly illus., facsims.) 30 cm.
Running title: 凌煙閣功臣圖像

1. China—Biography—Pictorial works. I. Title.

DS734.L537 70–840928

NL 0415979 DLC

Liu, Yuan-lung.
The Far East is not very far; letters from Liu Yuan-lung and Wang Shou-ming ₍*pseud.*₎ edited by Anna Melissa Graves. ₍Baltimore₎ Priv. print. ₍by the Waverly press, inc.₎ 1942.
xx, 317 p. incl. front. ports. 23½ cm.
"China's history and her social and economic condition during the period covered by the preceding letters. A few sources": p. 309.

I. Wang, Shou-ming, pseud. II. Graves, Anna Melissa, ed. III. Title.

Library of Congress DS778.L5A4 42-17921
₍5₎ 915.1

NL 0415980 DLC CSt-H OrCS CU NIC PHC PP PBm

Liu, Yüan-na.
俄語標準發音讀本 劉媛娜編 Учебник для изучения русского литературного произношения. Лю Юань-на. 北京 時代出版社 1955.
206 p. illus. 21 cm.

1. Russian language—Intonation. I. Title. II. Title: Uchebnik dlia izuchenia russkogo literaturnogo proiznoshenia.
Title romanized: O yü piao chun fa yin tu pên.

PG2361.L5 C 60–1360 ‡

NL 0415981 DLC

Liu, Yüeh.
捷聲速記術 劉越著 鄧綱編 改編3版 ₍南京₎ 江南出版社 1952.
6, 198 p. 18 cm.
At head of title: 自學函授教科適用

1. Shorthand, Chinese. I. Têng, Kang, ed. II. Title.
Title romanized: Chieh shêng su chi shu.

Z59.5.L57 C 68–989

NL 0415982 DLC

Liu, Yüeh.
速記發展簡史 劉越著 陳發淦勘校 ₍n. p.₎ 江南出版社 1951.
53 p. 18 cm. (速記叢書)

1. Shorthand, Chinese. I. Title.
Title romanized: Su chi fa chan chien shih.

Z53.L75 C 61–336 ‡

NL 0415983 DLC

Liu, Yüeh.
速記是什麼? 劉越著 ₍南京₎ 江南出版社 ₍1953₎
15 p. 19 cm. (速記叢書)

1. Shorthand. I. Title.
Title romanized: Su chi shih shih mo?

Z53.L753 C 67–3062

NL 0415984 DLC

Liu, Yüeh-fu.
國樂演奏曲集 劉樂夫 根生 伯廷編 濟南山東人民出版社 1955.
1, 59 p. 26 cm.
Includes instrumental music in number notation.

1. Music, Chinese. I. Title.
Title romanized: Kuo yüeh yen tsou ch'ü chi.

C 64–1780

Harvard Univ. Chinese-Japanese Library 6791
Library of Congress ₍1₎

NL 0415985 MH-HY

Liu, Yüeh-t'ing.
今日東北 劉躍挺著 九龍 自由出版社 民國 39 ₍1950₎
64 p. 19 cm.

1. Manchuria—Hist.—1945– 2. Communism—Manchuria. I. Title.
Title romanized: Chin jih Tung-pei.

DS783.7.L56 C 58–7364

Hoover Institution 3052
for Library of Congress ₍1₎†

NL 0415986 CSt-H DLC WU InU ViU

Liu, Yung-chi.
文心雕龍校釋 劉永濟編著 臺北 正中書局 民國 43 ₍1954₎
138 p. 21 cm. (中國文史叢書)

1. Liu, Hsieh, ca. 463–ca. 522. Wên hsin tiao lung. I. Title.
Title romanized: Wên hsin tiao lung chiao shih.

PL2263.L54 C 59–3106

NL 0415987 DLC

Liu, Yung-fu, 1837–1917.
劉永福歷史艸 羅香林輯錄 南京 正中書局 民國 25 ₍1936₎
2, 22, 231 p. ports. 22 cm. (史地叢刊)
Bibliography: p. 7–10 (2d group)
史草所述半爲黑旗將軍劉永福抗法禦日經過半爲劉氏剿撫南服土匪情況 作者欽人黃海安嘗隨永福効力行伍 永福晚年居里 黃爲之課兒孫讀書與永福晨夕晤對 意甚適也 永福令之草黑旗事蹟 自爲講述 日一二時 講罷黃輒錄之
I. Huang, Hai-an. II. Lo, Hsiang-lin, 1905– ed. III. Title.
Title romanized: Liu Yung-fu li shih ts'ao.

DS763.H7L5 C 67–1298

NL 0415988 DLC

Liu, Yung-ho, tr.
Mei kuei yüan
see under Weil, Ann, 1908-

Liu, Yung-kao.
天文駕駛 劉永誥編 ₍臺北₎ 招商局訓練委員會 民國 41 ₍1952₎
62 p. illus. 19 cm. (訓練教材甲種)

1. Nautical astronomy. I. Title.
Title romanized: T'ien wên chia shih.

VK555.L58 C 61–2428 ‡

NL 0415990 DLC ICU MH

六十年來中國國民黨與青年 ₍臺北₎ 中央委員會第四組編印 ₍1954₎
2, 134 p. 19 cm.

總理誕辰暨本黨建立六十週年紀念三民主義論文競賽社會青年組徵文選集

1. Chung-kuo kuo min tang. 2. Youth—China. I. Chung-kuo kuo min tang. Chung yang wei yüan hui. Ti ssŭ tsu.
Title romanized: Liu shih nien lai Chung kuo kuo min tang yü ch'ing nien.

JQ1519.A52L53 70–837120

NL 0415991 DLC

Liuban, A P
Анализ явлений доменного процесса. Ч. 1. Москва, Гос. научно-техн. изд-во лит-ры по черной и цветной металлургии, 1955.
471 p. illus. 23 cm.
No more published.
Includes bibliographies.
—— —— Microfilm copy (positive)
Made by the Library of Congress.
Negative film in the Library of Congress.
Microfilm Slavic 558 AC

1. Blast-furnaces. I. Title.
Title transliterated: Analiz iavlenii domennogo protsessa.

TN713.L49 55–41106 rev

NL 0415992 DLC

Liuban, A P
Исследование доменного процесса. Москва, Гос. научно-техн. изд-во лит-ры по черной и цветной металлургии, 1948.
200 p. illus. 23 cm.
Errata slip inserted.
"Литература": p. ₍197₎-200.

1. Blast-furnaces. 2. Metallurgy.
Title transliterated: Issledovanie domennogo protsessa.

TN713.L5 49–29357*

NL 0415993 DLC

Liubanskii, G
(Sblizhenie Srednei Azii s Evropoiu)
Сближеніе Средней Азіи съ Европою; или, Проэктъ о желѣзныхъ дорогахъ между городами Варшавою и Тифлисомъ и между Чернымъ моремъ и Каспіемъ. ₍Г. Любанскій₎. Санктпетербургъ ₍Въ Тип. Имп. Академіи наукъ₎ 1858.
56 p. illus. 24 cm.
Bound with Potekhin V. Селеніе Россъ. Санктпетербургъ, 1859.

1. Railroads—Russia. I. Title.

F864.P8558 73–216270

NL 0415994 DLC

VOLUME 336

Liubaro, Aisick.
... Emociones de inquietud, versos. Buenos Aires, Editorial Tor [1926]
7 p. l., 17-108 p., 2 l. 18½cm.

I. Title.

Library of Congress PQ7797.L54E6 34-29456
[3] 861.6

NL 0415995 DLC

Liúbaro, Aisick.
La isla de los alucinados [y otros cuentos de tierra adentro] Rosario, Libreria Ruiz, 1954. 161 p. 18cm.

1. Fiction, Argentine. I. Title.

NL 0415996 NN

DK268 .D9L5 1950 **Lîubarov, G M**
Феликс Эдмундович Дзержинский. Стенограмма публичной лекции, прочитанной в Москве 23 дек. 1949 г. Москва [Правда] 1950.
38 p. port. 22 cm.
At head of title: Всесоюзное общество по распространению политических и научных знаний.

1. Dzerzhinskiĭ, Feliks Ėdmundovich, 1877-1926.
Title transliterated: Feliks Ėdmundovich Dzerzhinskiĭ.
DK268.D9L5 1950 51-17693

NL 0415997 DLC

DK268 .D9L5 1950a **Lîubarov, G M**
Феликс Эдмундович Дзержинский. 2., доп. изд. стенограммы публичной лекции, прочитанной в Москве [23 дек. 1949 г.] Москва, Правда, 1950.
39 p. ports. 22 cm.
At head of title: Всесоюзное общество по распространению политических и научных знаний.

1. Dzerzhinskiĭ, Feliks Ėdmundovich, 1877-1926.
Title transliterated: Feliks Ėdmundovich Dzerzhinskiĭ.
DK268.D9L5 1950a 51-17692

NL 0415998 DLC

Lîubarskaîa, A I *comp.*
Твои товарищи; сборник рассказов. Перевод на эвенкийский язык Г. М. Василевич. Ленинград, Гос. учебно-педагог. изд-во, 1946.
160 p. illus. 23 cm.
Tungusic and Russian; added t. p. in Tungusic.
"Для эвенкийского школьника."

1. Tungusic language—Texts. 2. World War, 1939-1945—Fiction. I. Title. *Title transliterated:* Tvoi tovarishchi.
PL458.L5 52-31209

NL 0415999 DLC

Lîubarskiĭ, E I
Терпентин, канифоль и скипидар из корейского кедра. Владивосток, Тип. Дальневосточного гос. университета, 1929.
15 p. 26 cm. (Труды Дальневосточного краевого научно-исследовательского института, т. 1, вып. 5)
Title also in German.

1. Turpentine. 2. Gums and resins. 3. Pinus koraiensis. I. Title. (Series: Vladivostok. Dal'nevostochnyĭ kraevoĭ nauchno-issledovatel'skiĭ institut. Trudy, t. 1, vyp. 5)
Title transliterated: Terpentin, kanifol' i skipidar iz koreĭskogo kedra.
TP978.L49 59-59602

NL 0416001 DLC

TP978 .L5 **Lîubarskiĭ, E I**
Живой и мертвый терпентин; способы и продукты его обработки. Владивосток [Книжное дело] 19
v. 25 cm.

1. Turpentine. I. Title.
Title transliterated: Zhivoĭ i mertvyĭ terpentin.
TP978.L5 57-56344 ‡

NL 0416002 DLC

Lîubarskiĭ, I V
Памятка кузнеца свободной ковки. Москва, Гос. научно-техн. изд-во машиностроит. лит-ры, 1945.
67 p. diagrs. 20 cm.

1. Forging. I. Title.
Title transliterated: Pamîatka kuznefsa svobodnoĭ kovki.
TS225.L58 63-48061

NL 0416003 DLC

Lîubarskiĭ, Lev Nikolaevich.
Подготовка семян к посеву. Под общей ред. И. Д. Ладыгина и А. Ф. Тюрина. [Горький] Горьковское обл. изд-во, 1943.
15 p. 20 cm. (Колхозная массовая агроучеба; лекции для колхозных агрокружков)
At head of title: Горьковский сельскохозяйственный институт и Облзо.

1. Seeds. 2. Sowing. I. Title.
Title transliterated: Podgotovka semîan k posevu.
SB117.L5 58-54193 ‡

NL 0416004 DLC

Lîubarskiĭ, Lev Nikolaevich, ed

Russia (*1923-* *U. S. S. R.*) *Gosudarstvennaîa khlebnaîa inspekfsiîa.*
... Труды Центральной лаборатории, под редакцией и со вступительной статьей ... Л. Н. Любарского (Темы разрабатывались под руководством ... Н. С. Суворова) Москва, Издательство Наркомторгов СССР и РСФСР, 1929.

U739 .5 .L5 **Lîubarskiĭ, S**
Некоторые оперативно-тактические выводы из опыта войны в Испании. Москва, Гос. воен. изд-во, 1939.
70 p. illus. 20 cm.
At head of title: Академия Генерального штаба РККА.

1. Spain—Hist.—Civil War—1936-1939. I. Title.
Title transliterated: Nekotorye operativno-takticheskie vyvody iz opyta voĭny v Ispanii.
U739.5.L5 63-57413 ‡

NL 0416006 DLC

Lîubarskiĭ, Semen L'vovich, ed.

Russia (*1923-* *U. S. S. R.*) *Laws, statutes, etc.*
Единый сельскохозяйственный налог на 1929/30 год. Текст закона утвержденного 20 февр. 1929 г., с подробными объяснениями к каждой статье, примерами исчисления налога и вспомогательными таблицами. Под ред. М. И. Лифшица. Москва, Крестьянская газета, 1929.

Law **Lîubarskiĭ, Semen L'vovich.**
Льготы колхозам по сельхозналогу. Москва, Гос. изд-во, 1930.
95 p. 17 cm.

1. Agriculture—Taxation—Russia. I. Title.
Title transliterated: L'goty kolkhozam po sel'khoznalogu.
52-46982

NL 0416008 DLC

Lîubarskiĭ, Semen L'vovich, comp.

Russia (*1923-* *U. S. S. R.*) *Laws, statutes, etc.*
Положение о едином сельскохозяйственном налоге на 1926/27 год. С подробными об'яснениями к каждой статье, всеми таблицами и примерами исчисления налога с хозяйства. 2. испр. и доп. изд. Составлено А. Б. Райхманом и С. Л. Любарским, под руководством и ред. М. И. Лифшица. Москва, Крестьянская газета, 1926.

Lîubarskiĭ, Semen L'vovich, comp.

Law **Russia** (*1923-* *U. S. S. R.*) *Laws, statutes, etc.*
... Закон о едином сельско-хозяйственном налоге на 1928-29 год. Текст закона, утвержденного правительством Союза ССР 21 апреля 1928 г., с подробными пояснениями каждой статьи, таблицами и примерами исчисления налога. Составил ... С. Л. Любарский; под редакцией ... М. И. Лифшица ... Москва, Издательство "Крестьянская газета," 1928.

Lîubarskiĭ-Pis'mennyĭ, Evgeniĭ Petrovich, b. 1844? defendant.
Дѣло харьковскихъ банковъ. Москва, Печатня А. И. Снегиревой, 1904.
vii, 387 p. 20 cm. (Судебныя драмы)
At head of title: Л. Θ. Снегиревъ.
Trial of E. P. Lîubarskiĭ-Pis'mennyĭ and others, at the Ugolovnyĭ kassafsionnyĭ department of Pravitel'stvuîushchiĭ Senat, Dec. 11-12, 1903.
CONTENTS.—Кассаціонное производство.—Объясненія сторонъ.—Заключенія товар. оберъ-прокурора.—Мотивированное рѣшеніе Сената.—Отголоски печати.
1. Khar'kovskiĭ zemel'nyĭ bank. 2. Khar'kovskiĭ torgovyĭ bank. I. Snegirev, Leontiĭ F. II. Russia. Pravitel'stvuîushchiĭ Senat. Ugolovno-kassafsionnyĭ department. III. Title.
Title romanized: Dělo khar'kovskikh bankov.
72-268811

NL 0416011 DLC

Law **Lîubarskiĭ-Pis'mennyĭ, Evgeniĭ Petrovich, b. 1844?** *defendant.*
Дѣло о злоупотребленіяхъ въ харьковскомъ земельномъ и торговомъ банкахъ. Москва, 1903.
513, 4 p. 21 cm. (Судебныя драмы)
Trial of E. P. Lîubarskiĭ-Pis'mennyĭ and others at the Khar'kovskaîa sudebnaîa palata, Jan. 21-March 22, 1903.
1. Khar'kovskiĭ zemel'nyĭ bank. 2. Khar'kovskiĭ torgovyĭ bank. 3. Embezzlement—Russia. I. Russia. Sudebnaîa palata (Kharkov) II. Title.
Title transliterated: Dělo o zloupotrebleniîakh v khar'kovskom zemel'nom i torgovom bankakh.
56-54536

NL 0416012 DLC

Lîubashevskiĭ, Leonid Solomonovich.
Третья верста; пьеса. Ленинград, Искусство, 1938.
63 p. 17 cm.
At head of title: Д. Дэль.

I. Title. *Title transliterated:* Tret'fa versta.
PG3476.L645T7 66-97665

NL 0416013 DLC

VOLUME 336

Z68 .S654 Lfübavina, N., illus.

Sokolov-Mikitov, Ivan Sergeevich, 1892–
Засупоня. [Обложка, рисунки и клише работы Н. Любавиной. Петроград, 1918?]

SF377 .L56 **Lfübavskiĭ, A V**
Повышение шерстной продуктивности овец. Москва, Гос. изд-во сельхоз. лит-ры, 1952.
118 p. illus. 20 cm.
At head of title: А. В. Любавский, Б. Н. Филиппов.

1. Wool. 2. Wool trade and industry—Russia. I. Filippov, B. N., joint author. II. Title.
Title transliterated: Povyshenie sherstnoĭ produktivnosti oveŧ.

SF377.L56 53-16790

NL 0416015 DLC

SF375 .5 .R8L5 **Lfübavskiĭ, A V**
Ставропольская порода тонкорунных овец. Москва, Гос. изд-во сельхоз. лит-ры, 1953.
59 p. illus. 20 cm.
At head of title: А. В. Любавский, Б. Н. Филиппов.

1. Sheep breeds. I. Filippov, B. N., joint author. II. Title.
Title transliterated: Stavropol'skaîa poroda tonkorunnykh oveŧ.

54-42778 ‡

NL 0416016 DLC

Lfübavskiĭ, Aleksandr Dmitrievich.
Юридическія монографіи и изслѣдованія. С.-Петербургъ, 18
v. port. 23 cm.

1. Law—Russia—Addresses, essays, lectures. 2. Law—Addresses, essays, lectures.
Title transliterated: fÛridicheskīîa monografii i izslîêdovaniîa.

62-57652

NL 0416017 DLC

Lfübavskiĭ, Aleksandr Dmitrievich.
Нѣсколько вопросовъ изъ гражданскаго права. А. Любавскаго. Санктпетербургъ, Въ печатнѣ В. Головина, 1865.
cover-title, 49 p. 22cm.
Caption title: Судебныя рѣшенія по вопросамъ гражданскаго права.
Reprinted from Юридическій вѣстникъ, vol. XLVII.

1. Civil law—Russia—Cases. I. Title.

37-32988

NL 0416018 DLC

Law

Lfübavskiĭ, Aleksandr Dmitrievich, *ed.*
Новые русскіе уголовные процессы. Санктпетербургъ, Тип. "Общественная польза," 1868–
v. 23 cm.

1. Trials—Russia. I. Title.
Title transliterated: Novye russkie ugolovnye proŧessy.

55-50110

NL 0416019 DLC

Law

Lfübavskiĭ, Aleksandr Dmitrievich.
Объ упрощеніи внѣшней формы завѣщаній. Санктпетербургъ, 1865.
v, 259, 21 p. 26 cm.

1. Wills—Russia.
Title transliterated: Ob uproshchenii vnfêshneĭ formy zavfêshchaniĭ.

50-40117

NL 0416020 DLC

Lfübavskiĭ, Aleksandr Dmitrievich.
Опытъ коментарія русскихъ законовъ о давности. Александра Любавскаго. Санктпетербургъ [1865]
cover-title, 79 p. 21½cm.
Reprinted from Юридическій вѣстникъ, vol. XLVI.
Cover mutilated: part of imprint cut away in trimming.

1. Prescription (Law)—Russia. 2. Limitation of actions—Russia. I. Title.

37-32989

NL 0416021 DLC

Lfübavskiĭ, Aleksandr Dmitrievich.
Присяга, какъ доказательство въ дѣлахъ гражданскихъ [СПБ., 1862?]
[43]–102 p. 23 cm.
Caption title.
Detached from Журналъ Министерства юстиціи, v. 21, pt. 2.

1. Oaths—Russia. 2. Civil procedure—Russia. I. Title.
Title transliterated: Prisfâga, kak dokazatel'stvo v dfêlakh grazhdanskikh.

55-51047

NL 0416022 DLC

Law

Lfübavskiĭ, Aleksandr Dmitrievich, *ed.*
Русскіе уголовные процессы. Санктпетербургъ, Тип. "Общественная польза," 1866–68.
4 v. 22 cm.

1. Trials—Russia. I. Title.
Title transliterated: Russkie ugolovnye proŧessy.

55-50674

NL 0416023 DLC CSt OU

Law

Lfübavskiĭ, Aleksandr Dmitrievich.
Уголовныя дѣла, изъ практики Тульскаго окружнаго суда. А. Любавскаго. Тула, Тип. Тульск. губ. правленія, 1874.
127 p. 20 cm.

1. Trials—Russia. 2. Trial practice—Russia. 3. Russia. Okruzhnyĭ sud (Tula) I. Title.
Title transliterated: Ugolovnyîa dfêla, iz praktiki Tul'skago okruzhnago suda.

65-59873

NL 0416024 DLC

Lfübavskiĭ, K V *ed.*
Новое в технологии сварки. [Книга написана на основе исследований, проведенных ЦНИИТМАШ] Москва, Гос. научно-техн. изд-во машиностроит. лит-ры, 1955.
246 p. illus. 23 cm.
Includes bibliographies.

1. Welding. I. Moscow. Tŝentral'nyĭ nauchno-issledovatel'skiĭ institut tekhnologii i mashinostroeniîa. II. Title.
Title transliterated: Novoe v tekhnologii svarki.

TS227.L66 56-24093

NL 0416025 DLC

Lfübavskiĭ, K. V.
Welding with a consumable electrode in an atmosphere of protective gases, by K. V. Lyubavskii and N. M. Novoshilov. [Altadena, Cal., Henry Brutcher] 1953.
3 l. [9 l.] illus. 30 cm. (Brutcher translations, no. 3140)
Translated from Avtogennoe Delo, v. 24, 1953, no. 1, p. 4-8.

NL 0416026 PBL

D147 .L49 **Lfübavskiĭ, Matveĭ Kuz'mich, 1860–1936.**
Историческія судьбы славянства. Лекція, читанная 26 окт. 1914 г. Москва, 1915.
27 p. 23 cm.
At head of title: Комиссія по устройству чтеній для учащихся выпускныхъ классовъ среднихъ учебныхъ заведеній Московскаго учебнаго округа.

1. Slavs. *Title transliterated:* Istoricheskiîa sud'by slavîanstva.

D147.L49 50-51729

NL 0416027 DLC

Lfübavskiĭ, Matveĭ Kuz'mich, 1860–1936.
... Лекціи по древней русской исторіи до конца XVI вѣка. Изд. 3. Москва [Изданіе М. и С. Сабашниковыхъ] 1918.
2 p. l., 306, vi p. 22½cm.
At head of title: Проф. М. К. Любавскій.
"Читанныя въ [Московскомъ] университетѣ и на Высшихъ женскихъ курсахъ въ Москвѣ."—2d prelim. leaf.
Bibliography at end of each chapter.

1. Russia—Hist.—To 1533. 2. Russia—Hist.—1533-1613. *Title transliterated:* Lekŧii po drevneĭ russkoĭ istorii.

44-17498

Library of Congress DK71.L5 1918

NL 0416028 DLC NcU ScU OrU CaBVaU

Lfübavskiĭ, Matveĭ Kuz'mich, 1860–1936.
Литовско-русскій сеймъ; опытъ по исторіи учрежденія въ связи съ внутреннимъ строемъ и внѣшнею жизнью государства. Москва, Изд. Имп. Об-ва исторіи и древностей россійскихъ при Московскомъ университетѣ, 1900.
850, 232 p. 29 cm.
Includes legislation of Lithuania.
Bibliographical footnotes.

1. Lithuania. Soĭm. I. Lithuania. Laws, statutes, etc. II. Title.
Title transliterated: Litovsko-russkiĭ seĭm.

55-45760

NL 0416029 DLC CLU

VOLUME 336

Law

Li͡ubavskiĭ, Matveĭ Kuz'mich, 1860–1936.
Областное дѣленіе и мѣстное управленіе Литовско-русскаго государства ко времени изданія перваго Литовскаго статута; историческіе очерки. Москва, Унив. тип., 1892.
viii, 884, c, vi p. fold. col. map. 29 cm.
"Изъ 'Чтеній въ Императорскомъ Обществѣ исторіи и древностей россійскихъ при Московскомъ университетѣ.'"
Includes legislation of Lithuania.
Bibliographical footnotes.
1. Law—Lithuania. 2. Lithuania. Laws, statutes, etc. Statut Velikogo Kni͡azʹstva Litovskago. I. Lithuania. Laws, statutes, etc. II. Title.
Title transliterated: Oblastnoe di͡elenie ... Litovsko-Russkago gosudarstva.
55–45756

NL 0416030 DLC CaBVaU

Li͡ubavskiĭ, Matveĭ Kuz'mich, 1860–1936.
Образование основой государственной территории великорусской народности; заселение и объединение центра. Ленинград, Изд-во Академии наук СССР, 1929.
175 p. fold. map. 27 cm.
At head of title: Академия наук Союза Советских Социалистических Республик. Археографическая комиссия.
Bibliographical footnotes.
——— Photo-offset. [Orono, Me.] Academic International, 1969.
(The Russian series, v. 27)
DK71.L52 1969
1. Russia—History—To 1533. I. Title.
Title romanized: Obrazovanie osnovnoĭ gosudarstvennoĭ territorii velikorusskoĭ narodnosti.
DK71.L52 50–48908
SBN 87569-006-8

NL 0416031 DLC MnU

Li͡ubavskiĭ, Matveĭ Kuz'mich, 1860–1936.
Очеркъ исторіи Литовско-Русскаго государства до Люблинской уніи включительно. Съ приложеніемъ текста хартій, выданныхъ Великому Княжеству Литовскому и его областямъ. Москва, Изд. Имп. Об-ва исторіи и древностей россійскихъ, 1910.
876, ii p. 28 cm.
Includes bibliographies.
1. Lithuania—Hist. I. Lithuania. Laws, statutes, etc. II. Title.
Title transliterated: Ocherk istorii Litovsko-Russkago gosudarstva do Li͡ublinskoĭ unii.
DK511.L23L5 54–50743

NL 0416032 DLC OrU ScU IaU

DS11
.5
.L562

Li͡ubchenko, Arkadiĭ, 1899–
Щоденник. Торонто, Нові дні, 1951–
v. illus. 17 cm.
1. World War, 1939–1945—Personal narratives, Ukrainian.
Title transliterated: Shchodennyk.
D811.5.L562 57–27595 ‡

NL 0416033 DLC KU OrU

Li͡ubchenko, Arkadiĭ, 1899–
(Vybrani tvory)
Вибрані твори. [Харків] Держ. літературне вид-во, 1937.
421 p. 20 cm.
PG3948.L57A6 1937 73–203050

NL 0416034 DLC

Microfilm
AC–103

Li͡ubchenko, Panas Petrovych.
Lenins'kyĭ komunistychnyĭ soi͡uz molodi Ukraïny. *Tsentral'nyĭ komitet.*
Молоді фашисти української контрреволюції; до процесу СВУ. Статті П. Любченка [та інших] Харків, Держ. вид-во України, 1930.

Li͡ubchenko, Panas Petrovych.
Про проект Конституції УРСР; доповідь на надзвичайному XIV з'їзді Рад України, 25 січня 1937 року. [Київ] 1937.
Microfilm copy. Negative.
Collation of the original: 46 p. port.
1. Ukraine. Constitution. I. Title.
Title transliterated: Pro proekt Konstytutsiï URSR.
Mic 53–521

NL 0416036 DLC

Microfilm
Slavic
85
AC

Li͡ubchenko, Panas Petrovych.
Промова на 4-ій сессії ЦВК СРСР VII скликання. Київ, Партвидав, 1937.
Microfilm copy. Negative.
Collation of the original: 7 p.
1. Ukraine—Pol. & govt.
Title transliterated: Promova na chetvertiĭ sesiï.
Mic 53–600 rev

NL 0416037 DLC

Li͡ubchenko, Panas Petrovych.
Радянська Україна між XII і XIII З'їздами Рад; доповідь на XIII Всеукраїнському З'їзді Рад 15 січня 1935 р. Київ, Партвидав, 1935.
Microfilm copy. Negative.
Collation of the original as determined from the film: 46 p. port.
1. Ukraine. I. Title.
Title transliterated: Radi͡ans'ka Ukraïna mizh XII i XIII Z'ïzdamy Rad.
Microfilm Slavic 281 DK Mic 55–3058

NL 0416038 DLC

Li͡ubchenko, Panas Petrovych.
Сталинская Конституция и Советская Украина; речь на чрезвычайном VIII Всесоюзном Съезде Советов 26 ноября 1936. [Москва] Партиздат, 1936.
28 p. illus. 20 cm.
1. Ukraine—Pol. & govt.—1917–
Title transliterated: Stalinskai͡a Konstitut͡sii͡a.
JN6599.U4L5 54–49055 ‡

NL 0416039 DLC CSt-H

Microfilm
Slavic
205
AC

Li͡ubchenko, Panas Petrovych.
Українські націоналісти в боротьбі за реставрацію капіталізму. Харків, Держ. вид-во України, 1930.
Microfilm copy. Negative.
Collation of the original as determined from the film: 41 p.
1. Nationalism—Ukraine. I. Title.
Title transliterated: Ukraïns'ki natsionalisty v borot'bi za restavratsii͡u kapitalizmu.
~~Microfilm AC–127~~ Mic 53–777

NL 0416040 DLC

Li͡ubchenko, Panas Petrovych.
די וועגן און דער באנקראט פון דער אוקרייניזשער קאנטר־רעוואליוציע; רעדע אפן פראצעס פון ס. וו. או. כארקאוו, צענטרפארלאג. אלוקריינישע אפטיילונג. [Харків, 1930]
75 p. 19 cm.
1. Spilka vyzvolenni͡a Ukraïny, 1926–1930. 2. Ukraine—Hist.—1917–
Title transliterated: Di vegn un bankrot fun der ukraynisher kontr-revolutsye.
DK508.8.L548 59–59730 ‡

NL 0416041 DLC

4HC
Rus.
40

Li͡ubchenko, Panas Petrovych
Der Volkswirtschaftsplan der USSR für das Jahr 1936; Bericht vor der III. Session des ZEK der USSR am 7. Februar 1936. Kiew, Staatsverlag der nationalen Minderheiten der USSR, 1936.
69 p.

NL 0416042 DLC-P4

Microfilm
AC–83

Li͡ubchenko, Panas Petrovych.
З Варшавським договором проти п'ятирічки; до процесу СВУ. Харків, Держ. вид-во України, 1930.
Microfilm copy. Negative.
Collation of the original: 71 p.
1. Spilka vyzvolenni͡a Ukraïny, 1926–1930. I. Title.
Title transliterated: Z Varshavs'kym dohovorom proty p'i͡atyrichky.
Mic 52–867 rev

NL 0416043 DLC

Li͡ubchik, Mikhail Abramovich.
Аппараты автоматического управления электрическими машинами; учебные таблицы. Ленинград, Гос. энерг. изд-во, 1952.
1 portfolio (19 (i. e. 15) fold. col. plates) 23 x 28 cm.
Cover title.
At head of title: М. А. Любчик.
1. Electric controllers. I. Title.
Title romanized: Apparaty avtomaticheskogo upravlenii͡a ėlektricheskimi mashinami.
TK2851.L47 54–21133

NL 0416044 DLC

Li͡ubchik, Mikhail Abramovich
Аппараты неавтоматического управления электрическими машинами; учебные таблицы. Москва, Гос. энерг. изд-во, 1953.
portfolio (10 (i. e. 8) l.) 23 x 30 cm.
Cover title.
——— Microfilm.
Made by the Library of Congress.
Negative film in the Library of Congress.
Microfilm Slavic 731 T
1. Electric apparatus and appliances. I. Title.
Title transliterated: Apparaty neavtomaticheskogo upravlenii͡a ėlektricheskimi mashinami.
TK2851.L48 65–50823

NL 0416045 DLC

VOLUME 336

Lfûbchik, Mikhail Abramovich.
Коммутационные аппараты низкого напряжения; учебные таблицы. Москва, Гос. энерг. изд-во, 1954.
portfolio (10 (i. e. 8) l.) 23 x 29 cm.
Cover title.
——— Microfilm.
Made by the Library of Congress.
Negative film in the Library of Congress.
Microfilm Slavic 743 AC
1. Electric switchgear. I. Title.
Title transliterated: Kommutatŝionnye apparaty nizkogo naprfazhenifa.
TK2841.L54 65-50824
NL 0416046 DLC

Lfûbech, Ukraine
see
Lyubech, Ukraine.

Lfûbel'chik, Paltiel Jedidiah
see
Lubelchik, Paltiel Jedidiah.

Lfûber, Aglaida Andreevna.
Атлас спор и пыльцы палеозойских отложений Казахстана. Алма-Ата, 1955.
125 p. illus. 26 cm.
At head of title: Академия наук Казахской ССР.
Includes bibliography.
1. Pollen, Fossil. 2. Paleobotany—Paleozoic. 3. Paleobotany—Kazakhstan. I. Title.
Title transliterated: Atlas spor i pyl'fsy paleozoiskikh otlozhenii Kazakhstana.
QE993.L5 57-17014 ‡
NL 0416049 DLC

TJ1485
.L5
Lfûberefskii zavod imeni Ukhtomskogo, Lyubertsy.
Наклонно-подъемная косилка "Новый идеал" 4½; руководство по сборке, уходу и применению. [Ленинград?] Машгиз, 1946.
19 p. illus. 22 cm.
1. Mowing-machines. I. Title.
Title transliterated: Naklonno-pod"emnafa kosilka "Novyi ideal."
TJ1485.L5 52-21496
NL 0416050 DLC

Lfûbertsy, Russia
see Lyubertsy, Russia.

Liubetskii, H. Drutskii
see Drutskii-Liubetskii, H.

DK601
.L5
Lfûbetskii, Sergeĭ Mikhaĭlovich, d. 1881.
Отголоски старины (историческая мозаика) Москва, Тип. "Русскихъ вѣдомостей," 1867.
ii, 251 p. 22 cm.
1. Moscow—Hist. 2. Moscow—Soc. life & cust. 3. Fasts and feasts—Russia—Moscow. I. Title.
Title transliterated: Otgoloski stariny.
DK601.L5 55-53759
NL 0416053 DLC

Lfûbetskii, Sergeĭ Mikhaĭlovich, d. 1881.
Русь и русскіе въ 1812 году; книга для чтенія всѣхъ возрастовъ. Москва, Тип. П. Бахметова, 1869.
2 v. in 1. 21 cm.
1. Napoléon I, Emperor of the French, 1769-1821—Invasion of Russia, 1812. I. Title.
Title romanized: Rus' i russkīe v tysfâcha vosem'sot dvenadfsatom godu.
DC235.L54 68-48779 rev
NL 0416054 DLC MH

Lfûbetskii, Sergeĭ Mikhaĭlovich, d. 1881.
Старина Москвы и русскаго народа въ историческомъ отношеніи, съ бытовою жизнью русскихъ. Съ описаніемъ русскаго народнаго быта въ прошедшемъ и началѣ нынѣшняго столѣтій, нравовъ, обычаевъ, преданій, гульбищъ, увеселеній и проч. Москва, Тип. Н. Ф. Савича, 1872.
348, ii p. 22 cm.
1. Moscow—Hist. 2. Moscow—Soc. life & cust. 3. Fasts and feasts—Russia. I. Title.
Title transliterated: Starina Moskvy i russkago naroda.
DK600.L5 56-52879
NL 0416055 DLC

Lfûbetskii, V Drutskii-
see
Drutskii-Lfûbetskii, V knfaz'.

Lfûbich, A S
Скотоводческие совхозы и их задачи. [Москва] Сельхозгиз, 1931.
37 p. illus. 20 cm.
1. Stock and stock-breeding—Russia. I. Title.
Title transliterated: Skotovodcheskie sovkhozy i ikh zadachi.
SF55.R95L5 54-47123 ‡
NL 0416057 DLC

Liubich, O.
Schilderung der fälle von meningitis purulenta pneumococcica aus dem Kinderspital zu Basel der jahre 1907 u. 1908 ... Basel, 1909.
Diss. - Basel.
NL 0416058 MiU

PG3467
.L54R9
Lfûbich-Koshurov, I A
Рыцарь большого меча; легенда и быль. Москва, Изд. Д. П. Ефимова [1903]
86 p. illus. 22 cm.
I. Title. Title transliterated: Rytsar' bol'shogo mecha.
PG3467.L54R9 51-47759
NL 0416059 DLC

Lfûbich-Romanovich, Vasilii Ignat'evich, 1805-1888.
[Stikhotvorenifa]
Стихотворенія Василія Романовича Санктпетербургъ, Въ тип Плюшаръ, 1832.
170 p. 18 cm.
PG3337.L6S7 73-201957
NL 0416060 DLC

Lfûbichi, Russia
see Lyubichi, Russia.

Lfûbimenko, Inna Ivanovna (Borodina) 1878–
Anglo-Russian relations during the first English revolution. by Inna Lubimenko ...
(In Royal historical society, London. Transactions. London, 1871– 22cm. 4th ser., v. 11 (1928) p. 39-59)
Bibliographical foot-notes.
1. Gt. Brit.—Foreign relations—Russia. 2. Russia—Foreign relations—Gt. Brit. I. Title.
A C 36-1670
Newberry library for Library of Congress [DA20.R9 ser. 4, vol. 11]
[a38c1] (942.0062)
NL 0416062 ICN MB DLC

Lfûbimenko, Inna Ivanovna (Borodina) 1878–
The correspondence of the first Stuarts with the first Romanovs. By Madame Inna Lubimenko ...
(In Royal historical society, London. Transactions. London, 1871– 22cm. 4th ser., v. 1 (1918) p. 77-91)
1. Gt. Brit.—Foreign relations—Russia. 2. Russia—Foreign relations—Gt. Brit.
A C 36-1598
Title from Newberry Libr. Library of Congress [DA20.R9 ser. 4, vol. 1]
(942.0062)
NL 0416063 ICN MB

Lfûbimenko, Inna Ivanovna (Borodina) 1878–
Исторія торговыхъ сношеній Россіи съ Англіей. Юрьевъ, Тип. К. Маттисена, 1912–
v. 26 cm.
Bibliographical footnotes.
Contents.—вып. 1. XVI-ый вѣкъ.
1. Russia—Comm.—Gt. Brit. 2. Gt. Brit.—Comm.—Russia. I. Title.
Title transliterated: Istorifa torgovykh snoshenii Rossii s Angliei.
HF3628.G7L58 54-54765
NL 0416064 DLC GU

VOLUME 336

Lıūbımenko, Īnna Īvanovna (Borodīna) 1878-

Jean de Bretagne, comte de Richmond; sa vie et son activité en Angleterre, en Écosse et en France, 1266–1334. Paris, Picard, 1908. pp. xv, (3), 160 +.

John II, duke of Brittany

NL 0416065 MH CSmH PU CoU MiU PHC CtY NIC NNU

Lıūbımenko, Īnna Īvanovna (Borodīna) 1878-

Letters illustrating the relations of England and Russia in the seventeenth century.

Eng. hist. rev. 32:92-102.

NL 0416066 MnU

Lıūbımenko, Īnna Īvanovna (Borodīna) 1878-

A project for the acquisition of Russia by James II.

Eng. hist. rev. 29:246-56.

NL 0416067 MnU

Lıūbimenko, Īnna Īvanovna (Borodina) 1878–

Les relations commerciales et politiques de l'Angleterre avec la Russie avant Pierre le Grand, par Inna Lubimenko. Paris, Champion, 1933.

4 p. l., xx, 310 p., 1 l. 25cm. (*Added t.-p.:* Bibliothèque de l'École des hautes études ... Sciences historiques et philologiques. 261. fasc.)

"Bibliographie": p. [i]-xx.

1. Russia—For. rel.—Gt. Brit. 2. Gt. Brit.—For. rel.—Russia. 3. Russia—Comm.—Gt. Brit. 4. Gt. Brit.—Comm.—Russia. 5. British in Russia. 6. Russia company, London. I. Title.

34-10514

Library of Congress AS162.B6 fasc. 261

(064) 327.420947

NL 0416068 OU OCU PU PHC DDO MB MiU CLSU DLC NN NbU IaU CU MoU TU NcGU NBC NcU

Lıūbimenko, Īnna Īvanovna (Borodina) 1878–

The struggle of the Dutch with the English for the Russian market in the seventeenth century, by Madame Inna Lubimenko ...

(*In* Royal historical society, London. Transactions. London, 1871– 22cm. 4th ser., v. 7 (1924) p. 27–51)

Running title: Struggle for the Russian market.

Bibliographical foot-notes.

1. Netherlands — Commerce — Russia. 2. Russia — Commerce — Netherlands. 3. English in Russia. I. Title: Struggle for the Russian market.

A C 36-1641

Title from Newberry Library of Congress Libr. [DA20.R9 ser. 4, vol. 7]

(942.0062)

NL 0416069 ICN MB OCU

Lıūbimenko, Īnna Īvanovna (Borodina) 1878–

A suggestion for the publication of the correspondence of Queen Elizabeth with the Russian czars, by Inna Lubimenko ...

(*In* Royal historical society, London. Transactions. London, 1915. 22cm. 3d ser., v. 9, p. [111]–122)

1. Elizabeth, queen of England, 1533–1603. 2. Gt. Brit.—Foreign relations—Russia. 3. Russia—Foreign relations—Gt. Brit.

A C 36—1152

Newberry library for Library of Congress [DA20.R9 ser. 3, vol. 9]

[a40c1] (942.0062)

NL 0416070 ICN MB DLC

Lıūbimenko, Inna Ivanovna (Borodina), 1878-

Ученая корреспонденция Академии наук XVIII века, 1766–1782; научное описание, под общей ред. Д. С. Рождественского, под ред. Г. А. Князева и Л. Б. Модзалевского. Москва, Изд-во Академии наук СССР, 1937.

605 p. ports., facsims. 26 cm. (Академия наук Союза Советских Социалистических Республик. Труды Архива, вып. 2)

Pref. in Russian and French.

1. Akademiıā nauk SSSR — Hist. — Sources—Bibl. 2. Science—Bibl.—Catalogs. 3. Manuscripts. Russia—Catalogs. I. Rozhdestvenskiĭ, Dmitriĭ Sergeevich, 1876–1940. (Series: Akademiıā nauk SSSR. Arkhiv. Trudy, vyp. 2)

Title transliterated: Uchenaıā korrespondenfsiıā Akademii nauk.

AS262.A6135 no. 2 49-38487*

Z7409.L85

NL 0416071 DLC IU NNC IU

Lıūbimenko, Vladimir Nikolaevich, 1873–1937.

QK31 .B79U6 1942

U. S. *Work projects administration. Minnesota.*

... "A biographical history of plant physiology." Federal works agency, Minnesota work projects administration. University research project, Official project no. 165-1-71-124, State project no. 3-2171-50134, Sub-project no. 441. Sponsored by University of Minnesota, Department of agriculture, Saint Paul, Minnesota. [Saint Paul, 1942?]

Lıūbimenko, Vladimir Nikolaevich, 1873–1937.

Traité de botanique générale, par V. N. Lubimenko, traduit du russe par Mlle Anna Joukov, revu par MM. Ferdinand Lot ... [et] J. Friedel ... avec un préface de M. Molliard ... Paris, Gauthier-Villars et c^ie^, 1927–

v. illus. 24cm.

Bibliographies at end of sections.

1. Botany—Physiology. 2. Botany—Anatomy. [1, 2. Botany, Physiological and structural] I. Zhukova, Anna, tr. II. Lot, Ferdinand, 1866– III. Friedel, Jean, 1874–

Agr 28-616 Revised

Library, U. S. Dept. of Agriculture 463L74

NL 0416073 DNAL OU NIC

Lıūbimenko, Vladimir Nikolaevich, 1873-1937.

... Вегетацiонные опыты для опредѣленія вліянія химическихъ свойствъ почвъ и грунтовъ Велико-Анадольской лѣсной дачи на ростъ разведенныхъ въ степи лѣсныхъ породъ. С.-Петербургъ, Тип. М. А. Александрова, 1911.

1 p. l., 58 p. 25½cm. (... Лѣсной департаментъ. Труды по лѣсному опытному дѣлу въ Россіи. Выпускъ XXXIV)

Experiments for the determination of the influence of the chemical composition of the soil of the Veliko-Anadol'sk forest reserve upon the growth of forests on the steppes.

1. [Forest soils] 2. Soils—Russia. [2. Russia—Soils]

Agr 12-1217 Revised

Library, U. S. Dept. of Agriculture 57L74

NL 0416074 DNAL

Любимецъ Фортуны. Переводъ съ французскаго. Въ Москвѣ, Иждивенiемъ Н. Новикова, въ Унив. тип., 1782.

2 v. in 1. 17 cm.

Translated by Ivan Zakharov. Cf. V. S. Sopikov. Опытъ россійской библіографіи. 1904.

Title transliterated: Lıūbimets Fortuny.

PQ1947.A2L48 55-46651

NL 0416075 DLC

Lıūbımov, A. A., joint ed.

Utevskiĭ, Boris Samoĭlovich, *comp.*

... Борьба с детской беспризорностью; под редакцией Я. А. Перель и А. А. Любимова, с предисловием ... Н. А. Семашко, составил Б. С. Утевский. Москва [etc.] Наркомпрос РСФСР, Государственное учебно-педагогическое издательство, 1932.

Lıūbımov, A. A., joint ed.

Utevskiĭ, Boris Samoĭlovich, *comp.*

... Детский дом; под редакцией Я. А. Перель и А. А. Любимова, с предисловием ... Н. К. Крупской, составил Б. С. Утевский. Москва [etc.] Наркомпрос РСФСР, Государственное учебно-педагогическое издательство, 1932.

Lıūbımov, A. A., joint ed.

Iākovlev, Vasiliĭ Georgievich, *comp.*

... Детское коммунистическое движение; под редакцией Я. А. Перель и А. А. Любимова, с предисловием ... В. Г. Золотухина, составил В. Г. Яковлев, со вступительной статьей В. Г. Яковлева. Москва [etc.] Наркомпрос РСФСР, Государственное учебно-педагогическое издательство, 1932.

Lıūbımov, A. A., joint ed.

Ansheles, Iosif Isaakovich, *comp.*

... Красная армия и дети; под редакцией Я. А. Перель и А. А. Любимова, с предисловием ... С. Н. Орловского, составили: И. И. Аншелес, С. Д. Бейненсон [!], Б. С. Утевский. Москва [etc.] Наркомпрос РСФСР, Государственное учебно-педагогическое издательство. 1932.

Lıūbımov, A. A., joint ed.

Utevskiĭ, Boris Samoĭlovich, *comp.*

... Несовершеннолетние правонарушители; с предисловием ... П. А. Красикова, составил Б. С. Утевский, с вступительной статьей Б. С. Утевского. Москва [etc.] Наркомпрос РСФСР, Государственное учебно-педагогическое издательство, 1932.

Lıūbımov, A. A., joint ed.

Utevskiĭ, Boris Samoĭlovich, *comp.*

... Общество "Друг детей"; под редакцией Я. А. Перель и А. А. Любимова, с предисловием А. С. Бубнова (речь на съезде Общества "Друг детей" 24 мая 1931 г.) составил Б. С. Утевский. Москва [etc.] Наркомпрос РСФСР, Государственное учебно-педагогическое издательство, 1932.

Lıūbımov, A. A., joint ed.

Benenson, Sof'ıā Davidovna, *comp.*

... Охрана материнства и младенчества; под редакцией Я. А. Перель и А. А. Любимова, с предисловием ... А. П. Богат, составила С. Д. Бененсон, с вступительной статьей С. Д. Бененсон. Москва [etc.] Наркомпрос РСФСР, Государственное учебно-педагогическое издательство, 1932.

Lıūbımov, A. A., joint ed.

Vishnıāk, Vera Iosifovna, *comp.*

... Правовое положение ребенка в семье; под редакцией Я. А. Перель и А. А. Любимова, с предисловием ... Н. Н. Овсянникова, составила В. И. Вишняк, с вступительной статьей В. И. Вишняк. Москва [etc.] Наркомпрос [РСФСР] Государственное учебно-педагогическое издательство, 1932.

Lıūbımov, A. A., joint ed.

Utevskiĭ, Boris Samoĭlovich, *comp.*

... Преступления против несовершеннолетних; под редакцией Я. А. Перель и А. А. Любимова, с предисловием ... Л. М. Субоцкого, составил Б. С. Утевский, с вступительной статьей Б. С. Утевского. Москва [etc.] Наркомпрос РСФСР, Государственное учебно-педагогическое издательство, 1932.

VOLUME 336

Liubimov, A. A., joint ed.

Benenson, Sof'ia Davidovna, *comp.*
... Социальное обеспечение детей; под редакцией Я. А. Перель и А. А. Любимова, с предисловием ... И. А. Наговицына, составила С. Д. Бененсон, со вступительной статьей С. Д. Бененсон. Москва [etc.] Наркомпрос РСФСР, Государственное учебно-педагогическое издательство, 1932.

Liubimov, A. L., joint author.

TN85 .M43 vol. 35 **Dvorshchan, Evgenii Il'ich,** *fl.* 1934–
Барит. Е. И. Дворщан и А. Л. Любимов. Baryte. Ленинград, Глав. ред. геолого-разведочной и геодезической лит-ры, 1935.

Liubimov, Anatolii Nikolaevich.
Торгово-финансовый план магазина. Москва, Госторгиздат, 1952.
154 p. 22 cm.

1. Retail trade—Russia. I. Title.
Title romanized: Torgovo-finansovyi plan magazina.

HF5349.R9L58 54-20582 rev

NL 0416087 DLC

Liubimov, B.
Michal Fokin. [Z ruského originálu preložil Silvc Mikuš] Bratislava, Práca, 1949.
92 p. 16 cm. (Edícia Hrdinovia práce, sv. 4)

I. Title.

PG3476.L647M5 55-24412

NL 0416088 DLC

DK511 .U7L5

Liubimov, B
На Южном Урале. [Чкалов] Чкаловское изд-во, 1947.
86 p. 20 cm.

1. Ural Mountains—Descr. & trav.
Title transliterated: Na IUzhnom Urale.

DK511.U7L5 50-37270

NL 0416089 DLC

Liubimov, B
Прикамские встречи. Рисунки Н. Никифорова. Москва, Гос. изд-во детской лит-ры, 1952.
219 p. illus. 22 cm. (Наша родина)

1. Kama Valley—Descr. & trav. I. Title.
Title transliterated: Prikamskie vstrechi.

DK511.K17L5 53-15619 ‡

NL 0416090 DLC

DK651 .O7L5

Liubimov, B
В устье Орь-реки. Рисунки К. Арцеулова. Москва, Гос. изд-во детской лит-ры, 1949.
178 p. illus. 22 cm. (Наша родина)

1. Orsk, Russia. (Series: Nasha rodina)
Title transliterated: V ust'e Or'-reki.

DK651.O7L5 50-18879

NL 0416091 DLC

Liubimov, D. A., ed.

TS225 .U7

Ural'skii mashinostroitel'nyi zavod, *Sverdlovsk.*
Ковка и штамповка; [сборник. Редактор Д. А. Любимов] Свердловск, Гос. научно-техн. изд-во машиностроит. и судостроит. лит-ры [Урало-Сибирское отд-ние] 1954.

Liubimov, Gavriil Markovich, 1820–1899.
Историческое обозрѣніе способовъ содержанія христіанскаго духовенства отъ временъ апостольскихъ до XVII–XVIII вѣка. Санктпетербургъ, Въ Тип. военно-учеб. заведеній, 1851.
181 p. 24 cm.

1. Clergy—Salaries, pensions, etc. 2. Orthodox Eastern Church—Clergy—Salaries, pensions, etc. I. Title.
Title transliterated: Istoricheskoe obozrienie sposobov soderzhaniia khristianskago dukhovenstva.

BV770.L55 55-15580 ‡

NL 0416093 DLC

Liubimov, Gavriil Markovich, 1820–1899.
Церковныя торжества въ Ораніенбаумѣ, въ 1857 году. С. Петербургъ, Тип. Королева, 1859.
32 p. 24 cm.

1. Lomonosov, Russia. TSerkov' Sviatyia Zhivonachal'nyia Troitsy. I. Title.
Title transliterated: TSerkovnyia torzhestva v Oranienbaumie.

BX590.L65L5 54-55388 ‡

NL 0416094 DLC

BX590 .L65L5 1859a

Liubimov, Gavriil Markovich, 1820–1899.
Церковныя торжества въ Ораніенбаумѣ въ 1857 году. Изд. 2. Санктпетербургъ, 1859.
32 p. illus. 25 cm.

1. Lomonosov, Russia. TSerkov' Sviatyia Zhivonachal'nyia Troitsy. I. Title.
Title transliterated: TSerkovnyia torzhestva v Oranienbaumie.

BX590.L65L5 1859a 60-56962 ‡

NL 0416095 DLC

TC187 .L5

Liubimov, I B
Пособие для лебёдчика днооуглубительного флота. Москва, Морской транспорт, 1950.
143 p. illus. 23 cm.
At head of title: И. В. Любимов и Г. И. Федченко.
Errata slip inserted.
Bibliography: p. [140]

1. Dredging. I. Fedchenko, G. I., joint author.
Title transliterated: Posobie dlia lebëdchika.

51-19397

NL 0416096 DLC

Liubimov, I I
Записка къ проекту Пермско-Уральской желѣзной дороги. Санктпетербургъ, Тип. А. Каспари, 1870.
161, 37, 24 p. 3 fold. col. maps. 24 cm.

1. Trans-Siberian Railroad. 2. Railroads—Ural Mountain region.
Title transliterated: Zapiska k proektu Permsko-Ural'skoi zheleznoi dorogi.

HE3380.T7L5 60-57505

NL 0416097 DLC

[Liubimov, Isidor Evstigneevich] 1882-

HD5515 L78.32 The consumers' cooperatives in the economics of the USSR. Moscow, Centrosoyuz, 1927.
56 p. 19cm.
"A slight modification of a lecture delivered by the president of the managing board of the Centrosoyuz, I.E. Liubimov, before the Czecho-Slovacian cooperative delegation in May 1927."-p.3
Imprinte on cover: Sentrosoyus.
1.Cooperation - Russia. I.TSentral'nyi soiuz potrebitel skikh obshchestv. II. Title.

NL 0416098 CSt-H CSt NNC

Liubimov, Isidor Evstigneevich.
Потребительская кооперация в социалистическом строительстве СССР. Москва, Центросоюз, 1928.
78 p. 19 cm.

1. Cooperation—Russia. I. Title.
Title transliterated: Potrebitel'skaia kooperatsiia.

HD3515.L56 54-47671

NL 0416099 DLC

HC335 .L583

Liubimov, Isidor Evstigneevich.
Задачи легкой промышленности в 1936 г. и развитие стахановского движения. Москва, Гизлегпром, 1936.
53 p. 22 cm.

1. Russia—Manuf. I. Title.
Title transliterated: Zadachi legkoi promyshlennosti.

HC335.L583 61-57692

NL 0416100 DLC

Liubimov, Ivan Lukich, joint comp.

Russia (*1917– R. S. F. S. R.*) *Laws, statutes, etc.*
Действующие распоряжения по милиции: постановления, циркуляры, приказы и инструкции; систематический сборник с пояснениями. Составили В. А. Померанцев и И. Л. Любимов, под редакцией ... И. Ф. Киселева. 2. изд., значительно переработанное. Москва, Издательства Народного комиссариата внутренних дел РСФСР, 1928.

Liubimov, Ivan Lukich, joint comp.

Law

Pomerantsev, Vladimir Aleksandrovich, *comp.*
... Инструкция о порядке исполнения органами милиции судебных решений, приказов, определений и приговоров, а также решений земельных комиссий и вынесенных в силу ст. 121–а УПК постановлений следственных органов, с постатейными к ней раз' яснениями, под редакцией И. Ф. Киселева. Москва, Издательство Народного комиссариата внутренних дел, 1928.

VOLUME 336

Lîûbimov, Îvan Lukich, joint ed.

Russia (*1917– R. S. F. S. R.*) *T͡Sentral'noe administrativnoe upravlenie. Otdel milit͡sii.*
... Инструкция органам милиции о порядке производства дознаний, с постатейными к ней раз'яснениями, под редакцией ... И. Ф. Киселева. Москва, Издательство Народного комиссариата внутренних дел, 1928.

Lîûbimov, N. I.

TN281
.M68

Moscow. Vsesoiûznyĭ nauchno-issledovatel'skiĭ institut mineral'nogo syr'îa.
Пособие по бурению разведочных скважин стальной дробью-сечкой. [Написано Н. И. Любимовым] Москва, Гос. научно-техн. изд-во лит-ры по геологии и охране недр, 1954.

UD252
.L58

Lîûbimov, N N
Оборона СД и действия артиллерии; под ред. А. К. Сивкова. Москва, Изд. Артакадемии, 1941.
169 p. illus. 23 cm.
At head of title: Артиллерийская ордена Ленина Академия Красной Армии имени Дзержинского.
Errata slip inserted.
Bibliography: p. [167]

1. Russia (1923– U. S. S. R.) Armiîa. Pekhota—Drill and tactics. 2. Attack and defense (Military science)
Title transliterated: Oborona SD i deĭstviîa artillerii.

UD252.L58 50-46226

NL 0416105 DLC

Lîûbimov, Nikolaĭ Alekseevich, 1828–1897.

B1848
.R8L58

Descartes, René, 1596–1650.
Философія Декарта; переводъ "Разсужденія о методѣ," съ поясненіями, изложеніе ученій Декарта о мірѣ и человѣкѣ. Н. А. Любимова. С.-Петербургъ, Тип. В. С. Балашева, 1886.

JA98
.K3L5

Lîûbimov, Nikolaĭ Alekseevich, 1828–1897.
Михаилъ Никифоровичъ Катковъ и его историческая заслуга; по документамъ и личнымъ воспоминаніямъ. С.-Петербургъ, Тип. Т-ва "Общественная польза," 1889.
356 p. illus. 22 cm.

1. Katkov, Mikhail Nikiforovich, 1818–1887.
Title transliterated: Mikhail Nikiforovich Katkov.

JA98.K3L5 54-49064 ‡

NL 0416107 DLC

Lîûbimov, Nikolaĭ Alekseevich, 1828–1897.
Мой вкладъ; статьи, записки, чтенія, замѣтки. Москва, Въ Унив. тип., 1881–
v. 25 cm.

1. Universities and colleges—Russia. I. Title.
Title transliterated: Moĭ vklad.

LA837.5.L5 60-56977

NL 0416108 DLC

Lîûbimov, Nikolaĭ Alekseevich, 1828–1897.
Жизнь и труды Ломоносова. Москва, Въ Унив. тип. (Катковъ и ко.) 1872–
v. illus., port. 19 cm.
At head of title, v. 1– : Лицей Цесаревича Николая.
Bibliographical footnotes.

1. Lomonosov, Mikhail Vasil'evich, 1711–1765. I. Title.
Title transliterated: Zhizn' i trudy Lomonosova.

CT1218.L6L55 66-45694

NL 0416109 DLC

Lîûbimov, Nikolaĭ Ivanovich.
(Tōshi Tetsudō ni kansuru Ryubimofu Kyōju ikensho)
東支鐵道ニ關スルリユビーモフ教授意見書
(一九二二年採筆) [哈爾濱] 滿鐵·北滿經濟調
査所 昭和12[1937]
25 l. 28 cm. (北經經濟資料 第55號)
Cover title.
本意見書ハ一九二三年ニ在哈爾濱蘇聯總領事館へ送付シテ來タモノ

1. Chinese Eastern Railway. I. Minami Manshū Tetsudō Kabushiki Kaisha. Hokuman Keizai Chōsajo. II. Title. III. Series: Minami Manshū Tetsudō Kabushiki Kaisha. Hokuman Keizai Chōsajo. Hokkei keizai shiryō, dai 55-gō.

HE3290.C45L54 72-802041

NL 0416111 DLC

4HD
3205

Lîubimov, Nikolaĭ Nikolaevich
L'activité des concessions étrangères en U. R. S. S. Paris, 1929.
21 p.

NL 0416112 DLC-P4

Lîûbimov, Nikolaĭ Nikolaevich.
... Экономические проблемы Дальнего Востока (Вост. Китайская жел. дор.). Москва [Типография ЦУП ВСНХ] 1925.
49, [3] p. 22½cm.
At head of title: Центральное управление печати ВСНХ СССР. Н. Н. Любимов.
"Источники и материалы": p. [50]

1. Chinese eastern railway. 2. Manchuria—Econ. condit. I. Russia (1923– U. S. S. R.) Vyssbiĭ sovet narodnogo khozîaĭstva. T͡Sentral'noe upravlenie pechati. I. Title.

42-26536
Provisional

Library of Congress HC428.M3L5

NL 0416113 DLC

Lîûbimov, Nikolaĭ Nikolaevich, *ed.*
Финансовые системы иностранных государств ... Для финансово-экономических институтов. Москва, Госфиниздат, 1947.
244 p. 23 cm.

1. Finance. I. Title.
Title transliterated: Finansovye sistemy inostrannykh gosudarstv.

48-16070*

NL 0416114 DLC

Lîûbimov, Nikolaĭ Nikolaevich.

HJ191
R92M6

Moscow. Finansovo-ėkonomicheskiĭ institut.
Финансы капиталистических государств. Составлена бригадой МФЭИ под руководством Любимова Н. Н., под ред. Д. А. Буткова. Москва, Госфиниздат, 1934.

Lîûbimov, Nikolaĭ Nikolaevich.
Международный государственный кредит (1919–1943) Экономические и правовые проблемы. Под ред. М. И. Боголепова. [Москва] Госфиниздат, 1944.
96 p. 22 cm.

1. Banks and banking. 2. Loans. 3. Foreign exchange. I. Bogolepov, Mikhail Ivanovich, 1879– ed. II. Title.
Title transliterated: Mezhdunarodnyĭ gosudarstvennyĭ kredit.

HG3881.L5 49-31646

NL 0416116 DLC

Lîûbimov, Nikolaĭ Nikolaevich.
Международный капиталистический кредит—орудие империалистической агрессии. Москва, Госфиниздат, 1951.
166 p. 23 cm.
Errata slip inserted.

1. Debts, Public. 2. Economic policy. 3. Economic assistance, American. I. Title.
Title transliterated: Mezhdunarodnyĭ kapitalisticheskiĭ kredit.

HJ8083.L5 51-35201

NL 0416117 DLC OrU

Lîûbimov, Nikolaĭ Nikolaevich, ed.

HG221
.K8

Krotkov, Vasiliĭ Tikhonovich.
Очерки по денежному обращению и кредиту иностранных государств [учебное пособие] для финансово-экономических и кредитно-экономических институтов. Под ред. Н. Н. Любимова. Москва, Госфиниздат, 1947.

HF3626
.M58

Lîûbimov, Nikolaĭ Nikolaevich, ed.

Moscow. Institut vneshneĭ torgovli.
Внешняя торговля СССР. Под ред. А. М. Смирнова и Н. Н. Любимова. Москва, Внешторгиздат, 1954.

Lîûbimov, Nikolaĭ Pavlovich.
Таблицы процентных отношений (при трехзначных делителях, оканчивающихся на нуль) Москва, Гос. статистическое изд-во, 1955.
94 p. 17 cm.

1. Percentage I. Title.
Title transliterated: Tablit͡sy prot͡sentnykh otnosheniĭ.

HF5695.L5 57-26139 ‡

NL 0416120 DLC

Lîûbimov, Sergeĭ Petrovich.
Комсомольцам об Уставе КПСС. [Москва] Молодая гвардия, 1954.
125 p. 14 cm.

1. Kommunisticheskaîa partiîa Sovetskogo Soîuza. Ustav. 2. Vsesoîuznyĭ leninskiĭ kommunisticheskiĭ soîuz molodezhi. I. Title.
Title transliterated: Komsomol'tsam ob Ustave KPSS.

JN6598.K7L5 55-37835 rev

NL 0416121 DLC

VOLUME 336

Lfubimov, Sergeĭ Petrovich.
Речь В. И. Ленина на III Съезде комсомола "Задачи союзов молодежи." Стенограмма публичной лекции, прочитанной в Москве. Москва ‹Правда› 1949.
24 p. 22 cm.
At head of title: Всесоюзное общество по распространению политических и научных знаний.

1. Lenin, Vladimir Il'ich, 1870-1924. Zadachi soiuzov molodezhi. *Title transliterated:* Rech' V. I. Lenina na tret'em S"ezde komsomola.

HQ799.R9L53 52-17948 rev

NL 0416122 DLC

Lfubimova, Serafima Timofeevna, joint ed.

Vladimirov, Nikolaĭ Vasil'evich, *comp.*
... Справочник сельского совета; основные законы, инструкции и распоряжения о работе сельсоветов, составили: Н. В. Владимиров и А. В. Цейтлин, под редакцией: Б. В. Гибера, С. Т. Любимовой и Г. С. Михайлова. ‹Москва› Издание Московского облисполкома, 1930.

Lfubimova, Serafima Timofeevna.
Во имя победы; под ред. З. А. Гуриной. ‹Москва› Московский рабочий, 1947.
154 p. illus. 21 cm.
At head of title: С. Любимова, М. Рыбченкова.

1. Russia—Manuf. 2. World War, 1939-1945—Economic aspects—Russia. I. Rybchenkova, M., joint author. II. Title. *Title transliterated:* Vo imfa pobedy.

HD9735.R92L5 48-16074*‡

NL 0416124 DLC

SK602 R8L5

Lfubimova, V
Soviet children at summer camp. Moscow, Foreign Languages Pub. House, 1955.
39 p. illus.

At head of title: V. Lubimova.

1. Camping - Russia. 2. Children - Russia. I. Title.

NL 0416125 CU MH

Lfubimova, V V
Экономика Франции и положение трудящихся масс после Второй Мировой войны. Москва, Изд-во Академии наук СССР, 1952.
346 p. 23 cm.
At head of title: Академия наук СССР. Институт экономики.
Errata slip inserted.

1. Labor and laboring classes—France. 2. France—Econ. condit.—1945- I. Title. *Title transliterated:* Ėkonomika Frantsii ... posle Vtoroĭ Mirovoĭ voĭny.

HD8430.L5 53-37056

NL 0416126 DLC

Lfubimova, V. V., tr.

Тресты-миллиардеры во Франции. Перевод с французского В. В. Любимовой. Москва, Изд-во иностранной лит-ры, 1953.

Lfubimova, V V
Die Wirtschaft Frankreichs und die Lage der Werktätigen nach dem zweiten Weltkrieg. ‹Aus dem Russischen ins Deutsche übertragen von H. Heine und M. Brehm› Berlin, Verlag Tribüne, 1955.
195 p. 21 cm.

1. Labor and laboring classes—France. 2. France—Econ. condit.—1945- I. Title.

HD8430.L514 57-29247 ‡

NL 0416128 DLC NN NIC ICU

PG3476 .L65A19 1955

Lfubimova, Valentina Aleksandrovna, 1895-
Пьесы. Москва, Гос. изд-во детской лит-ры, 1955.
288 p. illus. 21 cm.
CONTENTS.—Сережа Стрельцов.—В начале мая.—Снежок.—В стороне.—Письмо в редакцию.

Title transliterated: P'esy.

PG3476.L65A19 1955 56-56563 ‡

NL 0416129 DLC

Lfubimova, Valentina Aleksandrovna, 1895-
Под солнечным небом; пьеса в четырех действиях, шести картинах. Москва, Искусство, 1952.
134 p. 14 cm.

I. Title. *Title transliterated:* Pod solnechnym nebom.

PG3476.L65P6 52-41865 rev ‡

NL 0416130 DLC

Lfubimova, Valentina Aleksandrovna, 1895-
Сережа Стрельцов; пьеса для подростков из школьной жизни в 4 действиях, 6 картинах. Москва, Искусство; ‹etc.› 1937.
94, ‹2› p. 17 cm.

I. Title. *Title transliterated:* Serezha Strel'fsov.

PZ67.L5 49-31713 rev

NL 0416131 DLC

Любимые мелодии; альбом популярных пьес для духового оркестра художественной самодеятельности. Москва, Гос. музыкальное изд-во, 19
miniature score (v.) and parts. 22 cm.
Arrangements for band.

1. Band music, Arranged—Scores and parts. *Title transliterated:* Lfubimye melodii.

M1200.L 64-46958/M

NL 0416132 DLC

PL314 .Z95R9 1945

Любимый Вождь; стихи поэтов южного Азербайджана. Баку, Азернешр, 1945.
50 p. port. 19 cm.

1. Azerbaijani poetry—Translations into Russian. 2. Russian poetry—Translations from Azerbaijani. 3. Stalin, Iosif, 1879- —Poetry. *Title transliterated:* Lfubimyĭ Vozhd'.

PL314.Z95R9 1945 51-19363

NL 0416133 DLC

Lfubinskaia, L M
Горючие газы и их сжигание в бытовых приборах. Москва, Гос. науч.-техн. изд-во нефтяной и горно-топливной лит-ры, 1946.
94 p. illus. 20 cm.
At head of title: Л. М. Любинская и Л. К. Пташный.

1. Gas—Heating and cooking. I. Ptashnyĭ, L. K., joint author. *Title transliterated:* Gorfuchie gazy i ikh szhiganie.

TH7453.L5 50-18997

NL 0416134 DLC

U115 .R9L48

Любить и уважать командира и комиссара, грудью защищать их в бою. Москва, Гос. воен. изд-во, 1940.
29 p. 17 cm. (Библиотека красноармейца)

1. Russia (1923- U. S. S. R.) Armiia—Handbooks, manuals, etc. (Series: Biblioteka krasnoarmeitsa) *Title transliterated:* Lfubit' i uvazhat' komandira.

U115.R9L48 50-48948

NL 0416135 DLC

Liubitskaia, L I Savich-
see Savich-Liubitskaia, Lidiia Ivanovna.

Liubitskaia, Lidiia Ivanovna
see Savich-Liubitskaia, Lidiia Ivanovna.

Lfubits'kyĭ, O., joint comp.

Russia (*1923- U. S. S. R.*) *Laws, statutes, etc.*
Фінансовий контроль. Збірка законодавчих актів і відомчих матеріалів. Упорядкували Д. Герцізон, О. Любицький. Київ, Укрфілія Держфінвидавництва СРСР, 1936.

Lfubker, Fridrikh
see
Lübker, Friedrich Heinrich Christian, 1811-1867.

Lfubliana
see Ljubljana.

Lfublianski bŭlgarski pametnik
see Lfublianski bŭlgarski rŭkopis.

Lfublianski bŭlgarski rŭkopis.
Люблянскиять български ржкопись отъ XVII вѣкъ, отъ С. Аргировъ. София, Държавна печатница, 1896.
‹463›-500 p. 27 cm.
Cover title.
"Отдѣлень отпечатъкъ отъ 'Сборникъ за народни умотворения, наука и книжнина,' кн. XII."

Microfilm 12658 BX

LC copy replaced by microfilm

1. Theology—Collections—Orthodox Eastern authors. I. Argirov, Stoian, 1870- ed. *Title transliterated:* Lfublianskiiat bŭlgarski rŭkopis.

BX250.L58 50-49608

NL 0416142 DLC

VOLUME 336

DK511 .C5D3

Li͡ublin, I. V.

Danilov, D D

... Советская Чувашия; национально-культурное строительство ... Москва, Коммунистическая академия. Институт литературы и искусства. Секция литературы СССР, Соцэкгиз, 1933.

Li͡ublino, *Russia*
see **Lyublino,** *Russia.*

Li͡ublinskai͡a, Aleksandra Dmitrievna.

Источниковедение истории Средних веков. Допущено в качестве учеб. пособия для гос. университетов. ₍Ленинград₎ Изд-во Ленинградского университета, 1955.

372 p. 27 cm.

Errata slip inserted at end of book.
Bibliography: p. ₍859₎-866.

1. Middle Ages—Historiography. I. Title.
Title transliterated: Istochnikovedenie istorii Srednikh vekov.

D116.L5 56-37798

NL 0416145 DLC CLSU NNC CtY

Li͡ublinskai͡a, Anna Aleksandrovna.
₍Detskiĭ sad i shkola₎
Детский сад и школа; сборник статей. Москва, Изд-во Академии педагог. наук РСФСР, 1954.

158 p. illus. 20 cm.

At head of title: Академия педагогических наук РСФСР. Ленинградский институт педагогики.

1. Kindergarten. I. Akademii͡a pedagogicheskikh nauk RSFSR, Moscow. Institut pedagogiki, Leningrad. II. Title.

LB1167.L5 56-42990 ‡

rev

NL 0416146 DLC

Li͡ublinskiĭ, Isaak Vasil'evich
see **Li͡ublinskiĭ, Isaĭ Vasil'evich,** 1844-1902.

Li͡ublinskii, Isaĭ Vasil'evich, 1844-1902, comp.

Russia. *Laws, statutes, etc.*

Сравнительный Уставъ о векселяхъ. Томъ XI Св. зак. ст. 540-684, съ разъясненіями по рѣшеніямъ Гражданскаго Кассаціоннаго, Четвертаго и Общихъ собраній департаментовъ Правительствующаго Сената и съ сравнительнымъ изложеніемъ постановленій нынѣ дѣйствующихъ во всѣхъ иностранныхъ государствахъ вексельныхъ уставовъ. Составилъ И. В. Люблинскій. С.-Петербургъ, Тип. И. С. Леви, 1887.

HV9076 .L5

Li͡ublinskiĭ, Pavel Isaevich, 1882-1939.

... Борьба с преступностью в детском и юношеском возрасте. (Социально-правовые очерки) Москва ₍Юридическое издательство Н.К.Ю.₎ 1923.

300, ₍2₎ p. 23cm.

At head of title: П. И. Люблинский ...
Bibliographical foot-notes.

1. Juvenile delinquency. I. Title.
Title transliterated: Bor'ba s prestupnost'i͡u.

44-43328

Library of Congress HV9076.L5

NL 0416149 DLC

Li͡ublinskiĭ, Pavel Isaevich, 1882-1939.

LAW

Moscow. Gosudarstvennyĭ institut po izuchenii͡u prestupnosti i prestupnika.

... Карательная политика капиталистических стран; сборник статей. ₍Москва₎ Государственное издательство Советское законодательство, 1933.

Li͡ublinskiĭ, Pavel Isaevich, 1882-1939.

... Международные съѣзды по вопросамъ уголовнаго права за десять лѣтъ (1905-1915). Петроградъ, Сенатская типографія, 1915.

vi, 379 p. 25½cm.

At head of title: Проф. П. И. Люблинскій.

1. Criminal law—Congresses. 2. Prisons—Congresses. 3. Criminal anthropology—Congresses.

42-26513

NL 0416151 DLC

Li͡ublinskiĭ, Pavel Isaevich, 1882-1939.

... На смѣну стараго права. Сборникъ статей по вопросамъ текущей правовой жизни. Петроградъ, Типо-литографія Руманова, 1915.

1 p. l., iii, 433, ₍1₎ p. 25½cm.

At head of title: Проф. П. И. Люблинскій.

1. Law—Russia—Addresses, essays, lectures. I. Title.

42-26514

NL 0416152 DLC

Li͡ublinskiĭ, Pavel Isaevich, 1882-1939.

Памяти трехъ русскихъ криминалистовъ: И. Я. Фойницкаго, Д. А. Дриля, Н. Д. Сергѣевскаго. С.-Петербургъ, Сенатская тип., 1914.

151 p. 23 cm.

Bibliographical footnotes.

1. Foĭnit͡skiĭ, Ivan I͡Akovlevich, 1847-1913. 2. Dril', Dmitriĭ Andreevich, 1846-1910. 3. Sergeevskiĭ, Nikolaĭ Dmitrievich, 1849-1908. I. Title. *Title transliterated:* Pami͡ati trekh russkikh kriminalistov.

56-53366

NL 0416153 DLC

Li͡ublinskiĭ, Pavel Isaevich, 1882-1939.

... Полиция, суд и тюрьмы Америки. ₍Москва, Государственное издательство Советское законодательство, 1933₎

151, ₍1₎ p. incl. front., illus. (map) col. plates. 23cm.

At head of title: П. И. Люблинский.
On recto of frontispiece: Государственный институт по изучению преступности.
"Книга ... представляет собою объединенные три доклада, прочитанные автором этой весной в секции уголовной политики капиталистических стран Государственного института по изучению преступности."—Предисловие.
Bibliography at the end of each chapter.

Contents.—Волков, Г. И. Предисловие.—Разложение полиции, обвинительного и судебного аппарата в САСШ.—Уголовная юстиция и внесудебная репрессия в отношении негров в САСШ.—Североамериканская пенитенциария последних лет.

1. Justice, Administration of—U. S. 2. Police—U. S. 3. Courts—U. S. 4. Prisons—U. S. I. Volkov, Grigoriĭ Ivanovich, 1892- II. Moscow. Gosudarstvennyĭ institut po izuchenii͡u prestupnosti i prestupnika. III. Title.

37-32990

NL 0416155 DLC

Li͡ublinskiĭ, Pavel Isaevich, 1882-1939.

Право амнистіи; историко-догматическое и политическое изслѣдованіе П. И. Люблинскаго. ₍С.-Петербургъ, Сенатская типографія₎ 1907.

1 p. l., viii, ₍3₎-363 p. 25cm.

1. Amnesty. 2. Amnesty—Russia. I. Title.

42-26515

NL 0416156 DLC

Li͡ublinskiĭ, Pavel Isaevich, 1882-1939.

... Преступления в области половых отношений. Москва ₍etc.₎ Издательство Л. Д. Френкель, 1925.

245, ₍1₎ p. 21cm.

At head of title: Проф. П. И. Люблинский.
"Литература по вопросу о половых преступлениях": p. 243-245.

1. Criminal law—Russia. 2. Sexual ethics. 3. Sexual perversion. 4. Prostitution—Russia. I. Title.

34-39020

NL 0416157 DLC

BF1569 .L5

Li͡ublinskiĭ, Pavel Isaevich, 1882-1939.

Процессы о вѣдовствѣ въ Англіи и судъ присяжныхъ. ₍С.-Петербургъ, 1913₎

₍193₎-259 p. 24 cm.

Caption title.
Detached from Журналъ Министерства народнаго просвѣщенія, no. 10, 1913.
Bibliographical footnotes.

1. Witchcraft. I. Title.
Title transliterated: Prot͡sessy o vi͡edovstvi͡e v Anglii i sud prisi͡azhnykh.

BF1569.L5 55-51186

NL 0416158 DLC

Liublinskii, Pavel Isaevich, 1882-1939.
The struggle against juvenile delinquency Moscow, 1923.
300 p. 1 l. 22½ cm.

NL 0416159 DL

Li͡ublinskiĭ, Pavel Isaevich, 1882-1939, ed.

Schneickert, Hans, 1876-

... Тайна преступника и пути к ее раскрытию. (К учению о судебных доказательствах). Перевод с немецкого под редакцией П. И. Люблинского. Москва, Издательство "Право и жизнь", 1925.

Li͡ublinskiĭ, Pavel Isaevich, 1882-1939.

... Техника, толкованіе и казуистика Уголовнаго кодекса. Пособіе къ практическимъ занятіямъ по уголовному праву. Петроградъ, Типо-лит. Руманова, 1917.

1 p. l., 267, ₍1₎ p. 23½cm.

At head of title: П. И. Люблинскій.

1. Criminal law—Russia. I. Title.

34-39021

NL 0416161 DLC

VOLUME 336

Lfublinskiĭ, Pavel Isaevich, 1882–1939.
Цѣли наказанія ₍сборникъ статей₎ СПБ, Образованіе, 1914.
135 p. 20 cm. (Новыя идеи въ правовѣдѣніи, сборникъ 1)
Bound with Prins, Adolphe. Защита общества и преобразованіе уголовнаго права. Москва, 1912. Copy 2.

1. Punishment. 2. Punishment—Russia. I. Title. (Series: Novyia idei v pravovîedîenii, sbornik 1)
Title transliterated: Tsîeli nakazaniîa.

HV8675.L75 54-49238

NL 0416162 DLC

Lfublinskiĭ, Pavel Isaevich, 1882–1939. ed.

Russia (1918– (R. S. F. S. R.)) *Laws, statutes, etc.*
Уголовно-процессуальный кодекс. Научно-популярный практический комментарий профессоров П. И. Люблинского и Н. Н. Полянского. ₍2. переработанное и дополненное изд.₎ Москва, Кооперативное издательство "Право и жизнь", 1928.

Lfublinskiĭ, Pavel Isaevich, 1882–1939.
... Условное осуждение в иностранном и советском праве. Москва, Издательство "Право и жизнь", 1924.
127, ₍1₎ p. 22cm.
At head of title: Издательство "Право и жизнь" под общей редакцией профессоров А. М. Винавера, М. Н. Гернета и А. Н. Трайнина. Проф. П. И. Люблинский.

1. Probation. 2. Probation—Russia. 3. Indeterminate sentence. 4. Indeterminate sentence—Russia. I. Title.

34-39022

NL 0416164 DLC

H8 .V6 Lfublinskiĭ, Pavel Isaevich, 1882-1939, ed.

Вопросы обществовѣдѣнія. 1–
С.-Петербургъ, 1908–

Lfublinskiĭ, Vladimir Sergîeevich.

Petrograd. Publichnaia biblioteka.
... Спутник читателя и посетителя. Составил библиотекарь В. С. Люблинский. Ленинград, Издание Государств. публичной библиотеки, 1930.

PQ2122 .A5 Lfublinskiĭ, Vladimir Sergoevich.

Akademiia nauk SSSR.
Вольтер; статьи и материалы, под ред. В. П. Волгина. Москва, 1948.

Lfubomirov, N I
XV Олимпийские игры. Москва, Физкультура и спорт, 1955.
327 p. illus. 21 cm.

1. Olympic Games, Helsingfors, 1952. I. Title.
Title transliterated: Piatnadtsatye Olimpiiskie igry.

GV722 1952.L57 56-57513 ‡

NL 0416168 DLC

Liubomirov, V I
Sport and physical culture in the U.S.S.R. [L, 1955]
1, xiv p. illus. (Soviet news booklet, 10)

NL 0416169 MH

Lfubomirov, Pavel Grigor'evich, 1885–1935.
Очерк истории Нижегородского ополчения 1611–1613 гг. Переиздание. Москва, Гос. социально-экон. изд-во, 1939.
339 p. 23 cm.

1. Russia—Hist.—Epoch of confusion, 1605–1613. 2. Gorki, Russia—Hist. I. Title.
Title transliterated: Ocherki istorii Nizhegorodskogo opolchenila.

DK111.L55 53-55839 ‡

NL 0416170 DLC OrU ViU CSt OOxM

TN85 .L5 Lfubomirov, Pavel Grigor'evich, 1885–1935.
Очерки по истории металлургической и металлообрабатывающей промышленности в России (XVII, XVIII и нач. XIX вв.). Географическое размещение металлопромышленности. ₍Ленинград₎ Гос. социально-экон. изд-во, 1937.
304 p. fold. maps. 20 cm.
Added t. p. in French.
Continuation of the author's Очерки по истории русской промышленности, published in Moscow, 1930.
Bibliographical references included in "Примечания" (p. 241–₍281₎)
1. Mineral industries—Russia. 2. Metallurgy. I. Title.
Title transliterated: Ocherki po istorii metallurgicheskoĭ i metalloobrabatyvaiushcheĭ promyshlennosti.

TN85.L5 52-55499

NL 0416171 DLC NN

HC333 .L52 Lfubomirov, Pavel Grigor'evich, 1885–1935.
Очерки по истории русской промышленности в XVIII и начале XIX вв.: организационная структура промышленных предприятий. ₍Москва₎ Прибой, 1930.
198 p. 21 cm.

1. Russia—Indus.—Hist. I. Title.
Title transliterated: Ocherki po istorii russkoĭ promyshlennosti.

HC333.L52 52-51986

NL 0416172 DLC

Lfubomirov, Pavel Grigor'evich, 1885–1935.
Очерки по истории русской промышленности; XVII, XVIII и начало XIX века. ₍Под общей ред. С. Г. Струмилина₎ ₍Москва₎ Гос. изд-во полит. лит-ры, 1947.
763 p. 23 cm.
Errata slip inserted.
Bibliographical footnotes.

1. Russia—Indus.—Hist. I. Strumilin, Stanislav Gustavovich, 1877– ed.
Title transliterated: Ocherki po istorii russkoĭ promyshlennosti.

HC333.L5 48-16048*

NL 0416173 DLC FU OrU CaBVaU

Lfubomirskiĭ, O
Михоэлс. Москва, "Искусство"; ₍etc.₎ 1938.
113, ₍3₎ p. front. (port.) illus. 20 cm.

1. Mikhoėls, Solomon Mikhaĭlovich, 1890–
Title transliterated: Mikhoėls.

PN2728.M5L5 49-31696

NL 0416174 DLC

Lfubomudrov, Sergeĭ Ivanovich, 1862–
Античные мотивы въ поэзіи Пушкина. С. Любомудровъ. Изд. 2. С.-Петербургъ, Типографія Н. Н. Клобукова, 1901.
68 p., 1 l. 17cm.

1. Pushkin, Aleksandr Sergeevich, 1799–1837. I. Title.

37-31009

NL 0416175 DLC

PG 3360 .Z8 L5 1901a Lfubomudrov, Sergeĭ Ivanovich, 1862–
Античные мотивы въ поэзіи Пушкина. С. Любомудровъ. Изд. 2. С.-Петербургъ, Типографія Н. Н. Клобукова, 1901.
68 p., 1 l. 17cm.

Photocopy. Ann Arbor, Mich., University Microfilms, 1966. On double leaves.

NL 0416176 OU RPB NBuU

PN3191 .R8G7 Lfubomudrov, Sergeĭ Ivanovich, 1862–

Gringmut, Vladimir Andreevich, 1851–1907.
Ученическіе спектакли въ женской классической гимназіи; статьи по поводу этихъ спектаклей В. А. Грингмута, Н. П. Шепелева и С. И. Любомудрова. Москва, Печатня А. И. Снегиревой, 1897.

HD9045 .R92N65 Lfubomudrov, V
Хлебное дело Северо-Кавказского края; пособие для работников по хлебному делу. Предисл. С. Гроссмана. Ростов н-Д., Северный Кавказ, 1928.
95 p. 23 cm.
At head of title: В. Любомудров. А. Мальцев. А. Никулин.

1. Grain trade—Caucasus, Northern. I. Title.
Title transliterated: Khlebnoe delo Severo-Kavkazskogo kraia.

51-50778

NL 0416177 DLC

TJ1280 .L55 Lfubomudrov, V N
Абразивные инструменты и их изготовление. Допущено в качестве учебника для станкостроит. и машиностроит. техникумов. Москва, Гос. научно-техн. изд-во машиностроит. и судостроит. лит-ры, 1953.
376 p. illus. 23 cm.
At head of title: В. Н. Любомудров, Н. Н. Васильев, Б. И. Фальковский.
Errata slip inserted.
Bibliography: p. ₍371₎–372.
1. Abrasives. 2. Grinding wheels. I. Vasil'ev, Nikolaĭ Nikolaevich. II. Title. *Title transliterated:* Abrazivnye instrumenty.

TJ1280.L55 54-35343

NL 0416178 DLC

Slavic-American Imprints Coll. 430.22 L58 Ljubomyrskyj, Stepan.
Zhorstoki svitanky; roman (v dvokh tshastynakh) Winnipeg, Novyj shlakh, 1947.
2 v. 23 cm. (Zhorstoki svitanky; druha tshastyna)
English translation of title: The cruel day-breaks; a novel (in two volumes)
rw

NL 0416179 IEdS

VOLUME 336

Liubomyrs'kyi, Stepan.
(Plem'ía vovkiv)
Плем'я вовків; роман. Вінніпег, Накладом і друком Нового шляху, 1951.
575 p. 20 cm.

1. World War, 1939-1945—Ukraine—Fiction. I. Title.

PG3979.L5P5 73-215483

NL 0416180 DLC

Любопытная; комедія въ двухъ дѣйствіяхъ. Въ Москвѣ, Въ Унив. тип. у Н. Новикова, 1780.
90 p. 19 cm.

Title transliterated: Líùbopytnaía.

PQ1947.A2L5 52-49544

NL 0416181 DLC

Любопытной, загадчивой, угадчивой и предсказчивой мѣсяцословъ на 1796 годъ и на слѣдующія. Для молодыхъ красавицъ. Въ Санктпетербургѣ, Иждивеніемъ I. К. Шнора.
100 p. front. 18 cm.
L. C. copy imperfect: date erased, then added in manuscript.
Dedication signed: Н. О.
Text, accompanying the calendar, translated from the German by Nikolaĭ Osipov; translation by G. Gromov of the same text included in Календарь на 1799 годъ стараго цыгана, ворожеи, угадчика. Cf. V. S. Sopikov. Опытъ россійской библіографіи, 1904, № 6385.

1. Almanacs, Russian. I. Osipov, Nikolaĭ Petrovich, 1751-1799, tr.
Title transliterated: Líùbopytnoĭ, zagadchivoĭ, ugadchivoĭ i predskazchivoĭ mîesíàtsoslov.

AY941.L5 60-59146

NL 0416182 DLC

Любопытный мѣсяцословъ московскій и Всероссійскія церкви, заключающій въ себѣ ... Господскіе, Богородичные праздники и всѣхъ святыхъ. На сей 1794 годъ. Москва, Въ Унив. тип., у Ридигера и Клаудія, 1794.
158, 399 p. 19 cm.
"Опытъ историческаго словаря всѣмъ монастырямъ, находящимся въ Россіи": p. 1-399.

1. Orthodox Eastern Church, Russian—Yearbooks. 2. Monasteries—Russia.
Title transliterated: Líùbopytnyĭ mîesíàtsoslov moskovskiĭ i Vserossiĭskíà tserkvi.

BX475.L5 55-51842

NL 0416183 DLC

Любопытный мѣсяцесловъ ... съ показаніемъ россійскихъ григоріанскихъ, жидовскихъ и турецкихъ лѣтъ и мѣсяцовъ, и съ приобщеніемъ пространнаго лѣтоисчисленія россійскихъ достопамятностей и проч. Изданъ въ свѣтъ отъ Издателя прежнихъ таковыхъ мѣсяцеслововъ.

Въ Санктпетербургѣ, Печатанъ при Артиллерійскомъ и инженерномъ шляхетномъ кадетскомъ корпусѣ, у Х. Ф. Клеэна.
v. 17 cm.
Published 1775-80. Cf. ÍU. ÍU. Bitovt. Рѣдкія русскія книги, 1905, № 2861-65.

Edited by V. G. Ruban.

1. Almanacs, Russian. I. Ruban, Vasiliĭ Grigor'evich, 1742-1795, ed.
Title transliterated: Líùbopytnyĭ mîesíàtseslov ... s pokazaniem rossiĭskikh, grigorianskikh, zhidovskikh i turetskikh lîet.

AY941.L53 61-55493

NL 0416185 DLC

Líùbosh, A. A., ed.
TH425 .K65
Krakovich, Abram Aleksandrovich.
Справочник: составителя смет по жилищному и гражданскому строительству. Под ред. А. А. Любоша. Ленинград, Гос. изд-во архитектуры и градостроительства, 1950.

Liuboshevskii, Dmitrii
see
Líùbashevskiĭ, Leonid Solomonovich.

HB3731 .A3L78
Líùboshits, L I
Questioni della teoria marxista-leninista delle crisi agrarie. Pref. di Ruggero Grieco. [Traduzione di Betto Aducci. Torino, Edizioni scientifiche Einaudi, 1955.
xviii, 475 p. (Biblioteca di cultura economica, 17)
Bibliographical footnotes.

1. Agriculture--Economic aspects.

Series.

NL 0416188 ICU NN MH NIC InU

Líùboshits, L I
Вопросы марксистско-ленинской теории аграрных кризисов. [Москва] Гос. изд-во полит. лит-ры, 1949.
467 p. 21 cm.

1. Agriculture—Economic aspects.
Title transliterated: Voprosy marksistsko-leninskoĭ teorii agrarnykh krizisov.

HB3731.A3L5 50-35461

NL 0416189 DLC CSt CaBVaU

Líùboslavskiĭ, G.
... Основанія ученія о погодѣ. Изд. 2. Петроградъ [Тип. Шредера] 1915.
[vii, 412 p. illus., diagrs. (part fold.) 26cm.
Principles of the study of the weather.
At head of title: Г. Любославскій.

1. Meteorology.

Agr 16-1158

Library, U. S. Dept. of Agriculture 340L74

NL 0416190 DNAL

Líùbov', knizhka zolotaía
see under [Gromov, Gleb Ivanovich]

Любовь Мильтона. Москва, Въ Тип. С. Селиванскаго, 1837.
122 p. 15 cm.

1. Milton, John, in fiction, drama, poetry, etc. 2. Milton, Mary (Powell) d. 1652—Drama. *Title transliterated:* Líùbov' Mil'tona.

PG3320.A1L5 55-45652

NL 0416192 DLC

Любовь Палирія и Дирфіи. Перевелъ съ французскаго на россійскій Степанъ Лобысевичъ. Въ Санктпетербургѣ, При Морскомъ шляхетномъ кадетскомъ корпусѣ, 1774.
149 p. 17 cm.
Bound with Книжка, содержащая въ себѣ разныя любовныя повѣсти. Въ Санктпетербургѣ, 1774.

I. Lobysevich, Stepan, tr.
Title transliterated: Líùbov' Paliríà i Dirfii.

PQ4675.K6 55-50721

NL 0416193 DLC

Любовь по вкусу; забавная повѣсть. Переведена съ нѣмецкова языка. Печатана въ Москвѣ, 1799.
116 p. 21 cm.

Title transliterated: Líùbov' po vkusu

PT1799.A1L5 55-46407

NL 0416194 DLC

Любовь превратна; или, Приключенія Милади графини Англезеи. Въ Санктпетербургѣ, Печатано при Артиллерійскомъ и инженерномъ шляхетномъ кадетскомъ корпусѣ, у содержателя тип. Х. Ф. Клеэна, 1779.
142 p. 16 cm.
Translated from French by Ivan Metal'nikov. Cf. V. S. Sopikov. Опытъ россійской библіографіи. 1904.

I. Metal'nikov, Ivan ÍAkovlevich, tr.
Title transliterated: Líùbov' prevratna.

PQ1947.A1L5 54-48980

NL 0416195 DLC

Любовь сильнее дружбы; повѣсть гишпанская. Переведена съ французскаго языка. Въ Санктпетербургѣ, При Имп. Академіи наукъ, 1764.
240 p. 17 cm.

Title transliterated: Líùbov' sil'nîe druzhby.

PQ1947.A1L54 55-50755

NL 0416196 DLC

Líùbovich, Artemii Moiseevich.

Russia (*1923-* *U. S. S. R.*) *Narodnyĭ komissariat pocht i telegrafov.*
... Контрольные цифры хозяйства связи на 1928/29-1932/33 гг. (Доклад А. М. Любовича в Госплане СССР). Москва, Издательство НКПТ, 1928.

HD9705 .R92L5
Líùbovich, ÍU O
Экономика машиностроительного завода. Москва, Гос. науч.-техн. изд-во машиностроит. лит-ры, 1948.
271 p. diagrs. 23 cm.

1. Machinery — Trade and manufacture — Russia. 2. Industrial management. I. Title.
Title transliterated: Ėkonomika mashinostroitel'nogo zavoda.

HD9705.R92L5 49-23093*

NL 0416198 DLC

VOLUME 336

Lıubovich, IU O
Ekonomika strojírenského podniku. Přel. Jaroslav Kašpar [z originálu ruského. Vyd. 1.] Praha, Průmyslové vydavatelství, 1950.
297 p. illus. 21 cm. (Knižnice podnikového hospodářství, sv. 34)

1. Machinery—Trade and manufacture—Russia. 2. Industrial management. I. Title.
HD9705.R92L53 52-32982 ‡

NL 0416199 DLC

Liubovich, IU. O., ed.
Dom inzhenera i tekhnika imeni F. É. Dzerzhinskogo, Moscow.
Система и практика материально-технического снабжения промышленных предприятий. [Редакторы: Ю. О. Любович, И. Л. Турецкий] Москва, Гос. научно-техн. изд-во машиностроит. лит-ры, 1954.

Lıubovich, Nikolaĭ Nikolaevich, 1855-1935.
(Marniks de Sent-Al'degond, kak politicheskiĭ pisatel')
Марниксъ де Сентъ-Альдегондъ, какъ политическій писатель. Н. Любовича. Кіевъ, Въ Унив. тип., 1877.
iii, 178 p. 25 cm.
"Изъ Университетскихъ извѣстій, 1877 г."
Includes bibliographical references.

1. Marnix, Philippe de, seigneur de Sainte-Aldegonde, 1538-1598. I. Title.
DH188.M35L58 73-215193

NL 0416201 DLC

Любовная школа; или, Подробное изъясненіе всѣхъ степеней и таинствъ любовной науки. Москва, Въ Унив. тип. у В. Окорокова, 1791.
61 p. 18 cm.

Title transliterated: Lıubovnaıa shkola.
PQ1947.A2L53 52-49543

NL 0416202 DLC

Lıubovniki i suprugi
see under [Gromov, Gleb Ivanovich]

Любовный вертоградъ; или, Непреоборимое постоянство Камбера и Арисены. Переведъ съ португальскаго на россійской языкъ Ѳедоръ Эминъ. Въ Санктпетербургѣ, 1763.
252 p. 19 cm.

I. Emin, Fedor Aleksandrovich, 1735-1770, tr.
Title transliterated: Lıubovnyĭ vertograd.
PQ9261.A1L5 1763 56-48608

NL 0416204 DLC

Любовный вертоградъ; или, Непреоборимое постоянство Камбера и Арисены. 2. изд. Переведъ съ португальскаго на россійской языкъ Ѳедоръ Эминъ. [Москва] 1780.
340 p. 18 cm

I. Emin, Fedor Aleksandrovich, 1735-1770, tr.
Title transliterated: Lıubovnyĭ vertograd.
PQ9261.A1L5 1780 55-53333

NL 0416205 DLC

Liubow, Fédor
See
Lyubov, Fiodor.

Liubowsky (Petrus). * Observationes medico-obstetriciæ. 66 pp. 8°. [*Dorpati, ex off. hered. Lindforsianorum*, 1838.

NL 0416207 DNLM

Lıubusha
see
Libuše, *8th cent.*

Lıubvin, V I
Обработка деталей редуцированием; анализ процесса, расчет и конструирование оборудования. Москва, Гос. научно-техн. изд-во машиностроит. лит-ры, 1949.
146 p. plates, diagrs. 20 cm.
Errata slip inserted.
Bibliography: p. [144]

1. Metal stamping.
Title transliterated: Obrabotka detaleĭ redufsirovaniem.
TS253.L5 51-20155

NL 0416209 DLC

S278 K9L5
Liuchow. Kwangsi Agricultural Experiment Station.
Bulletin 1-
Liuchow, 1939-
no.in v.

NL 0416210 CU

Liudger, Saint, Bp. of Münster, ca. 744-809.
... Heliand poema saxonicum seculi noni; ou, Poème de la vie de Jésus composé par ordre de l'empereur Louis le Débonnaire sous les auspices de Saint Luitger, évêque de Munster, en l'année 814
see under Heliand.

Liudger, Saint, Bp. of Münster, ca. 744-809.
Vita sancti Gregorii abbatis et rectoris ecclesiæ Trajectensis.
(In Patrologiæ cursus completus. Scriptores Latini. Series secunda. Tomus 99, col. 749-770. Parisiis. 1851.)
Appendix: Acta seu vita sancti Ludgeri, auctore Altfrido episcopo Monasteriensi. — Excerptum ex litaniis rhythmicis vitam sancti Ludgeri continentibus, Werthinæ scriptis. — Chartularium Werthinense.

K4595 — Gregorius, Abbot of Utrecht. 707?-780. — Werden, Germany. Hist.

NL 0416212 MB

Liudger und sein Erbe; dem siebzigsten Nachfolger des heiligen Liudger, Clemens August Kardinal von Galen, Bischof von Münster, zum Gedachtnis [by] Max Bierbaum [and others] München, Verlag Regensberg, 1948-50.

2 v. illus. (Westfalia sacra; Quellen und Forschungen zur Kirchengeschichte Westfalens, 1-2)

NL 0416213 MH NjPT PU

Liudgerus, episcopus Mimigardefordensis
see
Liudger, Saint, bp. of Münster, ca. 744-809

Люди и сталь; рассказы знатных людей "Красного Октября. Сталинград, Краевое гос. изд-во, 1935.
177 p. illus., ports. 20 cm.

1. Iron and steel workers—Stalingrad. 2. Krasnyĭ Oktıabr', Stalingrad.
Title transliterated: Lıudi i stal'.
HD8039.I52S85 51-49150

NL 0416215 DLC

HD8039 .M92R95
Люди нашего завода. [Составил П. Ромахин и др.; литературная обработка И. Романовского. Москва] Московский большевик, 1944.
42 p. ports. 15 cm. (Стахановцы военного времени)

1. Munition workers. I. Romakhin, P. II. Romanovskiĭ, I., ed. (Series: Stakhanovfsy voennogo vremeni)
Title transliterated: Lıudi nashego zavoda.
HD8039.M92R95 49-56166*

NL 0416216 DLC

Люди новаго времени; очеркъ ихъ убѣжденій, нравовъ и стремленій. Кострома, Тип. Андронникова, 1881.
103 p. 24 cm.

1. Russia—Soc. condit. 2. Youth—Russia. 3. Socialism in Russia.
Title transliterated: Lıudi novago vremeni.
HN523.L5 66-42428

NL 0416217 DLC

DK943 .L5
Люди солнечного Узбекистана; очерки. [Редактор М. И. Шевердин] Ташкент, Госиздат УзССР, 1951.
186 p. col. plates. 27 cm.

1. Uzbekistan. I. Sheverdin, M. I., ed.
Title transliterated: Lıudi solnechnogo Uzbekistana.
DK943.L5 52-26144

NL 0416218 DLC

VOLUME 336

Людмил Стоянов; юбилеен сборник. ⌐Съставили: Борис Делчев и Радой Ралин. Редактор: Борис Делчев. София⌐ Български писател ⌐1949⌐
186 p. illus. 21 cm.

1. Stoi͡anov, Li͡udmil, 1888– I. Delchev, Boris, ed. II. Ralin, Radoĭ, comp. *Title transliterated:* Li͡udmil Stoi͡anov.

PG1037.S68Z7 56–32768 ‡

NL 0416219 DLC

Microfilm Slavic 685 AC

Li͡udmirskai͡a, L
Советская Башкирия; очерк о документальном фильме. ⌐Москва⌐ Госкиноиздат, 1952.
Microfilm copy. Negative.
Collation of the original, as determined from the film: 27 p. illus., map.

1. Sovetskai͡a Bashkirii͡a (Motion picture) 2. Bashkiria—Descr. & trav. *Title transliterated:* Sovetskai͡a Bashkirii͡a.

Microfilm Slavic 685 AC Mic 57–5169

NL 0416220 DLC

GV1059 .L5

Li͡udmirskiĭ, L M
Фигурная езда на велосипеде. Москва, Физкультура и спорт, 1955.
69 p. illus. 20 cm.

1. Cycling. 2. Acrobats and acrobatism. I. Title. *Title transliterated:* Figurnai͡a ezda na velosipede.

GV1059.L5 57–17750 ‡

NL 0416221 DLC

Li͡udogovskiĭ, N
Практическое руководство для веденія дѣлъ охранительнаго судопроизводства въ общихъ и мировыхъ судебныхъ учрежденіяхъ. Съ приложеніемъ формъ необходимыхъ дѣловыхъ бумагъ, болѣе важныхъ опредѣленій различныхъ судебныхъ мѣстъ и рѣшеній Гражд. касс. деп. Сената, состоявшихся до 1877 г. С.-Петербургъ, 1878.
ii, 107, ii p. 22 cm.

1. Attachment and garnishment—Russia. I. Title. *Title transliterated:* Prakticheskoe rukovodstvo dli͡a vedenii͡a diel okhranitel'nago sudoproizvodstva.

55–50981

NL 0416222 DLC

Li͡udogovskiĭ, V M
Въ помощь начинающимъ хуторянамъ; записки изъ практики по полеводству и спеціальной культурѣ картофеля. Сѣдлецъ, Въ Тип. Губ. правленія, 1911.
52 p. illus. 22 cm.

1. Agriculture. I. Title. *Title transliterated:* V pomoshch' nachinai͡ushchim khutori͡anam.

S517.R8L5 54–46820 ‡

NL 0416223 DLC

Li͡udovik II, *King of Bavaria*
see
Ludwig II, *King of Bavaria,* 1845–1886.

Li͡udovik XVI, *korol' frant͡suzskiĭ i navarskiĭ*
see
Louis XVI, *King of France,* 1754–1793.

Li͡udovik XVII, *of France*
see
Louis XVII, *of France,* 1785–1795.

Liudprandus, Bp. of Cremona, d. ca. 972.
Lvitprandi ... Opera qvae extant. Chronicon et Adversaria nvnc primvm in lvcem exevnt, P. Hieronymi de la Higvera ... ⌐et⌐ D. Lavrenti Ramirez de Prado ... notis illvstrata. Antverpiae, Ex Officina Plantiniana Balthasaris Moreti, 1640.
xlviij, 592, ⌐38⌐ p. port. 34cm.
Engraved t. p.

NL 0416227 NIC ICN MH NjP

Liudprandus, *bp. of Cremona, d. ca.* 972.
Liudprandi Opera.
(*In* Monvmenta Germaniae historica ... avspiciis Societatis aperiendis fontibvs rervm germanicarvm medii aevi, edidit Georgivs Heinricvs Pertz ... Hannoverae, 1839. 42cm. Scriptorvm tomvs III, p. 264–363. facsim.)
Bibliographical foot-notes.
CONTENTS.—Antapodosis.—Liber de rebus gestis Ottonis Magni imperatoris.—Relatio de legatione constantinopolitana.

1. Europe—History—476–1492—Sources. 2. Otto I, der Grosse, emperor of Germany, 912–973. 3. Nicephorus II, Byzantine emperor, 912 (ca.)–969.

A C 37–2429
New York. Public library for Library of Congress [DD3.M8S4 t.3]
(943.0082)

NL 0416228 NN MH KyU MdBP OC1 OU DLC NN

---

943 W76sg v.4

Liudprandus, bp. of Cremona, d. ca.972.
Luidprandi episcopi cremonensis opera omnia ex Monumentis Germaniae historicis recudi fecit Georgius Heinricus Pertz ... Hannoverae, impensis bibliopolii Hahniani, 1839.
228p. (Added t.-p.: Scriptores rerum germanicarum in usum scholarum ex Monumentis Germaniae historicis recudi fecit Georgius Heinricus Pertz ⌐v.4⌐)
Index: Auctore v. cl. Ludowico Bethmann.
Contents.- Antapodosis.- Historia Ottonis.- Legatio.

NL 0416229 IU PHC CU NIC MH IU MnU MnCS PU

DD 3 G38 v.25

Liudprandus, bp. of Cremona, d. ca. 972.
Liudprands Werken. Nach der Ausg. der Monumenta Germaniae übers. von Freiherrn Karl v. d. Osten-Sacken. Berlin, F. Duncker, 1853.
xvi, 177 p. 20cm. (Die Geschichtschreiber der deutschen Vorzeit. 10. Jahrhundert, 2. Bd. ⌐v. 25⌐)

NL 0416230 NIC CaBVaU MiU MH

F 47 .5956 v.37

LIUDPRANDUS, bp. of Cremona, d.ca.972.
Liudprandi episcopi cremonensis opera omnia... Editio altera. Recognovit Ernestus Dümmler. Hannoverae,Hahn,1877.
xvii,181p. (Scriptores rerum germanicarum in usum scholarum ex Monumentis Germaniae historicis recusi)
Contents.—Antapodosis.—Historia Ottonis.—Legatio.—Index nominum.—Glossarium auctore Ludowico Bethmann.

NL 0416231 ICN PHC OU MH CU PPPD IU RPB

Liudprandus, *bp. of Cremona, d. ca.* 972.
Die werke Liudprands von Cremona. Dritte auflage, herausgegeben von Joseph Becker. Hannover und Leipzig, Hahnsche buchhandlung, 1915.
xl, 246 p. 23½cm. (*Added t.-p.:* Scriptores rerum germanicarum in usum scholarum ex Monumentis Germaniae historicis separatim editi)
Text in Latin. On added t.-p.: Liudprandi opera.
"Pertz und ihm folgend Dümmler legten dem text die Münchener handschrift, die sie irrig für das autograph hielten, zugrunde. Die vorliegende ausgabe zieht das gesamte handschriftenmaterial heran."—Einleitung, p. xxxv.
"Verzeichnis wiederholt und abgekürzt angeführter werke": p. ⌐xxxviii⌐–xl.
CONTENTS.—Antapodosis.—Historia Ottonis.—Legatio.
1. Europe—History—476–1492. 2. Otto I, der Grosse, emperor of Germany, 912–973. 3. Nicephorus II, Byzantine emperor, 912 (ca.)–969. I. Becker, Josef, 1883– ed.
Title from N. Y. Pub. Libr. A C 33–3990
Library of Congress [DD3.M82]

NL 0416232 NN CtY NCH PBm MH OC1W ICU OrU

Liudprandus, *bp. of Cremona, d. ca.* 972.
The works of Liudprand of Cremona ... translated for the first time into English with an introduction by F. A. Wright ... London, G. Routledge & sons, ltd., 1930.
3 p. l., 287 p. 23cm. (*Half-title:* Broadway medieval library)
CONTENTS.—Antapodosis (Tit-for-tat)—Liber de rebus gestis Ottonis (A chronicle of Otto's reign)—Relatio de legatione constantinopolitana (The embassy to Constantinople)

1. Europe—Hist.—476–1492. 2. Otto I, der Grosse, emperor of Germany, 912–973. 3. Nicephorus II, Byzantine emperor, 912 (ca.)–969. I. Wright, Frederick Adam, 1869– tr.

30—14105
Library of Congress D117.A2L5
⌐3812⌐ 940.1

NL 0416233 WaS OrCS PSC IdU NcGU PSt DDO OO NN MH WaU PPPD DLC ICU OC1W MH-AH MiU ViU MBrZ IdU-SB

Liudprandus, Bp. of Cremona, d. ca. 972.
The works of Liudprand of Cremona. Translated for the first time into English, with an introduction, by F. A. Wright.
New York. Dutton & Co. 1930. (5), 287 pp. 21½ cm., in 8s.
Contents. — Antapodosis. — Liber de rebus gestis Ottonis (A chronicle of Otto's reign). — Relatio de legatione Constantinopolitana (The embassy to Constantinople).

N8003 — Wright, Frederick Adam, ed. ...d tr., 1869–. — Germany. Hist. Otto I., 936–973. — Constantinople. Hist.

NL 0416234 MWelC MB MtBC MiU OCU OU OC1 NjPT MH PHC

D 117 A2 L783 1930b

Liudprandus,Bp,of Cremona,d.ca.972.
Works. Translated for the first time into English with an introd.by F.A.Wright. New York, Dutton, 1930.
287 p.
Photocopy. Ann Arbor,Mich., University Microfilms, 1966. 287 p.(on double leaves)

1.Europe--Hist.--476-1492. 2.Otto I,der Grosse, Emperor of Germany,912-973. 3.Nicephorus II, Byzantine emperor,912 (ca.)-969. I.Wright,Frederick Adam,1869- tr.

NL 0416235 MiU

Liudprandus, *Bp. of Cremona, d. ca.* 972.
Tutte le opere, 891–969, a cura di Alessandro Cutolo. ⌐Milano⌐ V. Bompiani, 1945.
271 p. illus. 21 cm. (Grandi ritorni)
CONTENTS.—La restituzione.—Le gesta di Ottone I.—La relazione di un'ambasceria a Constantinopoli.

1. Europe—Hist.—476–1492. 2. Otto I, der Grosse, Emperor of Germany, 912–973. 3. Nicephorus II, Byzantine Emperor, 912 (ca.)–969. I. Cutolo, Alessandro, 1899– ed. (Series)

D117.A2L515 940.1 A F 49–372*
New York. Public Libr. for Library of Congress †

NL 0416236 NN RPB NNC ICU CU MH DLC

VOLUME 336

DD3
.G36
v.31

Liudprandus, bp. of Cremona, 920-972.
Aus Liudprands werken. Nach der ausg. der Monumenta Germaniae übers. von freiherrn Karl v. d. Osten-Sacken. 2. aufl. Neu bearb. von W. Wattenbach. Leipzig, Dyk, 1889.
xx, 196 p. incl. 2 fold. geneal. tab. 19cm. (Added t.-p.: Die geschichtschreiber der deutschen vorzeit... [bd.31] 10. jahrh. 2. bd.)

1. Holy Roman empire--Hist.--843-1273.

NL 0416237 ICU ICN IU

Liudprandus, *bp. of Cremona, d. ca.* 972.
Aus Liudprands werken. Nach der ausgabe der Monumenta Germaniae übersetzt von freiherrn Karl v. d. Osten-Sacken. 2. aufl. Neu bearbeitet von W. Wattenbach. Leipzig, Dyksche buchhandlung [1890]
xx, 196 p. incl. 2 geneal. tab. on 1 fold. l. 19cm. (*Added t.-p.:* Die geschichtschreiber der deutschen vorzeit. 2. gesammtausgabe. 10. jahrhundert, 2. bd. [29. bd.])
CONTENTS.—Einleitung.—Das buch der vergeltung.—Liudprands Buch von den thaten des kaisers Otto des Grossen.—Liudprands Bericht über seine sendung nach Konstantinopel.
1. Europe—History—476-1492—Sources. 2. Otto I, der Grosse, emperor of Germany, 912-973. 3. Nicephorus II, Byzantine emperor, 912 (ca.)-969. I. *Osten-Sacken, Karl, freiherr von der, 1807-1869, tr. II. *Wattenbach, Wilhelm, 1819-1897, ed.
A C 39-44
Ohio state univ. Library for Library of Congres [DD3.G39 bd. 29]
(943.0082)

NL 0416238 OU CtY MH OCU

Liudprandus, bp. of Cremona, d. ca. 972.

Antonio, Nicolás, 1617-1684.
Bibliotheca hispana vetus, sive, Hispani scriptores qui ab Octaviani Augusti ævo ad annum Christi M. D. floruerunt. Auctore d. Nicolao Antonio Hispalensi ... Curante Francisco Perezio Bayerio ... qui et prologum, & auctoris vitæ epitomen, & notulas adiecit ... Matriti, apud viduam et heredes D. J. Ibarræ, 1788.

LIUDPRANDUS, bp. of Cremona, d.ca.972.
Una embajada occidental a Bizancio hace mil años (las relaciones diplomaticas entre el emperador Oton I de Alemania y el Basileus Niceforo Focas) Relacion de Liudprando de la embajada a Constantinopla.

***Separata de Cuadernos de historia diplomatica, II, 1955, p.293-347.**
At head of title: Luis García Arias.

NL 0416240 DDO

Liutprandus, bp. of Cremona, d. ca. 972.
Historia gestorum regum et imperatorum sive apodosis.— De rebus gestis Ottonis Magni imperatoris. — Relatio de legatione Constantinopolitana. — Appendix: Pseudo-Liutprandi Chronicon, et Adversaria.
(In Patrologiæ cursus completus. Scriptores Latini. Series secunda. Tomus 136, col. 769-1180. Lutetiæ Parisiorum. 1853.)

K4595 — Otto I., Emperor of Germany. 912-973. — Germany. Hist.

NL 0416241 MB

Liudprandus, bp. of Cremona, d. 972.
Liber de pontificum Romanorum vitis a Pseudo-Liutprando confectum.
(In Patrologiæ cursus completus. Scriptores Latini. Series secunda. Tomus 129, col. 1149-1256. Lutetiæ Parisiorum. 1853.)

K4594 — Liber pontificalis.

NL 0416242 MB

Liudprandus, bp. of Cremona, d ca. 972
Luitprandi Ticinensis Opusculum de vitis Romanorum pontificum. Item Albonis Floriacensis Epitome de viti eorundem ex Anastasii Bibliothecarii Historia excerpta. Moguntiae, Ex typ. I. Albini, 1602

161 p.

NL 0416243 MH DLC PPL

Liudprandus, bp. of Cremona, d. ca. 972.
Rerum Europae imperatoribus ac regibus gestarum. Basileae, 1551.
fol.

NL 0416244 NN

Rare Book Room
Bh3
110

Liudprandus, bp. of Cremona, d. ca. 972.
Liutprãdi Ticinensis ecclesiae Leuitae Rerum gestarum per Europam ipsius praesertim temporibus / libri sex. [Paris]Venundantur ab Jodoco Badio Ascensio & Ioanne Paruo. [Ad idvs Septemb. Anni. 1514]
4p.ℓ., XLII numb.ℓ. 26cm.
Described in Ph. Renouard, Bibliographie des impressions et des oeuvres de Josse Badius, Paris, 1908, vol.3, p.9-10.
Imperfect: title-border bled.

NL 0416245 CtY MH

Liudskanov, Aleksandŭr K., 1855-1922.

Bulgaria. *Ministerstvo na vŭtreshnite raboti i narodnoto zdrave.*
... Докладъ отъ Александръ К. Людскановъ, Министръ на вжтрѣшнитѣ работи и народното здраве, отъ 30 ноемв. 1911 г. Въ изпълнение постановлението на почитаемия Министерския Съвѣтъ отъ 15 сент. т. г., протоколъ № 72 имамъ честь до доложа, чеазъ посѣтихъ тритѣ държави, въ които е въведена пропорционалната избирателна система-Швейцария, Белгия и Сърбия, както и Франция, дѣто сжщата реформа е дневниятъ въпросъ отъ най-голѣма актуалность ... [София, 1911]

Liudvig, Emil'
see Ludwig, Emil, 1881-1948.

GB1755
.Y4L5

Liudvig, F V
Матеріалы къ изученію химическаго состава нѣкоторыхъ горько-соленыхъ озеръ степей—Солянойі, Абаканской, Сагайской и Качинской, Минусинскаго округа Енисейской губерніи. Юрьевъ, 1903.
198 p. illus., map. 24 cm.
Диссертація (магистръ фармаціи)—Tartu.
"Литература": p. 12-18.
1. Lakes—Russia—Yeniseisk (Government) 2. Water—Analysis. *Title transliterated:* Materialy k izuchenīiu khimicheskago sostava nīekotorykh gor'ko-solenykh ozer.

GB1755.Y4L5 50-44541

NL 0416248 DLC

Liuely ...
see Lively ...

Liues
see Lives ...

L'ĭuis, B
see
Lewis, Bernard, 1899-

L'ĭuis, Dzh.
see
Lewis, James Ogier, 1886-

L'ĭuis, Dzhordzh Genrikh
see
Lewes, George Henry, 1817-1878.

L'ĭuis, G. G.
see
Lewes, George Henry, 1817-1878.

L'ĭuis, I
see
Lewis, Ian Alexander D

L'ĭuis, Sinkler
see
Lewis, Sinclair, 1885-1951.

Люиза; или, Власть добродѣтели женскаго полу. Нравоучительная баснь, переведенная съ французскаго Иваномъ Шильтомъ. Въ Санктпетербургѣ, Печатано при Артиллерійскомъ и инженерномъ шляхетномъ кадетскомъ корпусѣ, иждивеніемъ содержателя тип. Х. Ф. Клеэна, 1780.
80 p. 20 cm.

I. Shil't, Ivan, tr. *Title transliterated:* Lĭuiza.

PQ1947.A1L588 56-50188

NL 0416257 DLC

Liūke, German
see
Lücke, Hermann, 1837-1907.

Liukko, A
Than täyttä totta; yksinäytöksinen näytelmä. [Hämeenlinna] Karisto [1951]

42 p. (Seuranäytilmiä, 552)

NL 0416259 MH

VOLUME 336

Li͡ukom, Elena Mikhaĭlovna.
... Моя работа в балете. Ленинград, Издание Ленинградского отделения Всероссийского театрального общества, 1940.

30, [2] p. front. (port.) plates. 27 x 20½ cm.

At head of title: Всероссийское театральное общество. Ленинградское отделение. Е. М. Люком ...

I. Vserossiĭskoe teatral'noe obshchestvo. Leningradskoe otdelenie. II. Title. *Title transliterated:* Moi͡a rabota v balete.

44-29073

Library of Congress GV1785.L85A3

NL 0416260 DLC MH

Li͡uksemburg, Mikhail Solomonovich
see
Li͡uksemburg, Moiseĭ Solomonovich.

Li͡uksemburg, Moiseĭ Solomonovich, joint ed.

Vsesoi͡uznyĭ kozhevennyĭ sindikat.
Справочник заготовителя кожевенного сырья и корья, под редакцией И. З. Лозинского, инж. М. С. Люксембурга, Н. В. Масалкова. [Москва] Всесоюзный кожевенный синдикат, 1929.

Li͡uksemburg, Moiseĭ Solomonovich.
Вопросы улучшения качества кожевенного сырья. Москва, Гос. науч.-техн. изд-во текст., легкой и полиграф промышл., 1947.

65 p. 20 cm.

Errata slip inserted.

1. Hides and skins. *Title transliterated:* Voprosy uluchshenii͡a kachestva kozhevennogo syr'i͡a.

TS967.L65 49-12815*

NL 0416263 DLC

Li͡uksemburg, Roza
see
Luxemburg, Rosa, 1870-1919.

Li͡ul'chenko, V. G., ed.

TJ1160
.R89

Russia (*1923- U. S. S. R.*) *Ministerstvo stankostroenii͡a. Vsesoi͡uznai͡a tekhnicheskai͡a kontora.*
Справочник инструментальщика. [Под общей ред. В. Г. Любченко] Москва, Машгиз, 1949.

Li͡umkis, I
עשעלאנענ גייענ קינ ביראבידזשאנ; רעפּארטאזש. מאסקווע, מעלוכע־פארלאג "דער עמעס." [Москва] 1948.

119 p. 17 cm.

1. Biro-Bidjan—Descr. & trav.
Title transliterated: Eshelonen geyen kayn Birobidzshan.

DK771.B5L5 57-56229 ‡

NL 0416266 DLC

Li͡umkis, I
פיאניסטנ. פארצייכענונגענ. קיעוו, מעלוכע־פארלאג פאר די נאציאנאלע מינדערהייטנ אינ אוססר. [Kiev] 1939.

61 p. ports. 19 cm.

CONTENTS.— יאקאוו פליער.—עמיל גילעלס.—אבראם לופער.—ראזע טא־מארקינא.

1. Pianists, Russian. *Title transliterated:* Pianistn.

ML397.L65 56-55645

NL 0416267 DLC

[Liun, Lina]
Chanzunettas da temp vegl Cuira, Libreria C. Bernhard [1913]

31 p. 31 cm.
Edited by Lina Liun and Martina Badrutt.
Engadine folksongs, with music.

NL 0416268 MH

Liun, Lina.
Elementary grammar of the Upper Engadine, with phrasebook, p.1-46. Translated from the German by Mildred Elizabeth Maxfield. Chur, 1936.

22 numb. l. 28 x 22 cm.
Typewritten.

NL 0416269 MH

459.98
L783o

Liun, Lina.
Oberengadinische Elementargrammatik mit Gesprächbüchlein und Wörterbüchlein für Deutschsprachige von Lina Liun und einigen andern Engadinern. 2.Aufl. Thusis, Roth [192-?]
iv,133p. 22cm.

1.Raeto-Romance language - Dialects - Engadin. 2.Raeto-Romance language - Grammar. I.Title.

NL 0416270 NcU MH

Liun iu
see
Confucius.
Analects.

PT8114
.R6
Rare Bk.
Coll.

Liunge, Andreas Peter, 1798-1879, ed.

Harpen.
[Kjøbenhavn]

AP42
.N87
Rare Bk.
Coll.

Liunge, Andreas Peter, 1798-1879, ed.

Nyt repertorium for moerskabs-læsning. 1.-6. bd.; 4. nov. 1829-30. juni 1832. Kjøbenhavn.

Liunge, Andreas Peter, 1798-1879.
Redaktør A. P. Liunges optegnelser. Ved Nic. Bøgh ... Kjøbenhavn, Det Hoffensbergske etabl., 1899.

1 p. l., 39 p. 23 cm.

"Særtryk af Personalhistorisk tidsskrift, fjerde række, I. bind."

I. Bøgh, Nicolaj Seidelin, 1843-1905.

17-11529

Library of Congress PT8143.L55Z5 1899

NL 0416274 DLC

Liunge, Andreas Peter, 1798-1879, ed.

Repertorium for moerskabs-læsning. nr. 1-24; 17. mai-28. oct. 1829. Kjøbenhavn.

Liunge, Andreas Peter, 1798-1879, tr.

Scott, *Sir* **Walter,** *bart.,* 1771-1832.
Walter Scott's samlede romaner, oversatte fra originalsproget ... Kjøbenhavn, P. G. Philipsen, 1855-71.

Liunge, Andreas Peter, 1798-1879, tr.

Scott, *Sir* **Walter,** *bart.,* 1771-1832.
Waverley eller Skotland for 60 aar siden. En historisk roman af Walter Scott. Oversat fra engelsk af A. P. Ljunge. 2. gjennemsete og forbedrede udg. Kjøbenhavn, P. G. Philipsen, 1857.

Liunge, Christian, d. 1779, tr.

Hofman, Tycho de, 1714-1754.
Historiske efterretninger om velfortiente danske adelsmænd, med deres stamme-tavler og portraiter. Ved Tycho de Hofman ... Oversatte, forøgede og forbedrede ... Kiøbenhavn, A. H. Godiches efterleverskes forlag, 1777-79.

Liungman, Annie.
Centunculus, dikter. Stockholm, L.Hökerberg [1939]

99 p. 23.5 cm.

NL 0416279 MH

Liungman, Annie.
Toner; dikter. Göteborg, Wettergren & Kerber [1926]
98 p.

NL 0416280 MH

Liungman, Carl Gudmund Waldemar
see
Liungman, Waldemar, 1883-

VOLUME 336

Liungman, Waldemar, 1883–
... Der kampf zwischen sommer und winter, von Waldemar Liungman. Helsinki, Suomalainen tiedeakatemia, Academia scientiarum fennica, 1941.
2 p. l., 187 p. maps (1 fold.) fold. tab., diagr. 23ᶜᵐ. (Folklore fellows; FF communications nr. 130)
Includes bibliographies.
1. Seasons. I. Title.
[Full name: Carl Gudmund Waldemar Liungman]
46-41430
Library of Congress GR1.F55 nr. 130
(398.062471) 394.262

NL 0416282 DLC NcD GU MoU FTaSU UU CoU ViU LU

GR355 .L7 LIUNGMAN, WALDEMAR, 1883–
Sagan om Bata och Anubis och den Orientalisk-europeiska undersagans ursprung. Viktor Rydbergsserien 1-3. Djursholm [Sweden] Förlags A.B. "Vald Litteratur", 1946. 116p. Map.
Cover-title.

NL 0416283 InU

BF1058 .S9L7 LIUNGMAN, WALDEMAR, 1883–
Sinnesvillor och sägenbildning samt därmed sammanhängende trosföreställningar. [n.p., n. pub., 1927?]
169-201 p.
Särtryk ur folkminnen och folktankar. Häfte 4, 1927.
Cover-title.
1. Hallucinations and illusions. 2. Folk-lore--Scandinavia. I. Tc. Folklore cd.

NL 0416284 InU

PT9531 .L5 Liungman, Waldemar, 1883–
Sveriges samtliga folksagor i ord och bild. [Stockholm] Lindfors Bokförlag AB, i distribution [1949-50]
2 v. illus.
"Bibliofilupplagan ... är tryckt i 500 exemplar varav detta är n:o 371, och är tryckt för University of California."
1. Legends - Sweden. 2. Folk literature - Sweden. I. Title.

NL 0416285 CU OU NIC MH ICU IU PPT InU TxU OrU

PT9531 .L5 Case B Liungman, Waldemar, 1883–
Sveriges samtliga folksagor i ord och bild [Stockholm] Lindfors Bokförlag AB, i distribution [1949-52]
3 v. illus.
Vol.3 has imprint: Djursholm, Förlagsaktiebolaget vald Litteratur.
Vol.3 has also special t.p.: Varifrån kommer våra sagor? Utkast till de svenska foldsagornas uppkomstoch utbredningshistoria; jämte översikstablå över förefintliga varianter i svenska arkiv och svenskt tryck.
Vol.1-2: "Bibliofilupplagan ... är tryckt i 500 exemplar varav detta är n:o 371".
Bibliography: v.3, p.[419]-453.

NL 0416287 CU MnU MiDW OCl NNC MdBJ

398.2 L74s 1954 Liungman, Waldemar, 1883– ed.
Sveriges samtliga folksagor i ord och bild. Stockholm, Djursholm, 1954–
v. illus. 24cm.
1. Folk-lore--Sweden. 2. Tales, Swedish. I. Title.

NL 0416288 IU ICN

Liungman, Waldemar, 1883–
En traditionsstudie över sagan om Prinsessan i jordkulan (Aarnes 870) av Waldemar Liungman ... Göteborg, Elanders boktryckeri aktiebolag, 1925.
2 v.in 1. 21 maps (20 fold., in pocket) 25½ᶜᵐ.
Akademisk avhandling.--Göteborgs högskola.
Vol.2: Bilagor och anmärkningar.
1.Tales, Swedish. 2.Tales, Scandinavian. 3.Folk literature--Themes, motives. I.Title: Prinsessan i jordkulan.

NL 0416289 MiU ICRL MH ICU ICN CtY CU IU IEN

Liungman, Waldemar, 1883–
Traditionswanderungen, Euphrat-Rhein; Studien zur Geschichte der Volksbräuche. Helsinki, Suomalainen Tiedeakatemia, 1937–38.
2 v. illus., maps, diagrs. 24 cm. (FF communications, nr. 118–119)
Summary in English: v. 2, p. [1124]–1147.
Bibliographical footnotes; bibliography: v. 2, p. [1207]–1220.
1. Mythology. 2. Cultus. 3. Nature-worship. 4. Religions. 5. Festivals. I. Title. (Series: Folklore Fellows. F. F. communications, nr. 118–119)
Full name: Carl Gudmund Waldemar Liungman.
GR1.F55 nr. 118–119 291.13 38–3574 rev*

NL 0416290 DLC PU OCl OU MoU GU FTaSU UU

Liungman, Waldemar, 1883–
Traditionswanderungen, Rhein-Jenissei; eine Untersuchung über das Winter- und Todaustragen und einige hierhergehörige Bräuche. Helsinki, Suomalainen Tiedeakatemia, Academia Scientiarum Fennica, 1941–45.
2 v. illus., fold. maps. 23 cm. ([Folklore Fellows] FF communications nr. 129, 131)
Includes bibliographical references.
1. Winter. 2. Dead (in religion, folk-lore, etc.) (Series)
Full name: Carl Gudmund Waldemar Liungman.
GR1.F55 nr. 129, 131 398.3 50–2555 rev

NIC
NL 0416291 DLC NN FTaSU MoU UU ViU LU GU OU NcD

PN1376 .L78 Liungman, Waldemar, 1883–
... Två folkminnesundersökningar: Brud icke mö och Liten Asa gåsapiga samt Kung Ingewalls dotter (Dg F 274, Aarnes 871 och 533) av Waldemar Liungman. Göteborg, Elanders boktryckeri, 1925.
viii, 73 p. illus. (maps) fold. tab. 23ᶜᵐ. (Folkloristiska studier och samlingar utg. av redaktionen för Folkminnen och folktankar. I)
1. Ballads—Hist. & crit. 2. Fairy tales—Hist. & crit.

NL 0416292 ICU OCl ICN IU

Liungman, Waldemar, 1883–
Varifrån kommer våra sagor? Utkast till de svenska folksagornas uppkomst- och utbredningshistoria. Jämte översiktstablå över förefintliga varianter i svenska arkiv och svenskt tryck. Djursholm, Förlagsaktiebolaget Vald Litteratur [1952]
537 p. (His Sveriges samtliga folksagor, v.3)

NL 0416293 MH

Liungman, Waldemar, 1883–
Das wahrscheinliche Alter des Volksmärchens in Schweden. Helsinki, Suomalainen Tiedeakatemia, 1955.
44 p. 24 cm. (FF communications, n:o 156)
1. Tales, Swedish—Hist. & crit. I. Title.
Full name: Carl Gudmund Waldemar Liungman.
GR1.F55 no. 156 57–34180 ‡

FTaSU NNC MoU UU
NL 0416294 DLC CU FMU MiU GU ViU CtY NcD OU NIC NN

Liuni, Francesco.
... La concezione italiana dello stato. Trani, Vecchi & c., 1934.
100 p. 22ᶜᵐ.
"Bibliografia": p. [9]–12.
1. State, The. 2. Political science—Hist.—Italy.
JA84.I 8L5 47–18035

NL 0416295 DLC NN

Liuni, Francesco.
Problemi agricoli del Mezzogiorno; con premessa di Arrigo Serpieri. Trani, Vecchi, 1951.
70 p. 22 cm.
1. Agriculture—Economic aspects—Italy, Southern. I. Title.
A 59–3682
New York Univ. Libraries HD1970
for Library of Congress

NL 0416296 NNU

Liupersol'skiĭ, Petr Ivanovich.
Храмовый городъ Дельфы съ оракуломъ Аполлона Пиѳійскаго въ древней Греціи; историческое изслѣдованіе П. Люперсольскаго. С.-Петербургъ, Въ Тип. В. Безобразова, 1869.
xv, 162 p. fold. map. 23 cm.
1. Delphi. I. Title.
Title romanized: Khramovyĭ gorod Del'fy s orakulom Apollona Pifiĭskago v drevneĭ Greĭsīi.
DF261.D35L58 72–218079

NL 0416297 DLC

Liure ...
see Livre ...

Liurette, Henri, 1878–
Le vol à voile dynamique des oiseaux; trente ans d'observations en A. O. F. Paris, F.-L. Vivien, 1955.
89 p. illus. 25 cm.
Includes bibliography.
1. Flight. I. Title.
QL698.L54 55–33219 ‡

NL 0416299 DLC

JN6598 .K71918 Liushin, Stepan Pavlovich, ed.
Из истории Волгоградской партийной организации. [Сборник статей]. Волгоград, [газ. "Волгогр. правда"], 19

VOLUME 336

Liuskova, Aleksandra Evgen'evna.
Meine Arbeit auf der Schweinefarm. Berlin, Kultur und Fortschritt, 1951.
33 p. (Kleine Bücherei der Gesellschaft für Deutsch-Sowjetische Freundschaft. Heft 17)

NL 0416301 DNAL

Liusnia, M., *pseud.*
see
Krauz-Kelles, Kazimierz, 1872-1905.

Liusternik, Lazar' Aronovich, 1899-
Elemente der Funktionalanalysis von L. A. Ljusternik ⌐und⌐ W. I. Sobolew. Berlin, Akademie-Verlag, 1955.
xi, 256 p. illus. 24 cm. (Mathematische Lehrbücher und Monographien, 1. Abt. Mathematische Lehrbücher, Bd. 8)
Bibliography: p. ⌐249⌐-252.

1. Functional analysis. I. Sobolev, V. I., joint author. (Series)

[QA320.L] A 56—4021

New York Univ. Libraries
for Library of Congress ⌐57d1⌐

CU TU MU MnU NcD PU-Math NIC RPB OU FMU ViU NN MoU
NL 0416303 NNU ICD DLC ICU OC1W OCU NcU MiU IU MH

Liusternik, Lazar' Aronovich, 1899-
Элементы функционального анализа. Москва, Гос. изд-во технико-теорет. лит-ры, 1951.
360 p. 21 cm.
At head of title: Л. А. Люстерник и В. И. Соболев.
Bibliography: p. ⌐354⌐-356.

1. Functional analysis. I. Sobolev, V. I., joint author. II. Title.
Title transliterated: Ėlementy funktsional'nogo analiza.

QA320.L55 55-43184

NL 0416304 DLC OrCS

Liusternik, Lazar' Aronovich, 1899- joint author.

QA315 .L3 1950
Lavrent'ev, Mikhail Alekseevich, 1900-
Курс вариационного исчисления. Изд. 2., перер. Допущено в качестве учебника для гос. университетов. Москва, Гос. изд-во технико-теорет. лит-ры, 1950.

Liusternik, Lazar' Aronovich, 1899-
... Méthodes topologiques dans les problèmes variationnels ... par L. Lusternik et L. Schnirelmann. Traduit du russe par J. Kravtchenko. Paris, Hermann & c^ie, 1934-
v. diagrs. 25 cm. (Exposés sur l'analyse mathématique et ses applications pub. sous la direction de m. J. Hadamard ... III
Actualités scientifiques et industrielles. 188-
"La présente brochure est la traduction de notre travail, publié en russe, d'abord, sous le titre 'Méthodes topologiques dans les problèmes du calcul des variations ⌐Топологические методы в вариационных задачах⌐' (1930) et complété par des recherches postérieures."—v. 1, Avant-propos.
Bibliographical foot-notes.
1. Calculus of variations. 2. Topology. I. Shnirel'man, Lev Genrikhovich, 1905- joint author. II. Kravtchenko, J., tr.

Q111.A3 no. 188 (508) 517.4 35—19045

NBuU PBm OO OCU OU NNC NBC NcD PBm N
NL 0416306 DLC NN OrCS PU ViU FMU IaU MH CSt CoU

QA408 .L5
Liusternik, Lazar' Aronovich, 1899-
Таблицы Бесселевых функций. Москва, Гос. изд-во технико-теорет. лит-ры, 1949.
430 p. 23 cm. (Математические таблицы, вып. 1)
At head of title: Л. А. Люстерник, И. Я. Акушский, В. А. Диткин.

1. Bessel's functions. (Series: Matematicheskie tablitsy, vyp. 1)
Title transliterated: Tablitsy Besselevykh funktsiĭ.

50-35489

NL 0416307 DLC

QA491 .L5 1941
Liusternik, Lazar' Aronovich, 1899-
Выпуклые тела. Изд. 2. Москва, Гос. изд-во техн.-теоретич. лит-ры, 1941.
136 p. illus., diagrs. 20 cm.

1. Polyhedra. I. Title. *Title transliterated:* Vypuklye tela.

QA491.L5 1941 49-32330

NL 0416308 DLC

N6995 .W5L5
Liutarovich, V
Росквіт беларускага совецкага мастацтва. Мінск, 1955.
30 p. 20 cm.
At head of title: Таварыства па распаўсюджанню палітычных і навуковых ведаў Беларускай ССР.

1. Art, White Russian. I. Title.
Title transliterated: Roskvit belaruskaha sovetskaha mastatstva.

N6995.W5L5 56-34221 ‡

NL 0416309 DLC

Liutaud, *Bp. of Vence.* 10 *cent.* Epistola ad Wenilonem Rothomagensem archiepiscopum de Wifado diacono. 2 pp. (Migne, J. P., *Patrol. s. Lat.* v. 129. p. 1392.)

NL 0416310 MdBP

Liutbert, Archbishop of Mainz. -889.
Epistola ad Ludovicum regem.
(In Patrologiæ cursus completus. Scriptores Latini. **Series secunda.** Tomus 129, col. 1051-1054. Lutetiæ Parisiorum. **1853.**)

K4594 — Louis, the German, King of the Germans. 843-876.

NL 0416311 MB

Liuter, Martin
see
Luther, Martin, 1483-1546.

Liutetskii, A
Открытое письмо къ учащейся молодежи. Москва, Тип. Г. Лисснера и А. Гешеля, 1899.
16 p. 22 cm.

1. Education—Addresses, essays, lectures. 2. Education—Russia.
Title transliterated: Otkrytoe pis'mo k uchashcheĭsia molodezhi.

LB775.L555 51-46926

NL 0416313 DLC

Liutetskii, A *ed.*
Замѣчательные уголовные процессы, разрѣшенные [illegible] Московскомъ окружномъ судѣ съ участiемъ присяжныхъ засѣдателей. Составлены, испр. и доп. приложенiем осмотровъ и плановъ А. Лютецкимъ. Москва, Тип. А. И. Мамонтова, 1867.
iv, 294 p. plans. 26 cm.

1. Trials—Russia. I. Russia. Okruzhnyĭ sud (Moscow) II. Title. *Title transliterated:* Zamiechatel'nye ugolovnye protsessy.

55-50101

NL 0416314 DLC

Liutgen, B
see
Lütgen, B

Liutgens, Avgust
see **Lütgens, August,** 1892-1933.

Liuther, Artur
see Luther, Arthur, 1876-1955.

868.71 L74a
Liuti, Augusto
La antesala del cielo, novela. Guatemala, Ediciones El Libro de Guatemala, 1948.
177p. 20cm. (El Libro en Guatemala, Coleccion contemporaneos, no.9)

KU TxU
NL 0416318 LU NBuU TxU IU MWelC CtY CU MH NcU OC1

Liuti, J L
... Apicultura, por J. L. Liuti ... Guatemala, C. A., Dirección general de agricultura, 1941.
44 p. 19^cm.
At head of title: Administración del general Jorge Ubico.

1. Bee culture. I. Guatemala. Dirección general de agricultura.
45-22723

Library of Congress SF531.L57

NL 0416319 DLC

HD8039 .R12R95
Liutikov, V
Политическая работа в поездных бригадах. ⌐Москва⌐ Московский рабочий, 1948.
55 p. 17 cm.
At head of title: В. Лютиков, М. Копелевич.

1. Railroads—Russia—Employees. 2. Communism—Russia. I. Kopelevich, M., joint author. II. Title.
Title transliterated: Politicheskaia rabota v poezdnykh brigadakh.

HD8039.R12R95 49-24953*

NL 0416320 DLC

Liutolfus, Presbyter of Mainz. Fl. 858.
De sancto Severo.
(In Monumenta Moguntina. [Bibliotheca rerum Germanicarum. Tomus 3.] Pp. 507-517. Berolini. 1866.)
Vita et translatio in Erphordiam anno 836.

G6531 — Severus, Saint, Archbishop of Ravenna. -390?

NL 0416321 MB

VOLUME 336

Lîūtostanskiĭ, Ippolit Iosifovich, 1835–1915.
Die Juden in Russland ... von J. J. Ljutostanski. Nach der zweiten auflage ⟨1880⟩ aus dem russischen übersetzt von Jul. baron Rosenberg. Bearbeitet von G. Arnold. [Berlin-Schöneberg, Verlag Deutsche kulturwacht, 1934]
2 v. 21cm.
"1. auflage."
Bibliography: v. 2., p. 5–6.
CONTENTS.—1. bd. Leben und treiben im jüdischen kahal.—2. bd. Jüdische ritual-morde in Russland.
1. Jewish question. 2. Ritual murder. I. Rosenberg, Jul., baron, tr. II. Arnold, G.
A C 34-3364
Title from N. Y. Pub. Libr. Printed by L. C.

NL 0416322 NN CU ICRL CtY

Liutostanskii, Ippolit Iosifovich, 1835-1915
Leben und Treiben im judischen Kahal.
Von J. J. L. [Berlin] 1880.
159 p. 8°. (Die Juden in Russland. Erster Band)

NL 0416323 PPDrop

Lîūtostanskiĭ, Ippolit Iosifovich, 1835–1915.
Объ употребленіи евреями (талмудистскими сектаторами) христіанской крови для религіозныхъ цѣлей, въ связи съ вопросомъ объ отношеніяхъ еврейства къ христіанству вообще. Изд. 2. Санктпетербургъ, Тип. Т-ва Общественная польза, 1880.
2 v. 25 cm.
1. Blood accusation. I. Title.
Title romanized: Ob upotreblenii evreĭami ... khristianskoĭ krovi dlîa religioznykh fŝeleĭ.
BM585.2.L58 1880 70-292343

NL 0416324 DLC WU

Lîūtostanskiĭ, Ippolit Iosifovich, 1835–1915.
Талмудъ и евреи. Сочиненіе И. Лютостанскаго. Москва, Тип. Л. Ѳ. Снегирева, 1879.
3 v. 25 cm.
Bibliography: v. 1, p. [ix]–xi.
1. Talmud—Commentaries. 2. Judaism—Controversial literature. 3. Jews—Rites and ceremonies. I. Title.
Title romanized: Talmud i evreï.
BM504.L57 76-293966

NL 0416325 DLC

Lîūtostanskiĭ, Ippolit Iosifovich, 1835–1915.
Талмудъ и евреи; компиляція изъ разныхъ талмудовъ и комментаріевъ. Изд. 3., испр. и доп. С.-Петербургъ, Тип. Т-ва худож. печати, 1902–09.
7 v. illus., col. map, ports. 25 cm.
Vols. 2–5 have imprint: С.-Петербургъ, Т-во худож. печати; v. 6: С.-Петербургъ, Тип. Т-ва Свѣтъ; v. 7: С.-Петербургъ, Отечественная тип.
1. Judaism—Controversial literature. 2. Jews—Civilization. 3. Jews—Nationality. I. Title.
Title romanized: Talmud i evreï.
BM585.L583 75-292513

NL 0416326 DLC

Lîūtostanskiĭ, Tomash-Ippolit
see
Lîūtostanskiĭ, Ippolit Iosifovich, 1835–1915.

Lîūtov, Pavel Timofeevich
see **Lutov, Paul Timothy**, 1900–

TK6553
.L55
Lîūtov, S A
Индустриальные помехи радиоприему и борьба с ними. Москва, Гос. энерг. изд-во, 1945.
142 p. illus. 22 cm.
1. Radio—Interference.
Title transliterated: Industrial'nye pomekhi radiopriemu.
TK6553.L55 50-17067

NL 0416329 DLC

TK6553
.L55
1951
Lîūtov, S A
Индустриальные помехи радиоприему и борьба с ними. Изд. 2., перер. Москва, Гос. энерг. изд-во, 1951.
239, [1] p. diagrs. 23 cm.
Bibliography: p. 238–[240]
1. Radio—Interference. I. Title.
Title transliterated: Industrial'nye pomekhi radiopriemu.
TK6553.L55 1951 51-31226

NL 0416330 DLC

Lîūtov, S A
Индустриальные помехи радиоприему и борьба с ними. Изд. 3., перер. Допущено в качестве учеб. пособия для электротехн. и энерг. вузов и факультетов. Москва, Гос. энерг. изд-во, 1952.
320 p. illus. 23 cm.
At head of title: С. А. Лютов.
Bibliography: p. [317]–320.
1. Radio—Interference. I. Title.
Title romanized: Industrial'nye pomekhi radiopriemu.
TK6553.L55 1952 68-34883

NL 0416331 DLC

Lîūtov, S A
Радиопомехи от электроустройств и их подавление. Москва, Гос. энерг. изд-во, 1952.
79 p. illus. 20 cm. (Массовая радиобиблиотека, вып. 156)
1. Radio—Interference. I. Title.
Title transliterated: Radiopomekhi ot ėlektroustroĭstv i ikh podavlenie.
TK6553.L56 54-17505 ‡

NL 0416332 DLC

Lîūtov, Viktor.
Упражненія въ чтеніи и переводахъ съ русскаго языка на нѣмецкій составленныя учителемъ русскаго языка Викторомъ Лютовымъ. Изданіе 3. исправленное и умноженное. Митава, Ѳ. Г. Лукасъ, 1852.
2 v. in 1. 18½cm.
1. Russian language—Chrestomathies and readers.
11-8007
Library of Congress PG2116.L5

NL 0416333 DLC

Lîūtovskiĭ, Ezhi
see
Lutowski, Jerzy.

Lîūtovskiĭ, Nikolaĭ Aleksandrovich, joint author.

Gurov, Petr Îakovlevich, 1881–
... Лесной кодекс Р.С.Ф.С.Р. в вопросах и ответах, с алфавитно-предметным указателем. С приложением текста Лесного кодекса, утвержденного сессией ВЦИК 6 июля 1923 года. Москва, Издательство Наркомзема "Новая деревия," 1924.

Liutpold III, Saint, margrave of Austria
see
Leopold III, Saint, margrave of Austria, 1073?-1136.

Liutprand, *Bp. of Cremona*
see **Liudprandus,** *Bp. of Cremona, d. ca.* 972.

Liutprandus, bp.
see
Liudprandus, bp. of Cremona, d. ca. 972.

[**Lîūtsenko, Efim Petrovich**] 1776–1854.
Похищеніе Прозерпины, въ трехъ пѣсняхъ, наизнанку. Въ Москвѣ, Въ Тип. А. Рѣшетникова, 1795.
93 p. 20 cm.
Preface signed: Е... Л...ко, А... К...кій.
I. Kotel'nitskiĭ, Aleksandr, joint author. II. Title.
Title transliterated: Pokhishchenie Prozerpiny
PG3315.L6P6 54-49847

NL 0416338 DLC

[**Lîūtsenko, Efim Petrovich**] 1776–1854.
Похищеніе Прозерпины, въ трехъ пѣсняхъ наизнанку. Изд. 2., вновь испр. и доп. Въ Санктпетербургѣ, Въ Театральной тип., 1805.
88 p. 18 cm.
By E. P. Lîūtsenko and A. Kotel'nitskiĭ.
I. Kotel'nitskiĭ, Aleksandr, joint author. II. Title.
Title transliterated: Pokhishchenie Prozerpiny.
PG3315.L6P6 1805 54-53672 ‡

NL 0416339 DLC

Lîūtts, Aleksandr Fedorovich.
Anlegung grosser Bauten. [Übersetzung: Anneliese Kuke] Berlin, Verlag Technik, 1953.
227 p. illus. 21 cm.
1. Surveying. 2. Building sites. I. Title.
TA545.L484 56-29272 ‡

NL 0416340 DLC

Lîūtts, Aleksandr Fedorovich.
Разбивка крупных сооружений; основные положения. Москва, Изд-во геодезической и картографической лит-ры, 1952.
224 p. diagrs. 23 cm.
Bibliography: p. 221–223.
1. Surveying. 2. Building sites. I. Title.
Title transliterated: Razbivka krupnykh sooruzhenii.
TA545.L48 1952 52-35137

NL 0416341 DLC

VOLUME 336

Liutwin
see
Lutwin, 13th cent.

NL

Lûtyĭ, I P
На передовой шахте. Ростов-на-Дону, Ростовское книжное изд-во, 1953.
Microfilm copy (negative) made in 1956 by the Library of Congress.
Collation of the original, as determined from the film: 33 p. illus., ports.
1. Coal mines and mining—Russia—Donets Basin. I. Title.
Title transliterated: Na peredovoĭ shakhte.
Microfilm Slavic 738 AC Mic 58-6159

NL 0416343 DLC

Liuzzi, Benedetto.
... Il Partito nazionale fascista nel diritto pubblico italiano. Roma, Società editrice del "Foro italiano", 1930.
1 p. l., [5]-96 p. 22½cm.
1. Partito nazionale fascista. 2. Italy—Constitutional law.
36-6386
329.945

NL 0416344 DLC ICU MH-L

95.3
L74 Liuzzi, Carlo.
Direttive per la coltivazione delle uve da tavola. Cagliari, Società editoriale italiana, 1931.
165 p.
1. Sardinia. Viticulture. 2. Grapes. Varieties. I. Cattedra ambulante di agricoltura per la Provincia di Cagliari.

NL 0416345 DNAL

Liuzzi, Fernando, 1884- 1940.
...Ballata e lauda alle origini della lirica musicale italiana.. [Roma, 1931.] 18 p. 26cm.
At head of title: R. Academia di S. Cecilia. Corso superiore di estetica e stilistica musicale (anno IV-1931-IX). Fernando Liuzzi.
"Estratto dall' annuario 1930-31 (cccxlvi-cccxlvii)."
Carnegie Corporation of New York.
1. Songs, Italian—Hist. and crit. 2. Songs, Sacred—Hist. and crit. I. Regia accademia di Santa Cecilia, Rome. II. Title.
October 13, 1933

NL 0416346 NN

780.72
L783c Liuzzi, Fernando, 1884-1940.
Corso superiore di estetica e stilistica musicale. Prelezione e sommario. [Rome] Accademia di Santa Cecilia, 1928.
25p. 28cm.
"Sommario delle lezioni successive": p.23-25.
"Estratto dall' Annuario della Regia Accademia di Santa Cecilia dal 1° luglio 1927 al 30 giugno (V-VI) pagg. 55-75."
1. Rome (City) Accademia di Santa Cecilia. Corso superiore di estetica e stilistica musicale.

NL 0416347 NcU

[Liuzzi, Fernando,] 1884-1940.
Drammi musicali dei secoli XI-XIV. I. Le vergini savie e le vergini folli... [Torino, 1930.] 82-109 p. illus. (music), 2 pl. (incl. facsim.) 25½cm.
Caption title.
Signed: Fernando Liuzzi.
Excerpt: Studi medievali. new ser. v. 3, fasc. 1.
Bibliographical footnotes.
1. Les vierges sages et les vierges folles., I. Title.
N. Y. P. L. August 31, 1933

NL 0416348 NN

Liuzzi, Fernando, 1884-1940.
...Due frammenti dell' Eneide, musicati in Roma nel seicento... Roma: Tipografia S. A. I. G. E., 1930. 495-504 p. 24½cm.
Cover-title.
The two fragments of Virgil's Aeneid were set to music by Mazzocchi with the titles "Dido furens" and "Nisus et Eurialus."
"Estratto dalla rivista 'Roma.'"
1. Mazzocchi, Domenico, 1592-1665. I. Virgil: Aeneid. II. Title.
October 13, 1933

NL 0416349 NN

Liuzzi, Fernando, 1884-
... L'espressione musicale nel dramma liturgico ... Torino, G. Chiantore, successore E. Loescher [1929]
2 p. l., 36 p. illus. (music) 24½cm.
"Estratto dagli Studi medievali, vol. II, fasc. 1, 21 aprile 1929—VII."
1. Mysteries and miracle-plays. 2. Drama, Medieval—Hist. & crit. 3. Music—Hist. & crit.—Medieval. 4. Chant (Plain, Gregorian, etc.) I. Title.
33-1042
Library of Congress ML178.L5
783.28

NL 0416350 DLC

Liuzzi, Fernando, 1884-
... Estetica della musica; studi e saggi. Firenze, Società anonima editrice "La Voce", 1924.
4 p. l., [3]-260 p., 2 l. 20½cm. (On cover: Biblioteca di filosofia contemporanea, diretta da Odoardo Campa. IX)
Contents.—Visibilità e udibilità.—Estetica "kreisleriana" (da E. T. A. Hoffmann a Roberto Schumann)—Un quesito di estetica musicale in Anatole France.—Opinioni.—Musica latina e musica tedesca.—"Tristano e Isolda" come poema drammatico.—"Ariane et Barbe-bleue" di M. Maeterlinck e P. Dukas.—Ernest Bloch.
1. Music—Philosophy and esthetics. 2. Music—Addresses, essays, lectures. I. Title.
25-4246
Library of Congress ML3845.L56

NL 0416351 DLC CLU NcD MH MB NN

780.9
L783g Liuzzi, Fernando, 1884-1940.
Il gusto barocco e la polifonia romana. [Rome] R. Accademia di S. Cecilia, 1930.
26p. 28cm.
Music lib.
At head of title: R. Accademia di S. Cecilia. Corso superiore di estetica e stilistica musicale (Anno III - 1930 - VIII)
"Estratto dall' Annuario della R. Accademia di Santa Cecilia 1929-30."
1. Music, Baroque. 2. Counterpoint - History. I. Rome (City) Accademia di Santa Cecilia. Corso superiore di estetica e stilistica musicale. II. Title.

NL 0416352 NcU

Liuzzi, Fernando, 1884-
...Il gusto barocco e la polifonia romana... [Roma, 1931.] 26 p. 27cm.
At head of title: R. Accademia di S. Cecilia. Corso superiore di estetica e stilistica musicale (anno III-1930-VIII). Fernando Liuzzi.
"Estratto dall' annuario 1929-30 (cccxlv-cccxlvi)."
1. Music—Italy. I. Regia accademia di Santa Cecilia, Rome. II. Title.
October 13, 1933

NL 0416353 NN

Liuzzi, Fernando, 1884-1940.
... La lauda e i primordi della melodia italiana ... [Roma] La Libreria dello stato, anno XIII. e. f. [1935]
2 v. col. fronts., plates (part col.) facsims. (music) 35½ cm.
Each plate accompanied by guard sheet with descriptive letterpress. Plates are reproductions of miniatures from the original manuscripts.
"Di questa opera ... sono stati stampati ... 500 esemplari numerati da 1 a 500. Esemplare numero 84."
Includes bibliographies.
Contents.—I. Albori della lirica musicale in Italia. Le melodie del Laudario 91 di Cortona. Le melodie del Laudario II, I, 122 di Firenze. Laude di Garzo, di Jacopone, di Ugo Panziera. Notazione e trascrizione. La melodia italiana fino all' "ars nova." Monumenti: Il Laudario 91 di Cortona; facsimili, trascrizioni, testi e note.—II. Monumenti: Il Laudario magliabechiano II, I, 122 di Firenze; facsimili, trascrizioni, testi e note.
1. Hymns, Italian. 2. Religious poetry, Italian. 3. Italian poetry—Early to 1400. 4. Church music—Italy—Hist. & crit. 5. Music—Manuscripts—Facsimiles. 6. Manuscripts, Italian—Facsimiles. I. Laudario di Cortona. II. Laudario magliabechiano. III. Cortona Biblioteca comunale e dell'Accademia etrusca. Mss. (91) IV. Florence. R. Biblioteca nazionale centrale. Mss. (Cod. Magl. II, I, 122) V. Title.
37-37927
Library of Congress M2.L76L3
783.6

NL 0416355 CtY PP PSt NSyU GU MB FTaSU OU NBC NcD IEN CU DLC CaBVaU MU ICU NIC NcU CLU PU-FA

783.9
L783m Liuzzi, Fernando, 1884-1940.
Melodie italiane inedite nel duecento. Genève, Leo Olschki, 1930.
36p. 28cm.
Music lib.
"Estratto dall'Archivum Romanicum, v. XIV, Nr. 4 - Ottobre-Dicembre 1930."
"Questo saggio offre, in riassunto, una parte della trattazione compresa nel volume La lauda della melodia italiana ..."
Includes the melodies of the hymns.
1. Catholic Church - Hymns. 2. Hymns, Italian. 3. Church music - Italy - History and criticism. I. Title

NL 0416356 NcU

LIUZZI, FERNANDO, 1884-1940.
Musica e poesia del trecento nel Codice vaticano rossiano 215. (IN: Pontificia di accademia romana di archaeologia. Rendiconti. [Roma] 26cm. v.13, fasc. 1-2 (1937) p. [59]-71)
Bibliographical footnotes.
1. Vatican. Biblioteca vaticana. Mss. (Rossiano 215) 2. Manuscripts, 14th cent.

NL 0416357 NN

Liuzzi, Fernando, 1884-1940.
... I musicisti in Francia ... di Fernando Liuzzi. Roma, Edizioni d'arte Danesi, 1946.
v. illus., plates, ports., facsims. (incl. music) 30 x 23½ cm. (Half-title: L'Opera del genio italiano all'estero. Ser. 2.)
Contents.—v. 1. I musicisti italiani in Francia dalle origini al secolo XVII.
1. Music—France. 2. Musicians, Italian. I. Title.
ML270.L6 47-27531

NL 0416358 PU-Mu IU NjP PP NcU GU DLC NcD WaU NIC NNC MB TxU NN MiU OU

Liuzzi, Fernando, 1884-1940, ed.
La passione nelle intonazioni del Laudario 91 di Cortona (secolo XIII)
see under Laudario di Cortona.

Liuzzi, Fernando, 1884-1940.
...Profilo musicale di Jacopone (con melodie inedite)... Roma: Bestetti e Tumminelli, 1931. 24 p. illus. (music.) 24cm.
"Dalla Nuova antologia, 16 settembre, 1931."
Bibliographical footnotes.
1. Jacopone da Todi, 1230-1306. I. Title.
August 31, 1933

NL 0416360 NN

VOLUME 336

Liuzzi, Fernando, 1884-1940.
Sei canti ad una voce con accompagnamento di pianoforte, di Fernando Liuzzi... Milano: Carisch & Jänichen [cop. 1914]. Publ. pl. nos. C. 13641–13646 J. 37 p. f°.

Italian words with music.
Contents: no. 1. Alba festiva. no. 2. Saffica. no. 3. Canzone d'Oriente. no. 4. Sogno dell' alba. no. 5. Ballatetta. no. 6. Soglia d' oblio.

1. Songs (Italian).

April 25, 1919.

NL 0416361 NN

Liuzzi, Fernando, 1884–1940.
...Tre canti popolari serbi sulla versione italiana di Pietro Kasandric, musicati per una voce e pianoforte da Fernando Liuzzi ... Milano: G. Ricordi & C., cop. 1915. Publ. pl. no. 115443. 11 p. f°.

Italian words with music for 1 voice with piano acc.
Words are Italian translations of Serbian folk songs.

1. Songs (Italian). 2. Folk songs (Serbian). 3. Kasandrić, Pietro, translator.

November 9, 1922.

NL 0416362 NN

M2003 .S8V4

Liuzzi, Fernando, 1884-1940. Le vergini savie e le vergini folli.
Sponsus.

... Le vergini savie e le vergini folli ("Sponsus") Dramma liturgico del secolo XI (dal m. s. lat. 1139 della Biblioteca nazionale di Parigi) liberamente interpretato per la scena moderna, da Fernando Liuzzi. [Roma? °1939]

Liuzzi, Ferruccio
... Arturo Rimbaud. Roma, A. F. Formiggini, 1925.
2 p.l., [7]-72 p. front. (port.) 16cm. (Added t.-p.: Profili, n. 85)

Added t.-p. within ornamental border.
"Nota bibliografica": p. 72.

1. Rimbaud, Jean Arthur, 1854-1891.

NL 0416364 NNC CtY PP

Liuzzi, Ferruccio A
... De delictis contra auctoritates ecclesiasticas (cann. 2331–2340) ... Romae, Officium libri catholici, 1942.

3 p. l., [ix]–xvi, 164 p. 25½cm.

At head of title: Ferrutius A. Liuzzi ... Commentarius de singulis delictis in iure canonico.
"Bibliographia": p. [xiii]–xvi.

1. Insubordination (Canon law) 2. Criminal law (Canon law) I. Title.

A F 47–951

Union theol. sem. Library for Library of Congress †

NL 0416365 NNUT DLC MBtS TxDaM DCU

Liuzzi, Guido, 1866–
... I servizi logistici nella guerra ... Milano, Corbaccio [1934]

2 p. l., 7–456, [1] p., 1 l. 5 fold. maps, tables (part fold.) diagrs. (part fold.) 20cm. (*Half-title:* Storia della guerra italiana. 15)

Some of the illustrative material is in pocket.
"Bibliografia": p. 11–[12]

1. European war, 1914–1918—Italy. 2. Logistics. 3. Italy. Esercito.

D569.A2L55 940.345 A 42–4189

Peabody inst., Baltimore. Library for Library of Congress [a46c1]†

NL 0416366 MdBP OC1 NN MB CtY DLC

DG 566 .L 78

LIUZZI,GUIDO, 1866-
Vittorio Emanuele III. Torino, Chiantore, 1935.
193 p. illus., ports. (Dal risorgimento al fascismo)

1. Vittorio Emanuele III, King of Italy, 1869-1947.

NL 0416367 InU

Liuzzi, Innocenzo.
Osservazioni sul colera morbus indiano fatte in Roma nell' estate dell' anno 1837; precedute dalla storia dell' invasione e da alcune riflessioni sull' indole e sulla natura del detto morbo. Roma: Salviucci, 1839. 95 p. 8°.

1. Cholera (Asiatic). Italy: Rome, 1837.

December 20, 1913

NL 0416368 NN DNLM

Liuzzi (Innocenzo). Progressi sulla medicina omiopatica. 11 pp. 8°. *Roma*, 1838. [P., v. 1452.]
Repr. from: Album, distrib. 7, Anno v.

NL 0416369 DNLM

WCB L783r 1835

LIUZZI, Innocenzo
Riflessioni sul cholera morbus asiatico. Roma, 1835.
16 p.

NL 0416370 DNLM

Liv, Égon
see
Livs, Egons.

Liv-, est- und curlaendisches privatrecht. Zusammengestellt auf befehl des herrn und kaisers Alexander II. St. Petersburg, Buchdr. der Zweiten abtheilung Seiner Kaiserlichen Majestät eigener kanzlei, 1864.

xl, 776, 172 p. 27½cm. (*Added t.-p.:* Provincialrecht der ostseegouvernements. 3. th.)

"Verzeichniss der quellen des Liv-, est- und curlaendischen privatrechts", followed by "Alphabetisches sachregister": 172 p. at end.

1. Law—Baltic Provinces. I. Livonia. Laws, statutes, etc. II. Esthonia. Laws, statutes, etc. III. Courland. Laws, statutes, etc.

26–8505

NL 0416372 DLC CLU

Liv och folkkultur. v. 1–
1948–
Stockholm.

v. illus., ports., maps. 26 cm. annual.

Issued by Samfundet för svensk folklivsforskning.

1. Sweden—Civilization—Period. I. Samfundet för svensk folklivsforskning.

DL601.L58 52–20985

NL 0416373 DLC CU KU N

W 1 LI996

LIV og helse.
Oslo [195-?]-
v. illus.
Continues Liv og sundhet.
1. Hygiene - Period.

NL 0416374 DNLM

PT7915 .L75

Liv og levned ..., udg. af Anders Uhrskov. København, H. Aschehoug & co., Dansk forlag, 1927–

v. illus., ports. 21½cm.

Title vignette.
Each vol. has also special t.-p.

1. Denmark—Biog. 2. Denmark—Soc. life & cust.

NL 0416375 ICU

Liv rust kammaren
see
Livrustkammaren.

Liva, Enrico
Origine del moto dei corpi celesti caldi.
Senigallia, 20 Novembre 1921.
Printed card. 9 x 14 cm.

NL 0416377 DNC

Liva, Enrico
Il potere calorico della materia nella gravitazione universale.
Senigallia, Tipografia Editrice Marchigiana, 1921.
12 p. 22cm.

NL 0416378 DN-Ob

Liva, Henry.
Some considerations on some scientific views, by Henry Liva. [Brooklyn? c1942] 8 p. 23cm.

With autograph of author.

1. Physics—Addresses, essays, lectures.

December 28, 1943

NL 0416379 NN

Liva, Henry
Temperature and attraction, by Henry Liva ... [Brooklyn, N. Y., Heilmeier press, c1942.
[3] p. 21½cm.

Caption title.

NL 0416380 NNC

Líva, Václav.
...Bouře nad Prahou; aneb, Švédové před Prahou a v Praze, r. 1648. Praha, V. Žikeš, 1948. illus. 16cm. (Žikešův pražský špalíček. sv. 7)

1. vyd.
Bibliography, p. 97-[99].

1. Fiction, Bohemian. 2. Thirty Years' war, 1618-1648—Fiction.

NL 0416381 NN MH InU

DB212 L58

Líva, Václav
Obležení Prahy roku 1648. V Praze, Kruh pro Studium Čs. Dějin Vojenských, 1936.
48 p. 25 cm. (Rozpravy Kruhu pro Studium Čs. Dejin Vojenských při Vědeckém Ústavu Vojenském, sv. 6)

1. Bohemia - Hist. - 1526- 2. Prague - Hist. I. Title(1) II.:Ser.: Prague. Vědecký Ústav Vojenský. Rozpravy, sv. 6.

NL 0416382 CtY

VOLUME 336

DB205
.4
.P7
Liva, Václav, ed.
Prameny k československým dějinám vojenským. sv. 1-
V Praze, Naše vojsko [1937-

Liva, Václav, ed.
Prameny k dějinám třicetileté války
see under Czechoslovak Republic.
Ministerstvo vnitra. Archiv.

Bq60A
+B45
3
Líva, Václav ed.
Pražská města, [1.vyd.] Praha, Archiv Bývalé země České, 1949.
199p. 2fold.maps(1 col.) 30cm. (Berní rula, sv.3)
Bibliographical footnotes.

NL 0416385 CtY

Div.S.
Pam.
Coll.
Liva, Victor.
... Prêtres a la barre ... Bruxelles, E. Wittmann, 1879.
69 p. 18½cm.
At head of title: Tout pour et par le peuple.

NL 0416386 NcD

Livable house series.
New York, 1917-

NL 0416387 DLC MiU

Livache, Achille.
FOR OTHER EDITIONS SEE MAIN ENTRY
McIntosh, John Geddes.
The manufacture of varnishes and kindred industries based on and including the "Drying oils and varnishes" of Ach. Livache, by John Geddes McIntosh ... 2d, greatly enl., English ed. ... London, Scott, Greenwood & son; New York, D. Van Nostrand co.; [etc., etc.] 1904-11.

Livache, Achille.
The manufacture of varnishes, oil crushing, refining and boiling and kindred industries, describing the manufacture and chemical and physical properties of spirit varnishes and oil varnishes; raw materials; resins; solvents and colouring principles; drying oils, their extraction, properties and applications; oil refining and boiling; the manufacture, employment and testing of various varnishes, tr. from the French of Ach. Livache ... greatly extended and adapted to English practice with numerous original recipes by John Geddes McIntosh ... London, Scott, Greenwood & co., 1899.
vii, 403 p. illus. 22 cm.

1. Varnish and varnishing. I. McIntosh, John Geddes, tr. *Translation of* Vernis et huiles siccatives.

TP935.L56 Agr 4-423
U. S. Dept. of Agr. Libr. 392L74
for Library of Congress [a56e1]†

NL 0416390 DNAL ICRL DN ICJ MB DLC Or

Livache, Achille
Rapport ... sur le travail de M. E. Fleurent, intitulé: Recherches sur la composition immédiate et élémentaire des matières albuminoïdes extraites du grain des céréales et des graines légumineuses; conséquences pratiques de cette étude.
Ann. sci. agron. 1898, tome 1, p. 418-421. Paris, 1898.

1. Cereals. Protein content. 2. Legumes. Protein content. I. Fleurent, Emile Charles Albert.
Agr 4-875
Library, U. S. Dept. of Agriculture

NL 0416391 DNAL

Law
Livache, Achille, joint author.
Porée, Henri.
Traité théorique et pratique des manufactures et ateliers dangereux, insalubres ou incommodes (établissements classés); conditions de leur autorisation et de leur exploitation, obligations et responsabilité de l'industriel à l'égard des voisins, par Henri Porée [et] Ach. Livache. Paris, Impr. et librairie générale de jurisprudence, 1887.

Livache, Achille
Vernis et huiles siccatives. Paris, Baudry & Cie, 1896.
316p.

NL 0416393 ICRL ICJ

Livacic Gazzano, Ernesto.
Literatura chilena; manual y antología [por] Ernesto Livacic Gazzano [y] Alejo Roa Bleck. [Santiago de Chile] Editorial Salesiana de Textos Escolares, 1955.
350p. 19cm.
Bibliography: p.105-106.
1. Chilean literature - Hist. & crit. I. Roa Bleck, Alejo, joint author.

NNC NcU WU FU
NL 0416394 TxU WaU NjP DPU RPB MH NN CU ICU CtY

Livacich, Serafín.
... Buenos Aires; páginas históricas para el primer centenario de la independencia ... Buenos Aires, Compañía sudamericana de billetes de banco, 1907.
1 p. l., [v]-viii, 291 p., 1 l. plates, fold. plans, facsims. 22½cm.
"Obras consultadas": 1 p. at end.

1. Buenos Aires—Hist.
A 17-383
Title from Leland Stanford Jr. Univ. Printed by L. C.

NL 0416395 CSt TxU CU CtY

Livacich, Serafín.
... Gloria argentina; relación sintética, descriptiva y filosófica de la historia argentina completa desde la revolución de mayo de 1810, hasta la reorganización nacional. Obra esencialmente original escrita con motivo del centenario. Buenos Aires, A. Moen y hermano, 1910.
1 p. l., [5]-153 p., 1 l. 18½cm.

1. Argentine Republic—Hist.—1810- I. Title.
19-11618
Library of Congress F2843.L78

NL 0416396 DLC MB

Livacich, Serafín.
... Historia de los Incas, ó sea Origen, progreso y fin de su imperio; extractado de la colección documental "Odriozola." Buenos Aires, Cabaut y cía, 1904.
64 p., 1 l. 23cm.
Extracted by Serafín Livacich from two works comp. by Manuel de Odriozola, "Documentos históricos del Perú," and "Colección de documentos literarios del Perú." *cf.* p. 6.
Contents.—Advertencia.—Fundación del imperio de los Incas.—Manco-Cupac.—Sinchi Roca.—Lloque Yupanqui.—Mayta Capac.—Capac-Yupanqui.—Inca Roca.—Yahuar-Huaca.—Viracocha.—Pachacutec.—Inca-Yupanqui.—Tupac-Yupanqui.—Huayna Capac.—Huascar.—Atahualpa. Religión de los Incas.
1. Incas. I. Odriozola, Manuel de.
16-24632
Library of Congress F3429.L78

NL 0416397 DLC NcD NcU ICU DAU CtY

Livacich, Serafín.
... Notas históricas ... Buenos Aires, 1916.
3 p. l., [v]-vii p., 1 l., 2, 520 p., 1 l. front. (port.) illus., double plan. 20½cm.
"Nuestra antigua prensa satírica": p. [446]-449.

1. Argentine Republic—Hist. 2. Argentine periodicals—Bibl.
16-17611
Library of Congress F2808.L78

NL 0416398 DLC NSyU

Livacich, Serafín.
... Recordando el pasado; historia argentina—tradiciones americanas—biografías—notas bibliográficas y literarias. Buenos Aires, J. Peuser, 1909.
viii, 172 p. 21cm.

1. Argentine Republic—Hist. 2. Argentine Republic—Biog.
11-28344
Library of Congress F2801.L78

NL 0416399 DLC

Livacich, Serafín, tr.
Seljan, Mirko.
... El salto del Guayrá. La chute du Guayrá. Buenos Aires [Impr. G. Kraft] 1905.

Livadas, Ch
Λόγος πανηγυρικός εἰς τήν ἀνάμνησιν τῆς κοιμήσεως τῆς Παναγίας. Ἐν Ἀθήναις, 1869.
23 p. 22cm.

NL 0416401 OCU

Livadas (Démosthènes) [1875-]. *De la coexistence de la môle hydatiforme et de la dégénérescence kystique des ovaires. 91 pp., 1 l. 8°. Lyon. 1906. No. 112.

NL 0416402 DNLM

M(055)
T414pu
no.2
Livadas, G C
Fish rains in western Macedonia. Thessalonike, 1954.
8 p. illus., map. 25 cm. (Thessalonike. Panepistemion. Ergasterion Meteorologias kai Klimatologias. Publications, 2)

NL 0416403 DAS

VOLUME 336

WC 765 qL784ma 1940
LIVADAS, Gregory A
'Η ἑλονοσία ἐν 'Ελλάδι 1930-1940· ἔρευναι, καταπολέμησις, ὑπὸ Γρηγορίου Α. Λιβαδᾶ καὶ 'Ιωάννου Κ. Σφάγγου. 'Αθῆναι, "Πυρσοῦ," 1940.
2 v. illus., ports.
Title transliterated: Hē helonosia en Helladi 1930-1940; ereunai, katapolemēsis.
Issued also in English.

Contains authors' signature.
1. Malaria - Greece I. Sphangos, John C Autographs - Livadas, Gregory A Autographs - Sphangos, John C

NL 0416405 DNLM

---

448 L74E
Livadas, Gregory A
E helonosia en Helladi (1946-47) Epeunai-katapolemesis. Athenai, 1948.
45 p.

Greek and English.

NL 0416406 DNAL

WC 750 L787h 1955
LIVADAS, Gregory A
'Η ἑλονοσία: ἱστορία, γεωγραφικὴ κατανομή, παρασιτολογία, παθογενεία, ἱστοπαθολογία, κλινική, θεραπεία, ἐντομολογία, ἐπιδημιολογία, καταπολέμησις. 'Αθῆναι [Δρούκας καὶ Κόνσολας] 1955.
255 p. illus.
Title transliterated: Hē helonosia.
Contains author's signature.
1. Malaria

NL 0416407 DNLM

WC 765 qL784m 1946
LIVADAS, Gregory A
Malaria control activities in Greece during 1946; by Gr. A. Livadas and George D. Belios. Athens, 1946.
22 ℓ. illus.
1. Malaria - Greece 2. Malaria - Prevention I. Belios, George D

NL 0416408 DNLM

Livadas, Gregory A
Malaria in Greece (1930–1940). Research-control. By Gregory A. Livadas ... and John C. Sphangos ... Athens, Pyrsos press, 1941, '40.
2 v. illus. (part col.) ports. $25\frac{1}{2}$cm.
Published also in Greek.
L.C. copy: illus., plates, group port, maps, plans, tables, diagrs. Bibliography: v.1, p. 21-22, 43.
1. Malarial fever—Greece. [1. Malaria—Greece] I. Sphangos, John C., joint author.
RC163.G9L5 Med 47-334†
U. S. Army medical library for Library of Congress [WC300qL784m 1941] 614.53

NL 0416409 DNLM WaU CtY-M DNAL ICU DLC

WC 765 L784me 1946
LIVADAS, Gregory A
'Η μέθοδος τοῦ ψεκασμοῦ τῶν καταφυγίων τῶν ἀνωφελῶν κωνώπων διὰ τοῦ νέου ἐντομοκτόνου DDT· πειραματικαὶ δοκιμασίαι. Adult spraying with DDT; experimental applications [ὑπὸ] Γρηγ. Α. Λιβαδᾶ [καὶ ἄ.] 'Αθῆναι, Διαλησμᾶ, 1946.
99 p. illus.
Title transliterated: Hē methodos tou psekasmou tōn kataphygiōn tōn anōphelōn kōnōpōn dia tou neou entomoktonou DDT; peiramatikai dokimasiai.

Continued in next column

Continued from preceding column

Lecture delivered in summary at a meeting of the Iatrocheirourgikē hetaireia Athēnōn, Mar. 6, 1946.
Contains summary in English.
Contains errata slip.
1. Malaria - Greece 2. Malaria - Prevention

NL 0416411 DNLM PPC DNAL NN

QV 256 L784t 1947
LIVADAS, Gregory A
'Η θεραπεία καὶ προφύλαξις τῆς ἑλονοσίας βάσει τῶν νεωτέρων δεδομένων· κινίνη, πλασμωκίνη, ἀτεβρίνη, παλουδρίνη - M 4888. 'Αθῆναι ['Απατσίδη] 1947.
26 p. illus.
Title transliterated: Hē therapeia kai prophylaxis tēs helonosias basei tōn neōterōn dedomenōn; kininē, plasmōkinē, atebrinē, paloudrinē - M 4888.

Contains summary in French.
Cover title.
Reprinted from Archeion Iatr. Epistēmōn, t. B, teuch. 11, 1-15 May 1947.
1. Drugs - Antimalarial 2. Malaria - Treatment

NL 0416413 DNLM

Livadas, Spyridonos Z.
... Η γπαμματικη του δημοτικού σχολειου. η γπαμματικαι και οπθογπαφικαι ασκησειο ειο την γοαφομένην ελληνεξην μετα ξανονων ενονων ... Κατα το αναλγοαμμα τον Υπουργειου της Παιδειας. Εκδοσισ νεα. Εκδοτησ Μιξαηλ Ι. Σαλιβεροσ. Εν αθηναισ, Βιβλιοπωλειον Μιξαηλ Ι. Σαλιβερου, 1917.
112 p. $21\frac{1}{2}$cm.
At head of title: ΣΠΥΡΙΔΩΝΟΣ Ζ. ΛΙΒΑΔΑ.
On cover: New York, N.Y. ΒΙΒΛΙΟΠΩΛΕΙΟΝ "ΑΤΛΑΣ".

1. Greek language, Modern—Grammar. I. Saliveros, Michael I., ed.

NL 0416414 ViU MB

[**Livadas, Theagenēs**] 1828–1902.
Ἄρτεμις Γ. Γενναδίου· βιογραφικαὶ ἀναμνήσεις. ὑπὸ Θ. Λ. (Ἐκ τῆς „Ἡμέρας" *ἀρθ.* 487 *τῆς* 31/12 *ἀπρ.* 1884) *Ἐν Βιέννῃ, ἐκ τῆς Καισαρο-βασιλικῆς τυπογραφίας*, 1884.
24 p. $18\frac{1}{2}$cm. [*With his* Artemis G. Gennadius; biographical reminiscences. London, 1890]
Vignettes on cover, t.-p., and at end of text.

1. Gennadios, Artemis (Benizelos) 1811–1884.

16-19262

Library of Congress DF803.9.G3L5

NL 0416415 DLC

Livadas, Theagenēs, 1828–1902.
Artemis G. Gennadius; biographical reminiscences by Dr. Th. Livadas ... London [Harrison and sons, printers] 1890.
24 p. $18\frac{1}{2}$cm.
Reprinted at the Imperial and royal press in Vienna from the "Hemera," no. 487 of the 31/12 April, 1884; and now tr. from the original Greek and printed privately.
With this is bound the original Greek.

1. Gennadios, Artemis (Benizelos) 1811–1884.

17-811

Library of Congress DF803.9.G3L5

NL 0416416 DLC

Pamph. v.421
LIVADEAS, Them
Philosophical discussions comprising articles concerning the new philosophy and philosophical sciences of Apostolos Makrakis and the philosophy of Spinoza and its pernicious errors. Chicago, Hellenic Christian Educational Society, 1948.
39p. 23cm.

NL 0416417 MH-AH PPPrHi OO

DR701 .S5L5
Livadeōs, Alexandros D
Τὸ 'Αλβανικὸν ζήτημα καὶ ἡ ἔναντι τούτου θέσις τοῦ 'Ελληνισμοῦ [ὑπὸ] 'Αλεξάνδρου Δ. Λιβαδέως. 'Εν 'Αθήναις, 1946.
23 p. 19cm.

1. Albania - History. I. Title.

NL 0416418 OCU

DR68 .L5
Livadeōs, Alexandros D
Βούλγαροι καὶ Βουλγαρισμοί [ὑπὸ] 'Αλεξάνδρου Δ. Λιβαδέως. 'Εν 'Αθήναις, 1945.
52 p. 21cm.

1. Bulgaria - History. I. Title.

NL 0416419 OCU DLC-P4

D829 .G8L5
Livadeōs, Alexandros D
Ἡ οἰκονομικὴ πλευρὰ τοῦ 'Ελληνικοῦ προβλήματος. Αθῆναι, 1945.
15 p. tables. 19cm.

At head of title: Α.Δ. Λιβάδεως.

NL 0416420 OCU

Livadeus, Alexandros D
see Livadeōs, Alexandros D.

Livadić, Branimir, 1871- ed.
Kranjčević, Silvije Strahimir, 1865–1908.
... Kroz život i djelo, priredio dr. Branimir Livadić. Zagreb, Minerva nakladna knjižara d. d., 1934.

PG 1618 .L 78 L 4
LIVADIĆ, BRANIMIR, 1871-
Legenda o Amisu i Amilu. Zagreb, Društvo hrvatskih književnika, 1913.
60 p. illus. (Savremeni hrvatski pisci, redovita izdanja Društva hrvatskih književnika, knj. 27.)

NL 0416423 InU OCl

PG 1658 .S6 M9
LIVADIĆ, BRANIMIR, 1871-
Novele. Zagreb, Nakl. Društva hrvatskih književnika. 1910.
129 p. illus., port. (Savremeni hrvatski pisci, redovita izdanja Društva hrvatskih književnika, knj. 8)
Bound with Šimunović, D. Mrkodol.

NL 0416424 InU

VOLUME 336

Hsg55 Livadić, Branimir, 1871-
L7424 Novele; novi izbor. Zagreb, 1932.
A1 169 p. 19 cm. (Izvanredno izdanje Matice
1932 Hrvatske za god. 1932)

NL 0416425 CtY

PG 1618 LIVADIĆ, BRANIMIR, 1871-
.L78 A17 Pjesme i pripoviesti. Uredio Stanko Gašparović. Zagreb, Suvremena biblioteka, 1944.
457 p. port. (Suvremena biblioteka. Izvanredno izdanje, knj. 18)

NL 0416426 InU FTaSU

Livadić, Branimir, 1871- ed.

Kranjčević, Silvije Strahimir, 1865–1908.
... Pred vizijama, priredio dr. Branimir Livadić. Zagreb, Minerva nakladna knjižara d. d., 1934.

Livadić, Branimir, 1871- ed.

Kranjčević, Silvije Strahimir, 1865–1908.
... Za čovjeka, priredio dr. Branimir Livadić. Zagreb, Minerva nakladna knjižara d. d., 1934.

Livadić, Branimir, 1871- ed.

Kranjčević, Silvije Strahimir, 1865–1908.
... Za narod, priredio dr. Branimir Livadić. Zagreb, Minerva nakladna knjižara d. d., 1933.

HX 365.5 LIVADIĆ, STJEPAN
.L 7 Politicki eseji. Zagreb ‹Stamparija "Grafika"› 1937.
91 p.

1. Socialism in Croatia.

NL 0416430 InU MH

LIVADIC, Vjekoslav.
Bosančice. Crte, pjesme, price i pripovjesti iz zivota Bosanskoga. Zagreb, 1882.

NL 0416431 MH

Livadić Wiesner, Branimir
see Livadić, Branimir, 1871-

Livaditi, Demetrio.
Operette umoristiche satiriche e filosofiche. New ed. edl. Bologna, Zanchelli, 1895.
433 p.

NL 0416433 PU

Livak, John Elmer, joint author.

Johnson, Treat Baldwin, 1875–
... Researches on pyrimidines. CXLIX. The synthesis of aryl substituted dihydrouracils and their conversion to uracil derivatives, by Treat B. Johnson and John E. Livak. [Easton, Pa., 1936]

Livan
see
Lebanon.

Livanii
see
Libanius.

Livanos, Constantine N 1889–
John Sakellaridis and Egyptian cotton. By C. N. Livanos ... Alexandria, Egypt, Printed by A. Procaccia, 1939.
4 p. l., 13–138 p. illus., fold. pl., ports., map, diagrs. $24\frac{1}{2}$cm.
Two portraits accompanied by guard sheet with descriptive letterpress.
Bibliography: p. 137–138.

1. Cotton—[Egypt] 2. Sakellaridis, John, 1845–1933.

Agr 40-613 Revised

U. S. Dept. of agr. Library for Library of Congress 281.372L74 [r41c2]

NL 0416437 DNAL NN

Livanov, A K
Приборы газопроводов контрольно-измерительные и автоматически регулирующие. Москва, Изд-во Министерства коммунального хозяйства РСФСР, 1952.
226 p. illus. 22 cm.
Bibliography: p. [225]

1. Gas manufacture and works—Apparatus. I. Title.
Title transliterated: Pribory gazoprovodov.

TP754.L5 53-25648

NL 0416438 DLC

Livanov, Antonii Valentinovich, 1876–
Матеріалы къ вопросу о вліяніи тромбокиназы на коллатеральное кровообращеніе въ связи съ общимъ ея дѣйствіемъ на организмъ; экспериментальное изслѣдованіе. С.-Петербургъ, Тип. Штаба Отдѣльнаго корпуса жандармовъ, 1912.
180 p. 22 cm. (Серія докторскихъ диссертацій, допущенныхъ къ защитѣ въ Императорской Военно-медицинской академіи въ 1911–1912 учебномъ году, № 35)
Diss.—Leningrad.
Vita.
Bibliography: p. [169]–177 2. Collateral circulation
1. Blood—Coagulation. I. Title.
Title transliterated: Materialy k voprosu o vlîiânii trombokinazy na kollateral'noe krovoobrashchenie.

QP91.L55 57-53413

NL 0416439 DLC

Livanov, Fedor Vasil'evich.
Раскольники и острожники; очерки и разсказы. [Изд. 1.] Санктпетербургъ, Въ Тип. М. Хана, 1868–73.
4 v. ports. 25 cm.
Includes bibliographical references.

1. Raskolniks. 2. Sects—Russia. I. Title.
Title romanized: Raskol'niki i ostrozhniki.

BX601.L58 76-277024

NL 0416440 DLC

QP372
L74
1954 Livanov, Mikhail Nikolaevich
Some results of electrophysiological investigations of conditioned reflex links. London, 1954.
‹9›-15 p. illus.

"From Fifty years of Pavlov's teaching, 1952."
From SCR Soviet medical bulletin, v. 1, no. 2, June 1954.

NL 0416441 NNC-M

Livanov, Nikolaĭ Aleksandrovich, 1876–
Acanthobdella peledina Grube, 1851, Морфологическое изслѣдованіе. Казань, Типо-лит. Имп. Университета, 1905.
271 p. 9 plates. 24 cm.

1. Acanthobdella peledina.

QL391.H6L6 39-10160 rev

NL 0416442 DLC

Livanov, Nikolaĭ Aleksandrovich, 1876–
Die Organisation der Hirudineen und die Beziehungen dieser Gruppe zu den Oligochäten, von N. Livanow ... Mit 33 Abbildungen im Text.
(*In* Ergebnisse und Fortschritte der Zoologie. Jena, 1931. $24\frac{1}{2}$cm. 7. Bd., p. [378]–484. illus.)
"Literaturverzeichnis": p. 477–484.

NL 0416443 ICJ

Livanov, Nikolaĭ Aleksandrovich, 1876–
Пути эволюции животного мира; анализ организации главнейших типов многоклеточных животных. Москва, Советская наука, 1955.
398 p. illus. 23 cm.
Includes bibliography.

1. Evolution. I. Title.
Title transliterated: Puti évolîûtsii zhivotnogo mira.

QH366.L58 57-24139 ‡

NL 0416444 DLC

Livanov, V A
Отжиг листового алыкледа; под ред. И. С. Виштынецкого и С. М. Воронова. Москва, Гос. изд-во обор. промышл., 1940.
123, [5] p. illus. 23 cm.
At head of title: В. А. Ливанов [и др.]
"Литература": p. [128]
—— —— Microfilm copy (negative)
Microfilm TS-7

1. Duralumin. 2. Aluminothermy. I. Title.
Title transliterated: Otzhig listovogo al'kleda.

TN775.L64 50-47256 rev

NL 0416445 DLC

Livanova, Tamara Nikolaevna.
Глинка; творческий путь. Москва, Гос. музыкальное изд-во, 1955.
2 v. illus., ports., music. 23 cm.
At head of title: Академия наук СССР. Институт истории искусств. Т. Ливанова, Вл. Протопопов.
Errata slip inserted.
"Список произведений М. И. Глинки": v. 2, p. 359–[370]

1. Glinka, Mikhail Ivanovich, 1804–1857. I. Protopopov, Vl.
Title transliterated: Glinka.

ML410.G46L49 56-27130

NL 0416446 DLC CaBVaU

VOLUME 336

ML300
.L5
Livanova, Tamara Nikolaevna.
Критическая деятельность русских композиторов классиков. Москва, Гос. музыкальное изд-во, 1950.
100 p. 17 cm. (Русская музыкальная культура)
Errata slip inserted.
Bibliographical footnotes.

1. Music—Russia—Hist. & crit. 2. Composers, Russian. 3. Musical criticism. (Series: Russkai͡a muzykal'nai͡a kul'tura)
Title transliterated: Kriticheskai͡a dei͡atel'nost' russkikh kompozitorov klassikov.

ML300.L5 51-15041

NL 0416447 DLC

Livanova, Tamara Nikolaevna.
Die Kritikertätigkeit der russischen klassischen Komponisten. [Übersetzung: Günter Comte, Redaktion: Wolfram Sterz.] Halle (Saale) Mitteldeutscher Verlag, 1953.
80 p. 21 cm. (Musik und Zeit, Bd. 4)

1. Music—Russia—Hist. & crit. 2. Composers, Russian. 3. Musical criticism. I. Title.

ML300.L515 56—26449 ‡

NL 0416448 DLC NBuU NN MH NcU

Livanova, Tamara Nikolaevna, *ed.*
М. И. Глинка; сборник материалов и статей. Москва, Гос. музыкальное изд-во, 1950.
388 p. ports., facsims., music. 23 cm.
Errata slip inserted.
"Неизданные письма М. И. Глинки": p. [5]-[36]

1. Glinka, Mikhail Ivanovich, 1804–1857. I. Glinka, Mikhail Ivanovich, 1804–1857.
Title transliterated: M. I. Glinka; sbornik materialov i stateĭ.

ML410.G46L5 51-29624

NL 0416449 DLC

Livanova, Tamara Nikolaevna.
Музыкальная драматургия И. С. Баха и ее исторические связи. Москва, Гос. музыкальное изд-во, 1948–
v. music. 23 cm.

1. Bach, Johann Sebastian, 1685–1750. I. Title.
Title transliterated: Muzykal'nai͡a dramaturgii͡a I. S. Bakha.

ML410.B13L54 52–66629

NL 0416450 DLC

Livanova, Tamara Nikolaevna.
Н. Я. Мясковский; творческий путь. Москва, Гос. музыкальное изд-во, 1953.
405, [3] p. ports., music. 23 cm.
Errata slip inserted.
"Перечень произведений Н. Я. Мясковского": p. 400-[406]

1. Mi͡askovskiĭ, Nikolaĭ I͡Akovlevich, 1881–1950.
Title transliterated: N. I͡A. Mi͡askovskiĭ.

ML410.M64L5 54–37954

NL 0416451 DLC

Livanova, Tamara Nikolaevna.
Очерки и материалы по истории русской музыкальной культуры. Москва, Искусство, 1938–
v. music (part fold.) 23 cm.

1. Music—Russia—Hist. & crit. I. Title.
Title transliterated: Ocherki i materialy po istorii russkoĭ muzykal'noĭ kul'tury.

ML300.L518 56–52363

NL 0416452 DLC MiU GU

Livanova, Tamara Nikolaevna.
Педагогическая деятельность русских композиторов-классиков. Москва, Гос. музыкальное изд-во, 1951.
99 p. 17 cm. (Русская музыкальная культура)

1. Music—Instruction and study—Russia. I. Title.
Title transliterated: Pedagogicheskai͡a dei͡atel'nost' russkikh kompozitorov-klassikov.

MT3.R8L5 52–27677 ‡

NL 0416453 DLC

Livanova, Tamara Nikolaevna.
Русская музыкальная культура XVIII века в ее связях с литературой, театром и бытом; исследования и материалы. Москва, Гос. музыкальное изд-во, 1952–53.
2 v. music. 27 cm.
At head of title: Академия наук СССР. Институт истории искусств.
"Между делом безделье или собрание разных песен; музыка Г. Теплова" (score, for 2 voices and continuo): v. 1, p. 189-245.
Vol. 2 includes vocal settings of folk music by various composers; the appendix includes selections from Карманная книжка для любителей музыки.
Includes bibliographies.
1. Music—Russia—Hist. & crit. I. Teplov, Grigoriĭ Nikolaevich, 1711–1779. II. Karmannai͡a knizhka dli͡a li͡ubiteleĭ muzyki. III. Title.
Title transliterated: Russkai͡a muzykal'nai͡a kul'tura.

ML300.L52 53–32121 rev

NL 0416454 DLC OrU

Livanova, Tamara Nikolaevna. Russkai͡a muzykal'nai͡a kul'tura. Suppl.
(Sbornik kantov ...)
Сборник кантов XVIII века (в извлечениях); из рукописных фондов Государственного исторического музея. Москва, Гос. музыкальное изд-во, 1952.

Livanova, Tamara Nikolaevna. Russkai͡a muzykal'nai͡a kul'tura XVIII veka. Suppl.
Bortni͡anskiĭ, Dmitriĭ Stepanovich, 1751–1825.
[Sinfonie concertante, piano & orchestra, B♭ major]
Симфония; копия автографа партитуры. [1790] Москва, Гос. музыкальное изд-во, 1953.

Livanova, Tamara Nikolaevna.
В. Г. Захаров; творческий путь. Москва, Гос. музыкальное изд-во, 1954.
264 p. port., music. 21 cm.
Errata slip inserted.
"Приложение" (p. 238-[260]) consists of music by V. G. Zakharov.

1. Zakharov, Vladimir Grigor'evich, 1901–
Title transliterated: V. G. Zakharov.

ML410.Z26L5 56–16180

NL 0416457 DLC

Līvānu atbrīvošanas pieminekļa celšanas komiteja.
...Līvānu atbrīvošanas atcerei... Sakopojis komit. loceklis Rūd. Zuters. Līvānos: Līvānu atbrīvošanas pieminekļa celšanas komiteja, 1935. 23 p. illus. (incl. facsim., ports.) 22½cm.

1. Livani, Latvia—Hist. I. Zuters, Rūdolfs.
January 31, 1941

NL 0416458 NN

Livarski vestnik.
[Ljubljana]
v. in illus. 24 cm. bimonthly.
Began publication in 1954. Cf. New serial titles, 1950-60.
Journal of Društvo livarjev Slovenije.
Summaries in French and German accompany some numbers.

1. Founding—Period. I. Društvo livarjev Slovenije.

TS200.L55 64-38383

NL 0416459 DLC

Ливарство. г. 1– (бр. 1–) 1954–
Београд.
v. in illus., ports. 24 cm. bimonthly.
Issued by Društvo livara NR Srbije (called 1954–57 Udruženje livara NR Srbije)

1. Founding—Period. I. Društvo livara NR Srbije.
Title transliterated: Livarstvo.

TS200.L57 61–48374

NL 0416460 DLC

Livas, Enrique C
... La universidad. Su misión y su marcha. [Por el] dr. Enrique C. Livas. [Monterrey] 1944.
[18] p. 20cm. (Universidad de Nuevo León ... Publicaciones del D. A. S. U. [i. e. Departamento de acción social universitaria])

1. Nuevo León, Mexico. Universidad, Monterey.

44-32641

Library of Congress LE7.N848.1943.L5

378.72

NL 0416462 DLC LNHT DPU TxU

G378.7212
N889
El
1945
Livas, Enrique C
La universidad: su misión y su marcha. 2. ed. [Monterrey] Universidad de Nuevo León, 1945.
[18]p. 20cm. (Publicaciones del D.A.S.U.)

1. Nuevo León, Mexico. Universidad, Monterey. I. Series: Nuevo León, Mexico. Universidad, Monterey. Departamento de Acción Social Universitaria. Publicaciones.

NL 0416463 TxU CU-B DPU

PA5610
.L565P3
1870
Livathinopoulos, A S
Παλμοὶ καὶ δάκρυα· ἤτοι συλλογὴ λυρικῶν ποιημάτων, ὑπὸ Α. Σ. Λιβαθηνοπούλου. Ἐν Κεφαλληνίᾳ, τυπ. Ἡ Πρόοδος, 1870.
62 p. 23cm.

NL 0416464 OCU

Livathinos, A N
see **Leibathēnos, Athanasios N** 1896–

VOLUME 336

PA5610
.L57H5
19--
Livathynopoulos, G
'Ιστορίες τῆς Κεφαλλωνιᾶς. ['Αθῆνα] ἐκδ. Γκοβόστη [19--]
63 p. 20cm.

At head of title: Γ. Λιβαθυνόπουλος.

1. Cephalonia

NL 0416466 OCU

Livathynopoulos, R
see
Libathynopoulos, Richardos, 1867–

Livaudais, Undine de.
... Mon guide, pour apprendre à lire, à écrire et à parler français, by Undine de Livaudais ... and René Samson ... Boston, New York [etc.] D. C. Heath and company [c1935]
xv, 549 p. front., illus., map. 19cm. (Heath's modern language series)
Contains songs with music.

1. French language—Grammar—1870– 2. French language—Chrestomathies and readers. I. Samson, René, joint author. II. Title.
35-6491
Library of Congress PC2111.L727
Copyright A 81439 448.242

NL 0416468 DLC OU OC1ND OCX OC1 PSC

Livaudais, Undine de.
... Mon guide, pour apprendre à lire, à écrire et à parler français, by Undine de Livaudais ... and René Samson ... Boston, New York [etc.] D. C. Heath and company [c1939]
xv, 571 p. front., illus., map. 19cm. (Heath's modern language series)
Includes songs with music.

1. French language—Grammar—1870– 2. French language—Chrestomathies and readers. I. Samson, René, joint author. II. Title.
39-8582
Library of Congress PC2111.L727 1939
Copyright A 127768 448.242

NL 0416469 DLC ViU WaS

Livay, Eliezer.
הנהלת־פנקסים. קורס שיטתי לתלמידי בתי־ספר וללומדים מעצמם. תל־אביב. "כפרות" תרצ"ה. [Tel-Aviv, 1935]
144 p. 23 cm.

1. Bookkeeping. I. Title.
Title transliterated: Hanhalat-pinkasim.
A 50-35 rev
New York. Public Libr.
for Library of Congress [r63b½]

NL 0416470 NN

TH7461
.L55
Livchak, I F
Изобретения усовершенствования в области центрального отопления. Москва, Гос. изд-во лит-ры по строительству и архитектуре, 1952.
140, [3] p. illus., diagrs. 23 cm.
Errata slip inserted.
Bibliography: p. 140–[141]

1. Heating. I. Title.
Title transliterated: Izobretenii͡a i usovershenstvovanii͡a v oblasti t͡sentral'nogo otoplenii͡a.
TH7461.L55 53-20057

NL 0416471 DLC

TH7653
L5
Livchak, I F
Вентиляция многоэтажных жилых домов. Москва, Гос. изд-во архитектуры и градостроительства, 1951.
169, [3] p. illus. 23 cm.
Errata slip inserted.
Bibliography: p. 169–[170]

1. Ventilation. I. Title.
Title transliterated: Ventili͡at͡sii͡a mnogoėtazhnykh zhilykh domov.
TH7653.L5 54-29891

NL 0416472 DLC

Livchen, René.
Net wages and real wages in Germany, by René Livchen ...
(*In* International labour review. July, 1944. v. 50, p. [65]–72)
Completes his Wage trends in Germany from 1929 to 1942, which appeared in the December 1943 International labour review.

1. Wages—Germany. 2. Cost [and standard] of living—Germany. I. Title. II. Title: Real wages in Germany.
L 44-168 Revised
U. S. Dept. of labor. Libr.
for Library of Congress [HD4811.I 65 vol. 50]
[r45d2] (331.05)

NL 0416473 DL

Livchen, René.
Wage trends in Germany from 1929 to 1942, by René Livchen ...
(*In* International labour review. December, 1943. v. 48, p. [714]–732)

1. Wages—Germany. I. Title.
L 44-58
U. S. Dept. of labor. Libr.
for Library of Congress [HD4811.I 65 vol. 48]
(331.05)

NL 0416474 DL

Livchen, René.
Wartime developments in German wage policy, by René Livchen ...
(*In* International labour review. August, 1942. v. 46, p. [136]–165)

1. Wages—Germany. 2. World war, 1939– —Economic aspects—Germany. [2. World war, 1939– —Labor—Germany] I. Title.
L 42-218
U. S. Dept. of Labor. Libr.
for Library of Congress [HD4811.I 65 vol. 46]
(331.05)

NL 0416475 DL

Livchitz (Debora). *Contribution à l'étude de l'accroissement des tendons. 16 pp. 8°. Lausanne, T. Geneux, 1920.

NL 0416476 DNLM

Livchitz (Haia). *Distribution du labferment dans l'organisme. 36 pp., 1 l. 8°. Lausanne. A. Simmen, 1907.

NL 0416477 DNLM

Livchiz, F.
See
Lifschitz, Feitel.

Live, Enya Harris.
Cooperative enterprise in Palestine. New York, Education department, Zionist organization of America, 1937.
31 p. 23 cm. (Zionist education series, 1)

NL 0416479 MH NBuG

Live, Israel, 1907–
... Studies with *Clostridium chauvoei* (blackleg) aggressin ... [by] Israel Live ... Philadelphia, 1940.
1 p. l., p. 137–162. 23cm.
Thesis (PH. D.)—University of Pennsylvania, 1940.
"Reprint from the Journal of immunology, vol. 39, no. 2."
"References": p. 161–162.

1. Clostridium chauvoei. 2. Toxins and antitoxins. 3. Anthrax, Symptomatic.
41-3235
Library of Congress SF962.L5 1940
Univ. of Pennsylvania Libr
619.2

NL 0416480 PU OC1 OCU OrU DLC

Live, Willie, pseud.
see Reed, William Lord.

The live and death of Mrs. Jane Shore
see The life and death of Jane Shore.

614.86205
L745
Live.
Pub. by National Safe Drivers Association.

1. Traffic accidents. Per soc etc. 2. Accidents. Prevention. Per soc etc. I. National Safe Drivers Association.

NL 0416483 OrU

Live and learn, Author of.

Read and reflect. The newspaper and general reader's pocket companion. Being a familiar explanation of classical and foreign words, phrases, and quotations of constant occurrence in the various journals, periodicals, and publications of the day. By the author of "Live and learn" ... London, J. F. Shaw and co. [1872?]

Live and learn: a guide for all who wish to speak and write correctly
see Over 1000 mistakes corrected.
Live and learn ...

Live and learn books.
Toronto: The Ryerson press [c1941 19½cm.
no.
Supersedes the New dominion books.

NL 0416486 NN

VOLUME 336

Live and let live. [Hartford, Conn.] 1936
see under [Travelers insurance company, Hartford, Conn.]

NL 0416489

Live and let live: a treatise on the hostile rivalships between the manufacturer and land-worker, with a more especial view of the present contest between the woollen manufacturers and wool-growers. London, Printed for J. Debrett, 1787.
vi, [7]-98 p. 22cm.

1. Wool trade and industry - Gt. Brit.

NL 0416488 NNC CtY

Live and let live; or, Domestic service illustrated
see under [Sedgwick, Catharine Maria] 1789-1867.

Live articles on industrial safeguards
see under Weekly underwriter.

Live articles on marine insurance
see under Weekly underwriter.

Live books resurrected.
London, T. Werner Laurie, ltd.

Editor: L. Stanley Jast.

NL 0416492 CtY

The live branch. No. IV
see under [Carey, Mathew] 1760-1839.

Live coals of fire. v. 1 (no. 1-21); Oct. 6, 1899-June 15, 1900. Lincoln, Neb., 1899-1900.
1 v. 51cm.

Caption title.
Weekly, Oct.-Nov. 1899; biweekly, Dec. 1899-June 1900.
"Official organ of the Fire-baptized holiness association of America."
B. H. Irwin, editor.
No more published.

I. Irwin, Benjamin H., ed. II. Fire-baptized holiness association of America.

Library of Congress BX7990.H6A3 26-18360

NL 0416494 DLC

A live collection, exhibited for several years past, at the Stock exchange, from ten o'clock till four, daily, Sundays and holidays excepted ... Wallbrook, Evans and Ruffy, printers [185-?]
broadside. 23 cm.

NL 0416495 MH-BA

Live fences. [Washington. 1855.] 8°. Illustr.
Report of the Commissioner of patents. Agriculture, 1854, pp. 393-418.
Signed "D. J. B."

NL 0416496 MH-A

17 "Live for Jesus"; ...
Boston, [1857]

NL 0416497 DLC

Live forever folk association.
The cosmic survey. [San Francisco, Live forever folk [c1922]
2 p. l., 3-81 p. front., illus. 23cm.

I. Title.

Library of Congress BF1999.L4 CA 23-362 Unrev'd

NL 0416498 DLC

The Live issue, advocating Christian social reform as against revolutionary socialism. New York, [Social Reform Press, 1913-].
Continued from vol. 2, no. 34, Oct. 18, 1913. illus. 46-57½cm.
Caption title.
Vol. 2, no. 34-35, have no subtitle.
Weekly.

NL 0416499 ICJ

Live life, Author of.
Anatomy of a gambler
see under title.

The live-long weary day (Den lieben langen Tag) A German melody. Words translated & music arr. by John P. Wendel. Piano. Cincinnati Published by W. C. Peters & Sons ... [c1856] Pl. no. 2677—4.
5 p. 34 cm.
No. 14 in a vol. with binder's title: Songs. [v. p., ca. 1835-65]
For voice and piano. English and German words.

1. Songs (Medium voice) with piano. I. Wendel, John P., arr. II. Title: Den lieben langen Tag.

M1.A152 no. 14 M 55-1786

NL 0416501 DLC

The live man's elegy: or, A hymn among the dead
see under [Defoe, Daniel] 1661?-1731.

Live Oak, Fla. Suwannee high school.

The Suwannean.

Live Oak, Fla., 19

The LIVE oak; the Pacific coast nature monthly.
v.

Angwin, Cal.: H.W. Clark, 19 24cm.
v
Monthly from Sept. to May.

1. Natural history—Per. and soc. publ.

NL 0416504 NN MiU

Live steam.
see
Engineers' and power users' magazine.

The live steam book, by "L.B.S.C." [pseud.] London, P. Marshall [1954] xiv, 209 p. illus. 24cm.

"Replacement of [the author's] 'Shops shed and road.'"—bookjacket.

1. Locomotives—Models. I. Lawrence, L. Shops, shed and road. t. 1954.

NL 0416506 NN WaS CaBVa

Live stock ....
see Livestock ....

Live stories. v. 1-
Nov. 1, 1913-
New York, Street & Smith [1913-
v. illus. 25cm.
Semimonthly, Nov. 1913-June 1914; monthly, Aug. 1914-
No number issued July 1914.
Title varies: Nov. 1, 1913-Nov. 1914, Women's stories.
Dec. 1914- Live stories.
Editor: Nov. 1914- C. A. MacLean.

1. MacLean, Charles A., ed.

16-4541

Library of Congress AP2.L649

NL 0416508 DLC

Live to help live
see under Conference of Labor Reformers, Boston, 1872.

Live wire. 803, Groote Kerk Gebou, Parliament Street, Cape Town, Union of South Africa.
Monthly.

Published by South African Telephone and Telegraph Association.

NL 0416510 NN

The Live wire. v. 1-4, v. 5, no. 1-2; Mar. 1907-Sept. 1908. New York, The F. A. Munsey co., 1907-08.
5 v. illus. (partly col.) 25cm. monthly.
Title varies: Mar. 1907-Jan. 1908, The Ocean.
Feb. 1908-Sept. 1908, The Live wire.
Merged into the Scrap book.

9-7209†

Library of Congress AP2.L6485

NL 0416511 DLC ICJ

AP
2
L798

The Live wire. no. 1-
Feb. 26? 1902-
Richmond, Va., Carlton McCarthy [1902-
v. 27.5 cm. daily.

Carlton McCarthy, editor and proprietor.

1. Richmond, Va. - Pol. & govt. 2. Periodicals (Titles) I. McCarthy, Carlton, 1847-1936, ed.

NL 0416512 Vi

VOLUME 336

LIVE WIRE; MAGAZINE OF THE ROYAL NAVAL ELECTRICAL BRANCH
(INCORPORATING THE ELECTRICAL ARTIFICERS APPRENTICES MAGAZINE)
FAREHAM, HANTS. 1949+ 3 TIMES A YEAR

NL 0416513 CaOOND

The **Live** wire ⌈pub. by the Buffalo Chamber of commerce⌉
see
Buffalo live wire.

Live wire game book
see under Plumb, Beatrice.

... A live woman in the mines; or, Pike county ahead!
see under [Delano, Alonzo] 1806-1874.

⌈**Liveing, E. H. T.**⌉
On an instrument for the detection and measurement of inflammable gas in the atmosphere of mines. ⌈London: L. Clark, Muirhead & Co., 1881.⌉ 12 p. incl. table. illus. 8°.

Caption-title.

1. Mines and mining—Gases. 2. Title.

March 12, 1930

NL 0416517 NN

Liveing, Edward.
On megrim, sick-headache, and some allied disorders: a contribution to the pathology of nerve-storms. By Edward Liveing, ... London, J. and A. Churchill, 1873.
x, 512, [2] p. 2 col. fold. pl., fold. tables. 24^{cm}.

NL 0416518 ICJ CtY PPC MH OClW-H DNLM WaU

Liveing, Edward George Downing, 1895–
Adventure in publishing; the House of Ward Lock, 1854–1954. London, Ward, Lock ⌈1954⌉
108 p. illus. 22 cm.

1. Ward, Lock and Company, ltd. 2. Publishers and publishing—Gt. Brit. I. Title.

Z325.W3L5 655.442 54-39738 ‡

OrU CaBVaU CLSU NbU
NL 0416519 DLC MsU NcU TxU MB CU NN NIC MH CtY LU

Liveing, Edward George Downing, 1895 -
Attack; an infantry subaltern's impressions of July 1st, 1916, by Edward G. D. Liveing; with an introduction by John Masefield. London: W. Heinemann ⌈1918⌉. xvii, 19-86 p. 12°.

"Appeared in Blackwood's magazine, December, 1917, under the title of 'Battle.'"
Describes the attack on the fortified village of Gommecourt which began the battle of the Somme.

1. European war, 1914- .—Personal narratives (English). 2. Somme (Battle of), 1916. 3. Title.

July 18, 1918.

NL 0416520 NN TxU ViU CSmH ICJ MH

Liveing, Edward George Downing, 1895 -
Attack; an infantry subaltern's impressions of July 1st, 1916, by Edward G. D. Liveing; with an introduction by John Masefield. New York, The Macmillan company, 1918.
114 p. 19½^{cm}. $0.75

"Appeared in Blackwood's magazine, December, 1917, under the title of 'Battle.'"
Describes the attack on the fortified village of Gommecourt which began the battle of the Somme.

1. European war, 1914- —Personal narratives, English. 2. Somme, Battle of the, 1916. I. Title.

Library of Congress D545.S7L5 18—8679

NjP
NL 0416521 DLC CtY OrP WaS OClW OU OOxM MH ICJ PBm

Liveing, Edward George Downing, 1895– ed.

Discovery; the popular journal of knowledge ... v. 1-19, Jan. 1920-Mar. 1938; new ser., v. 1-3, Apr. 1938-Mar. 1940. Cambridge ⌈Eng.⌉ The University press; ⌈etc., etc., 1920-40⌉

Z249 **Liveing, Edward George Downing, 1895-**
H315 **The House of Harrild, 1801-1948. London,**
Library **Harrild ⌈1949⌉**
School **ix,69 p. illus.,ports.,facsims.**

1. Harrild and Sons Ltd. 2. Printing machinery and supplies. I. Title.

NL 0416523 CU IU

Liveing, George Downing, 1827- 1924.
Chemical equilibrium the result of the dissipation of energy.
133087 By G D. Liveing, ... Cambridge, Deighton, Bell, and Co.; [etc., etc.], 1885.
viii, 97, [2] p. incl. diagrs. 3 illus. on 1 pl. 19^{cm}.

NL 0416524 ICJ CtY MH MWelC

Liveing, George Downing, 1827- 1924
Collected papers on spectroscopy, by G. D. Liveing ... and Sir J. Dewar ... with a supplementary paper not heretofore published and a classified index. Cambridge, University press, 1915.
xv, 566 p. illus., plates (part fold.) 27^{cm}.

1. Spectrum analysis. I. Dewar, Sir James, 1842-

16-12914

Library of Congress QC451.L75

NL 0416525 DLC CU CtY PBm PU OCl ICJ NN MiU OU WaS

Liveing, George Downing, 1827–1924.
Crystallization. By G. D. Liveing ...
(*In* Smithsonian institution. Annual report. 1892. Washington. 1893. 23½^{cm}. p. 269–280. diagrs.)
"From Nature, June 18, 1891; vol. XLIV, pp. 156–160."

1. Crystallography.

S 15–789

Smithsonian inst. Library for Library of Congress [Q11.S66 1892]

NL 0416526 DSI PP DLC MiU OU OClWHi WaS

Liveing, George Downing , 1827 - 1924.
& Dewar,(Sir) James
⌈Misc. reprints⌉ 1877-1895
Bound in 1v. il. pls. O

Contents: Spectra of flames. Line-spectrum of hydrogen. Absorption-spectrum of oxygen. Spectroscopic properties of dust. Spectrum of magnesium. Lines of metallic vapours. Spectra of sodium and potassium. Spectra of magnesium and lithium. Spectra of the compounds of carbon with hydrogen and nitrogen. History of the carbon spectrum. etc.etc.

NL 0416527 MCM

LIVEING, George Downing, 1827 - 1924.
On solution and crystallization. [London, 1888]

NL 0416528 MH

Liveing, George Downing, 1827–1924.
... On the spectrum of the more volatile gases of atmospheric air which are not condensed at the temperature of liquid hydrogen. Preliminary notice. By S. ⌈!⌉ D. Liveing ... and James Dewar ... ⌈London, Harrison and sons, printers, 1901⌉
cover-title, ⌈467⌉–474 p. 21½^{cm}.
From the Proceedings of the Royal society, vol. 67.

1. Spectrum analysis. I. Dewar, Sir James, 1842–1923.

Library of Congress QC454.L78 CA 6—2494 Unrev'd

NL 0416529 DLC

LIVEING, George Downing and DERVAR, J.
On the spectrum of the oxy-hydrogen flame. London,1888.

By George Downing Liveing and J.Dervar.

NL 0416530 MH

Liveing, George Downing, 1827 - 1924. 2555.16.1=**G.3853.2.1
On the transmutation of matter.
(*In* Cambridge Essays. Vol. 1, pp. 123-147. London. 1855.)

M8728 — Transmutation of matter, On the. — Matter.

NL 0416531 MB DNLM

LIVEING, George Downing, 1827 - 1924.
On the ultra-violet spectra of the elements. Pt. III. London,1888.

NL 0416532 MH

Liveing, George Downing, 1827-1924.
The recuperation of energy in the Universe. By G. D. Liveing.
Cambridge at the University Press, 1923.
cover title +(7) p. 22cm.

Cambridge Phil. Soc. Proc., 21, 1923, 569-575.

NL 0416533 DN-Ob

Liveing, Henry George Downing, 1861 *or* 2–
Records of Romsey abbey: an account of the Benedictine house of nuns, with notes on the parish church and town (A. D. 907–1558). Compiled from manuscript and printed records by Henry G. D. Liveing ... Winchester, Warren and son, 1906.
xxiii, 342 p. front., plates, ports., fold. maps, plan, facsim., geneal. tables (part fold.) 23½^{cm}.
"References" at end of most of the chapters.

1. Romsey abbey.

43-49086

Library of Congress DA670.R73L57

MdBP
NL 0416534 DLC ICU CtY NN OU PHC PU MH MB MiU

VOLUME 336

Liveing, Henry George Downing, 1861 or 2-
Records of Romsey abbey: an account of the Benedictine house of nuns, with notes on the parish church and town (A. D. 907-1558). Comp. from manuscript and printed records by Henry G. D. Liveing ... ‹Abridged ed.› Winchester, Warren and son, ltd., 1912.
xi, ‹1›, 292 p. front., plates, fold. maps, plan, facsims., geneal. tables. 22½cm.
"References" at end of chapters.
13-19090

NL 0416535 DLC AzU NcD IEG IU

WCE L784e 1873 LIVEING, Robert, 1834-1919.
Elephantiasis Graecorum, or true leprosy. Rev. and enl. London, Longmans, Green, 1873.
150 p. (Goulstonian lectures, 1873)

NL 0416536 DNLM PU

RL72 L5 1884 Liveing, Robert, 1834-1919.
A handbook on diseases of the skin, with especial reference to diagnosis and treatment, by Robert Liveing ... Fourth edition, revised. London, Longmans, Green, and co., 1884.
vii, 349p. 17cm.
1. Skin.-Diseases.-Diagnosis.

NL 0416537 NBuG

WR L784h 1887 LIVEING, Robert, 1834-1919.
A handbook on diseases of the skin, with especial reference to diagnosis and treatment. 5th ed. rev. and enl. London, Longmans, Green, 1887.
viii, 451 p.
1st. ed. published with title: A handbook on the diagnosis of skin diseases.

NL 0416538 DNLM PPC PU OC1W-H

WR L784h 1878 LIVEING, Robert, 1834-1919.
A handbook on the diagnosis of skin diseases. London, Longmans, Green, 1878.
vi, 266 p.
5th ed. published with title: A handbook on diseases of the skin.

NL 0416539 DNLM

Liveing, Robert, 1834-1919.
A handbook on the diagnosis of skin diseases. By Robert Liveing, ... New York, W. Wood & Co., 1879.
vi, [2], 266 p. 17½cm.

NL 0416540 ICJ OC1W-H DNLM IU RPM PPC PPHa PU

LIVEING, Robert, 1834-1919.
Notes on the treatment of skin diseases.
Lond. Longmans. 1870. (5), 90 pp. 24°.

NL 0416541 MB PPC

WR L784h 1871 LIVEING, Robert, 1834-1919.
Notes on the treatment of skin diseases. 2d ed. with additions. London, Longmans, Green, 1871.
104 p.

NL 0416542 DNLM PPC PU

Liveing, Robert, 1834-1919.
Notes on the treatment of skin diseases. 3rd. ed. London, Longmans, 1875.
116 p.

NL 0416543 PPC

RL61 877l Liveing, Robert, 1834-1919.
Notes on the treatment of skin diseases. 4th ed., rev. and enl. London, Longmans, Green, 1877.
6p.l., 127p. 15cm.
1. Skin - Diseases. I. Title.

NL 0416544 CtY-M

Liveing, Robert, 1834-1919.
Notes on the treatment of skin diseases. By Robert Liveing, ... Fourth edition, revised and enlarged. New York, W. Wood & Co., 1878.
[8], 127 p. 17½cm.

NL 0416545 ICJ DNLM KMK MiU OO

616.5 L784n4 Liveing, Robert, 1834-1919.
Notes on the treatment of skin diseases ... 4th ed., rev. and enl. New York, W. Wood & co., 1885.
127p.
1. Skin--Diseases.

NL 0416546 IU-M

Liveing, Susan.
A nineteenth-century teacher, John Henry Bridges ... by his niece, Susan Liveing; with a preface by Professor L. T. Hobhouse, and an introduction by Professor Patrick Geddes ... London, K. Paul, Trench, Trubner & co., ltd., 1926.
xv, 261, ‹1› p. front. (port.) 19½cm.
"List of published works by Dr. Bridges": p. ‹vii›-viii.
1. Bridges, John Henry, 1832-1906. I. Title.
29-12693
Library of Congress CT788.B7735L5

NL 0416547 DLC CtY NN OU

LIVELLI, Beneto.
Stanze alla venitiana del'origine e sucesso de la verra contra Turchi per fin alla ottegnuda vittoria. Con una barcelletta in laude delle gallie grosse. [Venice, 1572.]
24°. pp.(16). Wdct.
Dedication signed "Beneto Livelli."

NL 0416548 MH

Livellio, Ottavio, d.1634.
Epitome in quatuor libros institvtionvm iuris ciuilis. Denvo, et emendativs. Patavii, apud Laurentium Pasq., per Io. Ant. Iadram Bidellum, 1603.
169, [2] p. 19 cm.
1. Roman law. I. Corpus juris civilis. Institutiones. II. Title.

NL 0416549 DLC

Il liuello politico
see under [Leti, Gregorio] 1630-1701.

Lively, Anne Hathaway.
Somewhere in France.
In, Woodruff, Newton, Whims ... 1918.
24 cm. p. [1]-11.

NL 0416551 RPB

Lively, Charles Elson, 1890-
... The appearance and disappearance of minor trade centers in Minnesota, 1905-1930 ‹by› C.E. Lively... ‹Chapel Hill, University of North Carolina, 1931›
p. ‹71›-75. 25½cm.
"Reprinted from Social forces. Vol. X, no.1, October, 1931."
1. Economic surveys - Minnesota. 2 Minnesota - Economic conditions. I. Title.

NL 0416552 OU

Lively, Charles Elson, 1890-
The concern of Ohio agriculture in a system of old age relief by C. E. Lively ...
Columbus, Ohio, 1933.
19 numb. l.
(Ohio state university. Dept. of rural economics. Mimeograph bulletin no. 64)

NL 0416553 OU DL

Lively, Charles Elson, 1890-
Cost of family living on the farm; report of cost of living studies on 28 Ohio farm families, April 1, 1924 to April 1, 1928 by C. E. Lively
Columbus, Ohio state university, 1926.
8 numb. l.

NL 0416554 OU

Lively, Charles Elson, 1890-
Family living expenditures on Ohio farms...
Wooster, O., Ohio agricultural experiment station, 1930.
36 p. (Ohio agricultural experiment station Bulletin 468)
Thesis (Ph.D.) - University of Minnesota

NL 0416555 OU MH

VOLUME 336

SPEC-M HD 6993 .03 .L5 Lively, Charles Elson, 1890-
Family living on selected Ohio farms; an analysis of expenditures for living and other related factors, based upon 187 account book records. [n. p.] 1930.
137 L. illus.

Thesis--University of Minnesota.

#Cost and standard of living--Ohio. #Farm life.

NL 0416556 MoU

Lively, Charles Elson, 1890-
Family living on selected Ohio farms ... by Charles Elson Lively ... [Wooster, O., 1931]
cover-title, 1 p. l., 36 p. illus. (map) diagr. 22½cm.

Thesis (PH. D.)—University of Minnesota, 1931.
Vita.
Bulletin 468, November 1930, of the Ohio agricultural experiment station, Wooster (having title: Family living expenditures on Ohio farms) with cover containing thesis note and vita.
"References cited": p. 36.

1. Cost and standard of living—Ohio. 2. Farm life. I. Title.

Library of Congress HD6993.O3L5 1931 32-7110
Univ. of Minnesota Libr.
331.83109771

NL 0416557 MnU DLC MH

Lively, Charles Elson, 1890-
... Growth and decline of farm trade centers in Minnesota, 1905-1930 [by] C. C. Lively... St. Paul [1932]
48 p. maps, tables. 23cm. (University of Minnesota. Agricultural experiment station. Bulletin 287, July, 1932)

I. title: Farm trade centers in Minnesota. 1. Retail trade - Minnesota. 2. Retail trade - Minnesota - 1905-1930. 3. Retail stores - Rural areas - Minnesota.

NL 0416558 NNC MnHi

Lively, Charles Elson, 1890-
The growth cycle of the farm family by C. E. Lively...
Columbus, Ohio, 1932.
22 numb. l. (Ohio state university. Dept. of rural economics. Mimeograph bulletin no. 51)

NL 0416559 OU NcD

Lively, Charles Elson, 1890-
A method of determining rural social sub-areas with application to Ohio [by] C.E. Lively and R.B. Almack. Ohio State University and Ohio Agricultural Experiment Station. Farm Security Administration, Social Research Section, Region III, cooperating. Columbus, Ohio State University, 1938.
v. tables, maps. 30cm. (Ohio. State University, Columbus. Dept. of Rural Economics. Mimeograph bulletin, no. 106)

CONTENTS.- pt.1. Text and maps.

NL 0416560 GU NcD OClW

309.133 L74m Lively, Charles Elson, 1890-
... Movement of open country population in Ohio [by] C. E. Lively and P. G. Beck. Wooster, O., Ohio agricultural experiment station [1930]
48p. incl.map, tables, diagrs. (Ohio. Agricultural experiment station. Bulletin 467. November, 1930)

Bibliography: p.48.

1. Ohio--Population. 2. Sociology, Rural. I. Beck, Paul G., joint author.

NL 0416561 IU MH

Lively, Charles Elson, 1890-
Movement of open country population in three townships of northeastern Ohio, by C. E. Lively and P. G. Beck...
Columbus, Ohio, 1928.
33 p. (Ohio state university. Dept. of rural economics. Mimeograph bulletin no. 4)

NL 0416562 OU

Lively, Charles Elson, 1890-
Movement of open country population in three townships of southeastern Ohio, by C. E. Lively and P. G. Beck...
Columbus, Ohio, 1929.
22 numb. l. (Ohio state university. Dept. of rural economics. Mimeograph bulletin no. 5;)

NL 0416563 OU

Lively, Charles Elson, 1890-
Movement of open country population in two townships of northwestern Ohio, by C. E. Lively and P. G. Beck...
Columbus, Ohio, 1928.
1 p. l., 41 p. (Ohio state university. Dept. of rural economics. Mimeograph bulletin, no. 3)
The Ohio state university. Dept. of rural economics.)

NL 0416564 OU

449.15 L74 Lively, Charles Elson, 1890-
The physical status and health of farm tenants and farm laborers in southeast Missouri. Preliminary report. Columbia, Mo., University of Missouri,

NL 0416565 DNAL

SPEC-M RA 771 .L5 Lively, Charles Elson, 1890-
The physical status and health of farm tenants and farm laborers in southeast Missouri; preliminary report, by C. E. Lively. [Columbia, University of Missouri, 1942]
3 v. in 1. illus.
Caption title.
No. 1 also has title: The physical status and health of farm security clients in southeast Missouri.
No. 2-3, by C. E. Lively and Herbert F. Lionberger.
#Hygiene, Rural--Missouri.
#Agricultural laborers--Missouri.
(A)Lionberger, Herbert Frederick, 1912-

NL 0416566 MoU

LIVELY, Charles Elson, 1890-
Population mobility in selected areas of rural Ohio, 1928-1935. C.E.Lively and Frances Foott. Wooster, Ohio Agricultural Experiment Station, [1937].

23 cm. pp.(2),53. Charts.
"Bulletin 582."

NL 0416567 MH-PA

SPEC-M HB 3525 .M8 .L5 Lively, Charles Elson, 1890-
The population of Missouri: its conditions and trends [by] C. E. Lively. [n.p., 1941?]
15 p. illus.
Caption title.
"Prepared for U. S. Congress, House committee investigating national defense migration, 1941."
#Missouri--Population.
(A)The population of Missouri: its conditions and trends.

NL 0416568 MoU

~~MANN~~ HT 421 L78 Lively, Charles Elson, 1890-
Readings in rural sociology. Columbus, Ohio [c. 1933]
2 v. illus. (incl. map) tables. 28 cm.

Contents: Bk. I, Life in the farm family: Bk. II, Life in the neighborhood and community.

1. Country life. 2. Sociology. I. Title.

NL 0416569 NIC KyU ViU OU IU

Lively, Charles Elson, 1890-
Rural dramatics, a survey of the status of play production in Fairfield and Putnam counties, Ohio, by C. E. Lively and Merton Oyler...
[Columbus, O., Ohio state university, 1926]
21 [2] numb. l.

NL 0416570 OU

R 111 Z99 no. 48 Lively, Charles Elson, 1890-
Rural health and medical service in Missouri. Columbia, 1943.
16 l.

1. Hygiene, Rural. 2. Medicine, Rural. I. Title.

NL 0416571 NIC

Lively, Charles Elson, 1890-
Rural health facilities of Ross county, Ohio. (In Ohio, Agricultural experiment station. Bulletin. no. 412. Oct. 1927)

NL 0416572 OClW

Lively, Charles Elson, 1890-
... Rural migration in the United States, by C. E. Lively ... and Conrad Taeuber ... Washington, U. S. Govt. print. off., 1939.
xxi, 192 p. incl. illus. (maps) tables, diagrs., forms. plates. 25cm. ([U. S.] Works progress administration. Research monograph XIX)
At head of title: Works progress administration. F. C. Harrington, administrator. Corrington Gill, assistant administrator. Division of research. Howard B. Myers, director.
Issued also by the U. S. Farm security administration as its Social research report no. XVII under the title: Migration and mobility of rural population in the United States, by Conrad Taeuber and C. E. Lively.
"Publications of the Division of research": p. [2] of cover.
"Selected bibliography": p. 177-183.
1. Unemployed—U. S. 2. Country life—U. S. 3. Migration, Internal—U. S. I. *Taeuber, Conrad, 1906- joint author. II. Title.
Library of Congress HV85.A36 no. 19 39-29056 Revised 2
[r44g2]
HB2385.L5 (361.6082) 312.0973

NL 0416573 OrP WaWW OrU NcC PHC PSC PPT OU OClW OCU OO MB DLC MoU CaBVaU OrHi OrStbM WaTC OU AAP

Lively, Charles Elson, 1890-
Rural recreation in two Ohio counties, by C. E. Lively ... Columbus, The Ohio state university, 1927.
vii p., 1 l., 99 p. illus. (maps) 2 fold. tab. 25½cm. (On cover: [Ohio. State university] Contributions in rural economics no. 1)
Ohio state university studies. Graduate school series.
"The counties selected for this study were Gallia and Paulding."

1. Ohio—Soc. condit. 2. Recreation—Ohio. [2. Recreation, Rural] 3. [Rural surveys] I. [Title]
Agr 28-773 Revised
U. S. Dept. of agr. Library for Library of Congress 281.9Oh3 no. 1 GV54.O3A42
[r43c2]†

NL 0416574 DNAL NcD ViU DL DLC OOxM OCU OClW OU Mil

Lively, Charles Elson, 1890- ed.
Rural sociology; devoted to scientific study of rural life. v. 1- Mar. 1936-
[Baton Rouge, La.] Section on rural sociology, American sociological society [1936-

VOLUME 336

Lively, Charles Elson, 1890–
Rural young people, 16 to 24 years of age; a survey of the status and activities of 300 unmarried individuals in nine Ohio townships, by C.E. Lively and L. J. Miller.
Columbus, O., July, 1934.
27 numb. l.
(Dept. of rural economics, Ohio state university and Ohio agricultural experiment station, Mimeograph bulletin no. 73)

NL 0416576 OCl OU

Lively, Charles Elson, 1890-
Scouting the field of rural social relations by C. E. Lively.
[Columbus, O., 1933?]
8 numb. l.

NL 0416577 OU

Lively, Charles Elson, 1890–
Social aspects of land utilization. By Charles Elson Lively, Ohio Agricultural experiment station.
Columbus, Ohio, July, 1935.
10, 3 maps, 28cm. (With this is bound: His, Social planning for agriculture. 1935.)

NL 0416578 NcD OU

Lively, Charles Elson, 1890–
631.1
q L784S
Social planning for agriculture and its relation to all society. [By] C.E. Lively... October 16-18, 1935.
9 p. 28cm. (With: His, Social aspects of land utilization.)

"Paper read before the Annual conference of Agricultural extension workers, Ohio State University, October 16-18, 1935."

NL 0416579 NcD OU

Lively, Charles Elson, 1890-
Some aspects of rural social organization in Fairfield County, Ohio. Department of Rural Economics, Ohio State University and Ohio Agricultural Experiment Station, Mimeograph Bulletin, 91, 1936)

NL 0416580 OU

LIVELY, Charles Elson, 1890 –
Some relationships of the variable, cash expenditure for farm family living. Columbus, Ohio, 1931.

Manifold copy. 4°. ff.(1),21.
Cover serves as title-page.
"Department of rural economics, Ohio State University and Ohio Agricultural Experiment Station. Mimeograph bulletin no.36."

NL 0416581 MH OU

Lively, Charles Elson, 1890-
Some rural social agencies in Ohio.
Columbus, O., 1922.
(Ohio state university agricultural extension service. Bulletin, v. 18, no. 4)

NL 0416582 ODW

LIVELY, Charles Elson, 1890-
Some rural social agencies in Ohio; a study of trends, 1921-1931. Wooster, Ohio Agricultural Experiment Station, [1933].

23 cm. pp.(2),42. Charts.
"Bulletin 529."

NL 0416583 MH-PA OCl

Lively, Charles Elson, 1890-
Suggested changes in college curricula to meet present day needs.
[Columbus, O., 1934]
8 numb. l.

NL 0416584 OU

Lively, Charles Elson, 1890-
The trend of births, deaths, natural increase and migration in the rural population of Ohio.
Columbus, 1936.
10 mimeo. l. (Ohio. State university. Dept. of rural economics. Mimeograph bulletin no. 87)

NL 0416585 OU OClFRB

636.4
L748
Lively, Daniel O
Hog husbandry. [Portland, Ore., Oregon-Washington Railroad & Navigation Co. 192-?]
23p. illus., map. 23cm. (The money makers)

Cover title: Swine raising in the Pacific Northwest.

1. Swine. I. Title. II. Title: Swine raising in the Pacific Northwest. III. Series.

NL 0416586 OrU Or

STC
16608
copy 1
Lively, Edward, 1545?-1605.
... Annotationes in quinq; priores ex minoribus prophetis, cum Latina eorum interpretatione, eiusdem opera ac studio, ad normam Hebraicae veritatis diligenter examinata. Londini, typis Georgij Bishop, 1587.

A-N^8. (A1, blank except for signature, bd. after A8.) 8vo.
William Aldis Wright copy.

NL 0416587 DFo CSmH

FILM
Lively, Edward, 1545?-1605.
Edvardi Livelei ... Annotationes in quinq; priores ex minoribus prophetis, cum latina eorum interpretatione, eiusdem opera ac studio, ad normam Hebraicae veritatis diligenter examinata.
Londini typis Georgij Bishop ... M.D.LXXXVII.
University microfilms no.12354 (case 64, carton 380)
Short-title catalogue no.16608.

1. Bible. O.T. Minor prophets—Criticism, interpretation, etc.

NL 0416588 MiU DFo ViU

Lively, Edward, 1545?-1605.
A trve chronologie of the times of the Persian monarchie, and after to the destruction of Ierusalem by the Romanes. Wherein by the way briefly is handled the day of Christ his birth: with a declaration of the Angel Gabriels message to Daniel in the end of his 9. chap., against the friuolous conceits of Matthew Beroald. Written by Edward Livelie ... London, Printed by F. Kingston for T. Man [etc.] 1597.
5 p. l., [11]-258, [144] p. tables. 14½cm.
1. Persia—Hist.—Chronology. 2. Bible—Chronology. 3. Béroalde, Mathieu, d. 1576? Chronicum.

Library of Congress DS275.L7 5-6180†

NL 0416589 DLC OU WU CtY DFo NcD

FILM
Lively, Edward, 1545?-1605.
A trve chronologie of the times of the Persian monarchie, and after to the destruction of Ierusalem by the Romanes. Wherein ... briefly is handled the day of Christ his birth: with a declaration of the Angel Gabriels message to Daniel in the end of his 9. chap. against the friuolous conceits of Matthew Beroald. Written by Edvvard Livelie ... At London, Printed by Felix Kingston for Thomas Man, John Porter, and Rafe Iacson. 1597.
University microfilms no.15919 (case 68, carton 405)
Short-title catalogue no.16609.
1. Persia—Hist.—Chronology. 2. Bible—Chronology. 3. Béroalde, Mathieu, d. 1576? Chronicum.

NL 0416590 MiU ViU

Lively, Frank, joint comp.

Lilly, Armistead Abraham, 1878– comp.
West Virginia laws made plain; laws and legal forms prepared for the use of farmers, mechanics and business men, comp. by Hon. A. A. Lilly ... [and] Hon. Frank Lively ... [St. Joseph, Mo., Combe printing company] ©1916.

Lively, Frank, 1864-

Lively, William Thompson, 1891– comp.
... West Virginia laws made plain; laws and legal forms prepared for the use of farmers, mechanics and business men, compiled by Wm. T. Lively ... examined by Judge Frank Lively ... Kansas City, Mo., Bankers law publishing co., ©1925.

Lively, Gerald J
1909-
LI943p
The plea of the West, and other poems.
London, W. Stewart & Co. [1913?]
24 p. 18 cm.

Text within ornamental borders.

1. Canadian poetry. I. Title.

NL 0416593 RPB

Lively, H. C.
Primitive and ancient elements in Christian hymns. No pub., n. d.
40 l.

Bibliography: l.39-40.

NL 0416594 MiD

LIVELY, H. T.
American Railway Association freight claim division; address before 38th annual session freight claim division A.R.A. in Washington, D.C. May 21, 1929. n.p., [1929]

pp.5.

NL 0416595 MH

VOLUME 336

[Lively, James Madison,] 1852 –
Evolution of intellectual man. Mental economy, political economy, industrial economy. Book 1 [Easton, Pa.: Free Press Pub. Co., cop. 1911.] v. port. 8°.

On cover: Constructive energy.
Book 1. Mental economy.

1. Evolution (Mental). 2. Civilization.—History. 3. Title. 4. Title: Constructive energy.

June 16, 1921.

NL 0416596 NN MH

Lively, James Madison, 1852–
Science of mind; or, Individual and communal knowledge, by J. Madison Lively. [Portland, Or., Printed by the Metropolitan press] 1933.
6 p. l., [3]–211, [3] p. front. (port.) diagrs. 20½ cm.

1. Religion and science—1926–1945. I. Title.

BL240.L58 215 33—33470

NL 0416597 DLC OrU Or OrP

Lively, Luke, pseud.
The merry fellow; or, Jovial companion; being the wit's pocket-book and entertaining magazine...By Luke Lively, Gent. ...Dublin, Printed by J. Hoey, 1757.

NL 0416598 DFo

Lively, Robert A
The South in action; a sectional crusade against freight rate discrimination. Chapel Hill, Univ. of North Carolina Press, 1949.
viii, 98 p. map. 23 cm. (The James Sprunt studies in history and political science, v. 30)
Bibliography: p. [91]–98.

1. Railroads—Southern States—Freight. 2. Railroads—Southern States—Rates. I. Title. (Series)

F251.J28 vol. 30 385.1324 49–8233*
—— —— Copy 2. HE2126.L5

PSC PPPrHi GU-L NjR
NL 0416599 DLC IdPI OOxM CoU NIC TxU ViU OCU PU-L

Lively, William Irven, 1878-
Ananias of Arizona. Phoenix, Ariz., c1953.
54p. 22cm.

1.Tall tales I.Title

NL 0416600 CoD

1901
L7844ca
Lively, William Irven, 1878-
Camp and trail, incidents of pioneer life in Arizona. [Phoenix, Ariz.? 194-?]
70 p. 24 cm.

Poems.
Author's autographed presentation copy.

NL 0416601 RPB CoD

Lively, William Irven, 1878–
Cloud rifts, poems, by W. Irven Lively. Louisville, Ky., Pentecostal publishing co. [°1908]
199 p. front. (port.) 20½ cm.

8-20151

NL 0416602 DLC

Lively, William Irven, 1878–
Colorado, a legend of the Southwest, by W. Irven Lively ... [Los Angeles, Chicago color printing co., °1916]
[19] p. 19 cm. $0.50
In verse.

I. Title.

Library of Congress PS3523.I 88C6 1916 17–4321

NL 0416603 DLC

T811
L748l
Lively, William Irven, 1878-
The legend of Camelback Mountain. Sketches by Truman Helm. [Phoenix, Ariz.? A.T. Helm] c1928.
13p. illus. 21cm.

Poem.

NL 0416604 TxU RPB

Lively, Wm. Irven, 1878 -
The mystic mountains; a history of the Superstition mountains. [Phoenix, Ariz.] c1955. 29 p. illus. 23cm.

1. Superstition mountains.

NL 0416605 NN CU-B

Lively, William Irven, 1878–
The quest. Phoenix, Ariz., °1952.
108 p. 25 cm.
In verse.

I. Title.

PS3523.I 88Q4 811.5 52-19523 ‡

NL 0416606 DLC

Lively, William Spencer, 1855–
Lively's method of lightings. McMinnville, Tenn., W. S. Lively, °1907.
59 p. incl. front., illus. 27½ cm.

10-30071

Library of Congress
©

NL 0416607

Lively, William Thompson, 1891– *comp.*
... West Virginia laws made plain; laws and legal forms prepared for the use of farmers, mechanics and business men, compiled by Wm. T. Lively ... examined by Judge Frank Lively ... Kansas City, Mo., Bankers law publishing co., °1925.
cover-title, 100 p. 21½ cm.
"Presented by Carlville state bank, Carlville, West Virginia."
Edition of 1916 compiled by A. A. Lilly.

1. Business law—West Virginia. I. Lively, Frank, 1864– II. West Virginia. Laws, statutes, etc. III. Title.

Library of Congress HF1275.W4L6 25–18254

NL 0416608 DLC

Lively-Hamer, Marcelle
see Hamer, Marcelle (Lively)

Lively arts and book review
see under New York herald tribune.

The lively character of a contented and discontented cuckold, ala-mode de Anglitere, by what names or titles soever distinguished. With an apology for, and a defence of the fair and tender sex. Suited for the meridian of London. [London, Sold by the booksellers of London and Westminster, 1700] 4 p. 21cm. (4°.)

Wing 2590.
Caption-title and colophon.

1. Adultery—Gt. Br.

Card revised
February 1, 1950

NL 0416611 NN

A lively character of His Maiesties wisdome...
see under Gt. Brit. Sovereigns, etc., 1625-1649 (Charles I)

---

*EC65
A100
659l9
The lively character of some pretending grandees of Scotland to the good old cause. London, Printed in the year, 1659.
1p.l.,6p. 18.5cm.

NL 0416613 MH MiU

The lively character of the malignant partie: wherein their persons, who they are; their actions, what they have already done, and do daily further attempt; with their intentions, at what ends they ayme, are sufficiently set forth, fully described, and plainly evidenced to the indifferent judgement of any ordinary man, who hath had but a reasonable view of the strange passages of these later times. By one who cordially affects his soveraigne, and really respects the Parliament: which illustrious and renowned senate, hath (for the safetie of the king, and preservation of the kingdome) resolved upon the question, that in this malignant partie, they may not, must not, will not, cannot confide. [London?] Published and printed in the yeare of feares and jealousies, plots, projects, and policies, designes, dangers, and discoveries, 1642. 8 p. 20½cm. (4°.)

Astor library: Dixon collection, 167. Thomason, v. 1, p. 178. Union theological seminary: McAlpin collection, v. 2, p. 144.
Imperfect: lower edges cropped, imprint date cut away.

1. Great Britain—Hist.—Charles I, 1625–1649—Pamphlets.

NL 0416615 NN CtY MH CLU-C NNUT-Mc ICN TxU

VOLUME 336

[lively]
A liuely description of all the partes and properties of man
see [Underwood, Robert] fl. 1600. The little world.

---

*pEB65 A100 B675b v.5
A lively description of the destruction of Sodom and Gomorrah, in the year of the world, 2053.
London:Printed and sold by H.Hills,in Black-fryars,near the water-side. Price one penny. [1707]
broadside. 1 illus. 46.5x35.5cm.,mounted & bd.to 66cm.
Prediction of the destruction of London, in verse.
Narcissus Luttrell's copy, priced & dated in his hand: 1d 14. Novemb. 1707.
No. C55 of the Marquess of Bute broadsides.

NL 0416617 MH

... The lively history of Jack & the beanstalk
see under Jack and the bean-stalk.

The lively life of U. S. G., H. U. G., and U. H. G., the political triplets, and somewhat known to fame as the dummy candidate! Together with a series of vigorous illustrations and a useful hint as to how his friends ought to go to work to elect him. New York, 1868.
24, [1] p. illus. 11½cm.
Copyrighted by E. R. Van Winkle.

1. Grant, Ulysses Simpson, pres. U. S., 1822-1885.

Library of Congress E672.L77 10—32709 [a34b1]

NL 0416619 DLC OClWHi MiU-C

Lively livestock
see under Texas gulf sulphur company, incorporated.

The lively oracles given to us
see under [Allestree, Richard] 1619-1681.

Lively oracles, or living words. Acts VII.38. An essay on the importance...of the Holy Scriptures. By N. D. n.p. n.d.

NL 0416622 OClWHi

The lively picture of Lewis du Moulin
See under
[Daillé, Jean, 1594-1670.

A lively pourtraict of our new-cavaliers, commonly called Presbyterians, clearly shewing that His Majesty came not in upon their account. In a compendious narrative of our late revolutions. London, 1661.
15 p. 21cm. [Pamphlets on English history. 1648-1695. no. 8]

1. Presbyterians in Gt. Brit.

NL 0416624 CU NNUT-Mc CtY ICU OrP CtY MH MiD-B

A lively pourtraicture of the face of this commonwealth, exactly drawn by Lewis the Fourth, of France, of famous memory. [London] Printed 1659.
1 p. l., 14 p. 18½cm.

1. Gt. Brit.—Hist.—Commonwealth and protectorate, 1649-1660—Pamphlets. 2. Louis IV, d'Outre-mer, king of France, 921-954.

CA 17-556 Unrev'd

Library of Congress DA422.1659.L5

NL 0416625 DLC MdBP MH NjP NN CtY CLU-C InU ICN

A lively testimony to the living truth, given forth by Robert Jeckell upon his deathbed
see under Jeckell, Robert, d. 1676.

Liven, Alexander, baron von, 1843-1922
see Lieven, Alexander, baron von, 1843-1922.

Liven, Anatoliĭ Pavlovich, knyaz', 1872-
Der neue Mensch; Vortrag von Fürst A. Lieven gehalten den 25. Juni 1932 während der Freizeit des E. V. J. M. in Klein-Mesothen, Kreis Bauske, Lettland... [Riga: Akt.-Ges. "Riti"] 1932. 23 p. 18cm.

868221A. 1. Civilization—Hist., 20th cent.

February 17, 1937

NL 0416628 NN

Liven, Dar'ía Khristoforovna (Benckendorff) *kníaginía*
see
Lieven, Dar'ía Khristoforovna (Benckendorff) *kníaginía*, 1785-1857.

DK254 .K5A3
Liven, Leonid Pavlovich, kníaz', 1909- ed.
Kirill Vladimirovich, *grand duke of Russia*, 1876-1938.
My life in Russia's service—then and now, by H. I. H. the Grand Duke Cyril... London, Selwyn & Blount, 1939.

Liven, Petr Aleksandrovich, *kníaz'*, 1887-
... The birth of ballets-russes. Translated by L. Zarine. Boston and New York, Houghton Mifflin company, 1936.
3 p. l., 9-377 p. col. front., xxxiv pl. (incl. ports., facsim.) on 32 l., col. pl. 22½ cm.
At head of title: Prince Peter Lieven.
Printed in Great Britain.

1. Ballet. 2. Dancing—Russia. 3. Dancers. I. Zarin, Leonid Sergeevich, 1892- tr. II. Title.

GV1787.L5 1936a 792.80947 37—27074

NL 0416631 DLC MB OCl WaS OrP IdB Or WaSp ViU CU PP PU CtY

Liven, Petr Aleksandrovich, *kníaz'*, 1887-
... The birth of ballets-russes. Translated by L. Zarine. London, G. Allen & Unwin, ltd. [1936]
3 p. l., 9-377, [1] p. col. front., xxxiv pl. (incl. ports., facsim.) on 32 l., col. pl. 22 cm.
At head of title: Prince Peter Lieven.
Erratum slip inserted.

1. Ballet. 2. Dancing—Russia. 3. Dancers. I. Zarin, Leonid Sergeevich, 1892- tr. II. Title.

GV1787.L5 792.80947 37—388

NL 0416632 DLC OLak OEac OU NN MU WaU OrU WaSp CaBVa OkU FTaSU

Livenais, August, Jr.

SH451 .M3 1948
FOR OTHER EDITIONS SEE MAIN ENTRY
Major, Harlan, 1889-
Salt water fishing tackle. With special chapters by August "Primo" Livenais, Jr., and George W. Garey. Rev. ed. Drawings by F. B. Junghans. New York, Funk & Wagnalls Co. [1948]

Livén'chzhun
see
Li, Hung-chang, 1823-1901.

Livengood, Charles A.
... Cuban economic improvement by C. A. Livengood and Frank E. Coombs, American trade commissioners, Habana. Washington, Govt. print. off., 1924.
ii, 8 p. incl. tables. 24½cm. ([U. S.] Bureau of foreign and domestic commerce (Dept. of commerce) Trade information bulletin, no. 191)
Supplement to Commerce reports. Published by the Bureau of foreign and domestic commerce. February 11, 1924.

1. Cuba—Econ. condit. I. Coombs, Frank E., joint author. II. U. S. Bureau of foreign and domestic commerce. Commerce reports. Supplement. III. Title.

Library of Congress HF105.C285 no. 191 HC157.C9L5 24—26129

NL 0416635 DLC WaWW OU OCl OO MiU CU PP

Livengood, Charles A.
... Cuban market for paper and paper products, by Charles A. Livengood, American trade commissioner, Habana. Washington, Govt. print. off., 1924.
ii, 15 p. incl. tables. 24½cm. ([U. S.] Bureau of foreign and domestic commerce (Dept. of commerce) Trade information bulletin, no. 192)
Supplement to Commerce reports. Published by the Bureau of foreign and domestic commerce. February 18, 1924.

1. Paper making and trade—Cuba. I. U. S. Bureau of foreign and domestic commerce (Dept of commerce) Commerce reports. Supplement. II. Title.

Library of Congress HF105.C285 no. 192 HD9834.C82L5 24-26161

NL 0416636 DLC OU MiU OU OCl OO WaWW

[Livengood, Charles A]
... Spain: resources, industries, trade and public finance ... Washington, U. S. Govt. print. off., 1930.
ii, 47 p. incl. map, tables. 24cm. (U. S. Bureau of foreign and domestic commerce (Dept. of commerce) Trade information bulletin, no. 739)
At head of title: U. S. Department of commerce. R. P. Lamont, secretary. Bureau of foreign and domestic commerce. William L. Cooper, director.
"By Charles A. Livengood, American commercial attaché, and Julian Greenup, assistant commercial attaché, Madrid, and Philip M. Copp, Division of regional information."—p. 1.
1. Spain—Econ. condit.—1918- 2. Spain—Indus. 3. Spain—Comm. 4. Finance—Spain. I. Greenup, Julian, joint author. II. Copp, Philip Mauro, 1894- joint author. III. Title.

Library of Congress HF105.C285 no. 739 HC385.L5 31-26280

(382.061) 330.946

NL 0416637 DLC CaBVaU WaWW PP PPD MiU OU

VOLUME 336

Livengood, Charles H 1911-
The Federal wage and hour law. Philadelphia, 19 -
v. 23 cm.

Issued by the Joint Committee on Continuing Legal Education of the American Law Institute and the American Bar Association.
1. Wages - Minimum wage - U. S. 2. Overtime - U. S. 3. Children - Employment - U. S. I. Federal wage and hour law.

NL 0416638 CaBVaU DLC

Livengood, Charles H 1911-
The Federal wage and hour law, including the Fair labor standards amendments of 1949 (July 1951) Philadelphia, Committee on Continuing Legal Education ⌐1951⌐
xi, 196 p. 23 cm. (Committee on Continuing Legal Education Publications. Series two)
Includes bibliographies.

1. Wages—Minimum wage—U. S. 2. Overtime—U. S. 3. Children—Employment—U. S. I. Title. (Series: Committee on Continuing Legal Education. Publications)

331.2973 51-7024

NL 0416639 DLC MiEM TU TxU NcU WaU-L

Livengood, Charles Harris, 1911-
The Federal wage and hour law, including the Fair labor standards amendment of 1949 (March 1952) Philadelphia, Committee on Continuing Legal Education ⌐1952⌐
xi, 196 p. 23 cm. (Committee on Continuing Legal Education. Publications. Series two)
Including bibliographies.

1. Wages—Minimum wage—U. S. 2. Overtime—U. S. 3. Children—Employment—U. S. I. Title. (Series: Committee on Continuing Legal Education. Publications)

331.2973 52-3526 rev

NL 0416640 DLC NBuU-L TxU WaU

LIVENGOOD, George H
[Genealogical notes]
[Seattle, Wash. n.d.] 24v. in 26. illus. facsims. maps (part fold.)

Loose-leaf.

NL 0416641 WaS

S 21 C9 L5 Livengood, L M
History, organization, and functions of the bureaus and divisions in the Department of Agriculture. [n.p., n.d.]
Irregular paging. 28 cm.
Carbon copy of typescript.

1. U.S. Department of Agriculture - Hist.

NL 0416642 WaSpG

UH 460 L5 Livengood, L M
History, organization and functions of the Public Health and Marine Hospital Service. [n.p., n.d.]
290 p. 28 cm.
Carbon copy of typescript.

1. Hospitals, Military - U.S. - Hist. 2. U.S. Public Health Service - Hist.

NL 0416643 WaSpG

Livengood, William Winfred, 1881- *comp.*
Americana, as taught to the tune of a hickory stick. Introd. by Mary Ellen Chase. ⌐New York⌐ Women's National Book Association, 1954.
x, 70 p. illus., facsims. 24 cm.

1. Text-books—U. S. 2. American literature (Selections: Extracts, etc.) I. Title.

PS509.T4L5 810.8 54-2951

IdU OrAshS OrPS PSt PSC ODW OCl OClW TU MB ViU NN WaS GU CoU IdPI
NL 0416644 DLC PJB PPPL NcC OU PP PPT OOxM PU TxU

Livengood, William Winfred, 1881- comp.

Indiana University. Independent literary society.
Independent literary society of Indiana university; historical sketch, side lights from the press, register of members, comp. by William Winfred Livengood, A. B. '07. 1885-1907. Bloomington, Ind., The Society, 1908.

Livengood, William Winfred, 1881-
Our heritage ⌐by⌐ W. W. Livengood... An address delivered to the entire agency force of American book company, January 4, 1947, at...Cincinnati, Ohio. ⌐Cincinnati, 1947⌐ 32 p. 23cm.

1. American book company.

April 8, 1949

NL 0416646 NN NcD OC MH-BA N MH MB

LT23 .L78 Livengood, William Winfred, 1881-
Our textbooks; yesterday & today. ⌐New York⌐ Textbook Clinic, American Institute of Graphic Arts ⌐1953⌐
v, 22 p. illus.

1. Text-books--U. S. I. American Institute of Graphic Arts. Textbook Clinic.

NL 0416647 ICU NN ICU

Livengood, William Winfred, 1881- joint author.
Baldwin, James, 1841-1925.
Sailing the seas; the log of Tom Darke, by James Baldwin and W. W. Livengood; introduction by Edward N. Hurley ... illustrated by Kerr Eby and Leon D'Emo. New York, Cincinnati ⌐etc.⌐ American book company ⌐©1920⌐

Livengood, William Winfred, 1881- ed.

Shakespeare, William, 1564-1616.
... Shakespeare's Macbeth, ed. by W. W. Livengood ... New York, Cincinnati ⌐etc.⌐ American book company ⌐©1910⌐

Livengood, William Winfred, 1881-
The world at work, by W. W. Livengood ... with an introduction by C. A. Prosser ... New York, D. McNetton and company ⌐©1915⌐
xv, ⌐1⌐, 290 p. 19½cm. $1.00
A handbook to accompany 225 views.
"Books and bulletins": p. xiii-xiv.
"Suggested readings," at end of each chapter.

1. Economic conditions. I. Title.

Library of Congress HF1027.L5 15-14756

NL 0416650 DLC

Livens, George Henry.
The theory of electricity, by G. H. Livens ... Cambridge, University press, 1918.
vi p., 1 l., 717 p. illus., diagrs. 27½cm.

1. Electricity. I. Title.

Library of Congress QC518.L75 18-18163

ICJ NN MB IU CtY
NL 0416651 DLC CU OrPS PHC NjP MiU OU OCU ViU MdBJ

Livens, George Henry.
The theory of electricity, by G. H. Livens ... 2d ed. Cambridge ⌐Eng.⌐ The University press, 1926.
4 p. l., 427, ⌐1⌐ p. diagrs. 22½cm.

1. Electricity. I. Title.

Library of Congress QC518.L75 1926 27-18363

IU
NL 0416652 DLC WaS IdU CU NcD OU MiU OCU OCl MiHM

Livens, Herbert Mann.
Earth and her children, by Herbert Mann Livens. Illustrated by Horace Mann Livens, Fanny M. Minns, Geoffrey Livens, and others. London, Leipsic, T. F. Unwin, 1912.
2 p. l., 7-248 p. front., illus., plates (part double) 18cm.

1. Natural history—Juvenile and popular literature. I. Title.

A 13-429

Title from Enoch Pratt Free Libr. Printed by L. C.

NL 0416653 MdBE

S19 .I49 no.27 1943 Livens, J
L'étude du sol et sa nécessité au Congo Belge. ⌐Gembloux, J. Duculot⌐ 1943.
50 p. diagrs. 25cm. (Publications de l'Institut National pour l'Étude Agronomique du Congo Belge. Sér. technique, no. 27)
Bibliography: p. 50.

1. Soils—Kongo, Belgian. I. Ser.

NL 0416654 ViU IEN

LIVENS, LEO, 1896-

Sonata for pianoforte. [By] Leo Livens... London: The Anglo-French Music Co. Ltd. [1919] Publ.pl.no.A.F.M.Co. 60. 35 p. 31cm.

1. Sonatas—Piano.

NL 0416655 NN

Livenskiĭ, M., *pseud.*
see
Lifshits, Mikhail Iosifovich, 1888-

VOLUME 336

Livenson, Maksimilian Vil'gel'movich von.
... Поединокъ въ законодательствѣ и наукѣ ... С.-Петербургъ, Изданіе Д. В. Чичинадзе, 1900.

2 p. l., 139 p. 23 cm.

At head of title: Шт.-капитанъ Ливенсонъ.
"Уложеніе о наказаніяхъ, Проектъ новаго Уголовнаго уложенія, Воинскій уставъ о наказаніяхъ, Законъ 1894 года и иностранные кодексы."

1. Dueling. 2. Dueling—Russia. I. Russia. Laws, statutes, etc. II. Title. *Title transliterated:* Poedinok v zakonodatel'stvie i naukie.

43-30970

NL 0416657 DLC

TP445 .H88 1911 Rare bk. coll.

Livensperger, G. A.

Hydraulic Press Manufacturing Company.
A treatise on the manufacture of pure apple cider vinegar by the quick process, by H. J. Alwood and G. A. Livensperger, Yeast and Analytical Laboratory. [Rev. ed.] Mount Gilead, Ohio [°1911]

Līventāls, Teodors, 1882-

Riga. *Valde.*
Riga kā Latvijas galvas pilsēta. T. Līventāla un V. Sadovska redakcija. [Rigā, Rigas pilsētas valdes izdevums, 1932]

Līventāls, Teodors, 1882-
Rokas grāmata pilsētu pašvaldības darbiniekiem
see under Latvia. Laws, statutes, etc.

Liventsev, N
Опытные поездки с электровозами. Москва, Гос. трансп. жел-дор. изд-во, 1939.

86 p. diagrs. 23 cm. (Научно-исследовательский институт железнодорожного транспорта. [Издания] вып. 87)

1. Electric locomotives—Testing.
Title transliterated: Opytnye poezdki s ėlektrovozami.

TF975.L58 50-50918

NL 0416661 DLC

Microfilm Slavic 425 AC

Liventsev, Nikolaĭ Mitrofanovich, joint author.

Obrosov, A N
Электродиагностика и электростимуляция мышц при поражении периферических нервов; новые методики и аппараты. Москва, Медгиз, 1953.

Liventsev, Viktor Il'ich.
Партизанский край. Литературная запись: Г. Нехай. [Авторизованный перевод с белорусского Н. Кобзаревского] Ленинград, Молодая гвардия, 1951.

369 p. illus. 21 cm.

1. World War, 1939-1945—Underground movements—Russia. I. Niakhai, Ryhor, Osipavich, 1914- II. Title. *Title transliterated:* Partizanskiĭ kraĭ.

D802.R8L56 52-40722 rev

NL 0416663 DLC

Liveoak, *Fla.*
see
Live Oak, *Fla.*

Liver, Jacob.
ימי עזרא ונחמיה. ירושלים, המחלקה לעלית ילדים ונוער, מדור להדרכה, תשי"ג. [Jerusalem, 1952/53]

39 p. 19 cm. (עיונים, חוב' יד)

Bibliography: p. 39.

1. Bible. O. T. Ezra—Criticism, interpretation, etc. 2. Bible. O. T. Nehemiah—Criticism, interpretation, etc.
Title transliterated: Yeme 'Ezra u-Neḥemyah.

BS1355.L5 57-56215

NL 0416665 DLC

FL8 S9.9 L784g 1954

Liver, Peter, 1902-
Die Graubündner Kantonsverfassung des Jahres 1854; ihre Entstehung und geschichtliche Bedeutung. Zum Centenarium im Auftrag des Kleinen Rates dargestellt von Peter Liver. [Chur, Bischofberger] 1954.
63 p. 23cm.

1. Grisons. Constitution, 1854. I. Title.

NL 0416666 MiU-L MH-L

Pamphlet HD 1303

Liver, Peter
Mittelalterliches Kolonistenrecht und freie Walser in Graubünden. Nach einem im Zürcherischen Juristenverein am 15. Oktober 1942 gehaltenen Vortrag. Zürich, Polygraphischer Verlag, 1943.
40 p. map. 21cm. (Kultur- und staatswissenschaftliche Schriften, Heft 36)
1. Land tenure--Grisons (Canton)--Law. 2. Valaisians in Grisons (Canton) I. Title. II. Series: Zürich. Eidgenössische Technische Hochschule. Kultur- und staatswissenschaftliche Schriften, Heft 36.

NL 0416667 NIC MH

Liver, Peter.
Die öffentliche verwaltung und organisation der landschaft Rheinwald; ihre stellung im feudalstaat, im freistaat, gemeiner drei bünde und im kanton Graubünden; rechtsgeschichtliche und verwaltungsrechtliche studie, mit einem exkurs über die pflanzensuperficies, von Peter Liver ... [Chur, Gedruckt bei Sprecher, Eggerling & co.] 1936.
209 p. 23cm.
"Die Juristische fakultät der Universität Bern hat diese arbeit am 13. juli 1931 auf antrag von herrn prof. dr. Hans Fehr als dissertation angenommen, ohne damit zu den darin ausgesprochenen auffassungen stellung nehmen zu wollen."
"S. a. aus dem 66. jahresbericht der Historisch-antiquarischen gesellschaft von Graubünden."
"Quellen und literatur": p. [7]-10.
1. Rheinwald, Switzerland (Kreis)—Pol. & govt. I. Title.
Library of Congress JS6599.R5L5 [2] 42-41657

NL 0416668 DLC CU

BR115 .H5G8

Liver, Peter.

Guggisberg, Kurt, 1907-
Über christliche Geschichtsdeutung; Rektoratsrede von Kurt Guggisberg. Bericht über das Studienjahr 1953/54 (15. Oktober 1953 bis 14. Oktober 1954) erstattet vom abtretenden Rektor Peter Liver. Bern, Buchdr. P. Haupt [1955]

Liver, Peter, 1902-
Vom Feudalismus zur Demokratie in den graubuendnerischen hinterrheintaelern.
Inaug.diss. Zuerich, n.d. (Chur, 1929)

NL 0416670 ICRL

DD 497 L4 +

Liver, Peter
Die Walser in Graubünden. Bern, Hallwag, 1942.
15p. 30cm.

"Separatdruck aus dem Band 'Graubünden' der Bücherreihe Pro Helvetia."

1. Grisons - History. I. Title.

NL 0416671 MU

Liver, Peter, 1902-
... Der wille des gesetzes. Rektoratsrede von prof. Peter Liver. Bern, Haupt, 1954
32 p 21cm
At head of title: Berner rektoratsreden.
Bibliographical footnotes.

NL 0416672 MH-L

Le Liver des assises et plees
see under
Gt. Brit. Yearbooks, 1327-1377 (Edward III)

Liverance, W. B.
The Babcock test. Notes on its use in determining the percentage of fat in whole milk, skim-milk, butter-milk, cream, cheese and whey. East Lansing [1908]. 16 p. 8°. (Michigan. Agricultural experiment station. Circular 2.)

1. Milk.—Tests: Babcock method.

April 5, 1911.

NL 0416674 NN

Liverani, Antonio.
... Le società civili e di commercio in regime tributario ... Cesena, Tipografia S. A. I. C. A., 1929-
v. 24½cm.

1. Corporations—Italy—Taxation. 2. Taxation—Italy—Law. I. Title.

37-14946

NL 0416675 DLC

[**Liverani, Antonio,**] 1886-
La Brigata Venezia (83°-84° Reggimento fanteria) nella guerra italo-austriaca, 1915-1918. Firenze: Alfani e Venturi, 1920. 278 p. facsims., illus., maps, music, plates, ports. 4°.

Part of plates printed on both sides.
"La narrazione è stata curata dal Maggiore Liverani Cav. Antonio, con il materiale coordinato dalla Commissione incaricata." — [*Pref.*]

1. Army (Italian).—Regimental histories. 2. European war, 1914- —Regimental histories, Italy: Infantry: 83rd. 3. Title.

June 24, 1922.

NL 0416676 NN

Liverani, D
Il lamento; romance with an accompaniment for the piano forte. L, Welsh [182- ?]
Score (7 p.)
Bd. with Bellini, V. Norma (6) Selections: Mira, Norma, et al.

NL 0416677 MH

VOLUME 336

913.37 Liverani, Francesco, 1823-1894.
L75c Le catacombe e antichità cristiane di Chiusi descritte da monsig. Francesco Liverani. Siena, G. Bargellini, 1872.
348p. illus., plans.

Bibliographical foot-notes.

NL 0416678 IU MH MeLB

PA2402 Liverani, Francesco, *b.* 1823.
.L7 La chiave vera e le chiavi false della lingua etrusca. Saggio di epigrafi del Museo vaticano, britannico, di Firenze, di Parigi, Berlino, Lione, Cortona, Perugia, Chiusi, ec. interpretate in pro della storia, della lingua e delle arti di quel popolo, da Monsignor Francesco Liverani ... Siena, Tip. di L. Lazzeri, 1874.
97, [1] p. 18cm.

1. Etruscan language.

NL 0416679 ICU MH

Liverani, Francesco, b. 1823.
Confessions d'un protonotaire apostolique suivies de l'histoire d'une annexion pontificale; extraits du mémoire de Monsignor F. Liverani. Avec une introduction par Adalbert Philis. Paris, Poulet-Malassis et de Broise, 1861.

NL 0416680 MH

Liverani, Francesco, b. 1823.
La cour de Rome...
see under Andrea, Girolamo d', Cardinal.

Liverani, Francesco, 1823 - 1894. Arc 1033.12.1
Del nome di Santa Maria ad Praesepe che la Basilica Liberiana porta e delle reliquie della natività ed infanzia del Salvatore che conserva. Roma, B. Morini, 1854.
l. 8°. pp. (4), 116. 2 plates.

Rome-Santa Maria Maggiore-Relics

NL 0416682 MH MB PPD

Liverani, Francesco, 1823-94
Della vita e passione del venerabile servó di Dio Giovanni Sarcander, prete secolare di Skotschau, parroco di Holleschau, morto dagli eretici in Olmütz nell'anno 1620. Libri due. Macerata, Tip.di A.Mancini, 1855
248 p.

1. Jan Sarkander, Blessed, 1576-1620

NL 0416683 MH

Liverani, Francesco, 1823-1894. C 1276.1
Delle opere di Francesco Liverani. Orvieto, presso S. Pompei, etc. etc. [cover, 1858]-59.
5 vol. Ports. and other illus.
Vol. 1 has added title-page: "Orazioni lette agli ecclesiastici nell' Accademia liturgica di Roma presso i Lazzaristi a Monte Citorio e trattato sulle reliquie di Monsignore Francesco Liverani. 1858."

NL 0416684 MH

BX1810 Liverani, Francesco, 1823-1894.
L58 La dottrina cattolica e la rivoluzione italica. Firenze, F. Le Monnier, 1862.
248 p.

Bibliographical footnotes.

1. Popes - Temporal power 2. Roman question

NL 0416685 CU MH

945.56 Liverani, Francesco, 1823-1894.
L75d Il ducato e le antichità longobarde e saliche di Chiusi. Siena, 1875.
301p. plates.

"Codice diplomatico della città di Chiusi": p.[267]-287.

NL 0416686 IU MChB

DS25 Liverani, Francesco, 1823-1894.
.L7 Fra Giovanni da Pian di Carpine nel contado di Magione, viaggiatore e descrittore di Tartaria e Mongolia nel secolo XIII. Monografia di Monsignor Francesco Liverani. Perugia, Tip. V. Bartelli, 1876.
141 p. 23cm.
"Relazione del viaggio ... in Tartaria": p. 40-91.
"La Magione e i dintorni del Trasimeno all'era etrusca descritti da Monsignor Francesco Liverani": p. [103]-140.
Bibliographical foot-notes.

1. Giovanni di Plano Carpini, abp. of Antivari. 2. Tartars.

NL 0416687 ICU MWelC MH MB

LIVERANI, Francesco, 1823-1894.
Lessicografia italiana. 2a ed. accresciuta che contiene l'ultima parola sulla carte d'Arborea. Firenze, Tipografia dell'associazione,1871.

pp.41. 4245.28

NL 0416688 MH

LIVERANI, Francesco, 1823-1894.
Maestro Giovanni Bernardi da castelbolognese intagliatore di gemme. Faenza, 1870

Pamphlet. Ital 461.4

NL 0416689 MH

DG796 Liverani, Francesco, 1823-1894.
.L76 Il Papato, l'Impero e il regno d'Italia; memoria di monsignor Francesco Liverani, al conte de Montalembert. Firenze, G. Barbèra, 1861.
369 p.
"Documenti": p.[331]-365.

1. Papal States--Pol. & govt. 2. Church and state in Italy. 3. Popes--Temporal power

NL 0416690 ICU

Liverani, Francesco, 1823-1894.
Il papato, l' impero e il regno d' Italia; memoria. Roma: Coi tipi della Civiltà cattolica, 1861. xix, 410 p. 12°.

1. Catholic Church (Roman).—History, Italy, 1861. 2. Italy.—History, 1861. 3. Church and state, 1861.

April 23, 1912.

NL 0416691 NN

BX Liverani, Francesco, 1823-1894.
955 Il papato, l'impero e il regno d'Italia.
L78 2. ed. Firenze, G. Barbèra, 1861.
1861 335 p. 18cm.

1. Papacy--Hist.

NL 0416692 NIC CtY

DG796 Liverani, Francesco, 1823-1894.
L55 Il papato, l'impero e il regno d'Italia; memoria. 3.ed. Firenze, G. Barbèra, 1861.
308 p.

1. Papal States - Pol. & govt. 2. Church and state - Catholic Church. I. Title.

NL 0416693 CU NcD MH OCl IU

Liverani, Francesco, 1823-1894.
Il papato, l'impero e il regno d'Italia; memoria. 4a ed. Firenze, G. Barbèra, 1861.

NL 0416694 MH

Liverani, Francesco, 1823-1894, ed.
Spicilegium Liberianum
see under title

[LIVERANI, Francesco] 1823-1894.
Studi di storia siciliana di Isidoro La Lumia. Palermo, 1870.

NL 0416696 MH

Liverani, Francesco. 1823-1894. Sulle profession di legge romana ne' secoli XI-XII. 12 pp. (*Archiv. stor. ital.* 3 s. v. 18, 1873, p. 254.)

NL 0416697 MdBP

Liverani, Francesco Armando
Le associazioni di mestiere nelle civiltà antieche e moderne. Milano, Casa Editrice Dott. F. Vallardi, 1940.
viii, 422 p.

Bibliography: p. [415]-522.

1. Gilds. 2. Syndicalism.

NL 0416698 NNC

LIVERANI, GIUSEPPE.
...Catalogo delle porcellane dei Medici. Faenza: F. Lega [1936] 57 p. illus., plates. 25cm. (Piccola biblioteca del Museo delle ceramiche in Faenza. 2.)

"Bibliografia," p. 41-44.

1. Pottery, Italian. 2. Medici, House of. I. Ser.

NL 0416699 NN ICU MH

VOLUME 336

LIVERANI, GIUSEPPE.
Catalogo delle porcellane dei Medici. Faenza, F. Lega [1936] 57 p. illus., plates. 25cm. (Piccola biblioteca del Museo delle ceramiche in Faenza. 2)

Microfilm (Master negative)

NL 0416700 NN

Liverani, Giuseppe.
... Il Museo delle ceramiche in Faenza. (94 illustrazioni) Roma, La Libreria dello stato, a. xv E. F. [1936]

70 p. incl. plates. 18½cm. (Itinerari dei musei e monumenti d'Italia. [n. 57])

At head of title: Ministero della educazione nazionale. Direzione generale delle antichità e belle arti ...
Plans on p. [2] and [4] of cover.
Bibliography: p. 7-8.

1. Faenza. Museo internazionale delle ceramiche.

45-45613

Library of Congress NK3730.F25L5

738.074

NL 0416701 DLC OC1MA NN WaS NIC NNC

Liverani, Giuseppe
L'officina maiolicara cinquecentesca dei Bergantini per la storia della ceramica italiana [by] Giuseppe Liverani [and] Carlo Grigioni. Faenza, Stab. grafico F.Lega [1939]

35 p. plates. (Piccola biblioteca del Museo delle ceramiche in Faenza, 7)

NL 0416702 MH

J19
212m

Liverani, Giuseppe
Il Regio Istituto d'arte per la ceramica di Faenza. Firenze,F.Le Monnier,1941.
123p. 8 plates. 26cm.
"Bibliografia": p.[79]-96.

1.Faenza,Italy. Istituto d'arte per la ceramica.

NL 0416703 CtY MH

NK4315
.L78

Liverani, Giuseppe.
... Sull'origine della maiolica italiana ... Faenza, Fratelli Lega, 1937.
cover-title, 17 p. IV pl.
"Estratto da "Faenza", anno XXV, fasc.1, 1937, XV."
Bibliography: p.14-17.

1. Majolica. 2. Pottery--Italy.

NL 0416704 ICU

Liverani, Paolo
Cenno sopra le strade ferrate a pressione atmosferica in esercizio e proposta di miglioramento nel tubo di propulsione. Bologna, N. Zanichelli, 1877.
4 p.l., 93 p., 1 l., 3 pl. 8°.

NL 0416705 NN

LIVERANI, PAOLO.
Cenno sopra le strade ferrate a pressione atmosferica in esercizio e proposta di miglioramento nel tubo di propulsione. Bologna, N. Zanichelli, 1877. 93 p. 3 plates. 24cm.

Microfilm.

1. Railways, Compressed air. t. 1877.

NL 0416706 NN

WL
L784a
1886

LIVERANI, Vincenzo
L'âme est la fonction du cerveau, par Émile Ferrière; esame critico. Bologna, Tip. Arcivescovile, 1886.
419 p.
I. Ferrière, Émile, 1830- L'âme est la fonction du cerveau

NL 0416707 DNLM

Liverant, Sh
קראליקעס־צוכט. קיעוו, מעלוכע־פארלאג פאר די נאציאנאלע מינדערהייטן אין אוסר"ר, [Kiev] 1934
62 p. illus. 25 cm.

1. Rabbits. *Title transliterated: Krolikes-tsukht.*

SF453.L53 52-50453

NL 0416708 DLC

Liverati, Carlo Ernesto, 1805-1844.
Ricordi del terzo Congresso scientifico italiano ossieno ritratti di trentasei fra i suoi componenti disegnati dal vero dal cav. C. E. Liverati e accompagnati da brevi biografie. Firenze, Presso J. Grazzini, 1842.

[85] p. 35 port. 37cm.

1. Scientists. 2. Congresso degli scienziati italiani. 3d, Florence, 1841.

10-21901

Library of Congress Q54.C44 1841

NL 0416709 DLC NN

Liverati, Giovanni, 1772-ca. 1835.
Boot and saddle bonny Scott; a favorite song. Philada [i. e. Philadelphia] G. E. Blake [18—]
3 p. 36 cm.
For voice and piano.

1. Songs (High voice) with piano. I. Title.

M1.A13L M 60-1110

NL 0416710 DLC

LIVERATI, GIOVANNI, 1772-1835(ca.)
[LA PROVA GENERALE. CHI A VOI O UOMIN CREDE]
Chi a voi o uomin crede; aria in the opera of La prova generale, op. 17. London, Printed & sold by Birchall [182-?] Pl. no. 1101. 9 p. 34cm.

Caption title.
For voice and piano.

1. Songs, Italian.

NL 0416711 NN

Liverati, Giovanni, 1772-1835(ca.)
David. Dramma sacro in due atti
For libretti see under Posto, Antoni.

Liverati, Giovanni, 1772-1835(ca.)
The Nymph of the grotto
For libretti see under Dimond, William, fl. 1800-1830.

LIVERATI, Giovanni, 1772-ca. 1835
"Row the bit boatie," trio ... [S. S. T.] in the opera of Carron side ... [Accomp. for pianoforte.]
London. Mori & Lavenu. [183-?] (1), 5 pp. F°.

NL 0416714 MB

Liverdis, Balthazar Grangier de
see Grangier de Liverdis, Balthazar

Le livere de reis de Brittanie e Le livere de reis de Engleterre. Edited by John Glover ... Published by the authority of the lords commissioners of Her Majesty's Treasury, under the direction of the master of the rolls. London, Longmans, Green, Reader, and Dyer, 1865.

4, xx, 400 p. front. (fold. facsim.) 26 cm. (*Half-title:* [Gt. Brit. Public record office] Rerum britannicarum medii ævi scriptores; or, Chronicles and memorials of Great Britain and Ireland during the middle ages. [no. 42])

Old French and English on opposite pages.

Attributed to Peter of Ickham.
The Wroxham continuation, p. 302-321; The Sempringham continuation, p. 322-355.

1. Gt. Brit.—Kings and rulers. I. Peter, of Ickham, fl. 1290? supposed author. II. Glover, John, ed. III. Title: Le livere de reis de Engleterre.

DA25.B5 no. 42 A 28-2304

Chicago. Univ. Libr.
for Library of Congress [n58l½]†

NL 0416717 PPPD OC1 MH MnHi MdBP NjP DLC NBuU ViU CaBVaU KEmT RPB ICU IdPI OrPR OrU NcU MiU MWiW CtY NN

Micro-card Ed.

Le livere de reis de Brittanie e Le livere de reis de Engleterre. Ed. by John Glover. Pub. by the authority of the lords commissioners of Her Majesty's Treasury, under the direction of the master of the rolls. London, Longmans, Green, Reader, and Dyer, 1865.
4, xx, 400p. front. (fold. facsim.) 26cm. (Half-title: [Gt. Brit. Public record office] Rerum britannicarum medii aevi scriptores. [no.42])
Old French and English on opposite pages.
Attributed to Peter of Ickham.
Wroxham continuation, p.302-321; Sempringham continuation, p.322-355.
Microcard editinn (9 cds.)

NL 0416718 FMU IdPI

[Le livere de reis de Brittanie] The genealogy of the kings of Britain
see The genealogy of the kings of Britain.

VOLUME 336

Liveri di Valdausa, Napoleone, marchese de.
Libro d'oro della repubblica di San Marino, compilato dal patrizio marchese de Liveri di Valdausa... Foligno, F. Campitelli, 1914. xvii, 282 p. illus. 35cm.

Contains thirteen chapters, of which seven are by Liveri di Valdausa.

367069B. 1. San Marino (Republic)—Hist. 2. San Marino (Republic)—Biog.
March 21, 1947

NL 0416720 NN

LIVERIERO, Emilio.
Carlo Botta e i suoi tempi; orazione inaugurale, pronunciata il 16 nov. 1858. nel Collegio-convitto nazionale di Novara. Novara, G. Miglio,1858.

pp.28.

NL 0416721 MH

LIVERIERO, Emilio
Del sentimento religioso nelle lettere. Torino, 1875.

NL 0416722 MH

Liveright, Ada Fleisher.

American library association. *Committee on cooperation with the National education association.*
Report. 1934–
(*In* National education association of the United States. Addresses and proceedings, 1934. p. 171-172)

Liveright, Alexander Albert, 1907–
Union leadership training; a handbook of tools and techniques. ₍1st ed.₎ New York, Harper ₍1951₎
xvi, 265 p. illus. 22 cm.
"A publication of the Industrial Relations Center of the University of Chicago."
Bibliographical references included in "Chapter sources" (p. 251-259)

1. Trade-unions—Officers. I. Chicago. University. Industrial Relations Center. II. Title.

HD6490.O4L5 331.880 51-5176

NL 0416724 DLC NN MB TU TxU CU CaBVa Or OrCS OrP Wa WaS

Liveright, Alexander Albert, 1907 –
Your job: how to find it - how to hold it ... Chicago, The Jewish vocational service and employment center; Washington, B'nai B'rith vocational service bureau, c1940.
31 p. illus. 21½cm.

1. Applications for positions. 2. Vocational guidance. I. Jewish vocational service and employment center. II. B'nai B'rith vocational service bureau. III. Title.

NL 0416725 MiEM

Liveright, Mrs. Alice (Fleisher) 1882-
Pennsylvania. *State welfare commission.*
Report on state aid to private charitable institutions and agencies. By the State welfare commission ... ₍Harrisburg, 1935₎

Liveright, Alice Kaufmann, 1887–
Demonstration schools for teachers in service; a study representative of practices to and including the school year 1934–1935 ... ₍by₎ Alice Kaufmann Liveright. Philadelphia, 1938.
168, ₍4₎ p. incl. tables, forms. fold. form. 23cm.
Thesis (PH. D.)—University of Pennsylvania, 1938.
Bibliography: p. 166–168.

1. Teachers, Training of—U. S. I. Title.

39-1282
Library of Congress LB1715.L54 1938
Univ. of Pennsylvania. Libr.
₍5-5₎ 370.733

NL 0416727 PU OU OCl OOxM OO OCU CU NcU NIC KEmT MtU OrPR OrU DLC

Liveright, Alice Kaufmann, 1887– joint author.

Gates, Arthur Irving, 1890–
Tony and Jo-Jo ₍by₎ Gates, Liveright ₍and₎ Esterline. ₍New York, The Macmillan company, 1940₎

Liveright, Alice Kaufmann, 1887– joint author.

Gates, Arthur Irving, 1890–
Trails in the woods ₍by₎ Gates, Liveright ₍and₎ Esterline. ₍New York, The Macmillan company, 1940₎

Liveright, Frank

Newark museum association, *Newark, N. J.*
Numismatics; a list of books and pamphlets in the Frank I. Liveright collection. Newark, N. J., The Newark museum, 1939.

Law

Liveright, Horace, inc., defendant.

₍**Lewis, Gladys Adelina**₎ *plaintiff.*
... Georges Lewys, plaintiff, against Eugene O'Neill, Boni & Liveright, inc., Horace Liveright inc. and Theatre guild inc., defendant. In equity 49-219. Before: Honorable John M. Woolsey, district judge. New York, March 16th₍–April 22₎, 1931 ... ₍New York? 1931?₎

Liveright, Mrs. I. Albert

see

Liveright, Mrs. Alice (Fleisher) 1882-

Liveright, James.
Simple methods for detecting buying and selling points in securities, by James Liveright. New York, The Magazine of Wall street ₍°1923₎
156 p. 15½ cm.

1. Speculation. 2. Securities.

HG6021.L5 24—3780

NL 0416733 DLC NN OrU

LIVERIGHT, JAMES.
Simple methods for detecting buying and selling points in securities. 2. ed. New York, The Magazine of Wall street [c1923] 157 p. illus. 16cm.

Film Reproduction. Positive.
Imperfect: t.p. wanting when recataloged for filming.

1. Speculation. I. The Magazine of Wall street.

NL 0416734 NN

Liveright, James
Simple methods for detecting buying and selling points in securities. 3d ed.
New York, The Magazine of Wall street ₍c1926₎
133 p.

NL 0416735 OCl

Liveright, Pat.
Ideas into pictures, by Pat Liveright ... New York, Knight publishers, 1939.
2 p. l., 7-47 p. incl. front., illus., diagrs. 20½cm. (The Knight photographic library, edited by H. C. McKay, A. Sussman and S. G. Phillips)

1. Photography. I. Title.

Library of Congress TR147.L58 39-10615
Copyright AA 294114 770

NL 0416736 DLC OLak OCl

Livermoore, Ricardo Heredia y, *conde de Benahavis*
see
Heredia y Livermoore, Ricardo, *conde de Benahavis.*

PZ263 .L7805 1859
Livermore, Mrs.
The Christmas child. New York, J. A. Gray, 1859.
55 p.

NL 0416738 ICU

Livermore (A. E.)
How to make an accumulator. (In: Ward (H. S.) Practical radiography . . . *London,* 1896. 12°. pp. 16–24.)

NL 0416739 NN

Livermore, Mrs. A. L.

see

Livermore, Henrietta Jackson (Wells) "Mrs. A. L. Livermore."

Livermore, Aaron Russell
A sermon preached at the funeral of Mrs. Mary E. Hovey, wife of Mr. Dwight F. Hovey, and daughter of Dea. Rufus and Mrs. Elizabeth Dumock, who died July 22, 1852, aged 21 years. Hartford ₍Conn.₎ Elihu Geer, 1852.
15 p.

Published by request.

1. Hovey, Mary E ., d.1852. 2. Funeral sermons. I. Title

NL 0416741 CtHC

VOLUME 336

Livermore, Abiel Abbott, 1811-1892.
The Acts of the Apostles (with a commentary) see under Bible. N. T. Acts. English. 1844. Authorized. (Boston, Munroe) Also with dates: 1846 (London) 1850 (Boston) 1853 (B.) 1857 (B.) 1863 (New York) 1867 (N. Y.)

Livermore, Abiel Abbot, 1811-1892.
An address delivered before the Ladies' Bible association of Dublin, on August 7, 1839. By A. A. Livermore. Published by the request of the association. Keene [N. H.] Printed by J. & J. W. Prentiss, 1839.
12 p. 17 1/2 cm.

NL 0416743 CSmH

LIVERMORE, Abiel Abbot, 1811-1892.
The American physical man.
(Unitarian rev. and religious mag. Vol. 7. 1877.)

NL 0416744 MB

Livermore, Abiel Abbott, 1811-1892.
The ancient and honorable man. A discourse preached on the occasion of the death of Hon. John Quincy Adams, to the Unitarian church and congregation, Keene, N. H., on Sabbath afternoon, March 5, 1848. By A. A. Livermore ... Keene, Printed by J. W. Prentiss & co., 1848.
19 p. 20½cm.

1. Adams, John Quincy, pres. U. S., 1767-1848.

15-27872

Library of Congress E377.L78

NL 0416745 DLC NjP CtY OCl

Livermore, Abiel Abbot, 1811-1892.
Anti-tobacco. By Abiel Abbot Livermore. With a lecture on tobacco. By Rev. Russell Lant Carpenter. And On the use of tobacco. By G. F. Witter, M. D. Boston, Roberts brothers, 1883.
117 p. 16½cm.

1. Tobacco. I. Carpenter, Russell Lant. II. Witter, G. F.

7-33126

Library of Congress RC371.T6L66

NL 0416746 DLC OrP N PP PPL PU PPM ICJ

LIVERMORE, Abiel Abbot, 1811-1892.
Anti-tobacco. With a lecture on tobacco, By R.L. Carpenter. An on the use of tobacco, By G.F.Witter. B. 1888[cop. 1885].
12 x 17.

NL 0416747 MH

Livermore, A[biel] A[bbot] 1811-1892.
The Centennial international exhibition of 1876. A lecture delivered in the Court house, Meadville, Pa., before the City library association, December 8, 1874. By A. A. Livermore. [Meadville? Pa., 1875?]
10 p. 23½cm.

1. Philadelphia. Centennial exhibition, 1876.

5-38194†

Library of Congress T825.L1L7

NL 0416748 DLC PHi OO

Livermore, Abiel Abbot, 1811-1892, ed.
Christian hymns for public and private worship see under Cheshire pastoral association.

Livermore, Abiel Abbott, 1811-1892.
The Christian religion; its divinity, sufficiency, and perpetuity; a discourse preached to the First Congregational church and society of Cincinnati, 1852.
Cincinnati, Truman & Spfford, 1853.
25 p.

NL 0416750 OClWHi PPL

Livermore, Abbiel Abbot, 1811-1892.
A commentary on the four Gospels...
Belfast, ... 1844
see under Bible. N. T. Gospels. English. 1844. Authorized.

Livermore, Abiel Abbot, 1811-1892.
A discourse at Walpole [N. H.] Oct. 31, 1837, before the "Sunday school association in connection with the Cheshire pastoral association". [With an abstract of the first annual report of the association] Keene [N. H.] J. Prentiss, 1837.
24 p. 8°. [Waterman pamphlets, v. 157: 24]

NL 0416752 DLC

LIVERMORE, ABIEL ABBOT, 1811-1892.
A discourse delivered on Thanksgiving day, Dec. 7, 1837, in the Unitarian Church, Keene, N.H. By A.A.Livermore. Published by request of the society. Keene: J.Prentiss, 1837. 19 p. 21cm.

862636A. 1. Thanksgiving day—Sermons, 1837.

NL 0416753 NN RPB CSmH MB MeWC

Livermore, Abiel Abbot, 1811-1892.
Discourse on death of John Q. Adams to the Unitarian Church and Congregation Keene, N.H., March 5, 1848. Keene, 1848.
19 p.

NL 0416754 PHi

Livermore (Abiel Abbot) 1811-1892.
Discourses. *Boston: Crosby, Nichols & Co.*, 1854. viii, 426 pp. 8°.

NL 0416755 NN PPWa Nh OU CU MH MB OO

Livermore, Abiel Abbot, 1811-1892.
Discourses. Boston, D.C. Colesworthy, 1857.

NL 0416756 MH MB

Livermore, Abiel Abbot, 1811-1892
Don't drink: To our American boys.
n.p. Unitarian church temperance society, 18-?.
6 p.
(In Pamphlets on temperance binder's title, v. 4)

NL 0416757 OO

LIVERMORE, A[biel] A[bbot] 1811-1892.
Don't smoke: To our American boys. Boston Unitarian Temperance Society, [1881?]
8 p.
Cover serves as title-page.
At head of title: [no.5].

NL 0416758 MH

Livermore, Abiel Abbot, 1811-1892.
The Epistle of Paul to the Romans, with a commentary and revised translation ... see under Bible. N. T. Romans. English. 1854. Livermore. (Also with dates "1861?" and 1870)

Livermore, Abiel Abbot, 1811-1892.
The epistle to the Hebrews, the epistles of James, Peter, John and Jude, and the Revelation of John the divine... Boston, 1881
see under Bible. N. T. Epistles and Revelation. English. 1881.

Livermore, Abiel Abbot, 1811-1892.
The epistles of Paul to the Corinthians, Galatians, Ephesians, Philippians, Colossians, Thessalonians, Timothy, Titus and Philemon. Boston, 1881
see under Bible. N. T. Epistles of Paul. English. 1881.

Livermore, Rev. A[biel] A[bbot], 1811-1892.
The faith once delivered to the saints. A discourse delivered at the dedication of the Unitarian meeting house in Windsor, Vt., Dec. 9, 1846. Boston, W. Crosby & H. P. Nichols, 1847.
28 p. 8°.

NL 0416762 NN MnHi OO

Livermore, Abiel Abbot, 1811-1892.
The four anniversaries. A sermon preached to the Unitarian church and congregation in Keene, on Sabbath morning, Dec. 26, 1847. By A. A. Livermore. Published by request. Keene, Printed by J. W. Prentiss & co., 1848.
12 p. 22cm.

I. Title.

27-12449

Library of Congress BX9843.L52F6

NL 0416763 DLC Nh OCl

VOLUME 336

Livermore, Abiel Abbot, 1811-1892, *ed.*
The four Gospels; with a commentary.
Boston, Munroe, 1841-42.
see under Bible. N. T. Gospels. English. 1841-42. Authorized. Also: 1842 1843 1843-44 1844-45 1847-48 1850-51 1851-61 1854-55 1857-58 1870 (N. Y., Miller)

Livermore, Abiel Abbot, 1811-1892.
History of the town of Wilton, Hillsborough County, New Hampshire, with a genealogical register, by Abiel Abbot Livermore and Sewall Putnam ... Lowell, Mass., Marden & Rowell, printers, 1888.
xi, 575 p. plates, ports., plan. 23½cm.

1. Wilton, N. H.—Hist. 2. Wilton, N. H.—Geneal. I. Putnam, Sewall, joint author.

Library of Congress F44.W6L7 1—8079

NL 0416765 MWA DLC WaS ICU OU CtY MH Nh OClWHi NhDo

[LIVERMORE, Abiel Abbot, and others]
The issue in the West. [Shelbyville, Ill] [1856].
16 x 23.

NL 0416766 MH

LIVERMORE, Abiel Abbot, 1811-1892.
Lectures to Young Men on their Moral Dangers and Duties. B. 1846.

NL 0416767 MH

Livermore, Abiel Abbot, 1811-1892.
Lectures to young men on their moral dangers and duties. By Abiel Abbot Livermore. New ed. Boston, J. Munroe and company, 1847.
160 p. 18cm.

1. Young men.

10-11733†

Library of Congress BJ1671.L75

NL 0416768 DLC

Livermore, Abiel Abbot, 1811-1892.
Liberal Christianity. Its fruits.
Lakewood. 1886. 9 pp. 8°.

M6320 — T.r. — Liberalism. In religion.

NL 0416769 MB

[Livermore, Abiel Abbot] *ed.*
The marriage offering: a compilation of prose and poetry. Boston, W. Crosby and H. P. Nichols, 1848.
viii, 207 p. 17½cm.
Preface signed: A. A. L.

1. Marriage.

9-23560

Library of Congress HQ734.L6

NL 0416770 DLC N RPB

Livermore, Abiel Abbot, 1811-1892
The marriage offering: acompilation of prose and poetry. 3d ed.
Boston, Wm. Crosby and H. P. Nichols, 1849.
viii, 207 p.

NL 0416771 OO RPB

[Livermore, Abiel Abbot] *ed.*
The marriage offering: a compilation of prose and poetry. 7th ed. Boston, W. Crosby and H. P. Nichols, 1852.
1 p. l., viii, 207 p. front. 18cm.
Added t.-p., engr., with vignette.
Preface signed: A. A. L.

6-36319

NL 0416772 DLC MB

[Livermore, Abiel Abbot] *ed.*
The marriage offering: a compilation of prose and poetry. 7th ed. Boston, Crosby, Nichols, and co., 1853.
1 p. l., viii, 207 p. front. 19 cm.
Added t.-p., engr., with vignette.
Preface signed: A. A. L.

NL 0416773 OU

[Livermore, Abiel Abbot] 1811-1892.
Marriage offering; a compilation of prose and poetry. 1854.

NL 0416774 MiU PU

---

*AC85 Al191 Y858l

[Livermore, Abiel Abbot, 1811-1892, ed.]
The marriage offering: a compilation of prose and poetry. Fourteenth edition.
Boston:Crosby,Nichols,and company.117 Washington street.1858.
2p.l.,[iii]-viii,207p. front. 18.5cm.
Added engraved t.-p.
Preface signed: A.A.L.
Inscribed: Mr John B. Pratt of Boston and Miss Anne B. Alcott of Concord were this day married by Ephraim W. Bull Esqe assisted by their affectionate uncle Samuel J. May. Concord, May 23. 1860. May your union be as lasting and as happy as true love can make it.
Original decorated white cloth; edges gilt.

NL 0416776 MH OO

[Livermore, Abiel Abbot] 1811-1892, ed.
The marriage offering: a compilation of prose and poetry. 15th ed. Boston, W. Crosby and H. P. Nichols, 1859.
207 p.

NL 0416777 KMK RPB

Livermore, Abiel Abbot, 1811-1892.
Overcome evil with good. A discourse delivered at the installation of Rev. John Jay Putnam, as pastor of the First Congregational church and society, in Bolton, Mass. Sept. 26, 1849. By A. A. Livermore. Published by request of the society. Keene, N. H., Printed by J. W. Prentiss & co., 1849.
16 p. 22 1/2 cm. Green paper covers.
Collation followed by genuine blank leaf.

1. Putnam, John Jay. I. Title.

NL 0416778 CSmH Nh RPB

Livermore, Abiel Abbot, 1811-1892.
Physical education; a lecture delivered before the teachers of Hamilton and Butler Co. Ohio, on several different occasions, by A. A. Livermore ... Cincinnati, S. S. Rowe, 1855.
23 p. 20cm.
Published by request.

1. Physical education [and training] 2. School hygiene.

E 15-1480

U. S. Off. of educ. Library for Library of Congress GV361.L75 [a37b1]

NL 0416779 DHEW DNLM OHi MB OO OClWHi

Livermore, Abiel Abbot, 1811-1892.
... Reason and revelation. By Rev. A. A. Livermore, printed for the American Unitarian association. Boston, J. Munroe & co., 1838.
19 p. 19cm. (American Unitarian association. Tracts. 1st ser., no. 136)

I. Title.

22-23431

Library of Congress BX9843.L52R4

NL 0416780 DLC

Livermore, Abiel Abbot, 1811-1892.
Reason and revelation. A sermon delivered at the ordination of James Thurston, as pastor of the First Unitarian society in Windsor, Vt. By Rev. A. A. Livermore, of Keene, N. H. Windsor [Vt.] Printed by Tracy and Severance, 1838.
16 p. 22 cm.

1. Ordination sermons. 2. Thurston, James.

NL 0416781 CSmH PPAmP CtY NcD

Livermore, Abiel Abbot, 1811-1892.
Revisión de la guerra entre México y los Estados Unidos. Traducción, prólogo y notas de Francisco Castillo Nájera. México, 1948.
350 p. 23 cm.
Errata slip inserted.

1. U. S.—Hist.—War with Mexico, 1845-1848. 2. U. S.—Pol. & govt.—War with Mexico, 1845-1848. I. Title.

E404.L787 973.62 48-9794*‡

NL 0416782 DLC OOxM OU TxU CU

Livermore, Abiel Abbot, 1811-1892.
Two dedication sermons, Wilton, N. H., before the First Congregational church, Jan. 5, 1775, Jan. 10, 1861. New York, 1861.
33 p. O.

NL 0416783 RPB

Livermore, Abiel Abbot, 1811-1892.
Two Historical Sermons Unitarian Church Keene, N.H. Keene, 1850.
24 p. 4°

NL 0416784 MWA

Livermore, Abiel Abbot, 1811-92.
Union with God and man. [anon.] Boston, W. Crosby & H. P. Nichols, 1847.
16 p. 16°. [American unitarian association. Tracts. v. 21, 1st. series.]

NL 0416785 DLC

VOLUME 336

Livermore, Abiel Abbot, 1811-1892.
The war with Mexico reviewed. By Abiel Abbot Livermore. Boston, American peace society, 1850.
xii, 310 (*i. e.* 298) p. 19½cm.
Paging irregular: p. 298 numbered 310.
To this work was awarded the five hundred dollar prize offered by the American peace society "for the best review of the Mexican war on the principles of Christianity, and an enlightened statesmanship".
1. U. S.—Hist.—War with Mexico, 1845-1848. 2. U. S.—Pol. & govt.—War with Mexico, 1845-1848. I. Title.
Library of Congress E415.L77 2—15444
OCl MiU KMK FTaSU DAU MU TxHU
MB ICJ NWM NjR CU MnHi Nh MWA NcU NjP OClWHi OO OU
NL 0416786 DLC WaE NcD CtY PP PHi TxU ViU DN DNW

Livermore, Abiel Abbot, 1811-1892.
The war with Mexico reviewed. By Abiel Abbot Livermore. Seventh thousand. Boston, American peace society, 1850.
xii, 310 (*i. e.* 298) p. 18½cm.
p. 298 incorrectly numbered 310.
To this work was awarded the five hundred dollar prize offered by the American peace society "for the best review of the Mexican war on the principles of Christianity, and an enlightened statesmanship."
1. U. S.—Hist.—War with Mexico, 1845-1848. 2. U. S.—Pol. & govt.—War with Mexico, 1845-1848.
2-15445
Library of Congress E404.L78
NL 0416787 DLC NIC MiU I NN

Film 79 reel 243, no.4
Livermore, Abiel Abbot, 1811-1892.
The war with Mexico reviewed. Boston, American Peace Society, 1850.
(American culture series, 243:4)
Microfilm copy (positive) made by University Films, Ann Arbor, Mich.
Collation of the original: 310(i.e.298)p.
To this work was awarded the five hundred dollar prize offered by the American Peace Society "for the best review of the Mexican war on the principles of Christianity, and an enlightened statesmanship."
NL 0416789 FTaSU PSt KEmT ICRL

E404 L78
Livermore, Abiel Abbot, 1811-1892.
The war with Mexico reviewed. By Abiel Abbot Livermore. Boston: Wm. Crosby and H.P. Nichols. 1850.
xii, 310 (i.e. 298) p. 20 cm.
Page 298 incorrectly numbered 310.
To this work was awarded the five hundred dollar prize offered by the American Peace Society "for the best review of the Mexican War on the principles of Christianity, and an enlightened statesmanship."
NL 0416790 CU-A TxU GU OU

Livermore, Abiel Abbot, 1811-1892
What good has liberal Christianity done? n.p., [18-?]
6 p.
NL 0416791 OO

Livermore, Alfred S 1848-
A brief sketch of the life and work of A.S. Livermore against a monster evil. By A.S.Livermore ... Saginaw,Mich., Courier printing and binding co., 1890.
223,[1] p. 17½cm.
1.Tobacco habit.
HV5763.L78
NL 0416792 MiU OClWHi OO

Livermore, Alpheus, *defendant.*
The trial of Alpheus Livermore and Samuel Angier, before the Supreme judicial court of the commonwealth of Massachusetts, upon an indictment for the murder of Nicholas John Crevay, an Indian, committed November 23, 1813. Containing the evidence at large, the arguments of the solicitor general, and of the counsel for the prisoners, the charge of the Hon. Judge Sewall to the traverse jury, and his address on pronouncing sentence of death. ⟨From minutes taken at the trial.⟩ Boston: Published by Watson & Bangs, no. 7, State-street. 1813.
50 p. 23½cm.
1. Crevay, Nicholas John, d. 1813. I. Angier, Samuel, defendant. II. Sewall, Samuel, 1757-1814. III. Massachusetts. Supreme judicial court. IV. Title.
28-23596
NL 0416793 DLC CSt MH CtY MWA

Livermore, Ann, et als., plaintiffs.
... In the Supreme court of the state of California. Ann Livermore et als., plaintiffs and respondents. vs. Solomon Jewett et als., defendants and appellants. Transcript on appeal. S.L. Cutter, attorney for defendants and appellants. P. T. Colby and V. A. Gregg, attorneys for plaintiffs and respondents. Bakersfield: Kern county gazette job printing establishment, 1878.
cover-title, 1 p. l., [5]-106 p. 25 1/2 cm.
At head of title: No. .... [246 in ms.]
In ms. on t.-p.: C. E. Wilson attorney for respondent C. A. Livermore.
I. Jewett, Solomon, et als., defendants. II. California. Supreme court.
NL 0416794 CSmH

Livermore, Arthur, 1811-1905.
Seventy years ago. Reminiscences of Haverhill Corner, by Arthur Livermore. Woodsville, N. H., News print, 1902.
52 p. 22cm.
One hundred copies printed. no. 94.
1. Haverhill, N. H. I. Title.
18-3440
Library of Congress F44.H45L7
NL 0416795 DLC MWA MB

[**Livermore, Berta S**]
Indian legends of the Te-o-ne-sta [by] Benson Benley Stuart [*pseud.*] [Tionesta, Pa., 1943]
2 p. l., 3-121 p. front., plates. 21cm.
Narrative poem.
1. Munsie Indians—Poetry. I. Title.
43-14939
Library of Congress PS3523.I 887 I 5
811.5
NL 0416796 DLC OCl

Livermore, Berta S
Indian legends of the Te-o-ne-sta. 2d ed. [By] Berta S. Livermore. [Tionesta, Pa., 1946]
2 p. l., 3-121 p. front., plates. 21cm.
Narrative poem.
1. Munsie Indians—Poetry. I. Title.
46-20477
Library of Congress PS3523.I 887 I 5 1946
811.5
NL 0416797 DLC

Livermore, Charles F., plaintiff.
... Charles F. Livermore & others against Richard Bainbridge ... Argument of Edmund Randolph Robinson, of counsel for plaintiffs
see under Robinson, Edmund Randolph.

[**Livermore, Charles W**]
The ancient wreck. Loss of the Sparrow-hawk in 1626. Remarkable preservation and recent discovery of the wreck. Boston, A. Mudge & son, 1865.
38 pp. illus., map. 12°.
By C. W. Livermore and L. Crosby.
F72.C3L7 1-12130-M 1
NL 0416799 DLC MH MiU MB NN

[**Livermore, Charles W**]
Ye antient wrecke. Loss of the Sparrow-hawk in 1626. Remarkable preservation and recent discovery of the wreck. Boston, Printed by A. Mudge & son, 1865.
38 p. illus., map. 19cm.
By C. W. Livermore and L. Crosby.
An edition of same year, otherwise identical, has title: The ancient wreck.
1. Sparrow-hawk (Ship) 2. Cape Cod, Mass. 3. Massachusetts—Hist.—Colonial period (New Plymouth) I. Crosby, Leander, joint author. II. Title. III. Title: Loss of the Sparrow-hawk in 1626.
2—26827
Library of Congress F72.C3L71
NL 0416800 DLC

Livermore, Charles W.
Ye antient wrecke-1626. Loss of the Sparrow-Hawk in 1626. Remarkable preservation and recent discovery of the wreck. Boston, A. Mudge & Son, 1865.
39p. 12°.
NL 0416801 NN Nh OClWHi

[**Livermore, Charles W**]
Ye antient wrecke.—1626. Loss of the Sparrow-Hawk in 1626. Remarkable preservation and recent discovery of the wreck. Boston, Printed by A. Mudge & son, 1865.
44 p. illus. (incl. map) 19½cm.
By Charles W. Livermore and Leander Crosby.
1. Sparrow-Hawk (Ship) 2. Cape Cod, Mass. 3. Massachusetts—Hist.—Colonial period (New Plymouth) I. Crosby, Leander, joint author. II. Title. III. Title: Loss of the Sparrow-Hawk in 1626.
4—12564
Library of Congress F72.C3L72
NL 0416802 DLC RPJCB NNC

Livermore, Charles W
Loss of the "Sparrow-Hawk" in 1626. By C.W. Livermore and Leander Crosby. 1865.
NL 0416803 RP

[LIVERMORE, Charles W.]
[Photographs of the remains of an ancient ship, discovered on Cape Cod, supposed to have been the Sparrow-Hawk wrecked in 1626. Boston, 1865.
2 photographs.
By C.W.Livermore and Leander Crosby.
NL 0416804 MH

Livermore, Daniel.
Works by this author printed in America before 1801 are available in this library in the Readex Microprint edition of Early American Imprints published by the American Antiquarian Society.
This collection is arranged according to the numbers in Charles Evans' American Bibliography.
NL 0416805 DLC

VOLUME 336

LIVERMORE, Daniel.
The Calender of Maine, or Eastern Almanack, for 1797. Hallowell, [1796].
12°. pp.(24). US 10070.51

NL 0416806 MH

Livermore, Daniel. Journal.
14 pp. (Cook, F., Journ. of the military exped. of Sullivan, p. 178.)

NL 0416807 MdBP

Livermore, Daniel.
Journal of the march of general Poor's brigade, on the western expedition, May 7, 1779. Concord, McFarland, 1850.
29 p. 8°. [New Hampshire historical society's collections. v. 6]

NL 0416808 DLC MB

Livermore, Daniel Parker, 1818-1899.
Arguments against woman suffrage by Judge John Lowell & others... examined & ... answered. Melrose, 1885.
56 p.

NL 0416809 OO

LIVERMORE, Daniel Parker, 1818-1899.
The arguments against woman suffrage by Mrs. Clara T. Leonard, G. G. Crocker, Francis Parkman, and Mrs. Kate G. Wells, carefully examined and completely refuted. Melrose 1884.
pp.64.

NL 0416810 MH MB

JK1901 .L76 Livermore, Daniel Parker, 1818-1899.
Arguments against woman suffrage, by Rev. H.M. Dexter, D.D., carefully examined and completely answered. By D.P. Livermore. Boston, For sale by Cupples, Upham & co., 1886.
cover-title, 112 p. 20cm.

1. Woman--Suffrage. 2. Dexter, Henry Martyn, 1821-1890. Common sense as to woman suffrage.

NL 0416811 ICU

LIVERMORE, D[aniel] P[arker] 1818-1899.
Arguments against woman suffrage by H. M. Dexter. Carefully examined and completely answered by D.P. Livermore. [Melrose Mass., W.L. Williams], 1886.

Caption reads: -Reply to H. M. Dexter on woman suffrage.

Dr. Dexter's pamphlet was published with the title-:-Common sense as to woman suffage.

NL 0416812 MH

Livermore, Daniel Parker, 1818-1899.
Argument against woman suffrage by Hon. John J. Ingals carefully examined and completely answered.
Melrose, 1888.
48 p.

NL 0416813 OO

---

236 L784c Livermore, Daniel Parker, 1818-1899.
Comfort in sorrow; a token for the bereaved. [2d ed.] Chicago, D.P. Livermore, 1866.
vii, vi, 168p. 17cm.

1. Death. I. Title.

NL 0416814 IEN ICHi

Livermore, Daniel Parker, 1818-1899.
Essay on water baptism. A statement of reasons for believing that immersion is not the only Scriptural mode of water baptism.
Chicago, Livermore, n.d.
64 p.

NL 0416815 OO

Livermore, Daniel Parker, 1818-1899.
Female warriors.
(In Catt, Mrs. Carrie (Lane) Chapman, comp. The ballot and the bullet ... Philadelphia, 1897)

NL 0416816 DLC

Livermore, Daniel Parker, 1818-1899.

Tomlinson, Russell, 1808-1878.
Orthodoxy as it is; or, its mental influence and practical inefficiency and effects illustrated by philosophy and facts. By R. Tomlinson and D. P. Livermore ... Boston, A. Tompkins, 1845.

---

ar V 4993 Livermore, Daniel Parker, 1818-1899.
Proof-texts of endless punishment, examined and explained. Chicago, 1862.
288 p. 19cm.

1. Future punishment--Controversial literature. I. Title.

NL 0416818 NIC

Livermore, Daniel Parker, 1818-1899.
Proof-texts of endless punishment, examined and explained. By D. P. Livermore. Stereotyped ed. Chicago, Ill., D. P. Livermore, 1864.
xiv, [17]-384 p. 19cm.

1. Future punishment—Controversial literature. I. Title.

44-28891

Library of Congress BT837.L5 1864

NL 0416819 DLC MH IU ICHi KyWA NCaS MH-AH

Livermore, Daniel Parker, 1818-1899.
Woman suffrage defended by irrefutable arguments, and all objections to woman's enfranchisement carefully examined and completely answered. By D. P. Livermore ... Boston, Lee & Shepard, 1885.
vi p., 1 l., 224 p. 17½cm.

1. Woman—Suffrage. I. Title.

26-21183

Library of Congress JK1901.L5

NL 0416820 DLC TxU OO PU PSt ICJ

Livermore, Daniel Parker, 1818-1899. Woman's mental status. 9 pp. (Forum, v. 5, 1888, p. 90.)

NL 0416821 MdBP

Livermore, E. N.
Constitutional highways from servitude to liberty,...
Vancouver, [c1919]

HN64 .L57

NL 0416822 DLC

Livermore, Edith, tr.

Trubetskoi, Mikail, kniaz'.
Out of chaos; a personal story of the revolution in Russia, by Prince Michael Trubetzkoi ... New York, Longmans, Green & co.; [etc., etc.] 1907.

Livermore, Edith, tr.

Neumann, Angelo, 1838-1910.
Personal recollections of Wagner, by Angelo Neumann; tr. from the 4th German ed. by Edith Livermore. New York, H. Holt and company, 1908.

---

308 Z Box 738 Livermore, Edward A
Society whither bound. Providence, R. I. [United printing co., c1928.
30 p.

1. Socialism.

NL 0416825 NNC

Livermore, Edward M., et al., appellants.
Edward M. Livermore, and another, appellants, vs. Stephen Waterman, and others, appellees
see under Jenckes, Thomas Allen, 1818-1875.

Livermore, Edward M., appellant.
Edward M. Livermore and David B. Sexton, appellants, vs. Thomas A. Jenckes, Alexander Farnum, and Stephen Waterman, appellees
see under Jenckes, Thomas Allen, 1818-1875.

VOLUME 336

Livermore, Edward M.
... Edward M. Livermore and David B. Sexton vs. Thomas A. Jenckes, Alexander Farnum and Stephen Waterman. Pleadings and proofs for final hearing ... New York, 1856.
[144] p. 24 cm.
Cover-title.
Various paging.
In the Circuit court of the U.S. for the southern district of N.Y.

NL 0416828 RPB

Livermore, Edward St. Loe, 1762–1832.
Works by this author printed in America before 1801 are available in this library in the Readex Microprint edition of Early American Imprints published by the American Antiquarian Society.
This collection is arranged according to the numbers in Charles Evans' American Bibliography.

NL 0416829 DLC

LIVERMORE, EDWARD ST. LOE, 1762–1832.
Mr. Livermore's speech, in the House of Representatives, Friday morning, Jan. 6, on the bill from the Senate, making further provision for enforcing the embargo law. [Washington? 1809?] 25 p. 23cm.

Caption-title.

1. Embargo—U.S., 1807–1809

NL 0416830 NN NNU-W CaOTP MB CtY Nh NBu NNC

Livermore, Edward St. Loe, 1762-1832.
Observations occasioned by writings against alterations proposed in the convention to be made in the judiciary system. Ports., 1792.

NL 0416831 Nh

---

*AC8 L7518 792o
Livermore, Edward St. Loe, 1762-1832.
An oration delivered before the Grand lodge of ancient and honorable society of Free and accepted masons. of the state of New-Hampshire ... By Edward St. Loe Livermore, g. secr'y. At the request of the Grand lodge.
Portsmouth: Printed and sold by John Melcher, M,DCC,XCII.
23p. 24.5cm.
Evans 24479.

NL 0416832 MH MBFM DSC

Livermore, Edward St. Loe, 1762–1832.
An oration delivered July the fourth, 1813. At the request of the selectmen of Boston, in commemoration of American independence. By Edward St. Loe Livermore, esq. Boston: Printed by Chester Stebbins..... 1813.
40 p. 21½cm.

1. Fourth of July orations.

Library of Congress E286.B74 1813 37-9073
973.361

NL 0416833 DLC ICN CtY OU MH MWA RPB MH

Livermore, Edward St. Loe, 1762–1832.
An oration, in commemoration of the dissolution of the political union between the United States of America and France. Delivered on the seventeenth of July, 1799, at St. John's church, in Portsmouth, N. H. By Edward St. Loe Livermore ... Portsmouth, N. H., Printed at the Oracle press, by C. Peirce, 1799.
cover-title, [5]–28 p. 18½cm.

1. U. S.—For. rel.—France. 2. France—For. rel.—U. S.

Library of Congress E323.L78 10-15916

NL 0416834 DLC OC MBAt MH MWA Nh NHi NN MB RPJCB

F142 .S2S5
Livermore, Elizabeth.

Shourds, Thomas.
History and genealogy of Fenwick's colony [New Jersey] Bridgeton, N. J., G. F. Nixon, 1876.

Livermore, *Mrs.* **Elizabeth D.**
Zoë; or, The quadroon's triumph. A tale for the times By Mrs. Elizabeth D. Livermore. With illustrations by Henri Lovie, and Charles Bauerle ... Cincinnati, Truman and Spofford, 1855.
2 v. illus. 20cm.

Library of Congress PZ3.L752Z 7-16059†

NL 0416836 DLC InU ViHaI OCX OClWHi NjP OC OU

Livermore, Elizabeth D
Zoë; or, The quadroon's triumph. A tale for the times. With illustrations by Henri Lovie, and Charles Bauerle. Cincinnati, Truman and Spofford, 1855.
Microcard edition (15 cards). (Nineteenth century American literature on microcards. Series A: The Ohio Valley)

1. Ohio Valley—Fiction. I. Title.

NL 0416837 ViU CU MiU IU NcD ICRL WRU NcD KEmT

Livermore (Frank). *Des complications nerveuses du rhumatisme articulaire aigu. 56 pp. 4°. *Paris, 1868, No. 160.*

NL 0416838 Nh

Livermore, Frank S.
Notebook of printing for teachers and students, by Frank S. Livermore ... Fitchburg, Mass., State normal school practical arts press, 1925.
31 l. illus., diagr., fold. forms. 29½cm.

1. Printing, Practical—Study and teaching. I. Title.

Library of Congress Z122.L78 25-16825

NL 0416839 DLC

Livermore, Frank S.
Our dog, with the imagination of the dog's master, by Frank S. Livermore. [Fitchburg, Mass., ©1933]
[3] p. 1 mounted illus. 21½cm.
A poem.

1. Dogs—Poetry. I. Title.

Library of Congress PS3523.I 8908 1933 CA 33-329 Unrev'd
Copyright AA 118850 811.5

NL 0416840 DLC

[LIVERMORE, George], 1809-1865
A brief account of the Dana Hill public School, Cambridge, 1849. [Cambridge, 1849]

pp.19+. Front.
Cover: The Dana Hill public schools.

NL 0416841 MH

Livermore, George, 1809–1865.
Catalogue of the ... library of the late George Livermore, esq., of Cambridge, Mass.; being a magnificent collection of Bibles, New Testaments, Psalms, hymns, and catechisms ... Rare Americana ... To be sold by auction November 20th and three following days ... Charles F. Libbie & co., auctioneers. Boston, The Libbie show print, 1894.
2 p. l., 201 p. 8 facsim. (1 fold., incl. front.) 24½cm.

1. Bible—Bibl. 2. America—Bibl.—Catalogs.

Library of Congress Z997.L785 13-7051

NN MB
NL 0416842 DLC CU-A OU PU PPM MiU OO OClWHi MiU-C

[**Livermore, George,**] 1809–1865.
Cromwell's soldiers' Bible. [Cambridge? Mass., 1854?] broadside. 35 x 21½cm. bd. 23cm.
Signed and dated: G. L. Dana Hill, Cambridge, June 20th, 1854.
A description of "The souldiers pocket Bible." London, 1643.
Reprinted "From the Watchman and Reflector."

Lenox 418. 1. Bible. Selections. English. 1643: The souldiers pocket Bible. I. Title.
Revised November 5, 1934

NL 0416843 NN

Livermore, George, 1809–1865.
An historical research respecting the opinions of the founders of the republic on negroes as slaves, as citizens and as soldiers. Read before the Massachusetts historical society, August 14, 1862. By George Livermore. Boston, Printed by J. Wilson and son, 1862.
xiv, [2], 215, [1] p. 23½cm.

1. Negroes. 2. U. S.—Hist.—Revolution—Negro troops.

23-16220

E185.L778

MeB FTaSU OClWHi OO MiU OU OCl PPL
DNW CaNSWA NcWsW ViU NjP MH NIC RPJCB PBL PPG DI ICN
NL 0416844 DLC NcU WaTC FM GU-De ICMcC MoU NIC NN

Livermore, George, 1809–1865.
An historical research respecting the opinions of the founders of the republic on Negroes as slaves, as citizens, and as soldiers. Read before the Massachusetts historical society, August 14, 1862. By George Livermore. Boston, Printed by J. Wilson and son, 1862–[63]
xiv, [2], 236 p. 24 cm.
Supplement (p. [217]–236), issued 1863, has cover-title: Supplementary note and index to be added to the first edition of "An historical research, by George Livermore."
Also published (without supplement) in the Proceedings of the Massachusetts historical society, 1863, v. 6, p. 86–248.
1. Negroes. 2. U. S.—Hist.—Revolution—Negro troops.

E185.L78 4—19507

NL 0416845 DLC NIC PBL NcD NN OC CaBVaU

Livermore, George, 1809–1865.
An historical research respecting the opinions of the founders of the republic on negroes as slaves, as citizens, and as soldiers. Read before the Massachusetts historical society. August 14, 1862. By George Livermore. 3d ed. Boston, Pub. for the New-England loyal publication society, by A. Williams and company, 1863.
xviii, [2], 184 p. 24cm.
"Reprinted from the volume of 'Proceedings of the Massachusetts historical society' for the year 1862–63."—Note to the 3d edition.
1. Negroes. 2. U. S.—Hist.—Revolution—Negro troops. I. New-England loyal publications society.

Library of Congress E185.L79 6—34291

PBL MiU NIC WRU
NL 0416846 DLC NBuHi WHi MnHi KyU NIC NcD PSC PU

VOLUME 336

E
185
L78
1863 b

Livermore, George, 1809–1865.
An historical research respecting the opinions of the founders of the Republic on Negroes as slaves, as citizens, and as soldiers. Read before the Massachusetts Historical Society, August 14, 1862. 3d ed. Boston. Published for the New-England Loyal Publication Society by A. Williams, 1863.
xviii, 184 p. 21 cm.
"Reprinted from the ... 'Proceedings of the Massachusetts Historical Society' ... 1862–63."
Photocopy (Xerox by Micro Photo, 1969)
1. Negroes. 2. U. S. – Hist. – Revolution – Negro troops. 3. Negroes as soldiers. I New England Loyal Publication Society.

NL 0416847 Vi

Livermore, George, 1809–1865.
An historical research respecting the opinions of the founders of the republic on negroes as slaves, as citizens, and as soldiers. Read before the Massachusetts historical society, August 14, 1862. By George Livermore. 4th ed. Boston, A. Williams and company, 1863.
xviii, [2], 184 p. 23½ cm.
Title in red and black.
1. Negroes. 2. U. S.—Hist.—Revolution—Negro troops.
E185.L8 4—19506

NL 0416848 DLC WaT NcU MnHi PPL ViHaI MoS MdBP MB OKentU NN NjP PPAN TU

E
185
"L81

Livermore, George, 1809-1865.
An historical research respecting the opinions of the founders of the republic on Negroes as slaves, as citizens, and as soldiers. Read before the Massachusetts Historical Society, August 14, 1862. 5th ed. Boston, Printed by J. Wilson and son, 1863.
xviii, 184 p. 30 cm.
"Fifty copies printed on large paper."
1.Negroes. 2.U.S.-Hist.-Revolution-Negro troops. I.Title.

NL 0416849 WHi PSt ViHaI PPStarr

Livermore, George, 1809-1865.
Historical research respecting the opinions of the founders of the republic on negroes as slaves, as citizens, as soldiers...3d.ed. Boston, Williams, 1873.
184 p.

NL 0416850 PP

[Livermore, George] 1809–1865.
A merchant of the old school. A tribute to the memory of James Johnson. Boston, Printed for private distribution, 1855.
19 p. 22½cm.
Prefatory note signed: G. L. [i. e. George Livermore]
Author's autograph presentation copy to Eli French.
1. Johnson, James, 1783–1855. I. Title.
Library of Congress CT275.J67L5 9–13128

NL 0416851 DLC MWA MeB CtY MB NN

Livermore, George, 1809-1865.
Opinions of the early Presidents upon slavery and soldiers. N. Y., 1863.
8°

NL 0416852 MnHi

[Livermore, George] 1809–1865.
The origin, history and character of the New England primer: being a series of articles contributed to the Cambridge Chronicle, by "The Antiquary." Cambridge [Mass.] 1849. 22 l. 25 x 20cm.
Printed in single column, outer column blank.
No. 12 of 12 copies printed for private distribution.
Author's autographed presentation copy to Henry Stevens, esq.
1. New-England primer. I. Title.
Revised October 2, 1935

NL 0416853 NN MWA MB MH MiU-C

[Livermore, George] 1809–1865.
The origin, history and character of the New England primer. Being a series of articles contributed to "The Cambridge chronicle," by George Livermore ... New York, C. F. Heartman, 1915.
2 p. l., 7–94 p. incl. 10 p. of facsim. 23½cm. (On verso of half-title: Heartman's Historical series. no. 11)
"Reprinted from the edition of 1849 of which only twelve copies were printed."
"Number 15 of 31 copies printed on Nippon vellum. Also four copies printed on Japan vellum."
"There is added a fac-simile reprint of the only fragment extant of a New England primer printed by Christopher Sower in Germantown, 1764."
1. New England primer. I. Title.
16–15793
Library of Congress PE1119.A1N6

NL 0416854 DLC MWA ICN NjP MiU-C PU

Livermore, George, 1809-1865.
American antiquarian society, *Worcester, Mass.*
Remarks and resolutions commemorative of the Hon. Josiah Quincy, LL. D., by the American antiquarian society at their first meeting after his death. Worcester, Mass., 1864.

[Livermore, George] 1809–1865.
Remarks on public libraries. From "The North American review" for July, 1850. For private distribution only. Cambridge, Printed by Bolles and Houghton, 1850.
40 p. 20½cm.
Prefatory note signed: G. L.
1. Libraries—Addresses, essays, lectures. I. Title.
CA 32–779 Unrev'd
Library of Congress Z721.L78
22cm. 027

NL 0416856 DLC CtY CU NIC PPL MWA ICJ NN NRU RPB NjNbS

BV2370
.A64S92L7

LIVERMORE, GEORGE, 1809-1865.
Remarks on the publication and circulation of the Scriptures: suggested by Rev. W. P. Strickland's History of the American Bible society, and published as a review of that work in the Christian examiner for November, eighteen hundred and forty-nine. By George Livermore. Cambridge [Mass.] Printed at the University press, 1849.
31 p. 21½cm.
1. Strickland, William Peter, 1809-1884. History of the American Bible society.
DLC: YA14632

NL 0416857 ICU DLC ICN MB MH NN RPB CtY MB

Livermore, George, 1809-1865. ed.
FOR OTHER EDITIONS SEE MAIN ENTRY
Bible. *English. Selections. 1861. Geneva version.*
The soldier's pocket Bible. An exact reprint of the original edition of 1643, with a prefatory note by George Livermore ... Cambridge [Mass.] Printed for private distribution, 1861.

Z
992
.B88

Livermore, George, 1809-1865
The visible and invisible in libraries. Manchester, R. Holt, 1873.
20 p. 17cm.
Bound with [Brown, J. T.] "Bibliomania." Edinburgh, 1867.
"Reprinted from 'The Atlantic monthly,' November, 1855."
1. Libraries - Addresses, essays, lectures. 2. Books - addresses, essays, lectures. I. Title.

NL 0416859 WU

Livermore, George Griswold, 1886–
Take it from dad, by George G. Livermore. New York, The Macmillan company, 1920.
2 p. l., 3–173 p. incl. front., illus., plates. 19cm.
I. Title.
Library of Congress PN6161.L575 20—21986

NL 0416860 DLC NN WaSp

Livermore, George Griswold, 1886–
Team play; a story of the Owl and the clan, by George G. Livermore ... New York, The Macmillan company, 1921.
3 p. l., 3–249 p. front. 19½cm.
I. Title.
Library of Congress PZ7.L74Te 21–17271

NL 0416861 DLC

Livermore, George Robertson, 1878–
Gonorrhea and kindred affections; Gonorrhea in the male, chancroid and verruca acuminata, by George Robertson Livermore ... and Gonorrhea in the female, and the infectious granulomata, by Edward Armin Schumann ... New York, London, D. Appleton and company, 1929.

Livermore, George Whitefield, 1794-1870.
Paxton, *Mass.*
Centenary memorial of Paxton; or, The exercises of the hundredth anniversary of the incorporation of the town; including a historical address, by George W. Livermore ... an oration, by Rev. John F. Bigelow ... a poem, by Mr. George Gardner Phipps ... and other exercises under the direction of George N. Bigelow ... The celebration occurred, June 14, 1865. Worcester, Printed by E. R. Fiske & son, 1868.

LIVERMORE, George Whitefield, 1794-1870.
A valedictory address delivered before the Social Fraternity of Leicester Academy (Mass.). at the close of the autumnal term, Tuesday evening, Nov. 30, 1818. Leicester, H. Brown, 1818.
pp.14.

NL 0416864 MH MWA InU

VOLUME 336

Livermore, Harold Victor, 1914–
A history of Portugal. Cambridge [Eng.] University Press, 1947.
xvi, 502 p. plates, ports., maps (part fold.) 24 cm.
Bibliography: p. [471]–475.

1. Portugal—Hist.

DP538.L7 946.9 48–2845 rev*

CaBVaU CaBViP IdU Or OrP MtU Wa WaE
PPT PPEB PLF PHC MeB CSf CoU CLSU MB CtY NN MH CaBVa
NcGU WaWW ViU TxU OClW ICU NcD PSC OrU MiU MiEM Mi
NL 0416865 DLC WaT WaTC WaSp WaSpG WaS WaT OrU CU

Livermore, Harold Victor, 1914– ed.
Portugal and Brazil, an introduction. Made by friends of Edgar Prestage and Aubrey Fitz Gerald Bell in piam memoriam. Edited by H. V. Livermore with the assistance of W. J. Entwistle. Oxford, Clarendon Press, 1953.
xi, 418 p. illus., ports., maps. 23 cm.
Includes bibliographies.

1. Prestage, Edgar, 1869–1951. 2. Bell, Aubrey Fitz Gerald, 1882–1950. 3. Portugal—Civilization—Addresses, essays, lectures. 4. Portuguese philology—Addresses, essays, lectures. 5. Portugal—Colonies—Addresses, essays, lectures. 6. Brazil—Civilization—Addresses, essays, lectures.

DP504.L5 914.69 53-2979 rev

WaU TxU AAP PPComm
LU CaBVa IdPI MtU OrU OrPR NcD OO OClW ICU OCl MiU
TxU PBL PSt PP PBm WaSpG CtW WU NjR AU KU MAU WaS
NL 0416866 DLC NcRS MB N CU MH NN ViU TU CtY NcU

Livermore, Harriet, 1788–1868.
Addresses to the dispersed of Judah. By Harriet Livermore. With an appendix ... Philadelphia, Printed by L. R. Bailey, 1849.
268 p. 23cm.

1. Jews—Religion—Controversial literature.

Library of Congress BT1120.L5 37-23901 239

NL 0416867 DLC PPDrop PPGratz

LIVERMORE, Harriet, 1788-1868-
The counsel of God, immutable and everlasting. Philadelphia, L.R.Bailey, 1844, [cop.1841].
19 cm.

NL 0416868 MH OO

Livermore, Harriet, 1788–1868.
An epistle of love, addressed to the youth & children of Germantown, Pennsylvania, county of Philadelphia. By Harriet Livermore... Philadelphia: Printed by J. Rakestraw, 1826.
86 p. illus. 14cm.
"From the original manuscript."
In original illustrated covers.

237854B. 1. Juvenile literature, Religious. November 4, 1943

NL 0416869 NN PHi

Livermore, Harriet, 1788–1868.
An epistle of love, addressed to the youth & children of Germantown, Pennsylvania, County of Philadelphia. 2d edition. Philadelphia. Bakestraw. 1827. 84 pp. Vignette. 14½ cm., in 6s.

NL 0416870 MB NN

Livermore, Harriet, 1788-1868.
Glory of the Lord in the land of the living by redemption of the purchased possession. N.Y., 1842.
36 p.

NL 0416871 PHC

Livermore, Harriet, 1788–1868.
The harp of Israel, to meet the loud echo in the wilds of America. By Harriet Livermore ... Philadelphia, Printed for the authoress by J. Rakestraw, 1835.
180 p. 1 illus. 15½cm.
Title vignette.
"Hymns ... presented to the Cherokee nation and Indians everywhere."—p. 3.

I. Title.

Library of Congress PS2248.L43 28-14867

NL 0416872 DLC OCH ViU CtY NNUT CSmH

LIVERMORE, HARRIET, 1788-1868.
A letter to John Ross, the principal chief of the Cherokee nation; by Harriet Livermore, a pilgrim and stranger in the earth ...
Philadelphia:Published by Harriet Livermore. 1838.
24p. 15½cm.
Orig. printed yellow wrapper.

NL 0416873 PPRF

[Livermore, Harriet] 1788–1868.
Millennial tidings... Philadelphia: H. Livermore, 1831–39.
4 pams. in 1 v. 17cm.
No. 2, second ed.

235601B. 1. Millennium. I. Title. July 30, 1943

NL 0416874 NN PPPrHi NN DLC

Livermore, Harriet, 1788–1868.
A narration of religious experience. In twelve letters. By Harriet Livermore. With an appendix, containing her religious belief, and an original poem ... In two volumes .... vol. I. Concord [N. H.] Printed by Jacob B. Moore, for the author, 1826.
iv, [5]–282 p. 15cm.
No more published?

I. Title.

Library of Congress BR1725.L5A3 38-4811 922

NL 0416875 DLC

Livermore, Harriet, 1788–1868.
Scriptural evidence in favour of female testimony in meetings for Christian worship in letters to a friend.
— Portsmouth, N. H. Foster. 1824. 124 pp. 14½ cm., in 6s.
Inserted is a newspaper clipping with extracts from "Snow-Bound" relating to Miss Livermore, and with a biographical sketch of Dr. Moses H. Elliott, her early lover.

M5606 — T.r. — Women. As ministers of the Gospel. — Elliott, Moses H.,

NL 0416876 MB DLC

Livermore, Harriet, 1788-1868.
The Sparrow. Philadelphia
see under title

Livermore, Harriet, 1788–1868.
A testimony for the times. By Harriet Livermore ... New-York, The authoress, 1843.
xi, 123 p. 18½cm.

I. Title.

Library of Congress BT890.L73 34-10942 236.3

NL 0416878 DLC MeB PPLT PHi

Livermore, Harriet, 1788-1868.
Thoughts on important subjects. Philadelphia, Crissy & Markley, prs., 1864.

NL 0416879 MH

Livermore, Harriet, 1788-1868.
A wreath from Jessamine lawn; or, Free grace the flower that never fades. By Harriet Livermore ... Philadelphia, Printed for the authoress, 1831.
2 v. 15cm.

Library of Congress PZ3.L753W 7-16058†

NL 0416880 DLC NcD NcU NNC MiU PPL

M-film 810.8 Am35 4-13
Livermore, Harriet, 1788-1868.
A wreath from Jessamine lawn; or, Free grace the flower that never fades. By Harriet Livermore. Philadelphia, Printed for the authoress, 1831.
2 v.

Microfilm (positive) Ann Arbor, Mich., University Microfilms, 1966. 13th title of 15. 35 mm. (American fiction series, reel 4.13)

NL 0416881 KEmT CU

Livermore, Helen Ells.
Early Mexicans, prepared for the National society of colonial dames of America in the state of California, by Helen Ells Livermore. San Francisco, Calif., 1932.
15, [1] p. 23cm.
Bibliography: p. [16]

1. Mexico—Antiq. 2. Mexico—Hist.—Conquest, 1519–1540. I. National society of the colonial dames of America. California. II. Title.

Library of Congress F1219.L74 33-8501 913.72

NL 0416882 DLC WaS CU MB

VOLUME 336

Livermore, Henrietta Jackson (Wells) "*Mrs. A. L. Livermore*," 1864–
… How to raise money for suffrage … by Henrietta W. Livermore. January, 1917, ed. New York, N. Y., National woman suffrage publishing company, inc. [°1917]
16 p. 16cm. ("Efficiency booklet series") $0.05

1. Woman—Suffrage. I. Title.

Library of Congress JK1901.E3 [no. 3] 17-8595

NL 0416883 DLC

Livermore, Henrietta Jackson (Wells) "Mrs. A. L. Livermore."
Fairview garden school association, *Yonkers, N. Y.*
… School gardens, report of the Fairview garden association, Yonkers, N. Y. By Mrs. A. L. Livermore, chairman of the executive committee. [New York city, Dept. of child hygiene, Russell Sage foundation] 1910.

Livermore, Isaac.
An account of some bridges over Charles river [anon.] Cambridge [Ms.] chronicle press, 1858.
45 p. 8°. [Drake's Boston pamphlets, v. 19:2]

NL 0416885 MH NN DLC

Livermore, J. N.
Cooling buildings with ice; practical examples of the design and installation of ice-cooling apparatus in small buildings, by J. N. Livermore, C. M. Clemens, and P. S. Hosman. N. Y., Heating and ventilating, °1935.
21 p. diagr.

Bound with this: Electric motors for air conditioning and heating equipment, by L. Gwathmey and B. S. Weaver.

NL 0416886 MiD WaS

Livermore, Jesse Lauriston, 1877–1940.
How to trade in stocks; the Livermore formula for combining time element and price. New York, Duell, Sloan & Pearce [1940]
vii, 133 p. col. tables. 20 cm.
"First edition."

1. Speculation. 2. Stocks. 3. Stock-exchange—U. S. I. Title.

HG6015.L55 332.64 40-8064 rev 2

NL 0416887 DLC TU NcRS ViU PPT OCl OU NIC WaS

Livermore, Jonathan, 1770–1845.
An address, pronounced at Wilton, before the friends of the national administration, at the celebration of American independence, July 4, 1828. By Jonathan Livermore. Dunstable, N.H., Printed by Thayer & Wiggin, 1828.
16 p. 22cm.
[Moore pamphlets, v. 93, no. 8]

1. Fourth of July orations. 2. U. S.—Pol. & govt.—1825–1829. 3. Campaign literature, 1828—National Republican.

Library of Congress AC901.M7 vol. 93 19-13273

NL 0416888 DLC CSmH

Livermore, Jonathan, 1729–1809.
Two dedication sermons, delivered in Wilton, N. H., before the First Congregational church and society in that town; by Rev. Jonathan Livermore… January 5, 1775: and by Rev. Abiel Abbot Livermore… January 10, 1861… New-York: J. A. Gray, 1861. 33 p. 23cm.

1. Wilton, N. H.—Churches, Unitarian—First. I. Livermore, Abiel Abbot, 1811–1892. II. Unitarian Congregational church, Wilton. N. H. (First.)

October 26, 1943

NL 0416889 NN MWA RPB

Livermore, Josiah Randall.
A critical study of some of the factors concerned in measuring the effect of selection in the potato … by Josiah Randall Livermore … [Geneva, N. Y., 1927]
cover-title, p. 857–896. diagr. 22½cm.
Thesis (PH. D.)—Cornell university, 1927.
"Published as paper no. 155, Department of plant breeding, Cornell university, Ithaca, N. Y."
"Reprinted from the Journal of the American society of agronomy, vol. 19, no. 10, October, 1927."
"Literature cited": p. 895–896.

1. Potatoes.

Library of Congress SB211.P8L5 1927 28-10786

NL 0416890 DLC NIC OU

PZ6 .L58M3 Livermore, Kate.
Mary Lee, by Kate Livermore. New York, D.Appleton & company, 1860 [°1859]
vii, [8]-161p. front.,plates. 18cm.

NL 0416891 NNU-W CtY

FILM 4274 PR v.2 reel L9
Livermore, Kate
Mary Lee... New York, Appleton, 1860.
161 p. illus. (Wright American fiction, v.II, 1851-1875, no. 1563, Research Publications Microfilm, Reel L-9)

NL 0416892 CU KEmT

Livermore, Katherine, 1870- joint author.
Handy, Edward Smith Craighill, 1892–
Outline of Hawaiian physical therapeutics, by E. S. Craighill Handy, Mary Kawena Pukui [and] Katherine Livermore … Honolulu, Hawaii, The Museum, 1934.

Livermore, Kenneth Carter, 1886– **joint author.**
Warren, George Frederick.
… An agricultural survey; townships of Ithaca, Dryden, Danby and Lansing, Tompkins County, New York. By G. F. Warren and K. C. Livermore, assisted by C. M. Bennett, H. N. Kutschbach, E. H. Thomson, F. E. Robertson, E. L. Baker. Ithaca, N. Y., The University [1911]

Livermore, Kenneth Carter, 1886–
joint author.
Warren, George Frederick, 1874–
Laboratory exercises in farm management, by G. F. Warren … and K. C. Livermore … New York, The Macmillan company, 1910.

SB 191 O2 L78
Livermore, Kenneth Carter, 1886-
Natural cross fertilization in oats. [Ithaca, N. Y.] 1912.
16 l. mounted illus., tables (part fold.) 27 cm.

Minor thesis.

1. Oats. 2. Hybridization, Vegetable.

NL 0416896 NIC

SB 199 L78
Livermore, Kenneth Carter, 1886–
The renewal of old meadows on volusia silt loam soil without plowing [by] K. C. Livermore and A. L. Thompson. [Ithaca, N. Y.] 1914.
34 l. illus., tables (part fold.) 28 cm.

1. Meadows. I. Thompson, Arthur Lee.

NL 0416897 NIC

BX9803 A6 ser.4 no.6
Livermore, Leonard Jarvis
... Baptism, by Rev. L. J. Livermore. Boston, American Unitarian association [1880?]
9p. 20½cm. ([American Unitarian association. Tracts] Fourth series, no. 6)

1. Baptism.

NL 0416898 NBuG Nh

LIVERMORE, Leonard Jarvis.
The fading flower and eternal life. A sermon on the death of Ma[ria] A. Fiske.
[Bost.] n. d. 15 pp. 8°.

NL 0416899 MB

Livermore, Leonard Jarvis, comp.
Hymn and tune book, for the church and the home
see under American Unitarian association.

Livermore, Leonard Jarvis.
Perseverance in the war, the interest and duty of the nation. A sermon, preached in the church of the First parish, Lexington, Sunday, September 11, 1864. By L. J. Livermore … Boston, Press of T. R. Marvin & son, 1864.
16 p. 23½cm.
"Published by request of the congregation."

1. U. S.—Hist.—Civil war—Addresses, sermons, etc.

12-21469

Library of Congress E458.4.L78

NL 0416901 DLC Nh MB OClWHi

Livermore, Leonard Jarvis.
Sermon preached at the funeral of William Henry Harrington, in Clinton, Mass., May 20, 1855.
[Clinton? 1855.] 8 pp. 8°.

F3852 — Harrington, William Henry.

NL 0416902 MB MH

VOLUME 336

BV4305
L5
Livermore, Leonard Jarvis.
What we have to be thankful for; a sermon, on the occasion of the national Thanksgiving, preached at Lexington, Ms., August 6, 1863, by Rev. L. J. Livermore. Boston, Press of T. R. Marvin & son, 1863.
16p. 22½cm.

NL 0416903 NBuG TxDaM Nh MB

Livermore, Lot, 1815–
Diary relating to the winter of 1861-2, the hardest winter ever known in Oregon, and a trip to Salmon River Mines. (In Oregon Pioneer Assoc. Transactions. 1915)

NL 0416904 OrMonO

Livermore, *Mrs.* Marian (Sorlie) 1827–
Prairie flowers & heather bells; poems, by Marian S. Livermore. St. Joseph, Mo., American printing company, 1910.
viii, [3]-101 p. port. 20cm. $1.25

11-962

NL 0416905 DLC

Livermore, Mrs. Mary Ashton (Rice) 1820-1905.

[Willard, Frances Elizabeth] 1839–1898.
American women: fifteen hundred biographies with over 1,400 portraits; a comprehensive encyclopedia of the lives and achievements of American women during the nineteenth century, by a corps of able editors and contributors. Newly rev., with the addition of a classified index; also many new biographies and recent portraits ... New York, Chicago [etc.] Mast, Crowell & Kirkpatrick [c1897]

Livermore, Mary Ashton (Rice) 1820-1905.
Keep things stirred up.
= [Boston. 1890?] 6 pp. 16°.
An address delivered at a meeting of the Unitarian Temperance Society, May 30, 1890.
There is no title-page.

G5925 — Temperance. — Unitarian Temperance Society. Addresses.

NL 0416907 MB OO MH

Livermore, Mary Ashton (Rice) 1820-1905, ed.
Lily of the Valley
see under title

Livermore, Mrs. Mary Ashton Rice, 1820-1905.

Higginson, Thomas Wentworth, 1823–1911.
Massachusetts in the army and navy during the war of 1861–65. Prepared under the authority of the state by Thomas Wentworth Higginson ... Boston, Wright & Potter printing co., state printers, 1895–96.

Livermore, Mary Ashton (Rice) 1820-1905.
Mrs. Livermore on suffrage. Warren, Ohio, [1906?]
2 l. 16°. (National American Woman Suffrage Association. Political equality series, v.1., no. 10)
In: SNS p. v. b.

NL 0416910 NN

E
621
L79
Livermore, Mary Ashton (Rice) 1820-1905.
My story of the war: a woman's narrative of four years personal experience as nurse in the Union army ... with anecdotes ... portraying the lights and shadows of hospital life and the sanitary service of the war. Hartford, Conn., A.D. Worthington [1887]
700 p. illus. (part col.) ports. 23cm.
List and description of battle-flags: p. 15-65.
1. U.S. - Hist. - Civil war - Hospitals, charities, etc. 2. United States Sanitary Commission. 3. Flags - U.S. I. Title.

NL 0416911 CoU NIC MtU Or

Livermore, *Mrs.* Mary Ashton (Rice) 1820–1905.
My story of the war: a woman's narrative of four years personal experience as nurse in the Union army, and in relief work at home, in hospitals, camps, and at the front during the war of the rebellion. With anecdotes, pathetic incidents, and thrilling reminiscences portraying the lights and shadows of hospital life and the sanitary service of the war. By Mary A. Livermore ... Hartford, A. D. Worthington and company, 1888.
700 p. front., plates (part col.) port. 23cm.
List and description of battle-flags: p. 15-65.
1. U. S.—Hist.—Civil war—Hospitals, charities, etc. 2. United States sanitary commission. 3. Flags—U. S. I. Title.

2—18851

Library of Congress E621.L78

OCU ODW OClWHi
NL 0416912 DLC OrU-M KEMT MB PPFHi PCC MB NN NjP

Livermore, Mary Ashton (Rice) 1820-1905.
My story of the war: a woman's narrative of four years personal experience as nurse in the Union army, and in relief work at home, in hospitals, camps, and at the front, during the war of the rebellion. Hartford, A. D. Worthington, 1888.
700p. illus.

Microcard edition.

NL 0416913 ICRL OU OOxM TU PSt PHC

Livermore, *Mrs.* Mary Ashton (Rice) 1820–1905.
My story of the war: a woman's narrative of four years personal experience as nurse in the Union army, and in relief work at home, in hospitals, camps, and at the front, during the war of the rebellion. With anecdotes, pathetic incidents, and thrilling reminiscences portraying the lights and shadows of hospital life and the sanitary service of the war. By Mary A. Livermore ... Hartford, Conn., A. D. Worthington and company, 1889.
700 p. incl. front., illus., plates (part col.) ports. 23cm.
List and description of battle-flags: p. 15-65.
1. U. S.—Hist.—Civil war—Hospitals, charities, etc. 2. United States sanitary commission. 3. Flags—U. S.

4-22336

Library of Congress E621.L79

DNC WaTC WaS OrCS OrPR IdU CaBVaU
ViU PHi PP OU WU-M OrP MdBP MoU Wa CtY-M DNLM DSI
NL 0416914 DLC OO OCl OU NjP OClWHi MWA WaU MdBP

Livermore, Mary Ashton (Rice) 1820-1905.
My story of the war: a woman's narrative of four years personal experience as nurse in the Union army, and in relief work at home, in hospitals, camps, and at the front during the war of the rebellion. With anecdotes, pathetic incidents, and thrilling reminiscences portraying the lights and shadows of hospital life and the sanitary service of the war. Hartford, Worthington, 1890 [c1887]
700p.(78p.advertisements) plates(part col.)ports.(incl. front.) 23cm.
List and description of battle-flags: p.15-65.

NL 0416915 KU-M FTaSU NIC ViN MH UU OOxM MiU

Livermore, *Mrs.* Mary Ashton (Rice) 1820–1905.
My story of the war: a woman's narrative of four years personal experience as nurse in the Union army, and in relief work at home, in hospitals, camps, and at the front, during the war of the rebellion. With anecdotes, pathetic incidents, and thrilling reminiscences portraying the lights and shadows of hospital life and the sanitary service of the war. By Mary A. Livermore ... Hartford, Conn., A. D. Worthington and company, 1892.
700 p. incl. front., illus., plates (part col.) ports. 23cm.

NL 0416916 NcD

E621
.L78
1893
Livermore, Mary Ashton (Rice) 1820-1905.
My story of the war: a woman's narrative of four years personal experience as nurse in the Union army, and in relief work at home, in hospitals, camps, and at the front, during the war of the rebellion. Hartford, A. D. Worthington, 1893.
700 p. incl. front., illus., plates (part. col.) ports. 23cm.
List and description of battle-flags: p. 15-65.

NL 0416917 MB NSyU

E
621
.L79
Livermore, Mary Ashton (Rice) Mrs. 1820-1905.
My story of the war: a woman's narrative of four years personal experience as nurse in the Union army, and in relief work at home, in hospitals, camps, and at the front, during the war of the rebellion. With anecodotes, pathetic incidents, and thrilling reminiscences portraying the lights and shadows of hospital life and the sanitary service of the war. By Mary A. Livermore. Hartford, Conn., A. D. Worthington and company, 1896 [c1887]
700 p. incl. front., illus., plates (part col.) ports. 23 cm.
List and description of battle-flags: p. 15-65.

NL 0416918 OKentU MH

Livermore, Mary Ashton (Rice) 1820-1905.
The national pageant, and dramatic events in the history of New York, 1889
see under Pond, Cora Scott

Livermore, Mary Ashton (Rice) 1820-1905 4509a.331
Pen pictures: or, sketches from domestic life.
= Chicago. Griggs & Co. 1862. 216 pp. 16°.
Contents. — The life-long sacrifice. — The sale of the homestead. — The house of rest. — The sewing society. — La pueblo de los Angelos. — Lost and found. — The race with the mill-stream. — The mission of sorrow. — The last jewel. — The first quarrel. — The temple in the sky. — The song of the moonlight.

NL 0416920 MB ICN CtY ViU RPB ICHi

FILM
4274
PR
v.2
reel
L9
Livermore, Mary Ashton (Rice) 1820-1905.
Pen pictures; or, Sketches from domestic life. By Mrs. M. A. Livermore. Chicago, S. C. Griggs, 1862.
216 p. (Wright American fiction, v.II, 1851-1875, no. 1564, Research Publications Microfilm, Reel L-9)

NL 0416921 CU KEmT

Livermore, Mary Ashton Rice, joint ed.

Willard, Frances Elizabeth, 1839–1898, *ed.*
Portraits and biographies of prominent American women; a comprehensive encyclopedia of the lives and achievements of American women during the nineteenth century, edited by Frances E. Willard and Mary A. Livermore, assisted by a corps of able contributors; newly revised with the addition of a classified index ... New York, Chicago [etc.] The Crowell & Kirkpatrick co. [1901]

VOLUME 336

396 Livermore, Mary Ashton (Rice)
L78s Selections. Boston [c1892]
32p. front. (port.)

NL 0416923 IU

Livermore, Mary Ashton (Rice), 1820–1905.
Should women have a vote on the liquor traffic? By Mrs. Mary A. Livermore... ₍n. p., 189–?₎ 5 p. 8°.
Caption-title.
In: VTZ p. v. 138, no. 22.

1. Woman.—Suffrage. 2. Temperance.—Addresses, essays, lectures.
BLACK TEMPERANCE COLL. April 28, 1919.

NL 0416924 NN

Livermore, Mrs. Mary Ashton (Rice) 1820–1905
Story of my life; or, The sunshine and shadow of seventy years ... with hitherto unrecorded incidents and recollections of three years' experience as an army nurse in the great civil war, and reminiscences of twenty-five years' experiences on the lecture platform ... to which is added six of her most popular lectures ... with portraits and one hundred and twenty engravings from designs by eminent artists, made expressly for this work. Hartford, Conn. Worthington₍c1897₎
730p. illus.

NL 0416926 MWA MB CtY NcD Or WaTC ViHaI ViU ViN PPL PP OClWHi OO OCl

---

CT 275 L5 A3 1898
Livermore, Mrs. Mary Ashton (Rice) 1820-1905.
The story of my life; or, The sunshine and shadow of seventy years, by Mary A. Livermore, with hitherto unrecorded incidents and recollections of three years' experience as an army nurse in the great civil war, and reminiscences of twenty-five years' experience on the lecture platform, to which is added six of her most popular lectures, with portraits and one hundred and twenty engravings from designs by eminent artists.

Hartford, Conn., A.D. Worthington, 1898.
730p. illus.,plates 23cm.
Sold only to subscribers.

NL 0416928 MU AAP MiU MH PNt OU CoU

Livermore, Mary Ashton (Rice) 1820–1905.
The story of my life: or, The sunshine and shadow of seventy years, by Mary A. Livermore ... with hitherto unrecorded incidents and recollections of three years' experience as an army nurse in the great civil war, and reminiscences of twenty-five years' experiences on the lecture platform ... to which is added six of her most popular lectures ... with portraits and one hundred and twenty engravings from designs by eminent artists ... Hartford, Conn., A. D. Worthington & co., 1899.
xxxiv, 730 p. incl. fronts., illus., plates. 23 cm.
I. Title.
CT275.L5A3 1899 17—18747

NL 0416929 MtHi CU NIC WaS WaSpG MoU OU DLC NcRS NjP MiU OCl CtY NcGU MeB MU

Livermore, Mrs. Mary Ashton (Rice) 1820-1905.
Palmer, Alonzo Benjamin, 1815-1887.
The temperance teachings of science, intended for the general public and especially for young people, by A. B. Palmer ... Introduction by Mary A. Livermore. Boston, D. Lothrop and company ₍c1886₎

Livermore, Mary Ashton (Rice) 1820-1905.
Thirty years too late, a true story; and One in a thousand. Boston, Lockwood, Brooks ₍185-?₎
95 p. illus. 12cm.

NL 0416931 NNC

LIVERMORE, MARY ASHTON (RICE), 1820-1905.
Thirty years too late, a true story; and One in a thousand. By Mrs. Mary A.Livermore... Boston: Lockwood, Brooks, & Co. [1878] 96 p. illus. 12½cm.

783830A. 1. Fiction, American. 2. Temperance—Fiction. I. Title. II. Title: One in a thousand.

NL 0416932 NN ViU

FILM 4274 PR v.3 reel L22
Livermore, Mary Ashton (Rice) 1820-1905.
Thirty years too late, a true story: and One in a thousand. By Mary A. Livermore. Boston, Lockwood, Brooks [1878]
96 p. illus. (Wright American Fiction, v.III 1876-1900, no.3364, Research Publications, Inc. Microfilm, Reel L-22)

NL 0416933 CU

Livermore, *Mrs.* Mary Ashton (Rice) 1820–1905.
What shall we do with our daughters? Superfluous women, and other lectures, by Mary A. Livermore. Boston, Lee and Shepard; ₍etc., etc.₎ 1883.
208 p. 18cm.

1. Education of women. 2. Woman—Social and moral questions. I. Title. II. Title: Superfluous women. 7—28106
Library of Congress LC1481.L6

NL 0416934 DLC TxU NcGU PPD PP PPM MB

Livermore, Mrs. Mary Ashton (Rice) 1820-1905, joint ed.
Willard, Frances Elizabeth, 1839-1898, *ed.*
A woman of the century; fourteen hundred-seventy biographical sketches accompanied by portraits of leading American women in all walks of life; ed. by Frances E. Willard and Mary A. Livermore, assisted by a corps of able contributors. Buffalo, New York ₍etc.₎ C. W. Moulton, 1893.

Livermore, Mrs. Mary Ashton (Rice) 1820-1905) ed.
The Woman's journal. v. 1-48; Jan. 8, 1870-May 26, 1917. Boston and Chicago ₍etc.₎ 1870-1917.

Livermore, Mary Ashton (Rice), 1820–1905.
Woman's work in the temperance reform. By Mrs. Mary A. Livermore... ₍n. p., 1891?₎ p. 188–193. 8°.
Caption-title.
From: Essays, written for the National Temperance Convention, Saratoga, July 15, 1891.
In: VTZ p. v. 80, no. 26.

1. Temperance.—Addresses, essays, lectures.
BLACK TEMPERANCE COLL. July 25, 1918.

NL 0416937 NN

Livermore, Mary H. Raleigh, 1909.
Songs of the quiet hour.

NL 0416938 NcU

Livermore, *Mrs.* R S (Bailey)
The practical household assistant. A complete guide for the housekeeper. By Mrs. R. S. Livermore (née R. S. Bailey) Silver Creek, N. Y., The Local printing house, 1880.
1 p. l., 51 p. 20½cm.

1. Receipts. 2. Cookery.
Library of Congress TX153.L78 7-23936†

NL 0416939 DLC

Livermore, Rufus Putnam, *b.* 1860.
Livermore's trustees' handbook; a manual for the use of trustees, executors, administrators, assignees for the benefit of creditors, receivers, guardians, and committees of lunatics, idiots, and habitual drunkards. Containing a brief statement of their powers and duties, rights and liabilities, with practical suggestions and information for their guidance in the management of their trusts generally, and particularly as to matters relating to their accounts, and the settlement of them, upon their application to be discharged. By Rufus P. Livermore ... New York, L. K. Strouse & co., 1881.
2 p. l., 103 p. 22½cm.
1. Trusts and trustees—New York (State) I. Title: Trustees' handbook.
Library of Congress 37-39153

NL 0416940 DLC MH-L CtY PPB

Livermore, Rufus Putnam b. 1860
Livermore's trustees' handbook; a manual for the use of trustees, executors, administrators, assignees for the benefit of creditors, receivers, guardians, and committees of lunatics, idiots, and habitual drunkards... By Rufus P. Livermore... New York: L. K. Strouse & Co., 1885. 100 p. 2. ed., rev. 8°.

311537A. 1. Trusts and trustees—Jurisp.—U. S.—N. Y. August 19, 1927

NL 0416941 NN PCC

Livermore, S.
Account book. ms. 1752.

NL 0416942 NjP

Livermore, Samuel, 1786-1833.

Argument for the holders of the bills of exchange accepted by William M. Duncan and Sons, in the case of William Kenner & Co. vs. their creditors, before the Supreme Court of the State of Louisiana. ₍n. p., 1826?₎
16 p. 21 cm.

Caption title.

1. Bills of exchange. Cases. I. Kenner (William) & Company

NL 0416943 NcD

VOLUME 336

Livermore, Samuel, 1786-1833.
An argument, in a cause depending before the Supreme Court of Louisiana, between the Bank of the United States, the Bank of Louisiana, the Bank of Orleans and others, creditors of Joseph Saul, appellants; and Thomas H. Saul and others ... appellees: in which is discussed the question, whether in the case of a marriage contracted in a state governed by the common law of England, between parties there residing, but who afterwards remove to Louisiana and there acquire property, such property will be held in community between such husband and wife? By Samuel Livermore. New-Orleans, Printed by Benjamin Levy, 1827.
1 p.l., 80 p. 23cm.

NL 0416944 MHi

Livermore, Samuel, 1786–1833.
Dissertations on the questions which arise from the contrariety of the positive laws of different states and nations. By Samuel Livermore ... n.° I. Containing two dissertations. New-Orleans, Printed by B. Levy, 1828.
cover-title, 172 p., 1 l. 22cm.
No more published.
CONTENTS.—I. A general view of the nature of these questions and of the authors who have treated of them.—II. Of personal and real statutes, laws and customs, and of the general principles, which serve to distinguish them.
1. Conflict of laws. 2. International law, Private. I. Title.
Library of Congress 31-33479

NL 0416945 DLC IaU-L LNHT MBAt MB CtY OClWHi NNC OCLaw

Livermore, Samuel, 1786–1833.
A treatise on the law of principal and agent; and of sales by auction. By Samuel Livermore ... Baltimore: Printed for the author, by Joseph Robinson. 1818.
2 v. 22cm.
1. Agency (Law)—U. S. 2. Auctions—U. S. [2. Auctions and auctioneers—U. S.]
Library of Congress 31-33480

NL 0416946 DLC IU PU-L PPB NcD NcU NcRS ViU ViU-L

Livermore, Samuel, 1786–1833.
A treatise on the law relative to principals, agents, factors, auctioneers, and brokers. By Samuel Livermore ... Boston: Printed by Thomas B. Wait and co. 1811.
xii, 260 p. 22cm.
1. Agency (Law)—U. S. 2. Auctions—U. S. [2. Auctions and auctioneers—U. S.] 3. Brokers—U. S. [4. Factors—U. S.]
31-33478

NL 0416947 DLC NN NcD CtY PPB PPL MB MH NjR PP MBAt MH-L

Livermore, Samuel Truesdale, 1824–1892.
Block Island. I. A map and guide. II. A history (abridged). By Rev. S. T. Livermore, A. M. Hartford, Conn., Press of the Case, Lockwood & Brainard company, 1882.
125 p. incl. fold. map. plates. 20cm.
Preface states that much is taken from the author's "History of Block Island" published in 1877.
1. Block Island, R. I.
Library of Congress F87.B6L7 Rc-2998

NL 0416948 DLC PU CSmH OCl MWA

Coll L785 1888

Livermore, Samuel Truesdale, 1824-1892.
Block Island. I. A map and guide. II. A history (abridged) By Rev. S.T. Livermore, A.M. Hartford, Conn., Case, Lockwood & Brainard co., 1886 [i.e. 1888]
132 p. illus., incl. front., plates, fold. map. 19 cm.
On cover: 1888.
1. Maps-- Block Island--1886.

NL 0416949 RPB MH

C121 12d

Livermore, Samuel Truesdale, 1824-1892.
Block island. I. A map and guide. II. A history (abridged) ... Rev. and enl. Boston, Mass.,Press of L.Barta & co.,1893.
137p. 1 illus.,pl.,fold.map. 19½cm.
Preface states that much is taken from the author's history of Block Island published in 1877.

NL 0416950 CtY

Livermore, Samuel Truesdale, 1824-1892.
Block Island; an illustrated history, map and guide, by Rev. S. T. Livermore, A. M. Revised and brought down to date, 1901. A large number of illustrations, and a considerable amount of new reading matter, meteorological data, etc., have been added; ed. by Chas. E. Perry. Providence, R. I., For C. C. Ball by Snow & Farnham, printers [c1901]
45, [1], 46-156, [1] p. illus., plates, port. 18½cm.
1. Block Island, R. I. I. Perry, Charles E., ed.
Library of Congress F87.B6L71 1-26548

NL 0416951 DLC NIC NN OCl

Livermore, S[amuel] T[ruesdale] 1824-1892.
Checkers improved. Over 200 games and problems. Laws of the game; the move; classification, explanations, etc., for the new board without checks, and the old board with its 64 checks. By S. T. Livermore ... Hartford, Conn., Press of the Case, Lockwood & Brainard company, 1888.
71 p. 15½cm.
1. Checkers.
Library of Congress GV1463.L78 5-29234†

NL 0416952 DLC OCl

Livermore, Samuel Truesdale, 1824-1892.
A condensed history of Cooperstown, with a biographical sketch of J. Fenimore Cooper. By Rev. S. T. Livermore ... Albany, J. Munsell, 1862.
vii, [9]-276 p. 18½cm.
1. Cooperstown, N. Y.—Hist. 2. Cooper, James Fenimore, 1789-1851.
Library of Congress F129.C77L7 1-14891

NL 0416953 DLC MdBP OU NcD PPL PPM PHi NN MB MWA MdBP NN MnHi ViU TU PBL PPiU CaBVaU

Livermore, Samuel Truesdale, 1824–1892.
Harriet Livermore, the "Pilgrim stranger" ... By Rev. S. T. Livermore ... Hartford, Conn., Press of the Case, Lockwood & Brainard company, 1884.
223 p. front. (port.) 18½cm.
In part a criticism of Whittier's description of Miss Livermore in "Snow-bound."
"Specimens of Miss Livermore's poetry": p. 159-192.
1. Livermore, Harriet, 1788-1868. 2. Whittier, John Greenleaf, 1807-1892. Snow bound.
Library of Congress PS2248.L43Z6 28-9353

NL 0416954 DLC NRAB PHi PPFr MB MH

Livermore, Samuel Truesdale, 1824-1892.
A history of Block Island from its discovery, in 1514, to the present time, 1876, by Rev. S. T. Livermore ... Hartford, Conn., The Case, Lockwood & Brainard co., 1877.
371 p. 19½cm.
1. Block Island, R. I.—Hist. 2. Block Island, R. I.—Geneal.
Library of Congress F87.B6L8 Rc-2999

NL 0416955 DLC CU PHi PPL MWA Nh NN MH OClWHi OCl WaS

Livermore, Samuel Truesdale, 1824-1892
The Lord's supper as restricted to immersed believers. Hartford, Conn., Case, Lockwood & Brainard co., 1880.
53p. 11 1/2cm.

NL 0416956 NRAB

Livermore, Samuel Truesdale, 1824-1892.
Scripture index to Calvin's Institutes. [Manuscript.] [New York], 1851.
O.

NL 0416957 RPB

Livermore, Seward Wright.
American naval development, 1898-1914, with special reference to foreign affairs.
Thesis, Ph.D.- Harvard university, 1944. Department of history.
Typewritten.

NL 0416958 MH

Livermore, Shaw, 1902- joint author.

Tippetts, Charles Sanford, 1893–
Business organization and control; corporations and trusts in the United States, by Charles S. Tippetts ... and Shaw Livermore ... New York, D. Van Nostrand company, inc., 1932.

Livermore, Shaw, 1902- , joint author.
Tippetts, Charles Sanford, 1893–
Business organization and public control, by Charles S. Tippetts ... and Shaw Livermore ... 2d ed. New York, D. Van Nostrand company, inc. [1941]

Livermore, Shaw, 1902–
Early American land companies; their influence on corporate development, by Shaw Livermore ... New York, The Commonwealth fund; London, H. Milford, Oxford university press, 1939.
xxx, 327 p. 24cm. (Half-title: Publications of the Foundation for research in legal history, Columbia university School of law)
Thesis (PH. D.)—Columbia university, 1939.
Without thesis note.
Bibliography: p. [314]-318.
1. Land tenure—U. S.—Hist. 2. U. S.—Public lands. 3. Corporations—U. S. I. Title.
Library of Congress HD195.A3L5 39-6029 Revised
——— Copy 3. Thesis note, on label mounted on t.-p., "Vita" on leaf inserted at end.
[r42y4] 423.065

NL 0416961 DLC WaU-L MtU OrPR OrU OrP CaBVaU MB IdU WaS CU WaSpG OClW PPAmP NcD NcRS EaSp PU PSC PHi OO PU-L ViU-L ViU OCl OU OOxM OCU

VOLUME 336

Livermore, Shaw, 1902–
Investment, principles and analysis, by Shaw Livermore .. Chicago, Business publications, inc., 1938.
viii p., 1 l., 599 p. diagr. 23½cm.
"Listing securities on the New York stock exchange, by J. M. B. Hoxsey": p. 553–558.
"Selected references" at end of each chapter.

1. Investments—U. S. 2. Securities—U. S. I. Title.
38-5965
Library of Congress HG4521.L75
Copyright A 114568 332.67

NL 0416962 DLC CaBVaU OrU OrP OrCS PPT CoU KEmT MnU TU OCl OU OOxM OClW PSC

Livermore, Shaw, 1902–
Problems in investment, by Shaw Livermore ... and O. K. Burrell ... Chicago, Business publications, inc., °1938.
1 p. l., iii, 93 numb. l. 29cm.
Reproduced from type-written copy.
"Although ... [the problems] are in general intended for use with Investment, principles & analysis, by Livermore ... it is felt that they will provide suitable assignments to supplement other texts."—Foreword.

1. Investments—U. S. 2. Securities—U. S. I. Livermore, Shaw, 1902– Investment, principles and analysis. II. Burrell, Orin Kay, 1899– joint author. III. Title.
A 41-3091
Enoch Pratt free library for Library of Congress

NL 0416963 MdBE OrU NIC PSC OU ICU

Livermore, Solomon Kidder, 1779–1859.
On the practice of music. A discourse, pronounced at Pepperell, Massachusetts, May 17th, 1809, before The Middlesex Musical society. By Solomon Kidder Livermore ... Amherst, N. H. Printed by Joseph Cushing. 1809.
15 p. 20cm.

1. Music—Addresses, essays, lectures. I. Title.
28-12695
Library of Congress ML60.L5

NL 0416964 DLC CtY MH

---

*XH .809 .L75 0

Livermore, Solomon Kidder, 1779-1859.
An oration, pronounced at Temple, (N.H.) in commemoration of American independence, before the inhabitants of Temple, New-Ipswich, Peterborough, and Wilton, at their united celebration, July 4, 1809. By Solomon Kidder Livermore ... Amherst,N.H. Printed by Joseph Cushing. 1809.
16p. 20cm.(8vo)
Title vignette.
Shaw/Shoemaker 17924.

NL 0416965 MB Nh

Livermore, Thomas Leonard, 1844-1918.

Hamlin, Charles Sumner, 1861–
Addresses of Hon. Charles S. Hamlin, Horatio G. Curtis, esq., and Col. Thomas L. Livermore, before the Legislative committee on taxation. Boston, February 5th, 7th and 8th, 1901. Boston, Massachusetts anti-double-taxation league [1901]

LIVERMORE, Thomas Leonard, 1844-1918
The conduct of Generals McClellan and Halleck in August, 1862; and case of Fitz-John Porter. Read, June 11, 1877.
(In Military historical society of Massachusetts. Boston, 1886. Vol. 2, pp. 315-348.)

NL 0416967 MB

Livermore, Thomas Leonard, 1844-1918,
(The conduct of General McClellan... April-Dec. 1861... (n.p.,1917)
p. 315-353. 25 cm.
Paper read before Massachusetts historical society, May, 1917.

NL 0416968 DNW

Livermore, Thomas Leonard, 1844–1918.
Days and events, 1860–1866, by Thomas L. Livermore ... Boston and New York, Houghton Mifflin company, 1920.
x p., 2 l., [3]–485, [1] p. front. (port.) illus., fold. pl. 24½cm.

1. U. S.—Hist.—Civil war—Personal narratives. 2. New Hampshire infantry. 18th regt., 1864–1865. I. Title.
20—5734
Library of Congress E601.L78
[a40b1]

NL 0416969 DLC MiU OClWHi OCl NN MB PHC NcD TU KU NBuU OrP CaBVaU

Micro-card 57-10 no.294

Livermore, Thomas Leonard, 1844-1918.
Days and events, 1860-1866. Boston and New York, Houghton Mifflin, 1920. [Louisville, Ky., Lost Cause Press, 1958]
12 cards. (Travels in the Confederate States, no.294)
Microcard edition.
Collation of original: x, 485 p.

1. U. S.--Hist.--Civil war--Personal narratives. I. Title.

NL 0416970 AU PSt ICRL UU MsU

Livermore, Thomas Leonard, 1844-1918.
General Thomas in the record. (In: Critical sketches of some of the Federal and Confederate commanders... Boston, 1895. 8°. p. 209-244.)
Military Historical Society of Massachusetts. Papers. v. 10.

1. Thomas, George Henry. MILITARY SERVICE INST. December 11, 1911.

NL 0416971 NN OCl OO

Livermore, Thomas Leonard, 1844–1918.
History of the Eighteenth New Hampshire volunteers, 1864–5, by Thomas L. Livermore ... Boston, The Fort Hill press, 1904.
124 p. front., plates, ports. 24cm.

1. U. S.—Hist.—Civil war—Regimental histories—N. H. inf.—18th. 2. New Hampshire infantry. 18th regt., 1864–1865.
4—35436
Library of Congress E520.5.18th

NL 0416972 DLC I MB MWA OClWHi PPL PP NcD ViU ViN MtHi CaBVaU

Livermore, Thomas Leonard, 1844-1918
In memoriam Francis Amasa Walker.
n.p., n.d.
8°

NL 0416973 MWA

Livermore, Thomas Leonard, 1844-1918. *2355.12.50
McClellan.
(In Massachusetts Historical Society. Proceedings. Vol. 50, pp. 315-353. Boston. 1917.)
A review of his policy as a commander in the Civil War, in the light of contemporaneous records.

D7175 — MacClellan [McClellan], George Brinton, 1826-1885. — United States. Hist. Civil War. Military and naval studies.

NL 0416974 MB MH OO

Livermore, Thomas Leonard, 1844–1918.
Numbers and losses in the civil war in America, 1861–65, by Thomas L. Livermore ... Boston and New York, Houghton, Mifflin and company, 1900.
iv p., 1 l., 150 p., 1 l. 24½cm.
"This volume has grown from an essay which was read before the Military historical society of Massachusetts, February 23, 1897."—Pref.

1. U. S.—Hist.—Civil war—Statistics. 2. U. S.—Hist.—Civil war. 3. U. S.—Army—Statistics. I. Title.
37-14800
Library of Congress E491.L77
973.74

NL 0416975 DLC ViU OClWHi OU OCU ICN DI PHC PPM PP DNW MB MH NjP NN TxU PPL DNC

Livermore, Thomas Leonard, 1844–1918.
Numbers and losses in the civil war in America, 1861–65; by Thomas L. Livermore ... [2d ed.] Boston and New York, Houghton, Mifflin and company, 1901.
viii p., 1 l., 150 p., 1 l. 24cm.
"This volume has grown from an essay which was read before the Military historical society of Massachusetts, February 23, 1897."—Pref.

1. U. S.—Hist.—Civil war—Stat. 2. U. S.—Hist.—Civil war. 3. U. S.—Army—Stat. I. Title.
2—17110
Library of Congress E491.L78
[a36o1] 3.7

NL 0416976 DLC CaBVaU OrCS Or OrP WaSp WaS IU NIC FTaSU DNW Nh PU ODW OCl OO OClWHi MiU ViU MH

Livermore, Thomas Leonard, 1844–1918.
Numbers and losses in the Civil war in America, 1861–65; by Thomas L. Livermore ... [2d ed.] Boston and New York, Houghton, Mifflin and company, 1901. [i.e., 1909]
viii, [3], 1 l., 150 p., 1 l. 24cm.
"This volume has grown from an essay which was read before the Military historical society of Massachusetts, February 23, 1897."—Pref.
"July 1, 1909. Errata in and additions to ..." [3] p. inserted after p. viii.

NL 0416977 ViU

Livermore, Thomas Leonard, 1844-1918.
Patterson's Shenandoah campaign. [1862.]
(In Military Historical Society of Massachusetts. Papers. Revised edition. Vol. 1, pp. 1-58. Boston. 1895.)

D7274 — Shenandoah campaigns, 1861-1864.

NL 0416978 MB

Livermore, Thomas Leonard, 1844-1918. *"20th".21.34.8
The siege and relief of Chattanooga.
(In Military Historical Society of Massachusetts. Papers. Vol. 8, pp. 273-339. Boston. 1910.)
A discussion of the claims that the operations at and near Brown's Ferry, October, 1863, were planned by Gen. Rosecrans, before his removal from command.

D7344 — Chattanooga, Tenn. Hist. Civil War, 1861-1865. Campaign of 1863. — Rosecrans, William Starke. — Brown's Ferry, Tenn., Seizure of. 1863.

NL 0416979 MB

VOLUME 336

Livermore, Virgil Benjamin, 1863–
How to become a competent motorman, written by Virgil B. Livermore ... and James Williams ... being a practical treatise on the proper method of operating a street railway motor car, also giving details how to overcome certain defects ... [Brooklyn, N. Y., Eagle press] 1902.
1 p. l., 232 p. illus., diagr. 15½cm.

1. Electric railroads—Motormen's manuals. I. Williams, James joint author.

Library of Congress TF965.L78 2—16940

NL 0416980 DLC ICJ NN

TF 965 .L78 1903
Livermore, Virgil Benjamin, 1863-
How to become a competent motorman; being a practical treatise on the proper method of operating a street railway motor-car; also giving details how to overcome certain defects, by Virgil B. Livermore and James Williams. New York, D. Van Nostrand, 1903.
232 p. illus. (part col.) 16 cm.

1. Electric railroads--Motormen's manuals. I. Williams, James R.. joint author.

NL 0416981 MiU NIC

Livermore, Virgil Benjamin, 1863–
How to become a competent motorman; a practical book on the proper method of operating a street railway motor-car; with instructions how to overcome troubles on the road, by Virgil B. Livermore ... and James R. Williams ... New York, D. Van Nostrand company, 1908.
xiv, 247 p. incl. front., illus., diagrs. 16½cm.

1. Electric railroads—Motormen's manuals. I. Williams, James R., joint author.

Library of Congress TF965.L8 8—17267

NL 0416982 DLC WaS

Livermore, Virgil Benjamin, 1863–
How to become a competent motorman; a practical book on the proper method of operating a street railway motor-car; with instructions how to overcome troubles on the road, by Virgil B. Livermore ... and James R. Williams ... 2d ed.—rev. New York, D. Van Nostrand company, 1908.
xiv, 247 p. incl. front., illus. diagrs. 16½cm.

1. Electric railroads—Motormen's manuals. I. Williams, James R., joint author.

Library of Congress TF965.L82 8—17946

NL 0416983 DLC

Livermore, Virgil B[enjamin] 1863– and J. R. Williams.
How to become a competent motorman; a practical book on the proper method of operating a street railway motor-car; with instructions how to overcome troubles on the road. New York: D. Van Nostrand Co., 1909. xiv, 247 p., 2 pl. illus. 3. ed. rev. 16°.

NL 0416984 NN MiD MH PPSteph

[Livermore, William F]
Vest-pocket tactics; or, School of the knight. A complete instructor for all necessary and fancy movements. N[ew] Y[ork], Masonic publishing and supply company, 1895.
30 p. 13½cm.

1. Freemasons—Templars. I. Title.

Library of Congress HS751.L78 12-39766

NL 0416985 DLC

Livermore, William Roscoe, 1843–1919.
The American kriegsspiel. A game for practicing the art of war upon a topographical map. By W. R. Livermore ... Boston, New York, Houghton, Mifflin and company, 1882.
2 p. l., [iii]–xxiii, [2] p., 1 l., 128 p. 20cm. *and* atlas (1 p. l., iv (*i. e.* 6) pl. (part fold., part col.) x tab. on 11 l.) 21½ x 30½cm.

1. War games. I. Title.

Library of Congress U310.L69 18–12445

NL 0416986 DLC OU ICJ PPL CU IU ICN KMK WaTC

Film 3986
Livermore, William Roscoe, 1843-1919
The American Kriegspiel; a game for practicing the art of war. Boston, Houghton, Mifflin, 1882 [c1879]
128p. 20cm.
Microfilm (negative) Madison, University of Wisconsin Library, 1972. 1 reel.

NL 0416987 WU

Livermore, William Roscoe, 1843–1919.
The American kriegsspiel. A game for practicing the art of war upon a topographical map. By W. R. Livermore ... New and rev. ed. Boston, Mass., W. B. Clarke co., 1898.
xxvii, [2] p., 1 l., 132 p. 20cm. *and* atlas (1 p. l., v (*i. e.* 7) pl. (part fold., part col.) x tab. on 11 l.) 21½ x 30½cm.

1. War games. I. Title.

Library of Congress U310.L7 18–12446

NL 0416988 DLC DNW

Livermore, William Roscoe, 1843–1919.
America's place in history.
(*In* American antiquarian society, Worcester, Mass. Proceedings. Worcester, Mass., 1908. 24½cm. v. 19, p. 77–99)

1. U. S.—Hist.—Philosophy.

Library of Congress E172.A35 vol. 19
E172.9.L782 12—6404

NL 0416989 DLC MWA OO

Livermore, William Roscoe, 1843–1919.
America's place in history, by William R. Livermore ... Worcester, Mass., The Davis press, 1908.
25 p. incl. maps. 25½cm.
"Reprinted from the Proceedings of the American antiquarian society volume XIX."

1. U. S.—Hist.—Philosophy.

Library of Congress E177.L78 10-11213

NL 0416990 DLC

Livermore, William Roscoe, 1843-1919
Biographical notice of George Washington Cullum. n. imp.
[6] p.

NL 0416991 MiD-B

Livermore, William Roscoe, 1843–1919.
George L. Gillespie. By Col. W. R. Livermore ...
(*In* Professional memoirs, Corps of engineers, U. S. army, and Engineer department-at-large. Washington, 1917. 23cm. v. 9, no. 47, p. 503-507. front., port)

1. Gillespie, George Lewis, 1841-1911.

E S 17-103
Title from U. S. Engineer School Libr. Printed by L. C.

NL 0416992 DES MiU OU

Livermore, William Roscoe, 1843–1919.
George W. Cullum. By Col. W. R. Livermore ...
(*In* Professional memoirs, Corps of engineers, U. S. army, and Engineer department-at-large. Washington, 1919. 23cm. vol. XI, no. 58, p. 443-446. front. (port.))

1. Cullum, George Washington, 1809-1892.

E S 22-64
Title from U. S. Engineer School Libr. Printed by L. C.

NL 0416993 DES MiU OU

Livermore, William Roscoe, 1843- tr.
The German shelters on the Somme.
(*In* Professional memoirs, Corps of engineers, U. S. army, and Engineer department-at-large. Washington, 1917. 23cm. v. 9, no. 46, p. 399-406. illus.)

Livermore, William Roscoe, 1843-1919 tr.
How France subsists her armies at the front.
(*In* Professional memoirs, Corps of engineers, U. S. army, and Engineer department-at-large. Washington, 1917. 23cm. v. 9, no. 48, p. 692-706. illus.)

Livermore, William Roscoe, 1843-1919.
TC425 .H8A4 1907
U. S. *Army. Corps of engineers.*
... Hudson river from Troy to Waterford, N. Y. Letter from the acting secretary of war, transmitting, with a letter from the chief of engineers, reports of examination and survey of the Hudson river, with a view to extending the existing project to Waterford, N. Y. ... [Washington, Govt. print. off., 1907]

Livermore, William Roscoe, 1843–1919.
Jared Mansfield. By Col. W. R. Livermore ...
(*In* Professional memoirs, Corps of engineers, U. S. army, and Engineer department-at-large. Washington, 1919. 23cm. vol. XI, no. 55, p. 123-1.., front. (port.))

1. Mansfield, Jared, 1759-1830.

E S 22-34
Title from U. S. Engineer School Libr. Printed by L. C.

NL 0416997 DES MiU OU

Livermore, William Roscoe, 1843–1919.
John Gray Foster. By Col. W. R. Livermore ...
(*In* Professional memoirs, Corps of engineers, U. S. army, and Engineer department-at-large. Washington, 1919. 23cm. vol. XI, no. 56, p. 249-252. front. (port.))

1. Foster, John Gray, 1823-1874.

E S 22-44
Title from U. S. Engineer School Libr. Printed by L. C.

NL 0416998 DES MiU OU

VOLUME 336

Livermore, William Roscoe, 1843- 1919.
Manœuvres for infantry, by W. R. Livermore ... [San Antonio? Tex., 1884]
1 p. l., ii p., 2 l., 51, 27 p. 6 fold. pl. 15cm.

1. Infantry drill and tactics.

Library of Congress UD157.L78 CA 19-314 Unrev'd

NL 0416999 DLC NN

Livermore, William Roscoe, 1843–1919.
Manœuvres for infantry, by W. R. Livermore ... 2d ed. Principles and forms. New York, C. Scribner's sons, 1888.
xvii, 281 p. diagrs. 15cm.

1. Infantry drill and tactics. I. Title.

Library of Congress UD157.L8 12—36290

NL 0417000 DLC NN NIC AU

Livermore, William Roscoe, 1843–1919, *tr.*
Mining operations, especially for infantry. Mainly translated from a lecture to cadets at Saint-Maixent, France. By Col. W. R. Livermore ...
(*In* Professional memoirs, Corps of engineers, U. S. army, and Engineer department-at-large. Washington, 1918. 23cm. vol. x, no. 49, p. 123-139. illus., diagrs.)

1. Mines, Military. 2. Sapping. I. Title.

E S 22-95

Title from U. S. Engineer School Libr. Printed by L. C.

NL 0417001 DES MiU OU

Livermore, William Roscoe, 1843–1919
Outline of the territorial history of Germany. By Col. W. R. Livermore (retired).
(*In* Professional memoirs, Corps of engineers, U. S. army, and Engineer department-at-large. Washington, 1919. 23cm. vol. xi, no. 55, p. 1–27 incl. 9 maps)

1. Germany—History—Early period to 843. I. Title: Territorial history of Germany.

E S 22—31

U. S. Engineer sch. Libr. for Library of Congress [a41c1]

NL 0417002 DES MiU OU

LIVERMORE, William Roscoe, 1843 – 1919.
Report upon fog-signal experiments.
[Washington. Govt. pr. office. 1894.] 267–376 pp. Pl. Maps. 8°.
From United States. Light-house board. Report. 1894. Appendix 5 [*5956.56].

NL 0417003 MB CtNlCG PPM DWB DN-Ob OO ICJ

Livermore, William Roscoe, 1843-1919, tr.

Gay, Adrien.
Sapping operations, especially for infantry; from a lecture to cadets at Saint Maixent, France. By Capt. A. Gay, French army.
(*In* Professional memoirs, Corps of engineers, U. S. army, and Engineer department-at-large. Washington, 1918. 23cm. vol. x, no. 50, p. 196-210. illus., diagrs.)

Livermore, William Roscoe, 1843-1919

Ropes, John Codman, 1836-1899.
The story of the civil war; a concise account of the war in the United States of America between 1861 and 1865. By John Codman Ropes ... New York, G. P. Putnam's sons, 1933.

Livermore, W[illiam] R[oscoe], 1843-1919.
Suggestions for the development of the arts and sciences. [Boston,] 1897. 1 p.l., p. 31-42. 8°.
Repr.: Amer. Acad. of Arts and Sciences. Proc., v. 33, no. 3.

1. Art.—Development of. 2. Science.—Development of.
January 25, 1911.

NL 0417006 NN

Livermore, William Roscoe, 1843-1919.

Tunnels and galleries.
(*In* Professional memoirs, Corps of engineers, U. S. army, and Engineer department-at-large. Washington, 1918. 23cm. vol. x, no. 51, p. 306-308)

Livermore, William Roscoe, 1843-1919.
The Vicksburg campaign. (In: Military Historical Society of Massachusetts. Papers. Boston, 1912. 8°. v. 9, p. 538-571.)

1. United States.—History: Civil war: Military: 1862-63. Vicksburg.
July 15, 1912.

NL 0417008 NN

Livermore, William Roscoe, 1843-1919.

Alexander, Edward Porter, 1835–1910.
The Wilderness campaign. 1. Grant's conduct of the Wilderness campaign, by Gen. Edward P. Alexander ... 2. Lee's conduct of the Wilderness campaign, by Col. William R. Livermore ... 3. The Wilderness campaign from our present point of view, by Maj. Eben Swift ...
(*In* American historical association. Annual report ... for the year 1908. Washington, 1909. 24½cm. v. 1, p. 223-247)

F869 Livermore, Calif. Board of trade.
L75L7 Semi-tropical Livermore, Alameda county, California. Issued by the Livermore Board of trade. Livermore, The Livermore herald power printing house, 1887.
62, [2] p. illus. (incl. map) 22cm.

Illustrated t.-p.

1. Livermore, Calif.

NL 0417010 CLU CtY MnHi

Livermore, Calif. Lawrence Radiation Laboratory
see
California. University. *Lawrence Radiation Laboratory.*

Livermore, *Me.*
Annual reports of the selectmen, assessors, overseers of poor, treasurer, superintendent of schools, treasurer of ministerial and school funds, town clerk, and road commissioner ...

Livermore Falls, Me.,
v. tables. 23–24cm.
Report year irregular.

CA 34–1575 Unrev'd

Library of Congress JS13.L796 352.07418

NL 0417012 DLC

Livermore, Me.
Notes, historical, descriptive, and personal, of Livermore
see under [Washburn, Israel] 1813-1883.

Livermore, Me. Washburn memorial library
see
Washburn memorial library, *Livermore, Me.*

Livermore association.
Report to the Livermore association, U. S. A., made by Josiah Q. Hawkins, agent, A. D. 1865. Containing information already collected in America and England relative to the Livermore property in England: the crest and coat of arms of the family, likewise a genealogy of the Livermore family in England and America, so far collected ... Rutland, Livermore association, 1865.
38 p. 22cm.

1. Livermore family (John Livermore, 1606?–1684) I. Hawkins, Josiah Q., 1812–

Library of Congress CS71.L785 1865 9-15602

NL 0417015 DLC PHi IaHi NBLiHi MWA

CS71 Livermore association.
.L784 Report to the Livermore association,
1867 U.S.A., made by Josiah Q. Hawkins, agent, Brandon, Vt. ... Brandon, Vt., Livermore association, 1867.
cover-title, [8] p. illus.(coat of arms) 19cm.

NL 0417016 MnHi PPL

Livermore Falls, *Me.*
Annual reports of the municipal officers, superintendent of schools, and water and sewer districts of the town ...

Livermore Falls, Me.
v. tables. 23cm.

CA 34–2022 Unrev'd

Library of Congress JS13.L797 352.07418

NL 0417017 DLC NN

---

fF869 Livermore Herald.
L5L55 Special midwinter edition.

Livermore, Calif.
v. 40cm.

NL 0417018 CU-B

Livermore & Knight co.
Constructive psychological and mechanical analysis of catalog ... Ed. 2.
Providence, c1922.
83 p.

NL 0417019 OCl

Livermore & Knight Co.
Correct wedding customs
see under title

Livermore & Knight co.
Fifty years of the pioneer spirit; a retrospect of a half-century of endeavor which has produced a present-day organization equipped to render a very useful and complete service in advertising and printing. Providence, New York [etc.] Livermore & Knight co. [°1925]
[59] p. illus. 28cm.

I. Title.

Library of Congress HF6181.L5A3 26-4147

NL 0417021 DLC ICJ MiU OU

VOLUME 336

Livermore & Knight company, inc.
The hurricane and flood of September 21, 1938, at Providence, R. I. — A pictorial record. ⌐Providence, R. I.: Livermore & Knight co., 1938⌐ 16 l. illus. 25½cm.

Cover-title.

IXZ p.v.383

——— ⌐Providence⌐ The Providence-Biltmore hotel ⌐1938⌐

1. Storms—U. S.—R. I.— Providence. I. Title. II. Providence, R. I. Providence-Biltmore hotel.

June 12, 1942

NL 0417022 NN CU OU

Livermore & Knight co.
Let's analyze your catalog; a psychological and mechanical catalog analysis, prepared by the Catalog department of Livermore & Knight company. Providence, R.I., New York ⌐etc.,⌐ ⌐c1936⌐

89p. illus. 23cm.

Half-title: Make your catalog a better salesman.
"Third edition."

NL 0417023 MoU

[Livermore & Knight Co.]
99 salads and how to make them, with rules for dressing & sauce. New York [c1897]
see under Gorham manufacturing company.

TX740
L5
Agric.
Library

Livermore & Knight Co.
Ninety-nine salads and how to make them, with rules for dressing & sauce. San Francisco, Shreve & Co., Gold and Silver Smiths [c1897]
57 p.

"Copyrighted 1897 by Livermore & Knight Co., Providence, R.I."

1. Salads. I. Title.

NL 0417025 CU

Livermore & Knight co.
Trader's companion, issued by Livermore & Knight co., Providence and New York. ⌐New York, Livermore & Knight co., ©1917⌐

⌐47⌐ p. incl. forms. 10½ x 17½cm.

"Comprising alphabetical ticker abbreviations of active stocks listed on N. Y. stock exchange, high and low price record of 1916, with tape abbreviations, annual dividend rates and approximate ex-dividend dates, forms for brokers' accountings, with monthly recapitulation."
"The records ... are compiled up to January 1, 1917."

1. Stocks. I. Title.

17-13934

Library of Congress HG4923.L8

NL 0417026 DLC

Livermore & Knight co.
Your army, navy and Marine corps; a government service handbook, compiled and published by Livermore & Knight co. Providence, R. I. ⌐©1941⌐

31 p. incl. illus., forms. 23½cm.

1. U. S.—Army. 2. U. S.—Navy. 3. U. S. Marine corps. I. Title.

41-12080

Library of Congress UA23.L6

355.0073

NL 0417027 DLC

Livermore herald, Livermore, California.
Corral Hollow coal mines, special midwinter edition, Livermore Herald, Livermore, Alameda county, Cal. ... Livermore, Cal., 1896.
(10) p. illus.(incl.ports,maps, etc.) 29cm.

NL 0417028 DNLM

Livernash, Edward James, 1866- ed.
The Californian illustrated magazine ... v. 1-5; Oct 1891-Apr. 1894. San Francisco, The Californian publishing company ⌐1891-94⌐

LIVERNASH, Edward Robert.
An analysis of job evaluation procedures.

Typewritten. 28 x 21 cm. Charts.
Thesis, Ph.D. - Harvard University, 1941, Division of History, Government and Economics.
Abstract, ff.7, inserted in Copy B.

NL 0417030 MH

Livernash, Edward Robert.
... The Colorado labor market and its relation to unemployment compensation, by Edward Robert Livernash ... Boulder, Col., 1937.

2 p. l., 127-187 p. incl. tables. 24½cm. (⌐Colorado. University⌐ The University of Colorado studies, v. 24, nos. 3 and 4)

"This study was undertaken at the suggestion and with the aid of the Committee on social security of the Social science research council."—Pref.

On cover: Reprinted ... from University of Colorado studies, vol. 24, nos. 2 and 3 (i. e. 3 and 4) June, 1937.

1. Insurance, Unemployment—Colorado. 2. Unemployed—Colorado. I. Social science research council. Committee on social security. II. Title.

42-17299

Library of Congress AS36.C6 vol. 24, nos. 3-4
HD7096.U6C65
(082) 331.2544409788

NL 0417031 DLC PPT DL OU OC1W

M1630
18
.B57R32

Livernash, Will, comp.

Binns, Billy, comp.
... Billy Binns' Ranch, range and home songs ... Compiled and arranged by Will Livernash. New York, N. Y., Stasny music corporation, ©1937-

---

Livernash, Will, ed.

Dick Powell songs of romance; outstanding collection of love songs, compiled and edited by Will Livernash ... New York, Stasny music corp. ⌐1938⌐

64 p. illus. (incl. ports.) 30½ x 23cm.

With piano accompaniment; also chords for fretted instruments, and symbols for accordion.
Words in original language with English translation.

1. Songs—English words. I. Powell, Dick, 1904-

44-15110

Library of Congress M1629.L65D5

784.81

NL 0417033 DLC

Livernash, Will, comp.
Favorite songs of Hollywood stars; an outstanding collection of well known songs selected by 30 Hollywood screen celebrities, with notes of interest and pictures of these popular film favorites, compiled and arranged by Will Livernash ... New York, N. Y., Amsco music sales co., inc. ⌐©1939-

v. illus. (ports.) 30½ x 23cm.

With piano accompaniment; also chords for fretted instruments, and symbols for accordion.

1. Music, Popular (Songs, etc.)—U. S. I. Title.

44-43865

Library of Congress M1629.L65F3

NL 0417034 DLC

Livernash, Will, arr.
Songland favorites, a delightful collection of new songs with modern presentation, and a few well known favorites, compiled and arranged by Will Livernash, for voice, piano, guitar, banjo, ukulele and accordion ... New York city, Amsco music sales co., inc., ©1939-

v. 30½ x 23cm.

With piano accompaniment; also chords for fretted instruments and symbols for accordion.

1. Music, Popular (Songs, etc.)—U. S. I. Title.

45-46178

Library of Congress M1629.L65S6

NL 0417035 DLC

Livernash, Will, comp.
Tito Guizar's favorite Spanish and Mexican songs ... compiled and arranged by Will Livernash ... New York city, Amsco music publishing co., inc., ©1960 ⌐i. e. 1940⌐

96 p. illus. (incl. ports.) 30½cm.

Text on p. ⌐2⌐ of cover.
English and Spanish words.
Piano accompaniment; also chords in guitar tablature.

1. Music, Popular (Songs, etc.)—Mexico. I. Guizar, Tito.

44-28910

Library of Congress M1682.L5T5

NL 0417036 DLC OrP

Livernash & Peck.
A complete and concise business directory and descriptive pamphlet of Healdsburg, Geyserville and Windsor; Russian River, Dry Creek and Alexander Vallies. Containing the addresses of all business men resident within the above towns and territories. Facts and figures about the most charming portion of California. Issued ... by Livernash & Peck. Healdsburg, Cal., Healdsburg enterprise print., 1895.
cover-title, 32 p. 24cm.

Advertising matter included in paging.

NL 0417037 CU-B

LIVERNOIS, J. E.
Quebec illustrated in photo-gravure. N[ew Y[ork] The Albertype Co., [1895?]

obl. 24°. 16 plates.
The one page of text preceding the plates is signed E.T.D.C. Can 2359.73

NL 0417038 MH

Livernois, J. E.
Quebec of to-day, photo-gravures. New York: Albertype Co., 1894. 1 l., 27 pl. ob. 12°.

1. Quebec.—Views, 1894.

September 19, 1913.

NL 0417039 NN

F
1054
.5
.Q3L58x

Livernois, J. E.
Quebec of to-day. Photo-gravures. Quebec, J. E. Livernois, 1894.
Unpaged, illus. 18 cm.
Photo captions in French and English.

1. Quebec (City)--Descr. I. Title

NL 0417040 OKentU

VOLUME 336

LIVERNOIS, J. E.
Quebec of to-day; photo-gravures. N. Y. The Albertype, cop. 1897.
obl.12°. Can 2359.16

NL 0417041 MH

Livernois, J E ed.
Sainte Anne de Beaupré album, ed. by J. E. Livernois ... [Grand Rapids? Mich.] °1907.
[44] p. illus. 18 x 23cm.
French and English.
An earlier edition was published under title: Souvenir of the church of St. Anne de Beaupré.
1. Ste. Anne de Beaupre, Quebec. I. The James Bayne co., pub.
Library of Congress F1054.S17L8 7-41774

NL 0417042 DLC

971.411 Sa26l
Livernois, J E
St. Anne de Beaupré and the picturesque route from Quebec and Montmorency Falls. [Montreal? c1889]
32p.(p.26-32 advertisements) illus. 23cm.
Date on cover: 1902.
1. Ste. Anne de Beaupré, Quebec - Descr.

NL 0417043 TxU

[Livernois, J E] ed.
Souvenir of the church of St. Anne de Beaupré, together with a short historical sketch of the founding of the church and its evolution from the beginning of the seventeenth century to the present time. J. E. Livernois, photographer ... Grand Rapids, Mich., The J. Bayne co., 1902.
[40] p. incl. illus., plates. 18 x 23cm.
Text in French and English.
Published later under title: Sainte Anne de Beaupré album.
1. Ste. Anne de Beaupré, Quebec. I. The James Bayne co., pub.
Library of Congress F1054.5.S32L6 2—28719

NL 0417044 DLC

Liverovskii, A. V., ed.
TF200 .P852
(Postroĭka zheleznykh dorog ...)
Постройка железных дорог. 3. перер. изд. Под ред. Д. Д. Бизюкина и А. В. Ливеровского. Допущено в качестве учебника для вузов жел-дор. транспорта. Москва, Гос. трансп. жел-дор. изд-во, 1951.

TA713 .L58
Liverovskiĭ, A V
Строительство в условиях вечной мерзлоты. Ленинград, Гос. изд-во строит. лит-ры, 1941.
243 p. illus. 23 cm.
At head of title: А. В. Ливеровский и К. Д. Морозов.
Errata slip inserted.
Bibliography: p. 234.
1. Frozen ground. 2. Building. I. Morozov, Konstantin Dmitrievich, joint author.
Title transliterated: Stroitel'stvo v uslovīfakh vechnoĭ merzloty.
TA713.L58 50-46901

NL 0417046 DLC

TF220 .L5
Liverovskiĭ, A V
Укрепление откосов земляного полотна. Москва, Гос. трансп. жел-дор. изд-во, 1943.
79 p. diagrs. 20 cm. (В помощь строителям железных дорог)
At head of title: А. В. Ливеровский, А. В. Паталеев.
1. Railroads—Russia—Earthwork. I. Pataleev, Aleksandr Vasil'evich, 1901- joint author. (Series: V pomoshch' stroiteliām zheleznykh dorog)
Title transliterated: Ukreplenie otkosov zemlīanogo polotna.
50-51205

NL 0417047 DLC

Liverovskiĭ, Īuriĭ Alekseevich, joint author.
Pochvenno-botanicheskie isseldovaniīa
see under Lipshiīs, Sergeĭ Īul'evich, 1905-

Liverovskiĭ, Īuriĭ Alekseevich.
Почвы тундрово-болотной полосы в связи с земледелием на Севере; под ред. Л. И. Прасолова. Москва, Изд-во Академии наук СССР, 1937.
52, [2] p. illus. 22 cm. (Серия по почвоведению для агротехников, учителей и колхозного актива)
At head of title: Академия наук СССР. Почвенный институт им. В. В. Докучаева.
Errata slip inserted.
"Литература": p. [53]
1. Soils—Russia—Arctic regions. 2. Tundras. (Series: Seriīa po pochvovedeniīu dliā agrotekhnikov, uchiteleĭ i kolkhoznogo aktiva)
Title transliterated: Pochvy tundrovo-bolotnoĭ polosy.
S598.L5 49-53930*

NL 0417049 DLC DNAL

Liverovskiĭ, Īuriĭ Alekseevich.
Природа южной половины советского Дальнего Востока; физико-географическая характеристика. Москва, Гос. изд-во геогр. лит-ры, 1949.
379 p. illus., ports., maps. 21 cm. (Природа СССР; научно-популярные очерки)
At head of title: Академия наук Союза ССР. Институт географии. Ю. А. Ливеровский и Б. П. Колесников.
Errata slip inserted.
Bibliography: p. 355-[366] (Boris Pavlovich.
1. Physical geography—Dal'ne-Vostochnyĭ kraў. I. Kolesnikov, (Series: Priroda SSSR; nauchno-populīarnye ocherki)
Title transliterated: Priroda īuzhnoĭ poloviny sovetskogo Dal'nego Vostoka.
GB316.D3L5 50-39604

NL 0417050 DLC

Liverpool, Bishop of, 1880-1900
see
Ryle, John Charles, bp. of Liverpool, 1816-1900

LIVERPOOL, ANNETTE LOUISE (MONCK) FOLJAMBE, countess OF, d. 1948.
Countess of Liverpool's gift book of art and literature [Editor: A.W. Shrimpton] Christchurch, N.Z., Whitcombe and Tombs, 1915. 160 p. illus., ports. 26cm.
1. European war, 1914-1918--Gift books, literary miscellanies, etc.
I. Shrimpton, Arnold Wilfred, ed.

NL 0417052 NN

LIVERPOOL, ARTHUR WILLIAM DE BRITO SAVILE FOLJAMBE, 2d earl of, 1870-1941, comp.
The voyages of His Majesty's New Zealand hospital ships "Marama" and "Maheno". Auckland, N.Z., Whitcombe and Tombs, 1916-19. 4 v. illus. (incl. fronts., plates, ports.), tables. 19cm.
v.1 has title: The New Zealand hospital ship "Maheno."
1. European war, 1914-1918--Hospitals, charities, etc. 2. Hospital ships, New Zealand--Marama. 3. Hospital ships, New Zealand--Maheno.

NL 0417053 NN CtY

Liverpool, Arthur William de Brito Savile Foljambe, *earl of*, 1870-1941
see also
New Zealand. *Governor-general, 1912-1920 (Earl of Liverpool)*

1494 .332 .59f
Liverpool, Cecil George Savile Foljambe, Earl of, 1846-1907, comp.
Evelyn pedigrees and memoranda. Comp. by Cecil G.S. Foljambe. Priv.printed. London, Mitchell, 1893
114 p. illus. 45 cm
"Genealogical memoranda relating to the family of Shuckburgh": 20 p. at end.
1. EVELYN FAMILY I.T.

NL 0417055 NjP MH

Liverpool, Cecil George Savile Foljambe, earl of, 1846-1907.
The family of Ottley of Pitchford. By the Right Hon. Lord Hawkesbury... [London? 1897?] 20 p. 8°.
Caption-title.
132128A. 1. Ottley family. August 22, 1924

NL 0417056 NN

Liverpool, Cecil George Savile Foljambe, *earl of*, 1846-1907.
Hayton notes. By Lord Hawkesbury.
(*In* East Riding antiquarian society. Transactions ... Hull, 1904. 22cm. v. 11, p. 123-125. fold. geneal. tab.)
Pedigree of Rudston of Hayton: geneal. tab.
1. Registers of births, etc.—Hayton, Eng. 2. Rudston family. I. Title.
Library of Congress DA670.Y59E2 vol. 11 21-9497

NL 0417057 DLC

Liverpool, Cecil George Savile Foljambe, *earl of*, 1846-1907.
The house of Cornewall, by the Right Hon. Cecil G. S., 4th earl of Liverpool ... and Compton Reade. Hereford, Jakeman and Carver, 1908.
viii, 316 p. front., plates, ports., fold. geneal. tab. 26½cm.
Coat of arms in color on cover.
1. Cornwall family. I. Reade, Compton, 1834- joint author.
Library of Congress CS439.C7395 16-19783 Revised

NL 0417058 DLC IU NcD CtY PHi NN

Liverpool, Cecil George Savile Foljambe, earl of 1846-1907
Edwinstowe, *Eng.* (*Parish*)
The registers of Edwinstow, in the county of Nottingham, 1634-1758. Ed. by George W. Marshall ... With an appendix by Cecil G. Savile Foljambe ... Worksop, Printed by R. White, 1891.

Liverpool, Cecil George Savile Foljambe, earl of, 1846-1907.
Some East Riding families. By The Right Hon. the Lord Hawkesbury... Hull: W. Andrews & Co., 1899. 3 p.l., 36 p. 8°.
Repr.: East Riding Antiquarian Soc. Transac. v. 7. 1899.
1. Yorkshire.—Genealogy. January 10, 1921.

NL 0417060 NN WU NcD

VOLUME 336

[Liverpool, Cecil George Savile Foljambe, *earl of*] 1846–1907.
Three years on the Australian station ... London, Hatchard and co., 1868.
3 p. l., 282 p. front., illus., plates, fold. maps (1 in pocket) 22½cm.
"My son's log."—Pref., signed: Selina C. Milton.
For private circulation.

1. New Zealand—Descr. & trav. 2. Oceanica—Descr. & trav. I. Milton, Selina Charlotte (Jenkinson) Fitzwilliam, viscountess, 1812-1883. II. Title.

15-19661

Library of Congress DU21.L6

NL 0417061 DLC CtY

Liverpool, Charles Cecil Cope Jenkinson, 3d earl of, 1784-1851.
An account of the operation of the poor law amendment in the Uckfield union, in the county of Sussex, during the year ending Lady-day 1836 ... London, 1836.
v, [7]-43, [1] p. fold. map. 21 cm.

NL 0417062 CtY

Liverpool, Charles Jenkinson, 1st earl of, 1727-1808.
American material in the Liverpool papers, 1727-1828
see his The Liverpool papers.

Liverpool, Charles Jenkinson, 1st earl of, 1727-1808.
Gt. Brit. *Treaties, etc.*
A collection of all the treaties of peace, alliance, and commerce, between Great-Britain and other powers, from the treaty signed at Munster in 1648, to the treaties signed at Paris in 1783. To which is prefixed, A discourse on the conduct of the government of Great-Britain in respect to neutral nations, by the Right Hon. Charles Jenkinson ... London, Printed for J. Debrett, 1785.

Liverpool, Charles Jenkinson, 1st earl of, 1727-1808.
Society of ship-owners of Great Britain. Collection of interesting and important reports and papers ... 1807.

Liverpool, Charles Jenkinson, 1st earl of, 1727-1808.
Gt. Brit. *Treaties, etc.*
A collection of treaties of peace, commerce and alliance, between Great-Britain and other powers, from the year 1619 to 1734. To which is added, A discourse on the conduct of the government of Great-Britain, in respect to neutral nations. By the Right Hon. C. Jenkinson ... The whole being a supplement to A collection of treaties, between Great Britain and other powers, from the revolution, in 1688 ... London, Printed for J. Almon and J. Debrett, 1781.

Liverpool, Charles Jenkinson, 1st earl of, 1727-1808, supposed author.
The conduct of the late administration examined. 1767
see under Lloyd, Charles, 1735-1773.

Liverpool, Charles Jenkinson, 1st earl of, 1727-1808.
Constitutional maxims, extracted from a discourse on the establishment of a national and constitutional force ... London:printed 1757. Abridged and reprinted by order of the London corresponding society,1794.
1p.l.,[2]-12p. 21cm.

NL 0417068 CtY RPB OClWHi NjP NN

[Liverpool, Charles Jenkinson, 1st earl of,] 1727–1808.
Discours sur la conduite du gouvernement de la Grande Bretagne, à l'égard des nations neutres pendant la présente guerre. Traduit de l'Anglois. A la Haye: Chez P. de Hondt, 1759.
1 p.l., 79 p. 8°.

Knuttel 18723.

59129. 1. Great Britain—For. rel., 1756-1758. 2. Seven Years' war, 1756-1763. 3. Neutrality, 1756-1758. 4. Title.

November 26, 1929

NL 0417069 NN RPJCB ICN

[Liverpool, Charles Jenkinson, *1st earl of*] 1727–1808.
A discourse on the conduct of the government of Great Britain, in respect to neutral nations, during the present war. London, R. Griffiths, 1758.
1 p. l., 84 p. 26 x 20½cm.

1. War (International law) 2. Neutrality. I. Title.

5-430

Library of Congress JX5360.L6 1758

NL 0417070 DLC MiU-C MH-BA MB NN RPJCB CtY PHi MH CLL CaBVaU

758
L75
1759d

[Liverpool, Charles Jenkinson, 1st earl of]
1727-1808.
A discourse on the conduct of the government of Great-Britain, in respect to neutral nations, during the present war. Dublin,Printed for H.Bradley,1759.
71p. 17½cm.

NL 0417071 CtY

[Liverpool, Charles Jenkinson, *1st earl of*] 1727–1808.
A discourse on the conduct of the government of Great-Britain, in respect to neutral nations, during the present war. The 2d ed. London, R. Griffiths, 1759.
99 p. 21cm.
Imperfect: p. 73-99 wanting.

1. International law and relations. 2. Neutrality. I. Title.

5-431 Revised

Library of Congress JX5360.L6 1759

NL 0417072 DLC MH NIC PPL MiU-C NN

Liverpool, Charles Jenkinson, *1st earl of*, 1727-1808.
A discourse on the conduct of the government of Great Britain in respect to neutral nations. A new ed. By Charles, lord Hawkesbury. London, J. Debrett, 1794.
iv, 96 p. 22 x 12½cm.

1. International law and relations. 2. Neutrality.

5-428

Library of Congress JX5360.L6 1794

NL 0417073 DLC MH MB NcD PPL PHi CtY MiU-C PPL

Liverpool, Charles Jenkinson, *1st earl of*, 1727–1808.
A discourse on the conduct of the government of Great Britain, in respect to neutral nations. Written in the year 1758, by Charles Jenkinson, esq., now earl of Liverpool. A new ed. London, T. Cadell, jun. and W. Davies, 1801.
1 p. l., xlix, 108 p. 24cm.

1. International law and relations. 2. Neutrality.

5-429

Library of Congress JX5360.L6 1801
[Miscellaneous pamphlets, v. 922, no. 10]

NL 0417074 DLC MH MeB ICJ MiU-C NCH PU-L PHi CtY

Liverpool, Charles Jenkinson, *1st earl of*, 1727-1808.
A discourse on the conduct of the government of Great Britain, in respect to neutral nations. A new ed. By Charles, earl of Liverpool. London, Printed for J. Debrett, 1801.
111 p. 21cm.

1. International law and relations. 2. Neutrality.

34-5537

Library of Congress JX5360.L6 1801 a 341.3

NL 0417075 DLC NSyU

Liverpool, Charles Jenkinson, *1st earl of*, 1727–1808.
A discourse on the conduct of the government of Great Britain, in respect to neutral nations. Written in the year 1758, by Charles Jenkinson, esq., late earl of Liverpool. A new ed. Edinburgh, T. Clark, 1837.
100 p. 19½cm. (*In* The Cabinet library of scarce and celebrated tracts. v. 1. International law. p. [301]-400)
Double paging.

1. Neutrality. 2. Gt. Brit.—For. rel.

10—6965

Library of Congress JX1291.M343

NL 0417076 DLC PU-L PPB CSmH NN

UA
661
L7

[Liverpool, Charles Jenkinson, 1st earl of]
1727-1808.
A discourse on the establishment of a national and constitutional force in England. London, R. Griffiths, 1757.
82 p. 23 cm.

1. Gt. Brit. - Militia. 2. Gt. Brit. Army. I. Title.

NL 0417077 Vi RPB NN ICN CtY NIC KyU CaBVaU MH InU TxU

---

*EC75
L7565
757db

Liverpool, Charles Jenkinson, 1st earl of, 1727-1808.
A discourse on the establishment of a national and constitutional force in England. By Charles lord Hawkesbury.
London:Printed for John Stockdale,Piccadilly. 1794. <Price two shillings and six-pence.>
8°. 82p. 24.5cm.
On establishing a national militia.

NL 0417078 MH CSt ICU

Liverpool, Charles Jenkinson, 1st earl of, 1727-1808.
Draft of a report on the coin of this realm
see under Gt. Brit. Privy council. Committee on coins.

VOLUME 336

Liverpool, Charles Jenkinson, 1st earl of 1727-1808.
The Jenkinson papers, 1760-1766. Compiled by Ninetta S. Jusker. [Uncorrected proof copy] London, Macmillan, 1948.
xxix,443p. 22cm. (Studies in modern history)

1. Gt. Brit. Pol. & govt. 1760-1789.

NL 0417080 IEN

Liverpool, Charles Jenkinson, *1st earl of*, 1727-1808.
The Jenkinson papers, 1760-1766. Ed. with an introd. by Ninetta S. Jucker. London, Macmillan, 1949.
xxix, 451 p. 23 cm. (Studies in modern history)

1. Gt. Brit.—Pol. & govt.—1760-1789. (Series: Studies in modern history. London)

DA506.L65A4 942.073 49-9647*

NL 0417081 MtU CaBVaU CaBViP NNCU-G DLC PU OCl CtY NNC TxU ICU ViU NcD OrPR

Liverpool, Charles Jenkinson, 1st earl of, 1727-1808.
(Letter to the Duke of Northumberland, dated War-office, July 22, 1779, re the Middlesex and Westminster volunteers) (1779?)
1 l. 34 cm. (Inserted at p. (iii) of The maritime campaign of 1778.... London William Faden, 1779)

NL 0417082 MiU-C

Film 1080 .591 Liverpool, Charles Jenkinson, 1st Earl of, 1727-1808
The Liverpool papers [1727-1828]; a selection of material relating to the American colonies and the United States from the Liverpool papers in the British Museum, London. With an introd. by Geoffrey Seed.
3 reels. (British Association for American Studies./British records relating to America in microform)

Official papers acquired by Charles Jenkinson, 1st Earl of Liverpool and Robert Banks Jenkinson, 2d Earl of Liverpool.
Microfilm of originals in the British Museum.
1.Gt. Brit. - Colonies - America. 2.Gt. Brit. - For. rel. - U. S. 3.U. S. - For. rel. - Gt. Brit. I. Liverpool, Robert Banks Jenkinson, 2d Earl of, 1770-1828. II.Seed, Geoffrey. III. T. IV. Ser.

NL 0417084 NjP CU

Liverpool, Charles Jenkinson, 1st earl of, 1727-1808.

The Liverpool tractate, an eighteenth century manual on the procedure of the House of commons, edited with an introduction by Catherine Strateman ... New York, 1937.

Liverpool, [Charles Jenkinson] *1st earl of*, 1727-1808.
Principles of coinage; intended as a commentary on a letter to the king, on the coins of this realm, by the late earl of Liverpool. 1st, 2d, 3d, and 4th pts. [London, Printed by W. Glindon] 1829.
iv, 208 p. 21½cm.

1. Coinage—Gt. Brit.

Library of Congress HG938.L67 6-41151†

NL 0417086 DLC NcD

Liverpool, Charles Jenkinson, *1st earl of*, 1727-1808.
Remarks on paper currency; from A treatise on the coins of the realm, by the Earl of Liverpool, pub. in 1805.
(*In* [Overstone, Samuel J. Loyd, 1st baron] A select collection of ... tracts ... on paper currency and banking. London, 1857. 22cm. p. [349]-359)
[Financial pamphlets, v. 22]

1. Paper money.

CA 8-173 Unrev'd

Library of Congress

NL 0417087 DLC CU NN

Liverpool, Charles Jenkinson, 1st earl of, 1727-1808.
Gt. Brit. *Board of trade.* Report of a Committee of the lords of the Privy council ... 1888.

Liverpool, Charles Jenkinson, 1st earl of, 1727-1808.
Gt. Brit. *Board of trade.*
A report of the lords of the Committee of Privy council, appointed for all matters relating to trade and foreign plantations, on the commerce and navigation between His Majesty's dominions and the territories belonging to the United States of America. [London] 28th January, 1791.

Liverpool. Charles Jenkinson, 1st earl of, 1727-1808.
Gt. Brit. *Board of trade.*
Representation of the lords of the Committee of council, appointed for the consideration of all matters relating to trade and foreign plantations, upon the present state of the laws for regulating the importation and exportation of corn: and submitting to His Majesty's consideration some further provisions, which are wanting to amend and improve the said laws [March 8th, 1790] London, Printed for J. Stockdale, 1790.

Liverpool, Charles Jenkinson, 1st earl of, 1727-1808
A state of the allegations and evidence produced and opinions of merchants and other persons given, to the Committee of Council..made upon the representation of the West-India planters and merchants, purporting to show the distressed state of His Majesty's sugar colonies....(London) Printed in the year M.DCC.LXXXIV.
32, (3) p. 25 cm.

NL 0417091 MiU-C

[Liverpool, Charles Jenkinson, *1st earl of*] 1727-1808.
State of the country in the autumn of 1798 ... London, J. Wright, 1798.
32 p. 22½cm.

1. Gt. Brit.—Pol. & govt.—1789-1820. I. Title.

Library of Congress DA507.1798.L7 5-38333

NL 0417092 DLC CtY MH ViU LNHT RPJCB MH-BA InU

Beinecke Library NZ 798L1 [Liverpool, Charles Jenkinson, 1st Earl of] 1727-1808.
... State of the country in the autumn of 1798 ... London, Printed for J. Wright, 1798.
32 p. 21 cm.
At head of title: Second edition.
Manuscript note on t.p.: Ascribed to Ld. Hawkesbury.

NL 0417093 CtY IU MH-BA

[Liverpool, Charles Jenkinson, 1st Earl of] 1727-1808.
Tables and statements relating to money, bullion, and foreign exchanges, of 1772. (Reprinted from a rare and curious tract published in that year) [with title: Considerations on money, bullion, and foreign exchange. London? 1880?]
32p. tables. 20cm.

1. Currency question. Gt. Brit I. Title.

NL 0417094 IEN MH

Liverpool, Charles Jenkinson, *1st earl of*, 1727-1808.
A treatise on the coins of the realm; in a letter to the king. By Charles earl of Liverpool. Oxford, At the University press, for Cadell and Davies, London, 1805.
1 p. l., 268 p. 28cm.

1. Money—Gt. Brit.—Hist. 2. Coinage—Gt. Brit.

Library of Congress HG938.L655 6-41149

NL 0417095 DLC MH-BA KyU FU OU PU PPL CtY NN InU

Liverpool, Charles Jenkinson, 1st earl of, 1727-1808.

A treatise on the coins of the realm, being a concise account of all the facts relating to the currency, which bear upon the exchanges of Europe, and the principals of political science. By the late Charles, Earl of Liverpool. 2d ed. London, J. Hearne, 1846.
2 p.l., 283, [1] p. 22cm.

NL 0417096 NcD OO CtY

Liverpool, Charles Jenkinson, *1st earl of*, 1727-1808.
A treatise on the coins of the realm; in a letter to the king. By Charles 1st earl of Liverpool. London, E. Wilson, 1880.
xii, 295 p. 22½cm.
Edited, with an introduction, by J. W. Birch and H. R. Grenfell.

1. Money—Gt. Brit.—Hist. 2. Coinage—Gt. Brit. I. Birch, John William, ed. II. Grenfell, Henry Riversdale, 1824-1902, joint ed.

Library of Congress HG938.L66 6-41150

NL 0417097 OClW CU OkU DLC NIC CtY MH NjP TxU PHC ICJ MiU OCl

LIVERPOOL, Charles, Jenkinson, Earl of

Vindication of the Convention lately concluded between Great Britain and Russia, in six letters. Addressed to ---- t. p. w.

124 p.

NL 0417098 MH-L

VOLUME 336

Liverpool, Charles Jenkinson, 1st earl of, 1727-1808.
A vindication of the convention lately concluded between Great Britain and Russia. In six letters. 3d ed. London, J.Wright, 1801.
2 p.*l.*, 135 p. 21.5 cm.

NL 0417099 MH-BA MH-L MWA PPAmP

Liverpool, Edward Frederick Langley Russell, *baron Russell of*
see
Russell, Edward Frederick Langley Russell, *baron,* **1895-**

Liverpool, Robert Banks Jenkinson, 2d earl of, 1770-1828.
Additional papers, presented to the House of commons, by Lord Hawkesbury, respecting the discussions with France
see under Gt. Brit. Foreign office.

[**Liverpool, Robert Banks Jenkinson,** *2d earl of,*] 1770-1828.
Inquiry into the capacity of government to administer relief (and into the best mode of administering relief) to agricultural distress. With an examination into the actual operation of Mr. Peel's bill upon the existing prices. London, J. Hatchard and son, 1822.
1 p. l., 80 p. 21cm.
"Speech of the Earl of Liverpool, May 26, 1820."

1. Agriculture—Gt. Brit. 2. Gt. Brit.—Econ. condit. I. Title.

29-8198

Library of Congress HD1925.L55

NL 0417102 DLC ICU CtY MH-BA NN IU ICJ

Liverpool, Robert Banks Jenkinson, 2d Earl of, 1770-1828.
A letter addressed to the late Earl of Liverpool, in the year 1822, shewing that unjust taxation is the cause of the evils complained of; with a just system then suggested
see under title

LIVERPOOL, ROBERT BANKS JENKINSON, 2D EARL OF. Letter from Lord Hawkesbury to Robert Fulton, [May, 1804]. His Majesty's Ministers find it impossible to advance sums required by Fulton in the form pointed out by him; suggests that negotiations personally conducted might smoothe many difficulties: should he accept active employment from the British government, he may rely on the most liberal treatment. Photostat. 2 p.
In: Robert Fulton. Proposals made ..over the signature of "Robert Francis"...

NL 0417104 NN

Liverpool, Robert Banks Jenkinson, 2d earl of, 1770-1828.
A letter to the Earl of Liverpool, on the probable effect of a great reduction of corn prices, by importation
see under title

Liverpool, Robert Banks Jenkinson, 2d earl of, 1770-1828.
A letter to the Earl of Liverpool on the reports of the committees ...
see under Attwood, Thomas, 1783-1856.

Liverpool, Robert Banks Jenkinson, 2d earl of, 1770-1828.
The Liverpool papers [1727-1828]
see under Liverpool, Charles Jenkinson, 1st Earl of, 1727-1808.

Liverpool, Robert Banks Jenkinson, 2d earl of, 1770-1828.
Memoirs of the public life and administration of the Right Honourable the earl of Liverpool
see under title

Liverpool, Robert Banks Jenkinson, 2d earl of, 1770-1828.
Bullock, William, *fl.* 1827.
Mexiko in 1823; of, Beschrijving eener reis door Nieuw-Spanje ... door M. Beulloch ... voorafgegaan door eene inleiding van Sir John Byerley, en verrijkt met historische bescheiden en aanteekeningen, zoo van den vertaler, als van den schrijver ... Delft, Weduwe J. Allart, 1825.

F1213
.B952

Liverpool, Robert Banks Jenkinson, 2d earl of, 1770-1828.
Bullock, William, *fl.* 1808-1828.
Le Mexique en 1823, ou Relation d'un voyage dans la Nouvelle-Espagne, contenant des notions exactes et peu connues sur la situation physique, morale et politique de ce pays; accompagné d'un atlas de vingt planches; par m. Beulloch ... ouvrage traduit de l'anglais par M***. Précédé d'une introduction, et enrichi de pièces justificatives et de notes; par Sir John Byerley ... Paris, Alexis-Eymery, 1824.

Liverpool, Robert Banks, Jenkinson, 2d earl of, 1770-1828.
Papers relating to the prosecution against Edward Huggins, sen. at Nevis
see under Huggins, Edward, of Nevis, defendant.

[**Liverpool, Robert Banks Jenkinson,** *2d earl of,*] 1770-1828.
Reflections on the present state of the resources of the country. London, J. Stockdale, 1796.
27 p. 22½cm.

1. Gt. Brit.—Econ. condit. I. Title.

6—12212

Library of Congress HC246.L7

NL 0417112 DLC CtY NcD PU NN ICN InU MH-BA MH

Liverpool, Robert Banks Jenkinson, 2d earl of, 1770-1828.
A second letter to the Earl of Liverpool
see under Attwood, Thomas, 1783-1856.

Liverpool, Robert Banks Jenkinson, 2d earl of, 1770-1828.
Landor, Walter Savage, 1775-1864.
[Selections from seven first editions (1795-1854) of works by Walter Savage Landor; reproductions from copies belonging to the British museum, the Forster collection of the Victoria and Albert museum, South Kensington, and the Ashley library of T. J. Wise, London]

Liverpool, Robert Banks Jenkinson, 2d earl of, 1770-1828.
Speech of Lord Hawkesbury, in the House of commons, Friday, April 25th, 1800, on the incorporation of the parliaments of Great Britain and Ireland. London, Printed for J.Wright, 1800.
34p. 21½cm.

NL 0417115 CtY InU

Liverpool, Robert Banks Jenkinson, *2d earl of,* **1770-1828.**
The speech of the Earl of Liverpool, delivered in the House of lords, on Tuesday, the 26th day of February, 1822, on the subject of the agricultural distress of the country, and the financial measures proposed for its relief. With an appendix, containing several accounts therein referred to. London, J. Hatchard and son, 1822.
1 p. l., [5]-64, [8] p. 21cm.

1. Agriculture—Gt. Brit. 2. Gt. Brit.—Econ. condit. 3. Finance—Gt. Brit.

16-11930

Library of Congress HD1925.L5

NL 0417116 DLC PU NcD MH-BA

Liverpool, Robert Banks Jenkinson, 2d earl of, 1770-1828.
The speech of the Earl of Liverpool, delivered in the House of lords, on Tuesday, the 26th day of February, 1822, on the subject of the agricultural distress of the country, and the financial measures proposed for its relief. With an appendix, containing several accounts therein referred to. 2d ed. London, J.Hatchard and son [etc., etc.] 1822.
1 p.*l.*, [5]-64 p. tables (1 fold.) 21 cm.

NL 0417117 MH-BA

Liverpool, Robert Banks Jenkinson, *2d earl of,* 1770-1828.
The speech of the ... Earl of Liverpool, in the House of lords ... 1820, on a motion of the Marquis of Lansdown, "That a select committee be appointed to inquire into the means of extending and securing the foreign trade of the country." With an appendix, containing the official accounts referred to in the speech. London, J. Hatchard and son, 1820.
1 p. l., 56, [4] p. 21½cm.

1. Gt. Brit.—Commercial policy.

6—27211

Library of Congress HF3505.8.L78

NL 0417118 DLC NN MH-BA NcD PU CtY MB NN

Liverpool, Robert Banks Jenkinson, *2d earl of,* **1770-1828.**
The speech of the Earl of Liverpool, in the House of lords, on Monday, 14th April, 1823, upon laying on the table of the House, by His Majesty's command, certain papers relative to the negotiations at Verona, Paris, and Madrid, on the differences which had arisen between France and Spain. London, J. Hatchard and son, 1823.
1 p. l., [5]-55 p. 21cm.

1. Europe—Politics—1815-1848. 2. Gt. Brit.—For. rel.—1820-1830. 3. France—For. rel.—Spain. 4. Spain—For. rel.—France.

45-47000

Library of Congress D383.L5

NL 0417119 DLC LNHT NN NjP CtY

---

ar W
9535

Liverpool, Robert Banks Jenkinson, 2d earl of, 1770-1828.
The speech of the Right Hon. the Earl of Liverpool, in the House of Lords, on Friday 3rd, & Saturday 4th November, 1820, [on the second reading of the Bill of pains and penalties. 2d ed. London, J. Hatchard, 1820.
80 p. 22cm.

No. 10 in vol. lettered: Letters and papers about Queen Caroline.
1. Caroline Amelia Elizabeth, queen consort of George IV, 1768-1821.

NL 0417120 NIC MB NN

VOLUME 336

Liverpool, Robert Banks Jenkinson, 2d earl of, 1770-1828.
3y54 The speech of the Right Hon. the Earl of
109y Liverpool, in the House of lords, on Friday 3rd,
1820i & Saturday 4th November, 1820, on the second reading of the bill of pains and penalties. 3d ed. London, J. Hatchard and son, 1820.
80p. 20cm.

NL 0417121 CtY NN

F LIVERPOOL, ROBERT BANKS JENKINSON, 2d earl of, 1770-1828.
4563 Speech of the Right Honourable Lord Hawkes-
.425 bury, in the House of lords, on Friday, the 10th day of May, 1805, on the subject of the Catholic petition. 2d edition. London, J. Hatchard, 1805.
38p. 22cm. (with Hunter, William. Reasons for not making peace with Buonaparté... 1806)

NL 0417122 ICN MH

Liverpool, Robert Banks Jenkinson, *2d earl of,* **1770-1828.**
Substance of the speech delivered in the House of lords, on the 15th of March, 1824, by the Earl of Liverpool, on the Marquess of Lansdowne's motion for the recognition of the independence of the late Spanish colonies in South America by the British government. London, J. Murray, 1824.
44 p. 22cm.

1. Gt. Brit.—For. rel.—Spanish America. 2. Spanish America—For. rel.—Gt. Brit.

Library of Congress F2235.L78 11—21747

NL 0417123 DLC NcD OO

Liverpool, Robert Banks Jenkinson, *2d earl of,* **1770-1828.**
Substance of the speech of the Rt. Hon. the Earl of Liverpool, on the report of the bank committee.
(*In* The Pamphleteer. London, 1819. 22½cm. v. 14, p. [267]-284)

CA 6—356 Unrev'd

Library of Congress AP4.P2 vol. 14

NL 0417124 DLC MdBP ICN IU MH MnU PU

Liverpool, T. N. C.
... Anniversary of the birthday of Abraham Lincoln. Petition of T. N. C. Liverpool, Peter H. Clark, and other citizens of Cincinnati, Ohio ... Feb. 21, 1874, referred to the Comm. on the Judiciary and ordered to be printed. [Washington, 1874]
1 p. 23 cm. (43d Cong. 1st sess. House. Mis. doc. no. 148)
Dated Cincinnati, Feb. 12, 1874.

NL 0417125 RPB

There are no cards for numbers
NL 0417126 to NL 0418000

Liverpool.
——. Analysis of the returns of the conveniences attached to the street houses, courts, and court houses, warehouses, shops, offices, etc. within the borough of Liverpool. 2 tab. [*Liverpool, Liverpool Printing Co.*.]

NL 0418001 DNAL

Liverpool.
Burgess roll of the borough of Liverpool, 1846. Liverpool, Printed by T. Baines [1846?]

16 nos. in 1 v. 21cm.

1. Liverpool - Voting registers. I. Title.

NL 0418002 FU

Liverpool.
Children trading in streets. Report of the Children Trading in Streets Sub-Committee.
= Liverpool. 1901. 24 pp. 8°.

G8701 — Liverpool, Eng. Labor. — Children. Employment. — Peddling and itinerant industries.

NL 0418003 MB

DA Liverpool.
690 City of Liverpool. Selections from the
L8A19+ municipal archives and records, from the 13th
1883 to the 17th century inclusive. Extracted and annotated by Sir James A. Picton. Liverpool, G.G. Walmsley, 1883.
xii, 362 p. illus. 25cm.

"Published with the sanction of the City Council."

1. Liverpool --Hist.--Sources. I. Picton, Sir James Allanson, 1805-1889, ed.

RPB ICN MB ICU
NL 0418004 NIC CSmH IU MdBP MiU OCl MH NN CtY NjP

Liverpool.
...Official handbook. Published under the authority of the corporation. Liverpool: Littlebury Bros., 1908. 115 p. illus. (incl. plan.) 3. ed. 8°.

Advertisements interspersed.

1. Liverpool, England—Guidebooks, 1908.
N. Y. P. L. October 23, 1924

NL 0418005 NN

•DA690 Liverpool.
.L8A5 ... City of Liverpool. Official handbook.
1911 Published under the authority of the corporation, 1911. Liverpool [Eng.] Littlebury bros. [1911]
xxiv, 119 p. illus. 24 1/2cm.
At head of title: Sixth edition.
Includes advertising matter.

1. Liverpool—Descr.—Guide-books.

NL 0418006 MB

Liverpool.
... The city of Liverpool. Official handbook. Published under the authority of the corporation. 1936-7 [15th ed.] Liverpool, Littlebury bros., ltd. [1936]
48 p., 1 l., 120 p. illus. (incl. maps) 24½cm.
Includes advertising matter.

1. Liverpool—Descr.—Guide-books.

45-40359

Library of Congress DA690.L8A5 1937
914.272

NL 0418007 DLC

Liverpool.
... The city of Liverpool official handbook... 1939. Liverpool and Worcester [1939]
136 p. illus.
At head of title: 16th ed.
1. Liverpool. Descr.

NL 0418008 MiU

DA690 LIVERPOOL.
f.L8A3 ...Extension scheme. Memorial of corporation to
1894 the Local government board and shorthand notes of the inquiry. [Liverpool, 1894.
cover-title, 28 numb.l., 3,179 p. fold.map. 33cm.

1. Liverpool--Boundaries.

NL 0418009 ICU

Liverpool.
Gore's directory of Liverpool and its Environs
see under title

Liverpool.
History of the election, for members of Parliament, for the borough of Liverpool, 1806...
see under title

Liverpool.
List of emigrants to America from Liverpool, 1697-1707
see under title

Liverpool.
... Liverpool corporation act, 1893
see under Gt. Brit. Laws, statutes, etc., 1837-1901 (Victoria)

Liverpool.
Liverpool Corporation (General Powers) Bill. Superannuation clauses. Brief for the promoters — the Corporation of Liverpool, so far as regards the superannuation clauses... [Liverpool: C. Tinling & Co., Ltd., 1913.] 33 f. f°.
Cover-title.
At head of title: In Parliament. Session 1913. [no. 1.]

1. Pensions (Old age), Gt. Br.: Eng.: Liverpool. 2. Great Britain. Statutes.
N. Y. P. L. July 16, 1919.

NL 0418014 NN

Liverpool.
Liverpool corporation passenger transport, report of the general manager
see under Liverpool. Passenger Transport Dept.

Liverpool.
Liverpool. Descriptive guide illustrated with photo views. Published under the authority of the corporation of Liverpool. Liverpool: Littlebury Bros. [191-?] 48 p. illus. 16°.

1. Liverpool, Eng.—Guide-books.
N. Y. P. L. December 1, 1920.

NL 0418016 NN

VOLUME 336

Liverpool.
Liverpool in the reign of Queen Anne, 1705 and 1708; from a rate assessment book of the town and parish, giving one of the earliest known lists of inhabitants, with their respective holdings, according to streets. By Henry Peet ... [Liverpool, 1908]
175 p., 1 l. 2 pl., 2 fold. maps. 23cm. (Historic society of Lancashire and Cheshire, Liverpool. Transactions. Liverpool, 1908. v. 59 (new ser., v. 23) 1907, appendix)
Caption title.
1. Liverpool—Hist.—Sources. 2. Gt. Brit.—Hist.—Anne, 1702-1714. I. Peet, Henry, 1856- II. Title.
Library of Congress DA670.L19H6 vol. 59 24-3435

NL 0418017 DLC WaU KU NN CtY ICN

Liverpool.
Liverpool town books. Proceedings of assemblies, common councils, portmoot courts, &c., 1550-1862 ... edited for the corporation of the city of Liverpool by J. A. Twemlow ... Liverpool, Pub. for the University of Liverpool School of local history and records by the University press; London, Constable & company, ltd., 1918-
v. illus., fold. facsims. 26cm.
Bibliography: v. 1, p. 691-719.
Contents.—I. 1550-1571.
1. Liverpool—Hist.—Sources. I. Twemlow, Jesse Alfred, 1867- ed. II. Liverpool. University. School of local history and records. III. Title.
20-5764 Revised
Library of Congress DA690.L8A2

NL 0418018 DLC ICU NN PU CtY PU-L PHi

Liverpool.
Liverpool vestry books, 1681-1834, ed. by Henry Peet ...
Liverpool, The University press; [etc., etc.] 1912-
v. front., plans, facsims., fold. tab. 25cm.
On verso of half-title: The University of Liverpool. School of local history and records.
1. Liverpool—Hist.—Sources. 2. Liverpool—Poor. 3. Liverpool—Charities. I. Peet, Henry, ed. II. Liverpool. University. Faculty of arts. School of local history. III. Blease, Walter Lyon, 1884- IV. Title.
16-14955
Library of Congress DA690.L8A3

NL 0418019 DLC NN

Liverpool.
The Medical Relief Committee. Letter addressed to the General Board of Health, in reply to the Statements contained in Dr. Duncan's Report ... London, 1854.
16 p. 8°. [In v College Pamphlets]

NL 0418020 CtY

Liverpool.
Municipal archives and records, from A.D.1700/to the passing of the municipal reform act, 1835. Extracted and annotated by Sir James A. Picton. Liverpool, Walmsley, 1886.
432 p. 29 cm.
A continuation of its Selections from the municipal archives and records, from the 13th to the 17th century inclusive.
Limited edition.
1. Liverpool - Hist. - Sources. I. Picton, James Allanson, 1832-1910, ed.

NL 0418022 NjP RPB NcD MH

ar W 31845
Liverpool.
[Municipal papers. Liverpool, 1886-96]
14 pamphlets in 1 v. illus., maps (part fold.) 25cm.
Binder's title.
Contents.--[1] Report on the police establishment and the state of crime...1895.--[2] Report on the health of Liverpool during 1895, by E. W. Hope.--[3] Corporation tramways; report of city engineer as to works executed in tramway streets within the city from 1880 to 1885.--[4] Liverpool corporation tramways; report of the city engineer...1893.--[5] Hours of lighting and lamplighting; report of the city engineer...1894.--[6] The Measurement of illumination; report of the city engineer upon a paper by A. P. Trotter ...--[7] Liverpool electric lighting order, 1889. Scale of charges for testing.--[8] Liverpool electric lighting order, 1889. Electric testing; report of the city engineer...1891.--[9] Liverpool electric lighting order, 1889. Electric testing; further report of the city engineer...1891.--[10] Tests of illuminating power of gas in various towns; memorandum of the Special Lighting Committee...1895.--[11] Lighting of the city ...by electricity; report of the city engineer...1892.--[12] Gas statistics of various towns; report of the city engineer...1895.--[13] The new water supply of Liverpool, by J. Parry.--[14] Notes on the mechanical features of the Liverpool Water Works, and the supply of power by pressure from the public mains, and by other means, by J. Parry, water engineer...1892.

NL 0418027 NIC

JS3498 .P6
Liverpool.
The poll, for the election, of members of the Parliament, for the borough of Liverpool; taken between Colonel Tarleton, Bamber Gascoyne, jun., esq., the Rt. Hon. Richard lord Penrhyn, and Thomas Townley Parker, esq. Which begun at the Exchange on Monday the 21st of June, 1790. And ended the Monday evening following; before the worshipful Thomas Smyth, esq., mayor; Henry Blundell, and John Shaw, esquires, bailiffs. Also the addresses, songs, squibs, &c. With the list of those members who have represented this borough, since the year 1660. Liverpool, Printed by T. Johnson [1790?]

Liverpool, *plaintiff.*
Proceedings in an action at law, brought by the mayor, bailiffs, and burgesses, of the Borough of Liverpool, for the recovery of a penalty under a by-law made by them in Common Hall assembled. Containing the arguments of the counsel, as well as nisi prius, as upon the motion for a new trial in the Court of King's Bench; the proceedings on the second trial at Lancaster; and on a motion in the Court of King's Bench for a third trial, with the reasons at large of the Hon. the Justices of the said court for granting the same. Taken in short hand by Mr. Gurney. Liverpool, J. M'Creery, 1796.
xiii, 404 p. 23 cm.
Binder's title: Corporation of Liverpool v. Golightly.
I. Golightly, Thomas, defendant. II. Gt. Brit. Court of King's Bench. III. Gurney, Joseph, 1744-1815, reporter. IV. Title: Corporation of Liverpool v. Golightly.
47-41281*

NL 0418030 DLC

Liverpool.
Programme of the ceremony of opening the new labourers' dwellings in the Bevington street area by the Countess of Derby on Friday, June 14, 1912. [Liverpool, 1912]
47 p.

NL 0418031 MH

Liverpool.
Register of persons entitled to vote at any election of a member or members to serve in Parliament, which shall take place in and for the borough of Liverpool, between the last day of November, one thousand, eight hundred and forty six, and the last day of December, one thousand, eight hundred and forty seven. Liverpool, Printed by T. Baines [18--]
256 p. 34cm.
1. Liverpool - Voting registers. I. Title.

NL 0418033 FU

Liverpool.
A review of housing & planning, 1952. Prepared for the visit to the city of the Rt. Hon. Harold MacMillan, minister of housing and local government, 27th June, 1952. [Liverpool, 1952] 59 p. illus. plans. 18 x 23cm.
1. Cities—Plans—Gt.Br.—Eng.—Liverpool. 2. Housing—Gt.Br.—Eng.—Liverpool. I. 1952.

NL 0418034 NN

Liverpool.
...Theatres and places of public resort. Reports of the town clerk, the head constable, and the city engineer... Liverpool: H. Greenwood, 1882. 37 p. plans. 24½cm.
Mainly the report of the city engineer.
791379A. 1. Theatres—Safety—in theatres—Gt. Br.—Eng.—Liverpool. 2. Fires Gt. Br.—Eng.—Liverpool. I. Liverpool. Engineer's Office.
N. Y. P. L. December 16, 1935

NL 0418035 NN

Liverpool. American Chamber of Commerce.
At a general meeting of the American chamber of commerce held January 22d, 1808, to take into consideration a circular letter sent by Mr. Barber to each member, with a view of ascertaining what are deemed the regular and customary charges of commissions, &c., in this port [Liverpool].
Liverpool, printed by G.F.Harris, [1808].
Broadside, 33 x 20 1/2 cm.

NL 0418036 MHi

Liverpool. American Chamber of Commerce.
Centenary commemoration of the American chamber of commerce of Liverpool. Visit of the Hon. Whitelaw Reid, special envoy to the coronation of His Majesty King Edward VII from the United States of America and complimentary banquet to him, 17th July, 1902. Liverpool, Rockliff, 1902.
28 p.

NL 0418037 OOxM OClWHi

Liverpool. American chamber of commerce.
A letter to emigrants to the United States of America; containing useful information on the prices of labour and provisions; places of landing; modes of living, &c. &c., with an account of the commerce and agriculture of some of the principal towns and villages. By an Englishman, resident in the States. Liverpool, Printed by D. Marples, 1828.

VOLUME 336

FILM 13766 HF Liverpool. American Chamber of Commerce.
Minutes of the American Chamber of Commerce, Liverpool, 1801-1908; introduction by W. O. Henderson. [East Ardsley, Eng., Micro Methods] c1964.
3 reels. On film (positive) (British records relating to America in microform)

Microfilm. Original in Liverpool Public Libraries.

1. Gt. Brit. - Comm. - U.S. 2. U.S. - Comm. - Gt. Brit. I. Henderson, William Otto, 1904- , ed.

NL 0418039 CU NN

Liverpool. Architectural and housing department.
...A report of the city architect and director of housing on Speke
see under Liverpool. Housing Committee.

Liverpool. "Architecture of Liverpool," Exhibition, 1948.
An exhibition, "Architecture of Liverpool" at St. George's hall, Liverpool, coinciding with the British architects' conference and the centenary of the Liverpool architectural society. [Liverpool] 1948. 60 p. (chiefly illus.) 23cm.

At head of title: City of Liverpool.

1. Architecture—Gt. Br.—Eng.— Liverpool.

NL 0418041 NN IU

Liverpool. Art gallery
see
Liverpool. Public libraries, museums and art gallery. (Walker art gallery)

Liverpool. Associated Merchants
see Associated Merchants of Liverpool.

Liverpool. Association for the reduction of the duty on tea.
Liverpool. Citizens.
Report of the proceedings of the public meeting on tea duties, held in the borough sessions-house, Liverpool, on the 25th November, 1846. The worshipful the mayor in the chair. Pub. by the committee of the Liverpool association for the reduction of the duty on tea. Liverpool, T. Carter [1846]

Liverpool. Association for the reduction of the duty on tea.
The tea duties
see under Liverpool. Citizens.

Liverpool. Asylum for Orphan Boys
see Liverpool Asylum for Orphan Boys.

Liverpool. Athenæum Library.
Catalogue of the library of the Athenæum in Liverpool. To which are prefixed, the laws of the institution, and a list of the proprietors. Liverpool: printed by J. M'Creery, 1802. 2 p.l., xxxii, 174 p. 8°.

1. Bibliography.—Catalogues: Libraries (Society), Gt. Br.: Eng.: Liverpool.
N. Y. P. L. January 29, 1917.

NL 0418047 NN MiDSH

Liverpool. Athenaeum Library.
A catalogue of the library of the Athenaeum, Liverpool; by George Burrell... Liverpool, Harris and co., 1820. xxix, 404 p. 24cm.

471785B. I. Burrell, George.
N. Y. P. L. October 17, 1949

NL 0418048 NN ICN PPM MBAt

Liverpool. Athenaeum Library.
Catalogue of the library of the Athenaeum, Liverpool. To which are prefixed the laws of the institution and the rules for the circulation of books. London, Printed for the proprietors of the Athenaeum, Liverpool, by Whittingham and Wilkins, 1864.
xxxvi, 589 p. 23cm.
-- --- Supplement... Liverpool, Printed for the proprietors of the Athenaeum by G. G. Walmsley, 1875.
xxi, [1] p. 2 l., 87 p. 23cm.
[With its Catalogue]
1. Catalogs, Library.

NL 0418049 MnU WU

Liverpool. Athenaeum Library.
History of the Athenæum, Liverpool, 1798–1898, comp. by George T. Shaw, rev. by W. Forshaw Wilson. Liverpool, Printed for the Committee of the Athenæum by Rockliff Bros., 1898.
94 p. plates. 26 cm.

I. Shaw, George Thomas, 1863–1938. II. Wilson, W. Forshaw, ed.

Z792.L327 48–41338*

NL 0418050 DLC

Liverpool. Athletic society
see Athletic society, Liverpool.

Liverpool. Blind asylum
see
Liverpool. School for the indigent blind.

Liverpool. Blind children's home.
Annual report.
Liverpool,
v. 21½cm.
Report year ends April 30.

CA 9-5702 Unrev'd
Library of Congress HV1950.L7B6

NL 0418053 DLC

HV L786r LIVERPOOL. Blue Coat Hospital.
Report of the state of the Blue Coat Hospital.
Liverpool [1832?]-
v.
Includes the Annual report of the Liverpool Blue Coat Brotherly Society.

NL 0418054 DLC DNLM

Liverpool. Borough and water engineer
see Liverpool. Water engineer.

Liverpool. Borough Court.
see Liverpool. Court.

Liverpool. Borough Engineer
see Liverpool. City Engineer.

Liverpool. Borough prison. Annual reports of the governor, chaplain, and surgeon, presented to the court of gaol sessions for the year 1855-6. 34 pp. 8°. Liverpool, G. McCorquodale & Co., 1856.

NL 0418058 DNLM

Liverpool. Botanic garden.
A catalogue of plants in the Botanic garden at Liverpool. Liverpool, Printed by J. Smith, 1808.
vii, 298 p., 1 l. front. (fold. plan) 22cm.

Library of Congress QK73.L9A4 5-26097†

NL 0418059 DLC MH-A OkU CLSU

Liverpool. Brazilian association
see
Brazilian association of Liverpool.

Liverpool. British Pharmaceutical Conference, 1870
see British Pharmaceutical Conference, Liverpool, 1870.

Liverpool. Cathedral
see Liverpool Cathedral.

Liverpool. Catholic Blind Asylum. Annual reports of the committee to the subscribers. 24., 1865; 42.-44., 1886-8. 16° & 8°. Liverpool, 1865-89.
Established 1841.

NL 0418063 DNLM

Liverpool. Chamber of Commerce.
An abstract of the proceedings and resolutions of the several committees of the Chamber of Commerce for the port of Liverpool from their first establishment on the 24th June, 1774, to the 24th June, 1777... n.p. [1777]
16 p. 18 cm.

NL 0418064 RPB

VOLUME 336

Liverpool. Chamber of Commerce.
The Bank charter act of 1844, reprinted from the "Financial reformer." To which are added a Report and resolutions presented to the Liverpool Chamber of Commerce, 1856... London [etc., 1856]
36 p. 23 cm.

NL 0418065 CtY

Liverpool. Chamber of Commerce.
Comparative table of duties in the West African colonies and possessions from the Gambia to Loanda. [Compiled to July, 1900.]
= Liverpool, 1900. 4 tables. 8°.

F1748 — Tariffs. — Africa, West. Tariff.

NL 0418066 MB

Liverpool. Chamber of Commerce.
Fall in the value of silver...Memorial...transmitted to the First Lord of the Treasury...
Liverpool, 1876.
1 leaf. 26 cm.
Caption title.

NL 0418067 CtY

HD 2356 E51L7++ Liverpool. Chamber of Commerce.
Liverpool and industrial Merseyside, 19
Issued under the auspices of the Liverpool Chamber of Commerce. London, Bemrose Publicity Company, Limited [1942]
155 p. illus. 33cm.

1. Liverpool, Eng.--Industries. 2. Merseyside, Eng.--Industries. I. Title.

NL 0418068 NIC

HC 258 .L78 L7 Liverpool. Chamber of Commerce.
Liverpool and industrial Merseyside,1948.
London, Published for the Chamber of Bemrose Publicity Co. c1948?]
155 p.(p.[6]-48,120-155 advertisements) illus.(part col.) ports. 33 cm.

1.Liverpool-Indus. 2.Mersey Valley--Indus.

NL 0418069 MiU CtY MH N IEN

Liverpool. Chamber of commerce.
Liverpool: its trade and commerce; official handbook of the Liverpool chamber of commerce (incorporated) with classified trade indices in English, French, Spanish, Italian, and Russian; also trade mark section. 1st- issue; 1918-
Derby [etc.] Bemrose & sons, ltd., 1918-

HF3510 .L5L5 Liverpool. Chamber of commerce.
The Liverpool trade review.
[Liverpool] Liverpool chamber of commerce [19

Liverpool. Chamber of commerce.
... Mandats. Lettre de la Chambre de commerce de Liverpool au sujet de mandat français pour le Cameroun ... Mandates. Letter from the Liverpool Chamber of commerce concerning the French mandates for the Cameroons. Genève, 1921.
cover-title, 3, 3 p. 33cm.
At head of title: ... Société des nations.
Official no.: C.258.M.192.1921.
French and English on opposite pages, numbered in duplicate.
"Communiqué au Conseil et aux membres de la Société."
1. Mandates—Cameroons. I. League of nations.

A 46-5290

Woodrow Wilson memorial library
for Library of Congress [2]

NL 0418072 NNUN-W CSt-H

Liverpool. Chamber of commerce.
Merseyside manufacturers; classified list of industrial products manufactured by members of the Liverpool Chamber of commerce. Products arranged alphabetically. Liverpool: Chamber of commerce, inc. [1936?] 28 p. 22cm.
Cover-title.

1. Commerce—Direct.—Gt. Br. —Eng.—Liverpool.
N. Y. P. L. September 27, 1938

NL 0418073 NN

Liverpool. Chamber of Commerce.
... Questions put to the chamber by the Royal commission on the depression of trade and industry, and answers sent, in accordance with a resolution of the council, dated 7th October, 1885. Liverpool, Lee and Nightingale, 1885.
28 p. 21 cm.

NL 0418074 NcD

---

q385.2312 L756r Liverpool--Chamber of commerce.
Report of a special committee on light railways upon schemes having for their object reduction in the cost of the transit of merchandise between Liverpool and Manchester, and the adjacent districts, adopted by the committee, Friday, July 22nd, 1898 ... Liverpool, 1898.
132p. illus., maps, tables, diagrs. (part fold.)

NL 0418075 IU

Pam. Coll. 37421 Liverpool. Chamber of Commerce.
Report of proceedings at a banquet to the Rt. Hon. Joseph Chamberlain, M. P., Her Majesty's principal secretary of state for the Colonies, given by the Chamber at the Philharmonic Hall, Liverpool on Tuesday, the 18th January, 1898. Liverpool, C. Tinling, printers, 1898.
40 p. 22 cm.
1. Chamberlain, Joseph, 1836-1914. 2. Gt. Brit. Colonies. Addresses, essays, lectures

NL 0418076 NcU

Liverpool. Chamber of Commerce.
Report of the Council . . . at the Annual general meeting, 50th, 1900.
= Liverpool, 1900. v. 8°.

F1747 — Liverpool, Eng. Bus. assoc. — Boards of trade.

NL 0418077 MB MH-BA NjP

Liverpool. Chamber of Commerce.
Report of the Special Committee of Merchants and Lawyers, on the Bankruptcy Laws and of other Laws bearing upon Commercial Credit and Morality ...Liverpool, 1869.
16 p. 8°. [In v. College Pamphlets]

NL 0418078 CtY

Liverpool. Chamber of commerce.
... Report of the Special committee on mercantile reform and tribunals of commerce, read at a special meeting of the council, and ordered to be printed, 16th August, and adopted by the council, Sept. 6, 1852. London, E.Wilson [1852]
32 p. tables. 21.5 cm.

NL 0418079 MH-BA PU

Liverpool. Chamber of commerce.
... Report of the Special committee on the monetary system, and the Bank act of 1844, to the council. Received January 22nd, and ordered to be printed February 12th, 1857. [Liverpool, Benson & Mallett, printers, 1857]
48 p. 20cm.
At head of title: Liverpool Chamber of commerce, 1857.

1. Currency question—Gt. Brit. 2. Bank of England.

11-15308

Library of Congress HG939.L6

NL 0418080 DLC PU

Liverpool. Chamber of commerce.
Report of the Special committee on the state of trade in connection with the discrediting of silver as money ... Liverpool, Printed by Lee and Nightingale, 1879.
20 p.

Presented to the Council, and adopted, on Tuesday, the 25th March, 1879.

NL 0418081 MH-BA CtY IU NjP CU

Liverpool. Chamber of Commerce.
Session of Parliament, 1900. Companies Bill . . . Report of the Commercial Law Committee of the Council of the Chamber.
= Liverpool, 1900. 8 pp. 8°.

Dec. 28, 1903
F1878 — Great Britain. Acts and laws. Companies. — Corporation law. — Great Britain. Bus. assoc.

NL 0418082 MB

Liverpool. Chamber of Commerce.
The telegraphs (telephonic communication, etc.) bill, 1899. Proceedings at a deputation to the Right Hon. R. W. Hanbury . . . 3d May, 1899.
= Liverpool, 1899. 56 pp. 8°.

F1748 — Great Britain. Acts and laws. Telegraphs. — Telegraph. Law.

NL 0418083 MB

Liverpool. Chamber of Commerce.
Visit of the Chinese ambassador [Sir Chihchen Lofengluh] to Liverpool 14th December, 1899. Report of the proceedings.
= [Liverpool, 1899.] 8 pp. 8°.

F1748 — Lo Feng-Luh, Sir Chih Chen. — China. Comm.

NL 0418084 MB

Liverpool. Chapel for the Blind
see Liverpool. School for the Indigent Blind.

Ovf86 L672 910 Liverpool. Charters.
The charter, granted to the burgesses of Liverpool, by William III ... also, the charter of George II ... To which is added a summary of the proceedings of the burgesses and Common council from the reign of Elizabeth to the present time ... Liverpool, Printed for the editor, by Egerton Smith and co.,1810.
128p. 21cm.

NL 0418086 CtY

VOLUME 336

Liverpool. Charters.

Muir, Ramsay, 1872–
A history of municipal government in Liverpool, from the earliest times to the Municipal reform act of 1835 ... Part I: A narrative introduction, by Ramsay Muir ... Part II: A collection of charters, leases, and other documents, transcribed, translated and edited with illustrative material, by Edith M. Platt ... London, Pub. for the University press of Liverpool, by Williams & Norgate, 1906.

Liverpool. *Chief Constable.*
Report on the police establishment and the state of crime.

[Liverpool]
v. 25 cm.
At head of title, : Watch Committee for the city of Liverpool.

1. Liverpool—Police. 2. Crime and criminals—England—Liverpool. I. Liverpool. Watch Committee.

HV7730.L5A3 352.2 51-32257

NL 0418088 DLC NN DNLM MH

B LIVERPOOL. CHURCH OF HUMANITY.
239 Hymns and anthems for use in the Church of
.18521 Humanity. Liverpool, 1901.
63p. 16cm.

Without music.

NL 0418089 ICN

B LIVERPOOL. CHURCH OF HUMANITY.
239 Hymns for use in the Church of Humanity,
.18522 Liverpool. [Liverpool] 1891.
[31]p. 14cm.

Without music.

NL 0418090 ICN

Liverpool. Citizens.
... An Address from inhabitants of Liverpool, England, to the Hon. Abraham Lincoln, president of the United States of America. [Liverpool, 1863]
4p. 18cm.

Caption title.
At head of title: Draft.
Corrections and additions, including place and date, have been added in pen and ink.

NL 0418091 IHi

Liverpool. Citizens.
Proceedings of the public meeting on the India and China trade, held in the sessions room, Liverpool, on the 29th January, 1829, the Worshipful the Mayor in the chair. Published by the committee. Liverpool, Printed by E.Smith and co. [1829]
viii, [9]-47 p. 20.5 cm.

NL 0418092 MH-BA PU

Liverpool. Citizens.
Report of the proceedings of the public meeting on tea duties, held in the borough sessions-house, Liverpool, on the 25th November, 1846. The worshipful the mayor in the chair. Pub. by the committee of the Liverpool association for the reduction of the duty on tea. Liverpool, T. Carter [1846]
x, 70 p. 21cm.

1. Tea trade—Gt. Brit. 2. Tariff—Gt. Brit. I. Liverpool. Association for the reduction of the duty on tea.

12-21798

Library of Congress HF2651.T343L5

NL 0418093 DLC MH-BA CtY PU

Liverpool. Citizens.

C.2304 —— Report of the public meeting at Liverpool, on Wednesday, January 28, 1829, for the purpose of taking into consideration the best means of removing the restrictions imposed upon commerce by the present charter of the East India company. Comp. for the Oriental herald. London, W.Lewer, 1829.
39 p. 20 cm.
J.S.Buckingham, compiler?

NL 0418094 MH-BA OClW

Liverpool. Citizens.
v.102 The tea duties. Report of the second public meeting, held in the sessions-house, Liverpool, on the 14th January, 1848, Thos.B.Horsfall, esq., mayor, in the chair. To which is prefixed, The report of the parliamentary committee of last session. Pub. by the Liverpool association for the reduction of the duty on tea ... Liverpool, Smith, Rogerson, and co., 1848.
60p. 22cm.

NL 0418095 CtY

Liverpool. Citizens.
... To the right honourable the lords spiritual and temporal of the United Kingdom of Great Britain and Ireland, in Parliament assembled. The humble petition of the undersigned merchants, traders, and other inhabitants of the town of Liverpool ... [Liverpool, Eng.?] J.M'Creery [1812]
broadside. 32 x 20 cm.

At head of title: Copy of a petition from the inhabitants of Liverpool to the House of lords, presented by the Right Hon. the Earl of Derby, on Tuesday, May 5, 1812.

NL 0418097 MH-BA

Liverpool. City bacteriologist.
Report of the city bacteriologist on the electrical treatment of milk
see under Liverpool. Health Dept.

Liverpool. City beautiful conference, 1907
see "City Beautiful" conference, Liverpool, 1907.

Liverpool. City building surveyor.
Report...

NL 0418100 MiU

Liverpool. City Council
see Liverpool. Council.

Liverpool. City Engineer.

——. Abattoirs (Paris and Brussels). Return to an address of the House of Commons, dated 7 June, 1869, for "copy of report compiled for the health committee of Liverpool by the borough engineer, James Newlands, with reference to the establishment of the abattoir of La Villette in Paris, and the abattoir of Brussels". Ordered by the House of Commons to be printed, 7 Aug., 1869. 4 pp. fol. [London, 1869.]

NL 0418102 DNLM

Liverpool. City Engineer.

——. Account of the sewers, sewerage utilization company of Liverpool. [By Jas. Newlands, borough engineer.] MS. 6 l. fol. [n. p., n. d.]

NL 0418103 DNLM

Liverpool. City Engineer.

——. Disinfecting establishments erected from designs by the borough engineer [James Newlands, March, 1867]. 2 l., 2 pl. 8°. [Liverpool, 1867.]

NL 0418104 DNLM

Liverpool. City Engineer.
Liverpool sewers. Report of the City Engineer. 9, 22 p. 5 pl. 2 maps. O. Liverpool 1890.

NL 0418105 ICJ

Liverpool. City Engineer.

——. Narrative of the proceedings relative to the supply of salt water for the borough of Liverpool. By James Newlands. 20 pp. 8°. Liverpool, H. Greenwood, 1865.

NL 0418106 DNLM

LIVERPOOL. City Engineer.
Report on the sewer rate for the borough of Liverpool. Liverpool. Harris & co. [1849.] 15 pp. 8°.

NL 0418107 MB NN

Liverpool. City Engineer

——. Report of the borough engineer, in accordance with the resolution of the special improvement committee. 30 pp. 8°. Liverpool, G. McCorquodale & Co., 1859. [P., v. 1432.]
[By James Newlands]

NL 0418108 DNLM

Liverpool. City Engineer.
Report to the Health Committee of the borough of Liverpool on the sewerage and other works, under the Sanitary Act. By the Borough Engineer ... Liverpool, Printed by Harris and Co., 1848.
144, xxiii, iii p. 11 fold. plates. 23cm.

Signed: James Newlands.

NL 0418109 NNC DNLM MB

Liverpool. City Engineer.
...Theatres and places of public resort
see under Liverpool.

Liverpool. City Engineer.
Utilisation of refuse and sewerage.
see under Liverpool. Health Committee.

Liverpool. City lighting engineer's dept.
Annual report of the assistant lighting engineer. Liverpool,
v. 24.5 cm.

NL 0418112 MiU

VOLUME 336

Liverpool. City school of art.

Netherlands (*Kingdom, 1815– *) *Regeeringsvoorlichtingsdienst, London.*
Exhibition of works by Dutch masters of the seventeenth century organized by the lecture department of the Netherland government information bureau with the assistance of the Department of extra-mural studies of Liverpool university, the British council and the Department of education, arts and sciences of the Royal Netherland government in London. [Liverpool, Liverpool city school of art, 1944]

Liverpool. Cleveland Ragged School.
Annual report. Liverpool, D. Marples, 18
v. 26 cm.

NL 0418114 OKentU

Liverpool. Collector of customs
see Gt. Brit. Custom-house, Liverpool.

Liverpool. College.
English poetry. First book. To be learned by heart between the ages of eight and ten years. For use in the Collegiate schools, Liverpool. A new edition. Liverpool, Wareing Webb; London, Longman and company [ca. 1844-1857]
60 p. 18 cm.
This is one of a series of four similar volumes, three others being adapted for different ages. cf. Notice.

NL 0418116 NNUT

LF795 .L5A3 Liverpool.college.
Report of the proceedings at the opening of the Liverpool collegiate institution; including the inaugural address, delivered by the Right Honorable William Ewart Gladstone... Liverpool, W. Webb, 1843.
31p. front.,plan. 21p.

1. Gladstone, William Ewart,1809-1898.

NL 0418117 NNU-W CtY

Liverpool. Collegiate Institution
see
Liverpool. College.

Liverpool. Commercial Reference Library.
See
Liverpool. Public Libraries, Museums, and Art Gallery. Library. Commercial reference library.

Liverpool. Commission of inquiry into the subject of the unemployed.
... Full report of the Commission of inquiry into the subject of the unemployed in the city of Liverpool. 1894. Liverpool, 1894.
xxi, 119p. tables fold. 21½ cm.

NL 0418120 DL

Liverpool. Compton House Library
see Jeffery (J. &W.) & company, Liverpool. Compton House Library.

Liverpool. Conference on Christian missions
see
Conference on Christian missions, *Liverpool*, 1860.

Liverpool. Conference on various forms of cotton bills of lading, 1907
see Conference on various forms of cotton bills of lading, Liverpool, 1907.

Liverpool. Congregation of Protestant dissenters.
A form of prayer
see under Liverpool. Unitarian Church.

Liverpool. Consulado de la República de Colombia
see Colombia. Consulado. Liverpool.

Liverpool. Corporation
see Liverpool.

JS3495 f.A2 1925 LIVERPOOL. Council.
...City of Liverpool:Financial organisation. Report of Mr.Arthur Collins,F.S.A.A. London,E.E.Miller,parliamentary printer,1925.
cover-title,100 p. fold.diagrs. 33cm.
At head of title:Private and confidential.

1.Finance--Liverpool,Eng.

NL 0418127 ICU

Liverpool. Council.
... Education act, 1902. Scheme for the constitution of an education committee. Liverpool, C. Tinling and co., 1903.
6 p. illus. (coat of arms) 21 cm.
At head of title: City of Liverpool.
1. Education - Liverpool. 2. Liverpool. Education committee.

NL 0418129 CU

LIVERPOOL. Council.
...Epitome of the proceedings of the committees and sub-committees.

[Liverpool, 24cm.

Irregular.
Title varies slightly.

1. Liverpool—Govt.

NL 0418130 NN

Liverpool. Council.
Industrial Liverpool, prepared for the Liverpool city council
see under Liverpool. Finance and general purposes committee.

Liverpool. Council.
Municipal archives and records, from A.D. 1700 to the passing of the municipal Reform Act ...
see under Liverpool.

Liverpool. Council.
Proceedings of the Council. [Also, Reports of departments] Liverpool, 1865.
v. Maps. 8°.

NL 0418133 MB

Liverpool. Council.
...Standing orders of the Council.

[Liverpool, 32°.

1. Municipal government, Gt. Br.: Eng.: Liverpool.
N. Y. P. L. April 7, 1924.

NL 0418134 NN MiU

Liverpool. Council. Special committee as to contracts.
Report...Liverpool, 1891.
2 v. in 1. 24½ cm.

NL 0418135 DL

Liverpool. *Council. Special Committee on Tramways.*
... Tramways. Report of the Special Committee appointed by the Council on the 13th March, [7th May] 1897. ... Liverpool, J. R. Williams & Co., printers, 1897.
2 nos. in 1 vol. 24cm.
——— ... Report of deputation appointed to examine various tramway systems on the continent as to mechanical traction for tramways. Liverpool, 1897.
6 p. 24cm.
At head of titles: City of Liverpool.

NL 0418136 ICJ

Liverpool. Council of Voluntary aid
see Liverpool Council of Social Service.

Liverpool. Court.
Practice of the Borough Court of Liverpool
see under Grocott, John Cooper, 1793-1874.

VOLUME 336

Liverpool. Court of passage.

Johnson, Horace Maxwell.
Bills of costs in the High court of justice and Court of appeal, in the House of lords and the Privy council; with the scales of costs and tables of fees in use in the houses of Lords and Commons, relative to private bills; election petitions, parliamentary and municipal. Inquiries and arbitrations under the Lands clauses consolidation act, the Light railways act, and other arbitrations. Proceedings in the court of the Railway and canal commission. In the County court and the Mayor's courts. The scales of costs and tables of fees in use in the Court of passage, Liverpool, conveyancing costs, and costs between solicitors and their clients. With orders and rules as to costs and court fees and notes and decisions relating thereto. By Horace Maxwell Johnson... London. Stevens and sons, ltd. [etc.] 1897.

Liverpool. Court of passage.

Thompson, Vincent Thomas, 1829–1910, *ed.*
The County courts admiralty jurisdiction act, 1868 (31 & 32 Vict. c. 71), and the General orders of 1869, to which are added those of the Liverpool Court of passage: with notes and appendices. By Vincent T. Thompson ... London, H. Sweet, 1869.

WX
L785d
1896

LIVERPOOL. David Lewis Northern Hospital
The "David Lewis" Northern Hospital, Liverpool; Pennington & Son and C. W. Harvey, architects. [London, McCorquodale, 1896?]
14 p. illus.
"David Lewis Northern Hospital programme of the opening ceremony, on Thursday, March 13th, 1902" (4 p.) inserted.

NL 0418141 DNLM

WB
400
L785d
1952

LIVERPOOL. David Lewis Northern Hospital
Diet book of the David Lewis Northern Hospital, Liverpool, 1951. Liverpool, Lee & Nightingale [1952?]
68 p.
1. Diet in disease

NL 0418142 DNLM

Liverpool. Dental Hospital
see Liverpool Dental Hospital.

Liverpool. Dispensaries.
——. By-laws for the ... respecting the duties of the house surgeons and assistant house surgeons, to be signed by them in conformity with a resolution of the medical board. 6 pp. 18°. *Liverpool. Harbord & Johnston* 1873.

NL 0418144 DNLM

Liverpool. Dispensaries
——. General rules for the ... as approved and adopted at a general annual meeting of the governors held on the 23. February, 1859, and subsequently amended at general annual meetings of the governers held on the 22. February, 1866, and on the 22. February, 1872. 12 pp. 16°. *Liverpool, Liverpool Printing Co.*, 1872.

NL 0418145 DNLM

WX
2
FE5
L75D6r

LIVERPOOL. Dispensaries
Report.
Liverpool [1778?]-
v.
Issued 1901- with title: Annual report.

NL 0418146 DNLM

Liverpool. Education Committee.
The Calder Cookery book
see under Calder (F.L.) College of Education for Domestic Science.

in supplement

Liverpool. *Education committee.*
Education act, 1918. Memorandum by the director of education. Liverpool, Education committee, 1919.
2 p. l., [3]-62 p. 24cm.
Signed: J. G. Legge.

1. Education—England—Liverpool. I. Legge, James Granville, 1861– II. Title.

Library of Congress LA639.L5A5 1918 20-9884

NL 0418148 DLC ICJ

LIVERPOOL - Education committee.
General rules for the conduct of elementary schools provided or maintained by the council. Liverpool, C. Tinling & Co., Ltd., 1914.
pp. (8), 42.
Educ 882.464.15

NL 0418149 MH

Liverpool. Education Committee.
Handbook of employments in Liverpool
see under Liverpool. Juvenile Employment Committee.

Liverpool. Education committee.
Merseyside employments for boys and girls. (no. 1-10)
Liverpool, Liverpool education committee, 1930-
10 v. 21½ cm.

NL 0418151 DL

Liverpool. Education Committee.

LA209
.F6

Fletcher, William Charles, 1865–
Report on a visit to educational institutions in the United States. Liverpool, C. Tinling and Co., print. contractors, 1904.

Liverpool. Education committee.

Sadler, *Sir* Michael Ernest, 1861–
... Report on secondary education in Liverpool: including the training of teachers for public elementary schools. By Michael E. Sadler ... [2d ed.] London, Eyre and Spottiswoode [1904?]

Liverpool. Education Committee.
...Report on the medical inspection of school children for the year
Liverpool, 8°.

1. School children.—Medical inspection, Gt. Br.: Eng.: Liverpool.
N. Y. P. L. December 13, 1920.

NL 0418154 NN MdBJ-W Or

Liverpool. Education Committee.
Statistics of the Juvenile employment registry
see under Liverpool. Juvenile Employment Committee.

Liverpool. Egyptian Museum.
Catalogue. [Liverpool, Egyptian museum, 189-?] 47 p. 22cm.
Caption-title.

1. Egypt—Archaeology—Museums and collections—Gt. Br.—Eng.—Liverpool.
N. Y. P. L. June 5, 1947

NL 0418156 NN

Liverpool, Eisteddfod, 1884-
see
Eisteddfod, Liverpool, 1884-

Liverpool. European ju-jitsu association
see
European ju-jitsu association, *Liverpool.*

WX
2
FE5
L75E9a

LIVERPOOL. Eye and Ear Infirmary
Annual report.
Liverpool, 18
v.

NL 0418159 DNLM

Liverpool. F.L. Calder College of Domestic Science
see Calder (F.L.) College of Education for Domestic Science. in supplement.

Liverpool. Female Apprentices' Library.
An address delivered to the readers and nominees belonging to the Female Apprentices' Library, February 1, 1825. [Liverpool. Willmer & Co. 1825.] 4 pp. 8°.

NL 0418161 MB

Liverpool. Female Apprentices' Library.
The second report of the Female Apprentices' Library. [Liverpool. Willmer & Co. 1824.] 12 pp. Sm. 8°.

NL 0418162 MB

Liverpool. Female Apprentices' Library.
A catalogue of the books belonging to the Female Apprentices' Library, at Mrs. Ramsay's, 17 Renshaw Street. Prefixed, the rules of the Institution, and a friendly address to the readers. Liverpool. Willmer & Co. 1825. 24 pp. Sm. 8°.

NL 0418163 MB

VOLUME 336

Liverpool. Female Orphan Asylum
see Liverpool Female Orphan Asylum.

LIVERPOOL. Finance and general purposes committee.
Industrial Liverpool, prepared for the Liverpool city council. [Liverpool, 195-?] 40 p. illus., maps. 18x22cm.

1. Industries—Gt.Br.—Eng.—Liverpool. 2. Liverpool-Views. t. 195–.

NL 0418165 NN

Liverpool. Financial reform association.
see
Financial reform association, Liverpool

Liverpool. Free Public Library
see Liverpool. Public Libraries, museum and art gallery.

Liverpool. Free Public Museum
see
Liverpool. Public Libraries, Museums and Art Gallery. *Museum.*

Liverpool. Friends Institute.
see Liverpool Friends Institute.

VR65F
1863L
1873

Liverpool. Friends' Sabbath schools.

A selection of hymns and poetry compiled chiefly for the use of the Friends' Sabbath schoo Liverpool. Second edition.
Carlisle, Hudson Scott and sons, 1873, [pref. 1st 1863; 2nd ed. 1872]
4 p.l., 153 p. 12 cm.

Pieces unnumbered.
Ms. annotations by Prof. Bird.
Compiled by a few of the teachers of the Liverpool Friends' Sabbath schools. cf. pref.

NL 0418170 NNUT

Liverpool. Greenbank School
see Greenbank School, *Liverpool.*

Liverpool. Gypsy lore society
see Gypsy lore society.

Liverpool. Health Committee.
Abattoirs (Paris and Brussels)
see under Liverpool. City Engineer.

Liverpool. Health Committee.
Borough of Liverpool. Report of the operations under the Liverpool sanitary act. By John A. Tinne. Liverpool, Harris & co., 1849.
14 p. 8°.

NL 0418174 MB

Liverpool. Health Committee.
The common lodging houses of Liverpool. Report presented to the Town Council... Liverpool, 1859.
12 p. 8°. [In v. 322, College Pamphlets]

NL 0418175 CtY

WA
L785n
1882

Liverpool. Health Committee.
Notification of infectious diseases. Circular addressed by the chairman of the Health Committee tc the mayors of the boroughs, and the chairmen of the local board districts in which notification of infectious disease is compulsory, and the replies thereto. Ordered by the Health Committee to be printed, 14th September, 1882. Liverpool, Greenwood, 1882.
57 p.
Bound with Liverpool. Medical Officer of Health. Notification of infectious disease. Liverpool, 1882; and the Committee's Notification of infectious disease. Liverpool, 1882.
I. Title

NL 0418176 DNLM

Liverpool. Health Committee.

——. Notification of infectious disease. Evidence taken by the deputations appointed by the health committee. 260 pp. 8°. *Liverpool, H. Greenwood,* 1882.
Bound with: LIVERPOOL. Notification of infectious diseases. Circular. 8°. *Liverpool,* 1882.

NL 0418177 DNLM

Liverpool. Health Committee.

——. Notification of infectious diseases. Report of the medical officer of health/J. Stopford Taylor, upon the suggestions adopted at a meeting of the medical profession held on the 4th Sept., 1882. 6 pp. 8°. *Liverpool, H. Greenwood,* 1882.
Bound with: LIVERPOOL. Notification of infectious diseases. Circular. 8°. *Liverpool,* 1882.

NL 0418178 DNLM

Liverpool. Health Committee.
Report...as to the drainage of courts, cellars..
see under Fitzpatrick, H.

Liverpool. Health Committee.
Report of the medical officer of health, as to the comparative rate of morality
see under Duncan, William Henry.

Liverpool. Health Committee.
Report to the Health Committee of the borough of Liverpool on the sewerage and other works
see under Liverpool. City Engineer.

Liverpool. Health Committee.
Report to the health committee of the town council of the borough of Liverpool comprising a detail of the sanitary operations in the nuisance department
see under Fresh, Thomas.

Liverpool. Health Committee.

Utilisation of refuse and sewerage. Scheme, suggested in July, 1849, by the borough engineer, for the application of the refuse of the town to agricultural improvement and pauper support, as reported by a subcommittee, appointed to consider the subject. 12 pp. 8°. [*Liverpool, H. Greenwood,* 1849.]

NL 0418183 DNLM

Liverpool. Health Dept.
Causes of fever and other zymotic diseases in the city
see under Taylor, John Stopford.

Liverpoo Health dept.
...A century of progress; an account of the development of the Liverpool public health department since 1847. Liverpool [1947?] 24 p. illus., map. 19cm.
At head of title: 1847-1947.

1. 1947.

NL 0418185 NN

Liverpool. Health Dept.

——. Infectious disease. Report of the medical officer of health [J. Stopford Taylor]. 5 pp. 8°. *Liverpool, H. Greenwood,* 1883.

NL 0418186 DNLM

RA
242
.L8B3

Liverpool. Health dept.
... Port sanitary authority. Report of the Medical officer of health as to the work done by the officers ... Liverpool,
v.

NL 0418187 DLC DNLM ICJ RPB DL

Liverpool. Health Dept.

——. Report and evidence of the subcommittee on the causes of the excessive mortality of the town. To the health committee of the borough of Liverpool. xii, 305 pp., 4 l. 8°. *Liverpool, G. McCorquodale & Co.,* 1866.

NL 0418188 DNLM

QW
85
L785r
1914

LIVERPOOL. Health Dept.
Report of the city bacteriologist on the electrical treatment of milk, with details of experimental enquiry and apparatus.
Liverpool, Tinling, 1914.
22 p. illus.
Cover title.
Part of this information was previously given in a report presented to the Health Committee on June 17th, 1913.

NL 0418189 DNLM

VOLUME 336

Liverpool, Health Dept.
Report of the medical officer of health upon the work of the depots for the preparation of humanised sterilized milk for the use of infants whose mothers are unable to suckle them.
= Liverpool. 1904. 23 pp. 8°

G8351 — Milk. Sterilization of. — Infant diet. — Liverpool, Eng. Med.

NL 0418190 MB DL

Liverpool, Health dept.
Report on the health of...Liverpool...
Liverpool, 18-

RA242
.L8B1

NL 0418191 DLC NNC MiD NN MB DNLM

Liverpool. Historic society of Lancashire and Cheshire
see
Historic society of Lancashire and Cheshire, *Liverpool.*

Liverpool. Holy Trinity. Ragged Schools and Holy Trinity Certified Industrial Schools
see Holy Trinity Ragged Schools and Holy Trinity Certified Industrial Schools, Liverpool.

Liverpool. Holy Trinity church.
General report for the year ending December, 1865-67. Liverpool: T. Brakell, 1866-68. 2 pmp. 12°.
In: * C p. v. 1475, no. 13-14.

1. Liverpool, Eng.—Churches: Holy Trinity.
N. Y. P. L. May 19, 1914.

NL 0418194 NN

Liverpool Housing committee.
Artizans' and labourers' dwellings. Description and particulars as to rentals, etc., together with returns prepared by the manager relating to the work of the dwellings for the year 1909. Liverpool: C. Tinling & Co., Ltd., 1910. 86 p., 24 pl., 8 diagr. pap. 8°.
——— Same. (In: Liverpool. Council. Proceedings. 1909/10, v. 2, p. 1491-1646.)

1. Habitations for the working classes, Gt. Br.: England: Liverpool: 1910.
N. Y. P. L. January 3, 1912.

NL 0418195 NN MH

Liverpool Housing Committee.
...Artizans and labourers' dwellings and insanitary property. Report of the Housing Committee, together with returns prepared by the corporation surveyor, city treasurer and controller, the medical officer of health, and the manager. Liverpool: C. Tinling and Co., Ltd., 1913. 134 p. plates. 8°.
At head of title: 25th July, 1913. City of Liverpool.

1. Habitations for the working classes, Gt. Br.: England: Liverpool, 1913.
N. Y. P. L. March 31, 1924.

NL 0418196 NN ViU CtY MH ICJ

Liverpool. Housing committee.
Artizans' & labourers' dwellings & insanitary property: report of the housing committee...
Liverpool, Tinling, 1914.
105 p.

NL 0418197 OCIW

Liverpool. Housing Committee.
Artizans' and labourers' dwellings.
For earlier editions see under Liverpool. Surveyor's Dept.

Liverpool, Housing Committee.
... Housing ... 1914, 1928, 1931, 1934, 1937.
Liverpool, Housing dept., 1918-37
5 v. illus., plates, 24-26½ cm.
At head of title: City of Liverpool.
Title varies.
Filed with this: Programme of inspection, 1923.

NL 0418199 DL NNC NN ICJ

Liverpool. Housing Committee.
Housing of the working classes. Report of the visit of the deputation of the Housing Committee to Glasgow, Manchester, Salford, and London. December 19th, 1901. Liverpool: C. Tinling & Co., 1901. 48 p. 1 fold. plan, 41 pl. (9 fold.) cloth. 8°.
Cover-title.

1. Habitations for the working classes, Gt. Br.
N. Y. P. L. August 23, 1919.

NL 0418200 NN

Liverpool. Housing Committee.
... Housing problems in Liverpool
see under Liverpool University Settlement.

Liverpool. *Housing committee.*
... Preliminary report of the city architect and director of housing on housing and rehousing. (To be submitted to the meeting of the City council to be held on ... the 2nd February, 1944) ... Liverpool, 1943.
75, [1] p. incl. illus. (incl. maps, plans) tables. 24cm.

1. Housing—Liverpool. 2. Labor and laboring classes—Dwellings. 3. Cities and towns—Planning—Liverpool.
45-14230
Library of Congress NA7552.L5 1944

NL 0418202 DLC CtY

Liverpool. *Housing Committee.*
... Programme of inspection and description of Liverpool housing schemes. Ninety-first annual meeting of the British Association for the Advancement of Science, Liverpool, 12th to 19th Sept., 1923. Prepared by order of the Housing Committee ... Liverpool, Housing Dept., Municipal Buildings, 1923.
44 p. illus., 1 pl., maps, plans. 26½cm. *bound* 29cm.
At head of title: City of Liverpool.

NL 0418203 ICJ

710.1
L75r
Liverpool--Housing Committee.
A report of the city architect and director of housing on Speke, a self-contained and protected community unit, a township in the making. to be submitted to the meeting of the City Council to be held on Wednesday, the 23rd October 1946. Liverpool, 1946.
44p. illus., plans. 27cm.

1. Cities and towns--Planning--Liverpool.

NL 0418204 IU NNC NN

Liverpool. Housing committee.
... Speke estate; report of the director of housing on a proposal for the building of a self-contained community unit. (To be submitted to the City council, at its meeting to be held on Wednesday, the 21st day of October, 1936) ... Liverpool, Tinling, 1936.
17 p. 4 fold. maps. 24½cm.

At head of title: 17th October, 1936. City of Liverpool. Housing committee.
1. Housing - Liverpool. I. Title.

NL 0418205 NNC

Liverpool. Industrial Ragged Schools
see Liverpool Industrial Ragged Schools.

Liverpool. Infant Orphan Asylum. Annual reports of the committee to the subscribers. 10.-12., 1868-70. 8°. *Liverpool.* 1869-71.

NL 0418207 DNLM

WX
2
FE5
L75R8r
LIVERPOOL. Infirmary.
Report, list of subscribers, and statement of account, of the Liverpool Infirmary, Lunatic Asylum and Lock Hospital. 1st-102d; 1749-1850. Liverpool.
v. in
Title varies slightly.
Continued by the Report of the Liverpool Royal Infirmary.

I. Liverpool. Lock Hospital
II. Liverpool. Lunatic Asylum

NL 0418209 DNLM

WX
2
FE5
L75I5a
LIVERPOOL. Infirmary for Children.
Annual report.
Liverpool [1851?]-
v.

NL 0418210 DNLM

Liverpool. Inhabitants
see Liverpool. Citizens.

Liverpool. Inspector of Nuisances.
Report of the inspector of nuisances as to the drainage of courts, cellars, insanitary houses, etc.
see under Fitzpatrick, H.

VOLUME 336

MS Eng 1178 v.3 Liverpool. Institute.
Catalogue of the Autograph room, entirely filled with the collection of Mr. William Upcott, of Islington, London; with portraits. Third exhibition, Liverpool mechanics' institution, June and July, 1844.
Liverpool:Printed by D.Marples,Lord-street. [1844] Price sixpence.
cover-title,46p. 21.5cm.,bd.to 31cm.
Each leaf inlaid; bound on leaves 24-47 of a volume lettered on spine: Upcott, Evelyn, Pepys ...

NL 0418213 MH

Liverpool. Institute.
Liverpool institute addresses
see under title

Liverpool. Institute.
Report of the proceedings at the annual meeting of the members...containing the report of the directors.
no. 33.
(1857).
Liverpool, 1858. 16°.
In: *C p. v. 1476.

1. Mechanics' Institutions, Gt. Br.: Eng.: Liverpool.
N. Y. P. L. May 15, 1914.

NL 0418215 NN PPAmP

Liverpool. Institute.
Report of the proceedings of a public meeting held on the 29th January, 1844, in aid of the establishment of a girls' school in connexion with the Liverpool Mechanics' Institution. Liverpool: Smith, Rogerson, and Co., 1844. 23 p. 16°.
In: *C p. v. 1476.

1. Mechanics' Institutions, Gt. Br.: Eng.: Liverpool.
N. Y. P. L. May 15, 1914.

NL 0418216 NN

Liverpool. Institute and School of Art
see Liverpool. Institute.

Liverpool. Institute of hispanic studies
see
Institute of hispanic studies.

Liverpool. Institution for Infectious Diseases, Netherfield House
see Institution for Infectious Diseases, Netherfield House, Liverpool.

Liverpool. International congress of delegated representatives of master cotton spinners' and manufacterers' association, 3d, 1905
see International Cotton Congress, Liverpool 1905.

Liverpool. International cotton conference, 1913
see
International cotton conference, Liverpool, 1913

Liverpool. International exhibition, 1886.
Ascenseurs exposés par M. Louis Gonin ... et la Maison Gabert freres... M. P. Bony ... Ascensurs verticaux ou inclines ... Ascenseurs hydrauliques en rampe ...
Lausanne, G. Bridel, 1886.
26 ⌊5⌋ p.

NL 0418222 MiU

Liverpool. International exhibition, 1886.
Visitors' guide to Liverpool ... specially written for the Executive council of the Liverpool International exhibition. Liverpool, D. Marples & co. limited, printers, 1886.
cover-title, 108 p. illus. 20cm.
On spine: Visitors' illustrated guide to Liverpool.

1. Liverpool—Descr.—Guide-books. I. Title. II. Title: Visitors' illustrated guide to Liverpool.
42-51639
Library of Congress DA690.L8L75

NL 0418223 DLC

Liverpool. Jewish Centre for the Maintenance of literary efforts.
Account of the proceedings at the dedication of the Jewish Centre for the maintenance of literary efforts... Monday, 17th July, 1916. And at the inauguration of its literary activities Sunday, 29th Oct., 1916. With a report of the opening address delivered by Sir Edward Russell.
⌊Liverpool, 1916⌋
28 p.

NL 0418224 OCH

Liverpool. Joint Inquiry Committee on Unemployment among Young Persons in Liverpool
see Joint Inquiry Committee on Unemployment among Young Persons in Liverpool.

Liverpool. Juvenile Employment Committee.
Handbook of employments in Liverpool. Edited by F. J. Marquis...with a preface by Alderman F. J. Leslie... Liverpool: Liverpool Education Committee, 1916. 3 p.l., (i)x–xxvii, 277(1) p. 8°.

1. Occupations.—Choice of, Gt. Br.: Eng.: Liverpool. 2. Labor (Child), Gt. Br.: Eng.: Liverpool. 3. Marquis, F. J., editor.
N. Y. P. L. May 18, 1918.

NL 0418226 NN DL NjP

Liverpool. Juvenile Employment Committee.
...Report. 1st–
Liverpool, 1913– 8°.
At head of title: City of Liverpool. Education Committee.
1914/15 has title: Review of the work...for the year ended 31st July, 1915.

1. Child labor, Gt. Br.: Eng.: Liverpool. 2. Occupations.—Choice of, Gt. Br.: Liverpool. 3. Employment bureaus, Gt. Br.: Eng.: Liverpool.
N. Y. P. L. January 8, 1921.

NL 0418227 NN DL

Liverpool. Juvenile Employment Committee.
Statistics of the Juvenile employment registry for the year
Liverpool, 19 8°.
At head of title: City of Liverpool. Education Committee.
Statistics for the years 1911–15 were published in the Report of the committee for those years.

1. Child labor, Gt. Br.: Eng.: Liverpool. 2. Employment bureaus, Gt. Br.: Eng.: Liverpool.
N. Y. P. L. January 8, 1921.

NL 0418228 NN

Liverpool. Jubilee Exhibition, 1887.
Jamaica at the Liverpool Jubilee Exhibition, 1887, by C. Washington Eves... London: Spottiswoode & Co., 1887. 92 p. front., map, ports. 8°.

303885A. 1. Jamaica. 2. Economic history—West Indies—Jamaica. 3. Exhibitions, Liverpool, 1887—Jamaica exhibit. 4. Eves, Charles Washington, 1838–1899, compiler.
N. Y. P. L. July 16, 1927

NL 0418229 NN

WX 2 FE5 L75L2a LIVERPOOL. Ladies' Charity and the Lying-In Hospital
Annual report.
1st- 1869-
Liverpool.
v. in illus.

NL 0418230 DNLM

BM 296 L5L4.7 Liverpool. Liberal Jewish Congregation.
Bulletin.
[Liverpool]
v. 27 cm. weekly.
Each vol. includes annual report.

NL 0418231 OCH

Liverpool. Libraries, Museums & Arts Committee.
Bulletin. v. 1–6; July 1951–Mar. 1957. Liverpool, Liverpool Corporation.
5 v. illus. 26 cm. quarterly (irregular)
"A journal concerned with material belonging to or connected with the Liverpool Public Libraries, the Liverpool Public Museums and the Walker Art Gallery."
Superseded by the Liverpool bulletin: libraries number; the Liverpool bulletin: museums number; the Liverpool bulletin: Walker Art Gallery.
Vol. 6–8, 1956–60, bound with the Liverpool bulletin: Walker Art Gallery, v. 7–8, 1958/59–1959/60; the Liverpool bulletin: museums number, v. 7–8, 1958–1959/60; and the Liverpool bulletin: libraries number, v. 7–8, 1959–1959/60.
L. C. set imperfect: v. 2, v. 4, no. 3, v. 5, no. 3 wanting.
AS122.L43 71-617412

NL 0418232 DLC IU

DA28 .J .L56 Liverpool. Libraries, Museums & Arts Committee.
Liverpool. Public Libraries, Museums and Art Gallery. Walker Art Gallery.
Kings & queens of England; an exhibition organised by the Libraries, Museums & Arts Committee of the Liverpool City Council in honour of the coronation of Her Majesty, Queen Elizabeth II. Held at the Walker Art Gallery, Liverpool, May 6–Aug. 31, 1953. ⌊Liverpool, 1953⌋

Liverpool. Libraries, Museums and Arts Committee.
The public libraries of Liverpool
see under Liverpool. Public libraries, Museums and Art Gallery.

VOLUME 336

Liverpool. Literary and philosophical society
see
Literary and philosophical society of Liverpool.

Liverpool. Local executive committee. 1903.
City of Liverpool. Handbook compiled for the Congress of the Royal institute of public health. 1903. Issued by the Local executive committee. Ed. by E. W. Hope ... Liverpool, Lea & Nightingale [1903]
xi, 330 p. plates (partly col.) maps, plans. 29½cm.

1. Liverpool. 2. Liverpool—Sanit. affairs. 3. Hygiene, Public. I. Hope, Edward William, ed.

4-10531

Library of Congress RA488.L7R8

NL 0418236 DLC MB MiU OCU ICJ DNLM IaDm

---

381 L7511 Liverpool--Markets committee.
... The Liverpool corporation markets official handbook, describing the facilities afforded by the various markets in the city. Liverpool, Printed and published under the authority of the Liverpool corporation Markets committee by Littlebury bros., ltd. [1938]
95p. illus.
At head of title: 1938. City of Liverpool.
Advertising matter included in paging.

1. Liverpool--Markets.

NL 0418237 IU

Liverpool. Markets Committee.
...Report of the superintendent of markets.

Liverpool, 8°.

1. Markets, Gt. Br.: England: Liverpool.
N. Y. P. L. October 23, 1924

NL 0418238 NN MiU

Liverpool. Markets Committee.
A short description of the markets and market system...
see under Newlands, James, 1813-1871.

Liverpool. Markets Committee. Abattoir Meats and Cattle Markets Sub-committee.
The new Stanley abattoir meat and cattle markets, opened by the Right Honourable the Earl of Derby, K/G. 1931.
23 p.

NL 0418240 DNAL

WX 2 FE5 L75M4r **LIVERPOOL. Maternity Hospital**
Registrar's report.
Liverpool, 19
v.

NL 0418241 DNLM

Liverpool. Mayer Museum
see
Liverpool. Public Libraries, Museums and Art Gallery. *Museum.*

Liverpool. Mechanics' School of Arts
see **Liverpool. Institute.**

Liverpool. Medical Officer of Health.
Report of the Medical officer of Health
see under Liverpool. Health Dept.

Liverpool. Merchants.
Address [and petitions to the House of commons] 1808.

NL 0418245 MiU-C

Liverpool. Merchants.
Correspondence respecting the Guano Islands of Lobos de Tierra & Lobos de Fuera
see under Gt. Brit. Foreign Office.

Liverpool. Merchants.

Law of principal and factor. Statement of its defects, and the remedy, read at a meeting of deputations from the commercial associations of Liverpool, appointed to consider the state of the law, on the 26th January, 1842, and ordered to be printed. Liverpool, Printed by J. Mawdsley [1842?]

Liverpool. Merchants.
... To the right honourable the lords spiritual and temporal of the United Kingdom of Great Britain and Ireland
see under Liverpool. Citizens.

Kress Room Liverpool. Merchants and ship-owners.
Statements on behalf of the merchants and ship-owners of Liverpool, rate-payers to the dock estate, on the proposed application to Parliament, by the dock committee, for an act for the new constitution of the dock trust... [Liverpool, J. and J. Mawdsley, 1836]
[4] p. 32 cm.

Caption title
Indorsed: Liverpool dock bill. Petition and statement on behalf of the dock rate-payers.

NL 0418249 MH-BA

Liverpool. Mersey docks and harbour board
see
Mersey docks and harbour board, Liverpool.

Liverpool. Merseyside civic society
see
Merseyside civic society, *Liverpool.*

Liverpool. Museum
see
Liverpool. Public libraries, museums and art gallery. (Museum)

Liverpool. Music library.
See
Liverpool. Public libraries, museums, and art gallery. Music library.

Liverpool. New Scots Church. Committee of Management.
Correspondence...with the Rev. David Thom. Liverpool, 1824.
41 p. 8°. [In Biographical Pamphlets, vol. 78]

NL 0418254 CtY

Liverpool. New Scots Church. Committee of Management.
Further Correspondence...with the Rev. David Thom. Liverpool, 1825.
26 p. 8°. [In Biographical Pamphlets, vol. 78]

NL 0418255 CtY

Liverpool. Northern Hospital
see Liverpool Northern Hospital.

Liverpool. Observatory.
see Liverpool Observatory, Birkenhead, Eng.

Liverpool. Old Church
see **Liverpool. St. Nicholas' Church.**

Liverpool. Ophthalmic infirmary.
The practice in the Liverpool ophthalmic infirmary for the year 1834...Liverpool, Longman, 1835.
55 p.

NL 0418259 PPC

Liverpool. Ordinances.
Abstract of an act ... intituled, An act for the improvement, good government, and police regulation of the borough of Liverpool. Liverpool Mawdsley [1842]
48 p. Sm. 8°.

NL 0418260 MB

VOLUME 336

Liverpool. Ordinances.
Bye-laws with respect to new buildings, and with respect to ashpits in connection with buildings, and with respect to the removal of house refuse. Liverpool: C. Tinling and Co., Ltd., 1910. 9 p. 8°.

1. Building construction.—Jurisprudence, Gt. Br.: England: Liverpool: 1910.
N. Y. P. L. January 3, 1912.

NL 0418261 NN

Liverpool Ordinances.
Bye-laws with respect to the drainage of buildings and to water closets in connection with buildings. Liverpool: C. Tinling and Co., Ltd., 1904. 9 p. 8°.

1. Building construction.—Jurisprudence, Gt. Br.: England: Liverpool: 1904.
N. Y. P. L. January 3, 1912.

NL 0418262 NN

Liverpool, Ordinances.
----Acts of Parliament and orders regulating the sale of milk.... Liverpool,C. Tinling and Co., ltd., 1907.
23 p. 24 cm.

NL 0418263 DL

LIVERPOOL. Ordinances.
...Bye-laws... Liverpool: C.Tinling & Co., Ltd., 192
pam. col'd plan. 24cm.

1. Municipal charters and ordinances—Gt.Br.—Eng.—Liverpool.

NL 0418264 NN

LIVERPOOL. *Ordinances.*
By-laws respecting slaughter-houses.
Liverpool. Harris & co. [1849.] 10 pp. 8°.

B 9567

NL 0418265 MB

Liverpool, *Ordinances.*
Children trading in streets. Regulations made by the corporation pursuant to the Liverpool Corporation Act, 1902.
= Liverpool. 1903. 12 pp. 8°.

G8353 — Peddling and itinerant industries. — Children. Employment. — Liverpool, Eng. Labor.

NL 0418266 MB

Liverpool Ordinances.
...Extract from the Liverpool Corporation Act, 1913, being Part VII. thereof, relating to superannuation. Liverpool: C. Tinling & Co., Ltd., 1914. 23 p. 8°.

1. Pensions (Old age), Gt. Br.: Eng.: Liverpool.
N. Y. P. L. April 16, 1919.

NL 0418267 NN

Liverpool. Ordinances.
Liverpool building act, 1842, as amended by subsequent statutes, together with sections of other local acts relating to buildings, and bye-laws with respect to buildings and streets. With an index. [Liverpool,] 1898. 115, vii p. pap. 8°.

1. Building construction.—Jurisprudence, Gt. Br.: England: Liverpool: 1898. 2. Streets.—Jurisprudence, Gt. Br.: England: Liverpool: 1898.
N. Y. P. L. January 3, 1912.

NL 0418268 NN PU

Liverpool. Our Lady and St. Nicholas' Church
see **Liverpool. St. Nicholas' Church.**

Liverpool. Paradise St. chapel.
Lectures delivered in Paradise street chapel, Liverpool, in answer to a course of lectures against Unitarianism, in Christ church, Liverpool, by thirteen clergymen of the Church of England. Liverpool [etc.] 1839.
26 cm.

NL 0418270 CtY

Liverpool. Parochial Chapel of Our Lady and St. Nicholas
see **Liverpool. St. Nicholas' Church.**

Liverpool. Passenger Transport Dept.
Liverpool corporation passenger transport, report of the general manager. Liverpool.
v. fold. maps, tables, fold. diagrs.
Annual.
At head of title: City of Liverpool.
Title varies: Liverpool. Corporation tramways. Liverpool corporation tramways and omnibuses. Liverpool corporation passenger transport.
1914-1915 never published.

No more published.

NL 0418273 CU ICU MB PU MiD

Liverpool, Police courts.
Probation of offenders act, 1907, as amended by the criminal justice act, 1925. Report of the Probation committee of the justices upon the operation of the act, for the year 1928. n.t.p. n.p., [1929?].

8 p. table.

NL 0418274 MH-L

Liverpool, Police courts.
Report of the Theatres and public entertainments committee of the justices, for the year 1927/28, 1928. n.t.p. n.p., [1928?]-[1929].

2 nos. table.

NL 0418275 MH-L

Liverpool. Polska Szkoła Architektury
see **Liverpool. University.** *Polish School of Architecture.*

Liverpool. Port sanitary authority.
... Port sanitary authority. Report of the Medical officer of health as to the work done by the officers ...
see under Liverpool. Health dept.

Liverpool. Port sanitary authority.
Hope, E W.
... Report on actinomycosis (ray fungus disease) and tuberculosis in imported South American ox tongues, by E. W. Hope ... Liverpool, C. Tinling and co., ltd., 1914.

Liverpool. Post-war redevelopment advisory (special) committee.
City of Liverpool; illustrated brochure issued in connection with the introductory Town planning exhibition to be held at Radiant house, Bold street, Liverpool... Monday, 30th June to Saturday, 26th July 1947. [Liverpool] Post-war redevelopment advisory (special) committee, 1947. 46 p. illus. 24cm.

Cover-title: Town planning exhibition, 1947. Liverpool.

1. Cities—Plans—Gt. Br.—Eng. —Liverpool.
N. Y. P. L. March 23, 1951

NL 0418279 NN NcU NNC

Liverpool. *Post-war Redevelopment Advisory (Special) Committee.*
Report on the reconstruction proposals for the city. 1st-June 1946-
Liverpool.
v. maps (part fold.) 24 cm.

1. Cities and towns—Planning—Liverpool.

NA9187.L5A35 58-16130

NL 0418280 DLC

Liverpool. Public health department.
see Liverpool. Health Dept.

Liverpool. Public libraries, museums and art gallery.
... Annual reports ...
185
Liverpool, 185 -19
v. plates, ports., fold. plan. 24cm.
At head of title: 1933/34- City of Liverpool.
Report year ends August 31, 185 -1870/71; March 31, 1924/25-
63d-71st reports, 1915-1924, not published. Summaries for these years are contained in 72d report, 1924/25.
Title varies: 185 Annual report of the committee of the Free public library, and the Derby museum ...
186 -1866/67, 1872-1876, Annual report of the committee of the Free public library, museum, and gallery of arts ...

1867/68, Annual report of the committee of the Free public library, museum, gallery of arts and education ...
1868/69-1870/71, Annual report of the committee of the Free public library, museum and schools ...
1877-1894, Annual report of the committee of the Free public library, museum and Walker art gallery ...
1895-1909, Annual report of the committee of the Public libraries, museums, and art gallery ...
1910-1933/34, Annual reports to the Libraries, museums, and arts committee ...
1934/35- Annual reports to the Libraries, museums, arts and music committee ...

10-15444 Revised
Library of Congress Z792.L33

NL 0418283 DLC LU CU PU ICJ NjP NN MB MiU OCl PPPM

Liverpool. Public Libraries, Museums and Art Gallery.
Catalogue of exhibition, recording Merseyside at Bluecoat Chambers Corporation of Liverpool Art Gallery, Oct. 8th-Nov. 10th 1945; a record of pictures by Merseyside artists who have interpreted various features of the city and its surroundings as they see them. [Liverpool, 1945]
[28] p. (p. 7-27 illus.) 16 x 23 cm.

1. Paintings, British — Exhibitions. 2. Liverpool — Descr. & trav. — Views.
ND471.L5L5 759.2 47-27946*

NL 0418284 DLC

VOLUME 336

Liverpool. Public libraries, museums and art gallery.
The city of Liverpool, public museums, by Douglas A. Allan...director. Liverpool printed by C. Tinling & co., ltd.,1937.
31, (1) p. incl. front., illus. 19 cm.

NL 0418285 DSI

Z792 L335 Liverpool. Public Libraries, Museums and Art Gallery.
Liverpool Public Libraries centennary, 1850-1950. Liverpool, 1950.
39p. illus. 24½cm.

1. Liverpool. Public Libraries, Museums and Art Gallery.
I. Title.

NL 0418286 NBuG CaBVaU MdBP MB MoU NN LU MH InU

LIVERPOOL. Public libraries, museums and art gallery.
Liverpool public libraries; programme and guide.
Liverpool. v. illus. 24cm.

Annual.
For later file see its: Liverpool city libraries; programme and guide.

1. Libraries--Gt. Br.--Eng.--Liverpool. I. Title.

NL 0418287 NN

Liverpool. Public libraries, museums and art gallery.
The public libraries of Liverpool. Liverpool, Libraries, museums, arts and music committee, public libraries, 1939.
36 p. illus. (incl. ports.) fold. map. 24½cm.

1. Liverpool. Public libraries, museums and art gallery. Library. I. Title.

Library of Congress Z792.L335 39-22225
(2) 027.44272

NL 0418288 DLC ICU

Q 764
[Liverpool. Public Libraries, Museums and Art Gallery]
Liverpool reference libraries. [Liverpool? 1950]

NL 0418289 MH

Liverpool. Public Libraries, Museums and Art Gallery.
...Reports, on fitting up the new building, from the librarian, the curator, and the Rev. H. H. Higgins... Liverpool: T. Brakell, 1859. 10 f. 2 plans. f°.

At head of title: Liverpool Public Library and Derby Museum.

1. Libraries—Gt. Br.—Eng.—Liverpool. 2. Museums—Gt. Br.—Eng.—Liverpool.
N. Y. P. L. April 17, 1925

NL 0418290 NN

Liverpool. Public libraries, museums and art gallery. Library.
Brownbill, John, *comp.*
A calendar of that part of the collection of deeds and papers of the Moore family of Bankhall, co. Lanc., now in the Liverpool public library. By J. Brownbill ... With an appendix containing a calendar of a further portion of the same collection, now in the University of Liverpool School of local history and records. By Kathleen Walker ... [Liverpool] Printed for the Record society in co-operation with the Library, museum and arts committee of the Liverpool corporation, and the University of Liverpool School of local history and records 1913.

Liverpool. Public libraries, museums and art gallery. *Library.*
... Catalogue of books (fiction excepted) in all the branch libraries, compiled under the direction of the chief librarian, by W. E. Jones, librarian, Lending libraries' depot. Liverpool, Public library, 1925.
4 p. l., 751 p. illus. 25 cm.
At head of title: Liverpool public libraries.
—— ... Catalogue of works of non-fiction added to the lending libraries, 1925–1935. Liverpool, Libraries, museums, arts and music committee, Public libraries, 1935.
vi, 366 p. 24½ cm.

At head of title: City of Liverpool public libraries.
"Compiled under the direction of the chief librarian by W. S. Haugh."
Z921.L333 1935
—— ... Catalogue of works of non-fiction (excluding music and foreign literature) added to the lending libraries, 1935–1950. Liverpool, Libraries, museums and arts committee, Central public libraries, 1952.
626 p. map. 25 cm.
At head of title: City of Liverpool public libraries.
Z921.L333 1952
I. Jones, William E. II. Haugh, William Simon, 1910–
Z921.L333 26-11526 rev

NL 0418293 DLC NN ICJ MB OCl PPT IU

Liverpool. Public libraries, museums and art gallery. *Library.*
... Catalogue of the central lending library, William Brown street. Comp. under the direction of the chief librarian. New and enl. ed. Liverpool, C. Tinling & co., ltd., 1911.
iv, 386 p. 22½cm.
George T. Shaw, chief librarian.

I. Shaw, George T.
13-12901
Library of Congress Z921.L33C

NL 0418294 DLC

Liverpool. Public libraries, Museums and Art Gallery. Library.
Catalogue of the Liverpool free public library...1852. Liverpool [1852]
25.5 x 19 cm.

NL 0418295 CtY

Liverpool. Public libraries, museums and art gallery. *Library.*
Catalogue of the Liverpool free public library ... Liverpool, Printed by G. M'Corquodale & co., 1855.
vi, 278, viii p. 25½ x 19cm.

10-31229
Library of Congress Z921.L33 1855

NL 0418296 DLC

Liverpool. Public libraries, museums and art gallery. *Library.*
Catalogue of the Liverpool free public library ... Containing the books received up to December 31st, 1860. Liverpool, J. B. Williams & co., printers, 1862.
3 p. l., 498, xix p. 25½ x 19½cm.

CA 11-93 Unrev'd
Library of Congress Z921.L33 1860

NL 0418297 DLC

Liverpool. Public libraries, museums and art gallery. *Library.*
Catalogue of the Liverpool free public library ... Reference department ... Liverpool, J. R. Williams, printers, 1872–92.
3 v. front. (v. 2) 28cm.
Dictionary catalog.
Part 2 published by D. Marples & co., limited; pt. 3 published at the Free public library.
Three printed supplements to pt. 1, listing books received 1871/2, 1873/5 and 1876/7, are incorporated in pt. 2. Part 3 published 1892 supersedes a) the original pt. 3 published 1884 which contained books received 1881/83 and b) pt. 4 published 1887 which contained books received 1884/86.

CONTENTS.—[pt. 1] Books received up to Dec. 31st, 1870. Comp. by S. Huggins. 1872.—pt. 2. Books received from Jan., 1871 to Dec., 1880. Comp. under the direction of the chief librarian [Peter Cowell] 1881.—pt. 3. Books received from 1881 to 1891. Comp. under the direction of the chief librarian [Peter Cowell] 1892.

1. Catalogs, Dictionary. I. Huggins, Samuel, 1811–1885. II. Cowell, Peter, 1838–1909.
11—7045
Library of Congress Z921.L33 1892

NL 0418299 DLC MH CtY MB NIC NN NjP NjNbS

Liverpool. Public libraries, museums and art gallery. Library.
Catalogue of the Music library
see under Liverpool. Public libraries, Museums and Art Gallery. Music Library.

Liverpool. Public Libraries, Museums and Art Gallery. *Library.*
Catalogue of the Roscoe centenary exhibition, held in the exhibition hall of the Public Library, Liverpool, June 30th to July 18th, 1931. Liverpool, Libraries, Museums and Arts Committee, 1931.
15 p. plates, port. 18 cm.

1. Roscoe, William, 1753–1831. 2. Art—Liverpool—Catalogs. 3. Roscoe, William, 1753–1831—Bibl.

D15.R6L5 923.242 48-30545*

NL 0418301 DLC NN

Z921 .L44C 1885 Liverpool. Public libraries, museums & art gallery. Library.
... Catalogue of the South lending library ... New and revised edition ... Liverpool, A. Russell & Bayley, 1885.
viii, 282 p.

NL 0418302 ICU

Liverpool. Public Libraries, Museums and Art Gallery. Library.
Catalogue of works of nonfiction (excluding music and foreign literature)
see its ...Catalogue of books (fiction excepted)

Liverpool. Public libraries, museums and art gallery. *Library.*
... The centenary of the Liverpool and Manchester railway, 1830–1930; a list of printed & illustrated material in the Reference library. City of Liverpool, Libraries, museums and arts committee, 1930.
35 p. front., 2 illus. 21½cm.
At head of title: Liverpool public libraries.
"Compiled under the direction of the chief librarian [George H. Parry] by W. A. Phillips."
1. Liverpool and Manchester railway—Bibl. I. Phillips, W. A. II. Parry, George H. III. Title.
30-20447
Library of Congress Z7235.G7L8
016.385

NL 0418304 DLC CtY MH NN MB OCl

VOLUME 336

Liverpool. Public libraries, museums and art gallery. *Library.*
Ceremonies connected with the opening of the building for a free public library and museum, presented by William Brown, esq. to the town of Liverpool. Liverpool, G. McCorquodale & co., printers, 1861.
74 p. front. (plan) illus., pl. 22cm.
Title vignette (port.)
10-9400
Library of Congress Z792.L331

NL 0418305 DLC NN

Liverpool. Public libraries, museums, and art gallery. *Library.*
Ex bibliotheca Hugh Frederick Hornby. Catalogue of the art library bequeathed by Hugh Frederick Hornby, esq., of Liverpool, to the Free public library of the city of Liverpool. Compiled under the direction of the chief librarian by Henry E. Curran and Charles Robertson. Liverpool, Library, museum and arts committee, 1906.
5 p. l., 648 p. 28cm.
Alphabetical author catalog, annotated. Foreword by William A. Forwood, chairman; introduction by Peter Cowell, chief librarian.
"Index of artists": p. [575]-648.
1. Illustrated books—Bibl.—Catalogs. 2. Illustrators. 3. Engravers. I. Hornby, Hugh Frederick. II. Curran, Henry E., comp. III. Robertson, Charles, joint comp. IV. Cowell, Peter, 1838-1909, ed.
Library of Congress Z1023.L78 7—3179

NL 0418306 DLC NjNbS IU ICJ MB NBuU CtY

Liverpool. Public libraries, museums and art gallery. *Library.*
First supplement to the catalogue of the Liverpool free public library ... Reference department. Containing the books received from Jan. 1st, 1871, to Dec. 31st, 1872. With an appendix. Comp. under the authority of the Council, by Samuel Huggins. Liverpool, J. R. Williams & co., printers, 1873.
3 p. l., 105 p. 23cm.
I. Huggins, Samuel, 1811-1885.
CA 11-91 Unrev'd
Library of Congress Z921.L33 1873

NL 0418307 DLC

Liverpool. Public Libraries, Museums and Art Gallery. Library.
Hand-list of books on architecture in the Reference Department, William Brown street. Liverpool, The Free Public Library, 1894.
[4], 51 p. 22cm.

NL 0418308 ICJ NN MB

Liverpool. Public libraries, museums and art gallery. *Library.*
... Hand-list of books on architecture and the building trades in the reference department ... Liverpool, The Free public library, 1896.
4 p. l., 51 p., 2 l., [53]-81 p. 22cm.
Issued in 2 pt., 1894-96, each with special t.-p. Pt. [1]: ... Hand-list of books on architecture in the reference department ... Pt. [2]: ... Hand-list of books on the building trades in the reference department ... being a continuation of the "Hand-list of books on architecture."
——— Supplement. Liverpool, The Free public library, 1902.
2 p. l., 18 p. 21cm.
1. Architecture—Bibl. 2. Building—Bibl.
11-7019-20
Library of Congress Z921.L331A

NL 0418309 DLC IU ICJ NN PPD

Liverpool. Public libraries, museums and art gallery. *Library.*
... Hand-list of books on the decorative arts in the reference department ... Liverpool, The Free public library, 1899.
2 p. l., 113 p. 21½cm.
——— Supplement. Liverpool, The Free public library, 1902.
2 p. l., 17 p. 21½cm.
1. Decoration and ornament—Bibl.
11-7017-8
Library of Congress Z921.L331D

NL 0418310 DLC PPD ICJ NN

Liverpool. Public libraries, museums and art gallery. *Library.*
... Hand-list of reference works. [Liverpool, Northern publishing co., ltd., 1910]
35 p. 22cm.
Caption title.
At head of title: Liverpool public libraries. Reference department.
1. Reference books—Bibl.
Library of Congress Z921.L331R 11-1950

NL 0418311 DLC ICJ

Liverpool. Public libraries, museums and art gallery. *Library.*
... Liverpool prints and documents; catalogue of maps, plans, views, portraits, memoirs, literature &c. in the reference library relating to Liverpool and serving to illustrate its history, biography, administration, commerce and general condition and progress from earliest times. Comp. under the direction of the chief librarian. Liverpool, Library, museum and arts committee, Reference library, 1908.
viii, 374 p. 25½cm.
Introduction signed: Peter Cowell, chief librarian.
1. Liverpool—Bibl. 2. Liverpool—Descr.—Views—Catalogs. 3. Liverpool—Biog.—Portraits—Catalogs. I. Cowell, Peter, 1838-1909.
Library of Congress Z2024.L7L6 11-1951

NL 0418312 DLC NBuU CtY ICJ NN

Liverpool. Public libraries, museums and art gallery. Library.
Liverpool Public Libraries centennary, 1850-1950
see under Liverpool. Public Libraries, Museums and Art Gallery.

Liverpool. Public Libraries, Museums and Art Gallery. *Library.*
Liverpool Public Libraries. Descriptive handbook with illustrations & plans. Liverpool, Public Library, 1912.
[2], 124 p. incl. plates, ports., plans, tables. front. 26 x 19cm.

NL 0418314 ICJ OrCS DLC-P4 MiU

Liverpool. Public libraries, Museums and Art Gallery. Library.
Liverpool public libraries; programme and guide
see under Liverpool. Public libraries, museums and art gallery.

027.242 L785ℓ Liverpool. Public Libraries, Museums and Art Gallery. Library.
Proceedings of the one-day technical information conference, October 27th, 1955, leading to the formation of LADSIRLAC (Liverpool and District Scientific, Industrial and Research Library Advisory Council), together with a survey of the use made of the Liverpool Technical Library. Liverpool, Central Public Libraries, 1955.
36p. 25cm.
Cover title: Liverpool Technical Library. Conference proceedings and survey of its services.
"List of periodicals etc. required by local industry": p. 33-36.

NL 0418317 IU NNC

Liverpool. Public libraries, Museums and Art Gallery. Library.
Liverpool reference libraries
see under [Liverpool. Public Libraries Museums and Art Gallery]

Liverpool. Public Libraries, Museums, and Art Gallery. Library.
Report of the City Librarian on his visit to the United States as guest of the American government. Liverpool, 1955.
14 p.
Title on cover: American impressions.
1. Libraries - U. S. I. Title: American impressions.

NL 0418319 NNC NN ViW

Z 79 .L 768 LIVERPOOL. PUBLIC LIBRARIES, MUSEUMS, AND ART GALLERY. Library.
Special catalogue of prose fiction in the Liverpool free public library, established by the mayor, aldermen and burgesses, 1850. Reference department. Liverpool, A. Russell, 1876.
58p.
Inserted: presentation slip from the Library, museum and arts committee, to the Newberry library, dated Sept. 27, 1877.

NL 0418320 ICN NjP

Liverpool. Public libraries, museums and art gallery. *Library.*
Third supplement to the catalogue of the Liverpool free public library ... Reference department. Containing the books received from Jan. 1st, 1876, to Dec. 31st, 1877. Liverpool, A. Russell, printer, 1878.
4 p. l., 134 p. 28cm.
Comp. by the librarian, Peter Cowell.
I. Cowell, Peter, 1838-1909.
CA 11-92 Unrev'd
Library of Congress Z921.L33 1878

NL 0418321 DLC

Liverpool. Public libraries, museums and art gallery. *Library. Commercial reference library.*
A guide to the contents of the commercial books, directories, periodicals, reports, gazetteers, &c., available at the Commercial reference library, A3, Exchange buildings, Liverpool ... Liverpool, Libraries, museums & arts committee, 1931.
86 p., 1 l. front. 21½cm.
"Compiled under the direction of the chief librarian [George H. Parry] by George Halsall."
"Alphabetical index to commercial subjects" with class numbers: p. 9-82.
Z921.L34 1931

——... Recent additions to the Commercial reference library, A3, Exchange buildings. Supplement to "Business information handbook." Liverpool, Libraries, museums and arts committee, 1932.
15 p. 21½cm.
At head of title: Liverpool public libraries.
1. Commerce—Bibl.—Catalogs. 2. Classification—Books—Commerce. I. Halsall, George.
32-1904 Revised
Library of Congress Z921.L35
016.38

NL 0418323 DLC CtY DSI

Liverpool. Public libraries, museums, and art gallery. *Library.* Commercial reference library.
... Handbook to the Commercial reference library, A3 Exchange buildings, containing an index to commercial subjects, a catalogue of books and government papers in the library on commerce, shipping and related subjects, telegraphic codes, maps, British and foreign directories, periodicals, &c., comp. under the direction of the chief librarian. Liverpool, Libraries, museums and arts committee, 1920.
At head of title: Corporation of Liverpool. Free public libraries.
Mounted photograph of Commercial reference library on cover.
George T. Shaw, chief librarian.
Classified (Dewey decimal) with index of subjects.
1. Commerce—Bibl. 2. Classification—Books—Comm. 3. Classification, Decimal. 4. Catalogs, Classified (Dewey decimal) I. Shaw, George Thomas. II. Title.
21—7873
Library of Congress Z921.L33Co

NL 0418325 DLC ICJ OCl OU MB

VOLUME 336

Liverpool. Public Libraries, Museums and Art Gallery. *Library. Picton Reference Library.*
Select list of general dictionaries. Liverpool, 1950.
52 p. 20 cm.
Cover title.

1. Encyclopedias and dictionaries—Bibl.

Z7004.D5L58 016.413 53-16959

NL 0418326 DLC MB

Liverpool. Public Libraries, Museums and Art Gallery. *Library. Picton Reference Library.*
United States of America; select list of books in the Picton Reference Library ... Liverpool, 1951.
54 p. 24 cm.

1. U. S.—Bibl.—Catalogs.

Z1207.L68 016.9173 52-18706 ‡

NL 0418327 DLC NN MB

Liverpool. Public libraries, museums and art gallery. *Library. South district branch*
see
Liverpool. Public libraries, museums and art gallery *Library. Toxteth branch.*

Liverpool. Public libraries, museums and art gallery. *Library. Toxteth branch.*
Catalogue of the Free lending library ... of Liverpool, for the South district ... Liverpool, Printed by T. Brakell, 1857.
4 p. l., [7]-132 p. 21½cm.

10-31230

Library of Congress Z921.L33T 1857

NL 0418329 DLC

A111A
L75B
Liverpool. Public Libraries, Museums and Art Gallery. Museum.
Bulletin. v.1-3,no.2; Aug. 1897-May 1901. Liverpool.
1 v. illus. 26cm.

NL 0418330 CtY CU

Liverpool. Public libraries, museums and art gallery. Museum.
Catalogue of an exhibition of ivory carvings lent by the City of Liverpool public museums, mostly from the Mayer-Fejervary collection. London, Published by the Trustees of the British museum, 1954. 20 p. 3 illus. 22cm.
At head of title: British museum. Department of British and medieval antiquities.

1. Ivories—Collections—Gt. Br.—Eng.—Liverpool. I. British museum. Dept. of. British and medieval antiquities.

NL 0418331 NN DDO

Liverpool. Public Libraries, Museums and Art Gallery. *Museum.*
Catalogue of mediæval & later antiquities contained in the Mayer Museum, including the Mather collection of miniatures and medals relating to the Bonaparte family, by Charles T. Gatty, curator [Mayer Museum] Liverpool, G. G. Walmsley, 1883.
viii, 108 p. 20 plates. 29 cm.
Includes bibliographies.

1. Art—Liverpool—Catalogs. 2. Bonaparte family. I. Gatty, Charles Tindal.

N1410.A58 63-57270

NL 0418332 DLC NcGU N PBL NBuG DDO MB

913.3
L75c2
Liverpool. Public libraries, museums, and art gallery--Museum.
... Catalogue of the Mayer collection. Part I. The Egyptian, Babylonian, and Assyrian antiquities By Charles T. Gatty ... Pub. by order of the committee. 2d and rev. ed. London, Printed by Bradbury, Agnew & co., 1879.
83p. illus.

At head of title: Liverpool free public library, museum and gallery of art.

NL 0418333 IU DI-GS NBB NN NIC

Liverpool. Public libraries, museums, and art gallery. (Museum)

Codex Fejérváry-Mayer.
Codex Fejérváry-Mayer; manuscrit mexicain précolombien des Free Public museums de Liverpool (M 12014) publié en chromophotographie par le duc de Loubat ... Paris [Imprimé par P. Renouard] 1901.

DS52
.L76
(Or)
LIVERPOOL. PUBLIC LIBRARIES,MUSEUMS AND ART GALLERY. Museum. 5
Handbook and guide to the Aegean and Hittite collections on exhibition in the Public museums, Liverpool... (1st ed.) [Liverpool,Daily post printers,1931.
31 p. IV pl.incl.front.,map. 21½cm.
Preface signed:Douglas A.Allan,director of museums.

1.Islands of the Aegean--Antiq 2.Hittites.

NL 0418335 ICU

Liverpool. Public Libraries, Museums and Art Gallery. Museum.
Handbook and guide to the British birds...
see under Clubb, Joseph Albert.

Liverpool. Public libraries, Museums and Art Galery. Museum.
Handbook and guide to the Egyptian collection on exhibition in the Main hall of the Museums, Liverpool... Liverpool, C. Tinling & co., 1923.
2 p.l., 47 p. 12 pl., plan. 24 cm.
1. Egypt - Antiq. - Catalogs.

NL 0418337 CU

Liverpool.Public libraries, museums and art gallery. Museum.
Handbook and guide to the replicas and casts of Manx crosses on exhibition in the free public museums, Liverpool... 2d ed. [Liverpool] 1920.
19 p. plates. 22 cm.

1.Cross and crosses - Exhibitions.

NL 0418338 NjP MH

DA
670
.M1
L78h
Liverpool. Public Libraries, Museums and Art Gallery. Museum.
Handbook and guide to the replicas and casts of Manx crosses on exhibition in the Public Museums, Liverpool. 3d ed. Liverpool, Daily Post Printers, 1930.
22p. 4 plates. 22cm.
Imperfect: p.[1],-12,15-16,21-22 mutilated.

1. Cross and crosses - Isle of Man.
2. Man, Isle of - Antiq.

NL 0418339 NRU NNC

Liverpool. Public libraries, museums and art gallery. *Museum.*
Handbook and guide to the shipping gallery in the Public museums, Liverpool ... (1st ed.) [Liverpool, Printed by C. Tinling & co., ltd.] 1932-35.
2 v. fronts., plates. 21½ cm.
The preparation of this handbook is largely the work of Charles Carter. The responsibility for the steamship section is mainly that of Douglas A. Allan, director of museums. *cf.* Pref.

1. Ships. 2. Ship models. 3. Ship-building—Hist. I. Carter, Charles, 1906- II. Allan, Douglas Alexander, 1896-

VM6.L5A5 1932 623.8074 39-20821 rev

NL 0418340 DLC CtY

Liverpool. Public libraries, Museums and Art Gallery. Museum.
The Mayer papyri A & B
see under Papyri Mayer.

Liverpool. Public libraries, museums and art gallery. Museum.
Museum talk about animals which have no bones
see under Higgins, Henry Hugh, 1814-1893.

Liverpool. Public libraries, museums and art gallery. Museum.

Wright, Bryce M'Murdo.
Native silica, a treatise upon a series of specimens of quartz, rock crystal, chalcedony, agates and jaspers, as well as other earthy and metalliferous minerals (economic and decorative), with a chapter upon the formation of agates, cutting, polishing and staining, with a descriptive catalogue of the specimens forming the collection of the late Right Hon. the Earl of Derby, K. G., bequeathed by him to the Liverpool Free museum, by Bryce Wright ... London, Wyman & sons, limited, 1894.

Liverpool. Public libraries, Museums and Art Gallery. Museum.
The natural history of Sokatra and Abd el-Kuri
see under Forbes, Henry Ogg, 1851-1932, ed.

Liverpool. Public libraries, museums and art gallery. Museum.
Picton, *Sir* James Allanson, 1805-1889.
Primeval man. A lecture illustrative of the prehistoric remains in the ethnographical collection of the Liverpool museum. By J. A. Picton ... Liverpool, G. G.Walmsley, 1881.

VOLUME 336

Liverpool. Public libraries, museums and art gallery. *Museum.*
Synopsis of an arrangement of invertebrate animals in the Free public museum of Liverpool; with introduction; by the Rev. Henry H. Higgins ... Liverpool, Printed by D. Marples, 1874.
xix, [1], 104 p. front. 22cm. (Proceedings of the Literary and philosophical society of Liverpool. no. XXVIII (appendix))
Read before the ... society ... October, 1873.
1. Zoological specimens—Collection and preservation. 2. Invertebrates. I. Higgins, Henry Hugh, 1814-1893.
17-14214
Library of Congress AS122.L41 no. 28

NL 0418346 DLC ICJ IU MB MdBP PPAmP OCl MiU

Liverpool. Public libraries, museums and art gallery. *Museum.*
Synopsis of an arrangement of invertebrate animals in the Free public museum of Liverpool; with introduction; by the Rev. Henry H. Higgins ... 2d ed., with additions and appendix. Liverpool, Printed by D. Marples & co., limited, 1880.
xxi, [1], 105, x, [1] p. front., diagr. 21½cm.
Read before the Literary and philosophical society of Liverpool, October, 1873.
1. Zoological specimens—Collection and preservation. 2. Invertebrates. I. Higgins, Henry Hugh, 1814-1893.
11-33499
Library of Congress QL67.L6

NL 0418347 DLC CtY PPWa

Liverpool. Public libraries, museums and art gallery. Museum. Mss. 11162.
see
Papyri Mayer

Liverpool. Public libraries, museums and art gallery. Museum. Mss. 11186.
see
Papyri Mayer

Liverpool. Public libraries, museums and art gallery. Museum. Mss. (M 12014)
Codex Fejérváry-Mayer.
Codex Fejérváry-Mayer: an old Mexican picture manuscript in the Liverpool free public museums (12014/M) Pub. at the expense of His Excellency the Duke of Loubat ... elucidated by Dr. Eduard Seler ... Berlin and London [Edinburgh, Printed by T. and A. Constable] 1901-02.

Liverpool. Public Libraries, Museums and Art Gallery. *Music Library.*
Catalogue of music in the Liverpool Public Libraries. With an introd. by A. K. Holland. Liverpool, Libraries, Museums and Arts Committee, 1933.
vi, 874 p. 19 cm.
"Compiled under the direction of the chief librarian [George H. Parry] by J. A. Carr."
"All the music and musical literature in the Music Library, Reference Library, and Hornby Library, are contained in this catalogue."—p. v.
1. Music—Bibl.—Catalogs. I. Parry, George Henry, 1872-1963, comp.
ML136.L7M8 781.9731 34-5004 rev*

NL 0418351 DLC MiU NN ICN NcU

Liverpool. Public Libraries, Museums and Art Gallery. *Music Library.*
Catalogue of the Music Library. Liverpool, Central Public Libraries, 1954.
572 p. 25 cm.
1. Music—Bibl.—Catalogs.
ML136.L7M83 781.9731 57-18384

NL 0418352 DLC TU LU NBC CU NcU ICN NIC MB IaU ICU OU NcD CaBVaU NN CaBVa IU WaS NNC NNCU-G PSt TxU

Liverpool. Public Libraries, Museums and Art Gallery. *Music Library.*
The piano; its music and literature. [Compiled under the direction of the city librarian by K. H. Anderson] Liverpool, 1949.
viii, 102 p. 19 cm. (*Its* Catalogue, pt. 1)
1. Piano—Bibl. 2. Piano music—Bibl. I. Title. (Series)
ML128.P3L36 016.7862 59-17698

NL 0418353 DLC

Liverpool. Public Libraries, Museums and Art Gallery. *Walker Art Gallery.*
The autumn exhibition. [Catalogue] [Liverpool?]
v. illus. 17-22 cm. annual.
At head of title, : Corporation of Liverpool. Walker Art Gallery; : Walker Art Gallery.
First exhibition held 1871; none held 1917-18.
Title varies: -1921, Autumn exhibition of modern art; catalogue.—1922, Jubilee autumn exhibition; catalogue.
Other slight variations in title.
1. Art—Exhibitions.
N5056.L48 62-5903

NL 0418354 DLC NN

Liverpool. Public Libraries, Museum and Art Gallery. Walker Art Gallery.
[Blank forms, notices, plans of the building, etc.]
[Liverpool. 1853-69.] F°.
There is no title-page.
G1414 — Libraries. Administration.

NL 0418355 MB

Liverpool. Public Libraries, Museums and Art Gallery. Walker Art Gallery.
Rare Book Room Iq F531 1
A catalogue of paintings, etchings & drawings, Italy & other places, by A. Hugh Fisher. June 18 to 25, 1905. [Liverpool] Walker Gallery, 1905.
vii, [1] p. 19 cm.
1. Fisher, Alfred Hugh, 1867- Bibl.

NL 0418356 CtY

Liverpool. Public libraries, museums and art gallery (*Walker art gallery*)
... Catalogue of the museum of casts, architectural and sculptural. Liverpool, C. Tinling and co., printers, 1887.
xii, [13]-30, [2] p. 18cm.
At head of title: Corporation of Liverpool.
1. Sculpture—Liverpool—Catalogs.
9-11854†
Library of Congress N1410.A6

NL 0418357 DLC

Liverpool. Public libraries, museums and art gallery (*Walker art gallery*)
Catalogue of the Walker art gallery; ed. with an introduction and notes by Charles Dyall. London, Eyre & Spottiswoode, printers [1906]
50 p. illus., plan. 24cm. (*On cover:* Gems from the galleries. no. III)
"The official guide. Pub. by authority of the Liverpool corporation."
1. Art—Liverpool—Catalogs. 2. Paintings, Reproductions of. I. Dyall, Charles, ed.
8-36862†
Library of Congress N1410.A7

NL 0418358 DLC IU WaS Or MH NNC PPAFA

Liverpool. Public Libraries, Museums and Art Gallery. *Walker Art Gallery.*
Cleaned pictures; an exhibition of pictures from the collection of the Walker Art Gallery, Liverpool, mainly cleaned and restored in the years 1950-1955 by J. Coburn Witherop, with a historical and technical summary, and notes on the condition and treatment of the pictures, by J. Coburn Witherop. New catalogue entries by Ralph Fastnedge. 10th September to 22nd October, 1955. Liverpool [1955]
75 p. illus. 24 cm.
1. Paintings—Conservation and restoration. 2. Paintings—Liverpool—Catalogs. I. Title.
ND1650.L5 751.6 56-56063 ‡

NL 0418359 DLC UU IaU CtY MH OU PPiU NBuU NcD NBuC

W.C.L. 759.0838 L785D
Liverpool. Public Libraries, Museums and Art Gallery. Walker Art Gallery.
Descriptive catalogue of the permanent collection of pictures, compiled by Charles Dyall, curator. [Liverpool] 1889.
81 p. 19 cm.
At head of title: Corporation of Liverpool, Walker Art Gallery.
1. Art. Liverpool. Catalogs. I. Dyall, Charles.

NL 0418360 NcD MB

Liverpool Public libraries, museums and art gallery. *Walker art gallery.*
... Descriptive catalogue of the permanent collection of pictures, comp. by Charles Dyall, curator ... [Liverpool? 1894]
iv, [5]-96 p. 18½cm.
At head of title: Corporation of Liverpool.
"Published with the sanction of the Library, museum, and arts committee."
1. Art—Liverpool—Catalogs. I. Dyall, Charles, comp.
15-2359
Library of Congress N1410.A65 1894

NL 0418361 DLC

Liverpool. Public Libraries, Museums and Art Gallery (Walker art gallery).
Descriptive catalogue of the permanent collection of pictures, comp. by Charles Dyall. [Liverpool], pub. with the sanction of the Library, Museum and Art Committee, 1902.
112p.

NL 0418362 ICRL

Liverpool. Public libraries, museums and art gallery (*Walker art gallery*)
... Descriptive catalogue of the permanent collection of pictures, comp. by Charles Dyall ... [Liverpool] 1905.
iv, [5]-114 p. 21cm.
At head of title: Corporation of Liverpool.
Pub. with the sanction of the Library, museum, and arts committee.
1. Pictures—Liverpool—Catalogs. I. Dyall, Charles, comp.
8-36868†
Library of Congress N1410.A65 1905

NL 0418363 DLC

VOLUME 336

ND 497 .S91L79 Liverpool. Public Libraries, Museums and Art Gallery. Walker Art Gallery.
George Stubbs, 1724-1806. An exhibition held from 13th July to 25th August. [Catalogue. Liverpool, Published for the Libraries, Museums and Arts Committee of the Corporation of Liverpool, 1951]
26 p. illus.
At head of title: Corporation of Liverpool.

1. Stubbs, George, 1724-1806.

NL 0418364 ICU MH

Liverpool. Public Libraries, Museums and Art Gallery. Walker Art Gallery.
...Illustrated catalogue of the permanent collection... Liverpool: C. Tinling & Co., Ltd., 1927. xvi, 227 p. plates. sq. 8°.

573529A. 1. Paintings—Collections—Gt. Br.—Eng.—Liverpool.
N. Y. P. L. May 16, 1932

NL 0418365 NN CaBVaU

Liverpool. Public Libraries, Museums and Art Gallery. Walker Art Gallery.
Kings & queens of England; an exhibition organised by the Libraries, Museums & Arts Committee of the Liverpool City Council in honour of the coronation of Her Majesty, Queen Elizabeth II. Held at the Walker Art Gallery, Liverpool, May 6-Aug. 31, 1953. [Liverpool, 1953]
66 p. (chiefly illus., facsims., ports.) 25 cm.

1. Gt. Brit.—Kings and rulers—Portraits. 2. Portraits, British—Exhibitions. I. Liverpool. Libraries, Museums & Arts Committee. II. Title.

DA28.1.L56 79-260051 MARC

NL 0418366 DLC DNGA

Uy18 L75 892 Liverpool. Public libraries, museums and art gallery. Walker art gallery.
... Liverpool naval exhibition, 1892 ...
Liverpool, C.Tinling and co., 1892.
xx, 154p. plans. 18½cm.
At head of title: ... Corporation of Liverpool. James de Bels Adam, esquire, mayor.
Advertising matter: p.[i]-[xii]
William B. Forwood, chairman.

NL 0418367 CtY

HD497 H95W5 Liverpool. Public libraries, museums and art gallery. Walker art gallery.
... Memorial exhibition of pictures by Alfred W. Hunt, R.W. S. [Liverpool, pr. by Lee and Nightingale] 1897.
35 p. 20.5 cm.

1. Hunt, Alfred William, 1830-1896.

NL 0418368 CSmH

Liverpool. Public Libraries, Museums and Art Gallery. Walker Art Gallery.
Notes and sketches by Sickert
see under Arts Council of Great Britain.

Liverpool. Public Libraries, Museums and Art Gallery. *Walker Art Gallery.*
Picture book. no. 1-
[Liverpool, 1947-
v. illus. 22 cm.

1. Paintings—Liverpool.

ND471.L5L53 759.084 53-16108 ‡

NL 0418370 DLC OClMA NN

Liverpool. Public libraries, Museums and Art Gallery. Walker Art Gallery
Selected acquisitions of the Walker Art Gallery
see under Agnew (Thomas) and Sons, London.

Liverpool. Public libraries, museums and art gallery. *Walker art gallery.*
... Some acquisitions of the Walker art gallery, Liverpool, 1935-1945. May 1945. [Liverpool, 1945]
cover-title, 20 p. 40 pl. on 20 l. 21½cm.
At head of title: National gallery.
"Index of artists" on p. [3] of cover.
Catalogue of an exhibition at the National gallery.

1. Paintings—Exhibitions. I. London. National gallery.

Library of Congress N1410.A75 45-7180
[3] 708.2

NL 0418372 DLC PPPM

Liverpool. Public Libraries, Museums, and Art Gallery. Walker Art Gallery.
Twenty landscapes. Liverpool, University Press [1947]
[4] p. 20 plates. 22cm. (Walker Art Gallery picture book, no. 2)
"Published for the Libraries, Museums & Arts Committee of the Corporation of Liverpool."

NL 0418373 NIC MiDA CaBViP

759.2 W154t Liverpool. Public libraries, Museums and Art Gallery (Walker Art Gallery)
Twenty narrative pictures. [Liverpool] University press of Liverpool [1948]
[4] p. 20 plates (Walker Art Gallery picture book, no.3)

1.Painting, English. 2.Genre painting. I.Title.

NL 0418374 MiDA CaBViP

---

759 W154t Liverpool. Public libraries, museums and art Galler (Walker Art Gallery)
Twenty old masters. [Liverpool] University press of Liverpool [1948]
[4] p. 20 plates (Walker Art Gallery picture book, no.4)

1. Paintings. I. Title.

NL 0418375 MiDA CaBViP

Liverpool. Public libraries, Museum and Art Gallery. (Walker Art Gallery)
Twenty pictures by Liverpool artists. Liverpool, University Press [1951]
[23] p. plates. (Walker Art Gallery. Picture book, 6)

NL 0418376 MH

---

757 W154t Liverpool. Public libraries, museums and art gallery. Walker Art Gallery.
Twenty portraits. Liverpool, University press of Liverpool [1947]
[4] p. 20 plates (ports.) (Walker Art Gallery picture book, no. 1)

1. Portraits. I. Title.

NL 0418377 MiDA CaBViP

Liverpool. Public libraries, Museums and Art Gallery. (Walker Art Gallery)
Twenty sporting pictures. Liverpool, University Press [1949]
[22] p. plates. (Walker Art Gallery. Picture book, 5)

NL 0418378 MH

Liverpool. Public libraries, museums and art gallery. *Walker art gallery. Roscoe collection.*
... Catalogue of the Roscoe collection deposited by the trustees of the Royal institution. [Liverpool, C. Tinling and co.] 1893.
47, [1] p. 13½cm.
At head of title: Corporation of Liverpool.
"The Roscoe collection was formed by the late William Roscoe ... and on its dispersion was purchased by friends and placed in the Royal institution ... about the year 1840."—p. [2]
"The catalogue of the Roscoe collection is condensed from the Catalogue raisonné compiled by the late Theodore W. Rathbone."—p. 3.
1. Paintings—Liverpool—Catalogs. I. Roscoe, William, 1753-1831. II. Rathbone, Theodore W. III. Liverpool. Royal institution.

Library of Congress N1410.A8R7 1893 10-11785

NL 0418379 DLC

Art Library N1410 A82 1915 (LC) Liverpool. Public libraries, museums and art gallery. Walker art gallery. Roscoe collection.
Catalogue of the Roscoe collection and other pictures deposited by the trustees of the Liverpool Royal Institution. Liverpool, Northern Pub. Co., 1915.
52 p. 14 cm.
1. Paintings - Liverpool - Catalogs. 2. Roscoe, William, 1753-1831 - Art collections. I. Liverpool. Royal Institution.

NL 0418380 CtY WaS

Liverpool, England. Public Libraries, Museums and Art Gallery. Walker Art Gallery. Roscoe collection.
...Catalogue of the Roscoe collection and other paintings, drawings and engravings deposited by the trustees of the Liverpool Royal Institution; re-written by Maurice W. Brockwell. Liverpool: C. Tinling & Co., Ltd., 1928. 79 p. front., 20 pl. 8°.

572692A. 1. Paintings—Collections—Gt. Br.—Eng.—Liverpool. I. Brockwell, Maurice Walter, 1869- . II. Roscoe, William, 1753-1831. III. Royal Institution, Liverpool.
N. Y. P. L. May 20, 1932

NL 0418381 NN NNC CSmH MH MdBWA

Liverpool. Public Museums
see
Liverpool. Public Libraries, Museums and Art Gallery. *Museum.*

VOLUME 336

Liverpool. Radium institute and hospital for cancer and skin diseases.
... Medical board report ...

[Liverpool,
v. illus. 22½cm.

Cover-title.
At head of title: The Liverpool radium institute.

1. Hospital reports.

NL 0418383 NNC

Liverpool. Record society for the publication of original documents relating to Lancashire and Cheshire.

see

Record society for the publication of original documents relating to Lancashire and Cheshire

---

Liverpool. Reformed Presbyterian congregation.
Old bottles burst - new wine poured in; or, A record of the expulsion of the old members of the Reformed Presbyterian congregation, Liverpool... Liverpool, David Marples, printer, 1860.
31 p. 18 cm.

NL 0418385 NNUT PPPrHi

Lilly
PN 2596
.L68 R83

LIVERPOOL, --Royal Amphitheatre.
[Playbills. Liverpool, Eng., items

1. Playbills--Liverpool,Eng.

NL 0418386 InU

615.13
L78p

Liverpool.royal infirmary.
The pharmacopoeia of the Liverpool royal infirmary. Edinburgh, Neill, 1922.
42p. T.
Interleaved.

NL 0418387 IaU

WX
2
FE5
L75R8r

LIVERPOOL. Royal Infirmary
Report.
103d- 1851-
Liverpool.
v. in illus.

Continues the Report, list of subscribers, and statement of account of the Liverpool Infirmary, Lunatic Asylum and Lock Hospital.

Issues for 1851-88? have title: Report of the Liverpool Royal Infirmary, Lunatic Asylum, and Lock Hospital.
I. Liverpool. Lock Hospital II. Liverpool Lunatic Asylum

NL 0418389 DNLM

Liverpool. Royal Infirmary. *School of Medicine*
see Liverpool. University. *Faculty of Medicine.*

Liverpool. Royal institution.

Liverpool. Public libraries, museums and art gallery.
Walker art gallery. Roscoe collection.
... Catalogue of the Roscoe collection deposited by the trustees of the Royal institution. [Liverpool, C. Tinling and co.] 1893.

Liverpool. Royal institution.
Report.
Liverpool,
v. fold. plan. 20-23½cm.

Report year ends in Feb.
Title varies: Report of the state of the Liverpool Royal institution made to the meeting of the proprietors ...
Report of the committee of the Liverpool Royal institution ...
Address delivered at the annual meeting of the proprietors ...
Report adopted at the annual meeting of the proprietors of the Liverpool Royal institution ...
On cover: Report.

CA 9-2645 Unrev'd

Library of Congress AS122.L45

NL 0418392 DLC PU

Liverpool. Royal institution.
Roscoe collection

see

Liverpool. Public libraries, museums and art gallery. Walker art gallery. Roscoe collection

---

Liverpool. Royal institution. *Gallery of art.*
Descriptive and historical catalogue of the pictures, drawings, & casts, in the Gallery of art of the Royal institution, Colquitt street, Liverpool ... Liverpool, Printed by G. M'Corquodale & co., 1859.
viii, [2], 88 p. 21cm.

1. Art—Liverpool—Catalogs.

17-17667

Library of Congress N1408.A5 1860

NL 0418394 DLC

Liverpool. Royal institution. Gallery of art
A guide to the permanent gallery of art, and to the saloon of casts, at the Royal Institution, Liverpool. To be had at the institution. Liverpool. Whitty. 1844. 11 pp. Sm. 8°.

G767

NL 0418395 MB

Liverpool. Royal institution. *Museum.*
Catalogue of the mineralogical collection in the Museum of the Royal institution, Liverpool. Liverpool, Printed by Harris brothers, 1829.
xxiii, 109 p. 22cm.

Label on cover: Catalogue of the minerals, *Mammalia*, and birds in the Museum of the Liverpool Royal institution.
Appended: Catalogue of *Mammalia* in the Museum. v, 6 p.; Catalogue of birds in the Museum. v, 44 p.

Library of Congress QH71.L7A3 6-17166†

NL 0418396 DLC

Liverpool. Royal Institution. *School of Medicine and Surgery*
see Liverpool. University. *Faculty of Medicine.*

Liverpool. Royal Jubilee Exhibition, 1887.
See
Liverpool. Jubilee Exhibition, 1887.

WX
28
FE5
L7R8

LIVERPOOL. Royal Southern Hospital.
[Collection of publications]

The Library has a collection of miscellaneous publications of this organization kept as received. These publications are not listed or bound separately.

NL 0418399 DNLM

Liverpool. Royal Southern Hospital. Medical, surgical, and pathological reports of the ... 1901. v. 1. 310 pp., 6 pl. 8°. *Liverpool, Rockliff Bros., 1902.*
G. P. Newbolt, C. J. Macalister, Lin Dimond, editors.

NL 0418400 DNLM

Liverpool. Royal southern hospital.
Medical, surgical and pathological reports. 1912. Liverpool, Rockliff, 1903.

1 v. plates, charts, tables. 21.5 cm.

NL 0418401 MBCo

WX
2
FE5
L75R85r

LIVERPOOL. Royal Southern Hospital
Report.
1872-
Liverpool.
v. in
Continues the Report of the Southern Hospital.

NL 0418402 DNLM

Liverpool. Royal Southern Hospital,

——. Rules of the ... 18 pp. 8°. *Liverpool Townsend & Son, 1874.*

NL 0418403 DNLM

Liverpool. St. Mary's, Highfield Street.
The Catholic registers of Liverpool, now St. Mary's, Highfield street, 1741-73. /Contributed by Mrs. Seymour Spencer. Edited by Joseph S. Hansom. Historical notes by Joseph Gillow. Facsimile plates.
(In Catholic Record Society. Publications, vol. 9, Miscellanea 7, pp. 179-333. London. 1911.)

H6276 — Registers. Parish. — Hanso[m, J]oseph Stanislaus, ed. — Spencer, Mrs. Seymour, comp. — Gillow, Joseph, ed.

NL 0418404 MB

Liverpool. St. Nicholas' Church.
The earliest registers of the Parish of Liverpool (St. Nicholas's Church): christenings, marriages, and burials. Also an appendix being Report on the ecclesiastical records in the Diocese of Liverpool. Rochdale, Printed for the Lancashire Parish Register Society, by J. Clegg, 1909-63.
2 v. 23 cm. (Lancashire Parish Register Society. [Publications] 35, 101)

Pt. 2 has title: The registers of Our Lady & St. Nicholas, Liverpool; and imprint: Leyland, Preston, Printed for the Lancashire Parish Register Society, by R. Seed.

CONTENTS: [1] 1660-1704, with some of the earlier episcopal transcripts commencing in 1604, transcribed and edited by H. Peet.—pt. 2. 1705-1725, transcribed by E. B. Saxton, edited and indexed by R. Dickinson.

1. Registers of births, etc.—Liverpool. I. Peet, Henry, 1856-1935, ed. II. Dickinson, Robert, ed. III. Title. IV. Title: The registers of Our Lady & St. Nicholas, Liverpool. V. Series: Lancashire Parish Register Society. Publications, 35 [etc.]

CS435.L3 vol. 35, etc. 11-10106
[CS436.L517] rev

NL 0418405 DLC MB ICN IaU CaOTP NIC PHi NBu MH Vi

VOLUME 336

WX 2 FE5 L75SP2r **LIVERPOOL. St. Paul's Eye and Ear Hospital**
Report. 1st- 1872/73- Liverpool.
v.
Report year ends Aug. 31.

NL 0418406 DNLM

Liverpool. St. Peter's church.
Psalms, anthems and hymns, to be sung at the Parish church of St. Peter, the parochial chapel of St. Nicholas, and other churches, in Liverpool. Liverpool, printed by J. and J. Mawdsley, 1838.
3 p.l., [3]-127, [1] p. 15 cm.
A selection of psalms, 13 anthems, 69 hymns, 6 doxologies.

NL 0418407 NNUT

Liverpool. *School board.*
Suggestions to the managers of public elementary schools. 2d ed. London, W. Isbister, limited, 1880.
viii, 99, [1] p. incl. tables (partly fold.) 18½cm.

1. School management and organization—Liverpool.
E 9-1249
Library, U. S. Bur. of Education LB2902.L75S

NL 0418408 DHEW CtY

HV 2711 qL785r **LIVERPOOL. School for the Deaf and dumb**
Report. 1st- 1825-27- Liverpool.
v.

NL 0418409 DNLM

Liverpool. School for the Indigent Blind.
An address to the benevolent founders of the Chapel for the Blind, ... by the trustee. Liverpool, 1828.
xii+ 32+ 41 p. 8°. [In v. 1245. College Pamphlets]

NL 0418410 CtY

Liverpool. School for the Indigent Blind.
Regulations for the government of the several officers, with rules for the conduct & management of the pupils, adopted 1869. Liverpool, 1869.
1 v. O. (Bd. with Liverpool-School for Blind reports)

NL 0418411 OO

Liverpool. School for the indigent blind.
Report.
Liverpool,
v. illus. 21cm. annual.
Report year ends Dec. 31.
Full title, 1905: Report of the state of the School for the indigent blind. Commonly called the "Blind asylum" ... Liverpool, and the Wavertree branch school (for children) ...

CA 9-5695 Unrev'd
Library of Congress HV1950.L7S3

NL 0418412 DLC

W6 WA 304.L5 B8 Liverpool. School Health Service.
Report.
[Liverpool, 19— .-
v. illus.

1. School hygiene - Liverpool

NL 0418413 DNLM

Liverpool. School of Tropical Medicine
see **Liverpool. University.** *School of Tropical Medicine.*

Liverpool. Seamen's Orphan Institution
see Liverpool Seamen's Orphan Institution.

WX 2 FE5 L75R85r **LIVERPOOL. Southern Hospital**
Report.
Liverpool [1842?-71]
v. in
Continued by the Report of the Royal Southern Hospital.

NL 0418416 DNLM

332.6 L75c Liverpool. Stock exchange.
The centenary book of the Liverpool stock exchange, 1836-1936. [Liverpool, C. Tinling & co., ltd., 1936]
68p. incl.col.mounted front., illus., mounted plates(part.col.) mounted ports., mounted facsim.

Foreword signed: A. Alan Fish, chairman.
Bibliography: p.55.

NL 0418417 IU

Liverpool. Stock Exchange.

HG4502 .L5 **The Liverpool** Stock Exchange official weekly list.
[Liverpool]

Liverpool. Sub-committee on Dwellings for the Working Classes
..Report to the Sub-Committee on Dwellings for the Working Classes... Liverpool: G. M'Corquodale & Co., 1865. 6 p. table. 8°.

1. Habitations for the working classes—Gt. Br.—Eng.—Liverpool.
N. Y. P. L. August 19, 1926

NL 0418419 NN

Liverpool. Superintendent of Markets.
...Report of the superintendent of markets
see under Liverpool. Markets Committee

Liverpool, Surveyor's Department.
Artizans' and labourers' dwellings. Description and particulars as to rentals, etc.

1903. Liverpool: C. Tinling and Co., 1903. 31 p., 9 pl., 4 plans. 8°.
1904. ib., 1904. 39 p., 12 pl., 4 plans. 8°.
1905. ib., 1905. 47 p., 17 pl., 6 plans. 8°.
1906. ib., 1906. 53 p., 23 pl., 6 plans. 8°.

1. Habitations for the working classes, Gt. Br.: Eng.: Liverpool.
N. Y. P. L. August 31, 1917.

NL 0418421 NN

Liverpool. Surveyor's Dept.
Artizans' and labourers' dwellings
For later editions see under Liverpool. Housing Committee.

Liverpool. Technical instruction committee.
Annual report.
Liverpool, 18-

T173 .L79A3

NL 0418423 DLC

Liverpool. Theatre Royal.
[Play-bills. June 13, Aug. 25, 1796; Nov. 9, 1803; May 31, 1805; July 3, 1806; Aug. 25, 1808; June 21, 1809; July 1, Aug. 1, 1816; Dec 13, 1830; Sept. 29, Oct. 4, 7, 1836.]
— [Liverpool. 1796-1838.] 13 play-bills, in a portfolio, 30½ × 24½ cm.
Each programme includes the name of a famous performer.

M1038 — Theatre. Programmes.

NL 0418424 MB InU

Liverpool. Tidal Institute
see **Liverpool. University.** *Tidal Institute.*

Liverpool. Training School and Home for Nurses
see Liverpool Training School and Home for Nurses.

Liverpool, *Eng. Treasurer's dept.*
The accounts of the treasurer of the city of Liverpool ... with epitome and general abstract ...
Liverpool, 18
v. 24½cm.
Report year irregular.

1. Finance—Liverpool, Eng.
10-3575†
Library of Congress HJ9041.L6

NL 0418427 DLC PU ICJ MB

LIVERPOOL. Treasurer's dept.
The finances of the city of Liverpool. A review for the year 19

Liverpool, 19 25cm.
Report year ends March 31st.

1. Municipal finance—Gt. Br.—Eng.—Liverpool.

NL 0418428 NN

---

768 L785ps 1927 LIVERPOOL. Ullet Road Church.
Psalms & hymns of the church. Edited and pointed for chanting by Lawrence Redfern [and] James E. Wallace. For use in Ullet Road Church, Liverpool. [Liverpool, C. Tinling, 1927?]
178p. 19.5cm.

NL 0418429 MH-AH

Liverpool. Underwriters' Association
see Underwriters' Association, Liverpool.

VOLUME 336

Liverpool. Underwriters' registry for iron vessels
see
Underwriters' registry for iron vessels, Liverpool

NL 0418432 MB NNUT CBPac

Liverpool. Unitarian Church.
A form of prayer, and a new collection of Psalms for the use of a congregation of Protestant dissenters.
— London. Printed for the Society . . . M DCC LXIII. (3), 96, (20); (1), 165, (7) pp. 20 cm., in 4s.
The book is known as the Liverpool liturgy.

L1633 — Double main card. — Liverpool, England. Churches. Unitarian Church. (M1) — Common prayer, Book of. Church of England. Book of 1662. Adaptations. (M2)— Dissenters. (1)— Liverpool liturgy, The. (1)

Liverpool. United alkali company limited
see
United Alkali company limited

NL 0418434 CtY

Liverpool. University.
... Address to John Ruskin [on his recovery from illness, Nov. 1885]
1l. 28½cm.
Inserted also are the "Confidential" letter calling for signatures, dated Nov.27, 1885, 1l., and the form to be signed, 1l.

Liverpool. University.
Bulletin of Spanish studies: a record and review of their progress. v. 1- Dec. 1923-
[Liverpool, The University. 1923-

NL 0418436 DLC DHEW ICJ MB MiU NN

LF 374
Liverpool. University.
...Calendar,...
Liverpool, 18-

NL 0418437 DAS

(Liverpool.university.) S. L.
..."Configuration and climate of north-west England." 1924.
(7p.) 25½cm.

NL 0418438 CtNlC GEU

Liverpool. University.
Forwood lectures. Liverpool. 1,

Liverpool. University.
... In memoriam Robert Andrew Scott Macfie...
A catalogue of the gypsy books
see Liverpool. University. Library.
...A catalogue of the gypsy books...

NL 0418440 DLC OrPR CaBVaU DL NN

Liverpool. University.
... An industrial survey of Merseyside made for the Board of trade by the University of Liverpool ... London, H. M. Stationery off., 1932.
174 p. illus. (maps) diagrs. $24\frac{1}{2}^{cm}$.
At head of title: Board of trade.

1. Gt. Brit.—Indus. 2. Gt. Brit.—Econ. condit.—1918- 3. Liverpool—Indus. 4. Liverpool—Econ. condit. I. Gt. Brit. Board of trade. II. Title. III. Title: Merseyside, An industrial survey of.

Library of Congress HC258.L5L55 32-34619
338.094272

Liverpool. University.
Liverpool English texts and studies
see under title

Liverpool. University.
... A memoir on British resources of refractory sands for furnace and foundary purposes
see under Boswell, Percy George Hamnall, 1886-

Liverpool. University.
Primitiae; essay in English literature
see under title

NL 0418444 NcU

Liverpool. University.
Prospectus of the Liverpool school of architecture, together with an appendix descriptive of the department of civic design; session 1932-1933. Liverpool, University Press, 1932.
24 p. plans. 28 cm.
1. Architecture - Study and teaching.

NL 0418445 PPAmP

Liverpool. University.
Publications, 1-18. Liverpool. [University Press]

NL 0418446 DAS

Liverpool,university.
Rainfall of south west Scotland and the Solway district.
(8p.) figs. 25½ cm.
(Manifolded.)
44192

NL 0418447 PPAmP

Liverpool. University.
Report, 48-52, 54-56. Liverpool. [University Press]

NL 0418448 OO PU

Liverpool. University.
Report of senate upon research and other original work published or completed during the session 1913/14.
Liverpool, Univ. Pr., 19-

NL 0418449 DLC NN MiU PU

Liverpool. University.
... Roll of service, August, 1914 to November, 1918. Liverpool, University press, 1921.
vii, 87 p. $21\frac{1}{2}^{cm}$.
At head of title: The University of Liverpool.

1. European war, 1914-1918—Registers, lists, etc. I. Title.
30-11247

Library of Congress D639.E53L5

NL 0418450 ICU MiU DNLM

QP1 .L78
LIVERPOOL. UNIVERSITY.
The Sherrington lectures. 1-
Liverpool, Univ. Press, 1949-
v. in

1. Physiology—Collected works.

NL 0418451 OO NN OrP

Liverpool. University.
Shute lectures.
[New York] The Macmillan co., 19—?

Liverpool. University.
Jones, David Caradog.
... Social factors in secondary education ... [by] D. Caradog Jones. [Liverpool, Daily post printers, 1932]

OC1W ViU IU NN PU PSC WaU
NL 0418453 DLC CaBVaU CU MU NcD NcRA CtY OU MiU OO

Liverpool. University.
The social survey of Merseyside, edited by D. Caradog Jones, the School of social sciences and administration, University of Liverpool, with the assistance of J. E. McCrindell, H. J. H. Parker, C. T. Saunders. Secretary: N. L. Hume ... [Liverpool] University press of Liverpool; [etc., etc.] 1934.
3 v. fold. front., plates, maps (part fold.) plans, tables, diagrs., forms. 23^{cm}.

1. Lancashire, Eng.—Soc. condit. 2. Cheshire, Eng.—Soc. condit. 3. Liverpool—Soc. condit. 4. Social surveys. I. Jones, David Caradog, ed. II. Title. III. Title: Merseyside, The social survey of.

Library of Congress HN398.M4L5 34-41032
[3] 309.14272

NL 0418454 NNC

Liverpool. University.
Titles of theses accepted for higher degrees.
1950-
[Liverpool, 1950-
v. 22cm.

NL 0418455 DLC IaU NN KU CtY

Liverpool. University.
The University of Liverpool, 1903-1953; [a jubilee book. Liverpool, 1954]
63 p. col. plates, ports. 26 cm.
Text signed: S. D. [i. e. Stanley Dumbell]

1. Liverpool. University—Hist. I. Dumbell, Stanley.

LF375.A4 378.42 58-24906

VOLUME 336

Liverpool. University.
... Women's industries in Liverpool. An enquiry into the economic effects of legislation regulating the labour of women... London, 1904.
4 p.l., 64, [2] p. incl. tables. 21 cm.
Bibliography: p. following p. 64.
At head of title: Published for the University of Liverpool.

NL 0418456 CtY

QP501 .B47 Liverpool. University. Bio-Chemical Dept.
The Biochemical journal. v. 1- Jan. 1906- Cambridge [Eng.] University Press.

Sl25el 478 Liverpool. University. Bio-chemical dept.
Researches in bio-chemistry conducted in the Johnston laboratory, University of Liverpool Edited by Benjamin Moore ... and Owen T. Williams ... Liverpool, the Department of bio-chemistry, the University, 1911.
/v. illus.(incl.diagrs.) 24½cm.
Vol.II - 1908-1911.

NL 0418458 CtY

Liverpool. University. Botanical laboratory see Liverpool. University. Hartley botanical laboratories.

Liverpool. University. *Conference on Poland for teachers*, 1943
see
Conference on Poland for teachers, *University of Liverpool*, 1943.

Liverpool. University. Dept. of English Literature.
Primitiae; essays in English literature see under title

910.08 L785R Liverpool. University. Dept. of Geography.
Research paper. no. 1- Liverpool, 19
no. in v. illus., maps. 22 cm.

NL 0418462 NcD

Liverpool. University. *Dept. of oceanography.*
Established 1919 for the purpose of continuing and extending the work in marine biology and fisheries research which the Liverpool marine biology committee was founded to promote.

Liverpool. University. *Dept. of Oceanography.*
... L.M.B.C. memoirs on typical British marine plants & animals ... [Liverpool] 1899-1931.
Library has no. 1-30. illus., plates (part col.) 24cm.
At head of title: no. 1-29, Liverpool Marine Biology Committee; no. 30, Department of Oceanography, University of Liverpool.
Issued also in Liverpool Biological Society. Proceedings and transactions.

DLC FU ICJ CaBVaU CCC
NL 0418464 ICJ OC1W GU AzU NcD LU KEmT CU-Riv OO

Liverpool. University. *Dept. of Oceanography.*
The Marine Biological Station at Port Erin (Isle of Man) being the ... annual report of the ... Oceanography Department of the University of Liverpool ... Liverpool, 1888-1931.
Library has no. 1-44, 1885/87-1930. illus., plates, charts. 22cm.
Title varies: no. 1, The foundation and first season's work of the Liverpool Marine Biological Station on Puffin Island.
No. 2-5, Annual report of the Liverpool Marine Biological Station on Puffin Island.
No. 6-15, Annual report of the Liverpool Marine Biology Committee and their Biological Station at Port Erin.
Other slight variations.
The Liverpool Marine Biology Committee was discontinued Dec. 31, 1919, when its work was transferred to the Dept. of Oceanography, University of Liverpool.
Issued also in Liverpool Biological Society. Proceedings and transactions.

NL 0418466 ICJ DLC PPAN CaBVaU ICRL

SH351 .H5S65 no. 1 Liverpool. University. Dept. of oceanography. Port Erin biological station.
Special publications. [Liverpool] The University press of Liverpool limited; London, Hodder and Stoughton limited, 1923-
v. 24 cm.
Contents: no. 1 Smith, W.C. A short history of the Irish Sea herring fisheries during the eighteenth and nineteenth centuries. 1923.

NL 0418467 DLC

Liverpool. University. *Department of social science*
see
Liverpool. University. *Social science dept.*

Liverpool. University. Dept. of Zoology.
Society for Endocrinology.
The comparative endocrinology of vertebrates. Proceedings of a conference held at the Department of Zoology, University of Liverpool, from 12 to 16 July 1954. Edited on behalf of the Society for Endocrinology by I. Chester Jones & P. Eckstein. Cambridge [Eng.] University Press, 1955-56.

Liverpool. University. Development Committee.
Report...to the Council and Senate of the University on building progress, 1949-1954. Liverpool, University Press, 1955.
240 p. illus., photos., maps, sketches
(Being the first quinquennial review of the post-war development plan published in 1949 as "Proposals for the development of a site for the University of Liverpool.")

NL 0418470 MH-SD

Liverpool. University. Faculty of arts.
Otia Merseiana see under title

Liverpool. University. Faculty of Arts.
Prospectus of courses for the session 1911-12.
= [Liverpool.] 1911. v. 18½ cm., in 16s.

NL 0418472

Liverpool. University. Faculty of arts. School of local history see Liverpool. University. School of local history and records.

Liverpool. University. *Faculty of Arts. School of Social Sciences and Administration*
see
Liverpool. University. *School of Social Sciences and Administration.*

Liverpool. University. Faculty of Medicine.
Abridged prospectus.
Liverpool,
v. 18½cm.
At head of title: The University of Liverpool, Medical faculty.
CA 9-1268 Unrev'd
Library of Congress R773.L387

NL 0418475 DLC

W 19.5 FE5 L6R8 LIVERPOOL. University. Faculty of Medicine.
Catalogs, announcements of courses, requirements for admission and other publications relating to the academic program will be found under the above call number. Included also are similar publications of individual schools or departments of instruction of the institution.

NL 0418476 DNLM

LF 372m Liverpool. University. Faculty of Medicine.
Prospectus of courses.
Liverpool 19
v.

NL 0418477 DNLM

Liverpool. University. *Hartley botanical laboratories.*
... Publications of the Hartley botanical laboratories ... no. 1- Liverpool, 1924-
v. illus., plates, diagrs. 29½cm.
At head of title: The University of Liverpool.
1. Botany—Societies, etc.
35-22008
Library of Congress QK1.L77 580.722

NL 0418478 DLC MoU NcRS NcU MiU WU MH-G DSI

GN1 .A6 Liverpool. University. Institute of Archaeology.
Annals of archaeology and anthropology, issued by the Institute of Archaeology. v. 1-28; Sept. 1908-1948. Liverpool, University Press.

Liverpool. University. *Institute of archaeology.*
... Annual report, and prospectus, Liverpool,
v. 18cm.
At head of title, The University of Liverpool, XII.
CA. 16-797
Library of Congress CC23.L7

NL 0418480 DLC

Liverpool. University. Institute of archaeology.
Garstang, John, 1876-
... The burial customs of ancient Egypt as illustrated by tombs of the Middle Kingdom; being a report of excavations made in the necropolis of Beni Hassan during 1902-3-4 by John Garstang ... With coloured frontispiece by Mr. G. Hall-Neale, 15 plates and 231 photographic illustrations in the text. London, A. Constable & co., ltd., 1907.

VOLUME 336

Liverpool. University. Institute of archaeology

...Catalogue of Jettons or Casting-counters, for use on the counting-board or chequer, at the Institute of archaeology in the university of Liverpool... Liverpool, The university press; London, Constable & co., ltd., [1912]

cover-title, 21-62 p. 2 plates. 26 cm.

— —Supplementary list of Jettons. Liverpool, The university press; [etc.] [1912]
cover-title, 97-106 p. 1 plate. 26 cm.
"Reprinted from Annals of archaeology and Anthropology. Vol. V. July, October 1912.
1. Jettons. I. Barnard, Francis Pierrepont, 1854-1934

NL 0418482 CSmH

Liverpool. University. Institute of archaeology.

Excavations at Meroë, Sudan.

n. p. [1911].

SA 4687.591

NL 0418483 NjP

Liverpool. University. Institute of Archaeology.
.. Excavations at Meroë, Sudan, 1913. Fourth season ... with plans, photographs, and a description of the recent excavations by J. Garstang ... and W.S. George ... [Liverpool? 1913]
cover-title, 23 p. 7 pl. (2 fold.) incl. plans. 27.5 cm.
(Liverpool. University. Institute of archaeology. Guide to the 12th annual exhibition of antiquities discovered [1913])

NL 0418484 CtY

Liverpool. University. Institute of archaeology.
Excavations at Meroë, Sudan, 1914, fifth season; guide to the thirteenth annual exhibition of antiquities discovered, with... a description of the recent excavations by Professor J.Garstang... and W.J.Phythian-Adams... exhibition inaugurated by Sir Arthur J.Evans... [London? 1914]

16 p. plates, plans (part fold.) 27 cm.

NL 0418485 MH-P

Liverpool. University. Institute of archaeology.
Garstang, John, 1876–
Meroë, the city of the Ethiopians; being an account of a first season's excavations on the site, 1909–1910, by John Garstang ... With an introduction and chapter on decipherment by the Rev. A. H. Sayce ... and a chapter on the inscriptions from Meroë by F. Ll. Griffith ... Photographic illustrations by Horst Schliephack. Oxford, Clarendon press, 1911.

DS51 .M4G3

Liverpool. University. Institute of Archaeology. Neilson Expedition.

Garstang, John, 1876–
Prehistoric Mersin, Yümük Tepe in Southern Turkey; the Neilson Expedition in Cilicia. Oxford [Eng.] Clarendon Press, 1953.

Liverpool. University. Institute of commercial research in the tropics.

Aburi. Government botanical gardens.
... A catalogue of the Aburi gardens, being a complete list of all the plants grown in the Government botanical gardens at Aburi, Gold Coast, West Africa, together with their popular or local names, uses, habits, and habitats; prepared for the Institute of commercial research in the tropics, by A. E. Evans ... Liverpool, At the offices of the Institute; [etc., etc.] 1906.

HFG1 .L6

Liverpool. University. Institute of commercial research in the tropics.
...Quarterly journal. v. 1, no. 1-3; Jan. - Sept. 1906. Liverpool, [etc., 1906-]
3 nos. plates, maps. 24.5 cm.
Ceased publication with v. 3, no. 6, Jan. 1908.
v. 1, no. 1-2. Jan.-April, 1906. 2 nos.

NL 0418489 DLC

Liverpool. University. Johnston Laboratories
see Johnston laboratories.

Liverpool. University. Lancashire sea-fisheries laboratory.
... James Johnstone memorial volume. [Liverpool] University press of Liverpool, 1934.

Liverpool. University. Lancashire Sea-fisheries Laboratory.
Memoir...
see Lancashire Sea-fisheries memoir..

Liverpool. University. *Lancashire sea-fisheries laboratory.*
... Report on the Lancashire sea-fisheries laboratory at the University of Liverpool, and the Sea-fish hatchery at Piel ...
Liverpool,
v. illus., plates (part col.) maps, tables. 21½cm.
First report, 1892.
Drawn up by W. A. Herdman, assisted by Andrew Scott and James Johnstone.
Issued also in Proceedings and transactions of the Liverpool biological society. v. 7– 1892/93–
1. Fishes—Collected works. 2. Fish-culture—Collected works. I. Piel (Island) Sea-fish hatchery. II. Herdman, William Abbott, 1858– III. Scott, Andrew, A. L. S. IV. Johnstone, James, B. SC.

Library of Congress SH1.L78 CA 6-1495 Unrev'd

NL 0418493 DLC CU IU ICJ MiU

Liverpool. University. *Library.*
... A catalogue of the gypsy books collected by the late Robert Andrew Scott Macfie, sometime editor and secretary of the Gypsy lore society. Liverpool, 1936.

2 p. l., 178 p., 1 l. 25cm.

At head of title: University of Liverpool. In memoriam Robert Andrew Scott Macfie obiit ix die junii MDCCCCXXXV.
The collection was presented to the University of Liverpool library to be kept intact as a reference library. *cf.* Foreword.
"Prepared by Miss Dora E. Yates."

1. Gipsies—Bibl. I. Macfie, Robert Andrew Scott, 1868–1935. II. Yates, Dora Esther, 1879–

37-10995

Library of Congress Z5118.G5L7

016.397

NL 0418494 DLC CtY NcD MB CU NcU NIC NN

Liverpool. University. Library.
... A catalogue of the gypsy books collected by the late Robert Andrew Scott Macfie. sometime editor and secretary of the Gypsy lore society. Liverpool, 1936.
2 p.l., 178 p., 1 l. 23 cm.
At head of title: University of Liverpool. In memoriam Robert Andrew Scott Macfie obiit ix die junii MDCCCCXXXV.
"Prepared by Miss Dora E. Yates."
Negative microfilm by Library of Congress Photo Service.

NL 0418495 NcU

Liverpool. University. *Library.*
... A hand-list of academies and periodical publications in the university libraries, including the departmental libraries of the faculties of science, medicine and engineering, the class libraries of the faculty of arts, the institute of archaeology, and the school of tropical medicine. [Liverpool] At the University press of Liverpool, 1913.
4 p. l., 97, [46] p. 24½cm.
At head of title: University of Liverpool.
"... Arranged in a single catalogue under the seat of the society, government office, or place of publication ... with an alphabetical index of the titles."
1. Learned institutions and societies — Bibl. — Catalogs. 2. Periodicals—Bibl.— Catalogs.

Library of Congress Z6945.L78 21—7533

NL 0418496 DLC ICJ

Liverpool. University. *Library.*
Hand-list of incunabula in the University Library, Liverpool, by David I. Masson. Liverpool, Priv. print., 1949.
46 p. 25 cm.

1. Incunabula—Bibl.—Catalogs. I. Masson, David I.

Z240.L78 016.093 50-21526

NL 0418497 DLC KyU NcU NNC OClW

Liverpool. University. *Library.*
... Report ...
[Liverpool] The University press of Liverpool, 19
v. 21½cm.
At head of title: The University of Liverpool. University library.

Library of Congress Z792.L36 CA 33-497 Unrev'd

027.74272

NL 0418498 DLC NN MiU

Liverpool. University. *Medical Faculty*
see Liverpool. University. *Faculty of Medicine.*

Liverpool. University. *Oceanography dept.*
see
Liverpool. University. *Dept. of oceanography.*

Liverpool. University. *Polish School of Architecture.*
The Polish School of Architecture, 1942–1945, the University of Liverpool. [Editor: Bolesław Szmidt] [1st ed.] Liverpool [C. Birchall] 1945.
[2] l., iii–x, 248 p. illus., plans. 29 cm.
"Planning in Poland: short bibliography of publications in English, French and German": p. 174.

1. Architecture, Polish. 2. Architecture—Designs and plans. I. Szmidt, Bolesław, ed.

NA1191.L5 724.91 47-5327*

NL 0418501 DLC CaBVaU MB OU NBuC NIC

Liverpool. University. *Polska Szkola Architektury*
see Liverpool. University. *Polish School of Architecture.*

Liverpool. University. School of Architecture.
The book of the Liverpool School of Architecture
see under Budden, Lionel Bailey, 1887- ed.

VOLUME 336

Liverpool. University. School of architecture.
The Liverpool architectural sketch book; being the annual of the school of architecture of the University of Liverpool... London, Architectural review.

Library has
v.2-[4] 1911[i. e. 1912?]-1920

Title varies slightly.
None published 1914-1919

NL 0418504 MiD NN PSt OCU

Liverpool. University. School of Architecture.
Portfolio of measured drawings, School of Architecture, the University of Liverpool. v. 1- Liverpool: Univ. Press, 1906- v. plans, plates. 48cm.

Preface signed: C. H. Reilly. v. 2, "edited by C. H. Reilly and Patrick Abercrombie," published by C. Lockwood and Son, London.

1. Architectural drawing—Measured drawings. I. Abercrombie, Patrick, 1879- editor. II. Reilly, Charles Herbert, 1874- , editor.
N. Y. P. L. November 2, 1932

NL 0418505 NN ICJ CtY MB PU-FA

Liverpool. University. School of Architecture.
Prospectus of the Liverpool school of architecture
see under Liverpool. University.

Liverpool. University. School of architecture.

The Town planning review ... The journal of the Department of civic design at the School of architecture of the University of Liverpool ...

Liverpool, University press, 19

Liverpool. University. School of local history and records.
A calendar of that part of the collection of deeds and papers of the Moore family of Bankhall
see under Brownbill, John, comp.

Liverpool. University. School of local history and records.
The earliest registers of the parish of Liverpool (St. Nicholas' church)
see under Liverpool. St. Nicholas' church.

DA690
.L8A2

Liverpool. University. School of local history and records.

Liverpool.
Liverpool town books. Proceedings of assemblies, common councils, portmoot courts, &c., 1550-1862 ... edited for the corporation of the city of Liverpool by J. A. Twemlow ... Liverpool, Pub. for the University of Liverpool School of local history and records by the University press; London, Constable & company, ltd., 1918-

---

Liverpool. University. School of local history and records.
Liverpool vestry books, 1681-1834
see under Liverpool.

Liverpool. University. School of local history and records.

Vernon, William, 1588 (*ca.*)-1663, *comp.*
A Middlewich chartulary, compiled by William Vernon in the seventeenth century, edited by Joan Varley ... [Manchester, Eng.] The Chetham society and the Liverpool school of local history and records, 1941-

---

Liverpool. University. School of Russian studies.
Scheme of transliteration of the School of Russian studies. [Liverpool, 1913?]
1 p. 26 cm.
Also published in Russian review, 1913. v. 2, no. 4, p. [10]

NL 0418513 CU

HV9148
.L5B3

Liverpool. University. School of social sciences and administration.

Bagot, John Hendry, 1904-
Punitive detention, an inquiry into the results of treatment under Section 54 of the Children and young persons act, 1933, of juvenile delinquents in Liverpool during the years 1940, 1941 and 1942, by J. H. Bagot. London, J. Cape [1944]

Liverpool. University. School of Social Sciences and Administration.
The social survey of Merseyside
see under Liverpool. University.

Liverpool. University. *School of social sciences and administration. Social science dept.*
see
Liverpool. University. *Social science dept.*

Liverpool. University. School of Tropical Medicine
see Liverpool School of Tropical Medicine.

Liverpool. University. *Social Science Dept.*
The dock worker; an analysis of conditions of employment in the Port of Manchester. [Liverpool] University Press of Liverpool, 1954.
277 p. diagrs. 23 cm. (*Its* Social research series)
"Based on enquiries conducted in the Port of Manchester in 1950-51."
Bibliographical footnotes.

1. Longshoremen—Manchester, Eng. I. Title. (Series)
HD8039.L82G734 55-38144

NL 0418518 DLC WaU MdU GU MeB NBC NcD PHC IU CU MH NN TxU ICU MH-BA CaBVaU OrP OrU

Liverpool. University. *Social Science Dept.*
Employment relations in a group of hospitals; a report of a survey by the Department of Social Science of the University of Liverpool [drafted by] Joan Woodward [assisted by Joan Wright] London, Institute of Hospital Administrators [1950]
115 p. illus. 25 cm.

1. Hospitals—Gt. Brit. 2. Hospitals—Management and regulation. I. Woodward, Joan, M. A. II. Title.
RA986.L56 362.1 51-25386

NL 0418519 DLC ICU NNC DNLM MnU-B

T58
.L7

Liverpool. University. Social Science Dept.
Industrial leadership and joint consultation; a study of human relations in three Merseyside firms. Liverpool, The University Press, 1952.
207 p. 22 cm.

1. Efficiency, Industrial. 2. Industrial management. I. Title.

NL 0418520 TU

Liverpool. University. Social Science Dept.
Joint consultation in a Liverpool manufacturing firm
see under Scott, William Henry.

HM131
.N4

Liverpool. University. Social Science Dept.

Neighbourhood and community; an enquiry into social relationships on housing estates in Liverpool and Sheffield. [Liverpool] University Press of Liverpool, 1954.

Liverpool, university. Social science department.
New Merseyside series. [no. 1]-

[Liverpool] The Univ. press of Liverpool, 1935-
v. illus., maps. 21-22cm.

At head of title: The University of Liverpool. Social science department (nos. 1-14 add: Statistics division).
Supplements its Social survey of Merseyside published in 1934. (3 v.)
Nos. 1-2 issued without series title (no. 2 called new series [of the Social survey of Merseyside]).

[no. 1] Jones, D. C. Merseyside: trade and employment. 1935.
[no.] 2. Simey, T. S. Merseyside: co-ordination of passenger transport services. 1935.
[no.] 3. Jones, D. C. Merseyside: the relief of the poor. 1936.
[no.] 4. Jones, D. C. Trade revival in a depressed area. 1937.
[no.] 5. Holford, W. G. The future of Merseyside. 1937.
[no.] 6. Thomson, G. G. Social service; overlapping and co-ordination. 1938.
[no.] 7. Walshaw, R. S. Migration to and from Merseyside. 1938.
[no.] 8. Jones, D. C. Handbook of social statistics relating to Merseyside. 1938.
[no.] 9. Williams, Norman. Population problems of new estates with special reference to Norris Green. 1939.

[no.] 10. Liverpool university. Social science department. The economic status of coloured families in the port of Liverpool. 1940.
[no.] 11. Jones, D. C. New handbook of social statistics relating to Merseyside. 1940.
[no.] 12. Jones, D. C. Cost of living of representative working class families. 1941.
[no.] 13. Evans, O. E. Redeeming the time; a survey of the junior instruction centre movement. 1941.
[no.] 14. Smith, Wilfred. The distribution of population and the location of industry on Merseyside. 1942.
[no.] 15. Smith, Wilfred. Physical survey of Merseyside. 1946.
[no.] 16. Allen, G. C. The import trade of the port of Liverpool. 1946.
[no.] 17. Black, E. I. Old people's welfare on Merseyside. 1947.

NL 0418525 NN DL

LIVERPOOL. UNIVERSITY. Social science dept.
Occasional papers.
Liverpool, Liverpool university press.

NL 0418526 NN

[**Liverpool. University.** *Social science dept.*]
Our wartime guests—opportunity or menace? A psychological approach to evacuation. [Liverpool] The University press of Liverpool; London, Hodder & Stoughton ltd., 1940.
48 p. 21½cm.
"An inquiry into the problems of evacuation which has been pursued by research assistants in the Department of social science of the University of Liverpool."—p. 4.

1. European war, 1939- —Children. 2. European war, 1939- —Gt. Brit. I. Title.
41-19748
Library of Congress D810.C4L5
940.53161

NL 0418527 DLC OrU

VOLUME 336

Liverpool. University. Social science dept.

Conway, Edward S
Post-war employment, by Edward S. Conway, M. A. With an introduction by D. Caradog Jones ... London, J. Cape [1943]

NL 0418529 DLC NN CtY

[**Liverpool. University.** *Social science dept.*]
Preliminary report on the problems of evacuation ... [Liverpool] The University press of Liverpool; London, Hodder & Stoughton ltd., 1939.
32 p. incl. forms. 21½cm.
"The present investigation was organised by the University of Liverpool Department of social science in co-operation with the Liverpool university settlement under the direction of Dr. Gertrud Wagner ... The report is based on a series of 356 interviews in the neighbourhood of the settlement, and is preliminary to a fuller investigation."—p. 3.
1. World war, 1939- —Children. 2. World war, 1939- —Evacuation of civilians. I. Liverpool university settlement. II. Title. III. Title: Evacuation.
Library of Congress D810.C4L52 42-47570 940.53161

NL 0418530 DLC CaBVaU OrU NcU ICU MH NN NIC

Liverpool. University. *Social Science Dept.*
Social aspects of a town development plan; a study of the County Borough of Dudley. [Liverpool] University Press of Liverpool, 1951.
168 p. illus., maps (1 fold.) 23 cm.
"Prepared ... for the Town Council of the County Borough of Dudley."
1. Cities and towns — Planning — Dudley, Eng. (Worcestershire) I. Dudley, Eng. (Worcestershire) Town Council. II. Title.
NA9187.D8L5 711.13 53-2250

NL 0418532 DLC

Liverpool. University. Social Science Dept.
Social contacts in old age.
see under
Liverpool Personal Service Society.

Liverpool. University. *Social Science Dept.*
Youthful lawbreakers, a study of juvenile delinquency in Liverpool. [Liverpool] University Press of Liverpool, 1948.
47 p. map, diagrs. 22 cm.
At head of title: Liverpool Council of Social Service.
1. Juvenile delinquency—Liverpool. I. Liverpool Council of Social Service. II. Title.
HV9148.L5L5 364.36 48-4849*

NL 0418533 DLC NN

Liverpool. University. *Social science dept. Statistics division.*
... Cost of living of representative working class families. [Liverpool] The University press of Liverpool, 1941.
28 p. 22cm. (*Its* New Merseyside series, 12)
Prefatory note signed: D. Caradog Jones.
1. Cost and standard of living—Liverpool. I. Jones, David Caradog.
Library of Congress HD6669.L5L5 43-7769 331.831

NL 0418534 DLC NN

Liverpool. University. *Social science dept. Statistics division.*
... The economic status of coloured families in the port of Liverpool. [Liverpool] The University press of Liverpool, 1940.
23 p. 21½cm. (*Its* New Merseyside series, 10)
At head of title: The University of Liverpool. Social science department: Statistics division.
"The investigation of which this report is the outcome was undertaken at the suggestion of and under the auspices of the Liverpool association for the welfare of coloured people."—Foreword.
1. Negroes in Liverpool. 2. Liverpool—Soc. condit. I. Liverpool association for the welfare of coloured people. II. Title.
Library of Congress DA690.L8L8 42-34662 325.26094272

NL 0418535 DLC NcD

Liverpool. University. *Social Science Dept. Statistics Division.*
Handbook of social statistics relating to Merseyside. [Liverpool] Univ. Press of Liverpool, 1938.
82 p. 22 cm. (*Its* New Merseyside series, 8)
Prefatory note signed: D. Caradog Jones.
1. Liverpool—Stat. I. Jones, David Caradog. II. Series.
HA1118.L5L55 314.2 47-44015*

NL 0418537 DNAL NN KyU CtY

Liverpool. University. Social science dept. Statistics division.

Bagot, John Hendry, 1904-
Juvenile delinquency; a comparative study of the position in Liverpool and England and Wales, by J. H. Bagot ... with an introduction by D. Caradog Jones ... London, J. Cape [1941]

NL 0418538 DLC NN

Liverpool. University. *Social science dept. Statistics division.*
... Merseyside: co-ordination of passenger transport services. [Liverpool] The University press of Liverpool, 1935.
39, [1] p. double map. 22cm.
At head of title: The University of Liverpool. Social science department: Statistics division.
"Second of a new series of reports in which an attempt is made to keep up-to-date some of the more important information published in the "Social survey of Merseyside ... Present report ... prepared by Mr. T. S. Simey ... and Dr. C. D. Campbell ..."—p. [4]
1. Transportation—England—Cheshire. [1. Cheshire, Eng.—Transportation] 2. Transportation—England—Lancashire. [2. Lancashire, Eng.—Transportation] 3. Transportation—England—Liverpool. [3. Liverpool—Transportation] I. Campbell, Charles Douglas, 1905- II. Simey, Thomas Spensley, 1906- III. Title.
U. S. Dept. of agr. Library for Library of Congress 289L75 [HE243.Z7] [3] Agr 37-533

NL 0418539 DLC DL

Liverpool. University. *Social Science Dept. Statistics Division.*
Merseyside: the relief of the poor. [Liverpool] Univ. Press of Liverpool, 1936.
24 p. 22 cm. (*Its* New Merseyside series, 3)
Prefatory note signed: D. Caradog Jones.
1. Liverpool—Charities. I. Jones, David Caradog. II. Title. III. Series.
HV250.L5L56 361.6 48-12207*

NL 0418540 DLC NcD NN ICU

Liverpool. University. *Social Science Dept. Statistics Division.*
Merseyside: trade and employment. [Liverpool] Univ. Press of Liverpool, 1935.
39 p. 22 cm. (*Its* New Merseyside series, 1)
Preferatory note signed: W. Caradog Jones.
1. Liverpool—Comm. 2. Unemployed—Liverpool. I. Jones, David Caradog. II. Title. III. Series.
HF3510.L5L48 382 47-44009*

NL 0418542 DLC NN

Liverpool. University. *Social science dept. Statistics division.*
... Migration to and from Merseyside: home, Irish, overseas. [Liverpool] The University press of Liverpool, 1938.
40 p. diagrs. 21½cm. (*Its* New Merseyside series, 7)
At head of title: The University of Liverpool. Social science department: Statistics division.
"The present study of migration by Mr R. S. Walshaw is an offshoot of research which recently earned for him the degree of master of arts in the University of Liverpool."—p. 5.
1. Gt. Brit.—Emig. & immig. I. Walshaw, Ronald Stanley. II. Title. III. Title: Merseyside, Migration to and from.
Library of Congress JV7615.L5 40-29525 325.427

NL 0418543 NN

Liverpool. University. Social science dept. Statistics division.

Walshaw, Ronald Stanley.
Migration to and from the British isles; problems and policies, by R. S. Walshaw ... with an introduction by D. Caradog Jones ... London, J. Cape [1941]

NL 0418545 DLC

Liverpool. University. *Social science dept. Statistics division.*
... New handbook of social statistics relating to Merseyside. [Liverpool] The University press of Liverpool, 1940.
40 p. incl. tables. 22cm. (*Its* New Merseyside series, 11)
At head of title: The University of Liverpool. Social science department: Statistics division.
Prefatory note signed: D. Caradog Jones.
1. Liverpool—Soc. condit. 2. Liverpool—Stat. I. Jones, David Caradog.
Library of Congress HA1139.L54 42-14058 312.094272

Liverpool.university. Social science dept. Statistics
...New handbook of social statistics relating to Merseyside. Liverpool, Univ. press, 1948. 36 p. 22cm.
"A continuation of the series of Handbooks of social statistics of Merseyside produced by Mr. D. Caradog Jones."
1. Liverpool—Stat. 2. Liverpool—Soc. condit. 3. Mersey river and valley, Eng.—Soc. condit.

Liverpool. University. Social science dept. Statistics division.
New Merseyside series
see under Liverpool. University. Social science dept.

Liverpool. University. *Social Science Dept. Statistics Division.*
Social service: overlapping and co-ordination, an examination of the Liverpool Register of mutual assistance. [Liverpool] Univ. Press of Liverpool, 1938.
39 p. 22 cm. (*Its* New Merseyside series, 6)
Prefatory note signed: D. Caradog Jones.
1. Liverpool—Charities. I. Jones, David Caradog. II. Series.
HV250.L5L57 360.942 47-44014*

Liverpool. University. Thompson Yates Laboratories
see Thompson Yates Laboratories.

VOLUME 336

Liverpool. University. Tidal Institute.

Established in 1920. In 1929 merged with the Liverpool Observatory to form the Liverpool Observatory and Tidal Institute.

Liverpool. University. Tidal Institute.
Annual report. 1- 1920-
Liverpool,The University Press.
illus.,maps. 27cm.

Ceased publication with 1928.
For 1929- see Liverpool. Observatory and Tidal Institute. Annual report.

NL 0418548 CtY

Liverpool. University. Tidal Institute
see also
Liverpool Observatory, Birkenhead, Eng.
Liverpool Observatory and Tidal Institute, Birkenhead, Eng.

Liverpool. University College.
Founded 1881. From 1884 to 1903, one of the colleges of Victoria University.
In 1903 Victoria University was reconstituted, and University college, Liverpool, was granted a charter under the name of University of Liverpool.

Liverpool. University college.
... Calendar for the session
Liverpool,
v. 19
At head of title: Victoria university. University college, Liverpool.

CA 6-1496 Unrev'd

Library of Congress LF374

NL 0418551 DLC

W 19.5 FE5 L6U5

LIVERPOOL. University College.
Catalogs, announcements of courses, requirements for admission and other publications relating to the academic program will be found under the above call number. Included also are similar publications of individual schools or departments of instruction of the institution.

NL 0418552 DNLM

Liverpool.
University College, Prospectuses of day classes in arts and science, and of the evening lectures for the years 1882; 1882-3; 1885-6. 12°. *Liverpool*, 1882-5.

NL 0418553 DNLM

Liverpool.
University College,
——. Report of the council for the year 1884-5. 37 pp. 8°. *Liverpool, J. A. Thompson & Co.*, 1885.

NL 0418554 DNLM

655.13 L75c

Liverpool. University college--Library.
... A catalogue of the books, printed and in manuscript, bequeathed by the late Thomas Glazebrook Rylands of Highfields, Thelwall, Cheshire, esquire, to the library of University college, Liverpool. Compiled by John Sampson, librarian to the college. [Liverpool] The University press of Liverpool, 1900.
113p.
At head of title: In memoriam. Thomas Glazebrook Rylands.
Title vignette (coat of arms)

NL 0418555 IU NNC

Liverpool.
University College, *Medical Department*. Prospectuses for the sessions of 1875-6 to 1883-4; 1885-6; 1888-9. 8° & 12°. *Liverpool & Edinburgh*, 1875-88.

NL 0418556 DNLM

Liverpool.
University College,
Department.
——. Suggestions upon preliminary examinations, and other matters relating to the education of medical students. 19 pp. 8°. *Liverpool*, [1878?].

NL 0418557 DNLM

QZ L785d 1883

LIVERPOOL. University College. Pathological Museum
Descriptive catalogue ... Liverpool, 1883.
viii, 268 p.

NL 0418558 DNLM NN

Liverpool. Watch Committee.
Liverpool city police. Instructions. 1911. Liverpool: C. Tinling & Co., Ltd., 1911. 428, xliv p. 8°.

122781A. 1. Police, Gt. Br.: England: Liverpool.
N. Y. P. L. April 24, 1924.

NL 0418559 NN

Liverpool. Watch Committee.

HV7730 L6A3

Liverpool. *Chief Constable.*
Report on the police establishment and the state of crime.
[Liverpool]

Engineering K TD 257 A1 L78

Liverpool. Water Committee.
Borough of Liverpool. New water supply. Third report of the Special Sub-committee amended and adopted as the report of the Water Committee, together with the following appendices: 1. Report of Professor Frankland ... Liverpool, Printed by H. Greenwood, 1879.
30, xxxvi p. tables (1 fold.) 25cm.
No. 2 in vol. lettered: Liverpool waterworks; reports, 1876-1888 [etc.]
1. Liverpool --Water-supply. I. Frankland, Sir Edward, 1825-1899.

NL 0418561 NIC

Engineering K TD 257 A1 L78

Liverpool. Water Committee.
Borough of Liverpool. Water supply. Report of the Water Committee, pursuant to a resolution of the Council of the 4th March, 1874. Rev. pursuant to a resolution of the Council of the 26th June, 1876. Rev. 27th June, 1876. Liverpool, Printed by H. Greenwood, 1876.
44, xvi p. 5 fold. tables, fold. map. 25cm.
No. 1 in vol. lettered: Liverpool waterworks; reports, 1876-1888 [etc.]
1. Liverpoo 1--Water-supply.

NL 0418562 NIC

Liverpool. Water committee.
... Report of Mr. George F. Deacon as to the Vyrnwy Masonry dam. Liverpool, A. Russell, son & Bayley, 1885.
36 p., 1 l. front, tables, diagrs. (part. fold. 24 cm. (At head of title: City of Liverpool additional water supply)
1. Water-supply - Liverpool. I. Deacon, George Frederick.

NL 0418563 CU DNLM

Liverpool. Water engineer.
——. Liverpool Corporation Water Works. Vyrnwy supply. Annual report of the water engineer as to the progress of the works, dated 30th June, 1884. [By George F. Deacon.] 7 pp., 1 map, 2 diag. 8°. *Liverpool, H. Greenwood*, 1884.

NL 0418564 DNLM

K TD 257 A1 L7

Liverpool. Water Engineer.
Liverpool Corporation Water Works. Vyrnwy supply. Second annual report of the Water Engineer as to the progress of the works. Dated 30th June, 1883. Liverpool, Printed by H. Greenwood, 1883.
7 p. 3 fold. charts, fold. map. 25cm.

At head of title: City of Liverpool.
Report signed: George F. Deacon, Water engineer.

No. 3 in vol. lettered: Liverpool waterworks; reports, 1876-1888 [etc.]

1. Liverpool--Water-supply. 2. Waterworks--England--Liverpool. I. Deacon, George Frederick. II. Title.

NL 0418566 NIC

Liverpool. Water engineer.
——. Liverpool water supply. Report of James Simpson and James Newlands (to the chairman of the water committee of the council of the borough of Liverpool). 99 pp., 1 pl. 8°. *Liverpool, D. Marples*, 1849.

NL 0418567 DNLM

LIVERPOOL. Water engineer.
A century of progress, 1847-1947; an account of the development of the Liverpool water supply undertaking since 1847. Liverpool [1947?] 23 p. illus., map. 19 x 24cm.

L. 1947.

NL 0418568 NN

VOLUME 336

Engineering
K
TD
257
A1
L78

Liverpool. Water Engineer.
Progress of the Vyrnwy Waterworks; annual report of the engineer. Liverpool, J. R. Williams, printers, 1888.
41 p. 3 fold. maps, fold. plate. 25cm.

At head of title: City of Liverpool.
Report signed: George F. Deacon.
No. 5 in vol. lettered: Liverpool waterworks; reports, 1876-1888 [etc.]
1. Waterworks --England--Vyrnwy Valley. I. Deacon, George Frederick. II. Title. III. Title: The Vyrnwy Waterworks.

NL 0418569 NIC

Liverpool. Water engineer.
... Report of the borough and water engineer, as to prevention of waste of water, restoration of constant service, and waste water meters. Liverpool: H. Greenwood, 1873. 17 p. 21cm.

Prepared for the Water committee.
With bookplate of Charles H. Swan.

——— ——— [Liverpool] H. Greenwood, 1874. 16 p. chart. 21cm.

At head of title: (Revised) ...
With bookplate of Charles H. Swan.

1. Water supply—Liverpool. I. Liverpool. Water committee.
N. Y. P. L. April 23, 1942

NL 0418570 NN IU

Liverpool, Zoölogical Gardens. 3889.173
List of the animals in the Liverpool Zoological Gardens with notices respecting them.
Liverpool. Ross & Nightingale. 1835. 35 pp. Sm. 8°.

G317 — Animals.

NL 0418571 MB

Liverpool . (Diocese)
The Liverpool diocesan leaflet.

[Liverpool]
no. in v. 19 cm. monthly.

1. Church of England—Period. I. Title.

BX5107.L55L5 283.42 53-2129

NL 0418572 DLC

Liverpool (Diocese)
Year book and clergy list.
Liverpool.
v. 19 cm.

1. Liverpool, Eng. (Diocese)—Direct. 2. Clergy—Liverpool, Eng. (Diocese)

BX5107.L55A32 55-31188

NL 0418573 DLC

Liverpool (Diocese) Committee on Local Ecclesiastical Records. *2504.161
Collection and custody of local ecclesiastical records. Report presented to the Lord Bishop of Liverpool, March 14th, 1910. 30 pp. (In Liverpool, England, Parish. The earliest registers of the Parish of Liverpool . . . Rochdale. 1909.)

NL 0418574 MB

Liverpool (Diocese) Committee on local ecclesiastical records.
The earliest registers of the parish of Liverpool (St. Nicholas's church) christenings
see under Liverpool. St. Nicholas' church.

Liverpool (Parish)
see Liverpool. St. Nicholas's church.

Liverpool. [London? 18--?]
27½ x 43½cm fold. in 14 x 9cm.

"J. H. Franks sculpt."

1. Liverpool - Maps. I. Franks, J H

NL 0418577 NNC

Liverpool a few years since, by an old stager
see under [Aspinall, James] 1795 or 6-1861.

Liverpool Albion.
The Euphrates route to India ... London, E. Wilson [1857]
8 p. 22.5 cm.

"Reprinted from the 'Liverpool Albion', 20th July, 1857."
Bound with Andrew, Sir W.P., Letter to Viscount Palmerston ... 1857.

NL 0418579 MH-BA

Liverpool almanac, tide table, and annual advertiser ... with a variety of general and local information.

Liverpool, D. Ross and W. Nightingale

v. 19cm.

: Presented to the subscribers of The Liverpool chronicle.

NL 0418580 NNC

Liverpool Amateur Photographic Association.
Catalogue of an exhibition of the work of Alvin Langdon Coburn, at the Association's rooms, April 30th until May 14th 1906. Pref. by G. Bernard Shaw. [London, 1906] cover-title, [8]p. 20cm.

1. Coburn, Alvin Langdon, 1882- I. Shaw, George Bernard, 1856-1950.

NL 0418581 IEN NIC CtY

Liverpool Amateur Photographic Association.
The history of the Liverpool amateur photographic association

see under

Good, George.

Liverpool Amateur Photographic Association
see also
Historic Society of Lancashire and Cheshire, *Liverpool.*

R.B.R. Liverpool and Charleston Steamship Company.
Liverpool and Charleston steamships.
Proceedings of a meeting held at the hall of the Bank of Charleston, February 22, 1861. Charleston [S. C.] Steam-Power Presses of Evans & Cogswell, 1861.
7 p. 23 cm.

1. Steamboat lines. Charleston, S. C. I. Confederate imprint. II. Title.

NL 0418584 NcD

Liverpool and District Association of Assistant Librarians.
Annual report.
[no.]
[Liverpool, 19 4°.
no.

19 typewritten.

1. Libraries.—Assoc. and organizations, Gt. Br.: England.
N. Y. P. L. April 5, 1921.

NL 0418585 NN

Liverpool and District Association of Assistant Librarians
see also Association of Assistant Librarians. Liverpool division.

Liverpool and District Regional Survey Association.
Population maps (13) for region around estuaries of Mersey and Dee, showing relative density of population in townships for years 1801, 1811, 1821, 1831, 1841, 1851, 1861, 1871, 1881, 1891, 1901, 1911 and 1921,.. [Liverpool, 1921?] 1 p.l., 13 maps. sq. f°.

277493A. 1. Population—Gt. Br.—Eng.—Dee river and valley. 2. Population—Gt. Br.—Eng.—Mersey river and valley. 3. Dee river and valley, Eng.—Maps. 4. Mersey river and valley, Eng.—Maps.
N. Y. P. L. March 18, 1927

NL 0418587 NN

Liverpool and district regional survey association.
Hewitt, William.
The Wirral peninsula: an outline regional survey, by W. Hewitt ... [Liverpool] The University press of Liverpool, ltd.; London, Hodder & Stoughton, ltd., 1922.

Liverpool and district regional survey association.
Hewitt, W.
... Workplaces and movement of workers in the Merseyside area based on the census returns, 1921. [By] W. Hewitt, B. SC. [Liverpool] University press of Liverpool, ltd.; London, Hodder & Stoughton, ltd., 1928.

Liverpool & Great Western Steamship Company. No. 1 in 6266.72
Official guide. . . . Appended, a tourist guide . . . for the use of passengers visiting Great Britain, and the continent of Europe, or the United States and Canada.
= Liverpool. Guion & Co. [1878?] Irregularly paged. Plates. Maps. Plans. 8°.

F5500 — Guide-books.

NL 0418590 MB

Liverpool and London and Globe insurance Company Limited.
1848–1898. Fifty years of work in the United States of America; being an account of the entry into the United States of the company now known as the Liverpool and London and Globe, in the year 1848 and of its work there for fifty years; with which is included a brief history of the establishment and general operations of the company. New York [J. C. & W. E. Powers Press] 1898.
124 p. illus., ports., plan. 24 cm.

I. Title: Fifty years of work in the United States of America.

HG8598.Z9L54 368.065 41-34224 rev*

NL 0418591 DLC WaS OrCS CU NcD NcU PHi

C.7470 **Liverpool & London & Globe insurance company limited.**
. . . Instructions to agents. London, R.Kinder [1848?]
47 p. fold. table. 21 cm.

NL 0418592 MH-BA

VOLUME 336

Liverpool and London and Globe Insurance Company limited.
1936; Our centenary year...
see under Simpson, Sir James Dyer.

Liverpool & London & Globe Insurance Company ltd.
Recurso de casación que el representante común de las compañías "North British and Mercantile" y "Liverpool and London and Globe," interpone contra la ejecutoria pronunciada ...
see under Alexanderson, Pablo, plaintiff.

HG8597
.A6
Liverpool and London and Globe insurance company limited.
Report and accounts ... 1949-
[Liverpool, 1949-
v.

1. Insurance - Gt. Brit. 2. Gt. Brit. - Insurance. I. Serials - Gt. Brit. - Annuals, etc.

NL 0418595 DS

Liverpool & London & Globe Insurance Company Limited.
Seventy-five years in the United States, 1848–1923. [New York, 1924?] 48 p. col'd front., ports. 4°.

1. Insurance, Fire—Companies—Gt. Br.
N. Y. P. L. April 25, 1925

NL 0418596 NN MB OC1W OC1 MH-BA NcU

Liverpool and London war risks insurance association, limited.
Gt. Brit. *Board of trade.*
Government war risks insurance scheme. Text of agreements made between His Majesty's government and the war risks insurance associations ... London, H. M. Stationery off., Darling and son, limited [printers] 1915.

Liverpool and Manchester geological journal. v. 1-
1951-
[Birkenhead, Eng.]
v. plates, maps (part fold.) diagrs. 20 cm. annual.

Supersedes the Proceedings of the Liverpool Geological Society and the Journal of the Manchester Geological Association.
Published by the Liverpool Geological Society and the Manchester Geological Association.

1. Geology—Societies, etc. I. Liverpool Geological Society. II. Manchester Geological Association.

QE1.L49 58-34636

KU OU TxU NNM ICJ
NL 0418598 DLC MoU PPT OU NNC CaBVaU OrCS OrU NbU

W 1
LI929F
The LIVERPOOL and Manchester medical and surgical reports. v. 1-6; 1873-78.
Liverpool.
6 v. illus.
Formed by the union of the Liverpool medical and surgical reports and the Manchester medical and surgical reports.
Superseded by the Liverpool medico-chirurgical journal.

NL 0418599 DNLM

Liverpool and Manchester photographic journal
see
British journal of photography.

HE
3020
.L78
A4
1832
Liverpool and Manchester railway company.
... Answer of the directors to an article in the Edinburgh review, for October, 1832. Liverpool, Printed by Wales and Baines, 1832.
32 p. 23 cm.
Signed: Chas. Lawrence, chairman.
"Letter from Mr. Earle to Dr. Lardner": p. 18-32.

I. Lawrence, Charles. II. Earle, Hardman. III. Lardner, Dionysius, 1793-1859.

NL 0418601 MiU CSmH CtY

Liverpool and Manchester railway company.
The book & programme of the Liverpool & Manchester railway centenary, LMR 1830 - LMS 1930 ...
see under Anderson, Matthew.

Liverpool and Manchester Railway Company.
Catalogue of the exhibition of literature, portraits, maps, plans and drawings, and of model railway locomotives, ancient and modern, held at St. George's hall, Liverpool, 13–20 September 1930, in commemoration of the opening on 15 September 1830 of the Liverpool and Manchester Railway. Liverpool[: The Northern Pub. Co., Ltd.], 1930. 56 p. front., plates. 21½cm.

Advertising matter interspersed.

720668A. 1. Railways—Exhibitions— Gt. Br.—Eng.—Liverpool, 1930.
N. Y. P. L. August 16, 1934

NL 0418603 NN

Liverpool and Manchester Railway Company.
...The centenary of the Liverpool and Manchester railway, 1830–1930
see under Liverpool. Public libraries, Museums and Art Gallery. Library.

Liverpool and Manchester railway company.
Descriptive catalogue of the padorama; of the Manchester and Liverpool rail-road, containing 10,000 square feet of canvass, now exhibiting at Baker street, Portman square, illustrated with twelve lithographic views, taken on the spot, by artists of acknowledged talent. London: Printed by E. Colyer, 1834. 16 p. front., plates. 22½cm.

Frontispiece and five plates signed: Drawn by H. West. E. Colyer, litho.

905761A. 1. Panoramas. I. Title.
N. Y. P. L. January 5 1938

NL 0418605 NN

Liverpool and Manchester Railway Company.
A guide to the Liverpool & Manchester railway
see under title

Liverpool and Manchester railway company.
Liverpool & Manchester rail-road bill. Reasons in favour of the bill. Second reading, in the House of commons, on Monday, 28th of February, 1825. [London] J. Bullock, printer [1825]
2 l. 32 cm.

NL 0418607 MH-BA

Liverpool and Manchester railway company.
Walker, James Scott, 1793–1850.
Liverpool and Manchester railway. Report to the directors on the comparative merits of loco-motive & fixed engines, as a moving power. By James Walker ... Second edition, corrected. London, Pub. by John and Arthur Arch, 1829.

Liverpool and Manchester railway company.
Liverpool and Manchester railway travelling, with an account of the times of departure and arrival of the different trains, fares, &c,&c; also, lists of the coaches from Liverpool, Manchester, and Chester, to various parts of the kingdom, and of the steam packets from Liverpool to Ireland, Scotland, Wales, and different parts of the coast... Liverpool, Printed by E. Smith and co.; reproduced by H. Blacklock & co., limited, Manchester [1831]
12p. 21.5cm.

NL 0418609 KU

Liverpool and Manchester railway company.
... Prospectus. [Liverpool, Printed by W. Wales and co., 1824]
[3] p. 32 cm.
Charles Lawrence, chairman.

NL 0418610 MH-BA

The Liverpool and Birkenhead official red book.
[no.]
Liverpool: Littlebury[, 190 12°.
v.
Annual.

1. Liverpool, Eng.—Yearbooks. 2. Liverpool, Eng.—Registers. 3. Birkenhead, Eng.—Yearbooks. 4. Birkenhead, Eng.—Registers.
N. Y. P. L. February 18, 1930

NL 0418611 NN

The Liverpool and Merseyside official red book.
Liverpool, Littlebury Bros.
v. 20 cm. annual.
Began publication in 1899.
On spine, : Liverpool official red book.
Issues for include "Liverpool 'Who's who.'"

1. Liverpool—Registers. 2. Liverpool—Biog. 3. Mersey Valley.

DA690.L8L85 49-22083*

NL 0418612 DLC

Liverpool and slavery: an historical account of the Liverpool-African slave trade ... Compiled from various sources and authentic documents ... with an interesting plate of the famous slave ship, the "Brookes" of Liverpool ... By a genuine "Dicky Sam" ... Liverpool, A. Bowker & son, 1884.
xii, 137 p. fold. pl. 22cm.
"The edition is limited to 500 copies."

1. Slave-trade — Gt. Brit. 2. Slave-trade — Africa. 3. Liverpool—Comm. I. A genuine "Dicky Sam."

43-48631

Library of Congress HT1162.L5

ICU CtY ICN CSmH OC1WHi
NL 0418613 DLC IEN CU NcD TNF MH MdBP PSC-Hi NIC

Liverpool & Texas Steamship Company.
The complete guide to Texas
see under title

VOLUME 336

1843E
L75 Liverpool Anti-Monopoly Association.
First annual report of the council of the Liverpool Anti-Monopoly Association for the year 1842, read at the annual meeting of the members, held January 25, 1843: the treasurers' account, and a list of members. 2d ed. Liverpool, Smith Rogerson, 1843.
37 p. 21cm.

NL 0418615 NNC MH-BA

Slavery
E
441
M46
v.60
no.3
Liverpool Anti-Slavery Society.
A report of the proceedings of the meeting of the Liverpool Anti-Slavery Society, held in the music hall, Bold-street, on Tuesday and Wednesday, the 19th and 20th December, 1837. With an appendix. Liverpool, Printed by E. Smith, 1838.
73 p. 22 cm.
May anti-slavery pamphlets, v. 60.
1. Slavery--Societies.

NL 0418616 NIC

Slavery
E
441
M46
v.42
no.4
v.43
no.2
v.44
no.8
Liverpool Anti-Slavery Society.
[Resolutions] at a meeting of the Committee held on Monday morning, the 16th of November, 1840. Liverpool, D. Marples [1840]
7 p. 23 cm.
May anti-slavery pamphlets, v. 42-44.
1. Slavery.

NL 0418617 NIC

WB
37170
The Liverpool Apollonius, or the geometrical and philosophical repository. no.1-2, London, Sherwood, Jones [etc., etc.] 1823-24.
2 no.
"By J.H. Swale."
1. Mathematics - Periodicals, etc. I. Swale, J H

NL 0418618 MBdAF DAU

The Liverpool architectural sketch book
see under Liverpool. University. School of architecture.

Liverpool Architectural Society.
Liverpool Architectural Society (incorporated) [Council, list of committees, annual report, etc.]
Liverpool.
v. illus. 22 cm.
1. Architecture—Societies.
NA12.L84 720.6242 50-41297 ‡

NL 0418620 DLC

Liverpool architectural society (incorporated)
Proceedings.
Liverpool, 18
v. plates, diagrs. 21½cm.
List of members in 1881/82.
1. Architecture—Societies.
Library of Congress NA12.L8 CA 9—1713 Unrev'd

NL 0418621 DLC

Liverpool art club.
... Catalogue of a loan collection of the works of Josiah Wedgwood exhibited at the Liverpool art club, February, 1879. Comp. by Charles T. Gatty. Liverpool, The Club, 1879.
xxiv, [25]-175, [1] p. illus. 21cm.
I. Gatty, Charles T., comp.
8-22884
Library of Congress

NL 0418622 DLC CtY NN

Liverpool art club.
NK7101
L5L5
... Catalogue of the exhibition of goldsmiths' art ... 2d ed. Liverpool, Liverpool art club, 1874.
54 p. 21.5 cm.
1. Goldsmithing. 2. Silversmithing.

NL 0418623 CSmH

Liverpool art club.
...Exhibition of illuminated manuscripts... Liverpool, Liverpool art club, 1876. 60 p. 22cm.
"Illuminated manuscripts," p. [7]-26, signed: John Newton.
1. Illumination of books and manuscripts—Exhibitions—Gt. Br.—Eng.—Liverpool. I. Newton, John, of Liverpool.
N. Y. P. L. January 8, 1945

NL 0418624 NN

Liverpool art club.
Ex-libris exhibition. Some notes on the decorative treatment of English ex-libris from 1574–1830; with a list of the book-plate designers of to-day, by J. Carlton Stitt ... Being the catalogue of an exhibition of English ex-libris, held at the Liverpool art club, January, 1895. Liverpool, D. Marples & co., printers [1895]
45 p. 21½cm.
1. Book-plates—Exhibitions. 2. Book-plates, English. I. Stitt, James Carlton.
16-25314
Library of Congress Z994.E5L5

NL 0418625 DLC

Liverpool art club.
... Loan collection of wood engravings ... Liverpool, Liverpool art club, 1878.
58 p. 22cm.
Committee of management: John Newton, T. Shadford Walker.
1. Wood-engravings—Exhibitions. 2. Wood-engravings—Hist.
9-25564†
Library of Congress NE1010.L6 1878

NL 0418626 DLC

Liverpool Association for the reduction of the duty on tea
see Liverpool. Association for the reduction of the duty on tea.

Liverpool association for the welfare of coloured people.
Liverpool. University. *Social science dept. Statistics division.*
... The economic status of coloured families in the port of Liverpool. [Liverpool] The University press of Liverpool, 1940.

Liverpool astronomical society.
Annual report...
Liverpool,
QB1
.L724

NL 0418629 DLC

Liverpool astronomical society.
... Catalogue of the library. Liverpool, Blevin & son, printers, 1888.
20 p. 22cm. [*With its* Journal. Liverpool [1888] v. 6]
8-4021
Library of Congress, no. QB1.L7.

NL 0418630 DLC

Liverpool astronomical society.
Laws of the Liverpool astronomical society. Revised 23rd October, 1886. [Liverpool, Printed by J. Blevin, 1886]
8 p. 21cm.
7-7265†
Library of Congress QB1.L73

NL 0418631 DLC

Liverpool astronomical society.
... List of members 1st March, 1887. Liverpool, W. Blevin & son, 1887.
cover-title, 16 p. 21½ cm.
At head of title: Liverpool astronomical society.

NL 0418632 DN-Ob

Liverpool Asylum for Orphan Boys. Annual reports of the committee to the subscribers for the years 1868–70. 8°. *Liverpool*, 1869–71.

NL 0418633 DN-Ob

Liverpool Biological Society.
Proceedings and transactions.
Liverpool.
v. illus.
Published 1886-1952/53.
Vols. 1-3 published as its Proceedings.

NL 0418634 ICRL PPAmP OkS FTaSU

Liverpool Cathedral
The form and order of the service that is to be performed and of the ceremonies that are to be observed in the consecration of the Cathedral Church of Christ, Liverpool by the Right Reverend Father in God, Albert Augustus, lord bishop of Liverpool in the presence of Their Majesties King George V and Queen Mary, on Saturday the nineteenth day of July, in the year of Our Lord one thousand nine hundred and twenty-four. [London: H. Milford, 1924.] 62 p. illus. (music.) 4°.
Contains the music of hymns, anthems, responses, etc., included in the service.
1. Cathedrals—Gt. Br.—Eng.—Liverpool.
N. Y. P. L. October 16, 1926

NL 0418635 NN PPPD

Liverpool. Cathedral.
The form and order of the service that is to be performed, and of the ceremonies that are to be observed ... within the Cathedral church of Christ, Liverpool on the occasion of the hallowing of the kinship of Liverpool with the sea ... on Sunday the ninth day of February in the year of our Lord one thousand nine hundred and thirty. [Liverpool, 1930]
1. Rites and ceremonies - Liverpool.

NL 0418636 CtY

VOLUME 336

Liverpool. Cathedral.
The form and order of the service that shall be used at the offering of the banner of the Royal institute of British archtects, 30 May, 1948. [Liverpool, Eaton press, 1948]

14 p.

NL 0418637 MH

Liverpool Cathedral.
Guidebook. n.p., n.d.

NL 0418638 PPLT

LIVERPOOL. CATHEDRAL.
The hallowing of the king's grace and the rejoicings over the king's majesty; for use in private devotions or by groups of king's pilgrims in the Liverpool Cathedral during the celebrations of the twenty-five auspicious years of the reign of King George V. [Liverpool, Eng., 1935] 10 p. 22cm.

866208A. 1. Liturgy—Church of England. 2. George V, king of Great Britain, 1865-1936.

NL 0418639 NN

Liverpool. Cathedral.
Liverpool Cathedral interpreters' book. [Liverpool, 1936]
50 p. plates, fold. plan. 19cm.

NL 0418640 NNC

Liverpool cathedral committe.
The building of the new Liverpool Cathedral
see under Harris, Charles, comp.

Liverpool cathedral committee.
Liverpool cathedral. Liverpool, Pub. by H. Young & sons, ltd., for the Liverpool cathedral committee, 1937.
16, [34], 17-20 p., 1 l. incl. plan. 34 plates (incl. front.) 28½cm.

Frontispiece accompanied by transparent guard-sheet with descriptive letterpress.

1.Liverpool. Cathedral.

NL 0418642 NNC IEN

Liverpool cathedral committee.
...Official handbook...
see under Cotton, Vere Egerton, 1888- comp.

Liverpool Cathedral Official handbook
see under Cotton, Vere Egerton, 1888- comp.

Liverpool Blue Coat Brotherly Society.
Annual reports of the trustees and committee of the Liverpool Blue Coat Brotherly Society to the members and friends. 27.-33., 1865-71: 38.-41., 1876-9; 43., 1881; 45., 1883. 8°. Liverpool, 1866-84.

NL 0418645 DNLM

HV250 Liverpool central relief and charity organization
.L7L7 society.
Annual report.
Liverpool,
v. 21-21½cm.

I.Liverpool-Charities.

NL 0418646 ICU DNLM

Liverpool Central Relief and charity organization Society.

——. Statements shewing operations and financial position of various local charitable institutions, issued with the best of local charities for which subscriptions and donations are received. 36 pp. 8°. Liverpool, Liverpool Printing Co., 1883.

NL 0418647 DNLM

HV250 Liverpool central relief and charity organization society.
.L7L72 Statements shewing operations and financial position of
1902 various Liverpool charitable institutions. Issued with the list of local charities for which subscriptions and donations are received at the office of the Liverpool central relief and charity organization society ... [Liverpool] Liverpool printing and stationery co., 1902.
64 p. illus. 20½cm.

1. Liverpool—Charities.

NL 0418648 ICU

Liverpool chamber of commerce (incorporated)
see
Liverpool. Chamber of commerce

Liverpool chemists' association.
Transactions, and annual report of the Liverpool chemists' association, with a list of officers & members, and additions to library & museum during the session. Session
Liverpool,
v. 21cm.

The proceedings of these meetings are more fully reported in the "Pharmaceutical journal" and "Chemist and druggist."

Library of Congress [33b1] QD1.L8 CA 6-1349 Unrev'd

NL 0418650 DLC

Liverpool chemists' association. *Library.*
A catalogue of the library of the Liverpool chemists' association with the laws, bye-laws, &c. Liverpool, Printed by Fearnall & co., 1877.
26 p. 21½cm.

1. Chemistry—Bibl.—Catalogs.

Library of Congress Z5526.L78 10—21070

NL 0418651 DLC

Liverpool Chess Club.
...Report...
18

[Liverpool, 18 21½cm.
no.
Report year ends Sept. 30th.

1. Chess—Clubs.
N. Y. P. L. June 8, 1933

NL 0418652 NN

Liverpool chess club; a short sketch
see under [Edgar, J S]

D LIVERPOOL CHURCH DEFENSE ASSOCIATION.
245 Proceedings of a meeting of clergy and laity,
.509 held at the Clarendon Rooms, Liverpool, on Tuesday, Dec. 5, 1859, on the present position of the church-rate question, including the address of J.M. Knott, Esq. ... Liverpool, A. Holden, 1859.
16p. 16cm.

"Reprinted from the Northern Daily Times."
Exact text of Knott's address not given.
"Quotations made by Mr. Knott, in illustrating the address. (From the 'Nonconformist', printed in the 'Liberator', September 1, 1859)": p.[13]-14.

NL 0418654 ICN

261.7
L785c Liverpool Citizen Sunday Council.
A city set free; a message from the churches to the citizens of Liverpool. Liverpool, Lee and Nightingale, 1930.
50p. 19cm.

1. Christianity and politics. 2. Church work. 3. Church societies. 4. Citizenship. Liverpool. I. T[itl]e.

NL 0418655 IEN

Liverpool city school of art
see
Liverpool. City school of art.

Liverpool college
see
Liverpool. University college

338.0942 The Liverpool commercial list, comprising
S519L1 Liverpool, Runcorn, St.Helens, Warrington and Widnes. year of issue;
By Seyd & co.ld. London,
v. 32cm.

1.Liverpool - Industries. 2.Gt.Brit. - Industires.

NL 0418658 CSt

VOLUME 336

Liverpool committee for excavation and research in Wales and the marches.
... Annual report... 1st- 1908-
Liverpool, At the university press, 1909-
v. 26 cm.

1. Wales—Antiq.

NL 0418659 CSmH PU

Liverpool compass committee.
First and second [and third] reports of the Liverpool compass committee to the Board of trade, 1855 & 1856 [and 1857-1860] ... London, Printed by G. E. Eyre and W. Spottiswoode, for H. M. Stationery off., 1857-62.
2 v. illus., diagrs. (part fold.) charts (part fold.) 33 cm.
Signed: Thos. Brocklebank, chairman, Liverpool compass committee.
On t.-p. of 1855 & 1856, "with letters from the astronomer royal thereupon."
1. Compass, Deviation of. 2. Magnetism of ships. I. Brocklebank, Sir Thomas, 1814-1906. II. Title.
QC849.L7 14—6519

NL 0418660 DLC DAS NjP DSI PU DN-Ob

Liverpool compass committee.
Magnetism of ships...with additional papers by Archibald Smith. & F. J. Evans. 1869.
6627

NL 0418661 DAS PPF

Liverpool corn trade association, limited.
Bye-laws of the Liverpool corn trade association, limited. In force on and after 1st June, 1911. [Liverpool, 1911]
3 p. l., 84 p. 22cm.
17-3201
Library of Congress HD9041.8.L5L6

NL 0418662 DLC

Liverpool Corn Trade Association, limited.
Bye-laws ... in force on and after 1st April, 1929. [Liverpool, 1929]
87 p.

1. Grain trade. Societies. 2. Grain exchanges. Liverpool.

NL 0418663 DNAL

HD9041 .8 L5L6 Giannini

Liverpool corn trade association, limited
The Liverpool corn trade association, 1853-1953. This brochure has been prepared to commemorate the centenary of the Association. Liverpool [1953]
64 p. illus.

1. Liverpool corn trade association, limited. 2. Grain trade - Liverpool.

NL 0418664 CU NN DNAL

HD9070 .4 .L64

Liverpool cotton association, limited.
Actual stock of all growths of cotton other than American held in Liverpool on the 1st December 1911.
Liverpool, 1911

NL 0418665 DLC DNAL

286.372 L75

Liverpool Cotton Association, limited.
A brief outline of the trading system recommended in the Hopkins Committee's report. [Liverpool, 1951?]
4 p.

1. Cotton trade. Gt.Brit.

NL 0418666 DNAL

Liverpool cotton association, limited.
Bye-laws of the Liverpool cotton association, limited. Liverpool, Turner, Routledge & co., 1883. 55 p. 25cm.

NL 0418667 NN CtY

Liverpool cotton association, limited.
Bye-laws of the Liverpool cotton association, limited. Liverpool, Turner, Routledge and co., printers, 1907.
viii, 77 p. incl. blank forms. 28½cm.
CA 17-3840 Unrev'd
Library of Congress HD9081.1.L6

NL 0418668 DLC

Liverpool cotton association, limited.
... Dockham's cotton merchants directory, embracing cotton factors, buyers, brokers, commission dealers, merchants, importers, exporters, f. o. b. sellers and future brokers, also Liverpool cotton association, ltd. members and foreign associate members. United States and Canada, 1923-
Boston, Dockham publishing company, °1923-

Liverpool cotton association, limited.
General by-laws, trading rules, clearing house rules and forms of contracts of the Liverpool cotton association, limited. Adopted 18th March, 1912. To come into force on 1st June, 1912. Liverpool, Turner, Routledge & co., printers, 1912.
68 numb. l., 1 l., [64] p. (forms 1-18b) 33½cm.
22-19095
Library of Congress HD9081.1.L6 1912

NL 0418670 DLC

Liverpool cotton association, limited.
The Liverpool cotton association annual circular ...
Liverpool,
v. 28½ x 23½cm.
Caption title.
1. Cotton trade—Societies. 2. Cotton trade—Stat.
12-25529
Library of Congress HD9070.4.L6

NL 0418671 DLC

MANN HD 9081 .8 L7 L7

Liverpool cotton association, limited.
Rules and forms of contracts of the Liverpool cotton association, ltd. Liverpool, Turner Routledge, 1924.
1 v. 34 cm.

1. Cotton trade - England - Liverpool.
I. Title.

NL 0418672 NIC

284.3729 L75

Liverpool Cotton Association, limited.
Value differences ... American cotton, based on universal standards for grade and on U.S.A. staple standards.
Liverpool.

1. Cotton. Prices.

NL 0418673 DNAL

Liverpool Council of Social Service.
Bulletin. v. -4 (no. -112), Jan. 19, 1943-Dec. 1946; new ser., no. 1- Sept. 1947-
[Liverpool]
v. 21-26 cm. monthly (irregular)
Supersedes Flowing tide.
Title varies: -Feb. 1944, Wartime bulletin of information; Apr. 1944-Dec. 1946, Bulletin of information.
INDEXES:
No. 63-88 (Issued as no. 89)
No. 90-111 (Issued as no. 112)
1. Liverpool—Charities.
HV250.L5L512 361.8 53-35516

NL 0418674 DLC NN

Liverpool council of social service.
The Flowing tide; a magazine of social service
see under title

Liverpool Council of Social Service.
Liverpool and the Liverpool Council of Voluntary Aid. A record of 21 years. Liverpool: Liverpool Council of Voluntary Aid, Inc. [, 1931.] 28 p. 8°.
Compiled by Mr. F. G. D'Aeth. — *cf. Pref.*
554909A. 1. Charities—Gt. Br.—Eng.—Liverpool. I. D'Aeth, Frederic George.
N. Y. P. L. November 30, 1931

NL 0418676 NN

Liverpool Council of Social Service.
D'Aeth, Frederic George.
Liverpool social workers' handbook ... prepared for the Liverpool council of voluntary aid by Frederic G. D'Aeth. Liverpool, D. Marples & co., 1913.

NA9188 .L6S5

Liverpool council of social service.
Shennan, Alfred Ernest.
... The post-war reconstruction of Liverpool, by Alderman A. Ernest Shennan ... Delivered at the annual meeting in the Town hall, on 10th December, 1941. Foreword by the Lord Mayor of Liverpool (Sir C. Sydney Jones ...) [Liverpool, Liverpool council of social service and the Merseyside civic society, 1942]

Liverpool Council of Social Service.
Report.
[Liverpool]
v. illus. 25 cm. annual.
Report year ends Sept. 30.
HV250.L5L514 361.8 51-40280 ‡

NL 0418679 DLC NN

VOLUME 336

Liverpool Council of Social Service.
Report on the uses of leisure in Liverpool. [Liverpool, 1923.]
28 p. incl. tables. 8°.
Issued under its earlier name: Liverpool Council of Voluntary Aid.

1. Working classes.—Intellectual life, Gt. Br.: Eng.: Liverpool. 2. Recreation, Gt. Br.: Eng.: Liverpool. 3. Leisure.
N. Y. P. L. December 1, 1924

NL 0418680 NN DL

HV9148 .L5L5
Liverpool Council of Social Service.
Liverpool. University. *Social Science Dept.*
Youthful lawbreakers, a study of juvenile delinquency in Liverpool. [Liverpool] University Press of Liverpool, 1948.

Liverpool Council of Voluntary Aid
see
Liverpool Council of Social Service.

Liverpool Crematorium Company. *6230a.43
Annual report of the council. 11th. 1902.
= [Liverpool, 1902.] (3) pp. F°.

F4417 — Cremation.

NL 0418683 MB

Liverpool Crematorium Company.
The Liverpool Crematorium, Anfield.
Liverpool [1897]
4 p. illus.

NL 0418684 ICJ

Liverpool currency reform association
see Currency reform association, Liverpool.

D760 .8 .L6B6
Liverpool daily post and echo ltd.
Bombers over Merseyside, this was Merseyside's 'finest hour': the authoritative record of the blitz, 1940–1941 ... Liverpool, Daily post and echo ltd., 1943.

Liverpool daily post and echo ltd.
Country heritage; the stately homes of the north west counties and north Wales. [Liverpool] 1951.
112 p. illus. 28 cm.

1. Architecture, Domestic—Gt. Brit. I. Title.
NA7328.L58 728.3 52-41954 ‡

NL 0418687 DLC CSt

NA9188 .L5M4
Liverpool daily post and echo ltd.
Merseyside civic society, *Liverpool.*
Merseyside of the future; report of the Merseyside civic competition organised by the Merseyside civic society in association with the Liverpool daily post. Edited by James R. Spencer. Liverpool, Daily post and echo ltd., 1944.

DA690 .L8P63
Liverpool Daily Post and Echo ltd.
Pictures from the Post.
[Liverpool] Liverpool Daily Post & Echo.

Liverpool daily post and mercury.
...The ambassador of commerce for the city and port of Liverpool and the adjoining boroughs.
[Liverpool, 1924]

HC258 .L5L5

NL 0418690 DLC

Liverpool daily post and mercury.
...The ambassador of commerce; ...
[Liverpool, 1927]

HC258 .L5L5 1927

NL 0418691 DLC

Liverpool daily post and mercury.
...The foundations of Liverpool's greatness,...
[Liverpool, 1927]

HC258 .L5L52

NL 0418692 DLC

Liverpool Dental Hospital. Annual reports of the committee to the subscribers. 8.-10., 1868-70; 17., 1877. 17 pp. 8°. *Liverpool, D. Marples & Co., 1869-78.*

NL 0418693 DNLM

The Liverpool directory
see Liverpool's directory.

Liverpool Dispensaries
see Liverpool. Dispensaries.

Liverpool Domestic Mission Society.
Reports [of the ministers to the poor], resolutions of the annual meeting...and statement of accounts for the year.

Liverpool & London 16°.
v.
In: *C p. v. 1476.
1855 includes Reports of J. Wilson and [T.] Jones.
Also another part of 1857: Report of S. A. Steinthal.
2d report issued in 1838.

1. Missions (Home), Gt. Br.: Eng.: Liverpool.
N. Y. P. L. May 13, 1914.

NL 0418696 NN MB

**T.29.7
Liverpool Dramatic Censor, The, or theatrical recorder; containing strictures on actors . . . and a critical analysis of every popular dramatic composition represented at the Theatre Royal . . . With biographical sketches of celebrated dramatists. Vol. 1.
= Liverpool. Troughton. 1806. 286 pp. Plates. 14½ cm., in 6s.

J657 — Liverpool, England. Theatres. Theatre Royal. — Drama. Period. — Periodicals.

NL 0418697 MB NNC

Liverpool East India Association.
East India and China trade. [Liverpool, 1830]
2 p. 33 cm.
Caption title.

NL 0418698 CtY

Liverpool East India association.
Report of a committee of the Liverpool East India association, appointed to take into consideration the restrictions on the East India trade. Presented to the association at a general meeting, 9th May 1822, and ordered to be printed. Liverpool, Printed for the association, by J. Smith, 1822.
58, 40 p. 20 cm.
On t.-p. in manuscript: James Cropper (part of note at top trimmed off)

Appendix (40 p. at end) contains reports of the Select committee on foreign trade of the House of lords and of the House of commons.

1. East India company (English) 2. Gt. Brit. - Comm. - East Indies. 3. East Indies - Comm. - Gt. Brit. I. Gt. Brit. Parliament. House of lords. Select committee on foreign trade. II. Gt. Brit. Parliament. House of commons. Select committee on foreign trade.

NL 0418700 Vi ICN CtY IEN CaBViPA MiD MH-BA ICU OO

Micro 3
Liverpool East India Association.
Report of a committee of the Liverpool East India Association, appointed to take into consideration the restrictions on the East India trade. Presented to the Association at a general meeting, 9th May, 1822, and ordered to be printed. Liverpool, Printed for the Association by J. Smith, 1822.
2cards(3sides). 7.5x12.5cm. (Slavery Pamphlets)
Micro-opaque. Louisville, Ky., Lost Cause Press, 1962.
Collation of the original: 58,40p

NL 0418701 PSt CaBViPA

Liverpool East India association.
Report of the Committee of the Liverpool East India association, on the subject of the trade with India. Presented to the association at a general meeting, 21st March, 1828. Liverpool, G. Smith [etc., etc.] 1828. 40 p. 21cm.

1. Commerce—Gt. Br. and India, 1828. 2. Commerce—India and Gt. Br., 1828. 3. East India company.
N. Y. P. L. April 25, 1945

NL 0418702 NN MH MH-BA MB IU

Liverpool East India Association.
Report on the funds and finances of the East India company, presented to the Liverpool general committee on the East India and China trade. [Liverpool, 1828?]
4 p. 33 cm.
Caption title.

NL 0418703 CtY

VOLUME 336

Liverpool East India Association.
Statement of the reasons for the removal of all restrictions on the trade with India, and on the residence of British subjects in that country, and for throwing open the trade with China. Issued by the Liverpool committee, as central committee for the principal cities and towns of the kingdom. [Liverpool, 1828]
4 p. 33 cm.
Caption title.

NL 0418704 CtY

HD8039 .L82G769
Liverpool Economic and Statistical Society.
Williams, Richard, B. A.
... The first year's working of the Liverpool docks scheme, by R. Williams ... London, P. S. King & son, 1914.

Liverpool economic and statistical society.
Liverpool joint research committee.
How the casual labourer lives. Report of the Liverpool joint research committee on the domestic condition and expenditure of the families of certain Liverpool labourers. Read before and pub. by the Liverpool economic and statistical society ... Liverpool, The Northern publishing co., ltd., 1909.

HD8039 .L82G77
Liverpool economic and statistical society.
Williams, Richard.
The Liverpool docks problem, by R. Williams ... ⌊Liverpool, The Northern publishing co., ltd., 1912⌋

Liverpool economic and statistical society
Transactions.

NL 0418708 DL

Liverpool Engineering Society.
Journal. v.1- Aug.1955-
Liverpool.

Supersedes the society's Bulletin.
Absorbs and continues the session numbering of the society's Transactions (in Crerar set, 87th session- 1960/61-)
I. Its Transactions, 87th session- 1960/61-
620.51 620.6151

NL 0418709 ICJ

Liverpool engineering society.
Report.
⌊Liverpool, 18
v. 21-22cm.
Report year irregular.
"Rules of the society" and "List of members" in each vol.
Title varies: 1884-85, Annual report.
1886-87, Annual report and statement of accounts.
1889-1892/93, Report ... and statement of accounts.
Continued in its Transactions, beginning with v. 15, 1893/94; the separate issue was later resumed, with title as in 1893/94 (with slight variation)
Library of Congress TA1.L72 CA 6-2136 Unrev'd

NL 0418710 DLC ICJ

Liverpool engineering society.
Transactions of the Liverpool engineering society. v. 1-
Liverpool, The Society, 1881-
v. illus., plates, ports., map, tables, diagrs. 21½cm.
Editors: ⌊1877/80⌋ Wilfrid S. Boult.—1880/81-18 Edward H. Allies.—18 Robert L. Tapscott and Wilfrid S. Boult.—1885-86, Thomas L. Miller.—1887-⌊1891/92⌋ J. H. T. Turner ⌊i. e. J. H. T. Tudsbery⌋—⌊1892/93⌋- R. C. F. Annett.
Annual reports of the society were issued separately up to and including the 19th session, 1892/93, since which they have been included in the Transactions beginning with v. 15, 1893/94.
An index to Transactions for preceding years (1875 to current year) is issued with each volume, beginning with v. 20.
1. Engineering—Societies. I. Boult, Wilfrid S., ed. II. Allies, Edward H., ed. III. Tapscott, Robert L., ed. IV. Miller, Thomas L., ed. V. Tudsbery, John Henry Tudsbery, 1859-1939, ed. VI. Annett, R. C. F., ed.
Library of Congress TA1.L7 6—16865

NL 0418711 DLC ViBlbV PPF ICJ NcRS FMU OCl ICJ MiU

Liverpool engineering students' society.
see
Liverpool engineering society.

Liverpool English reprints. London.
No.1,1948-

NL 0418713 NcGU

820.6 L785
Liverpool English texts and studies. ⌊no.1⌋- 1948-
⌊Liverpool⌋
General editor: 1948- Kenneth Muir.

NL 0418714 MiU CtNlC DCU NNC MH

Liverpool enquiry and employment bureau for educated women.
... Annual report. 10. 1907.
(Liverpool, 1907-15)
8 v. 26 cm.

NL 0418715 DL

⌊Liverpool Evangelical Sunday School Union⌋
Papers read at the Sunday school conference held at Liverpool, September, 1865. Also the introductory sermons by Rev. R. W. Forrest, and Rev. W. M. Taylor. Liverpool: Evangelical Sunday School Union ⌊1866⌋. xii, 145 p. 12°.
In: ZEC p. v. 63, no. 10.
1. Sunday-schools, Great Britain.—Conferences: Liverpool, 1865. 2. Sunday-schools.—Organization and management. 3. Forrest, Rev. R. W. 4. Taylor, Rev. W. M.
N. Y. P. L. September 29, 1913.

NL 0418716 NN

Liverpool Fabian Society
see Fabian Society, Liverpool.

Liverpool Female Orphan Asylum. Annual reports. 1868-70; 1874. 27 pp. 8°. *Liverpool, E. Smith & Co.* 1869-75.

NL 0418718 DNLM

Liverpool Financial Reform Association
see Financial Reform Association, Liverpool.

Liverpool first edition club.
...Catalogue of the first exhibition by members of finely printed books from modern presses, May 21-24, 1930. With a foreword by Eric Gill. The Basnett gallery, The Bon marché (Liverpool) ltd. Liverpool. ⌊Liverpool, 1930⌋ 31(1) p. 21cm.
"Printed at the Fanfare press ⌊London⌋"
1. Books—Exhibitions—Gt. Br.—Eng.—Liverpool, 1930.

NL 0418720 NN CLU NNC MiD ICN CLU-C WaSpG NN CSt IEN

Liverpool Friends Institute.
Report of the Proceedings of the Inaugural Meeting of the Liverpool Friends' Institute held 10th mo. 23rd, 1860, also of the General Meeting of subscribers held 10th mo. 22d, 1860. Liverpool, 1860.

NL 0418721 PSC-Hi

Beinecke Library Z17 00476
The Liverpool general advertiser: or, The commercial register. no.1- Dec. 27, 1765-
[Liverpool: Printed by W. Nevett and Co., etc.]
43cm. weekly.
1. Periodicals

NL 0418722 CtY

Liverpool geographical society.
Transactions and 1st- annual report of the council of the Liverpool geographical society ... 1892-
Liverpool ⌊1893⌋-
v. in illus., plates, maps. 21½-24½cm.
Report year ends December 31.
Title varies: 1892, Report of the council of the Liverpool geographical society.
1893-95, Annual report of the council ...
1896- Transactions and annual report of the council ...
"Catalogue of books, articles, guides, handbooks, maps, &c., of the ... society": 22 p., appended to 4th report.
List of members in 2d- reports.
1. Geography—Societies.
Library of Congress G7.L78 17-14197

NL 0418723 DLC IU ICJ

Liverpool geological association.
Proceedings ...
Liverpool, 1881-1910.
v. in illus., plates (part col.) maps, diagr. 21-22cm.
Title varies: 1880/81-1886/87 (⌊v. 1⌋-7) ... Transactions.
1887/88- ... Journal.
1909/10, Proceedings of the Liverpool geological association.
Includes annual reports of the association.
Amalgamated with the Liverpool geological society in 1910, under the name of the latter.
1. Geology—Societies.
13-10028
Library of Congress QE1.L5

NL 0418724 DLC CaBVaU

Liverpool geological society.
Laws of the Liverpool geological society. As revised, November 12th, 1878. Liverpool, C. Tinling & co., printers, 1878.
11 p. 21cm.
Corrected to 1891 in ms.
CA 10-1088 Unrev'd
Library of Congress QE1.L65 1878

NL 0418725 DLC

QE1 .L49
Liverpool Geological Society.
Liverpool and Manchester geological journal. v. 1- 1951-
⌊Birkenhead, Eng.⌋

VOLUME 336

Liverpool Geological Society.
Proceedings. v. [1]– (session 1/2–); 1860/61–
Liverpool [etc.]
v. illus., maps (part fold., part col.) 22 cm.
Title varies: 1860/61–1873/74, Abstract of the proceedings.
With v. 1 is bound: Morton, G. H. The geology and mineral veins of the country around Shelve, Shropshire. Liverpool, 1869.

1. Geology—Societies.

QE1.L6 13–10029 rev*

NL 0418727 DLC ICJ CCC

QE 51 .44 L59 **Liverpool Geological Society**
A retrospect of fifty years' existence and work. By W. Hewitt. Liverpool, C. Tinling and Co., Ltd., Printers, 1910.
117 p. 21 cm.
At head of t.-p.: The Liverpool Geological Society ...

1. Liverpool Geological Society. I. Hewitt, William

NL 0418728 ICF

W1 L1929N **The Liverpool health of towns' advocate.** no. 1-20; Sept. 1845-July 1847. Liverpool, J. Wamsley [etc.]
20 no. in illus.
Issued by Liverpool Health of Towns' Association.
Edited by J. Sutherland.
No more published?
I. Liverpool Health of Town's Association.
II. Sutherland, John, 1808-1891, ed.

Lack no. 20

NL 0418729 DNLM

Liverpool Health of Town's Association.
The Liverpool health of towns' advocate
see under title

Liverpool Hebrews' Educational Institution and Endowed Schools.
Report of the ceremonial and proceedings in connection with laying the foundation stone of the new schools... Aug. 31st, ... with a list of donations, etc.
Liverpool, E. Smith & Co., [1852]
24 p.

NL 0418731 OCH

Liverpool Hospital for Consumption and Diseases of the Chest, Mount Pleasant. Annual reports of the committee to the subscribers and governors. 4., 1867; 12., 1875. 8°. *Liverpool*, 1868–76.
Established 1864.

NL 0418732 DNLM

Liverpool Hospitals Commission.
Report on the voluntary hospitals of Liverpool. [Liverpool] Univ. Press of Liverpool, 1935.
x, 184 p. 25 cm.

1. Liverpool—Hospitals.

RA988.L5L5 362.1 Med 47–2386*

NL 0418733 DLC NNC

Liverpool hospitals joint advisory committee.
... The demand for rehabilitation and convalescent treatment. A report on a survey conducted in Liverpool hospitals during the three weeks, 5th to 25th March, 1945. [Liverpool] 1946.
28 p. 21½cm.

1. Disabled—Rehabilitation [etc.—Gt. Brit.] 2. Hospitals, Convalescent. 3. Liverpool—Hospitals. [3. Hospitals—Liverpool]

Med 47–1105

U. S. Army medical library for Library of Congress [W6P3] [2]

NL 0418734 DNLM

Liverpool Industrial Ragged Schools (certified). Annual reports of the committee to the subscribers. 3., 1851; 17., 1865; 18., 1866. 8°. *Liverpool*, 1852–67.
Established 1849.

NL 0418735 DNLM

Liverpool Industrial Ragged Schools (certified). Annual report of the committee to the subscribers. 22., 1870. 19 pp. 8°. *Liverpool, D. Marples*, 1870.
Established 1849.

NL 0418736 DNLM

Liverpool Industrial Ragged Schools.
Report of the 1st Annual Meeting, held. 4th Febr., 1850. ... Liverpool, 1850.
42 p. 8°. [In v. 1258, College Pamphlets.]

NL 0418737 CtY

Liverpool Infant Orphan Asylum
see Liverpool. Infant Orphan Asylum.

Liverpool institute addresses. [Liverpool? 1887?]
[266] p. 18cm.
Binder's title.
Various paging.
Imperfect: p. 9–20 of the address on Natural selection for science and for art, by B. W. Richardson, wanting.
CONTENTS.—Education for men of business. An address, delivered in the Liverpool institute, 1st December, 1874, by James Bryce.—National culture and recreation antidotes to vice. An address, delivered in the Liverpool institute, 8th December, 1875, by Henry Cole.—Higher and secondary education. An address, delivered in the Liverpool institute, 8th November, 1876, by M. E. G. Duff.—On the cultivation of the imagination. An address, delivered in the Liverpool institute, 29th November, 1877, by G. J. Goschen.—How the study of history is let and hindered.

An address, delivered in the Liverpool institute, 19th November, 1879, by E. A. Freeman.—The place and function of poetry in education. An address, delivered in the Liverpool institute, 26th November, 1880, by Lewis Morris.—On science and art in relation to education. An address, delivered in the Liverpool institute, February 16th, 1883, by Professor Huxley.—Success. An address, delivered in the Liverpool institute, December 19th, 1884, by William Rathbone.—Liberal education, past and present: a retrospect and a contrast. An address, delivered in the Liverpool institute, 21st December, 1885, by G. O. Morgan.—Natural selection for science and for art. An address, delivered in the Liverpool institute, 17th December, 1886, by B. W. Richardson.—The subjects and objects of study. An address, delivered in the Liverpool institute, 25th October, 1887, by John Lubbock.
1. Education—Addresses, [essays], lectures, [etc.]

E 15-2668

Library, U. S. Bur. of Education LB41.L75

NL 0418740 DHEW

Liverpool institute of archaeology.
see
Liverpool. University. Institute of archaeology.

WY 19 L782a **LIVERPOOL Institution for the Training and Employment of Nurses**
Annual report.
Liverpool [1855?]-
v. in
Reports for 1871-83 include several miscellaneous publications.

NL 0418742 DNLM

Liverpool Institution for the training and employment of Nurses.
——. Fundamental laws. 2 pp. 8°. [*Liverpool, n. d.*]

NL 0418743 DNLM

Liverpool Institution for the training and employment of Nurses.
——. Rules. 3 pp. 4°. [*Liverpool, n. d.*]
——. The same. 2 l. 4°. [*Liverpool*, 188-.]

NL 0418744 DNLM

Liverpool: its trade and commerce; official handbook of the Liverpool chamber of commerce (incorporated) with classified trade indices in English, French, Spanish, Italian, and Russian; also trade mark section. 1st– issue; 1918–
Derby [etc.] Bemrose & sons, ltd., 1918–
v. illus., plates. 25½cm.

1. Liverpool—Comm. 2. Liverpool—Indus. I. Liverpool. Chamber of commerce.

Library of Congress HF302.L75 20-9349

NL 0418745 DLC CU PPC NN ICJ

Liverpool joint research committee.
How the casual labourer lives. Report of the Liverpool joint research committee on the domestic condition and expenditure of the families of certain Liverpool labourers. Read before and pub. by the Liverpool economic and statistical society ... Liverpool, The Northern publishing co., ltd., 1909.
xxxvi p., 1 l., 114 p. fold. tables. 22cm.
Pages xxxiii–xxxvi, 1 leaf duplicated.

1. Cost and standard of living—Liverpool. 2. Labor and laboring classes—Liverpool. I. Liverpool economic and statistical society, pub. II. Title.

Library of Congress HD7023.L7 10–15797

NL 0418746 DLC WaS CU ICJ NN MiU

Liverpool journal of commerce
see
The Journal of commerce and shipping telegraph, *Liverpool*.

Liverpool labour chronicle
see The labour chronicle and trades union reporter.

4HV 525 Liverpool Ladies' Union of Workers Among Women and Girls.
Women workers; papers read at a conference convened by the Liverpool Ladies' Union of Workers Among Women and Girls in November 1891. Liverpool, G. G. Walmsley, Printer, 1892.
267 p.

NL 0418749 DLC-P4

Liverpool library.
Catalogue of the Liverpool library at the Lyceum, Bold-street. Liverpool, Printed by J. Smith, 1814.
392 p. 21½cm.
Error in paging: numbers 263–264 repeated, 283–284 omitted.
Classified, with indexes of authors and anonymous works.

38-34698

Library of Congress Z921.L328

017.1

NL 0418750 DLC

VOLUME 336

017.1
L756 LIVERPOOL LIBRARY.
Catalogue of the Liverpool library. MDCCCL. Liverpool, T.Brakell, printer, 1850.

6 p.l., [7]-30, 532p. 22cm.

Title vignette.
"This library... is believed to be the only instance of the combination on a large scale, of the proprietary principle with that of circulation."- Pref.

1. Catalogs, Library. 2. Libraries, Subscription.

NL 0418751 MnU

MICROFILM
A3105 Liverpool Library
A catalogue of the present collection of books in the Liverpool Library, to which is prefixed a copy of the laws and a list of the subscribers. [Liverpool] Printed by John Sadler, 1760.
38 p.

Microcopy of the original.

1. Library catalogs.

NL 0418752 WaU

Liverpool Licensed Victuallers' Association.
Annual report.
no. 38-
(1868)-
Liverpool, 1868- 16°.

1. Saloons, Gt. Br.: Eng.: Liverpool.
N. Y. P. L. May 12, 1914.

NL 0418753 NN

Liverpool life
see under Shimmin, Hugh, d. 1879.

Liverpool liturgy
see Liverpool. Unitarian Church.
A form of prayer ...

The Liverpool, London & Paris guide and continental indicator ...
see under Guion line of United States mail streamers.

Liverpool marine biology committee.

Founded 1885; discontinued Dec. 31, 1919, when its work was transferred to the newly established Department of oceanography of the University of Liverpool.
The committee, during its existence, conducted work at Liverpool, 1885-1919; at Puffin Island, Anglesey, 1887-1892; and at Port Erin, Isle of Man, 1892-1919.
The Puffin Island station was taken over by Dr. Philip J. White, Prof. Reginald Phillips, and others connected with the University college of North Wales, at Bangor, who formed a local committee to carry on the work.

Liverpool marine biology committee.
... Annual report ... [1st]- [1886/87-
Liverpool, 1888-1919.

v. illus., plates (part col.) ports., maps, plans, tables. 21½cm.

Title varies: 1886/87, The foundation and first season's work of the Liverpool marine biological station on Puffin Island. By W. A. Herdman.
1887/88-1891, Annual report of the Liverpool marine biological station on Puffin Island. By W. A. Herdman. 2d-5th.
1892-1919, Annual report of the Liverpool marine biology committee, and their Biological station at Port Erin (Isle of Man) By W. A. Herdman ... 6th-33d. (With slight variations)

Issued also in Proceedings and transactions of the Liverpool biological society.
"Guide to the aquarium" is included in the 15th report; a 2d edition of the same is included in the 19th report.
Historical sketches of the committee and its work are to be found in the 16th and 33d reports.
The committee was discontinued Dec. 31, 1919, when its work was transferred to the Department of oceanography of the University of Liverpool; the reports of the Marine biological station at Port Erin are continued by the department in a style uniform with the reports of the committee.

1. Biology—Societies, etc. I. Herdman, William Abbott, 1858-

Library of Congress QH323.P8A2 21-6534

NL 0418759 DLC MdBJ CtY ICRL ICJ IU PBm

Liverpool marine biology committee.
The first report upon the fauna of Liverpool bay and the neighbouring seas, written by the members of the Liverpool marine biology committee, and edited by W. A. Herdman. With ten plates and two maps. London, Longmans, Green & co., 1886.

iv, 372 p. incl. tables. x pl. (1 col.) 2 fold. maps. 23cm.

At head of title: L. M. B. C. reports. no. 1.

1. Marine fauna. I. Herdman, Sir William Abbott, 1858-1924, ed.

A 18-1508

Harvard univ. Library
for Library of Congress [a47b1]

NL 0418760 MH ICJ

Liverpool Marine Biological Committee.
... L.M.B.C. memoirs on typical British marine plants & animals...
see under Liverpool. University. Dept. of Oceanography.

Zool. Mus.
Liverpool Marine biology committee.
Memoirs [Prospectus]. Dec.1899.

vii p.

NL 0418762 MH-Z

Liverpool Marine Biology Committee.
Memoirs on Br. marine plants & animals.
Liverpool, 1899-
v. 1-

NL 0418763 NjP

Liverpool marine biology committee.
... Report upon the fauna of Liverpool Bay and the neighbouring seas, written by the members of the Liverpool marine biology committee.
London, 1886-

v. plates (part col.) maps. 22½cm. (L. M. B. C. reports. no. 1)

First report issued as appendix to Proceedings of the Literary and philosophical society of Liverpool. no. XL. (Issued also separately)
Editor: 1886- W. A. Herdman.

1. Marine fauna—England. I. Herdman, William Abbott, 1858- ed.

17-14215

Library of Congress AS122.L41 no. 40

NL 0418764 DLC IU CU MiU

Liverpool marine biology committee
see also
Liverpool. University. *Dept. of oceanography.*

Liverpool marine biology committee. *Port Erin biological station.*
... Guide to the aquarium: being a short account of some of the common marine animals of the neighbourhood. With illustrations ... Liverpool, C. Tinling & co., printers, 1901.

[41]-84 p. illus. 21cm. (*In* Liverpool marine biology committee. 15th annual report)

1. Marine fauna—Irish Sea.

Library of Congress QH323.P8A2 5-23849

NL 0418766 DLC

Liverpool marine biology committee. *Port Erin biological station.*
... Guide to the aquarium: being a short account of some of the common marine animals of the neighbourhood. With illustrations ... Liverpool, C. Tinling & co., printers, 1902.

44 p. illus. 31cm.

Also issued in the 15th Annual report of the Liverpool marine biology committee, 1901.

1. Marine fauna—Irish Sea.

9-1905

Library of Congress QL79.P8A3

NL 0418767 DLC

Liverpool marine biology committee. *Port Erin biological station.*
... Guide to the aquarium: being a short account of some of the common marine animals of the neighbourhood, drawn up by Professor W. A. Herdman ... With many illustrations, mostly prepared for this work by Herbert C. Chadwick ... 2d ed. ... Liverpool, C. Tinling & co., ltd., printers, 1906.

[55]-131 p. illus. 21cm. (*In* Liverpool marine biology committee. 19th annual report)

1. Marine fauna—Irish Sea. I. Herdman, William Abbott, 1858-
II. Chadwick, Herbert Clifton.

Library of Congress QH323.P8A2 6-17465

NL 0418768 DLC CU

Liverpool marine biology committee. Port Erin biological station
see also Liverpool. University. Dept. of oceanography. Port Erin biological station.

W 1
L193 The LIVERPOOL medical and surgical reports.
v. 1-5; Oct. 1867-Oct. 1871.
London.
5 v. illus.

United with the Manchester medical and surgical reports to form the Liverpool and Manchester medical and surgical reports.

NL 0418770 DNLM PPC ICJ

Liverpool Medical Institution.
——. City of Liverpool. Amendment to the building and sanitary act. Suggested amendments. 2 l. 4°. [*Liverpool*, 1881.]
Private; printed for members only.

NL 0418771 DNLM

Liverpool Medical Institution. Report of the discussion on the exclusion of homœopathic practitioners, and on the publication of the proceedings of the institution, January 28, 1859. 52 pp. 12°. *London, T. Richards*, 1859. [P., v. 1108.]

NL 0418772 DNLM

VOLUME 336

Z 675.M4 L785c 1861
Liverpool Medical Institution. Library.
Catalogue ... with the laws and a list of members. Liverpool, Brakell, 1861.
xxii, 206, 36 p.

"Supplement ... 1876" (36 p. at end with special title-page)

1. Medicine - Bibliography - Catalogs

NL 0418773 DNLM

Liverpool Medical Missionary Society. Report for the year 1874, and of the annual meeting. 1l., 1874. 38 pp., 2 l. 12°. *Liverpool*, 1875.

NL 0418774 DNLM

QZ 200 L785c 1928
LIVERPOOL Medical Research Organization.
Cancer and cancer research; a series of articles for the lay public. Manchester, Sherratt & Hughes, 1928.
75 p.
"These articles appeared first during March, April, and May, 1928, in the Liverpool Daily Post and Mercury."
1. Cancer 2. Cancer research

NL 0418775 DNLM

Liverpool medical research organization.

Bell, William Blair, 1871- *ed.*
Some aspects of the cancer problem; an account of researches into the nature and control of malignant disease commenced in the University of Liverpool in 1905, and continued by the Liverpool medical research organization (formerly the Liverpool cancer committee), together with some of the scientific papers that have been published; edited by W. Blair Bell ... [London, Baillière, Tindall and Cox, 1930.

Liverpool Medical School
see **Liverpool. University.** *Faculty of Medicine.*

W 1 LI93L
The LIVERPOOL medico-chirurgical journal. v. 1-52; July 1881-1948. Liverpool.
52 v. in 41. illus., ports.

Publication suspended 1917-28, 1940-42.
Supersedes the Liverpool and Manchester medical and surgical reports.
Title varies slightly.
Journal of the Liverpool Medical Institution.
Includes the proceedings or transactions of the Liverpool Medical Institution.

1. Medicine - period. 2. Surgery - period. I. Liverpool Medical Institution

NL 0418779 DNLM ICRL MnRM

Beinecke Library Z17 00939
Liverpool mercantile gazette. v.1-
1817-
Liverpool[Printed and published by J. and J. Smith]
$5\frac{1}{2}$cm. weekly.

Title varies: -Dec. 1838, Myers's mercantile advertiser; and weekly reporter of imports & exports for the principal ports of Great Britain.
Ceased publication June 28, 1875.

NL 0418780 CtY

A Liverpool Merchant.
Germany versus Denmark; being a short account of the Schleswig-Holstein question
see under Prange, Francis.

A Liverpool merchant.
A letter to the Right Hon. Thos. Spring Rice
see under Hall, John, of Liverpool.

A Liverpool merchant.
Letters on the Bank of England
see under Hall, John, of Liverpool.

A Liverpool merchant.
Letters on the proposed United banks of England
see under Hall, John, of Liverpool.

A Liverpool merchant.
Unpublished cruelties on the high seas
see Bright, Henry Arthur, 1830-1884.

The Liverpool mercury, and Lancashire, Cheshire, and general advertiser.
v. 1- (no. 1-
July 5, 1811-
Liverpool, Egerton Smith [etc.] 1811-
v. cm.

Microfilm copy (positive) on reels.

Weekly, 1811- ; twice a week,
Title varies: 1811- The Liverpool mercury; or, Commercial, literary, and political herald.
Ceased publication with issue for Nov. 12, 1904.
Merged into Liverpool daily post.

NL 0418787 NNC

Liverpool Mercury.
... Free trade facts and fair trade fallacies ...
see under title

Liverpool Mercury.
Free trade to India
see under title

326.4 L756l
Liverpool mercury.
Letters on the means of abolishing slavery in the West Indies, and improving the condition of the slaves: with remarks on Mr. M'Donnell's pamphlet, entitled Compulsory manumission. London, Wightman and Cramp, 1827.
3p.l.,70p. $21\frac{1}{2}$cm.

1. Slavery in the West Indies. 2. M'Donnell, Alexander. Compulsory manumission. I. Title.

NL 0418790 TxU

Liverpool Mercury. *2497.11
Publicity the true cure of social evils. /Liverpool life: its pleasures, practices, and pastimes.
Liverpool. Smith & Co. 1857. 2 v. in 1. 18 cm., in 8s.
Reprinted from "The Liverpool Mercury."

M51 — T.r. — Prostitution. — Liverpool, England. Soc. sci.

NL 0418791 MB

Liverpool mercury.

Trollope, Anthony, 1815-1882.
The tireless traveler; twenty letters to the Liverpool mercury by Anthony Trollope, 1875. Edited, with an introduction, by Bradford Allen Booth. Berkeley and Los Angeles, University of California press, 1941.

Liverpool microscopical society.
Annual report.
Abstract of proceedings.
Liverpool,
v. illus., plates. $21\frac{1}{2}$cm.
The 51st and 52d reports are combined in one issue.
List of members in each report.

1. Microscope and microscopy—Societies.

Library of Congress QH201.L5 23-13932

NL 0418793 DLC

QH201 .L48
Liverpool microscopical society.
Journal. v. 1, no. 1-4. Liverpool, Turner, Routledge and co., 1889-91.
nos. in v. illus., plates. 22cm. Irregular.
No. 3 (appendix): Twenty-first annual report of the Liverpool microscopical society ... January, 1890.
No more published.
L. C. set incomplete: nos. 1 and 4 wanting.

1. Microscope and microscopy—Societies.

Library of Congress QH201.L48 43-19077

NL 0418794 DLC

Liverpool Music Library
see
Liverpool. Public Libraries, Museums and Art Gallery. *Music Library.*

Liverpool Natural History Society
see Natural History Society of Liverpool.

Liverpool naturalists' field club.
—— Appendix [notes of additions. Liverpool]. 1873. 8°. pp. 14.

NL 0418797 MH-A

Liverpool naturalists' field club.
The flora of Liverpool. A list of the indigenous flowering plants and ferns growing within fifteen miles of the Liverpool exchange and two miles of Southport. Pub. by the Liverpool naturalists' field club ... Liverpool, Printed by W. Fearnall, 1872.
vi, 178 p., 2 l. 22cm.

1. Botany—England—Lancashire. 2. Botany—England—Cheshire.

Library of Congress QK306.L78 4-23818†

NL 0418798 DLC MH-A

VOLUME 336

Liverpool naturalists field club.

Green, Conrad Theodore, 1863– *ed.*
The flora of the Liverpool district, illustrated by drawings and photographs. Edited by C. Theodore Green ... Liverpool, D. Marples & co., 1902.

Temp. cd.
Liverpool Naturalists' Field Club.
Proceedings and natural history notes for the area.
Liverpool.
v. illus. annual.

Continued by the club's Proceedings ..., articles, notes.

NL 0418800 ICRL IaAS

QH1 L92 **Liverpool naturalists' field club.**
Report of the Liverpool naturalists' field club..
Liverpool, 186-

NL 0418801 DLC

Liverpool naturalists' field club.
—— Second appendix. [Liverpool.] 1875. 8°. pp. 24.

NL 0418802 MH-A

... Liverpool naval exhibition, 1892 ...
see under Liverpool. Public libraries, museums and art gallery. Walker art gallery.

Liverpool Northern Hospital. Annual report of the committee to the subscribers. 42., 1873; 50., 1883. 12°. *Liverpool, T. Brakell, 1876–84.*

NL 0418804 DNLM

Liverpool Observatory, Birkenhead, Eng.
Founded in 1838 and moved in 1867 to Bidston, Birkenhead, as the Liverpool Observatory of the Mersey Docks and Harbour Board. In 1929 merged with the University of Liverpool Tidal Institute to form the Liverpool Observatory and Tidal Institute.

Liverpool Observatory, *Birkenhead, Eng.*
Direction and strength of the wind at the Liverpool Observatory, 1852–1857. Liverpool, G. M'Corquodale [185–?]
1 l. 4 pl. 44 x 45 cm.
Cover title.
Signed: John Hartnup.

1. Winds. I. Hartnup, John, 1806–1885.
8-10967 rev*
QC940.G7L5

NL 0418806 DLC

Liverpool Observatory, *Birkenhead, Eng.*
Report of the director ... and meteorological results deduced from the observations taken.
[Liverpool] Liverpool Print. and Stationery Co. [etc.]
v. in illus., tables. 25 cm.
Report year varies.
Reports for 1873–74, 1875–78, 1917–19 and 1920–21 issued in combined form.
Title varies slightly.
Pub. by order of the Mersey Docks and Harbour Board.
Ceased publication with report for 1928?
1. Meteorology—England—Liverpool. I. Mersey Docks and Harbour Board, Liverpool.
QC989.G7L5 8-7030 rev*‡

NL 0418807 DLC PU DAS CtY

Liverpool Observatory, *Birkenhead, Eng.*
see also **Liverpool Observatory and Tidal Institute,** *Birkenhead, Eng.*

Liverpool Observatory and Tidal Institute, Birkenhead, Eng.
Established in 1929 by the merger of the Liverpool Observatory with the University of Liverpool Tidal Institute. Partially supported by grants from the University and the Liverpool Steam Ship Owners' Association.

Liverpool Observatory and Tidal Institute, *Birkenhead, Eng.*
Annual report.
Liverpool.
v. illus. 27 cm.

QC989.G7L514 551.5072 48-42668*‡

NL 0418810 DLC DAS CtY

Liverpool Observatory and Tidal Institute, *Birkenhead, Eng.*
Storm surges in the North Sea, by R. H. Corkan, Liverpool Observatory & Tidal Institute. [Birkenhead] 1948.
2 v. illus., charts. 27 cm ([U. S. Hydrographic Office] H. O. Misc. 15072)
"Undertaken ... at the request of the London County Council."

1. Tides—North Sea. I. Corkan, R. H. II. London. County Council. (Series: U. S. Hydrographic Office. Miscellaneous no. 15072)
GC341.L58 551.461 49-46492*

NL 0418811 DLC WaU

Liverpool Observatory and Tidal Institute, *Birkenhead, Eng.*
see also **Liverpool Observatory,** *Birkenhead, Eng.;* **Liverpool. University.** *Tidal Institute.*

The Liverpool Observer.
Sermons delivered at various places of worship, on Sunday, 4th July, 1858, to inaugurate the first annual festival of the temperance societies of Toxteth park. [Liverpool, 1858] 14 p. 20cm.
Caption-title.
"Issued with the 'Liverpool Observer'."
Sermons by S. A. Steinthal, Francis Bishop, John Wilson and W. Wilkinson.

1. Temperance—Addresses, essays, lectures. I. Steinthal, S. Alfred.
January 8, 1951

NL 0418813 NN

Liverpool official red book
see **The Liverpool** and Merseyside official red book.

Liverpool Ophthalmic Infirmary
see Liverpool. Ophthalmic Infirmary.

Liverpool organization ltd.
Directory of Merseyside manufacturers ... [1st- ed.]
Liverpool, Liverpool organization ltd. [1931-

Liverpool organization, ltd.
Industrial Liverpool and Birkenhead.
Liverpool, Liverpool organization ltd., 1929.
51[5]p. front., photos., maps, tables. 28cm.

NL 0418816 NBuG

Liverpool Organization Ltd.
Industrial Liverpool and Birkenhead, 1930. Liverpool: Liverpool Organization, Ltd.[, 1930.] 51 p. incl. mounted front., tables. illus. (part mounted, incl. chart, maps, plans.) [2. ed., rev.] 4°.
On book jacket: City of Liverpool. Visit of the Rt. Hon. the lord mayor of Liverpool and the lady mayoress of Liverpool (Alderman and Mrs. Edwin Thompson) to His Honour the mayor of New York city (the Honourable James J. Walker), May 4th–12th 1931. With the lord mayor's compliments.
Decorative end-papers.

560009A. 1. Economic history—Gt. Br.—Eng.—Liverpool. 2. Economic history—Gt. Br.—Eng.—Birkenhead. I. Liverpool, England. Lord Mayor. 1931– (Edwin Thompson).
May 20, 1932

NL 0418817 NN NNC

Liverpool overhead railway company.
...Report of the directors together with statement of accounts...
1
Liverpool, 1 38cm.
nos.
Semiannual, 1 –12; annual, 1913–
Title varies slightly.
Cover-title: 1 –12, Half-yearly report and accounts [no.] –49; 1912– Yearly report and accounts.

NL 0418818 NN

PN 6120 .P4 L54 Liverpool pantomimes, &c. Liverpool, London, 1875-1895.
1 v. (various pagings) illus. 20 cm.
Binder's title.
A collection of Christmas pantomimes performed at the Alexandra Theatre and other theaters in Liverpool, and a London theater.
Contents. - Robinson Crusoe, by J. F. McArdle and F. W. Green. - Robin Hood, by the author of "The piebald possum of the panting prairie", and other moral and instructive works. - Blue Beard, by T. F. Doyle. - Jack the giant killer, by T. F. Doyle. - Aladdin in a new light, by C. Millward. - Dick Whittington and his cat. - The forty thieves, by W. Jones. - Robinson Crusoe, by G. Thorn. - Dick Whittington, by Sir A. Harris, C. Raleigh & H. Hamilton. - Whittington and his cat, by E. L. Blanchard.

NL 0418819 WU

Liverpool Peace Society.
Report [of the committee and of the annual meeting].
1870.
Liverpool, 1870. 12°.
In: *C p. v. 1475, no. 11.

1. War and peace.—Associations, Gt. Br.: Eng.
May 20, 1914.

NL 0418820 NN

Liverpool Permissive Bill Association.
Annual report.
no. 1
Liverpool [1872]. 8°.
v.

BLACK TEMPERANCE COLL.
1. Local option, Gt. Br.: Eng.: Liverpool.
March 13, 1920.

NL 0418821 NN

VOLUME 336

HQ1064 G7L5 Liverpool Personal Service Society.
Social contacts in old age. Report of a survey undertaken by the Liverpool Personal Service Society in conjunction with the Department of Social Science of the University of Liverpool. [Liverpool] University Press of Liverpool, 1953.
viii, 35 p. tables.

1. Old age. I. Liverpool. University. Social Science Dept. II. Title.

NL 0418822 CU CtY

LIVERPOOL PHILOMATHIC SOCIETY.
Proceedings. v. 29- ; 1883/84-
Liverpool. no. 8°.

Publication suspended between 1938/39 and 1946/47.

1. Societies, Learned--Gt. Br.

NL 0418823 NN

Liverpool Photographic Club
see
Liverpool Amateur Photographic Association.

Liverpool photographic journal.
see
British journal of photography.

Liverpool Photographic Society
see
Liverpool Amateur Photographic Association.

Liverpool polytechnic society.
Annual report.
[Liverpool, 18
v. 21½-22½cm.
Report year ends in December.
List of members in each report.
Reports are included in the society's Journal for those years: 1891- have separate t.-p.: Report ... and statement of accounts ...

Library of Congress T1.L52 CA 6-2061 Unrev'd

NL 0418827 DLC

Liverpool polytechnic society.
Journal.
Liverpool, 18
v. illus., fold. map, diagrs. 21½-22cm.
52d-53d sessions, 1889-90, have title: Proceedings of the Liverpool polytechnic society ... [cover-title: Journal]

1. Technology—Societies. 2. Industrial arts—Societies.

Library of Congress T1.L6 CA 6—2062 Unrev'd

NL 0418828 DLC

Liverpool polytechnic society.
Laws of the Liverpool polytechnic society. [Liverpool, A. Russell, printer, 18—?]
4 p. 21cm.
Caption title.

CA 7-1242 Unrev'd
Library of Congress T1.L63

NL 0418829 DLC

Liverpool police-aided association for clothing the destitute children of the city.
Annual report, list of subscribers, statement of account.
Liverpool, 1907-
9 v. 21½ cm.
Report year ends October 31st.
The number 24 omitted in numbering of reports.

NL 0418830 DL

Wing Z 104 .51 Liverpool printing & stationery co., limited.
Specimens of printing types, ornamental borders, &c., in use at the Liverpool printing & stationery co's (limited) printing works, Mercer court, Redcross street, Liverpool. [Liverpool]1882.
O.

Printed on rectos only.

NL 0418831 ICN

W 1 LI931 LIVERPOOL Queen Victoria District Nursing Association
Report.
1898-
Liverpool.
v.

NL 0418832 DNLM

WY L783s 1899 LIVERPOOL Queen Victoria District Nursing Association
A short history and description of district nursing (the nursing of the poor in their own homes) in Liverpool. [Liverpool, Marples, 1899?]
31 p.

NL 0418833 DNLM

Liverpool Regional Hospital Board.
The recovery home

see under

Joint Committee of the Liverpool Regional Hospital Board and the Board of Governors of the United Liverpool Hospitals.

Liverpool Religious Tract Society
see Religious Tract Society, Liverpool.

The Liverpool repository, of literature, philosophy, and commerce. / By an association of literary gentlemen ... v. 1; Jan.-Dec. 1826. Liverpool, C. Gray, 1826.
2 p. l., 792 col. 23cm. monthly.

Library of Congress AP4.L442 7-22237†

NL 0418836 DLC KU

Liverpool reprints.

Liverpool, University press.

Editor : nos. 1- , L. C. Martin.

1. English literature—Collections. I. Martin, Leonard Cyril, 1886- , ed.

NL 0418837 NN FU CtNIC

Liverpool Royal Infirmary
see Liverpool. Royal Infirmary.

Liverpool Sailors' Homes, Dispensary, and Nautical School. Annual report of the committee to the supporters and friends. 35., 1879. 36 pp. 12°. *Liverpool, J. R. Williams & Co.*, [1880].

NL 0418839 DNLM

Liverpool Sailors' Home, Registry, and Savings Bank. Annual report of the committee of management to the friends and supporters for the year 1869. 23 pp. 12°. *Liverpool, Daily Courier.* 1870.

NL 0418840 DNLM

Liverpool sale and pedigree co., inc.
Liverpool, N. Y.
The Breeder's horn
see under title

Liverpool School of Tropical Diseases
see Liverpool School of Tropical Medecine.

Liverpool school of tropical medicine.

The African mail; an illustrated weekly journal founded to meet the rapidly growing interest in West & Central African questions. An independent organ representing the commercial, industrial & political interests of West Africa generally. v. -5, -Oct. 4, 1907; [new ser.] v. 1-10, Oct. 11, 1907-Jan. 5, 1917. Liverpool, New York [etc.] 19 -17.

Liverpool school of tropical medicine.
... Annals of tropical medicine and parasitology, issued by the Liverpool school of tropical medicine ...
[Liverpool, etc., 1907]-
v. illus., plates, port., maps, diagrs. 26cm.
Editor: 1907- Ronald Ross.

1. Tropics—Diseases and hygiene. 2. Trypanosomiasis. I. Ross, Ronald, 1857- ed. II. Title.

8-160
Library of Congress RC960.L76

NL 0418844 DLC ICJ

Liverpool School of Tropical Medicine.
Annual report
see its Report.

W 19.5 L784 LIVERPOOL School of Tropical Medicine.
Catalogs, announcements of courses, requirements for admission, and other publications relating to the academic program will be found under the above call number. Included also are similar publications of individual schools or departments of instruction of the institution.

NL 0418846 DNLM

VOLUME 336

WC 680 qL785 LIVERPOOL School of Tropical Medicine.
[Collection of publications]
The Library has a collection of miscellaneous publications of this organization kept as received. These publications are not listed or bound separately.

NL 0418847 DNLM

Liverpool school of tropical medicine.

Moore, Benjamin.
... Concerning the treatment of experimental trypanosomiasis, [by] Benjamin Moore, M. Nierenstein and John L. Todd ... Issued by the Liverpool school of tropical medicine. Liverpool, At the University press; [etc., etc.] [1908]

Liverpool school of tropical medicine.
... Historical record, 1898–1920. Liverpool, University press, 1920.
viii, 103, [1] p. front., plates, ports., plan, facsims. 22cm.
At head of title: Liverpool school of tropical medicine.
"Who's who in the Liverpool school of tropical medicine": p. 67–72.
"Papers published by members of the staff while at the school": p. 77–100.

1. Liverpool school of tropical medicine.

Library, U. S. Dept. of Agriculture 448L75 Agr 20-1984

NL 0418849 DNLM IEdS MnU-B IEN PPC ICJ MiU

Liverpool school of tropical medicine.

Patton, Walter Scott, 1876–
Insects, ticks, mites and venomous animals of medical and veterinary importance ... Croydon, H. R. Grubb, ltd., 1929–

Liverpool School of Tropical Medicine. 3793.29
Instructions for the prevention of malarial fever, for the use of residents in malarial places. 2d edition.
Liverpool. University Press. 1900. (4), 14 pp. [Memoir I.] 8°.
This school was at first called the Liverpool School of Tropical Diseases.

F4973 — Malaria.

NL 0418851 MB DNLM PU

Liverpool school of tropical medicine.
... Memoir I-- new series, no. 3 ... Liverpool London [etc.] 1899-1927.
23 v. illus., plates (part col.) maps, tables. 21.5-29 cm.
At head of title: no. 1, Liverpool school of tropical diseases; no. 2-new ser. no. 3, Liverpool school of tropical medicine.
1st series: 21 v., 1899-1906. --New series: 3 v., 1924-1927.
Replaced during 1907-1923 by Annuals of tropical medicine and parasitology.

No. 6 never published.

NL 0418853 MiU PPC DNLM

LF 362 Liverpool School of Tropical Medicine.
Prospectus and courses of instruction.
Liverpool 19
v. illus.

NL 0418854 DNLM MiU

Liverpool school of tropical medicine.
... Record of the school during six years of war, 1939–1945. Liverpool [1946?]
48 p. front. 22cm.

1. Liverpool school of tropical medicine—Hist. 2. Medical colleges—Gt. Brit. [2. Medical schools—Gt. Brit.]

Med 47-1076

U. S. Army medical library for Library of Congress [L385A4 1946]

NL 0418855 DNLM MH

Liverpool School of Tropical Medicine.
Report.
Liverpool.
v. 22 cm. annual.
Report year ends July 31.

R773.L3955 610.71142 54-15277 ‡

NL 0418856 DLC DNLM MH

Liverpool school of tropical medicine.
... Report of the malaria expedition of the Liverpool school of tropical medicine and medical parasitology
see under Ross, Sir Ronald, 1857-1932.

Liverpool school of tropical medecine.

Austen, Ernest Edward, 1867–
... Report of the proceedings of the Expedition for the study of the causes of malaria, despatched to Sierra Leone, West Africa, under the leadership of Major Ronald Ross ... by the Liverpool school of tropical diseases, July 29th, 1899. By Ernest E. Austen ... London, Printed for H. M. Stationery off., by Darling & son, ltd., 1899.

Liverpool School of Tropical Medicine. Runcorn Research Laboratories.
[Results of work done at the Runcorn Research Laboratories]
see under Breinl, Anton and others.

Liverpool School of Tropical Medicine. Yellow Fever Bureau.
Reports on questions connected with the investigation of non-malarial fevers in West Africa
see under Gt. Brit. Yellow Fever Commission (West Africa)

Liverpool Seamen's Orphan Institution. Annual reports of the committee to the subscribers. 1.-2., 1869-70. 8°. *Liverpool*, 1870-71.
Opened May, 1869, as a "Temporary Home".

NL 0418861 DNLM

Liverpool shipowners association.

Chamberlain, Joseph, 1836–
Alleged overloading of ships. Mr. Chamberlain's speech to the deputation of shipowners on the 8th March, 1883, and the correspondence resulting therefrom, with other matter bearing on the subject. Printed for the Liverpool shipowners association. [Liverpool, Lee and Nightingale, printers] 1883.

Liverpool Shipwreck and Humane Society. Annual reports of the committee to the subscribers. 30., 1868-9; 31., 1869-70. 8°. *Liverpool*, 1869-70.
Instituted 1839.

NL 0418863 DNLM

Slavery E 441 M46 v.27 no.7 Liverpool Society for Promoting the Abolition of Slavery.
An address from the Liverpool Society for the Abolition of Slavery, on the safest and most efficacious means of promoting the gradual improvement of the Negro slaves in the British West India Islands, preparatory to their becoming free labourers, and on the expected consequences of such change. Liverpool, Printed by J. & G. Smith, 1824.
18 p. 23cm.
No. 7 in a vol. lettered: Pamphlets on slavery, vol. 3.
May anti-sla very pamphlets, v. 27.

NL 0418864 NIC CtY MiD MB OO TxU PSt NcD

Liverpool society for promoting the abolition of slavery.
Declaration of the objects of the Liverpool society for promoting the abolition of slavery, 25th March, 1823. London, Hatchard & son; [etc., etc., 1823]
14 p. 20½ cm.

HT853.L58 3-14101
——— Copy 2. [Slavery pamphlets, v. 34, no. 3] HT857.S5 vol. 34, no. 3

NL 0418865 DLC ICN NcD TxU NIC OO CtY Vi

W 1 NA749 LIVERPOOL Society for the Prevention of Cruelty to Children
Annual report. 1st-71st; 1883-1953.
Liverpool.
71 v. illus.
Continued by the Annual report and balance sheet of the Liverpool and District Branch of the National Society for the Prevention of Cruelty to Children.
1. Child welfare - Gt. Brit. 2. Child welfare - Period.

NL 0418866 DNLM

Liverpool society of fine arts.
...Exhibition of ancient and modern paintings, engravings, and photographs, MDCCCLX, Queen's hall, Bold street... Liverpool: C. Tinling [1860] 11 p. 24cm.

NL 0418867 NN

DA763 .A1P2 v.2 LIVERPOOL SOCIETY OF HIGHLANDERS.
Evictions in the Highlands. The correspondence of the Liverpool society of Highlanders, with Mr. Gladstone...and the Earl of Roseberry...in reference to agrarian evictions in the Highlands and islands of Scotland. Republished from the "Oban times," of April 8th, 1882...slightly revised, by J. MacKenzie MacLeod... Liverpool, D. Russell, printer, 1882.
12 p. 22cm.
[Pamphlets on Scotland, v.2, no.6]

NL 0418868 ICU

Liverpool steam ship owners' association.
Annual report.
Liverpool,
v. 23cm.
Report year ends December 31.
Full title, : Annual report of the Liverpool steam ship owners' association ...

1. Shipping—Gt. Brit.

15-18447

Library of Congress HE564.E4L5

NL 0418869 DLC OU CU MdBJ

VOLUME 336

[Liverpool steam ship owner's association]
The coasting trade. ...
[Liverpool?] 1920

HE824
.L45

NL 0418870 DLC

Liverpool Steam Ship Owners' Association.
...International commerce, communications and transit. The work that must be done to make effective the steps already taken by the League of Nations for the security and maintenance of freedom of communications and of transit and equitable treatment for commerce in international trade. [Liverpool,] 1924. 38 p. 8°.

1. Commerce, Foreign. 2. Transportation. 3. Communications.
February 16, 1925

NL 0418871 NN

Liverpool steam ship owners' association.
... The oversea trade of the United Kingdom. Report on the present congestion of traffic, 12th January, 1915. [Liverpool? 1915]
11 p. 23cm.
Signed: Norman Hill, secretary.

1. Shipping—Gt. Brit. 2. Gt. Brit.—Comm. I. Hill, Sir Arthur Norman, 1863– II. Title.

16-24679
Library of Congress HE824.L5 1915 a

NL 0418872 DLC

Liverpool steam ship owners' association.
... The oversea trade of the United Kingdom. Report on the present congestion of traffic, 12th January, 1915. [Liverpool? 1915]
10 p. incl. tables. 22½cm.
Signed: Norman Hill, secretary.

1. Shipping—Gt. Brit. 2. Gt. Brit.—Comm. I. Hill, Sir Arthur Norman, 1863– II. Title.

15-5885
Library of Congress HE824.L5

NL 0418873 DLC CtY

Liverpool steam ship owners' association.

Chamber of shipping of the United Kingdom.
... Report of the committee appointed to advise as to the measures requisite for the maintenance of the British mercantile marine ... [London, Witherby & co.] 1917.

Liverpool steam ship owners' association.

Hill, *Sir* **Arthur Norman, 1863–**
... Statement by Sir Norman Hill, the secretary of the Liverpool steam ship owners' association. [Liverpool? 1914].

Liverpool steam ship owners' association
see also
General council of British shipping, *London.*

Liverpool Stock Exchange
see **Liverpool. Stock Exchange.**

The Liverpool Stock Exchange official weekly list.
[Liverpool]
no. in v. 44 cm.
"Published by authority of the Committee of the Liverpool Stock Exchange."

1. Securities—Gt. Brit. I. Liverpool. Stock Exchange.
HG4502.L5 332.63 52-21190 ‡

NL 0418878 DLC

... **Liverpool** studies in Spanish literature ... Edited by E. Allison Peers. Liverpool, Institute of Hispanic studies, 1940–
v. 22 cm. (Studies in Hispanic literatures; general editor: E. Allison Peers)
CONTENTS.—First series. From Cadalso to Rubén Darío.

1. Spanish literature—Hist. & crit. I. Peers, Edgar Allison, ed. II. Institute of Hispanic studies.
PQ6039.L55 860.9 A 41-4725
Wellesley College. Libr. for Library of Congress [a48d1]†

TxLT FU MiU FTaSU MH IU ICU OrU MsSM
NL 0418879 MWelC DLC NcD OU ICU NNC TxU ViU TU NcD

Beinecke Library
Z17
00467d

Liverpool times. no.1-
May 28, 1756-
[Liverpool: Printed and published by R. Williamson, etc.]
46cm. weekly.

Title varies: May 28, 1756-
1766- Williamson's
Liverpool advertiser and mercantile chronicle; -Dec.30, 1828, Billinge's
Liverpool advertiser.
Ceased publication Feb.5, 1856.

NL 0418880 CtY NPV

Liverpool town planning and housing exhibition, 1914.
... Transactions of conference held March 9 to 13, 1914, at Liberty buildings, Liverpool, ed. by S. D. Adshead and Patrick Abercrombie. [Liverpool, The University press of Liverpool [1914]
168 p. plates, map, plans (part fold.) 24½cm.

1. Cities and towns—Planning—Congresses. 2. Art, Municipal—Gt. Brit. 3. Garden cities. 4. Labor and laboring classes—Dwellings. I. Adshead, Stanley Davenport, 1868– ed. II. *Abercrombie, Patrick, 1879– joint ed.

15—6097
Library of Congress NA9000.L5

NL 0418881 DLC CU NcD CtY MB DL MiU OCl OClW

The Liverpool tractate, an eighteenth century manual on the procedure of the House of commons, edited with an introduction by Catherine Strateman ... New York, 1937.
xcii p., 1 l., 107 p. 22½cm.
Thesis (PH. D.)—Columbia university, 1937.
Vita.
Published also as Studies in history, economics and public law, ed. by the Faculty of political science of Columbia university, no. 430.
The tractate, Additional ms. 38456 in the British museum, is v. 267 of the Liverpool papers, a collection of papers of Charles Jenkinson, first earl of Liverpool, and his sons, the second and third earls. The title-page of the tractate, composed about 1763, is lacking and evidence of its authorship is slight. cf. Introd.
Bibliography: p. lxxxi-xcii.

1. Gt. Brit. Parliament. House of commons—Rules and practice. I. Strateman, Catherine, 1912– ed. II. British museum. Mss. (Additional 38456) III. Liverpool, Charles Jenkinson, 1st earl of, 1727–1808.

38-6233
Library of Congress JN593.L5 1937
Columbia Univ. Libr. 328.4205

NL 0418883 NNC PBm PU PSC DLC

The Liverpool tractate, an eighteenth century manual on the procedure of the House of commons, edited with an introduction by Catherine Strateman, PH. D. New York, Columbia university press; London, P. S. King & son, ltd., 1937.
3 p. l., v-xcii p., 1 l., 105 p. 23 cm. (*Half-title:* Studies in history, economics and public law, ed. by the Faculty of political science of Columbia university. no. 430)
Issued also as thesis (PH. D.) Columbia university.
The tractate, Additional ms. 38456 in the British museum, is v. 267 of the Liverpool papers, a collection of papers of Charles Jenkinson, first earl of Liverpool, and his sons, the second and third earls. The title-page of the tractate, composed about 1763, is lacking and evidence of its authorship is slight. cf. Introd.
Bibliography: p. lxxxi-xcii.

1. Gt. Brit. Parliament. House of commons—Rules of practice. I. Strateman, Catherine, 1912– ed. II. British museum. Mss. (Additional 38456) III. Liverpool, Charles Jenkinson, 1st earl of, 1727-1808.

38—6232
Library of Congress H31.C7 no. 430
JN593.L5 1937a
[a50e½] (308.2) 328.4205

NL 0418885 DLC WaS OrP MB ViU OCU OO

The Liverpool trade review.
[Liverpool] Liverpool chamber of commerce [19
v. in 25-27cm. monthly.
Began publication in 1902. cf. Willing's press guide.

1. Liverpool—Comm.—Period. I. Liverpool. Chamber of commerce.

45-46278
Library of Congress HF3510.L5L5
382.05

NL 0418886 DLC

The Liverpool tragedy: shewing, how Mr. Robert Fuller, of Liverpool, Lancashire, Grazier, and his wife, for the sake of gold, murdered their own son, after he had been above ten years from them in the East-Indies. Col: Printed by J. Butler, Worcester.

NL 0418887 DFo

Liverpool Training School and Home for Nurses. Annual reports of the committee to the subscribers. 1.- 1862- 8°. Liverpool, 1862-85.
1.-19. bound in 2 v. Established 1862.

NL 0418888 DNLM

Liverpool Training School and Home for Nurses. Annual reports of the committee to the subscribers. 24.-38., 1885-99. 8°. Liverpool, 1886-1900.

NL 0418889 DNLM

610.73
L756o

LIVERPOOL TRAINING SCHOOL AND HOME FOR NURSES.
Organization of nursing; an account of the Liverpool nurses' training school, its foundation, progress, and operation in hospital, district, and private nursing, by a member of the Committee of the home & training school, with an introduction and notes by Florence Nightingale. Liverpool, A. Holden, 1865.
103 p. front., map, plan.

NL 0418890 WaU

Liverpool training school and home for nurses.
... Proposed plan for the training and employment of women in hospital, district, and private nursing. Liverpool, A. Holden [1861?]
34 p. 21.5 cm. [Medical pamphlets, v. 31]

NL 0418891 CtY

VOLUME 336

Liverpool Training School and Home for nurses.
——. Regulations as to training probationer nurses. 2 l. 4°. [Liverpool, n. d.]

NL 0418892 DNLM

Liverpool training school and home for nurses.
Report from the committee of the Liverpool training school and home for nurses, on the cholera outbreak in 1866. [Liverpool, The Liverpool printing and stationery company, limited, 1867]
19 p. 21.5 cm. [Medical pamphlets, v. 31]
From Fifth annual report of the Liverpool training school and home for nurses, 1866.

NL 0418893 CtY DNLM

Liverpool Training School and Home for Nurses.
——. The rules of the society. 2 l. 4°. [Liverpool, n. d.]

NL 0418894 DNLM

Liverpool Training-Ship "Indefatigable". Annual reports of the committee to the subscribers. 4.-6., 1868-70. 8°. Liverpool, 1869-71.
Established for the sons and orphans of sailors.

NL 0418895 DNLM

Liverpool trials, May 1898. No pub.
16 mount. photographs. 23 1/2 cm.
Binder's title.
Photographs of the competition and prize winning steam cars.

NL 0418896 MiD

Liverpool union bank.
The deed of settlement of the Liverpool union bank established 1st May, 1835, under the authority of an Act of Parliament... with an abstract of the Act.
Liverpool, W. Forshaw, 1835.
78 p.

NL 0418897 OU

Liverpool Unitarian Tract Society
see Unitarian Tract Society, Liverpool.

Liverpool United Typographical Society.
Articles of the Liverpool United Typographical Society, as agreed to, June 20th, 1837.
Liverpool, Mitchell, Heaton & Mitchell, 1838.
21 p. 19cm.

1. Trade-unions.

NL 0418899 NNC

Liverpool University Settlement.
...Housing problems in Liverpool; a survey of six areas of bad housing, with special reference to the Housing act, 1930. Liverpool[, 1931]. 39 p. incl. tables. illus. (plans), plates. 24½cm.

703519A. 1. Habitations for the working class—Gt. Br.—Eng.—Liverpool.
May 7, 1934

NL 0418900 NN

Liverpool university settlement.

[Liverpool. University. Social science dept.]
Preliminary report on the problems of evacuation ... [Liverpool] The University press of Liverpool: London, Hodder & Stoughton ltd., 1939.

Liverpool Welsh national society.
Morris, Sir Lewis, 1833–1907.
... Inaugural address delivered by Mr. Lewis Morris, M. A., Royal institution, Liverpool, Thursday evening, Oct. 8th, 1885 ... Liverpool, I. Foulkes [1885]

Liverpool Welsh national society.
Transactions 1885-
Liverpool, [1886-]
Library has:
2d sess. 1886|87

NL 0418903 CSmH

Liverpool Women's Industrial Council.
Report of an enquiry into the occupations of girls after leaving the elementary schools, & into the industrial training for women's trades. Liverpool [Handley Bros., 1899?]. 8 p. 8°.
Cover-title.

1. Woman.—Occupations, Gt. Br.: Eng.: Liverpool. 2. Woman.—Education (Industrial and technical), Gt. Br.: Eng.: Liverpool.
December 7, 1915.

NL 0418904 NN

Liverpool women's war service bureau.
Report.
Liverpool, 191
v. 21cm.
Report year ends August 7.

17-8355
Library of Congress D639.W7L5

NL 0418905 DLC DL ICJ

286.85
L752
Liverpool wool brokers' association.
East Indian wool sales.
Liverpool.

Includes those with title East Indian wool auctions; East Indian wool.

NL 0418906 DNAL

286.85
L752M
Liverpool wool brokers' association.
Miscellaneous wool auctions.
Liverpool.

Have also in this call no. those entitled "River Plate, etc., wool auctions."

NL 0418907 DNAL

Liverpool workshops and home teaching society for the outdoor blind.
Annual report.
Liverpool,
v. 21cm.
Report year ends Dec. 31.

CA 9-5701 Unrev'd
Library of Congress HV1950.L7L7

NL 0418908 DLC DNLM OO

Liverpool's directory; a reprint of the names and addresses from Gore's directory ... to which are added a street directory, and lists of professional men and tradesmen.
[no.] 1-

Liverpool: H. Young & Sons, Ltd., 1907- 8°.
v. fronts. (facsims.), plans, ports.

1. Liverpool—Directories. I. Shaw, George Thomas, 1863–1938, editor. II. Shaw, Isabella, editor. III. Gore, John, 1738–1803.
September 22, 1931

The frontispieces are reproductions of the title-pages of the original editions, reading: Gore's Liverpool directory... (slight variations.) (See entry under Gore's directory of Liverpool.)
Title varies slightly.
No. 1 includes: A history of the Liverpool directories from 1766 to 1907, by G. T. Shaw.
Editors: [no.] 1- G. T. Shaw ([no.] 1, 3 with I. Shaw).

NL 0418910 NN InU ICRL

Liverpool's directory.
Liverpool's first directory; a reprint of the names and addresses from Gore's directory for 1766. To which is added a street directory for the same year, compiled by George T. Shaw and Isabella Shaw. Also a history of the Liverpool directories from 1766 to 1907 by George T. Shaw. Liverpool, H. Young, 1907.

vii, 76 p. facsim., fold. map., port. 23cm.
1. Liverpool. Directories. I. Gore, John, 1738-1803. I. Shaw, George T

NL 0418911 MnU NN MB IEN MH NNC CSmH

942.2L75
L756
1767
Liverpool's directory.
Liverpool's second directory; a reprint of the names and addresses from Gore's directory for 1767. To which are added a street directory, and lists of professional men and tradesmen, compiled by George T. Shaw. Liverpool, H. Young, 1928.
67 p. facsim. 23cm.
Reprinted from the Transactions of the Historic Society of Lancashire and Cheshire. v.78, 1926. cf. Label following t.-p.
1. Liverpool, Directories. I. Gore, John, 1738- 1803. II. Shaw, George T

NL 0418912 MnU

VOLUME 336

Liversage, Vincent.
Economics of production of grade "A" (tuberculin-tested) milk ₍by₎ V. Liversage ... Oxford, Clarendon press, 1926.
58 p. 22cm.

1. Milk—₍Cost of production₎ I. Oxford. University. Institute for research in agricultural economics. II. Title.

Library, U. S. Dept. of Agriculture 44L75 Agr 27-831

NL 0418913 DNAL NIC IU

Liversage, Vincent.
Land tenure in the colonies, by V. Liversage ... Cambridge ₍Eng.₎ The University press, 1945.
ix, 151 p. 19cm.
"References": p. ₍146₎-148.

1. Land tenure. 2. Gt. Brit.—Colonies—Land tenure. I. Title.

Library of Congress HD1251.L5 45-7313
333.3

NL 0418914 DLC CU GU CSt-L NcD NcRA CtY TxU PU-L NNUN PSC ViU PP OU TxU OrCS OrU WaS Wa CaBVaU CaBViP

Nc97 B58 +947L
Liversage, Vincent.
Swaziland development. [n.p., 1947?]
41 p. map. 33 cm.

Cover title.
Lithographed.

1. Swaziland - Econ. condit.

NL 0418915 CtY NNC

Liversay, Florence Randal.
Shepherd's purse. Toronto, 1923.
66 p. 19 cm.

NL 0418916 RPB

Liversedge, Alfred John.
Commercial engineering, by "A general manager" (Alfred J. Liversedge) ... Manchester, London, Emmott & co., ltd., 1912.
xv, 389, ₍1₎ p. tables. 22cm. (*Half-title:* The "Mechanical world" series)
"The present work reproduces in book form a series of articles which recently appeared in the Mechanical world."—Pref.
Appendix. Prices of materials: p. 361-363.

1. Engineering—Estimates and costs. I. Title.

Springfield, Mass. City library for Library of Congress ₍r41b2₎ A 14-1363 Revised

NL 0418917 MSC MiU ICJ NN ICU

---

ar W 48831
₍Liversedge, Alfred John₎
Engineering estimates, costs and accounts. London, C. Lockwood, 1890.
xii, 256 p. 22cm.

NL 0418918 NIC ICJ MH-BA MiU MB

₍Liversedge, Alfred John₎
Engineering estimates, costs, and accounts; a guide to commercial engineering, with numerous examples of estimates and costs of millwright work, miscellaneous productions, steam engines ... By a general manager. 2d ed. London, C. Lockwood and son, 1896.
xii, 256 p. incl. tables. 22cm.

1. Engineering—Estimates and costs. I. Title.

Stanford univ. Library for Library of Congress ₍r41c2₎ A 11-508 Revised

NL 0418919 CSt CaBVaU ICRL CU OCl NIC

---

ar W 48833
₍Liversedge, Alfred John₎
Engineering estimates, costs, and accounts, by a general manager. 3d ed., rev. and corr. London, C. Lockwood, 1911.
xx, 256 p. 22cm.

I. A general manager. II. Title.

NL 0418920 NIC OCU NN CU

Liverseege, Henry, 1803-1832.
Engravings from the works of Henry Liverseege. London, Hodgson, Boys and Graves; ₍etc., etc., 1832-35₎
2 p. l., front. (port.) 35 pl. 43½cm.
Engr. t.-p., with vignette.

Library of Congress ND497.L8A3 11-33630

NL 0418921 DLC PU PP NN CaBVa

Liverseege, John Francis.
Adulteration and analysis of foods and drugs; Birmingham methods and analyses of samples; review of British prosecutions during half a century, by J. F. Liverseege ... with a foreword by the Right Honourable Neville Chamberlain ... London, J. & A. Churchill, 1932.
xv, 599 p. incl. tables, diagrs., forms. 25½cm.

1. Food adulteration and inspection—Gt. Brit. 2. Food—Analysis. 3. Drugs—Adulteration and analysis. I. Title.

Library of Congress TX531.L5 33-764
614.30942

NL 0418922 DLC DNLM MBCo CtY OU NN

Liversidge, Archibald, 1847-
... Address by Professor Liversidge ... (president) ₍at the seventh session of the Australasian association for the advancement of science, Jnuary 6, 1898. Sydney, W. A. Gullick, government printer, 1898₎
cover-title, 53, ₍1₎ p. 22cm.
At head of title: Australasian association for the advancement of science. Sydney session, 1898.
Issued also in Report of the seventh meeting of the Australasian association for the advancement of science. Sydney, 1898. p. 1-53.

1. Chemistry—Addresses, essays, lectures.

Library of Congress Q93.A93 1898 7-23404†

NL 0418923 DLC PU-S PPAN

Liversidge, Archibald, 1847-
The Bingera diamond field. Sydney, 1873.
8°

NL 0418924 NN

Liversidge, A(rchibald), 1847-
The Deniliquin or Barratta meteorite, second notice. (Sydney, Richards, 1883).

NL 0418925 MA

B 633.61 L75d
Liversidge, Archibald, 1847-
Disease in the sugar cane. Queensland. By Professor Liversidge... Sidney, Gibbs, Shallard, and co. [1876?]
cover-title, 34p. tables. 18cm.

1. Sugar-cane--Diseases and pests. I. Title.

NL 0418926 LU MH NN

Liversidge, Archibald, 1847-
Iron and coal deposits at Wallerawang, New South Wales. [Sydney, 1875]
8°

NL 0418927 NN

Liversidge, Archibald, 1847-
List of scientific papers and reports by Professor Archibald Liversidge ... Sydney, F. Cunninghame and co., printers ₍1882?₎
8 p. 25cm.

1. Geology—Bibl.

Library of Congress Z8512.5.L5 6-7493†

NL 0418928 DLC DI-GS PPAmP

Liversidge, A₍rchibald₎ 1847-
Map of the minerals of New South Wales, &c. By A. Liversidge ... With a list of the mineral localities. London, E. Stanford; ₍etc., etc., 1888₎
cover-title, 32 p. fold. map. 24½cm.
Text and map in envelope.

1. Mines and mineral resources—New South Wales.

Library, U. S. Geol. survey GS 6-887

NL 0418929 DI-GS

Liversidge, Archibald, 1847-
New South Wales. *Dept. of mines.*
... Mineral products of New South Wales, by Harrie Wood ... Notes on the geology of New South Wales, by C. S. Wilkinson ... And description of the minerals of New South Wales, by Archibald Liversidge ... Also catalogue of works, papers, reports, and maps on the geology, palæontology, mineralogy, &c., &c., of the Australian continent and Tasmania, by Robert Etheridge, junr. ... and Robert Logan Jack ... Sydney, T. Richards, government printer, 1882.

Liversidge, Archibald, 1847-
The minerals of New South Wales. By Archibald Liversidge ... ₍1st ed. Sydney, 1875?₎
63 p., 1 l. 21cm.
Caption title.
Read before the Royal society of New South Wales, 9 December, 1874, and published in the Transactions of the society for that year.

1. Mineralogy—New South Wales.

Library, U. S. Geol. survey GS 7-1039

NL 0418931 DI-GS

Liversidge, Archibald, 1847-
Minerals of New South Wales. Archibald Liversidge ... ₍1st ed. corrected₎ Sydney, T. Richards, government printer, 1876.
cover-title, 63 p. 21½cm.
First published in the Transactions of the Royal society of New South Wales for 1874.

1. Mineralogy—New South Wales.

Library, U. S. Geol. survey GS 7-1040

NL 0418932 DI-GS NjP NN

VOLUME 336

Liversidge, Archibald, 1847–
The minerals of New South Wales. By Archibald Liversidge ... 2d ed. ⌊Sydney, T. Richards, printer, 1882⌋
137, xiii p. 26½cm.
From the Royal society of New South Wales. Transactions, 1874, p. 65-199.

Subject entries: Mineralogy—New South Wales.
8-24170

Library of Congress, no. QE384.N5L8.

NL 0418933 DLC NjR N CtY MB

Liversidge, Archibald, 1847–
The minerals of New South Wales, etc., by A. Liversidge. ⌊3d ed.⌋ ... London, Trübner & co., 1888.
viii, 326 p. front. (fold. map) illus., plates (partly fold.) 25cm.
First published in the Transactions of the Royal society of New South Wales for 1874.

1. Mineralogy—New South Wales.

Library, U. S. Geol. survey G S 7-1041

PPAmP
NL 0418934 DI-GS MdBP MiHM NjR NIC CtY OOxM PPF NcU

Liversidge, Archibald, 1847-
New South Wales. *Dept. of mines.*
... Mines and mineral statistics of New South Wales, and notes on the geological collection of the Department of mines, comp. by direction of the Hon. John Lucas, M. P., minister for mines. Also remarks on the sedimentary formations of N. S. Wales, by the Rev. W. B. Clarke ... and notes on the iron and coal deposits, Wallerawang, and on the diamond fields, by Professor Liversidge ... Sydney, T. Richards, government printer, 1875.

LIVERSIDGE, Archibald, 1847–
Note on some bismuth minerals, molybdenite, and enhydros. n.p., [1892].

NL 0418936 MH

Liversidge, Archibald, 1847-
Notes upon some minerals from New Caledonia ...
[Sydney, 1880]
"Read before the Royal society of N. S. W., 1 September, 1880."

NL 0418937 CtY

Liversidge, Archibald, 1847-
On some New South Wales minerals ...
[Sydney, 1880]
"Read before the Royal society of N. S. W., 3 November, 1880."

NL 0418938 CtY NN MH

Liversidge, (Archibald), 1847– On the amylolytic ferment of the pancreas. pp. 45–51. 8°. *Cambridge, Macmillan & Co.,* 1873. [P., v. 1489.]
In: Stud. from. Physiol. Lab., Univ. Camb., 1873, pt. 1.
Repr. from: J. Anat. & Physiol., Lond., 1872–4, viii.

NL 0418939 DNLM

LIVERSIDGE, Archibald, 1847–
On the chemical composition of certain rocks, New York Wales, etc., [Sydney, 1883]

NL 0418940 MH

Liversidge, Archibald, 1847–
On the composition of some wood enclosed in basalt. By A. Liversidge ... ⌊Sydney, T. Richards, government printer, 1881⌋
3 p. illus. 21½cm.
Caption title.
"Read before the Royal society of New South Wales, 1 December, 1880."

1. Trees, Fossil.

Library of Congress QE991.L78 6—22497

NL 0418941 DLC

Liversidge, Archibald, 1847–
... 1. On the presence of magnetite in certain minerals and rocks. 2. On iron rust possessing magnetic properties. By A. Liversidge ... ⌊Hobart, Tasmania, 1892⌋
26 p. 21½cm.

"Reprinted from the Transactions of the Australasian association for the advancement of science, Hobart meeting, 1892."

NL 0418942 NNC MH

Liversidge, Archibald, 1847–
President's address, delivered to the Royal society of New South Wales, 5 May, 1886.
(Sydney, 1886. YA 17887
41p.

NL 0418943 DLC NN

Liversidge, Archibald, 1847–
... President's address, by A. Liversidge ... Sydney, The Society; ⌊etc., etc.⌋ 1901.
cover-title, 29 p. 21cm.
At head of title: Royal society of New South Wales. Sydney.

I. Royal society of New South Wales, Sydney.
15-2735

Library of Congress Q93.N58L5

NL 0418944 DLC

Liversidge, Archibald, 1847–
Report upon certain museums for technology, science, and art, also, upon scientific, professional, and technical instruction, and systems of evening classes in Great Britain and on the continent of Europe. By Archibald Liversidge ... Ordered by the council to be printed, 13 July, 1880. Sydney, T. Richards, government printer, 1880.
v, xxx, 237 p. 33cm.
At head of title: 1879–80. New South Wales. Legislative council.
Submitted to the minister for justice and public instruction.
"A list of certain publications relating to technical education, museums, and allied matters": p. 225–228.
1. Education. 2. Technical education. I. New South Wales. Dept. of justice and public instruction.
7–27823†

Library of Congress T69.L8

NL 0418945 DLC Nh ICRL ICJ PPAmP CtY NN ICJ

Liversidge, Archibald, 1847-
Tables for qualitative chemical analysis, arranged for the use of students, by A. Liversidge ... 2d ed. London, Macmillan and co., ltd., 1904.
126 p. 25 cm.
1. Chemistry, Analytic-Qualitative.

NL 0418946 CU

Liversidge, Archibald, 1847–
Upon the composition of some New South Wales coals. By A. Liversidge ... ⟨Read before the Royal society of N. S. W., 8 December, 1880.⟩ ⌊Sydney, T. Richards, gov't printer, 1881⌋
32 p. incl. tables. 21½cm.
Caption title.

1. Coal—Analysis. 2. Coal—New South Wales.
8-23851†

Library of Congress TP326.A8N5 1881

NL 0418947 DLC

Liversidge, Douglas, 1913–
White horizon. London, Odhams Press ⌊1951⌋
255 p. illus. 22 cm.

1. Palmer Peninsula. 2. John Biscoe (Ship) I. Title.

G890.P3L5 1951 919.9 51-36649 rev ‡

NL 0418948 DLC WaE WaSp CaBVa CaBViP KMK

Liversidge, Henry Douglas
see
Liversidge, Douglas, 1913–

Liversidge, Horace Preston, 1878–
Electric service in Philadelphia, since 1881 ⌊by⌋ H. P. Liversidge ... New York, The Newcomen society of England, American branch, 1945.
36 p. incl. mounted col. front., illus. 23cm.
Text on p. ⌊2⌋ and ⌊4⌋ of cover.
"This Newcomen address, based upon contemporary records preserved by Philadelphia electric company, was delivered during the '1945 Philadelphia dinner' ... held in ... the Bellevue-Stratford, Philadelphia ... on November 28, 1945."

"First printing: November 1945. Second printing: November 1945."

1. Philadelphia electric company. I. Newcomen society for the study of the history of engineering and technology, London. American branch. II. Title.
HD9685.U7P54 621.3 47-4471

NL 0418951 DLC CaBVaU IdU NN ICU ICJ MH CU

Liversidge, Horace Preston, 1878-
History of Association...
see under **Electrical Association of Philadelphia.**

387.1 qL785 **Liversidge, Horace Preston, 1878-**
The importance of the port and foreign trade to the Philadelphia area. Address on acceptance of annual award of Foreign Traders Association of Philadelphia, inc. Philadelphia, September 22, 1953. [Philadelphia, Publicity Dept., Philadelphia Electric Co., 1953]
12 p. 29 cm.

1. Philadelphia. Harbor. I. Title.

NL 0418953 N NN PPD PPCPC PSt

Liversidge, Horace Preston, 1878-
Opportunities for youth in the electric utility industry, by H. P. Liversidge ... New York, Edison electric institute ⌊1937⌋
⌊7⌋ p. port. 29½cm.

"Originally presented before the fifth annual convention of the Edison electric institute, Chicago, Ill., June 2, 1937."
I. Title: Electric utility industry.

NL 0418954 NNC

VOLUME 336

Liversidge, Joan.
Furniture in Roman Britain. With foreword by J. M. C. Toynbee. London, A. Tiranti, 1955.
75 p. illus. 19 cm. [Chapters in art, v. 27]

1. Furniture, Roman. 2. Gt. Brit.—Antiq. I. Title.

NK2315.L5 749.2937 56-3229 ‡

NL 0418955 OC1MA DAU NNC OCU MB NN TxU PU TNJ ICU MB DDO MdBWA DSI CoU DLC MiU WaU OC1 NcD PP PPD CtY IU NIC

Liversidge, John G[eorge].
Engine-room practice; a handbook for the royal navy and mercantile marine; treating of the management of the main and auxiliary engines on board ship. London: Charles Griffin and Co., Ltd., 1899. xi, 292 p. diagr., illus., tables. 12°.

1. Marine engineering. 2. Title.
March 8, 1915

NL 0418956 NN DN NIC ICJ OC1 MiD

Liversidge, John George.
Engine-room practice. A handbook for the royal navy and mercantile marine; treating of the management of the main and auxiliary engines on board ship. By John G. Liversidge, ... Fifth edition, revised. London, C. Griffin & Co., ltd., 1906.
xi, 390 p. 111 illus., v fold. diagr. 20cm.

NL 0418957 ICJ CU

Liversidge, John George.
Engine-room practice. A handbook for the royal navy and mercantile marine: treating of the management of the main and auxiliary engines on board ship. London: C. Griffin & Co., 1911. xi, 394 p., 5 diagr. 7. ed. 8°.
Proudfit collection.

1. Marine engines.—Systematic works, 1911.
August 31, 1911

NL 0418958 NN

Liversidge, John G[eorge].
Engine-room practice. A handbook for the royal navy and mercantile marine: treating of the management of the main and auxiliary engines on board ship... London: C. Griffin & Co., 1914. xi, 412 p. illus. 8. ed. 8°.

1. Marine engine.
September 18, 1914.

NL 0418959 NN

Liversidge, John George.
Engine-room practice. A handbook for the royal navy and mercantile marine; treating of the management of the main and auxiliary engines on board ship. 10th edition revised London, C. Griffin & Co., ltd., 1918.
412 p.

NL 0418960 MiU

Liversidge, John George.
Engine-room practice. A handbook for the Royal navy and mercantile marine: treating of the management of the main and auxiliary engines on board ship. By John G. Liversidge ... With 13 plates and 132 other illustrations. 11th ed., thoroughly rev. throughout. London, C. Griffin & company, limited, 1923.
xiii, 429 p. illus., XIII fold. pl., diagrs. 20cm.

1. Marine engineering—Handbooks, manuals, etc. I. Title.

24-2640

Library of Congress VM605.L5 1923

NL 0418961 DLC NN

Liversidge Institution of Industry, Boston.
[Report] 1893.
= Boston, 1893. Plate. 8°.

F4695 — Children. Charities for. — Boston, Mass. Hosp. — Boston, Mass. Char.

NL 0418962 MB

LIVERSIDGE INSTITUTION OF INDUSTRY, Boston.
Statements respecting the institution, with the constitution and by-laws. Oct., 1881.
= Boston, 1881. 22 pp. Plate. 8°

NL 0418963 MB DNLM MH

225
L75

Liverton's Tamar Valley horticultural guide.
Bere Alston, South Devon [Eng.]

1. Horticulturists. Directories.
2. Nurseries (Horticulture) Directories.
I. Liverton & Co. II. Title: Liverton's Tamar Valley market guide.

NL 0418964 DNAL

The Livery Club of the Worshipful Company of Musicians.
see London. Musicians' Company.

The livery rake, and country lass. An opera
see under [Phillips, Edward] fl. 1730-1740.

... The Livery triumphant; a letter to the Right Hon. the Lord Mayor, on his conduct respecting the later Common hall... to which are subjoined the Proceedings at large of the Common hall ... and an account of the festival of the Livery at the London tavern ... London [1809]
30 p.
3d ed.
No. 3 of a volume of pamphlets.

NL 0418967 NjP

A livery-man.
An address to the livery-men of the city of London...
see under title.

A Liveryman.
The ax laid to the root of the corrupt tree
see under title

A liveryman.
A brief extract, or summary of important arguments advanced by some late distinguished writers
see under title

A liveryman and grocer.
A letter to the Right Honourable Grocer
see under title

A Liveryman of London.
An essay on the effects of the inequitable modes of pursuing trade
see under title

A livery-man of the city of London.
A letter from a livery-man of the city of London, to a member of the honourable House of commons ...
see under title

The livery-man; or, Plain thoughts on publick affairs. In which the present situation of things, some late writings concerning the liberty of the press, the general disposition of the people, the insults offered to the city of London, and the true nature and infallible characteristicks of publick spirit, in contradistinction to that of a faction, are consider'd and explain'd ... London, Printed for J. Smith, 1740.
viii, 64 p. 21cm.

1. Gt. Brit.—Pol. & govt.—1727-1760. 2. Public opinion.

CA 17-565 Unrev'd

Library of Congress DA503.1740.L5

NL 0418974 DLC CtY MH NPV

The livery-man's answer to letter, dated at White-Hall, January, 22d. 1727-8. [London? 1728]
broadside. 22 cm. [Anonymous poetical pamphlets. 18th century. Broadsides. no. 28]

NL 0418975 OCU

The livery man's reasons, why he did not give his vote for a certain gentleman
see under [Defoe, Daniel] 1661?-1731.

Lilly Library

A liveryman's reply to Sir Crisp Gascoigne's address. Shewing that gentleman's real motives, and his whole conduct, concerning Canning and Squires. London, Printed for W. Reeve, 1714.
2 p.l., [3]-53 p. 8vo

NL 0418977 InU MH

VOLUME 336

A liveryman's reply to Sir Crisp Gascoigne's address. Shewing that gentleman's real motives, and his whole conduct, concerning Canning and Squires. London, W. Reeve, 1754.
33 p. 20cm.

1. Gascoyne, Sir Crisp, 1700–1761. An address to the liverymen of London. 2. Canning, Elizabeth, 1734–1773. 3. Squires, Mary, d. 1762.
45-48427

NL 0418978 DLC MH OCl MnHi CtY

Liverzani, Bartolomeo, ed.
Resolutiones a Sacra Congregatione Concilii in causis anno 1740 propositis editae ...
see under Congregatio Concilii.

Liverziani, Giuseppe.
Grammatica della musica, o sia Nuovo, e facile metodo per istruirsi nell' intero corso della musica, non per anche posto in ordine da alcuno, ove premesse le notizie istoriche, e le proprietà della medesima, s'insegnano fin dai più remoti principj le regole per ben cantare, e suonare il cembalo, indi si procede allo studio del contrappunto. e composizione prattica. Di Giuseppe Liverziani ... Parte prima. Roma, Nella stamperia P. Cracas, 1797.
xvi, 88 p. incl. front. (port.) 20cm.
No more published.
1. Music—Manuals, text-books, etc.
6-43880
Library of Congress MT7.L5L73

NL 0418980 DLC CU

Lives, adventures and exploits of Frank and Jesse James. With an account of the tragic death of Jesse James, April 3d, 1882. The last daring feats of the James confederacy, in the robbery and murder on the Rock Island train, July 14th, 1881; and at Glendale, Mo., Sept. 17th 1881. [n. p., 1882?] 96 p. incl. front. illus. 22cm.
Cover-title.

266411B. 1. James, Jesse Woodson, 1847–1882. 2. James, Frank, 1844–1915. 3. Robbers and robberies—U. S.
June 5, 1944

NL 0418981 NN NcD

Lives, adventures and exploits of Frank and Jesse James
see also The James boys. A thrilling story of the adventures and exploits of Frank and Jesse James; ...

The lives and adventures of celebrated claimants; an account of the extraordinary careers of some remarkable impostors, from Maturin Bruneau, soi-disant Louis XVII of France to Arthur Orton, pretended Sir R. C. Richborne, bart...
London & New York, Ward, Lock and co., n.d.
163 p.

NL 0418983 OCl PPL

The LIVES and adventures of Jack Shepherd, Dick Morris, William Nevison and Sawney Beane, notorious thieves and highwaymen. Manchester, W. Willis, 1839.
nar.12°. pp. 24. Front. engraved.

NL 0418984 MH

---

*EC75 A100 755l

The lives and adventures of the German Princess [i.e. Mary Carleton], Mary Read, Anne Bonny, Joan Philipe, Madam Churchill, Betty Ireland, and Ann Hereford. With a folio print of the German Princess with her suppos'd husband and lawyer; and other copper plates.
London: Printed for M.Cooper, Pater-noster-row; W.Reeve, Fleet-street; and C.Sympson, at the Bible-warrhouse[!], Chancery-lane. MDCCLV ...
1p.l., 108p. fold.port. 17cm.
Title vignette.
Pages 36, 44 misnumbered 26, 96.

Although the text includes biographies of all the persons named in the title, p.108 has note "The end of the first part", and copper plates other than the "folio print" are not present.
The lives of the female pirates, Mary Read and Anne Bonny are taken from Charles Johnson's "A generall history of the pyrates" (1724).

NL 0418986 MH

---

*Defoe 30 .726 .A10L

The lives and amours of queens and royal mistresses. Extracted from the historians of England, France, Turky and Spain. With some intrigues of popes. London, Printed in the year 1726.
viii, 186 p. 19cm.

1. Queens. 2. Courts and courtiers.

NL 0418987 MB

D107.3 L5

The lives and amours of queens and royal mistresses, with some intrigues of popes, extracted from the histories of England, France Turkey, Spain and Italy. London, 1727.
152 p. 19 cm.
Contents. - Isabel, queen of England under king John. - Fredegund, under Chilperic, king of France. - Roxelana, under Soliman the second emperor of the Turks. - Maria de Padilla, under Don Pedro, king of Spain. - Marozia, under several popes.

NL 0418988 CtY ICN

---

*Defoe 30 .726 .A10Lb

The lives and amours of queens and royal mistresses ... With some intrigues of popes. Extracted from the histories of France, England, Turkey, Spain and Italy. Gloucester [Eng.] Printed by R. Raikes, 1746.
131 p. 18cm.

1. Queens.

NL 0418989 MB

Lives and anecdotes of illustrious men
see under [Hawks, Francis Lister] 1798-1866.

The lives and battles of Tom Sayers, the champion of England, and John C. Heenan, "the Benicia boy." With full accounts of their various contests in the ring ... To which is added the new rules of the ring ... New York, R. M. De Witt [1860]
94, [1]-vi p. incl. front., port. 14cm.
In double columns.

1. Sayers, Thomas, 1826–1865. 2. Heenan, John C., 1835–1873. 3. Boxing.
Library of Congress GV1131.L78 5-29627†

NL 0418991 DLC NN MnU

The lives and bloody exploits of the most noted pirates, their trials and executions, including correct accounts of the late piracies, committed in the West Indias, and the expedition of Commodore Porter; also those committed on the brig Mexican, who were executed at Boston, in 1835 ... Hartford, Con., E. Strong, 1836.
1 p. l., [5]–298 p. 1 illus., plates. 18cm.
Title vignette.
Earlier editions (1825, 1829, 1834) published under title: The history of the pirates ... Later editions (1855, 1860) under title: The history of the lives and bloody exploits of the most noted pirates ...
1. Pirates. I. Strong, Ezra, pub.
32-1217
Library of Congress F2161.H674 923.41729

NL 0418992 DLC NN PU MH

The lives and bloody exploits of the most noted pirates, their trials and executions, including the correct accounts of the late piracies, committed in the West Indies, and the expedition of Commodore Porter; also, those committed on the Brig Mexican, who were executed at Boston, in 1835 ... Hartford, Con.: Ezra Strong, 1839.
298p. front., plates. 19½cm.

NL 0418993 NBu MH-L MB

The lives and characters of all the English poets
see [Jacob, Giles] 1686-1744.
The poetical register; or, the lives and characters of all the English poets

---

Lives and characteres of English dramatick poets ...
see under Langbain, Gerard, 1609-1658.

920.042 L758

The lives and characters of the most illustrious persons, who died in the years, 1713, 1714, and 1715. Viz, Dr. Compton, bishop of London. Dr. Sprat, bishop of Rochester. Dr. Burnett, bishop of Salisbury. Dr. Radcliffe. Thomas, marquiss of Wharton. Dr. Burnett, maste of the Charter-house. J. Partridge, gent. With true copies of their last wills and testaments. London, Printed for E. Curll and J. Pemberton, 1716.
[378]p.

Various pagings.
Apparently a continuation or imitation of John Le Neve's Lives and characters of the most illustrious persons who died in the years 1711-1712. The compilation has been attributed to the bookseller, Edmund Curll. cf. Raphael King ltd. Rare books. Catalogue 32.

NL 0418997 IU KU DFo ICU InU IU ViU ICN RP FU CSmH

XB 123 L78

The lives and characters of the principal personages in the early part of the history of America. Philadelphia, Published by Bennett & Walton, No. 31, Market street. 1812.
103p. 13½cm.
"Printed by John F.Gilbert, Frankford, Pa."
Contents. - Christopher Columbus. - Fernando Cortes. - Montezuma. - Pizarro, Almagro, & Luque.
1. Colombo, Cristoforo. 2. Cortés, Hernando. 3. Montezuma II, emperor of Mexico. 4. Pizarro, Francisco, marqués. 5. Almagro, Diego de. 6. Luque, Fernando.

NL 0418998 NRU PP NjR

VOLUME 336

G535 L55 Lives and confessions of John Williams, Francis Frederick, John P. Rog, and Peter Peterson, who were tried at the United States Circuit court in Boston, for murder & piracy; sentenced to be executed Jan. 21, 1819; and afterwards reprieved till Feb. 18, 1819 ... Boston, Printed by J. T. Buckingham ₍c1819₎
cover-title, iv₍5₎-36p. 24cm. in 25½cm.
Sabin: 41584.

NL 0418999 NBuG MH MB

... Lives and confessions of John Williams, Francis Frederick, John P. Rog, and Peter Peterson, who were tried at the United States circuit court in Boston, for murder & piracy; sentenced to be executed Jan. 21, 1819; and afterwards reprieved till Feb. 18, 1819 ... ₍2d ed.₎ Boston, Printed by J. T. Buckingham ₍1819₎
iv, ₍5₎-40 p. 23cm.
"The sketches ... were taken from the declaration of the persons themselves, whose lives they purport to be."—Pref.
I. Williams, John, 1789-1819. II. Frederick, Francis, d. 1819. III. Rog, John Peterson, 1789-1819. IV. Peterson, Peter, 1790-1819.
16—21843
Library of Congress HV6245.L45

NL 0419000 DLC DN NBu MWA MH MB

Lives and Confessions of Zebadiah Payne ...
see under [Haynes, Milton A]

*
331.881 M738 The lives and crimes of the "Mollie Maguires"; the confessions and execution. With an account of the organization of this terrible secret society; a full account. Philadelphia, Published by Barclay ₍1877₎
88 p. illus., ports. 24 cm.

NL 0419002 KyU MH

The lives and crimes of the "Mollie Maguires." The confessions and execution. With an account of the organization of this terrible secret society.
Phila., Barclay & co., c1878.
88 p.

NL 0419003 OCl

...The lives and crimes of the "Mollie Maguires." The confessions and execution. With an account of the organization of this terrible secret society. Philadelphia, Barclay & co. ₍1879₎ 100 p. illus. 24cm.
At head of title: A full account.
On cover: The life and execution of Jack Kehoe, king of the "Mollie Maguires."
"Argument of Franklin B. Gowen, esq.," p. 65-88.

1. Murder—U. S.—Pennsylvania. 2. Molly Maguires. 3. Kehoe, John. I. Gowen, Franklin Benjamin, 1836-1889.
N. Y. P. L. December 12, 1947

NL 0419004 NN

The lives and criminal trials of celebrated men
see under [Jardine, David] 1794-1860.

The lives and daring deeds of the most celebrated pirates and buccaneers of all countries... Philadelphia, G.G. Evans ₍18--?₎
288 p.incl.col.front. plates. 19 cm.

1.Pirates. 2.Buccaneers. 3.Brigands and robbers.

NL 0419006 NjP DLC CtNlCG CSmH T CaBViPA OClWHi

The Lives and Deaths of the Holy Apostles...
London, Dorman Newman, 1685.
Small 8vo. A, blank and lacking. Old sheep.
Woodcuts in the text.
Preface signed: P.D.

NL 0419007 CSmH

Lives and discoveries of famous travellers
see under [Cochrane, Robert] comp.

The Lives and dying confessions of Richard Barrick, and John Sullivan, high-way robbers.
Printed and sold at Worcester. Sold also by Edward Houghton, Post Rider. [1784.] pp.12. 12mo.
Evans 18559

NL 0419009 MWA

1044
Lives and exploits of pirates and buccaneers. Philadelphia, 1857.

NL 0419010 MBBC PHC

The Lives and exploits of the most celebrated robbers and banditti of all countries. With many engravings. Philadelphia, Geo. G. Evans ₍ca. 1860₎
284 p. plates. 20 cm.

NL 0419011 PLatS PU

The LIVES and exploits of the banditti and robbers of all nations. Philadelphia, R.W. Pomeroy, 1836.
1 v. illus. 19cm.
Vol. 2.
Complete work in 2 v.

1. Robbers and robberies.

NL 0419012 NN

Lives and exploits of the most distinguished voyagers, adventurers and discoverers in Europe, Asia, Africa, America, the South seas, and polar regions...by J. A. St. John, Sir Hugh Murray, and others. Hartford, H. Huntington, 1840.
650 p. illus. ports.

I. St. John, James Augustus. II. Murray, Hugh.

NL 0419013 MiD IU NjP CU KyU

Lives and exploits of the most noted highwaymen, robbers and murderers, of all nations
see under [Whitehead, Charles] 1804-1862.

The lives and exploits of the most noted robbers, buccaneers, and pirates of all countries. Philadelphia, F.Bell, 1846.
2 v. in 1.

NL 0419015 MH OClWHi

Case I 201 .496 The LIVES and exploits of the most noted robbers, buccaneers, and pirates of all countries ... Philadelphia, F.Bell, 1849.
2v.in 1. col.fronts.(ports.),illus. 20cm.
Title vignettes.
The text is suspiciously similiar to that of Charles MacFarlane's The lives and exploits of banditti and robbers in all parts of the world, first published in 1833.

NL 0419016 ICN

The lives and exploits of the most noted robbers, buccaneers and pirates of all countries...
Phila., 1854

HV6246 .L5

NL 0419017 DLC

tG535 L5 The Lives and exploits of the most notorious pirates and their crews,/by a sea captain. London, T. Allman ₍18--₎
324 p. front. 13cm.

1. Pirates. I. A sea captain.

NL 0419018 CU

Lives and exploits of pirates. Phil.,1842.

NL 0419019 NcU

*Defoe 30 .728 .A10L The lives and last wills and testaments of the following eminent persons. I. Dr. Gilbert Burnet. II. Dr. Thomas Burnet. III. Dr. George Hickes. IV. Dr. Daniel Williams. V. Joseph Addison. VI. Mr. Mahomet. With several other valuable tracts, now first collected into a volume. London, Printed for H. Curll, 1728.
12 pts. in 1 v. 20cm.
Pamphlets also issued separately here brought

1. Wills—Gt. Brit.

NL 0419021 MB

Lives and legends of the English bishops and Kings ..
see under Bell, Nancy R E (Meugens) d. 1933.

VOLUME 336

Lives and Legends of the evangelists, apostles ...
see under [Bell, Nancy R E (Meugens)] d. 1933.

The lives and memorable actions of many illustrious persons of the eastern nations, such as khalifas, soltans, wazirs, or prime-ministers, generals, philosophers, poets, &c. who have distinguish'd themselves .. Extracted from the most authentick oriental chronologers and historians. Never before Englished. London: Printed for J. Wilcox ... 1739.
[7],300 p. 17cm.
"These short memorials ... was designed and begun to be trans- lated into English, by the late ... George Sale ... and since his death, the translations have been compleated by a gentleman who resided in Turkey near twenty years."- Advertisement.
Signatures: [A]4, B-N12, O8 (O7-8, advertisements)
From the library of C.K. Ogden.
Bound in old calf, rebacked.

NL 0419024 CLU-C

The lives and most remarkable maxims of the antient philosophers
see under [Fénelon, François de Salignac de La Mothe-] 1651-1715.

The lives and portraits of curious and odd characters, compiled from authentic sources... Worcester [Mass.] T. Drew, 1852.
192 p. illus. 17cm.

165476B. 1. Eccentric persons.
N. Y. P. L. May 19, 1942

NL 0419026 NN MH

The Lives and portraits of remarkable characters, drawn from the most authentic sources. A new ed. v. 1-2. London, Printed and published by W. Lewis, 1819.
2 v. in 1. ports. 25 cm.
A new ed. of the Eccentric magazine; or, Lives and portraits of remarkable persons, originally compiled and edited successively by Henry Lemoine and James Caulfield and published by G. Smeeton, London, 1812-13. A reissue was printed and sold by G. Smeeton and J. Caulfield, London, 1814. Cf. Brit. Mus. Cat.

1. Eccentrics and eccentricities.

CT9990.E312 64-58809

NL 0419027 DLC PU MH

... The lives and public services of General U. S. Grant, U. S. A. and of Hon. Schuyler Colfax, speaker of the House of representatives. Philadelphia, 1868.
24 p. illus. (ports.) 21½cm.
At head of title: <no. 182.>

1. Grant, Ulysses Simpson, pres. U. S., 1822-1885. 2. Colfax, Schuyler, 1823-1885.

Library of Congress E672.L775 10—32710

NL 0419028 DLC OClWHi PHi PPL

---

x823
D36co1 The lives and singular adventures of the three Jacks of Rosemary Lane; more particularly the life of Colonel Jack, in whose memoirs is pourtrayed a long chain of successful occurrences, which happened during his gradation through the following stages; beggar boy, pickpocket, footpad — the whole forming a display of the tricks and manoeuvres practised by highwaymen and their colleagues ... Written with a view to put on their guard the inhabitants of this extensive metropolis against those infamous pests of society. London, Printed and sold by S. Fisher [1801]
72p. front. 17cm.
Upper margins closely trimmed.

Caption title: The life and singular adventures of Colonel Jack.
A much abridged and entirely rewritten version of Defoe's The history of the most remarkable life and extraordinary adventures of — Colonel Jacque.

NL 0419031 IU ICN

Lives and speeches of Abraham Lincoln and Hannibal Hamlin. Columbus, O., Follett, Foster, 1860.
406 p. plate, ports. 20 cm.
CONTENTS.—Life of Abraham Lincoln, by W. D. Howells.—Memorabilia of the Chicago convention.—Speeches of Abraham Lincoln.—Life and speeches of Hannibal Hamlin, by John L. Hayes.
1. Lincoln, Abraham, Pres. U. S., 1809-1865. 2. Hamlin, Hannibal, 1809-1891. I. Howells, William Dean, 1837-1920. Life of Abraham Lincoln. II. Hayes, John Lord, 1812-1887. Life and speeches of Hannibal Hamlin.
E457.L78 5-40585 rev*
——Copy 10.
Lincoln's own marginal notes and corrections have been copied into this copy by Paul M. Angle from photocopies of pertinent pages in the Illinois State Historical Library.
Includes a holograph note by W. D. Howells and a newspaper clipping about Lincoln's notations.

WaS InU NIC NNC WU KU AU MWA MoU MH NcU OKentU CLSU NjP PU KyBgW ViW OO OClWHi MiU-C MH RPB DI
NL 0419032 DLC ICN NBu NRU CoU AAP MoSW OOxM PP

RAB
L736hoh
1860b Lives and speeches of Abraham Lincoln and Hannibal Hamlin. [2d complete ed.] Columbus, Ohio, Follett, Foster; Chicago, S. C. Griggs; Pittsburgh, Hunt & Miner; Cleveland, Ingham & Bragg, 1860.
406p.ports.20cm.
Textual change: The text at page 74, beginning with line 3, has been changed to read: "It was charged by Douglas that a Republican Convention met at Springfield and passed the resolutions found below. This was an error. No Convention was held at Springfield, but the resolutions were offered at a small meeting in Kane County of which Lincoln knew nothing."
Contents.--Life of Abraham Lincoln by W. D. Howells.--Memorabilia of the Chicago convention.--Speeches of Abraham Lincoln.--Life and speeches of Hannibal Hamlin, by John L. Hayes.

NL 0419035 OC ViU ICHi MH InU

Lives and speeches of Abraham Lincoln and Hannibal Hamlin. New York, W. A. Townsend & co.; Columbus, Follett, Foster & co., 1860.
xv, 17-406 p. pl., 2 port. (incl. front.) 18½cm.
CONTENTS.—Life of Abraham Lincoln, by W. D. Howells.—Memorabilia of the Chicago convention.—Speeches of Abraham Lincoln.—Life and speeches of Hannibal Hamlin, by John L. Hayes.

1. Lincoln, Abraham, pres. U. S., 1809-1865. 2. Hamlin, Hannibal, 1809-1891. I. Howells, William Dean, 1837-1920. II. Hayes, John Lord, 1812-1887.

Library of Congress E457.L78 12—3256
[41c1]

OCl
NL 0419036 DLC CaBVaU OrPR N IEN IU CLSU NjP NN MH

Lives and sufferings of the English martyrs
see under [Burnet, Gilbert] bp., of Salisbury, 1643-1715, supposed author.

The lives and times of the popes, by the Chevalier Artaud de Montor. The most sumptuously extra-illustrated work ever made, New York, anno Domini MCMX. [New York, Plandome press, 1940?]
[19] p., 1 l. 6 facsim. (1 double) on 4 l. 28cm.
"Only one hundred copies of this monograph have been printed ... No. 43."

1. Artaud de Montor, Alexis François, 1772-1849. Histoire des souverains pontifes romains.

Library of Congress BX955.A73L5 44-44916

NL 0419038 DLC

The lives and times of the United Irishmen: Lord Edward Fitzgerald. Dublin [1846?]
142p.

NL 0419039 IU

... The lives and tragical deaths of beautiful females. By a clergyman, of Brunswick, Me. ... Boston [1858?]
cover-title, 36 p. incl. 2 pl. 24½cm.

Library of Congress 6-37488†

NL 0419040 DLC

Lives and trials of Archibald Hamilton Rowan, Rev. William Jackson
see under Macnevin, Thomas, 1814-1848, ed.

Lives and voyages of Drake, Cavendish, and Dampier
see under [Johnstone, Christian Isobel] 1781-1857.

The liues, apprehension, araignment & execution, of Robert Throgmorton, William Porter, Iohn Bishop, gentlemen. Together with the prayer which themselues made, & exercised both after their cõuiction & at their execution, who were al executed at S.Thomas a Watrings, on Fryday being the 26 of Februarie. 1608. for certaine robberies, & a muther [is] committed on Bagshot-Heath. London, Printed [by E. Allde] for H.Gosson, 1608.
Short-title catalogue no.24053 (carton 941)
1.Throgmorton, Robert, d.1608.

NL 0419043 MiU

The || lives, ap || prehensions Arraignments, and || *Executions, of the* 19. *late* || Pyrates. Namely:
Capt. Harris. Iennings. Longcastle. Downes. Haulsey. and their companies.
As they were seuerally indited on St. Mar- || grets Hill in *Southwarke*, on the 22. of || *December* last, and executed the || Fryday following. || London ¶ Printed for *Iohn Busby* the elder [1609?]
[60] p. 20cm.
Signatures: A-G4, H2.
Title vignette (woodcut of ship)
1. Pirates. I. Harris, James, d. 1608?

Library of Congress G535.L6 18-13067

NL 0419044 DLC ICU MiU-C CSmH DFO

VOLUME 336

FILM

The lives,apprehensions arraignments,and executions,of the 19.late pyratos. Namely: Capt. Harris. Iennings. Longcastle. Downes. Haulsey. and their companies. As they were seuerally indited on St.Margrets Hill in Southwarke,on the 22.of December last,and executed the Fryday following. London, Printed for I.Busby [1609]
University microfilms no.21681 (carton 725)
Short-title catalogue no.12805.
1.Pirates. I.Harris,James,d.1608.

NL 0419045 MiU

Lives, English and forein: containing the history of the most illustrious persons of our own and other nations, from the year 1550, to the year 1690. By several hands... London: B. Tooke, 1704. 2 v. 8°.

Extra title-page to each volume reading: Lives, English and forein...Including the history of England, and other nations of Europe...
Binder's title: Lives of illustrious persons.

1. Biography.
May 29, 1913.

NL 0419046 NN CLU-C NSchU NNC IEN

Lives in a lowland parish
see under [Green, Charles Edward] 1866-1920.

Lives made sublime.
see under Steel, Robert, 1827-1893.

Lives of Adam Wallace and Walter Mill
see under Lawson, John Parker, d. 1852.

The lives of alchemystical philosophers
see under [Barrett, Francis]

Lives of Alexander Henderson and James Guthrie, with specimens of their writings
see under Henderson, Alexander, 1583-1646.

Lives of Alfred the Great, Sir Thomas More, and John Evelyn. London, J. Burns [n.d.]
45, 48, 31 p. illus. 17 cm.
With this is bound: Lives of Englishmen. 1st-3d ser. London, J. Burns, 1845.
1. Gt. Brit. Biog. 2. Alfred the Great, King of England, 849-901. 3. More, Sir Thomas, Saint, 1478-1535. 4. Evelyn, John, 1620-1706.

NL 0419052 IEG

Lives of all the lords chancellors, lords keepers, and lords commissioners, of the great seal of England; from William the Conqueror, to the present time: but more at large of those two great opposites, Edward earl of Clarendon, and Bulstrode lord Whitlock. With a parallel of their actions. To which is added, an appendix of many rare and valuable speeches, letters, &c., referring to the said lives ... By an impartial hand ... London, R. Bonwicke, W. Freeman [etc.] 1712, '08
2 v. 20cm.
Vol. 1, second edition, with additions.
Vol. 2 has imprint: London, R. Burrough and J. Baker, 1708.
1. Clarendon, Edward Hyde, 1st earl of, 1609-1674. 2. Whitelocke, Sir Bulstrode, 1605-1675. 3. Gt. Brit. Lord high chancellor 4. Judges—Gt. Brit. I. An impartial hand. II. Oldmixon, John, 1673-1742, supposed author.
Library of Congress DA28.4.L15 17—12808 [a38b1]

MnU-L CLL NcD ICU NjP CtY CoU ViU PU-L
NL 0419053 DLC MiU-L IU CSt-Law WaU-L CLU-C TxU NcU

Lives of all the presidents of the United States, to which is added the Declaration of independence, and the Constitution of the United States. Boston, Printed by S. Harris, 1843.
24 p. 22½cm.
Copyrighted by Jeremiah Greenleaf.

1. Presidents—U. S.—Biog. I. Greenleaf, Jeremiah, 1791-
5-36848
Library of Congress E176.1.L58

NL 0419054 DLC

The lives of all the Roman emperors
see under [Brathwaite, Richard] 1588?-1673.

Lives of American merchants, eminent for integrity ...
see under [Frost, John] 1800-1859.

Lives of Andrew Jackson and General Marion: embracing anecdotes of their characters... Boston Lee and Shepard; New York, C. T. Dillingham, 1881
2 v. in 1. fronts.(ports.) 20 cm. [Lettered on cover: Famous generals]

Life of Andrew Jackson first published in 1845? cf. Pref.
"Life of General Marion" has separate t.-p. and paging, with imprint: Boston, Lee and Shepard; New York, Lee, Shepard, and Dillingham [n.d.]

1. Jackson, Andrew pres. U. S., 1767-1845. 2. Marion, Francis, 1732-1895.

NL 0419057 Vi T OClWHi

Lives of Anthony Wayne and Sir Henry Vane
see under [Armstrong, John] 1758-1843.

The LIVES of Arthur lord Balmerino, William earl of Kilmarnock, George earl of Cromertie, Jenny Cameron and Simon lord Lovat. The first two executed on Tower-hill; the third reprieved... London, Printed for C. Whitefield, 1746. 308 p. illus., ports. 20cm.

Added t.p. for each life.
"Some memoirs of the life and history of William Murray," p.[298]-308.

1. Balmerino, Arthur Elphingston, 6th baron, 1688-1746.
2. Kilmarnock, William Boyde, 4th earl of, 1704-1746.
3. Cromarty, George Mackenzie, 3d earl of, ca. 1702-1766.
4. Cameron, Jenny. 5. Lovat, Simon Fraser, 12th baron, 1677?-1747.
6. Jacobite rebellion, 1745-1746.

NL 0419060 NN CLU PU

Lives of Baron Steuben, [by Francis Bowen] Sebastian Cabot, [by Charles Hayward, Jr.] and William Eaton [by Cornelius C. Felton]
see under [Bowen, Francis] 1811-1890.

Lives of benefactors
see under [Goodrich, Samuel Griswold] 1793-1860.

Lives of Blaine and Logan
see under [Williams, C R]

Lives of British dramatists. By Thomas Campbell, William Gifford, Leigh Hunt, George Darley, &c., &c. .. Philadelphia, Carey and Hart, 1846.
2 v. in 1. 18cm. (Half-title: Carey and Hart's library for the people)
Paged continuously.
With the exception of the memoirs of Ben Jonson "these volumes contain memoirs and critical remarks prefixed to Mr. Moxon's series of the elder British dramatists." cf. Pref.
CONTENTS.—Remarks on the life and writings of William Shakespeare, by Thomas Campbell.—Memoirs of Ben Jonson, by William Gifford.—Lives of Beaumont and Fletcher, by George Darley.—Lives of Massinger and Ford, by Hartley Coleridge.—Biographical and critical notices of Wycherley, Congreve, Vanbrugh, and Farquhar, by Leigh Hunt.
1. Dramatists, English.
13-27148
Library of Congress PR653.L5

PPL OCU KyLx PU-F PPA MB OCl
NL 0419064 DLC MWA PPULC GU WaU NN NcU PP ViU N NjP

Lives of British Physicians
see under [Macmichael, William] 1784-1839.

Lives of celebrated American Indians
see under [Goodrich, Samuel Griswold] 1793-1860.

CT107 .L5 The LIVES of celebrated children. Boston, C. Tappan, 1845.
iv p., 1 l., [7]-157 p. 16cm.
CONTENTS.—Edward the Sixth, king of England.—Jane Grey.—Henry Christian Heinecken.—Agatha Watrin.—Francesco Micheli.—Juliette d'Aubencourt—Henry, duke of Nemours.—Hal-Mehi-Cantamir.—Volney Beckner.—Francis Mariette.—Louis, duke of Burgundy.—Lilia Fondana.—Ambroise Bouflers.—Marcella Apollodora.—Lucius Valerius.—Louis the Seventeenth, the 'martyr king'.—Francis Beauchateau.—John Philip Baratier.—Michael Verin.
1. Children—Biography.

NL 0419067 ViU MB

[Lives of celebrated Greeks. London: J. Burns, 1845.]
xxviii, 152 p. 12°.
By A.J.H.

1. Lycurgus. 2. Solon. 3. Aristides. 4. Themistocles. 5. Cimon. 6. Pericles. 7. Nicias. 8. Alcibiades. 9. Title.
N. Y. P. L. June 18, 1913.

NL 0419068 NN NBuG

[Lives of celebrated Greeks. London,1855.
By A.J.H.

NL 0419069 DSI

Lives of celebrated women, London, 1833
see under [Cochelet, Louise, "Mme. Parquin"] fl. 1809, supposed author.

Lives of celebrated women: by the author of Peter Parley's tales...
see under [Goodrich, Samuel Griswold] 1793-1860.

VOLUME 336

Lives of celebrated women. Joan of Arc, the maid of Orleans (1412–1431,) by Jules Mitchelet [sic]. Mary, queen of Scots, (1542–1587,) by Alphonse de Lamartine. Vittoria Colonna, (1490–1547,) by T. A. Trollope. New York: W. L. Allison [187–] 61, 53, 74, 28 p. front. (port.) 19cm.

On cover: Arundel edition.
"Josephine. Empress of the French; Charlotte Corday; Madame de Staël," 28 p. at end.

822628A. 1. Jeanne d'Arc, Saint, 1412–1431. 2. Mary, queen of Scots, 1542–1587. 3. Colonna, Vittoria, marchesa di Pescara, 1490–1547. I. Michelet, Jules, 1798–1874. II. Lamartine, Alphonse Marie Louis de Prat de, 1790–1869. III. Trollope, Thomas Adolphus, 1810–1892.
N. Y. P. L. June 11, 1937

NL 0419072 NN NcGU MWA DCU

Lives of celebrated women: Joan of Arc, by Jules Mitchelet; Mary, Queen of Scots, by Alphonse de Lamartine; Vittoria Colonna, by T.A.Trollope. New York, J.W.Lovell co. [189-]

Spine: Lovell's universal series.

NL 0419073 MH

Lives of certain fathers of the church in the fourth century
see under [Lear, Henrietta Louisa (Farrer) 1824-1896.

Lives of Charles Lee and Joseph Reed
see under [Sparks, Jared] 1789-1866, ed.

The lives of children
see under Johns Hopkins half-century committee.

The lives of Christopher Columbus, the discoverer of America, and Americus Vespucius, the Florentine ... Boston, Marsh, Capen, Lyon, and Webb, 1840.
1 p. l., 278 p. front. (port.) illus. 16cm.

1. Colombo, Cristoforo. 2. Vespucci, Amerigo, 1451–1512.

Library of Congress E111.L77 3—2803

NL 0419077 DLC MWA MB ICN MH

The lives of Christopher Columbus, the discoverer of America, and Americus Vespucius, the Florentine... N.Y., Harper, 1847.
278 p. illus., ports. 16cm.

1 Colombo, Cristoforo.
2 Vespucci, Amerigo, 1451-1512.

NL 0419078 NjPT

The **lives** of Christopher Columbus, the discoverer of America, and Americus Vespucius the Florentine ... New York, Harper & brothers, 1854.
1 p. l., 278 p. front. (ports.) illus. 16cm.

1. Colombo, Cristoforo. 2. Vespucci, Amerigo, 1451–1512.

A 21-1470

Title from H. E. Huntington Libr. Printed by L. C.

NL 0419079 CSmH PCC

4749a.18
Lives, The, of Christopher Columbus, the discoverer of America, and Americus Vespucius, the Florentine.
New York. Harper. 1870. (2), 278 pp. Portraits. Plates. 15 cm., in 8s.

L9791 — Columbus. Christopher. — Vespucci, Amerigo, 1451-1512.

NL 0419080 MB

*
BR1705
.L55
1828
The lives of Clemens Romanus, Ignatius, and Polycarp. Philadelphia: American Sunday School Union, 1828.
126 p. illus. 15cm.
Bookplate of Sycamore Church Sunday School Library.

1. Clemens Romanus. 2. Ignatius, Saint, Bp. of Antioch, 1st cent. 3. Polycarpus, Saint, Bp. of Smyrna. I. Sunday-School Union of the Methodist Episcopal Church.

NL 0419081 ViU

The **lives** of Clemens Romanus, Ignatius, and Polycarp ... Revised by the editors. New-York, B. Waugh and T. Mason, for the Sunday school union of the Methodist Episcopal church, 1833.
94 p. illus. 13½cm.

1. Clemens Romanus. 2. Ignatius, Saint, bp. of Antioch, 1st cent. 3. Polycarpus, Saint, bp. of Smyrna. I. Sunday-school union of the Methodist Episcopal church.

34-9079

Library of Congress BR1705.L55 922.1

NL 0419082 DLC

The lives of Cleopatra and Octavia
see under [Fielding, Sarah] 1710-1768.

Lives of Columbus, Washington, and Franklin. Philadelphia, 1851.

NL 0419084 DLC

Lives of Count Rumford, Zebulon Montgomery Pike and Samuel Gorton
see under [Renwick, James] 1790-1863.

DS282
.L5
1891
The lives of Cyrus and Alexander. New York, Hunt & Eaton, 1891.
404 p. 17cm. (Young peoples series)

Also published separately under titles: The life of Cyrus; and The life of Alexander the Great.

1. Cyrus, the Great, King of Persia, d. B. C. 529. 2. Alexander the Great, B. C. 356-323.

NL 0419086 ViU

Lives of David R. Porter and Joseph Ritner, the two candidates for the office of governor of Pennsylvania, compiled from authentic sources and contrasted... [n. p.] 1838. 24 p. 19½cm.

1. Porter, David R., b. 1788. 2. Ritner, Joseph, 1780–1869.
N. Y. P. L. January 29, 1941

NL 0419087 NN NIC MH

The lives of distinguished foreigners
see under [Nougaret, Pierre Jean Baptiste] 1742-1823.

Lives of distinguished shoemakers ... Portland [Me. Davis & Southworth, 1849.
iv p., 2 l., [9]-340 p. 19 cm.

1. Shoemakers.

Portland, Me. Pub. Lib. for Library of Congress CT9730.S5L6 A 34—1442

NL 0419089 MeP OrU PP PPT NcD

The Lives of Dr. Edward Pocock, the celebrated orientalist, by Dr. Twells; of Dr. Zachary Pearce, bishop of Rochester, and of Dr. Thomas Newton, bishop of Bristol, by themselves; and of the Rev. Philip Skelton, by Mr. Burdy... London, Printed for F. C. and J. Rivington, by R. and R. Gilbert, 1816.
2 v. 22cm.
Preface signed: A. C.

1. Pocock, Edward, 1604–1691. 2. Skelton, Philip, 1707–1787. I. Twells Leonard, d. 1742. II. Pearce, Zachary, bp. of Rochester, 1690–1774. III. Newton, Thomas, bp. of Bristol, 1704–1782. IV. Burdy, Samuel, 1760?–1820 V. C., A., ed. VI. A. C., ed.

Library of Congress CT781.L5 23-2544

NL 0419090 DLC NNUT NcD CtY TxU NN OCl

Lives of early Methodist preachers
see under [Jackson, Thomas] 1783-1873, ed.

Lives of Ebenezer Erskine, William Wilson, and Thomas Gillespie, fathers of the United Presbyterian Church
see under Harper, James, 1795-1879.

Lives of Edward Preble and William Penn. Boston: Little, Brown and Co., 1864. xiv, 408 p., 1 port. 12°. (Library of American biography.)

Life of Edward Preble, commodore in the navy of the United States, by Lorenzo Sabine. Life of William Penn, by George E. Ellis.

CENTRAL RESERVE.
1. Preble, Edward. 2. Penn, William. 3. Sabine, Lorenzo. 4. Ellis, George Edward. 5. Series.
N. Y. P. L. May 25, 1914.

NL 0419093 NN CSmH

Lives of eminent American physicians and surgeons of the nineteenth century
see under Gross, Samuel David, 1805-1884, ed.

VOLUME 336

The lives of eminent & remarkable characters, born or long resident in the counties of Essex, Suffolk, & Norfolk. Embellished with 68 portraits. London, Printed for Longman, Hurst, Rees, Orme, and Brown; [etc., etc.] 1820.

[140] p. port. 21½cm.

Subject entries: 1. Essex, Eng.—Biog. 2. Suffolk, Eng.—Biog. 3. Norfolk, Eng.—Biog.

2-29236

Library of Congress, no. DA670.E14L6.

NL 0419095 DLC TxU MH PSt IU NcD NN ViU CtY PU-FA PP PPL

The lives of eminent and remarkable characters born or long resident in the counties of Essex, Suffolk, & Norfolk. Embellished with 68 portraits. London, Printed for Longman, Hurst, Rees, Orme, and Brown; [etc., etc.] 1820.

[116] p. port. 18½cm.

Imperfect (?)

Subject entries: 1. Essex, Eng.—Biog. 2. Suffolk, Eng.—Biog. Norfolk, Eng.—Biog.

2-29236

Library of Congress, no. DA670.E14L7.

NL 0419096 DLC

Lives of eminent Anglo-Saxons; illustrating the dawn of Christianity and civilization in Great Britain ... London, The religious tract society [1850]

2 v. 14½cm.

1. Anglo-Saxons. I. Religious tract society, London.

37-23882

Library of Congress BR749.L75 [2] 274.2

NL 0419097 DLC PPAmS

DA28 F67

Lives of eminent British statesmen. London, Longman, Orme, Brown, Green & Longmans [1831?]-39.

7 v. illus., ports. 17-18 cm.

Vol. 1 imperfect: t. p. wanting.

Bibliographical footnotes.

Contents. - v. 1. Sir Thomas More [by Sir J. Mackintosh] Cardinal Wolsey. Archbishop Cranmer. William Cecil, Lord Burleigh [by J. Macdiarmid] - v. 2 Sir John Eliot, by J. Forster. Thomas Wentworth, Earl of Strafford, by J. Forster. - v. 3. John Pym, by J. Forster. John Hampden, by J. Forster. - v. 4. Sir Henry Vane, the Younger, by J. Forster. Henry Marten, by J. Forster. - v. 5. Robert Cecil, Earl of Salisbury, by T. P. Courtenay. Thomas Osborne, Earl of Danby and Duke of Leeds, by T. P. Courtenay. - v. 6-7. Oliver Cromwell, by J. Forster.

1. Statesmen, British. I. Mackintosh, Sir James, 1765-1832. II. Macdiarmid, John, 1779-1808. III. Courtenay, Thomas Peregrine, 1782-1841. IV. Title: Eminent British statesmen.

NL 0419099 MeB OrU ViU NN CU

Lives of eminent British statesmen
see also Eminent British statesmen.

Lives of eminent individuals, celebrated in American history ...
see under [Sparks, Jared] 1789-1866, ed.

CT104 .L58 1st ser. 1860

Lives of eminent men. First series. Boston, Shepard, Clark & Brown [1860?]

194 p. 16cm. (The Parlor library)

1. Biography.

NL 0419102 ViU OClWHi

Lives of eminent men. 2nd ser. Boston, Shepard, Clark & Brown, n.d.

6, 95-286p. 16cm. (Parlor Library)

Sub-title: Cabinet of Biography.

NL 0419103 PPPrHi DLC

509.2 L785

Lives of eminent naturalists, with engraved portraits accompanying each. Edinburgh, W.H. Lizars, 1840.

6 pts. in 1 v. ports. 18cm.

First published in the Naturalist's library.

Each biography separately paged.

Contents.-Sir Hans Sloane, by J.Moule.-Pliny, by A.Crichton.-Werner, by J.Duncan.-Camper, by R.Hamilton.-John Hunter, by A. Crichton.-Maria Sibilia Merian, by J. Duncan.

1.Naturalists.

NL 0419104 CSt

... Lives of eminent person; consisting of Galileo, Kepler ...
see under Society for the diffusion of useful knowledge, London.

Coxe collection BX595 L5

Lives of eminent Russian prelates: I. Nikon, sixth patriarch of Moscow. II. Saint Demetrius, metropolitan of Rostoff. III. Michael, metropolitan of Novgorod and S. Petersburg. London, Joseph Masters, 1854.

xvi,147p. 17½cm.

"The lives of S. Demetrius and Michael ... are simply translations from the Russian ... [by] the Rev. R. W. Blackmore ... The Life of Nikon and the Introduction have been compiled from English materials, by the Rev. R. Thornton ..."

NL 0419106 NBuG DLC PU

[The lives of eminent saints.] New York, P.J Kenedy, 1904.

"The young Christian's library, no. 7."
Title taken from spine.

NL 0419107 MH

The lives of eminent Scotsmen
see under Society of Ancient Scots, London.

Lives of English authors, a biographical history of English literature.
London, New York, T. Nelson & sons, 1890.
9-323 p.

NL 0419109 MiU OCl

Lives of English popular leaders; I.
see under Maurice, Charles Edmund, 1843-

Lives of Epaminondas, of Philip of Macedon, ... 1602
see under Plutarchus.

Lives of Ezra Stiles, John Fitch and Anne Hutchinson
see under [Kingsley, James Luce] 1778-1852.

... The lives of Father Antonio Talpa, and the Ven. Father Eustachio, of the Naples Oratory
see under [Marciano, Giovanni] d. 1713.

... The lives of Father Joseph Anchieta, of the Society of Jesus, the Ven. Alvera von Virmundt ...
see under [Berettari, Sebastiano] 1543-1622.

The lives of Father Paul Segneri, S. J., Father Pinamonti, S. J. ...
see under [Massei, Giuseppe] 1626-1698.

Lives of Gen. Franklin Pierce and William R. King
see under Democratic Party. National Committee, 1852-1856.

... The lives of General U. S. Grant, and Henry Wilson. This work is a complete history of the lives of General Ulysses S. Grant, and of the Hon. Henry Wilson, from their birth up to the present time. With portraits of General U. S. Grant, Hon. Henry Wilson and other illustrative engravings. Philadelphia, T. B. Peterson & brothers [°1872]

1 p. l., 11-373 p. front., plates, port. 19cm.

At head of title: The lives of "Grant and Wilson."

1. U. S.—Hist.—Civil war—Campaigns & battles. 2. Grant, Ulysses Simpson, pres. U. S., 1822-1885. 3. Wilson, Henry, 1812-1875.

4-12744

Library of Congress E470.L78

NL 0419117 DLC OrP MU PHi

The lives of General U. S. Grant, and Schuyler Colfax. This work is a complete history of the lives of General Ulysses S. Grant, and of the Hon. Schuyler Colfax, from their birth up to the present time ... Philadelphia, T. B. Peterson & brothers [°1868]

1 p. l., 13-362 p. front., plates, ports. 18½cm.

1. Grant, Ulysses Simpson, pres. U. S., 1822-1885. 2. Colfax, Schuyler, 1823-1885.

29-2667

Library of Congress E672.L783 [2]

NL 0419118 DLC PU PPL

VOLUME 336

Lives of Good Servants ...
see under [Manning, Anne] 1807-1879.

LIVES of great and celebrated characters of all ages and countries, comprising heroes conquerors, jugglers and other curiosities of human nature. Philadelphia, Leary, Getz & co., 1860.

pp.767. Front. and illustr.

NL 0419120 MH PPL

LIVES of great and celebrated characters, of all ages and countries; comprising heroces, conquerors, jugglers, and other curiosities of human nature. New York Wold publishing house,1875.

pp.767. Ports and illustr.

Cover reads: World edition".

NL 0419121 MH

Lives of great and celebrated characters, of all ages and countries: comprising heroes, conquerors, statesmen, authors, artists, extraordinary humorists, misers, mountebanks, kings and queens, jugglers, and other curiosities of human nature. Compiled from authentic materials. Illustrated by several hundred engravings. = New York. World Publishing House. 1876. 767 pp. Illus. Portraits. Ornamental capitals. Autograph facsimile. Vignettes. 23 cm., in 4s.

F.1186 — Biography. Colls.

NL 0419122 MB

... "Lives of great men." Boston [The Directors of the Old South work] 1908.

cover-title, [168] p. 18½cm. (Old South leaflets. xxvi. 1908)

Various paging.
The t.-p. reads: The Old South leaflets. Twenty-sixth series, 1908.
The Old South lectures for 1908, which these papers supplement, were arranged with reference to the fact that 1908 was the third centennial of the birth of Milton and 1909 the centennial of the other great men treated in the course: Lincoln, Gladstone, Winthrop, Holmes, Tennyson, Darwin, Mendelssohn.

CONTENTS.—[1] Milton's treatise on education.—[2] Lincoln's first message to Congress (message to Congress in special session, July 4, 1861)—[3] Gladstone's "Kin beyond sea." 1878.—[4] Winthrop, R. C. The centennial of independence (from his Fourth of July oration, Boston, 1876)—[5] Holmes, O. W. The inevitable trial (from Dr. Holmes's Fourth of July oration before the city authorities of Boston, 1863)—[6] Gladstone on Tennyson (from Gladstone's essay on Tennyson in the "Quarterly review," October, 1859)—[7] The education of Darwin (the first section of Darwin's autobiography, written in 1876)—[8] Winthrop, R. C. Music in New England (address at the opening of the first musical festival in Boston, May 21, 1857)

10-13092

NL 0419123 DLC

Lives of illustrious men ...
see under [Plutarchus]

Lives of illustrious seamen ... including several hundred naval characters ... To which is prefixed a brief history of the rise and progress of the British navy ... London, Printed by J. Cundee for T. Hurst [etc.] 1803.

xx, 436 p. front., 12 port. 13cm.

1. Gt. Brit. Navy—Biog.

Library of Congress DA72.L7 4-34889

NL 0419125 DLC CaBViP DN MiU-C

...Lives of Indians. [Boston: Allen and Ticknor, 1833-34?] 24 p. 12°. (Scientific tracts. v. 3, no. 1.)

Caption-title.

1. Indians (N. A.)—Biography. 2. Series.
N. Y. P. L. September 27, 1922.

NL 0419126 NN

Lives of J. Edwards and D. Brainerd
see under [Sparks, Jared] 1789-1866, ed.

Lives of James Buchanan and John C. Breckinridge
see Buchanan and Breckinridge. Lives of James Buchanan and John C. Breckinridge.

Lives of James Otis [by Francis Bowen] and James Oglethorpe [by William B. O. Peabody]
see under [Bowen, Francis] 1811-1890.

E440
L785

Lives of John C. Breckinridge and Gen. Joseph Lane, the National Democratic candidates for President and Vice-President of the United States. With the National Democratic platform, and their letters of acceptance. Campaign ed. New York, Van Evrie, Horton & Co. [1860?]
30 p. ports. 24cm.

1. Presidents - U.S. - Election - 1860.
2. Campaign literature, 1860 - Democratic.
3. Breckinridge, John Cabell, 1821-1875.
4. Lane, Joseph, 1801-1881.

NL 0419130 GU

Lives of John Jay and Alexander Hamilton
see under [Renwick, Henry Brevoort] 1817-1895.

Lives of John Ribault, Sebastian Rale and William Palfrey
see under [Sparks, Jared] 1789-1866.

Lives of John Stark, Charles Brocken Brown ...
see under [Everett, Edward] 1794-1865.

Lives of John Sullivan, Jacob Leisler, Nathaniel Bacon, and John Mason. Boston: C. C. Little, 1848. 3 p.l., (i)vi-x, 438 p., 1 map. 12°. (Library of American biography. Series 2. v. 3.)

Life of J. Sullivan, by O. W. B. Peabody.
Administration of J. Leisler, by C. F. Hoffman.
Memoir of N. Bacon, by W. Ware.
Life of J. Mason, by G. E. Ellis.

1. Sullivan, John. 2. Leisler, Jacob. 3. Bacon, Nathaniel. 4. Mason, John, 1600-72. 5. Peabody, Oliver William Bourn. 6. Hoffman, Charles Fenno. 7. Ware, William. 8. Ellis, George Edward.
N. Y. P. L. November 29, 1911.

NL 0419134 NN NNC

The lives of John Trueman, and Richard Atkins
see under [Gilpin, William] 1724-1804.

Lives of Jonathan Edwards
see under [Miller, Samuel] 1769-1850.

Lives of Leonard Calvert, Samuel Ward and Thomas Posey
see under [Burnap, George Washington] 1802-1859.

Lives of Lord Herbert of Cherbury and Thomas Ellwood
see under Herbert, Edward Herbert, baron, 1583-1648.

Lives of Maha Raja Apurva Krishna bahadur ...
see under [Taeb Allāh, munshī]

The lives of Mark Rashton, the drunkard! Dan Coultford, the gambler. Miles Daring, the thief. Bloody Bill Blank, the murderer. New York, Philadelphia, Turner & Fisher, 1842.

32 p. incl. front., plates. 14½cm.

1. Crime and criminals.

15-9592

Library of Congress HV6245.L6

NL 0419140 DLC

The lives of Martin Luther and John Calvin, the two great reformers.

This work is available in this library in the Readex Microprint edition of Early American Imprints published by the American Antiquarian Society.
This collection is arranged according to the numbers in Charles Evans' American Bibliography.

NL 0419141 DLC

Lives of Martin Luther and John Calvin, the two great reformers.
Phila., 1799.
105p 24°

NL 0419142 MWA RPJCB

The lives of Master John H. Powers, the wonderful Kentucky giant boy, and of his sister Miss Mary Jane Powers, known as Barnum's fat lady ... A true narrative of their parentage, birth, early life, astounding growth, habits of life, remarkable travels and interesting experiences. Philadelphia, Barclay & co. [1876]

46 p. 15½cm.

Portraits on covers.

1. Powers, John H., 1858- 2. Powers, Mary Jane, 1848-

CA 18-1650 Unrev'd

Library of Congress GV1835.P6L5

NL 0419143 DLC OClWHi

VOLUME 336

Lives of missionaries, Greenland: Hans Egede; Matthew Stach and his associates. London, Society for Promoting Christian Knowledge [186-]

224 p. illus., port. 17 cm.

"Published under the direction of the Committee of General Literature and Education, appointed by the Society for Promoting Christian Knowledge."

1. Egede, Hans Poulsen, 1686-1758. 2. Stach, Matthäus, 1711-1787. 3. Moravian Church—Missions. 4. Missions—Greenland. I. Society for Promoting Christian Knowledge. General Literature Committee.

BV3695.E4L59 70-237701
266'.023'0922 [B]
MARC

NL 0419144 DLC NN ICN

NK8
L758 Lives of missionaries. North America. Published under the direction of the Committee of General Literature and Education, appointed by the Society for Promoting Christian Knowledge. London, Society for Promoting Christian Knowledge [185-?]
252 p. illus. 17 cm.

Contents.- John Eliot.- Bishop Seabury.- Bishop Chase.- Bishop Stewart, of Quebec.- Rev. J.G. Mountain.

1. Missionaries. 2. Eliot, John, 1604-1690. 3. Seabury, Samuel, Bp., 1729-1796. 4. Chase, Philander, Bp., 1775-1852. 5. Stewart, Charles James, Bp. of Quebec, 1775-1837. 6. Mountain, Jacob George, 1818-1856. I. Society for Promoting Christian Knowledge, London. General Literature Committee /(2)

NL 0419146 CtY-D CtY ICN

Lives of missionaries. Southern India. Ziegenbalg. Schwartz. Jaenicke. Gerické. London, Society for promoting Christian knowledge [1863?]
352 p. illus. 17 cm.

"Published under the direction of the Committee of general literature and education, appointed by the Society for promoting Christian knowledge."

NL 0419147 CtY-D

LIVES of notorious and daring highwaymen, robbers, and murderers. Compiled from authentic sources. Halifax, W. Milner [18--] 324 p. 14cm.

1. Criminals--Biog.--Gt. Br.

NL 0419148 NN

BX8693
.L7 Lives of our leaders. Character sketches of living presidents and apostles of the church of Jesus Christ of latter-day saints. With portraits. Salt Lake City, The Deseret news, 1901.

264 p. incl. front., ports. $18\frac{1}{2}$ cm.

"First appeared in the Juvenile instructor."—Pref.

CONTENTS.—Lorenzo Snow [by] O. F. Whitney.—G. Q. Cannon [by] J. H Anderson.—J. F. Smith [by] E. H. Anderson.—F. D. Richards [by] O. F. Whitney.—Brigham Young [by] S. Y. Gates.—F. M. Lyman [by] E. H. Anderson.—J. H. Smith [by] E. F. Parry.—George Teasdale [by] H. J. Cannon.—H. J. Grant [by] E. H. Anderson.—J. W. Taylor [by] E. F. Parry.—M. W. Merrill [by] J. M. Tanner.—A. H. Lund [by] J. M. Sjodahl.—M. F. Cowley [by] E. H. Anderson.—A. O. Woodruff [by] N. L. Morris.—Rudger Clawson [by] Nephi Anderson.—Reed Smoot [by] O. F. Whitney.

NL 0419149 ICU NjP MH

The **lives** of Philip Howard, earl of Arundel, and of Anne Dacres, his wife. Edited from the original mss. by the Duke of Norfolk, E. M. London, Hurst and Blackett, 1857.

viii, 317 p. 19 cm.

"Probably written by the countess' confessor."—Dictionary of nat. biog.

1. Arundel, Philip Howard, 1st earl of, 1557-1595. 2. Arundel, Anne (Dacres) countess of, 1557-1630. I. Norfolk, Henry Granville Fitzalan-Howard, 14th duke of, 1815-1860, ed.

Library of Congress DA358.A7L6 1-18581

NL 0419150 DLC TxU PU NcD OC1 WU PPL PV

Lives of remarkable characters, who have distinguished themselves from the commencement of the French revolution to the present time. From the French ... London, Longman, Hurst, Rees, Orme, and Brown, 1814

v. $21\frac{1}{2}$ cm.

Tr. from "Biographie moderne, ou Dictionnaire historique des hommes qui se sont fait un nom en Europe depuis 1789 jusqu'en 1802 (par MM. Alphonse de Beauchamp, Caubrières, Giraud, Michaud, de Coiffier et autres) Leipsick (Paris) 1802."

1. France—Hist.—Revolution—Dictionaries. 2. France—Hist.—Consulate and empire, 1799-1815. 3. France—Biog.—Dictionaries. I. Beauchamp, Alphonse de, 1767-1832, ed.

13-17802

Library of Congress DC145.L6

NL 0419151 DLC NIC ICU

PZ6
.L59 Lives of remarkable youth... Philadelphia, Presbyterian board of publication, n.d.
182p. 16cm.

NL 0419152 NNU-W RPB NcD

LIVES OF REMARKABLE YOUTH, of both sexes.
= Philadelphia. Littell. 1830. 222 pp. [Juvenile library.] 24°.
Contents. — Sir Thomas Lawrence. — Angela de la Moriniere. — Mozart. — The admirable Crichton. — Volney Beckner. — Candiac de Montcalm. — Blaise Pascal. — Lady Jane Grey. — Edward the Sixth.

NL 0419153 MB MWA NjP PSt MH PU

The lives of Richard Turpin, and William Nevison, two notorious highwaymen: containing a particular account of all their adventures until their trial and execution at York. York: James Kendrew, printer [17--?]
28 p. front. 20cm.

NL 0419154 NNC

Lives of Richard Turpin and William Nevison, two notorious highwaymen: containing a particular account of all their adventures, until their trial and execution at York. York [18--]
35 p.
The life of William Nevison, by Capt. Johnson: p. [30]-35.
I. Johnson, captain.

NL 0419155 NjP

Lives of Robert Cavelier de La Salle and Patrick Henry. Boston, C. C. Little and J. Brown, 1844.

4 p. l., [vii]-xx, 398, [2] p. $17\frac{1}{2}$ cm. (*Added t.-p.:* The library of American biography. Conducted by Jared Sparks. Second series. vol. I)

Also added t.-p., engraved, with portrait, and third added t.-p.: The library of American biography ... vol. XI.

CONTENTS.—Life of Robert Cavelier de La Salle, by Jared Sparks.—Life of Patrick Henry, by Alexander H. Everett.

1. La Salle, Robert Cavelier, sieur de, 1643-1687. 2. Henry, Patrick, 1736-1799. I. Sparks, Jared, 1789-1866. II. Everett, Alexander Hill, 1790-1847.

34-25063

Library of Congress E176.S81 2d ser., vol. 1

NL 0419156 DLC ICN CSmH

Lives of Robert Cavelier de La Salle and Patrick **Henry**. Boston, C. C. Little and J. Brown, 1848 [i. e. 1855]

4 p. l., [vii]-xx, 398, [2] p. $18\frac{1}{2}$ cm. (*Added t.-p.:* The library of American biography. Conducted by Jared Sparks. Second series. vol. I)

Added t.-p. has imprint: Boston, Little, Brown, and company, 1855.
Also added t.-p., engraved, with portrait, dated 1844, and third added t.-p.: The library of American biography ... vol. XI, 1847.

CONTENTS.—Life of Robert Cavelier de La Salle, by Jared Sparks.—Life of Patrick Henry, by Alexander H. Everett.

1. La Salle, Robert Cavelier, sieur de, 1643-1687. 2. Henry, Patrick, 1736-1799. I. Sparks, Jared, 1789-1866. II. Everett, Alexander Hill, 1790-1847.

Library of Congress F1030.5.L58 34-25064

NL 0419157 DLC

Lives of Robert Fulton, Joseph Warren, ...
see under [Renwick, James] 1790-1863, ed.

---

*Defoe
30
.711 **The lives of Roger Mortimer, earl of March,**
.A10 **and of Robert, earl of Oxford, &c. prime minis-**
L11b **ters in the reigns of Edward the Second, and Richard the Second.** The 2d ed. London, Printed for A. Baldwin, 1711.
48 p. 19cm.
Probably printed from standing type of the 1st edition.
Publication occasioned by the elevation of Robert Harley to the peerage.

1. March, Roger Mortimer, earl of, 1287?-1330. 2. Oxford, Robert De Vere, earl of, 1362-1392. 3. Oxford, Robert Harley, earl of, 1661-1724.

NL 0419160 MB TxU InU MH CtY

Lives of Roger Williams, Timothy Dwight and Count Pulaski
see under [Gammell, William] 1812-1889.

The lives of St. Alphonsus Liguori, St. Francis de Girolamo ...
see under [Wiseman, Nicholas Patrick Stephen] Cardinal, 1802-1865.

Lives of St. Francis of Assisi, and of St. Clare. New York and London, Burns and Oates, n.d.
132 p.

NL 0419163 WaSpG DHN

PX
7286
J83
L7
E5 The lives of St. Joseph Calasanctius, founder of the Pious Schools, and of the Blessed Ippolito Galantini, founder of the Congregation of Christian Doctrine. London, Richardson, 1850.
xiv, 460 p. front. (port.) 20cm. (The Saints and servants of God)
1. Joseph Calasanctius, St., 1556-1658. 2. Galantini, Ippolito, Blessed, 1565-1619. 3. Congregation of Christian Doctrine. I. Sorgenti, Fabio.

NL 0419164 DCU

LIVES of St.Paul Miki,St.John de Goto,and St.James Kisai,martyrs,of the Society of Jesus Canonized June 8,1862. New York,Rennie,Shea & Lindsay,1862.

16°. pp.31,(1).

NL 0419165 MH

... The lives of St. Thomas of Villanova, archbishop of Valentia ... and of St. Francis Solano.
see under [Maimbourg, Claude]

The lives of saints, collected from authentick records, of church history
see under [Fell, Charles] 1687-1763

VOLUME 336

Lives of saints, with excerpts from their writings. Introd. by Father Thomas Plassmann; editorial supervision by Father Joseph Vann. Roslyn, N. Y., Published for the Classics Club by W. J. Black [1953]
496 p. 20 cm.

1. Saints. 2. Religious literature (Selections: Extracts, etc.) I. Vann, Joseph, Father, 1907- ed.

BR1710.L5 922.22 54-17181 ‡

NL 0419168 DLC

Lives of saints, with excerpts from their writings. New York, J. J. Crawley [1954-
v. col. illus., col. ports. 22 cm.

1. Saints. 2. Religious literature (Selections: Extracts, etc.)

BR1710.L52 922.22 54—37560

NL 0419169 DLC KAS WaSpG OrStbM NbU DCU NcC NcGU NcRS MB PSt

The **lives** of saints, with other feasts of the year ...
see under Rivadeneira, Pedro de, 1527-1611.

Lives of Scottish poets ...
see under Society of Ancient Scots, London.

The lives of Sir Walter Raleigh and Capt. John Smith; with an account of the Governors of Virginia, to the year 1781. By a Virginian. Shepherd's-Town; printed by Maxwell & Harper. 1817.
121. [1] p. 16.5 cm.

NL 0419172 NcD WHi

---

*EC75 A100 755l5

The lives of Stephen M'Daniel, John Berry, James Egan, (alias Cahagan) and James Salmon, thief-takers. Containing, a full account of the evidence on which they were convicted, which opens such a scene of villainy as is scarce to be paralell'd in history. Together with Mr. Cox's narrative, by whose vigilance and industry, they were discovered, taken and brought to justice. With the evidence they gave against Kelly and Ellis at the assizes at Maidstone. Likewise the case of Kidden, the porter, who was wrongfully convicted of a robbery on the highway; and executed at Tyburn, on the evidence of M'Daniel, Berry, Blee, and other thief-takers;
London:Printed for H.Owen,printer of the St. James's evening post,White-fryars,and C.Sympson at the Bible-warehouse,Chancery-lane.1755. <Price six pence.>
8°. 32p. 20.5cm.

NL 0419174 MH

The lives of sundry notorious villains
see under [Behn, Aphra (Amis)] 1640-1689.

The lives of the adepts in alchemystical philosophy..
see under Barrett, Francis.

The **lives** of the ancient philosophers, containing an account of their several sects, doctrines, actions, and remarkable sayings. Extracted from Diogenes Laertius Causabon, Menagius, Stanley, Gassendus, Charleton, and others, the best authors upon that subject. With an appendix containing the lives of several later philosophers not confined to particular sects; taken from Eunapius. And an account of the women philosophers, written originally in Latin by Æg. Menagius to Madam Dacier. And an introduction representing the state of learning and philosophy in the eastern part of the world, before it flourished in Greece ... London, J. Nicholson [etc.] 1702.
8 p. l., xxx, [2], 564, [12] p. plates. 20cm.
1. Philosophers, Ancient.

Library of Congress B171.L5 13-11908

NL 0419177 DLC CLU-C NcD CtY PPL PV MB

C 27 .514

LIVES of the apostles and early martyrs of the church. By the author of "The trial of skill". New York,J.& J.Harper,1832.
v. front. 16cm. (Boy's and girl's library. no.1)

"Harper's stereotype edition."

NL 0419178 ICN

Lives of the apostles and early martyrs of the church [Designed for Sunday reading] by the author of "The trial of skill." N. Y., Harper, 1848.
204 p. illus. S.

NL 0419179 NcD

BS2440 .L5

Lives of the apostles and early martyrs of the church. (Designed for Sunday reading) By the author of "The trial of skill". New York, Harper, 1858.
204p. front. 16cm. (Boy's and girl's library no. 1)

1. Apostles. 2. Martyrs.

NL 0419180 NNU-W

[LIVES of the Apostles and Evangelists, the Christian Fathers, and Schoolmen, Reformers of the Church, and other eminent Modern Divines and of the Kings and Queens of England from Henry VIII to [ ] Anne. L? About [1705].

Title page wanting. The volume has 294 pages besides the "Table " 2 pages, at the end. There is also an engraving, entitled "The Reformation. "The preface is signed" J. S."

NL 0419181 MH

The Lives of Helen Jewett, and Richard P. Robinson
see under [Wilkes, George] 1820?-1885.

... The lives of Hernando Cortes, the discoverer of Mexico, and Francisco Pizarro, the conqueror of Peru. Boston, B. H. Greene, 1840.
viii, [13]-194 p. front., pl. 26cm. (American juvenile biography)

1. Cortés, Hernando, 1485-1547. 2. Pizarro, Francisco, marqués, 1470?-1541.

Library of Congress F1230.L78 13-14402

NL 0419183 DLC

Lives of holy saints, prophets, patriarchs ...
see under [Marbeck, John] ca. 1510-ca. 1585

... The **lives** of Horatio Seymour and Frank P. Blair, jr. ... Philadelphia, T. B. Peterson & brothers [1868]
1 p. l., 19-95 p. 20cm.
At head of title: Seymour and Blair.—Campaign edition.

1. Seymour, Horatio, 1810-1886. 2. Blair, Francis Preston, 1821-1875. 3. Campaign literature, 1868—Democratic.

Library of Congress E415.9.S5L7 14-10152

NL 0419185 DLC OClWHi

The lives of illustrious and eminent persons of Great Britian. Embellished with sixty-eight portraits. London: Printed for Longman, Hurst, Rees, Orme, and Brown, 1820.
[142] p. incl. ports. 17½cm.
CONTENTS.—Richard Porson.—John Pearson.—Matthew Parker.—Sir Robert Walpole.—Horatio Walpole, Lord Walpole.—Sir Henry Spelman.—Sir Cloudesley Shovel.—Horatio Viscount Baron Nelson.—Edward, Lord Thurlow.—Sir Nicholas Bacon.—Thomas Gainsborough.—Mrs. Sarah Trimmer.—Thomas Cavendish.—William Alabaster.—Mary Beale.—Thomas Beacon.—Baron Thomas Dimsdale.—Thomas Stanley.—John Ray.—Philemon Holland.—Frances Quarles.—Margaret, Duchess of Newcastle.—Sir John Hawkwood.—Dr. John Bastwick.—Horatio Walpole, fourth Earl of

CONTENTS.—Continued.
Orford.—Thomas Herring.—William Ames.—Right Hon. William Windham.—Edward Jerningham.—Sir Edward Coke.—Sir John Fastolff.—Duke of Grafton.—Marquis Cornwallis.—William Smith.—Rev. Thomas Harmer.—Cardinal Wolsey.—John Overall.—John Lydgate.—Richard Sibbs.—Thomas Brand-Hollis.—John Harriott.—Robert Edward, Lord Petre.—Sir Thomas Smith.—Samuel Purchas.—John Thurloe.—Sir Francis Vere.—Horace Vere.—John Joshua Kirby.—John Elwes.—Stephen Gardiner.—William Hoare.—Lieut.-General Thomas Talmash.—Richard Morton.—Ralph Brownrig.—Arthur Jackson.—Humphrey Repton.—Edward Miller.—John Day.—George Edwards.—William Sancroft.—Thomas, Lord Audley.—Edmund Hickeringill.—George Gascoigne.—John Disney.—Samuel Clarke.—Sir Thomas Barnardiston.—Sir John Holt.

1. Biography. 2. Gt. Brti.—Biog.

NL 0419187 ViU

Lives of the apostles of Jesus Christ, 1836
see under Bacon, David Francis, 1813-1866.

... The lives of the Blessed Leonard,of Port Maurice, and of the blessed Nicholas Fattore
see under [Giuseppe Maria da Masserano] Father.

Lives of the brethren of the Order of preachers, 1206-1259
see under [Gerard de Frachet] d. 1271.

---

tDA74 L5

The Lives of the British admirals, displaying ... the conduct and heroism of the naval commanders of Great Britain and Ireland ... intended not only to instruct and entertain but also to animate the youth of this country ... London, F. Newbery, 1776-77.
2 v. in 1. ports. 13cm.

1. Admirals - Gt.Brit. 2. Gt.Brit. - Navy - Biog. 3. Admirals - Ireland.

NL 0419190 CU

VOLUME 336

The lives of the British admirals,displaying the most striking colours,the conduct and heroism of the naval commanders of Great Britain and Ireland... pt.1. Lond.,E.Newbery,1787.

NL 0419191 InU NN

The lives of the British hymn-writers
see under Wright, Thomas, 1859-1936.

Lives of the British poets: with specimens of their writings. Edinburgh, W. P. Nimmo, 1873.
viii, [9]-376 p. plates, ports. 17cm.

1. Poets, English.

NL 0419193 ViU MiD

PR 105 L57 Lives of the British poets; with specimens of their writing. London, William P. Nimmo, 1878.
viii, 384 p. 20 cm.

1. Authors, English. 2. Poets, English.

NL 0419194 WaSpG

The lives of the British reformers
see under [Stokes, George] 1789-1847.

Lives of the brothers Humboldt, Alexander and William ...
see under Klencke, Hermann, 1813-1881.

Lives of the Caesars
see under [Sinclair, Catherine] 1800-1864.

Lives of the candidates, election statistics and party platforms
see Carlisle, John Griffin, 1875-1910. Contest of 1888. Lives of the candidates ...

The lives of the cardinals Richelieu and Mazarin. With illustrations. London, Office of the "National illustrated library," 1854.
2 p. l., 115, [1] p. incl. 4 illus. (ports.) 8 pl. 18½cm.

Subject entries: 1. Richelieu, Armand Jean du Plessis, cardinal, duc de, 1585-1642. 2. Mazarin, Jules, cardinal, 1602-1661.
4-619

Library of Congress, no. DC123.9.R5L7.

NL 0419199 DLC

The lives of the cardinals Richelieu and Mazarin . . . London, Office of the "National illustrated library,' 1854.
2 p. l., 115, [1] pp. incl. pl., port. 17½cm. [With [Dixon, Henry H.] 1822-1870. The post and the paddock. London [pref. 1856]]
2-6279

NL 0419200 DLC

Lives of the chief fathers of New England. [Boston, Massachusetts Sabbath school society, 1846-49]
6 v. front. (port., v. 5) illus. 19 cm.

CONTENTS.—I. M'Clure, A. W. The life of John Cotton. 1846.—II. M'Clure, A. W. The lives of John Wilson, John Norton and John Davenport. 1846.—III. Adams, N. The life of John Eliot. 1847.—IV. Albro, J. A. The life of Thomas Shepard. 1847.—V. Pond, E. The lives of Increase Mather and Sir William Phipps. 1847.—VI. Hooker, E. W. The life of Thomas Hooker. 1849.

1. New England — Biog. 2. New England — Hist. — Colonial period. I. Massachusetts Sabbath school society, pub.

Library of Congress F3.L68 5—39201

MeB MiD
NL 0419201 DLC MC MiU OClWHi OClW MB OO PPPrHi PHi

---

x920.074 L758 1870 Lives of the chief fathers of New England. [Boston, 1870]
6v. 21cm.

"Library edition, 100 copies."
Originally published, 1846-1849, by the Massachusetts Sabbath School Society.

NL 0419202 IU CU CtY

... The lives of the companions of S. Philip Neri, the first fathers of the Oratory
see under [Ricci, Giacomo] d. 1703.

... The lives of the companions of St. Alphonso Liguori ... London [etc.] T. Richardson and son. 1849.
xii, 503 p. incl. front. (port.) 20cm. (The saints and servants of God. [15])

CONTENTS.—Introduction. [Extract from the "Maximes spirituelles" of F. Guilloré]—Life of Father D. Alexander de Meo, by Father Tannoja.—Life of Father D. Paul Cafaro, by St. Alphonso de Liguori.—Life of Father D. Januarius Maria Sarnelli, by St. Alphonso de Liguori.—Life of Father D. Angelo Latessa, by Father Tannoja.—Life of Father D. Cæsar Sportelli, by Father D. Joseph Landi.—Life of Father D. Dominic Blasucci, by Father Tannoja.—Short notice of the same father, by Father D. Joseph Landi.—Life of Brother Gerard Majella, by Father Tannoja.—Life of Brother Joachim Gaudiello, by Father Tannoja.—Life of Brother Vitus Curzius, by St. Alphonso de Liguori.—Life of Brother Francis Tartaglione, by Father Tannoja.

1. Redemptorists. 2. Catholic church—Biog. I. Tannoja, Antonio Maria, d. 1808. II. Liguori, Alfonso Maria da, Saint, 1696-1787. III. Landi, Giuseppe.

Library of Congress BX4655.S3 vol. 15 30—22406 [a38b1]

NL 0419204 DLC CtY

Lives of the early Medici, as told in their correspondence
see under Ross, Janet Ann (Duff-Gordon) 1842-1927, ed. & tr.

Lives of the English Bishops from the Restauration to the Revolution
see under [Salmon, Nathanael] 1675-1742.

Lives of the English martyrs. Second series: The martyrs declared venerable ... edited by Edwin H. Burton, D. D., and J. H. Pollen, S. J. London, New York [etc.] Longmans, Green and co., 1914-
v. 19cm.

1. Catholics in England. 2. Martyrs—England. 3. Christian biography. 4. Persecution. I. Burton, Edwin Hubert, 1870-1925, ed. II. Pollen, John Hungerford, 1858- joint ed. III. Title: The martyrs declared venerable.

Library of Congress BX4676.L5 1914 29—4172

NL 0419207 DLC NIC PV PPL CtY NN

Lives of the English martyrs, declared blessed by Pope Leo XIII. in 1886 and 1895.
see under Camm, Bede, 1864-1942, ed.

Lives of the English sacred poets...
see under Willmott, Robert Eldridge Aris, 1809-1863.

Lives of the English saints ... London, James Toovey, 1844-45.
14 v. in 4. fronts. 17½cm.
No.1 and no.12 have titles respectively: The Cistercian saints of England,and The life of St.Augustine of Canterbury,apostle of the English.
Cardinal Newman had intended to edit the entire series,but declined all responsibility after the publication of nos.1 & 2. *cf.* Pref. to the edition of 1900.
Bibliographical foot-notes.
Contents.-no.1.St.Stephen [by J.B.Dalgairns] 3d ed., 1845.-no.2.Family of St.Richard:St. St.Richard,St.Willibald,St.Walburga,St.Winibald [by T.Meyrick] 2d ed ,1844.-no.3,12.St.Augustine [by F.Oakeley] 1844-45.-no.4.Hermit saints:St.Gundleus [by J.H.Newman] St.Helier [by J.B.Dalgairns] St.Herbert [by J.Barrow] St.Edelwald [by ?] St.Bettelin [by J.H.Newman] St Neot [by J.A.Froude] St. Bartholomew [by T.Mozley] 1844.-no 5.St.Wulstan [by R.W.Church] St.William [by R.A.Coffin] 1844.-no.6.St Paulinus,St.Edwin,St.Ethelburga,St.Oswald,St.Oswin,St. Ebba,St.Adamnan,St.Bega [by F.W.Faber] 1844.-no.7.St. Gilbert [by J.B.Dalgairns, after W.Lockhart] 1844.-no.8. St.Wilfrid [by F.W.Faber] 1844.-no.9,11. St.German [by J.Walker] 1844.-no.10.Stephen Langton [by M Pattison] 1845.-no.13. St.Aelred [by J.B.Dalgairns] St.Ninian [by M.Pattison] 1845.-no.14.St Edmund [by M.Pattison] St. Waltheof,St.Robert [by J.B.Dalgairns] St.Richard [by R. Ornsby] 1845.
1.Saints,English. 2.Hermits. I.Newman,John Henry, cardinal,1801-1890,ed

CtY NNUT MiU CMenSP MWelC
NL 0419212 DCU PPEB CaBVaU IMunS MH PPPD IU NRU MB

D 9877 .621 The LIVES of the English saints, written by various hands at the suggestion of John Henry Newman, afterwards cardinal... With an introduction by Arthur Wollaston Hutton. London,S.T.Freemantle,1900-01.
6v.

Half-title: Newman's lives of the English saints.
Contents.—v.1. Introduction by A.W.Hutton. St. Stephen Harding [by J.D.Dalgairns] St. Wilfrid [by F.W.Faber]—v.2. The family of St. Richard: St. Richard; St. Willibald; St. Walburga; St. Winibald [by Thomas Meyrick] St. German [by John Walker]—v.3. Hermit saints: St. Gundleus [by J.H.Newman]; St. Helier [by J.D.Dalgairns] St. Herbert [by John Barrow]; St. Edelwald [by J.H.Newman?]; St. Bettelin [by J.H.Newman and J.D. Dalgairns]; St. Neot [by J.A.Froude]; St. Bartholomew [by Thomas Mozley] St. Augustine [by Frederick Oakeley]—v.4. St. Gilbert [by J.D.Dalgains]; Northumbrian saints: St. Paulinus; St. Edwin; St. Ethelburga; St. Oswald; St. Oswin; St. Ebba; St. Adamnan; St. Bega [by F.W.Faber] St. William [by R.A.Coffin]—v.5. St. Wulstan [by R.W.Church] St. Aelred [by J.B.Dalgairns] St. Ninian [by Mark Pattison] St. Waltheof and St. Robert of Newminster [by J.D.Dalgairns]—v.6. St. Edmund [by Mark Pattison] St. Richard [by Robert Ornsby] Stephen Langton [by Mark Pattison] Appendices: A provisional calendar of English saints, compiled by J.H.Newman in 1843. Authorship of the "Lives of the English saints". Biographical notices of the authors.

NL 0419216 ICN OO InU NIC MBtS DCU TxU MB OCU OCl

VOLUME 336

UG78.6 L758 The Lives of the English saints written by various hands at the suggestion of John Henry Newman. With an introd. by Arthur Wollaston Hutton. Philadelphia, J.B. Lippincott, 1901.
6 v. illus., ports. 21 cm.

Half-title: Newman's Lives of the English saints.
First published 1844-45.
Bibliographical references included in footnotes.

Contents.- v. 1. St. Stephen Harding. St. Wilfrid.- v. 2. The family of St. Richard. St. German.- v. 3. Hermit saints. St. Augustine.- v. 4. St. Gilbert. Northumbrian saints. St. William.- v. 5. St. Wulstan. St. Aelred. St. Ninian. St. Waltheof and St. Robert of Newminster.- v. 6. St. Edmund. St. Richard.

Stephen Langton. Appendices. I. Newman's calendar of the English saints. II. Authorship of the lives in the series. General index.

1. Saints, English. I. Newman, John Henry, cardinal, 1801-1890, ed. (2) II. Hutton, Arthur Wollaston, 1848-1912. (2)

NL 0419219 CtY-D

The lives of the English saints, written by various hands at the suggestion of John Henry Newman, afterwards cardinal. With an introduction by Arthur Wollaston Hutton. New York, Scott-Thaw Company, 1903.
6v. 20.5cm.

NL 0419220 MH-AH

Lives of the evangelists and apostles
see under [Hildreth, Hosea]

Lives of the excellent commanders
see under Nepos, Cornelius.

---

922 L758 The lives of the fathers, martyrs, and other principal saints: compiled from original monuments, and other authentick records: illustrated with the remarks of judicious modern criticks and historians ... London, Printed in the year 1756.
v.

1. Martyrologies. 2. Saints. 3. Fathers of the church.

NL 0419223 IU

MSS M6006 The Lives of the fathers of the deserts. And of some holy women. With some of their most remarkable actions and sayings. In four volumes. Vol. I. Translated from the French of Mr. Arnauld D'andilly, Doctor of the House and Society of the Sorbon. By J.M. [n.p.] Anno 1757.
ms. lvi,291 p.,2 l. 17cm.

NL 0419224 NIC

Lives of the fathers of the deserts
see also Les vies des Saints Peres deserts..

Lives of the Fathers of the Eastern Desert ...
see under [Challoner, Richard] bp., 1691-1781.

WZ 140 FA1 L8R8L Lives of the fellows of the Royal College of Physicians of London. London, The College, 1955-
v.
Earlier volumes, by William Munk, have title: The roll of the Royal College of Physicians of London.
Title on spine: Munk's Roll.
Vol. 4 edited by G. H. Brown; v. 5 edited by Richard R. Trail.
1. History of Medicine - biog. 2. Physicians - Gt. Brit. 3. Royal College of Physicians, London. I. Brown, G. H., ed. II. Trail, Richard Robertson, 1894- ed.

NL 0419227 DNLM

Lives of the fellows of the Royal College of Physicians of London
see also Royal College of Physicians of London.
The roll of the Royal College of Physicians.

Lives of the Fellows of the Royal College of Surgeons of England
see under Plarr, Victor Gustave, 1863-1929.

The lives of the felons, or American criminal calendar. Compiled in part from the New-York "National police gazette", and corrected, enlarged and revised on careful comparison with the criminal records of the various states ... New-York, G. F. Nesbitt, printer, 1846.
iv, [7]-96 p. incl. illus., plates, ports. port. 23cm.

1. Crime and criminals—U. S. [1. Criminology—U. S.] I. The National police gazette
Library of Congress 10-20125 Revised

NL 0419230 DLC ViU NN MH OClW

Lives of the French, Italian, and German philosophers ...
see under Fontenelle, Bernard Le Bovier de, 1657-1757.

Lives of the heroes of the American revolution ...
see under [Frost, John] 1800-1859.

The LIVES of the holy apostles...according to the accounts of Holy Scripture and the best ecclesiastical writers. Illustrated with their several effigies, curiously engraved. London, Printed for J. Watts, 1716.

232 p. illus. 17 cm.

1. Apostles.

NL 0419233 CaBVaU

The lives of the holy evangelists and apostles; with their martyrdoms...
see under [Cave, William] 1637-1713.

Lives of the illustrious. London, Partridge, 1856.
5 v. 23 cm.
Pub. 1852-55 under title: The Biographical magazine.

1. Biography.
CT104.B522 49-55985*

NL 0419235 DLC NN NNUT CtY

Lives of the illustrious (The Biographical magazine) London, J. P. Edwards, 1852-54.
5 v. 23 cm.
Vols. 3-5 have imprint: Partridge, Oakey.
Pub. 1852-55 under title: The Biographical magazine.
Errata slips inserted.

1. Biography.
CT104.B52 49-44100*

NL 0419236 DLC NN MB

The lives of the loyal "ronins"...
see under Chiushingura

Lives of the 'lustrious
see under Stephen, Sidney, pseud.

LIVES of the most celebrated British admirals; containing a concise account of the characters, and an accurate detail of the gallant achievements, of the most distinguished naval heroes... Edinburgh: Printed by and for Oliver & Boyd, 1808. 223 p. front. 14½cm.

Title vignette.

641659A 1. Admirals, British.

NL 0419239 NN

Lives of the most eminent British naval heroes; comprehending details of their achievements, in various quarters of the globe, forming a complete naval history, from the reign of Henry VII. to the present time... Leith: A. Allardice, 1809. vii, 428 p., 3 pl. (incl. front.) 12°.

1. Navy (British).—History: Biography.
N. Y. P. L. December 5, 1917.

NL 0419240 NN NjP

Lives of the most eminent English poets ...
see under [Johnson, Samuel] 1709-1784.

Lives of the most eminent foreign statesmen.
see under [Crowe, Eyre Evans] 1799-1868.

Lives of the most eminent literary and scientific men of France
see under [Shelley, Mary Wollstonecraft (Godwin) 1797-1851.

VOLUME 336

Lives of the most eminent literary and scientific men of Great Britain
see under [Dunham, Samuel Astley] d. 1858.

Lives of the most eminent literary and scientific men of Italy, Spain ...
see under Shelley, Mary Wollstonecraft (Godwin) 1797-1851.

Lives of the most eminent modern painters
see under [Burgess, James] 18th cent.

Lives of the most eminent saints of the Oriental deserts ...
see under [Challoner, Richard] bp., 1691-1781.

The lives of the most famous English poets
see under [Winstanley, William] 1628?-1690?

Lives of the most remarkable criminals who have been condemned and executed for murder, highway robberies, housebreaking, street robberies, coining, or other offenses, from the year 1720 to the year 1735. Collected from original papers and authentic memoirs. London, Reeves and Turner, 1873.
485p. 23cm.

1. Crime and criminals - Gt. Brit. 2. Crime and criminals - Biog

NL 0419249 FMU NN

Lives of the most remarkable criminals who have been condemned and executed for murder, highway robberies, housebreaking, street robberies, coining, or other offences; from the year 1720 to the year 1735. Collected from original papers and authentic memoirs. London, Reeves and Turner, 1874.
2 v. front. 19½cm.
A faithful reproduction of the original of 1735. *cf.* Pref.

1. Crime and criminals—Gt. Brit. 2. Crime and criminals—Biog.

Library of Congress HV6945.A4L7 2—5447

NL 0419250 DLC OU ICU MB NcD CtY PU TxU PPDrop

Lives of the most remarkable criminals who have been condemned and executed for murder, the highway, housebreaking, street robberies, coining or other offences, collected from original papers and authentic memoirs, and published in 1735, edited by Arthur L. Hayward. London, G. Routledge & sons, ltd., 1927.
xv, 640 p. front., plates. 25½ x 20cm.

1. Crime and criminals — Gt. Brit. 2. Crime and criminals — Biog. I. Hayward, Arthur Lawrence, 1885- ed.

Library of Congress HV6945.A4L7 1927 a 28-11907

NL 0419251 DLC CaBVaU OrU NcGU

Lives of the most remarkable criminals, who have been condemned and executed for murder, the highway, housebreaking, street robberies, coining or other offences, collected from original papers and authentic memoirs, and published in 1735, edited by Arthur L. Hayward. New York, Dodd, Mead & company, 1927.
xv, 640 p. front., plates. 26 x 20 cm.
Printed in Great Britain.

1. Crime and criminals—Gt. Brit. 2. Crime and criminals—Biog. I. Hayward, Arthur Lawrence, 1885- ed.

HV6945.A4L7 1927 28—6965

PPYH CLSU NIC CU OKentU
NL 0419252 DLC WaU-L MB NN PU OO OCU MiU OCl CLSU

Lives of the poets of Great Britain and Ireland
see under Cibber, Theophilus, 1703-1758.

Lives of the poets-laureate
see under [Austin, Wiltshire Stanton] 1826-1875.

Lives of the poisoners ... New York, Richard K. Fox [1882]
58 p. [Police Gazette library of sensation, no. 2]

NL 0419255 DLC

The lives of the popes... London, The religious tract society [n.d.]
2 v., illus., 14½cm.

Contents: 1. From the rise of the Roman church to the dawn of the Reformation, A.D. 100-1431.- 2. From the dawn of the Reformation to Pope Pius the Ninth, A.D. 1431-1852.

NL 0419256 NjPT ViLxW NIC

BX955 .L5 1876

The lives of the popes. Edited by Thomas O. Summers. Nashville, Published by A. H. Redford, Agent for the M. E. Church, South, 1876.
4 v. 16 cm.
Prefatory note dated 1855.
Contents.-v.1. From the rise of the Roman Church to the age of Gregory VII. A.D. 100-1046.-v.2. From the age of Gregory VII, to the dawn of the Reformation. A.D. 1046-1431.-v.3. From the dawn of the Reformation to the Romanist reaction. A.D. 1431-1605.-v.4. From the Romanist reaction to Pope Pius Ninth. A.D. 1605-1855.

1. Popes. I. Summers, Thomas Osmond, 1812-1882, ed

NL 0419258 T NcD

Coxe collection BX1070 K53

The lives of the popes. From A. D. 100 to A.D. 1858. Revised by Daniel P. Kidder. New York, Carlton & Phillips, 1853.

566p. 19cm.

I. Title. 1. Popes.

NL 0419259 NBuG NjPT NNU GEU CU PPLT

The lives of the popes, Author of. Annals of Christian martyrdom
see under title

BX955 .L5

The lives of the popes from A. D. 100 to A. D. 1858. New York, Carlton & Phillips, 1855.
566p. 19cm.

NL 0419261 NNU-W CU NNU

The lives of the present candidates for president and vice-president of the United States, containing a condensed and impartial history of the lives, public acts, and political views of the present candidates, with the platforms of the parties they represent, their portraits from life, their letters of acceptance, etc. Cincinnati, H. M. Rulison; [etc., etc., 1860]
ii, 3-139 p. port. 21cm.
CONTENTS.—Life of John Bell.—Life of Edward Everett.—Life of Abraham Lincoln.—Life of Hannibal Hamlin.—Life of Stephen A. Douglas.—Life of Herschel V. Johnson.—Life of John C. Breckinridge.—Life of General Joseph Lane.—The Douglas Democratic convention.—The anti-Douglas Democratic convention.—How Congress elects the president and vice-president.
1. U. S.—Biog.

Library of Congress E440.L78 3—1629

NL 0419262 DLC CSmH

... Lives of the presidents
see under [McCarthy, J J]

Lives of the presidents of the United States. Chicago, W.B.Conkey co. [1904]

204 p. ports., illus. 19.5 cm.

NL 0419264 MH

Lives of the presidents of the United States. Chicago, W.B.Conkey co. [1905?]

203 p. port., illus. 19.5 cm.

NL 0419265 MH

Lives of the presidents of the United States ... Chicago, New York, M. A. Donohue & company [1911?]
2 p. l., 148 p. incl. front., illus. (incl. ports.) 19cm.

1. Presidents—U. S.—Biog.

34-38745

Library of Congress E176.1.L589 923.173

NL 0419266 DLC

Lives of the presidents of the United States ... New York, The New York book company, 1911.
2 p. l., 148 p. incl. front., illus. (incl. ports.) 18½cm.

1. Presidents—U. S.—Biog.

29-12048

Library of Congress E176.1.L59

NL 0419267 DLC

The lives of the primitive fathers
see under Cave, William, 1637-1713.

VOLUME 336

The LIVES of the Primitive Fathers for the Four First Centuries, and Part of the Fifth To which is added a Discourse concerning the State of Religion during those Ages, 2d ed. 2 vol. L. 1715.

Port.

NL 0419269 MH

The lives of the princes of the illustrious house of Orange, continued down to the present time. Collected from the best authorities, both printed and manuscript. Illustrated with copper plates and a genealogical table. London, W. Mears, 1734.

1 p. l., iv, [2], 224 p. double front. (ports.) fold. geneal. tab. 20½cm.

1. Orange-Nassau, House of.

43-22207

Library of Congress DJ150.L5

NL 0419270 DLC NjP MH InU CtY MnU PBL TxU

Lives of the queens of England see under Strickland, Agnes, 1796-1874.

5515 .977 .59 The lives of the Right Reverend Father in God, Thomas Wilson, D.D.,and of the Right Reverend Father in God, Mark Hildesley, D.D., bishops of Sodor and Man. London, Rivington, 1821.

48 p. 18 cm.

Ms.note on t.-p.: by Clement Cruttwell? and, for the life of Mark Hildesley: by Weeden Butler?

NL 0419272 NjP

Lives of the saints ... London, 1869 see under [Riancey, Henri León Camusat de] 1816-1870.

Lives of the saints. The apostles of Great Britain. — [London.] Talbot. [19—?] 230, (2) pp. Plates. Map. 11½ cm.

K9179 — Great Britain. Hist. Relig. — Saint-

NL 0419274 MB

Lives of the saints (Scottish) see Legends of the saints (Scottish)

BX4654 .L75 Mss room Lives of the saints commemorated in the first 37 days of the calendar. A Dutch work of the 15th cent.

[214] p. 21cm.

Latin manuscript in Gothic characters; rubricated. Presented by Miss Shirley Farr.

1. Manuscripts, Latin. 2. Saints—Biog.

NL 0419276 ICU

The lives of the saints; or, Notes ecclesiological and historical see under [Dickinson, William Leeson]

Lives of the Serbian saints, by Voyeslav Yanich and C. Patrick Hankey. London, Society for Promoting Christian Knowledge; New York, Macmillan, 1921.

xx, 108 p. plate, ports. 19 cm. (Translations of Christian literature, ser. 7)

Translated from a martyrology issued, in the middle of the last century, for the use of the church throughout Serbia.

1. Saints, Serbian. I. Janić, Vojislav, 1890– ed. and tr. II. Hankey, Cyril Patrick, joint ed. (Series)

BR45.T67L5 21-21903 rev

NL 0419278 DLC MB NN MH CU OCl OU MiU PBm

The Lives Of The III. Normans, Kings of England see under [Hayward, Sir John] 1564?-1627.

The lives of the two illustrious generals, John, duke of Marlborough, and Francis Eugene, prince of Savoy ... London, A. Bell [etc.] 1713.

4 p. l., 3 p., 1 l., 5-174 p., 1 l., 175-283 p. 2 port. 19cm.

Each biography has special t.-p. Dedication signed: C. M.

1. Marlborough, John Churchill, 1st duke of, 1650-1722. 2. Eugène i. e. François Eugène, prince of Savoie-Carignan, 1663-1736. I. M., C. II. C. M.

13-10259

Library of Congress D281.L5

NL 0419280 DLC NjP DFo CLU-C CtY OrU PBm

... The lives of the venerable servant of God, Fabrizio dall'Aste ... and of the venerable servant of God, Father Mariano Sozzini see under [Marciano, Giovanni] d. 1713.

Lives of Thomas Warton, Joseph Warton ... see under [Singer, Samuel Weller] 1783-1858.

The lives of those eminent antiquaries Elias Ashmole, esquire, and Mr. William Lilly, written by themselves; containing, first, William Lilly's history of his life and times, with notes, by Mr. Ashmole: Secondly, Lilly's life and death of Charles the First: and lastly, the life of Elias Ashmole, esquire, by way of diary. With several occasional letters, by Charles Burman, esquire. London, T. Davies, 1774.

7, 399 p. front. (2 port.) 22cm.

"Advertisement to the reader," signed: T. D. [i. e. T. Davies]

1. Charles I, king of Great Britain, 1600-1649. I. Lilly, William, 1602-1681. II. Ashmole, Elias, 1617-1692. III. Burman, Charles. IV. Davies, Thomas, 1712-1785, ed.

13-18585

Library of Congress DA92.L5

NL 0419283 PP OrU MdBP ICN ICU MB PPL PU NjP ViU DLC CU NIC CU-S CaBVaU NcD IaU CtY NB

The lives of those eminent antiquaries John Leland, Thomas Hearne, and Anthony à Wood; with an authentick account of their respective writings and publications, from original papers. In which are occasionally inserted, memoirs relating to many eminent persons, and various parts of literature. Also several engravings of antiquity, never before published ... Oxford, J. and J. Fletcher [etc.] 1772.

2 v. fronts., plates (part fold.) port. 23cm.

Part II of v. 1 has special t.-p.: The life of Mr. Thomas Hearne ... from his own manuscript copy ... Oxford, 1772. Edited by W. Huddesford and T. Warton.

Continued in next column

Continued from preceding column

The life of Leland is by Huddesford; the lives of Hearne and à Wood are autobiographical with additions.

CONTENTS.—vol. I, pt. I. The life of John Leland ... to which is added: I. The antient treatise of Leland's New years gyfte to K. Henry, with the commentaries of J. Bale, first printed in the year 1549 [reprint of The laboryouse journey & serche of John Leylande ... Emprented at London, 1549]; II. A summary account of the said J. Bale. pt. II. The life of Mr. Thomas Hearne.—vol. II. The life of Mr. Anthony à Wood.

1. Leland, John, 1506?-1552. 2. England—Antiq. 3. Authors, English. I. Huddesford, William, 1732-1772, ed. II. Warton, Thomas, 1728-1790, joint ed. III. Hearne, Thomas, 1678-1735. IV. Wood, Anthony à, 1632-1695.

13-21175

Library of Congress DA92.H8

NL 0419285 MH WaU TxU NN IU DFo OCl NPV OrU LU CU CLSU DFo InU DLC NN WaSpG CSmH MdBP NcD MiU CtY IaU

... Lives of Ulysses S. Grant, and Schuyler Colfax ... Containing, also, a correct genealogical summary of the Grant family ... Cincinnati, Padrick & co., 1868.

1 p. l., xiii-xiv, 15-104 p. front., ports. 22½cm.

People's edition for the campaign. "Life of Colfax": p. 79-103.

1. Grant, Ulysses Simpson, pres. U. S., 1822-1885. 2. Colfax, Schuyler, 1823-1885. 3. Grant family.

10-32711

Library of Congress E672.L781

NL 0419286 DLC OClWHi

The lives of Vasco Nunez de Balboa, the discoverer of the Pacific ocean, Hernando Cortes, the conqueror of Mexico, and Francisco Pizarro, the conqueror of Peru. Boston, Marsh, Capen, Lyon, and Webb, 1840.

276 p. 16cm.

1. Balboa, Vasco Núñez de, 1475-1519? 2. Cortés, Hernando, 1485-1547. 3. Pizarro, Francisco, marqués, 1470?-1541.

12-34239

Library of Congress E125.B2L7 [a37b1]

NL 0419287 DLC MiD MWA MdBP NcRS PV ViU

The Lives of Vasco Nunez de Balboa, the discoverer of the Pacific ocean, Hernando Cortes, the conqueror of Mexico, and Francisco Pizarro, the conqueror of Peru. Boston, Marsh, Capen, Lyon, and Webb, 1840.

4 p. l., [5]-276 p. 16cm. (Added t.-p.: The School library ... Juvenile ser. Vol. XII)

1. Balboa, Vasco Núñez de, 1475-1519. 2. Cortés, Hernando, 1485-1547. 3. Pizarro, Francisco, marqués, 1470?-1541.

44-30291

Library of Congress E125.B2L7 1840 a

NL 0419288 DLC

SP. COLL. The Lives of Vasco Nunez de Balboa, the discoverer of the Pacific Ocean, Hernando Cortes, the conqueror of Mexico, and Francisco Pizarro, the conqueror of Peru. New York, Harper, 1847.

276, 12 p. 16 cm.

Publisher's advertisements: 12 p. at end.

1. Balboa, Vasco Núñez de, 1475-1519. 2. Cortés, Hernando, 1485-1547. 3. Pizarro, Francisco, marqués, 1470?-1541.

NL 0419290 CU-S PPL TxU

The lives of Vasco Nunez de Balboa, the discoverer of the Pacific ocean, Hernando Cortes, the conqueror of Mexico, and Francisco Pizarro, the conqueror of Peru. New York, Harper & brothers, 1854.

276 p. 16cm.

1. Balboa, Vasco Núñez de, 1475-1519. 2. Cortés, Hernando, 1485-1547. 3. Pizarro, Francisco, marqués, 1470?-1541.

A 21-1471

H. E. Huntington library for Library of Congress [E125.B]

NL 0419291 CSmH OO

VOLUME 336

The lives of Vasco Nunez de Balboa, the discoverer of the Pacific Ocean, Hernando Cortes, the conqueror of Mexico, and Francisco Pizarro, the conqueror of Peru.
New York, Harper & brothers, 1860.
276 p.

NL 0419292 MiU

Lives of William Pinkney, William Ellery ... see under [Wheaton, Henry] 1785-1848.

The lives of women saints of our contrie of England, also some other liues of holie women written by some of the auncient fathers. (c. 1610-1615.) Ed. for the first time from ms. Stowe 949 by C. Horstmann. London, Pub. for the Early English text society by N. Trübner & co., 1886.
xiii, 241, [1] p. 22½cm. (On cover: Early English text society. [Original series] 86)

1. Saints, English. 2. Saints, Women. I. *Horstmann, Carl, ed. II. British museum. Mss. (Stowe 949) 12—17030

Library of Congress PR1119.A2 no. 86

MiU OCU OO ODW NjNbS NcGU PP PU PHC PBm PSC NjP PPPD MB NcU OU
NL 0419294 DLC PSt CU-S OrU CaBVaU WaSpG OU MdBP

The Lives of women saints of our contrie of England, also some other liues of holie women written by some of the auncient fathers. (c. 1610-1615) Edited for the first time from ms Stowe 949 by C. Horstmann. London, Published for the Early English Text Society by N. Trübner & Co., 1886.
xiii, 241 p. 23cm. [Early English Text Society. Original series, no. 86]

Micro-opaque. [Washington, Microcard Editions, 1950] 5 cards. 7.5 x 12.5 cm. (Fo-50: 6643-6647)

NL 0419295 NNC

The lives, prophecies, visions, and revelations of Christopher Kotterus, and Christina Poniatonia [properly Poniatovia], two eminent prophets in Germany. Containing predictions concerning the Pope, King of France, and the Roman Empire. Printed from the original published in 1664. [L., [1794].

pp. 48. (PROPHETICAL extracts, V.)

NL 0419296 MH

The lives, robberies, and surprizing adventures, of those memorable robbers of antiquity see under [Johnson, Charles] fl. 1724-1736.

Lives that speak.
New York, Chicago, Fleming H. Revell company.

NL 0419298 CtY

L923.9 Lives there a man who has not heard the
A55 fame of the high exploits of the Portuguese? Lisbon, Editorial império [1939]
[4] p. 39cm.

Printed in colors.
"This chart gives the names of the Portuguese who took part in the discovery of the American continent indicating the dates of their achievements ... the Portuguese cartographers who were concerned with America and their oldest American maps."

NL 0419299 LNHT

The lives, trial, confession and execution of John Slowes & Geo. King, two of the Townsend gang, who were executed at Cayuga, C. W., on the 18th day of May, 1855, for the murder of John H. Nelles. Buffalo: Published by Thomas Messenger, 1855.

1p.l.,16p. 23cm.

Xeroxed copy of an incomplete original owned by Brock University; title-page, p. 6 p. 11-16 present.

NL 0419300 NBu

Lives, trials, and execution of criminals. Philadelphia, J. B. Perry; New York, Nafis & Cornish, 1842.
2 p. l., p. 125-241 incl. front., illus., plates. 14½cm.

CONTENTS.—Johnson, the printer.—Catharine Cashiere.—Trial and sentence of Michael M'Garvey.—Louis Gaiarre.—Joel Clough, the murderer of Mrs. Mary W. Hamilton.—Antoine Le Blanc.—John A. Murel, the great western land pirate.—The murder of Suydam, by Peter Robinson.

1. Crime and criminals—U. S. 2. Trials (Murder)
24-19570

NL 0419301 DLC

Livesay, Ann
see Livesay, Elizabeth Ann.

Livesay, Dorothy, 1909-
Call my people home. [Poems] Toronto, Ryerson Press [1950]
24 p. 22 cm. (Ryerson poetry chap books, 143)
Cover title.
"Five hundred copies ... printed."

I. Title.

PR6023.I 8C3 811.5 51-40306

CaBViPA CaBViP
NL 0419303 DLC WU INS LU TxU IU NN RPB CaBVa CaBVaU

Livesay, Dorothy, 1909-
Day and night, poems by Dorothy Livesay. Toronto, The Ryerson press [1944]
4 p. l., 48 p. 21½cm.

I. Title.
44-7827
Library of Congress PR6023.I 8D3
[3] 811.5

NN
NL 0419304 DLC CaBViPA CaBViP CaBVaU Wa CaOTU OCH

Tr.R. Livesay, Dorothy, 1909-

Green pitcher. [Poems] Toronto, Macmillan Company of Canada, 1928.
16 p. 20 cm.

Cover title.
Author's autograph presentation copy to Lionel Stevenson.

NL 0419305 NcD CaBVaU RPB CaOTU

Livesay, Dorothy, 1909-
New poems. Toronto, Emblem Books, 1955.
[15] p.

NL 0419306 CaOTU CaBVaU IaU RPB

Livesay, Dorothy, 1909-
Poems for people. [1st ed.] Toronto, Ryerson Press [1947]
40 p. 21 cm.

I. Title.

PR6023.I 8P6 811.5 47-29048*

CaBViPA CaBViP
NL 0419308 DLC CaBVaU CaBVa MH ICU NN TxU InU CaOTU

Livesay, Dorothy, 1909-
Signpost, by Dorothy Livesay. Toronto, The Macmillan company of Canada ltd., 1932.
ix, 61, [1] p. 20½cm.
Poems.

I. Title.
33-9970
Library of Congress PR6023.I 8S5 1932
[3] 821.91

CaBVaU
NL 0419309 DLC CaBVaU NcD CaOTU OTU OCU CaBViPA

F Livesay, Dowell.
784 Denver and the middle trail; the story
D4 of a city and a road of destiny, by Dowell
L58 Livesay. [Denver, Welch-Haffner Printing Company, c1927]
63p. illus.

1. Denver--Descr. I. Title.

NL 0419310 UU

LIVESAY, Edward Alexander.
An experimental study of hybrid vigor or heterosis in rats. [Dissertation], Harvard University, 1928.

Typewritten. 4°. ff.(3). 51, (16). Charts.

NL 0419311 MH OCU

Livesay, Edward Alexander
An experimental study of hybrid vigor or heterosis in rats by Edward Alexander Livesay... [New Haven, Conn., 1930?]
17-54 p.

NL 0419312 OCU

QE115
.K4
no. 2 Livesay, Elizabeth Ann.
Geology of the Mammoth Cave National Park area. Lexington, 1953.
40 p. illus., maps, table. 23 cm. (Kentucky. Geological Survey Series IX. Special publication no. 2)
Bibliography: p. 40.

1. Geology—Kentucky—Mammoth Cave. 2. Mammoth Cave, Ky. (Series: Kentucky. University. Geological Survey. Series IX. Special publication no. 2)

G S 54-7

U. S. Geol. Survey. Libr. for Library of Congress [3]

NL 0419313 DI-GS OC1W MsU NNC OCU DLC

1944 Livesay, Elizabeth Ann.
L758 The ostracode family Cytheridae ... [Urbana, Ill., 1944]
83 numb.l.

Thesis (B.S.)--University of Illinois, 1944.
Typewritten.
Bibliography: leaves 81-83.

1. Cytheridae. I. Title.

NL 0419314 IU

VOLUME 336

Livesay, Elizabeth Ann.
The past speaks to you; the story of geology in Illinois. Springfield, 1951.
31 p. illus., maps. 23 cm. (Illinois. State Museum, Springfield. Story of Illinois series, no. 7)
Bibliography: p. 2.

1. Geology—Illinois. I. Title. (Series)
[F541.I4 no. 7] A 51-10511
Illinois. Univ. Library for Library of Congress [2]

NL 0419315 IU OKentU DNAL

PN4913 .L5A3 Livesay, Florence (Randal) 1874- ed.

Livesay, John Frederick Bligh, 1875-1944.
The making of a Canadian. Ed., with a memoir, by Florence Randal Livesay. Toronto, Ryerson Press [1947]

Livesay, Florence (Randal) 1874- tr.

PZ3 .K979 Mar Kvitka, Hryhorii Fedorovych, 1778-1843.
Marusia. Translated by Florence Randal Livesay from the Ukrainian. Introd. by Lord Tweedsmuir. New York, E. P. Dutton, 1940.

819.3 L758s

Livesay, Florence(Randal) 1874-
Savour of salt. London & Toronto, Dent, 1927.
vii, 227,[1]p. 20cm.

NL 0419318 TxU CaBVa CaBVaU RPB NcD IaU MH

Livesay, Florence (Randal) 1874-
Shepherd's purse, by Florence Randal Livesay... Toronto: The Macmillan Co. of Canada, Ltd., 1923. 66 p. 12°.
Poems partly reprinted from various sources.

149987A. 1. Poetry (English). 2. Title. October 1, 1924
N. Y. P. L.

NL 0419319 NN CaBVaU TxU NcD CaOTU MH RPB ICU

Livesay, Florence (Randal) 1874- ed. and tr.
Songs of Ukraina, with Ruthenian poems, translated by Florence Randal Livesay. London [etc.] J. M. Dent & sons limited; New York, E. P. Dutton & co., 1916.
175 p. 19 cm.
Ukrainian national anthem (words, English translation, and music): p. 172-175.

1. Folk-songs, Ukrainian. 2. Ukrainian poetry—Translations into English. 3. English poetry—Translations from Ukrainian. I. Title.
PG3986.E3L5 17-26397

CU TxU NcD NN FU
NL 0419320 DLC CaBVa CaBVaU OrP WaSp WaS CaBViP MB

513.62 L758e Livesay, George Roger, 1924-
An extension of the notion of unicoherence with an application to mappings of spheres. Urbana [1952]
19l. 28cm.

Thesis—University of Illinois.
Typewritten (carbon copy)
Vita.
Bibliography: leaf 18.
1952 L758 ——— Thesis copy.

NL 0419321 IU

Livesay, John Frederick Bligh, 1875-1944.
Canada's hundred days; with the Canadian corps from Amiens to Mons, Aug. 8-Nov. 11, 1918. By J. F. B. Livesay. Toronto, T. Allen, 1919.
x p., 1 l., 421 p. front. (port.) 3 fold. maps. 25 cm.

1. European war, 1914-1918—Regimental histories—Canada. 2. European war, 1914-1918—Campaigns—France. I. Title.
D547.C2L5 20-12261

NL 0419322 DLC CaBVa CaBVaU NcD MB NN DN

Livesay, J[ohn] F[rederick] B[ligh], 1875- 1944.
-he Canadian press and allied organizations. [N.p.n.pub.]1924.
15p.O.

NL 0419323 CaBViP

Livesay, John Frederick Bligh, 1875-1944.
The Canadian press, its birth and development, by J. F. B. Livesay... [n. p., 1939?]
cover-title, 19 p. 22cm.
"Reprinted from the Quebec Chronicle-telegraph of June 21, 1939."

1. Canadian press association. I. Title.
44-11961
Library of Congress PN4901.C3L5
[2] 071.

NL 0419324 DLC

PS2123 .E4L5 1927 Livesay, John Frederick Bligh, 1875-1944.

Henry James and his critics. [By] J. F. B. Livesay. [n. p., 1927?]
[80]-88 p. 24cm.
Detached from The Dalhousie review.

1. Edgar, Pelham, 1871-1948. Henry James, man and author. 2. James, Henry, 1843-1916—Style.

NL 0419325 ViU

Livesay, John Frederick Bligh, 1875-1944.
The making of a Canadian. Ed., with a memoir, by Florence Randal Livesay. Toronto, Ryerson Press [1947]
x, 181 p. plate, port. 20 cm.

1. Journalists—Correspondence, reminiscences, etc. I. *Livesay, Florence (Randal) 1874- ed. II. Title.
PN4913.L5A3 920.5 48-17467

NL 0419326 DLC MtBC CaBVa CaBViP TxU NIC NN

Livesay, John Frederick Bligh, 1875-1944.
Peggy's Cove, by J. F. B. Livesay. Toronto, The Ryerson press [1944]
viii p., 1 l., 100 p. incl. front., illus. (incl. ports.) 21cm.
Some of the sketches appeared originally in the Vancouver (B. C.) daily province.

1. Peggy's Cove, Nova Scotia.
45-3089
Library of Congress F1030.5.P4L5
[5] 917.1622

NL 0419327 DLC CaBVa CaBVaU CaBViP OCl TxU

Livesay, R.
The prisioners of 1776; a relic of the revolution...
see under Herbert, Charles, 1757-1808.

Livesay, Thayne Miller, joint author.
Adams, Romanzo Colfax, 1868-
The peoples of Hawaii, a statistical study, by Romanzo Adams, T. M. Livesay, E. H. Van Winkle ... Honolulu, Hawaii, Institute of Pacific relations, 1925.

Livesay, Thayne Miller.
... A study of public education in Hawaii, with special reference to the pupil population, by Thayne M. Livesay ... Honolulu, University of Hawaii, 1932.
vii, 120 p. diagr. 23cm. (University of Hawaii. Research publications. no. 7)
Bibliography: p. 119-120.

1. Education—Hawaiian islands. 2. Hawaiian islands—Population.
33-27774
Library of Congress LA2252.L5
[3] 370.9969

NL 0419330 DLC OrCS CaBVaU WaS WaWW OU DI OCl OCU

Livesay, Verna Helen (Thomas) 1908-

Miles, Rufus Edward, 1876-
Overcrowding in Ohio correctional institutions for men, and factors affecting their future population; report prepared by R. E. Miles, statistics by Verna Thomas. Columbus, O., The Ohio institute, 1938.

Livesay, Verna Helen (Thomas) 1908-

HV98 .O3O3 1939 Ohio institute, *Columbus.*
Public aid in Ohio, 1937-1939 (inclusive) A comparative picture of non-institutional public aid in Ohio. Columbus, O., The Ohio institute, 1940.

Livesay, Verna Helen (Thomas) 1908-

HV98 .O3O3 1940 Ohio institute, *Columbus.*
Public aid in Ohio, 1937-1940, a four-year picture of non-institutional public aid in Ohio. Columbus, O., The Ohio institute, 1941.

Livesay, W B
Notes on graphic statics
see under Illinois. University. Dept. of Architecture.

G780 .L24 Livesay, William, 1846-1913, ed.

Lamont, *Sir* James, 1828-1913.
Yachting in the Arctic seas; or, Notes of five voyages of sport and discovery in the neighbourhood of Spitzbergen and Novaya Zemlya. Edited and illustrated by W. Livesay. London, Chatto and Windus, 1876.

Livesey, A H Henderson
The green heart of London [by] A. H. Henderson Livesey. The history of the royal parks & residences. London: Ward Lock & co., ltd. [1937] 16 l. illus. 25cm.
Cover-title.
Plans on p. [2-3] of cover.

1. London—Descr., 1900- 2. Parks—Gt. Br.—Eng.—London.
N. Y. P. L. March 30, 1939

NL 0419336 NN

VOLUME 336

Livesey, A H Henderson.
The green heart of London [by] A. H. Henderson Livesey; the history of the royal parks & residences. [London, Ward, Lock & co., ltd., 1941]
cover-title, [32] p. incl. illus., plates. 25cm.
Maps on p. [2] and [3] of cover.

1. London—Descr.—Views. I. Title.
42-15577
Library of Congress DA684.L6
[2] 914.213

NL 0419337 DLC

Livesey, A. H., Henderson
The only way; a commentary on current party controversies, by Captain A. H. Henderson-Livesey. [London:] Social Services, Ltd., 1927. 79 p. 12°.

1. Liberal party—Gt. Br. 2. Great Britain—Politics, 20th cent. 3. Lloyd-George, David, 1863– 4. Grey, Edward, 1st viscount, 1862–
N. Y. P. L. June 13, 1928

NL 0419338 NN Mi

Livesey, A. H., Henderson
Sex and public life, by Captain A. H. Henderson-Livesey. [London:] Social Services, Ltd.[, 1926.] 198 p. 12°.

287745A. 1. Woman—Emancipation. 2. Title.
N. Y. P. L. March 30, 1927

NL 0419339 NN MiU

Livesey, A. H., Henderson
...The women police question, by Captain A. H. Henderson-Livesey, with an introduction by Ashley Brown. [London:] League of Womanhood[, 1926?]. 16 p. 8°. (League of Womanhood, London. Pam. no. 1.)
Cover-title.

1. Woman—Police—Gt. Br. 2. Ser.
N. Y. P. L. May 20, 1927

NL 0419340 NN

Livesey, A. J.
Bushell's hospital bicentenary, 1735-1935
see under Bushell's hospital, Goosnargh, Eng.

[Livesey, Algernon Montague]
Poems 1903-1923. Cambridge, Galloway & Porter, 1924.
22.5 x 18.5 cm.
"250 copies of this book have been printed."

NL 0419342 CtY

Livesey, Charles Atkins, 1916- joint author.
TL724 .1 .M35L4
Lewis, Howard Thompson, 1888–
Materials management, a problem of the airframe industry, by Howard T. Lewis ... and Charles A. Livesey ... Boston, Mass., Harvard university, Graduate school of business administration, Bureau of business research, 1944.

Livesey, Dela.
Cameos of beauty... Ilfracombe, A. H. Stockwell, 1949. 31 p. 18cm.

NL 0419344 NN

SK 31 L5
Livesey, Edward.
The big game. With engravings by H. Dixon and a frontispiece by William Wood. London, John Westhouse, 1947.
206p. illus. 18cm.
" I have tried to retell in this book some of the...adventures of the great English explorer and hunter, Sir Samuel William Baker." E. L.
1. Animals, Habits and behavior of 2.Hunting. I. Baker, Sir Samuel William, 1821-1893. Wild beasts and their ways. II. T.

NL 0419345 CtU

Livesey, F J.
... Laundry accounts, by F. J. Livesey, F. C. A. London, Gee & co., 1905.
xii, 124 p. 22cm. ("The Accountants' library." vol. XXXVIII)
On verso of half-title: "The Accountants' library." (Second series) Ed. by the editor of "The Accountant."

1. Laundry—Accounting.
6—36616
Library of Congress HF5601.A2

NL 0419346 DLC NN ICJ MiU CU

LIVESEY, Francis B.
[Circulars in defense of Francis Schlatter] No. 4-10. [Sykesville, Md.] 1896.

NL 0419347 MH

Livesey, Sir George Thomas, 1834–
Co-partnership, by Sir George Livesey. A paper read before the Institution of gas engineers, June 16, 1908. London, Printed by King, Sell, & Olding, ltd. [1908?]
1 p. l., 30, iii, [1] p. 21½cm.

1. Profit-sharing.
9-22283
Library of Congress HD3487.L6

NL 0419348 DLC NN

Livesey, Sir George Thomas, 1834-
Co-partnership conference of the Labour Association at Newcastle-on-Tyne, October 14th, 1899; paper on the profit-sharing scheme of the South Metropolitan Gas Company. London, Printed by McCorquodale & Co., 1899.
39p.

NL 0419349 ICRL RPB

Livesey, Sir George Thomas, 1834-
Eight-hours system in gas-works. 1 pp. (Fortn. Rev. n. s. v. 52, 1892, p. 185.)

NL 0419350 MdBP

Livesey, H F F
The locomotives of the L. N. W. R. London, Railway Pub. Co., 1948.
100 p. illus. 23 cm.

1. Locomotives—Hist. 2. London and North-Western Railway.
TJ603.L5 621.132942 49-14840*

NL 0419351 DLC ICJ WaS

LIVESEY, J.
Darlith ar ddirwest. A gyfieithuyd gan John Pryse. Llanidloses, E.Hughes,1837.
pp.37-.

NL 0419352 MH

Livesey, James, 1625?-1682.
The spirit of the Lord in power and at liberty, as at first to give a being to; so still to give a blessing by His ordinances. In three sermons, preacht at Great Budworth ... London, Printed by A. M. for R. Clavel, 1674.
184 p. 15cm.
WILLIAM ANDREWS CLARK MEMORIAL LIBRARY

NL 0419353 CLU-C

Livesey, John.
Enchiridion Judicum, or, Jehosaphats charge to his judges, opened, in a sermon before the Judges, and the Sheriffe of the County Palatine of Lancast. Together with Catastrophe magnatum . . . [and Series decretorum Dei . . .].
London. Printed by R. I. for Tho. Parkhurst. 1657. (3), 320, (7) pp. Sm. 8°.

E8435 — T.r. May 18, 1903

NL 0419354 MB CtY

Livesey, John.
Psychesemia; or the greatest Loss on Matth. XVI, XXVI. In a short Discourse occasioned by the ... loss of ... Mr. H. Chetham ... London, 1660.
8°.
Bound with his Enchiridion.

NL 0419355 CtY

[Livesey, Joseph,] 1794–1884.
The alarm! [Preston, Eng.: C. Greenall, printer, 1872?] 4 p. 8°.
Caption-title.
Signed: J. Livesey.
In: VTZ p. v. 90, no. 9.

BLACK TEMPERANCE COLL.
1. Temperance.—Addresses, essays, lectures. 2. Title.
N. Y. P. L. May 22, 1918.

NL 0419356 NN

Livesey, Joseph, 1794–1884.
Autobiography of Joseph Livesey. London: National Temperance League Publ. Depot [1886]. 2 p.l., (1)4-98, xi p. 8°.
Edited by W. Livesey.

NAT. TEMPERANCE COLL.
1. No subject. 2. Livesey, William, b. 1816, editor.
N. Y. P. L. September 4, 1917.

NL 0419357 NN

Livesey, Joseph, 1794-1884.
Call things by their right names
see under title

[Livesey, Joseph,] 1794–1884.
A friendly address to all sorts of drinkers. [Preston, Eng.? C. Greenall, printer? 1872.] 1 l. 8°.
Caption-title.
Signed: J. Livesey.
In: VTZ p. v. 90, no. 10.

BLACK TEMPERANCE COLL.
1. Temperance.—Addresses, essays, lectures.
N. Y. P. L. May 21, 1918.

NL 0419359 NN

VOLUME 336

[Livesey, Joseph,] 1794–1884.
A friendly address to shopkeepers, tradesmen, and the middle classes generally. [Preston, Eng.: C. Greenall, printed, 187–?] 4 p. 8°.

Caption-title.
Signed: Joseph Livesey.
In: VTZ p. v. 90, no. 11.

1. Temperance.—Addresses, essays, lectures. BLACK TEMPERANCE COLL.
N. Y. P. L. May 21, 1918.

NL 0419360 NN

Livesey, Joseph, 1794–1884.
Is temperance likely to drop or raise wages?
see under title

[Livesey, Joseph,] 1794–1884.
Joseph Livesey and his teetotalism. [Preston, 18—?] 1 l. 24°.

Caption-title.
Signed: J. Livesey.
In: VTZ p. v. 97, no. 6.

1. Temperance.—Addresses, essays, lectures. BLACK TEMPERANCE COLL.
N. Y. P. L. June 28, 1918.

NL 0419362 NN

Livesey, Joseph, 1794–1884.
A lecture on malt liquor. By Joseph Livesey. London: Norwich Temperance Depot [186–?]. 14 p. 12°.

Cover-title.
In: VTZ p. v. 133, no. 6.

1. Malt liquor. BLACK TEMPERANCE COLL.
N. Y. P. L. February 4, 1919.

NL 0419363 NN

Livesey, Joseph, 1794-1884.
A Lecture on malt liquor. Preston, 1870. 16 p. 8°. [In v. 42, Biographical Pamphlets]

NL 0419364 CtY

Livesey, Joseph, 1794–1884.
The life and teachings of Joseph Livesey, comprising his Autobiography, with an introductory review of his labours as reformer and teacher by John Pearce, and an appendix containing press and pulpit notices of Mr. Livesey's writings and life... London: National Temperance League's Depôt [pref. 1885]. clxviii, 176, 16 p., 3 port. (1 mounted.) 8°.

His "Lecture on malt liquor," 16 p. at end.

1. Temperance, Gt. Br. 2. Pearce, John, editor. BLACK TEMPERANCE COLL.
N. Y. P. L. June 19, 1917.

NL 0419365 NN

Livesey, Joseph, 1794–1884.
The life and teachings of Joseph Livesey, comprising Joseph Livesey as reformer and teacher, by John Pearce — the Autobiography — the malt liquor lecture — press and pulpit notices, etc. Edited by John Pearce... London: National Temperance Publ. Depot, 1887. clxviii, 176, 16 p., 3 port. (1 mounted.) illus. 2. ed. 8°.

1. Temperance, Gt. Br. 2. Pearce, John, editor. BLACK TEMPERANCE COLL.
N. Y. P. L. June 19, 1917.

NL 0419366 NN MnU

Livesey, Joseph, 1794-1884.
——. Malt, malt liquor, malt tax, beer, and barley; being a reply to Sir Fitzroy Kelley [*et al.*] on the repeal of the malt tax. 16 pp. 8°. *London, W. Tweedie*, [n. d.].

NL 0419367 DNLM

Livesey, Joseph, 1794-1884, ed.
The Moral reformer, and protestor against the vices, abuses and corruptions of the age. By J. Livesey. v. 1–3; Jan. 1831–Dec. 1833. London, Sherwood and co., 1831–33.

Livesey, Joseph, 1794–1884.
A new lecture on malt liquor. By Joseph Livesey. Preston [Eng.]: Printed by C. Greenall, 1870. 16 p. 8°.

In: VTZ p. v. 90, no. 1.

1. Beer and brewing. BLACK TEMPERANCE COLL.
N. Y. P. L. May 21, 1918.

NL 0419369 NN CtY DNLM

[Livesey, Joseph,] 1794–1884.
New Year's address, 1875. To drinkers and non-drinkers. [Preston, Eng.: C. Greenall, printer, 1875.] 4 p. 8°.

Caption-title.
Signed: J. Livesey.
In: VTZ p. v. 90, no. 12.

1. Temperance.—Addresses, essays, lectures. BLACK TEMPERANCE COLL.
N. Y. P. L. May 21, 1918.

NL 0419370 NN

[Livesey, Joseph,] 1794–1884.
New Year's address, 1875. To the people of Preston. [Preston, Eng.: C. Greenall, printer, 1875.] 4 p. 8°.

Caption-title.
Signed: J. Livesey.
In: VTZ p. v. 90, no. 13.

1. Temperance.—Addresses, essays, lectures. BLACK TEMPERANCE COLL.
N. Y. P. L. May 21, 1918.

NL 0419371 NN

[Livesey, Joseph,] 1794–1884.
New Year's address, 1876. To the people of Preston. [Preston, Eng.: C. Greenall, printer, 1876.] 4 p. 8°.

Caption-title.
Signed: J. Livesey.
In: VTZ p. v. 90, no. 14.

1. Temperance.—Addresses, essays, lectures. BLACK TEMPERANCE COLL.
N. Y. P. L. May 21, 1918.

NL 0419372 NN

Livesey, Joseph, 1794–1884.
The New Year's gift, by J. Livesey. [Preston, Eng.: C. Greenall, printer, 1874.] 4 p. 8°.

Caption-title.
At head of title: 1874.
In: VTZ p. v. 90, no. 15.

1. Temperance.—Addresses, essays, lectures. 2. Title. BLACK TEMPERANCE COLL
N. Y. P. L. May 22, 1918.

NL 0419373 NN

[Livesey, Joseph, 1794-1884]
A plea for perfect sobriety. [Preston, Greenall, 1850]

4 p. 22 cm.
Signed at end: J.Livesey.
Without title-page. Caption title

NL 0419374 MH

Livesey, Joseph, 1794–1884.
Reminiscences of early teetotalism. By J. Livesey... Preston: "Staunch Teetotaler," 1872. 56 p. New ed., with additions. 8°.

In: VTZ p. v. 48, no. 11.

1. Temperance, Gt. Br. BLACK TEMPERANCE COLL.
N. Y. P. L. November 23, 1917.

NL 0419375 NN CtY

Livesey, Joseph, 1794–1884.
"Something must be done," by J. Livesey. [Preston, Eng.: C. Greenall, printer, 187–?] 4 p. 8°.

Caption-title.
In: VTZ p. v. 90, no. 16.

1. Temperance.—Addresses, essays, lectures. 2. Title. BLACK TEMPERANCE COLL.
N. Y. P. L. May 22, 1918.

NL 0419376 NN

Livesey, Joseph, 1794–1884.
The staunch teetotaler. London, Tweedie, 1869.
vi, 884 p. port. 22 cm.
Originally issued monthly in 24 nos., from Jan. 1867 to Dec. 1868.

1. Temperance. 2. Liquor problem. I. Title.
HV5060.L55 49-36533*

NL 0419377 DLC

Pam. Coll. Livesey, Joseph, 1794-1884.
A temperance lecture based on the tee-total
16746 principle; including an exposure of the great delusion as to the properties of malt liquor ... Preston, 1836.
35 p. 21½cm.

1. Temperance

NL 0419378 NcD NN DNLM

Livesey, Joseph, 1794–1884.
A temperance lecture based on the tee-total principle; including an exposure of the great delusion as to the properties of malt liquor, the substance of which has been delivered in the principal towns of England. By J. Livesey... Preston [Eng.]: Printed and published by J. Livesey [187–?]. 16 p. 8°.

In: VTZ p. v. 90, no. 29.

1. Temperance.—Addresses, essays, lectures. BLACK TEMPERANCE COLL.
N. Y. P. L. May 21, 1918.

NL 0419379 NN

LIVESEY, Joseph, 1794-1884, editor.
Temperance melodies, selected from Paxton Hood & others. Intended chiefly to encourage social temperance singing meetings. Preston, printed by A.V.Myers, for J.Livesey, [1850?].

12 cm. pp.63, (1).

NL 0419380 MH

VOLUME 336

Livesey, Joseph, 1794–1884, and T. H. Barker.
True policy vindicated. A friendly correspondence between Mr. Joseph Livesey and Mr. T. H. Barker... Manchester: United Kingdom Alliance [1870?]. 12 p. 16°.

Repr.: Social reformer, April and May 1870.
In: VTZ p. v. 97, no. 5.

BLACK TEMPERANCE COLL.
1. Local option, Gt. Br. 2. Barker, Thomas H. 3. Title.
N. Y. P. L. July 1, 1918.

NL 0419381 NN

Livesey, Joseph, 1794–1884.
True temperance teaching; shewing the errors of the alliance and the Permissive Bill. By Joseph Livesey... London: W. Tweedie, 1873. 16 p. 8°.

Reprinted in part from the Temperance star.
In: VTZ p. v. 90, no. 17.

BLACK TEMPERANCE COLL.
1. Local option, Gt. Br. 2. Title.
N. Y. P. L. May 21, 1918.

NL 0419382 NN NIC

[Livesey, Joseph, 1794-1884]
What can be done for Liverpool? [Preston, C.Greenall, 185- ?]

4 p. 23.5 cm.
Signed at end: J.Livesey.
Without title-page. Caption title.

NL 0419383 MH

[Livesey, Joseph,] 1794–1884.
Why repeal the malt tax? Norwich: S. Jarrold [186–?]. 8 p. 12°.

Signed: J. Livesey.
In: VTZ p. v. 185, no. 3.

BLACK TEMPERANCE COLL.
1. Malt liquor.—Taxation, Gt. Br. 2. Title.
N. Y. P. L. May 31, 1919.

NL 0419384 NN

Livesey, Richard.
An exposure of Mormonism, being a statement of facts relating to the self-styled "Latter Day Saints," and the origin of the Book of Mormon, by Richard Livesey... Preston: Printed by J. Livesey, 1838. 12 p. 8°.

1. Mormonism, Anti.
N. Y. P. L. November 8, 1923.

NL 0419385 NN

LIVESEY, RICHARD.
An exposure of Mormonism; being a statement of facts, relating to the self-styled "Latter Day Saints," and the origin of the Book of Mormon. By Richard Livesey... Wrexham: Printed by W. Bayley, 1840. 12 p. 21cm.

804023A. 1. Mormons and Mormonism, Anti.

NL 0419386 NN CtY

Livesey, Richard.
The prisoners of 1776; a relic of the revolution
see under Herbert, Charles, 1757-1808.

Livesey, Thomas J.
Granville history readers. [Revised and brought up to date by S. Benson Thorp.]
— London. Burns & Oates. [1902.] 4 v. Illus. Portraits. Plates. Sm. 8°.
Contents. — 1. Stories from English history. 2. History of England from the Roman period to the Wars of the Roses. 3. From the Wars of the Roses to the present reign. 4. Notable events in England's history as narrated by the best writers.

E7880 — English language. Read. Mar. 19, 1903 T.r. — Great Britain. Hist. — Thorp. S. Benson, ed.

NL 0419388 MB

Livesey, Thomas J., and S. B. Thorp.
History of England, by T. J. Livesey and S. Benson Thorp... London: Burns & Oates, Ltd. [, 1906.] 173 p. incl. tables. 16°.

301281A. 1. Great Britain—Hist. 2. Thorp, S. Benson, jt. au.
N. Y. P. L. June 8, 1927

NL 0419389 NN NNUT

DA130
.L52 Livesey, Thomas J ed.
History of England from the early Britons to the Wars of the Roses. New and rev. ed. London, Burns & Oates [1902]
iv, 207 p. illus. 18 cm. (The Granville history readers, no. 2)

1. Gt. Brit.--History--To 1485.
2. Gt. Brit.--History, Juvenile. I. Title.
II. Series.

NL 0419390 LU

Livesey, Thomas J
How to teach grammar: illustrated in a series of notes of lessons. By T. J. Livesey ... London, Moffatt and Paige [1881]
vii, 147 p. 17.5cm.

1. English language - Study and teaching.

NL 0419391 NNC

Livesey, Thomas J.
The primer of English history from B.C. 55 to A.D. 1920. By T. J. Livesey.
London. Burns, Oates & Washbourne, Ltd. [1920.] (1), 175, (1) pp. Genealogical tables. 16½ cm., in 8s.
Two copies.

N3204 — T.r. — Great Britain. Hist.

NL 0419392 MB

DA
32
.8
L5 Livesey, Thomas J
Stories from English history. London, Burns & Oates [n.d.]
vi, 122 p. illus. 18 cm. (Granville history readers, no. 1)

1. Gt. Brit.--History, Juvenile.
I. Title. II. Series.

NL 0419393 LU

Livesey, W
The mining crisis, its history and meaning to all workers, by W. Livesey ... London, Simpkin, Marshall, Hamilton, Kent & co., ltd., 1921.
vi, 89 p. 18½ cm.

1. Coal trade—Gt. Brit. 2. Coal-miners—Gt. Brit. 3. Miners' federation of Great Britain. 4. Coal mines and mining—Government ownership—Gt. Brit. I. Title.

HD9551.6.L5 22—7421

NL 0419394 DLC CaBViP MB NN ICJ

LIVESEY, W.
The mining crisis; its history and meaning to all workers, 2d ed. London, Simpkin, Marshall, Hamilton, Kent & co., Ltd., 1922.

NL 0419395 MH

385.232 Livesey, William.
L758f A financial scheme for the relief of railway companies, submitted to directors, shareholders, and the public for their consideration. In two parts. London [1866]
cover-title, 38p. tables.

NL 0419396 IU

Livesey, William, b. 1816, ed.
Autobiography of Joseph Livesey
see under Livesey, Joseph, 1794-1884.

Livesey, William, b. 1816.
Fifty years ago; or, Early Preston teetotalism. By William Livesey. Read at the conference in connection with the Crystal Palace Temperance Jubilee. London: National Temperance League Publ. Depot [1882]. 8 p. 8°.

Repr.: Temperance record.
In: VTZ p. v. 89, no. 13.

BLACK TEMPERANCE COLL.
1. Temperance.—History, Gt. Br.: Eng.: Preston. 2. Title.
N. Y. P. L. May 17, 1918.

NL 0419398 NN

Livesey & Crowther Ltd., Manchester and Leicester.
Elastics.
[Manchester. 1932.] 3-68 pp. Illus. Plates. Diagram. Tables. 22 cm.

D2242 — Elastic fabrics.

NL 0419399 MB MiD

Livesly, *captain, defendant.*
The remarkable case of Potter Jackson ... giving an account of the most cruel treatment, he received from Captain Livesly, (commander of the Lord Stanly slave-ship) and his chief mate; by assaulting, imprisoning, putting in irons, and cruelly flogging him ... Written by himself. With the trial, before the Right Hon. Lord Ellenborough in the Court of King's bench, Guildhall, London, on Thursday, July 10, 1806; when the jury returned a verdict, five hundred pounds damages!!

London, Printed for and sold by the unfortunate sufferer, at R. Butters' [1807?]
iv, [9]-31 p. fold. front. 20½cm.

I. Jackson, Potter, b. 1774, plaintiff. II. Gt. Brit. Court of King's bench. III. Title.
45-32272
Library of Congress [Slavery pamphlets, v. 6, no. 5a]
——— Another issue. dated 1807.
Contains prefatory note, HT857.S5 vol. 6, no. 5a
[2]

NL 0419401 DLC

Liv-Estländisches Bureau für Landeskultur.
Bericht.
(In Livländische Gemeinnützige und Ökonomische Sozietät. Bericht)

NL 0419402 NN

VOLUME 336

S242 .L5 Liv-Estländisches Bureau für Landeskultur.
Mitteilungen des liv-estländischen Bureau für landeskultur der Versuchsstation und des Baltischen Moorvereins. Jahrbuch. [Dorpat, 1909-]
1 v. 8°.
1. Title. 2. Estonia. Landeskultur-bureau. Versuchsstation. 3. Baltischer Moorverein, Tartu.

NL 0419403 DLC IU

Livestock.
(*In* U. S. Dept. of agriculture. Yearbook of agriculture, 1933 p. 219-273. illus., diagrs. 23½cm. Washington, 1933)
Consists of a number of short articles by various authors.

1. Domestic animals—U. S.
Agr 33-534
Library, U. S. Dept. of Agriculture 1Ag84Y 1933
Library of Congress [S21.A35 1933]
[6°]

NL 0419404 DNAL CaBVaU OCl OU

Livestock and animal products statistics
see under Canada. Bureau of Statistics.

... Livestock and dairy farming
see under [Berry, John Coulter]

284.34 L75 Livestock and Home-Produced Meat Policy Committee.
Marketing of fat stock: deficiency payment system for guarantee of price. London, 1950.
10 p.
Includes press notice with title: A new plan for the marketing of fat stock (2 p.)

NL 0419407 DNAL

Livestock and meat council.
A program for solving wartime meat problems, submitted by the Livestock and meat council... Distributed to the cattle producers of Wyoming by the Wyoming stock growers association ... [Cheyenne, 1943] 7 p. 23cm.
BZAC p.v.254
—— —— Second copy.

1. World war, 1939-1945—Food supply—U. S. 2. Meat—Trade and stat.—U. S. I. Wyoming stock growers association, Cheyenne, Wyo.
N. Y. P. L. January 29, 1946

NL 0419408 NN DNAL

Livestock and meat council.
That our boys shall have meat; how new meat management plan can solve America's wartime meat problem. [Chicago?] Livestock and meat council [1943] 30 p. illus. 23cm.

1. Meat—Trade and stat.—U. S., 1943. 2. World war, 1939- — Food supply—U. S.
N. Y. P. L. April 6, 1944

NL 0419409 NN DNAL

HD9411 qL5 1954 Agriculture Room Livestock and Meat Marketing Conference, Oregon State College.
[Proceedings] Jan.6 & 7, 1954, Corvallis, Ore. [Corvallis, Ore., 1954]
[141] l. tables. 28cm.
Various paging.
1.Meat industry and trade - Ore. 2.Animal industry - Ore. 3.Animal industry - Cong.

NL 0419410 OrCS

The **Livestock** and meat situation.
[Washington]
no. in v. diagrs. 27 cm. bimonthly (irregular)
Began publication in Jan. 1947. Cf. Monthly catalog of United States Government publications, Apr. 1947.
Vols. for -Mar. 1961 issued by the Bureau of Agricultural Economics; May 1961- by the Agricultural Marketing Service; by the Dept. of Agriculture, Economic Research Service.
1. Animal industry—U. S. 2. Meat industry and trade—U. S. I. U. S. Bureau of Agricultural Economics. II. U. S. Agricultural Marketing Service. III. U. S. Dept. of Agriculture. Economic Research Service.
HD9414.A25 59-30695 rev

NL 0419411 DLC

Live stock associations. [International and national]
(*In* U. S. Dept. of agriculture. Yearbook, 1918. p. 448. 23cm. Washington, 1919)

1. Domestic animals—[Breeders' societies]
Agr 19-787 Revised
Library, U. S. Dept. of Agriculture 1Ag84Y

NL 0419412 DNAL OU

Live-stock associations. [National and state]
(*In* U. S. Dept. of agriculture. Yearbook, 1917, p. 595-603; 1919, p. 502-508; 23cm. Washington, 1918-)
1917 has title: National and state livestock associations and allied organizations.

1. Domestic animals—[Breeders' societies]
Agr 18-639 Revised
Library, U. S. Dept. of Agriculture 1Ag84Y

NL 0419413 DNAL

Live-stock associations and the markets. Registered live stock in the United States, December 31, 1903.
(*In* U. S. Dept. of agriculture. Bureau of animal industry. Annual report, 20th, 1903, p. 523-557. pl. XXII. 23cm. Washington, 1904)

1. Domestic animals—Statistics. 2. Stock and stock-breeding—Societies. [2. Domestic animals—Breeders' societies]
Agr 20-490
Library, U. S. Dept. of Agriculture 1An5 1903

NL 0419414 DNAL

Livestock auction markets in New Jersey.
See under
[Young, J L]

The **Livestock** book. [Staff of writers: W. R. Thompson, and others] State College, Miss., W. R. Thompson, and J. McKinney, Memphis, °1952.
370 p. illus. 24 cm.

1. Stock and stock-breeding. I. Thompson, Wilfred Roland, 1904-
SF65.L49 636.08 52—14694 ‡

NL 0419416 DLC WaSp MtU TU KMK

Livestock book. Rev. and edited by the editors of Successful farming. Rev. ed. Des Moines, Meredith Pub. Co., c1955.
122 p. illus. 31 cm.
Published in 1972 under title: Livestock.

1. Stock and stock-breeding. 2. Veterinary medicine. I. Successful farming.
SF65.L49 1955 636.08 55-2037 ‡

NL 0419417 DLC

Seneca Library Zc10 L74 The Live stock breeders' directory of the United States and Canada ... June 1887-
Saint Louis, Mo.
24 cm.
Compiled and published by Philip H. Hale.
Includes advertising matter.
1. Stock and stock-breeding - U.S. - Direct. I. Hale, Philip H comp.

NL 0419418 CtY DNAL

Livestock breeding at the crossroads.
(*In* U. S. Dept. of agriculture. Yearbook of agriculture, 1936, p. 831-862. illus. 23½cm. Washington, 1936)
"Many workers in the Department have contributed to this article, and much valuable historical and genetic material was supplied by J. L. Lush, head of the Animal breeding subsection, Iowa State college".—cf. foot-note, p. 831.

1. Stock and stock-breeding. [1. Domestic animals—Breeding]
Agr 37-242
U. S. Dept. of agr. Library 1Ag84Y 1936
for Library of Congress [S21.A35 1936]
[7°]

NL 0419419 DNAL CaBVaU OCl

Livestock Conference, Port. of. Spain, Trinidad, 1950.
Animal husbandry in the Caribbean: report ...
see under Caribbean Commission.

SF 1 L54 Livestock Conservation, Inc.
Annual meeting.
Chicago.

NL 0419421 KMK DNAL

Livestock Conservation, inc.
Livestock conservation news
see under title

---

41 L752 Livestock Conservation, inc.
More meat and milk: how to get them through livestock conservation. [Chicago, 1952?]
7 p.
1. Veterinary hygiene. 2. Veterinary medicine. U.S.

NL 0419423 DNAL

VOLUME 336

VET. MEDICINE
SF1
L5
Livestock Conservation, inc.
Proceedings «of the» annual meeting.
«Chicago»
v. illus. 22 cm.
Some nos. have also distinctive titles.

1. Stock and stock-breeding - Societies, etc.

NL 0419424 OU GU OrCS

HD9433
.U4
qN35
Livestock Conservation, Inc.
Report, 19
«Chicago, 19
v. illus. 21½-28cm. annual.

Formed by the union of the National Live Stock Loss Prevention Board, and National Livestock Sanitary Committee, Feb. 1951.
This set includes reports of former National Live Stock Loss Prevention Board, which were issued with distinctive title, 1939-1948.

1. Meat industry and trade - U.S. 2. Animal industry. x:

NL 0419425 OrCS MtBC MtU DNAL

49
L754
Livestock-conservation news. v.1
Chicago, Livestock Conservation.

1. Domestic animals. Periodicals.
2. Marketing of live stock. Periodicals.
I. Livestock Conservation, inc.

NL 0419426 DNAL

The Live Stock Dealers' and Butchers' Association of New Orleans, plaintiff.
Affidavit "Z". Supreme Court of the United States. No. 475. Inbau, Aycock & Co., plaintiff in error
see under title

Livestock enterprises ₍by₎ H. P. Davis ... L. Wermelskirchen ... ₍and others₎ edited by Kary C. Davis ... Philadelphia ₍etc.₎ J. B. Lippincott company ₍°1928₎
ix, 492 p. incl. illus., pl., diagrs. 22cm. (*On cover:* Lippincott's farm enterprise series)
On verso of half-title: Farm enterprise series.
"Reference books": p. 463.

1. Stock and stock-breeding—U. S. I. Davis, Herbert Perry, 1889– II. Davis, Kary Cadmus, 1867– ed.

28-30415 Revised
Library of Congress SF65.L5 1928
Copyright A 2186 ₍r37g2₎ 636

NL 0419428 DLC DNAL OCl ICJ

Livestock enterprises ₍by₎ H. P. Davis, W. H. Smith, L. Wermelskirchen ... ₍and others₎ Chicago, Philadelphia, J. B. Lippincott company ₍°1937₎
ix, 492 p. illus., diagrs. 21½cm. (*Half-title:* Profitable enterprise series)
On cover: Enterprise series.
Previous edition edited by Kary C. Davis.
"Reference books": p. 463-464; bibliography at end of some of the chapters.

1. Stock and stock-breeding—U. S. I. Davis, Herbert Perry, 1889–

37-6109
Library of Congress SF65.L5 1937
——— Copy 2.
Copyright A 102533 ₍5₎ 636

NL 0419429 DLC Or NcRS NIC DNAL LU

Livestock enterprises ₍by₎ H. P. Davis, W. H. Smith, L. Wermelskirchen ₍and others₎ ... Edited by R. W. Gregory. Chicago, Philadelphia ₍etc.₎ J. B. Lippincott company ₍1946₎
ix, 492 p. incl. illus. (incl. maps, diagrs.) forms. 21½cm.
"Second revised edition."—Pref.
Includes bibliographies.

1. Stock and stock-breeding—U. S. ₍1. Domestic animals₎ I. Davis, Herbert Perry, 1889– II. Gregory, Raymond William, 1893– ed.
SF65.L5 1946 636 Agr 47-79

U. S. Dept. of agr. Library for Library of Congress 40L75S 1946 ₍5₎†

NL 0419430 DNAL CU PSt ICJ DLC

Livestock farming
see under [Corn belt farm dailies]

49
L759
The Livestock feeder.
Omaha, Neb., National Livestock Feeders Association.

1. Stock breeders' societies. I. National Livestock Feeders Association.

NL 0419432 DNAL

Livestock feeder
The American breeder, with which is combined Carlson's Rural review, v.9-
Kansas City, Mo., 1916-

NL 0419433 OU ICRL

Live stock feeding association, *Pleasant Hill, O.*
How to feed for bigger live-stock profits ... Pleasant Hill., O., Live stock feeding association ₍°1919₎
10 v. illus. (incl. port.) 22cm.
"A brief foreword," signed: C. C. Palmer.

1. Feeding and feedings stuffs. I. Palmer, Charles Conger, 1892– II. Title.
Library of Congress SF95.L5 20-842

NL 0419434 DLC ICJ

... Livestock for small farms
see under [Erskine, Ralph] 1889-

40
L755
Live stock growers' directory of marks and brands for the state of Oregon. Portland, Kilham Stationery & Printing Co., 1918.
360 p.

NL 0419436 DNAL OrU OrHi OrP

Film
CD
3119
B3
U5
reel 21
Live stock in Utah.
6l.
Microfilm (positive) of holograph.
Also titled: Stock-raising in Utah.
Stocking of Utah ranges in 1849-1854; cattle as a medium of exchange; horse-breeding practices; claims for Utah horses made by H.J. Faust, 1877; sheep-raising.
1. Cattle--Utah. 2. Mormons and Mormonism--Hist.--Sources. 3. Horse breeding. 4. Sheep--Utah.

NL 0419437 UU

Live stock in war-time
see under [Curtiss, Charles Franklin] 1863-

The Live stock indicator.
[Des Moines, Ia., Kansas City, Mo.]

14
9342

NL 0419439 DLC

The live-stock industry in 1906.
(*In* U. S. Dept. of agriculture. Yearbook, 1906, p. 492-498; 23cm. Washington, 1907-)

1. Domestic animals—Statistics.

Library, U. S. Dept. of Agriculture Agr 7-1951

NL 0419440 DNAL MiU OU

Livestock insect control in Kansas
see under [Kelly, Edward Owen Guerrant] 1880-

The Live stock inspector. Devoted exclusively to live stock interests. v. 1- Apr. 1895-
Woodward, Okl. ₍etc.₎ W. E. Bolton, 1895-
v. in illus. (incl. ports.) 33½-38cm.
Caption title.
Monthly, Apr. 1895-June 1898; semimonthly, July 1898-
Official organ of the Oklahoma live stock association.
Merged into the Farmers star and live stock inspector, Sept. 3, 1909.

1. Stock and stock-breeding—Period. I. Oklahoma live stock association.
8-27252 Revised
Library of Congress SF1.L6

NL 0419442 DLC

Live stock journal.
London.
v. illus. weekly.
Ceased June 1933.
Continues Fancier's gazette.

NL 0419443 ICRL MnU-A DNAL WaS CaBViP

Live Stock Journal.
Types of hackney horses. Selected from the "Live Stock Journal" collection.
— London. Vinton & Co., Ltd. 1892. Unpaged. Illus. 24 × 36 cm.

H8529 — Horse.

NL 0419444 MB OU

Live stock journal.
Types of shire horses selected from the Live stock journal collection. London, Vinton, 1894.

NL 0419445 PU

Live stock market and meat trade review
see
Livestock market review.

VOLUME 336

Livestock market news statistics and related data
see under U.S. Agricultural Marketing Service. Livestock Division.

Livestock market review.
Ottawa.

v. in maps, tables. 25-28 cm. annual.

Began publication in 1919. Cf. List of the serial publications of foreign governments.
Title varies: 19 -31, Live stock market and meat trade review.—1932-49, Annual market review.
Vols. for 19 -32 issued by Canada. Markets Intelligence and Stock Yards Services (varies slightly); 1933-36 by Canada. Live Stock Branch. Market Services; 1937- by Canada. Dept. of Agriculture. Marketing Service (1950- by its Market Information Section); 19 by Canada. Dept. of Agriculture. Production and Marketing Branch. Markets Information Section.

1. Stock and stock-breeding — Canada. 2. Meat industry and trade—Canada. I. Canada. Markets Intelligence and Stock Yards Services. II. Canada. Live Stock Branch. Market Service. III. Canada. Dept. of Agriculture. Marketing Service. IV. Canada. Dept. of Agriculture. Production and Marketing Branch.

HD9433.C18A3 62-56760

ICU NN
NL 0419449 DLC DNAL CaBVaU IU NbU CU WU TU MH ICJ

280.38
L753 Livestock marketeer. v.1

Cleveland, O., American stock yards association,

NL 0419450 DNAL

Livestock marketing in the Southern region
see under [Johnson, Jack D]

Live stock markets. v.1-46, no.5; Jan. 1891-May 1936. Chicago, Clay, Robinson & Co., John Clay & Co. ₍etc.₎
46v. illus. 34cm.

Title varies: 1891-June 27, 1901, Live stock report.- July 4, 1901-May 22, 1908, Weekly live stock report (varies slightly.- May 29, 1908-Oct. 31, 1913, Clay, Robinson & Company's live stock report.- Nov.7, 1913-Dec.8, 1921, Live stock report.

NL 0419452 KU MnU-A ICRL

Livestock, meats and wool market statistics and related data
see U.S. Agricultural Marketing Service. Livestock Division.
Livestock market news statistics and related data.

Live stock men's association of America.
Directory, 3d ed., of the Live stock men's association of America (incorporated under the laws of Tennessee) ... Knoxville, Tenn., S. B. Newman & co., 1914.
₍1₎, iii, 429 p. illus. 15cm.

1. Stock and stock breeding—U. S.—Direct.

Library of Congress SF25.L5 14-13226

NL 0419454 DLC

Live Stock Men's Association of America.
Directory, fifth edition, of the Live Stock Men's Association of America (incorporated under the laws of Tennessee). .... Mt. Juliet, Tenn., Freeman Press, 1916.
xxix, 408 p. 15½cm.
6 plank pages for memoranda at end.

NL 0419455 ICJ

7₋2
L74

Live stock national bank of Chicago.
March 12, 1868, March 12, 1938; then and now, a contrast. ₍Chicago₎ The Live stock national bank of Chicago, c1938₎
₍28₎ p. illus. 24cm.

On cover: 70th anniversary.
Running title: 70 years of progress.

NL 0419456 NNC

Livestock outlook news
see Illinois farm outlook.

1.913
C3L753 Livestock Production and Marketing Conference.
Summary of subject matter covered at meetings of Interregional Livestock Production and Marketing Conference, 1948-1952. Washington, 1953.

Issued Feb. 1953.

1. Marketing of live stock. Congresses. 2. Stock breeders' congresses. I. U.S. Extension Service. Division of Agricultural Economics.

NL 0419458 DNAL

Live-stock Publishing Co., Chicago.
Illustrated American horse book
see under title

Live Stock report
see Live Stock Market.

Live Stock Sanitary Committee, Sioux City, Iowa
see Sioux City, Iowa, Live Stock Sanitary Committee.

Live-stock shipments from Canada, Argentina, and Australia to England.
(*In* U. S. Dept. of agriculture. Bureau of animal industry. Annual report, 12th-13th, 1895-1896, p. 77-83. 23cm. Washington, 1897)

1. Meat industry and trade.

Agr 20-491
Library, U. S. Dept. of Agriculture 1An5 1895-1896

NL 0419462 DNAL OU OO

Live stock shippers protective league.
Before the interstate commerce commission, ex parte no. 57. ₍1917₎
39 p.

NL 0419463 DNAL

Live stock society of America.
Premium list of the annual stock and farm show, 1895. N.Y., 1895.
v.1

NL 0419464 Nh

Live stock Tribune [monthly]
illus.
Library has: v. 12-13 Jan. 1907 - Dec. 1908.
No more published after v. 14, no. 9, Sept. 1909.

NL 0419465 WaSp

Livet,
Rapport de M. Livet sur les vitraux exposés par MM. Maréchal et Gugnon le 24 juin 1843. Metz, Typographie de S. Lamort, 1843.
40p. (Académie royale de Metz. Lettres, sciences, arts, agriculture.)

NL 0419466 ICRL

LIVET, C. S. F.
Gnomonique, ou Art de tracer les cadrans solaires. Metz, Mme Thiel, etc., etc., 1839.

Plates.

NL 0419467 MH PLH

Livet, Charles Louis, 1828-1897.
Catalogue des documents relatifs à l'histoire de France, conservés aux archives de la Torre do Tombo, à Lisbonne, par M. Charles Livet ... Paris, Imprimerie impériale, 1869.
2 p. l., ii, 72 p. 23cm.
Half-title: Documents relatifs à l'histoire de France conservés aux archives de Lisbonne.

1. France—Hist.—Sources. 2. France—For. rel.—Portugal. 3. Portugal—For. rel.—France. I. Portugal. Arquivo nacional. II. Title.

Library of Congress CD1888.F8L5 2-16266

NL 0419468 DLC

Livet, Charles Louis, 1828-1897, ed.

Somaize, Antoine Baudeau de.
Le dictionnaire des précieuses, par le sieur de Somaize. Nouv. éd., augm. de divers opuscules du même auteur relatifs aux précieuses, et d'une clef historique et anecdotique par m. Ch.-L. Livet ... Paris, P. Jannet, 1856.

Livet, Charles Louis, 1828-1897.

Le Boulanger de Chalussay,
Elomire hypocondre; comédie par Le Boulanger de Chalussay. Réimprimé sur l'édition originale (Paris, 1670) avec une reproduction du frontispice et une Note sur les ennemis de Molière par Ch.-L. Livet. Paris, I. Liseux, 1878.

VOLUME 336

Livet, Charles Louis. 1828—1897 Episode de l'histoire des Jésuites. L'autodafé du P. Malagrida. 35 pp. (*Rev. hist.* v. 18, 1882, p. 323.)

NL 0419471 MdBP

840.9
L785E
Livet, Charles Louis, 1828-1897.
Études sur la littérature française a l'époque de Richelieu et de Mazarin ... Paris, Techener, 1852-53.
3 v. 21½cm.

Contents.- I. Bois-Robert.

1. French literature. 17th century. History and criticism. I. Title.

NL 0419472 NcD

PC2057 **Livet, Charles Louis,** 1828-1896.
.L7 La grammaire française et les grammairiens du xvie siècle, par Ch.-L. Livet ... Paris, Didier et cie. [etc.] 1859.
viii, 536 p. 22cm.

1. French language—Grammar—Hist.

IaU NjP
NRU MH IU OU NIC TNJ NBuU NcD MiU OO NNU-W PHC
NL 0419473 ICU CaBVaU PU MdBP CU CtY PBm ViLxW ICN

Livet, Charles Louis, 1828-1897.

Bussy, Roger de Rabutin, *comte* **de,** 1618-1693.
Histoire amoureuse des Gaules, par Bussy Rabutin, revue et annotée par m. Paul Boiteau; suivie des romans historico-satiriques du xviie siècle recueillis et annotés par m. C. L. Livet ... Paris, P. Jannet [etc.] 1856-76.

Livet, Charles Louis, 1828-1897, ed.

Pellisson-Fontanier, Paul, 1624-1693.
Histoire de l'Académie française par Pellisson et d'Olivet, avec une introduction, des éclaircissements et notes par M. Ch.-L. Livet. Paris, Didier et c^ie, 1858.

Livet, Charles Louis, 1828-1897, ed.

[**Boudin,** *Mme.*]
Les intrigues de Molière et celles de sa femme; ou, La fameuse comédienne, histoire de la Guérin; réimpression conforme à l'édition sans lieu ni date, suivie des variantes, avec préface et notes, par Ch.-L. Livet. Nouv. éd., considérablement augm. et ornée d'un portrait d'Armande Béjart. Paris, I. Liseux, 1877.

Livet, Charles Louis, 1828-1896.
... Le Journal officiel de Paris pendant la commune (20 mars-24 mai 1871) Histoire—extraits, facsimile du dernier n° (24 mai) Paris, L. Beauvais, 1871.
286 p. fold. facsim. 18½cm.
At head of title: Ch.-L. Livet.

1. Journal officiel de la République française. 2. Paris—Hist.—Commune, 1871.

NL 0419477 ICU IEN IaU IU TxFTC CtY NjR MB NN MH-BA

Livet, Charles Louis, 1828-1897.
Lexique de la Langue de Moliere.
Paris.1845; v.2,1846; v.3, 1847.

NL 0419478 OrU

Livet, Charles Louis, 1828-1897.
Lexique de la langue de Molière comparée à celle des écrivains de son temps, avec des commentaires de philologie historique et grammaticale par Ch. L. Livet ... Paris, Impimerie nationale, 1895-97.
3 v. 25cm.
"Ouvrage couronné par l'Académie française."

1. French language—Dictionaries. 2. Molière, Jean Baptiste Poquelin, 1622-1673. 3. French language—Hist.

Library of Congress PQ1867.L5 3—30397

NcD CtY PU PP PHC PSC PBm OCl OU OCU OO
NL 0419479 DLC MtU MeB ViU CU WU PSt DAU PPT NcU MB

Livet, Charles Louis, 1828-1897, ed.
La muze historique; ou, Recueil des lettres en vers contenant les nouvelles du temps, écrites à Son Altesse Mademoizelle de Longueville, depuis duchesse de Nemours (1650-1665) par J. Loret
see under Loret, Jean, 1595-1665.

Livet, Charles Louis, 1828-1897, ed.

Saint-Amant, Marc Antoine Gérard, *sieur* **de,** 1594-1661?
Oeuvres complètes de Saint-Amant. Nouv. éd. pub. sur les manuscrits inédits et les éditions anciennes. Précédée d'une notice et accompagnée de notes, par m. Ch.-L. Livet. Paris, P. Jannet, 1855.

E
5
C 816917
LIVET, CHARLES LOUIS, 1828-1897.
Philippe Cospeau, nommé en France Philippe de Cospéan. Sa vie et ses œuvres, 1571-1646. Paris, Alvares, 1854.
122p. 19cm.

Bibliography: p.[73]-78.
"Oraison funebre de Henry le Grand": p.[79]-122.

NL 0419482 ICN NjP MH

DC
1218
.A2
L78
Livet, Charles Louis, 1828-1897.
Portraits du grand siècle. Paris, É.Perrin, 1885.
463 p.
Includes bibliography.

1.France--Biog. I.Title.

MeB
NL 0419483 MiU CaBVaU OrU OrPR NcWsW IU WU CoU MH

DC121 **Livet, Charles Louis,** 1828-1896.
.8 Portraits du grand siècle, par Ch.-L. Livet. 2. éd. Paris,
.A1L8 É. Perrin, 1886.
[3], iv, 463, [1] p. 18½cm.
CONTENTS.—Madame de Fiesque.—Marie Mancini.—Mademoiselle de Valois.—Madame de Chantal.—Louis XIV.—Antoine Corneille.—Charles de Simiane.—Saint-Amant.—Philippe Cospeau.—Fléchier.—Racan.

NL 0419484 ICU NIC CtY PPD

Livet, Charles Louis, 1828-1896.
Précieux et précieuses; caractères et mœurs littéraires du XVIIe siècle, par Ch. L. Livet ... Paris: Didier & Cie, 1859. 3 p.l., (i)iv-xxxvi, 442 p., 1 l. 8°.

Contents: Introduction. Madame de Rambouillet. L'abbé Cotin. Madame Cornuel. L'abbé d'Aubignac. Georges de Scudéry. Mademoiselle de Gournay. René Le Pays. Maitre Jean Grillet. Bois-Robert. Appendice.—La guirlande de Julie.

1. French literature.—History an[d] criticism, 17th century. 2. Précieuses. 3. Authors (French).
N. Y. P. L. February 28, 1917.

NL 0419485 NN WaSpG CaBVaU KMK CtY MA MH OU

Livet, Charles Louis, 1828-1897.
Précieux et précieuses; caractères et mœurs littéraires du xviiie siècle par Ch.-L. Livet. 2. éd. ... Paris, Didier et ce., 1860.
2 p. l., xxxvi, 442 p., 1 l. 18½cm.
CONTENTS.—Introduction.—Madame de Rambouillet.—L'abbé Cotin.—Madame Cornuel.—L'abbé d'Aubignac.—Georges de Scudéry.—Mlle. de Gournay.—René Le Pays.—Maitre Jean Grillet.—Bois-Robert.—Appendice: La guirlande de Julie.

1. French literature—17th cent.—Hist. & crit. 2. France—Soc. life & cust. 3. Précieuses. I. Title.

1—27927

Library of Congress PQ245.L6 1860

NL 0419486 DLC NN ODW LU

PQ 245
.L 69
LIVET,CHARLES LOUIS,1828-1897.
Précieux et précieuses; caractères et moeurs littéraires du XVIIe siècle. 2. éd. Paris, Didier et cie, 1870.
36+442 p.

1. French literature--17th cent.-- Hist & crit.
2. Précieuses.

NL 0419487 InU NcD

4PQ
Fr
1589
Livet, Charles Louis, 1828-1897.
Précieux et précieuses; caractères et moeurs littéraires du XVIIe siècle. 3. éd... Paris, H. Welter, 1895.
442 p.

MiU InStme PU
NL 0419488 DLC-P4 CtY OClW OCU OOxM OU PHC MH CU

PQ
245
L6
1895
Livet, Charles Louis, 1828-1897.
Précieux et précieuses; caratères et moeurs littéraires du XVIIe siècle. 4. éd. Paris, H. Welter, 1895.
xxxv, 442 p. 18 cm.

First edition, 1859.
Contents.- Madame de Rambouillet.- L'abbé Cotin.- Madame Cornuel.- L'abbé d'Aubignac.- Georges de Scudéry.- Mademoiselle de Gournay.- René Le Pays.- Maître Jean Grillet.- Bois-Robert.- Appendice: La guirlande de Julie.

1. French literature - 17th cent. - Hist. & crit. 2. France - Soc. life & cust. 3. Précieuses. I. Title.

NL 0419490 CU-S OrPR NcD NjP MeU

Livet, Charles Louis, 1828-1897.
... Précieux et précieuses; caractères et mœurs littéraires du xviie siècle. 3. éd. Leipzig, Paris, H. Welter, 1897.
2 p. l., xxxv, 442 p., 1 l. 22cm. (Collection de reproductions en facsimilé et de reimpressions d'ouvrages rares du xixe siècle. no. iv)
1st edition, 1859.
CONTENTS.—Madame de Rambouillet.—L'abbé Cotin.—Madame Cornuel.—L'abbé d'Aubignac.—Georges de Scudéry.—Mademoiselle de Gournay.—René Le Pays.—Maitre Jean Grillet.—Bois-Robert.—Appendice: La guirlande de Julie.

1. French literature—17th cent.—Hist. & crit. 2. France—Soc. life & cust. 3. Précieuses.

1-27928

Library of Congress PQ245.L6 1897

NL 0419491 DLC MtU NjP PHC PSC ViU

VOLUME 336

Livet, Eugène, 1820-
... L'Institution Livet et l'enseignement dans la seconde moitié du XIXe siècle. Histoire de cet établissement. Naissance de l'enseignement technique en France. Nantes, C. Mellinet, 1905.
2 p.l., [7]-64 p. 25.5 cm.

NL 0419492 CtY

LIVET, Fred.
Contribution a l'étude du role des électrolytes dans la teinture du coton par les colorants substantifs. [Thèse]. Lyon, Imp. Réunies, 1929.

NL 0419493 MH-C CtY

Livet, Georges.
Le duc Mazarin, gouverneur d'Alsace, 1661-1713; lettres et documents inédits. Paris, F.-X. Le Roux, 1954.
205 p. ports., facsim. 26 cm. (Publications de l'Institut des hautes études alsaciennes, t. 10)
Bibliography: p. [183]-201.

1. Mazarin, Armand Charles de La Porte, duc de, 1632-1713. (Series: Strasbourg. Université. Institut des hautes études alsaciennes. Publications, t. 10)

DC130.M388L5 56-20478

NL 0419494 DLC MiU TxU OU MH NNC ICU CtY IaU

Livet, Georges
Les guerres de religion (1559-1598)
Paris, Presses Universitaires de France, 19
128 p. 16 cm. (Que sais-je?)

Bibliography: p. [125]-126.

1. France - Church history - 16th cent.
I. Title.

NL 0419495 NNG

QE 268
.L 78
1938 Q
GEOLOGICAL

Livet, Georges.
... Sur le terrain houiller du Gard ... [Montpellier?] L'Auteur, 1938.
1 p.l., 298 p. incl. illus. (incl. maps, profiles) tables, diagrs. 32½cm.

Thèse - Univ. de Montpellier.
Part of the illustrative material is colored.
Reproduced from manuscript and type-written copy.
"Listes bibliographiques": p.5-14.

NL 0419496 MdBJ NNC CtY DLC-P4

Livet (Guillaume) [1856-]. *De l'emploi du carbure de calcium en chirurgie (et particulièrement dans le traitement du cancer de l'utérus). 76 pp. 4°. *Paris*, 1896, No. 403.

NL 0419497 DNLM

Livet, Guillaume, 1856-
... Miramar, l'homme aux yeux de chat. Paris, J. Tallandier [1913]
2 p. l., 300 p. 18½cm. (Les romans mystérieux) fr. 3.50

I. Title.

Library of Congress PQ2623.I 8M5 1913 14-3784

NL 0419498 DLC

Livet, Guillaume, 1865- joint author.
Bisson, Alexandre Charles Auguste, 1848-1912.
... Nick Carter; pièce en 5 actes et 8 tableaux. Paris, Librairie théâtrale, 30, rue de Grammont, 1910.

Livet, Guillaume, 1856-
... Pietro Darena, le semeur de morts. Paris, J. Tallandier, °1913.
2 p. l., 288 p. 18½cm. (Les romans mystérieux) fr. 3.50

I. Title.

Library of Congress PQ2338.L65P5 1913 13-16874

NL 0419500 DLC

PQ
2338
L785a

Livet, Guillaume Antoine François Marie
... A travers la porte; saynète en un acte en vers ... Paris, E.Dentu, 1884.
27p. 18½cm.

NL 0419501 NRU

Livet, Henri Philippe.
...Deucalion; suite magique. À la porte éternelle. Paris: La Comédie humaine, 1937. 83 p. 19½cm.

1. Poetry, French. I. Title. II. Title: À la porte éternelle.
N. Y. P. L. August 4, 1938

NL 0419502 NN

Livet, Léon de, marquis de Barville. La Tunisie; ses eaux et ses forêts. Paris. 1880. 8°. pp. [4], ii, 42.
"Fortu," pp. 11-42.

NL 0419503 MH-A

Livet, Roger.
Ici Carsicis, photos et texte par Roger Livet. Grenoble, B. Arthaud [1941]
2 p. l., 7-80, [2] p., 1 l. illus. (incl. map) 25½ x 20cm.

1. Cassis, France—Descr.—Views. I. Title.

46-40906

Library of Congress DC801.C285L5
[2] 914.491

NL 0419505 DLC ICU NN CU

Livet gaar videre. [n. p.] 1944. 20 l. illus. 28cm.
Mostly illus.

1. World war, 1939-1945— Aerial operations—Germany.
N. Y. P. L. May 6, 1949

NL 0419506 NN MH

Livet i Danmark. 1937-47—
København, A. G. Hassing.
v. illus., ports. 31 cm. decennial.
Editors: 1937-47, A. Kjerulf.—1947-57— H. Hetsch.

1. Denmark—Hist.—Christian x, 1912-1947. 2. Denmark—Civilization. I. Kjerulf, Axel, 1884- ed. II. Hetsch, Haagen, ed.

DL255.L55 52-42532 rev

NL 0419507 DLC NN MnU IEN CU

Livet i prestegaarden. Nogle volmente alvorsord naermest til landets prestefruer fra en af dem. Med forord af sogneprest E.F. Eckhoff. Kristiania, P.T. Malling, 1887.
78p. 18cm.

NL 0419508 IEN

LIVETS BOG'S BUREAU, Copenhagen.
Informilo pri Martinus. [København, Livets bog's bureau, 1946?] 20 p. 22cm.

Film reproduction. Positive.

1. Esperanto--Books in. I. Title.
Mrs. Dave H. Morris Collection

NL 0419509 NN

Livets högtider
see under Wikman, Karl Robert Vilkhad, 1886-

Livets Ord udi Doedens Stund.
see under [Hersleb, Peder] 1689-1757.

... Livets Röst.
see under [Christensen, Cai Löve] 1878-

Livett, Grevile Mairis.
The architectural history of the church of St. Leonard, Hythe. By the Rev. G. M. Livett ... London, Mitchell, Hughes and Clarke, 1913.
38 p. illus., plates (part fold.) fold. plans. 23cm.
The folded plates and plans are in pocket.
Reprinted from "Archaeologia cantiana", vol. xxx.

1. Hythe, Eng. St. Leonard's (Church)

24-8096

Library of Congress NA5471.H8L5

NL 0419513 DLC

Livett, Grevile Mairis.
Brief notes on the architecture of Rochester Cathedral church. (In Munro, A. G., and B. P. Row. Rochester & Chatham. Pp. 28-43. London. [1913?])

K9333 — Rochester Cathedral, Rochester, England.

NL 0419514 MB

Livett, Grevile Mairis.
Southwell minster. An account of the Collegiate and Cathedral Church of Southwell, architectural, archæological, and historical, by Grevile Mairis Livett... Southwell: J. Whittingham, 1883. 160 p. incl. tables. front., plan, plates. 12°.

1. Cathedrals—Gt. Br.—Eng.— Southwell.
N. Y. P. L. December 19, 1924

NL 0419515 NN

VOLUME 336

Livett, Grevile Mairis.
West Hythe church and the sites of churches formerly existing at Hythe. By the Rev. G. M. Livett ... London, Mitchell, Hughes and Clarke, 1913.
14 p. plates, 2 plans (1 fold.) 23cm. ⌊*With his* The architectural history of the church of St. Leonard, Hythe ... London, 1913⌋
Reprinted from "Archaeologia cantiana", vol. xxx.

1. West Hythe, Eng. St. Mary's (Church)

24-8099

Library of Congress NA5471.H8L5

NL 0419516 DLC

Livezey (Abraham). Lecture, introductory to the course, on the practice of medicine/to the class of the New England Female Medical College, delivered Feb. 17th, 1852. 14 pp., 1 l. 8°. *Boston, A. Mudge*, 1852.

NL 0419517 DNLM PPHa PHi

WB
L784n
1853

LIVEZEY, Abrm.
A new compendium of the principles and practice of medicine, embracing the most recent improvements in the science, by Abrm. Livezey and J. Emerson Kent. New York, Redfield, 1853.
239 p.
I. Kent, J Emerson

NL 0419518 DNLM

Livezey, Frederick M.
A recurrent - impulse generator, by Fred M. Livezey. [Cincinnati] 1951.
26 l. diagrs. 29 cm.
Thesis (Electrical Engineer) - Univ. of Cincinnati, 1951.
Bibliography: l. 25-26.

NL 0419519 OCU

Livezey, Charles Augustus.
Gatherings of the Livezey Clan, 1905-1946
see under Livezey association.

Livezey, Herman.
In unison, a new primitive in a new jungle; libretto for symphony: poems in counterpart and counterpoint. Caldwell, Idaho, Caxton Printers, 1951.
254 p. 24 cm.

I. Title.

PS3523.I 93 I 6 811.5 51-13961 ‡

NL 0419521 DLC IdU IU NcD FMU CU MB MH

Livezey, Herman.
Sleet, by Herman Livezey. Camden, N. J., The Walt Whitman foundation, 1927.
xi, 84 p. 19½cm.
Poems.

I. Title.

Library of Congress PS3523.I 93S6 1927 27-12854

NL 0419522 DLC TxU

Livezey, Robert Lee.
A comparative vertebrate ecology of typical and atypical oak areas, by Robert Lee Livezey ... ⌊Corvallis, Ore.⌋ 1943.
5 p.l., 73 numb. l. incl. illus. (mounted photos) plates, tables, diagrs. 28cm.

NL 0419523 OrCS

Thesis
1946
L787

Livezey, Robert Lee, 1920-
A synoptic key to the Salientian eggs of the United States. ⌊Ithaca, N. Y.⌋ 1946.
89 l. illus. 27 cm.

Thesis (Ph. D.) - Cornell Univ., June 1946.

1. Anura. 2. Eggs. I. Title.

NL 0419524 NIC

Livezey, Shella Cossin.
I look at life, by Shella Cossin Livezey. New York: Fortuny': ⌊1940⌋ 64 p. front. (port.) 19cm.

1. Poetry, American. I. Title.
N. Y. P. L. January 11, 1941

NL 0419525 NN

Livezey, William Edmund, 1903-
Alfred Thayer Mahan, American expansionist... by William Edmund Livezey...
⌊Columbus⌋ The Ohio state university, 1937.
2 p. l., 266 numb. l.
Thesis (Ph.D.) - Ohio state university.

NL 0419526 OU

Livezey, William Edmund, 1903–
Mahan on sea power, by William E. Livezey. Norman, University of Oklahoma press, 1947.
xiii, 334 p., 1 l. illus. (maps, facsims.) plates, ports. 22cm.
"First edition."
"Books and articles by Mahan": p. 301-311. "Selected bibliography": p. 312-326.

1. Mahan, Alfred Thayer, 1840-1914. 2. Sea-power. 3. U. S.—History, Naval. I. Title.
E182.M254 923.573 47-2156

ICJ MB MH ICU OFH TxU TU ViU
CaBViP NcRS OrPS MiU NIC NBuU MeB NcD MU KEmT PHC
NL 0419527 DLC OU NcD WaS IdPI OKentU WaSpG Or OrU

E182
.M254
1954

Livezey, William Edmund, 1903-
Mahan on sea power. Norman, University of Oklahoma press ⌊1954⌋
xiii, 334 p. illus., ports., maps, facsims. 22cm.
"Books and articles by Hanan": p. 301-311.
"Selected bibliography": p. 312-326.

1. Mahan, Alfred Thayer, 1840-1914. 2. Sea-power. 3. U. S.—History, Naval. I. Title.

NL 0419528 MB NBuC NNS

Livezey, William Edmund, 1903- joint author.

DS685
.G75

Grunder, Garel A
The Philippines and the United States, by Garel A. Grunder and William E. Livezey. ⌊1st ed.⌋ Norman, University of Oklahoma Press ⌊1951⌋

Livezey association.
Gatherings of the Livezey clan, 1905–1946. ⌊Teaneck, N. J., 1946⌋ 20 p. 23cm.
Written by Charles Augustus Livezey for the Livezey association.

1. Livezey family. I. Livezey, Charles Augustus.
N. Y. P. L. December 9, 1949

NL 0419530 NN

Livezey association.

CS71
.L7855
1934

Smith, Charles Harper, 1878–
The Livezey family, a genealogical and historical record, assembled for the Livezey association, by Charles Harper Smith. Philadelphia, Pa. ⌊George H. Buchanan company⌋ 1934.

LIVFÖRSÄKRINGSBOLAGENS SAMHÄLLSEKONOMISKA NÄMND.
Skrift.
[Stockholm] Norstedt.

NL 0419532 NN

LIVI, Carlo, 1823-1877.
Della monomania in relazione col foro criminale, e più specialmente della monomania instintiva e della follia morale. Reggio nel' Emilia, 1877.
43 p.
"Dalla Rivista sperimentale di freniatria e medicina legale, anno II."

NL 0419533 MH-L

Livi, Carlo, 1823-77.
Del Manicomio di San Niccolo di Siena e relazione statistica del quinquennio 1859-63 per il Prof. Carlo Livi, medico soprintendente. Siena, Tip. nell'Istit. dei Sordo-Muti, 1864.
25 p. incl. tables. 29½cm.

NL 0419534 MH-L

Livi (Carlo) [1823-77]. Parole dette nella solenne distribuzione de' premi agli alunni del manicomio di S. Niccolo di Siena. 11 pp. 8°. *Firenze, N. Fabbrini*, 1858.
Repr. from: Tempo. Gior. di med., chir. e sc. affini, fasc. xii.

NL 0419535 DNLM

Livi, Filiberto.
La giunta municipale e le sue attribuzioni. ⌊Cuneo⌋ Casa editrice I. C. A., 1951.
18 p. 22 cm. (Collana legislativa e amministrativa, 29)

1. Municipal corporations—Italy. 2. Municipal government—Italy. I. Title.
A 52-7458

Illinois. Univ. Libr. for Library of Congress ⌊1⌋

NL 0419536 IU

Livi, Filiberto.
Il sindaco nel diritto italiano. Como, Tip. editrice C. Nani, 1951.
62 p. 17 cm. (Biblioteca pratica "Raccolta Ostinelli," n. 157)

1. Municipal corporations—Italy. 2. Mayors—Italy. I. Title.
A 52-6753

Illinois. Univ. Library for Library of Congress ⌊1⌋†

NL 0419537 IU DLC

VOLUME 336

Livi, Giovanni, 1855- 1908.
Ancora su Piero di Dante e il Petrarca...

NL 0419538 NIC

LIVI, GIOVANNI, 1855-
La Corsica e Cosimo I de'Medici, studio storico. Firenze, Fratelli Bencici, 1885. xiii, 413 p. 22cm.

1. Corsica--For. rel. --Tuscany. 2. Tuscany--For. rel. --Corsica. 3. Cosimo I, de Medici, the Great, grand-duke of Tuscany, 1519-1574.

NL 0419539 NN MH OCl

380.92
D262l Livi, Giovanni, 1855-
Dall'archivio di Francesco Datini, mercante pratese; celebrandosi in Prato addi XVI d'agosto MDCCCCX, auspice la Pia casa de Ceppi il V centenario della morte di LUI. Firenze, Presso F. Lumachi, 1910.
v, 59 p. illus., facsims. 33 cm.

1. Datini, Francesco di Marco, 1335 (ca.)-1410. I. Title.

NL 0419540 OkU ICN MH-BA

Livi, Giovanni, 1855-
Dante: suoi primi cultori, sua gente in Bologna. Con documenti inediti, facsimili e illustrazioni figurate. — Bologna. Cappelli. 1918. xi, 291 pp. Illus. Plates. Facsimiles. Genealogical charts. 24 cm., in 8s.

M2768 — Dante Alighieri. Biog. and crit. — Bologna, Italy.

NL 0419541 MB CU CtY InU NN MoU RPB MH IU NSyU ICN

Livi, Giovanni, 1855-
... Dante e Bologna; nuovi studi e documenti. Bologna, N. Zanichelli [1921]
2 p. l., [vii]-ix p., 2 l., [3]-239 p., 2 l. incl. geneal. tables. facsims. 24cm.
Contents.—pte. 1. Sulla priorità ed antica preminenza bolognese nel culto di Dante.—pte. 2. Alighieri e Aldighieri, secondo documenti bolognesi ed altri, editi ed inediti.—pte. 3. Di alcuni personaggi della Divina commedia (I. Sul maestro Adamo e la sua patria in particolare. II. Personaggi pisani. Conti Guidi da Romena. Pier da Medicina. Fabbro dei Lambertazzi.)—Indice analitico delle persone, dei luoghi e delle cose piú notevoli.

1. Dante—Appreciation—Bologna. 2. Alighieri family. 3. Dante—Characters. I. Title.

22-11390

Library of Congress PQ4384.B7L5

NL 0419542 DLC NcD WU

Livi, Giovanni, 1855-
Gasparo da Salò e l'invenzione del violino. 19 pp. (Nuov. antol. 3 s. v. 34, 1891, p. 663.)

NL 0419543 MdBP

945.422 Livi, Giovanni, 1855-
L76g Il Guicciardini e Domenico d'Amorotto; ricerche di Giovanni Livi con XXV lettere dello storico illustre ed altri documenti inediti. Reggio d'Emilia, S. Calderini, 1875.
95p. fold.facsim.

"Lettura fatta nell'adunanza della R. Deputazione di storia patria della sotto-sezione reggiana il dì 20 agosto 1875."
"Documenti": p.[55]-95.

NL 0419544 IU

Livi, Giovanni, 1855-
Il Guicciardini e Domenico d'Amorotto, narrazione storica Nuova ed. ampliata. Bologna, G. Romagnoli, 1879.
pp. xiv, (1), 244 +.

Guicciardini|Amorotto|

NL 0419545 MH IU

PQ
4353
M63L76 Livi, Giovanni, 1855-
Maestro Feduccio de' Milotti, medico certaldese, caro a Dante in Ravenna. Castelfiorentino, Tip. Giovannelli e Carpitelli, 1927.
18 p.

Includes bibliographical footnotes.

1. Milotti, Feduccio de'. I. Title.

NL 0419546 CLU

Livi, Giovanni, 1855-
...Materie scrittorie e librarie. Firenze, Ufficio della "Rassegna nazionale", 1895.
14 p.

NL 0419547 NjP

LIVI, Giovanni, 1855-
Memorie dantesche degli anni 1323 e 1325. Da documenti inediti bolognesi. Roma, Nuova antologia, 1904.

pp. 23. Facsims. and other illustr.
"Dalla Nuova Antologia, 1° aprile 1904."
Inserted is a newspaper-cutting entitled "A Difesa d'una Congettura iconografica dantesca."

NL 0419548 MH

Livi, Giovanni. 1855—. I mercanti di seta lucchesi in Bologna nei secoli XIII e XIV. 27 pp. (Archiv. stor. ital. 4 s. v. 7, 1881, p. 29.)—Delle relazioni dei Corsi colla Repubblica fiorentina e con Giovanni de' Medici, delle Bande nere. 22 pp. (Archiv. stor. ital. 4 s. v, 13, 1884, p. 415.)—Gasparo da Salò e l'invenzione del violino. 19 pp. (Nuov. antol. 3 s. v. 34, 1891, p. 663.)

NL 0419549 MdBP

944.05 Livi, Giovanni, 1855-
N16Wli Napoleone all'isola d'Elba; secondo le carte di un archivio segreto ed altre, edite ed inedite. Milano, 1888.
316p.

NL 0419550 IU CSmH MH DLC-P4

Livi, Giovanni, 1855- Modena, 1878.
Nuovi documenti relativi a F. Petrarca .

NL 0419551 NIC

Livi, Leone.
Memorie e notizie istoriche della terra di Montecatini in Valdinievole. Firenze, G. Fiatti, 1811.
pp. 155.

Montecatini. Italy||

NL 0419552 MH CtY IU

Livi, Leone.
Memorie e notizie istoriche della terra di Montecatini in Valdinievole. Nuova ed. per cura di Giocondo Gentili. Pescia, Tip. Vannini, 1874. xv, 144 p. 21cm.

1. Montecatini di Val di Nievole, Italy—Hist. I. Gentili, Giocondo, ed. II. Gentili, Giocondo.

NL 0419553 NN

Livi, Livio, 1891-
...Cenni di statistica applicata; appendice ai "Principi di statistica," per uso degli studenti di scuole medie. Padova: Casa editrice Dott. A. Milani, 1928. iv, 42 p. incl. tables. 8°.

388731A. 1. Statistics, Vital.
N. Y. P. L. December 22, 1928

NL 0419554 NN

330.5 Livi, Livio, 1891-
GI Un censimento di Roma avanti il sacco borbonico
ser.3 [Roma, Athenaeum, 1914]
v.48 100p. tables, diagrs. [With Giornale degli economisti e rivista di statistica. ser.3,v.48. Roma, 1914]

Caption title.
Supplement to Giornale degli economisti e rivista di statistica. ser.3,v.48.

1. Rome (City)--Census.

NL 0419555 IU

GN
57
J4L5 Livi, Livio, 1891-
Gli ebrei alla luce della statistica. Caratteristiche antropologiche e patologiche ed individualità etnica. Firenze, Libreria della Voce [pref. 1918]
278 p. 20 cm.

1. Jews--Anthropometry. I. Title

NL 0419556 OCH MH MB

Livi, Livio, 1891-
...Gli Ebrei alla luce della statistica; caratteristiche antropologiche e patologiche ed individualità etnica. [v. 1–] Firenze: Libreria della Voce [1920–] v. diagr., tables. 8°.

"Un secondo volume verrà dedicato allo stato e al movimento della loro popolazione, estendendo il più possibile le ricerche ai tempi trascorsi." — Introduzione.
Bibliographical footnotes.

1. Jews. 2. Statistics (Vital), Jews.
N. Y. P. L. December 28, 1921.

NL 0419557 NN NcU MH

Livi, Livio, 1891-

Economia; rivista mensile di politica economica e di scienze sociali ... anno 1– (v. 1–); giugno 1923– Trieste, Circolo di studi economici, 1923–

Livi, Livio, 1891-
The effects of war on the population of Italy. Roma: Provveditorato generale dello stato, 1925. 8 f. incl. tables. charts. 4°.

"This paper represents a contribution by Livio Livi." — f. [2.]

626347A. 1. European war, 1914-1918—Population and the war—Italy. 2. Population—Italy, 1914-1925. I. Italy. Provveditorato generale dello stato.
N. Y. P. L. May 22, 1933

NL 0419559 NN

VOLUME 336

LIVI, Livio, 1891-
Elementi di statistica. Padova, A.Milani, 1926.

NL 0419560 MH

Livi, Livio, 1891-
Elementi di statistica. Padova, Milani, 1927.
371 p.

NL 0419561 PP

MANN HA 29 L78 Livi, Livio, 1891-
Elementi di statistica. Seconda edizione riveduta. Padova, G. Litotipo, 1929.
[9]-382 p. illus. 24 cm.

Bibliographical foot-notes.

1. Statistics. I. Title.

NL 0419562 NIC

HA 29 .L832 1932 Livi, Livio, 1891-
Elementi di statistica. 3. ed. rev. Padova, CEDAM, 1932.
409p. illus. 25cm.

1933 appears on the cover.

1. Statistics.

NL 0419563 KU

Livi, Livio, 1891-
Elementi di statistica. 8.ed. Padova, Cedam, 1948

NL 0419564 MH KU

Livi, Livio, 1891-
Elementi di statistica. 9. ed. Padova, CEDAM, 1953.
350 p. illus. 25 cm.
At head of title: Centro per la statistica aziendale.

1. Statistics.

HA29.L832 1953 54-22149 ‡

NL 0419565 DLC NN

HA29 .L832 1955 Livi, Livio, 1891-
Elementi di statistica. 10 ed. Padova, CEDAM, 1955.
379 p. illus. 25 cm.

At head of title: Centro per la statistica aziendale.

1 Statistics

NL 0419566 NjR

Livi, Livio, 1891-
... I fattori biologici dell' ordinamento sociale; introduzione alla demografia ... Padova, CEDAM, Casa editrice dott. Antonio Milani, 1937.
1 p. l., [5]-302 p., 1 l. incl. tables, diagrs. 25½cm.
Bibliographical foot-notes.

1. Sociology. 2. Demography. 3. Biology. I. Title.
A C 39-17

New York. Public library for Library of Congress [2]

NL 0419567 NN NcD NNC

[LIVI, LIVIO,] 1891-
Italy's economic and financial effort during the war. Roma: Provveditorato generale dello stato, 1925. 20 f. incl. tables. 4°.

"This paper represents a contribution by Prof. Livio Livi."—f.2.

626347A. 1. European war, 1914-1918—Economic aspects—Italy. I. Italy. Provveditorato generale dello stato.

NL 0419568 NN

Livi, Livio, 1891-
...Lezioni di demografia, con appendice sul dinamismo dei fenomeni economici. Padova: Cedam, 1936. vi, 325 p. incl. tables. illus. (charts.) 25½cm.

930786A. 1. Population.
N. Y. P. L. April 22, 1938

NL 0419569 NN

Livi, Livio, 1891-
... Nozioni di statistica e politica demografica, [di] Livio Livi. Padova, Casa editrice Dott. Antonio Milani, 1938.
1., 148 p. 25.5 cm.

NL 0419570 NcD

Livi, Livio, 1891-
... Un nuovo criterio nella valutazione degli effetti dell' emigrazione sulla razza ... Trieste, Tip. del Lloyd Triestino [1924?]
cover-title, 27 p. 24½cm.
"Estratto de 'Economia', anno II, n. 10-11, vol. V, ottobre-novembre 1924, editore il Circolo di studi economici, Trieste."

1. Italy—Emig. & immig.

Library of Congress JV8131.L5 29-634

NL 0419571 DLC

Livi, Livio, 1891-
... La previsione delle crisi e la disciplina dell' attività produttiva. Firenze, Rinascimento del libro, 1934.
117 p. incl. tables, diagrs. 27cm.
At head of title: Scuola di statistica della R. Università di Firenze.
Bibliographical foot-notes.

1. Business cycles. 2. Over-production. 3. Economic policy. I. Title.
A C 36-231

Title from N. Y. Pub. Libr. Printed by L. C.

NL 0419572 NN CtY NIC

Livi, Livio, 1891-
Prime linee par una storia demografica di Rodi e delle isole dipendenti dall'età classica ai nostri giorni. Firenze, G. C. Sansoni, 1944.
211 p. maps. 25 cm. (Università degli studi di Firenze. Centro di studi coloniali. [Pubblicazioni] 27)

1. Rhodes—Population. I. Series: Florence. Università. Centro di studi coloniali. Pubblicazioni, 27.

HB3598.R5L5 312 47-7688*

NL 0419573 DLC CU CLU MH

Livi, Livio, 1891-
Principi di statistica. 3. ed. Padova, CEDAM, 1943.
vi, 186 p. map, diagrs. 23 cm.

1. Statistics.

HA29.L55 1943 311.2 A F 47-7096*

Northwestern Univ. Libr. for Library of Congress [1]†

NL 0419574 IEN MH NN DLC

Livi, Livio, 1891-
Principi di statistica. 6. ed. Padova, CEDAM, 1953.
152 p. illus. 23 cm.

1. Statistics.

HA29.L834 1953 54-22151 ‡

NL 0419575 DLC

Livi, Livio, 1891-
...Principi di statistica ad uso degli studenti di scuole medie e delle persone colte. Padova: Casa editrice Dott. A. Milani, 1927. xii, 162 p. incl. tables. diagrs., forms. 8°.

1. Statistics—Methods.
N. Y. P. L. June 12, 1928

NL 0419576 NN MH

Livi, Livio, 1891-
...La produzione delle assicurazioni sulla vita in regime di monopolio. Trieste: C. U. Trani, 1922. 13 p. incl. tables. 8. (Circolo di studi economici, Trieste. Scritti di politica economica. no. 4.)

1. Insurance (Life), Italy. 2. Insurance (State), Italy. 3. Series.
N. Y. P. L. May 21, 1924.

NL 0419577 NN

ar X 2170 Livi, Livio, 1891-
Ricerche storico-geografiche sull'insediamento umano e sulle vicende demografiche delle isole italiane dell'Egeo. Roma Reale Accademia d'Italia, 1940.
83 p. illus., maps. 26cm.

"Estratto da 'Viaggi di studio' promossi dalla Fondazione Volta istituita dalla Società Edison di Milano, volume V."

1. Islands of the Aegean.

NL 0419578 NIC

VOLUME 336

Livi, Livio, 1891–
La rilevazione della ricchezza e del reddito nazionale; questioni concettuali e di metodo. Firenze, Edizioni del Centro per la statistica aziendale, 1952.
318 p. illus. 25 cm.
Includes bibliography.

1. Wealth. 2. Income. I. Title.
HA40.W4L5 54-24064 ‡

NL 0419579 DLC PPT NjR NN

Livi, Livio, 1891–
...Lo spirito di previdenza e il monopolio delle assicurazioni sulla vita. Trieste: C. U. Trani, 1922. 24 p. incl. tables. 8°. (Circolo di studi economici, Trieste. Scritti di politica economica. no. 1.)
Cover-title.

1. Insurance (Life), Italy. 2. Insurance (State), Italy. 3. Series.
N. Y. P. L. April 16, 1924.

NL 0419580 NN DLC

Livi, Livio, 1891–
... Trattato di demografia ... Padova, CEDAM, Casa editrice dott. A. Milani, 1940–
v. diagrs. 25cm.
Each volume has also special t.-p.
"Trattato i cui tre volumi possono dirsi uno sviluppo della ... precedente opera 'I fattori biologici dell' ordinamento sociale.' Anzi, il primo di essi ... non è, in sostanza, che una seconda edizione di questo precedente lavoro."—Pref.
Bibliographical foot-notes.
CONTENTS.—v. 1. I fattori bio-demografici nell' ordinamento sociale.—v. 2. Le leggi naturali della popolazione.

1. Demography. 2. Population. 3. Vital statistics.
HB881.L55 A F 47-2975
Illinois. Univ. Library for Library of Congress [2]†

NL 0419581 IU DNLM CU NN NjP MH NcD DLC CU

LIVI, LIVIO, 1891-
Trattato di demografia. Padova, CEDAM, 1940-41 [v.1, 1941] 2 v. diagr. 25cm.
Film reproduction. Negative.
Vol. 1-2.
Each volume has also special t.-p.

"Trattato i cui tre volumi possono dirsi uno sviluppo della... precedente opera 'I fattori biologici dell' ordinamento sociale.' Anzi, il primo di essi... non è, in sostanza, che una seconda edizione di questo precedente lavoro."--Pref.
Bibliographical footnotes.
CONTENTS.--v.1. I fattori bio-demografici nell'ordinamento sociale.--v.2. Le leggi naturali della popolazione.

1. Population.

NL 0419583 NN

Case MS 8A 91
LIVI, ORFEO
Cosi facea mio nonno? Mazurka per banda di Orfeo Livi. Bologna, 1875.
score([11]p.) 28cm.

Manuscript on paper.

NL 0419584 ICN

GN 60 .L78
Livi, Ridolfo, 1856-1920.
Antropologia nei suoi rapporti con la medicina sociale. Milano, F. Vallardi [pref. 1907]
x, 356 p. illus., tables, maps. (Trattato di medicina sociale. II: Sanità psichica.)

1. Somatology. 2. Anthropometry. I. Title.

NL 0419585 ICU DLC-P4

Livi (Ridolfo) [1856-1920]. Antropologia nei suoi rapporti con la medicina sociale. x, 356 pp. 8°. Milano, F. Vallardi [1908].
Forms pt. 8 of Sanità psichica, diretta da A. Tamburini.

NL 0419586 DNLM

WA T776 pt. 2 v. 2 1910
LIVI, Ridolfo, 1856-1920.
Antropologia nei suoi rapporti con la medicina sociale. Milano, Vallardi [1910]
x, 356 p. illus. (Trattato di medicina sociale, pt. 2 [v. 2])
Series

NL 0419587 DNLM

Livi, Ridolfo, 1856–1920.
... Antropometria ... Con 33 incisioni. Milano, U. Hoepli, 1900.
3 p. l., 237 p. incl. illus., tables, diagrs. 15½cm. (Manuali Hoepli)

1. Anthropometry.

Library of Congress GN51.L78 5-5249

NL 0419588 DLC MB DNLM ICJ DSI

GN 58 .I8 L78
Livi,Ridolfo,1856-1920.
Antropometria militare. Risultati ottenuti dallo spoglio dei fogli sanitarii dei militari delle classi 1859-63,eseguito dall'Ispettorato di sanità militare per ordine del Ministero della guerra. Incaricato della direzione dei lavori d.r Ridolfo Livi ... Roma, Presso il Giornale medico del regio esercito, 1896-1905.
2 v. illus.(maps,diagrs.) diagrs.on VIII pl. (part fold.) 30½cm. and atlas of XXIII (i.e.28) pl.(maps, part fold.,and fold.diagrs.) 30½ x 25cm.
"Indice degli autori citati": v.1,verso of third prelim.leaf; v.2,p.[vi].

NL 0419589 MiU MnU IEN DNLM MB ICU MH NIC DSI CU

LIVI, Ridolfo, 1856-1920.
Dello sviluppo del corpo (statura e perimetro toracico) in rapporto co professione e colla condizione sociale.
Roma. Voghera. 1897. 40 pp. Tables. 8°.

Sheet D 1085 Dec. 10, 1898

NL 0419590 MB MH DNLM CtY

LIVI, Ridolfo, 1856-1920.
Note di statistica antropometrica italiana-Classificazione delle stature e determinazione della statura media dei coscritti delle leve diterra negli anni 1875-79. per ogni circondari del regno Tarole.

Plates. (In ANNALDI statistica. Ser.3a,1883, VIII. 119-156.)

NL 0419591 MH

Livi, Ridolfo, 1856–1920.
Saggio dei risultati antropometrici ottenuti dallo spoglio dei fogli sanitarii delle classi 1859–1863, eseguito all'Ispettorato di sanità militare sotto la direzione del dott. Ridolfo Livi ... Roma, E. Voghera, 1894.
48 p. incl. tables, diagrs. 6 fold. maps. 31½cm.
"Presentato in omaggio ai membri della XIV sezione del XI Congresso medico internazionale—(Roma, 1894)"

1. Anthropometry—Italy.

Library of Congress GN58.I 8L58 30-245

NL 0419592 DLC MB DNLM

LIVI, Ridolfo, 1856-1920.
Saggio di geografia del militarismo in Italia.
Torino. Roux, Frassati & co. 1897. 12 pp. Maps. 8°.

NL 0419593 MB

HT1191 .L75
LIVI,RIDOLFO,1856-1920.
...La schiavitù domestica nei tempi di mezzo e nei moderni;ricerche storiche di un antropologo. Padova, A.Milani,1928.
xii,348 p.incl.front.(port.) 23cm.
Bibliographical foot-notes.

1.Slavery in Italy.

NL 0419594 ICU OrU CtY

Livi, Ridolfo, 1856-1920.
Sulla interpretazione delle curve seriali in antropometria. Rome, Tip. dell'unione cooperativa editrice, 1895.
34 p.

NL 0419595 PU-Mu

GN L785s 1884
LIVI, Ridolfo, 1856-1920
Sulla statura degli italiani; studio statistico antropologico. Firenze, Arte della stampa, 1884.
79 p. illus.
Cover title.

NL 0419596 DNLM

LIVI, Rodolfo, 1856-1920.
Sullo sviluppo del dente del giudizio.
= Torino. Bruno. [1894.] 7 pp. Chart. 8°.
Reprinted from Atti della società romana di antropologia, vol. 1 [*3822.90.1].

NL 0419597 MB

Livi, Ridolfo, 1856-1920
——. La vaccinazione nell' esercito e l' antivaccinismo. 2. ed. 83 pp. 8°. Roma, 1899.

NL 0419598 DNLM

Livi, Rūbin
see
Levy, Reuben.

Livi, Thomas
see
Levi, Thomas.

Livi, Yves
see
Montand, Yves, 1921-

Livi, Yvo
see his stage name
Montand, Yves, 1921-

VOLUME 336

Livi-Prûvansâl, I
see
Lévi-Provençal, Évariste, 1894-1956.

LIVIABELLA, LINO, 1902-
La giornata di Lucio; suite facile per pianoforte. Milano, Suvini-Zerboni [c1947] 7 p. illus. 31cm.
CONTENTS.--Lucio si sveglia.--Lucio studia.--Lucio giuoca.--Lucio ha sonno.
1. Children's music (Piano) I. Title.

NL 0419604 NN

M1002 .L68 M6 Liviabella, Lino, 1902-
[Monte Mario]
Monte Mario, poema sinfonico per orchestra. [Milano, Ricordi [c1939] score (68p.) 29cm.
Duration: 15 min.

NL 0419605 NcU

---

fM2114.5 L5N5 Liviabella, Lino, 1902-
Ninna nanna al bambino Gesù, per voce infantile e pianoforte. Parole e musica di Lino Liviabella. Milano, Edizioni Suvini Zerboni [1948]
8p. 31cm.
For voice and piano.
Duration: 4 min.
1. Sacred songs (Medium voice) with piano. 2. Christmas music. I. Title.

NL 0419606 IaU

LIVIABELLA, LINO, 1902-
Il presepio; sei composizioni brevi per pianoforte. Milano, Suvini Zerboni [c1945] 20 p. illus. 32cm.
CONTENTS.--Le stradine d'argento.--La pecorella.--I Bambini.--La stella cometa.--I re magi.--La ninna nanna della Madonna.
1. Christmas music (Piano) 2. Piano. I. Title.

NL 0419607 NN

LIVIABELLA, LINO, 1902-
Quartetto in fa minore. Milano, Edizioni Suvini Zerboni [c1940] score (21 p.) and 4 parts. 32cm.
Duration: 15 min.
MOVEMENTS.--Allegro.--Andante nostalgico.--Allegro.
1. Chamber music, 20th cent. --Quartets. 2. Violin in quartets (2 violins, viola, violoncello)

NL 0419608 NN MB

LIVIABELLA, LINO, 1902-
Riderella; fiaba musicale per pianoforte a quattro mani. Milano, Suvini-Zerboni [c1949] 39 p. illus. 32cm.
For piano, 4 hands.
CONTENTS.--Il ruscello.--La fuga nel mare.--La città azzurra.--Il pianto di Riderella.--La pietà del sole.--Il ruscello.
1. Children's music (Piano, 4 hands) I. Title.

NL 0419609 NN

Liviabella, Lino, 1902-
[Sonata ciclica, violoncello & piano]
... Sonata ciclica, per violoncello e pianoforte ... Milano [etc.] G. Ricordi & c.; New York, G. Ricordi & co., inc.; [etc., etc.] 1939.
1 p. l., 26 p. and pt. 34½cm.
Publisher's plate no.: 124448.
1. Violoncello and piano music.
46-33343
Library of Congress M233.L6886

NL 0419610 DLC

Liviabella, Lino, 1902-
... Sonata in un tempo, per violino e pianoforte ... Milano [etc.] G. Ricordi & c.; New York, G. Ricordi & co., inc.; [etc., etc.] 1940.
1 p. l., 17 p. and pt. 34½cm.
Publisher's plate no.: 124666.
Score (violin and piano) and part.
Performance time, 10 minutes.
1. Sonatas (Violin and piano)
46-34297
Library of Congress M219.L79S6

NL 0419611 DLC

LIVIABELLA, LINO, 1902-
Suite-giocattolo; quadretti pianistici per bambini piccolissimi. Milano, Suvini Zerboni [c1953] 19 p. illus. 31cm.
For piano, for 2, 3 or 4 hands.
CONTENTS.--La gocciolina.--Il tamburino.--Valzer.--Cucù.--Le campane (omaggio a Mussorgsky)--Capriccetto finale.
1. Children's music (Piano, 2 hands) 2. Children's music (Piano, 3 hands) 3. Children's music (Piano, 4 hands) I. Title.

NL 0419612 NN

Hd66 L140 Liviah, Cino
... La fata delle stelle (fiabe). Milano, Bietti[1921?]
189p.,1l. illus. 18½cm.
Contents. - La fata delle stelle. - Stellino. - Barbabianca. - Trillino e Trillina. - Il flauto magico. - Stelluccio e Stelluccia.

NL 0419613 CtY

Livian, Marcel.
... L'entente balkanique et l'après-guerre actuelle. Paris, Librairie générale de droit & de jurisprudence, 1940.
2 p. l., 188 p. 25cm.
Imprint date changed in ms. to 1942.
"Bibliographie générale": p. [183]-185.
1. Balkan entente, 1934- I. Title.
45-34028
Library of Congress D465.L5
[2] 949.6

NL 0419614 DLC CtY MH-L MiU NN CU

Livian, Marcel.
Le régime juridique des étrangers en France; recueil des lois, décrets et arrêtés en vigueur, commentaires et renseignements pratiques avec une introduction sur l'histoire des étrangers en France et une étude sur les différents aspects de la question des étrangers, par Marcel Livian ... Préface de Marius Moutet ... Paris, Librairie générale de droit & de jurisprudence, R. Pichon et R. Durand-Auzias, administrateurs, 1936.
vii, 234 p., 1 l. 23cm.
Bibliographical foot-notes.
1. Aliens—France. I. France. Laws, statutes, etc. II. Title.
A C 37-227
New York. Public library for Library of Congress [2]

NL 0419615 NN ICU IU NBuU-L

Augustan DA 503 .L74
Livia's [i.e. Caroline Wilhelmina's] advice to Augustus [i.e. George II] persuading clemency in the case of Cinna, who, was taken in actual rebellion against the government. Collected from the Roman historians ... London, Printed for T. Payne, 1722.
vii, 32 p.
A political satire.

NL 0419616 InU OClWHi

Livido, Fisonio, *pseud.*
Transcorso politico di Fisonio Livido disinteressato, circa gli affari per gl' Vscocchi infra la signoria, & l'arciduca, oltre gl'addotti dal Borone, Tordisiglia, Vrbani Minucio, & altri. [n. p., 1613?]
[32] p. 22cm.
Signatures: A-F⁴, G².
1. Uskoks.

NL 0419617 MiU

[Livie, John]
Graecae linguae conjugationes; temporibus suis quibusque locis ita dispositis, ut simplici fere intuitu eorundem cernatur formatio. In usum ... Annae Damer. Londini, 1791.
1p.l.,69p. 24cm.
"Composed by the celebrated scholar Livie; published for presents only": Martin, Bibl. cat. of privately printed books. 2d ed. p.215.

NL 0419618 CtY

Livie-Noble, F S
The school psychologist. London, Duckworth [1947]
256 p. 19cm.
Bibliography: p. 248-252.
1. Educational psychology. I. Title.
LB1051.L73 370.15 47-27206*

NL 0419619 DLC CaBVaU WaU OU CtY NNC

Rare Book Room Hd29 L761 A8 Liviera, Giovanni Battista, b. 1565.
Apologia di Gio. Battista Liviera contro l'eccell.te Sig. Favstino Svmmo Padovano. Intorno alle tragedie di lieto fine. In Padova,Appresso Lorenzo Pasq. impressor della Mag: Vniu. de Legisti.1590.
[24]p. 20cm.
The printer surname was Pasquati.
Signatures: A-C⁴.

NL 0419620 CtY

PQ4627 .L55C9 1588 Rare Bk Liviera, Giovanni Battista, b.1565.
Cresfonte, tragedia ... Padova, P. Meietto, 1588.
[8], 48 l. 14cm.
Title vignette (printer's device?); initials.

NL 0419621 ICU ICN MH

Liviera, Giovanni Battista, b. 1565.
Il Cresfonte; tragedia. (In: Scelta di rare e celebri tragedie. [Venezia, 1731] 8°. p. 1-88.)
1. Drama (Italian). 2. Title.
N. Y. P. L. March 7, 1912.

NL 0419622 NN

VOLUME 336

x854L76 Liviera, Giovanni Battista, b.1565.
0g Givstina vergine, e martire santissima, hierotragedia. Serraualle di Vinetia, M. Claseri, 1590.
58l. 14cm.

NL 0419623 IU

PQ4627 Liviera, Giovanni Battista, b.1565.
.L5506 Givstina vergine e martire santissima, hiero-
1605 tragedia ... Serraualle di Vinetia, M. Claseri,
Rare 1605.
Bk 58 l. 13cm.
Title vignette.

1. Justina of Padua, Saint, 1st cent.--Drama. I. Title.

NL 0419624 ICU

LIVIERA, GIOVANNI BATTISTA, b. 1565.
Risposta per lo ecc: Sig. Favstino Svmmo Padovano all'apologia del Signor Giovan Battista Liviera Vicentino. In Padova, appresso Lorenzo Pasquati, 1590.
14 numb.l. 4to

Bound with Summo, F. Dve discorsi l'vno intorno contrasto tra il S. Speron Speroni Padova, 1590.

NL 0419625 InU

Livierato (P[anagine] E.) [1860-]. Cause del battito cardiaco e varie teorie emesse. 32 pp. 8°. *Milano, F. Vallardi*, [1900].
Forms no. 28 of: Confer. clin. ital., Milano, 1900, 449.

NL 0419626 DNLM

QZ LIVIERATO, Panagine E., 1860-
T776 Malattie dell'apparato circolatorio.
v.4 Milano [190-?]
1900 (In Trattato completo di patologia e terapia speciale medica, diretto dal prof. Achille de Giovanni. Milano. [v. 4] p. 1-265)
Series: Trattato completo di patologia e terapia speciale medica [v. 4]

NL 0419627 DNLM

PA5610
.L575E3 Livieratos, P E
1877 'Η ἐκδίκησις. Δρᾶμα εἰς πέντε πράξεις. 'Εν Κεφαλληνία, 1877.
63 p. 23cm.

NL 0419628 OCU

Livieratos, Spyridon, 1908-
... Le seuil rénal du glycose chez les diabétiques; notions théoriques; son intérêt pratique pour le diagnostic et la conduite du traitement ... Paris, 1936.
Thèse - Univ. de Paris.
"Bibliographie": p. [167]-178.

NL 0419629 CtY DNLM

Livieres de Artecona, Raquel.
... La cocinera paraguaya (libro adoptado como texto oficial para las escuelas públicas por resolución del h. Consejo nacional de educación) Asunción, La Colmena s. a., 1931.
111 p. 21cm.

1. Cookery, Paraguayan. I. Title.

45-51001

Library of Congress TX725.L53

NL 0419630 DLC TxU DPU

641.55892
A786m Livieres de Artecona, Raquel.
La moderna cocina paraguaya. Asunción [Zamphiropolos] 1952.
161p.

"Libro adoptado como texto oficial para las escuelas públicas por resolución del Consejo Nacional de Educación."

1. Cookery, Paraguayan. I. Title.

NL 0419631 ICarbS

Livigni, Filippo.
ML50
.2
.C677C5 Cimarosa, Domenico, 1749-1801.
1794 [Il convito. Libretto. Italian]
Case
Il convito; dramma giocoso per musica. Udine, Ristampato per il Murero [1794]

Livigni, Filippo.
ML50
.2
.C677C5 Cimarosa, Domenico, 1749-1801.
1796 [Il convito. Libretto. Italian & Portuguese]
Case
Il convito; dramma giocoso per musica. Lisbona, nella Stamperia di S. T. Ferreira, 1796.

Livigni, Filippo.
I due castellani burlati
see under Fabrizi, Vincenzo, b. 1765.

Livigni, Filippo. La frascatana.
ML50
.2
.F84P2 Paisiello, Giovanni, 1740-1816.
1782 [La frascatana. Libretto. German]

La frascatana. Ein singspiel in drey aufzügen. Die musick von Paisello. [n. p.] 1782.

Livigni, Filippo. La Frascatana.
ML50
.2
.F84P217 Paisiello. Giovanni, 1740-1816.
[La Frascatana. Libretto. German]

La Frascatana; oder, Das Mädchen von Fraskati. Ein Singspiel in drey Aufzügen. Die Musik von Paisello. [n. p.] 1782.

Livigni, Filippo. Giannina e Bernardone.
ML50
.C578G5 Cimarosa, Domenico, 1749-1801.
1932 [Giannina e Bernardone. Libretto. Italian]

Giannina e Bernardone; dramma giocoso in due atti di Filippo Livigni. Sesto San Giovanni, A. Barion, 1932.

Livigni, Filippo.
La moglie capricciosa ...
see under Gazzaniga, Giuseppe, 1743-1818.

Livigni, Filippo.
Puntigli gelosi; dramma giocoso per musica. Venezia, M. Fenzo, 1783.
pp. 62 +.

NL 0419639 MH

Livigni, Filippo.
I viaggiatori felici...
see under Anfossi, Pasquale, 1727-1797.

Livii, Tit
see
Livius, Titus.

Liviā
see
Libya.

DL 750 LIVIJN, CLAS, 1781-1844
.L 7 A4 Bref, från fälttågen i Tyskland och Norge 1813 och 1814; utg. med en inledning af Johan Mortensen. Stockholm, Ljus, 1909.
270 p.

1. Livijn, Clas, 1781-1844.

NL 0419644 InU CtY MnU MH

[Livijn, Clas, 1781-1844]
*GC8 Pique-Dame. Berichte aus dem Irrenhause in
L1937 Briefen ... Nach dem Schwedischen von L. M.
825ib Fouqué.
Berlin, bei August Rücker. 1826.

xvi, 200p. 18.5cm.
Translation of his Spader Dame, 1824.

NL 0419645 MH

FILM Livijn, Clas, 1781-1844.
839.73 Pique-Dame. Berichte aus dem Irrenhause in
L76sGl Briefen. Nach dem Schwedischen von L. M. Fouqué. Berlin, A. Rücker, 1826.
200p.
Translation of Spader dame; en berättelse i brev funne på danviken.
Microfilm (negative) Berlin, Deutsche Staatsbibliothek, Reprographische Abt., 1970.
1 reel. 35mm.
Microfilm imperfect: p.20-21 and 62-63 are out of order and inserted at end; p.36-37 are missing.

NL 0419646 IU

VOLUME 336

PT9774 Livijn, Clas, 1781-1844.
A1 Samlade skrifter. Utgifne af Adolf Iwar Arwidsson.
1850 Orebro, N.M. Lindh, 1850-52.
2 v.

I. Arwidsson, Adolph Ivar, 1791-1850.

NL 0419647 CU WaU CtY

LIVIJN, Clas, 1781-1844.
Spader Dame, en berättelse i bref funne pa
Danviken. [Stockholm, 1909.]

pp. 80.
"Bihang" to Mila Hallman,Clas Livijn,
Separately paged.

NL 0419648 MH

PT9774 Livijn, Clas, 1781-1844.
S7 Spader dame; en berättelse i brev funne på Danviken. Förord
1953 av Bo Grandien. Illustrerad av Gunnar Brusewitz. Stockholm,
Wahlström & Widstrand [1953]
135 p. illus., port.

NL 0419649 CU IU MnU

Livijn, Klas Johan
see
Livijn, Clas, 1781-1844.

Livin, Saint.
see
Lebwin, Saint, d. ca. 773.

Livin, Antwerp
see
Lathem, Lievin van, d. 1492 or 3.

Livin, Claudius, Joh., respondent.
... Dissertatio academica, de Cannensi Pugna..
see under Ekerman, Petrus, 1696-(7)-
1783, praeses.

Livin, Magnus Claudii.
*De sanctimonia templorum, quod consentiente
amplissimo ordine ... praeside ... Fabiano
Törner ... examini modeste submittit ...
M.C. Livin, Ostrogothus ... 1729 ... solitis.
Upsaliae, Werner [1729]
2 p.l., 44 p. 2 l. 8°.

NL 0419654 NN

LIVINEC, Jean.
Le nouveau régime des ports de commerce auto-
nomes. La question des ports francs. Thèse,
Rennes. Morlaix, Imp. Hamon, [1925].

pp. 54.
"Bibliographie", pp. [5-7].

NL 0419655 MH CtY

Livinec (Jean) [1884-]. *Les infections à
tétragènes. 81 pp. 8°. Montpellier, 1911.
No. 87

NL 0419656 DNLM CtY

Livineius, Joannes
see Lievens, Jan, 1546(ca.)-1599.

Livinejus, Johannes
see Lievens, Jan, 1546(ca.)-1599.

Living. v. 1- Jan. 1939-
[Menasha, Wis., etc., The National conference on family relations, 1939-
v. 27cm. quarterly.

1. Social problems—Period. 2. Family. 3. Marriage. I. National
conference on family relations.

42-51034

Library of Congress HQ1.L5
[5] 392.05

NL 0419659 DLC DNLM NcD

Living; community magazine for Bay Shore, Babylon, Bright-
waters, Amityville, Lindenhurst, Copiague, the Islips.
v. 1

Bay Shore, Great South Bay pub. corp., 1948
v. illus. 31cm.

Weekly, June 19-July 17, 1948; biweekly, Aug. 7-
Subtitle varies.

1. Periodicals—U. S.
N. Y. P. L. March 13, 1950

NL 0419660 NN

Living ... devoted to man and his transcendental nature.
v. 1-2; Dec. 1936-Dec. 1938. [New York, Living associates,
The School of applied philosophy, 1936-38]
2 v. in 1. illus., diagrs. 28cm. monthly (except July-Aug.)

Photolithographed.
No number issued for Dec. 1937.
Edited by May B. Mayer.
No more published?

I. Mayer, May (Benzenberg) ed. II. New York. School of applied
philosophy.

41-40816

Library of Congress BF1995.L65
[2] [159.913205] 131.3205

NL 0419661 DLC OrCS

The Living age. v. 1-360; May 11, 1844-Aug. 1941. New
York, The Living age company, inc.; [etc., etc., 1844-1941]
360 v. illus. (incl. ports., maps) plates. 22½-30½cm.

Weekly, 1884-Sept. 1926; semimonthly, Oct. 1926-Apr. 1928; monthly,
May 1928-Aug. 1929; semimonthly, Sept. 1929-July 1930; monthly, Aug.
1930-1941.
Vols. 37-56 called also ser. 2, v. 1-20; v. 57-88, ser. 3, v. 1-32; v. 89-
115, ser. 4, v. 1-27; v. 116-199, ser. 5, v. 1-84; v. 200-218, ser. 6, v. 1-19;
v. 219-287, ser. 7, v. 1-69; v. 288-331, ser. 8, v. 1-44.
1844-96 have title: Littell's living age.
Vols. 1-334 were published in Boston.
Absorbed Every Saturday: a journal of choice reading, in Nov. 1874.
No more published.

L. C. set incomplete: Apr. 6, June 1, 1918; Mar.-Aug. 1939 wanting.
Indexes:
Vols. 1-100, 1844-Mar. 1869.

I. Littell, Eliakim, 1797-1870. II. Littell, Robert S., 1831-1896.
III. Title: Littell's living age.

4-12671 Revised

Library of Congress AP2.L65

FM CtNIC MnNC MnU CoU ViU-L MoCA MdU
OrSaW WaT WaSp MtU OrCS OrLgE OrAshS OrU WaTC PU
OClWHi NIC PPL CU-M CaBVaU CaBVa CaBViP COMC CSfH
MB OOxM MiU OCU NjP NcD OU PU PHi PV PSC PBm CCC
NL 0419663 DLC AzTes MWH MeB DSI NN GEU Nc PHC Nh

The Living age.

The Eclectic magazine; foreign literature. v. 1-63, 1844-64;
[v. 64-121] (new ser. v. 1-68), 1865-98; v. 132-145 (3d ser.
v. 1-14), 1899-1905; v. 146-147, v. 148 no. 1-6, 1906-June
1907. New-York and Philadelphia, Leavitt, Trow & co.;
[etc., etc.] 1844-1907.

AI 3 The living age. (Indexes)
.G8
no. 5 [Griswold, William McCrillis] 1853-1899, comp.
A general index to vols. I-XCVI [of the Eclectic magazine and
to v. 37-148 of the Living age] Bangor, Me., Q. P. index, 1881.

PS625 The Living age.
.L78 Plays,synopses,etc.from the Living age. At-
Atkinson kinson collection.
Coll. 3 nos. 19-24cm.

For individual entries see the Atkinson card
catalog.

NL 0419667 ICU

[Living American art, inc., New York]
[Color plates of American paintings] [New York, 1939]
4 p.l., 34 col'd pl. 54cm.

"Some notes about the artists included," 4 p. mounted on prelim. leaf 3-4.
Bound by The New York public library, 1942.

156816B. 1. Paintings, U. S.
N. Y. P. L. March 6, 1942

NL 0419668 NN

Living American art, inc.
Contemporary American artists; portfolio of
color prints.
New York, c1936-39.

NL 0419669 OClW

VOLUME 336

f759.1 L76f Living American art, inc., New York.
Famous American paintings. [New York] Living American art [1941?]
8 col.pl.

Issued in portfolio; title from cover.
"An explanation of the price of this portfolio and some notes about the artists included" ([4]p.) laid in.

1. Paintings, American. 2. Artists, American. I. Title.

NL 0419670 IU MiD

Living American Art, Inc.
First portfolio of color reproductions of paintings. Living American Art, Inc.

NL 0419671 OrU

Living American art, Inc.
July portfolio of 2 prints: Kantor, Morris: Still Life Strater, Henry: Winter in the Verde Valley. Living American Art.

NL 0419672 OrU

Living and learning (*Radio program*)
Widening horizons; the broadcast discussions in the series "Living and learning" describing the aims and purpose of education. With foreword by P. R. Morris ... Worcester [Eng.] Littlebury and company ltd. [1943]
2 p. l., 9-127 p. 19cm.
"These twelve discussions were broadcast during January and April, 1943, in the Home service of the British broadcasting corporation."—p. 10.

1. Education—Aims and objectives. 2. Education—Gt. Brit. I. Title.
44-26357
Library of Congress LB775.L56
[3] 370.1

NL 0419673 DLC

RA380.5 L786 Living and moving or horses railways & coaches. London: Darton and Clark [ca.1860] [28]p.col.illus.21cm.

Cover-title.
Illustrated end papers.
Original blue printed wrappers.

1. Children's lit. (RA cat only)
2. Transportation--Juvenile literature.

NL 0419674 OC ICN

The living and the dead
see under [Neale, Erskine] 1804-1883.

The living and the dead: a letter to the people of England, on the state of their churchyards, with practicable suggestions on their improvement. By a philanthropist. London, Whittaker & co. [etc., etc.] 1841. 81 p. 21cm.

1. Dead—Care and disposal—Gt. Br. I. A philanthropist.
N. Y. P. L. May 9, 1949

NL 0419676 NN DNLM

The living animals of the world, a popular natural history
see under Cornish Charles John, 1859-1906.

Living art; Chardin, Ingres, Delacroix, Corot, Daumier, Bresdin, Guys, Van Gogh, Gauguin, Rousseau, le Douanier, Picasso, Delaunay, Rouault ... [New York, J. B. Neumann, 193-?]
[48] p. illus. 25½cm. (The art lover library. II)
"A note to collectors of art" (p. [46]-[48]) signed: J. B. Neumann.

1. Paintings, French—Catalogs. I. Neumann, Jsrael Ber, 1887-
39-3604
Library of Congress ND541.L5
[2] 759.4

NL 0419678 DLC

Living art: Chardin, Ingres, Delacroix, Corot, Daumier, Bresdin, Guys, Van Gogh, Gauguin, Rousseau, le douanier, Picasso, Delaunay, Rouault... [New York: Printed by M. Spiegel, inc., 1930?] 25 l. illus. 26cm. (The art lover library ... v. 2.)

Text and full page illus. on opposite pages.
"A note to collectors of art" signed: J. B. Neumann.

1. Paintings—Catalogues. I. Title. II. Ser.
N. Y. P. L. July 2, 1940

NL 0419679 NN

Living art; twenty facsimile reproductions after paintings, drawings and engravings and ten photographs, after sculpture by contemporary artists. New York: Dial Pub. Co. [1923.] 2 v. plates. f°.

Printed in Germany.
no. 129 of 500 copies printed.

J. S. BILLINGS MEM. COLL.
1. Paintings.—Reproductions. 2. Prints.—Reproductions. 3. Sculpture. 4. Artists.—Biography.
N. Y. P. L. July 2, 1924

NL 0419680 NN PPiU ICU NRU MWelC MH

The Living arts, a portfolio reflecting the literary and artistic taste of our time. no. 1-
Oct. 1921-
New York [etc.] C. Nast [1921-
v. illus. (part col.) plates (part col.) 24½cm. bimonthly.
Editors: Oct. 1921- Lucien Vogel, Michel Dufet.
"Printed in Paris at the press of George Lang."

1. Art—Period. I. Vogel, Lucien, 1886- ed. II. Dufet, Michel, ed.
25-540
Library of Congress AP2.L7

NL 0419681 DLC NhD NIC

Living authors; a book of biographies
see under [Kunitz, Stanley Jasspon] 1905- ed.

Living authors at the New York bar
see under [Guernsey, Rocellus Sheridan] 1836-1918.

The living Bible (B. Hall, ed.)
see under Bible. English. Selections. 1928. Authorized. Also with dates 1937, 1938.

The living Bible (R.O. Ballou, ed.)
see under Bible. English. Selections. 1952. Authorized.

Living biographies of great composers...
see under Thomas, Henry, 1886-

Living biographies of great scientists
see under Thomas, Henry, 1886-

Living Catholic authors
see under Webster Groves, Mo. Gallery of living Catholic authors.

Living catholic authors past and present
see under Schuster, George N

DS710 L785 The Living China; a pictoral record.
-
Shanghai, Liang You Print. & Pub. Co.
v. illus. (part col.) ports. (part mounted col.) plans. 32cm. annual.
Added t.-p. in Chinese (transliterated): Chung-kuo ta-kuan t'u-hua nien-chien.
Hoover Library
Chinese and English.
Editors: 19 - Wu Luen Tak [and others]
1. China - Views. I. Wu, Lien-tê, 1879- ed. II. Title: Chung-kuo ta-kuan t'u-hua nien-chien.

NL 0419690 CSt-H OrP Or

XB56 L785 The living Christ ... New York, Warren and Wyman [n.d.]
46p. 15cm.
"Originally published in the 'Church monthly'."

NL 0419691 NNUT

The living Christ. [New York? 1893]
see under [Bentley, John Theo. Doré]

The living Christ.

PN6120 .E2L4 Lehman, Valerie (Robertson) 1895-
The living Christ, a sacred pageant for Easter, by Valeria R. Lehman; music by I. H. Meredith ... New York, N. Y., Tullar-Meredith co., °1934.

The living Christ and other tracts
see under American tract Society.

There are no cards for numbers
NL 0419695 to NL 0420000

VOLUME 336

The Living church. v. 1- 1878-
Chicago, C. W. Leffingwell ⌐etc., 1878–1900⌐; Milwaukee, Wis., The Young churchman company; ⌐etc., etc.⌐ 1900-

v. illus., plates. 34–37½cm (v. 1, no. 28–v. 7: 50½cm) weekly.

Editors: 1878–79, S. S. Harris, John Fulton.—May 17, 1879–Jan. 27, 1900, C. W. Leffingwell.—Feb. 3, 1900- F. C. Morehouse.
Absorbed Our diocese in Feb. 1880.

1. Protestant Episcopal church in the U. S. A.—Period. I. Harris, Samuel Smith, bp., 1841–1888, ed. II. Fulton, John, 1834–1907, ed. III. Leffingwell, Charles Wesley, 1840–1928, ed. IV. Morehouse, Frederic Cook, 1868–1932, ed.

22—25331

Library of Congress BX5800.L

MH-AH NcD MB
NL 0420001 DLC WHi ICRL CtY-D I MoSC KyLxCB FDS OC1

The Living church.

Morehouse, Clifford P *ed.*
The Anglican communion throughout the world; a series of missionary papers from the field, reprinted from the Living church and edited by Clifford P. Morehouse ... Milwaukee, Wis., Morehouse publishing co.; London, A. R. Mowbray & co. ⌐°1927⌐

BX5995 The Living church.
.K4L7 Bishop Kemper centennial number.
⌐Milwaukee, Wis., 1935.
p.⌐249⌐-264. illus.(incl.ports.,facsim.,) 31cm.

Extracted from the Living church, vol. 93,no.12, September 21, 1935.

NL 0420003 MnHi

THE LIVING CHURCH
The church in Oregon. ⌐744 N. Fourth St., Milwaukee, Wis., Author, 1942⌐
42 p. illus.

Special issue of The Living church, June 7, 1942.

NL 0420004 Or

The Living church.
A draught outpoured; an anthology of Anglican verse; poems published in "The Living church", 1924–1934, edited by Portia Martin. Milwaukee, Wis., Morehouse publishing co. ⌐°1934⌐

xii, ⌐1⌐, 142 p. 19cm.

1. Religious poetry. 2. Poetry—Collections. I. Martin, Portia, ed. II. Title. III. Title: Anglican verse.

35-82

Library of Congress PR1191.L5
——— Copy 2.
Copyright A 77716 ⌐2⌐ 811.50822

NL 0420005 DLC WaWW

The Living church.

The Layman's magazine of the Living church. v. 1-
Feb. 1940-
⌐Milwaukee, Morehouse-Gorham co., 1940-

The Living church.
Lyrics of the Living church; original poems compiled from "The Living church", edited by C. W. Leffingwell. Chicago, A. C. McClurg and company, 1891.

xviii, ⌐19⌐-275 p. incl. front., illus. 19½cm.

1. Religious poetry, American. I. Leffingwell, Charles Wesley, 1840–1928, ed. II. Title.

34-40198

Library of Congress PS595.R4L4
Copyright 1891: 37876 811.0822

NL 0420007 DLC WaS NBuG OC1

Living Church, The.
The Story of the Round Table Conference that preceded the general convention of 1910. Being a reprint of two editorials printed in the Living Church of Jan. 14 and 21, 1911, respectively. Milwaukee: Young Churchman Co., 1913. 22 p. 8°.

1. Protestant Episcopal Church in the U. S. of America.—History, 1910. 2. Protestant Episcopal Church in the U. S. of America.—Name.
N. Y. P. L. September 3, 1914.

NL 0420008 NN

A living church; the first hundred years of the Brick Church in Rochester
see under Hallock, Gerard Benjamin Fleet, 1856- ed.

The Living church annual
see **The Episcopal Church** annual.

Living church annual and churchman's almanac.
see
Episcopal Church annual.

The Living church. General convention daily. v. 1, no. 1-14; Sept. 10–Oct. 24, 1934. ⌐Camden, N. J., Morehouse publishing co.⌐ 1934.

1 v. illus. (incl. ports.) 40½cm. daily (except Sunday)

Caption title.
No. 1 is a pre-convention issue; no. 2 is dated Oct. 10, 1934.
Edited by C. P. Morehouse.
No more published.

1. Protestant Episcopal church in the U. S. A. General convention, 1934. I. Morehouse, Clifford Phelps, 1904- ed.

43-48873

Library of Congress BX5820.A3 1934
⌐2⌐ 283.73

NL 0420012 DLC ICU

The Living church quarterly
see **The Episcopal Church** annual.

"The Living church" series.
Royden, A.M. The church and woman. n.d.

NL 0420014 OrP

The living descendants, of William Healy, of Cambridge, Mass.
see under [Healy, Clarence Loveland]

Living dog, A, is better than a dead lion. The vanity of human glory. A design for the monument of General Wolfe. [Etching.] [London.] 1760. Size, 11¾ × 8¾ inches. Portrait. Contains an allusion to the Battle of Minden.

K3935 — Minden, Prussia. Hist. Battle, 1759.— Wolfe, General James. 1726–1759 Caricatures. — Vanity, The, of human glory.

NL 0420016 MB

Living dramatists: Pinero, Ibsen, d'Annunzio
see under Hermann, Oscar.

Living English poets. MDCCCLXXXII. Boston, Roberts brothers; ⌐etc., etc.⌐ 1883.

xx, 339 p. front. 18cm.
Selections from their works.

1. English poetry—19th cent.

18-2763

Library of Congress PR1223.L6

NL 0420018 DLC MH ViU

---

*PR1223
.L6 Living English poets. MDCCCLXXXII. London,
1883a K. Paul, Trench, & co., 1883.
xix, 325 p., 1 l. front. 20 1/2cm.
Selections from their works.

1. English poetry—19th cent.

NL 0420019 MB IU CtY NNC MWA NcD NjP PPL NcU CLU NN

Living English poets, 1893. [Selections from their works. New ed.] London, K. Paul, Trench, Trübner & Co. 1893.
pp. xxiii, 285. Front.

Eng. poetry–Coll.||

NL 0420020 MH MB PPL CtY NIC InU CaBVaU

Rare
P[illegible]
1223 Living English poets, 1893. London, Kegan
L78+ Paul, Trench, Trübner, 1893.
1893a xiii,285 p. front. 26cm.

Large paper edition; fifty copies only printed.
Signed Charles Whittingham & co.

NL 0420021 NIC InU

The living epistle: an evangelical monthly devoted to the spread of Biblical knowledge, scriptural holiness and pure literature.
Cleveland, W.F. Schneider, v. 1-
1866-
v. 24 cm.
Edited by Jacob Young.
1. Holiness - Period.

NL 0420022 KyWAT

The living female writers of the south. 1872
see under Tardy, Mrs. Mary T.

The living female writers of] Virginia [1872] 6823
, (In The living female writers of the South. 1872. p. 379-441)
Includes Mrs. Margaret J. Preston, Mrs. S. A. Weiss, Miss M. J. Haw, Mrs. Mary Wiley, Miss M. E. Heath, Miss Virginia E. Davidson, Mrs. J. W. McGuire, Miss Sallie A. Brock, Miss Susan C. Hooper, Matilda S. Edwards, Mrs. Mary McCabe, Mary J. S. Upshur, Miss Sarah J. C. Whittlesey, Helen G. Beale, Miss Cornelia J. M. Jordan, Laura R. Fewell, Mrs. Lizzie Pettit Cutler, Mary E. Woodson, M. Virginia Terhune, Mrs. William C. Rives, Mary Tucker Magill, Miss Emily V. Mason, Mary Eugenie McKinne.

NL 0420024 Vi

VOLUME 336

"The living flame"
see under Catholic Charities Diocese of Brooklyn.

Living for Jesus, a compilation by more than three hundred Christian ministers. Cincinnati, O., The Standard publishing company [1944]
375 p. 15½cm.

1. Devotional exercises. 2. Calendars.

44-51034

Library of Congress BV4810.L57
[3] 242

NL 0420026 DLC

Living for young homemakers. v. 1-
autumn 1947-
New York, Street & Smith Publications.
v. illus. (part col.) 33 cm.
Frequency varies.
Title varies: 1947-Apr./May 1949, Mademoiselle's living.

1. Architecture, Domestic—Period. 2. Interior decoration—Period.

NA7100.L5 728.605 51-17541

GDS NN FTaSU NcRS NcGU AzTeS
NL 0420027 DLC OrCS MtBC WaS MB CaBVa MiD FU I TxLT

R021.2
L761
The living generation; a report of an experiment in liberal adult education [in] the San Bernardino-Riverside area of Southern California February 1 to April 8, 1954. [San Bernardino?, 1954]
38 l.

Cover title.

1. LIVING GENERATION (Radio program)
2. Adult education

NL 0420028 MiD

Living German literature. New York, F. Ungar Pub. Co. [1945- v. 1, 1954]
v. 24 cm.
Vols. 1-2 by R. Lohan; v. 3 by H. M. Rosenwald.
CONTENTS.—v. 1. Living German literature. 4th ed., rev. and enl.—v. 2. The golden age of German literature.—v. 3. The age of romanticism.

1. German literature (Selections: Extracts, etc.) 2. German language—Readers. I. Lohan, Robert. II. Rosenwald, Henry M.

PT1105.L5 830.82 54-37274 rev 2 ‡

TxU OrU UU FTaSU
NL 0420029 DLC WaWW OrU WaTC KMK NBuU NBuC IU NcD

Living, The, God; a testimony...to God's present power and willingness to hear and to bless his faithful people. Philadelphia: Presbyterian Board of Education, 1866. 24 p. 12°.

Suppl. to Home and foreign record.

1. Revivals (Religious), U. S.: Delaware, 1865. 2. Presbyterian Church in the U. S. A., Delaware, 1865. 3. Presbyterian Board of Publication, Phila.
N. Y. P. L. July 25, 1913.

NL 0420030 NN DLC

The living God; what matters who wrote it. New York & London, G. P. Putnam's sons, 1923.
3 p. l., 86 p. 20½cm.

Library of Congress PS3500.A1L5 24-4564

NL 0420031 DLC OrU NcD

Living Gospel songs & choruses; a little book to meet a big need. Expressly adapted to evangelistic meetings, Sunday schools, and young people's meetings... Published in round and shaped notes. Chicago, Tabernacle Publishing Co., c1925.
1 v. (unpaged) music. 20cm.

NL 0420032 NjPT OrP

Living graduates and non-graduates of Yale University
see under Yale University.

Living History, inc., Shenandoah, Iowa.

E461
.H3
Harper's weekly; a journal of civilization. v. 4- (no. 209-); Dec. 29, 1860-
New York [Shenandoah, Iowa, Living History, 1960-

Living hymns for use in the Sabbath school, Christian endeavor meetings, the church and the home ... c. 1890.
see under Wanamaker, John, 1838-1922, comp.

Living hymns (The small hymnal) A book of worship and praise for the developing life, suitable for Sunday schools ...
see under Chalmers, William Everett, 1868-1928, ed. and comp.

Living in freedom; a sketch of independent Lithuania's achievements
see under Supreme Lithuanian Committee of Liberation.

"Living in industrial civilization," Conference on, Corning, N.Y., 1951.
See
Conference on "Living in industrial civilization," Corning, N.Y., 1951.

Living in London: a comedy, in three acts
see under [Jameson, Robert Francis] of Inner Temple.

Living in our community. Resource volume.
Towson, Md., Board of Education of Baltimore County, 19
v. illus. 24 cm.

1. Baltimore Co., Md. I. Baltimore Co., Md. Board of Education.

F187.B2L5 975.271 54-28954 ‡

NL 0420040 DLC

Living in River Oaks.
See
[River Oaks magazine]

... Living in the atomic age, a resource unit for teachers in secondary schools
see under Hand, Harold Curtis, 1901- ed.

Living is our business, a dramatic up-to-the-minute story, side by side with tabloid summary of the Marsh report
see under [Highe, Edward]

A living issue
see under [Dodge, Richard Irving] 1827-1895.

Living issues of the campaign of 1904, including lives of Roosevelt and Fairbanks... comprising a complete history of all the great political campaigns of our country; with an introd. by Hon. Murat Halstead... n. p. ©1904.
384 p. illus.

The life of Roosevelt rev. & pub. later under title: "Adventurous life and heroic deeds of Theodore Roosevelt."

NL 0420045 MiD MH IaU T

M
2117
.L58
Living jewels, songs for all occasions [by] Otis L. McCoy [and others] Cleveland, Tenn., Tennessee Music and Printing Co., c1949.
160p. 22cm.

With music.

1. Hymns, English. I. McCoy, Otis L., ed.

NL 0420046 OrU

The Living King, special Easter service for the Sunday school with selections for the choir. Chicago, c1917.
29 [2] p. 22 cm.
Cover title.

NL 0420047 RPB

VOLUME 336

CB663
+L58
Living leaders; an encyclopedia of biography. Special edition for Daviess and Martin Counties, Indiana. [n.p.] American Pub. Co., 1897.
519, [4], 57 p. plates, ports. 28 cm.

1. U.S. - Biog. 2. Daviess Co., Ind. 3. Martin Co., Ind.

NL 0420048 CtY

Living leaders of the world: comprising graphic biographies of the men and women of greatest eminence, influence, wealth, power, or fame.... Prepared by...L. Wallace, J. Parton...and others. Chicago: Hubbard Bros. ⌜cop. 1889⌝ 614 p., 5 pl., 9 port. illus. 4°.

1. Biography. 2. Wallace, Lew.
N. Y. P. L. March 1, 1912.

NL 0420049 NN ICN MH MiD DNW DLC

YA
..S495
Living letters. Philadelphia [c1841].
54p.

(Sunday school books; arr. numerically.)

NL 0420050 DLC

The **living** light. Anonymous. Santa Barbara, Calif., J. F. Rowny press ⌜1951⌝ xi, 13-227 p. 23cm.
By various authors.

NL 0420051 NN WaS

---

*
PS1431
.L55
1831
Living literary characters, no. iv. James Fenimore Cooper.
(In The new monthly magazine and literary journal. 22½cm. 1831, pt. I, p. 356-362, port.)

1. Cooper, James Fenimore, 1789-1851.

NL 0420052 ViU

Living literature. New York, Harcourt, Brace, 1948-
v. illus., ports. 25 cm.
CONTENTS.—

grade 10. People in literature, by L. B. Cook, Walter Loban and R. M. Stauffer.

1. Literature—Collections. I. Cook, Luella Bussey, 1890- ed. II. Title: People in literature.

PN6014.L66 808.8 48-6406 *

NL 0420053 DLC ICU

HQ
1061
.L78
Living longer; ⌜some aspects of the problems of old age,by C.O.S.Blyth Brooke,and others⌝ A series of lectures organised by the Institute of Public Administration (South-West Regional Group) with the co-operation of the University College of the South West and the National Council of Social Service. London, National Council of Social Service, 1954.
71,⌜1⌝ p. 22 cm. (Exeter papers)
Bibliography: p.⌜71⌝
1.Old age. I.Brooke,C.O.S.Blyth.

NL 0420054 MiU MnU NN

---

*
PS646
.F5
.L585
1822
Living manners, or The true secret of happiness, a tale. Philadelphia: Published by Anthony Finley, 1822.
108 p. 15cm.
Wright 1702.

NL 0420055 ViU

FILM
4274
PR
v.1
reel
L7
Living manners; or, The true secret of happiness. A tale. Philadelphia, A. Finley, 1822.
108 p. (Wright American fiction, v.1, 1774-1850, no.1702, Research Publications Microfilm, Reel L-7)

NL 0420056 CU

---

*pEB7
A100
710ℓ
The living man's elegie or Doctor Sacheverell's much lamented silence, March ⅌ 23 1710.
[London? 1710]
broadside. 35.5x27cm.
In verse.
Engraved throughout; ornamental border contains death emblems and a portrait of Hoadly.

NL 0420057 MH

The living martyr and the unholy alliance
see under [West, George Montgomery] 1789-

LIVING Marxism; international council correspondence. v.[1] no.11-v.6, no.4; Sept. 1935-winter, 1943 (Incomplete)
Chicago. v. tables.
23-30cm.

Microfilm (negative)
FULL RECORD OF HOLDINGS IN CENTRAL SERIAL RECORD
Frequency varies.

1935-37, reproduced from typewritten copy.
Published by the United workers party, 1935; by the Groups of council communists of America, 1936-39.
Title varies: 1935-37, International council correspondence; for theory and discussion (Sept. 1935, cover title: Council correspondence, English edition; for theory and discussion; 1942-43, New essays.

1. Bolshevism--Per. and soc. publ. I. Groups of council communists of America. II. United workers party of America. III. Title: International council correspondence; for theory and discussion. IV. Title: New essays.

NL 0420060 NN

A living memorial to a mental health leader: Alexander Caswell Ellis. [Austin, Tex.] The Hogg Foundation For Mental Hygiene [1955?]
14p. port. 21½cm.
Includes papers by Roy Bedichek and William C. Adamson.

1. Ellis, Alexander Caswell, 1871-1948. I. Bedichek, Roy, 1878- II. Adamson, William Colbert, 1919- III. Texas. University. Hogg Foundation.

NL 0420061 TxU

A living memorial to Ernst Reuter
see under
International Rescue Committee.

The living memorial to Lincoln
see under [Jones, Richard Lloyd] 1873-

ZP
L761
The Living message.
Toronto.
v. 25-29 cm. monthly.

Title varies: -22, The Letter leaflet.
Published by the Woman's Auxiliary to the Missionary Society of the Church of England in Canada, -July 1947; by the Woman's

Auxiliary of the Church of England in Canada, Aug. 1947-53; by the Woman's Auxiliary of the Anglican Church of Canada, 1954-

1. Anglican Church of Canada - Missions - Period. 2. Women - Missions - Period. 3. Missions - Period. I. Anglican Church of Canada. Woman's Auxiliary. II. Title: The Letter leaflet. (2)

NL 0420065 CtY-D

The **Living** museum. v. 1-
May 1939-
⌜Springfield, Illinois State museum, 1939-
v. in illus. 23½ cm. monthly.

1. Natural history—Period. 2. Natural history—Illinois. I. Illinois. State museum, Springfield.

QH1.L925 069.0973 47-5764

WvU TxU NNC LNHT LU DSI OkS KU CLSU DNAL MtBC
NL 0420066 DLC FU NbHi CaBViP OrCS CoU NN AzTeS OC1

... **Living** my religion (series) The questions and answers of the revised Baltimore catechism, explained and correlated with Bible and church history; basic new Baltimore catechism texts for elementary grades, by Very Rev. Monsignor W. R. Kelly ... Rev. Edmund J. Goebel ... ⌜and⌝ Sister Mary Imelda ... ⌜New York⌝ Benziger brothers, inc., 1942-
v. col. illus. 20cm.
Title from p. ⌜2⌝ of cover.
At head of title: The Kelly-Goebel-Imelda graded new Baltimore catechisms.
CONTENTS.—Primer. Our Heavenly Father, by W. R. Kelly and Sister Mary Imelda.
1. Baltimore catechism. 2. Catholic church—Catechisms and creeds—English. I. Kelly, William doswell, 1891- II. Goebel, Edmund Joseph, 1896- III. Wallace, Mary Imelda, sister, 1884-

Library of Congress BX1961.L5 42-23829
⌜2⌝ 238.2

NL 0420067 DLC MBtS

VOLUME 336

The Living newspaper.

Federal theatre project.
Federal theatre plays. 1. Triple-A plowed under, by the staff of the Living newspaper. 2. Power, a living newspaper, by Arthur Arent. 3. Spirochete, a history, by Arnold Sundgaard. New York, Random house [°1938]

PS 634 F293+ no.9 Living newspaper.
Injunction granted, written by the Editorial Staff of the Living newspaper. As presented by the Living newspaper at the Biltmore Theatre, New York City, 1936. [New York, 1936]
[6], 101,xv numb. l. 28cm. (Federal Theatre Project. National Play Bureau. Federal Theatre playscript publication, no. 9)
"Third edition of the Living newspaper... Arthur Arent, managing editor"

NL 0420069 NIC OU OrPR IaU NNBG

812.1 L785i Living newspaper
...Injunction granted; written by the editorial staff of the Living news paper... [New York, National play bureau, Federal theatre project] 1937.
101,[1] xvl. diagr. 4. (Federal theatre project. National play bureau. Federal theatre playscript, no.9)
Mimeographed.
Bibliography: l.A.

NL 0420070 IaU OrPR OClW

808.2 F317n no.9-S LIVING NEWSPAPER.
... Injunction granted, written by the editorial staff of the Living newspaper ... [New York, National service bureau, Federal theatre project, 1938]
6p.l.,101 numb.l.,1l.,xv numb.l. illus. 28½cm. (National service bureau publication no.9-S)
"Third edition."
Reproduced from typewritten copy.
I. Title. II. Series (contents)

NL 0420071 TxU RPB

Drama PS3523 I88N5 Living newspaper. Editorial staff.
... "1935." Written by the Editorial staff of the Living newspaper, Arthur Arent, managing editor. Entire production under the supervision of Morris Watson. As presented by the Living newspaper of the Federal theatre project, New York city. [New York city, Play bureau, Federal theatre project] 1936.
3p.l.,88 numb.l. 28cm. (Federal theatre project. Federal theatre playscript. no. 3)
At head of title: Play bureau, Federal theatre project
Reproduced from typewritten copy.

NL 0420072 NBuG OrPR IdU

---

812 L765t The Living newspaper.
... Triple A plowed under; written by the editorial staff of the Living newspaper under the supervision of Arthur Arent. Produced under the supervision of Morris Watson ... [New York, 1936]
73 numb.l.
At head of title: National play bureau. Federal theatre project.
Mimeographed.
Bibliography: leaves 3-4.
I. Arent, Arthur. II. Federal theatre project. III. Title.

NL 0420073 IU OrPR OClW OU RPB NBuG

Living 1949 (Radio program).
Second class citizens; NBC's weekly drama document... [New York, National broadcasting co., c1949] 15, [1] p. 22cm.
Cover-title; at head of title: FREC, Radio depository, NAB.
"Each week Living 1949 presents as a public service some 'significant' aspect of the times in which we live—as in this broadcast where problems of our older people are considered."
Bibliography, p. [16]

1. Drama, Radio, American. 2. Aged—Drama. I. National broadcasting company, inc.

NL 0420074 NN

Living on other people's means ...
See under
[Lee, Mrs. Hannah Farnham (Sawyer)] 1780-1865.

Living painters of France and England; fifteen etchings from representative pictures with descriptive letterpress. London, Remington & co.; Paris, Librairie de l'art, 1882.
18 l. 15 pl. 45cm.
Initials, head and tail pieces.

1. Painters, French. 2. Painters, British.
12—1592
Library of Congress ND1230.L7

NL 0420076 DLC NN

Living paper series.
The higher criticism
see under title

Living papers on present day themes; Christian evidences, doctrines and morals. New York, F. H. Revell co. [1881-] v. 20 cm.

NL 0420078 MBC OOxM

Living papers on present day themes; Christian evidences, doctrines and morals ... New York, Chicago, Fleming H. Revell company [1892-
v. 19cm.

1. Apologetics—19th cent. 2. Bible—Evidences, authority, etc. 3. Theology, Doctrinal—Addresses, essays, lectures. 4. Christian ethics—Addresses, essays, lectures.
42-41957.
Library of Congress BT1095.L5
[2]

NL 0420079 DLC ICU

Living philosophies, by Albert Einstein, John Dewey, Sir James Jeans ... [and others] New York, Simon and Schuster, 1931.
6 p. l., 3-334 p. front., ports. 24½ cm.
On cover: A series of intimate credos.
CONTENTS.—Albert Einstein.—Bertrand Russell.—John Dewey.—R. A. Millikan.—Theodore Dreiser.—H. G. Wells.—Fridtjof Nansen.—Sir James Jeans.—Irving Babbitt.—Sir Arthur Keith.—J. T. Adams.—H. L. Mencken.—Julia Peterkin.—Lewis Mumford.—G. J. Nathan.—Hu Shih.—J. W. Krutch.—Irwin Edman.—Hilaire Belloc.—Beatrice Webb.—W. R. Inge.—J. B. S. Haldane.—Biographical notes.
1. Philosophy, Modern. 2. Philosophers. I. Einstein, Albert, 1879-1955.
B804.L5 190 31-27199

OrSaW WaTC WaSpG WaSp Wa WaS PU-PSW IdU IdPS IdB MtBC OrCS OrStbM Or OrPR PrLgE OrU CBSK CaBVaU TxU WaU CaBVa IdPI PPFr CoU KEmT PPT PP NcRA OCH PJB PPEB PPLas OCU NIC MtBC OU
NL 0420080 DLC OO MiU ODW OClh PU ViU PPGi MB

Living philosophies by Albert Einstein, John Dewey, Sir James Jeans and others... New York, Simon and Schuster, 1933.
334 p.

NL 0420082 PHC

Living philosophies, by Albert Einstein, John Dewey, Sir James Jeans ... and others. Louisville, Ky., American printing house for the blind, 1937.
3 v.

NL 0420083 OCl

B 804 L78 1942 **Living philosophies**, by Albert Einstein, John Dewey, Sir James Jeans [and others] New York, The World Publishing Co. [1942]
334 p. illus. 21cm.
On cover: A series of intimate credoes.
"Tower Book Edition"
1. Philosophy. I. Einstein, Albert, 1879-

NL 0420084 NIC

A living picture of London...
See under
[Badcock, John] fl. 1816-1830.

Living pictures of the animal world. A rare and most unique collection of exquisite photographs from living specimens only. With an introduction by Alfred H. Miles. London, The Werner Company, [1903].
[4], 196 p. illus. 28x34cm

NL 0420085 ICJ

Living pictures, the Church of the living Messiah
see under [Feild-Palmer, Harold] 1871-

822.08 L762 Living plays. [New York, C. Wiley, 1824]
4v. in 1. 18cm.
Binder's title
Each play has special t.p. and separate paging.
Contents.- The poor gentleman, by G. Colman.- Three weeks after marriage, by A. Murphy.- Blue devils, by G. Colman.- The spoil'd child by P. Hoare.

NL 0420087 IU ICU NNC

The living poem... 1877 [c1877]
see under Hershey, Eusebius, b. 1823.

Living poetry quarterly
see **Folio.**

VOLUME 336

PR 1221 .L786 THE LIVING POETS OF ENGLAND; SPECIMENS OF the living British poets, with biographical and critical notices, and an essay on English poetry. Paris, Printed for L. Baudry ⌊etc.⌋, 1827.
2 v.

1. English poetry—19th cent.—Selections, extracts, etc.

NL 0420090 InU MH MdBJ OCIND NcD CtY

The Living pulpit of the Christian Church: a series of discourses, doctrinal and practical... see under Moore, William Thomas, 1832-1926.

The Living pulpit, or Eighteen sermons see under Wilson, Elijah.

The living questions of the age see under [Walker, James Barr] 1805-1887.

Living quill. Padroni, Calif. Monthly.

NL 0420094 NN

The Living races of mankind: a popular illustrated account of the customs, habits, pursuits, feasts & ceremonies ... see under Hutchinson, Henry Neville, 1856-1927.

Living record of the Jensen family see under Jensen, Charles C., 1872-

---

Living record of the Olaus Johnson family see under [Johnson, Anna] 1892-

---

A liuing remembrance of Master Robert Rogers, Marchant aduenturer & Leatherseller of London deceased ... the 22. of September. And was buried ... 1. of October 1601. London, for M. Allde [1601]
Broadside
Laid (no. 72) in the same vol. with: Awdelay or Awdeley, John. Ecclesi. XX. 1569. Britwell sale, Nov. 1919, no. 16 (72)

NL 0420098 CSmH

The living remnant and other Quaker tales see under [O'Brien, Edith Florence]

Living room furniture designs, with scale drawings and working details... ⌊London:⌋ Evans Bros., Ltd.⌊, 1927.⌋ 48 p. diagrs., illus. 8°. (Woodworker ser.)

1. Furniture—Design and manufacture. 2. Ser.
N. Y. P. L. October 11, 1928

NL 0420100 NN

The LIVING sacrifice, an offering to the Lord. A funeral oration: set forth at a meeting of the people call'd Quakers, on the burial of Joseph Silk of Godmanchester, who died on the 30th of November last and was buried on the 3d of December, 1713. Painted [!] at Stamford in Lincolnshire, [1713?].
17 cm. pp.16.

NL 0420101 MH

4A 3506 LIVING Scottish poets. [London, E.Benn Ltd., 1931]
30,[1]p. 21cm. (The Augustan books of modern poetry)

Bibliography: p.[31]

NL 0420102 ICN

Living sermons; a book of twenty sermons by representative evangelists of the Church of Christ. Cincinnati, O., F. L. Rowe, 1925.
227 p. 20cm.

Library of Congress BX7327.A1L5 25-27558

NL 0420103 DLC

A living skeleton!! Authentic memoir of that singular human prodigy Claude Seurat, denominated the living skeleton, who arrived in London from the continent in July, 1825, in which is contained a circumstantial detail of his person, as collected from the most scrutinizing observation of his structure, together with an account of his manners, habits, &c., from his birth to the present time. Illustrated with three engravings...drawn from the life, by Robert Cruikshank. London: J. Fairburn ⌊1825⌋ 20 p. front. (folder of 3 ports.) 22cm.

171492B. 1. Seurat, Claude Ambroise, 1798-
N. Y. P. L. July 28, 1942

NL 0420104 NN MdBJ DNLM

Living songs: for the Sunday school, the Epworth league, prayer meetings, revivals, and all special occasions of Christian work and worship 1892 see under Cunnyngham, William George Etler, ed.

Living standards in Pakistan. A group study see under Pakistan Institute of International Affairs.

Living standards on the farm.
(*In* U. S. Dept. of agriculture. Yearbook of agriculture, 1932, p. 549-572. illus. 23½cm. Washington, 1932)
Consists of a number of short articles by various authors.

1. Cost and standard of living—U. S. 2. Farm life.
Agr 33-270
Library, U. S. Dept. of Agriculture 1Ag84Y 1932
Library of Congress [S21.A35 1932]
[7*]

NL 0420107 DNAL OCl OU

The living temple... see under Howe, John, 1630-1705.

The living temple: a brief memoir of Jane Bethel see under Bethel, Jane.

A living testimony from the power and spirit of our Lord Jesus Christ ... see under Friends, Society of. London Yearly Meeting of Women Friends.

Living the later years, a conference on old age, Marshall college, 1950.
Living the later years... A conference on old age sponsored by the Department of sociology in association with Marshall college and the civic organizations of Huntington, June 20-21, 1950... ⌊Huntington, 1950⌋ ix, 162 p. 28cm.

582287B. 1. Age, Old. I. Marshall college, Huntington, W. Va.
N. Y. P. L.

NL 0420111 NN LU

BARRETT The Living Theatre, Inc.
Beyond the mountains [by] Kenneth Rexroth. [New York, © 1951]
Published as a play program for the Living Theatre production of Beyond the Mountains.
1. Rexroth, Kenneth, 1905-

NL 0420112 ViU

Aq El46 J952t Rare Books Col The Living Theatre, Inc.
Stein, Picasso, Eliot. [New York, 1952?]
16p. 22cm. in envelope in folder 28cm.
Cover title.
Program of a production of Ladies' voices by Gertrude Stein, Desire by Pablo Picasso, and Sweeney Agonistes by T.S. Eliot, at the Cherry Lane Theatre, New York City, opening Mar. 2, 1952.
I. Eliot, Thomas Stearns, 1888-

NL 0420113 TxU MoSW

A living theatre; the Gordon Craig School; the Arena Goldoni; the Mask; see under Craig, Edward Gordon, 1872-

VOLUME 336

Living thoughts ...
see under Means, Mrs. Charlotte A., comp.

Living thoughts in words that burn, from poet, sage and humorist
see under [Beezley, Charles F] ed.

The Living thoughts library, edited by Alfred O. Mendel. ₍no. 1₎–
New York ₍etc.₎ Longmans, Green and co., 1939– v. fronts. (ports.) 18½cm.
Also known as Longmans' living thoughts library.

1. No subject. I. Mendel, Alfred O., ed. II. Longmans' living thoughts library.
N. Y. P. L. March 31, 1941

YBX ₍no. 1₎ Schopenhauer, Arthur. The living thoughts of Schopenhauer, presented by Thomas Mann. ₍1st ed.₎ 1939.
NBY ₍no. 2₎ Thoreau, H. D. The living thoughts of Thoreau, presented by Theodore Dreiser. ₍1st ed.₎ 1939.
NKW ₍no. 3₎ Montaigne, M. E. de. The living thoughts of Montaigne, presented by André Gide. ₍1st ed.₎ 1939.
•QDX ₍no. 4₎ Tolstoi, L. N., graf. The living thoughts of Tolstoi, presented by Stefan Zweig. ₍1st ed.₎ 1939.
PQF ₍no. 5₎ Darwin, C. R. The living thoughts of Darwin, presented by Julian Huxley ... assisted by James Fisher. ₍1st ed.₎ 1939.
NKE ₍no. 6₎ Rousseau, J. J. The living thoughts of Rousseau, presented by Romain Rolland. ₍1st ed.₎ 1939.
YBX ₍no. 7₎ Nietzsche, F. W. The living thoughts of Nietzsche, presented by Heinrich Mann. ₍1st ed.₎ 1939.
NNCC ₍no. 8₎ Mazzini, Giuseppe. The living thoughts of Mazzini, presented by Ignazio Silone. ₍1st ed.₎ 1939.
YBG ₍no. 9₎ Spinoza, Benedictus de. The living thoughts of Spinoza, presented by Arnold Zweig. ₍1st ed.₎ 1939.
NKW ₍no. 10₎ Voltaire, F. M. A. de. The living thoughts of Voltaire, presented by André Maurois. ₍1st ed.₎ 1939.
SFG ₍no. 11₎ Marx, Karl. Das Kapital. English. Rühle. The living thoughts of Karl Marx... ₍1st ed.₎ 1939.
SEB ₍no. 12₎ Paine, Thomas. The living thoughts of Tom Paine, presented by John Dos Passos. ₍1st ed.₎ 1940.
YBX ₍no. 13₎ Pascal, Blaise. The living thoughts of Pascal, presented by François Mauriac. ₍1st ed.₎ 1940.
SEB ₍no. 14₎ Jefferson, Thomas, 3d pres. U. S. The living thoughts of Thomas Jefferson, presented by John Dewey. ₍1st ed.₎ 1940.
SEC ₍no. 15₎ Macchiavelli, Niccolò di Bernardo dei. The living thoughts of Machiavelli, presented by Count Carlo Sforza. ₍1st ed.₎ 1940.
NBQ ₍no. 16₎ Emerson, R. W. The living thoughts of Emerson, presented by Edgar Lee Masters. ₍1st ed.₎ 1940.
₍no. 17₎ Confucius. The living thoughts of Confucius, presented by Alfred Doeblin. ₍1st ed.₎ 1940.
₍no.₎ 18. Kant, Immanuel. The living thoughts of Kant, presented by Julien Benda. ₍1st ed.₎ 1940.

NL 0420122 NN OO OCU Mi

The living thoughts of the prophet Muhammad
see under Koran. English. Selections.

Living through the older years
see under Conference on Aging. [1st] University of Michigan, 1948.

HV4925 .L5 Living tissue.
₍Boston, 19
v. illus. (incl. ports.) 28½cm. monthly (except July and Aug.)
Official organ of the New England anti-vivisection society.
Began publication in 1915. *cf.* Union list of serials.

1. Vivisection—Period. I. New England anti-vivisection society.
45-50004
Library of Congress HV4925.L5 ₍2₎ 179.405

NL 0420125 DLC NN

Living to Christ. A mother's memorial
see under [Cobb, Mrs. Sanford]

Living to do good
see under [Sweetser, Seth] 1807-1878.

Living together in the modern world
see under
Creative Educational Society, Mankato, Minn.

The living torch, A.E.
see under [Russell, George William] 1867-1935.

The Living truth, *Greenville, Ala.*
The Living truth ... Extra ed. Feb. 1904. Prominent men, leading business houses, items of general interest ... ₍Greenville, 1904₎
cover-title, ₍64₎ p. illus. (incl. ports.) 24½cm.
Advertisements interspersed.

1. Greenville, Ala.
Library of Congress F334.G8L7 4-29420†

NL 0420130 DLC

Living twig of Christ's vine, though little known. ₌Stamford, Conn., Ukrainian Catholic Seminary, 1945₌.
23 p. illus. 20 cm. (₌Pamphlets, v.60₌)
Contents.--Explanation of the Holy Liturgy, by Rev. Desmond A. Schmall, S.J.--Ukrainian Catholics, by Most Reverend Ambrose Senyshyn.

NL 0420131 PLatS

Living units for men, Cornell University
see under Katz, Robert D

Living voices of living men: practical sermons by bishops and clergy of the church, intended for family and lay reading. New York, T. Whittaker, 1887.
vi, 256p. 19cm.
Preface signed George F. Cushman.

1. Sermons. Collections. I. Cushman, George F.
Printed by Wesleyan University Library

NL 0420133 CtW NNUT

WW L785 (2) Living voices of living men; practical sermons by bishops and clergy of the church intended for family and lay reading. ₍Second series₎ New York, T. Whittaker, 1889.
vi, 339p. 19cm.
Preface signed: George F. Cushman.

NL 0420134 NNUT

The living wage, by H. N. Brailsford, John A. Hobson, A Creech Jones, E. F. Wise. A report submitted to the National administrative council of the Independent labour party. London, Independent labour party publication department ₍1926₎
3 p. l., 55 p. 18cm.

1. Wages—Gt. Brit. 2. Gt. Brit.—Economic policy. I. Brailsford, Henry Noel, 1873– II. Hobson, John Atkinson, 1858– III. Jones, Arthur Creech, 1891– IV. Wise, Edward Frank, 1885– V. Independent labour party (Gt. Brit.)
Library, U. S. Dept. of Labor L 27-41

NL 0420135 DL OClWHi MtU TU FU MH-BA PHC NN

Living water for the thirsty...
₌Goldsboro', N.C., Published by Board of missions₌ n.d.
4 p. (Confederate tracts, no. 32)

NL 0420136 OClWHi

Living water songs, suitable for all kinds of religious services ... [after 1909]
see under Benson, John T comp.

YA 5593 Living waters; drawn from the fountains of Holy Scripture and sacred poetry. For daily use... New York, 1850.
200p.

(Sunday school books; arr. numerically.)

NL 0420138 DLC

Living waters; or, Messages of joy; with an introduction by Dwight Goddard. New York, Brentano's ₍©1919₎
x p., 1 l., 140 p. 19½ cm.

1. Spiritualism. I. Goddard, Dwight, 1861–
BR125.L742 20—2428

NL 0420139 DLC

VOLUME 336

The Living way.
San Francisco, 1870-

BR1
.L85

NL 0420140 DLC CU

Living whist
see under [Grant, Horatio N]

The Living wilderness ... published by the Wilderness society.
v. 1- (no. 1-);
Sept. 1935-
[Washington, D. C., 1935-
v. illus. (incl. maps) 28 cm. annual.

Caption title.
Editor: 1935- R. S. Yard.

1. Natural history—U. S. 2. Natural history—Yearbooks. 3. Wilderness areas—Period. I. Yard, Robert Sterling, 1861-1945, ed. II. Wilderness society.

QH1.L93 574.973 42—15142

OrCS OrMonO MtBC CaBVaU
NdU NMSeS TU FU NbU AzTeS IaAS CaBVaU WaS WaT
CL ICRL INS CtY Vi CSt LNL MtBC PSt MoS OC DBB
NL 0420142 DLC NIC ICJ ViU MsSM P ArU CoD GU-L

Living with Christ
see under [Lucian Alphonsus, brother]
1913-

634.6805 Living with flowers.
LI
Chicago.
v. illus. 15-21cm. monthly.

NL 0420145 IU

LIVING with flowers.
Lansing, Mich. J. Henry co., 1962-
v. 1

NL 0420146 WaS

A living without a boss ... New York and London, Harper & brothers, 1911.
4 p. l., 230, [1] p. front., plates. 18½cm.

1. U. S.—Soc. condit. 2. Country life.
Library of Congress HN64.L6 11—23028

NL 0420147 DLC OrP ICJ MB NN OO

The living witness; a lawyer's brief for Christianity
see under [Pendarvis, George Henry]
1854-

Living witnesses; or, Voices from the Inebriates' Home. [n. p 1876?] 16, iv p. 8°.

Caption-title.
In: VTZ p. v. 91, no. 10.

BLACK TEMPERANCE COLL.
U. S.: N. Y.: Fort Hamilton.

1. Inebriates.—Hospitals and asylums, N. Y. P. L. June 6, 1918.

NL 0420149 NN

The living word. February 27, 1899.
Brooklyn, 1899.
v. 2 no. 3 24 cm.
Caption title

NL 0420150 RPB

The living word; or, Bible truths and lessons... (Boston, Ginn, 1872)
see under [Parsons, James Challis]
1833-1897.

The living word; the Bible abridged for public and private reading (H. H. Saunderson, ed.)
see under Bible. English. Selections. 1924?

Living words for needy souls [by] various authors. London, Stow Hill Bible and Tract Depot, n.d.

64 p.

NL 0420153 CLamB

Living writers, being critical studies broadcast in the B.B.C. Third programme ...
see under Phelps, Gilbert.

HC385 Livingood, Charles A.
.L5
... Spain; resources, industries, trade and public finance ... Washington, 1930.
1 pam. 8°.

NL 0420155 DLC

Livingood, Charles Jacob, 1866- tr.

Daudet, Alphonse, 1840-1897.
L'Arlésienne (The woman from Arles); a play in three acts and five scenes, by Alphonse Daudet; translated into English by Charles J. Livingood; produced by the Cincinnati Stuart Walker company, under direction of Stuart Walker; photographs by Nancy Ford Cones. Cincinnati, O., Print. priv. by D. W. Roberts [°1930]

Livingood, Clarence S., 1911- joint author.

Pillsbury, Donald Marion, 1902-
Manual of dermatology, issued under the auspices of the Committee on medicine of the Division of medical sciences of the National research council, by Donald M. Pillsbury, M. D., Marion B. Sulzberger, M. D. [and] Clarence S. Livingood, M. D. Philadelphia & London, W. B. Saunders company, 1942.

Livingood, Frederick George.
Eighteenth century Reformed church schools. Part xxxv of a narrative and critical history prepared at the request of the Pennsylvania German society. [By] Frederick George Livingood ... Norristown, Pa., 1930.
xix, [2], 313 p. front., illus., plates, ports., facsims. 26cm.
"Edition 200 copies."
"Reprinted from Proceedings of the Pennsylvania German society, vol. XXXVIII."
Forms pt. 35 of the series "Pennsylvania: the German influence in its settlement and development", published in the Proceedings and addresses of the Society.
Bibliography: p. [299]-313.
1. Reformed church in the United States—Education. 2. Church schools—Pennsylvania. 3. Education—Pennsylvania — Hist. 4. Schools, German—Pennsylvania. I. Pennsylvania-German society. II. Title.
Library of Congress LC586.R35L5 30-28276
[3] 377.84109748

NL 0420158 DLC PSt NNC CaBVaU NcD MH InU OCU OO

Livingood, Frederick George.
Eighteenth century Reformed church schools. Part xxxv of a narrative and critical history prepared at the request of the Pennsylvania German society. [By] Frederick George Livingood ... Norristown, Pa. [Norristown press] 1930.
xix, [1] p., 1 l., 313 p. front., illus., plates, ports., facsims. 25½cm. [Pennsylvania: the German influence in its settlement and development. pt. xxxv]
In Pennsylvania-German society. [Proceedings and addresses] ... Oct. 21, 1927. 1930. v. 38.
Bibliography: p. [299]-313.
1. Reformed church in the United States — Education. 2. Church schools—Pennsylvania. 3. Education—Pennsylvania—Hist. 4. Schools, German—Pennsylvania. I. Title.

30-28426
Library of Congress F146.P23 vol. 38

NL 0420159 DLC NRCR PWcS MH-AH PU PHi PPT

LIVINGOOD, Frederick George.
German Reformed Church education in Pennslyvania during the eighteenth century. Thesis Harvard University, 1925.

Typewritten. 4°. ff. xxxiii,645. Facsim. plates and maps.
"Bibliography", ff. 596-644.
"Vita", f,645,

NL 0420160 MH

Livingood, G B.
For the glory of America, by G.B.Livingood. [Philadelphia, Franklin printing company, 1919?]
143,[1] p.incl.illus.(incl.plans),col.pl.,ports. col.front. 31cm.

Two of the portraits (plates) are preceded by guard sheet with descriptive letter-press.
An account of the Traylor engineering and manufacturing company,Allentown,Pa.

1.Traylor engineering and manufacturing company,Allentown,Pa.

NL 0420161 MiU NN

Livingood, Harry H.
The Livingood manual of chemistry; an outline of elementary and applied chemistry, arranged for the student of embalming, by H. H. Livingood ... Kansas City, Kan., The Williams institute of embalming [°1929]

112 p. 22cm.

Blank pages for "Notes" included in the paging.

1. Chemistry—Outlines, syllabi, etc. I. The Williams institute of embalming and sanitary science, Kansas City, Kan.

29-21579
Library of Congress QD41.L7

NL 0420162 DLC

Livingood, James Weston, joint author.

F444
C4G6
Govan, Gilbert Eaton, 1892-
The Chattanooga country, 1540-1951: from tomahawks to TVA, by Gilbert E. Govan and James W. Livingood. [1st ed.] New York, Dutton, 1952.

VOLUME 336

Livingood, James Weston.
The history of the commercial rivalry between Philadelphia and Baltimore for the trade of the Susquehanna Valley, 1780-1860. Ann Arbor, University Microfilms [1952]
([University Microfilms, Ann Arbor, Mich.] Publication no. 2998)
Microfilm copy of typescript. Positive.
Collation of the original, as determined from the film: iv, 289 l. illus., maps, tables.
Thesis—Princeton University.
Published in 1947, without thesis statement, under title: The Philadelphia-Baltimore trade rivalry.
Bibliography: leaves 269-289.
1. Philadelphia—Comm. 2. Philadelphia—Hist. 3. Baltimore—Comm. 4. Baltimore—Hist.
Microfilm AC-1 no. 2998 Mic 56-4170

NL 0420164 DLC

Livingood, James Weston.
The Philadelphia-Baltimore trade rivalry, 1780-1860. Harrisburg, Pennsylvania Historical and Museum Commission, 1947.
vii, 195 p. maps. 24 cm.
"The original manuscript was presented as a doctoral dissertation (Princeton Univ.)"
Bibliography: p. 166-187.
1. Philadelphia—Comm. 2. Philadelphia—Hist. 3. Baltimore—Comm. 4. Baltimore—Hist.
HF3163.P5L5 381 A 47-29*
Pennsylvania. State College. Library for Library of Congress [a49k3]†

NL 0420165 NcD OrU Or ScU FU WaS WaTC TU MiU PSt PPT PPD DLC PU-W ViU MB ICU CU CtY NNC NcU OO CU

Livingood, James Weston, joint author.

LD891 .C72G6
Govan, Gilbert Eaton, 1892-
The University of Chattanooga: sixty years, by Gilbert E. Govan and James W. Livingood. Chattanooga, University of Chattanooga, 1947.

Livingood, John, 1913-
... A partition function with the prime modulus P> 3 ... [by] John Livingood ... Philadelphia, 1945.
[1], 194-208 p. 24½cm.
Thesis (PH. D.)—University of Pennsylvania, 1944.
"Reprint from the American journal of mathematics, LXVII, 2."
Bibliography: p. 208.
1. Convergence. 2. Series, Infinite. 3. Functions, Modular. 4. Partitions (Mathematics)
A 45-4357
Pennsylvania. Univ. Libr. for Library of Congress QA295.L58 [3]† 512.4

NL 0420167 PSt DLC PSC NNC PU

Livingood, John Jacob, 1903-
The arc spectrum of platinum ... by John Jacob Livingood. [Minneapolis, Minn., 1929]
cover-title, p. 185-198. 25½cm.
Thesis (PH. D.)—Princeton university, 1929.
From Physical review, v. 34, July 15, 1929.
1. Spectrum analysis. 2. Platinum.
Library of Congress QC462.P5L5 1929 29-28035
Princeton Univ. Libr.

NL 0420168 NjP OU MH DLC

Livingood, John Jacob, 1903-
Experimental atomic physics
see under Harnwell, Gaylord Probasco, 1903-

Livingood, John N B
Analysis of spanwise temperature distribution in three types of air-cooled turbine blade, by John N. B. Livingood and W. Byron Brown. Washington, U. S. Govt. Print. Off., 1950 [i. e. 1951]
ii, 18 p. illus. 30 cm. ([U. S.] National Advisory Committee for Aeronautics. Report 994)
Cover title.
"References": p. 18.
1. Aeroplanes—Turbojet engines—Blades. I. Brown, William Byron, 1894- joint author. (Series)
TL521.A33 no. 994 51-60291
*629.14353 629.13435
—— Copy 2. TL709.L56

NL 0420170 DLC

Livingood, John N B
Analysis of temperature distribution in liquid-cooled turbine blades, by John N. B. Livingood and W. Byron Brown. Washington, U. S. Govt. Print. Off., 1952.
ii, 21 p. illus. 30 cm. (U. S. National Advisory Committee for Aeronautics. Report 1066)
Cover title.
Bibliography: p. 21.
1. Aeroplanes—Turbojet engines—Blades. 2. Heat—Transmission. I. Brown, William Byron, 1894- , joint author. (Series)
TL521.A33 no. 1066 52-61776
*629.14353 629.13435
—— Copy 2. TL700.L57

NL 0420171 DLC PP

Livingood, John N. B., joint author.

TL521 .A33 no. 1220
Eckert, Ernst R G 1904-
Calculations of laminar heat transfer around cylinders of arbitrary cross section and transpiration-cooled walls with application to turbine blade cooling, by E. R. G. Eckert and J. N. B. Livingood. Washington, U. S. Govt. Print. Off., 1955 [i. e., 1956]

Livingood, John N. B., joint author.

TL521 .A33 no. 1182
Eckert, Ernst R G 1904-
Comparison of effectiveness of convection-, transpiration-, and film-cooling methods with air as coolant, by E. R. G. Eckert and John N. B. Livingood. [Washington] 1954 [i. e. 1955]

Livingood, John N. B., joint author.

TL521 .A33 no. 1118
Eckert, Ernst R G 1904-
Method for calculation of laminar heat transfer in air flow around cylinders of arbitrary cross section (including large temperature differences and transpiration cooling) by E. R. G. Eckert and John N. B. Livingood. Washington, U. S. Govt. Print. Off., 1953.

Livingood, Louis Eugene, d. 1898, ed.

Balzac, Honoré de, 1799-1850.
Contes de Balzac; ed., with introduction and notes by George McLean Harper ... and Louis Eugene Livingood ... New York, W. R. Jenkins; Boston, C. Schoenhof [1893]

Livings, A.
Twelve white flowers, by Frances Livings, and A. Livings. London: Hamilton, Adams & Co., 1888. viii, 47 p. plates. 8°.
"Artist, Frances Livings ... author, A. Livings." — cf. p. [ii].
455030A. 1. Flowers. 2. Livings, Frances. 3. Title.
N. Y. P. L. March 18, 1930

NL 0420176 NN CSmH

Livings, Bess, illus.

Gage, Anne.
Little Brown Bear, story by Anne Gage; pictures by Bess Livings. New York, Grosset & Dunlap, inc., °1934.

Livings, Bess, illus.

[Lowe, Samuel Edward] 1884-
Little rabbit, by Helen Hart [*pseud.*] pictures by Bess Livings. Racine, Wis., Whitman publishing co. [°1934]

Livings, Frances.
Twelve White Flowers
see under Livings, A.

Livings, Theodore, ed.

McDonald, David, 1803-1869.
A treatise on the powers and duties of justices of the peace, mayors, marshals, and constables in the state of Indiana, and on substantive law and procedure, with practical forms and citations, by David McDonald. Revised and enlarged by Louis O. Schroeder. New ed., by Theodore Livings. Cincinnati, The Robert Clarke company, 1896.

[Livingston,]
An address to the Legislature of New-Jersey, on the subject of internal improvements. [n. p., 182-]
27 p. 23½cm.
Signed: Livingston.
1. Camden and Amboy railroad and transportation company. 2. Delaware and Raritan canal company.
CA 7-5068 Unrev'd
Library of Congress HE2791.C185 182-

NL 0420181 DLC

[Livingston.]
An address to the legislature of New-Jersey, on the subject of internal improvements. n. p. [1835.] 27 p. 8°.
Caption-title.
Signed: Livingston.
1. Railways, U. S. (Indiv.): Camden and Amboy. 2. Trenton and New Brunswick Turnpike Company. 3. Title.
N. Y. P. L. October 17, 1917.

NL 0420182 NN

[Livingston,] pseud.
Letters to the President of the United States, in relation to the French spoliations prior to 1800. [n. p., 1841]
46 p. 22½cm.
Signed: Livingston.
1. French spoliation claims. I. Title.
Library of Congress JX238.F75 1841 10-6851

NL 0420183 DLC TxU

VOLUME 336

PZ 5 .L788 Livingston,Mrs.
Love each other; or,Strive to be good. Stories designed to advance the young in virtue and morality. Lowell, S.Wilkins; Boston, Dayton & Wentworth, 1854 [c1851]
106 p. illus. 16 cm.
Includes stories and poems by various authors.

1.Children's literature. I.Title.

NL 0420184 MiU RPB NNC

PZ211 .L78 Livingston, Mrs. ed.
Love each other; or, Strive to be good. Stories designed to advance the young in virtue and morality. Philadelphia, J. W. Bradley, [c1855]
106 p. illus.

NL 0420185 ICU

Livingston, Mrs.
Love each other; or, Strive to be good. Stories designed to advance the young in virtue and morality. By Mrs. Livingston. Boston, Crown and Emery; 1857.
106 p. incl. plates. front. 15 cm.
Prose and poetry.

NL 0420186 RPB

Livingston, Mrs.
Strive to be good; or, Stories designed to advance the young in virtue and morality. By Mrs. Livingston. New York, Fletcher, 1852.
106 p. front., plates.

Contents.--The clever boy, by Mrs. S. C. Hall. --A child's prayer, by W. J. Hamersley.--Grace Vernon.--The cameleopard, or giraffe.--Flattery. --Skating and coasting.--The ostrich.--The garden. --The squirrel.-- The power of kindness.--What good can I do?--The child's prayer, by Elizabeth Doton.--Little Clara, by J. M. Fletcher.--The angel, from the Danish of Hans Christian Andersen.--Cedar trees, by Mary Howitt. --A story about a dog, by T. S. Arthur.--Song of the snowbird, by Rev. F. C. Woodworth.
I. Title.

NL 0420188 NNC

Livingston, A W.
Livingston and the tomato. Being the history of experiences in discovering the choice varieties introduced by him, with practical instructions for growers. By A. W. Livingston. Columbus, O., A. W. Livingston's sons [1893]
1 p. l., [7]-172, [4] p. front. (port.) illus. 19½cm.

1. Tomatoes.

Library of Congress SB349.L78 11—25634

NL 0420189 DLC MBH NN OU NIC

Livingston, Albert Arthur
see
Livingston, Arthur, 1883-

617.61 L786d Livingston, Alexander.
... Dental histology ... Edinburgh, E. & S. Livingstone, 1929.
142p. illus., diagrs. (Outlines of dental science. vol.X.)

1. Histology, Dental

NL 0420191 IU-M OU OC1W OC1W-H DNLM ICRL

Livingston, Alexander C.
...Dynamical similarity in fluid flow. By Alex. C. Livingston ... London: The Draughtsman pub. co., ltd. [1938] 46 p. illus. (incl. charts.) 21½cm.

At head of title: The Association of engineering and shipbuilding draughtsmen. "Session 1937-38." "Bibliography," p. 46.

1. Hydrodynamics, 1938. I. Association of engineering and shipbuilding draughtsmen.
N. Y. P. L. December 20, 1940

NL 0420192 NN

Livingston, Alfred.
Buying a home in Southern California. Dubuque, Iowa, W. C. Brown Co. [°1950]
vi, 74, [1] p. illus. 24 cm.
"Check list of desirable and undesirable factors to be considered when buying a home ..." ([1] p.) has special t. p.

1. Architecture, Domestic—California. 2. Homesites. I. Title.
NA7235.C2L5 728 51-5025

NL 0420193 DLC

Livingston, Alfred.
... Geological journeys in southern California, by Alfred Livingston, jr. [and] William C. Putnam. Los Angeles, California, 1933.
104 p. incl. front., illus., maps, tab., diagrs. 23cm. (Los Angeles junior college. Publication no. 1, Geology ser. no. 1, January 30, 1933)
Contains bibliographies.

1. Geology—California, Southern. I. Putnam, William Clement, 1908- joint author. II. Title.
G S 34—185
U. S. Geol. survey. Library for Library of Congress G(276) L6jp no. 1 QE89.L5

NL 0420194 DI-GS DLC CU-I OKentU OrP OrU

D557.5 L75 Livingston, Alfred
Geological journeys in southern California, by Alfred Livingston, jr. ... Los Angeles, Lymanhouse [1939]
xi, 154, iv p. illus., maps, diagrs. 23½cm.
"Second edition (rewritten and revised)"
Bibliography at end of each chapter.
1. Geology - California, Southern.

NL 0420195 NNC OrP

Livingston, Alfred.
Geological journeys in southern California. [2d ed., rewritten and rev.] Dubuque, W. C. Brown Co. [°1949]
xi, 154, iv p. illus., maps. 23 cm.
Includes bibliographies.

1. Geology—California, Southern. I. Title.
QE89.L5 1949 557.94 50-3536

NL 0420196 DLC CSt

Livingston, Alfred Erwin, 1883-
... The comparative toxicity of thymol and carvacrol (isothymol) by A. E. Livingston, physiologist, United States Public health service ... Washington, Govt. print. off., 1921.
16 p. incl. tables, diagrs. 23½cm.
Reprint no. 666 from the Public health reports, v. 36, no. 23, June 10, 1921 (p. 1317-1331)
Running title: Thymol and carvacrol (isothymol)

1. Thymol. 2. Carvacrol. I. U. S. Public health service. Public health reports. Reprint 666. II. Title.
Library of Congress RM666.T5L5 21-26853
[5]

NL 0420197 DLC MiU

Livingston, Alfred Erwin, 1883-
The effect of castration on the weight of the pituitary body and other glands of internal secretion in the rabbit ... by Alfred Irwin Livingston ... [Boston] 1916.
1 p. l., p. 153-185. diagrs. 26½cm.
Thesis (PH. D.)—Cornell university, 1914.
"Reprinted from the American journal of physiology, vol. XL, no. 2, April, 1916."
Bibliography: p. 184-185

1. Castration. 2. Pituitary body.
Library of Congress QP251.L5 16-15553
Cornell Univ. Libr.

NL 0420198 NIC MiU DLC

Livingston, Alfred Erwin, 1883-
The management of greenhouses and frames, by Alfred E. Livingston ... London, C. Lockwood & son, 1927.
4 p. l., 127 p. illus. 19cm. (*Lettered on cover: Lockwood's manuals*)

1. Greenhouses.
Library, U. S. Dept. of Agriculture 90L76 Agr 27-832

NL 0420199 DNAL NN

Livingston, Alfred Erwin, 1883-
... Mercury fulminate as a skin irritant. By A. E. Livingston ...
(*In* U. S. Hygienic laboratory. Bulletin. Washington, Govt. print. off., 1920. 23cm. no. 126, p. 203-211. fold. tab.)
Bibliography: p. 210-211.

1. Mercury—Toxicology. I. Title.
Library of Congress RA421.U4 no. 126 20-27586
——— Copy 2. RA1242.T7V7

NL 0420200 DLC NcD MiU OU OCU OO OC1 MB

Livingston, Alfred Erwin, 1883- joint author.
Voegtlin, Carl, 1879-
... The toxic action of "parazol" (crude dichlordinitrobenzene). By Carl Voegtlin, A. E. Livingston, and C. W. Hooper ...
(*In* U. S. Hygienic laboratory. Bulletin. Washington, Govt. print. off., 1920. 23cm. no. 126, p. 183-202 incl. tables. diagrs. (part fold.))

Livingston, Alfred Erwin, 1883-
Your flower garden and the things that matter, by Alfred E. Livingston... London: C. Lockwood & Son, 1929. xi, 208 p. col'd front., plates. 12°.

433685A. 1. Horticulture.
N. Y. P. L. September 28, 1929

NL 0420202 NN

VOLUME 336

Livingston, Alfred Tennyson, 1849-1923.
The sea and other verses. By Alfred Tennyson Livingston. ⟨For private distribution⟩ [Buffalo, N. Y., Kittinger printing co.] 1891.
126 p. 24½cm.

I. Title.
Library of Congress PS3523.I 9484 1891 33-31980
Copyright 1892: 2533 811.49

NL 0420203 DLC NBi

Livingston, Alice E., comp.
Colville, William Wilberforce Juvenal, 1862-
Glints of wisdom, helpful sayings for leisure moments; abstracts from lectures delivered by W. J. Colville ... Comp. from epitomized reports by Alice E. Livingston ... Boston, Colby & Rich, 1895.

Livingston, Anne.
Daily worker. Words by Will Ferris. Music by Anne Livingston. N. Y.: Pierre Degeyter music club [1935?] 1 l. 28cm.
Score: S.A.T.B. Another version for 1 voice and piano. English words. Caption-title.

1. Bolshevism—Songs. I. Ferris, Will. Daily worker. II. Pierre Degeyter music club of New York City.
N. Y. P. L. June 11, 1937

NL 0420205 NN

Livingston, Anne.

Statewide recreation project (*Florida*)
Hand-book on rhythm-bands. Recreational music. Work projects administration of Florida. [Jacksonville] Statewide recreation project [1940]

Livingston, Anne.
Leadership training in recreation, 1951-1952; summary of the course, Social recreation and playground activities, offered at Chattahoochee, Florida, March 10-12, 1952. Gainesville, General Extension Division of Florida, University of Florida [1952]
unpaged. illus. 28 cm.

1. Recreation leadership.
GV14.5.L5 793.07 52-62849 ‡

NL 0420207 DLC

Livingston, Anne.
...Social recreation institute... Oct. 14-18, 1946
see under Austin, Tex. Recreation dept.

Livingston, Anne Home (Shippen) 1763-1841.
Nancy Shippen, her journal book; the international romance of a young lady of fashion of colonial Philadelphia, with letters to her and about her. Compiled and edited by Ethel Armes ... Philadelphia, London, J. B. Lippincott company, 1935.
3 p. l., 5-348, [1] p. col. front., 1 illus., plates, ports., facsims. (incl. music) fold. geneal. tab., coat of arms. 23cm.
Plans on lining-papers.
"First edition."
Bibliography: p. 317-[321]

1. Shippen family. 2. Livingston family. I. Armes, Ethel Marie, ed. II. Title.
35-32239
Library of Congress E302.6.L67L6
[a43k1] 920.7

00 OU
MoU NcD PP PPT PHi PPA PHC ViU OC1W OLak OC1h OC1
NL 0420209 DLC WaS OrP IdU MiU CoFS NIC NN MB CU

---

*
PS586
.Z92
.L56S2
1817
Livingston, Anne Home (Shippen) 1763-1841.
Sacred records, abridged in verse. Consisting of some of the parables and miracles, the life, death, resurrection and ascension of the Blessed Saviour. Philadelphia: Printed and published for the Author, by T. S. Manning. 1817.
iv, [5]-124 p. 18½cm.
Wegelin, 1042.

NL 0420210 ViU RPB

[LIVINGSTON, Anson].
Petition, in behalf of the heirs of Henry Brockholst Livingston, for half pay and arrears of pay, for services under resolve of Oct.21, 1780, a[ ] March 8, 1785. [Wash. 1[]59.]

pp. 6.

NL 0420211 MH

Livingston, Archibald R
Wild flowers [of Colorado, California and Oregon] n.p. n.d.
23 v.of mounted col.photographs. 21 X 30cm.

Contents.
[v.1-3] Colorado.
[v.4-15] Fremont county, Colorado.
[v.16-19] California.
[v.20] Southern California except where marked New Mexico and Arizona.
[v.21-23] Oregon: Jackson and Josephine counties.

NL 0420212 OrU

Livingston, Armitage T.
Verses, by Armitage T. Livingston. Philadelphia, 1915.
61 p. 19½cm.

Library of Congress PS3523.I 945 1915 16-735

NL 0420213 DLC

Livingston, Armstrong, 1885-
The doublecross, by Armstrong Livingston ... New York, R. D. Henkle co., inc. [c1929]
316 p. 19½cm.

I. Title.
Library of Congress PZ3.L759Do 29-10176
——— Copy 2.

NL 0420214 DLC MH

Livingston, Armstrong, 1885-
In cold blood, by Armstrong Livingston. Indianapolis, The Bobbs-Merrill company [c1931]
4 p. l., 11-316 p. 19½cm.
"First edition."

I. Title.
Library of Congress PZ3.L759 In 31-23468

NL 0420215 DLC MB

Livingston, Armstrong, 1885-
The juju-man, by Armstrong Livingston and Thomas H. Griffiths ... New York, Siebel publishing corporation, 1926.
3 p. l., 277 p. 20½cm.

I. Griffiths, Thomas H., joint author. II. Title.
Library of Congress PZ3.L759Ju 27-16677

NL 0420216 DLC OC1 OO

Livingston, Armstrong, 1885-
Light-fingered ladies; a detective story. New York city, Chelsea house [c.1927]

NL 0420217 MH

Livingston, Armstrong, 1885-
Magic for murder, by Armstrong Livingston. London, Skeffington & son, ltd. [1936]
3 p. l., 11-254 p. 19cm.

I. Title.
Library of Congress PZ3.L759Mag 36-9854

NL 0420218 DLC

Livingston, Armstrong, 1885-
Magic for murder. [2d ed.] NY, Delta Library [c1945]
127 p. (PDC, 2)
A cavalcade book

NL 0420219 MH

LIVINGSTON, ARMSTRONG, 1885-
The monk of Hambleton, by Armstrong Livingston. Cleveland, O.; New York, N.Y., International fiction library [c1928]
1 p.l.,9-318 p. 19½cm.

679073A. 1. Fiction, English. I. Title.

NL 0420220 NN

Livingston, Armstrong, 1885-
The monk of Hambleton, by Armstrong Livingston. New York, R. D. Henkle co., inc., 1928.
v p., 1 l., 9-318 p. 19½cm.

I. Title.
Library of Congress PZ3.L759Mo 28-4239

NL 0420221 DLC ODW

Livingston, Armstrong, 1885-
The monster in the pool, by Armstrong Livingston. Indianapolis, The Bobbs-Merrill company [c1929]
320 p. 19½cm.

I. Title.
Library of Congress PZ3.L759Mon 29-16669

NL 0420222 DLC

VOLUME 336

Livingston, Armstrong, 1885-
The monster in the pool, by Armstrong Livingston NewYork, Chicago, A. L. Burt co., c1929.
320 p.

NL 0420223 OO

Livingston, Armstrong, 1885-
... Murder is easy! New York, R. Speller [c1936]
304 p. 19½cm.
At head of title: By Livingston Armstrong.
"First edition."

I. Title.
Library of Congress PZ3.L759Mr 37-1609

NL 0420224 DLC

Livingston, Armstrong, 1885-
The murder trap, by Armstrong Livingston. Indianapolis, The Bobbs-Merrill co. [c1930]
320 p. 19½cm.
"First edition."

I. Title.
Library of Congress PZ3.L759Mu 31-526

NL 0420225 DLC MB

Livingston, Armstrong, 1885–
The murdered and the missing, by Armstrong Livingston and Capt. John G. Stein. New York, Stephen-Paul, 1947.
xi p., 1 l., 242 p. 19½cm.
"First edition."

1. New York (City) Police dept. Missing persons bureau. 2. Crime and criminals—New York (City) I. Stein, John G., 1887– joint author. II. Title.
HV6795.N5L6 364.9747 47-20477

NL 0420226 DLC CU-I TxU

Livingston, Armstrong, 1885-
The mystery of the twin rubies, by Armstrong Livingston. New York, Moffat, Yard and company, 1922.
v, 330 p. 19½cm.

I. Title.
Library of Congress PZ3.L759My 23-2974

NL 0420227 DLC CtY MB

Livingston, Armstrong, 1885-
...Night of crime. New York: Sovereign house [c1938]
315 p. 19½cm.

26690B. 1. Fiction, English. I. Title.
N. Y. P. L. March 28, 1941

NL 0420228 NN

LIVINGSTON, ARMSTRONG, 1885-
On the right wrists; a detective story, by Armstrong Livingston. New York city: Chelsea House [c1925]
314 p. 19½cm.

118466B. 1. Fiction, English. I. Title.

NL 0420229 NN

Livingston, Armstrong, 1885-
Trackless death, by Armstrong Livingston. Indianapolis, The Bobbs-Merrill company [c1930]
328 p. 19½cm.
"First edition."

I. Title.
Library of Congress PZ3.L759Tr 30-10978

NL 0420230 DLC

Livingston, Arthur, publisher.
Picturesque Poughkeepsie together with views of Vassar college
see under title

---

*Livingston, Arthur, 1883- tr.

Montessori, Maria, 1870-
The advanced Montessori method ... by Maria Montessori ... tr. from the Italian ... New York, Frederick A. Stokes company [c1917]

---

*Livingston, Arthur, 1883- tr.

Blasco Ibáñez, Vicente, 1867-1928.
The Borgias; or, At the feet of Venus, by Vicente Blasco Ibañez ... version from the Spanish by Arthur Livingston. New York, E. P. Dutton & co., inc. [c1930]

***Livingston, Arthur, 1883- tr.**

Croce, Benedetto, 1866-
The conduct of life, by Benedetto Croce, authorised translation by Arthur Livingston. New York, Harcourt, Brace and company [c1924]

---

*Livingston, Arthur, 1883- tr.

Pirandello, Luigi, 1867-1936.
Each in his own way, and two other plays, by Luigi Pirandello, from the Italian by Arthur Livingston. New York, E. P. Dutton & company [c1923]

Livingston, Arthur, 1883-
Essays on modern Italian literature. New York, Vanni [1950]
197 p. 18 cm. (Old and new sheaves)

1. Italian literature—20th cent.—Addresses, essays, lectures.
Full name: Albert Arthur Livingston.
PQ4087.L5 850.904 50-2600
[7]

PPD DLC
NL 0420236 FTaSU WaSp OrU NN NcU CoU GU UU TxU ViU

---

*Livingston, Arthur, 1883- joint author.

Nardelli, Federico Vittore, 1891-
Gabriel the archangel ⟨Gabriele d'Annunzio⟩ [by] Federico Nardelli and Arthur Livingston. New York, Harcourt, Brace and company [c1931]

Livingston, Arthur, 1883- tr.

Farrère, Claude, 1876-
The house of the secret (La maison des hommes vivants) by Claude Farrère; authorized translation by Arthur Livingston. New York, E. P. Dutton & company [c1923]

Livingston, Arthur, 1883-
*SCA James Howell e la città vergine (1618-1651)
.5276 Roma, Tip. F. Centenari, 1912.
.1 12 p. 24cm.
"Estratto dal 'Fanfulla della Domenica' N.20, del 19 Maggio 1912."

1. Howell, James, 1594?-1666. Survey of the signorie of Venice. 2. Venice--Pol. & govt.

NL 0420239 MB

---

*Livingston, Arthur, 1883- tr.

Blasco Ibáñez, Vicente, 1867-1928.
The Knight of the Virgin, by Vicente Blasco Ibañez .. translation by Arthur Livingston. New York, E. P. Dutton & co., inc. [c1930]

---

*Livingston, Arthur, 1883- tr.

Pirandello, Luigi, 1867-1936.
The late Mattia Pascal (Il fu Mattia Pascal) by Luigi Pirandello; translated from the Italian by Arthur Livingston. New York, E. P. Dutton & company [c1923]

Livingston, Arthur, 1883- tr.

Laveille, Auguste Pierre, 1856-1928.
A life of Cardinal Mercier, by Monsignor A. Laveille ... translated by Arthur Livingstone [!] New York, London, The Century co. [c1928]

Livingston, Arthur, 1883- tr.

Machiavelli, Niccolò, 1469-1527.
The living thoughts of Machiavelli, presented by Count Carlo Sforza ... New York, Toronto, Longmans, Green and co., 1940.

Livingston, Arthur, 1883- tr.

FOR OTHER EDITIONS SEE MAIN ENTRY

Mazzini, Giuseppe, 1805-1872.
The living thoughts of Mazzini, presented by Ignazio Silone. London [etc.] Cassell and company, limited [1939]

---

*Livingston, Arthur, 1883- tr.

Blasco Ibáñez, Vicente, 1867-1928.
The Mayflower (Flor de mayo); a tale of the Valencian seashore, by Vicente Blasco Ibañez; tr. from the Spanish by Arthur Livingston. New York, E. P. Dutton & company [c1921]

VOLUME 336

Livingston, Arthur, 1883- ed.

Da Ponte, Lorenzo, 1749–1838.
Memoirs of Lorenzo Da Ponte, translated by Elisabeth Abbott from the Italian; edited and annotated by Arthur Livingston. Philadelphia & London, J. B. Lippincott company, 1929.

Livingston, Arthur, 1883- tr.

Blasco Ibáñez, Vicente, 1867–1928.
Mexico in revolution, by V. Blasco Ibañez ... tr. by Arthur Livingston and José Padin. New York, E. P. Dutton & company [°1920]

---

*Livingston, Arthur, 1883- ed. and tr.

Pareto, Vilfredo, 1848–1923.
The mind and society <Trattato di sociologia generale> by Vilfredo Pareto; edited by Arthur Livingston; translated by Andrew Bongiorno and Arthur Livingston, with the advice and active cooperation of James Harvey Rogers ... New York, Harcourt, Brace and company [°1935]

Livingston, Arthur, 1883- tr.

Aubry, Octave, 1881–
Napoleon, soldier and emperor, by Octave Aubry; authorized translation by Arthur Livingston; with 25 illustrations in doubletone. Philadelphia, New York [etc.] J. B. Lippincott company, 1938.

Livingston, Arthur, joint tr.

Blasco Ibáñez, Vicente, 1867–1928.
A novelist's tour of the world, by Vicente Blasco Ibáñez ... authorized translation by Leo Ongley and Arthur Livingston ... New York, E. P. Dutton & company [°1926]

---

*Livingston, Arthur, 1883- ed. and tr.

Pirandello, Luigi, 1867–1936.
The one-act plays of Luigi Pirandello ... edited by Arthur Livingston; translations by Elisabeth Abbott, Arthur Livingston and Blanche Valentine Mitchell. New York, E. P. Dutton & company [°1928]

Livingston, Arthur, 1883- tr.

Blasco Ibáñez, Vicente, 1867–1928.
... The phantom with wings of gold, a novel; translation by Arthur Livingston. New York, E. P. Dutton & co. inc. [°1931]

Livingston, Arthur, *1883–*
Una poesia di Gian Francesco Busenello in Inghilterra (1657–1667). [By] Arthur Livingston.
— Venezia. Istituto veneto di arti grafiche. 1908. 21 pp. 24 cm.
"Estratto da l'Ateneo veneto anno 31, fasc. 1, luglio-agosto 1908."

?700 — Busenello, Giovanni Francesco.

NL 0420253 MB MH

Livingston, Arthur, 1883- tr.

Blasco Ibáñez, Vicente, 1867–1928.
The pope of the sea, an historical medley, by Vicente Blasco Ibañez ... from the Spanish by Arthur Livingston. New York, E. P. Dutton & company [°1927]

Livingston, Arthur, 1883- ed.

Mosca, Gaetano, 1858–
The ruling class (Elementi di scienze politica) by Gaetano Mosca. Translation by Hannah D. Kahn. Edited and revised, with an introduction, by Arthur Livingston. 1st ed. New York and London, McGraw-Hill book company, inc., 1939.

---

*Livingston, Arthur, 1883- tr.

Aubry, Octave, 1881–
St. Helena, by Octave Aubry; authorized translation by Arthur Livingston; with 43 illustrations in doubletone. Philadelphia, London, J. B. Lippincott company, 1936.

Livingston, Arthur, 1883- tr.

Aubry, Octave, 1881–
The second empire, by Octave Aubry; translated by Arthur Livingston; 27 illustrations. Philadelphia, New York, J. B. Lippincott company [°1940]

Livingston, Arthur, 1883- tr.

Ferrero, Guglielmo, 1871–
The seven vices, a novel of Italy in our own times, by Guglielmo Ferrero, authorized translation by Arthur Livingston and Elisabeth Abbott ... New York, Harcourt, Brace and company [°1929]

---

*Livingston, Arthur, 1883- tr.

Scheffer, Paul.
... Seven years in soviet Russia, with a retrospect; authorized translation by Arthur Livingston. London & New York, Putnam [1931]

Livingston, Arthur, *1883–*
Some early Italian parallels to the locution *the Sick Man of the East.* (In Modern Language Association of America. Publications. Vol. 25, pp. 459–485. Baltimore. 1910.)

H5598 — Sick Man of the East. The phrase.

NL 0420260 MB

Livingston, Arthur, 1883-

Busenello, Giovanni Francesco, 1598–1659.
I sonetti morali ed amorosi di Gian Francesco Busenello (1598–1659) Testo critico per cura di Arthur Livingston. Venezia, Prem. stab. grafico G. Fabbris di S., 1911.

Livingston, Arthur, 1883- tr.

PZ10
.3
.Q48
So 5

FOR OTHER EDITIONS SEE MAIN ENTRY

Quiroga, Horacio, 1879–1937.
South American jungle tales, by Horacio Quiroga. Authorized translation from the Spanish (Cuentos de la selva) by Arthur Livingston, illustrated by A. L. Ripley. New York, Dodd, Mead & company, 1943.

Livingston, Arthur, 1883- joint tr.

Blasco Ibáñez, Vicente, 1867–1928.
The torrent (Entre naranjos) by Vicente Blasco Ibañez, tr. from the Spanish by Isaac Goldberg and Arthur Livingston. New York, E. P. Dutton & company [°1921]

---

*Livingston, Arthur, 1883- tr.

Albertini, Alberto, 1879–
Two years [by] Alberto Albertini; translated from the Italian by Arthur Livingston. New York, The Viking press, 1936.

---

*Livingston, Arthur, 1883- tr.

Blasco Ibáñez, Vicente, 1867–1928.
Unknown lands, the story of Columbus, by Vicente Blasco Ibañez ... translated from the Spanish by Arthur Livingston. New York, E. P. Dutton & co., inc. [°1929]

PQ4617 **Livingston, Arthur,** 1883
.B2Z8L7 ... La vita veneziana nelle opere di Gian Francesco Busenello. Venezia, V. Callegari, 1913.

[5], 483 p. front. (port.) 24cm.
At head of title: Arthur Livingston.
"Bibliografia di G. F. Busenello": p. 402–463.

1. Busenello, Giovanni Francesco, 1598–1659. 2. Venice—Soc. life & cust.

NL 0420266 ICU NN CtY PBm MH CU RPB MeB ICN ViU NRU

---

*Livingston, Arthur, 1883- tr.

Moravia, Alberto, 1907–
... Wheel of fortune; translation by Arthur Livingston. New York, The Viking press, 1937.

517.3 Livingston, Arthur Eugene.
L762 Some Hausdorff means which exhibit the Gibbs' phenomenon. 1952.
40 l.

Thesis, Ph.D., Oregon, Dept. of Mathematics.
Bibliography: l.40.

NL 0420268 OrU

---

*F612 Livingston, Mrs. B J , comp.
.M46L7 Scrapbook of newspaper clippings chiefly concerning Martin County, Minnesota. Fairmont, Minn., 191-?
2 v. ports. 30cm. (v.2:24x29cm.)

Includes clippings of the columns: Center chain, and Links from the center chain, which probably appeared in the Martin County sentinal.

NL 0420269 MnHi

Livingston, Bill, 1911–

I wish you the best of everything tho' I got the worst of it all. Words and music by Bill Livingston, Arthur Terker & Sammy Mysels. New York, H. S. Gordon inc. [c1939]

First line: You brought me heaven with your tender charms.
Chorus: You made me love you.

Printed for the Music Division

I. Terker, Arthur. II. Mysels, Sammy. III. Song index (3).
N. Y. P. L. April 10, 1946

NL 0420270 NN

VOLUME 336

Livingston, Brockholst, 1757-1823.

Works by this author printed in America before 1801 are available in this library in the Readex Microprint edition of Early American Imprints published by the American Antiquarian Society.
This collection is arranged according to the numbers in Charles Evans' American Bibliography.

Revised card; previously printed with heading: Livingston, Henry Brockholst, 1757-1823.

NL 0420271 DLC

[Livingston, Brockholst] 1757-1823.
Democracy, an epic poem, by Aquiline Nimblechops, Democrat. [i.e. Brockholst Livingston] Canto first. New York, Printed for the author, about 1790.
80 p.
uncut copy.

NL 0420272 NN PPL

[Livingston, Brockholst] 1757-1823.
Democracy: an epic poem, by Aquiline Nimble-Chops, Democrat [pseud.] Canto first. New-York: Printed for the author [1794]
20 p. 20cm.
"Printed in New-York, in March, 1794 ... Written in consequence of a tumultous meeting of the citizens of that place, instigated by a few popular demagogues, for the purpose of prescribing to Congress the adortion of hostile measures against Great Britain. The second canto ... was prepared for the press immediately after the appearance of the first, but the timidity of the booksellers, and the peculiar circumstances of the times prevented its publication." cf. The Echo, edited by R. Alsop and T. Dwight, p. 196.
Extracts from cantos 1 and 2 appeared in "The Echo."
1. U. S.—Pol. & govt.—1789-1797. 2. U. S.—For. rel.—1789-1797. I. Title.
Library of Congress E311.L78 9-7784
——— Copy 2. [With Randolph, Edmund. A vindication of Mr. Randolph's resignation. Philadelphia, 1795] E311.R2 copy 2

MWA NHi MB NN RPB RPJCB PBL
NL 0420273 DLC MiU-C ViU ICN NcD TxU ICU CtY MBAt

[Livingston, Brockholst] 1757-1823.
Democracy. [Canto first]
(In The Magazine of history, with notes and queries. Tarrytown, N. Y., 1922. 26½cm. Extra number. no. 84, p. [37]-59)
Author's name appears in Preface.
"Printed in New York, in March, 1794 ... Written in consequence of a tumultuous meeting of the citizens of that place, instigated by a few popular demagogues, for the purpose of prescribing to Congress the adoption of hostile measures against Great Britain. The second canto ... was prepared for the press immediately after the appearance of the first, but the timidity of the booksellers, and the peculiar circumstances of the times prevented its publication." cf. The Echo [ed. by R. Alsop and T. Dwight] 1807, p. 196.
Extracts from cantos 1 and 2 appeared in "The Echo".
1. U. S.—Pol. & govt.—1789-1797. 2. U. S.—For. rel.—1789-1797. I. Title.
name: Henry Brockholst Livingston 22-24419
Library of Congress E173.M24 no. 84

NL 0420274 DLC MB MiU OCl

M/0290 L786at
Livingston, Burton Edward, 1875-
Atmometers of porous porcelain and paper, their use in physiological ecology. [Brooklyn, N.Y.] [1935]
p.438-472. illus., map. 25½cm.
(Reprinted from Ecology, v.16, no.3., July, 1935

NL 0420275 DAS

Livingston, Burton Edward, 1875-
Atmometry and the porous cup atmometer; [by] Burton Edward Livingston. [Baltimore,] 1915. 1 p.l., 21-30, 51-74, 95-111, 143-149 p. diagr. 8°.
Repr.: Plant world. v. 18, 1915.

1. Atmometer.
N. Y. P. L. September 28, 1917.

NL 0420276 NN NjP IU

QC916 .L75
Livingston, Burton Edward, 1875-
Atmometry and the porous cup atmometer [by] Burton Edward Livingston ... [Washington, D. C.] 1915.
[61] p. illus. 28cm.
Various paging.
Reprinted from the Plant world, vol. 18, 1915.

1. Atmometer.

NL 0420277 ICU

Livingston, Burton Edward, 1875-
Atmometric units & Vapor tension deficit.
1917

NL 0420278 DAS

Livingston, Burton Edward, 1875-
Atmospheric influence on evaporation and its direct measurement.
(In U. S. Dept. of agriculture. Weather bureau. Monthly weather review. v. 43, p. 126-131 incl. diagrs. 31cm. Washington, 1915)
"References and notes": p. 131.

1. Evaporation.
Agr 15-930
Library, U. S. Dept. of Agriculture 1W37M vol. 43

NL 0420279 DNAL DLC NN OO OU

Livingston, Burton Edward, 1875- ed.
Botanical abstracts; a monthly serial furnishing abstracts and citations of publications in the international field of botany in its broadest sense. v. 1-15; Sept. 1918-July/Nov. 1926. Baltimore, Williams & Wilkins company, 1918-27.

Livingston, Burton Edward, 1875-
... Chemical stimulation of a green alga, by Burton Edward Livingston. New York, 1905.
cover-title, 34 p. illus. 24cm. (Contributions from the New York botanical garden. no. 63)
From the Bulletin of the Torrey botanical club, 32. 1905.

1. Stigeoclonium. 2. Plants, Effect of chemicals on.
CA 9—314 Unrev'd
Library of Congress QK1.N515 no. 63

NL 0420281 DLC OU OO MiU

Livingston, Burton Edward, 1875-
Climatic areas of the United States as related to plant growth. By Burton Edward Livingston. [Philadelphia,] 1913. (1)258-275 p., 3 maps. 8°.
Cover-title.
Repr.: Proc. of the Amer. Philosophical Soc. v. 52, April 1913.

1. Botany.—Ecology, U. S.
N. Y. P. L. September 28, 1917.

NL 0420282 NN DAS OO

Livingston, Burton Edward, 1875-
The distribution of the plant societies of Kent county, Michigan. (In: Michigan. Geological Survey Board. Annual report...1901. Lansing, 1901. 8°. p. 79-108, 1 chart.)

1. Botany, U. S.: Mich.: Kent county.
N. Y. P. L. August 7, 1912.

NL 0420283 NN

Livingston, Burton Edward, 1875-
The distribution of vegetation in the United States, as related to climatic conditions [by] Burton E. Livingston and Forrest Shreve. [Washington] Carnegie institution of Washington, 1921.
xvi, 590 p. maps (2 fold.) tables, diagrs. 25½cm. (On verso of t.-p.: Carnegie institution of Washington. Publication no. 284)
"Literature cited": p. 587-590.

1. Botany—Geographical distribution. 2. Botany—U. S. 3. U. S.—Climate. I. Shreve, Forrest, 1878-
21—15878
Library of Congress QK115.L8
——— Copy 2. [s33k5]

CaBVaU OrCS OClWHi DAS OCU OO OU MiU
NcU PU NIC MH CU NNBG NcD MH-A NcRA ViU MB ICJ OrP
NL 0420284 DLC Wa WaWW OrU OrPR CoU IdU WaSp MH-GM

Livingston, Burton Edward, 1875-
... The effect of the osmotic pressure of the medium upon the growth and reproduction of organisms ... Chicago [University of Chicago press] 1903.
1 p. l., [123]-144 p. 22cm.
Thesis (PH. D.)—University of Chicago.
"The chapter constituting this dissertation is taken from a larger work, entitled The rôle of diffusion and osmotic pressure in plants, which has appeared as volume VIII, second series, of the Decennial publications of the University of Chicago."

1. Osmosis.
7-40987
Library of Congress QH611.L76

NL 0420285 DLC OU NN NjP NIC

Livingston, Burton Edward, 1875
Further studies on the properties of unproductive soils. By Burton Edward Livingston, assisted by Charles A. Jensen, J. F. Breazeale, F. R. Pember, and J. J. Skinner.
Washington. 1907. 71 pp. Plates. [United States. Department of Agriculture. Bureau of Soils. Bulletin. 36.] 23 cm.
Literature, pp. 57-62.

H1086 — Jensen, Charles A., jt. auth. — Breazeale, James F., jt. auth.—Pember, F. R., jt. auth. — Skinner, J. J., jt. auth. — Soil.

NL 0420286 MB DNAL MiU OO

Livingston, Burton Edward, 1875- , and E. B. Shreve.
Improvements in the method for determining the transpiring power of plant surfaces by hygrometric paper. [By] Burton E. Livingston...and Edith B. Shreve... [Baltimore,] 1916. p. 287-309. Tables. 8°.
Cover-title.
Repr.: Plant world. v. 19, Oct. 1916.

1. Plants.—Transpiration. 2. Shreve, Edith Bellamy, jt. au.
N. Y. P. L. September 28, 1917

NL 0420287 NN

Livingston, Burton Edward, 1875-
——— The laboratory of plant physiology [at Johns Hopkins University. Baltimore. 1916]. 8°. Plate and plans.
From the Johns Hopkins university circular, 1916, N. S., I, 40-45.

NL 0420288 MH-A

Livingston, Burton Edward, 1875-
A modification of the Bellani porous plate atmometer. [New York,] 1915. 6 p. diagr. 8°.
Caption-title.
Signed: Burton E. Livingston.
Repr.: Science. New series. v. 41, June 11, 1915.

1. Atmometer.
N. Y. P. L. September 28, 1917.

NL 0420289 NN

VOLUME 336

Livingston, Burton Edward, 1875–
Osmotic pressure and related forces as environmental factors. ₍By₎ Burton Edward Livingston. ₍Baltimore,₎ 1913. p. 165–176. 8°.

Cover-title.
Repr.: Plant world. v. 16, June 1913.

1. Plants.—Osmosis.
N. Y. P. L. September 28, 1917.

NL 0420290 NN

Livingston, Burton Edward, 1875– joint auth.

Hutchins, Lee M 1888–
Oxygen-supplying power of the soil as indicated by color changes in alkaline pyrogallol solution. By Lee M. Hutchins ... and Burton E. Livingston ...

(In U. S. Dept. of agriculture. Journal of agricultural research. vol. xxv, no. 3, p. 133-140. 25cm. Washington, 1923)

Livingston, Burton Edward, 1875–
Paper atmometers for studies in evaporation. By Burton E. Livingston. ₍Baltimore,₎ 1911. (1)282–289 p. diagr. 8°.

Cover-title.
Repr.: Plant world. v. 14, 1911.

1. Atmometer. 2. Evaporation.
N. Y. P. L. September 29, 1917.

NL 0420292 NN DAS

Livingston, Burton Edward, 1875–
Physiological temperature indices for the study of plant growth in relation to climatic conditions, by Burton Edward Livingston.

(In Physiological researches. Baltimore, Md., 1916. 26½cm. Vol. 1, p. 399-420. incl. tables, charts, 1 diagr.)
Botanical contribution from the Johns Hopkins University, no. 49.
"Literature cited," p. 420.

NL 0420293 ICJ OO OU

Livingston, Burton Edward, 1875– ed.
FOR OTHER EDITIONS SEE MAIN ENTRY

Palladin, Vladimir Ivanovich, 1859–1922.
Plant physiology, by Vladimir I. Palladin ... Authorized English ed. based on the German translation of the 6th Russian ed. and on the 7th Russian ed. (1914) Edited by Burton Edward Livingston ... with 173 illustrations. Philadelphia, P. Blakiston's son & co. °1918.

Livingston, Burton Edward, 1875–
Present problems in soil physics as related to plant activities. ₍By₎ Professor Burton E. Livingston. ₍Salem, Mass.₎ 1912. p. 294–301. 8°.

Caption-title.
Repr.: Amer. naturalist. v. 46, May 1912.

1. Soils.—Moisture.
N. Y. P. L. September 28, 1917.

NL 0420295 NN

Livingston, Burton Edward, 1875–
A quarter century of growth in plant physiology. ₍By₎ Burton Edward Livingston. ₍Baltimore,₎ 1917. 15 p. 8°.

Cover-title.
Repr.: Plant world. v. 20, Jan. 1917.

1. Botany (Physiological and structural).
N. Y. P. L. September 28, 1917.

NL 0420296 NN

Livingston, Burton Edward, 1875–
The relation of desert plants to soil moisture and to evaporation, by Burton Edward Livingston. Washington, D. C., Carnegie institution of Washington, 1906.

78 p. illus., diagrs. 25½ cm. (On verso of t.-p.: Carnegie institution of Washington. Publication no. 50)
"Literature cited": p. 77–78.

1. Plants, Effect of evaporation on. 2. Botany—Ecology.

QK921.L78 6—34017

IdU
DAS ViU ICJ MB NN OCl TU OClW OO MiU OU OCU CU OrP
NL 0420297 DLC CaBVaU Wa WaWW OrCS WaSp OrU NcD MHA

Livingston, Burton Edward, 1875–
Relation of soil moisture to desert vegetation... ₍By₎ Burton Edward Livingston. ₍Chicago:₎ University of Chicago Press, 1910. p. 241–256. diagr. 8°.

Cover-title.
Repr.: Botanical gazette, v. 50, Oct. 1910.

1. Soils.—Moisture. 2. Botany.—Ecology. 3. Deserts.
N. Y. P. L. September 28, 1917.

NL 0420298 NN

Livingston, Burton Edward, 1875–
The relation of soils to natural vegetation in Roscommon and Crawford counties, Michigan. (In: Michigan. Geological Survey Board. Annual report...1903. Lansing, 1905. 8°. p. 9-31, 1 chart.)

1. Soils and vegetation, U. S.: Mich.
N. Y. P. L. August 7, 1912

NL 0420299 NN

Livingston, Burton Edward, 1875– , and W. H. Brown.
Relation of the daily march of transpiration to variations in the water content of foliage leaves. ₍By₎ Burton Edward Livingston and William Henry Brown. ₍Chicago, 1912.₎ p. 309–330. Tables. 8°.

Caption-title.
Repr.: Botanical gazette, v. 53.

1. Plants.—Transpiration. 2. Brown, William Henry, 1884– , jt. au.
N. Y. P. L. September 29, 1917.

NL 0420300 NN

Livingston, Burton Edward, 1875–
The relation of the osmotic pressure of the cell sap in plants to arid habitats. ₍By₎ Burton Edward Livingston. ₍Baltimore,₎ 1911. (1)154–164 p. 8°.

Caption-title.
Repr.: Plant world. v. 14, 1911.

1. Plants.—Osmosis.
N. Y. P. L. September 28, 1917.

NL 0420301 NN

Livingston, Burton Edward, 1875–
... Relation of transpiration to growth in wheat ... ₍by₎ Burton Edward Livingston. ₍Chicago₎ University of Chicago press ₍1905?₎

₍1₎ p., p. 178–195. illus. 25cm. (Contributions from the Hull botanical laboratory, LXVII (i. e. LXXVII))
Reprinted from the Botanical gazette, 40:178–195, September, 1905.

1. Plants—Transpiration. ₍1. Plant transpiration₎ 2. Wheat ₍Growth₎
Agr 11–2067 Revised
Library, U. S. Dept. of Agriculture 451C431 no. 77

NL 0420302 DNAL MiU

Livingston, Burton Edward, 1875–
The rôle of diffusion and osmotic pressure in plants, by Burton Edward Livingston ... Chicago, The University of Chicago press, 1903.

xiii p., 1 l., 149 p. 23cm. (Chicago. University. The decennial publications. 2d series, v. 8)
Bibliography: p. 2

1. Plants, Motion of fluids in. 2. Osmosis.

Library of Congress QH611.L78 3—9911

NIC NjP NcRA MiU OU OCl OClW TU OOxM ViU
NL 0420303 DLC MB NN ICJ MtU IdU OrPR WaWW OrCS WaTC

Livingston, Burton Edward, 1875–
A schematic representation of the water relations of plants, a pedagogical suggestion; ₍by₎ Burton Edward Livingston. ₍Baltimore,₎ 1911. p. 214–217. 8°.

Caption-title.
Repr.: Plant world. v. 15, 1912.

1. Plants.—Transpiration. 2. Soils.—Moisture.
N. Y. P. L. September 29, 1917.

NL 0420304 NN

Livingston, Burton Edward, 1875–
A single index to represent both moisture and temperature conditions as related to plants, by Burton Edward Livingston.

(In Physiological researches. Baltimore, Md., 1916. 26½cm. Vol. 1, p. 421-440. incl. tables, 1 chart.)
Botanical contribution from the Johns Hopkins University, no. 51.
"Literature cited," p. 439-440.

NL 0420305 ICJ DAS OU OO

Livingston, Burton Edward, 1875–
... Studies on the properties of an unproductive soil. By Burton Edward Livingston, J. C. Britton, and F. R. Reid. Washington, Govt. print. off., 1905.

39 p. 23cm. (U. S. Dept. of agriculture. Bureau of soils. Bulletin 28)

1. Soil fertility. I. Britton, John Carr, joint author. II. Reid, Frederic Robertson, joint author.
Agr 6—577
U. S. Dept. of agr. Library for Library of Congress 1So3B no. 28 ₍a41b1₎

NL 0420306 DNAL OO MiU MB NN

Livingston, Burton Edward, 1875–
A study of the relation between summer evaporation intensity and centers of plant distribution in the United States. ₍By₎ Burton Edward Livingston. ₍Baltimore,₎ 1911. (1)206–222 p. diagr., tables. 8°.

Caption-title.
Repr.: Plant world. v. 14, 1911.

1. Evaporation, U. S. 2. Botany.—Ecology, U. S.
N. Y. P. L. September 29, 1917.

NL 0420307 NN DAS

Livingston, Burton Edward, 1875– , and G. J. Livingston.
Temperature coefficients in plant geography and climatology ... ₍By₎ Burton Edward Livingston and Grace Johnson Livingston. ₍Chicago,₎ 1913. p. 349–375. Charts, tables. 8°.

Cover-title.
Repr.: The botanical gazette, v. 56, Nov. 1913.

1. Botany.—Ecology. 2. Botany, Regional. 3. Livingston, Grace Johnson, jt. au.
N. Y. P. L. September 28, 1917.

NL 0420308 NN DAS

VOLUME 336

Livingston, Burton Edward, 1875–
The water-relation between plant and soil, by Burton E. Livingston and Lon A. Hawkins. The water-supplying power of the soil as indicated by osmometers, by Howard E. Pulling and Burton E. Livingston. Washington, D. C., Carnegie institution of Washington, 1915.
84 p. incl. tables, diagrs. 25½ cm. (*On verso of t.-p.:* Carnegie institution of Washington. Publication no. 204)
Botanical contributions from the Johns Hopkins university, no. 38-39.
"Literature cited": p. 47–48, 84.
1. Plants—Transpiration. 2. Soil moisture. I. Hawkins, Lon Adrian, 1880– joint author. II. Pulling, Howard Edward. III. Title.
QK871.L6 15—9720

MiU OCl OO CoU OrP IdU WaSp WaWW OrPR OCU
NL 0420309 DLC TU OrCS Wa OrU CaBVaU NcD OU MB ICJ

Livingston (C. E.) A treatise on displacement of the womb, with suggestions for treatment. 20 pp. 16°. *Toledo, Ohio, The B. F. Wade Co.,* [n. d.]

NL 0420310 DNLM

Livingston, Mrs. C.M., joint author.
Divers women
see under [Alden, Isabella (Macdonald)] "Mrs. G.R. Alden," 1841-

Livingston, *Mrs.* **C M.**
Katy Hunter's homes. By Mrs. C. M. Livingston. Boston, D. Lothrop & co.; Dover, N. H., G. T. Day & co. [°1876]
4, 7–126 p. front., pl. 17cm.
Library of Congress PZ7.L761K 7–19394†

NL 0420312 DLC OKentU

Livingston, *Mrs.* **C M.**
The night before Christmas. A Christmas exercise. By Mrs. C. M. Livingston. Boston, D. Lothrop & co.; Dover, N. H., G. T. Day & co. [1876]
15, [1] p. 16½cm.
1. Christmas plays. I. Title.
CA 36-1285 Unrev'd
Library of Congress PN6120.C5L5
Copyright 1876: 406 [2] 812.4

NL 0420313 DLC

Livingston, *Mrs.* **C M.**
Susan's sheaves and other stories. By Mrs. C. M. Livingston. New York, The National temperance society and publication house, 1887.
364 p. front. 19½cm.
CONTENTS.—Susan's sheaves.—Mrs. Dale's diamonds.—Where he found her.—Their Christmas presents.— Topknot.— John Trent's discoveries.—That cellar door.—Books and bread.—Who is to blame?—Mrs. Raynor's new nurse-maid.
Library of Congress PZ3.L761S 7-19401†

NL 0420314 DLC

FILM 4274 PR v.3 reel L22
Livingston, Mrs. C. M. 1
Susan's sheaves and other stories. By Mrs. C. M. Livingston. New York, The National temperance society and publications house, 1887.
364 p. front. 19 1/2 cm.
(Wright American Fiction, v. III, 1876-1900, no. 3365, Research Publications, Inc. Microfilm, Reel L-22)
Contents.-Susan's sheaves.-Mrs. Dale's diamonds.-Where he found her.-Their Christmas presents.-Topknot.-John Trent's discoveries.-

That cellar door.-Books and bread.-Who is to blame.-Mrs. Raynor's new nurse-maid.

NL 0420316 CU

FILM 4568
Livingston, C S
Investigation of dynamite A. G. plant at Troisdorf, Germany by C. S. Livingston, D. T. Lewis, and E. R. Rechel. [n. p., n.d.
Microfilm copy (negative)—Library of Congress.
Collation of the original: 11 p.
"CIOS Target Number 2/74-2e (11)."
1. Factory inspection—Germany—Troisdorf.

NL 0420317 ViU

Livingston, Catherine.
Poems on several occasions. Written by Catherine Livingston. London: Printed for the author, and sold by D. Ogilvy and Son, 1797. 4 p.l., 46 p. 4°.
This copy originally belonged to William Maxwell of New York, one of the subscribers, and contains annotations in pencil by his grandson. A manuscript note on the title-page reads: I presume Catherine Livingston was a New York lady.
A letter in another hand, inserted, suggests that the author may have been the sister of Edward Livingston and wife of the Rev. Mr. Garretson.
Lenox copy.
AVERY COLLECTION.
1. No subject. 2. Garrettson, Catherine Livingston, 1752–1849, supposed author.
N. Y. P. L. August 4, 1915.

NL 0420318 NN WU

Livingston, Charles Adolphe, 1864–
Palingenesia [by] Charles A. Livingston. [New York, H. Harrison, °1940]
31 p. 19cm.
A poem.
I. Title.
41-7111
Library of Congress PS3523.I 9425P3 1940
[2] 811.5

NL 0420319 DLC

[**Livingston, Charles Adolphe**] 1864-
The path of the soul. [By] Livy [*pseud.*] [Gouverneur, N. Y., The Livy press] 1903.
4 p. l., 56 p. 16½cm.
3-12040

NL 0420320 DLC

PQ1628 .I25 L58
Livingston, Charles Harold, 1888-
Bertrand de la Borderie, un disciple de Clément Marot. Paris, H. Champion, 1930.
68p.
"Extrait de la Revue du Seizième Siècle, tome XVI, 1929."
1. La Borderie, Bertrand de,. 2. Marot, Clément, 1495?-1544. I. Title.

NL 0420321 NcU

843 P5377cYl
Livingston, Charles Harold, 1888-
Les cent nouvelles nouvelles de Philippe de Vigneulles ... par Charles H. Livingston ... Paris, É. Champion, 1924.
47p. 24cm.
"Extrait de la Revue du seizième siècle, tome X, 1923."
1. Philippe de Vigneulles, 1471-1527 or 8. Cent nouvelles nouvelles.

NL 0420322 MiU TxU CU KPT MH IU IaU

Livingston, Charles Harold, 1888-
Deux historiettes de Philippe de Vigneulles, par Charles H. Livingston... (In: Mélanges de linguistique et de littérature offerts à M. Alfred Jeanroy. Paris, 1928. 4°. p. [469–]476.)
478012A. 1. Philippe, de Vigneulles, 1471–1527 or '28.
N. Y. P. L. July 1, 1930

NL 0420323 NN OO

848 L116ZL
Livingston, Charles Harold, 1888-
Un disciple de Clément Marot, Bertrand de La Borderie, par Charles H. Livingston... Paris, Honoré Champion, 1930.
68p. 24cm.
"Extrait de la Revue du seizième siècle, tome XVI, 1929."
1. La Borderie, Bertrand de, 1507-
2. Marot, Clément, 1495?-1544. I. Title.

NL 0420324 LU CtY MH ICarbS

Livingston, Charles Harold, 1888-
The fabliau "Des deux anglois et de l'anel."
(*In* Modern Language Association of America. Publications. Vol. 40, pp. 217–224. Menasha. 1925.)
N3499 — Fables. — Des deux anglois et de l'anel. Fable.

NL 0420325 MB

Livingston, Charles Harold, 1888- ed.
Gliglois.
Gliglois, a French Arthurian romance of the thirteenth century, edited with an introduction by Charles H. Livingston .. Cambridge, Harvard university press, 1932.

LIVINGSTON, Charles Harold, 1888-
The Heptameron des Nouvelles of Marguerite de Navarre; a study of Nouvelles 28,34,52 and 62. [New York? 1923].
Pamphlet.
Cover serves as title-page.
"Reprinted from The Romanic Review,Vol.XIV, no.2-3,April-September, 1923",pp.97-118.

NL 0420327 MH

VOLUME 336

Livingston, Charles Harold, 1888–
Le jongleur Gautier le Leu; étude sur les fabliaux. Cambridge, Harvard University Press, 1951.
xii, 377 p. 24 cm. (Harvard studies in Romance languages, v. 24)
"Les fabliaux et dits de Gautier le Leu; textes et variantes": p. [139]–287.
Includes bibliographical references.

1. Gautier le Leu, 13th cent. I. Gautier le Leu, 13th cent. (Series)
A 52-9208
Harvard Univ. Library for Library of Congress [5]

NL 0420328 CaBVaU MH NcU MB TxU ViU IaU GU DAU NN IdU MtU

LIVINGSTON, Charles Harold, 1888–
The Latin prefix ex in French. Thesis, Harvard University, 1916.
Manuscript. ff. vi, 454.[456]
"Bibliography, ff. 360-388.

NL 0420329 MH

636.1 L761 Livingston, Charlotte.
Laet, a Percheron legend. [Columbus? O., 1940?]
69p. incl.illus., ports.
Cover-title: Sire of sires. Laet.
Illustrations on front and back cover.
"Laet blood breeds on" tipped in at end.

1. Percheron horse. I. Title. II. Title: Sire of sires.

NL 0420330 IU

Livingston, Charlotte L
Ancestry of Mrs. Levi Parsons Morton (Anna Livingston Reade Street) [n. d.]
92 p. illus., col. coats of arms. 35 cm.
Manuscript.

1. Street family (Nicholas Street, 1603?-1674)
CS71.S914 50-56250

NL 0420331 DLC

Livingston, Clermont, 1850–
Livingston, Edwin Brockholst, 1852–
The Livingstons of Callendar, and their principal cadets. A family history by Edwin Brockholst Livingston ... [Edinburgh, Scott & Ferguson] 1887–[92]

Livingston, Clifton W *comp.*
An introduction to the design of underground openings for defense; edited by Le Roy W. Goodwin. Golden, 1951
vi, 304 p. illus., diagrs. (1 fold. in pocket) 23 cm. (Quarterly of the Colorado School of Mines, v. 46, no. 1)
Includes bibliographies.
CONTENTS.—Protective standards for underground defense, by E. H. Leavey, Jr.—The mechanics of rock failure, by J. P. Cogan.—A review of rock pressure problems, by R. P. Shoemaker.—A method for the determination of stresses around an opening under impact loads, by G. E. Hesselbacher, Jr.—Rock tunneling for underground protective construction, by B. D. Jones.—Heating, ventilating and air conditioning of underground installations, by I. M. Rice.

1. Underground construction. 2. Mining engineering. I. Title. II. Title: Underground openings for defense. (Series: Colorado School of Mines, Golden. Quarterly, v. 46, no. 1)
TN210.C68 vol. 46, no. 1 623.3 51-62406
——— Copy 2. TA712.L5
TA712 L5

NL 0420334 DLC MB DI RPB MoU MU CaBVaU WaS

Livingston, David
see
Livingstone, David, 1813–1873.

TF 216 .L79 Livingston, David, C. E.
Treatise on the setting out of railway curves, with full tables of the angles, distances, and offsets required; especially arranged for the use of measurements in feet and imperial links, but also adapted for the use of any other unit of measurement. London, New York, E.& F.N.Spon, 1873.
viii,147 p. diagrs. 19 cm.

1.Railroads--Curves and turnouts.

NL 0420336 MiU

Livingston, David, 1874–
The book of David; or, "I am" in the Bible; a series of thirteen discourses wherein is interwoven a network of Scripture testimony and positive substantiation from many sources, verifying the "I am" teachings, as put forth by the ascended master, the prince—recorded and done under his authority, inspiration and guidance, and by his express wish to the author, through the media of his recording messengers Mr. and Mrs. G. W. Ballard ... by David Livingston. Los Angeles, "Star of empire" publishing company [°1937]
xxiv, 339 p. 19½cm.
Includes blank pages for "Notes".
I. Ballard, Guy W., 1878– II. Ballard, Edna (Wheeler) "Mrs. G. W. Ballard." III. Title. IV. Title: David, The book of.
Library of Congress BF1999.L5 38-954
——— Copy 2.
Copyright A 110150 [2] [159.9611] 133

NL 0420337 DLC

Livingston, David Palmer.
Training schedule for national guard ... by Capt. David P. Livingston ... [Corning, Ia., Printed by Free press publishing co.] °1924–
pt. 23cm.
Cover-title.

1. Military education—U. S. 2. U. S.—Militia. I. Title.
Library of Congress U408.3.L5 CA 25-404 Unrev'd

NL 0420338 DLC DAS

Livingston, Don.
Film and the director. New York, Macmillan [1953]
209 p. illus. 22 cm.
Includes bibliographies.

1. Moving-pictures—Production and direction. I. Title.
PN1995.9.P7L5 *792.93 791.4 53—13433 ‡

NL 0420339 MiU PU OCl FTaSU OClW OrPS OrP WaT MtBC MsU OU PSt TxU DI PP PPT PPLas PBL ViU MB NN IdPI DLC IdU OrU CaBVaU CaBVa WaS Or GU MoSW

Livingston, Donald G
The effects of varying group organization upon perception of power and benefit. Ann Arbor, University Microfilms [1951?]
([University Microfilms, Ann Arbor, Mich.] Publication no. 3209)
Microfilm copy of typescript. Positive.
Collation of the original: 162 l. tables.
Thesis—University of Kansas.
Bibliography: leaves 152-155.

1. Power (Social sciences) 2. Social psychology.
Microfilm AC-1 no. 3209 Mic 54-659

NL 0420340 DLC

Livingston, Douglas Clermont, 1877–
... The copper deposits of the Seven Devils and adjacent districts (including Heath, Hornet creek, Hoodoo, and Deer creek), by D. C. Livingston and F. B. Laney ... Moscow, University of Idaho, 1920.
v, 105 p. front. (maps) 13 pl., charts (part fold., 2 in pocket) 23cm. [Idaho. Bureau of mines and geology. Bulletin no. 1]
At head of title: State of Idaho. D. W. Davis, governor. Bureau of mines and geology. Francis A. Thomson, secretary.
Published in cooperation with the United States Geological survey.
Literature: p. 3.

1. Copper mines and mining—Idaho. I. Laney, Francis Baker, 1875–1938, joint author. II. U. S. Geological survey. III. Title.
G S 21—12
U. S. Geol. survey. Library for Library of Congress (283) B no. 1 TN443.I 2L5 [a40g1]

NL 0420341 DI-GS WaS WaTC CU NN DLC MtBuM

Livingston, Douglas Clermont, 1877–
... A geologic reconnaissance of the mineral and Cuddy Mountain mining district, Washington and Adams counties, Idaho, by D. C. Livingston. [Boise, 1925?]
3 p. l., 24 l. II pl. (fold. maps) 27½cm. (Idaho. Bureau of mines and geology. Pamphlet no. 13)
Mimeographed.
Bibliographical references.

1. Mines and mineral resources—Idaho. 2. Geology—Idaho. I. Title.
G S 25-126
——— Copy 2.
Library, U. S. Geological Survey (283) P no. 13

NL 0420342 DI-GS MtBuM WaS MoU CU OU

Livingston, Douglas Clermont, 1877–
... The geology and ore deposits of the Dixie mining district, Idaho with metallurgical notes, by D. C. Livingston and C. A. Stewart. Moscow, Id., University of Idaho, 1914.
cover-title, 11 p. fold. map. 23cm. (Idaho. University. Bulletin, vol. IX, no. 2)

1. Geology—Idaho. I. Stewart, Charles Arthur, 1885– joint author.
Library, U. S. Geol. survey G S 14-310

NL 0420343 DI-GS ICJ WaS OrCS

Livingston, Douglas Clermont, 1877– joint author.
Varley, Thomas.
... A preliminary report on the mining districts of Idaho, by Thomas Varley, Clarence A. Wright, Edgar K. Soper and Douglas C. Livingston (in cooperation with the University of Idaho) Washington, Govt. print. off., 1919.

Livingston, Douglas Clermont, 1877–
Umpleby, Joseph Bertram, 1883–
... A reconnaissance in south central Idaho, embracing the Thunder mountain, Big creek, Stanley basin, Sheep mountain, and Seafoam districts, by J. B. Umpleby and D. C. Livingston ... Moscow, University of Idaho, 1920.

Livingston, Douglas Clermont, 1877–
... Tungsten, cinnabar, manganese, molybdenum, and tin deposits of Idaho, by D. C. Livingston, with notes on the antimony deposits, by Francis A. Thompson. Moscow, Id., 1919.
72 p. plates, maps (part fold.) fold. plans. 23cm. (University of Idaho. School of mines. vol. XIV. Bulletin no. 2)

1. Tungsten—Idaho. 2. Cinnabar—Idaho. 3. Manganese ores—Idaho. 4. Molybdenum. 5. Tin ores—Idaho. 6. Antimony. 7. Mines and mineral resources—Idaho. I. Thomson, Francis Andrew, 1879–
G S 19—112
U. S. Geol. survey. Library for Library of Congress S(283) Id4 vol. 14, no. 2 TN24.I 2L5 [a41g1]

NL 0420346 ICJ OCl IdPI OO OCU DI-GS WaTC MtBuM WaS OrCS IdB OdU OOxM CU

VOLUME 336

Livingston, Edward.
A personal history of the San Francisco earthquake and fire in 1906, by Edward Livingston, sr. San Francisco ₍Printed by the Windsor press₎ 1941.
3 p. l., 3-45, ₍1₎ p. pl., group port., facsims. 24½ x 18½cm.

1. San Francisco—Earthquake and fire, 1906.

Library of Congress F869.S3L67 41-20687
₍5₎ 979.461

NL 0420347 DLC CU C

Livingston, Edward, 1764-1836.

Works by this author printed in America before 1801 are available in this library in the Readex Microprint edition of Early American Imprints published by the American Antiquarian Society.
This collection is arranged according to the numbers in Charles Evans' American Bibliography.

NL 0420348 DLC

Livingston, Edward, 1764-1836.
The complete works of Edward Livingston on criminal jurisprudence; consisting of systems of penal law for the state of Louisiana and for the United States of America; with the introductory reports to the same. To which is prefixed an introduction by Salmon P. Chase ... New York, National prison association of the United States of America, 1873.
2 v. 25cm.
CONTENTS.—v. 1. Prefatory note. Introduction. Act of Assembly of Louisiana, 10 February 1820. Resolution of the Assembly of Louisiana, 21 March 1822. Appointment of Edward Livingston. Preliminary report on the plan of a penal code. Introductory report to the System of penal law. Introductory report to the Code of crimes and punishments. Introductory report to the Code of procedure. Introductory report to the Code of evidence. Introductory report to the Code of reform and prison discipline.—v. 2. A system of penal law: A Code of crimes and punishments; a Code of procedure; a Code of evidence; a Code of reform and prison discipline. Extracts from the System of penal law for the United States. A book of definitions.
1. Criminal law—Louisiana. 2. Punishment—Louisiana. 3. Criminal procedure—Louisiana. 4. Evidence (Law)—Louisiana. 5. Crime and criminals—Louisiana. 6. Prisons—Laws and regulations. 7. Criminal law—U. S. 8. Criminal procedure—U. S. I. Chase, Salmon Portland, 1808-1873.

18-16868

NL 0420350 NcU MnU-L OU NcD PHC PPL PU-L PP ICJ NN MiU OCl ViU-L DLC PPWa WaU-L OKentU WaS PPT DAU MB IdB

La 345.2 L93 1823ZL
[Livingston, Edward] 1764-1836.
A l'honorable Senat et a la Chambre des representans de l'etat de la Louisiane, reunis en Assemblée générale. Les juristes soussignés, chargés de la révision du Code civil, ont l'honneur de rapporter. [Nouvelle-Orléans, Imprimé par J.C. de St. Romes, impr. de l'etat, 1823]
13p. 23cm.

Caption title.
Signed: Edew. [ ] Livingston, Moreau Lislet, P. Derbigny.

NL 0420351 LU

Livingston, Edward, 1764-1836.

Louisiana. *Laws, statutes, etc.*
Additions et amendemens au Code civil de l'État de la Louisiane, proposés, en vertu de la résolution de la législature du 14 mars 1822, par les juristes chargés de ce travail. Nouvelle-Orléans, Imprimé par B. Levy & co., 1823.

Livingston, Edward, 1764-1836.
Address Delivered On The Installation Of The Louisiana Lodge, By Edward Livingston, W.M. Est Et Fideli Tuta Silentio Merces ... Hor. Printed At The Request Of The Brethren Of The Lodge. John Mowry, Printer. New Orleans, n.d. circa 1807.
41 x 52 cm. Broadside.
Arranged in double column, with waved rule between the columns.
Masonic vignette on either side of title.

NL 0420353 CSmH

Livingston, Edward, 1764-1836.
Address to the people of the United States, on the measures pursued by the executive with respect to the batture at New-Orleans: to which are annexed, a full report of the cause tried in the Superior court of the terriry ₍!₎ of Orleans: the Mémoire of Mr. Derbigny: an examination of the title of the United States: the opinion of counsel thereon: and a number of other documents necessary to a full understanding of this interesting case. By Edward Livingston ... New-Orleans:—Printed by Bradford & Anderson. 1808.
2 v. 19½cm.
Vol. 1: 2 p. l., ₍iii₎-L p.; v. 2: 50, xxix, 68, lxxv, 15 p.

Vol. 1 is an advance issue of the "Address", with the announcement on a 2d preliminary leaf (omitted in later issue): ... The report of the cause as tried in the supreme court, is unavoidably omitted, but will be forwarded to each member of Congress in a few days—it is now in the press and will be published here about the first of November.
F379.N5L68
——— ₍Another issue₎ New-Orleans:—Printed by Bradford & Anderson. 1808.
L, 50, 15, xxix, 68, lxxv p. 20½cm.
In one volume, without the announcement following t.-p. in first (advance) issue, and with groups of paging in different order.
1. New Orleans batture. I. Derbigny, Pierre Auguste Charles Bourisgay, 1767-1829.

Library of Congress ₍r27e2₎ 3-32018 Revised
F379.N5L682
——— Copy 2. ₍Miscellaneous pamphlets, v. 528₎ 18½cm.
AC901.M5 vol. 528
Some of the leaves have page numbers trimmed

NL 0420355 LNHT MH-L LU PPiU PPL NjR PPAmP ViU DLC PHi CSmH N CtY NjP AU NNC MWA MdBP

Livingston, Edward, 1764-1836.
[Alphabetical and class lists of pamphlets collected by Edward Livingston and T. P. Barton
see under Barton, Thomas Pennant, 1803-1869.

Livingston, Edward, 1764-1836.
An answer to Mr. Jefferson's justification of his conduct in the case of the New Orleans batture. By Edward Livingston ...
(*In* Jefferson, Thomas. The proceedings of the government of the United States, in maintaining the public right to the beach of the Missisipi, adjacent to New-Orleans ... (n. p., n. d.) 25cm. p. ₍105₎-299)

1. New Orleans batture. 2. Jefferson, Thomas, pres. U. S., 1743-1826. The proceedings of the government of the United States, in maintaining the public right to the beach of the Missisipi, adjacent to New-Orleans ...

Library of Congress F379.N5J42 21-4363

NL 0420357 DLC ViU

Livingston, Edward, 1764-1836.
An answer to Mr. Jefferson's justification of his conduct in the case of the New Orleans batture. By Edward Livingston ... Philadelphia, Printed by W. Fry, 1813.
xi, 187 p. 2 fold. plans. 22cm.

1. New Orleans batture. 2. Jefferson, Thomas, pres. U. S., 1743-1826. The proceedings of the government of the United States, in maintaining the public right to the beach of the Missisipi, adjacent to New-Orleans ...

Library of Congress F379.N5L7 1-10868

NL 0420358 ViU PPAmP NjP MiU-C ScU DLC TU NcU NcD PHi PU-L PPL PU AU NN MH

Livingston, Edward, 1764-1836.
An answer to Mr. Jefferson's justification of his conduct in the case of the New Orleans batture. By Edward Livingston... ₍Baltimore, 1814.₎ p. ₍105₎-299. 2 fold. plans. 8°.
Repr.: Amer. Law Jour., v. 5, no. 18. Baltimore, 1814.
Bound with: T. Jefferson, The proceedings of the government... ₍Baltimore, 1814.₎ 8°.

1. Jefferson, Thomas, 3d president of the U. S.: The proceedings of the government of the U. S. 2. New Orleans batture.
N. Y. P. L. June 30, 1916.

NL 0420359 NN

HV 8698 L78a
Livingston, Edward, 1764-1836
Argument ... against capital punishment. New York, New York state society for the abolition of capital punishment, 1847.
24p. 22½cm.
"Taken from the Introduction to the 'Criminal code of Louisiana, by Edward Livingston.'" - Pref.
With this are bound: Massachusetts. General court. House of representatives. Committee on capital punishment. Report relating to capital punishment. 1836; New York (State) Legislature. Assembly. Select committee on the abolition of capital punishment. Report. [1847]

NL 0420361 NRU NjP NcD MB NN MH PHi MiU-L

Livingston, Edward, 1764-1836.
Catalogue of the library of Edward Livingston .. to be sold at auction, Monday-Thursday, December 7th-10th, 1885. New York, Bangs & Co., 1885.
119 p. 8°.
Partly priced.

NL 0420362 NN

Livingston, Edward, 1764-1836, comp.

Louisiana. *Laws, statutes, etc.*
Civil code of the state of Louisiana. By authority. New-Orleans, Printed by J. C. de St. Romes, 1825.

Livingston, Edward, 1764-1836.
Claim to the Batture of Suburb. St. Mary. New Orleans, 1808.
University of Alabama

NL 0420364 AU

Livingston, Edward, 1764-1836.

Louisiana. *Laws, statutes, etc.*
Code de procédure civile de l'État de la Louisiane. ₍Nouvelle-Orléans? 1823?₎

VOLUME 336

Livingston, Edward, 1764-1836.
Code de réforme et de discipline formant la troisième partie du système de lois pénales préparé pour l'état de la Louisiane. Par Édouard Livingston... Québec: Imprimé par ordre du Conseil législatif, par T. Cary & Co., 1831. 44 p. 4°.
Not adopted as law.—cf. Introd., The complete works of Edward Livingston... New York, 1873.

1. Prisons—Regulations—U. S.—Louisiana.
N. Y. P. L. January 12, 1926

NL 0420367 NN

Livingston, Edward, 1764-1836.
Code of evidence. [New Orleans, 182-]
73 p. 31½cm. [With his Introductory report to the code of evidence of the state of Louisiana. [New Orleans, 182-]]
Caption title.

1. Evidence (Law)—Louisiana.
A 14-350
Title from Univ. of Chicago HV8665.L71 Printed by L. C.

NL 0420368 ICU

Livingston, Edward, 1764-1836.

Louisiana. Laws, statutes, etc.
Code of practice, in civil cases, for the state of Louisiana. [New Orleans, 1825]

NL 0420370 DLC NN ICU

Livingston, Edward, 1764-1836.
Code of procedure, for giving effect to the Penal code of the state of Louisiana. Prepared under the authority of a law of the said state, by Edward Livingston, LL. D. New-Orleans, Printed by B. Levy, 1825.
263 p. 30½cm.
No. 4 in a volume of publications lettered: Livingston.
Not adopted as law. cf. Introd., The complete works of Edward Livingston ... New York, 1873.
"Corrections," p. 257-263, consist of suggestions for the amendment of "the different codes which form this 'System of penal law,' prepared for the state of Louisiana ... annotations on the Penal code ... by Judge Gould of Connecticut ... together with corrections of typographical errors."
1. Criminal procedure—Louisiana.
18-16863

NL 0420371 DLC NN ICJ CU MeB

Livingston, Edward, 1764-1836.
A code of reform and prison discipline: to which is prefixed an introductory report to the same, by Edward Livingston. With an introduction by Salmon P. Chase ... New York, National prison association of the United States [1872]
viii, 140 p. 23½cm.
"Brought out under the auspices of the American prison association."—Introd.

1. Prisons—Laws and regulations. I. American prison association.
17-8651
Library of Congress HV8751.L5

NL 0420372 DLC ICU Nh

Livingston, Edward, 1764-1836.
Code of reform and prison discipline, being the third part of the system of penal law prepared for the state of Louisiana. By Edward Livingston, LL. D. New-Orleans, Printed by B. Levy, 1826.
1 p. l., 51, 65 p. 30½cm.
No. 1 in a volume of publications lettered: Livingston.
At head of the caption title, Introductory report to the Code of reform and prison discipline, is written: Roberts Vaux. From his friend, Edward Livingston.
Not adopted as law. cf. Introd., The complete works of Edward Livingston ... New York, 1873.
"Introductory report to the Code of reform and prison discipline": 51 p.
1. Prisons—Laws and regulations. 2. Punishment. 3. Crime and criminals—Louisiana.
18-16866

NL 0420373 NN MH

Livingston, Edward, 1764-1836.
Code of reform and prison discipline; being the third part of the system of penal law prepared for the state of Louisiana. By Edward Livingston... Quebec: Printed by order of the Legislative Council, by T. Cary & Co., 1831. 44 p. 4°.
Not adopted as law—cf. Introd., The complete works of Edward Livingston... New York, 1873.

1. Prisons—Regulations—U. S.—Louisiana.
N. Y. P. L. January 12, 1926

NL 0420374 DLC

[Livingston, Edward] 1764-1836.
Commercial code for the state of Louisiana. New-Orleans, Printed by B. Levy, 1825.
1 p. l., 260 p. 31½cm.
Proposed commercial code, not adopted by the legislature.

1. Commercial law—Louisiana. I. Title.
18-16861

NL 0420375 DLC ICU

[Livingston, Edward] 1764-1836.
Definitions of all the technical words used in the System of penal law prepared for the state of Louisiana. [New Orleans? 18—]
27 p. 30½cm.
Half-title.
Caption title: System of penal law. Book of definitions
No. 5 in a volume of publications lettered: Livingston.
"These definitions are intended to show the sense in which the words defined are employed in the System of penal law, not to define or fix their general signification in the language."
1. Criminal law—Louisiana. 2. Law—Dictionaries. I. Title.
18-16862

NL 0420376 DLC LNHT CtY InU

Lilly Library
Livingston, Edward, 1764-1836.
Discurso de Mr. Livingston, contra la ley de expulson [!] de extranjeros, dada en los Estados-Unidos de América. Acompañado de un prólogo y de un comentario del traductor. Edición de la Voz de México. México, Imprenta de la "Voz de México," 1873.
1 p. l., v, 31 p. 18½cm.
Translation of "The speech of Edward Livingston, esq. on the third reading of the Alien bill", delivered in the House of representatives, June 21, 1798, printed by J. Carey, Philadelphia [1798?]
Cover-title: "Acompañado de un prólogo y de un comentario del lic. Luis E. de la Sierra."
"Comentario": p. 13-31, signed Luis G. de la Sierra.
1. Alien and sedition laws, 1798. I. Sierra, Luis G. de la, tr.
In paper cover. 3—5900
Library of Congress E327.L785

Livingston, Edward, 1764-1836.
Emancipate your colonies!
see under Bentham, Jeremy, 1748-1832.

Livingston, Edward, 1764-1836.
Examination of the Title of the United States to the Land called The Batture - By Edward Livingston, Dec. 10, 1807. New Orleans, 1808.
68 p. 13 x 19 cm.
Bibliotheca Parsoniana.

NL 0420378 NHi PPL

Livingston, Edward, 1764-1836.
Exposé d'un système de législation criminelle pour l'État de la Louisiane et pour les États-Unis d'Amérique, par Edward Livingston ... précédé d'une préface par m. Charles Lucas ... et d'une notice historique par m. Mignet ... Paris, Guillaumin et cie, 1872.
2 v. in 1. 22cm.
Vol. 2 includes Livre de définitions de tous les mots techniques employés dans le Système de législation criminelle préparé pour l'État de la Louisiane, and Appendice: Parties détachées d'un Code pénal pour les États-Unis d'Amérique en ce qui concerne les délits généraux directement justiciables du gouvernement fédéral.

Continued in next column

Continued from preceding column

1. Criminal law—Louisiana. 2. Punishment—Louisiana. 3. Criminal procedure—Louisiana. 4. Evidence (Law)—Louisiana. 5. Crime and criminals—Louisiana. 6. Prisons—Laws and regulations. 7. Criminal law—U. S. 8. Criminal procedure—U. S. I. Lucas, Charles Jean Marie, 1803-1889. II. Mignet, François Auguste Marie Alexis, 1796-1884.
18—16869

NL 0420380 NcU NcD CtY ViU-L MH MiU-C PU-L OU MiU PP OCl PHC DLC WaS WaU-L NBu ICJ NN CU-AL PPDrop

Livingston, Edward, 1764-1836.
Extracts from the projected penal code: containing the fourth section of the thirteenth chapter, third book: entitled "Of offences which affect written contracts." So many of the definitions contained in the first book as apply to terms employed in the said chapter. That part of the fourth book which contains the forms of proceeding. And of the fifth book which gives the rules of evidence, applicable exclusively to those offences. To which is prefixed an extract from a preliminary discourse, indicating the changes that have been made, and assigning the reasons for adopting them ... New Orleans, Printed by B. Levy & co., 1823.
1 p. l., 31, [2] p. 31½cm. [With his Introductory report to the system of penal law. [New Orleans, 182-]]

1. Criminal law—Louisiana.
A 14-354
Title from Univ. of Chicago HV8665.L7 Printed by L. C.

NL 0420382 ICU CtY MH-L ICU MB MBAt

Livingston, Edward, 1764-1836.
Extracts from two reports made to the General Assembly of Louisiana, by Edward Livingston...containing his arguments for the abolishment of capital punishments. Providence: Knowles, Vose & Co., 1838. 24 p. 8°.

1. Punishment (Capital).
N. Y. P. L. June 21, 192

NL 0420383 NN TxU PHi CtY RPB N MH

Livingston, Edward, 1764-1836.

A faithful picture of the political situation of New Orleans, at the close of the last and the beginning of the present year 1807. Boston, Re-printed from the New-Orleans edition, 1808.

[Livingston, Edward] 1764-1836.
French spoliations, prior to 1800. [New York, Bryant & Boggs, printers, 184_]
16 p. 24 cm.

Caption title.
"The ... report, by the Honorable Edward Livingston ... is reprinted from the Documents of the U. S. Senate."
No. [1] in a volume of pamphlets with binder's title: Miscellanea Americana, v. 1.

1 French spoliation claims.

NL 0420385 NSchU MnHi MH-L

Livingston, Edward, 1764-1836.
Introductory report to the code of evidence of the state of Louisiana. [New Orleans, 182-]
68 p. 31½cm.
Caption title.

1. Evidence (Law) 2. Evidence (Law)—Louisiana.
A 14-355
Title from Univ. of Chicago HV8665.L71 Printed by L. C.

NL 0420386 ICU IU NcD

VOLUME 336

Livingston, Edward. 1764-1836.
Introductory report to the code of prison discipline: explanatory of the principles on which the code is founded. Being part of the "System of penal law, prepared for the State of Louisiana." London. Miller. 1827. (1), 78 pp. 8°.
The system of penal law, prepared for the State of Louisiana," is on shelf-number 3610.5.

G959 — Louisiana. Prisons, etc. — Prisons and prison discipline.

NL 0420387 MB MH-L LU NN

Livingston, Edward, 1764-1836.
Introductory report to the Code of prison discipline: explanatory of the principles on which the code is founded. Being part of the System of penal law, prepared for the state of Louisiana. By Edward Livingston. Philadelphia, Carey, Lea & Carey. 1827.
2 p. l., [3]-78 p. 22cm.

1. Prisons. 2. Prisons—Louisiana.

10-32170

Library of Congress HV9475.L2L8

NL 0420388 PPM PPA IGK PHi NN AU DLC LU ViU MiU-C DNLM NcD PHC PPL PU

[Livingston, Edward] 1764-1836.
Introductory report to the Code of procedure. [New Orleans, 1827]
58 p. 30½cm.
Caption title.
No. 2 in a volume of publications lettered: Livingston.
Date at end of report: 15th Sept. 1827.
Relates to the Code of procedure for giving effect to the Penal code of Louisiana, written by Livington, but never adopted as law.

1. Criminal procedure—Louisiana. I. Title.

18-16565

NL 0420389 DLC ICU MBAt PPAmP IU

Livingston, Edward, 1764-1836.
Introductory report to the code of reform and prison discipline. [New Orleans, Printed by B. Levy, 182-]
71 p. 31½cm. [With his Introductory report to the code of evidence of the state of Louisiana. [New Orleans, 182-]]
Caption title.

1. Prisons. 2. Prisons—Louisiana—Laws and regulations.

A 14-357

Title from Univ. of Chicago HV8665.L71 Printed by L. C.

NL 0420390 ICU IU-L

[Livingston, Edward] 1764-1836.
Introductory report to the System of penal law, prepared for the state of Louisiana. [New Orleans, 182-]
185 p. 30½cm.
Caption title.
No. 3 in a volume of publications lettered: Livingston.
Contents.—pt. 1. Of the actual state of our Penal code, and the necessity of a reform.—pt. 2. Review of proposed code. Punishment of death.

1. Criminal law—Louisiana. 2. Punishment—Louisiana. I. Title.

18—16864

NL 0420391 DLC MH-L ICU

Livingston, Edward, 1764-1836.

New York (City) Mayor's court.
Judicial opinions, delivered in the Mayor's court of the city of New-York, in the year 1802 ... New-York: Printed and published by D Longworth, at the Shakespeare gallery, near the theatre. 1803. [n. p., 19—]

Livingston, Edward, 1764-1836.

White, Joseph M 1781-1839.
Legal opinions of the Honorable Joseph M. White ... Honorable Daniel Webster ... and Edward Livingston... in relation to the title of the Duke of Alagon. New-York, H. Cassidy, printer, 1836.

Livingston, Edward, 1764-1836.
Letter from Edward Livingston...to Roberts Vaux, on the advantages of the Pennsylvania system of prison discipline, for the application of which the new penitentiary has been constructed near Philadelphia, &c. &c. Philadelphia: J. Harding, 1828. iv, (1)6-15 p. 8°.

1. Prisons.—Discipline: Pennsylvania system.
N. Y. P. L. August 22, 1921.

NL 0420394 PHi PPL-R PBa MH PU NN NNC OC1W MnU ICU GU CU ViU MB PHC MH

Livingston, Edward, 1764-1836.
A letter relative to the criminal code, from Edward Livingston, esq. to the General assembly of the state of Louisiana. By order of the Senate. New-Orleans, Printed by J. C. de St. Romes, state printer, 1823.

7 p. 21 1|2 cm.
Report of the committee to whom was referred the report of Edward Livingston, esqr. the jurist appointed to prepare a Criminal code, and the progress made therein: p. 6-7.
Autograph on title.
1. Criminal law—Louisiana. I. Louisiana General assembly. Senate.

NL 0420395 CSmH

E356
.N5L4
Rare bk.
Coll.

Livingston, Edward, 1764- 1836.

A letter to Edward Livingston, esq., delegate from Louisiana to the general Congress at Washington-city, on the subject of the speech delivered by him, at Washington, at the late celebration of the anniversary of the 8th of January, 1815. Natchez [Miss.] The author, 1828.

Livingston, Edward. 1764-1836.
Letter ... to Roberts Vaux, on the advantages of the Pennsylvania system of prison discipline for the application of which the new penitentiary has been constructed near Philadelphia, &c.
see his Letter from Edward Livingston... to Robert Vaux.

Livingston, Edward, 1764-1836.

Adams, John Quincy, pres. U. S., 1767-1848.
... Letters from the Hon. John Quincy Adams, to Edward Livingston, grand high priest of the General grand royal arch chapter of the United States. Hartford, Connecticut antimasonic tract association, 1834.

Livingston, Edward, 1764-1836.

FOR OTHER EDITIONS SEE MAIN ENTRY

Louisiana. Laws, statutes, etc.
Louisiana legal archives. Volume 1. A republication of the projet of the Civil code of Louisiana of 1825. Volume 2. A republication of the projet of the Code of practice of Louisiana of 1825. Published pursuant to Act 286 of the legislature of Louisiana of 1936, E. A. Conway, secretary of state. New Orleans, Printed by T. J. Moran's sons, 1937.

Livingston, Edward, 1764-1836.
Message from the President of the United States [transmitting a report from the secretary of state] in relation to the consular establishment of the United States
see under U.S. Dept. of state.

---

*A
1800
.U6A5
Feb.20

Livingston, Edward, 1764-1836.
Mr. Livingston's motion. 20th February, 1800. Committed to the Committee ... to whom was committed ... the Message of the President, transmitting the papers, relative to the requisition for, and delivery of Jonathan Robbins. [Philadelphia, 1800]
4 p. 20½cm.
1. Robbins, Jonathan, d. 1799. 2. U. S.—For. rel.—Gt. Brit. 3. Gt. Brit.—For. rel.—U. S.

NL 0420401 ViU PU NjP RPJCB

AC901
.M5

Livingston, Edward.
Note to Mr. Jefferson.
14 p. (Miscellansous pamphlets, 528:3)

NL 0420402 DLC

Rare Book Dept.
*XG
.182
.56
no.8

Livingston, Edward, 1764-1836.
... Opinion de m. Édouard Livingston sur la peine de mort. Extrait du Rapport servant d'introduction au système de loi pénale préparé pour l'état de la Louisiane ...
[Paris] De l'imprimerie de Plassan et cie, rue de Vaugirard, No 15. [1830?]

38p. 21.5cm.;bd.to 23cm.
Caption title; imprint from p.38.
At head of title: Extrait de la Revue encyclopédique (juillet 1830) ...
Blue wrappers preserved.

NL 0420403 MB

LIVINGSTON, Edward, 1764-1836.
Opinion sur le duel et sur la manière de le réprimer. P. 1829.

pp. 23.

NL 0420404 MH

Livingston, Edward, 1764-1836.
Project of a new penal code for the state of Louisiana. By Edward Livingston... London: Baldwin, Cradock and Joy, 1824. x, 146 p. 23cm.
"Published in America...under the title of a 'Report made to the General assembly of...Louisiana, on the plan of a penal code.'"

1. Criminal law—U. S.—Louisiana. I. Louisiana. Legislature.
N. Y. P. L. Card revised February 26, 1941

NL 0420405 NN NBu MH-L WaU-L NcU CtY ScU TxU

Livingston, Edward, 1764-1836.
Rapport fait à l'Assemblée générale de l'état de la Louisiane, sur le projet d'un Code pénal, pour ledit état. Par Édouard Livingston ... Nouvelle-Orléans, Impr. de B. Levy & co., 1822.
170 p., 1 l. 23½cm.

1. Criminal law—Louisiana. 2. Law—Codification. I. Louisiana General assembly.

19-14651

Library of Congress

NL 0420406 DLC MB CtY MnU NN PPL L-M

VOLUME 336

Livingston, Edward, 1764–1836.

Rapport sur le projet d'un Code pénal fait à l'Assemblée générale de l'état de la Louisiane, par m. Édouard Livingston, suivi des observations sur les Conditions nécessaires à la perfection d'un Code pénal, par m. Mill, avec une introduction et des notes par m. A. H. Taillandier ... Paris, Antoine-Augustin Renouard, 1825.

xxxij, 223, [1] p. 21cm.

Includes the report of Edward Livingston, Moreau Lislet and P. Derbigny on the revision of the Civil code (p. [177]–190)

1. Criminal law—Louisiana. 2. Law—Louisiana—Codification. I. Louisiana. General assembly. II. Mill, James, 1773–1836. III. Taillandier, Alphonse Honoré, 1797

19–14653

NL 0420407 DLC NcD CtY LNHT MiU-C NN

Livingston, Edward, 1764-1836.
Rapport sur le projet d'un code penal, fait par M. Ed. Livingston. Extrait de la Revue encyclopedique, juin, 1826.
11 p.

NL 0420408 MB

Livingston, Edward, 1764–1836.

Remarks on the expediency of abolishing the punishment of death. By Edward Livingston ... Philadelphia, J. Harding, printer, 1831.

iv, [5]–42 p. 23cm.

1. Capital punishment.

Library of Congress HV8698.L7 10–34450

——— Copy 2. 21½cm. [With Philadelphia. Committee of twenty-five on capital punishment. The impropriety of capital punishment. Philadelphia, 1842] HV8699.U5T8

NL 0420409 DLC PPB PPL MnU-L NN

Livingston, Edward, 1764–1836.

Report made to the General assembly of the state of Louisiana, on the plan of a Penal code for the said state. By Edward Livingston ... New-Orleans, Printed by B. Levy & co., 1822.

159 p. 23cm.

1. Criminal law — Louisiana. 2. Law — Louisiana — Codification. I. Louisiana. General assembly.

19-14652

MnU NBLiHi Nb NcD P NjP OU TxU-L
M MB MBAt MHi MBC MdHi MiD-B NcD AU OU NN MoSW NNLI
NL 0420410 DLC ViU LU MB CaBVaU CU-Law IU LNHT LU-L

Micro-fiche s425

Livingston, Edward, 1764–1836.

Report made to the General Assembly of the state of Louisiana, on the plan of a Penal code for the said state New-Orleans, Printed by B. Levy & Co., 1822.

Microcard edition (4 cards).

Sabin 41614.

1. Criminal law—Louisiana. 2. Law—Codification. I. Louisiana. General Assembly.

NL 0420411 ViU PSt OU ICRL TxU

Livingston, Edward, 1764-1836.

Louisiana. *Laws, statutes, etc.*

... A republication of the projet of the Civil code of Louisiana of 1825 ... A republication of the projet of the Code of practice of Louisiana of 1825. Published pursuant to Act 236 of the legislature of Louisiana of 1936, E. A. Conway, secretary of state. New Orleans, Printed by T. J. Moran's sons, 1937.

Livingston, Edward, 1764-1836.

[Timlow, William]

A review of the arguments of the Hon. Edward Livingston and others, on the subject of capital punishment. 2d ed. ... Goshen, N. Y., Printed by Clark & Montanye, 1850.

Livingston, Edward, 1764–1836.

The speech of Edward Livingston, esq. on the third reading of the Alien bill. Philadelphia: Printed: by James Carey, no. 19. Carter's alley [1798?]

16 p. 23½cm.

Delivered in the House of representatives, June 21, 1798.

1. Alien and sedition laws, 1798.

3–5899

Library of Congress E327.L78

——— Copy 2. [Miscellaneous pamphlets, v. 850, no. 3] AC901.M5 vol. 850

NL 0420414 DLC NcD ViU MH NjP PPiPT NN MBAt RPJCB

Livingston, Edward, 1764–1836.

Speech of Edward Livingston in the Senate of the United States, February, 1831, on the Turkish mission, in answer to Mr. Tazewell, of Virginia. Washington: Printed by Gales and Seaton, 1831. 47 p. 8°.

1. U. S.—Government: Treaty power. 2. Tazewell, Littleton Waller, 1774–1860.
N. Y. P. L. October 2, 1916.

NL 0420415 NN LU GHi DLC ViU ViN

Z 973.561 L762s

Livingston, Edward, 1764-1836.
Speech of Mr. Livingston, of Louisiana, on Mr. Foot's resolution, proposing an inquiry into the expediency of abolishing the office of surveyor general of public lands, and for discontinuing further surveys, &c. Delivered in the Senate of the United States, Feb. 29, 1830. Charleston [S.C.] Printed by J.S. Burges, 1830.
24p. 22cm.

1. Foot's resolution, 1829. Sp.: Littlefield Fund.

NL 0420416 TxU DLC PPAmP PU MH MiU CSmH

Livingston, Edward, 1764–1836.

Speech of Mr. Livingston, of Louisiana, on Mr. Foot's resolution, proposing an inquiry into the expediency of abolishing the office of surveyor general of public lands, and for discontinuing further surveys, &c. Delivered in the Senate of the United States, February 29, 1830. Washington, Printed by D. Green, 1830.

58 p. 22cm.

[Markoe pamphlets, v. 2, no. 7]

1. Foot's resolution, 1829.

19–12197

Library of Congress AC901.M2 vol. 2

——— Copy 2. [Miscellaneous pamphlets, v. 955, no. 12] AC901.M5 vol. 955 [2]

NL 0420417 DLC N ViU OClWHi

HE204 .L5 Toner Coll.

Livingston, Edward, 1764-1836.
Speech of Mr. Livingston, of Louisiana, on the subject of internal improvement. Delivered in the House of representatives U. S., February 9, 1824. Washington, Printed by Gales & Seaton, 1824.
36 p. 22 cm.

Caption title: Speech ... on the bill for obtaining the necessary surveys on the subject of roads and canals.

1. Roads--U. S. 2. Canals--U. S.

NL 0420418 DLC LU MH NN

Livingston, Edward, 1764-1836.
A system of penal law for the state of Louisiana. London, 1824.
8vo.

NL 0420419 NN

Livingston, Edward, 1764–1836.

A system of penal law, for the state of Louisiana: consisting of a Code of crimes and punishments, a Code of procedure, a Code of evidence, a Code of reform and prison discipline, a Book of definitions. Prepared under the authority of a law of the said state. By Edward Livingston. To which are prefixed a preliminary report on the plan of a penal code, and introductory reports to the several codes embraced in the system of penal law. Philadelphia, J. Kay, jun., & brother; Pittsburgh, J. I. Kay & co. [1833]

v. 745 p. 24 cm.

Not adopted as law by the Louisiana General assembly. *cf.* Introd., The complete works of Edward Livingston ... New York, 1873.

1. Criminal law—Louisiana. 2. Punishment—Louisiana. 3. Criminal procedure—Louisiana. 4. Evidence (Law)—Louisiana. 5. Crime and criminals—Louisiana. 6. Prisons—Louisiana—Laws and regulations.

18—16870

TU N MH-L WaU-L CLL
NL 0420421 DLC MiU MH NN NcD PU-L PU PP ViU-L TxU IU

Livingston, Edward, 1764–1836.

A system of penal law for the United States of America: consisting of a Code of crimes and punishments; a Code of procedure in criminal cases; a Code of prison discipline; and a Book of definitions. Prepared and presented to the House of representatives of the United States, by Edward Livingston ... Printed by order of the House of representatives. Washington, Printed by Gales & Seaton, 1828.

x p., 1 l., 142, 187, 51, 45, 21 p. 31½cm.

Followed by no legislation. *cf.* Introd., The complete works of Edward Livingston ... New York, 1873.

1. Criminal law—U. S. 2. Punishment. 3. Criminal procedure—U. S. 4. Crime and criminals—U. S. 5. Prisons—Laws and regulations.

18-16867

ViU-L MB MH NN NjP MWA OU MiU
NL 0420422 DLC WaU-L NBuU-L NcU OClW NjP NcD PU-L

Livingston, Edward, 1764–1836.

System of penal law, prepared for the state of Louisiana; comprising codes of offenses and punishments, of procedure, of prison discipline, and of evidence applicable as well to civil as to criminal cases. And a book, containing definitions of all the technical words used in this system. Prepared under the authority of a law of the said state. By Edward Livingston, LL. D. New-Orleans, Printed by B. Levy, 1824.

164 p. 30 x 19cm.

Not adopted as law by the Louisiana General assembly. *cf.* Introd. The complete works of Edward Livingston ... New York, 1873.

1. Criminal law—Louisiana. 2. Punishment. 3. Criminal procedure—Louisiana. 4. Evidence (Law) — Louisiana. 5. Crime and criminals—Louisiana. 6. Prisons—Laws and regulations.

3-25017

Library of Congress

NL 0420423 DLC WaU-L LU CtY PHi

Film 144

Livingston, Edward, 1764-1836.
System of penal law, prepared for the State of Louisiana, comprising codes of offences and punishments, of procedure, of prison discipline, and of evidence applicable as well to civil as to criminal cases. And a book, containing definitions of all the technical words used in the system. Prepared under the authority of a law of the said state. New Orleans, Benjamin Levy, 1842.

Microfilm of the original in the Library of Congress: Positive.
Collation of the original as determined from the film: 164p.

1. Criminal law—La. 2. Punishment. 3. Criminal procedure—La. 4. Crime and criminals—La. I. Title.

NL 0420425 LU

VOLUME 336

Livingston, Edward, 1764-1836.
Système de loi pénale pour l'état de la Louisiane, comprenant les codes, 1. Des délits et des peines. 2. De procédure. 3. De discipline des prisons. 4. Des preuves; ce dernier applicable au civil comme au criminel; et un livre contenant les définitions de tous les mots techniques dont il est fait usage dans ce système. Préparé en vertu d'une loi de l'état, par Edouard Livingston. Nouvelle Orléans, B. Levy, 1825.
1 v. (various pagings)

Title-page preceded by "Rapport servant d'introduction au Système de loi pénale preparé pour l'état de la Louisiane" (227 p.) and "Table: Offenses créées, par statuts, dans la Louisiane, depuis sa cession aux États-Unis" (vii p.)

NL 0420427 NNC MH-L

[Livingston, Edward] 1764-1836.
To the Honorable the Senate and House of representatives of the state of Louisiana, in General assembly convened. The subscribers, jurists, appointed for the revision of the Civil code, respectfully report. [New Orleans, Printed by J. C. de St. Romes, state printer, 1823]
13 p. 23cm.
Caption title.
Signed: Edw. Livingston, Moreau Lislet, P. Derbigny.
1. Law—Louisiana. 2. Law—Codification. I. Louisiana. General assembly. II. Moreau Lislet, Louis. III. Derbigny, Pierre Auguste Charles Bourisgay, 1767-1829. IV. Title.
19-14650

NL 0420428 DLC ICN MdHi MnU

617.55 qL786 Livingston, Edward Meakin, 1895-
... A clinical study of the abdominal cavity and peritoneum ... [N.Y., P.B.Hoeber, 1930]
576p. illus. 27cm.

"Supplement to the American journal of surgery."
1.Abdomen. Diseases. Diagnosis. 2.Abdomen. Surgery. 3.Peritoneum. Diseases. Diagnosis. 4.Peritoneum. Surgery. I.American journal of surgery. Supplement. II.Title.

NL 0420429 N

Livingston, Edward Meakin, 1895-
... A clinical study of the abdominal cavity & peritoneum, by Edward Meakin Livingston ... 372 illustrations. New York, P. B. Hoeber, inc., 1932.
xxii, 866 p. incl. illus., facsims., diagrs. 27½cm. (Hoeber's surgical monographs)
"References": p. 780-792.
1. Abdomen—Diseases—Diagnosis. 2. Peritoneum—Diseases—Diagnosis. 3. Abdomen—Surgery. 4. Peritoneum—Surgery. I. Title.
32-7138
Library of Congress RD540.L5
——— Copy 2.
Copyright A 47961 [3] 617.5507

NL 0420430 DLC OClW-H NcU-H NcD MiU PPC PPHa

Livingston, Edward Meakin, 1895-
End-results in the treatment of gastric cancer; an analytical study and statistical survey of sixty years of surgical treatment, by Edward M. Livingston ... and George T. Pack ... with a foreword by Bowman C. Crowell ... New York, London, P. B. Hoeber, inc. [c1939]
x, 179 p. incl. front., illus., tables. diagrs. 26cm.
Illustrated lining-papers; includes blank pages for "Notes".
On cover: Cancer of the stomach.
"The material in this volume is preprinted from the Treatment of cancer and allied diseases by 142 international authors, edited by George T. Pack and Edward M. Livingston."
Bibliography: p. 164-175.
1. Stomach — Cancer. 2. Stomach — Surgery. I. Pack, George Thomas, 1898- joint author. II. Title.
39-12930
Library of Congress RC261.L79
——— Copy 2.
Copyright A 128278 [2] [616.33] 616.994

NL 0420431 DLC OrU-M CaBVaU OU PPC

Livingston, Edward Meakin, 1895- joint author.

Foote, Edward Milton, 1866-
Principles and practice of minor surgery; a textbook for students and practitioners, by Edward Milton Foote ... and Edward Meakin Livingston ... 6th ed., illustrated by four hundred and twenty engravings chiefly from original drawings and photographs. New York, London, D. Appleton and company, 1929.

Livingston, Edward Meakin, 1895- joint ed

Pack, George Thomas, 1898- *ed.*
Treatment of cancer and allied diseases, by one hundred and forty-seven international authors; edited by George T. Pack ... and Edward M. Livingston ... with 1500 illustrations ... New York, London, P. B. Hoeber, inc. [c1940]

Livingston, Edward P.
An address delivered on the 1st of Aug. 1831, before the Philolexian and Peithologian societies, of Columbia college. New York, 1831.
28 p. 8°.

NL 0420434 MB DLC CSmH NN

Livingston, Edwin Brockholst, 1852-
The Livingstons of America.
2 p. (Mag. Am. Hist. v. 25, 1891, p. 416)

NL 0420435 MdBP

Livingston, Edwin Brockholst, 1852-
The Livingstons of Callendar, and their principal cadets. A family history by Edwin Brockholst Livingston ... [Edinburgh, Scott & Ferguson] 1887-[92]
xviii, 656, civ p. front., plates, ports., facsims. (1 fold.) coats of arms (part col.) fold. geneal. tab. 31cm.
Title vignette: colored coat of arms.
"Privately printed for Clermont and Edwin Brockholst Livingston. Impression: seventy-five copies, of which this is no. 58."
Issued in 5 numbers, in portfolios; number 6 to contain Addenda and corrigenda, errata, index, &c., not published.
Bound in two volumes.
Pedigree showing the American ancestry of the author's family: p. 476.

CONTENTS.—pt. I, no. I-IV. Scotland. section I. The Livingstons of Livingston and the Livingstons, lords of Callendar. section II. The earls of Linlithgow. section III. The earls of Callendar. section IV. The earls of Newburgh. section V. The viscounts of Kilsyth. section VI. The Livingstons of Jerviswood and Newbigging, and Sir Thomas Livingston, viscount of Teviot. section VII. The Livingstons in France.—pt. II, no. V. America. section I. The manor of Livingston, New York. section II. The political history of the manor of Livingston, and of the Livingstons of New York, during colonial and revolutionary times. section III. Clermont.
1. Livingston family. 2. Livingston family (Robert Livingston, 1654-1728) I. Livingston, Clermont, 1850- II. Title.
20-20492
Library of Congress CS71.L787 1887

NL 0420437 DLC NN

Livingston, Edwin Brockholst, 1852-
The Livingstons of Callendar, and their principal cadets; the history of an old Stirlingshire family, by Edwin Brockholst Livingston ... New ed., entirely rewritten and greatly enl. ... Edinburgh, Printed at the University press for the author, 1920.
xix, 511 p. front. (fold. facsim.) plates, ports., col. coats of arms. 26½cm.
"Contains a set of coloured heraldic plates from drawings specially executed for this new edition by Mr. Graham Johnston, heraldic artist to the Lyon court."
"A chronology of the most notable events in the history of the Livingstons of Callendar": p. xv-xviii.
"Notes and references": p. 139-143.
1. Livingston family. I. Johnston, Graham, illus. II. Title.
Library of Congress CS479.L7 1920 20-22842

NL 0420438 DLC MB MH NN NjP OClWHi

Livingston, Edwin Brockholst, 1852-
The Livingstons of Livingston manor; being the history of that branch of the Scottish house of Callendar which settled in the English province of New York during the reign of Charles the Second; and also including an account of Robert Livingston of Albany, "The nephew", a settler in the same province, and his principal descendants, by Edwin Brockholst Livingston ... [New York, The Knickerbocker press] 1910.
xxxiii, 590 p. plates (part col.) ports., map, facsims. (part fold.) 2 fold. geneal. tab. (incl. front.) 24½cm.
"275 copies only printed by private subscription."
"List of authorities": p. 564-575.
1. Livingston family. 2. Livingston family (Robert Livingston, 1654-1728) 3. Livingston family (Robert Livingston, d. 1725)
Library of Congress CS71.L787 1910 10—5281

NL 0420439 DLC CtY NjP NN MiU

Livingston, Eleanor.
Come sweet love. Words and music by Eleanor Livingstone... New York, M. Witmark & sons [c1904]
First line: The world seems dark and dreary.
Portrait of Eleanor Livingstone on t.-p.
Printed for the Music Division
1. Livingston, Eleanor—Port. I. Song index (2).
N. Y. P. L. May 26, 1949

NL 0420440 NN

[Livingston, Elizabeth]
Stephanie. A novel. By Tom Lee [*pseud.*] London, Ward and Downey, 1890.
302 p. 19½cm.
Library of Congress PZ3.L7 7-19400†

NL 0420441 DLC

MF328.34 L762 Livingston, Ellis Noel.
Senate investigating committees, 1900-1938. [Minneapolis] 1953.
iii,327l.

Microfilm (positive)
Thesis- University of Minnesota.
Bibliography: l.325-327.

1. Governmental investigations. U.S. I. Title.

NL 0420442 OrU

Livingston, Ernest M.
The oxidation of hydrogen sulphide ... by Ernest M. Livingston ... [Ithaca, N. Y., 1931]
cover-title, 1 p. l., 8 p. diagrs. 26½cm.
Thesis (PH. D.)—New York university, 1931.
Reprinted from an article, by H. Austin Taylor and Ernest M. Livingston, published in the Journal of physical chemistry, v. 35, no. 9, Sept. 1931.
1. Hydrogen sulphide. 2. Oxidation. I. Taylor, Henry Austin, 1899- joint author.
32-5481
Library of Congress QD181.S1L55 1931
New York Univ. Libr. [2]

NL 0420443 NNU DLC OU

Livingston, Essex R.
Oration: delivered before the Cherryfield Washington temperance society, July 4, 1842. By Essex R. Livingston. Published by the Cherryfield Washington temperance society. Bangor [Me.] Smith & Sayward, printers, 1842. 22 p. 23cm.

1. Temperance—Addresses, essays, lectures. 2. Independence day—Speeches, 1842. I. Cherryfield Washington temperance society, Cherryfield, Me.
N. Y. P. L. September 25, 1940

NL 0420444 NN

VOLUME 336

Livingston, Ethel.
A difference in clocks; a sketch in one scene, by Ethel Livingston. Boston, W. H. Baker & co., 1900.
12 p. 19cm. (On cover: Baker's edition of plays)

I. Title.

Library of Congress PS3523.I 943D5 1900 0-4143 Revised
Copyright 1900 A 10425 [r30c2] 812.5

NL 0420445 DLC MH

Livingston, Everett Gordon, 1901-
Fifty full-scale drawings of woodturning problems. Iowa State College, Industrial Arts., Ames, 1934.
pamphlet

NL 0420446 OrCS PSt

Livingston, Everett Gordon, 1901- joint author.
Hunter, William Luther.
A guide to magazine articles on industrial arts education and vocational industrial education, by William L. Hunter and Everett G. Livingston. Ames, Industrial arts department, Iowa state college [1934]

Livingston, Everett Gordon, 1901- comp.
Industrial sheets in industrial arts education, a symposium prepared under the direction of Everett G.Livingston. Ames, Ia., Industrial arts department, Iowa state college, 1934.

5p.l.,103 numb.l. illus.(incl.diagrs.) 28½cm.

"Formulated by a group of graduate students ... during the second summer term of 1934 at Iowa state college."--cf. Preface.
Reproduced from type-written copy.

NL 0420448 MoU OrCS OOxM

Livingston, Everett Gordon.
Keene's cement craft [by] Everett G. Livingston. Amos, Iowa: Iowa State College [1935] 49 f. diagrs., illus. 4°.
Bibliography, p. 49.

1. Cement. 2. Title. 3. Modelling. 4. Handicraft.
N. Y. P. L. April 3, 1936

NL 0420449 NN OU OCl OClh

Livingston, Flora Virginia (Milner) 1862-
... Bibliographical data relating to a few of the publications of Algernon Charles Swinburne
see her Swinburne's proof sheets and American first editions ...

Livingston, Flora Virginia (Milner) 1862-
[Livingston, Luther Samuel] 1864-1914.
Bibliography of the separate publications of Luther S. Livingston.
(In The papers of the Bibliographical society of America. Chicago, Ill. [1915] 25cm. v. 8, 1914, no. 3-4, p. 121-134)

Livingston, Flora Virginia (Milner) 1862-
Prideaux, William Francis, 1840-1914.
A bibliography of the works of Robert Louis Stevenson, by Colonel W. F. Prideaux, C. S. I. A new and rev. ed., edited and supplemented by Mrs. Luther S. Livingston ... London, F. Hollings, 1917.

Livingston, *Mrs.* **Flora Virginia (Milner)** 1862-
Bibliography of the works of Rudyard Kipling, by Flora V. Livingston ... New York, E. H. Wells and company, 1927.
xviii, 523 p. facsims. 22cm.
"Chronological list" 1879-1926: p. [v]-xviii.
Z8465.L78
—— Copy 2.
Copyright A 976328
—— Supplement to Bibliography of the works of Rudyard Kipling (1927) by Flora V. Livingston ... Cambridge, Harvard university press, 1938.
xv, 333 p. illus. (port.) 22cm.
1. Kipling, Rudyard, 1865-1936—Bibl.
27-10104 Revised
Library of Congress Z8465.L78 Suppl
—— Copy 2.
Copyright A 116790 [r39f2]

NSyU FTaSU InU MsU MtU MoSW NBuU MoU PPT TU TxU PU MH PSt CU MShM NN NjP MB TxU NcD OCU OO OU OCl CaBVa OrCS OrU WaSp
NL 0420453 DLC WaS PU NIC PBm PP PU PSC PPT MH ViU

Livingston, Flora Virginia (Milner) 1862-
... Books, autographs and manuscripts ....
see under title

[LIVINGSTON, Mrs. Flora Virginia (Milner).] 1862-
[A collection of photostats procured by Mrs.Livingston while preparing her Bibliography of the Works of Rudyard Kipling.]

The collection contains photostats of original manuscripts, title-pages, newspapers, articles, broadsides, etc.

NL 0420455 MH

[LIVINGSTON, Mrs. Flora Virginia (Milner), 1862-]
Drunk as Davy's sow.

Typewritten. 29 cm. ff.7.
Without title-page. Caption title.
Typescript made by Mrs.Livingston of letters and comments relating to a controversy in the columns of the London Sunday Times over the origin of the expression "drunk as Davy's sow".
A carbon record by L.H.Chandler from which this copy was made is inserted at end. Two newspaper clippings, one containing the letter from Kipling which constitutes his contribution to the controversy, inserted at front.

NL 0420456 MH

Livingston, *Mrs.* **Flora Virginia (Milner)** 1862-
A footnote to bibliography, by Flora V. Livingston.
(In The Colophon. [New York, ©1931] 27½ x 21½cm. pt. 7 [no. 4] [4] p. illus. (facsim.))
Title from Contents to pt. 7 of the series: A footnote to Kipling bibliography.

1. Kipling, Rudyard, 1865-1936. Recessional. I. Title.
A C 38-1907
Grosvenor library for Library of Congress Z1007.C71 pt. 7, no. 4 [Z1007.C71 pt. 7, no. 4]
[4] (010.5)

NL 0420457 NBuG DLC OCl

Livingston, Mrs. Flora Virginia (Milner) 1862-
Harvard university. *Library.*
The Harcourt Amory collection of Lewis Carroll in the Harvard college library, compiled by Flora V. Livingston. Cambridge, Mass., Priv. print. [Harvard university press] 1932.

Livingston, Flora Virginia (Milner) 1862-
Dickens, Charles, 1812-1870.
Charles Dickens's letters to Charles Lever, edited by Flora V. Livingston, with an introduction by Hyder E. Rollins. Cambridge, Harvard university press, 1933.

Livingston, Mrs. Flora Virginia (Milner) 1862-
Milton portraits in the Harvard College Library compared with the Grolier Club Catalogue
see under Harvard University. Library.

[LIVINGSTON, Mrs. Flora Virginia (Milner).]
[Scrapbook kept by Mrs.Livingston containing cuttings from various periodicals, most of which are portraits and caricatures of Rudyard Kipling.]

31.5 x 25.5 cm.

NL 0420461 MH

[LIVINGSTON, Mrs. Flora Virginia (Milner).]
[Scrapbook kept by Mrs.Livingston containing programs, letters, announcements, etc., relating to the Kipling Society.]

37 x 27 cm.

NL 0420462 MH

[LIVINGSTON, Mrs. Flora Virginia (Milner).]
[Scrapbook material collected by Mrs.Livingston, consisting mainly of portraits and caricatures of Rudyard Kipling, mostly cuttings from various periodicals.]

57 x 41 cm.

NL 0420463 MH

[LIVINGSTON, Mrs. Flora Virginia (Milner).]
[Scrapbook material collected by Mrs.Livingston, consisting of cuttings from various periodicals containing poems and stories by Rudyard Kipling and pictures and articles relating to him and his work.]

Portfolio. 41 x 53.5 cm.

NL 0420464 MH

[LIVINGSTON, Mrs. Flora Virginia (Milner).]
[Scrapbook material collected by Mrs.Livingston, containing cuttings from newspapers and magazines, etc. relating to Rudyard Kipling and his work].

44 x 29.5 cm.

NL 0420465 MH

VOLUME 336

[LIVINGSTON, Mrs. Flora Virginia (Milner).]
[Scrapbook material containing cuttings from various periodicals relating to Rudyard Kipling and his work.]

Portfolio. 71 x 53.5 cm.

NL 0420466 MH

[LIVINGSTON, Mrs. Flora Virginia (Milner).]
[Scrapbooks kept by Mrs. Livingston containing typescripts from various periodicals, of stories, articles, and poems attributed to Kipling].

7 vol. 37 x 27 cm.
Mrs. Livingston believes the attribution to be false in many cases.
Typescripts of articles by Mrs. J.L. Kipling in the Pioneer Mail, May-October, 1888, are in vol. II, ff. 30-57.

NL 0420467 MH

[LIVINGSTON, Mrs. Flora Virginia (Milner).]
[Scrapbooks kept by Mrs. Livingston from 1920-1937, containing cuttings from newspapers and magazines, etc., mainly items of Kipling interest.]

15 vol. 29.5 x 21 cm. Ports. and other illustr.

NL 0420468 MH

Livingston, Flora Virginia (Milner) 1862-
Supplement to Bibliography of the works of Rudyard Kipling (1927)
see her Bibliography of the works of Rudyard Kipling.

Livingston, Flora Virginia (Milner) 1862-
Swinburne's proof sheets and American first editions. Bibliographical data relating to a few of the publications of Algernon Charles Swinburne, with notes on the priority of certain claimants to the distinction of "Editio princeps," by Flora V. Livingston. Cambridge, Mass., Priv. print. [by the Cosmos press] 1920.

30, [2] p. incl. facsims. 21½cm.

1. Swinburne, Algernon Charles, 1837-1909—Bibl.

21-2472 Revised

Library of Congress Z8857.L78

NL 0420470 DLC NSyU NIC NcU MH NcD TxU MB PBL NN

Livingston, Florence Bingham.
The custard cup, by Florence Bingham Livingston. New York, George H. Doran company [°1921]

vi p., 1 l., 9-297 p. 19½cm.

I. Title.

21-6897

Library of Congress PZ3.L7623Cu

NL 0420471 DLC Or WaS MB

Livingston, Florence Bingham.
This man and this woman, by Florence Bingham Livingston. Garden City, N. Y., Doubleday, Doran & company, inc., 1928.

2 p. l., 310 p. 19½cm.

I. Title.

Library of Congress PZ3.L7623Th 28-9653

NL 0420472 DLC MB

Livingston, Florence Bingham.
Under a thousand eyes, by Florence Bingham Livingston ... illustrations by Maurice L. Bower. New York, Cosmopolitan book corporation, 1923.

4 p. l., 456 p. front., plates. 19½cm.

I. Title.

23-7724

Library of Congress PZ3.L7623Un

NL 0420473 DLC LU ViU NN OClh OCl MB

Livingston, Frank H.
Tuberculosis; its cause, prevention, and care, by Frank H. Livingston. New York, The Macmillan company, 1930.

xii p., 1 l., 191 p. 20½cm.

1. Tuberculosis.

30-29805

Library of Congress RC311.L8
Copyright A 29641 [3] 616.246

NL 0420474 DLC ICJ OrP OrAshS OrP NN OCl PU

Livingston, George, 1886-
Field crop production; a text-book for elementary courses in schools and brief courses in colleges, by George Livingston ... New York, The Macmillan company, 1914.

xix, 424 p. front., illus. 19½cm. (*Half-title: The rural text-book series, ed. by L. H. Bailey*)

1. Agriculture.

14-8200

Library of Congress SB185.L46

NL 0420475 DLC CU NIC NcRA ViU ICJ MB NN TU OrCS OOxM OO OU OCl

---

Livingston, George, 1886-
Field crop production; a textbook for elementary courses in schools and brief courses in colleges, by George Livingston...
New York, The Macmillan company, 1920.
424 p. (The rural text-book series, ed. by L. H. Bailey)

NL 0420476 MiU

Livingston, George, 1886-
Laboratory manual of cereals and forage crops, by Geo. Livingston ... and Malon Yoder ... Columbus, O., R. G. Adams & company, 1913.

90 p. incl. forms. 27cm.

1. Grain. 2. Forage plants. I. Yoder, Malon, joint author.

14-975

Library of Congress SB185.L5

NL 0420477 DLC ICJ

Livingston, George, 1886-
Laboratory manual of cereals and forage crops, by Geo. Livingston ... and F. W. Stemple ... Columbus, O., R. G. Adams & company, 1915.

147 p. incl. illus., forms. 27cm. $0.90

Part of pages blank for "Instructor's notices, explanations, etc."

1. Grain. 2. Forage plants. 3. Agriculture—Laboratory manuals I. Stemple, Forrest Wilbur, 1881- joint author.

15-24707

Library of Congress SB185.L5 1915

NL 0420478 DLC NcRS ICJ

Livingston, George, 1886-
... Marketing grain at country points. By George Livingston and K. B. Seeds ... Washington, Govt. print. off., 1917.

cover-title, 45 p. illus., diagr. 23cm. (U. S. Dept. of agriculture. Bulletin no. 558)

Contribution from the Office of markets and rural organization.

1. Grain. 2. Grain trade—U. S. [1. 2. Cereals—Marketing] I. Seeds, Karl Beaver, 1879- joint author. II. Title.

Agr 17-813

U. S. Dept. of agr. Library 1Ag84B no. 558
for Library of Congress 821.A7 no. 558
——— Copy 2. HD9006.L6

NL 0420479 DNAL OU DLC NN WaWW

Livingston, George, 1886-
... The wheat standards and their application. By George Livingston ... [Washington, Govt. print. off., 1918]

12 p. 23cm. (U. S. Dept. of agriculture. Bureau of markets. Service and regulatory announcement. no. 35)

Address delivered before the Annual convention of the Oklahoma grain dealers and millers association, Oklahoma City, Okla., May 22-23, 1918.

1. [Wheat—Standards]

Agr 18-871

Library, U. S. Dept. of Agriculture 1M34S no. 35

NL 0420480 DNAL OO

SF427 .C815

Livingston, Gerald M.

Connett, Eugene Virginius, 1891- ed.
American sporting dogs; chapters by Gerald M. Livingston [and others] Illus. from paintings by Edwin Megargee and from photos. [1st ed.] New York, D. Van Nostrand Co. [1948]

FILM 5943 HF

Livingston, Gilbert
Building account book ... 1770-1772. [New York? 1770-72]
1 v. On film.

Microfilm copy of original manuscript in the library of the New York historical society.

1. Accounting - To 1800. 2. Building - Accounting.

NL 0420482 CU

FILM 6004 HF

Livingston, Gilbert
Correspondence of Gilbert Livingston, attorney-at-law, 1730-1796. Poughkeepsie, N.Y., etc., 1730-96.
1 v. On film.

Microfilm copy of original manuscripts in the New York Public Library.

1. Commercial correspondence.

NL 0420483 CU

VOLUME 336

Livingston, Goodhue
The matching of different expressions of personality; recognition of the authorship of stories

Thesis - Harvard, 1954

NL 0420484 MH

Livingston, Gordon.
Livingston's guide book to St. John and the St. John River, with an account of the fishing grounds of New Brunswick, by Gordon Livingston. St. John, N. B., Printed by H. Chubb & co., 1870.
1 p. l., 138, ii p. 14½cm.
Advertising matter included in paging.

1. St. John, N. B.—Descr.—Guide-books. 2. New Brunswick—Descr. & trav.—Guide-books.
18-4487
Library of Congress F1044.5.S14L7

NL 0420485 DLC MWA CaNSWA

Rare Books and Special Collections
Livingston, Gordon
Livingston's hand book and visitors' guide to Saint John, with an account of Fredericton and the St. John River. Saint John, N.B., Printed by H. Chubb, 1869.
133, iii p.

Includes advertisements.
In box.

NL 0420486 CaOTU MWA

Livingston, Grace
see Hill, Mrs. Grace (Livingston) 1865-

Livingston, Mrs. Grace J.
Annotated bibliography of evaporation. 1908.

NL 0420488 DAS

Livingston, Mrs. Grace J.
An annotated bibliography of evaporation. (1909)
unacc nub.

NL 0420489 DI-GS

Livingston, *Mrs.* **Grace J.**
An annotated bibliography of evaporation. By Mrs. Grace J. Livingston ... [Washington, Weather bureau, 1910]
cover-title, 121 p. 24½cm.
Reprinted from Monthly weather review for June, September and November, 1908, and February, March, April, May and June, 1909.

1. Evaporation—Bibl. I. U. S. Dept. of agriculture. Weather bureau.
Agr 10-1754 Cancel*
Library, U. S. Dept. of Agriculture 1W378L

NL 0420490 DNAL MB NN NjP

Livingston, Mrs. Grace J., comp.
Alden, Isabella (Macdonald) *"Mrs. G. R. Alden,"* **1841–**
Pansies for thoughts, from the writings of Pansy—Mrs. G. R. Alden. Comp. and arranged with an appropriate text for each day by Grace Livingston ... Boston, D. Lothrop company [1888]

Livingston, Guy, 1881–
Hot air in cold blood, by Brigadier-General Guy Livingston ... with 20 illustrations. [London] Selwyn & Blount ltd., 1933.
xvi, 17–288 p. front., plates, ports., facsims. 23½cm.

1. Aeronautics, Military—Gt. Brit. 2. Gt. Brit.—Army—Military life. 3. European war, 1914–1918—Aerial operations. I. Title.
33-16234
Library of Congress D602.L5 1933
——— Copy 2.
Copyright A ad int. 17842 [3] 940.44942

NL 0420492 DLC MH DAL

Livingston, Harold.
The coasts of the earth. Boston, Houghton Mifflin, 1954.
278 p. 22 cm.

I. Title.
PZ4.L786Co 54-5701 ‡

PP OClTem OCl PPLas
NL 0420493 DLC OrU Or OrP WaSp NNJ OCH GU NN PPDrop

M1 A13C6 no.25
Livingston, Hattie
Young folks at home. Written and composed expressly for Wood's Minstrels, Minstrel's Hall, 444 Broadway. Composed by Miss Hattie Livingston. Words written by Frank Spencer. 13th ed. New York, T.S.Berry & Co., 297 Broadway, 1852.
5p. 34cm. (In [Collection of songs published in the U.S. 1840-1860, no.25])
For voice and piano with choral refrain for S.A.T.B.
1. Vocal quartets with piano. I. Title.

NL 0420494 IaU ViU

LIVINGSTON, HATTIE
Young folks at home; written & composed expressly for Wood's minstrels. Words written by Frank Spencer. New York, T. S. Berry, c1852.
5 p.

Microfilm (master negative).
For chorus.
13th ed.
First line: 'Twas in a southern grave I dwelt.

NL 0420495 NN

---

* M1 .A13N .L48Y6 1854
Livingston, Hattie.
Young folks at home. 18th ed. Guitar, piano: 25¢ nett. New York, Berry & Cordon [!] 297 Broadway; New Orleans, H. D. Hewitt ... ©1854.
5 p. 32cm.
At head of title: Words written by Frank Spencer.
Dunbar, cs.; Swain, engvr.
1. Songs with piano. 2. Choruses, Secular (Mixed voices, 4 pts.) with piano. I. Title.

NL 0420496 ViU

Livingston, Hattie.
The young folks at home. [Song, with accompaniment for pianoforte.] Written by Frank Spencer. Music by Hattie Livingston. — [New York. 186-?] 5 pp. 33½ cm.
The title-page is lacking.

L9708 — Double main card. — Livingston, Hattie. (M1) — Spencer, Frank. (M2) — T.r. (1) — Songs ref. made.

NL 0420497 MB

Livingston, Hazel.
Stolen love, by Hazel Livingston. New York, Grosset & Dunlap [©1929]
2 p. l., 275 p. 19½cm.

I. Title.
29-2735
Library of Congress PZ3.L7624St

NL 0420498 DLC

Livingston, Helen.
see Livingstone, Helen, 1877-

Livingston, Helen E.
National health insurance. Washington, 1950.
xv, 78 p. 26 cm. (Public affairs bulletin no. 85)
Bibliography: p. 71–73.

1. Insurance, Health—U. S. (Series: U. S. Library of Congress. Legislative Reference Service. Public affairs bulletin no. 85)
JK1108.A35 no. 85 331.25442 50-62954

NL 0420500 DLC MB NcU DNLM MtBC CaBViP OrPS

Livingston, Helen (Hay) Countess of Linlithgow
see Linlithgow, Helen (Hay) Livingston, Countess of.

Livingston, Helen Raddon.
Look, say and do. [Salt Lake City] Deseret News Press, ©1947.
45 p. col. illus. 16 x 24 cm.

1. Readers and speakers—1870– I. Title.
PE1119.L55 372.4 48-20564*

NL 0420502 DLC

Livingston, Henry, *ed.*
"The money-maker;" or, How to get rich. Being a practical guide to business success, applicable to all trades and professions, and particularly designed as a help to those out of employment. New York, H. Livingston, pub. & ed. [©1868]
320 p. 13½cm.

1. Success. 2. Receipts. I. Title.
7-8033
Library of Congress HF5386.L75

NL 0420503 DLC

Livingston, Henry, 1748–1828.
Journal of Major Henry Livingston, of the Third New York continental line, August to December, 1775. By Gaillard Hunt ... Philadelphia, 1898.
28 p. 25cm.
"Reprinted from the Pennsylvania magazine of history and biography for April, 1898."

1. Canadian invasion, 1775–1776. 2. U. S.—Hist.—Revolution—Personal narratives. I. Hunt, Gaillard, 1862–1924, ed.
5-23351
Library of Congress E231.L78

NL 0420504 DLC

Livingston, Henry Brockholst
see
Livingston, Brockholst, 1757–1823.

VOLUME 336

FILM 9747 ML Music Library
Livingston, Herbert
The Italian overture from Alessandro Scarlatti to Mozart. Chapel Hill, [N.C.] 1952.
iii, 343 ℓ. On film (Negative)

Microfilm copy of typescript.
Thesis - University of NOrth Carolina.
Bibliography: Books and articles: leaves 315-324; Scores: leaves 326-343.

--- ----- Musical supplement.
vii ℓ., score (198 p.) On film (Negative)

Contents. - La statira (Sinfonia) Il prigioniero fortunato (Sinfonia); by A. Scarlatti. - Pyrrhus and Demetrius (Overture); by N. Haym. - Elpida (Overture); by L. Vinci. - Cair Mario (Overture); by N. Jommelli. - Il geloso in cemento; by P. Anfossi. - Love in a village (Overture); by C. F. Abel. Der Aerndtekranz (Sinfonia); by J. A. Hiller.

NL 0420507 CU

Livingston, Herbert Klossner, 1918–
Adsorption and the free surface energy of solids. Chicago, 1941.
v, 70 l. diagrs. 32 cm.
Thesis—University of Chicago.
Typescript (carbon copy)
Bibliographical footnotes.

1. Adsorption. 2. Surface energy.

QC182.L52 1941 62-57166

NL 0420508 DLC ICU

Livingston, Herbert Klossner, 1918–
... Adsorption and the free surface energy of solids ... by Herbert Klossner Livingston ... [n. p., 1942]
8 p. incl. tables, diagrs. 26½ x 20cm.
Part of thesis (PH. D.)—University of Chicago, 1941.
"Reprinted from the Journal of the American chemical society, vol. 64, no. 10, October, 1942."
Bibliographical foot-notes.

1. Adsorption. I. Title: Surface energy of solids.

A 43-786

Chicago. Univ. Library for Library of Congress QC182.L52 [2]† 582.7

NL 0420509 ICU DLC

Livingston, Herbert Klossner, 1918–
Surface and interfacial tensions of oil-water systems in Texas oil sands.
(In Petroleum technology. York, Pa., 1938-48. 23 cm. v. 1, no. 4, Nov. 1938. 13 p. diagrs.)
American Institute of Mining and Metallurgical Engineers. Technical publication no. 1001 (Class G, Petroleum Division, no. 68)
Bibliography: p. 13.

1. Petroleum. 2. Surface tension. I. Title: Interfacial tensions of oil-water systems.
[TN860.P55 vol. 1, no. 4] P O 51-259

U. S. Patent Office. Library for Library of Congress [1]

NL 0420510 DP

Livingston, Herbert Klossner, 1918–
Surface energy relationships in petroleum reservoirs.
(In Petroleum technology. York, Pa., 1938-48. 23 cm. v. 5, no. 6, Nov. 1942. 6 p.)
American Institute of Mining and Metallurgical Engineers. Technical publication no. 1526 (Class G, Petroleum Division, no. 174)
Bibliography: p. 6.

1. Petroleum. 2. Surface tension. 3. Fluid mechanics. I. Title.
[TN860.P55 vol. 5, no. 6] P O 52-109

U. S. Patent Office. Library for Library of Congress [1]

NL 0420511 DP

LIVINGSTON, HERBERT STANTON, 1916-
The Italian overture from A. Scarlatti to Mozart. Chapel Hill, 1952. 2 v. 28cm.

Micro-opaque. Rochester, N.Y., University of Rochester press, c.1958. 14 cards. 7.5 x 12.5 cm.
Thesis--University of North Carolina.
Vol. 2 contains musical examples in score.
Bibliography: v.1, leaves 314-343.
1. Overtures. 2. Overtures-- Collections--To 1800. 3. Overture.

NL 0420512 NN OU NSyU

Law
Livingston, Herman, defendant.

Sutherland, Josiah.
... The people of the state of New-York, agt. Herman Livingston. Ejectment for 150 acres of wood land, part of the manor of Livingston, points and argument of Josiah Sutherland, esq., one of the counsel for defendant, upon the law and evidence establishing the title to said manor, at Albany, before the Hon. William B. Wright, on the 27th of May, 1850. Hudson, P. D. Carrique's print, 1850.

Livingston, Ida Goldschmidt-
see
Goldschmidt-Livingston, Ida.

Livingston, Ida Mae Case
see
Case, Ida Mae

Livingston, Irvin S
Flax afire. [1st ed.] New York, Pageant Press [1953]
69 p. 24 cm.
Poems.

I. Title.

PR6023.I 84F6 811.5 53-12693 ‡

NL 0420516 DLC NcD

Livingston, J. A.
see
Livingston, Joseph A

---

331 L762d
Livingston, J J
Die dampfkraft und unsere soziale lage. Vortrag gehalten im Deutschen gesellig-wissenschaftlichen verein in New York am 10. februar 1886. New York, 1886. 20p.

NL 0420518 IU PU

368.3 L78m
Livingston, J M
The medical aspect of the selection of life assurance risks. Waterloo, Ont., Mutual life assurance co. of Canada, 1937.
cover-title, 48p. tables. O.
Math.
Delivered before the Life insurance institute of Canada, Feb.11,1937.

NL 0420519 IaU

Livingston, Jack.
... Livingston's international casting directory see under title

---

Livingston, James Duane.
The society of the Early Eighties of Columbia college. [N.Y., 1933]
[12] p. 24 cm.

NL 0420521 RPB

Livingston, James W.
French combination instruction book. New York, [c1880]

TT520 .L78

NL 0420522 DLC

Livingston, James W.
French combination of squares. New York, c1884

TT520 .L785

NL 0420523 DLC

Livingston, Jay, 1915–

...Kitty. Words and music by Jay Livingston and Ray Evans New York, Paramount music corp. [c1946]

First line: She's teasin', she's pleasin'.
Chorus: She's a pert little flirt.
At head of title: Inspired by the Paramount picture "Kitty."

Printed for the Music Division
1. Kitty. 2. Motion pictures. I. Evans, Ray. II. Song index (3).
N. Y. P. L. April 18, 1947

NL 0420524 NN

Livingston, Jay, 1915–

On the other end of a kiss. Music and words by Jay Livingston and Ray Evans. New York, Famous music corp., c1946.

First line: Banker, buyer, lawyer, flyer.
Chorus: Your brain is sharp.

Printed for the Music Division
1. Kissing. I. Evans, Ray. II. Song index (3).
N. Y. P. L. April 18, 1947

NL 0420525 NN

Livingston, Jay, 1915–

...To each his own. Words and music by Jay Livingston and Ray Evans. New York, Paramount music corp. [c1946]

First line: Wise men have shown.
Chorus: A rose must remain.

Printed for the Music Division
1. Motion pictures—To each his own. I. Evans, Ray. II. Song index (3).
N. Y. P. L. April 18, 1947

NL 0420526 NN

VOLUME 336

LIVINGSTON, JERRY, 1909-

Go Go Go Go. Words by Mack David. Music by Jerry Livingston. New York, Famous music corp., c1951.

1. Songs, Popular—1890- I. David, Mack, 1912-

NL 0420527 NN

Livingston, Jerry, 1909-

It's Sunday down in Caroline. Words by Marty Symes and Al. J. Neiburg. Music by Jerry Levinson. New York, Santly bros. inc., c1933.

First line: No wonder they call it Sunday.
Chorus: Lazy sun is shinin'.

Printed for the Music Division

1. Sunday. 2. U. S.—South Carolina. I. Symes, Marty. II. Neiburg, Al. J. III. Song index (3)
N. Y. P. L. August 30, 1948

NL 0420528 NN

Livingston, Jerry, 1909-

It's the talk of the town. Words by Marty Symes & Al. J. Neiburg. Music by Jerry Levinson. New York, Santly bros. inc., c1933.

First line: We were more than lovers.
Chorus: I can't show my face.

Printed for the Music Division

1. Quarrels. I. Symes, Marty. II. Neiburg, Al. J. III. Song index (3).
N. Y. P. L. August 30, 1948

NL 0420529 NN

Livingston, Jerry, 1909-

My piggy bank is jing-a-ling again. Lyric by Robert Burk. Music by Jerry Livingston. New York, Santly-Joy-Select inc., c1940.

First line: Happy, happy days!

Printed for the Music Division

1. Banks. 2. Prosperity. I. Burk, Robert. II. Song index (2).
N. Y. P. L. December 5, 1947

NL 0420530 NN

Livingston, Jerry, 1909-

Odds and ends (of an old love affair). Lyrics by Al J. Neiburg. Music by Jerry Levinson. New York, Keit-Engel inc., c1933.

First line: I was yours and you were mine.
Chorus: I found a rose pressed in a book.

Printed for the Music Division

1. Keepsakes. 2. Memories. I. Neiburg, Al J. II. Song index (3).
N. Y. P. L. August 30, 1948

NL 0420531 NN

Livingston, Jerry, 1909-

Teresa. Lyric by Mack David. Music by Jerry Livingston... New York, Robbins music corp. [c1951]

First line: This must be the night I've waited for
Printed for the Music Division.

1. Teresa. I. David, Mack, 1912- II. Song index

NL 0420532 NN

Livingston, Jerry, 1909-

Under a blanket of blue. Words by Marty Symes & Al. J. Neiburg. Music by Jerry Levinson. New York, Santly bros. inc., c1933.

First line: There's starlight shining from the skies.

Printed for the Music Division

1. Love-making. I. Symes, Marty. II. Neiburg, A. III. Song index (2).
N. Y. P. L. September 2, 1948

NL 0420533 NN

Livingston, Jerry, 1909-

Yum, yummy yummy, yum-yum. Words by Mack David. Music by Jerry Livingston. New York, Shapiro, Bernstein & co. inc. [c1949]

Printed for the Music Division

1. Apples. I. David, Mack, 1912- II. Song index (1).
N. Y. P. L. January 9, 1950

NL 0420534 NN

Livingston, Jesse Elsmer, 1909-

The inheritance of resistance to *Ustilago nuda* [by] J. E. Livingston ... [n. p., 1942]

cover-title, 451-466 p. incl. tables, diagrs. 26cm.

Based on thesis (PH. D.)—University of Missouri, 1940.
"Reprinted from Phytopathology, June, 1942, vol. XXXII, no. 6."
"Literature cited": p. 466.

1. Ustilago nuda. 2. Barley—Diseases and pests. I. Title.

A 44-422

Missouri. Univ. Library for Library of Congress SB608.B2L5
[2] † 633.16

NL 0420535 MoU DLC

Livingston, Joel Thomas, 1867-

A history of Jasper County, Missouri, and its people, by Joel T. Livingston ... Chicago, New York [etc.] The Lewis publishing company, 1912.

2 v. front., illus. (incl. facsims.) plates, ports. 27½ x 21cm.

Paged continuously.

1. Jasper Co., Mo.—Hist. 2. Jasper Co., Mo.—Biog.

21-11167

Library of Congress F472.J3L7

NL 0420536 DLC TxU MWA NN ICN

Livingston, Johannes.
see Livingston, John Henry, 1746-1825.

E339
.L68

Livingston, John.
... American portrait gallery, containing portraits of men now living; with biographical and historical memoirs of their lives and actions. By John Livingston ...
New York [J. Livingston] London, S. Low, Ion & co.; [etc., etc.] 185
pts. ports. 23cm.

AC901 .W4 vol.2, no.14 Office
---- ----Copy 2, vol. IV, pt. III.
[Wells pamphlets, v. 2, no. 14]
Cover-title wanting.
I. Title.

NL 0420538 DLC ViU MH OClW

Livingston, John.

Analysis of the Erie reorganization bill, with a clear statement, based upon official documents and figures ... demonstrating its unlimited powers and dangerous character ... Prepared for and at the request of holders of more than $15,000,000 Erie railway shares, and respectfully submitted for the consideration of the Legislature. By John Livingston ... New York, 1876.

76 p. 23cm.
Affidavits of Peter H. Watson and Henry N. Smith in the case of the Erie railway company against Jay Gould before the New York Supreme court ([4] p. 34½ x 21½cm fold. to 21½ x 8½cm) laid in.

1. Erie railway company. 16-17254

Library of Congress HE2791.E689 1876

NL 0420539 DLC OFH

Livingston, John, ed. N.p.,n.d.
[Biographical sketches of distinguished American lawyers.]

Contents, North Carolina:
Hon. Robert Strange.- Hon. William Horn Battle

NL 0420540 NcU MH-L

---

s.c.
923.4
L76b

Livingston, John
Biographical sketches of distinguished Americans, now living. Philosophy teaching by example... New York and London, The author, 1853.
viii, 504 p. (U.S. Monthly Law Magazine and Examiner. vol. VI, no.6, July to Dec. 1852

1. U.S. - Biography. 2. Lawyers - U.S. I. United States Monthly Law Magazine and Examiner. II. Title.

NL 0420541 ScU CU NN MH OClWHi PBL MHi

Livingston, John.

... Biographical sketches of eminent American lawyers, now living ... Ed. by John Livingston ... [New York, 1852-
23cm.

1. Lawyers—U. S.

11-22244

Library of Congress E339.L685

NL 0420542 DLC MHi MiD-B NN MWA OClWHi

Case
K
006
.493

LIVINGSTON, JOHN, comp.
...Catalogue giving the name and residence of an efficient and reliable practising lawyer, for every county in the United States and Canada; with a complete list of counties. Compiled from official and special reports, received from judicial and county officers...to which is added instructions and forms... New York, Law and Collection Office,
v. 23cm.

Monthly.
Supersedes his Law register.

NL 0420543 ICN

[?]S 655
.4
[?]

Livingston, John.
Catalogue, giving the name and residence of an efficient and reliable practising lawyer for nearly every county in the United States, with a complete list of counties and county towns: compiled from official and special reports, received from judicial and county officers, and from other reliable sources, and designed to insure efficiency, facility, and safety in the collection of claims, and the transaction of other legal business throughout the United States: for the use of

Continued in next column

VOLUME 336

Continued from preceding column

merchants, manufacturers, bankers, and all business men, as well as for members of the legal profession. 2d ed., revised and corrected. New York, Law and Collection Agency, 1857.
xxiii, [17]-88 p. 21.4cm.

No.12 in a collection with made-up title: Addresses, treatises, messages and letters, etc. on various subjects, collected by Richard F. Burges. El Paso, 1854-58.

1. Lawyers - U. S. Directories.

NL 0420544 TxHU NcU OClWHi NjP NcD ViU

Livingston, John.
The Erie railway: its history and management, from April 24, 1832, to July 13, 1875 ... Together with complete lists, containing the names of holders of all the common and preference shares ... Being a report to the bond and shareholders by John Livingston ... New York, J. Polhemus, printer, 1875.
92, ii p. 22½cm.

1. Erie railway company. I. Title.

A 18-779

Title from Bureau of Railway Economics. Printed by L. C.

NL 0420545 DBRE OClWHi ICJ MB PBL

Livingston, John.]
George Fisher, secretary and translator to the California Land Commission... [New York, 1854.] 441-446 p., 1 port. 8°.

Excerpt: J. Livingston, Portraits of eminent Americans. New York, 1853-54. v. 3.
In: *C p. v. 1453, no. 13.

1. Fisher, George, 1795- 1. Title. MILITARY SERVICE INST.
N. Y. P. L. June 3, 1913.

NL 0420546 NN

[LIVINGSTON, JOHN.]
George Fisher, secretary and translator to the California land commission, is a native of Hungary ...
[Washington, D.C. ?1858?]
6p. 22½cm.
Caption title.
Reprinted from his Portraits of eminent Americans now living ...
Signatures: [-]⁴ ([-]⁴ blank).
No. 1 in a brown cloth volume, inscribed by Fisher in May 1858 to Lew is Cass; ms. spine label: George Fish[er].

NL 0420547 PPRF

S.C.
p92
J64L

[Livingston, John]
Hon. Chancellor Johnston, of South Carolina (In: Biographical sketches of eminent American Lawyers, now living... ed. by John Livingston. March, 1852, part 1. p. 72-77.)

Detached xeroxed copy in pamphlet binder.

1. Johnston, Job.

NL 0420548 ScU

Livingston, John.
... Hon. Richard S. Coxe, LL. D., of Washington, D. C.
(*In his* Portraits of eminent Americans now living ... New York 1853-54. 24cm. v. 1, p. 247-254. port.)

1. Coxe, Richard Smith, 1792-1865.

19-755

Library of Congress E339.L69
—— Copy 2, detached CT275.B8645L5

NL 0420549 DLC

[LIVINGSTON, John]
Hon. William Parker, of Boston, president of the Boylston bank. [A biographical sketch. N.Y. 18-].

pp. 23-30 of some vol. of his Portraits of eminent Americans.
Port. of Von Parker.

NL 0420550 MH

[Livingston, John]
John F. Moreland, M.D., of Heard County, Georgia. [New York, London and Paris, 1854]
289-298 p. 8 vo. Portrait.
Excerpt from: Livingston, John. Portraits of Eminent Americans now Living. New York, London and Paris, 1854. Vol. III.
Note: A complete copy of Livingston's work is also in the library (see entry on p. 557)

NL 0420551 GU-De

Livingston, John.
... The law register; comprising the lawyers in the United States: the state record; containing the state and county officers, the organization, jurisdiction, and terms of the courts for every state and territory: the official directory for the United States; containing the officers of the federal government ... the officers and terms of the federal courts: the collector's assistant: giving the laws for collecting debts, executing deeds, verifying claims, and taking testimony, with forms for every state ... the whole constituting an official and business union directory. Prepared from official returns

by John Livingston ... 18 -[1868] New York, The Merchants' union law company [etc.] 18 -[°68]
v. front. (1852: port.) 18½-26½ cm.

Published annually, 1849-1854; irregularly in 1856 (for May, 1856-May, 1858), 1859, 1860, 1866 and 1868. No more published after 1868?
1849 and 1851 not in L. C. set.
Title varies: 1850, The United States lawyers' directory and official bulletin ...
1851-1856, Livingston's law register ...
1859-1860, Livingston's United States law register, and official directory ...
1866, The official directory and law register for the United States ...
1868, The law register; comprising the lawyers in the United States ...

Publisner varies.
"Manual of the American legal association: containing its plan, constitution and secretary's report ... New-York city, 1850": 1850, 31 p. at end.
"Catalogue of the newspapers and periodicals published in the United States ... compiled ... by Hon. J. C. G. Kennedy ... New-York, 1852": 1852, 56 p. at end.
1. Lawyers—U. S.—Direct. 2. U. S.—Registers. 3. Collection laws—U. S. 4. Forms (Law)—U. S. 5. American newspapers—Direct. 6. American periodicals—Direct. I. American legal association. II. Kennedy, Joseph Camp Griffith, 1813-1887. III. Title. IV. Title: The United States lawyers' directory and official bulletin. V. Title: Livingston's law register. VI. Title: Livingston's United States law register. VII. Title: The official directory and law register for the United States.

40—23509

NcD ViU IHi
CtY PPL ICJ ICN I NcD ViU-L GU-L NBuU-L NN OFH
NL 0420554 DLC Nh NNU-W MB PU-L NcU NN MH-L CtW CSmH

Livingston, John, ed.

Livingston's monthly law magazine ... By John Livingston. v. 1-3, v. 4, no. 1; Jan. 1853-Jan. 1856. New York, 1853-56.

LIVINGSTON, John.
Manual of the North American Legal Association containing its regulations and by-laws; together with the name and address of an efficient and trustworthy lawyer for every county and city in the United States, with the counties alphabetically arranged. New York, 1849.

70+(1). p.

NL 0420556 MH-L

[Livingston, John]
Memoir of Joseph Henry Lumpkin, Chief Justice of Georgia. [New York, 1851]
34-43 p. 8vo. Portrait.
Excerpt from: United States Monthly Law Magazine. Edited by John Livingston. New York, 1851. Vol. IV, July and August, 1851.
Note: Reprinted in Livingston's Portraits of Eminent Americans now Living. New York and London, 1853, Vol. II, p. 779-788.

NL 0420557 GU-De

[Livingston, John]
Mulford Marsh, of Savannah, Georgia. [New York and London, 1853]
289-293 p. 8 vo. Portrait.
Excerpt from: Livingston, John. Portraits of Eminent Americans now Living. New York and London, 1853, Vol. II.
Note: A copy of Livingston's complete work is also in the library (see following entry)

NL 0420558 GU-De

LIVINGSTON, John,
The official directory and law register for the United States, 1866.
N. Y., 1866. xiv, 600 pp. 8°.
Two copies.
An edition of 1856 bears the title, "Livingston's Law register [*7635.4], and an edition of 1868 the title, "The law register" [*7635.6].

NL 0420559 MB OClWHi MH CtY WaU-L

Livingston, John.
New chapters of Erie: Respectfully submitted for the consideration of members of the legislature, pending their votes upon the Erie Reorganization bill. ...By Hon. Josiah Deadhead [John Livingston], member from Sligo, a bad man who avows that he is a robber and a jobber. New York, March 1876.
7 p.

NL 0420560 OFH

Livingston, John.
... The perils of the nation. Bribery, dishonesty, usurpations and despotism of the railway corporations, and their relation to the politics of the day, the remedy to be used. Read—discuss—diffuse. Address by John Livingston, before the Workingmen and farmers' union, at Owego, Tioga County, New York, September 22, 1877. [New York, Evening post print, 1877?]
cover-title, 88 p. fold. tab. 23cm.

1. Railroads—Passes. 2. Railroads—U. S.—Finance. I. Title.

A 26-564

Title from Bureau of Railway Economics. Printed by L. C.

NL 0420561 DBRE NN OFH

Livingston, John.
Portraits of eminent Americans now living: with biographical and historical memoirs of their lives and actions. By John Livingston ... New York, Cornish, Lamport & co., 1853-54.
4 v. ports. 23cm (v. 4: 24cm)

Vols. 3-4 have imprint: New York [The author] 157 Broadway; London, S. Low, son & co.; [etc., etc.]
Originally issued in parts, with cover-title: American portrait gallery, containing portraits of men now living ...

1. U. S.—Biog. I. Title.

5-37664

Library of Congress E339.L69

PU PPL MWA ViU MiU OClWHi MB NWM
NL 0420562 DLC NcU WaU-L OKentU ViU RPB MeB PHi PP

VOLUME 336

Livingston, John.
Portraits of eminent Americans now living; including President Pierce and his cabinet: with biographical and historical memoirs of their lives and actions. By John Livingston ... New York [R. Craighead, printer]; London, S. Low, son & co.; [etc., etc.] 1854.
xvi, 542 p. ports. 23cm.

1. U. S.—Biog. I. Title.

Library of Congress E339.L692 8—2682

NL 0420563 DLC GU ViU TxU OClWHi

Livingston, John.
United States Lawyer's Directory and Official Bulletin ...
see his ... The law register.

[Livingston, John] of Canada
A British report on Canada, 1711.
Toronto, 1920.
48-54 p. 8°
(R'pt. from Canadian Hist. Rev., Mar., 1920)

NL 0420565 MWA

RC206 .L5 Toner Coll.
Livingston, John, of New Orleans.
The cause and remedy for yellow fever, as explained in a few articles published in the Daily city item. By J. Livingston ... New Orleans, A. W. Hyatt, print, 1879.
cover-title, 16 p. 15cm.

Imperfect: cover wanting; title supplied from the copy in the library of the Surgeon-general's office.

1. Yellow fever.

NL 0420566 DLC DNLM

Livingston, John, 1603-1672.
A brief historical relation of the life of Mr J. Livingston ... written by himself ... Glasgow, Printed by W. Duncansen. for A. Stevenson, 1754.
2 pts. in 1 v. 16½cm.
Imperfect copy; t.-p. of part I, missing. Title taken from British museum. Catalogue.
Part II has title: Memorable characteristics and remarkable passages of divine providence, exemplified in the lives of a considerable number of the most eminent divines ...

1. Livingstone, John, 1603-1672. 2. Scotland—Biog.

NL 0420567 MiU InU

Livingston, John, 1603-1672
A brief historical relation of the life of Mr. John Livingstone ... Edinburgh and London, J. Johnstone, 1848.
290 p., 1 l.
"Printed from Stevenson's ed. of 1754 with alterations and emendations in phraseology and punctuation ... according to the ... ed. of the Wodrow society." - Prefatory notice.

NL 0420568 GDC

Livingston, John, 1680-1720
see
Livingstone, John, 1680-1720

FILM 300 no.113
Livingston, John, 1919-
Bank reserve requirements and how their effectiveness as an instrument of monetary control may be enhanced. Ann Arbor, University Microfilms [1955]
1r. ([University Microfilms] Publication 10,594)
Microfilm copy (positive) of typescript. Thesis - Cornell University.
1.Bank reserves - U.S. 2.Currency question - U.S. I.Title.

NL 0420570 CLSU NIC

T45 F4 no. 909
Livingston, John A
The cerium metal and lighter flint industry in Germany and Austria, by John A. Livingston and Henry Kent. [n.p.] 1946.
18 p. tables. 28 cm. (Office of Military Government for Germany (US). Field Information Agency, Technical. Final report no.909)
Cover title.
1. Cerium. 2. Flint. I. Kent, Henry, jt. auth. (Series: Field Information Agency, Technical. Final report 909.)

NL 0420571 DI

Livingston, John H.
"One-two"; the story of the fifth national air tour as related by the winner, John H. Livingston ... Troy, O., The Waco aircraft company [c1930]
31, [1] p. illus. (incl. ports., map) 21½cm.
Contains advertising matter.

1. Aeronautics—Flights. I. Waco aircraft company, Troy, O. II. Title. III. Title: National air tour, The story of the fifth.

Library of Congress TL540.L55A3 30-9851
——— Copy 2.
Copyright A 20689 [2] 629.13

NL 0420572 DLC WaS

Livingston, John Henry, 1746-1825.
Works by this author printed in America before 1801 are available in this library in the Readex Microprint edition of Early American Imprints published by the American Antiquarian Society.
This collection is arranged according to the numbers in Charles Evans' American Bibliography.

NL 0420573 DLC

Livingston, John Henry, 1746-1825.
An address delivered at the commencement held in Queen's College in New-Jersey, September 25, 1810. By J. H. Livingston, D.D., professor of theology, and president of Queen's College. New-Brunswick: Printed by Abraham Blauvelt. 1810. 31 p. 8°.
Contains a valuable historical sketch of the college.

1. Colleges, etc., U. S.: Rutgers College.
N. Y. P. L. January 27, 1915.

NL 0420574 NN NjR CtY InU NjNbS CSmH MiU-C

Livingston,John Henry,1746-1825.
An address to the Reformed German churches in the United States. By John H.Livingston,D.D.--S.T.P. New-Brunswick: Printed by William Myer. 1819.
36 p. 21cm.
Urges the establishment of a theological seminary for the Reformed German church.
Bound with his A sermon,delivered before the New-York missionary society ... April 3,1804. New-York, 1804.
1.Reformed Church in the U.S.

NL 0420575 MiU-C NjNbS

Livingston, John H[enry] 1746-1825.
Analysis of a system of theology, compiled from lectures delivered by the late J. H. Livingston, D.D., by the Rev. A. Neal. no. 1. New York: J. F. Sibell, 1831. 1 no. 8°.

1. Theology (Systematic). 2. Neal, Ava, compiler.
N. Y. P. L. July 5, 1913.

NL 0420576 NN

Livingston, John Henry, 1746-1825.
Analysis of a system of theology composed chiefly from lectures delivered by the late John H. Livingston. [Ed.] by Rev. Ava Neal. New York, J.F. Sibell, 1832.
339, (1) p. 18 cm.

NL 0420577 NRCR PPPrHi NjNbS

Livingston, John Henry, 1746-1825.
A dissertation on the marriage of a man with his sister in law. By John H. Livingston ... New-Brunswick: Printed by Deare & Myer. 1816.
179 p. 22cm.
Half-title: Incestuous marriage.

1. Marriage with deceased wife's sister. 2. Church discipline. 3. Reformed church in the United States—Discipline.

Library of Congress HQ1028.L78 9-9881

NL 0420578 DLC CSt NHi MH NjNbS NcD MWA PPL NjR NN

Livingston, John Henry, 1746-1825.
The flight of the prophetic angel.
(In Fish, Henry Clay. History and repository of pulpit eloquence, v. 2, p. 425-441)

NL 0420579 RPB

Livingston, John Henry, 1746-1825.
A funeral service, or Meditations adapted to funeral addresses. Selected from the Sacred Scriptures. By John H. Livingston ... New-Brunswick: Printed by Abraham Blauvelt. 1812.
ix, [1], [11]-87, [1] p. 20½cm.

1. Funeral service. I. Title.

Library of Congress BV199.F8L5 24-7288

NL 0420580 DLC InU MiU-C CtY NjNbS PPPrHi

Livingston, John Henry, 1746-1825.
Glory of the Redeemer; sermon, before the N.Y. Missionary Soc., Apr. 23, 1799.
N.Y., 1799.
48 p. 8°

NL 0420581 MWA NIC NN

Livingston, John Henry, 1746-1825.
Memoirs of the Rev. John Henry Livingston ...
see under Gunn, Alexander, 1784-1829.

VOLUME 336

Livingston, John Henry, 1746–1825.
Oratio inauguralis de veritate religionis christianae, quam, coram veneranda ecclesiarum Belgicarum Synodo, Neo Eboraci convocata, publice in aede sacra habuit, Johannes H. Livingston... Ad diem xix Maji, M DCC LXXXV. Neo-Eboraci: Excudebant Samuel et Johannes Loudon... [1785.] 1 p.l., 111 p. 12°.

Evans 19061.
Lenox copy.

1. Apologetics (Christian).
N. Y. P. L. May 29, 1924.

NjNbS
NL 0420583 NN MH InU CtY NjP MH MBAt NHi DLC PPL

Livingston, John Henry, 1746-1825.
Oratio inauguralis de veritate religionis Christianae quam, corum venerande ecclesiarum Belgicarum synodo neo eboraci convocata publice in aede socia habuit ... Neo-Eborae [1875?]
49 p. 23 cm.
Added title page in English

NL 0420584 RPB

Livingston, John Henry, 1746-1825, comp.
FOR OTHER EDITIONS SEE MAIN ENTRY
Reformed church in America.
The Psalms and hymns, with the Catechism, Confession of faith and Liturgy of the Reformed Dutch church in North America. Selected at the request of the General synod. By John H. Livingston ... New-York: Printed and sold by George Forman, corner of Partition and Greenwich-streets. 1814.

Livingston, John Henry, 1746-1825.
Reformed church in America.
The Psalms of David, with hymns and spiritual songs, having the proper metre prefixed to each. Also, the Catechism, Compendium, Confession of faith and Liturgy, of the Reformed church in the Netherlands. For the use of the Reformed Dutch church in North-America. Albany: Printed and sold, by Charles R. and George Webster, at their printing-office and bookstore, in the white house, corner of State & Pearl streets. M,DCC,XCVI.

Rare
BV [Livingston, John Henry] 1746-1825.
2075 [A sermon, delivered before the New York
S48 Missionary Society, at their annual meet-
no.3 ing, April 3, 1804. To which are added, an Appendix, the Annual report of the directors, and other papers relating to American missions. New York, Printed by T. & J. Swords, 1804]
[97] p. 22cm.

No. 3 in vol.

New York Missionary Society.
CUL copy imperfect: lacks t. p. and p. [97]; title taken from another copy.
With autograph: Anth. M. Post.

OO NjP PMA ABH
NL 0420588 NIC MB ViW MiU-C DGU NIC CtY CSmH OClWHi

---

252 Livingston, John Henry, 1746-1825.
L762s A sermon, delivered before the New York
1807 Missionary Society, at their annual meeting, April 3,1804. By John H. Livingston, D.D.S.T.P. To which are added, an appendix, and other papers relating to American missions. Worcester: Printed by Thomas & Sturtevant, 1807.
68p. 23cm.

1. Sermons, American. 2. Missions, Foreign --Addresses, essays, lectures.

NL 0420589 IU MWA MH

Livingston, John Henry, 1746–1825.
A sermon, delivered before the New York missionary society, at their annual meeting, April 3, 1804. By John H. Livingston, D. D., T. P. To which are added, an appendix, and other papers relating to American missions. Greenfield [Mass.] Printed by John Denio, 1809.
72 p. 21½ cm.
Appendix: p. [38]–72.

1. Missions—Sermons.

A 38—346

New York. State Libr.
for Library of Congress [66c½]

NL 0420590 NN TxU CSt OClW MWA MH

Livingston, John Henry, 1746-1825.
A sermon before the New York missionary society, April 3, 1804 [with] appendix. 3. ed. Providence, 1832.
48 p. D.

NL 0420591 RPB

AC901 Livingston, John Henry, 1746-1825.
.M5 A sermon delivered before the New York missionary society, at their annual meeting April 3, 1804. 2d ed. Providence, 1832.
48 p. (Miscellaneous pamphlets, 355:4)

NL 0420592 DLC

Livingston, John Henry, 1848– 1927
The Livingston manor; address written for the New York branch of the Order of colonial lords of manors in America, by John Henry Livingston ... [Baltimore? 191–?]
37 p. incl. illus., col. pl., ports., facsim. 23½cm. [Order of colonial lords of manors in America. New York branch. Publications]

1. Livingston manor. 2. Livingston family.

20-16023

Library of Congress E186.99.O6N5
—— Copy 2. F127.C8L78

NL 0420593 DLC NcD OClWHi

Livingston, John Henry, 1848–1927.
The minor manors of New York; address prepared for the New York branch of the Order of colonial lords of manors in America, by John Henry Livingston ... [n. p.] 1923.
31 p. incl. illus., pl. 24cm. [Order of colonial lords of manors in America. New York branch. Publications. no. 12]

1. New York (State)—Hist.—Colonial period. 2. Manors—New York (State) I. Title.

23-12562 Revised

Library of Congress E186.99.O6 no. 12
—— Copy 2. F122.L76

NL 0420594 DLC NN

Livingston, John Henry, 1746-1825.
Two sermons, delivered before the New York missionary society;
see under title

Livingston, John Robert, 1755–1851.
The petition of John R. Livingston & Robert J. Livingston, to the Legislature of New-Jersey, respecting steamboats; with the laws of the states of New-York and New-Jersey, and affidavits of sundry persons respecting the improvements said to be made by Daniel Dod and others, on the machinery of R. Fulton. New-York, Printed by Pelsue & Gould, 1814.
43 p. 20cm.

Continued in next column

Continued from preceding column

Preceded by "The memorial of John R. Livingston & Robert J. Livingston, to the Legislature of New-York, respecting steam-boats": 8 p.

1. Fulton, Robert, 1765–1815. 2. Steam-navigation—U. S. I. Livingston, Robert James, 1760–1827.

17-9973

Library of Congress VM618.L6
—— Copy 2. 21½cm.
An act of the state of New Jersey, concerning steamboats; testimonies of B. Henry Latrobe and Charles Staudinger, before the Court of common pleas of Alleghany County, Pa.: 15 p. inserted.
Imperfect: the memorial wanting.

NL 0420597 DLC PPL PBL NN

Livingston, John W
The bank as a clearing house for the settlement of interline freight bills. New Brunswick [N.J.] Rutgers University, 1954.
iii, 113 l. forms.
Bibliography: l. 110-113.
Thesis - Rutgers University. American Bankers Association. Graduate School of Banking.

NL 0420598 MH-BA

Livingston, Joseph A
... Reconversion—the job ahead, by J. A. Livingston. [New York, Public affairs committee, inc., 1944]
cover-title, 32 p. illus., diagrs. 21 cm. (Public affairs pamphlets. No. 94)
Text on p. [3] of cover.
"First edition, June, 1944."

1. U. S.—Indus. 2. Reconstruction (1939-1951)—U. S. I. Title.

HC106.4.L588 338.91 44-6650 rev

OrPR MtU CaBViP PSt PPT PHC PSC
NL 0420599 DLC OLak OCU OO OU ODW OrU ViU OrCS PPD

Livingston, Joseph A.
Some of the most thrilling and heart-melting accounts of life among the legal maniacs... Carthage, N. Y.: J. A. Livingston & Co., 1853. 16 p. 8°.

Title from cover.

1. Temperance.—Tracts.
N. Y. P. L. January 22, 1914

NL 0420600 NN

[**Livingston, Josiah.**]
Our street; memories of Buccleuch place. Edinburgh: J. Thin, 1893. 1 p.l., 79(1) p. 12°.

Signed: Josiah Livingston.

1. Edinburgh.—Social life. 2. Streets, Gt. Br.: Edinburgh: Buccleuch Place.
N. Y. P. L. November 22, 1919.

NL 0420601 NN

Livingston, Julius Sterling, 1918-
Making steel, prepared by J.Sterling Livingston in cooperation with the American Iron and Steel Institute. [Washington?, U.S. Naval Supply Corps. Reserve [1948]
[11] p. illus. (Industries that supply the Navy series)

NL 0420602 MH-BA

VOLUME 336

Livingston, Julius Sterling, 1916-
Oil production, prepared by J.Sterling Livingston in cooperation with the American Petroleum Institute. [Washington?] U.S. Naval Supply Corps Reserve [1949]
8 p. illus. (Industries that supply the Navy series)

NL 0420603 MH-BA

Livingston, Julius Sterling, 1916-
Single department procurement of paint
see under Harvard University. Graduate School of Business Administration. Mobilization Analysis Center.

Livingston, Kate
see Caldwell, Mrs. Kate (Livingston)

PR 6023 I 84D6 Livingston, Kenneth.
The Dodd cases. London, Methuen [1933]
250 p. 20cm.

NL 0420606 CoU

Livingston, Kenneth.
... The Dodd cases ... Garden City, N. Y., Pub. for the Crime club, inc., by Doubleday, Doran & company, inc., 1934.
5 p. l., 307 p. 19½cm.
"First edition."

I. Title.
Library of Congress PZ3.L76246Do 34-36039

NL 0420607 DLC MB

Pam. Coll. 23631 Livingston, Knox
In memoriam. Judge Joshua Hilary Hudson. Memorial address at the memorial services of the Supreme Court and bar, in Columbia, S. C., Jan. 20, 1909. [Columbia, S. C.? 1909?]
18 p. port. 24 cm.

1. Hudson, Joshua Hilary, 1832-1909

NL 0420608 NcD

Livingston (L.) & Hosack (David). Observations on the Ballston waters. 8 pp. 8°. [New York, 1810, vel subseq.] [Also, in: P., v. 746.]

NL 0420609 DNLM

LIVINGSTON, L F
The Columbia basin and industry: chemical wizardy to unfold vast markets for agriculture: address ... delivered before the Agricultural bureau and Columbia basin committee of Spokane chamber of commerce ... January 6, 1936. n.p. [1936]
[4] p.

NL 0420610 Or

Wason HE7207+ L78 Livingston, L F [writer on postal service]
The postal system of the Chinese Treaty Ports. Catonsville, Md. [1947]
v. illus. 28cm.

1. Postal service--China. 2. Postage-stamps--China. I. Title.

NL 0420611 NIC

710.1 L896g Livingston, Lawrence.
General plan, Los Altos, Calif., planning area. [Los Altos, 1954]
21 l. 11 plans. 28cm.

Cover title.

1. Cities and towns--Planning--Los Altos, Calif.

NL 0420612 IU NcU PPCPC

Livingston, Lee.
Buster Bear's surprise; pictures by Miloche and Kane, story by Lee Livingston. Akron, O., New York, The Saalfield publishing company [1946]
[58] p. incl. front., illus. (part col.) 17cm. [Little treasure series]

I. Title.
PZ10.3.L726Bu 47-15738

NL 0420613 DLC

Livingston, Lee.
Just a minute Jimmy; story by Lee Livingston, pictures by Doris and Marion Henderson. Akron, O., New York, The Saalfield publishing company [1946]
[58] p. illus. (part col.) 17cm. [Little treasure series]

I. Title.
PZ7.L7612Ju 47-15739

NL 0420614 DLC

Livingston, Lela (Lingenfelter) 1899-
Pyle family history, 1594-1954, by Lela Livingston [and others. n. p.] H. Pyle [1954 or 5]
76 p. 22 cm.

1. Pyle family.
CS71.P995 1955 56-46835 ‡

NL 0420615 DLC NN

HF3161 .W2A47 1945 Livingston, Leo, 1914-
Washington (State) State planning council.
Commerce of Snohomish county. Prepared and published by the Washington State planning council. A community study sponsored by Snohomish county Public utility district no. 1. [Olympia? 1945?]

Livingston, Leon Ray, 1872-
The adventures of a female tramp, by A-No. 1, the famous tramp, written by himself from actual experiences of his own life. 7th ed. Erie, Pa., A-No. 1 Pub. Co., °1914.
133 p. illus. 20 cm.
L. C. copy replaced by microfilm.
Microfilm no. 28586

1. Tramps—U. S. I. A-No. 1. II. Title.
[HV4505.L58 1914] 78-263235 MARC

NL 0420617 DLC

[Livingston, Leon Ray] 1872-
The curse of tramp life, by A—no. 1, the king of hoboes; a true story of actual tramp life written by himself. Illustrated by the famous artist Joseph Earl Shrock. 1st ed. ... Cambridge Springs, Pa., A—no. 1 publishing co., °1912.
133 p. illus. 19½cm. $0.25

1. Tramps. I. Title.
Library of Congress HV4505.L63 12-26397

NL 0420618 DLC ICJ OrU NN

Livingston, Leon Ray, 1872-
The curse of tramp life, by A-No. 1, the famous tramp. A true story of actual tramp life written by himself. Illustrated by the famous artist Joseph Earl Shrock. 6th. ed. Cambridge Springs, Pa., A-No. 1 Pub. Co., c1912.
133 p. illus., port.
1. Tramps. I. Title.

NL 0420619 CLU

[Livingston, Leon Ray] 1872-
From coast to coast with Jack London, by A-no 1, the famous tramp, written by himself from personal experiences. 1st ed. ... Erie, Pa., The A-no 1 publishing company, °1917.
136 p. incl. front. (facsims.) illus. 19 cm.

1. Tramps. 2. London, Jack, 1876-1916. I. Title.
HV4505.L68 17—25253

NL 0420620 DLC ViU TxU NcD

Am L847Yf.4 Livingston, Leon Ray, 1872-
From coast to coast with Jack London; by A-No.1 [pseud.], the famous tramp, written by himself from personal experiences. 4th ed. Erie, Pa., A-No.1, °1917.
136p. illus. 19cm.

1. Tramps. 2. London, Jack, 1876-1916. I. Title.

NL 0420621 IEN

[Livingston, Leon Ray,] 1872-
From coast to coast with Jack London, by A. no. 1, the famous tramp, written by himself from personal experiences.... Erie, Pa.: The A. No. 1 Pub. Co., cop. 1917. 136 p. illus. 6. ed. 12°.

1. Vagrants and vagrancy. 2. London, Jack, 1876-1916. 3. Title.
N. Y. P. L. June 27, 1924

NL 0420622 NN NBu

[Livingston, Leon Ray] 1872-
Here and there with A-no. 1, America's most famous tramp, written by himself. 1st ed. ... Erie, Pa., The A-no. 1 publishing company, °1921.
128 p. illus. 19½cm.
Portrait on p. 2 of cover.

1. Tramps. I. Title.
Library of Congress HV4505.L694 21-10616

NL 0420623 DLC NN

VOLUME 336

Livingston, Leon Ray, 1872-
Hobo-camp-fire-tales, by A-No. 1 [pseud.] America's most famous tramp, written by himself. 2d ed. Cambridge Springs, Pa., A-No.1 publishing co., c1911
133 p.

NL 0420624 OCl

[Livingston, Leon Ray,] 1872-
Hobo-camp-fire-tales, by A — no. 1, America's most famous tramp. Written by himself... Cambridge Springs, Pa.: A — no. 1 Pub. Co., cop. 1911. 133 p. illus. 7. ed. 12°.

1. Vagrants and vagrancy, U. S. 2. Title.
N. Y. P. L. January 16, 1924.

NL 0420625 NN CtU

[Livingston, Leon Ray] 1872-
Life and adventures of A—no. 1, America's most celebrated tramp. Written by himself. Rev. ed., illustrated from life ... Corry, Pa., The "A—no. 1" publishing co., °1908.
98 p. illus. (incl. port.) 20½cm.

1. Tramps.

Library of Congress HV4505.L62 8-31179
(Copyright 1908 A 220676)

NL 0420626 DLC

[Livingston, Leon Ray] 1872-
Life and adventures of A-no. 1, America's most celebrated tramp. Written by himself ... Corry, Pa., Self mastery press, °1908.
2 p. l., [9]-96 p. illus. (partly col.) incl. port. 26½cm.

1. Tramps.

Library of Congress HV4505.L6 8-11814

NL 0420627 DLC ICJ

B L7862f1 1910 [Livingston, Leon Ray,] 1872-
Life and adventures of A-No.1, America's most celebrated tramp, written by himself. 4th rev. ed. Cambridge Springs, Pa., A-No.1 Pub. Co., 1910.
137p. port., illus. 20cm.

1. Tramps. I. Title.

NL 0420628 IU AU

[Livingston, Leon Ray] 1872-
Life and adventures of A — no. 1, America's most celebrated tramp. Written by himself. 12. ed. ... Cambridge Springs, Pa., A — no. 1 pub. co., c1910. 137 p. illus. 19cm.

516150B. 1. Vagrants and vagrancy —U. S.
N. Y. P. L. December 11, 1945

NL 0420629 NN

[Livingston, Leon Ray] 1872-
Life and adventures of A-no. 1, America's most celebrated tramp. Written by himself. 21st ed. Erie, Pa., A-No.1 Publishing Co., c1910.
137p. illus. 20cm.

1. Tramps.

NL 0420630 CLSU

[Livingston, Leon Ray] 1872-
Mother Delcassee of the hoboes, and other stories, by A-no. 1, the famous tramp, written by himself from personal experiences. 1st ed. ... Erie, Pa., The A-no. 1 publishing company, °1918.
136 p. illus. 19½cm.
Author's portrait on p. [2] of cover.
Advertising matter: p. 129-136.
CONTENTS.—Capturing the wrong hobo.—Mother Delcassee of the hoboes.—The lifelong complaint of Lanky Jim.—How tramp "Seldom Seen" gained his unique nickname.—The lure of phoney gold.

1. Tramps. I. Title.

Library of Congress HV4505.L69 18-19589

NL 0420631 DLC NN

[Livingston, Leon Ray] 1872
The snare of the road, by A-no. 1, the famous tramp, written by himself from personal experiences ... 1st ed. ... Erie, Penn'a, A-no. 1 publishing company, °1916.
134 p. illus. 19cm. $0.25

1. Tramps. I. Title.

Library of Congress HV4505.L67 16-21999

NL 0420632 DLC ICJ TxU

[Livingston, Leon Ray] 1872-
The trail of the tramp, by A no 1, the famous tramp, written by himself from actual experiences of his own life. Illustrated by Joseph Earl Shrock. 1st ed. ... Cambridge Springs, Pa., The A no 1 publishing co., 1913.
137 p. illus. 19cm. $0.25
Portrait of author on inside of cover.

1. Tramps. I. Title.

Library of Congress HV4505.L64 13-19302

NL 0420633 DLC ICJ ViU

[Livingston, Leon Ray] 1872-
Traveling with tramps, by A no. 1, America's most famous tramp, written by himself. 1st ed. ... Erie, Pa., The A no. 1 publishing company, °1920.
135 p. illus. 19½cm.
Portrait of p. 2 of cover.

1. Tramps. I. Title.

Library of Congress HV4505.L692 20-20933

NL 0420634 DLC MiU

4PZ 531 Livingston, Leon Ray, 1872-
The ways of the hobo, by A-No 1 [pseud.] 4th ed. Erie, A-No 1 Pub. Co., c1915.
131 p.

NL 0420635 DLC-P4

[Livingston, Leon Ray] 1872-
The wife I won, by A-no. 1, the famous tramp-author. His greatest adventure, written by himself from personal experiences. Sixth edition ... Erie, Pa.: The A-no. 1 pub. co. [1919?] 135 p. illus. 19½cm. (On cover: Books on tramp life ... no. 10.)
Portrait on p. [2] of cover.

1. Vagrants and vagrancy. I. Title.
N. Y. P. L. April 19, 1939

NL 0420636 NN MH MiU N CFIS

Livingston, Leonidas F 1832-1912
The tariff. Speech ... in the House ... March 24, 1897. Washington [Gov't print. off.] 1897.
12 pp. 8°.
HF1755 .L8 1-4640

NL 0420637 DLC

LIVINGSTON, LOIS B.
The simple art of wall decoration, by Lois B.Livingston. Brooklyn, N.Y.: Baeck Wall Paper Co. [192-?] 25 p. illus. (1 col'd), 25 col'd pl. 15 x 23cm.

Plates are samples of Muralia wallpaper in color, with descriptive text on accompanying leaves.

865765A. 1. Wall paper. I. Baeck Wall Paper Company, Brooklyn.

NL 0420638 NN

Livingston, Lorraine, *comp.*
Approved enduring favorites ... compiled by Lorraine Livingston ... illustrated by Edna Braun ... [St. Louis] St. Louis, Mo., unit, Women's overseas service league [°1932]
v, [1], 170 p. illus. 23½cm.
Contains blank pages for "Special recipes".

1. Cookery, American. I. Women's overseas service league. St. Louis unit. II. Title.

Library of Congress TX715.L765 32-35184
Copyright A 58294 [2] 641.5

NL 0420639 DLC KMK

Livingston, Louis J *comp.*
Medical and dental red book. A register of all the physicians, surgeons, dentists, druggists, nurses, etc., of Cleveland and vicinity, together with a digest of the state laws, and the city laws pertaining to these professions and other miscellaneous matter. Compiled by Louis J. Livingston. Cleveland, The Helman-Taylor co., 1899.
372 p. illus. (incl. port.) 17cm.
Includes advertising matter.
1. Physicians—Cleveland. 2. Dentists—Cleveland. 3. Pharmacists—Cleveland. 4. Nurses—Cleveland. 5. Cleveland—Direct. I. Title.

Library of Congress R712.A3C6 99-2724 Revised
Copyright 1898: 47461 [r33b2] 610.5

NL 0420640 DLC OClW-H

Livingston, Louis J., comp.
Pythian directory of Indianapolis, Ind. and suburbs ... Comp. ... by Louis J. Livingston ... Indianapolis, Ind., L. J. Livingston, 1897.

Livingston, Louis Joseph, 1856-
... Hail, the Kaiser! The tribute of a native American By Louis J. Livingston ... Also A message to the German people and A toast to the hyphen. St. Paul, Minn., L. J. Livingston, 1915.
20 p. 21½cm. $0.25

1. Wilhelm II, German emperor, 1859- I. Title.

Library of Congress DD229.5.L5 15-25327

NL 0420642 DLC

VOLUME 336

Livingston, Louise, 1883–
A promise; songs and sonnets. San Antonio, Naylor Co. [1952]
36 p. 20 cm.

I. Title.

PS3523.I 944P7 811.5 52-33546 ‡

NL 0420643 DLC NN

Livingston, Luther Samuel, 1864-1914, ed.

Z1000 .A51 **American** book-prices current. A record of literary properties sold at auction in the United States. v. 1– 1894/95–

Livingston, Luther Samuel, 1864–1914.
Auction prices of books; a representative record arranged in alphabetical order from the commencement of the English Book-prices current in 1886 and the American book-prices current in 1894 to 1904, and including some thousands of important auction quotations of earlier date; edited by Luther S. Livingston ... New York, Dodd, Mead & company, 1905.
4 v. 20cm.
"Edition limited to seven hundred and fifty copies."
"In making this selection it has been the aim to include every important book (selling above the limit of price) in the following broad classes: 1. Books printed in England, or books in the English language printed abroad ... 2. Americana, in its broadest sense ... 3. Books printed ... in the various countries of Continental Europe before 1520 ..."
CONTENTS.—v. 1. A-Dick.—v. 2. Dickens-La Peyrere.—v. 3. Lapham-Richards.—v. 4. Richardson-Zwingli.
1. Books—Prices. 2. America—Bibl. 3. English literature—Early modern (to 1700)—Bibl. 4. Bibliography—Rare books. I. Book prices current. II. American book prices current. III. Title.
5-9722 Revised
Library of Congress Z1000.L65

ODW MiU-C WaT OrP WaS WaSp MiU
PBm PU MH NNUT NcD OCl RPJCB ViU MWA MB ICJ OU
PSt FTaSU FMU WU NjPT NN PPLas PP PPL PBa PHC
NL 0420645 DLC NSyU MoU KMK GU-De PPRF NjP DO

Livingston, Luther Samuel, 1864-1914
Beverly Chew and his books. [New York?, New York Evening Post Co. ?, 1912?]
8 p. 17 cm.
"Reprinted from the Nation [v. 95, p. 405-406] 50 copies."
Presentation copy to Grenville Kane, signed by the author.
Bound with the author's The Robert Hoe library. [New York ?, 1912?]

NL 0420647 NjP MiU MH CSmH

Z 1004 .L7 A4 Livingston, Luther Samuel, 1864-1914.
A bibliographical puzzle. The 1770 editions of Goldsmith's "Deserted village." [New York, 1901]
4, [1] p. illus. (facsims.) 24½cm.
Caption title.
Signed: Luther S. Livingston.
"About 20 copies were printed from the types of The Bookman, with headlines cut out and pages renumbered."--G. P. Winship. Luther S. Livingston, p. 124.
In case lettered: Livingston. Bibliographical works.
1. Goldsmith, Oliver, The deserted village.--Bibl.

NL 0420648 MiU MH

[LIVINGSTON, LUTHER SAMUEL, 1864-1914.]
A bibliographical record, 1895-1913. [Scarsdale, N.Y.], Privately printed, January, 1914. 22p., 1l. 16cm.
Imprint from front cover; printed at the University press, Cambridge, U.S.A.
Compiled and issued by Mr. Livingston, as a record of his work.
Orig. printed tan wrapper; stitched.

NL 0420649 PPRF MH MiU

[**Livingston, Luther Samuel**] 1864–1914.
Bibliography of the first editions in book form of the works of Alfred, lord Tennyson; the description of a set brought together by Dodd, Mead & company, with notes referring to items not included in the set. New York, Dodd, Mead & company, 1901.
ix, [1], 95, [1] p., 1 l. front. (port.) illus., facsim. 24½cm.
"Of this volume, 306 copies have been printed, of which 56 are on large paper, with two extra illustrations." Large paper copy.
Introduction signed: L. S. L. [i. e. Luther Samuel Livingston]
1. Tennyson, Alfred Tennyson, baron—Bibl. I. Title.
2—995
Library of Congress Z8866.L78
——— Copy 2. Large paper copy.

NL 0420650 DLC OrU InU NcD PP PU PSC MiU TxU MB NjP

Livingston, Luther Samuel, 1864–1914.
A bibliography of the first editions in book form of the writings of Charles and Mary Lamb published prior to Charles Lamb's death in 1834, by Luther S. Livingston. New York, Printed for J. A. Spoor at the De Vinne press, 1903.
xv, 209 p. incl. facsim. front., ports., facsims. (part fold.) 24cm.
"One hundred copies only printed from type at the De Vinne press: ten copies on Japan paper, numbered from 1 to 10. Ninety copies on Van Gelder paper, numbered from 11 to 100. no. 9."
Inserted between p. (viii) and p. ix: Charles Lamb [a chronology]
"Appendix: The books of the two John Lambs": p. 195–203.
1. Lamb, Charles, 1775–1834—Bibl. 2. Lamb, Mary Ann, 1764–1847—Bibl.
3-10610 Revised
Library of Congress Z8474.L5

NL 0420651 DLC WU MiD RPB MH ViU NjP MiU OCl TxU

Livingston, Luther Samuel, 1864–1914.
... A bibliography of the first editions in book form of the writings of Henry Wadsworth Longfellow; comp. largely from the collection formed by the late Jacob Chester Chamberlain with assistance from his notes and memoranda, by Luther S. Livingston. New York, Priv. print. [The De Vinne press] 1908.
3 p. l., v–xiv, 131, [1] p. front. (port.) 24cm. (The Chamberlain bibliographies)
"Five hundred copies printed on old Stratford paper and fifty copies on Van Gelder. 150."
1. Longfellow, Henry Wadsworth—Bibl. I. Chamberlain, Jacob Chester, 1860–1905.
8-31655
Library of Congress Z8515.L78

PPL
MeB NBu PSt NcD MH MiU-C NN MB NjP TxU OO OCl PSC
NL 0420652 DLC NcGU OCU NIC ICarbS FMU WaU MoSW IdU

Livingston, Luther Samuel, 1864–1914.
... A bibliography of the first editions in book forms of the writings of James Russell Lowell, comp. largely from the collection formed by the late Jacob Chester Chamberlain, with assistance from his notes and memoranda, by Luther S. Livingston. New York, Priv. print. [The De Vinne press] 1914.
xvii, 136 p., 1 l. front. (port.) 24cm. (The Chamberlain bibliographies)
"Five hundred copies printed on Old Stratford paper and fifty copies on Van Gelder. Van Gelder copy no. 12."
1. Lowell, James Russell, 1819–1891—Bibl. I. Chamberlain, Jacob Chester, 1860–1905.
14—2201
Library of Congress Z8521.L40

PU ICJ MB NN OU
NL 0420653 DLC NcGU WaS ViU PSt MeB FMU MiD TU NcD

[**Livingston, Luther Samuel**] 1864–1914.
Bibliography of the separate publications of Luther S. Livingston.
(*In* **The papers of the Bibliographical society of America. Chicago Ill. [1915] 25cm. v. 8, 1914, no. 3–4, p. 121–134**)
"This is a reprint of Mr. Livingston's own A bibliographical record, 1895–1913, privately printed by him in January, 1914 ... Eight additional titles which were noted in his own copy have been expanded ... by Mrs. Livingston."
1. Livingston, Luther Samuel, 1864–1914—Bibliography. I. Livingston, Mrs. Flora V. (Milner) II. Title.
C D 31–67
Library of Congress Card Div. Z1008.B51P vol. 8, no. 3–4

NL 0420654 DLC MiU OClW OU OCU PPT

(Livingston, Luther Samuel) 1864-1914.
"The book hunter. The works of Captain John Smith
259-264 p. illus. 25.4 cm.
Article in the Bookman, October, 1898. vol. VIII.
No. 2 Bound with this are seven other magazine artic.
1. Andrews, W.L. - Portraiture of the American Revolutionary War 2 pts. in 1. illus.
2. Andrews, W.L. - The first illustrated magazine published in New York. Pp. 234-39. illus.

NL 0420655 MiU-C

Livingston, Luther Samuel, 1864-1914, ed.

Brereton, John, *fl.* 1603.
A briefe and true relation of the discouerie of the north part of Virginia, by John Brereton; reproduced in facsimile from the first edition of 1602, with an introductory note by Luther S. Livingston. New York, Dodd, Mead & company, 1903.

Livingston, Luther Samuel, 1864-1914, ed.

Smith, John, 1580–1631.
Captain John Smith's circular or prospectus of his Generall historie of Virginia, New-England, and the Summer Isles; reproduced from the only known copy in the collection of the Society of antiquaries, London, with notes. Cambridge, Priv. print., 1914.

Livingston, Luther Samuel, 1864-1914.

Milton, John, 1608–1674.
Comus, "a maske presented at Ludlow castle. 1634": by John Milton. Reproduced in facsimile from the first edition of 1637, with an introductory note by Luther S. Livingston. New York, Dodd, Mead & company, 1903.

LIVINGSTON, Luther Samuel, 1864-1914.
[Correspondence addressed to L. S. Livingston by distinguished book collectors, bibliographers, and dealers].

Manuscript and typewritten. 4 boxes.

NL 0420659 MH

Livingston, Luther Samuel, 1864-1914.

Franklin, Benjamin, 1706–1790.
Benjamin Franklin's Dialogue with the gout, with an account of the first editions by Luther S. Livingston. Cambridge [Printed by C. P. Rollins at the Dyke mill, Montague, Mass.] 1917.

Twain Z£i IN: spec Livingston, Luther Samuel, 1864-1914.
The first books of some American authors: Mark Twain ... [by Luther S. Livingston. New York, Dodd, Mead, 1899]
563-564p. facsim. 26cm.
Detached from The Bookman, vol. VIII, no. 6.

1. Clemens, Samuel Langhorne, 1835-1910. The celebrated jumping frog of Calaveras County I. TITLE.

NL 0420661 IEN ViU

VOLUME 336

[Livingston, Luther Samuel] 1864-1914.
First editions of Algernon Charles Swinburne. The bibliographical description of a collected set of the first editions of writings of the last of the great Victorian poets. New York, Offered for sale by Dodd & Livingston [1913]
59p. 25cm.

Cf. Wise, S.L.,p.281;Wise B.B.,p.558,no.31.
Insert: typed letter, designating printing date, signed "John S. Mayfield", tipped in back free endpaper.
----Copy 2: As issued.
Inscription: Robert H. Dodd to William F. Gable.

1. Swinburne, Algernon Charles, 1837-1909.-- Bibliography. I. Title.

NL 0420662 NSyU CSmH

[Livingston, Luther Samuel] 1864-1914.
First editions of George Meredith; being the description of a collected set of his books, some with autographic annotations, and including manuscript agreements with his publishers and the original autograph manuscript of "The tragic comedians." New York, Dodd & Livingston [1912?]
37 p. 24cm.

1. Meredith, George, 1828-1909—Bibl. I. Title.

41-41463

Library of Congress Z8568.8.Z9L58

[2] 012

NL 0420663 DLC MiU CtY FU

Livingston, Luther Samuel, 1864-1914, ed.

E125
.V5V475

Vespucci, Amerigo, 1451-1512.
The first four voyages of Americus Vespucius: a reprint in exact facsimile of the German edition printed at Strassburg, by John Grüniger, in 1509. New York, Dodd, Mead & company, 1902.

[Livingston, Luther Samuel] 1864-1914.
The four folios of Shakespeare's plays; an account of the four collected editions together with a census of the known perfect copies of the first folio. A description of an exceptionally desirable set now offered for sale by Dodd,Mead & company, New York. [N.Y.,Dodd,Mead & company, 1907] 32p. 24½cm.

Initials L.S.L. in ink on title-page.

NL 0420665 MWelC

Livingston, Luther Samuel, 1864-1914.
Franklin and his press at Passy; an account of the books, pamphlets, and leaflets printed there, including the long-lost 'Bagatelles', by Luther S. Livingston. New York, The Grolier club, 1914.
xii p., 1 l., 216 p., 1 l. front. (port.) illus., pl., facsims. (part fold.) 24½cm.

"One of an edition of three hundred copies on Van Gelder paper and three copies on Alton mill paper, printed during the month of May, 1914."

1. Franklin, Benjamin, 1706-1790. I. Title: Passy press.

14-20677

Library of Congress Z232.F8L6

NL 0420666 DLC NcU NjP TxHU FU CoU NN MiU-C OClWHi MH OkU CSmH MoSW ICU MB ICJ CSmH RPJCB IaU

[Livingston, Luther Samuel] 1864-1914.
The Harry Elkins Widener Stevenson collection.
Pamphlet
Caption title.
Signed L.S.L.
"Reprinted from The Nation. 50 copies."

I.Harvard university. Library. Widener collection.

NL 0420667 CtY MiU ViU KU CSmH MH PPRF

Livingston, Luther Samuel, 1864-1914.
(In memoriam) Luther S. Livingston
see Winship, George Parker, 1871- Luther S. Livingston.

Livingston, Luther Samuel, 1864-1914.

Franklin, Benjamin, 1706-1790.
Benjamin Franklin's Letters to Madame Helvétius and Madame La Freté, with an explanatory note by Luther S. Livingston. Cambridge [Printed at the Harvard university press] 1924.

[LIVINGSTON, LUTHER SAMUEL, 1864-1914.]
A literary curiosity from Charles Lamb's library; discovery of a book that has hitherto baffled Lamb students.
[New York,1899.]
p.453-458. illus.(facsims.) 25½cm.
Caption title.
Detached from The Bookman, Jan. 1899.
Three-quarter red mor.; t.e.g.
Bound with Dodd, Mead & co.'s Description of a few books from Charles Lamb's library ... New York, [ca.1899].

NL 0420670 PPRF

Livingston, Luther S[amuel] 1864-1914.
Longfellow, Lowell, Holmes, Bryant.
(The first books of some American authors. II)
(From- The Bookman, Oct. 1898. 25 cm. p. 138-144. facsim.

NL 0420671 RPB

[Livingston, Luther Samuel] 1864-1914.
News for bibliophiles.

423
+1

(In The Nation. New York,1913. 30½cm. v.96, p.494-496)
Signed: L.S.L.
On Franklin's Way to wealth.

NL 0420672 CtY

Livingston, Luther Samuel, 1864-1914.
Notice to booksellers ... [n.p.,19-?]

421
+1769by

1l. 26½x33cm. 21 copies.
Facsimiles of the title-pages of four editions of Barbeu Du Bourg's Code de l'humanité with notice that Livingston desired to obtain copies of every edition of that work.

NL 0420673 CtY

Livingston, Luther Samuel, 1864-1914.

Franklin, Benjamin, 1706-1790.
Benjamin Franklin's Parable against persecution, with an account of the early editions by Luther S. Livingston. Cambridge [Mass., The Montague press] 1916.

X337
1

[Livingston, Luther Samuel] 1864-1914.
The Robert Hoe library ...

Caption title.
Signed: L.S.L.
"Reprinted from The Nation, 50 copies."

I.Hoe, Robert, 1839-1909.

NL 0420675 CtY

Livingston, Luther Samuel, 1864-1914
The Robert Hoe library. [New York?, New York Evening Post Co.?, 1912?]
8 p. 17 cm.

"Reprinted from the Nation [v.95,p.505-506] 50 copies."
Presentation copy to Grenville Kane, with the author's initials.
Bound with the author's Beverly Chew and his books. [New York?, 1912?]

NL 0420676 NjP MH CSmH

Livingston, Luther Samuel, 1864-1914.
Rudyard Kipling's first book. [New York] 1899.
32 p. facsims. 18 cm.

"Twenty copies separately printed from the types of the Bookman." Author's holograph note to G. M. Williamson laid in.

1. Kipling, Rudyard, 1865-1936—Bibl. 2. Kipling, Rudyard, 1865-1936. Schoolboy lyrics.

Z8465.L79 52-45198

NL 0420677 DLC CU-S CtY CSmH MH

Livingston, Luther Samuel, 1864-1914.

Some notes on three of Lamb's juveniles... [n.p., Priv.print., 190-?] [18] p. illus.

Caption-title.
Limited edition.
Presentation copy to L.H.Chubbuck signed by the author.

1.Lamb,Charles,1775-1834.

NL 0420678 NjP MH IaU

Livingston, Luther Samuel, 1864-1914.

Franklin, Benjamin, 1706-1790.
Benjamin Franklin's Story of the whistle, with an introductory note by Luther S. Livingston, and a bibliography to 1820. Cambridge [Harvard university press] 1922.

Livingston, Luther Samuel, 1864-1914, comp.
The works of Mark Twain (Samuel Langhorne Clemens) the description of a set of first editions of his books. New York, Dodd and Livingston [191-?]
63 p. 25 cm. (in binder, 27 cm.)

"Seventy-five copies only printed".

NL 0420680 WU

Livingston, Luther Samuel, 1864-1914.

[Dows, Tracy] 1871-
The works of Rudyard Kipling: the description of a set of the first editions of his books, in the library of a New York collector. With facsimiles. New York, Dodd, Mead & company, 1901.

Livingston, Mrs. Luther Samuel
see Livingston, Flora Virginia (Milner) 1862-

VOLUME 336

Livingston, Luzern Gould.
The nature and distribution of plasmodesmata in the tobacco plant ⌊by⌋ L. G. Livingston ... ⌊Brooklyn, 1935⌋
p. 75–87 incl. 2 pl. on 1 l. 25½cm.
Caption title.
Thesis (PH. D.)—University of Wisconsin, 1933.
Thesis note stamped on p. 75.
From the American journal of botany, v. 22, Jan. 1935.
"Literature cited": p. 84.
1. Tobacco. 2. Plant cells and tissues. 3. Mosaic disease. I. Title: Plasmodesmata in the tobacco plant.
35-38083
Library of Congress QK725.L5 1933
Univ. of Wisconsin Libr. ⌊2⌋ 581.875

NL 0420683 WU DLC

Livingston, Malcolm Rogers.
QE129 .A2 no. 43
Mississippi. *Geological, Economic and Topographical Survey.*
Warren County mineral resources. University, 1941.

Livingston, Marcia M., joint author.
Aunt Hannah and Martha and John
see under
Alden, Isabella (Macdonald) "Mrs. G.R. Alden", 1841-1930.

Livingston, Marcia M , joint author.
Profiles
see under
Alden, Isabella (Macdonald) "Mrs. G.R. Alden", 1841-1930.

Livingston (Marcus). *Beobachtungen über Caries sicca. 29 pp., 1 l., 1 pl. 8°. *Berlin, G. Schade,* [1877].

NL 0420687 DNLM

Livingston, Mrs. Margaret Vere (Farrington) 1863-
Almost true tales. Stories by Washington Irving—Nathaniel Hawthorne—Thomas Bulfinch—M. V. Farrington—Charles Kingsley—and "Ouida." Illustrated. New York and London. G. P. Putnam's sons ⌊1912?⌋

Livingston, Mrs. Margaret Vere (Farrington) 1863-
Andrew Jackson Davis and the harmonial philosophy [Boston, c1912]
BF1283 .D4L5

NL 0420689 DLC

Livingston, Margaret Vere (Farrington) 1863-
Fra Lippo Lippi, a romance, by Margaret Vere Farrington ... New York ⌊etc.⌋ G. P. Putnam's sons, 1890.
vii p., 1 l., 225 p. front., plates. 22cm.
1. Lippi, Fra Filippo, 1412?-1469—Fiction. I. Title.
7—19396
Library of Congress PZ3.L7625F
⌊a45d1⌋

NL 0420690 DLC NIC TxU OO OCl OCU PPL MB PPMoI

FILM 4274 PR v.3 reel L22
Livingston, Margaret Vere (Farrington) 1863-
Fra Lippo Lippi, a romance, by Margaret Vere Farrington ... New York ⌊etc.⌋ G. P. Putnam's sons, 1890.
vii p., 1 l., 225 p. front., plates. 22cm.
(Wright American Fiction, v. III, 1876-1900, no. 3366, Research Publications, Inc. Microfilm, Reel L-22)
1. Lippi, Fra Filippo, 1412?-1469—Fiction. I. Title.

NL 0420691 CU

Livingston, Margaret Vere (Farrington) 1863-
Fra Lippo Lippi; a romance. 2d ed. NY, Putnam, 1891
vii, 225 p. illus.

NL 0420692 MH

813.4 L765f 1892
Livingston, Margaret Vere (Farrington) 1863-
Fra Lippo Lippi, a romance, by Margaret Vere Farrington. 2nd ed. New York, G. P. Putnam's Sons, 1892.
vii, 225p. front., plates.
1. Lippi, Fra Filippo, 1412?-1469--Fiction. I. Title.

NL 0420693 ICarbS

Livingston, Margaret Vere (Farrington) 1863-
Fra Lippo Lippi, a romance. 3d ed. New York, etc., G.P.Putnam's sons, 1899.
vii, 225 p. port., plates. 22 cm.

NL 0420694 MH

Livingston, Margaret Vere (Farrington), 1863–
Sauce for the goose; a farce in one act, by Margaret Vere F. Livingston. Boston, W. H. Baker & co., 1899. 11 p. 19cm. (Baker's edition of plays.)
1. Drama, American. I. Title.
N. Y. P. L. July 10, 1947

NL 0420695 NN CtY MH NBuG

Livingston, *Mrs.* Margaret Vere (Farrington) 1863–
Tales of King Arthur and his knights of the Round table, by Margaret Vere Farrington; with illustrations by Alfred Fredericks and others. New York and London, G. P. Putnam's sons, 1888.
vii, ⌊1⌋, 276 p. front., illus. 21½cm.
1. Arthur, King—Juvenile literature. I. Title.
Library of Congress PZ8.1.M788L 11-15070

NL 0420696 MB OCIW DLC OrP WaS MtU ViU PV PPGi PBa PP OU OO

Livingston, Margaret Vere (Farrington) 1863-
Tales of King Arthur and his knights of the round table... New York and London, J.P. Putnam's sons, 1889.
276 p.

NL 0420697 PPAN

Livingston, Mrs Margaret Vere (Farrington) 1863-
Tales of King Arthur and his knights of the Round Table, with illustrations by Alfred Fredericks and others. New York: G. P. Putnam's Sons, 1910. vii(i), 276 p., 1 pl. illus. 12°.
1. Arthur, King. 2. Title. CENTRAL CIRCULATION.
N. Y. P. L. April 25, 1911.

NL 0420698 NN

Livingston, Mario, 1878–
El corazón de los hombres. Buenos Aires, Librería Perlado ⌊1947⌋
322 p. 21 cm.
I. Title.
A 49-6545*
New York. Public Libr. for Library of Congress ⌊1⌋

NL 0420699 NN

Livingston, Mario, 1878–
Ese beso de ayer, por Mario Livingston... Buenos Aires: "Libreria del colegio," 1939. 201 p. 21cm.
Poems.
212068B. 1. Poetry, Argentine. I. Title.
N. Y. P. L. April 16, 1943

NL 0420700 NN

Livingston, Mario, 1878-
... Óyeme. Buenos Aires, "Librería del colegio", 1936.
2 p. l., ⌊7⌋-220, ⌊4⌋ p. 20cm.
Poems.
I. Title.
38-29479
Library of Congress PQ7797.L54309
⌊2⌋ 861.6

NL 0420701 DLC NcU

Livingston, Marjorie (Prout), 1893–
Delphic echo, by Marjorie Livingston. London, A. Dakers ⌊1948⌋ 431 p. 21cm.
498787B. I. Title.
N. Y. P. L. November 25, 1949

NL 0420702 NN MH

Livingston, Marjorie (Prout) 1893-
The future of Mr. Purdew, a novel by Marjorie Livingston. London, Wright & Brown ⌊1936⌋
vi, 7-320 p. 19cm.
I. Title.
36-33140
Library of Congress PZ3.L7626Fu

NL 0420703 DLC

VOLUME 336

Livingston, Marjorie (Prout) 1893-
The key of the castle, by Marjorie Livingston ... London, Wright & Brown [1937]
287 p. 19cm.

I. Title.
37-12423
Library of Congress PZ3.L7626Ke

NL 0420704 DLC

[**Livingston,** *Mrs.* **Marjorie (Prout)**] 1893-
The loquacious vessel [by] Mark Vinton [*pseud.*] ... London, Hutchinson & company, ltd., 1938.
304 p. 19cm. (First novel library. no. 75)

I. Title.
39-2056
Library of Congress PZ3.L7626Lo

NL 0420705 DLC

Livingston, Marjorie (Prout) 1893-
Moloch, by Marjorie Livingston ... London, A. Dakers limited [1942]
295 p. 19½cm.
"First published 1942."

I. Title.
43-2470
Library of Congress PZ3.L7626Mo

NL 0420706 DLC

Livingston, Marjorie (Prout) 1893-
Muted strings. London, A. Dakers [1946]
445 p. 19 cm.

I. Title.
A 48-7352*
Harvard Univ. Library for Library of Congress [1]

NL 0420707 MH

Livingston, Marjorie (Prout) 1893-
... The new Nuctemeron (the twelve hours of Apollonius of Tyana) preface by Sir Arthur Conan Doyle, and explanatory note by the amanuensis. London, Rider & co., 1930.
143 p. 19cm.
"This remarkable script purports to be produced under the direct inspiration of Apollonius of Tyana."—Pref.

1. Spiritualism. I. Apollonius, of Tyana. II. Title.
30-23814
Library of Congress BF1311.A6L5
Copyright A ad int. 14183 [2] 133.9

NL 0420708 DLC UU MH NN

Livingston, Mark.
Naughty Elizabeth. New York, Town topics pub. co., 1901.
247 p. 12°. (Tales from Town topics, no. 40)
1-15201—M 4 Aug. 8

NL 0420709 DLC

Livingston, Martha Child, 1889-1946.
Passing by, and other poems by Martha Child Livingston. Los Angeles, Calif., Wetzel publishing co., inc. [1946]
4 p. l., 11-39 p. 21cm.

I. Title.
PS3523.I 945P3 811.5 47-16122

NL 0420710 DLC

Livingston, Mary Georgia, 1890-

PZ3 .S848 T 99
Stevenson, Robert Louis, 1850-1894.
Treasure Island, adapted by M. Georgia Livingston. New York, Globe Book Co. [1948]

Livingston, Mary Walton.

U. S. *National archives.*
... Preliminary inventory of the War labor policies board records. Compiled by Mary Walton Livingston and Leo Pascal. Washington, 1943.

Livingston, Maturin, *plaintiff.*
The trial of the Hon. Maturin Livingston, against James Cheetham, for a libel; held at the sittings, on the twenty eighth of Nov. 1807. Before the Hon Judge Spencer. Taken in short hand, by William Sampson, Esq. ... New-York, Printed and published by S. Gould, law bookseller and law stationer, opposite the City-hall, 1807.
63 p. 20½cm.
Trial for the alleged libelous inference that the plaintiff enabled his brother, Peter R. Livingston, to win money, unfairly, in a game of cards.
I. Cheetham, James, 1772-1810, defendant. II. Sampson, William, 1764-1836.
47-35705

NL 0420713 DLC CtY NIC CSt IU NjP NNU-W PP PPL

910.4 L762
Livingston, Max L
Around the world with Julian M. and Max L. Livingston. [Chicago, Cuneo Press, 1927.
263p. illus. 26cm.

1. Voyages around the world. I. Livingston, Julian M jt. auth. II. Title.

NL 0420714 OrU

Livingston, Milton Stanley, 1905-
High energy accelerator design, by the Brookhaven Accelerator Project, M.S. Livingston, Chairman. Upton, N.Y., 1948.
2 p.l., 63 p. illus. 28 cm. (Brookhaven National Laboratory, Associated Universities, inc. Technical report, no. 1)

NL 0420715 OU

Livingston, Milton Stanley, 1905-
High-energy accelerators. New York, Interscience Publishers, 1954.
157 p. illus. 21 cm. (Interscience tracts on physics and astronomy, 2)

1. Particle accelerators. I. Title.
QC786.L5 *539.73 54-11776 ‡

IdU CaBVaU MtBC OClW WaSpG CaBVaU OrU PBL PPD MiU PPF PHC PSt NcD PU OrPR OrCS NSyU KEmT ViU NN TxU MB ICJ TU PP PV OCU OO OU
NL 0420716 DLC NBuC OrPS WaWW WaS OrSaW TxU MiU

U428 I5A6 L56-47 R
Livingston, Milton Stanley, 1905-
Problems in research and development. Washington, 1955.
ii, 20 p. 26 cm. (U.S. Industrial College of the Armed Forces. Publication no. L56-47)
Cover title.

1. Research. I. Title. (Series)

NL 0420717 DI

Livingston, Milton Stanley, 1905-
The production of high velocity hydrogen ions without the use of high voltages, by Milton Stanley Livingston ... [Berkeley, Calif., 1931]
1 p.l., 29 numb. 1. mounted diagrs. 29 cm.
Thesis (Ph.D.) - Univ. of California, May 1931.
"References": p. 29.
-- ----- Another copy.
1. Hydrogen. 2. Ions - Migration and velocity.

NL 0420718 CU

Livingston, Milton Stanley, 1905-

Cherenkov, P A *ed.*
Циклотрон; сборник статей. Перевод. Москва, Гос. изд-во технико-теорет. лит-ры, 1948.

Livingston, Miriam Drake.
Beacon lights, by Miriam Drake Livingston. New York, The Pyramid press [°1938]
4 p. l., 84 p. 23½cm.
Verse.

1. Religious poetry. I. Title.
40-37886
Library of Congress PS3523.I 946B4 1938
——— Copy 2.
Copyright [2] 811.5

NL 0420720 DLC NN

Livingston, Miriam Drake.
Meditations for all minds, by Miriam Drake Livingston. Poetry. [Columbus, O., The F. J. Heer printing co., °1936]
69 p. 22½cm.
Title from cover.

I. Title.
36-29808
Library of Congress PS3523.I 946M4 1936
——— Copy 2.
Copyright A 99655 [2] 811.5

NL 0420721 DLC

Livingston, Mortimer.
New York and Havre steam navigation company.
Argument to be submitted to the Committee of ways and means, in regard to the renewal of the contracts with the line of steamships to Bremen and Havre. New York, W. C. Bryant & co., 1852.

Livingston, Myrtle Athleen (Smith), 1902-
For unborn children. A play in one act. By Myrtle A. Smith Livingston. (Crisis. New York, 1926. 8°. v. 32, p. 122-124. port.)

1. Negro drama. 2. Title.
N. Y. P. L. September 20, 1927

NL 0420723 NN

VOLUME 336

Livingston, Neil, d. 1899, ed.

Bible. *O. T. Psalms. English. Paraphrases. 1864.*
The Scottish metrical psalter of A. D. 1635, reprinted in full from the original work; the additional matter and various readings found in the editions of 1565, &c. being appended, and the whole illustrated by dissertations, notes, & fac-similes. Edited by the Rev. Neil Livingston. Glasgow, Printed from stone, by Maclure & Macdonald, 1864.

Livingston, Neil, d. 1899, ed.

Bible. *O. T. Psalms. English. Paraphrases (1635) 1935.*
The Scottish psalter of 1635, edited with modal harmonies by Richard Runciman Terry. London, Novello and company limited; New York, The H. W. Gray co. ⌐1935⌐

Livingston, Noël B.
Sketch pedigrees of some of the early settlers in Jamaica. Comp. from the records of the Court of chancery of the island with a list of the inhabitants in 1670 and other matter relative to the early history of the same. By Noël B. Livingston. ⌐Kingston, Jamaica, The Educational supply company, 1909⌐
139, iv p. 21cm.

1. Jamaica—Geneal. 2. Jamaica—Hist.—Sources. I. Title.
14-17186
Library of Congress F1865.L78

NL 0420726 DLC NN MWA NcD MiD-B MBBC NjP CtY

Livingston, Norman Francis, 1913- joint author.

Roberts, Ray Harland, 1890-
... Carbon dioxide exchange rhythm and fruitfulness in plants of different reproductive habits. By R. H. Roberts ... James E. Kraus and Norman Livingston ...
(*In* U. S. Dept. of agriculture. Journal of agricultural research. v. 54, no. 5, Mar. 1, 1937, p. 319-343. illus., diagrs. 23½cm. Washington, 1937)

Livingston, *Mrs.* Ophelia (Mead) 1807-1873.
Poems. By Mrs. O. M. Livingston. ⌐Cambridge, Mass.⌐ Printed at the Riverside press, and for sale by Hurd and Houghton, New York, 1868.
viii, 242 p. 18cm.

28-9326
Library of Congress PS2248.L53

NL 0420728 DLC CtY MH MB

621.39 Livingston, Orrin William, 1905-
L76i Industrial electronics, by O. W. Livingston and Harry L. Palmer. Scranton, Pa., International Textbook Co.[1941?]
v, 101, 89p. illus., diagrs. 20cm. ([International Textbook Company. Bluebooks] 603B)
Contents.- Theory of industrial electronic tubes, by O. W. Livingston.- Electron tubes in industry, by H. L. Palmer.
1. Vacuum-tubes. I. Livingston, Orrin William, 1905- Theory of industrial electronic tubes. II. Palmer, Harry L. Electron tubes in industry. III. Title.

NL 0420729 IU

Livingston, Orrin William, 1905-
... Theory of industrial electronic tubes, prepared especially for home study ... ⌐Scranton, °1937⌐
cover-title, 101 p. illus. 19cm.
At head of title: International correspondence schools, Scranton, Pa. "Serial 5226, edition 1."

1. Vacuum-tubes. I. International correspondence schools, Scranton, Pa.
43-40176
Brief cataloging
Library of Congress QC544.V3L55 1937a
⌐2⌐ 537.53

NL 0420730 DLC WaS

Livingston, Patrick
A short account of that faithful servant of the Lord, and diligent la bourer in his vineyard, George Gray....London, T. Sowle, 1692.
30 p. 16 cm.
Half-title missing. Preface by Alexander Seston.

NL 0420731 MiU-C

Livingston, Paul Yount, 1893-
Glad tidings to the meek, and other sermons, by Paul Y. Livingston ... New York ⌐etc.⌐ Fleming H. Revell company ⌐°1933⌐
64 p. 19½cm.

1. Lutheran church—Sermons. 2. Sermons, American. I. Title.
33-34599
Library of Congress BX8066.L5G6
——— Copy 2.
Copyright A 65879 ⌐3⌐ 252.041

NL 0420732 DLC NJQ

Livingston, Paul Yount, 1893-
Say thou art mine; evangelical sermon series, by Paul Y. Livingston ... introduction by Professor Daniel J. Klinedinst ... New York ⌐etc.⌐ Fleming H. Revell company ⌐°1937⌐
128 p. 2 port. (incl. front.) 19½cm.
"Thank God for victory" (words and music) : p. ⌐4⌐

1. Lutheran church—Sermons. 2. Sermons, American. I. Title.
37-23650
Library of Congress BX8066.L5S3
——— Copy 2.
Copyright A 109249 ⌐2⌐ 252.041

NL 0420733 DLC

Livingston, Penn Poore, 1899-
... Geology and ground-water resources of the Big Spring area, Texas, by Penn Livingston and Robert R. Bennett ... Washington, U. S. Govt. print. off., 1944.
v, 113 p. incl. tables. plates, maps (2 fold. in pocket) diagrs. 23cm. (U. S. Geological survey. Water-supply paper 913)
Part of the illustrative material is folded.
"Prepared in cooperation with Texas state Board of water engineers and the city of Big Spring."

1. Geology—Texas—Howard co. 2. Water-supply—Texas—Howard co. 3. Water, Underground—Texas—Howard co. I. Bennett, Robert Raymond, 1913- joint author. II. Texas. Board of water engineers III. Big Spring, Texas.
G S 44-48
U. S. Geol. survey. Library for Library of Congress [TC801.U2 no. 913] ⌐12⌐ (628.10973)

NL 0420734 DI-GS

Livingston, Penn Poore, 1899-

GB1025
.T4A5
1947

Texas. *Water Commission.*
Ground-water resources of Bexar County, Texas, by Penn Livingston. Prepared in cooperation with the U. S. Dept. of the Interior, Geological Survey. ⌐Washington⌐ 1947.

Livingston, Penn Poore, 1899- joint author.

TC801
.U2
no. 919

Sayre, Albert Nelson, 1901-
... Ground-water resources of the El Paso area, Texas, by A. N. Sayre and Penn Livingston. Prepared in cooperation with the El Paso Water board and the Texas state Board of water engineers. Washington, U. S. Govt. print. off., 1945.

Livingston, Penn Poore, 1899-

GB705
.T4A5
1947

Texas. *Water Commission.*
Relationship of ground water to the discharge of the Leona River in Uvalde and Zavala Counties, Texas, by Penn Livingston. Prepared in cooperation with the United States Dept of the Interior, Geological Survey. ⌐Washington⌐ 1947.

Livingston, Penn Poore, 1899-
... Underground leakage from artesian wells in the Flowell area, near Fillmore, Utah, by Penn Livingston and George B. Maxey ... ⌐Salt Lake City⌐ 1944.
37 p. illus. (incl. map) 22½cm. (Utah. State engineer's office. Technical publication no. 1)
"Prepared in cooperation with the United States Dept. of the interior, Geological survey, 1944."

1. Artesian wells—Utah—Millard co. 2. Water-supply—Utah—Millard co. 3. Fillmore, Utah—Water-supply. I. Maxey, George Burke, 1917- joint author. II. U. S. Geological survey. III. Title.
G S 47-193
U. S. Geol. survey. Library for Library of Congress ⌐3⌐

NL 0420738 DI-GS

Livingston, Peter, *b.* 1823.
Poems and songs, principally relating to Scottish manners and customs. 3d ed. Dundee, Pub. for the author, to be had of W. Livingston, 1846.
128+ p. 18 cm.

L. C. copy imperfect: p. 97-112 and all after p. 128 wanting.
PR4890.L6 1846 48-39715*

NL 0420739 DLC

Livingston, Peter, *b.* 1823.
Poems and songs, principally relating to Scottish manners and customs. By Peter Livingston ... 4th ed. Dundee, The author, 1847.
viii, ⌐9⌐-158 p. front. (port.) 17cm.
Title-page mutilated, upper part cut away.

25-25713
Library of Congress PR4890.L6 1847

NL 0420740 DLC

Livingston, Peter, b. 1823.
Poems and songs, principally relating to Scottish manners and customs, by Peter Livingston... Dundee: the author, 1848. viii, (1)10-160 p. 5. ed. 12°.

1. Poetry (Scottish).
N. Y. P. L. October 26, 1915.

NL 0420741 NN

Livingston, Peter, *b.* 1823.
Poems and songs, principally relating to Scottish manners and customs. By Peter Livingston ... 6th ed. Dundee, The author, 1849.
viii, ⌐9⌐-160 p. 17½cm.

25-25714
Library of Congress PR4890.L6 1849

NL 0420742 DLC

VOLUME 336

 Livingston, Peter, 1823-
Poems and songs; with lectures on the genius and works of Burns and the Rev. George Gilfillan; and letter of Sir John Franklin and the Arctic regions. 8th ed. Dundee, Printed by J. Durham for W. Livingston, 1852.
125 p. 20 cm.
1. Burns, Robert, 1759-1796. 2. Gilfillan, George, 1813-1878. 3. Franklin, Sir John, 1786-1847. I. Title

NL 0420743 CaBVaU

Livingston, Peter, b.1823.
Poems and songs; with lectures on the genius & works of Burns, and the Rev. Geo. Gilfillan, and letter on Sir John Franklin, and the Arctic regions. By Peter Livingston ... 10th ed. Dundee, Printed by J. Pellow, 1858.
xii,[13]-137p.,20cm.

NL 0420744 CaBViPA

 Livingston, Peter, b. 1823.
Poems and songs; with lectures on the genius & works of Burns, and the Rev. Geo. Gilfillan, and letter on Sir John Franklin and the Arctic regions, by Peter Livingston... 10th ed. Dundee, Printed by J. Pellow, 1859.
xii, [13]-137p. 19½cm.

1. Burns, Robert, 1759-1796. 2. Gilfillan, George, 1813-1878. 3. Franklin, Sir John, 1786-1847. 4. English poetry.

NL 0420745 LU

Livingston, Peter, *b.* 1823.
Poems and songs; with lectures on the genius and works of Burns, and the Rev. George Gilfillan: and letters on Dr. Dick, the Christian philosopher, and Sir J. Franklin & the Arctic regions. By Peter Livingston ... 10th ed. Dundee, Printed by J. Pellow, 1865.
xii, [13]-140 p. 19½cm.

1. Burns, Robert, 1759-1796. 2. Gilfillan, George, 1813-1878. 3. Franklin, Sir John, 1786-1847.
7—28479
Library of Congress PR4890.L6 1865

NL 0420746 DLC NN NIC

Livingston, Peter, *b.* 1823.
Poems and songs; with lectures on the genius and works of Burns, and the Rev. George Gilfillan: and letters on Dr. Dick, the Christian philosopher, and Sir J. Franklin & the Arctic regions. By Peter Livingston ... 10th ed. Edinburgh, Printed by Mould & Tod, 1874.
xii, [13]-140 p. 19½cm.

NL 0420747 CtY

Livingston, Peter, 1823-
Poems and songs; with lectures on the genius and works of Burns and George Gilfillan; and letters on Dr. Dick, the Christian philosopher, and Sir John Franklin and the Arctic regions. 10th ed. Edinburgh, Mould & Tod, 1881.
pp. 143.

Burns|Gilfillan|Dick|Franklin|| 6

NL 0420748 MH CaBVaU

Livingston, Philip, 1716–1778.
Works by this author printed in America before 1801 are available in this library in the Readex Microprint edition of Early American Imprints published by the American Antiquarian Society. This collection is arranged according to the numbers in Charles Evans' American Bibliography.

NL 0420749 DLC

[Livingston, Philip] 1716-1778.
The inhabitants of the city and county of New York. The wisest men in all ages...[at end.]: A citizen. New York, March 4,1775.

NL 0420750 RPJCB

Livingston, Philip, 1716-1778.
[Letter to Messrs. Gardiner and Jepson] Newport, June 23, 1760. ms.
Laid in Brotherhead, W., The centennial book of the signers...[1876]

NL 0420751 RPJCB

[Livingston, Philip] 1716–1778.
The other side of the question: or, A defence of the liberties of North-America. In answer to a late Friendly address to all reasonable Americans, on the subject of our political confusions. By a citizen. New-York: Printed by James Rivington, fronting Hanover-Square. M, DCC, LXXIV.
29, [1] p., 1 l. 20cm.
[Hazard pamphlets. v. 44, no. 3]
Signatures: A-D[4].
At end ([D4] recto) Announcement of early publication of the letters of the Earl of Chesterfield.

A reply to Thomas Bradbury Chandler's A friendly address to all reasonable Americans.

1. U. S.—Pol. & govt.—Revolution. 2. Chandler, Thomas Bradbury, 1726-1790. A friendly address to all reasonable Americans on the subject of our political confusions. I. Title.
27-4698 Revised
Library of Congress AC901.H3 vol. 44
——— Copy 2. [Miscellaneous pamphlets, v. 757, no. 3] AC901.M5 vol.

MiU-C PPL ICN MWA MB NN RPJCB PPL PHi ViU CaOTP
NL 0420753 DLC MnHi NIC NNC InU MH CtY OClWHi MWiW-C

Film
E
8 Livingston, Philip, 1716-1778
THE OTHER SIDE OF THE QUESTION; OR, A defence of the liberties of North America ... By a citizen. N.Y., Printed by James Rivington, fronting Hanover Square,1774.

Negative film reproduction.
Original in British Museum.
Collation of original as determined from film: 29p.
Filmed with [Crouch,Nathaniel, The English empire in America.

NL 0420754 InU

[Livingston, Philip] 1716–1778.
The other side of the question: or, A defence of the liberties of North-America. In answer to a late Friendly address to all reasonable Americans, on the subject of our political confusions. By a citizen. New-York, Printed by James Rivington, 1774. Tarrytown, N. Y., Reprinted, W. Abbatt, 1916.
33 p. 26½cm. (The Magazine of history with notes and queries. Extra number. 52, pt. 1)
A reply to Thomas Bradbury Chandler's A friendly address to all reasonable Americans.
1. U. S.—Pol. & govt.—Revolution. 2. Chandler, Thomas Bradbury, 1726-1790. A friendly address to all reasonable Americans, on the subject of our political confusions. I. Title.
16-24710 Revised
Library of Congress E173.M24 no. 52

NL 0420755 DLC NIC MB MiU OCl

[Livingston, Philip] 1716–1778.
To the inhabitants of the city and county of New-York. [New York. Printed by J. Holt, 1775]
broadside. 40 x 27 cm. fold. to 22 x 27 cm.
Signed: A citizen.

1. U. S.—Pol. & govt.—Revolution. 2. New York (State)—Pol. & govt.—Revolution. 3. U. S. Continental Congress. I. Title.
E211.L77 48-39006*

NL 0420756 DLC MiU-C

LIVINGSTON, R. A.
Remarks on total abstinence. n.p., n.d.

NL 0420757 MH

 Livingston, Ralph.
Fluorophosphoric acids. [Cincinnati] 1943.
66 l. illus. 29cm.

Thesis (Dr. of Science) - Univ. of Cincinnati, 1943.
Bibliographical foot-notes.

1. Cincinnati. University - Theses Dr. of Science. 1943. I. Title.

NL 0420758 OCU

Livingston, Robert.
Monetary reform and bi-metallism: a paper read before the Kirkcaldy chamber of commerce ... May 26th, 1892. Kirkcaldy [Scotland] : Macbean & Miller, 1892.
20 p. tables, charts.

NL 0420759 MH-BA

Livingston, Robert, *pseud.*
see
Scaife, Roger Livingston, 1875-

Livingston, Robert, 1898-
see
Livingston, Robert Stanley, 1898-

Livingston, Robert B 1911-
An ecological study of the Black Forest, Colorado. [n. p., 1949]
[123]-144 p. illus., map, tables. 27 cm.
Cover title.
Thesis—Duke University.
"Reprinted from Ecological monographs, 19 ... April, 1949."
"Literature cited": p. 144.

1. Forest ecology. 2. Forests and forestry—Colorado.
QK938.F6L58 634.946 A 51-4446
Duke Univ. Library for Library of Congress [1]†

NL 0420762 NcD DLC

Livingston, Robert C.
Illustrated catalogue of ... the unpublished correspondence
see under American Art Association.

VOLUME 336

Livingston, Robert Gerald.
The Carinthian Slovenes; a historical study of provincial loyalty

Honors thesis - Harvard, 1953

NL 0420764 MH

Livingston, Robert Greig.
A comparison of the use of polaroid and colored filters in the multiplex aeroprojector. Rolla, 1947.

29 p. illus. 23 cm. (Missouri. University. School of Mines and Metallurgy. Bulletin. Technical series, v. 17, no. 4)

"Mining and metallurgical investigations under the auspices of the United Statues Department of Interior, Bureau of Mines and the University of Missouri School of Mines and Metallurgy."
Bibliography: p. 29.

1. Photogrammetric pictures. I. Title: Multiplex aeroprojector. (Series)
TA1.M75 vol. 17, no. 4 778.38 A 48-5056*

Missouri. Univ. Libr. for Library of Congress [a50d1]†

NL 0420765 MoU CoU TxU OCU ViU DLC

Livingston [Robert I]
This Indenture, made the Day of in the Year of our Lord, one Thousand Seven Hundred and between Livingston, Esq. Lord Proprietor of the Lordship and Manor of Livingston, in the County of Columbia ... [etc.] [A blank form of lease] [n. p.] T. Green leaf, [17-?]
broadside. f°.
Manuscript endorsement of Robert L. Livingston.

NL 0420766 NN

Livingston, Robert James, 1760-1827.

Livingston, John Robert, 1755–1851.
The petition of John R. Livingston & Robert J. Livingston, to the Legislature of New-Jersey, respecting steamboats; with the laws of the states of New-York and New-Jersey, and affidavits of sundry persons respecting the improvements said to be made by Daniel Dod and others, on the machinery of R. Fulton. New-York, Printed by Pelsue & Gould, 1814.

Livingston, Robert L
Memorial, presented to the House of Representatives, Dec. 1831.
49 p. 8°.
In vol. 2 of "Pamphlets-American Revolution".

NL 0420768 CtY

Livingston, Robert Louis, 1918–
The molecular structures of dimethyl silicon dichloride, methyl silicon trichloride and trifluorosilicon chloride, by R. L. Livingston and L. O. Brockway. [n. p., 1944]

[94]-98 p. illus. 26 cm.

Cover title.
Part of R. L. Livingston's thesis—University of Michigan.
"Contribution from the Chemistry Laboratory of the University of Michigan."
"Reprinted from the Journal of the American Chemical Society, 66 ... (1944)"

1. Silicon. 2. Chlorides. I. Brockway, Lawrence Olin, 1907– joint author.
QD181.S6L67 A 53-6019

Michigan. Univ. Libr. for Library of Congress [1]†

NL 0420769 MiU DLC

Livingston, Robert R 1718–1775.
Works by this author printed in America before 1801 are available in this library in the Readex Microprint edition of Early American Imprints published by the American Antiquarian Society.
This collection is arranged according to the numbers in Charles Evans' American Bibliography.

NL 0420770 DLC

Livingston, Robert R., 1718–1775.
The address of Mr. Justice Livingston to the House of Assembly of New-York, in support of his right to a seat. New-York printed: Boston, N. E.: Re-printed, and sold by D. Kneeland, and by E. Russell, 1769. 15 p. 4°.

Evans 11314. Sabin 41635.

1. Representation—U. S.—New York, 1769. 2. New York (colony). General Assembly.
N. Y. P. L. April 4, 1929

NL 0420771 NN MWA PPRF PPL CSmH

+J
5851
.51
LIVINGSTON, ROBERT R 1718-1775.
Speech of Mr. Justice Livingston, made on Friday the 25th of January, in support of his claim to a seat in the House of the General assembly. [New York, Holt, 1771]
4p. 36cm.

Photostat reproduction (negative) from the copy in the New York public library.
Caption title.

NL 0420772 ICN

Livingston, Robert R., 1746–1813.
Works by this author printed in America before 1801 are available in this library in the Readex Microprint edition of Early American Imprints published by the American Antiquarian Society.
This collection is arranged according to the numbers in Charles Evans' American Bibliography.

NL 0420773 DLC

FILM
5942
HF
Livingston, Robert R., 1746-1813.
Account ... 1761-1787. Clermont [1761-87]
1 v. On film.

Microfilm copy of original manuscript in the library of the New York historical society.

1. Accounting - To 1800.

NL 0420774 CU

Livingston, Robert R., 1746-1813.
Biographical sketch of ...
see under De Peyster, Frederic, 1796-1882.

Livingston, Robert R., 1746-1813.
Chancellor Robert R. Livingston of New York and his family
see under Delafield, Joseph Livingston, 1871-

Livingston, Robert R., 1746–1813.
Essay on sheep; their varieties—account of the merinoes of Spain, France, &c. Reflections on the best method of treating them, and raising a flock in the United States; together with miscellaneous remarks on sheep and woollen manufactures. By Robert R. Livingston ... New York, Printed by T. and J. Swords, 1809.

186 p. 22cm.

1. Sheep.
6—8321

Library of Congress SF375.L78

NBu MH MU NIC CU
NL 0420777 DLC OClWHi MWA NjP PSt MiU-C NN MB CU-A

Livingston, Robert R., 1746-1813.
Essay on sheep. Trenton, 1810.
149 p.

NL 0420778 PU MWA

Livingston, Robert R 1746-1813.
Essay on sheep; their varieties—account of the merinos of Spain, France, &c. Reflections on the best method of treating them, and raising a flock in the United States: together with miscellaneous remarks on sheep, and woollen manufactures. By Robert R. Livingston ... 2d ed., much enl., and illustrated by engravings ... New-York, Printed and sold by Collins and Perkins, 1810.

164 p., 1 l. front. 18½cm.

Printed by order of the Legislature of the state of New-York.

1. Sheep.
6—5851

Library of Congress SF375.L79

NL 0420779 DLC PBL CU NcU CtY MH MB ICJ ViU InU

Livingston, Robert R., 1746–1813.
Essays on sheep: their varieties—account of the merinoes of Spain, France, &c. Reflections on the best method of treating them, and raising a flock in the United States; together with miscellaneous remarks on sheep and woollen manufactures. By Robert R. Livingston ... Concord, N. H., D. Cooledge, 1813.

143 p. 17cm.

1. Sheep.
Agr 28-1149

U. S. Dept. of agr. Library for Library of Congress 45L76E [SF375.L]

CaBVaU CSt TU
NL 0420780 DNAL MH MU MB MWA NcD CtY MiU-C PMA ViW

Livingston, Robert R., 1746-1813, attributed author.
Examen du Gouvernement d'Angleterre, compare aux Constitution Des Etats-Unis
see under [Stevens, John] 1749-1838.

Livingston, Robert R., 1746-1813, plaintiff.

Examination of the chancellor's opinion in the case of Rob. R. Livingston and Rob. Fulton, *vs.* James Van Ingen, Lansing & others. [Albany] Printed at the office of the Albany register, 1812.

[**Livingston, Robert R**] 1746–1813.
Examination of the treaty of amity, commerce, and navigation, between the United States and Great-Britain, in several numbers: by Cato [*pseud.*] [New York] Re-published, from the Argus, by Thomas Greenleaf, 1795.

96 p. 20cm.
Also published in the American remembrancer, Philadelphia, 1795–1796 under title: Observations on Mr. Jay's treaty.
"The authorship of this pamphlet has been ascribed to Hamilton, and to William Smith; but in a letter to James Monroe, Mr. Livingston states that he has replied to Camillus 'over my old signature—Cato.'"—P. L. Ford, Bibliotheca Hamiltoniana, 1886, p. 47.
1. Jay's treaty, 1794. 2. U. S.—For. rel.—Gt. Brit. 3. Gt. Brit.—For. rel.—U. S. 4. U. S.—For. rel.—Constitutional period, 1789–1809. I. Title.
19-10567

Library of Congress E314.L78
—— —— Copy 2. [Duane pamphlets, v. 55, no. 5]
AC901.D8 vol. 55; AC 901 .M5, v. 923

NL 0420783 DLC MH PU ViU MWA NHi PHi NN MB PPL

Livingston, Robert R 1746-1813.
Experiments and observations on lucerne ...
[Albany, N. Y., 1794]
cover-title: 65-94 p. 24 cm.
Bound with his Letter ... on the subject of green-gage plums.
From the Society for the promotion of useful arts, Albany, N. Y., Transactions, v. 1, pt. 2.

NL 0420784 PPAN

VOLUME 336

Livingston, Robert R., 1746-1813.
Illustrated catalogue of important revolutionary letters
see under Keane, James Richard, 1859-

Livingston, Robert R., 1746-1813.
In the court for the trial of impeachments and the correction of errors
see under Van Ingen, James, respondent.

Livingston, Robert R 1746-1813.
... The invention of the steamboat. An historical account of the application of steam for the propelling of boats; a letter from Chancellor Livingston to the editors of the "American medical and philosophical register," published in that journal in January, 1812 (vol. ii. p 256). [Boston, Directors of the Old South work, 1902]
16 p. 20cm. (Old South leaflets. [General series. v. 5] no. 108)
Caption title.
Robert Fulton to Aaron Ogden (1814) on the invention of the steamboat: p. 6-11.
"Fulton's letters on the first voyage of the Clermont": p. 11-13.
"The first voyage of the Clermont. Reminiscences of H. Freeland, in a letter to J. F. Reigart, 1856": p. 13-14.
1. Steam-navigation— U. S. 2. Steamboats. I. Fulton, Robert, 1765-1815.
20-20775
Library of Congress E173.O44 vol. 5

NL 0420787 DLC GEU ViU WaS OrPR PHi PPL

Livingston, Robert R., 1746-1813.
Invention, The, of the steamboat. An historical account of the application of steam for the propelling of boats . . .
[Boston, 1902.] 20 pp. [Old South Leaflets. General series. No. 107.] 12°.
Letters relative to the invention of the steamboat, from Robert Fulton to Aaron Ogden, to the editor of the American Citizen, to Joel Barlow; from H. Freeland to J. F. Reigart, from Chancellor Livingston to the editors of the American Medical and Philosophical Register.

E5675 — S.r. — Fulton, Robert. 1765-1815 — Steamboats.

NL 0420788 MB

Livingston, Robert R., 1746-1813.
The letters of Robert R. Livingston; the diplomatic story of the Louisiana purchase, by Edward Alexander Parsons.
(*In* American antiquarian society, Worcester, Mass. Proceedings. Worcester, Mass., 1943. 25cm. v. 52, p. [363]-407)

1. Louisiana purchase. I. Parsons, Edward Alexander, 1878- ed.
A 44-409
Newberry library for Library of Congress [E172.A35 vol. 52]
[3] (973.062)

NL 0420789 ICN

[**Livingston, Robert R.**] 1746-1813.
Observations on Mr. Jay's treaty.
(*In* The American remembrancer. Philadelphia, 1795-[96] 21½cm. v. 1, p. 114-122, 147-174, 219-252; v. 2, p. 3-13; v. 3, p. 63-67)
Caption title.
In 16 parts; signed: Cato.
Also published separately, New York, 1795, under title: Examination of the treaty of amity, commerce, and navigation, between the United States and Great Britain ...
"The authorship of this pamphlet has been ascribed to Hamilton, and to William Smith; but in a letter to James Monroe, Mr. Livingston states that he has replied to Camillus 'over my old signature—Cato'."—P. L. Ford, Bibl. Hamiltoniana, 1886, p. 47.
1. Jay's treaty, 1794. 2. U. S.—For. rel.—Gt. Brit. 3. Gt. Brit.—For. rel.—U. S. 4. U. S.—For. rel.—Constitutional period, 1789-1809. I. Title.
9—758
Library of Congress E311.A48

NL 0420790 DLC MiU

1746-1813.
Livingston, Robert R. On the effects of the shade of trees upon vegetation. Extract of two letters to Mr. Mitchill. [New York, *etc.* 1794.] 8°.
Transactions of the Society instituted in the state of New York for the promotion of agriculture, arts, and manufactures, 1794, i, pt. 2, pp. 169-173.

NL 0420791 MH-A

Lilly
VM 140
.F9 L 78
LIVINGSTON, ROBERT R ,1746-1813
The opinions of the judges of the Supreme Court, delivered in the Court of Errors, in the cause of Robert R. Livingston and Robert Fulton vs. James Van Ingen, and twenty others. Albany, Printed by S. Southwick, 1812.
12,12,23,[1] p. 21.5 cm.

Sabin 41637.
Bound in green cloth.

NL 0420792 InU NN

Livingston, Robert R 1746-1813.
An oration delivered before the Society of the Cincinnati of the state of New-York; in commemoration of the fourth day of July... New-York, Printed by Francis Childs, 1787.
2 p.l.,22 p. 19.5 cm.
pp. 19-22 contain an address to the "newly admitted members" by Colonel Morgan Lewis.

NL 0420793 MiU-C MdBJ-G MWA PPL CtY CSmH PHi

Livingston, Robert R., 1746-1813.
The original letters of Robert R. Livingston, 1801-1803, written during his negotiations of the purchase of Louisiana. To which is prefixed: A brief history of the Louisiana Purchase from original documents, by Edward Alexander Parsons. New Orleans, Louisiana Historical Society, 1953.
126 p. 27 cm.
Bibliographical footnotes.

1. Louisiana Purchase. I. Parsons, Edward Alexander, 1878- A brief history of the Louisiana Purchase.

E333.L7 973.46 53-40258

NL 0420794 DLC MB LU NBuC ICN OU

Livingston, Robert R. 1746-1813. Two unpublished letters. 2 pp. (*Mag. Am. Hist.* v. 21, 1889, p. 256.)

NL 0420795 MdBP

Livingston, Robert Simpson, 1914-
Heavy particles and X-rays produced during deuteron bombardment in the cyclotron, by Robert Simpson Livingston ... [Berkeley, Calif., 1941]
1 p.l., 39 numb. l. incl. mounted plates, tables, diagrs. 29 cm.
Thesis (Ph. D.) - Univ. of California, Sept. 1941.
Bibliographical foot-notes.
1. Deuterons. 2. X-rays. 3. Protons.

NL 0420796 CU

Livingston, Robert Stanley, 1898-
The activity of hydrobromic and hydrochloric acids and their catalytic actions in the decomposition of hydrogen peroxide, by Robert Stanley Livingston ... [Easton, Pa., 1926]
3 pt. diagrs. 23½cm.
Special thesis t.-p. attached to the cover of [pt. 1]
Thesis (PH. D.)—University of California, 1925.
Reprinted from the Journal of the American chemical society, 47, 1925 and 48, 1926.
"Note": 1 leaf laid in [pt. 1]

CONTENTS.—[pt. 1] The catalytic decomposition of hydrogen peroxide in an acid chlorine-chloride solution, by R. S. Livingston and W. C. Bray.—[pt. 2] The activity of hydrobromic acid in pure aqueous solution and in solutions containing sulfates, by R. S. Livingston.—[pt. 3] The interpretation of rate measurements as a function of the activity product of hydrobromic acid, by R. S. Livingston.

1. Catalysis. 2. Hydrogen peroxide. 3. Hydrobromic acid. 4. Hydrochloric acid. I. Bray, William Crowell, 1879- joint author.
CA 26-689 Unrev'd
Library of Congress QD501.L8 1925

NL 0420798 DLC

Livingston, Robert Stanley, 1898- joint author.
Hurd, Frank Wilson, 1909-
Photosensitized oxidation of aqueous solutions: dye-sensitized oxidation of potassium iodide solutions ... by Frank Wilson Hurd ... [Baltimore, 1941]

Livingston, Robert Stanley, 1898-
Physico chemical experiments, by Robert Livingston ... New York, The Macmillan company, 1939.
xi, 257 p. illus., diagrs. 21½cm.
"Abbreviations and references": p. 247.

1. Chemistry, Physical and theoretical—Laboratory manuals. I. Title.
39-3780
Library of Congress QD457.L5
——— Copy 2.
Copyright A 124856 [2] 541.072

PJB OClND
OrCS KEmT CU NcD PPF PPD PPT OU OCU OLak ICJ ViU
NL 0420800 DLC WaT MtBuM OrP WaWW IdU-SB ICJ OrU

Livingston, Robert Stanley, 1898-
Physico chemical experiments. Rev. ed. New York, Macmillan Co., 1948.
xiii, 267 p. diagrs. 22 cm.
"Abbreviations and references": p. 257.

1. Chemistry, Physical and theoretical—Laboratory manuals. I. Title.
QD457.L5 1948 541.072 48-10129*

NL 0420801 DLC OrPR PU PSt PV OU PHC MiU

QD181
.U7M2
Livingston, Robert Stanley, 1898- joint author.
McBrady, John J 1916-
A study of reversible and irreversible photobleaching of uranium compounds in homogeneous solutions. [n. p., 1946]

Pamphlet
Q
6+
Livingston, Robert Teviot.
Decision theory [by] R. T. Livingston and D. B. Hertz. Contributed by the Management Division and Junior Committee for presentation at the annual meeting, New York, N. Y., November 30 - December 5, 1952 of the American Society of Mechanical Engineers. New York, American Society of Mechanical Engineers [1953?]
10 p. illus. 29cm. (American Society of Mechanical Engin eers. Paper no. 52A-106)

NL 0420803 NIC

Livingston, Robert Teviot.
The engineering of organization and management. 1st ed. New York, McGraw-Hill Book Co., 1949.
xii, 247 p. diagrs. 24 cm. (The McGraw-Hill engineering management series)
Includes bibliographies.

1. Industrial management. I. Title.

HD31.L5 658 49-8132*

CU
NNC OClCC TxU PSt PP PPD ScU ViU CoU IU NcRS CLSU
NL 0420804 DLC CaBVaU MtBC Wa WaS OrCS MtU ICU TU

658.01
L7621
Photo-
copy
Livingston, Robert Teviot.
The integration of theories of organized behavior [by] R.T. Livingston and D.B. Hertz. [New York, The American Society of Mechanical Engineers, 1953]
[1],15p. 26½cm.
Photocopy (negative) made from the original in the Engineering Societies Library, New York.
"Advance copy released for publication upon presentation."
"Contributed by the Management Division for presentation at the Spring meeting,

Continued in next column

VOLUME 336

Continued from preceding column

Columbus, Ohio, April 28-30, 1953 of the American Society of Mechanical Engineers."
Bibliography: p.14-15.

1. Organization. I. Hertz, David Bendel, 1919- joint author. II. American Society of Mechanical Engineers. Management Division. III. Title.

NL 0420806 TxU

[Livingston, Robert Teviot]
... Gas and electricity, 1941-1942. [1942]
1 v. diagrs. 28cm. (Information course no. 2)

Various pagings.
Reproduced from type-written copy.
Contents.--1. Electricity and how it is made. --2. Electric distribution.--3. Gas and how it is made.--4. Gas distribution.--5. Operating department procedures.

NL 0420807 NNC

Livingston, Robert Teviot.
How to speak easily ... Riverhead, N. Y., Harry Lee pub. co., c1941.
6 p. l., 211 p.

1. Oratory.

NL 0420808 NNC

Livingston, Robert Teviot.
Light industry or heavy taxes ... 1946.
1 p. l., 21 p.

1. Long Island - Industries.

NL 0420809 NNC

Livingston, Robert Teviot.
Philosophy of management. [1947?]
1 v.

Loose-leaf.

1. Management.

NL 0420810 NNC

Livingston, Robert Teviot.
The seven C's of public relations. [1940]
377-381 p. port.

From Edison electric institute bulletin, vol. 8, no. 8, Aug., 1940.
I. Title: Public relations.

NL 0420811 NNC

Livingston, Robert Teviot.
The value of management. [1945]
10 p.

From Technical valuation, vol. 6, no. 7, July, 1945.

1. Management.

NL 0420812 NNC

Livingston, Robert Teviot.
What does a good neighbor cost? a study in community planning ... 1945.
1 p. l., 26 p.

1. Regional planning. I. Title.

NL 0420813 NNC

Livingston, Ruby Erwin.
Steal away home, a dramatic reading of the sunny South, by **Ruby Erwin** Livingston ... Franklin, O., Eldridge entertainment house, inc., ©1929.
9 p. 19cm. (*On cover:* Eldridge popular monologs)

I. Title.

CA 36-1209 Unrev'd

Library of Congress PN4305.M6L55
Copyright AA 35589 [2] 815.5

NL 0420814 DLC

Livingston, S B
Citizenship and the age of maturity. Inaugural address read before the Society of Medical Jurisprudence, New York, January 9, 1899. [New York ?, 1899 ?]
8 p. 4°.
n.t.p.

NL 0420815 NN

HC106 .4 .A6376 Livingston, S. Morris.

American management association.
... Analyzing postwar market potentials, by S. Morris Livingston ... Donald H. Davenport ... [and] Richard V. Gilbert ... New York, N. Y., American management association, ©1944.

Livingston, S. Morris.
The building construction industry and our postwar national economy; ... Chicago building congress, Oct. 22, 1942.

NL 0420817 OClFRB

330.973 L7622 Livingston, S Morris.
Domestic business outlook, address at the 27th Annual Agricultural Outlook Conference, Washington 25, D.C., October 31, 1949. [Washington, 1949]
5p. 27cm.

Caption title.
Processed.

1. U.S. Economic conditions. 1945-
I. Title.

NL 0420818 OrU DNAL

HF5415 .U5 1943 Livingston, S. Morris.

FOR OTHER EDITIONS SEE MAIN ENTRY

U. S. *Bureau of foreign and domestic commerce.*
... Markets after the war, an approach to their analysis, by S. Morris Livingston. Washington, 1943.

1.941 F2In22 Livingston, S Morris.
The outlook for the national income. [Washington, 1947]
5 p.

NL 0420820 DNAL

Livingston, St. Clair.

Steen-Hansen, Ingeborg.
... Fra tre fronter. Med det Røde kors paa slagmarkerne i Belgien, Frankrig og Serbien. Med 17 illustrationer efter forfatterindens originalfotografier. Kristiania, A. Cammermeyer, 1916.

Livingston, St. Clair.
Under three flags; with the Red cross in Belgium, France and Serbia, by St. Clair Livingston and Ingeborg Steen-Hansen. London, Macmillan and co., limited, 1916.
xiii, 238 p. 18½cm.

1. European war, 1914- —Personal narratives. 2. European war, 1914- —Hospitals, charities, etc. I. Steen-Hansen, Ingeborg, joint author. II. Title.

16-14235

Library of Congress D640.L55

NL 0420821 DLC MB NN PPL OClWHi OU CtY NcD OrP Or WaT

Livingston, Samuel, 1908-
The diagnosis and treatment of convulsive disorders in children. Springfield, Ill., Thomas [1954]
314 p. illus. 27 cm.

1. Convulsions. I. Title: Convulsive disorders in children.

RJ496.C7L5 618.92 54—6569 ‡

NL 0420822 DLC OrU-M IdPI FU-HC ICJ Wa ViU OClW-H PPJ PPC PPT-M NcD ICJ OU PPWM PBL OClW PRaW

LIVINGSTON, Schuyler William.
Our law and the social order; English commencement part by Schuyler William Livington [!], at the Harvard commencement exercises, June 20, [1929].

Typewritten. 29 x 21 cm. ff.5.
Without title-page. Caption title.

NL 0420823 MH

Livingston, Sidnee.
Something to do in bed; text by Sidnee Livingston; illustrations by Pierre Simonet. New York, Hillman-Curl, inc., 1936.
[61] p. illus. 28½cm.
Illustrated lining-papers.

I. Title.

37-1159

Library of Congress NC1429.L55
——— Copy 2.
Copyright A 102380 [3] 741

NL 0420824 DLC

Livingston, Sigmund, 1872-
An address; stupidity or stereotypy. Institute of Human Relations, sponsored by the National Conference of Christian and Jews, Inc., Feb.8,1945, Atlanta, Georgia. [n.p.,1945?]

15 p.

I. Livingston, Sigmund, 1872- . Stupidity or stereotypy

NL 0420825 MH

VOLUME 336

Livingston, Sigmund, 1872–
Facts about fictions concerning the Jew, by Sigmund Livingston, chairman, Anti-defamation league. [Chicago? 1938]
cover-title, 31 p. 21cm.
"Delivered as a message to the supreme convention of B'nai B'rith in session at Washington, D. C., May 9, 1938."—p. 27.

1. Jewish question. 2. Communism. 3. Propaganda, German. I. Title.
Library of Congress DS145.L63 38-25853
[3] 296

NL 0420826 DLC OCH OClWHi NN PHi

Livingston, Sigmund, 1872–1946.
Must men hate? [By] Sigmund Livingston. New York and London, Harper & brothers [1944]
xv p., 1 l., 344 p. 20 cm.
"First edition."
"Seven hundred Jews who have made notable contributions to modern civilization": p. 240–267. "Jews in the American armed forces in the present war who received official awards": p. 268–325.
Bibliography: p. 331–332.

1. Jewish question. 2. Jews in the U. S. 3. Jews—Biog. 4. Jews as soldiers. I. Title.
Library of Congress DS145.L64 44—5528
[a48e³3] 296

MtBuM WaTC OrSaW
MsU KyLxT KyU KyLxCB KyU-A OrP OrCS OrU OrPR Or WaS
NL 0420827 DLC PPT NcD OCl OU OCH ViU PSt PPM PP NIC

296
L787m.2 Livingston, Sigmund, 1872-
Must men hate? [2d ed.] New York, Harper [1944]
xv,344p. 20cm.

Bibliography: p. 331-332.

1. Jewish question. 2. Jews in the U.S. 3. Jews. Biog. 4. Jews as soldiers. I. Title.

NL 0420828 IEN NcGU GU ICJ

DS145
.L64
1944a Livingston, Sigmund, 1872-
Must men hate? [By] Sigmund Livingston, Cleveland, O., Crane press [1944]
xv p., 1 l., 287 p. 21cm.
"Revised edition."
"Seven hundred Jews who have made notable contributions to modern civilization": p.240-267.
Bibliography: p. 274-275.
1. Jewish question. 2. Jews in the U. S. 3. Jews--Biog. I. Title.

NL 0420829 MB KyLxT MeB KyU MH OCH OBlC

296
L787m Livingston, Sigmund, 1872-
Must men hate? [Forum Books ed.] Cleveland, World Pub. Co. [1945]
xv,286p. 21cm.

"Seven hundred Jews who have made notable contributions to modern civilization": p.240-267.
Bibliography: p.273-74.

1. Jewish question. 2. Jews in the U. S. 3. Jews - Biog. 4. Jews as soldiers. I. Title.

NL 0420830 WaSp MtU

Livingston, Sigmund, 1872-
A problem of American Jewry. Chicago, 1935.

28 p. 21 cm.

NL 0420831 MH PPDrop

Livingston, Sigmund, 1872–
Protocols of the wise men of Zion; a spurious and fraudulent document manufactured to deceive and to engender religious and racial hatred. By Sigmund Livingston. [Chicago, Educational commission, B'nai B'rith, 1934]
cover-title, 16 p. 20½cm.

1. "Protocols of the wise men of Zion." 2. Jewish question.
Library of Congress DS145.P7L5 34-22815
——— Copy 2. [3] 296

NL 0420832 DLC NcD OCl OCH

Livingston, Sigmund, 1872-

Anti-defamation league.
Questions and answers concerning the Jew. Prepared and published by Anti-defamation league of B'nai B'rith. Chicago, Ill. [1942]

Livingston, Stuart, 1865-1923.

The history of Professor Paul. Hamilton, Hunter & Grant [1889]

102 p. 19 cm.

NL 0420834 CaBVaU

Livingston, Stuart, 1865–1923.
In various moods. Poems. By Stuart Livingston. Toronto, W. Briggs; [etc., etc.] 1894.
ix, [11]–100 p. 19½cm.

I. Title.
Library of Congress PR4890.L63 I 5 39-4612

NL 0420835 DLC NBuG CaBVaU TxU RPB CaOTU MH RPB

Livingston, Thomas.
An address delivered at Jefferson college, before the Association of alumni ... Sept., 26,1833 ... Pittsburgh, pr. by Wilson & Marks,1834.
25 p.

NL 0420836 ViU

Livingston, Thomas, 1652?-1711
see Livingstone, Thomas, 1652?-1711.

Livingston, Vanbrugh.
An inquiry into the merits of the Reformed doctrine of "imputation," as contrasted with those of "Catholic imputation;" or, The cardinal point of controversy between the Church of Rome and the Protestant high church: together with miscellaneous essays on the Catholic faith, by Vanbrugh Livingston ... With an introduction by the Rt. Rev. John Hughes ... New York, Casserly & sons, 1843.
xx, 242 p. 19cm.
On cover: Catholic imputation.
1. Grace (Theology) 2. Catholic church—Doctrinal and controversial works—Catholic authors. I. Hughes, John, abp., 1797–1864. II. Title: Catholic imputation.
Library of Congress BT761.L7 35-34410
——— Copy 2. 234.1

NL 0420838 DLC CtY MH NjP PV

Livingston, Vanbrugh.

New York. Citizens.
Proceedings of the public demonstration of sympathy with Pope Pius IX., and with Italy, in the city of New York, on Monday, November 29, A. D. 1847. Prepared under the supervision of the Committee of arrangements. New York, Printed by W. Van Norden, 1847.

Livingston, Vanbrugh.
Remarks on the "Oxford theology" in connection with its bearing upon the law of nature.
New York. Taylor & Co. 1841. 227, (1) pp. 16°.
The title-page is mutilated.

F4995 — Tractarian Movement, 1833–1841. — Theology. Doctrinal.

NL 0420840 MB MH DLC NcD MWA NN CtY MiU PPL PPPrHi

Livingston, W W
A historical system of chronology, for beginners in the study of history. Compiled from the best autorities. Designed for the use of schools and families. By W. W. Livingston, esq. St. Clairsville, [Ohio] Howard & Cowen, 1853.
276 p. 18 cm.

1. Chronology Historical. 2. Chronology, Histori , Tables. I. Title.

NL 0420841 DAU

LIVINGSTON, Walter, 1740–1797.
An abridged statement of Walter Livingston's claim.
N. t. p., n. p. [1823?] 3 pp. 8°.

NL 0420842 MB

Livingston, Walter, 1895–
The mystery of Burnleigh manor, by Walter Livingston. New York, The Mystery league, inc., 1930.
286 p. 19½cm.
"First edition."

I. Title.
Library of Congress PZ3.L7627My 30-28178

NL 0420843 DLC OrU WaE OClU CSt-H

Livingston, Walter, 1895–
The mystery of Villa Sineste, by Walter Livingston. New York, The Mystery league, inc., 1931.
286 p. 19½cm.
"First edition."
Sample pages of The Hunterstone outrage, by Seldon Truss: p. [271]–286.

I. Title.
Library of Congress PZ3.L7627Myv 31-22796

NL 0420844 DLC PP

F1038
.L78 [Livingston, Walter Ross]
The first responsible party government in British North America.

(In The Canadian historical review,June, 1926. Toronto, 1926. 25 1/2 cm. v. 7, p. 115-136)

NL 0420845 DLC

VOLUME 336

Livingston, Walter Ross.
... Responsible government in Nova Scotia; a study of the constitutional beginnings of the British commonwealth, by W. Ross Livingston ... Iowa City, The University, 1930.
280 p. illus. (map) 23½cm. (University of Iowa. Studies in the social sciences. vol. IX, no. 1)
On cover: University of Iowa studies. First series, no. 176.
Bibliography: p. 265–272.

1. Nova Scotia—Pol. & govt.—1763–1867. I. Title.

Library of Congress H31.I 8 vol. 9, no. 1 30-27573
[3] (306.2) 342.71609

MH NcD ViU-L NIC
MoU INS PV PP PSC PBm ODW OCU MiU OClW ViU PU CSmH
NL 0420846 DLC NBuU WaWW OrSaW CaBViP Or OrU CaBVaU

Livingston, Walter Ross.
... Responsible government in Prince Edward island, a triumph of self-government under the crown, by W. Ross Livingston ... Iowa City, The University, 1931.
136 p. illus. (map) 23½cm. (University of Iowa. Studies in the social sciences. vol. IX, no. 4)
On cover: University of Iowa studies. New series no. 215.
Bibliography: p. 130–131.

1. Prince Edward island—Pol. & govt. I. Title. 31-27667

Library of Congress H31.I 8 vol. 9, no. 4
—— —— Copy 2. JL382.L5
[3] (306.2) 342.71700

PBm OCU ODW OO MiU ViU PU MH NcD FMU
NL 0420847 DLC CaBVaU OrU OrSaW WaWW PV PP PHC PSC

Livingston, William.
An address delivered before the Female Benezet Philanthropic Society, of Albany, January 1, 1822, it being the anniversary of the abolition of the African slave trade. Albany, Printed by Packard & Van Benthuysen, 1822.
12 p. 23 cm.
Cover title: Facts and observations on the African slave Trade.
1. Slave-trade. Addresses, essays, lectures. 2. Amer. impr. New York (State) Albany. Packard & Van.

NL 0420848 N

W 4 LIVINGSTON, William.
L68 Dissertatio medica inauguralis de scrophula ... Lugduni
1788 Batavorum, Fratres Murray, 1788.
L.1 21 p. 24 cm.
Diss. - Leyden.

NL 0420849 DNLM

Livingston, William.
Sicut cedrus libani; to his eminence John Cardinal Farley, archbishop of New York, New York, O'Connor, 1912.

NL 0420850 OClJC

Livingston, William.

Retail shoe salesmen's institute, *Boston.*
Stockkeeping, by the staff editors, Retail shoe salesmen's institute, in collaboration with A. O. Day ... J. F. Knowles ... William Livingston [and others] ... Boston, Retail shoe salesmen's institute [c1920]

Livingston, William, 1723–1790.
Works by this author printed in America before 1801 are available in this library in the Readex Microprint edition of Early American Imprints published by the American Antiquarian Society.
This collection is arranged according to the numbers in Charles Evans' American Bibliography.

NL 0420852 DLC

[**Livingston, William**] 1723–1790.
An address to His Excellency Sir Charles Hardy, knt., captain general and governor in chief of the province of New-York, and territories thereon depending in America, and vice-admiral of the same. By the author of a weekly paper, entitled, The Watch-tower. New York, 1755.
13 p. 29cm. [*With* The Independent reflector]

1. Columbia university—Hist. I. Hardy, Sir Charles, 1716?–1780.
11-7452
Library of Congress AP2.A2 I 4

NL 0420853 DLC CtY

Livingston, William, 1723–1790.

PS739
.A8
Rare Bk
Coll

[**Dwight, Timothy**] 1752–1817.
America; or, A poem on the settlement of the British Colonies. Addressed to the friends of freedom, and their country, by a gentleman educated at Yale-College. New Haven. Printed by T. and S. Green [1780?]

Livingston, William 1723–1790.
An answer to A bill in the chancery of New-Jersey, at the suit of John earl of Stair, and others, commonly called proprietors of the eastern division of New-Jersey, against Benjamin Bond
see under Board of general proprietors of the eastern division of New Jersey.

[Livingston, William] 1723–1790.
The art of pleading
see under title

Livingston, William, 1723–1790.

Clarke, Thomas.
The bill of complaint in the chancery of New-Jersey, brought by Thomas Clarke, and others, against James Alexander, esq.; and others, commonly called the Proprietors of East New-Jersey. Wherein the title of the people of Eliza-beth-Town, to the controverted lands, is fully exhibited, and the objections of the pretended proprietors, stated, and refuted. Now published from the original filed in the Court of chancery, in 1754, to satisfy many who are curious to know the foundation of a private debate of the greatest importance in America. New-York, Printed by William Weyman, 1760.

Livingston, William, 1723–1790.
Brief aan den recht eerwaardigen vader in God John. lord bisschop van Landaff. Veroirzaakt door eenige gezegden in Zyne Lordschap's leerreeden, op den 20sten februarii 1767. uitgesprooken, waar in de Americaansche colonien met eene aanmerkelyke en onverdiende schande beswaard woorden. Door William Livingston. Uit het Engelsch vertaald. Utrecht, A. van Paddenburg, 1774.
2 p. l., 34 p. 21cm.

6-44461

NL 0420858 DLC

Livingston, William, 1723–1790.
A brief consideration of New York with respect to its natural advantages, its superiority in several instances over some of the neighboring colonies, by William Livingston. Reprinted from the Independent reflector, 1753; edited by Earl Gregg Swem ... Metuchen, N. J., Printed for C. F. Heartman, 1925.
2 p. l., v, 24 p. 23cm. (*On verso of half-title:* Heartman's historical series, no. 39)
Imprint reads: Forty-one copies printed for Charles F. Heartman. Metuchen, New Jersey, 1925.
"No. ... of forty-one copies printed." This copy not numbered.
1. New York (State)—Descr. & trav. I. Swem, Earl Gregg, 1870– ed. II. Title.
25-18694
Library of Congress F122.L776

NL 0420859 DLC NcD ViW MWA MH NjP MB NN

Livingston, William, 1723-1790.
The choice of a rural life; a poem.
[Written by W. L., esq., Gov. of N. J.]
(In Moore, John Hamilton, d. 1807, comp. The young gentleman and lady's monitor, and English teacher's assistant. 2d. Hartford ed. Hartford, 1804. 17 cm. p. 320-337)

NL 0420860 RPB

Livingston, William, 1723-1790.
Circular letter to the Colonels of militia of the State of New Jersey, when Gen Howe's army threatened the State. Burlington, Nov, 24,1776.

NL 0420861 PPL

Livingston, William, 1723-1790.
Collection of tracts from the late newspapers on Protestant bishops in American Colonies
see under title

Livingston, William, 1723-1790
English grammar calculated in conjunction with the syntactical atlas. Middlebury, Francis Burnap. 1817.
84 p.

NL 0420863 MWA VtHi

Livingston, William, 1723-1790.
Examen du gouvernment d'Angleterre, compare aux constitutions des États-Unis ...
see under [Stevens, John] 1749-1838.

Livingston, William, 1723-90.
A funeral elogium on the Reverend Mr. Aaron Burr, late president of the College of New-Jersey. New-York: H. Gaine, 1757. 1 p.l., 22 p. sq. 8°, in twos.

1. Burr, Rev. Aaron, 1716-57.
N. Y. P. L. June 30, 1914.

NL 0420865 NN MWA MH NjP CtHi PHi NjN MHi CU CSmH

Livingston, William, 1723–1790.
A funeral elogium on the Reverend Mr. Aaron Burr, late president of the College of New-Jersey.
New-York, Printed: Boston; Re-printed by Green and Russell, . . . for J. Winter . . . MDCCLVIII. 23 pp. 19 cm., in 2s.
This is said to be the earliest American book having a Shakespearean quotation on the title-page.

L5033 — Burr, Aaron, D.D., 1714–1757. — Green & Russell, printers.

NjP CSmH MWA
NL 0420866 MB DFo MH NjP NjR MiU-C MH DLC CtY MHi

Livingston, William, 1723-1790, ed.
The Independent reflector
see under title

VOLUME 336

Livingston, William, 1723–1790.
A letter to the Right Reverend father in God, John, lord bishop of Landaff; occasioned by some passages in his lordship's sermon, on the 20th of February, 1767, in which the American colonies are loaded with great and undeserved reproach. By William Livingston. Boston, Re-printed and sold by Kneeland and Adams, next to the treasurer's office, in Milk-street, 1768.
26 p. 19cm.
1. Ewer, John, bp. of Bangor, d. 1774. A sermon preached ... February 20, 1767. 2. U. S.—Religion.
Library of Congress BR520.E9L7 1768 a 23-1327

NL 0420868 DLC NHi MH MWA CtY NN MiU-C MB MBAt MiAlbC

FILM
Livingston,William,1723-1790.
A letter to the Right Reverend Father in God, John,lord bishop of Landaff; occasioned by some passages in his lordship's sermon,on the 20th of February,1767, in which the American colonies are loaded with great and undeserved reproach ... Boston: Re-printed and sold by Kneeland and Adams. MDCCLXVIII.
University microfilms. American culture series no.171 (roll 14)
Original in the William L.Clements library.

NL 0420869 MiU KEmT

Livingston, William, 1723–1790.
A letter to the Right Reverend father in God, John, lord bishop of Landaff; occasioned by some passages in his lordship's sermon, on the 20th of February, 1767; in which the American colonies are loaded with great and undeserved reproach. By William Livingston. New-York: Printed. London: Reprinted for J. Buckland; E. and C. Dilly; and G. Keith, 1768. 31 p. 8°.
Sabin 41642.
Title-page and p. [3] slightly cropped.
1. Ewer, John, bp. of Bangor, d. 1774: A sermon preached... February 20, 1768. 2. New England—Hist., Colonial. 3. Indians, N. A.—New England—Missions.
N. Y. P. L. April 9, 1929

NL 0420870 NN RPJCB MH MB

Livingston, William, 1723–1790.
A letter to the Right Reverend father in God, John, lord bishop of Landaff; occasioned by some passages in his lordship's sermon, on the 20th of February, 1767, in which the American colonies are loaded with great and undeserved reproach. By William Livingston. New-York: Printed for the author: and to be sold by Garrat Noel, near the Coffee-house. MDCCLXVIII.
2 p. l., 25 p. 19cm.
1. Ewer, John, bp. of Bangor, d. 1774. A sermon preached ... February 20, 1767. 2. U. S.—Religion.
Library of Congress BR520.E9L7 1768 19-10116
——— Copy 2. [Hazard pamphlets, v. 14, no. 3] AC901.H3 vol. 14, no 3

N MWiW-C NcD PPAmP MH CtY NN RPJCB MiU-C PPL CtHi
NL 0420871 DLC MWA OClWHi PPPrHi NHL IaU NjP MiEM

Livingston, William, 1723-1790.
A memoir of the life of William Livingston
see under Sedgwick, Theodore, 1811-1859.

Livingston, William, 1723-1790, ed.

Makemie, Francis, 1658–1708.
A narrative of a new and unusual American imprisonment, of two Presbyterian ministers, and prosecution of Mr. Francis Makemie, one of them, for preaching one sermon in the city of New-York. By a learner of law, and lover of liberty. New-York. Re-printed and sold by H. Gaine, 1755.

[Livingston, William] 1723-1790.
Observations on government ...
see under [Stevens, John] 1749-1838.

Livingston, William, 1723-1790.
The petition of the trustees of the College of New-York, to his honour the lieutenant governor, praying to be incorporated
see under Columbia university.

[LIVINGSTON, William, 1723-1790.]
Philosophic solitude, or The choice of a rural life, a poem. By a gentleman educated at Yale college. New York, printed by J.Parker 1747.
sm.4°. pp. 44.
First edition.
A manuscript note on title-page incorrectly attributes it to Abraham Livingston. The true name has been supplied on p.11 and blanks filled throughout the book. by another hand.

NL 0420876 MH RPJCB CSmH MHi RPB

FILM
Livingston,William,1723-1790.
Philosophic solitude: or,The choice of a rural life. A poem. By a gentleman educated at Yale College. New York: Printed by J. Parker, 1747.
University microfilms. American culture series no.139 (roll 12)
Original in the Massachusetts historical society library.

NL 0420877 MiU CU KEmT

[Livingston, William,] 1723–1790.
Philosophic solitude: or, The choice of a rural life: a poem. By a gentleman educated at Yale College... New-York: Printed, 1747. Boston: Reprinted and sold by B. Mecom, 1762. xii p., 1 l., 15–46 p. 8°.
Evans 9160.
1. Poetry, American. 2. Title.
N. Y. P. L. July 16, 1929

NL 0420878 NN MH NjP MeB

Y
285
.L 7615 [LIVINGSTON, WILLIAM] 1723-1790.
Philosophic solitude; or, The choice of a rural life: a poem. By a gentleman educated at Yale college... The 3d edition. New York,Holt [1769]
40p.
Photostat reproduction (positive) from the Library of Congress copy.

NL 0420879 ICN RPB

[Livingston, William] 1723-1790.
Philosophic solitude; or, The choice of a rural life: a poem. By a young gentleman educated at Yale college. Trenton,Re-printed by I.Collins,1782.
28p. 20cm.

NL 0420880 CtY PBL ViU NjR NjP NjHi

[Livingston, William] 1723-1790
... Philosophic solitude. (Written by W. L., esq. Gov. of N.J.)
At head of title: The choice of a rural life.
(In Moore, John Hamilton, d. 1807, comp. The young gentleman and lady's monitor, and English teacher's assistant. London, 1794 17 cm. p. 316-333)
Imperfect: p. 395-96, [30] p. wanting.

NL 0420881 RPB

Livingston, William, 1723-1790.
Poems: Philosophic solitude; or, The choice of a rural life; 13ed: [also] The progress of science, spoken at Harvard University, 1788, by Samuel Dexter never before published. New York, 1790.
19 p. D.

NL 0420882 RPB NHi

[Livingston, William] 1723-1790.
The querist ...
see under title

[Livingston, William,] 1723–1790.
A review of the military operations in North America; from the commencement of the French hostilities on the frontiers of Virginia, in 1753, to the surrender of Oswego, on the 14th of August, 1756. Interspersed with various observations, characters, and anecdotes; necessary to give light into the conduct of American transactions in general; and more especially into the political management of affairs in New-York. In a letter to a nobleman. To which are added, Col. Washington's journal of his expedition to the Ohio, in 1754, and several letters ... found in the cabinet of Major General Braddock, after his defeat near Fort Du Quesne ... Dublin, P. Wilson, and J. Exshaw, 1757.
276 p. 16½cm.
First edition of the "Review" was printed in London, R. and J. Dodsley, 1757. It has been attributed to various persons. Samuel Jones, in the New-York historical society, Collections, v. 3, 1821, p. 361, says: "This pamphlet was written in New-York, and it is believed ... that William Smith [1728–1793] afterwards chief justice of Canada, was the author; that he copied it himself, never permitting either of his clerks to see a word of it; that the manuscript was carefully nailed up ... and sent to London to be printed. The pamphlets when received from London were not publicly distributed ..." (Cited in Documentary history of the state of New York, 1849–51, v. 4, p. 1054) In Smith's posthumous "History of the late province of New York", 1829, v. 2, p. 255–256, it is stated that William Alexander (who later called himself Lord Stirling) acknowledged having given the manuscript to the printer, but denied the authorship, but Smith neither hints at himself being the author, nor offers any suggestions as to who wrote the pamphlet. It is now generally believed that Alexander had the manuscript from his brother-in-law, Livingston, to whom it is attributed by his biographer Sedgwick (*cf.* Amer. quart. rev., 1833, v. 14, p. 12–13) by Halkett and Laing, Cushing, Sabin and the best authorities.
1. U. S.—Hist.—French and Indian war, 1755–1763. 2. Braddock's campaign, 1755. 3. New York (State)—Hist.—Colonial period. I. Smith, William, 1728–1793. II. Alexander, William, called Lord Stirling, 1726–1783. III. Title.
Library of Congress E199.L78 2-15681

MWiW-C ViU OClU
NL 0420886 DLC OClWHi OFH MWA CaOTU CtY MiU-C RPJCB

M-film
973
Am3
244-7 Livingston, William, 1723-1790.
A review of the military operations in North America, from the commencement of the French hostilities on the frontiers of Virginia, in 1753, to the surrender of Oswego, on the 14th of August, 1756. Interspersed with various observations, characters, and anecdotes; necessary to give light into the conduct of American transactions in general; and more especially into the political management of affairs in New-York. In a letter to a nobleman. To which are added Col. Washington's journal of his expedition to the

Continued in next column

VOLUME 336

Continued from preceding column

Ohio, in 1754, and several letters...found in the cabinet of Major General Braddock, after his defeat near Fort Du Quesne... Dublin, P. Wilson, and J. Exshaw, 1757.
276 p.

Microfilm (positive) Ann Arbor, Mich., University Microfilms, 1963. 7th title of 12. 35 mm. (American culture series, reel 244.7)

1. U. S. - Hist. - French and Indian War, 1755-1763. 2. Braddock's Campaign, 1755. 3. New York (State) - Hist. - Colonial period. I. Title.

NL 0420889 KEmT PSt WaU ICRL

[Livingston, William] 1723–1790.
A review of the military operations in North-America; from the commencement of the French hostilities on the frontiers of Virginia in 1753, to the surrender of Oswego, on the 14th of August, 1756. Interspersed with various observations, characters, and anecdotes; necessary to give light into the conduct of American transactions in general; and more especially into the political management of affairs in New York. In a letter to a nobleman. London, R. and J. Dodsley, 1757.
2 p. l., 144 p. 28cm.

A defense of General Shirley's conduct of operations during the war. "In this work Mr. Livingston is said, I know not on what authority, to have been assisted by William Smith and John Morine [!] Scott. For the facts which it contains, he was probably indebted to his brother-in-law, Mr. Alexander, afterwards Lord Stirling, who was about this time secretary to General Shirley."—Sedgwick, T. A memoir of the life of William Livingston, New York, 1833, p. 114.

1. U. S.—Hist.—French and Indian war, 1755-1763. 2. Braddock's campaign, 1755. 3. New York (State)—Hist.—Colonial period. 4. Shirley, William, 1694-1771. I. Smith, William, 1728-1793. II. Scott, John Morin, 1730-1784. III. Alexander, William, 1726-1783. IV. Title.
42-51893

Library of Congress E199.L7815

NL 0420891 DLC OCl MB NNC MH CaOTU MnU IU NcD CtY NN MiU-C ViU FTaSU PPL CaNSWA

[Livingston, William] 1723–1790.
A review of the military operations in North-America, from the commencement of the French hostilities on the frontiers of Virginia in 1753, to the surrender of Oswego, on the 14th of August, 1756. Interspersed with various observations, characters, and anecdotes; necessary to give light into the conduct of American transactions in general; and more especially into the political management of affairs in New York. In a letter to a nobleman. London: Printed, for R. and J. Dodsley in Pall-Mall. 1757. New-England, Re-printed, in the year. 1758.
98 p. 20½ x 16cm.

A defense of General Shirley's conduct of operations during the war. "In this work Mr. Livingston is said, I know not on what authority, to have been assisted by William Smith and John Morine [!] Scott. For the facts which it contains, he was probably indebted to his brother-in-law, Mr. Alexander, afterwards Lord Stirling, who was about this time secretary to General Shirley."—T. Sedgwick, A memoir of the life of William Livingston, New York, 1833, p. 114.

1. U. S. — Hist. — French and Indian war, 1755-1763. 2. Braddock's campaign, 1755. 3. New York (State)—Hist.—Colonial period. 4. Shirley, William, 1694-1771. I. Smith, William, 1728-1793. II. Scott, John Morin, 1730-1784. III. Alexander, William, 1726-1783. IV. Title.

Library of Congress E199.L78 3-8985

NL 0420892 DLC MWA NBuHi NjP CtY CtHi MWiW-C RPJCB NN

[Livingston, William] 1723–1790.
A review of the military operations in North-America; from the commencement of the French hostilities on the frontiers of Virginia, in 1753, to the surrender of Oswego, on the 14th of August, 1756. Interspersed with various observations, characters, and anecdotes; necessary to give light into the conduct of American transactions in general; and more especially into the political management of affairs in New-York. In a letter to a nobleman. New-York: Printed by Alexander and James Robertson, 1770.
170 p. 21½cm.

Continued in next column

Continued from preceding column

First edition, London, R. and J. Dodsley, 1757.
A defense of General Shirley's conduct of operations during the war. "In this work Mr. Livingston is said, I know not on what authority, to have been assisted by William Smith and John Morine [!] Scott. For the facts which it contains, he was probably indebted to his brother-in-law, Mr. Alexander, afterwards Lord Stirling, who was about this time secretary to General Shirley."—T. Sedgwick, A memoir of the life of William Livingston, New York, 1833, p. 114.

1. U. S.—Hist.—French and Indian war, 1755-1763. 2. Braddock's campaign, 1755. 3. New York (State)—Hist.—Colonial period. 4. Shirley, William, 1694-1771. I. Smith, William, 1728-1793. II. Scott, John Morin, 1730-1784. III. Alexander, William, called Lord Stirling, 1726-1783. IV. Title.
18-10875

Library of Congress E199.L786
——— Copy 2. [Hazard pamphlets, v. 24, no. 7] AC901.H3 vol. 24

NL 0420894 DLC PPL MWA NIC NjR MWiW-C NN RPJCB

[Livingston, William] 1723–1790.
A review of the military operations in North-America, from the commencement of the French hostilities on the frontiers of Virginia in 1753, to the surrender of Oswego, on the 14th of August, 1756; in a letter to a nobleman. Interspersed with various observations, characters, and anecdotes; necessary to give light into the conduct of American transactions in general, and more especially into the political management of affairs in New-York.
(In Massachusetts historical society. Collections, for the year 1800. Boston, 1801. 22½ cm. p. 67-163)

"This valuable letter is said to have been written by the late Gov. [William] Livingston, and his friends, Messrs. W[illiam] Smith and [John Morin] Scott, lawyers, New-York."—Note, p. 67.
Apropos of this note, Sedgwick, in his life of Livingston, p. 114-117, speaking of the "Review," says: "For the facts which it contains, he [Livingston] was probably in a considerable degree indebted to his brother-in-law, Mr. Alexander, afterwards Lord Stirling ... and ... it may be supposed that they took an interest, perhaps an active one, in its composition and progress, but the work as it now stands bears strong marks of being the production of a single hand ... The manuscript was first given to the press in England through the hands of Mr. Alexander, and the work was immediately afterwards reprinted in the colonies."

First edition published London, R. and J. Dodsley, 1757.

1. U. S.—Hist.—French and Indian war, 1755-1763. 2. Braddock's campaign, 1755. 3. New York (State)—Hist.—Colonial period. 4. Shirley, William, 1694-1771. I. Alexander, William, called Lord Stirling, 1726-1783, attributed author. II. Smith, William, 1728-1803, attributed author. III. Scott, John Morin, 1730-1784, attributed author.

F61.M41 2—15682

NL 0420897 DLC OCl MWA

[Livingston, William] 1723–1790.
A soliloquy ... [Philadelphia?] Printed [by J. Dunlap?] in the year 1770.
1 p. l., 15 p. 18½ x 14½cm.
[Hazard pamphlets, v. 39, no. 7]
An anonymous satire on Lieutenant-Governor Colden of New York, occasioned by Governor Dunmore's suit against him for a moiety of the salary and fees received by Colden after Dunmore's appointment.
Incorrectly attributed to William Goddard.

1. Colden, Cadwallader, 1688-1776.

7-21585

Library of Congress AC901.H3 vol. 39

NL 0420898 DLC N NN PPL ViU

[Livingston, William] 1723–1790.
A soliloquy ... 2d ed. [Philadelphia?] Printed [by J. Dunlap?] in the year 1770.
1 p. l., 15 p. 22cm.
An anonymous satire on Lieutenant-Governor Colden of New York, occasioned by Governor Dunmore's suit against him for a moiety of the salary and fees received by Colden after Dunmore's appointment.
Incorrectly attributed to William Goddard.

1. Colden, Cadwallader, 1688-1776.

Library of Congress F122.L78 7-21584

NL 0420899 DLC

Livingston, William, 1723-1790.
Speech to the Honourable the Council, and the General Assembly of New Jersey.
Gentlemen,
Having already laid before the Assembly, ------.
Wil. Livingston.
Haddonfield, Feb. 25, 1777.
pp. (4).

NL 0420900 PPL

Livingston, William, 1723–1790.
Unpublished correspondence of William Livingston and John Jay; introduction and notes, by Frank Monaghan ... Newark, N. J., New Jersey historical society, 1934.
24 p. 23½cm.

I. Jay, John, 1745-1829. II. Monaghan, Frank, 1904- ed.
34-38746

Library of Congress E302.6.L75L7
——— Copy 2. [2] 923.273

NL 0420901 DLC CtY

Livingston, William, 1723-1790.
A vindication of the Bishop of Landoff's Sermon from the Gross Misrepresentations ...
see under [Inglis, Charles, bp. of Nova Scotia] 1734-1816.

Livingston, William, 1723-1790
see also
New Jersey. Governor, 1776-1790 (William Livingston)

LIVINGSTON, William, 1808-1870.
Duain agus orain, le Uilleam Mac Dhunleibhe. Glasgow, W. Gilchrist, 1865.

NL 0420904 MH

Livingston, William, 1808–1870.
Duain agus orain le Uilleam Mac Dhunleibhe, am Bard Ileach ... air an cur a mach air iarrtus agus fo iuil a' chomuinn ilich. Glasgow, A. Sinclair, 1882.
xvii, 239 p. 18½cm.
On cover: Livingston's Gaelic poems.
Preface signed: R. Blair.

I. Blair, Robert, 1837 (ca.)-1907, ed. II. Title. III. Title: Gaelic poems.
46-40653

Library of Congress PB1648.L5 1882

NL 0420905 DLC CU NIC MH NN

Livingston, William, 1808–1870.
Duain Ghaelic, le Uilleam Mac Dhun-Leibhe...with a brief sketch proving the authenticity of Ossian's poems. Edinburgh: Maclachlan & Stewart, 1858. 191 p. 16°.

118979A. 1. Poetry (Scottish): Gaelic. 2. Ossian.
N. Y. P. L. April 16, 1924.

NL 0420906 NN MH

Livingston, William, 1857–
Poems for loyal hearts, by Rev. William Livingston ... New York, P. J. Kenedy & sons, 1914.
7 p. l., 173 p. 18 cm.
Reprinted in part from various periodicals.

PS3523.I 95P6 1914 14—16932

NL 0420907 DLC

VOLUME 336

Livingston, William, 1857-
The queen city.
In, Historical society of Newburgh Bay and the Highlands ... Centennial number May 8, 1900. Newburgh, N. Y., 1890. 23 cm. 78 p. p. 28.

NL 0420908 RPB

Livingston, William, 1857-
The shepherds' watch! By Rev. William Livingston .. Troy, N. Y., W. J. Woods, 1892.
5 l. front. 19½cm.
Cover illustrated in colors.
In verse.

1. Christmas—Poetry. I. Title.

Library of Congress PS3523.I 9584 1892 33-32480
Copyright 1892: 36279 811.5

NL 0420909 DLC

Livingston, William, 1911-
Friends. Song for voice and piano. Words and music by Wm. Livingston. New York, G. Schirmer inc. [c1942]
First line: I once knew a man of wealth and fame.

1. Songs, U. S. I. Song index (2).

NL 0420910 NN

Livingston, William Farrand.
Israel Putnam, pioneer, ranger, and major-general, 1718-1790, by William Farrand Livingston. New York & London, G. P. Putnam's sons, 1901.
3 p. l., v-xviii p., 1 l., 442 p. front., plates, ports., facsims. 20cm. (*Half-title:* American men of energy)
Bibliography: p. xi-xviii.

1. Putnam, Israel, 1718-1790.

Library of Congress E207.P9L78 1-25819
Copyright A 14241 [a37j1] 923.573

NL 0420911 DLC OrU WaT WaS WaE OrP DI N NBuU NIC OO PPM PPL PPD PP OCl DN PU MB NN MeB ICU

Livingston, William Farrand.
Israel Putnam, pioneer, ranger, and major-general, 1718-1790. New York: G. P. Putnam's Sons, 1905. xviii(i), 442 p., 4 fac., 25 pl., 4 port. 12°. (American men of energy.)
Bibliography, p. xi-xviii.

NL 0420912 NN

Livingston, William Farrand.
Prominent American families. V.—The Livingstons. A family famous in the annals of Scotland and of America... [New York, 1896.] p. 585-594. illus., port. 8° in 4° binder.
Caption title.
Excerpt: Munsey's mag., April, 1896.

1. Livingston family.
N. Y. P. L. July 26, 1915.

NL 0420913 NN

Livingston, William H., ed.
Insurance and commercial magazine.
see under title

Livingston, William H.
Statistics in relation to the practice and standing of board & non-board fire insurance companies of the United States. By Wm. H. Livingston ... New York [W. H. Livingston] 1875.
10 p. 21 x 9½cm.

1. Insurance, Fire—U. S.—Stat.

Library of Congress HG9765.L7 CA 9-3283 Unrev'd

NL 0420915 DLC

Livingston, William Kenneth, 1892-
The clinical aspects of visceral neurology, with special reference to the surgery of the sympathetic nervous system, by W. K. Livingston ... Springfield, Ill., Baltimore, Md., C. C. Thomas [°1935]
xi, 254 p., 1 l. illus., col. plates, diagrs. 25½cm.
Bibliography: p. 227-239.

1. Nervous system—Surgery. 2. Nervous system, Sympathetic. 3. Viscera—Diseases. I. Title: Visceral neurology, The clinical aspects of.

Library of Congress RD595.L5 35-3522
Copyright A 80564 [3] 617.48

NL 0420916 DLC ICJ OrU OrU-M NcD PPJ OU PPC PPHa ViU

Livingston, William Kenneth, 1892-
Pain mechanisms; a physiologic interpretation of causalgia and its related states, by W. K. Livingston ... New York, The Macmillan company, 1943.
xiii, 253 p. illus., plates, diagrs. 22 cm.
Bibliography: p. 241-248.

1. Pain. 2. Causalgia. I. Title.

Library of Congress RC73.L6 43-8940
[a51h1] 612.884

NL 0420917 DLC IParkA OU OO PPHa PPC PPJ DNLM OrU WaSpG Wa NIC KMK PPSKF CaBVaU OrU-C Or

---

Livingston, William Kenneth, 1892-
Pain mechanisms; a physiologic interpretation of causalgia and its related states, by W. K. Livingston ... New York, The Macmillan company, 1944.
xiii, 253 p. illus., plates, diagrs. 22cm.
Bibliography: p. 241-248.
"June, 1944."

NL 0420918 Vi

RC73 .L6 1947
Livingston, William Kenneth, 1892-
Pain mechanisms; a physiologic interpretation of causalgia and its related states. New York, Macmillan Co. 1947.
xiii, 253 p. illus., plates, diagrs. 22cm.
Bibliography: p. 241-248.

1. Pain. 2. Causalgia. I. Title.

NL 0420919 MB

WA 670 qL787s 1919
LIVINGSTON, William Kenneth, 1892-
Sanitary survey of Dover, Massachusetts. [Boston, Harvard Medical School, 1919]
59 l. illus.
Typewritten copy.

NL 0420920 DNLM

Livingston, William Samuel.
The social contract in American political theory ... 1943.
Thesis. Ohio state university.

NL 0420921 OU

Livingston, William Towle, 1893-
How to read the financial page of a newspaper, by William T. Livingston ... [New York] Alexander Hamilton institute incorporated, °1940.
1 p. l., 36 numb. l. port. 27½ x 21½cm. ([Alexander Hamilton institute, New York] Report no. 357)
Reproduced from type-written copy.

1. Finance. 2. Money. 3. Stock-exchange—U. S. 4. Banks and banking—U. S. I. Title.

Library of Congress HG154.L6 1940 42-49656
[2] 332.6

NL 0420922 DLC

Livingston, William Towle, 1893-
How to read the financial page of a newspaper, by William T. Livingston ... [New York] Alexander Hamilton institute incorporated, 1942.
1 p. l., 36 numb. l. port. 27½ x 21½cm. ([Alexander Hamilton institute, New York] Report no. 357)
Reproduced from type-written copy.
"Latest revision, 1942."

1. Finance. 2. Money. 3. Stock-exchange—U. S. 4. Banks and banking—U. S. I. Title.

Library of Congress HG154.L6 1942 42-50754
[3] 332.6

NL 0420923 DLC

Livingston, Rev. William W.
Historical discourse delivered in the Congregational church, Jaffrey, N.H., Aug. 2, 1896. Peterboro, 1896.

NL 0420924 Nh

Livingston, Rev. William W.
Veteran's mission; a sermon before the G.B. McClellan Post, 1891, Jaffrey, N.H. Peterboro, 1891.

NL 0420925 Nh

Livingston, Y Esther.
Transgression, a novel by Y. Esther Livingston. New York, N. Y., The Hobson book press, 1945.
3 p. l., 199 p. 21½cm.
Reproduced from type-written copy.

I. Title.

Library of Congress PZ3.L7628Tr 45-7904

NL 0420926 DLC NN

Livingston, Y Esther.
The valiant coward. Philadelphia, Dorrance [°1950]
310 p. 20 cm.

I. Title.

PZ3.L7628Val 51-1776

NL 0420927 DLC

Livingston-Herbage, Julian
see Herbage, Julian.

Livingston, Ala. State normal school
see Alabama. State Teachers College, Livingston.

VOLUME 336

Livingston, Ala. State Teachers College
see
Alabama. State Teachers College, *Livingston.*

Livingston, Miss. Citizens.

Shackelford, Thomas.
[Proceedings] of the citizens of Madison County, Mississippi, at Livingston, in July, 1835, in relation to the trial and punishment of several individuals implicated in a contemplated insurrection in this state. Prepared by Thomas Shackelford, esq. Jackson, Mi., Printed by Mayson & Smoot, 1836.

Livingston, Montana. Chamber of commerce.
"Livingston, Montana." Livingston, Mont. n.d.
4 p.

NL 0420932 OClWHi

Livingston, Montana. Chamber of Commerce.
We will welcome you to Livingston and Park county in the glorious treasure state of Montana ... [Livingston, Post print, 1909]

cover-title, [50] p. illus. 23 1/2cm

NL 0420933 MtU

A 974.739 f L78l
Livingston, N. Y. Linlithgo Reformed Church.
Records. [1722-1889] Photostat copy by New York State Library. [Albany. 1936-45.
2 v. in 5 (v. 1, pt. 1-4, 531 l.) 38 cm.

Partial contents.--List of ministers.--Baptisms, 1723-1889.-- Members, 1722-1885.--Marriages, 1723-1800; 1816-1817; 1827-1867; 1869-1884.--Consistory minutes, etc., 1722-1829--Families, 1828, 1844--Catechumens, 1816.
1. Registers of births, etc. Livingston, N.Y. H.I. New York (State) Livingston.

NL 0420934 N

Livingston, N. Y. Potts memorial hospital for the rehabilitation of the tuberculous
see Potts Memorial Hospital, Livingston, N. Y.

Livingston, N. Y. St. John's Evangelical Lutheran church.
Records of St. John's Evangelical Lutheran church at Manorton, in the town of Livingston, Columbia County, N. Y. Transcribed by the New York genealogical and biographical society. Ed. by Royden Woodward Vosburgh. New York, 1913.
2 v. 36cm.
Autographed from typewritten copy.
1. Registers of births, etc.—Livingston, N. Y. I. Vosburgh, Royden Woodward, ed. II. New York genealogical and biographical society.
13-16527
Library of Congress F129.L73L7

NL 0420936 DLC

KFI 152 .Z9L5
Livingston & Bach.
The laws and legal forms of Illinois; for the convenience of farmers, mechanics, merchants, bankers, and lawyers. Compiled by Livingston & Bach, Attorneys at law, Bloomington, Illinois. Bloomington, Ill., The Pantagraph, 1898.
165p. illus.

1. Business law--Illinois. I. Title.

NL 0420937 INS

711.40973 N22l
Livingston and Blayney.
Navajo, New Mexico, development plan [by] Livingston and Blayney [and] John Carl Warnecke and Associates. [Presented to the Tribal Council of the Navajo Tribe. San Francisco, 19 -
v. illus., maps. 28cm.

NL 0420938 IU

Livingston & co., *London.*
Telegraphic cypher code in use by Livingston & co. March, 1877. London, Spottiswoode & co., 1877.
iv, 683 p. 18½cm.

1. Cipher and telegraph codes—Cotton trade.
CA 7—4032 Unrev'd
Library of Congress HE7677.C8L7

NL 0420939 DLC

Livingston Baptist association
see Baptists. New York. Livingston association.

Livingston city directory
see under Polk, R. L., & co.

Livingston County, Ill. Board of Supervisors.
Livingston county, Illinois in the World war. Winnie Sparks, editor. [Bloomington, Ill., 192-]
656 p. illus., ports. 28cm.

1. Livingston county, Ill.--Biog. 2. European war, 1914-1918--U.S.--Ill--Livingston county. I. Sparks, Winnie, ed. II. Sparks, Winnie. t. 192-

NL 0420942 NN WHi IU

379.773 L76f
Livingston Co., Ill.--School Survey Committee.
Final report. [n.p.] 1947.
12p. fold.map. 28cm.

Cover title.

1. Educational surveys. 2. Public schools--Livingston Co., Ill.

NL 0420943 IU

Livingston Co, Ky.
... Record of marriages in Livingston county, Kentucky
see under Burns, Annie (Walker) 1894-

Livingston Co., Ky.
... Record of wills in Livingston county, Kentucky
see under Burns, Annie (Walker) 1894-

Livingston Co., Mich.
... Rural cemeteries of Livingston County
see under Daughters of the American Revolution. Michigan. Philip Livingston Chapter, Howell.

Livingston Co., Mich. Board of County Road Commissioners.
Report. 1st- 191 -

NL 0420947 MiU

Livingston Co., N. Y.
A history of Livingston County, New York
see under Doty, Lockwood Lyon, 1827-1873.

S336.74785 qL787
Livingston Co., N. Y.
Recommendations for tentative budget.
[Geneseo]
v. in 44 x 28 cm

1. Budget. Livingston Co., N. Y.

NL 0420949 N

Livingston co., *N. Y. Board of supervisors.*
Proceedings ...
[Caledonia, N. Y.,
v. front., tables. 23cm.
On cover, : ... Supervisors' proceedings ...
Issued by the Board of supervisors.
35-11421
Library of Congress J83.N7L5
[2] 352.074785

NL 0420950 DLC CSmH NBuU-L

Livingston Co., N. Y. High School.
Prospectus ... to be opened the first of October, 1827, on Temple Hill, Geneseo, N. Y. Geneseo, n.p., August, 1827.
8 p. O.

NL 0420951 N

Livingston Co., N. Y. High School.
View of the Livingston County High-School, on Temple-Hill, Geneseo ...
see under title

Livingston Co., *N. Y. Superintendent of Highways.*
Department of Highways map of Livingston County, New York. Charles A. Smith, supt. Conesus, N. Y., 1954.
col. map 71 x 55 cm.
Scale ca. 1:90,000.
"Copyright ... W. P. Munger, Kenmore, N. Y."
"Livingston County road index" on verso.

1. Livingston Co., N. Y.—Road maps. I. Munger, William Peres.
G3803.L5 1954.L5 Map 54-347

NL 0420953 DLC

VOLUME 336

Livingston Co., N. Y. Teachers' Institute.
see Teachers' Institute, Livingston Co., N. Y

630.5 Livingston County agricultural news.
qL787 v. 1- 1919- Mt. Morris, N.Y.
v. illus. 28-38 cm.

Published by Livingston County Extension Service Association; 1919-1933, Livingston County Farm Bureau Association; 1934-1943, Livingston County Farm and Home Bureau Association; 1944-1955, Livingston County Farm and Home Bureau and 4-H Club Association.

Title varies 1919-1933 and 1944-55, Livingston County Farm Bureau news; 1934-43, Livingston County Farm and Home Bureau news;
Nov. 1945-Nov. 1947 include supplement.

1. Agriculture. New York (State) Livingston County. I. Livingston County Extension Service Association.

NL 0420956 N DNAL

The Livingston county business directory, embracing a list of the business firms of the cities and villages of Livingston county, a list of county and township officers and public school teachers, a directory of churches and secret societies, containing also, portraits and biographies of many prominent citizens ... Odell, Ill., C. A. Stuck, 1898.

240 p. illus. (incl. ports.) 24cm.

1. Livingston co., Ill.—Direct. 2. Livingston co., Ill.—Biog.

98-1580 Revised

Library of Congress F547.L78A18 1898

NL 0420957 DLC

43.9
L76 Livingston County (N. Y.) Cooperative Artificial Breeding Association, inc.
Annual report.

Mt. Morris, N. Y.

NL 0420958 DNAL

Livingston county directory
Howell, Mich. [19
v. 23½cm.

Cover-title.

1. Livingston co., Mich.—Direct.

39-14747

Library of Congress F572.L8A18

NL 0420959 DLC

Livingston County directory for the years 1873-4 ... together with a sketch of the County
see under Keating, John W., comp.

Livingston county farm and home bureau news
see Livingston county agricultural news.

Livingston county farm bureau news
see Livingston county agricultural news.

974.785 Livingston County Historical Society, Geneseo, N. Y.
L786A
Annual meeting. 1st-41st, 1877-1917. Dansville, N. Y., A. O. Bunnell, printer.
41 v. in 23 cm.
No more published?
Bound with v. 2-5: its Constitution, by-laws and certificate of incorporation. Mt. Morris, N. Y., 1877.

1. Livingston Co., N. Y. History. Societies, etc. I. Livingston County Historical Society, Geneseo, N. Y. Constitution, by-laws and certificate of incorporation.

NL 0420963 NcD MnHi OClWHi MiD NBuG NRU CU Nh NIC

Livingston County Historical Society, Geneseo, N. Y.
... Boyd and Parker, heroes of the American revolution
see under Doty, Lockwood Richard, 1858-1937.

Livingston county historical society, Geneseo, N. Y.

De Long, Hermon Wells, 1851-
Conesus lake in history, by H. W. De Long. [Geneseo? N. Y., 1915?]

Livingston County historical society, *Geneseo, N. Y.*
A history of the treaty of Big Tree, and an account of the celebration of the one hundredth anniversary of the making of the treaty, held at Geneseo, N. Y., September the fifteenth, eighteen hundred ninety-seven. [Dansville, N. Y.] Livingston County historical society [1897?]

103 p. front., plates, ports., map. 23½cm.

1. Big Tree, Treaty of, 1797. 2. Holland purchase. 3. New York (State)—Hist.

4-17873 Revised

Library of Congress F127.H7L7

NL 0420966 DLC MWA MiU MB

The Livingston Farrand memorial meeting, January 30, 1940 ...
see under New York Academy of Medicine.

... Livingston folio, Montana
see under [Iddings, Joseph Paxson] 1857-1920.

The LIVINGSTON library. To be sold by auction, May 26th and 27th, 1885. G. A. Leavitt & co., auctioneers. New York, 1885.

pp. 46.

NL 0420969 MH

Livingston Manor, *N. Y. Board of education.*
The pioneer; a commemorative book published by the Livingston Manor Central school Board of education on the occasion of the dedication of the Livingston Manor Central school, Livingston Manor, New York, May 19, 1939. [Union City, N. J., New city printing co., °1939]

48 p. illus. (incl. ports., maps, plans, facsims.) 28cm.

"By Joseph F. Willis."—p. [2]

1. Livingston Manor, N. Y. Central school. 2. Livingston Manor, N. Y.—Hist. I. Willis, Joseph F. II. Title.

E 42-15

U. S. Off. of educ. Library for Library of Congress LA339.L6A6 [2]

NL 0420970 DHEW

917.49 Livingston Manor Corporation, New Brunswick, N. J.
L787
Livingston manor [and metropolitan New Jersey. New Brunswick? N. J., 1907?]
36 p. illus., map. 18 x 26 cm.

Cover title.

1. New Jersey. Descr. & trav. I. Title.

NL 0420971 N

Livingston Mining Co. of New York.
[Prospectus] New York, [186-]
20 p. 1 pl. 8°.
In: VHC p.v. 2.

NL 0420972 NN

Livingston Parish, *La. Development Board.*
Livingston Parish resources and facilities; survey. [Baton Rouge] State of Louisiana, Dept. of Public Works, Planning Division [1954?]

77 p. illus., maps (part fold., part col.) 28 cm.

1. Livingston Parish, La. I. Title.

F377.L6A52 55-62538

NL 0420973 DLC LU

LIVINGSTON PARK SEMINARY, Rochester, N. Y.
The story of sixty years, 1858-1918. [Rochester, N. Y. 1918?] 76 p. illus., ports. 20cm.

1. Woman--Education--Indiv. inst.--U. S.--N. Y.--Rochester.

NL 0420974 NN

Livingston republican.
Geneseo, N. Y., S. P. Allen.
64cm. weekly.

Began publication Sept. 19, 1837.

NL 0420975 CtY

F127 Livingston Republican, Geneseo, N. Y.
G19L6 [Centennial number to commemorate Sullivan's Indian campaign] Geneseo, N. Y., 1879.

4p. illus. 69cm. (Vol. 43, no. 6, Sept. 18, 1879)

NL 0420976 NBuG

VOLUME 336

Livingston Republican, Geneseo, N. Y.
Geneseo's centennial, September 11th, 1890
see under title

M1747.18 L4 Livingstone,
... Livingstone's Scotch comic songs. [No imprint, 1800?]

32p. 13cm.

Caption title; title page wanting.
At head of title: Third collection of.
1. Scottish ballads and songs.
2. Humorous songs, Scottish.

NL 0420978 NBuG

Livingstone, Addie.
When my soldier is married to me. Serio comic ballad. [With accompaniment for pianoforte.]
Cincinnati. Church. [1863.] 5 pp. [Sounds from the battle field.] Decorated title-page. 33½ cm.

NL 0420979 MB

Livingstone, Dame Adelaide Lord (Stickney) 1887-
National declaration committee (Gt. Brit.)
The peace ballot; the official history, by Dame Adelaide Livingstone (secretary, National declaration committee) in collaboration with Marjorie Scott Johnston, with a statistical survey of the results by Walter Ashley, conclusion by Viscount Cecil, chairman ... London, V. Gollancz ltd., 1935.

Livingstone, Alexander P., compiler.
Complete story of San Francisco's terrible calamity of earthquake and fire; the most appalling disaster of modern times; immense loss of life and hundreds of millions of property destroyed; compiled from stories told by eye-witnesses, by Alexander P. Livingstone... To which is added graphic accounts of the eruptions of Vesuvius and many other volcanos, explaining the causes of volcanic eruptions and earthquakes; embellished with a great number of superb photographs taken before and after this frightful calamity. [San Francisco?:] The Continental Pub. House[, 1907?]. ix, 272 p. incl. front., plates, ports. 8°.

328301A. 1. San Francisco, Cal. —Hist., 1906. N. Y. P. L. February 4, 1928

NL 0420981 NN ODW NjP

Livingstone, Alice.
A sealed book, by Alice Livingstone ... with eight full page illustrations. New York, R. F. Fenno & company [°1906]
384 p. 8 pl. (incl. front.) 20cm.

I. Title.

Library of Congress PZ3.L7638e 7—5060

NL 0420982 DLC OO

Livingstone, Arthur A.
... The Bryozoa. Supplementary report ... Sydney, 1928.
1 p.l., ii, [5]-93 p. illus., VII pl. 31 cm. (Australasian Antarctic expedition, 1911-1914. Scientific reports. Series C. Zoology and botany, vol. IX, pt. I)

NL 0420983 CtY

Livingstone, Arthur A.
Studies on Australian Bryozoa... no.1- (In Australian museum, Sydney. Records ... v. 14, ...

NL 0420984 OO

Livingstone, Belle.
Belle of Bohemia; the memoirs of Belle Livingstone. London, J. Hamilton ltd. [1927]
318 p. front., ports. 22cm.
"First printing, January, 1927; second printing, January, 1927."
"These memoirs appeared serially in the Cosmopolitan."—p. 315.

I. Title.

Library of Congress CT275.L56A3 28-5677

NL 0420985 DLC TxU FMU OrU CtY OWorP CU MH CU-A NN

Livingstone, Belle.
Letters of a Bohemian. London, Greening & co., ltd., 1906.

NL 0420986 MH

Livingstone, Beulah.
Metropolitan opera house, December 19, 1913; souvenir of the Pavlowa carnival for the benefit of the Music school settlement, illustrated by M. A. Stocking ... By Beulah Livingstone. New York, The Theatre magazine co., °1913.
[16] p. illus. (incl. ports.) 25cm. $0.25

1. Pavlova, Anna. 2. Ballet. 3. Music school settlement, New York. I. Title: Pavlowa carnival.

Library of Congress GV1785.P3L5 14-6196

NL 0420987 DLC

792.94 V161 XL Livingstone, Beulah.
Remember Valentino; reminiscences of the world's greatest lover. [n.p.] c1938.
85p. illus. 21cm.

1.Valentino, Rudolph, 1895-1926.
I.Title.

NL 0420988 CLSU NcD

LIVINGSTONE, BEULAH.
Remember Valentino; reminiscences of the world's greatest lover. [New York?] c1938. 85 p. ports. 21cm.
Film reproduction. Positive.

1. Valentino, Rudolf, 1895-1926.

NL 0420989 NN

Livingstone, Mrs. C. M., joint author.
Alden, Isabella (Macdonald) "Mrs. G. R. Alden," 1841-
By way of the wilderness, by "Pansy" (Mrs. G. R. Alden) and Mrs. C. M. Livingstone ... Boston, Lothrop publishing company [1899]

Livingstone, C R
The earth is red, by C. R. Livingstone. London, Macmillan & co. ltd, 1946.
2 p. l., 110, [1] p. 19cm.

I. Title.

Library of Congress PZ3.L7613Ea 46-17061

NL 0420991 DLC OCl CaBVa

Livingstone, Charles, 1821-1873, joint author.
Livingstone, David, 1813-1873.
... Explorations dans l'Afrique australe et dans le bassin du Zambèse depuis 1840 jusqu'à 1864; ouvrage traduit par Mme Henriette Loreau, abrégé par J. Belin-de Launay, avec 4 gravures et une carte. 7. éd. Paris, Hachette et c^ie, 1883.

Livingstone, Charles, 1821-1873, joint author.
Livingstone, David, 1813-1873.
Explorations du Zambèse et de ses affluents et découverte des lacs Chiroua et Nyassa, par David et Charles Livingstone, 1858-1864; ouvrage traduit de l'anglais, avec l'autorisation de l'auteur, par m^me H. Loreau. Contenant 47 gravures et 4 cartes. Paris, L. Hachette et c^ie, 1866.

[Livingstone, Charles, 1821-1873.
[Journal of travels in Africa, with his brother, David Livingstone]. n.p., n.d.
4 v.

NL 0420994 OO

Livingstone, Charles, 1821-1873, joint author.
FOR OTHER EDITIONS SEE MAIN ENTRY
Livingstone, David, 1813-1873.
Narrative of an expedition to the Zambesi and its tributaries; and of the discovery of the lakes Shirwa and Nyassa. 1858-1864. By David and Charles Livingstone. With map and illustrations. New York, Harper & brothers, 1866.

Livingstone, Charles, 1821-1873.
Livingstone, David, 1813-1873.
A popular account of Dr. Livingstone's expedition to the Zambesi and its tributaries: and of the discovery of lakes Shirwa and Nyassa, 1858-1864. Abridged from the larger work. London, J. Murray, 1887.

[Livingstone, Colin Hamilton] comp.
The Citizen guide to Brooklyn and Long island. The city's resources and residences, the island's retreats and resorts ... Brooklyn [Printed by The Jersey City printing company] 1893.
4 p. l., 320 p. illus. (incl. maps) 18½cm.
Published anonymously.
Copyrighted by R. Wayne Wilson and company.

1. Brooklyn—Descr.—Guide-books. 2. Long island—Descr. & trav.—Guide-books. I. Title.

Library of Congress F129.B7L7 3—18825

NL 0420997 DLC NN NB NBLiHi

Livingstone, Colin Hamilton, comp.
The Sun's guide to New York. Replies to questions asked every day by the guests and citizens of the American metropolis ... [Jersey City, The Jersey City printing company] 1892.

VOLUME 336

[Livingstone, Cora Luetta] 1874–
Glimpses of pioneer life for little folks ... Chicago, New York, A. Flanagan company [1904]
166 p. col. front., illus., col. pl. 19cm.

I. Title.

Library of Congress (✱) (PZ7.L) 4–18494

NL 0420999 OrP

Livingstone, Cora Luetta, 1874-
Glimpses of pioneer life... Chic., A. Flanagan company, 1923.
160 p.

NL 0421000 OU OClh

Livingstone, David.
New commerce with ancient markets, by David Livingstone. Published by the Los Angeles chamber of commerce under its Greater harbor program. [Los Angeles] 1939.
5 p. l., 73 numb. l. diagrs. 27½ x 21½cm.
Half-titles (10 leaves) not included in pagination.
Reproduced from type-written copy.

1. Los Angeles—Comm.—Asia. 2. Asia—Comm.—Los Angeles. I. Los Angeles. Chamber of commerce. II. Title.

Library of Congress HF3163.L7L5 42-2344
382.0979494

NL 0421001 DLC MH CLSU

LIVINGSTONE, David.
The Transvaal Boers.
[Edin. Constable. 1881.] 23 pp. 8°.

NL 0421002 MB

Livingstone, David, 1813-1873.
[Barclay, George Lippard]
All honor to Stanley! Dr. David Livingstone's discoveries in Africa ... Horrors of the internecine wars and internal slave trade! The diamond fields. Also, M. De Challue's [!] adventures & discoveries in Africa. Numerous engravings. Philadelphia, Barclay & co. [1873]

Livingstone, David, 1813–1873.
Analysis of the language of the Bechuanas. By David Livingstone. [London, Printed by W. Clowes and sons, 1858]
40 p. 27½ x 22cm.
"Printed for private circulation among the members of Livingstone's Zambesi expedition ... It was written in 1852."

1. Sechuana language—Grammar.

Library of Congress PL8651.L5 43-19007

NL 0421004 DLC NN

MZ54 L763au Livingstone, David, 1813-1873.
Autobiography of David Livingstone and extracts referring to his three journeys, discoveries and influence. Hamilton, Printed by the Hamilton Advertiser [192-?]
[32] p. illus., port. 13 x 19 cm.

Reprinted for the Scottish National Livingstone Memorial, Blantyre, Lanarkshire.

1. Africa, South - Missions. I. Scottish National Livingstone Memorial, Blantyre, Lanarkshire. Afr

NL 0421005 CtY-D

Livingstone, David, 1813-1873.
Dr. Livingstone's Cambridge lectures, together with a prefatory letter by the Rev. Professor Sedgwick... Ed. with introduction, life of Dr. Livingstone, notes and appendix, by the Rev. William Monk... Cambridge [Eng.] Deighton, Bell and co. [etc., etc.] 1858. xxx, xciii, 181 p. front., maps. 19cm.

235267B. 1. Africa, South—Descr. and trav., 1800-1900. 2. Missions, Foreign—Africa. I. Sedgwick, Adam, 1785-1873. II. Monk, William, ed.
July 19, 1943

NL 0421006 NN IEdS NcD WU NjP MBU WaU CtY-D InU

Livingstone, David, 1813–1873.
Dr. Livingstone's Cambridge lectures, together with a prefatory letter by the Rev. Professor Sedgwick ... Ed. with introduction, etc., by the Rev. William Monk ... With a portrait and maps. 2d ed. Cambridge [Eng.] Deighton, Bell and co.; [etc., etc.] 1860.
viii, 380 p. front. (port.) 2 fold. maps. 18½cm.

1. Africa, South—Descr. & trav. 2. Missions—Africa. I. Monk, William, ed. II. Sedgwick, Adam, 1785–1873. III. Title.

Library of Congress DT731.L78 5-15660

NL 0421007 DLC CtY NN IEN

Livingstone, David, 1813-1873.
David Livingstone memorial
see under Federated Caledonian society of South Africa.

Livingstone, David, 1813-1873.
David Livingstone: The story of his life and travels
see under title

Livingstone, David, 1813–1873.
... David Livingstone; voyages d'exploration au Zambèze et dans l'Afrique centrale, 1840–1873. Abrégés par H. Vattemare. 3. éd. Paris, Hachette et cie, 1882.
224 p. front. (port.) illus. (incl. map) 22cm. (Bibliothèque de lecture des écoles et des familles)

1. Africa, Central—Descr. & trav. I. Vattemare, Hippolyte, d. 1882, ed.

Library of Congress DT731.L72 27-1281

NL 0421010 DLC

916.7 L788D Livingstone, David, 1813-1873.
Dernier journal du docteur David Livingstone relatant ses explorations et découvertes de 1866 a 1873. Suivi du récit de ses derniers moments rédigé d'après le rapport de ses fidèles serviteurs Chouma et Souzi par Horace Waller ... Ouvrage traduit de l'Anglais avec l'autorisation des éditeurs par Mme H. Loreau et contenant 60 gravures et 4 cartes. Paris, Hachette, 1876.
2 v. front. (port.), plate, fold. map. 24cm.

NL 0421011 NcD

Livingstone, David, 1813-1873.
Despatches addressed by Dr. Livingstone, Her Majesty's consul, inner Africa, to Her Majesty's secretary of state for foreign affairs, in 1870, 1871, and 1872. London: Harrison and Sons, n. d. 24 p. f°. (Great Britain. Foreign Office.)

In: Great Britain. Parliament. Sessional papers. 1872, v. 70.

1. Africa.—History, 1870-72.
June 20, 1913.

NL 0421012 NN

Livingstone, David, 1813-1873.
... Dr. David Livingstone's discoveries in Africa
see [Barclay, George Lippard]
All honor to Stanley. Dr. David Livingstone's discoveries in Africa.

Livingstone, David, 1813-1873.
Dr. Livingstone's 17 years' explorations ...
see under Coombs, John Hartley.

LIVINGSTONE, [David], 1813-1873.
Dreissig jahre Afrika, Livingstones missions- und forschungs-reisen in Afrika. Berichte aus seinen reisewerken ausgewählt und zusammengefasst von Julius Schäffer. Leipzig, R. Voigtländer, [191-?].

pp. 155.
Verso of title-page reads:- Voigt-länders quellenbücher. 95.

NL 0421015 MH IEN

Livingstone, David, 1813-1873.
Entdeckungen in Afrika. Philadelphia, Barclay u. Co., 1873.

NL 0421016 PPG

Livingstone, David, 1813-1873.
[Entdeckungsreisen im süden und innern von Afrika während der jahre 1840 bis 1873, nach David Livingstones werken und hinterlassenen aufzeichnungen bearb. von Richard Oberländer. 6. durchgesehene und ergänzte aufl. viii, 302p. front., il. Leipzig und Berlin, O. Spamer, 1883. (Das buch der reisen und entdeckungen, 3)

NL 0421017 OCl

---

967 V878Yw Livingstone, David, 1813-1873.
Erforschungsreisen im Innern Afrika's. In Schilderungen der bekanntesten alteren und neuern Reisen insbesondere der grossen Entdeckungen im südlichen Afrika während der Jahre 1840-1856. 2.verm. Aufl. Leipzig, O. Spamer, 1860.
vi, 318p. illus., col. plates (1 fold.) map. 20cm. (Malerische Feierstunden. 1.Serie. 2. Abth. Afrika, I)

With Wagner, H. Schilderungen der Reisen und Entdeckungen des Dr. Eduard Vogel... Leipzig, 1860.

1. Africa. Disc. & explor. I. Title.

NL 0421019 IEN

DT731 .L723 1868 Livingstone, David, 1813-1873.

Explorations dans l'Afrique australe et dans le bassin du Zambèse depuis 1840 jusqu'à 1864; ouvrage traduit par Henriette Loreau, abrégée par J. Belin-de Launay. Paris, L. Hachette, 1868.
xix, 339 p. plates, port., map. 18cm. (Bibliothèque rose illustrée)
Abridgment of Mme. Loreau's translations of 'Missionary travels', etc., and 'Narrative of an expedition to the Zambesi', etc., by David and Charles Livingstone.
1. Africa, South—Descr. & trav. 2. Africa, Central—Descr. & trav. 3. Missions—Africa, South. I. Livingstone, Charles, 1821-1873, joint author.

NL 0421020 ViU

VOLUME 336

916.7
L78e.2 Livingstone, David, 1813-1873.
Explorations dans l'Afrique australe et dans le bassin du Zambèse depuis 1840 jusqu'a 1864. Ouvrage traduit par Henriette Loreau; abrégé par J. Belin-de Launay. 2. éd. Paris, L. Hachette, 1869.
xx,339p. illus. 18cm.

Abridgment of Mme. Loreau's translations of Missionary travels, etc., and Narrative of an expedition to the Zambesi, etc., by David and Charles Livingstone.

NL 0421021 IEN MH

Livingstone, David, 1813-1873.
Explorations dans l'Afrique australe et dans le bassin du Zambèse depuis 1840 jusqu'à 1864 [par] David & Charles Livingstone. Ouvrage traduit par Mme. Henriette Loreau, abrège par J. Belin-de-Launay. 3. éd. Paris, Hachette, 1874.
xx, 339 p. illus., fold. map. port. 18 cm.
Abridgment of Mme. Loreau's translations of "Missionary travels", etc., and "Narrative of an expedition to the Zambesi", etc., by David and Charles Livingstone. -cf. Library of Congress Catalog of Printed Cards, v. 89, p. 95.

NL 0421022 NcD

MZ54
L763miF
1879 Livingstone, David, 1813-1873.
Explorations dans l'Afrique australe et dans le bassin du Zambèse depuis 1840 jusqu'à 1864 [par] David & Charles Livingstone. Ouvrage traduit par Henriette Loreau. Abrégé par J. Belin-de Launay. 4. éd. Paris, Hachette, 1879.
xx, 339 p. illus., map, port. 19 cm. (Bibliothèque rose illustrée)

Abridgment of Mme Loreau's translation of Missionary travels ... (Explorations dans l'Afrique australe) by David Livingstone, and Narrative of an expedition tc the Zambesi (Explorations du Zambèse) by David and Charles Livingstone.

NL 0421024 CtY-D

Livingstone, David, 1813-1873.
... Explorations dans l'Afrique australe et dans le bassin du Zambèse depuis 1840 jusqu'à 1864; ouvrage traduit par Mme Henriette Loreau, abrégé par J. Belin-de Launay, avec 4 gravures et une carte. 7. éd. Paris, Hachette et c[ie], 1883.
2 p. l., xx, 339 p. plates, map. 18[cm].
At head of title: David et Charles Livingstone.
"Abridgment of Mme. Loreau's translations of 'Missionary travels', etc., and 'Narrative of an expedition to the Zambesi', etc., by David and Charles Livingstone."
1. Africa, South—Descr. & trav. 2. Africa, Central—Descr. & trav. 3. Missions—Africa, South. I. Livingstone, Charles, 1821-1873, joint author. II. Loreau, Mme. Henriette, b. 1815, tr. III. Belin de Launay, Jules Henri Robert, 1814-1883, ed.
26-23487
Library of Congress DT731.L743 1883

NL 0421025 DLC

Livingstone, David, 1813-1873.
Explorations dans l'intérieur de l'Afrique australe et voyages à travers le continent, de Saint-Paul de Loanda à l'embouchure du Zambèze, de 1840 à 1856, par le r[d] d[r] David Livingstone. Ouvrage traduit de l'anglais, avec l'autorisation de l'auteur, par m[me] H. Loreau. 2. éd. Paris, Hachette et c[ie], 1873.
3 p. l., 687 p. illus., plates. 25[cm].

1. Africa, South—Descr. & trav. 2. Missions—Africa, South. I. Loreau, Mme. Henriette, b. 1815, tr.
33-32437
Library of Congress DT731.L743 1873 916.8

NL 0421026 DLC NcD

Livingstone, David, 1813-1873.
Explorations du Zambèse et de ses affluents et découverte des lacs Chiroua et Nyassa, par David et Charles Livingstone, 1858-1864; ouvrage traduit de l'anglais, avec l'autorisation de l'auteur, par m[me] H. Loreau. Contenant 47 gravures et 4 cartes. Paris, L. Hachette et c[ie], 1866.
4 p. l., 580 p. illus., plates, fold. maps. 24[cm].

1. Africa, Central—Descr. & trav. I. Livingstone, Charles, 1821-1873, joint author. II. Loreau, Mme. Henriette, b. 1815, tr. III. Title.
Translation of Narrative of an expedition to the Zambesi.
36-2478
Library of Congress DT731.L762 916.7

NL 0421027 DLC NN

MZ54
L763nF Livingstone, David, 1813-1873.
Explorations du Zambèse et de ses affluents et découverte des lacs Chiroua et Nyassa, par David et Charles Livingstone, 1858-1864. Ouvrage traduit de l'anglais avec l'authorisation des auteurs, par Mme. H. Loreau. Paris, Librairie Hachette, 1881.
580 p. illus., 4 fold. maps. 24 cm.

Translation of Narrative of an expedition to the Zambesi and its tributaries.

NL 0421028 CtY-D

Livingstone, David, 1813-1873
Explorations in Africa ...

See under
Ingersoll, Lurton Dunham

Livingstone, David, 1813-1873.
Inéditos do Dr. David Livingstone? Por Filipe Gastão de Almeida de Eça. Lourenço Marques, Imprensa Nacional de Moçambique, 1953.
24 p. illus. 29 cm.
"Separata do Documentário 'Moçambique,' nº. 73, de março de 1953."

I. Eça, Filipe Gastão de Moura Coutinho de Almeida de, 1895- ed. II. Title.
DT731.L716 58-42253 ‡

NL 0421030 DLC CSt

Livingstone, David, 1813-1873.
The last journals of David Livingstone, in Central Africa, from 1865 to his death. Continued by a narrative of his last moments and sufferings obtained from his faithful servants Chuma and Susi, by Horace Waller ... London, J. Murray, 1874.
2 v. fronts. (v. 1, port.) illus., plates, facsims., fold. maps. 22 cm.

1. Africa, Central—Descr. & trav. I. Waller, Horace, 1833-1896, ed. II. Title.
DT731.L77 1874 -916.7 4-16739

Wa WaTC WaS Or WaSpG IdB
PPA WaSp OKentU OrSaW CaBVaU MdBP MB WaT IEN I
CaBVa CtY-D CaBViP MH-P OrPR PP PPRCI PPL CtY NN
NL 0421031 DLC IEN MdBP OrP WaU IU FU OU NjP

Livingstone, David, 1813-1873.
The last journals of David Livingstone, in Central Africa ... Chicago, Jansen, McClurg, & Company, 1875.
541 p. illus., front., drawings, plates, maps. 24 cm.
Edited by Horace Waller.

NL 0421032 C-S

Livingstone, David, 1813-1873.
The last journals of David Livingstone, in central Africa, from 1865 to his death. (Abridged from the original London edition.) With a narrative of his last moments and sufferings, obtained from his faithful servants Chumah and Susi, by Horace Waller ... With portrait, maps, and illustrations ... Hartford, Conn., R. W. Bliss & company; Newark, N. J., F. C. Bliss & co.; [etc., etc.] 1875.
1 p. l., [ix]-xvii, [1], [19]-448 p. incl. plates, ports., facsim. front., 2 maps. 23[cm].
1. Africa, Central—Descr. & trav. I. Waller, Horace, 1833-1896, ed. II. Title.
Library of Congr DT731.L77 1875 5—15659

PPPD PPT PP PBa PPD PU ICJ
NL 0421033 DLC WaS ICJ NjNbS InAndC-T TNF CoU NIC

Livingstone, David, 1813-1873.
The last journals of David Livingstone, in Central Africa. From eighteen hundred and sixty-five to his death. Continued by a narrative of his last moments and sufferings. Obtained from his faithful servants, Chuma and Susi, by Horace Waller ... New York, Harper & brothers, 1875.
2 p. l., [3]-541 p. front. (port.) illus., plates, 2 maps, facsims. 23½[cm].
Imperfect: maps wanting.

1. Africa, Central—Descr. & trav. I. Waller, Horace, 1833-1896, ed. II. Title.
17-9532
Library of Congress DT731.L77 1875 a

CtY-D PPAN
ViU TU MB NcA FMU PPG DN OCl MiU OU OO MB NN
NL 0421034 DLC FTaSU CU PPWe KyLx PPFr MH NjP NcU

916.7
L788l
1880 Livingstone, David, 1813-1873.
The last journals of David Livingstone, in Central Africa, from 1865 to his death. Continued by a narrative of his last moments and sufferings obtained from his faithful servants Chuma and Susi, by Horace Waller... London, J. Murray, 1880.
2 v. fronts (v.1 port.) illus., plates, facsims., fold.maps. 23cm.

One map in pocket, v.l.

1. Africa, Central - Descr. & trav. I. Waller, Horace, 1833-1896, ed. II. Title.

NL 0421036 FU TU CtY-D NBuC OCU OClW

Livingstone, David, 1813-1873.
[Letter written from near Lake Bangweolo, South Central Africa, July, 1868]
7 p.
"Privately printed for the perusal of Dr. Livingstone's personal friends only."
Bound with other pamphlets in volume given binder's title: Mélanges.
1. Africa, Central - Disc. & explor.

NL 0421037 CU

Livingstone, David, 1813-1873.
Letters from David Livingstone, the distinguished African explorer. Written in 1856.
(In Essex Institute, Salem. Historical collections. Vol. 12, pp. 285-294. Salem. 1874.)
To Sir Edmund Gabriel.

K797 — Gabriel, Sir Edmund.

NL 0421038 MB

Livingstone, David, 1813-1873.
Letzte Reise von David Livingstone in Centralafrica von 1865 bis zu seinem Tode 1873. Vervollständigt durch einen Bericht über seine Leiden und letzten Augenblicke nach den Erzählungen seiner treuen Diener Chuma und Susi, von Horace Waller, ... Rechtmässige deutsche Ausgabe besorgt von Dr. Josef M. Boyes. Mit Portrait, 2 Karten, vielen Illustrationen und Facsimiles. Hamburg, Hoffmann & Campe, 1875.
2 vol. in 1. 2 front. (1 port.), illus., 16 pl., 2 fold. maps (1 in pocket), 2 facsim. (1 fold.) 22½[cm].

NL 0421039 ICJ

VOLUME 336

DT 731 L734 Livingstone, David, 1813-1873.
Life and explorations of David Livingstone, the great missionary explorer in the interior of Africa: comprising all his extensive travels and discoveries as detailed in his diary, reports and letters, and including his famous last journals ... Together with the explorations of Barth, Baker, Speke, Du Chaillu, and others, and a full account of the Herald-Stanley expedition. St. Louis, Valley Pub. Co., [1874]
643 p. illus. 21 cm.

At head of title: The story of the brave Scotchman!

1. Africa, Central—Descr. & trav. 2. Africa, South—Descr. & trav. I. Title.

NL 0421041 IEdS T CU NN

Livingstone, David, 1813-1873.
Life and explorations of David Livingstone
see also his The story of the brave Scotchman.

Livingstone, David, 1813-1873.
Life and labors of David Livingstone
see under Chambliss, J E

Livingstone, David, 1813-1873.
... The life and services of Dr. David Livingstone.
see under American geographical society, New York.

---

916 L763z Livingstone, David, 1813-1873.
Livingstone and his African explorations: together with a full account of the Young Stanley, and Dawson search expeditions; chapters on ancient & modern Nile discovery; on the Central African slave trade, &c., &c., New York, Adams, Victor & Company, 1872.
xii, 292 p. front. port. map.
Imperfect: spine slightly damaged; spoiled.

1. Livingstone, David, 1813-1873. 2. Africa - Descr. & trav. 3. Missions - Africa. I. Title.

NL 0421045 MsSM WaE

Livingstone, David, 1813-1873.
Livingstone, der Missionär
see under [Kiesewetter, Fr]

Livingstone, David, 1813-1873.
Livingstone's Africa. Perilous adventures and extensive discoveries in the interior of Africa, from the personal narrative of David Livingstone ... together with the remarkable success and important results of the Herald-Stanley expedition, as furnished by H. M. Stanley ... To which is added a sketch of other important discoveries in Africa, including the celebrated diamond diggings at Colesberg Kopje. Illustrated with numerous engravings ... Phila. & Boston, Hubbard bros.; [etc., etc., ©1872]
3 p. l., v-xvi, 3-598 p. incl. front., illus., plates, ports. 20cm.
1. Africa, South—Descr. & trav. 2. Africa, Central—Descr. & trav.

Library of Congress DT731.L79 5-15661

CSmH Nh ODW
IaU TNJ-R OU WaU ViU AAP CtY-D CU-I NIC OrU WaWW
NL 0421047 DLC CU CLSU MeWaC PSt OCl TNJ PP NcD IEN

Livingstone, David, 1813-1873.
Livingstone's travels, edited by James I. Macnair; with geographical sections by Ronald Miller. London, Dent [1954]
xvi, 429 p. illus., ports., maps. 22 cm.
Compiled from the author's works entitled: Missionary travels and researches in South Africa, Narrative of an expedition to the Zambezi and its tributaries, and Last journals.
Bibliography: p. 415-418.

1. Africa, South—Descr. & trav. 2. Africa, Central—Descr. & trav. 3. Missions—Africa, South. I. Macnair, James Irvine, 1869- ed. II. Title.

DT731.L747 1954 916.8 54-3788

PU OCl NcU FTaSU CU NcD IU PPLT PPD PSC PPWe
MtBC OrP CLU CNoS MB FU CoU KU TxU PP NjPT PPT
NL 0421048 DLC RP IEdS OYesA N CaBVa CaBViP CaBVaU

Livingstone, David, 1813-1873.
Livingstone's travels and researches in South Africa; including a sketch of sixteen years' residence in the interior of Africa, and a journey from the cape of Good Hope to Loanda on the west coast, thence across the continent, down the river Zambesi, to the eastern ocean. From the personal narrative of David Livingstone ... To which is added a historical sketch of discoveries in Africa. New Haven, H. Mansfield, 1858.
xiv, 9-440 p. incl. front., illus., plates. 20 cm.

NL 0421049 OWoC

Livingstone, David, 1813-1873.
Livingstone's travels and researches in South Africa; including a sketch of sixteen years' residence in the interior of Africa, and a journey from the Cape of Good Hope to Loanda on the west coast, thence across the continent, down the river Zambesi, to the eastern ocean. From the personal narrative of David Livingstone ... To which is added a historical sketch of discoveries in Africa ... Philadelphia, J. W. Bradley [©1858]
xiv, 9-440 p. incl. front., illus., plates. 20cm.
Published also, the same year, with title: Missionary travels and researches in South Africa.
1. Africa, South—Descr. & trav. 2. Missions—Africa, South.

Library of Congress DT731.L74 5-15252

OCl OO OClWHi ViU OClU ViHaI
NL 0421050 DLC KEmT CtY-D WaU Or WaS MWA PNt PP OU

Efg 840d Livingstone, David, 1813-1873.
Livingstone's travels and researches in South Africa; including a sketch of sixteen years' residence in the interior of Africa, and a journey from the Cape of Good Hope to Loanda on the west coast, thence across the continent, down the river Zambesi, to the eastern ocean ... To which is added a historical sketch of discoveries in Africa. Illus. with numerous engravings. Philadelphia, J.W.Bradley, 1859.
xiv, 3-442p. incl. front., illus., plates. 20cm.

NL 0421051 CtY MH OCl TNF

Livingstone, David, 1813-1873.
Livingstone's travels and researches in South Africa; including a sketch of sixteen years' residence in the interior of Africa, and a journey from the Cape of Good Hope to Loanda on the West Coast, thence across the continent, down the River Zambesi, to the Eastern Ocean. To which is added a historical sketch of discoveries in Africa. Phila., Evans, 1859.
xiv, 442 p. incl. front., illus., plates.
Published also under title: Missionary travels and researches in South Africa.

NL 0421052 MBU NcRS

DT731 .L74 1859 Livingstone, David, 1813-1873.
Livingstone's travels and researches in South Africa; including a sketch of sixteen years' residence in the interior of Africa and a journey from the Cape of Good Hope to Loanda on the West Coast, thence across the continent, down the river Zambesi, to the Eastern Ocean. From the personal narrative of David Livingstone ...

Continued in next column

Continued from preceding column

To which is added a historical sketch of discoveries in Africa ... Philadelphia, J. E. Potter and company [©1859]
xiv, 3-442 p. incl. front., illus., plates. 18cm.

Published also under the title: Missionary travels and researches in South Africa.

1. Africa, South—Descr. & trav. 2. Missions—Africa, South.

NL 0421055 MB CaOTP OCl

Livingstone, David, 1813-1873.
Livingstone's travels and researches in South Africa; including a sketch of sixteen years' residence in the interior of Africa, and a journey from the Cape of Good Hope to Loanda on the West Coast, thence across the continent, down the River Zambesi, to the Eastern Ocean. From the personal narrative of David Livingstone ... To which is added a historical sketch of discoveries in Africa ... Philadelphia, J. W. Bradley, 1861.
xiv, [3]-442 p. incl. front., illus., plates. 20cm.
Published also under title: Missionary travels and researches in South Africa.
1. Africa, South—Descr. & trav. 2. Missions—Africa, South.

Library of Congress DT731.L74 1861 22-18188

NL 0421056 DLC NcD

Livingstone, David, 1813-1873.
Livingstone's travels and researches in South Africa, ... Philadelphia, Bradley, 1864.
442p.

NL 0421057 MiU

Livingstone, David, 1813-1873.
Livingstone's travels and researches in South Africa
see also his Travels and researches ...

Livingstone, David, 1813-1873.

BV3625 .M32W3 **Wallis, John Peter Richard,** 1880- *ed.*
The Matabele mission, a selection from the correspondence of John and Emily Moffat, David Livingstone and others, 1858-1878, edited by J. P. R. Wallis. London, Chatto & Windus, 1945.

DT731 L742 1857 Livingstone, David, 1813-1873.
Missionary travels, by David Livingstone ... New York, Harper & brothers; London, Ward, Lock & co., ltd. [1857]

xv, 617p. 18cm. (The world library)

Title within ornamental border.
Half-title: Missionary travels and South Africa.

1. Africa, South.-Description. 2. Missions.-Africa, South. I. Title.

NL 0421060 NBuG OrU PPT

Livingstone, David, 1813-1873.
Missionary travels and adventures in Africa
see under [Adams, Henry Gardiner] 1811 or 12-1881

VOLUME 336

Livingstone, David, 1813-1873.
Missionary travels and researches in South Africa; including a sketch of sixteen years' residence in the interior of Africa, and a journey from the Cape of Good Hope to Loanda, on the west coast; thence across the continent, down the river Zambesi, to the eastern ocean. By David Livingstone ... With portrait; maps by Arrowsmith; and numerous illustrations. London, J. Murray, 1857.
ix, [1], 687, [1] p. front. (port.) illus., plates (part col. and fold.) 2 fold. maps, fold. plan. 22½ cm.
1. Africa, South.—Descr. & trav. 2. Missions—Africa, South. I. Title.
DT731.L739 5—15250

ICJ CSmH OrPS CLU MH-P OrU PPL PSC NN PPD TxU DNLM InU CU NjR NcD-MC TU OCU NIC CtY FU CtY-D
NL 0421062 DLC NcU OKentU PU IEN NcU OClW IU TxU MB

Livingstone, David, 1813-1873.
Missionary travels and researches in South Africa: including a sketch of sixteen years' residence in the interior of Africa, and a journey from the cape of Good Hope to Loanda on the west coast; thence across the continent, down the river Zambesi, to the eastern ocean. By David Livingstone ... With portrait; maps by Arrowsmith; and numerous illustrations. New York, Harper & brothers, 1858.
2 p. l., [ix]-xxiv, 732 p. incl. illus., plates. front. (port.) doub. pl., 2 fold maps, fold. plan. 23 cm.
Published also, the same year, with title: Livingstone's travels and researches in South Africa.
1. Africa, South—Descr. & trav. 2. Missions—Africa, South. I. Title.
DT731.L742 5—15251

Or ICJ CaBVaU IdU OrPR MsSM TxU PU PU-Mu KyLx KyU PPRETS PPAN WaT WaTC CtHT-W NBC OCl OO ODW MB ICJ WaS MWA UU FTaSU CtY-AO NjP NcD TU MdBP AAP NcA CtY PU MiU NN PP
NL 0421063 DLC OClStM PPL PV NcU PPG DN DNLM CtY-D

Livingstone, David, 1813-1873.
Missionary travels and researches in South Africa; including a sketch of sixteen years' residence in the interior of Africa, and a journey from the cape of Good Hope to Loanda on the west coast; thence across the continent, down the river Zambesi, to the eastern ocean. By David Liningstone ... 25th ed. ... N. Y., Harper & bros., 1859.
xxiv, 755 p. front.(port.) maps 24 cm.

NL 0421065 ViLxW MH ViU Or

MZ54 L763mi 1860 Livingstone, David, 1813-1873.
Missionary travels and researches in South Africa; including a sketch of sixteen years' residence in the interior of Africa, and a journey from the Cape of Good Hope to Loanda on the west coast; thence across the continent, down the river Zambesi, to the eastern ocean. With port., maps by Arrowsmith; and numerous illustrations. 25th ed. New York, Harper, 1860.
xxiv, 755 p. illus., port., fold. maps, fold. plan, tables. 24 cm.
Previous ed. published under title: Livingstone's travels and researches in South Africa.

NL 0421067 CtY-D PPWa MdBP MB OU OO

Livingstone, David, 1813-1873.
Missionary travels & researches in South Africa ... N. Y., 1865.

NL 0421068 NjNbS

Livingstone, David, 1813-1873.
Missionary travels and researches in South Africa; including a sketch of sixteen years' residence in the interior of Africa... New York: Harper & Bros., 1868. 2 p.l., (i)x-xxiv, 755 p., 1 pl., 1 port. 25. ed. 8°.

NL 0421069 NN PPT PPAN

LIVINGSTONE, David, 1813-1873.
Missionary travels and researches in South Africa. Including a sketch of sixteen years' residence in the interior of Africa, and a journey from the Cape of Good Hope to Loanda on the west coast, thence across the continent, down the river Zambesi, to the eastern ocean. Maps by Arrowsmith. 25th ed., with copious index. New York, Harper & Brothers, 1870.
24 cm. pp.xxiv, 755. Port., maps and other illustr.

NL 0421070 MH ViLxW

MZ54 L763mi 1872 Livingstone, David, 1813-1873.
Missionary travels and researches in South Africa; including a sketch of sixteen years' residence in the interior of Africa, and a journey from the Cape of Good Hope to Loanda on the west coast; thence across the continent, down the river Zambesi, to the eastern ocean. With port.; maps by Arrowsmith; and numerous illustrations. 25th ed. New York, Harper, 1872
xxiv, 755 p. illus., double plate, port., 2 fold. maps, fold.plan. 24 cm.

NL 0421071 CtY-D CtY CaBVa

Livingstone, David, 1813-1873.
Missionary travels and researches in South Africa: including a sketch of sixteen years' residence in the interior of Africa...25th.ed. with copius index. N.Y., Harper, 1876.
755 p.

NL 0421072 PP

Livingstone, David, 1813-1873.
Missionary travels and researches in South Africa. By David Livingstone ... With notes by Frederick Stanley Arnot ... With map and illustrations. New ed. London, J. Murray, 1899.
xiv, 447 p. incl. front., illus. plates, fold. map. 21cm.
1. Africa, South—Descr. & trav. 2. Missions—Africa, South. I. Arnot, Frederick Stanley, ed.
17-5281
Library of Congress DT731.L742 1899

NL 0421073 DLC MH KyLoU

Livingstone, David, 1813-1873.
Missionary travels & researches in South Africa, including a sketch of sixteen years' residence in the interior of Africa, by David Livingstone ... London, New York [etc.] Ward, Lock & co. [1899]
xv, 617 p. front. (port.) plates. 19½cm.
1. Africa, South—Descr. & trav. 2. Missions—Africa, South. I. Title.

NL 0421074 MiU CtY-D

DT752 .L72 1905 Livingstone, David, 1813-1878.
Missionary travels and researches in South Africa. By David Livingstone... With notes by Frederick Stanley Arnot. New ed. London, Maclaren, 1905.
447 p.
1. Africa, South - Descr. & trav. 2. Missions - Africa, South. I. Arnot, Frederick Stanley, ed.

NL 0421075 NBuU

MZ54 L763mi 1912 Livingstone, David, 1813-1873.
Missionary travels and researches in South Africa. With notes by Frederick Stanley Arnot. London, J. Murray, 1912.
xiv, 468 p. illus., fold. map. 20 cm.
1. Africa, South - Descr. & trav. 2. Africa South - Missions. 3. Africa, Central - Descr. & trav. 4. Africa, Central - Missions. I. Arnot, Frederick Stanley, 1858-1914.

NL 0421076 CtY-D ODW NSyU CU

916.7 L763mTGl Livingstone, David, 1813-1873.
Missionsreisen und Forschungen in Süd-Afrika während eines sechzehnjährigen Aufenthalts im Innern des Kontinents. Autorisierte, vollständige Ausg. für Deutschland. Aus dem Englischen von Hermann Lotze. Leipzig, H. Costenoble, 1858.
2v. in 1. illus., plates, ports., 2 maps. 23cm.
Translation of Missionary travels and researches in South Africa.
1. Africa, South - Descr. & trav. 2. Missions - Africa, South. I. Title.

NL 0421077 TxU

Livingstone, David, 1813-1873.
Narrative of an expedition to the Zambesi and its tributaries; and of the discovery of the lakes Shirwa and Nyassa. 1858-1864. By David and Charles Livingstone. With map and illustrations. London, J. Murray, 1865.
xiv p., 1 l., 608 p. double front., illus., plates, fold. map. 23cm.
1. Africa, Central—Descr. & trav. I. Livingstone, Charles, 1821-1873, joint author.
5-15249
Library of Congress DT731.L75

PPAN PP PBm PPA CtY MdBP ViU LU IEN CaBVaU WaSpG
NL 0421078 DLC FMU InU CU NBC PPL ICJ OClW OCU PBa

Livingstone, David, 1813-1873.
Narrative of an expedition to the Zambesi and its tributaries; and of the discovery of the lakes Shirwa and Nyassa. 1858-1864. By David and Charles Livingstone. With map and illustrations. New York, Harper & brothers, 1866.
xxii, 638 p. incl. illus., plates. double front., fold. map. 23cm.
1. Africa, Central—Descr. & trav. I. Livingstone, Charles, 1821-1873, joint author.
5—15248
Library of Congress DT731.L752

MoU CoU AAP WU ViU WaU NN I NcD NjP PPG NcA MiU OCl OO DN PPFr NjNbS NjP OClW
NL 0421079 DLC OrP Wa Or WaS NIC GU NjR CtY-D FU CU

Livingstone, David, 1813-1873.
Narrative of an expedition to the Zambesi and its tributaries; and of the discovery of the lakes Shirwa and Nyassa. 1858-1864. By David and Charles Livingstone ... New York, Harper & brothers [1893]
xxii, 638 p. incl. illus., plates. front., fold. map. 24cm.
First published in 1865.
1. Africa, Central—Descr. & trav. I. Livingstone, Charles, 1821-1873, joint author. II. Title.
4—16740
Library of Congress DT731.L76
916.7 [s25h1] G742

NL 0421080 DLC WaT

MZ54 L763nG Livingstone, David, 1813-1873.
Neue missionsreisen in Süd-Afrika unternommen im auftrage der englischen regierung. Forschungen am Zambesi und seinen nebenflüssen nebst entdeckung der Seen Schirwa und Nyassa in den jahren 1858 bis 1864. Von David und Charles Livingstone. Autorisirte vollständige ausgabe für Deutschland. Aus dem englischen von J.E.A. Martin. 2. aufl. Wohlfeile volksausg. Jena, H. Costenoble, 1874.

Continued in next column

VOLUME 336

Continued from preceding column

2 v. in 1. illus., plates (1 fold.) fold. map. 22 cm. (Bibliothek geographischer reisen und entdeckungen älterer und neuerer zeit, 8. bd.)

Translation of Narrative of an expedition to the Zambesi and its tributaries.

NL 0421082 CtY-D

916.7 L763nTGa 1869 Livingstone, David, 1813-1873.
Neueste Erforschungsreisen im Süden Afrika's und auf dem Eilande Madagascar. In Schilderungen von David Livingstone's neuesten Forschungen während der Jahre 1858-1864; der Universitätsmission, der Reisen von Chapman [et. al] sowie der Reisen aus Madagascar in alter und neuer Zeit. Bearb. von Richard Andree. 2., umgearbeitete und ergänzte Aufl. Leipzig, O. Spamer, 1869.
2v. in 1. illus. 20cm. (Das Buch der Reisen und Entdeckungen. Afrika. Livingstone, der Missionär. II)
Cover title: Neueste Entdeckungsreisen im Innern Afrikas.
CONTENTS.--1. Abth. Reisen im Süden und Innern des afrikanischen Kontinents.--2. Abth. Land und Leute von Madagascar.

NL 0421084 TxU

Livingstone, David, 1813-1873.
... Perilous adventures and extensive discoveries in the interior of Africa ...
see his Livingstone's Africa.

Livingstone, David, 1813-1873.
Personal life
see under Blaikie, William Garden, 1820-1899.

Livingstone, David, 1813-1873.
A popular account of Dr. Livingstone's expedition to the Zambesi and its tributaries: and of the discovery of lakes Shirwa and Nyassa. 1858-1864. Abridged from the larger work. London, J. Murray, 1887.
xii, 416 p. fold. front., illus., plates. fold. map. 19½cm.
Title vignette.
"In laying the result of their discoveries before the public, it was arranged that Mr. Charles Livingstone should place his voluminous notes at the disposal of his brother; they are incorporated in the present work, but in a necessarily abridged form."—Notice.
1. Africa, Central—Descr. & trav. I. Livingstone, Charles, 1821-1873.
A 13-642
Title from Univ. of Chicago DT731.L754 Printed by L. C.

NL 0421087 ICU MtU

MZ54 L763np Livingstone, David, 1813-1873.
A popular account of Dr. Livingstone's expedition to the Zambesi and its tributaries: and of the discovery of lakes Shirwa and Nyassa: 1858-1864. London, J. Murray, 1894.
xii, 416 p. illus.(1 fold.) fold. map. 19 cm.
Title vignette.
"In laying the result of their discoveries before the public, it was arranged that Mr. Charles Livingstone should place his voluminous notes at the disposal of his brother: they are incorporated in the present work, but in a necessarily abridged form." - Notice.
1. Africa, Central - Missions. 2. Africa, Central - Descr. & trav. I. Livingstone, Charles, 1821-1873.

NL 0421089 CtY-D

MZ54 L763mi 1861 Livingstone, David, 1813-1873.
A popular account of missionary travels and researches in South Africa. London, J. Murray, 1861.
ix, 436 p. illus. (1 fold.) fold. map. 20 cm.
1. Africa, South - Descr. & trav. 2. Africa, South - Missions. 3. Africa, Central - Descr. & trav. 4. Africa, Central - Missions. I. Title.

NL 0421090 CtY-D MB MH CtY ViU CaBVaU IEN

Livingstone, David, 1813-1873.
A popular account of missionary travels and researches in South Africa. New ed. London, J. Murray, 1868.
ix,436 p. illus.,map. 20 cm.
1.Africa, South—Desc. & trav. 2. Missions—Africa, South.

NL 0421091 NIC MH

Livingstone, David, 1813-1873.
A popular account of missionary travels and researches in South Africa. By David Livingstone ... New ed. London, J. Murray, 1875.
ix, 436 p. fold. front., illus., plates, fold. map. 19½cm.
Title vignette.
1. Africa, South—Descr. & trav. 2. Missions—Africa, South.
A 13-644
Title from Univ. of Chicago DT731.L755 Printed by L. C.

NL 0421092 ICU NSyU MtU NBuU CoU FMU OClJC

DT731 .L748 Livingstone, David, 1813-1873.
Путешествия по Южной Африке с 1840 по 1856 гг. [Под ред. А. С. Баркова, сокр. перевод с английского Н. М. Пульхритудова] Москва, Гос. изд-во геогр. лит-ры, 1947.
323 p. plates, port., fold. map. 27 cm.
1. Africa, South—Descr. & trav. 1801-1900. 2. Missions—Africa, South.
Title transliterated: Puteshestvīā po ÎUzhnoĭ Afrike.
DT731.L748 49-18369*‡

NL 0421093 DLC

Livingstone, David, 1813-1873.
Some letters from Livingstone, 1840-1872, edited by David Chamberlin; with an introduction by R. Coupland ... London, New York [etc.] Oxford university press, 1940.
xxvii, [1], 280 p. front. (port.) illus. (map) facsims. 22cm.
"Books on Livingstone and the Arab slave-trade": p. xxvii.
I. Chamberlin, David, ed.
41-1115
Library of Congress DT731.L775
[922.842] 923.942

NL 0421094 NcD NNC PPL OCl OCU PPT DLC NBuU OO CtY-D IEN CU WaSpG WaS MU

DT731 .L776 Livingstone, David, 1813-1873.
The story of the brave Scotchman! Life and explorations of David Livingstone, the great missionary explorer, in the interior of Africa: comprising all his extensive travels and discoveries as detailed in his diary, reports and letters, and including his famous last journals. Philadelphia, John E. Potter and company, 1874.
643 p. fronts. (ports.), illus. 21 cm.

NL 0421095 TU PPT Mi

Livingstone, David, 1813-1873.
The story of the brave Scotchman
see also his Life and explorations of David Livingstone.

---

968 L78s Livingstone, David, 1813-1873.
Südafrika und Madagaskar geschildert durch die neueren Entdeckungsreisenden, namentlich Livingstone und Ellis. [Hrsg. von C.B.Lorck] Leipzig, C.B. Lorck, 1860.
416p. 20cm. (Carl B. Lorck's Hausbibliothek, 64)
1. Africa, South. Disc. & explor. 2. Madagascar. Disc. & explor. I. Ellis, James J., jt. auth. II. Lorck, Carl Berendt, 1814-1905, ed. III. Title.

NL 0421097 IEN OCl

Livingstone, David, 1813-1873, and Ellis, William.
Südafrika und Madagaskar. 1865.
416 p.

NL 0421098 PPFr

Livingstone, David, 1813-1873.
Travels and researches in South Africa. Including a sketch of sixteen years' residence in the interior of Africa, and a journey from the Cape of Good Hope to Loanda on the West coast, thence across the continent, down the River Zambesi to the Eastern ocean. From the personal narrative of David Livingstone. To which is added a historical sketch of discoveries in Africa. Philadelphia, J.W. Bradley, 1860.
Colored plates and other illustr.

NL 0421099 MH IaU OrP

DT 731 .L745 1905 Livingstone, David, 1813-1873.
Travels and researches in South Africa ... London, Amalgamated Press, 1905.
xxiv,656p. 17cm. (Harmondsworth library, no.14)
Originally published under titles: Missionary travels and researches in South Africa, and Livingstone's travels and researches in South Africa.
1. Africa, South. Descr. & trav. 2. Missions. Africa, South. I. Title.

NL 0421100 OrU

Livingstone, David, 1813-1873.
... Travels and researches in Sth. Africa, by Dr. David Livingstone. London, Herbert Joseph limited [1937]
349 p. incl. front. (map) 19cm. (Great explorations; ed. by Hugh J. Schonfield. [v. 2])
Cover-title: Livingstone's travels in S. Africa.
Title vignette.
First published under title: Missionary travels and researches in South Africa. cf. Editorial note.
1. Africa, South—Description and travel. 2. Missions—Africa, South.
A 39-975
New York. Public library for Library of Congress [DT731.L]

NL 0421101 NN

Livingstone, David, 1813-1873.
Travels and researches ...
see also his Livingston's travels and researches in South Africa.

VOLUME 336

Livingstone, David, 1813–1873.
L'ultimo giornale di Livingstone, 1866–1873... Milano: Fratelli Treves, 1876. xv, 213 p. front. (port.), illus., map. 8°. (Biblioteca di viaggi. [v.] 40.)

221889A. 1. Africa, Central—Descr. and trav., 1850–1875. August 25, 1926

NL 0421103 NN

DT351 .S35 Livingstone, David, 1813-1873.

Saussus, Roger, 1902–
Vers le Congo: Livingstone et Stanley. Illus. d'A. de Vinck. Namur, Grands Lacs [1952]

Livingstone, David, 1813–1873.
I viaggi di Livingstone.
— Milano. Fratelli. 1887. xv, 514 pp. Illus. Portraits. Plates. Maps. [Africa. 2.] 24 cm., in 4s.

H6300 — Africa. Series. — Africa, South. Geog.

NL 0421105 MB

Livingstone, David, 1813-1873.

Oswell, William Edward.
William Cotton Oswell, hunter and explorer; the story of his life, with certain correspondence and extracts from the private journal of David Livingstone, hitherto unpublished; by his eldest son, W. Edward Oswell ... With an introduction by Francis Galton ... London, W. Heinemann, 1900.

Livingstone, David, 1813-1873.
Wonders of Africa; the life-history of Doctor Livingston, the great explorer
see under title

Livingstone, David, 1813-1873
see also Rhodes-Livingstone Museum, Livingstone, Zambia.

Beinecke Library Iq M167 936L Livingstone, David Stanley.
Full and by ... with an introduction by William McFee. London, Faber and Faber limited [1936]
2 p.ℓ., 7-258 p. 21 cm.

"First published in January MCMXXXVI."

1. Livingstone, David Stanley - Presentation inscription to W.McFee. I. McFee, William, 1881-1966.

NL 0421109 CtY AU

Livingstone, David Stanley.
Full and by [by] David Stanley Livingstone; with an introduction by William McFee. New York, Dodge publishing company [°1936]
xx, 233 p. illus. 21ᶜᵐ.
"First edition."

I. McFee, William, 1881– II. Title. 36-7581

Library of Congress PZ3.L7633Fu

NL 0421110 DLC NN GU TxU CaBVa MB

Livingstone, E. & S., publishers.
Pathology
see under title

Livingstone, Elizabeth.
Two studies in supervision

see under

National Institute of Industrial Psychology, London.

SB945 .T68R4 1937 Livingstone, Erskine McFarlane, 1909- joint author.

Reed, William Doyle, 1897–
... Biology of the tobacco moth and its control in closed storage. By W. D. Reed ... and E. M. Livingstone ... [Washington, U. S. Govt. print. off., 1937]

Livingstone, Erskine McFarlane, 1909- joint author.
Reed, William Doyle, 1897–
... A pest of cured tobacco, *Ephestia elutella* Hübner. By W. D. Reed ... and Erskine Livingstone and A. W. Morrill, jr. ... Washington [U. S. Govt. print. off.] 1933.

Livingstone, Erskine McFarlane, 1909- joint author.
Reed, William Doyle, 1897–
... Trapping experiments for the control of the cigarette beetle [*Lasioderma serricorne* Fab.] By W. D. Reed ... and A. W. Morrill, jr., and E. M. Livingstone ... [Washington, U. S. Govt. print. off., 1935]

Livingstone, Esther Louise.
The literary career of A. E. Housman... [Cincinnati, 1941.
Thesis.

NL 0421116 OCU

JQ653 Z96L3 L57 Livingstone, George.
The Tamilians in Ceylon and a federal constitution. Colombo, Ilankai Tamil Arasu Kadchi [1952?]
71 p.

1. Ceylon - Languages. 2. Ceylon. Constitution. I. Title.

NL 0421117 CU

Livingstone, H.

Threlkeld, Lancelot Edward, 1788–1859.
An Australian language as spoken by the Awabakal, the people of Awaba, or lake Macquarie (near Newcastle, New South Wales) being an account of their language, traditions, and customs: by L. E. Threlkeld. Re-arranged, condensed, and ed., with an appendix, by John Fraser ... Sydney, C. Potter, govt. printer, 1892.

Q161 .N4 Livingstone, Helen, 1877-

New York state vocational and practical arts association.
Applied science essential to the needle trades. Prepared by the following trade teachers in the New York city vocational high schools: Nancy Angelier ... Mary M. Stern ... Emma S. Janofsky ... [and] Marie R. Scalea ... Cover design by Dora Bagnoud ... Illustrations by Eugene H. Peterson ... Under the direction of Gilbert G. Weaver [and] Helen Livingston [!] ... [Albany] Pub. for the New York state vocational and practical arts association by Delmar publishers, inc.. 1945.

Livingstone, Helen, 1877–
Everyday beauty culture [by] Helen Livingstone ... and Ann Maroni ... Illustrated by Gladys Gazarian ... Bloomington, Ill., McKnight & McKnight [1945]
115 p. illus. 26½ x 20ᶜᵐ.

1. Beauty, Personal. 2. Beauty shops. I. Maroni, Ann, joint author. II. Title. 45-85129

Library of Congress RL76.L5 646.7

NL 0421120 DLC Or CaBVa IdB WaT NcGU PP PPD OCl OClW

Livingstone, Helen, 1877–
Everyday grooming, by Helen Livingstone and Ann Maroni; illustrated by Mary M. Graf. Bloomington, Ill., McKnight & McKnight [1951]
165 p. illus. 24 cm.

1. Beauty, Personal. I. Title.

RA778.L82 646.7 51-6849 ‡

NL 0421121 DLC CU Wa WaT WaE DNLM WaSp

Livingstone, Helen, 1877–
Food service; for restaurant, coffee shop, hotel, cafeteria, home. Bloomington, Ill., McKnight and McKnight Pub. Co. [°1950]
117 p. illus. 27 cm.

1. Restaurants, lunch rooms, etc. 2. Cookery for institutions, etc. I. Title.

TX945.L5 647.95 51-7362 ‡

NL 0421122 DLC WaE Wa Or CaBVa OrCS N MiD DNAL MB NN LU MoU

T65 .B68 Livingstone, Helen, 1877- joint author.

Bollinger, Elroy William, 1897–
Metodologia do ensino industrial [por] Elroy W. Bollinger [e] Helen Livingstone. Rio de Janeiro, Ministério da Educação e Saúde, Comissão Brasileiro-Americana de Educação Industrial, 1950.

Livingstone, Helen, 1877–
... Suggested reference list for a girls' vocational high school library, prepared by Helen Livingstone ... [Albany, The University of the state of New York press, 1945]
1 p. l., 17 p. 23ᶜᵐ. (New York (State) University. Bulletin no. 1293)

1. Occupations—Bibl. 2. Vocational guidance—Bibl. 3. School libraries (High school) I. Title.

A 45-4487

Teachers college library, for Library of Congress Columbia univ. Z7164.C81L76 † 016.371425

NL 0421124 NNC-T ODW DLC

Livingstone, Helen, 1877–
Teaching homemaking; adult education; copyrighted ... [by] Helen Livingstone [and] Naomi Voegele. [New York, Organization service associates] °1937.
4 p. l., 49 p., 1 l. 28ᶜᵐ.
Mimeographed.
Includes bibliographies.

1. Domestic economy—Study and teaching. 2. Education of adults. I. Voegele, Naomi, joint author. II. Title.

40-8719

Library of Congress TX165.L5
Copyright AA 266113 640.7

NL 0421125 DLC OrCS OClW PPT

VOLUME 336

Livingstone, Helen, 1877-
The teaching of related trade information for women's trades, prepared by Helen Livingstone ... New York city, The Hamilton company ⌐194-?⌐
4 p. l., 2-122 numb. l. 27½cm. (Industrial teacher-training monograph series)
Reproduced from type-written copy.
Includes "References."
1. Vocational education. 2. Vocational guidance. 3. Woman—Employment. I. Title.
Penn. state college. Libr. for Library of Congress A 44-488
NL 0421126 PSt

TX 331 L78 Livingstone, Helen, 1877-
Training for household service occupations in the American home. Rev. New York City, 1936.
100, ⌐2⌐ p. tables. 28 cm.
Bibliography: p. ⌐101-102⌐
1. Domestic education. 2. Servants. I. Title.
NL 0421127 NIC WaS

Livingstone, Helen Carroll.
The White House book of etiquette, an authoritative and authentic statement of the manners of society, by Helen Carroll Livingstone ... illustrated with portraits of mistresses of the White House from Mrs. Washington to Mrs. Roosevelt. Chicago, The Madison book co. ⌐1903⌐
249 p. incl. front., illus., plates, ports. 21½cm. 3-19658
NL 0421128 DLC

BM 535 L5 Livingstone, Isaac.
Illustrations of co-operation between Jews and non-Jews in educational and other fields. [London, Jews' College, 1954?]
21 p. 19 cm. (Michael Friedländer Memorial lecture, 6)
1. Christianity and other religions--Judaism. 2. Judaism--Relations--Christianity. I. Title II. Series
NL 0421129 OCH CtY

BM 560 .L5 Livingstone, Isaac.
Jewish life interpreted, by I. Livingstone. London, Goldston, 1939.
212 p.
#Judaism.
#Jews--Rites and ceremonies.
(A)Jewish life interpreted.
NL 0421130 MoU OClTem OCH OCl

Livingstone, Isaac.
Jews and Christians: a plea for goodwill and fellowship. Sermon ... May 7th, 1933...
⌐Bath: Sharp and sons, 1933⌐.
16 p.
NL 0421131 OCH NNJ

PZ 3 .L7452 Ne Livingstone, J C
The negro prince; or, The victims of Dahomey. London, C. H. Clarke, 1862.
331p.
Bound with Balfour, C. L. Retribution. Glasgow, 1863.
NL 0421132 ScU

Livingstone, James B., joint comp.
Campbell, Gus W comp.
Buddies, a collection of world war poems, "written by our buddies for our buddies"; collected by Gus W. Campbell ⌐and⌐ James B. Livingstone. De Kalb, Ill., The Barb city book company ⌐°1930⌐

WB 100 L787a 1929 LIVINGSTONE, James Livingstone.
Aids to medicine. 4th ed. London, Baillière, Tindall and Cox, 1929.
x, 414 p. illus. (Students' aids series)
1. Medicine - Handbooks
NL 0421134 DNLM

Livingstone, James Livingstone.
Aids to medicine, by James L. Livingstone ... 5th ed. London, Baillière, Tindall and Cox, 1935.
viii, 422 p. illus. 16½cm.
1. Medicine—Practice. I. Title.
U. S. Surg.-gen. off. Library for Library of Congress [RC46] S G 37-46
NL 0421135 DNLM CaBVaU ICU

RC46 L4 1944 LIVINGSTONE, James Livingstone.
Aids to medicine, by James L. Livingstone. 5th ed. London, Baillière, Tindall and Cox, 1944.
422p. illus. 17cm.
1. Medicine - Practice I. Title
NL 0421136 CtY-M

Livingstone, Janey C.
Historic Silver Islet, the story of a drowned mine.
24p. illus. port. Fort William, ⌐Times-Journal Presses⌐, n.d.
NL 0421137 CaOTU

Livingstone, Jeffrey.
Build your own summer camp or cabin. New York, McGraw-Hill ⌐°1955⌐
152 p. illus. 21 x 24 cm.
1. Summer homes. 2. Architecture, Domestic—Designs and plans. I. Title.
TH4835.L5 694 54—7364 ‡
MiU OU
IU MtBC IdB PSt CaBVa Or OrP Wa WaS WaSp WaT OC1W
NL 0421138 DLC OCl OOxM NcC NcRS TxU PPD TU NN MB

Livingstone, Jennie.
Organic constituents of oil shales and related rocks. ... (In Colorado. University. Studies... Boulder, Col., 1928. v. 16, no. 2, 149-70.)
NL 0421139 OU OrP

C 7445 .885 LIVINGSTONE, JEREMIAH LENNOX.
Church property. First fruits and tenths in England and Ireland, being the petition of J. Lennox Livingstone, presented to the House of Commons, 18th March, 1835. By the Rt.Hon.Lord John Russell, relative to the claims of lay-patrons of churches in England and Ireland. London, E. Wilson, 1835.
156p. 22cm.
Binder's title: Tracts on church property and church reform. 1835-40.
NL 0421140 ICN RPB NNC

C 7445 .885 LIVINGSTONE, JEREMIAH LENNOX.
A letter to the most noble the Marquis of Clanricarde, on Irish church property; the usurpation of the rights of lay patrons by the Irish bishops: and the recent attempt made by government to extinguish those rights for the purpose of creating a surplus fund. London, E. Wilson, 1836.
31p. 22cm.
Binder's title: Tracts on church property and church reform 1835-40.
NL 0421141 ICN

⌐Livingstone, John⌐
Christopher Columbus, digest relating to discoveries. ⌐Chicago, 1893⌐
60 numb. l. 31 x 23½cm.
No. t.-p. Proof-sheets, with manuscript corrections; each leaf signed "J. L."
In double columns. Bound oblong.
1. Colombo, Cristoforo. I. Title. 2—7924
Library of Congress E111.L78
NL 0421142 DLC

Livingstone, John, 1603-1672
see Livingston, John, 1603-1672.

⌐Livingstone, John⌐ 1680-1720.
A British report on Canada, 1711 ⌐edited⌐ by James F. Kenney ... ⌐Toronto⌐ The University of Toronto press, 1920.
cover-title, p. 48-54. 26cm.
Caption title: Notes and documents; a British secret service report on Canada, 1711.
The report of Major Livingstone is a transcript of the original in the Public record office, London, C. O. 42, v. 13. Title of original: 1710. A view of Canada taken by Major John Livingstone with acco^t. of fortifications and number of men.
The transcript, with editor's notes, is reprinted from the Canadian historical review, March, 1920.
1. Canada—Defenses. 2. Quebec (City)—Fortifications. I. Kenney, James F., ed. II. Title.
29-30086
Library of Congress F1030.L78
NL 0421144 DLC MH MWA MB NN

Livingstone, John, 1838-
Fuel losses. The present day problem. I have solved it, consider what that means. [Montreal, 1908]
2 l. f°.
n. t.-p.
Two circulars by same author, inserted, relative to patent 853, 099, a device for saving fuel.
NL 0421145 NN

Livingstone, John, 1838-
How justice was cheated: a narrative of ... conspiracies by rich and influential men ... and a narrative of criminal manipulations of proceedings by lawyers to deceive judges ... [New York, Platt Press, cop. 1906]
76 p. 8°.
NL 0421146 NN

Livingstone, John, 1838-
How to save 50 per cent. now spent on coal; also the utility of hollow bolts as stays and as factors bettering combustion, comprised in a practical paper read before the St. Louis railway club ... and a practical paper read before the New York railway club ... by John Livingstone. [New York, Printed by Roy press, °1905]
62 p. 23cm.
1. Locomotives.
Library of Congress TJ608.L7 6-24585
NL 0421147 DLC NN ICJ

VOLUME 336

Livingstone, John A
Address on presentation of a portrait of the late Risden Tyler Bennett, to the Supreme Court of North Carolina, by his family, 22 November 1933 [n.p., n.d.]
21 p. 24 cm.

1. Bennett, Risden Tyler, 1840-1913.

NL 0421148 NcU-L

Livingstone, John A
The law and its ideal. Raleigh, Bynum Printing Co., 1926. 16p. 16cm.
Reprinted from News and observer.

1. N.C.--Lawyers

NL 0421149 NcU NcD

Livingstone, John A.
Open court: Rotation of Superior court judges.

Extract from North Carolina law review, Dec.1927, v.6, no.1.

NL 0421150 NcU

---

*F259 .B4 1933 Livingstone, John A

Risden Tyler Bennett; address by John A. Livingstone, presenting the portrait of Risden Tyler Bennett ... to the Supreme Court. Acceptance address by Walter P. Stacy. [n. p.] 1933.
21 p. port. 24cm.
Cover title.

1. Bennett, Risden Tyler, 1840-1913. I. Stacy, Walter P II. North Carolina. Supreme Court.

NL 0421151 ViU NcD-L

Livingstone, John H.
see Livingston, John Henry, 1746-1825.

B4568 .O74L4 Livingstone, Leon.
Ortega y Gasset's philosophy of art. New York, 1952.
609-654 p. 25cm.

Thesis - Brown University.
Reprinted from PMLA, v.67, no.5, September, 1952.

NL 0421153 OCU OCIW

Livingstone, Mabel.

Le Roy, Kate Warner.

Flower fair, and other poems; music by Kate Warner Le Roy, poems by Mabel Livingstone ... New York city, Musette publishers, °1941.

Livingstone, Mabel.
"Have a good time."
see under Le Roy, Kate Warner.

Livingstone, Mabel.
My prayer was heard
see under Donaldson, Molly.

CD1072 .A3 Livingstone, Matthew, 1837-1917.

Scotland. *General registry office of births, deaths and marriages.*
A guide to the public records of Scotland deposited in H. M. General register house, Edinburgh; by M. Livingstone ... Edinburgh, H. M. General register house, 1905.

Livingstone, Matthew, 1837-1917.
Scotland.
Registrum secreti sigilli regum Scotorum. The register of the Privy seal of Scotland ...
Edinburgh, H. M. General register house, 1908-

---

*EC65 L7636 667p Livingstone, Patrick, 1634?-1694.
Plain and downright-dealing with them that were with us, and are gone out from us; and also to them that are of the same mind with them who are gone from us, and yet come to meetings ... Also, there is annexed something in answer to a paper, given forth by one whose name is set down under M.T. By Patrick Livingstone ...
London, Printed in the year, 1667.
24p. 18.5cm.
On wearing hats during prayers.

NL 0421159 MH PSC-Hi PHC PHi CtY DFo CSmH InRE

Mm72 L763 1847 Livingstone, Patrick, 1634-1694.
Selections from the writings of Patrick Livingstone; a faithful minister of the gospel in the Society of Friends, and a patient sufferer for the same; who was born at Montrose, in Scotland, in 1634, and died in 1694. Now first published from the original manuscript volume. Together with a brief memoir of him ... London, C.Gilpin, 1847.
3p.ℓ., [5]-395p. 19½cm.
Edited by Lydia Ann Barclay.

NL 0421160 CtY PHC PSC-Hi

---

*EC65 L7636 670t [Livingstone, Patrick, 1634?-1694]
To all friends every where to whom this may concern, to go abroad among them to be lead in the fear of God by them.
[London, 1670]
8p. 19cm.
Caption title.
Dated & signed at end: From the prison by Newgate the 7th. of the 10th. month, 1670. Your friend Patrick Livingstone.

NL 0421161 MH PSC-Hi PHC CtY CSmH

---

*pEB65 A100 B675b v.3 Livingstone, Patrick, 1634?-1694.
To the King and both houses of Parliament.
[London, 1670]
broadside. 38.5x31cm., mounted & bd. to 66cm.
Dated & signed: London the 8th of the 9th month, 1670. Your Friend Patrick Livingstone.
No. B1 of the Marquess of Bute broadsides.

NL 0421162 MH

---

*EC65 L7636 667t Livingstone, Patrick, 1634?-1694.
Truth owned and deceit denyed and witnessed against: or, A clear manifestation of truth and its servants: as also a manifestation of falshood and deceit, with its servants. Wherein many several things are spoken to in plainness of speech, and in love to them who are willing to try all things, and to hold fast that which is good. Also many things are spoken to concerning the Book of common-prayer. And something annexed touching election and reprobation. Also there are some queries touching womens speaking in the church; which is annexed for the priests, or any of the contrary mind to answer if they can, or else be silent, that say, that no woman may speak in the church. Given forth by ... Patrick Livingston ...
London, Printed in the year, 1667.
47p. 19.5cm.
"Some queries to them that deny womens speaking in church" (p.45-47) signed: W.D.
Imperfect: p.45-47 slightly mutilated.

NL 0421164 MH PHi PPL MH PSC-Hi PHC CSmH

Livingstone, Paul Clyde.
Seeing America on the cuff, as told to Frank Gill, jr., by Paul Livingstone. Hollywood, Murray & Gee [°1940]
7 p. l., [13]-233 p. illus. 21½cm.
"This edition limited to eleven hundred copies."

1. U. S.—Descr. & trav. 2. Automobiles—Touring. I. Gill, Frank, jr. II. Title.

40-29765

Library of Congress E169.L78

Copyright 917.3

NL 0421165 DLC OrU

Livingstone, Peter Kininmonth.
The Boys' Brigade in Kirkcaldy, from its beginnings to the present time. Kirkcaldy, Allen Lithographic Co., 1953.
78 p. illus.

NL 0421166 MH

Livingstone, Peter Kininmonth.
Flax and linen in Fife through the centuries. Kirkcaldy, 1951.
43 p. illus.

NL 0421167 MH DNAL MiU

Livingstone, Peter Kininmonth, *comp.*
Flax and linen in Fife through the centuries. Kirkcaldy, 1952.
48 p. illus. 22 cm.

1. Linen—Scotland—Fife. 2. Flax—Scotland—Fife. I. Title.

TS1715.S3L5 677.11 52-65038 ‡

NL 0421168 DLC NN

Livingstone, Peter Kininmonth.
A history of Kirkcaldy, covering the years 1843-1949. Prepared by P.K. Livingstone in connection with his work for the third statistical account of Fife, published in Sept., 1952. Kirkcaldy, Allen Lithographic Co. 1955
95 p. illus.

NL 0421169 MH

VOLUME 336

Livingstone, Peter Kininmonth.
Kirkcaldy and its libraries; an account of the libraries in Kirkcaldy prepared for the centenary celebrations. [Kirkcaldy] 1950. 35 p. illus. 23cm.

1. Libraries—Gt. Br.—Scot.— Kirkcaldy.

NL 0421170 NN

Livingstone, R.
The mechanical design and construction of commutators, by R. Livingstone ... London, "The Electrician" printing and publishing company, limited; New York, The D. Van Nostrand co.; [etc., etc., 1907]
iv p., 1 l., 93 p. incl. tables, diagrs. 22cm. (On cover: "The Electrician" series)

1. Commutation (Electricity). I. Title.

NL 0421171 DP OCl NcSC NN

Livingstone, R.
The mechanical design and construction of generators. By R. Livingstone ... London, "The Electrician" printing and publishing company, limited; New York, The D. Van Nostrand co.; [etc., etc., 1914]
3 p. l., [v]-vi, 222 p. illus., 2 fold. pl., 2 fold. tab., fold. diagr. 22cm. (*On cover:* "The Electrician" series)

1. Dynamos. I. Title.

A 15-133

Title from Leland Stanford Jr. Univ. Printed by L. C.

NL 0421172 CSt WaS CU MiU OCl IU NN

Livingstone, R. of Australia.
Matriculation examination questions in English. Prahran, n.d.
20 p.

NL 0421173 CSt

LIVINGSTONE, R.W.

See LIVINGSTONE, Richard Winn, 1880-1933.

705.5 B642w 1954 LIVINGSTONE, Richard.
Tolerance in theory and in practice. London, The Council of Christians and Jews, 1954.
23p. 22cm. (Robert Waley Cohen memorial lecture, 1954)

NL 0421175 MH-AH

Livingstone, Richard Winn, 1880-1933, ed. and tr.
Caesar, C. Julius.
Caesar, books IV (20-38) ... [-VII] of the Gallic war, partly in the original and partly in translation, edited by R. W. Livingstone ... and C. E. Freeman ... Oxford, The Clarendon press; London, New York [etc.] H. Milford, 1924, '22.

Livingstone, Sir Richard Winn, 1880–
The classics and national life, by Sir Richard Livingstone. With a vote of thanks by Gilbert Murray... London [etc.] Oxford univ. press, 1941. [Classical association. Presidential addresses. 1941]

1. Classical education. I. Classical association.

April 30, 1945

NL 0421177 NN MH MA ICN NcD

Livingstone, *Sir* Richard Winn, 1880–
The classics and national life, by Sir Richard Livingstone. With a vote of thanks by Gilbert Murray. The presidential address delivered to the Classical association on 22nd April 1941. London, New York [etc.] Oxford university press [1942]
31, [1] p. 16cm.
"Published 1941, reprinted 1942."

1. Greek literature. 2. Hellenism. I. Title.

A 42-5348

Harvard univ. Library for Library of Congress

NL 0421178 MH CaBVaU LU MiD OCU NcD OU OO OClW IU

Livingstone, *Sir* Richard Winn, 1880–
... The Danish folk schools, by Sir Richard Livingstone. [New York, 1944]
1 p. l., 8 numb. l. 28 x 21½cm. (News background inc. Report no. 15)
Caption title: The way out.
Reproduced from type-written copy.
"From 'The future in education' by Sir Richard Livingstone. Cambridge university press; The Macmillan company, 1942."

1. Folk high schools. 2. Education—Denmark. 3. Education—Gt. Brit. I. Title.

Library of Congress LA876.L5 45-10

374.9489

NL 0421179 DLC

Livingstone, *Sir* Richard Winn, 1880–
A defence of classical education, by R. W. Livingstone. London, Macmillan and co., limited, 1916.
xi, 278 p. 19cm.

1. Classical education.

17—12623

Library of Congress LC1011.L5

NL 0421180 DLC CaBVaU WaS IdU NIC PV PBm OCl MiU OCU OO OOxM ViU IU MB NN PSC PU NcD NjP CtY

M-film 370.1 L763d Livingstone, Richard Winn, 1880-
A defence of classical education. London, Macmillan, 1917 [c1916.
xi, 278 p.

Microfilm (negative) Emporia, Kan., William Allen White Library, 1970. 1 reel. 35 mm.

1. Classical education.

NL 0421181 KEmT

Livingstone, R[ichard] W[inn], 1880-1933.
A defence of classical education. London: Macmillan and Co., Ltd., 1917. 278 p. 12°.

NL 0421182 NN PPT KEmT

Livingstone, Richard Winn.
A defense of classical education. Lond., 1918.
278 p.

NL 0421183 PHC

Livingstone, *Sir* Richard Winn, 1880–
Education and the spirit of the age. Oxford [Eng.] Clarendon Press, 1952.
114 p. 19 cm.

1. Education—Philosophy. 2. Civilization, Modern. I. Title.

LB775.L568 370.4 52—11081 ‡

NL 0421184 DLC NSyU CtY NN MH TxU OU MiU MeB NcGU NcU PU FMU CoU ScU CaBVaU WaSpG OrCS OrU OrMonO CaBVa OrLgE

Livingstone, *Sir* Richard Winn, 1880–
Education for a world adrift, by Sir Richard Livingstone ... Cambridge [Eng.] The University press, 1943.
xv, [1], 158 p., 1 l. 18cm. (*Half-title:* Current problems; general editor: Ernest Barker. 17)

1. Education—Aims and objectives. 2. Education—Gt. Brit. I. Title.

43-6566

Library of Congress LB775.L57

370.1

NL 0421185 DLC OrU CaBViP CaBVa NcGU NcC OCl OU PSC

370.11 L763e 1944 Livingstone, Sir Richard Winn, 1880-
Education for a world adrift, by Sir Richard Livingstone. Cambridge [Eng.] University press, 1944.
xv, 158p. 18cm. (Current problems; 17)

Includes bibliographical footnotes.

1. Education. Aims and objectives. 2. Education. Gt. Brit. I. Title.

NL 0421186 KU MB MH

Livingstone, *Sir* Richard Winn, 1880–
The future in education. Cambridge [Eng.] University Press, 1941.
ix, 127 p. 18 cm. (Current problems)
Bibliographical footnotes.

1. Education of adults. 2. Education—Gt. Brit. I. Title. (Series)

LC5256.G7L5 374.0942 A 41-2962 rev*

Harvard Univ. Library for Library of Congress [r55h2]†

NL 0421187 MH NcGU PSt DLC ViU OOxM OCl PWcS PSC PU WaWW NIC CaBVaU ICJ IdPI MtBC OrP

LA 632 .L79 1942 Livingstone, Sir Richard Winn, 1880-
The future in education, by Sir Richard Livingstone ... Cambridge [Eng.] At the University press, 1942.
ix, [1], 127 p. 17½cm. (Half-title: Current problems [no.6, General editor: Ernest Barker)
"First edition, March 1941. Reprinted ... May 1942."

1. Education—Aims and objectives. 2. Education of adults. 3. Education—Gt. Brit. I. Title.

NL 0421188 MiU FU ViU OU ICN

Livingstone, Sir Richard Winn, 1880-
The future in education, ... Cambridge [Eng.] The University press, 1943.
127 p.

NL 0421189 OClW

VOLUME 336

Livingstone, Sir Richard Winn.
The future in education. Cambridge, Eng., University press, 1944.
127 p.

NL 0421190 PP

Livingstone, Sir Richard Winn, 1880-
The future in education. Cambridge [Eng.] Univ.Press, 1945.
ix, 127 p. (Current problems, 6)

NL 0421191 MH

Livingstone, *Sir* Richard Winn, 1880-
The Greek genius and its meaning to us, by R. W. Livingstone ... Oxford, Clarendon press, 1912.
250 p., 1 l. 23cm.

1. Civilization, Greek. 2. Greek literature—Hist. & crit. I. Title.
12—40662
Library of Congress DF77.L5

WaWW CaBVaU OrCS NjP MiU MB NN IU ICJ ViU PSC PU PHC PPL ICJ OrP WaS
NL 0421192 DLC CoU CU NIC CtY NcD OOxM OCl OO PBm

Livingstone, *Sir* Richard Winn, 1880-
The Greek genius and its meaning to us, by R. W. Livingstone ... 2d ed. Oxford, The Clarendon press, 1915.
250 p., 1 l. 23½cm.

1. Civilization, Greek. 2. Greek literature—Hist. & crit. I. Title.
23—26570
Library of Congress DF77.L5
[a39e1]

CaBVaU OClW PPT CtY MB NcGU UU MtU AAP OrPR Or WaWW OrP
NL 0421193 DLC KyLxT InStme NcD NBuC KMK NcU PCC PBa

Livingstone, R[ichard] W[inn], 1880-1933.
The Greek genius and its meaning to us. London: Oxford Univ. Press, 1924. 250 p. 8°.

1. Title. 2. Greek literature.
July 17, 1928

NL 0421194 NN DDO OCX MB MH KyLoU TxFTC

Livingstone, Richard Winn, 1880-1933.
The Greek genius and its meaning to us, by R. W. Livingstone... London: Oxford University Press, 1924. 250 p. [2. ed.] 8°.

161574A. 1. Culture, Greek. 2. Greek literature—Hist. and criticism.
January 12, 1925

NL 0421195 NN OO OClW CtY ViU

LIVINGSTONE, R[ichard] W[inn] 1880-1933.
The Greek genius and its meaning to us. [3rd ed.] 3rd impression. London, H.Milford, 1924.

NL 0421196 MH

Livingstone, Richard Winn.
The Greek genius and its meaning to us. [2d ed.] London: Oxford univ. press [1933] 250 p.

1. Greek literature I. Title.
February 23, 1939

NL 0421197 NN

DF 77 L5 1939
Livingstone, *Sir* Richard Winn, 1880-
The Greek genius and its meaning to us, by R. W. Livingstone ... [2d ed.] London, Oxford University Press [1939]
250 p., 1 l. 23½ cm.
"Second edition, 1915; reprinted photographically ... 1939."

NL 0421198 CBDP

DF77 .L5 1946
Livingstone, Sir Richard Winn, 1880-
The Greek genius and its meaning to us. [2d ed.] London, Oxford University Press [1946]
250 p. 23 cm.

1. Civilization, Greek. 2. Greek literature—Hist. & crit. I. Title.

NL 0421199 MB

DF77 .L5 1949
Livingstone, Richard Winn, 1880-
The Greek genius and its meaning to us, by R. W. Livingstone. [2d ed.] [Oxford] Oxford University Press [1949]
250 p. 22cm.

1. Civilization, Greek. 2. Greek literature—Hist. & crit. I. Title.

NL 0421200 ViU MB IEN NRU

Livingstone, *Sir* Richard Winn, 1880-
Greek ideals and modern life, by Sir R. W. Livingstone ... Cambridge, Mass., Harvard university press, 1935.
4 p. l., [vii]-x, 175, [1] p. 21½ cm. (*Half-title: Martin classical lectures.* [vol. v])
Printed in Great Britain.
Errata slip inserted after p. x.
CONTENTS.—Introduction.—The growing influence of Hellenism.—Greek humanism.—Humanism in politics and economics.—The age of Plato; an analogy.—Christianity and Hellenism.

1. Hellenism. 2. Philosophy, Ancient. 3. Civilization, Greek. 4. Humanism. I. Title.
PA25.M3 vol. 5 913.38 A 35—1658
Oberlin College. Library for Library of Congress [a59r52w1]†

MH-AH FU CLSU MiU ICarbS OO ODW ViU NN PSt PP MiU PHC PSC PU MU MB NN DLC WaPS OrCS NcU
NL 0421201 OO OrSaW OrPR WaWW MtU IdPS OCl OCU

Livingstone, Sir Richard Winn, 1880-
Hēllenika idanika kai sygchronē zōē. Metaphrasis D. Chondros. [Athens] Apostolikē Diakonia tēs Ekklēsias tēs Hellados [1950]
115 [1] p.
Added t.-p.: Greek ideals and modern life.

NL 0421202 MiD

DF229 .T5C7 1943
Livingstone, Sir Richard Winn, 1880- ed. and tr.
Thucydides.
... The history of the Peloponnesian war, edited in translation by Sir R. W. Livingstone ... London, New York [etc.] H. Milford, Oxford university press, 1943.

Livingstone, *Sir* Richard Winn, 1880-
Leadership in education. London, New York, Oxford University Press, 1950.
25 p. 23 cm. (Walker Trust lectures on leadership, no. 10)

1. Teaching. I. Title. (Series)
A 51-9887
Teachers College Libr., Columbia Univ. for Library of Congress

NL 0421204 NNC-T ICU NN CU MH

Livingstone, Sir Richard Winn, 1880-
Lebendiges Griechentum. Greek ideals and modern life. [Von] Sir R. W. Livingstone. [Berechtigte Übers. aus dem Englischen von Hellmut Jaesrich] Hamburg, M. von Schröder, 1947.
191 p.
1. Hellenism. 2. Philosophy, Acient. 3. Civilization, Greek. I. (A) Lebendiges Griechentum.

NL 0421205 MoU MnU

Livingstone, *Sir* Richard Winn, 1880- *ed.*
The legacy of Greece; essays by Gilbert Murray, W. R. Inge, J. Burnet ... [and others] ed. by R. W. Livingstone. Oxford, The Clarendon press, 1921.
3 p. l., [ix]-xii, 424 p. illus., plates. 19½ cm.
CONTENTS.—The value of Greece to the future of the world, by G. Murray.—Religion, by W. R. Inge.—Philosophy, by J. Burnet.—Mathematics and astronomy, by Sir T. L. Heath.—Natural science, by D'Arcy W. Thompson.—Biology, by C. Singer.—Medicine, by C. Singer.—Literature, by R. W. Livington.—History, by A. Toynbee.—Political thought, by A. E. Zimmern.—The lamps of Greek art, by P. Gardner.—Architecture, by Sir R. Blomfield.

1. Greece. I. Title.
DF77.L6 913.38 22—10803

OClND Ky-LE CaQMM AU NIC CtY PPD PHC PU PBm ODW OCU OCl
NL 0421206 DLC NcD PBa PPLas OClU ViU OO OCX KyWAT

Livingstone, Richard Winn, 1880- ed.
The legacy of Greece; essays by Gilbert Murray, W.R. Inge, J. Burnet ... [and others] ed. by R.W. Livingstone. Oxford, The Clarendon press, 1922.
3 p. ℓ., [ix]-xii, 424 p. illus., plates. 20 cm.

PPLT NjP MB OCX CtY-D
NL 0421207 TU NjNbS KyLoU CU-M InStme NNUN PPT PP

913.38 L763ℓ 1921r
Livingstone, Richard Winn, 1880- ed.
The legacy of Greece; essays by Gilbert Murray, W.R. Inge, J. Burnet ... [and others] ed. by R.W. Livingstone. Oxford, The Clarendon press, 1923.
3p.ℓ.,[ix]-xii, 424p. illus.,plates. 19½cm.
"Third impression."
CONTENTS.—The value of Greece to the future of the world, by G. Murray.—Religion, by W.R. Inge.—Philosophy, by J. Burnet.—Mathematics and astronomy, by Sir T.L. Heath. Natural science, by D'Arcy W. Thompson.
(Continued on next card)

Biology, by C. Singer.—Medicine, by C. Singer.—Literature, by R.W. Livingstone.—History, by A. Toynbee.—Political thought, by A.W. Zimmern.—The lamps of Greek art, by P. Gardner.—Architecture, by Sir R. Blomfield.

1. Greece. I. Title.

NL 0421209 TxU ViU CtY PSC PU OU MH

Livingstone, R[ichard] W[inn], 1880-1933.
The legacy of Greece; essays; edited by R. W. Livingstone. Oxford: The Clarendon Press, 1924. 424 p. pl. 12°.
Contents: The value of Greece to the future of the world, by Gilbert Murray. Religion, by W. R. Inge. Philosophy, by J. Burnet. Mathematics and astronomy, by Sir T. L. Heath. Natural science, by D'Arcy W. Thompson. Biology, by Charles Singer. Literature, by R. W. Livingstone. History, by Arnold Toynbee. Political thought, by A. E. Zimmern. The lamps of Greek art, by Percy Gardner. Architecture, by Sir Reginald Blomfield.

1. Greece—Religion (anal.). 2. Greece—Hist. (anal.) 3. Greece—Government and politics (anal.). 4. Greece—Art (anal.). 5. Greek literature (anal.). 6. Philosophy (Greek) (anal.).
February 24, 1927

NL 0421210 NN PV PRosC OClUr ViU MH

VOLUME 336

Livingstone, *Sir* **Richard Winn,** 1880- *ed.*
The legacy of Greece; essays by Gilbert Murray, W. R. Inge, J. Burnet ... [and others] edited by R. W. Livingstone. Oxford, The Clarendon press [1928]
3 p. l., [ix]-xii, 424 p. illus., plates. 19 cm.
"Impression of 1928, first edition, 1921."
CONTENTS.—The value of Greece to the future of the world, by G. Murray. — Religion, by W. R. Inge. — Philosophy, by J. Burnet. — Mathematics and astronomy, by Sir T. L. Heath.—Natural science, by D'Arcy W. Thompson.—Biology, by C. Singer.—Medicine, by C. Singer.—Literature, by R. W. Livingstone.—History, by A. Toynbee.—Political thought, by A. E. Zimmern.—The lamps of Greek art, by P. Gardner.—Architecture, by Sir R. Blomfield.
1. Civilization, Greek. I. Title.
DF77.L6 1928 938 31-15045 rev

NL 0421211 DLC PPLas ViU PU CtY FMU NcD NBuU MSHM

WZ 51 L788L 1937 LIVINGSTONE, Sir Richard Winn, 1880- ed.
The legacy of Greece. Oxford, Clarendon Press [1937]
xii, 424 p. illus.
1. Medicine - Greek & Roman

NL 0421212 DNLM MB PPWe CtY

Livingstone, *Sir* **Richard Winn,** 1880- *ed.*
The legacy of Greece; essays by Gilbert Murray [and others] ... edited by R. W. Livingstone. Oxford, The Clarendon press [1942]
4 p. l., 424 p. illus., plates. 19cm.
"First published 1921, reprinted ... 1942."
CONTENTS.—The value of Greece to the future of the world, by Gilbert Murray.—Religion, by W. R. Inge.—Philosophy, by J. Burnet.—Mathematics and astronomy, by Sir T. L. Heath.—Natural science, by D. W. Thompson.—Biology, by Charles Singer.—Medicine, by Charles Singer.—Literature, by R. W. Livingstone.—History, by Arnold Toynbee.—Political thought, by A. E. Zimmern.—The lamps of Greek art, by Percy Gardner.—Architecture, by Sir Reginald Blomfield.
1. Civilization, Greek. I. Title.
44-7800
Library of Congress DF77.L6 1942
938

NL 0421213 DLC NcD CBDP

Livingstone, Richard Winn, ed.
The legacy of Greece. Essays. Oxford, Clarenden, 1947.

NL 0421214 NcU

Livingstone, Sir Richard Winn, 1880- ed.
The legacy of Greece; essays by G.Murray [and others] Oxford, Clarendon Press [1951]
424 p. illus., plates

NL 0421215 MH-FA

Livingstone, Richard Winn, *1880*-1933.
Literature.
(*In* Livingstone, Richard Winn, compiler and editor. The legacy of Greece. Pp. 249-287. Oxford. 1921.)
Relates to the influence of Greek literature on English literature.

M486o — English literature. Influence of other literatures. Greek.

NL 0421216 MB OOxM

Livingstone, *Sir* **Richard Winn,** 1880- *ed.*
The mission of Greece; some Greek views of life in the Roman world, edited by R. W. Livingstone ... Oxford, The Clarendon press, 1928.
xi, [1], 302 p., 1 l. plates, ports. 19½cm.
CONTENTS.—Introduction.—Epicurus.—The cynics.—The stoics: Epictetus.—The stoics: Marcus Aurelius.—A philosophic missionary: Dion Chrysostom.—Plutarch.—A popular preacher: Maximus Tyrius.—A theosophist: Apollonius of Tyana.—The sophists: Polemon and Herodes Atticus.—A prince of neurotics: Aelius Aristides.—Lucian.—Epilogue.
1. Philosophy, Ancient. 2. Greek literature—Translations into English. 3. English literature—Translations from Greek. I. Title.
Library of Congress B165.L5 29—12641

KEmT MU WaWW WaS OrPR CaBVaU CaBVa OrCS
MiU OO OCU PBm PPLas NcGU NcD PU NBuC ICarbS KMK
NL 0421217 DLC TNJ CSt MB PSC PPT PHC ViU NN OCl

Livingstone, Richard Winn.
Mycenai. Ox., Blackwell, 1901.
12 p.

NL 0421218 PU

Livingstone, *Sir* **Richard Winn,** 1880-
On education, by Sir Richard Livingstone ... containing two books previously published separately, The future in education and Education for a world adrift; with a foreword by Virginia C. Gildersleeve ... Cambridge [Eng.] The University press; New York, The Macmillan company, 1944.
5 p. l., [v]-ix, [1], 127 p., 1 l., [vii]-xv, [1], 158 p. 19½cm.
"First printing."
1. Education—Aims and objectives. 2. Education of adults. 3. Education—Gt. Brit. I. Title. II. Title: The future in education. III. Title: Education for a world adrift.
44-5234
LB775.L5
[25] 370.1

PPPL OU ViU ICJ OO OCl PSt PBm LU
OrU WaT CaBVa KyWAT KEmT KyLxCB KyU NBuC PV NcD DNAL
NL 0421219 DLC MtU Or IdPI OrStbM CaBVaU OrPR WaWW

LB775 .L58 Livingstone, Sir Richard Winn, 1880-
On education, by Sir Richard Livingstone ... containing two books previously published separately, The future in education and Education for a world adrift, with a foreword by Virginia C. Gildersleeve ... Cambridge [Eng.] The University press; New York, The Macmillan company, 1945.
5 p. l., [v]-ix, [1], 127 p., 1 l., [vii]-xv, [1], 158 p. 19 1/2cm.
1. Education—Aims and objectives. 2. Education of adults. 3. Education—Gt. Brit. I. Title. II. Title: The future in education. III. Title: Education for a world adrift.

NL 0421220 MB PHC OCU PU KMK ViU MH WU NNUN PPT CU

Livingstone, *Sir* **Richard Winn,** 1880-
On education: The future in education and Education for a world adrift. Cambridge [Eng.] University Press, 1954.
281 p. 19 cm.
1. Education—Aims and objectives. 2. Education of adults. 3. Education—Gt. Brit. I. Title. II. Title: The future in education. III. Title: Education for a world adrift.
LB775.L58 1954 370.1 54—2471 ‡

PWcT OClW PIm MsU MH OOxM PPT CBGTU NcU
IU MH MiD NN NIC ICN TU PBL PP MB OCl CaBVaU PU MiU
NL 0421221 DLC OrMonO OrU CaBVa MtU OrCS OrLgE NNC

Livingstone, *Sir* **Richard Winn,** 1880-
On speaking the truth, by Sir Richard Livingstone ... Being the third of the Sir Robert Falconer lectures delivered at the University of Toronto, November, 1945. Toronto, Can., The University of Toronto press, 1946.
3 p. l., 38 p. 17 cm. [Falconer lectures, University of Toronto. 1945]
1. Truthfulness and falsehood. I. Title.
BJ1421.L5 177.3 48-1145

NL 0421222 DLC CaBViP CaOTU MB OClW

Livingstone, *Sir* **Richard Winn,** 1880- *ed.*
The pageant of Greece, edited by R. W. Livingstone. Oxford, The Clarendon press, 1923.
xi, [1], 436 p. front., illus. (map, plan) ports. 19½cm.
Short bibliography: p. [x]-xi.
1. Greek literature—Translations into English. 2. English literature—Translations from Greek. I. Title.
23—17680
Library of Congress PA3621.L5

PPLas MtU IdU OrPR CaBVa OrCS Or MtBuM
NN NjP MB IU OCU OOxM MiU OU PPA PBm PHC PBa PU PPL
NL 0421223 DLC KyLoU NIC MiU ICN LU CtY OCX IEG MeB

Livingstone, *Sir* **Richard Winn,** 1880- *ed.*
The pageant of Greece, edited by R. W. Livingstone. Oxford, The Clarendon press, 1924.
xi, [1], 436 p. front., illus. (incl. map, plan) ports. 19½cm.
"Impression of 1924. First edition 1923."
"Short bibliography": p. [x]-xi.
1. Greek literature—Translations into English. 2. English literature—Translations from Greek. I. Title.
28—10660
Library of Congress PA3621.L5 1924

NN PP PSC ODW OCl OClW MH
NL 0421224 DLC OrSaW WaWW CoU CaBVaU CaBViP OrP TU

Livingstone, Richard Winn, *compiler and editor, 1880*-1933.
The pageant of Greece. By R. W. Livingstone. Edition abridged for use in schools.
Oxford. Clarendon Press. 1925. 240 pp. Illus. Portraits. Plates. Plan. Diagrams. Map. 18 cm., in 8s.
Selections translated from classical Greek writers.

N2202 — T.r. — Greece. Lit. Ancient Greek. Coll.

NL 0421225 MB

Livingstone, Richard Wunn, 1880- ,ed.
The pageant of Greece... Oxford, The Clarendon press, 1928.
436 p.

NL 0421226 PPT FMU

Livingstone, Sir Richard Winn, 1880- ed.
The pageant of Greece, edited by R. W. Livingstone. Oxford, The Clarendon press, 1945.
xi, [1], 436 p. front., illus. (incl. map, plan) ports. 19.5 cm.
"Impression of 1945. First edition 1923."
"Short bibliography": p. [x]-xi.
(Red cloth)

NL 0421227 KU-M

Livingstone, *Sir* **Richard Winn,** 1880- *ed.*
The pageant of Greece, edited by R. W. Livingstone. Oxford, The Clarendon press [1947]
xi, [1], 436 p. front., illus. (incl. map, plan) ports. 19½ cm.
"First published 1923. Reprinted ... 1947."
"Short bibliography": p. [x]-xi.

NL 0421228 CBDP

Livingstone, *Sir* **Richard Winn,** 1880-
Plato & modern education, by Sir Richard Livingstone. The Rede lecture, 1944. Cambridge [Eng.] The University press; New York, The Macmillan company, 1944.
35, [1] p. 19½cm.
1. Plato. 2. Education—Aims and objectives. I. Rede lectures.
44-47092
Library of Congress LB85.P7L5 1944 a
370.1

ViU
NL 0421229 DLC OrLgE OrCS CaBVa AAP TxU MU NIC NcD

Livingstone, *Sir* **Richard Winn,** 1880-
Plato & modern education, by Sir Richard Livingstone ... The Rede lecture, 1944. Cambridge [Eng.] The University press, 1944.
35, [1] p. 19cm.
1. Plato. 2. Education—Aims and objectives. I. Rede lectures.
44-7933
Library of Congress LB85.P7L5 1944
[a45e1]

PPLas PJB OO OCU OClW OU PSt TU FTaSU
NL 0421230 DLC MtU OrPR WaS CaBVaU AAP NcD NcGU

VOLUME 336

Livingstone, Sir Richard Winn, 1880- ed.

Plato.
Portrait of Socrates, being the Apology, Crito, and Phaedo of Plato in an English translation, with introductions and notes, by Sir R. W. Livingstone ... Oxford, The Clarendon press, 1938.

CB 3 W301 1930/31
Livingstone, Sir Richard Winn, 1880-
The position and function of classical studies in modern English education.
(In Warburg Institute. Vorträge der Bibliothek Warburg. Nendeln/Liechtenstein. 24 cm. v.9 (1930-1931), p.[251]-277)

(Series: Warburg Institute. Vorträge der Bibliothek Warburg, 1930/31)

NL 0421232 CU-S

Livingstone, *Sir* Richard Winn, 1880–
Ruskin, by R. W. Livingstone ... London, G. Cumberlege [1945]
20 p. 25½cm. (The British academy. Annual lecture on a master mind. Henriette Hertz trust, 1945)
"From the Proceedings of the British academy. Volume XXXI."
"Read 23 May 1945."

1. Ruskin, John, 1819–1900.
A 47-2634
Rochester. Univ. Library for Library of Congress PR5263.L7

NL 0421233 NRU CaBVaU MiU IU MH NN CtY MdBJ

---

824 R89Yl 1946
LIVINGSTONE, Sir RICHARD WINN, 1880-
Ruskin, by R.W. Livingstone ... London, G. Cumberlege [1946]
20p. 25½cm. (The British academy. Annual lecture on a master mind. Henriette Hertz trust, 1945)
"From the Proceedings of the British academy. Volume XXXI."
"Read 23 May 1945."
"First published 1945 ... Third impression October, 1946."

1. Ruskin, John, 1819-1900. I. Series: The British academy, London. Henriette Hertz trust. Annual lecture on a master mind.

NL 0421235 TxU CoU DLC

Livingstone, *Sir* Richard Winn, 1880–
Ruskin.
(*In* British Academy, London. (Founded 1901) Proceedings, 1945. London [1947] 26 cm. v. 31, p. [85]-102)
Annual lecture on a master mind, Henriette Hertz Trust, read 23 May, 1945.

1. Ruskin, John, 1819-1900. (Series: British Academy, London. (Founded 1901) Annual lecture on a master-mind, Henriette Hertz Trust, 1945)
AS122.L5 vol. 31 A 51-449
Wisconsin. Univ. Libr. for Library of Congress †

NL 0421236 WU DLC

Livingstone, Sir Richard Winn, 1880– ed.

Plato.
... Selected passages, chosen and edited by Sir R. W. Livingstone ... London, New York [etc.] H. Milford, Oxford university press [1940]

Livingstone, *Sir* Richard Winn, 1880–
Some tasks for education, by Sir Richard Livingstone ... London, Toronto [etc.] G. Cumberlege, Oxford university press [1946]
vii, 98 p. 19cm.

1. Education. 2. Teaching. I. Title.
LB1033.L5 1946 370.1 47-18522
Toronto;

CaBViP CaBVaU CtY-D MtBC MtU Or OrP OrU Wa OrPS
NL 0421238 DLC MH ViU CtY MB NcD ICU PSC MeB CaBVa

AC 901 H34 no.23
Livingstone, Sir Richard Winn, 1880-
Some thoughts on university education.
[New Haven, Edward W. Hazen Foundation, 1948?]
21p. 23cm. (Hazen pamphlets, no. 23)

1. Education, Higher - Addresses, essays, lectures. I. Title. (Series)

NL 0421239 MU IU NNC OU KAS

Livingstone, *Sir* Richard Winn, 1880–
Some thoughts on university education. London, Pub. for the National Book League by the Cambridge Univ. Press, 1948.
28 p. 19 cm. (National Book League fifth annual lecture)
"Delivered ... at Friends House ... London ... October 29, 1947."

1. Education, Higher. I. Title. (Series: National Book League, London. Annual lecture, 5)
LB2325.L54 378.01 48-11906 rev*

PU NIC KEmT TU ViU
MH ICU PPT CaBVa CaBViP WaSpG CaBVaU OrCS OrP OrU
NL 0421240 DLC NN PJB NcGU OCH TxU MB MtBC CtY-D

LIVINGSTONE, Sir Richard Winn, 1880-
Thoughts on the education of character. Durham, Eng., Doncaster Grammar School, 1954.
12p. 22cm. (Vaughan Memorial Lecture, 2)

NL 0421241 MH-AH

177.3 L76v
Livingstone, Sir Richard Winn, 1880
Veracity. London, Lindsey Press [1937]
39 p. 19 cm. (Essex Hall lectures, 1937)

1. Truth. I. Title. II. Series.

NL 0421242 LU

U717 .G7W5
Livingstone, Sir Richard Winn, 1880–
Window to a fuller life; contributors: Sir Richard Livingstone [and others] ... [London] The editor, R. A. F. quarterly, 1945.

Livingstone, Rinaldo R.
Livingstone's historical and statistical chart of California. [San Francisco, 1885]
1 p. l., 5 double l., 1 l. illus. (incl. ports.) 41½ x 34½cm.
Caption title.
"Introduction" signed and dated: Rinaldo R. Livingstone. San Francisco, Cal., March 10, 1885.

1. California—Hist. 2. California—Stat.
Library of Congress F861.L78 Rc-T22

NL 0421244 DLC ICN

Livingstone, Robert, joint author.
North Pacific albacore
see under
Powell, Donald E

Livingstone, Robert G
Primary carcinoma of the vagina. [1st ed.] Springfield, Ill., C. C. Thomas [1950]
viii, 73 p. illus. 23 cm. (American lecture series, publication no. 38. American lectures in obstetrics and gynecology)
Bibliography: p. 71-73.

1. Vagina—Cancer. I. Title. (Series: American lecture series, no. 38. Series: American lectures in obstetrics and gynecology)
RG257.L5 1950 618.15 50-7710

ICU DNLM PPT-M CU-M ICJ NBuU N NcD-MC
NL 0421246 DLC IdPI OrU-M OrCS CaBVaU PPC ViU NcU

Livingston, Sir Thomas, 1652?-1711.
Sir Thomas Levingstons Letter to the Honourable Major General Mackay, Commander in Chief of their Majesties Forces in Scotland, giving a true Account of the Battel at Crombdel ... [caption-title] Colophen, London, for Tho. Salusbury, 1690.
2 p. small folio. Bound (36) with: [W., L.] A full and True Account Of The Later Brave Action Perform'd by the Innis-killing-Men ... London, 1690.
Note: The Bridgewater Library copy, 4 G 9 (36)

NL 0421247 CSmH

British Tracts 1690 +L76
Livingstone, Sir Thomas, 1652?-1711.
A true and real account of the defeat of General Buchan, and Brigadeer Cannon, their high-land army, at the battel of Crombdell; upon the 1st of May; 1690. Conform to a letter, sent by Sir Thomas Livingston Collonel ... to Major General Mackay, giving a particular account of the said defeat, with a list of the officers taken at the said battel, and at the castle of Lethen-dee. Licensed May 8th, 1690. Edinburgh, Printed by the heir of Andrew Anderson, 1690.
1 p.l., 2 p. 30 cm.

NL 0421248 CtY

Beinecke Library 1971 +62
Livingstone, Sir Thomas, 1652?-1711.
A true and real account of the defeat of General Buchan, and Brigadier Cannon, their highland army, at the battel of Crombdell; upon the 1st of May, 1690. Conform to a letter, sent by Sir Thomas Livingston ... to Major General Mackay, giving a particular account of the said defeat; with a list of the officers taken at the said battel, and at the castle of Lethen Dee. Licensed, May 16th, 1690. [London, Printed for Rich. Chiswell at the Rose and Crown in St. Paul's Church-Yard [1690]]

[2] p. 30 x 19 cm.
Binder's title: Tracts Ireland.
Caption title.
Wing T-2575.

NL 0421250 CtY

Livingstone, Thomas J , S.J.
The magic fiddle: a musical fairy drama in five acts. Chicago, Ill., Loyola University Press, 1921.
62 p.

NL 0421251 WaSpG RPB

Livingstone, Tristram.
Rubaiyat for a music devotee... Boston, 1936.
9 p.

NL 0421252 OCl

VOLUME 336

Livingstone, Uilleam
see Livingston, William, 1808-1870.

Livingstone, W B.
A new mode of correcting exercises, adapted to Indian schools and colleges. By W. B. Livingstone ... Calcutta, Thacker, Spink and co., 1881.
v. 23cm.

1. English language—Composition and exercises. [1. English language—Teaching—India] 2. Education—India. 3. [English language—Teaching—Secondary schools]

E 15—1440
U. S. Off. of educ. Library for Library of Congress LB1631.I 4L7 [a41b1]

NL 0421254 DHEW

Livingstone, W. B.
A new system of short-hand. By W. B. Livingstone... Berhampore: W. B. Livingstone, 1882. 11 p. plates. 8°.
Cover-title.

1. Shorthand—Systems, English, 1882.
May 18, 1926

NL 0421255 NN CtY

Bon. Coll. No.12046
[LIVINGSTONE, WILLIAM, minister of Lanark, Scotland]
The conflict in conscience of a deare Christian, named Bessie Clarksone, in the parish of Lanerk, which shee lay under three yeare and an half. With the conference that past betwixt her pastor and her at diverse times. Newly corrected and amended. Edinburgh, Printed by J.Wreittoun,1631;Edinburgh,re-printed for Webster & Son,1820.
46p. 18cm.
Preface signed: W.L.

NL 0421256 ICN

FILM
Livingstone,William,minister of Lanark,Scotland.
The conflict in conscience of a deare Christian, names Bessie Clarksone in the parish of Lanerk, which shee lay vnder three yeare & an half. With the conference that past betwixt her pastor and her at diuerse times. Newly corr.and amended. Edinbvrgh, Printed by I.Wreittoun, 1631.
Short-title catalogue no.16611 (carton 809)

NL 0421257 MiU

Livingstone, William, 1808-1870
see
Livingston, William, 1808-1870.

Livingstone, William, 1844-1925.
Livingstone's history of the Republican party. A history of the Republican party from its foundation to the close of the campaign of 1900, including incidents of Michigan campaigns and biographical sketches ... Detroit, Mich., W. Livingstone [1900]
2 v. fronts., illus., pl., ports. 27½cm.

1. Republican party—Hist. 2. Michigan—Biog.
Library of Congress JK2356.L78 1-31197 Revised

NL 0421259 DLC NNC MiU

Livingstone, William Allan.
The Great Lakes problem; or, The "twenty foot channel". Detroit, 1891.
unp. illus.

NL 0421260 MiD-B OClWHi MiU

Micro-film 668
Livingstone, William D
The Princeton apologetic as exemplified by the work of Benjamin B. Warfield and J. Gresham Machen, a study in American theology, 1880-1930. [New Haven, Conn] 1948.
vii, 371, g, ℓ.
Thesis--Princeton University.
Bibliography and bibliographical footnotes.
Microfilm (positive) Ann Arbor, Mich., University Microfilm, 1969. 1 reel. 35mm.

1. Theology, Doctrinal--History--19th cent. 2. Theology, Doctrinal--History--20th cent. 3. Machen, John Gresham, 1881-1937. 4. Warfield, Benjamin Breckinridge, 1851-1921. I. Title.

NL 0421261 CBGTU PPiPT

Livingstone, William Pringle.
Black Jamaica; a study in evolution, by W. P. Livingstone. London, S. Low, Marston and company, limited, 1899.
4 p. l., 298 p. plates, port. 19½cm.

1. Negroes in Jamaica. 2. Jamaica—Hist. I. Title.
Library of Congress F1871.L78 3—8395

NL 0421262 DLC OU MChN NIC CtY OCl OClW DN MB ViHaI

Livingstone, William Pringle.
Black Jamaica; a study in evolution. 2d ed. London, S.Low, Marston and co., ltd., 1900.
298 p. ports. 19 cm. (Low's Indian and colonial library)

NL 0421263 MH CU WaU

Livingstone, William Pringle.
Christina Forsyth of Fingoland; the story of the loneliest woman in Africa, by W. P. Livingstone... London: Hodder and Stoughton, 1918. xiii(i), 236 p. front. (port.), illus. (map), plates. 12°.

1. Forsyth, Christina (Moir), 1844- . 2. Missions (Foreign), Africa (South East).
July 2, 1919.

NL 0421264 NN IEN MH NNC WU IU

Livingstone, William Pringle.
Christina Forsyth of Fingoland; the story of the loneliest woman in Africa... London, Hodder & Stoughton [c1919]
248 p., illus., port., map, 20cm.

NL 0421265 NjPT

Livingstone, William Pringle.
Christina Forsyth of Fingoland; the story of the loneliest woman in Africa, by W. P. Livingstone ... New York, George H. Doran company [c1919]
x p., 2 l., 15-248 p. front., illus. (map) plates, ports. 19½cm.

1. Forsyth, Mrs. Christina (Moir) b. 1844. 2. Missions—Africa, South.
Library of Congress BV3625.F5L5 19—9751

NL 0421266 DLC Or CtY OrU NjNbS NcD OClW MB NN CU TNF PPT PPL MiEM

Livingstone, William Pringle.
A Galilee doctor; being a sketch of the career of Dr. D. W. Torrance of Tiberias, by W. P. Livingstone ... London, Hodder and Stoughton [1923]
x, 283 p. front. (port.) 9 pl. (incl. maps, plans) 22cm.
Plates printed on both sides.

1. Torrance, David Watt, 1862-1922. I. Title.
A 23-2362
Title from General Theol. Sem. Printed by L. C.

NL 0421267 NNG CU DNLM NN PCC

Livingstone, William Pringle.
A Galilee doctor; being a sketch of the career of Dr. D. W. Torrance of Tiberias, by W. P. Livingstone ... New York, George H. Doran company [1923]
x, 283 p. front., plates, ports., map. 22cm.
Printed in Great Britain.

1. Torrance, David Watt, 1862-1922. 2. Missions—Palestine. I. Title.
Library of Congress BV3202.T6L5 24-5336

NL 0421268 DLC MH-AH

Livingstone, William Pringle.
A Galilee doctor; being a sketch of the career of Dr. D.W. Torrance of Tiberias, by W.P. Livingstone... London, Hodder and Stoughton [1925]
x, 295 p., front., plates, ports., map, 22cm.

NL 0421269 NjPT MBCo

Livingstone, William Pringle.
Laws of Livingstonia; a narrative of missionary adventure and achievement, by W. P. Livingstone ... London, Hodder and Stoughton, limited [1921]
i, [1], 385, [1] p. front., plates, ports., maps (1 fold.) plans. 23cm.
"Works by Robert Laws": p. [xii]

1. Laws, Robert, 1851- 2. Missions—Nyasaland. I. Title.
Library of Congress BV3625.N8L5 22-13899

NL 0421270 DLC CtY-D CaBVaU IU ICU NcD NcU CtY NN MB NBuU NBuC KyWAT

Livingstone, William Pringle.
Laws of Livingstonia; a narrative of missionary adventure and achievement by W. P. Livingstone ... New York,Doran[1921]
xi, [1], 385, [1] p. front., plates, ports., maps (1 fold.) plans. 23 cm.
"Works by Robert Laws": p. [xii]

NL 0421271 MU

---

266 L425Yt
Livingstone, William Pringle.
Laws of Livingstonia; a narrative of missionary adventure and achievement. London, Hodder and Stoughton [1922]
xi,385p. port.,plates,maps.(1 fold.) 23cm.

1. Laws, Robert, 1851-1934. 2. Missions. Nyasaland. I. Title.

NL 0421272 IEN

VOLUME 336

Livingstone, William Pringle.
Laws on Livingstonia; a narrative of missionary adventure and achievement, by W. P. Livingstone ... London, Hodder and Stoughton, limited [c1923]
ix, [1], 385, [1] p. front., plates, ports., maps (1 fold.) plans.

NL 0421273 WaU

BV 3625 .N8L5 1933 Livingstone, William Pringle.
Laws of Livingstonia; a narrative of missionary adventure and achievement, by W. P. Livingstone. [3d ed.] London, Hodder and Stoughton, limited [1933]
385 p.

#Laws, Robert, 1851-
#Missions--Nyasaland.
Laws of Livingstonia.

NL 0421274 MoU

BV 3625 N82 L78 1921 Livingstone, William Pringle.
The life of Robert Laws of Livingstonia. A narrative of missionary adventure and achievement. New York, Doran [ca. 1921]
ix, 385 p. illus. 22cm.

Published in London in 1921 under title: Laws of Livingstonia.

1. Laws, Robert, 1851- 2. Missions--Nyasaland. I. His Laws of Livingstonia.

NL 0421275 NIC ViU NcD InU NNC ODW IEN NN NjNbS

---

266 S628Yl.mXD **Livingstone, William Pringle.**
Mary Slessor; den hvide dronning i Okoyong, en sand fortaelling [af] W.P. Livingstone. Med forfatterens tilladeise frit gengivet after "The white queen of Okoyong" og "Mary Slessor of Calabar" ved M. Wolff. [Aalborg] Dansk Forenet Sudan-Mission, 1917.
206p. illus., ports. 21cm.

NL 0421276 IEN

MY39 Sl28 XL76m Livingstone, William Pringle.
Mary Slessor of Calabar, pioneer missionary. 8th ed. New York, Doran [n.d.]
xi, 353 p. illus., ports., maps. 21 cm.

1. Slessor, Mary Mitchell, 1848-1915.
2. Calabar - Missions.

NL 0421277 CtY-D OC1W OC1h IEN NN

Livingstone, William Pringle.
Mary Slessor of Calabar, pioneer missionary; by W. P. Livingstone... London: Hodder and Stoughton, 1915. xi, 347 p., front. (port.), 2 maps, 9 pl. 8°.

1. Slessor, Mary Mitchell, 1848-1915. 2. Missions (Foreign), Africa: Nigeria. 3. Calabar, Africa.
May 5, 1916.

NL 0421278 NN WaU

Livingstone, William Pringle.
Mary Slessor of Calabar, pioneer missionary, by W. P. Livingstone ... 4th ed. London, New York [etc.] Hodder and Stoughton, 1916.
xi, 347 p. front., plates, port. 23cm.

1. Slessor, Mary Mitchell, 1848-1915. 2. Missions—Calabar, Old.

Brockton, Mass. Public libr. for Library of Congress A 16-1078 [BV3625.N5L]

PPL PP OC1W
NL 0421279 MBrocK OrP NNC CaBVaU TU MtU OU OC1 PPLT

Livingstone, William Pringle.
Mary Slessor of Calabar, pioneer missionary, by W. P. Livingstone ... 5th ed. London, New York [etc.] Hodder and Stoughton, 1916.
xi, 347 p. front. (port.) plates, maps. 23 cm.

NL 0421280 KEmT

Livingstone, William Pringle.
Mary Slessor of Calabar, pioneer missionary, by W. P. Livingstone ... 6th ed. London, New York [etc.] Hodder and Stoughton, 1916.
xi, 347 p. front. (port.) plates, maps. 23cm.

1. Slessor, Mary Mitchell, 1848-1915. 2. Missions—Calabar, Old.
16—22663

Library of Congress BV3625.N6S62

NcD NcGU NjNbS OO ODW TNF MB OKentU
NL 0421281 DLC WaS Or MiU WaWW CaBVa CU-I Or Wa WaT

BV3625 .N5L5 1916a **Livingstone, William Pringle.**
Mary Slessor of Calabar, pioneer missionary. 7th ed. London, New York, Hodder and Stoughton, 1916.
xi, 347 p. plates, ports., maps. 22cm.

1. Slessor, Mary Mitchell, 1848-1915. 2. Missions—Calabar, Old.

NL 0421282 MB PPT

LIVINGSTONE, W[illiam] P[ringle].
Mary Slessor of Calabar, pioneer missionary. 9th ed. London, etc., Hodder and Stoughton, 1917.

Ports, plates and map. Afr. 555.20.5

NL 0421283 MH

Livingstone, William Pringle.
Mary Slessor of Calabar, pioneer missionary by W. P. Livingstone ... 16th ed. London, Hodder and Stoughton [c192-?]
xi, 34. p. front. (port.) plates, maps. 23 cm.

NL 0421284 OrU

BV3625 N6S66 L5 1923 Livingstone, William Pringle
Mary Slessor of Calabar, pioneer missionary, by W. P. Livingstone. Popular edition. London, Hodder and Stoughton [1923]
x, 347 p. port.

1. Slessor, Mary Mitchell, 1848-1915.

NL 0421285 CU

276.69 S639zL Livingstone, William Pringle.
Mary Slessor of Calabar, pioneer missionary. by W.P. Livingstone ... Popular ed. London, Hodder and Stoughton, 1924.
x, 352p. illus. 20cm.

1. Slessor, Mary Mitchell, 1848-1915.
2. Missions - Calabar, Old.

NL 0421286 NcU

266.51669 L788m 1926 Livingstone, William Pringle.
Mary Slessor of Calabar, pioneer missionary, by W. P. Livingstone. Popular ed. London, Hodder and Stoughton [1926].
x, 352 p. port. 21cm.

"First edition printed November 1915."

1. Slessor, Mary Mitchell, 1848-1915. 2. Missions - Calabar, Nigeria.

NL 0421287 FU

Livingstone, William Pringle.
Mary Slessor of Calabar, pioneer missionary, by W. P. Livingstone... London: Hodder and Stoughton, Ltd.[, 1930.] x, 352 p. front. (port.) 12°.

"Popular edition."
First published in 1915.

548365A. 1. Slessor, Mary Mitchell, 1848-1915. 2. Missions, Foreign—Africa—Nigeria. 3. Calabar, Africa.
October 6, 1931

NL 0421288 NN

Livingstone, William Pringle,
Mary Slessor, the white queen; a true story of adventure, heroism and faith... London, Hodder and Stoughton [n.d.]
127 p. 20cm.

"Originally published as 'The white queen of Okoyong.'"

1 Slessor, Mary Mitchell, 1848-1915

NL 0421289 NjPT

Div.S. 922 S632LI Livingstone, William Pringle.
Mary Slessor, the white queen; a true story of adventure, heroism and faith, by W. P. Livingstone. London, Hodder and Stoughton [c1949]
127 p. 20 cm.

"First published in this form ... 1931."
"Originally published as The white queen of Okoyong."

1. Slessor, Mary Mitchell, 1848-1915. I. Title.

NL 0421290 NcD

Livingstone, William Pringle.
The master life; the story of Jesus for to-day, by W. P. Livingstone ... London, J. Clarke & co., limited [c1925]
xi, 13-319, [1] p. incl. front. (map) 23cm.

1. Jesus Christ—Biog. I. Title.

Library of Congress BT301.L54 25-12635

NL 0421291 DLC IEG

VOLUME 336

Livingstone, William Pringle.
The master life, the story of Jesus for to-day, by W. P. Livingstone ... New York, George H. Doran company [°1925]
xii p., 1 l., 15-405 p. incl. front. (map) 20cm.

1. Jesus Christ—Biog. I. Title.
Library of Congress BT301.L54 1925 a 25-17835
[s27c2]

NL 0421292 DLC ODW MB PPPD OrP

Livingstone, William Pringle, ed.
Master Missionary Series
see under title

Livingstone, William Pringle.
The new outlook; an ideal of life for today. Lond., Hodder and Stoughton, 1917.
258 p.

NL 0421294 OO

Livingstone, William Pringle.
A prince of missionaries, the Rev. Alexander Hetherwick, C. B. E., D. D., M. A., of Blantyre, Central Africa, by W. P. Livingstone ... With 4 illustrations and map. London, J. Clarke & co., limited [1931]
ix, 11-205, [1] p. front., illus. (map) plates, ports. 19cm.

1. Hetherwick, Alexander, 1860- I. Title.
Library of Congress BV3625.N82H4 35-3721
922.568

NL 0421295 DLC CtY NN

Livingstone, William Pringle.
The race conflict; a study of conditions in America, by W. P. Livingstone... London: S. Low, Marston & Co., Ld., 1911. 4 p.l., 7-185(1) p., col'd front., fold. map. 12°.

1. Negro, U. S.
January 29, 1917.

NL 0421296 NN MiU CtY

Livingstone, William Pringle.
Shetland and the Shetlanders. With 31 half-tone plates. London, New York, T. Nelson [1947]
x, 229 p. plates, maps (on lining-papers) 19 cm.

1. Shetland—Islands.
DA880.S5L5 914.11 47-26992*

NL 0421297 DLC CaBVa

Livingstone, William Pringle.
The story of David Livingstone, by W. P. Livingstone... London: The Livingstone Press[, 1929]. 125 p. front. (port.), illus. (map), plates. 12°.
Plates printed on both sides.
Map on front end paper, illustration on back end paper.

453834A. 1. Livingstone, David, 1813-1873.
January 18, 1930

NL 0421298 NN

Livingstone, William Pringle.
The story of David Livingstone, by W. P. Livingstone ... New York and London, Harper & brothers, 1930.
5 p. l., 161 p. front., illus. (map) plates, ports. 20cm.
Map on lining-paper.

1. Livingstone, David, 1813-1873.
Library of Congress DT731.L8L55 30-6388

NL 0421299 DLC TNJ-R PP PCC PPT NcD MB WaS Or

Livingstone, William Pringle.
The story of Mary Slessor for young people. The white queen of Okoyong; a true story of adventure, heroism and faith, by W. P. Livingstone ... New York, George H. Doran company [°1917]
xii p., 1 l., 208 p. illus. 20cm.

1. Slessor, Mary Mitchell, 1848-1915. I. Title. II. Title: The white queen of Okoyong.
Library of Congress BV3625.N6S6 17-4476

NL 0421300 DLC Or KyU KyLxCB OLak InAndC-T

Livingstone, William Pringle.
The story of Mary Slessor for young people. The white queen of Okoyong; a true story of adventure, heroism and faith. Garden City, N.Y., Doubleday, 1929, [c.1917]
208 p. illus. 20 cm.

NL 0421301 TU

Livingstone, William Pringle.
Villien Valkoinen Kuningatar Mary Slessor, lähetyksen uranuurtaja kalabarissa. Helsinki, Suomen lähetysseura, 1927.
310p. map 20cm.

In Finnish.

NL 0421302 Mi

266
3628Yl
Livingstone, William Pringle.
The white queen of Okoyong, Mary Slessor; a true story of adventure, heroism and faith. London, New York, Hodder & Stoughton, 1916.
xii, 208p. front. (col.) illus. 19cm.

1. Slessor, Mary Mitchell, 1848-1915. I. Title.

NL 0421303 IEN

Livingstone, William Pringle.
The white queen of Okoyong, Mary Slessor; a true story of adventure, heroism and faith, by W. P. Livingstone... London: Hodder and Stoughton, 1917. xii, 208 p., col'd front. illus. 12°.

1. Slessor, Mary Mitchell, 1848-1915. 2. Missions (Foreign), Africa: Nigeria. 3. Calabar, Africa.
June 25, 1918.

NL 0421304 NN

Livingstone, William Pringle.
The wonder of it! A century of world-wide missionary service ... Edinburgh, Foreign mission committee of the Church of Scotland, [1932]
94 p. illus. incl. maps. 18.5 cm.

NL 0421305 CtY

Livingstone, Win C.
The belle of the Island city, or, The wreck of the Southern Star. A romance of Galveston. By Win. C. Livingstone ... New York, Katahdin publishing company [1896]
1 p. l., 11-112 p. $18\frac{1}{2}$cm. (*On cover:* New York 10 cent library, no. 6)

CA 8-1658 Unrev'd
Library of Congress PZ3.L764B

NL 0421306 DLC

Livingstone, Win C.
For the flag. A tale of western adventure. By Wm. [!] C. Livingstone ... New York, Katahdin publishing company [1896]
1 p. l., 11-150 p. 18cm. (*On cover:* New York 10 cent library. no. 11)
On cover: By Win C. Livingstone.

CA 8-1659 Unrev'd
Library of Congress PZ3.L764F

NL 0421307 DLC MH

Livingstone, Win C.
... The wreck of the Southern star. By Win C. Livingstone ... Boston, Mass., Atlantic news company, °1893.
3 p. l., 11-92 p. illus. 19cm. (The Hub ten cent library, v. 1, no. 2)

I. Title.
Library of Congress PS2248.L54 31-35340
813.49

NL 0421308 DLC

Livingstone-Blevins, F
"The Dowager minster" of Lincoln; or, The story of Stow-in-Lindsey. A topographical and descriptive account illustrating its claim to be the Saxon Sidnacester with translations of Saxon charters and Domesday book... St. Marks, Lincoln, Melton [19--]
cover-title, 20 p. illus. 20 cm.
1. Stow, Eng. St. Mary's church.

NL 0421309 NjP MH

Livingstone-Stanley, Serena, pseud.
see Lindsay, Joan (Weigall)

L968.94
L788s
Livingstone, Zambia.
Report on outline advisory development plan for the expansion of Livingstone, Northern Rhodesia, to accomodate the Federal Capital of the Federation of Rhodesia and Nyasaland. Lusaka, J. C. Collings & Partner [1953]
16l. fold. maps. 34cm. [With Livingstone, Northern Rhodesia, Municipal Council. Submission of case for the expansion of Livingstone, Northern Rhodesia... <Livingstone, 1953>]

1. Livingstone, Northern Rhodesia. 2. Rhodesia and Nyasaland. Capital. I. Collings (J.C.) & Partner. II. Title.

NL 0421312 IEN

VOLUME 336

Livingstone, Zambia. David Livingstone Memorial Museum
see
Rhodes-Livingstone Museum, *Livingstone, Zambia.*

L968.94
L788s
Livingstone, Zambia. Municipal Council.
Submission of case for the expansion of Livingstone, Northern Rhodesia to accomodate the federal capital of the Federation of Rhodesia and Nyasaland. [Livingstone, 1953]
cover title, 6*l*. fold. map. 34cm.

With this is bound Livingstone, Northern Rhodesia. Report on outline advisory development plan for the expansion of Livingstone, Northern Rhodesia, to accomodate the federal capital of the Federation of Rhodesia and Nyasaland. Lusaka [1953]

NL 0421315 IEN

Livingstone, Zambia. Rhodes-Livingstone Institute
see Rhodes-Livingstone Institute, Lusaka, Zambia.

Livingstone, Zambia. Rhodes-Livingstone Museum
see
Rhodes-Livingstone Museum, *Livingstone, Zambia.*

... Livingstone. Paris, Lafitte & cie [c1914]
see under [Keim, Albert] 1876-

Livingstone and Stanley. The story of the opening up of the Dark Continent.
London. Chambers. [1900.] 151 pp. Illus. Portraits. Plates. [Heroic lives.] 17½ cm., in 8s.

H4244 — S.r. — Livingstone, David. 1813-1873. — Stanley, Sir Henry Morton. 1841-1904.

NL 0421319 MB

Livingstone centenary, a practical program for its celebration. March 19, 1813-1913. [Lond., Lond. missionary soc., 1913?]
[16] p.

NL 0421320 OO

Livingstone college, *Salisbury, N. C.*
Catalogue.
Salisbury, N. C., 18
v. plates. 22cm.

CA 9-1200 Unrev'd

Library of Congress LC2851.L8

NL 0421321 DLC NjP NcU

Livingstone College, Salisbury, N. C.
Quarter centennial of Livingstone College and industrial school, Salisbury, N. C., May 19-24, 1907. [Salisbury, N. C.] J. E. Mason, Secretary [1907]
[16] p. illus. 23 cm.
"J. C. Price memorial souvenir."

1. Livingstone College Salisbury N. C.—History. I. Title.

LC2851.L8A6 72-194925
MARC

NL 0421322 DLC

Livingstone College year book, containing hints to travelers in matters of health, outfit, and travel. 96 pp., 2 pl. 12°. Leyton, 1904.

NL 0421323 DNLM

WX
2
FE5
D38L7a
[Livingstone Cottage Hospital *for Dartford and District, Dartford, Eng.*]
Annual report and statement of accounts.
1st- 1895-
Dartford.
v.

NL 0421324 DNLM

Livingstone, Crouse & company, *Detroit.*
Detroit banks and trust companies, statistical data as compiled by Livingstone, Crouse & company ... Detroit, Mich. [The Mulford company] °1928.
4 p. l., 11-35, [1] p. 29cm.

1. Banks and banking—Detroit. 2. Banks and banking—Stat. I. Title.

Library of Congress HG2613.D62L7 28-14218

NL 0421325 DLC OCIFRB

Livingstone, der Missionär
see under [Kiesewetter, Fr]

The LIVINGSTONE lectures.
[Sydney]

"A series of public lectures sponsored by the Livingstone trudt, Camden college, Sydney."

NL 0421327 NN

Livingstone Mail.
Livingstone, Northern Rhodesia.
v. weekly.
Microfilm ed., positive copy.
Began 1906.

NL 0421328 ICRL

Livingstone Memorial Museum, *Livingstone, Zambia*
see
Rhodes-Livingstone Museum, *Livingstone, Zambia.*

Livingstone. Ontdekkingsreizen inde binnenlanden van Arika
see under Oosterzee, Hendrik Marinus Christiaan Doornick van, 1806-1877.

The Livingstone search and relief expedition ...
see under [Henn, Thomas Rice] 1814-1901.

The Livingstones; a story of real life
see under [Dalrymple, Georgiana A

Livingstonia Mission of the Free Church of Scotland.
The Lake Regions of Central Africa. The Livingstonia Mission of the Free Church of Scotland in Nyasa-Land. Third Quinquennial narrative (with new map) Glasgow: Edinburgh Press, 1891.
36 p., 1 map 8°.

NL 0421333 NN

LIVINGSTON'S biographical magazine, New York. Vol. III, no. 1 (May 1, 1853.)
pp.(viii), 40. Ports. US 42503.5

NL 0421334 MH

Livingston's family guest. Lynn.
v. [3]

NL 0421335 N

Livingston's guide book to St. John and the St. John River ...
see under Livingston, Gordon.

... Livingston's international casting directory ...
[v. 1
New York: Jack Livingston, c1931 28cm.
v. illus. (ports.)
Monthly.

1. Actors and acting—Biog. 2. Actors and acting—Direct.
January 26, 1943

NL 0421337 NN

Livingston's law register
See
Livingston, John, ed.
The law register.

VOLUME 336

Livingston's monthly law magazine ... By John Livingston. v. 1–3, v. 4, no. 1; Jan. 1853–Jan. 1856. New York, 1853–56.
4 v. ports. 23½cm.
No more published?

1. Law—Period.—U. S. I. Livingston, John, ed.

20—2181

MoSW-L GEU LU
NL 0421339 DLC PU-L OClWHi NN OClW P WaU-L NcU

Livingston's United States law register
see
Livingston, John.
The Law register.

Livington, Schuyler William
see Livingston, Schulyer William.

Livinhac, Léon, *Bp.*, 1846–1922.
Instructions de Monseigneur Livinhac aux missionnaires d'Afrique (Pères blancs) Maison-Carrée (Alger) Impr. des Pères blancs, 1938.
vii, 423 p. 23 cm.

1. White Fathers—Collected works. 2. Monastic and religious life—Collected works. I. Title.

BX4181.A3L5 N E 65–329

NL 0421342 DLC

Livinhac, Leon, Bp., 1846-1922.
Près des Grands Lacs. Par les missionnaires de S. Ém. le cardinal Lavigerie. Extrait des Missions catholiques.
Lyon. Bureau des Missions catholiques. 1885. (4), 146 pp. Portraits. Plates. 24 cm., in 8s.
Contents. — Le Nyanza, lettre de Mgr. Livinhac. — De Tanganyka, par Mgr. Charbonnier.

L2790 — Double main card. — Livinhac, ——, Bishop of Pacando. (M1) — Charbonnier, Jean Baptiste. (M2) — T.r. (1) — Lavigerie, Charles Martial Allemand, cardinal, 1828-1892. (1) — Nyassaland, Africa. Missions. (1) — Société de missionaires d'Alger. (1)

NL 0421343 MB

[Livinhac, Léon] Bp., 1846-1922.
Près des grands lacs, par les missionnaires de S. Ém. le cardinal Lavigerie... Lyon: Missions catholiques, 1886. 195 p. front., map, plates, ports. 8°.

Repr.: Missions catholiques.
Contents: Partie 1. LIVINHAC[, L.]. Le Nyanza; lettre. Partie 2. CHARBONNIER[, J. B.]. Le Tanganyka.

1. Missions, Foreign—Africa, German East—Catholic Church, (Roman.) 2. African tribes—Africa, German East. 3. Charbonnier, Jean Baptiste, jt. au. 4. Title.

October 21, 1925

NL 0421344 NN CtY

LIVINI, A.
Scienze fisiche e poesia; argomenti per compiti scritti proposti agli allievi della R. Scuola Normale di Messina. Firenze, Letture di Famiglia, 1882.

NL 0421345 MH

Livini, Ferdinando, 1862-

Istituto sieroterapico milanese Serafino Belfanti.
Endocrinologia. Lezioni tenute ai rr. istituti clinici di perfezionamento in Milano, per iniziativa dell'Istituto sieroterapico millanese, dai signori professo. Livini, Rondoni, Pepere, Pende e Coronedi. [Milano] Istituto sieroterapico milanese, 1922.

Livini, Ferdinando, 1862–
... Intorno alla struttura della trachea. Ricerche di istologia comparata del dott. Ferdinando Livini ... (con 1 tavola) Firenze, Tip. G. Carnesecchi e figli, 1897.
48 p. fold. pl. (col.) 27½cm. (Pubblicazioni del R. Istituto di studi superiori pratici e perfezionamento in Firenze. Sezione di medicina e chirurgia. [no. 16])
At head of title: Istituto anatomico di Firenze diretto dal prof. G. Chiarugi.

1. Trachea.

Library of Congress R65.F5 no. 16 14-16421
QL847.L5

NL 0421347 DLC DNLM NN

WI
qL788s
1900

LIVINI, Ferdinando, 1862-
Le tissu élastique dans les organes du corps humain. 1. mémoire, Sa distribution dans l'appareil digestif. [Tr. de l'italien] Turin, Clausen, 1900.
46 p. illus.
Translation of Sulla distribuzione del tessuto elastico in varii organi del corpo umano, 1. nota.
No more published.

NL 0421348 DNLM PPWI CtY

Livini, Gregorio. Venezia, 1830.
Lezione sopra il sonetto del Petrarca,...

NL 0421349 NIC

Livino de Carvalho, Carlos
see
Carvalho, Carlos Livino de.

Livinsky, Isidore.
Reminiscences of Poland, her revolutions and her rights. A brief sketch of the causes of the revolutions from 1830 to the incorporation of Cracow with the Austrian Empire; with a short local description of the city of Cracow. By Isidore Livinsky, a Polish refugee. London: C. Gilpin, 1848. xvi, 96 p. 16°.

1. Poland.—History: Revolution of 1830-32. 2. Poland.—History: Revolution of 1846.

November 1, 1920.

NL 0421351 NN

Livinus, Saint and martyr, Apostle of Flanders. -657.
Epistola . . . ad Florbertum Gandæ abbatem.
(In Patrologiæ cursus completus. Scriptores Latini. Series secunda. Tomus 87, col. 345-346. Parisiis. 1851.)
Prefixed is Vita sancti Livini . . . , auctore Bonifacio coævo. This is catalogued separately.

K4596 — Florbertus, Saint, Abbot of St. Pierre, Gand, Belgium.

NL 0421352 MB MdBP

Livio Agrippa
see
Agrippa, Livio.

Livio, Bragadin
see Bragadin, Livio.

Livio, Juan Carlos.
... Lluvia de pétalos; poesías, cuentos, aguafuertes porteñas. [Buenos Aires] 1935.
99, [1] p. incl. 2 port. 18cm.
At head of title: Juan Carlos Livio y Salvador del Priore (Juancho)

I. Priore, Salvador del. II. Title.

41-30780

Library of Congress PQ7797.L544L6

861.6

NL 0421355 DLC

388.3145
L7641
1938

Livio, Livi.
Indagine sulla frequenza dei sinistri automobilistici in rapporto agli automezzi in circolazione ed al chilometraggio. [Rome] Reale Automobile Club d'Italia, 1938.
118p. tables. 25cm.

1. Traffic surveys. I. Title.

NL 0421356 KU

Livio de Castro, Tito
see Castro, Tito Livio de, 1864-1890.

Livio Martini, Juan
see
Martini, Juan Livio.

Livirani, Pietro Paolo.
Die festo sollemni ob memoriam inventae crucis, Joanni Benedicto Folicaldio...sodales crucis. [Faventiae, 1843]
8°

NL 0421359 NN

Livirani, Pietro Paolo.
In nuptias T. Rasponii com. et Angelae Frontaliae [ode...Faventiae, 1842]
8°

NL 0421360 NN

LIVIRANI, Pietro Paolo.
Odae. Bononiae, 1847.

Portrait.

NL 0421361 MH NN

VOLUME 336

Livisay, Leonidas Franklin.
Antigenic value of pneumococcal protein adsorbed on colloidal alum... ₍Columbus, Ohio state university, 1934₎.
Thesis.

NL 0421362 OU

Bonaparte Collection No.6983 LIVIU, ANDREAS.
Anleitung zur erlernung der romanischen sprache... Teschen, K.Prochaska, 1852.
253p. 19cm.

NL 0421363 ICN CaBVa

Livius Andronicus.
...Dramatum reliquiae...recensuit, quoad fieri potuit in ordinem digessit, illustravit, E.C.C. Klussmann. Rudolstadt, ₍1849₎
26 p.

NL 0421364 PBm PU NjP

Livius Andronicus.
Fragmenta collecta et inlustrata
see under Düntzer, Heinrich, 1813-1901, ed.

Livius Andronicus.
Livi Andronici Fragmenta collegit M. Lenchantin de Gubernatis. Aug. Taurinorum, Mediolani ₍etc.₎ In aedibus Io. Bapt. Paraviae et sociorum ₍1937₎
xxxv, 48 p. 19½cm. (On verso of half-title: ... Corpus scriptorum Latinorum Paravianum. 63)

I. Lenchantin de Gubernatis, Massimo, 1884- ed.

NL 0421366 NNC PU OCU IaU ICU

Livius Andronicus.
Livi Andronici et Cn. Naevi Fabularum reliquiae. Emendavit et adnotavit Lucianus Mueller. Berolini, Apud S. Calvarium, 1885.
72p. 23cm.

I. Naevius, Cn. II. Müller, Lucian, 1836-1898, ed.

NL 0421367 IU InU MH OO NPV NcD NjP ViU NIC OrU

Livius Andronicus.
Livio Andronico e la traduzione artistica
see under
Mariotti, Scevola.

Livius Andronicus.
L'Odyssia, 1951
see under Borelli, Isa.

Livius Andronicus.
Odyssiae reliquiae ex recensione Ottomari Guentheri. Sedini, 1864. 4°.

NL 0421370 MdBP PU NjP

ar X 2967 no.26 Livius Andronicus.
Odyssiae reliquiae ex recensione Ottomari Guentheri. Stettin, F. Hessenland, 1864.
10 p. 26cm.

Separate from "Programm" (Schulnachrichten)--Friedrich-Wilhelms-Gymnasium, Greiffenberg.
No. 26 in a vol. lettered: Programmes: Latin literature I.

NL 0421371 NIC

Livius, pseud.
...La costruzione fascista dell'impero. II edizione. Roma: Casa editrice Pinciana, 1936. 148 p. illus. (maps.) 21cm.

911325A. 1. Colonies and colonization, Italian. 2. Colonies and colonization, Italian—Govt. I. Title.
December 29, 1937

NL 0421372 NN NcD

963.057 L788et Livius, pseud.
L'Etiopia contro l'Italia. Roma, Pinciana, 1936.
IN: afri 119p. photos. 19cm. (L'Italia ha conquistato l'impero)
At head of title: La marcia imperiale dell'Italia in Africa.

1. Ethiopia--Social life and customs I. TITLE.

NL 0421373 IEN

DT837 .8 .L79 Livius, pseud.
L'Italia ha conquistato l'Impero. Roma, Pinciana, 1936.
6 v. illus.
At head of title: La marcia imperiale dell'Italia.
Contents:--v.1. L'Etiopia contro l'Italia.--v.2. Dalla occupazione di Assab alla conquista di Cufra.--v.3. La preparazione della guerra con l'Etiopia.--v.4. Dal Mareb a Macallè.--v.5. Da Gorrahei a Neghelli.--v.6. Le quattro battaglie sul fronte settentrionale e la conquista di Addis Abeba.

NL 0421374 ICU

Livius, Charles Barham, d. 1865.
All in the dark, or the banks of the Elbe
For libretti see under title

822 L76m Livius, Charles Barham, d.1865.
The biter bit; or, Maid or wife, a musical comedy in two acts by Barham Livius. Printed from the acting copy. As now performed at the principal American and English theatres. Clyde, Ohio, A. D. Ames ₍n.d.₎
19p. 19cm. (Ames' series of standard and minor drama, no.87)
Bound with the author's Maid or wife. London, 1821.
"Performed at the Theatre Royal, Drury Lane, November 5th, 1821."

NL 0421376 IU RPB MH CLSU

Livius, Charles Barham, d. 1865.
The freyschütz; or, The wild huntsman of Bohemia
see under Weber, Karl Maria Friedrich Ernst, Freiherr von, 1786-1826.

TC 769 .L79 Livius, Charles Barham, d.1865.
A letter addressed to canal proprietors on the practicability of employing steam power on canals. London, J.Hatchard, 1842.
24 p. fold.plate. 21 cm.

1.Canals--Steam-navigation.

NL 0421378 MiU

Livius, Charles Barham, *d.* 1865.
Maid or wife; or, The deceiver deceived: a musical comedy, in two acts, by Barham Livius, esq. The music composed by the author. Printed from the acting copy, with remarks, biographical and critical, by D.—G. ... As now performed at the Theatres Royal ... London, J. Cumberland ₍n. d.₎
34 p. front. 15cm. (Cumberland's British theatre. London, ca. 1825-55. v. 33 (no. 1))
Remarks by George Daniel, editor of the series.
Without music.
Reissued in Davidson's shilling volume of Cumberland's plays, v. 29 (no. 1)
I. Title.
Library of Congress PR1243.C8 vol. 33 21-14092

NL 0421379 DLC MsU NN MdBP MH MiU OCU PU-F

Livius, Charles Barham, d.1865
Maid or wife; or, The deceiver deceived: a musical comedy, in two acts, by Barham Livius, esq. The music composed by the author. Printed from the acting copy, with remarks, biographical and critical, by D.--G. ... As now performed at the Theatres Royal ... London, J. Cumberland [n.d]; [Louisville, Falls City Microcards, 1965?]
34 p. 15cm. (Cumberland's British theatre. London, ca. 1825-55. v.33 [no.1]) (FCM25363-4)
Microcard ed. 1 card. 7 1/2 x 12 1/2 cm.

Remarks by George Daniel, editor of the series.
Without music.
Reissued in Davidson's shilling volume of Cumberland's plays, v.29 [no.1]
Also published under title: The biter bit.

NL 0421381 RPB

Livius, Charles Barham, *d.* 1865.
Maid or wife; or, The deceiver deceived: a musical comedy, in two acts, by Barham Livius, esq. The music composed by the author. Printed from the acting copy, with remarks, biographical and critical, by D.—G. ... As performed at the Theatres Royal ... London, G. H. Davidson ₍n. d.₎
34 p. front. 15cm. (Davidson's shilling volume of Cumberland's plays. London, ca. 1849-55. v. 29 (no. 1))
Reissue of Cumberland's British theatre, no. 247 (v. 33 (no. 1))
Remarks by George Daniel, editor of the original series.
Without music.
Memoir and portrait of Mrs. Fitz-William.
1. Fitzwilliam, Mrs. Fanny Elizabeth (Copeland) 1801-1854. I. Title.
20-14597
Library of Congress PR1243.C82 vol. 29

NL 0421382 DLC MH IU OO

VOLUME 336

Lilly
PR 4890
.L 65 M3
1821

LIVIUS, CHARLES BARHAM, d. 1865
Maid or wife; or, The deceiver deceived. A musical comedy, in two acts. Performed at the Theatre Royal, Drury-Lane, for the first time, November 5, 1821. By Barham Livius ... London, W. Sams, 1821.
4 p.l., 40 p. 21 cm.
First edition.
Prompt book for the Boston Museum Theatre, with American cast in ms. and marked for production.
Bound in quarter red morocco.

NL 0421383 InU IU MiU NIC ICU MH

[Livius, Charles Barham] d. 1865.
Songs, duets, etc. in the new grand opera of Masaniello
see under Auber, Daniel François Esprit, 1782-1871.

W.C.L.
M780.88
A512VC
no.7

Livius, Charles Barham, d. 1865.
[Maid or wife. 'Twas nature's gay day; arr.]
'Twas nature's gay day; the celebrated dinner song sung in the musical comedy of Maid or wife. Philad[elphi]a, Pub. & sold by Geo. Willig [ca. 1830]
3 p. 34 cm.
Caption title.
For voice and piano. Acc. originally for orchestra.
[No. 7] in a vol. of songs and piano music ca. 1830, with binder's title: Music.
1. Operas. Excerpts. Vocal scores with piano. 2. Songs (High voice) with piano. I. Title.

NL 0421385 NcD

Livius, Peter, 1727–1795.
The memorial of Peter Livius, esq. one of His Majesty's Council for the province of New Hampshire, in New England, to the Lords commissioners for trade and plantations; with the governor's answer, and the memorialist's reply, printed article by article, also their lordships report thereon, to His Majesty, and the opinion of the attorney, and solicitor general, in 1752, referred to by the governor. [London] 1773.
1 p. l., 50 p. 21cm.
1. New Hampshire—Pol. & govt.—Colonial period. 2. Land grants—New Hampshire. I. New Hampshire (Colony) Governor, 1767–1775 (John Wentworth) II. Gt. Brit. Board of trade. III. Title.
8—18439
Library of Congress F37.L78

NL 0421386 DLC RPJCB NjP MH

Livius, Peter, 1727-1795.
Proceedings between Sir Guy Carleton, late governor of the province of Quebec, and Peter Livius, esquire, chief justice...
see under Dorchester, Sir Guy Carleton, 1st baron, 1724-1808.

Livius, Peter, 1727-1795.
Proceedings in the case of Peter Livius, esq. [London, 1795?]
1p.l.,46p. 20cm.(8vo)
On Livius's dismissal as Chief Justice of Quebec by Sir Guy Carleton, and his appeal to the Lords of the Committee of Council for Plantation Affairs.

NL 0421388 MB RPJCB

Livius, Peter, 1727-1795.
Two reports on the matter of complaint of Mr. Livius against Governor Wentworth
see under Gt. Brit. Board of trade.

LIVIUS, Thomas. Stiverd, 1829?-1903.
Die allerseligste Jungfrau bei den vätern der ersten sechs jahrhunderte. Uebersetzung aus dem englischen von Philipp, pring von Arenberg und Heinrich Dhom. Trier, Paulinus-druckerei, 1901-07.
2 vol.

NL 0421390 MH

BT
1014
.L78

Livius, Thomas Stiverd, C.S.S.R., 1829?-1903.
The Blessed Virgin in the Fathers of the first six centuries. With a preface by His Eminence the Cardinal Archbishop of Westminster. London, Burns and Oates, New York, Benziger, 1893.
xxvii, 481 p. 23 cm.
Bibliographical footnotes.
1. Mary, Blessed Virgin - History of Doctrines - Early Church. I. Title.

OrStbM
NL 0421391 DCU MBtS ODaU CSt PBm CtY PV PLatS

BX
7684
.F98
L7

Livius, Thomas Stiverd, 1829?-1903.
Father Furniss and his work for children. London, Art and Book Company, 1896.
193 p. front. 17cm.
1. Furniss, John, C.S.S.R.

NL 0421392 DCU

BS1015
L5

Livius, Thomas Stiverd, 1829?-1903.
Mary in the Epistles, or the implicit teaching of the Apostles concerning the Blessed Virgin contained in their writings; illustrated from the Fathers and other authors, with introductory chapters, by the Rev. Thomas Livius ... London, Burns & Oates, 1891.
viii, 291 p. 16cm.
1. Mary, Blessed Virgin-Apostolic writings. I. Title.

NL 0421393 MBtS CtY ViRUT

Livius, Thomas Stiverd, 1829?-1903.
Mary in the Epistles, or the implicit teaching of the Apostles concerning the Blessed Virgin. New York, Catholic Pub. Society, 1891.
291 p.

NL 0421394 OCX OClJC

Livius, Thomas Stiverd, 1829?–1903.
S. Peter, bishop of Rome; or, The Roman episcopate of the prince of the apostles. Proved from the fathers, history, and archæology, and illustrated by arguments from other sources. By the Rev. T. Livius ... London, Burns & Oates, limited; New York, Catholic publication society co., 1888.
xxii, 560 p. 22cm.
1. Apostolic succession. 2. Peter, Saint, apostle.
25-15263
Library of Congress BV665.L5

NL 0421395 DLC NRCR MU MoSU KStMC OClJC

Livius, Titus
Arrangement

1. Manuscripts
2. Ab urbe condita-Collections of all extant books.
3. Ab urbe condita-One or more books. Epitome see Periochae
4. Periochae
5. Selections

6. Selective index

All groups are arranged by language and within language alphabetically by title regardless of subtitle. The editions in Latin always precede the editions in translations.

---

1. Manuscripts

Livius, Titus. *Mss.* (*Codex Puteanus*)
... Histoire romaine de Tite-Live ... reproduction réduite du manuscrit en onciale, latin 5730 de la Bibliothèque nationale. Paris, Imprimerie Berthaud frères [1907]
4 v. (portfolios) 20cm.
At head of title: Bibliothèque nationale. Département des manuscrits.
Introduction signed: H. O. [*i. e.* Henry Omont]
Tome I: t.-p., and description of the ms. (7 p.), fold. pl. (facsimile, full size, of fol. 281 verso), and fol. 1–120 (incl. 48bis).—t. II: t.-p., and fol. 121–240 (161 omitted).—t. III: t.-p., and fol. 241–360 (297 and 306 omitted).—t. IV: t.-p., and fol. 361–470 (incl. 464bis, and 465bis)
Facsimile of the Codex Puteanus (now Ms. lat. 5730 in the Bibliothèque nationale, Paris) containing the third decade, or book XXI (chap. 20 §8–chap. 21 §13; chap. 29 §6–chap. 30 §11; chap. 41 §13 to end (chap. 63)); books XXII–XXIX; book XXX (chap. 1–30 §14; chap. 37 §3–chap. 38 §3)
1. Manuscripts, Latin—Facsimiles. 2. Manuscripts. France—Facsimiles. I. Paris. Bibliothèque nationale. Département des manuscrits. II. Omont, Henri Auguste, 1857–
27-5394
Library of Congress Z115Z.L78

NL 0421400 DLC ICN ViW IU NcGU MiU OCU OCl MB ICN

Livius, Titus. *Mss.* (*Codex vindobonensis lat. 15*)
Livius. Codex vindobonensis lat. 15 phototypice editus. Praefatus est Carolus Wessely. Lugduni Batavorum, A. W. Sijthoff, 1907.
2 p. l., xcv p., facsim.: 193 numb. l. 41½cm. (*Added t.-p.:* Codices graeci et latini photographice depicti duce Scatone de Vries ... t. XI)
1. Manuscripts, Latin—Facsimiles. I. Wessely, Carl, 1860–1930.
7-40263 Revised
Library of Congress Z114.C67 vol. 11

NL 0421401 DLC NcU NcD NjP NN MH PP MiU OCU OCl

---

2. Ab urbe condita-Collections of all extant books.

Livius, Titus.
Ab urbe condita.
For operas, etc., based on this work see Porrino, Ennio, 1910– Gli orazi; Respighi, Ottorino, 1879–1936. Lucrezia.

VOLUME 336

Latin

PA6452 A3 F7 Livius, Titus
Titi Livii Ab urbe condita ... für den Schulgebrauch ... Leipzig, B. G. Teubner, 1865-1873.
3 pts. in 1 v. 22 cm.
Contents.- Liber I ... erklärt von Joseph Frey.- Liber II ... erklärt von Joseph Frey.- Liber XXI ... erklärt von Eduard Wölfflin.

NL 0421405 RPB PBm MH MA CtY ViU

PA 6452 A3T89 Livius, Titus.
Ab urbe condita; für den Schulgebrauch erklärt von Carl Tücking. Paderborn, F. Schöningh, 1872-79.
7 v. in 3. 21cm.
Books 21-22 are 2. Aufl.
I. Tücking, Karl, ed.

NL 0421406 NIC PU

PA6452 .A3T9 1874 LIVIUS,TITUS.
Titi Livii Ab urbe condita... Für den schulgebrauch erklärt von dr.Karl Tücking... Paderborn und Münster,F.Schöningh,1874-92.
7 v.in 1. 21cm.

NL 0421407 ICU MoU

Livius, Titus.
Ab urbe condita; für den schulgebrauch erklärt von Moritz Müller und Franz Luterbacher, liber Leipzig, 1879-1905.
20 v.

NL 0421408 PHC

878.4 MR55 Livius, Titus.
Ab urbe condita; texte latin publié avec une notice sur la vie et les ouvrages de Tite-Live, des notes critiques et explicatives, des remarques sur la langue, un index des noms propres historiques et géographiques et des antiquités, par O. Riemann et E. Benoist. Paris, Hachette, 1892 [v.1, 1908]-1909.
3 v. illus.,fold.maps. 16cm. (Classiques latins)
Vol.[1] 12th ed., rev.; v.[2] new ed.; v.[3] 9th ed., rev.
Vol.[3] by O. Riemann and T. Homolle.
Contents.- [1] libri XXI-XXII.- [2] libri XXIII-XXV.- [3] libri XXVI-XXX.
I. Riemann, Othon, 1853-1901, ed. II.Benoist, Eugène, 1831-1887, ed.

NL 0421410 CSt

---

ar W 29603 Livius, Titus.
Ab urbe condita; edidit Antonius Zingerle. Ed. maior. Vindobonae et Pragae, F. Tempsky, 1899-1907.
5 v. in 1. 22cm.
Issued in fascicles.
I. Zingerle, Anton, 1842-1910, ed.

NL 0421411 NIC

Livius, Titus.
Titi Livi Ab Urbe condita. Oxonii, E Typographeo Clarendoniano, 1914–
v. 19 cm. (Scriptorum classicorum bibliotheca Oxoniensis)
Includes bibliographical references.
CONTENTS.—T. 1. Libri I–V. Recognoverunt R. S. Conway et C. F. Walters.—T. 2. Libri VI–X. Recognoverunt C. F. Walters et R. S. Conway.—T. 4. Libri XXVI–XXX. Recognoverunt R. S. Conway et S. K. Johnson.—T. 5. Libri XXXI–XXXV. Recognovit A. H. McDonald.
I. Conway, Robert Seymour, 1864–1933, ed. (Series)
PA6105.S8L5 1914 14–14418 rev
PA6452.A2 1914

PPT NjP NBuU InU MA DDO NcU TU NIC OU OO NSyU NcGU NcD PHC PU PSC MiU PBm ViU
NL 0421412 DLC MB OCU CU ICN CoU IU UU MH TNJ LU ScU

PA 6452 A2 1940 Livius, Titus.
Ab urbe condita. Firenze, "La Nuova Italia" [194-
v. 20 cm. (I classici della Nuova Italia, 8-9, 15, 40, 48)
Classici latini.
Edition varies.
Editors vary.
1. Rome - Hist. I. Title.

NL 0421413 CU-S

---

871 L5 1909 Livius Patavinus, Titus.
Ab urbe condita libri. Wilhelm Weissenborns erklärende ausgabe. Neu bearbeitet von H. J. Müller. Berlin,
v. (Sammlung griechischer und lateinischer schriftsteller mit deutschen anmerkungen)
I. Muller, H. J., ed. II. Weissenborn, Wilhelm, ed.

NL 0421414 IU MiU

PA6452 .A2 1829 LIVIUS,TITUS.
T.Livii Ab urbe condita libri. Recognovit Immanuel Bekkerus. Selectas virorum doctorum notas in usum scholarum addidit M.F.E.Raschig... Editio stereotypa... Berolini,G.Reimer,1829-
v. 18cm.

MoU
NL 0421415 ICU CU PU PBm IMunS PLatS ViLxW MH InU

PA6452 .A2 1829a LIVIUS,TITUS.
T.Livii Ab urbe condita libri. Recognovit Immanuel Bekkerus. Selectas virorum doctorum notas in usum scholarum addidit M.F.E.Raschig ... Londini,apud Black,Young et Young,1829-
v. 18cm.
1.Rome--Hist.

NL 0421416 ICU

---

871 L5 1836 Livius, Titus.
T. Livii Ab urbe condita libri. Recognovit Immanuel Bekkerus. Selectas virorum doctorum notas in usum scholarum addidit M. F. E. Raschig. Ed. stereotypa ... Londini, 1836.
v.

NL 0421417 IU

PA6452 .A2 1851 Livius, Titus.
Titi Livi Ab urbe condita libri. Iterum recognovit Wilh. Weissenborn ... Lipsiae, In aedibus B. G. Teubneri, 1851-
6 v. 17½cm.
CONTENTS.—pars 1. Lib.I-VI.—pars 2. Lib.VII-XXIII.—pars 3. Lib.XXIV-XXX.—pars 4. Lib.XXXI-XXXVIII.—pars 5. Lib.XXXIX-CXL.—pars 6. Fragmenta et index.
1. Rome—Hist. I. Weissenborn, Wilhelm, 1803-1878, ed.

NL 0421418 ViU IU PU ICU MH NjP

PA6104 .L5 1852 Livius, Titus.
Titi Livi Ab urbe condita libri. Recognovit Wilh. Weissenborn ... Lipsiae, Sumptibus et typis B. G. Teubneri, 1852-53.
6 v. in 5. 17½cm. [Bibliotheca scriptorum graecorum et romanorum Teubneriana. S.r.]
Vol.6 bound with vol.5, has special t.-p., and is paged separately.
1. Rome—Hist. I. Weissenborn, Wilhelm, 1803-1878, ed. II. Ser.

NL 0421419 ViU NNC

Livius, Titus.
Titi Livi Ab urbe condita libri; erklaert von W.Weissenborn... Leipzig,Weidmann,1853-60.
7v.in 5. 20cm.

NL 0421420 MWelC MiU

Livius, Titus.
Titi Livi Ab urbe condita libri. Erklært von W. Weissenborn ... Berlin, Weidmann, 1853-1866.
10 v. 20½cm.
10.bd.: 20cm.
1. Rome—Hist. I. Weissenborn, Wilhelm, 1803-1878, ed. II. Title: Ab urbe condita libri.

NL 0421421 ViU

Livius, Titus.
Ab urbe condita libri. Weissenborn. Zweite auflage. Berlin, Weidmann, 1854-56.

NL 0421422 OClJC ScU

PA 6452 .A2 1856 Livius, Titus.
Ab urbe condita libri. Erklaert von W. Weissenborn. 2. Aufl. Berlin, Weidmann, 1856-81.
10 v. (Sammlung griechischer und lateinischer Schriftsteller mit deutschen Anmerkungen)
Bd. -10 besorgt von H. J. Müller.
Rome--History.
(A) Weissenborn, Wilhelm, 1803-1878, ed.
(A) Müller, Hermann Johannes, 1844-1903? ed.

NL 0421423 MoU PU PBm

Livius, Titus.
Titi Livi ab urbe condita libri. Edidit Martinus Hertz ... Ed. stereotypa. Lipsiae, ex officina Bernhardi Tauchnitz, 1857–63 [64]
4 v. 20½cm.
In 8 parts with special t.-p. for each.
CONTENTS.—vol. I. pars I. De vita ac scriptis T. Livii Patavini prolusio. Adnotatio critica. Liber I–V. 1857. pars II. Liber VI–X. Periocha libri XI–XX. 1857.—vol. II. pars I. Adnotatio critica. Liber XXI–XXV. 1860. pars II. Liber XXVI–XXX. 1860.—vol. III. pars I. Adnotatio critica. Liber XXXI–XXXV. 1862. pars II. Liber XXXVI–XXXX. 1862.—vol. IV. pars I. Adnotatio critica. Liber XXXXI–XXXXV. 1863. pars II. Adnotatio critica. Librorum XLVI–CXXXXII periochae. Librorvm deperditorvm fragmenta. Index rervm. 1864.
I. Hertz, Martin Julius, 1818–1895, ed.
7–16251

NL 0421424 DLC ICU MiU NjP PU CaBVaU CtY ViU InU

VOLUME 336

PA6452 .A2 1858 Livius, Titus.
Titi Livi Ab urbe condita libri. Erklaert von W. Weissenborn ... Berlin, Weidmann, 1858-1877.
10 v. in 11. 19½cm. (On cover: Sammlung griechischer und lateinischer schriftsteller mit deutschen anmerkungen)
Series note on cover of vol.3, pts.1 & 2.
Edition varies: v.1, 5. verb. aufl.; v.2-4, 4. verb. aufl.; v.5, 3. aufl. v.6-10, no edition note.
1. Rome—Hist. I. Weissenborn, Wilhelm, 1803-1878, ed. II. Ser.

NL 0421425 ViU

---

878 L5.V 1858 Classics Lib'y Livius, Titus.
Ab urbe condita libri. Edidit Martinus Hertz. Editio stereotypa. Lipsiae, Tauchnitz, 1858.
4v. 21cm.

I. Hertz, Martin Julius, 1818-1895, ed.

NL 0421426 TxU MH

Livius, Titus.
Ab urbe condita libri, erklaert von W. Weissenborn... Berlin, Weidmannsche buchhandlung, 1859-70.
10 v.

NL 0421427 OU

Livius, Titus.
Titi Livi Ab urbe condita libri. Erklært von W. Weissenborn ... 3. aufl. Berlin, Weidmann, 1860-
10 v. 20cm.

1. Rome—Hist. I. Weissenborn, Wilhelm, 1803-1878, ed. II. Title: Ab urbe condita libri.

NL 0421428 ViU

PA6452 A2 1860a Livius, Titus.
Titi Livi Ab urbe condita libri; recognovit Wilh. Weissenborn. Lipsiae, sumptibus et typis B.G. Teubneri, 1860-63.
v.

Contents.-

pars 2. Lib. VII-X. Epitom. Lib. XI-XX. Lib. XXI-XXIII.

NL 0421429 CU

PA 6452 .A2 1861 Livius, Titus.
Ab urbe condita libri. Erklärt von W. Weissenborn. 3. Aufl.
Berlin Weidmann, 1861-
v. in (Sammlung griechischer und lateinischer Schriftsteller mit deutschen Anmerkungen)
Bd. besorgt von H. J. Müller.
#Rome--History.
(A) Weissenborn, Wilhelm, 1803-1878, ed.
(A) Müller, Hermann Johannes, 1844-1903? ed.

NL 0421430 MoU CtY

Livius, Titus.
Ab urbe condita libri, erklaert von W. Weissenborn. Berlin, 1863-73, Weidmannsche Buchhandlung. 10v. in 5.

NL 0421431 MA MiU KAS MWelC IaDuC

PA 6452 .A2 1866 Livius, Titus.
Ab urbe condita libri. Erklärt von W. Weissenborn. 4. Aufl.
Berlin, Weidmann, 1866-
v. in (Sammlung griechischer und lateinischer Schriftsteller mit deutschen Anmerkungen)
Bd. besorgt von H. J. Müller.
#Rome--History.
(A) Weissenborn, Wilhelm, 1803-1878, ed.
(A) Müller, Hermann Johannes, 1844-1903? ed.

NL 0421432 MoU NjP ViU PU ICN PBm

Livius, Titus.
Ab urbe condita libri. Erklaert von W. Weissenborn... Berlin, Weidmannsche buchhandlung, 1867-81.
10 v. in 17.

NL 0421433 OCU

Livius, Titus.
Titi Livi Ab urbe condita libri. Erklaert von W. Weissenborn ... Berlin, Weidmann, 1867-1882.
10 v. 19½cm.
Edition varies: 1.bd., 7. aufl.; 2.bd., 5. aufl.; 3.bd., 4. verb. aufl.; 4.bd., 6. verb. aufl.; 5.bd., 4. aufl.; 6.bd., 3. verb. aufl.; 7., 8., 9.bde., 2. verb. aufl.; 10.bd., 2. aufl.
Vols. 1, 2, 5, and 10 ed. by H. J. Müller.

1. Rome—Hist. I. Weissenborn, Wilhelm, 1803-1878, ed. II. Müller, Hermann Johann, 1844-1912, ed. III. Title: Ab urbe condita libri.

NL 0421434 ViU

Livius, Titus.
Titi Livi Ab urbe condita libri. Iterum recognovit Wilh. Weissenborn... Lipsiae, In aedibus B. G. Teubneri, 1868-73.
6 v. in 5. 18cm.

Pars 1-2, 1873; pars 3, 1872; pars 4, 1871; pars 5, 1873; pars 6, 1868.

I. Weissenborn, Wilhelm, 1803-1878, ed. *Card revised January 21, 1948*

NL 0421435 NN

Livius, Titus.
Ab urbe condita libri. Iterum recognovit Wilh. Weissenborn. ... Editio stereotypa. Lipsiae, 1898 in aedibus B. G. Teubneri, 1868-1912.
6 v. in 3.

NL 0421436 MiU

---

871 L5 1869 Livius, Titus.
Ab urbe condita libri. Iterum recognovit Wilh. Weissenborn. Lipsiae, In Aedibus B. G. Teubneri, 1869-1871 [v.1, 1870]
6v. in 5. 18cm.

Title of v.3-6 varies slightly.
Vol.1, copy 2 and v.2, copy 3: 1889.

NL 0421437 IU MH

Livius, Titus.
Titi Livi Ab urbe condita libri. Erklært von W. Weissenborn ... 5. verb. aufl. Berlin, Weidmann, 1871-
10 v. 19½cm. (Sammlung griechischer und lateinischer schriftsteller mit deutschen anmerkungen)

1. Rome—Hist. I. Weissenborn, Wilhelm, 1803-1878, ed. II. Title: Ab urbe condita libri. III. Ser.

NL 0421438 ViU MoU NcD PU

Livius, Titus
Titi Livi ab urbe condita libri. Iterum recognovit Wilh. Weissenborn. Lipsiae, 1871-73.
6 v. in 5 16°

NL 0421439 NN OOxM MdBP

---

878 L5 W43 N8 Livius,Titus.
...Ab urbe condita libri.Iterum recognovit Wilh.Weissenborn...Leipzig, B.G. Teubner, 1873-1881.
6 v. in 5 17½cm.

NL 0421440 MiU

Livius, Titus.
Ab urbe condita libri; erklärt von W. Weissenborn... Ber., 1873-83.
10 v.

NL 0421441 PBm OClW RPB

878.4 A2 W4 1873 v.1-10 Livius, Titus
T. Livi Ab urbe condita libri. Erklärt von W. Weissenborn... Bearbeitet von H. J. Müller... Berlin, Weidmannsche Buchhandlung, 1873-1890.
10v. in 5.

I. Weissenborn, Wilhelm, 1803-1878, ed. II. Müller,H.J.,jt.ed. III. Title: Ab urbe condita.

NL 0421442 TNJ

Livius, Titus.
Ab urbe condita libri. 8. aufl. Berlin, Weidmann, 1873-91.
10 v. in 5.

NL 0421443 OU

PA6453 .A2 1885 Livius, Titus.
T.Livi Ab urbe condita libri, erklärt von W.Weissenborn... Berlin, Weidmann, 1873-94.
10 v. 20 cm.
Contents.- 1.bd. Buch I-II,8.aufl.von H.J.Müller. 1885-94. 2 pts.in 1 v. - 2. bd. Buch III-V, 5.aufl.besorgt von H.J. Müller. 1881-82. 2 pts.in 1 v. - 3.bd. Buch VI-X, 5.aufl.besorgt von H.J.Müller.

1886-90. 2 pts.in 1 v. - 4.bd.hft.1-2. Buch XXI-XXII, 8.aufl.,neubearb.von H.J. Müller. 1888-91; hft.3. Buch XXIII, 7. aufl.besorgt von H.J.Müller. 1883. 3 pts. in 1 v. - 5.bd. Buch XXIIII-XXVI, 4.aufl. besorgt von H.J.Müller. 1880. 2 pts.in 1 v. - 6.bd. Buch XXVII-XXX, 3.verb,aufl. 1878. 2 pts.in 1 v. - 7.bd.Buch XXI-

XXXIIII, 3.aufl.von H.J.Müller. 1883. 2 pts.in 1 v. - 8.bd. Buch XXV-XXXVIII, 2 verb.aufl. 1873. - bd.9. Buch XXXVIIII-XXXXII, 2.verb.aufl. 1876. 2 pts.in 1 v. - bd.10. Buch XXXXIII-XXXXV, und fragmente; 2.aufl.besorgt von H.J.Müller. 1880-81. 2 pts.in 1 v.
I.Weissenborn, Wilhelm, 1803-1878, ed II.Müller, Hermann Johannes, 1844-1912, ed

NL 0421446 OCU

VOLUME 336

PA6452
A2
1885
Livius, Titus
Ab urbe condita libri. Erklärt von W. Weissenborn. ₍Bearbeitet₎ von H. J. Müller. Berlin, Weidmann, 1873-96 ₍v. 1, pt. 1, 1885₎
10 v. 20 cm.

Contents. - 1. Bd. Libri 1-2. 8. Aufl. 1885-94. - 2. Bd., 1. Heft. Liber 3. 5. Aufl. 1881. - 2. Bd., 2. Heft. Libri 4-5. 6. Aufl. 1896. - 3. Bd. Libri 6-10. 5. Aufl. 1886-90. - 4. Bd., 1.-2. Heft. Libri 21-22. 8. Aufl. 1888-91. - 4. Bd.,

Contents - Continued
3. Heft. Liber 23. 7. Aufl. 1883. - 5. Bd., 1. Heft. Libri 24-25. 5. Aufl. 1895. - 5. Bd., 2. Heft. Liber 26. 4. Aufl. 1880. - 6. Bd. Libri 27-30. 3. verb. Aufl. 1878. - 7. Bd. Libri 31-34. 3. Aufl. 1883. - 8. Bd. Libri 35-38. 2. verb. Aufl. 1873. - 9. Bd. Libri 39-42. 2. verb. Aufl. 1875-76. - 10. Bd. Libri 43-45 et Fragmenta.

2. Aufl. 1880-81.

NL 0421449 MeB

PA
6452
A2
1873
Livius, Titus.
Ab urbe condita libri; erklärt von W. Weissenborn. Berlin, Weidmann, 1873-99 ₍v. 1, 1885₎
10 v. in 11. 21cm. (Sammlung griechischer und lateinischer Schriftsteller mit deutschen Anmerkungen. Griechische Schriftsteller)
All except Bd. 6, Hft. 1 and Bd. 8-9 are edited by H. J. Müller.

NL 0421450 NIC

Livius, Titus.
Ab urbe condita libri, erklärt von W. Weissenborn. Ed. 4. Berlin, 1874.

NL 0421451 ODW

PA6452
A2
1875
Livius, Titus. Latin.
Ab urbe condita libri; erklärt von W. Weissenborn. 6., verb. Aufl. Berlin, Weidmann, 1875-
v.

Contents.-

4. Bd., 1. Hft. Buch XXI.

NL 0421452 CU InU MH MoU ViU NcU PU PBm PU TNJ

Livius, Titus.
Ab urbe condita libri... recognovit Wilh. Weissenborn... Lipsiae, in aedibus B. G. Teubner, 1877-82.
6 v. in 5.

NL 0421453 OU

PA6452
A2
1878a
CLASSICS
DEPT.
Livius, Titus. Latin.
Titi Livi Ab urbe condita libri. Iterum recognovit Wilh. Weissenborn ... Ed. stereotypa. Lipsiae, in aedibus B.G. Teubner, 1878-95.
6 v. 18cm.

Titles of v.2-6 vary slightly.

Contents. - pars 1. Liber I-VI. 1894. - pars 2. Lib.VII-XXIII. Iterum recognovit Wilh. Weissenborn. 1878. - pars 3. Lib.XXIV-XXX. Ed. primam cur. Guilelmus Weissenborn. Ed. altera, quam cur. Mauritius Müller. Ed. stereotypa. 1894. - pars 4. Lib.XXXI-XXXVIII. Ed. primam cur. Guilelmus Weissenborn. Ed. altera, quam

cur. Mauritius Müller. Ed. stereotypa. 1895. - pars 5. Lib.XXXIX-CXL. Recognovit Wilh. Weissenborn. Ed. stereotypa. 1894. - pars 6. Fragmenta et index. Recognovit Wilh. Weissenborn. 1892.

I. Weissenborn, Wilhelm, 1803-1878, ed.
II. Müller, Moritz, ed.

NL 0421455 CU

PA6452
A2
1879
Livius, Titus
Titi Livi ab urbe condita libri; erklaert von W. Weissenborn. 7. Aufl. Besorgt von H. J. Müller. Berlin, Weidmannsche Buchlandlung, 1879-1882.
3 v. in 1. 21 cm.

NL 0421456 RPB PBm PU ViU

PA
6452
.A2
1880
Livius, Titus.
Ab urbe condita libri, ex recensione Andreae Frigellii. Gothae, F. A. Perthes, 188-?
v.

Partial contents.--v. 2, fasc. 1. Liber 21.
No more published?

#Rome--Hist.--Republic, 265-30 B. C.
#Punic War, 2d, 218-201 B. C.
Frigell, Anders.

NL 0421458 MoU

PA6452
.A3W475
LIVIUS, TITUS.
Titi Livi Ab urbe condita libri. Recognovit Wilh. Weissenborn ... Lipsiae, in aedibus B. G. Teubneri ₍188-
6 v. (On cover: Bibliotheca scriptorum graecorum et romanorum Teubneriana)

1. Rome--Hist.

NL 0421459 ICU

PA
6452
.A2
1880
Livius, Titus.
T. Livi Ab urbe condita libri. Wilhelm Weissenborns erklärende Ausg. neu bearb. von H.J. Müller. Berlin, Weidmann, 1880-1910.
10 v. in 13 20 cm.
Edition varies: Bd. 1, 4(2. Heft): 9. Aufl.; Bd.2: 6. Aufl.; Bd.3, 5: 5. Aufl.; Bd.4(3. Heft): 8. Aufl.; Bd.6: 4. Aufl.; Bd.7-9: 3. Aufl.; Bd.10: 2. Aufl.
I. Weissenborn, Wilhelm, 1803-1878, ed.
II. Müller, Hermann Johann, ed.

NL 0421460 DCU NcU InU RPB

PA
6452
A2
1880
Livius, Titus.
Ab urbe condita libri. Wilhelm Weissenborns erklärende Ausg. Berlin, Weidmannsche Buchhandlung, 1880-1921 [v. 1, 1908]
10 v. 21 cm.

Contents. - 1. Bd., 1. Hft., Buch I, 9 Aufl., 1908. 1. Bd., 2. Hft., Buch II, 8. Aufl., 1894. - 2. Bd., 1. Hft., Buch III, 6. Aufl., 1900. 2. Bd., 2. Hft., Buch IIII und V, 6. Aufl., 1896. - 3. Bd., 1 Hft., Buch VI-VIII, 5. Aufl., 1886. 3. Bd. 2 Hft., Buch VIIII-X, 5. Aufl., 1890. - 4. Bd., 1. Hft., Buch XXI, 10 Aufl., 1921. 4. Bd., 2. Hft., Buch XXII, 9. Aufl., 1905. - 5. Bd., 1. Hft., Buch XXIII und XXV, 5. Aufl., 1895. 5. Bd., 2.

Hft., Buch XXVI, 5. Aufl., 1911. - 6. Bd., 1. Hft., Buch XXVII und XXVIII, 4. Aufl., 1910. 6. Bd., 2. Hft., Buch XXVIIII-XXX, 4. Aufl., 1899. - 7. Bd., 1. Hft., Buch XXXI-XXXII, 3. Aufl., 1883. 7. Bd., 2. Hft., Buch XXXIII-XXXIIII, 3. Aufl., 1883. - 8. Bd., 1. Hft., Buch XXV-XXVI, 3. Aufl., 1906. 8. Bd., 2. Hft., Buch XXXVII-XXXVIII, 3. Aufl., 1907. - 9. Bd., 1. Hft., Buch XXXVIIII und XXXX, 3. Aufl., 1909. 9. Bd., 2 Hft., Buch XXXXI und XXXXII, 3. Aufl., 1909. - 10. Bd., 1 Hft., Buch XXXXIII-XXXXIIII, 2. Aufl., 1880. 10. Bd., 2. Hft., Buch XXXXV und Fragmente, 2. Aufl., 1881.

I. Weisseborn, cs Wilhelm, 1803-1878.

NL 0421462 CU-S IU PPT

PA6452
A2
1880
Livius, Titus.
T. Livi Ab vrbe condita libri. Wilhelm Weissenborns erklärende ausgabe, neu bearbeitet von H.J. Müller ... Berlin, Weidmannsche buchhandlung, 1880-1924.
10 v. in 14. 20cm. (On cover: Sammlung griechischer und lateinischer schriftsteller)

Title varies slightly.

Contents. - v.1:1. buch I. 9.aufl. 1908. - v.1:2. buch II. 8.aufl. 1894. - v.2:1. buch III. 6.aufl. 1900. 2:2. buch IIII und V. 6.aufl. 1896. - v.3:1. buch VI-VIII. Erklärt von W.

Weissenborn und H.J.Müller. Neubearb. von Otto Rossbach. 6.aufl. 1924. - v.3:2. buch VIIII-X. 5.aufl. 1890. - v.4:1. buch XXI. Erklärt von W. Weissenborn und H.J.Müller. Neubearb. von Otto Rossbach. 10.aufl. 1921. - v.4:2. buch XXII. 9.aufl. 1905. - v.4:3. buch XXIII. 8.aufl. 1907. - v.5:1. buch XXIIII und XXV. 5.aufl. 1895. 5:2. buch XXVI. 5.aufl. 1911. - v.6:1. buch XXVII und XXVIII. 4.aufl. 1910. 6:2. buch

XXVIIII-XXX. 4.aufl. 1899. - v.7:1. buch XXXI, XXXII. 3.aufl. 1883. 7:2. buch XXXIII, XXXIIII. 3.aufl. 1883. - v.8:1. buch XXXV-XXXVI. 3.aufl. 1906. 8:2. buch XXXVII-XXXVIII. 3.aufl. 1907. - v.9:1. buch XXXVIIII und XXXX. 3.aufl. 1909. 9:2 buch XXXXI und XXXXII. 3.aufl. 1909. - v.10:1. buch XXXXIII, XXXXIIII. 2.aufl. 1880. 10:2. buch XXXXV und Fragmente. 2.aufl. 1881.

NL 0421465 CU CaBVaU

PA6452
.A2
1881
Livius, Titus.
T. Livi Ab urbe condita libri. Recognovit H. J. Mueller ... Berolini, Apud Weidmannos, 1881-82.
4 v. 20cm.

1. Rome—Hist. I. Müller, Hermann Johann, 1844-1912, ed.

NL 0421466 ViU CtY

PA6453
.A3
1899
Livius, Titus.
Titi Livi Ab urbe condita libri. Editionem primam curavit Guilelmus Weissenborn. Editio altera... Lipsiae, in aedibus B.G. Teubneri, 1881-1912.
6 pts. in 11 v. 18½ cm. (On cover: Bibliotheca scriptorum graecorum et romanorum Teubneriana. ₍S.r.₎)
Vols. not issued consecutively.
pts. 1-4, ed. by Moritz Müller.
Pt. 5, ed. by W. Heraeus.

Continued in next column

VOLUME 336

Continued from preceding column

pt.6, first edition.

Contents.- Pars I,fasc.1-2. Libri I-VI 1899,1902. - Pars II,fasc.1. Libri VII-X. 1899. - Pars II,fasc.2. Libri XXI-XXIII. 1894. - Pars III,fasc.1-2. Libri XXIV-XXX 1881,1884. - Pars IV,fasc.1-2.Libri XXXI-XXXVIII. 1887,1890. - Pars V,fasc.1-2.Libri XXXIX-CXLII. 1908,1912. - Pars VI.Fragmenta et index. 1892.

I.Weissenborn,Wilhelm, 1803-1878, ed. II.Müller,Moritz, ed. III.Heraeus,Wilhelm, 1862- ed.

NL 0421469 OCU ODW InU ViU

Livius, Titus
T. Livi Ab urbe condita libri. Erklärt von W. Weissenborn. 5.Aufl. besorgt von H.J. Müller ... Berlin, Weidmannsche Buchhandlung, 1882.

v. 19cm.
Library has volumes 2, 3
Volume 3 published 1854. On cover: Sammlung Griechischer und Lateinischer schriftsteller mit deutschen anmerkungen.

I. Weissenborn, Wilhelm, 1803-1878, ed.
II. Müller, Hermann Johannes, ed.

NL 0421470 PLatS

Livius, Titus.
Ab urbe condita libri, iterum recognovit Wilh. Weissenborn. Lipsiae, Teubner, 1882-85.
5 v. in 3. 17 cm.

NL 0421471 TU

PA6452 A2 1885
Livius, Titus. Latin.
Titi Livi Ab urbe condita libri. Iterum recognovit Wilh. Weissenborn ... Lipsiae, in aedibus B.G. Teubneri, 1882-86.
5 v. 18cm.

Titles v.3-5 vary slightly.

Contents. - pars 1. Liber I-VI. 1885. - pars 2. Liber VII-XXIII. 1886. - pars 3. Lib.XXIV-XXX. Ed. primam cur. Guilelmus Weissenborn. Ed. altera, quam cur. Mauritius Müller. 1884. - pars 4. Lib.XXXI-XXXVIII. Recognovit Wilh. Weissenborn. 1885. - pars 5. Liber XXXIX-CXL. Recognovit Wilh. Weissenborn. 1882.

NL 0421472 CU

PA6452 A2 1887
Livius, Titus
Ab urbe condita libri. Iterum recognovit Wilh. Weissenborn. Lipsiae, in aedibus B. G. Teubneri, 1882-89 [pt. 1, 1887]
6 pts in 3 v. 18 cm. (Bibliotheca scriptorum graecorum et romanorum Teubneriana)

Contents. - pars 1. Libri 1-6. - pars 2. Libri 7-23. - pars 3. Libri 24-30. - pars 4. Libri 31-38. - pars 5. Libri 39-40. pars 6. Fragmenta et index.

NL 0421473 MeB

Livius, Titus.
Ab urbe condita libri. Lipsiae, Teubnere, 1882-91.
6v. in 3.

NL 0421474 PHC

PA6452 .A2 1883
LIVIUS,TITUS.
T.Livi Ab urbe condita libri edidit Antonius Zingerle... Vindobonae et Pragae,sumptus fecit F.Tempsky;[etc.,etc.]1883-94.
7 v.in 2. 18cm. (Added t.-p.:Bibliotheca scriptorum graecorum et romanorum edita curante Carolo Schenkl)

NL 0421475 ICU OCU ViU PU

PA6452 .A2 1884
Livius, Titus.
Titi Livi Ab urbe condita libri. Iterum recognovit Wilh. Weissenborn ... Lipsiae, In aedibus B. G. Teubneri, 1884-
6 v. 17½cm.

CONTENTS.—pars 1. Lib.I-VI.—pars 2. Lib.VII-X. Epitom. lib.XI-XX., lib.XXI-XXIII.—pars 3. Lib.XXIV-XXX.—pars 4. Lib.XXXI-XXXVIII.—pars 5. Lib.XXXIX-XLV. Epitom. lib.XLVI-CXL.—pars 6. Fragmenta et index.

1. Rome—Hist. I. Weissenborn, Wilhelm, 1803-1878, ed.

NL 0421476 ViU NIC

---

871 L5 1885
Livius, Titus.
Ab urbe condita libri. Erklärt von W. Weissenborn. 8.Aufl. von H. J. Müller. Berlin, Weidmann, 1885-
v. in 20cm.

NL 0421477 IU OO NjP FTaSU MoU PPCCH

Livius, Titus.
Ab urbe condita libri, iterum recognovit Wilh. Weissenborn. Lipsiae, Teubner, 1885-
5 v. in 3. 18 cm.

NL 0421478 TU MH

PA6452 .A3L9
LIVIUS,TITUS.
Titi Livi Ab urbe condita... Für den schulgebrauch erklärt von Franz Luterbacher. Leipzig, B.G.Teubner,1885-
v. map. 21cm.
Liber XXI,3.,verb.aufl.;liber XXII-XXIII,2., verb.aufl.
Libri XXI-XXII have imprint:Gotha,F.A.Perthes.

NL 0421479 ICU MiU

Livius,Titus.

[T.Livi] Ab urbe condita libri. Wilhelm Weissenborns erklärende ausgabe neu bearbeitet von H.J.Müller... Berlin,Weidmann,1886-1908.

10v.in 4. 20cm.
v.1,9 aufl.,v.2,6 aufl.,v.3,4 aufl.,v.4 9 aufl.,v.5,5 aufl.,v.6,4 aufl.,v.7,3 aufl.,v.8,3 aufl.,v.9,3 aufl.,v.10,2 aufl.

NL 0421480 OrPR

PA6452 .A2 1886
Livius, Titus.

Ab urbe condita libri. Wilhelm Weissenborns erklärende Ausgabe. Neu bearb. von H. H. Müller. Berlin, Weidmann, 1886-1908.
6 v. in 1. 20cm.
Title page v. 3, pt. 1, varies slightly:Besorgt von H. J. Müller.
CONTENTS.—Bd.1.Hft. 1. Buch 1. 9. Aufl. 1908.—Bd.1. Hft. 2. Buch 2. 8. Aufl. 1894.—Bd.2. Hft. 1. Buch 3. 6. Aufl. 1900.—Bd.2. Hft. 2. Buch 4 und 5. 6. Aufl. 1896.—Bd.3. Hft. 1. Buch 6-8. 5. Aufl. 1886.—Bd.3. Hft. 2. Buch 8-10. 5. Aufl. 1890.
I. Wessenborn, Wilhelm, 1803-1878. II. Müller, Herman Johann, 1844-1912, ed.

NL 0421481 ViU

PA6452 .A2 1887
Livius, Titus.
Ab urbe condita libri. Wilhelm Weissenborns erklärende ausgabe, neubearbeitet von H.J. Müller. Berlin, Weidmann, 1887-
v. 21 cm.

I. Weissenborns, Wilhelm. II. Muller, H.J.

NL 0421482 TU

PA6452 .A2 1888
Livius, Titus.
T. Livi Ab vrbe condita libri apparatv critico adiecto edidit Avgvstvs Lvchs ... Berolini, Apvd Weidmannos, 1888-
v. 20cm.

1. Rome—Hist. I. Luchs, August, ed.

NL 0421483 ViU OO OU MiU InU MH NIC CtY PBm OU

Livius, Titus.
Titi Livi ab urbe condita libri. Iterum recognovit Wilh. Weissenborn. Lipsiae [Leipzig] in aedibus B. G. Teubneri, 1889-91.
6 v. in 5. 17 cm.

NL 0421484 ViLxW NjP ViU MH

Livius, Titus.
Ab urbe condita libri; Wilhelm Weissenborns erklärende ausgabe; neu bearbeitet von H. J. Müller. Berlin, Weidmann, 1890-1924.
5 v. in 10.
Library has v. 1, pt. 1, v. 2 pt. 1-2; v. 3, tp. 1-2; v. 4, pts. 1-4; v. 5 pts. 1-2.

NL 0421485 IdU

PA6452 .A2 1890
LIVIUS,TITUS.
T.Livi Ab urbe condita libri. Edidit Antonius Zingerle... Vindobonae et Pragae,sumptus fecit F.Tempsky;[etc.,etc.]1890-
v. 18½cm.

NL 0421486 ICU NjP

Livius, Titus.
... Ab urbe condita libri; Wilhelm Weissenborns erklärende ausgabe; neu bearbeitet von H. J. Müller ... 8.aufl. Berlin, 1891.
19 cm.
v. 4.2 only.

NL 0421487 RPB

Livius, Titus.

Titi Livi ab urbe condita libri. Editionem primam curavit Guilelmus Weissenborn. Editio altera, quam curavit Mauritius Müller. Pars IV. Lib. xxxi.-xxxviii. Lipsiae, B. G. Teubneri, 1891.

xxv, 415 p. 18.5cm.

NL 0421488 CaBVaU

VOLUME 336

PA 6104 .L5 1891 Livius, Titus.
Titi Livi Ab urbe condita libri. Iterum recognovit Wilh. Weissenborn. Ed. stereotypa. Lipsiae, B. G. Teubner, 1891-1897.
6 v. in 3. 18cm. (Bibliotheca scriptorum graecorum et romanorum Teubneriana)

Contents.--pars 1. lib. I-VI. 189_.--pars 2. lib. VII-XXIII. Ed. primam cur. Guil. Weissenborn. Ed. alteram cur. Mauritius Müller. 189_.--pars 3. lib. XXIV-XXX. Ed. primam cur. G. Weissenborn. Ed. altera quam cur. M. Müller. 1894.--pars 4. lib. XXXI-XXXVIII. Ed. primam cur. G. Weissenborn. Ed. altera, quam cur. M. Müller. 1895.--pars 5. lib. XXXIX-CXL. Recognovit Wilh. Weissenborn. 1897.--pars 6. Fragmenta et index. 1891.

NL 0421491 NIC MH

Livius, Titus.
Titi Livi ab urbe condita libri. Editionem primam curavit Guilelmus Weissenborn. Editio altera, quam curavit Mauritius Müller. Lipsiae, B. G. Teubner, 1894-
5 v. S.

NL 0421492 NcD ViU MH CU

Livius, Titus.
Ab urbe condita libri, editionem primam curavit Weissenborn, editio altera, ... Lipsiae, Teubner, 1896.
Editio stereotypa. 180 p.

NL 0421493 OCl

Livius, Titus.
Titi Livi ab urbe condita libri. Iterum recognovit Wilh. Weissenborn ... Ed. Lipsiae, B.G. Teubner. 1897-1901.

NL 0421494 InU

Livius, Titus.
Titi Livi ab urbe condita libri. Iterum recognovit Wilh. Weissenborn ... Ed. stereotypa. Lipsiae, B. G. Tevbner, 1898-1901.
6 v. 17½cm. (*On cover:* Bibliotheca scriptorum graecorum et romanorum Teubneriana)
Titles of v. 2-6 vary slightly. Vols. 5-6 are reprints of the 1st edition, 1851.
CONTENTS.—pars 1. lib. I-VI. 1899.—pars 2. lib. VII-XXIII. Ed. primam cur. Guil. Weissenborn. Ed. alteram cur. Mauritius Müller. 1901.—pars 3. lib. XXIV-XXX. Ed. primam cur. G. Weissenborn. Ed. altera, quam cur. M. Müller. 1900.—pars 4. lib. XXXI-XXXVIII. Ed. primam cur. G. Weissenborn. Ed. altera, quam cur. M. Müller. 1898.—pars 5. lib. XXXIX-CXL. Recognovit Wilh. Weissenborn. 1899.—pars 6. Fragmenta et Index. 1900.
I. Weissenborn, Wilhelm, 1803-1878, ed. II. Müller, Moritz, ed.
2—27832
Library of Congress PA6104.L5 1899

NL 0421495 DLC WaS OrPR PSC OC1JC PU PV OO

PA6104 .L5 1899 Livius, Titus.
Ab urbe condita libri. Iterum recognovit Wilh. Weissenborn. Editio stereotypa. Lipsiae, In aedibus B. G. Teubneri, 1899-
v. 18cm. (Bibliotheca scriptorum graecorum et romanorum Teubneriana)
CONTENTS.—pars. I. facs. 1. lib. 1-3. fasc. 2. lib. V-6. 1899 (2 v.)—
I. Weissenborn, Wilhelm, 1803-1878, ed. II. Ser.

NL 0421496 ViU WaWW

870.8 T351 L 78 **Livius, Titus,**
Ab urbe condita libri; editionem primam curavit Guilelmus Weissenborn; editio altera, quam curavit Mauritius Mueller... Leipzig, Teubner, 1901-1906.
6v. 17½cm. (Bibliotheca... Teubneriana)
I.Title. II.Weissenborn, Wilhelm, ed. III.Mueller, Maurice, ed. IV. Series: Bibliotheca Teubneriana.

NL 0421497 OWorP

PA6104 .L5 1902 Livius, Titus.
Ab urbe condita libri. Editionem primam curavit Guilelmus Weissenborn. Editio altera, quam curavit Mauritius Müller. Lipsiae, B. G. Teubneri, 1902.
v. 18cm. (Bibliotheca scriptorum graecorum et romanorum Teubneriana)
1. Rome—Hist. I. Weussenborn, Wilhelm, 1803-1878, ed. II. Müller, Moritz, ed. III. Ser.

NL 0421498 ViU

878.4 L764we Livius, Titus.
Ab urbe condita libri. Editionem curavit Guilelmus Weissenborn. Editio altera, quam curavit Mauritius Müller. Editio stereotypa. Lipsiae, in aedibus B.G. Teubneri, 1903-1906. [v.1, 1906]
6 v. 18 cm. (Bibliotheca scriptorum graecorum et romanorum Teubneriana)

NL 0421499 KyU

Livius, Titus, 59 B. C.-17 A. D.
Ab urbe condita libri; editionem primam curavit Guilelmus Weissenborn; editio altera, quam curavit Mauritius Mueller. (Pars V edidit Guilelmus Heraeus) Leipzig, Teubner, 1909-1912.
6 v. 17.5 cm. (On cover: Bibliotheca ... Teubneriana)
I. Title. II. Weissenborn, Wilhelm, ed. III. Mueller, Maurice, ed. IV. Heraeus, Wilhelm.

NL 0421500 OWorP

Livius, Titus.
Titi Livi Ab urbe condita libri. Ed. primam curavit Guilelmus Weissenborn. Ed. altera, quam curavit Mauritius Müller ... Ed. stereotypa. Lipsiae, in aedibus B.G. Teubneri, 1905-10.
6 v. 18 cm. (On cover: Bibliotheca scriptorum graecorum et romanorum Teubneriana)
Titles v. 5, 6 vary slightly.
Contents.-pars 1. Lib. I-VI. 1910. - pars 2. Lib. VII-XXIII. 1909. - pars 3. Lib XXIV-XXX. 1909. - pars 4. Lib. XXXI-XXXVIII. 1909. - pars 5:1. Lib. XXXIX-XL. Ed. primam curavit Guilelmus Weissenborn. Ed. altera, quam curavit Guilelmus Heraeus. 1908. pars 5:2. Lib. XLI-CXLII. Ed. primam curavit Guilelmus Weissenborn. Ed. altera quam curavit Guilelmus Heraeus. 1912. - pars 6. Fragmenta et index Recognovit Wilh. Weissenborn. Ed. stereotypa. 1905.
I. Weissenborn, Wilhelm, 1803-1878. ed. II. Müller, Moritz. ed.

NL 0421502 CU

Livius, Titus.
Ab urbe condita libri. Editionem primam curavit Guilelmus Weissenborn, editio altera, quam curavit Mauritius Müller. Editio stereotypa. Lipsiae, In Aedibus B.G.Teubneri, 1910 1911.
6 v.
Cover: Bibliotheca scriptorum graecorum et romanorum teubneriana.

NL 0421503 MH

PA 6452 .A2 1921 Livius, Titus.
T. Livi Ab urbe condita libri. Erklärt von W. Weissenborn und H.J. Müller. Neubearb. von Otto Rossbach. Berlin, Weidmann, [1921?]-
10 v. in 20 cm. ([Sammlung griechischer und lateinischer Schriftsteller mit deutschen Anmerkungen])
Edition varies:
Bd. 3 (1. Heft): 6. Aufl., 1924.

NL 0421504 DCU NIC PBm MWelC

Livius, Titus.
Titi Livi Ab vrbe condita libri praefatio, liber primvs; ed. by H. J. Edwards ... Cambridge, University press, 1912.
lvii, 232 p. fold. map. 18cm. (Pitt press series)
I. Edwards, Henry John, ed.
A 13-1487
Title from Wisconsin Univ. Printed by L. C.

NL 0421505 WU OrU CaBVaU

Livius, Titus. Whole works. Latin.
Ab urbe condita libri; ed. primam curavit Guilelmus Weissenborn; ed. altera quam curavit Mauritius Mueller. Lipsiae, Teubner, 1923. 4v.

NL 0421506 MA OU

Livius, Titus.
Ab urbe condita libri; erklaert von Weissenborn, ... Berlin, Weidmann, 1924.
21 v.

NL 0421507 OCU NIC

Livius, Titus.
Titi Livi ab urbe condita libri, editionem primam curavit Guilelmus Weissenborn. Editio altera quam curavit Mauritius Mueller ... Editio stereotypa. Lipsiae, B.G. Teubner, 1926.
4 v. 17.5 cm. (Bibliotheca scriptorvm graecorvm et romanorvm Tevbneriana)
Contents.- pars I. Libri I-X. - pars II. Libri XXI-XXX. - pars III. Libri XXXI -XL. - pars IV. Libri XLI-CXLII. Fragmenta. Index.

NL 0421508 CtY MH

Livius, Titus.
Titi Livi Ab urbe condita libri. Editionem primam curavit Guilelmus Weissenborn. Editio altera quam curavit Mauritius Mueller... Editio stereotypa. Lipsiae,In aedibus B.G.Teubneri, 1930-1933. 4v. 17½cm. (On cover: Bibliotheca scriptorum graecorum et romanorum Teubneriana
Vol.I, 1932; v.2, 1933; v.3-4, 1930.

NL 0421509 MWelC OO MH

VOLUME 336

Livius, Titus.
Titi Libi ab urbe condita libri. Editionem primam curavit Guilelmus Weissenborn, editio altera quam curavit Lipsiae in aedibus B. G. Teubneri 1938.
v. 17 cm. (Bibliotheca scriptorum Graecorum et Romanorum Teubneriana)

NL 0421510 NcD

Livius, Titus.
Titi Liuij Decades. nouiter impreese. [L.A. Giunta's device] [Colophon: ... Venetiis per
Gnq3 Ioannem [Rubeum] ac Bernardinum eius fratrem
+c493c Vercellenses ... Impressae. Anno domini. M.ccccc. vi. xxvii .nonas ianuarii. Imperãte Serenissimo Leonardo Lauridano ...] [1506]
20,CCLIII numb.ℓ. illus. 32½cm.
Title and device (Kristeller,Italienische Buchdrucker- & Verlegerzeichen,no.217) printed in red; woodcut initials.

Edited by M.A. Sabellico; with L.A. Florus' epitomes to each book.
Many of the woodcuts are signed F; the woodcuts to the 1st book of the 1st and 3d Decades respectively, are rendered in facsimile in L.S. Olschki, Le livre illustré au XVe siècle,no.185; the woodcut on L_{ix} verso, in Perrins, Italian book-illustrations, no.66.

Signatures: $A^8a^8b^4c$-ℓ^8m-$n^{10}A$-$K^8L^{10}aa$-ii^8 (ii_8 blank)
[Bound with Quintilianus, Marcus Fabius. ed. Regio.Quintilianus cum commento [Venice?1506]

NL 0421513 CtY InU NjP MH

PA 6452 A2 1511 Cage

Livius, Titus.
... Decades cum figuris nouiter impresse.
Colophon: Venetiis, A. Philippo Pincio Mantuano Impressae, 1511.
xx, cliii l. A^8, a-b^6, d(i.e. c)-l^8, m-n^{10}, A-K^8, L^{10}, aa-ii^8. (A1, title-page, mutilated, pasted to A2, 2h1 misbound after 2i3)
W. T. Smedley copy

NL 0421514 DFo MdBP MH

PA 6452 A2 1535 Cage

Livius, Titus.
... Decades tres cum dimidia... Beati Rhenani & Sigismundi Gelenij... annotationes. Addita est Chronologia Henrici Glareani, ab ipso recognita & aucta... Basileae, In officina Frobeniana, 1534-35.
Colophons:... Per Hieronymum Frobenium & Nicolaum Episcopium...

3 pts. in 1 v. Pt.1: 69 [7] 244, 243 [1] 211 [1] p. α-$ε^6$, $ζ^8$, a-t^6, u^8, 2a-$2t^6$, $2u^8$, 3a-$3q^6$, $3r^4$, $3s^6$; pt.2: 91 [41] p. A-F^6, G^4, H-K^6, L^8; pt.3: [56] [32] p. a-d^6, e^4, [2d]a-[2d]b^6, [2d]c^4. Fo.

Separate title-page to pt.2 reads:... Historiarum ab vrbe condita decadis quintae libri quinque ... to pt.3: Chronologia siue temporum supputatio in omnem Romanam historiam... per Henricum Glareanum...
According to the description given in Graesse, Trésor... 1950, v.4,p.227 two leaves of index and one leaf of errata are lacking.
Title cut out and mounted.
Smedley - Sir Thomas Wardle copy.

NL 0421516 DFo IU

---

xq871 L5 1541

Livius, Titus.
Latinae historiae principis decades tres cũ dimidia, longe tamen quàm nuper emaculatiores, quod nunc demum ad uetera contulerimus exemplaria, ubi quantum sit deprehensum mendorum, facile indicabunt doctissimae in hunc authorem Beati Rhenani & Sigismundi Gelenij adiunctae annotationes. Addita est Chronologia Henrici Glareani, ab ipso recognita & aucta, cum indice copiosissimo. Venetiis [Apvd Haeredes L. Ivnta] 1541.
312ℓ. 31cm.

NL 0421517 IU

KB 1543 L5 f

Livius, Titus.
Decades tres cvm dimidia, longe tamen quâm nvper emaculatiores ... Beati Rhenani & Sigismundi Gelenij adiunctae annotationes. Addita est Chronologia Henrici Glareani, ab ipso recognita & aucta... Basileae, Per Ioan. Hervagivm, 1543.
2 p.ℓ.,70,[1],244,243,211,91,[137] p. 38cm.
Printer's device on title pages and verso of last leaf; initials.
"Historiarvm ... decadis qvintae libri qvinqve" and "Chronologia ... per Henricvm Glareanvm" have special title pages.

"Titi Livii ... decadvm XIIII epitome": p. [1]-[40] at end.
Dedication by Gelen.
Manuscript annotations.
Title page mutilated.
I.Florus, Lucius Annaeus. Epitoma. Latin. Gelen. 1543. II.Glareanus, Henricus, 1488-1563. III.Gelen, Sigmund, 1497-1554, ed. IV.Rhenanus, Beatus, 1485-1547, ed.
878.4.JG31.f

NL 0421519 CSt

Livius, Titus.
T. Livii Patavini Latinae historiae principis decades tres, cvm dimidia ... emendatiores, compluribus locis partim Caelii Secvndi Cvrionis industria, partim collatione meliorum codicum suâe integritati restitutis. Eiusdem Caelii S. C. praefatio, summam continens de mensuris, ponderibus req3 nummaria Romanorum & Graecorum ... L. Flori epitomae ... Beati Rhenani & Sigismundi Gelenij ... annotationes. Chronologia Henrici Glareani ... Index. Basileae, Per Ioannem Hervagium, 1549.
[12], 829, [18] p. 1 l. 38cm.

NL 0421520 NNC MeB

Rare PA 6452 A2++ 1552

Livius, Titus.

T. Livii Patavini historiae Romanae principis Decades tres cvm dimidia, sev libri XXXV, ex XIIII Decadibus relicti, longe quàm hactenus ... correctiores, & emendatiores. Qvibvs accesservnt Simonis Grynaei de utilitate legendae historiae, praefatio. Bartholomaei Marliani ... de origine urbis Romae, caput. Messalę Coruini ... libellus, ad Octauianum Augustum: in quo omnis Romana historia ...

describitur. Sexti Ruffi ... de historia Romanorum breuis libellus. L. Flori Epitome in singulos omnium decadum libros T. Liuij. Henrici Loriti Glareani ... annotationes, in eas quae extant decadas. Chronologia eiusdem in uniuersam Romanam historiam ... Eiusdem Chronologiae index alphabeticus ... Laurentij Vallae iudicium de quibusdam apud Liuium locis ... Emendationes eiusdem in sex priores

libros de secundo bello Punico. M. Antonij Sabellici, Beati Rhenani, Sigismundi Gelenij ... annotat. Io. Velcurionis introductio in uniuersam Romanam historiam. Caelij Secundi Curionis libellus de mensuris, ponderibus, réque nummaria Romanorum & Graecorum ... Tabula concionum atque orationum omnium T. Liuij ... Rerum... ac verborum in T. Liuio memorabilium ... index. Lvtetiae Parisiorum,

Continued in next column

Continued from preceding column

ex officina Michaelis Vascosani, 1552.
[18], 388, 18, 114, [74] l. 34cm.

"L. Flori Epitome ..." has separate foliation.
"Henrichi Loriti Glareani ... in omneis, quae quidem extant, T. Liuii ... decadas, annotationes, cum eiusdem Chronologia in totam Romanam historiam ... Vallae iudicium de quibusdam apud Liuium locis ... Adiectae sunt & M. Antonii Sabellici annotationes in Liuium" has separate foliation and special t. p., with imprint: Lvtetiae Parisiorum, apud Michaelem Vascosanum, & Audoenum Paruum, 1552.

NL 0421525 NIC NNC NN NcU MH CtY NjP

Case 6A 214

LIVIUS, TITUS.
T. Livii ... Romanae historiae principis decades tres, cvm dimidia, partim Caelii Secvndi Cvrionis industria, partim collatione meliorum codicum iterum diligenter emendatae. Eiusdem Caelii S. C. Praefatio ... Simonis Grynaei De utilitate legendae historiae. Bartholomaei Marliani De origine urbis Romae compendium. Tabvla concionum atq3 orationum T. Liuij ... L.

Flori epitomae, ita iam singulis libris praemissae, ut argumenti loco esse studiosis lectoribus queant ... Item, annorum series, iuxta regum, consulum, tribunorum, &c. ... Breve compendium, siue argumentum totius Romanae historiae ab vrbe condita. Ratio temporum eorum quae primo Liuianae historiae libro continentur. Doctorum uirorum in hunc

autorem Annotationes, Glareani annotationibus, suis locis commodè & diligenter insertae. Chronologia Henrici Glareani, ab ipso recognita & aucta. Eiusdem chronologia, in alphabeticum ordinem ... à Iodoco Badio Ascensio redacta ... Basileae, Per I. Hervagios, 1555.
[8]ℓ.,829,[14]p.; [138]ℓ. 39cm.

Signatures: a^8, a-z^6, aa-zz^6, aaa-zzz^6, AAA^5; A-Z^6.
Title vignette (printer's device) A different form of the device on verso of last leaf.
The 2d pt. (unpaged) has special t.-p.: Henrichi Loriti Glareani ... in omneis, quae

quidem extant, T. Liuij ... historici decadas, annotationes, cum eiusdem chronologia in totam Romanam historiam, nunc primùm non sine foenore recognita. Cui Badij Ascensij elenchus ad alphabeti ordinem deductus ... accesit. Deinde Laurentij Vallae, M. Antonij Sabellici, Beati Rhenani, Sigismundi

Gelenij, Theodorici Morelli, in Liuium totum castigationes ... Postremò Ioannis Velcurionis annotationes eruditae, quibus Liuiana historia ... illustratur...
Blind-stamped pigskin binding dated 1558.

NL 0421531 ICN MiU InU MnU ICU RPB MWiW-C

Livius, Titus.
T.Livii Patavini...decades tres, cvm dimidia; partim Caelii Secvndi Cvrionis industria, partim collatione meliorum codicum iterum diligenter emendatae... L.Flori Epitome... Doctorum uirorum...annotationes, Glareani annotationibus, suis locis...insertae... Basileae, Per Ioannes Heruagios, 1555.
2 reels.
Microfilm.

Continued in next column

VOLUME 336

Continued from preceding column

Original owned by Lucius Wilmerding, jr.
From the library of Gabriel Harvey (1545-1630) with his ms.notes in Latin and English.

I. Curione, Celio Secondo, 1503-1569, ed.

NL 0421533 NjP

Rare PA 6452 A2++ 1501

Livius, Titus.
Titi Livii Decadis. [Venetiis, Per Georgium de Rusconibus, 1501]
[20], 229 l. 34cm.
Text preceded by 20 unnumbered leaves containing dedicatory epistle, table and "L. Flori Epitoma decadum ..."
Manuscript notes in margins and at end.

NL 0421534 NIC InU

Case Y 672 .L 5052

LIVIUS, TITUS.
...Latinæ historiæ principis decas prima cum Epit. L. Flori antrorsum appositia... Lugduni, Apud hæredes S.Vincentii, 1537.
[15], 648, [63]p. 18cm. (with Glareanus, Henricus. Chronologia... 1537)
Printer's device on t.-p.
Colophon (on recto of last leaf): Excudebant Lugduni Melchior et Gaspar Trechsel fratres. 1536.

NL 0421535 ICN MB

Rare Book Room Gn240 c531b

Livius, Titus.
Titi Livii ... Decas prima [-]
Lvgdvni, Apvd Seb.Gryphivm, 1548.
v. 12cm.
Described in Baudrier, Bibliographie lyonnaise, VIII, p.228.

NL 0421536 CtY

---

871 L5 1554

Livius, Titus.
T. Livii Patavini latinae historiae principis Decas prima[-qvinta] Lvgdvni, apvd Seb. Gryphivm, 1554.
v.
Printer's device on t.-p. of each volume.

NL 0421537 IU NNC NIC DNW NjP CtY

Rare Book Room Gn240 b511

Livius, Titus.
Titi Livii Patavini historici Dechades ... [Lyons, Balthazard de Gabiano, ca.1511]
3v. 17cm.
Edited by Augustinus Becharius.
Described in H.L.Baudrier, Bibliographie lyonnaise, 7. série, p. 18-19. "Cette édition ... est antérieure à celle d'Alde 1518-1520 ... et ... ne peut être considérée comme une contrefaçon."
Imperfect: vol.2-3 wanting.

NL 0421538 CtY

Livius, Titus.
T. Livivs Patavinvs Historicvs dvobvs libris avctvs. Cvm L. Flori Epitome et annotatis in libros VII. Belli Maced. [Mogvntiae, In aedibvs Ioannis Scheffer, 1518]
[56], 730, [29] p. 35cm.
Edited by Nicolas Carbach and Wolfgang Augustus.
Imprint from colophon.
A 2d t.-p. following the preliminary matter reads: T. Tivivs Patavinvs Historicvs dvobvs volvminibvs recens ex vetvsto codice Moguntin. Bibliothecae avctvs.
The text is followed by the announcement of Carbach and various readings in the books of Livy, De bello Macedonis. (Carbach's announcement, as well as Erasmus' preface, is dated 1519)
This copy is a different issue from the other Columbia copy (B87LI B13) It does not include the Index T. Livii. Text on verso of leaf a3 begins Vvlphganvs Angvstvs lectoris S. Text on verso of leaf a3 in the other copy begins Index copiosissimvs ...

NL 0421541 NNC CU CSt MWiW-C PBm CtY InU NN MH IEN MdBP

Livius, Titus.
T[itus] Liuius ... duobus libris auctus: cum L. Flori Epitome. Addito ... Leonardo Aretino de primo bello Punico. Ac imaginibus res gestae exprimentibus. [Venetiis, Per M. Sessam & P. de Rauanis socios, 1520]
295 l. illus. 34 cm.
Edited by Lucas Panaetius.
Woodcuts partly signed: z. a. (i. e. Zoan Andrea)
1. Rome—History. I. Panaetius, Lucas, Olchinensis, ed. II. Florus, Lucius Annaeus. Epitome. 1520. III. Bruni, Leonardo Aretino, 1369-1444. De primo bello Punico. 1520.
PA6452.A5 1520 Rosenwald Coll. 70-27290

NL 0421542 DLC ICN CtY CSt MnU NNC DFo

Livius. 1518-33. Asulanus.
Ex XIIII. T. Livii decadibvs. Prima, tortia, qvarta [et quinta], in qua praeter fragmenta III & X libri, quae in Germania nuper reperta, hic etiam continentur, multa adulterina expunximus, multa uera recepimus, quae in alijs non habentur. Epitome singulorum librorum XIIII decadum. Historia omnium XIIII decadum in compendium redacta ab L. Floro. Polybij lib. V de rebus romanis latinitate donati à Nicolao Perotto. Index copiosissimus rerum omnium memorabilium ... [Venice, 1518-33]
5v. 16.5cm.
Colophons: v.1-4.Venetiis in aedibvs Aldi, et Andreae soceri ... M. D. XVIII[-M. D. XXI.]--v.5.Venetiis in aedibvs haeredvm Aldi Manvtii romani, et Andreae Asvlani soceri, mense maio. M.D.XXXIII.
Printer's marks on title-pages and on verso of last leaf in each vol.
Numerous errors in foliation.
"Errata": v.1, p.[3-12] at end; v.2, leaves [351-355].
Contents (each vol. with special t.-p.): v.1. Titi Livii patavini Decas prima.--v.2.Titi Livii patavini Decas tertia.--v.3.Titi Livii patavini Decas qvarta.--v.4.Titi Livii patavini Decadvm epitomae. Lvcii Flori Rervm ab vrbe condita libri IIII. Polybii Historiarvm libri qvinqve in latiam[!] conversi lingvam, Nicolao Perotto interprete.--v.5.Titi Livii patavini Decadis qvintae libri qvinqve.
Edited by Franciscus Asulanus.
Vols.1-3 have extensive indexes (those in v.2-3 with special title-pages); according to Renouard, these occur bound either at the beginning or at the end of the volumes; in this set they are bound at the beginning.

NL 0421546 NjP ViU MWiW-C MA CSt CU ICN MH IU MBSi MH NNC CtY NjP ICU OU NcD OCU InU RPJCB

Livius, Titus. ed. Torresani.
Ex XIIII. T.Livii Decadibvs Prima Tertia Qvarta, Cuius Tertio libro prima pars, quae desyderabat, & Decimo quicquid ferè in calce non habebamus, additum est. uerum praeter haec ueluti fragmenta quartae Decadi adiuncta ... multa adulterina expunximus ... beneficio unts ueterum exemplarium adiuti ... Polybii libri V de rebus Romanis in latinum traducti à Nicolao Perotto, quos in locum secundae Decadis substituimus ... [Colophon: Venetiis In Aedibvs Aldi, Et Andreae Soceri[M.D.XX.Mense Octobri]-Mense Febrvario. M.D.XXI] [1520-21]
14pl., 106numb.l., 10l., 102 numb.l., 127numb.l., 1l., 71numb.l., 1l. 29½cm.
Edited by F. Torresani; index by G.Malatesta.
Each part of Livius has individual colophon and, excepting Florus' epitomes, separate foliation; Polybius has a separate preface by Torresani.
Title-page and colophon devices.
Signatures: $A^8B^6a\text{-}m^8n^{10}*^{10}aa\text{-}mm^8nn^6**^{10}$ $aaa\text{-}qqq^8A\text{-}I^8$.
With Florus' epitomes to the Livius.

NL 0421549 CtY ViU NcU ICU NNC NN InU DFo

PA6452 .A2 1522 Rare bk

LIVIUS, TITUS.
Ex XIIII. T. Livii decadibvs. Prima, tortia, qvarta nuper maxima diligentia recognitae, collatis simul tum antiquissimis quot quot reperta sunt exemplaribus, tum illis quae hactenus et Venetijs & in Germania excusa fuerunt. Epitome singulorum librorum XIIII decadum. Historia omnium XIIII decadum in compendium redacta à L. Floro. Polybij libri. V. de rebus Romanis latinitate donati à Nicolao Perotto. Index copiosissimus rerum omnium notatu dignarum. [Florentiae, per haeredes P. Iuntae, 1522-32]
6 v. in 4. 16cm.
Title leaf and index bound at end of [v.1]
Each volume has special half-title only; [v.1-3]: Titi Livii Patavini decas prima [tertia-qvarta]; [v.4]: T. Livii Patavini Historiarvm ab vrbe condita decadis qvintae libri qvinqve nvnc primvm excvsi; [v.5] Titi Livii Patavini decadvm XIIII epitomae. Lvcivs Florvs; [v.6] Polybii Historiarvm libri qvinqve in latinam conversi lingvam, Nicolao Perotto interprete.
Giunti's device on title leaves and on leaves at end of volumes.
Colophons of [v.1-3, 6] dated 1522. Colophon of [v.4]: Impressvm Florentiae in aedibvs Bernardi Ivntae anno XXXII. svpra M. et D. Colophon lacking in [v.5], which was apparently issued with [v.6], though the two often occur separately.
Dedicatory epistle by Niccolò degli Angeli.
A reprint of the Aldine edition edited by Francesco Torresani, except [v.4], which preceded the Aldine edition of the fifth decade, dated 1533.
With index to the first, third and fourth decades by J. Malatesta.
1. Rome--Hist.

NL 0421553 ICU InU MH ICN

Livius, Titus.
T. Livii Patavini scriptoris clarissimi, ex XIIII decadibvs historiae romanae ab vrbe condita, decades, prima, tertia, quarta, & quintae dimidium, singulari cum studio ac iudicio, tum diligenti obseruatione annotationum Beati Rhenani & Sigismundi Gelenii recognitae ac restitutae: quibus velut corollarii vice accesserunt L. Flori epitomae in singulos omnium decadum libros. Henrici Loriti Glareani, patricii claronensis apud Heluetios, annotationes in eas quae extant decadas: & Chronologia in vniuersam historiam

Continued in next column

VOLUME 336

Continued from preceding column

romanam. Eiusdem Chronologiae alphabeticus elenchus per Iodocum Badium collectus. Laurentii Vallae iudicium de quibusdam apud Liuium locis: ex quo eruditus lector, qua cura ac diligentia authores sint legendi, facilè discere poterit. Item emendationes eiusdem in sex priores libros de secundo bello punico. M. Antonii Sabellici annotationes pauculae. Rerum maximè memorabilium index copiosissimus. Parisiis, ex officina

Michaëlis Vascosani, in via quae est ad diuum Iacobum, sub Fontis insigni. M. D. XLIII. Cum priuilegio.
47 p. l., 348 numb. l., [28] p., 66 numb. l., [54] p. 1 illus. 33.5 x 24 cm.
Initials.
Leaves printed on both sides.
Errors in foliation: 67 repeated, 70 omitted;

140, 164, 317, 335, and 343-344 numbered 142, 166, 318, 325, and 344-345 respectively; in second section of numbered leaves, 10-11 numbered 18-19.
The Annotations of Glareanus has special t.-p.: Henrichi Loriti Glareani, patricii claronēsis apud Helvetios, in omneis, qvae qvidem extant, T. Livii Patauini clarissimi historici decadas,

annotationes, cum eiusdē Chronologia in totam romanam historiam ... Parisiis, imprimebat Michaël Vascosanus sibi & Odoino Paruo. M. D. XLII.
Mounted on verso of fly-leaf is a manuscript letter from Edmund Halley to Abraham Hill, Bishopsgate street, London, dated Feb. 10, 1706/7, relating to the editions of this work published by Michael Vascosanus; Halley's comments

and corrections in Latin throughout.
1. Rome - Hist. I. Rhenanus, Beatus, 1485-1547. II. Gelen, Sigmund, 1497-1554. III. Florus, Lucius Annaeus. IV. Glareanus, Henricus, 1488-1563. V. Badius Ascensius, Jodocus, 1462-1535. VI. Valla, Lorenzo, 1406-1457. VII. Sabellico, Marco Antonio Coccio, called, 1436-1506. VIII. Halley, Edmund, 1656-1742.

NL 0421559 Vi OCU ICU MiU NcD

Livius, Titus.
... Historiae Romanae ab urbe condita ... cum commentariis omnium interpretum ... His adjecimus, ultrà brevem Livii, L. etiam Flori, Epitomen: Sigonii Chronologiam, Pomponii Laeti De antiquitatibus Romanorum, & plaeraque alia ad Romanam historiam pertinentia ... Lutetiae Parisiorum, Apud Gulielmum Julianum, 1573.
[22] 850, 534,[44] p. 34 cm.

NL 0421560 DLC DFo

Livius, Titus.
Historiae Romanae decades. Rome, Conradus Sweynheym and Arnoldus Pannartz [1469]
Hain-Copinger 10128; Goff L-236.

NL 0421561 DLC CSmH

Livius, Titus.
Historiae Romanae decades. [Rome] Ulrich Han (Udalricus Gallus) [before 3 Aug. 1470]
Hain-Copinger 10129; Goff L-237.

NL 0421562 DLC MH NjP IU

Livius, Titus.
Historiae Romanae decades. [Venice] Vindelinus de Spyra, 1470.
Hain-Copinger 10130; Goff L-238.

NL 0421563 DLC CSmH MH

Livius, Titus.
Historiae Romanae decades. Rome, Conradus Sweynheym and Arnoldus Pannartz, 16 July 1472.
Hain-Copinger 10131; Goff L-239.

NL 0421564 CSmH NNC

Livius, Titus.
Historiae Romanae decades. Milan, Philippus de Lavagnia, 1478.
Hain-Copinger 10132; Goff L-240.

NL 0421565 ViU

Livius, Titus.
Historiae Romanae decades. Milan, Antonius Zarotus, for Johannes de Legnano, 23 Oct. 1480.
Hain-Copinger 10133; Goff L-241.

NL 0421566 DLC DFo MH

Livius, Titus.
Historiae Romanae decades. [Treviso] Michael Manzolus, 31 Oct. 1480.
Hain-Copinger-Reichling 10134; Goff L-242.

NL 0421567 NNC

Livius, Titus.
Historiae Romanae decades. Treviso, Joannes Rubeus, Vercellensis, 1482.
Hain-Copinger 10135; Goff L-243.

NL 0421568 DLC NNC MH CtY

Livius, Titus.
Historiae Romanae decades. Treviso, Joannes Rubeus, Vercellensis, 1485.
Hain-Copinger 10136; Goff L-244.

NL 0421569 DLC NCC CtY MH CSmH InU NcU

Livius, Titus.
Historiae Romanae decades. Venice [Matteo Capcasa (di Codeca)] 5 Nov. 1491.
Hain 10137; Goff L-245.

NL 0421570 DLC MH ICN

Livius, Titus.
Historiae Romanae decades. Milan, Uldericus Scinzenzeler, for Alexander Minutianus, 25 May 1495.
Hain-Copinger 10140; Goff L-246.

NL 0421571 DFo ICU CtY

Livius, Titus.
Historiae Romanae decades. Venice, Philippus Pincius, for Lucantonio Giunta, 3 Nov. 1495.
Hain-Copinger 10141; Goff L-247.

NL 0421572 DLC MH CtY NNC CSmH

Livius, Titus.
Historiae Romanae decades. Venice, Bartholomaeus de Zanis, 20 June 1498.
Hain-Copinger (Add) 10142; Goff L-248.

NL 0421573 NNC MH CSmH ICN IU CU

Livius, Titus.
Titi Livii Patavini Historiæ romanæ libri, qui supersunt, duplici divisione in capita distincti, periochis insuper, variis lectionibus, chronologia, & rhetoricis exercitationibus illustrati ... Patavii, Ex typographia Seminarii, Apud Joannem Manfrè, 1727.
4 v. 17cm.

NL 0421574 NNC MWA

Livius, Titus.
Titi Livii Patavini Historiæ romanæ libri, qui supersunt ... variis lectionibus, chronologia, & rhetoricis exercitationibus illustrati ... Augustæ Taurinorum, 1731-32.
4v. front.

In double columns.
Vol.1 has added t.-p.: Titi Livii

Patavini historia. Ad usum regiarum scholarum.
Vol.2-4 have special t.-p. only.
Colophon date of v.2: 1742.
The device of the printer, D. A. Fontana, on t.-p. and at end of each vol.

Pirated from the revision by Jac. Jobetti and M. A. Ferracci of Gronovius' edition of 1679.
Contains also Florus, L. A. Epitome.
"Caroli Sigonii Chronologia in T. Livii Historias ab urbe condita": v.4, p. 231-248.

"Exercitationes rhetoricæ in orationes Titi Livii Patavini": 227p. at end of v.4, with separate t.-p., bearing imprint Taurini, 1732.

NL 0421578 IU

Livius, Titus
Titi Livii Patavini Historiæ Romanæ libri, qui supersunt, duplici divisione in capita distincti, periochis insuper, variis lectionibus, chronologia, & rhetoricis exercitationibus illustrati ... Patavii, Ex typographia Seminarii, Apud Joannem Manfrè, 1733
17cm.

The text of Gronov, revised by Jacopo Giacometti and Marco Antonio Ferracci.
Added engraved title-page.

NL 0421579 NNC

Livius, Titus.
Historiarum. Oxonii, J. H. Parker, 1852.
2 v. 14cm.

Edited by K. F. S. Alschefski. Cf. Pref.
Contents.--t. 1. lib. 1-10.--t. 2. lib. 21-30.

I. Alschefski, Karl Friedrich Siegmund, ed.

NL 0421580 NIC

VOLUME 336

PA6452 .A2 1853
Livius, Titus.
T. Livii Historiarum ... Oxonii et Londini, J. H. Parker, 1853.
2 v. in 4. 14cm. (Lettered on cover: Oxford Greek and Latin classics)
Vol.1, parts I-II, and vol.2, parts I-II each paged continuously.
CONTENTS.—t.1, pt.1. Lib.I.-V.—t.1, pt.2. Lib.VI.-X.—t.2, pt.1. Lib.XXI-XXIV.—t.2, pt.2. Lib.XXV-XXX.
1. Rome—Hist. I. Alschefski, Karl Friedrich Siegmund, 1805-1852. II. Ser.

NL 0421581 ViU CtY MB CtMW IaU

Livius, Titus.
T. Livii historiarum. Oxonii et Londini, Johannes Henricus et Jacobus Parker, 1865.
2 v. in 4 pts. 13 cm.

NL 0421582 ViLxW

Livius,Titus
Historiarum ab urbe condita... Amsterdam,Danielem Elzevirium,1664-78. v.1-3.

NL 0421583 InU

PA 6452 .A2 1777
Livius, Titus.
T. Livii Patavini Historiarvm ab vrbe condita. Cvm indice rervm et verborvm. Halae, Orphanotrophei, 1760-77 [v. 1, 1777]
3 v.
#Rome--History.

NL 0421584 MoU

PA6452 A2R9
Livius, Titus.
Titi Livii Patavini Historiarum ab urbe condita./ Ad optimas editiones castigati accurante Tho. Ruddimanno. Edinburgi, W. Ruddiman, 1772.
4 v. 19cm.

1. Rome - Hist. I. Ruddiman, Thomas 1674-1757, ed.

NL 0421585 NCH MH InU CU

Livius, Titus.

Titi Livii Historiarum ab urbe condita libri qui extant. Cum supplementis, tam librorum qui à X, ad XXI. desiderantur, quàm lacunarum quae in libris qui extant reperiuntur. Sumptis è Freinshemio, Crevierio & aliis, et indice copiosiore, quippe supplementorum materia locupletato. Londini: J. & R. Tonson, & J. Watts, 1749.
7 v. front. 17½cm.
Vol. 2-7 have title: Titi Livii Historiarum.
Imperfect: v.3, p. 360- wanting.
1. Rome—Hist. I. Freinsheim, Johann, 1608-1660. II. Crevier, Jean Baptiste Louis, 1693-1765.

NjP CSmH IU
NL 0421586 ViU ViLxW CtY NNG RPB PLatS MH PV PP

---

q871 L5 1555
Livius, Titus.
T. Livii Patavini, Historiarum ab urbe condita, libri, qvi extant, XXXV. Cvm vniversae historiae epitomis, à Carolo Sigonio emendati: Cuius etiam scholia simul eduntur, quibus ijdem libri, atque epitomae partim emendantur, partim etiam explanantur. Venetiis, apud Paulum Manutium, Aldi f., 1555.
4 p.l., 478, 98 numb.l., 40 l. 36cm.

Signatures: A4, a-z8, aa-zz8, aaa-nnn8, ooo6; A-Z4, AA4, BB2, a-k4(verso of last leaf blank)

Device of Aldus on title-pages; initials.
"Caroli Sigonii Scholia" has special t.-p.

I. Sigonio, Carlo. 1524?-1584

NL 0421588 IU ICN ICU InU NNC CtY NcD INS WU MH NN

---

q871 L5 1566
Livius, Titus.
T. Livii Patavini, Historiarum ab vrbe condita. libri, qvi extant, XXXV. Cvm vniversae historiae epitomis. Adiunctis scholijs Caroli Sigonii, quibus ijdem libri, atque epitomae partim emendantur, partim etiam explanantur. Secvnda editio - Venetiis, apud Paulum Manutium, Aldi f., 1566.
5 l., 399 numb.l., 1 l., 107 numb.l. 32cm.

Signatures: a6(a6 blank) a-e8, f6, A-Z8, Aa-Zz8, Aaa-Ddd8(verso of Ddd7 blank) A-N8, O4(last leaf blank)

Device of Aldus on title-pages and on verso of last leaf of first part. Initials.
"Caroli Sigonii Scholia" has special t.-p.

I. Sigonio, Carlo, 1524?-1584.

NL 0421590 IU CtY PU InU NNC

Livius, Titus.
T.Livii...Historiarum ab vrbe condita, libri qvi exstant XXXV, cvm vniversae historiae epitomis. Caroli Sigonij scholia...ab auctore...aucta. Venetiis, In aedibus Manutianis, 1572.
399,109 numb.*l*.
The Scholia have special t.-p.
With this is bound Sigonio, C. Caroli Sigonii Livianorvm scholiorvm aliqvot defensiones... 1572.
I.Sigonio, Carlo,1524?-1584,ed.

NL 0421591 NjP CU MnU PPD NcU InU CSt NNC IU CtY MH

PA 6452 A2 1592 Cage
Livius, Titus.
... Historiarum ab vrbe condita libri qui extant XXXV cum vniuersae historiae epitomis. Additis Caroli Sigonii scholijs... ab auctore multis in partibus postremo auctis, & emendatis... Venetiis, Apud Aldum, 1592.
Colophon.

[8] 398 [194] p. Fo.
Graesse, Trésor... 1950, v.4, p.228 and A.A. Renouard, Annali delle edizioni Aldine... 1953,

p.250 describe copies having 99 unnumbered leaves at the end, although Folger copy with 97 leaves seems to be complete.
Smedley copy.

NL 0421593 DFo CU MH InU MA CtY RPB

Livius, Titus.
T. Livii Patavini Historiarum ab urbe condita libri qui supersunt, Mss. codicum collatione recogniti, annotationibusque illustrati. Oxonii, e theatro Sheldoniano, 1708.
6 v. 2 fold. pl. 22½cm.
Title vignette.
Volumes 2-6 have half-title only.
Edited by T. Hearne. *cf.* Brit. mus. Catalogue.
I. Hearne, Thomas, 1678-1735, ed.

NL 0421594 MiU CLU-C DFo CtY MH ViLxW

Livius, Titus.
T. Livii Patavini Historiarum ab urbe condita libri qui supersunt. Londini, ex officina J. Tonson, & J. Watts, 1722.
1 p. l., [32], 419 p. front. 15cm.

NL 0421595 MiU NjP MH

Livius, Titus.
Titi Livii Patavini Historiarum ab urbe condita libri qui supersunt, cum omnium epitomis, ac deperditorum fragmentis: ad optimas editiones castigati, accurante Tho. Ruddimanno ... Edinburgi, in aedibus T. & W. Ruddimanni, 1751.
4 v. 17cm.

I. Ruddiman, Thomas, 1674-1757, ed.

ICU InU OCU CtY
NL 0421596 MiU NN ViLxW OCl PMA NIC PHi PPL MH ICN

A 6452 A2 752 Rare)
Livius. Titus.
... Historiarum ab urbe condita libri qui supersunt, cum omnium epitomis ac deperditorum fragmentis: ad optimas editiones castigati, accurante Thoma Ruddimanno. Edinburgi, In Aedibus T. et W. Ruddimanni, 1752.
4 v. front.

I. Ruddiman, Thomas, 1674-1757, ed.

NL 0421597 ICU MH

---

878 L5h 1764 Rare Books Col
Livius, Titus.
Titi Livii Patavini Historiarum ab urbe condita libri qui supersunt, cum omnium epitomis, ac deperditorum fragmentis: ad optimam editionem celeberrimi Tho. Ruddimanni fideliter expressi ... Edinburgi, J. Wood, 1764.
4v. 17½cm.
Autograph of Levi Lincoln on each t.p.
Bookplated of William Lincoln.
I. Ruddiman, Thomas, 1674-1757, ed.

NL 0421598 TxU NcD PPL NNUT NjP

Livius,Titus Patavinus.
Historiarum ab urbe condita libri, qui supersunt,omnes,cum notes integris.. nec non ineditis Jani Gebhardi,Car.And Dukeri,& aliorum:Curante Arn.Drakenborch,qui & suas adnotationes adjecit. Accedunt supplementa deperditorum T.Livii librorum a Joh.Freinshemio concinnata...Amsterdam,J.Wetstenium & G.Smith,1741. v.4.

NL 0421599 InU

VOLUME 336

LIVIUS,TITUS
T. Livii Patavini Historiarum ab urbe condita libri, qui supersunt, omnes, cum notis integris Laur. Vallae, M. Ant. Sabellici, Beati Rhenani, Sigism. Gelenii, Henr. Loriti Glareani, Car. Sigonii, Fulvii Ursini, Franc. Sanctii, J. Fr. Gronovii, Tan. Fabri, Henr. Valesii, Jac. Perizonii, Jac. Gronovii; excerptis Petr. Nannii, Justi Lipsii, Fr. Modii, Jani Gruteri; nec non ineditis Jani Gebhardi, Car. And.

Dukeri, & aliorum: curante Arn. Drakenborch, qui & suas adnotationes adjecit. Accedunt Supplementa deperditorum T. Livii librorum a Joh. Freinshemio concinnata ... Amstelaedami, Lugduni Batavorum, 1738-1746.
7 v. front., plates, ports., fold. facsim. 4to

Title in red and black.
Head and tail pieces; initials.
Contents.-I. Liber I-IV. 1738.-II. Liber V-IX. 1738.-III. Liber X-XXVI. 1740. -IV. Liber XXVII-XXXVI. 1741.-V. Liber XXXVII-XLV. Supplementa Liviana a libro quadragesimo sexto, auctore Johanne Frein-

shemio ⌊Liber XLVI-LX⌋ 1743.-VI. Supplementa, Liber LXI-CXL. Fragmenta deperditorum librorum T. Livii. 1744.- VII. Praefatio, by A. Drakenborch. Vita Titi Livii, ex G. J. Vossio, etc. 1746.

NL 0421603 InU NIC NcU OU CtY RPB MiU ViU CU MH MdBP

PA6452 .A2 1814
LIVIUS,TITUS.
T.Livii Patavini Historiarum ab urbe condita libri qui supersunt omnes,ex recensione Arn.Drakenborchii. Accedunt notæ integræ ex editionibus J.B.L.Crevierii. Cum indice rerum locupletissimo. Oxonii,e prelo Bartlett et Newman(superrime Collingwood et sociorum); [etc.,etc.]1814.
4 v. 21½cm.

1.Rome--Hist.

NL 0421604 ICU MH IU PSC

PA 6452 A2 1818
Livius, Titus.
T. Livii Patavini Historiarum ab urbe condita libri qui supersunt omnes, ex recensione Arn. Drakenborchii. Accedunt notae integrae ex editionibus J. B. L. Crevierii. Cum indice rerum locupletissimo. Oxonii, excudebat W. Baxter; Londini, impensis J. Parker et R. Bliss et R. Priestley, 1818.
4 v. 21 1/2 cm.
1.Rome - History. I.Drakenborch, Arnoldus, 1684-1748. II.Crévier, Jean Baptiste Louis, 1693-1765.

NL 0421605 IMunS MH

Livius, Titus.
T. Livii Patavini Historiarum ab urbe condita libri, qui supersunt, omnes, cum notis integris Laur. Vallae, M. Ant. Sabellici ... nec non ineditis Jani Gebhardi ...Lipsiae, In commissis apud C. H. F. Hartmannum, 1820-1828.
15 v. in 23 pts. 21 cm.

NL 0421606 ViU ViLxW

PA6452 A2 1820
Livius, Titus.
T. Livii Patavini Historiarum ab urbe condita libri, qui supersunt, omnes, cum notis integris Laur. Vallae, M. Ant. Sabellici, Beati Rhenani ... et aliorum: curante Arn. Drakenborch, qui et suas adnotationes adjecit. Accedunt supplementa deperditorum T. Livii librorum a Jo. Freinshemio concinnata. Stutgardiae, Ex typographia societatis Wuertembergicae, 1820-1827.

15 vols. 21cm.

NL 0421607 NBuG WaPS InU PPL CtY PU PP CU NcD ODW MWelC NjP MnCS MdBP MH ViU PLatS

PA 6452 A2 1821
Livius, Titus.
T. Livii Patavini Historiarum ab urbe condita libri qui supersunt omnes, ex recensione Arn. Drakenborchii. Accedunt notae integrae ex editionibus J. B. L. Crevierii, cum indice rerum locupletissimo. Oxonii, excudebat W. Baxter;impensis J. Parker, [etc.],Londini, R. Priestley,[etc.],1821.
4 v. 21 1/2 cm.
1.Rome - History. I.Drakenborch,Arnoldus, 1684-1748. II.Crévier,Jean Baptiste Louis, 1693-1765.

NL 0421608 IMunS ViU CtY RPB IU NIC OCX

PA 6452 A2 1824
Livius, Titus.
T. Livii Patavini Historiarum ab urbe condita libri, qui supersunt, omnes, cum deperditorum fragmentis et epitomis omnium. Ad optimas editiones emendavit, selectamque lectionum varietatem textui subjecit Leon. Tafel. Stutgardiae, typis et impensis J.B.Metzleri, 1824-
v. 18 1/2 cm. (Bibliotheca romana in usum scholarum edita, v.1-)
1.Rome - History. I.Tafel, Leon ed.

NL 0421609 IMunS InU ICU NjP CU PLatS

PA6452 A2 1825
Livius, Titus. Latin.
⌊Historiarum ab urbe condita libri qui supersunt omnes; ex recensione Arn. Drakenborchii. Accedunt notae integrae ex editionibus J.B.L. Crevierii, cum indice rerum locupletissimo. Oxonii, excudebat W. Baxter, 1825⌋
4 v.

Imperfect: title page of v.1 wanting; title supplied from v.2.

NL 0421610 CU NNC TU

Livius, Titus
T. Livii Patavini Historiarum ab urbe condita libri qui supersunt omnes, ex recensione Arn. Drakenborchii. Accedunt notae integrae ex editionibus J.B.L. Crevierii. Cum indice rerum locupletissimo. Oxonii, W. Baxter, 1828.
4v. 22cm.

1. Rome - History. I. Drakenborch, Arnoldus, 1684-1748. II. Crévier, Jean Baptiste Louis, 1693-1765.

NL 0421611 KAS

1842
LIVIUS, Titus.
Historiarum ab urbe condita libri qui supersunt omnes,ex recensione Arn.Drakenborchii. Praeter varietatem lectionum Gronovianae, Crevierianae,Kreyssigianae,et Bekkerianae, accedunt notae integrae ex editionibus J.B.L. Crevierii. Londini,impensis Whittaker et Soc., etc.,etc.,1842.

3 vol. 23 cm.

NL 0421612 MH PSC PV

Livius, Titus.
T. Livii Patavini historiarum ab urbe condita libri qui supersunt xxxv; cum supplementis librorum amissorum a J. Freinshemio concinnatis; recensuit & notis illustravit J. B. L. Crevier. Parisiis [Paris] sumptibus & impensis Gabrielis-Francisci Quillau et Joannis Desaint, 1735-1742.
6 v. 25 cm.

NL 0421613 ViLxW PU CtY ViU ICU KyU

PA6452 .A2 1747
LIVIUS,TITUS.
T.Livii...Historiarum ab urbe condita libri qui supersunt XXXV. Recensuit,& notis ad usum scholarum accommodatis illustravit J.B.L.Crevier ... Parisiis,apud Desaint,& Saillant,1747-48.
3 v. 17cm.

1.Rome--Hist.

NL 0421614 ICU MH CU InU

Livius, Titus.
Historiarum ab urbe condita libri qui supersunt XXXV. Parisiis, apud J. Barbou, 1768-1774.
3 v. in 6.

NL 0421615 OCU MB

Livius, Titus.
Titi Livii Patavini Historiarum ab urbe condita libri qui supersunt xxxv. Recensuit J. N. Lallemand. ... Parisiis, typis Barbou, 1775.
7 v. front. (port.) 16½cm.
Book-plate: James Corry.

1. Lallemand, Jean Nicolas, ed.

NL 0421616 MiU IEN PV NNC KyU NcD OCU MWiW-C InU CtY MA MH

---

ar W 29596
Livius, Titus.

Historiarum, ab urbe condita, libri qui supersunt XXXV. Textum recognovit, selectis variorum notis illustravit, suasque aliquot adjecit Johannes Walker. Dublinii, E typographeo academico, et sumptibus academicis, 1797-1813.
8 v. 21cm.

Vol. 8: Index.

NL 0421617 NIC

PA6452 .A2 1813
LIVIUS,TITUS.
T.Livii...Historiarum ab urbe condita libri qui supersunt XXXV. Recensuit et notis ad usum scholarum accommodatis illustravit J.B.L.Crevier... Londini,impensis J.Mawman,1813.
3 v. 21½cm.
Each vol. in 2 parts.

1.Rome--Hist.

NL 0421618 ICU PBm PU

Livius, Titus.
Titi Livii Patavini Historiarum ab urbe condita libri qui supersunt XXXV. Recensuit, et notis ad usum scholarum accommodatis illustravit J.-B.-L. Crevier ... Parisiis, Ulyssipone, 1820.
6 v. 18 cm.

NL 0421619 CtY

VOLUME 336

x871 L5 1702 Livius, Titus.
Titi Livi Patavini Historiarum decades quæ supersunt; juxta editionem Gronovianam diligenter recensitæ: lemmatibus historicis ad paginarum oras ornatæ; atque indice rerum uberrimo perinde ac utilissimo locupletatæ. Adjiciuntur tabulæ geographicæ, historiam Romanam egregie illustrantes. Londini, Apud W. Freeman, & J. Walthoe, 1702.
2v. (1423p.) 2 fold.maps. 20cm.
Vol. 2 has half title only.

NL 0421620 IU ViU

Livius, Titus.
Titi Livii Patavini Historiarvm libri. Amsterdami, apud Guiljelm Blaeu, MDCXXXIII.
1 p. l., 1007 p. 13cm.
Engraved t.-p., illustrated.
"Epitome Flori in reliqvos Titi Livii libros qui desiderantur": p. 985-1007.

I. Florus, Lucius Annaeus.
34-18910
Library of Congress PA6452.A2 1633 878.4

NL 0421621 DLC NjP InU

Livius, Titus.
Titi Livii Historiarum libri ex recensione Heinsiana. Lvgd. Batavorvm, ex officina Elzeviriana, anno 1634.
3 v. 1 illus. 13cm.
Vol. 1 has t.-p. engraved by Corn. Cl. Duysendt.
Printer's mark on t.-p. of v. 2-3.
Vols. 2-3 have title: T. Livii Patavini Historiarvm ab vrbe condita tomus secundus [tertius]

1. Rome—Hist. I. Heinsius, Daniel, 1580-1655, ed.
5-30707
Library of Congress PA6452.A2 1634 [a31c1] 878.4

FTaSU
NL 0421622 DLC NcD CSt PU OCU InU NN IEN MoSW NjP

PA6452 .A2 1635 Rare bk Livius, Titus.
Titi-Livii patavini Historiarium libri ... Amstelodami, apud J. Jansonium, 1635.
2 v. 13cm.

1. Rome--Hist.

NL 0421623 ICU ViU OCU

Rare PA 6452 A2 1644 Livius, Titus.
Historiarum libri ex recensione I. F. Gronovii. Lvgd[uni] Batavorvm, Ex Officina Elzeviriana, 1644-45 [v.1, 1645]
4 v. pl. 13cm.
Vol. 1 has t. p. engraved by Corn. Cl. Duysendt, dated 1645.
Vols. 2-4 have title vignettes: Elsevier device (the solitary).
Vols. 2-3 have title: T. Livii Patavini Historiarvm ab vrbe condita tomus secundus [-tertius]
This set includes and additional fourth volume, which has title: Joh. Fred. Gronovii Ad T. Livii Patavini libros svperstites notae. Accessit Ismaelis Bullialdi Epistola de solis defectu, cujus Livius lib. XXXVII meminit. Lvgd[uni] Batav[orum] Ex Officina Elzeviriorum, 1645. (Issued also separately)
With the Epitome of L. Florus.
A. Willems: Les Elzevier, no. 590 (p. 145)

NL 0421626 NIC MeB ICU MH OCU NcU CU PU ViU CtY MiU

Z239.9 E49L5 1654 t Livius, Titus.
Historiarum libri ex recensione I.F. Gronovii. Lvgd.Batavorvm, Ex officina Elzeviriana, 1653-54 (v.1, 1654)
3 v. 1 illus. 14cm.
Printer's device on t.p. (v.2-3); headpieces; initials.
Vol.1 has engraved general t.p. only; v.2-3 have special title pages: Historiarvm ab urbe condita, tomus secundus [-tertius]
I.Gronovius, Joannes Fredericus, 1611-1671, ed.

NL 0421627 CSt ViU NN MB OO DFo PU CU NIC MdU NNC

Livius, Titus.
Titi Livii Patavini Historiarum libri. Amstelodami, apud I. Ianssonium, 1661.
850, [6] p. 16cm.
Engraved t.-p.

NL 0421628 MiU InU OU MH PBL

SPECIAL COLLECTIONS GONZALEZ LODGE 1672 L76 Livius, Titus.
Titi Livii Patavini Historiarum libri, Cum notis selectissimis Sigonii, Glareani, Gruteri, Godelevaei, T. Fabri, Gronovii & variorum. Accurante Joanne Tillemonio [pseud.] ... Parisiis, Apud viduam Claudii Thiboust, et Petrum Esclassan, 1672-
16cm.
Title-vignette.
Added engraved title-page.

NL 0421629 NNC

Livius, Titus.
Titi Livii Patavini Historiarum libri qui extant. Interpretatione et notis illustravit Joannes Dujatius ... jussu christianissimi regis, in usum serenissimi delphini. Accessêre librorum omnium deperditorum supplementa, per Jo. Freinshemium; ... Parisiis, apud F. Leonard, 1679-82.
6 v. illus., pl., maps, fold. plan. 25½cm.
Added t.-p., engraved.
Each volume has special t.-p.
I. Doujat, Jean, 1609?-1688, ed. II. Freinsheim, Johann, 1608-1660.

NL 0421630 MiU MH NSyL DLC MWA MWelC TxU ICN PBm

PA 6452 A8 1714 Livius, Titus.
Titi Livii Patavini Historiarum libri qui extant, Interpretatione et notis illustravit Joannes Dujatius...in usum serenissimi Delphini; et librorum omnium deperditorum integra supplementa Joannis Freinshemii; accessere in hac nova editione Joannis Clerici notae. Venetiis, apud Carolum Bonarrigum, 1714-1715.
6 v. 24 cm.
1.Rome - History. I.Doujat, Jean, 1609?-1688, ed. II.Freinsheim, Johann,1608-1660. III.Le Clerc, Jean, [16]57-1736

NL 0421631 IMunS InU ICU OClStM MiDW

878.4 L788P Livius, Titus.
[T. Livii Patavini Historiarum libri qui supersunt, ex editione et cum notis J. Clerici. Adjecta est diversitas lectionis Gronovianae, cum praefatione J. M. Gesneri. Lipsiae, In Officina Weidmanniana, 1743]
3 v. 18 cm.
1. Rome. Hist. I. Le Clerc, Jean, 1657-173[6]
II. Gronovius, Joannes Fredericus, 1611-1671.
III. Gesner, Johann Matthias, 1691-1761.

NL 0421632 NcD KU NRU

Livius,Titus
Historiarum libri,qui supersunt, ex editione cum notes I.Clerici,adiecta est diversitas lectionis Gronovianae,cum praefatione I.M.Gesneri... Leipzig,Weidmann,1755. v.1-3.

NL 0421633 InU

Livius,Titus
Historiarum libri qui supersunt,... Editio altera emendatior. Mannheim, T.Loeffler,1821. v.1-3.

NL 0421634 InU

870.8 V247 49-68 Livius, Titus.
T. Livii Patavini Historiarum libri qui supersunt, ex editione G.A. Ruperti, cum supplementis notis et interpretatione, in usum Delphini, variis lectionibus, notis variorum, recensu editionum et codicum indice locupletissimo et glossario Liviano accurate recensiti. Londini, A.J. Valpy, 1828.
20 v. illus. 22 cm.
On spine: Valpy, Auctores latini, 49-68.
Provenance: The Rev. E.A. Dalrymple, Maryland Diocesan Library.

MH ODW OCU
TU FTaSU MWelC PHC PBm ICN InU ICU OO MB NN CtY OU
NL 0421635 NNG NIC RPB PU PLatS MoSU MdBP MiD NjP

Livius, Titus.
T. Livii Patavini Historiarum libri qui supersunt cum deperditorum fragmentis et epitomis omnium, ex recensione Arnoldi Drakenborchii, cum notis integris J. B. L. Crevierii et indice rerum locupletissimo. Accessit, praeter varietatem lectt. Gronovianæ, Crevierianæ, Doeringianæ et Rupertinæ necnon codicum duorum manuscriptorum, glossarium Livianum, sive index latinitatis exquisitioris. Ex schedis Aug. Guil. Ernesti emendavit plurimisque accessionibus locupletavit Godofr. Henr. Schæfer. Londini, sumptibus Ricardi Priestley, 1825.
4 v. 21½cm.
1. Rome—Hist. I. Drakenborch, Arnoldus, 1684-1748. II. Crévier, Jean Baptiste Louis, 1693-1765. III. Gronovius, Joannes Fredericus, 1611-1671. IV. Ernesti, August Wilhelm, 1733-1801. V. Schäfer, Gottfried Heinrich, 1764-1840.
Library of Congress PA6452.A2 1825 41-30691

NL 0421636 DLC IMunS NNC MH InU OO

Livius, Titus.
T. Livii Patavini Historiarum libri qui supersunt cum deperditorum fragmentis et epitomis omnium. Ad optimarum editionum fidem scholarum in usum, curavit G. H. Lünemann ... Hannoverae, in bibliopolio A. Hahniano, 1828-29.
3 v. 20½cm. (Nova bibliotheca romana classica ... adornavit G. H. Lünemann. t. IX-XI)

I. Lünemann, Georg Heinrich, 1780-1830, ed.

NL 0421637 MiU PU InU

Livius, Titus.
Titi Livii Patavini Historiarum libri qui supersunt, cum indice rerum. Ad vetustorum librorum fidem accurate recogniti. Nova editio stereotypa ... Lipsiae, sumtibus et typis Caroli Tauchnitii, 1848.
6 v. 14cm.

1. Rome—Hist.
34-32048
Library of Congress PA6452.A2 1848 878.4

NL 0421638 DLC MsU PSt ViU NjP InU MH

VOLUME 336

Livius, Titus.
Titi Livii Patavini Historiarum libri qui supersunt, cum indice rerum. Ad vetustorum librorum fidem accurate recogniti. Nova editio stereotypa ... Lipsiae, sumptibus Ottonis Holtze; [etc., etc.] 1866-67 [v. 4, '66]
6 v. in 3. 14cm.
On t.-p., v. 2-6: Editionis stereotypae C. Tauchnitianae nova impressio.

1. Rome—Hist.
37-39549
Library of Congress PA6452.A2 1866
878.4

NL 0421639 DLC CLU-C MdBP

Livius, Titus.
Titi Livii Patavini Historiarum libri qui supersunt, cum indice rerum. Ad vetustorum librorum fidem accurate recogniti. * Lipsiae, sumptibus Ottonis Holtze [1877-88?]
6 v. in 5. 14cm.
* Editionis stereotypae C. Tauchnitianae nova impressio.

NL 0421640 ViU

878.4
L788HEA
Livius, Titus.
[Historiarvm libri qvi svpersvnt omnes ex recensione Arn. Drakenborchii ... Accessit praeter varietatem lectt Gronovianae et Creverianae glossarivm Livianvm, cvrante Avgvsto Gvil. Ernesti. Lipsiae, E Libraria Veidmanni Heredd. et Reichii, 1769.
v. illus. 21 cm.

NL 0421641 NcD MoU MH InU KyU

878.4
X3
Livius, Titus.
T. Livii Patavini [Historiarvm libri qvi svpersvnt omnes ex recensione Arn. Drakenborchii vna cvm libri XCI. fragmento anekdoto Giovenazzio-Brvnsiano et indice rervm locvpletiss. Acessit praeter varietatem lectt Gronovianae et Creverianae glossarivm Livianvm, cvrante Avgvsto Gvil. Ernesti. Francofvrti et Lipsiae, n.p. 1778.
4v front 18cm

NL 0421642 MnCS

Livius, Titus.
[Historiarum libri qui supersunt omnes ex recensione Arn. Drakenborchii. Londoni, Ritchie & J. Sammells, 1779.

NL 0421643 OClJC

873
L788
1779
Livius, Titus.
Titi Livii Patavini [historiarvm libri qui supersunt omnes. Mannhemii, cura & sumptibus Societatis literatae, nunc apud Tobiam Loeffler, 1779-1780.
12 v. in 4. 17cm.
J.B.L. Crévier praefatio in vitam et scripta Livii. cf. Brit. Mus.

1. Rome--Hist. I. Crévier, Jean Baptiste Louis, 1693-1765.

NL 0421644 TxDaM CU MWA InU

Livius, Titus.
T. Livii Patavini [Historiarum libri qui supersunt omnes cum integris Jo. Freinshemii supplementis. Praemittitur vita a Jacobo Philippo Tomasino conscripta, cum notitia literaria. Accedit index studiis Societatis Bipontinae. Editio accurata. Biponti, ex typographia Societatis, 1784-86.
13 v. in 8. 20cm.
Title vignettes.
I. Tomasini, Jacopo Filippo, 1597-1654. II. Freinsheim, Johann, 1608-1660.

InU NN OClJC OOxM
NL 0421645 MiU MoU PLatS RPB OCU CtY PBa PU MH MB

Livius, Titus.
T. Livii Patavini [Historiarum libri qui supersunt omnes, ex recensione Arn. Drakenborchii ... Londini, M. Ritchie & J. Sammells, 1794.
8 v. front. (port.) 23½cm.
Vol. 8 has title: Index et glossarium in T. Livii ... Historiarum libros ...

I. Drakenborch, Arnoldus, 1684-1748, ed.

MWiW-C
NL 0421646 MiU NIC MsU NN ICN MH InU ViU CLSU

PA6452
.A2
1801
LIVIUS,TITUS.
T.Livii...Historiarvm libri qvi svpersvnt omnes ex recensione Arn.Drakenborchii cvm indice rervm locvpletiss. Accessit praeter varietatem lectt. Gronovianae et Creverianae Glossarivm Livianvm cvrante Avgvsto Gvil.Ernesti. Editio nova emendatior... Lipsiae,in libraria Weidmanniana,1801-04.
5 v. 18cm.
Vol.5 has added t.-p.:Glossarivm Livianvm sive latinitatis exqvisitioris. Ex schedis Avgvsti Gvil.Ernestii emendavit plvrimisqve accessionibvs locvpletavit Godofr. Henr.Schaefer.

NL 0421647 ICU PLF NcD MoU

PA6452
.A2
1807
Livius, Titus.
T. Livii Patavini Historiarvm libri qui svpersvnt omnes. Procemio breviariis librorvm indice rervm locvpletissimo tabvlis chronologicis historicisqve et commentario perpetvo seorsvm edito instrvcti a Ge. Alex. Rvperti ... Gottingae, Svmtibvs C. F. Rvprecht, 1807-09.
6 v. 17½cm.
CONTENTS.—v.I-IV. Historiarvm libri qvi svpersvnt omnes.—v.V-VI. Commentarivs perpetvvs in T. Livii Patavini Historiarvm libros ... conscriptvs a Ge. Alex. Rvperti, v.I-II.
1. Rome—Hist. I. Ruperti, Georg Alexander, 1758-1839, ed.

NL 0421648 ViU ICU NNC MH InU OCU

PA6452
A2
1811
Livius, Titus.
T. Livii Patavini Historiarum libri qui supersunt omnes ... Editio nova emendatior. Halae, impensis Orphanotrophei, 1811-1816.
3 v. 19cm.

Contents. - v.1. Books 1-10. Epitome Books 11-20. 1815. - v.2. Books 21-30. 1816. - v.3. Books 31-45. Epitomae librorum deperditorum. 1811.

NL 0421649 OU InU MH

PA
6452
.A2
1819
Livius, Titus.
T. Livii Patavini Historiarum libri qui supersunt omnes. Editio nova emendatior. Halae, Orphanotrophei, 1819.
3 v.
Rome--History.

NL 0421650 MoU MiU

LIVIUS, Titus.
Historiarum libri qui supersunt omnes. Ad optimorum librorum fidem accurate editi. Ed. stereotypa. Tom. 1-v. Lipsiae, [1821].

5 vol. 24°. Ports.

NL 0421651 MH PU NcD MiU

PA6452
.A2
1822
LIVIUS,TITUS.
T.Livii...Historiarum libri qui supersunt omnes ... Editio nova emendatior. Halae,impensis Orphanotrophei,1822-23.
3 v. 19x10½cm.

1.Rome--Hist.

NL 0421652 ICU

Livius, Titus.
T. Livii Patavini [Historiarum libri, qui supersunt omnes [et] deperditorum fragmenta. Ex recensione Arn. Drakenborchii ad codicum bambergensis et vindobonensis fidem passim refictis a Ioanne Theophilo Kreyssig. Annotationes Crevierii, Strothii, Ruperti, aliorumque selectas; animadversiones Niebuhrii, Wachsmuthii, et suas addidit Travers Twiss ... Oxonii, impensis D. A. Talboys, 18
v. 23cm.
1. Rome—Hist. I. Twiss, Sir Travers, 1809-1897, ed. II. Kreyssig, Johann Gottlieb, 1779-1854.
45-45555
Library of Congress PA6452.A2

NL 0421653 DLC OCX

Livius, Titus.
T. Livii Patavini Historiarvm libri qvi svpersvnt omnes et deperditorvm fragmenta ... Lipsiae, In Libraria Weidmannia, 1823-1827.
4 v. 21 1/2 cm.

NL 0421654 ViU PBm PU CtY OCU MdBP InU MH

PA6452
.A2
1828
Livius, Titus.
[Historiarum libri qui supersunt omnes et deperditorum fragmenta. Ex recensione Arn. Drakenborchii ad Codicum bambergensis et vindobonensis fidem passim refícta edidit Ioannes Theophilus Kreyssig. Editio [stereotypa ... Lipsiae, Ex officina Tauchnitii, 1828.
viii, 582 p. port. 31cm.
1. Rome—Hist. I. Kreyssig, Johann Gottlieb, 1779-1854, ed.

NL 0421655 ViU CU NjP ViLxM InU NcU

4PA
Latin
69
Livius, Titus.
Historiarum libri qui supersunt omnes et deperditorum fragmenta. Ex recensione Arn. Drakenborchii ad codicum Bambergensis et Vindobonensis fidem passim refícta edidit Ioannes Theophilus Kreyssig. Editio stereotypa. Lipsiae, Sumtibus C. Tauchnitii, 1829-
v. 1-4

NjP NIC ViU IU CtY MeB KAS
NL 0421656 DLC-P4 NN DCU-H IaDuG MiU MH ViLxW PPL

Livius, Titus
... Historiarum libri qui supersunt omnes et deperditorum fragmenta. Monachii, Sumptibus librariae scholarum regiae, 1839-1841.

v. 20 cm.
Each volume has separate title page.
Library has Tom. 1-4 and 6.

NL 0421657 PLatS InU

Livius, Titus
Historiarum libri qui supersunt omnes et deperditorum fragmenta; ex recensione Arn. Drakenborchii ad codicum bambergensis et vindobonensis fidem passim reficta a Ioanne Theophilo Kreyssig. Annotationes Crevierii, Strothii, Ruperti, aliorumque selectas; animadversiones Niebuhrii, Wachsmuthii, et suas addidit Travers Twiss, I. C. B. Oxonii, Impensis D. A. Talboys, 1840-41.
4 v.

OCU MiU
NN DCU NcU TNJ ViU NIC ViLxW NjP MA MH InU MWelC
NL 0421658 MiD RPB CtY NNUT InStme MeB CtMW MdBP

VOLUME 336

Livius, Titus.
T. Livii Patavini Historiarum quæ supersunt, ex recensione Arn. Drakenborchii. Cum indice rerum. Accedunt gentes et familiæ romanorum, auctore R. Streinnio. Necnon Ernesti Glossarium Livianum, auctius nonnihil, et in locis quamplurimis emendatum ... Oxonii, e typographeo Clarendoniano, MDCCC.
6 v. 18cm.
Signatures.
1. Rome—Hist. I. Drakenborch, Arnoldus, 1684-1747?, ed. II. Strein, Richard, 1538-1600 or 01. III. Ernesti, August Wilhelm, 1733-1801. Glossarium Livianum.

NL 0421659 ViU MH IU ViLxW PU PMA MsSM

PA6452 **Livius, Titus.**
.A2 Titi Livii Historiarum quod extat. Ex recensione I. F.
1678 **Gronovii.** Amstelodami, apud D. Elzevirium, 1678.
Rare bk [1], 788 p. 15cm.
room Engraved t.-p.; head and tail pieces; initials.

1. Rome—Hist. I. Gronovius, Joannes Fredericus, 1611-1671, ed.

CtY PPL PBa N CU CSt CU-A MeB
NL 0421660 ICU MiAC ODW PU NNC IEN MB PP InU MH

Tzz
097.9 **Livius, Titus.**
Sm51Liv **Titi Livii Historiarum quod exstat, cum integris Joannis Freinshemii supplementis. Emendatioribus & suis locis collocatis, tabulis geographicis & copioso indice. Recensuit et notulis auxit Joannes Clericus. Amstelaedami, Apud H. Wetstenium; Traiecti ad Rhenum, Apud G. van de Water, 1710.**
10v. fold. maps. 17cm.
From the library of Ashbel Smith.
1. Smith, Ashbel, 1805-1886 - Association copy.

NL 0421661 TxU PU MH InU MeB DLC OClJC PPL

Livius, Titus.
Titi Livii [Historiarum quod extat, cum perpetius **Gronovii et** variorum notis.] Amstelodami, apud **Ludovicum & Danielem** Elzevirios, 1665, 64. 3 v.
Vols. 2-3 have title: T. Livii Patavini Historiarum ab vrbe condita.

NN PU CU
NL 0421662 DLC CtY NjP NNC OCU OCl ICU IaU MH MiD

Livius, Titus.
Titi Livii Historiarum quod extat, cum perpetuis **Car.** Sigonii et J. F. Gronovii notis. Jac. Gronovius probabit, suasque et aliorum notas adjecit. **Amstelodami, apud D.** Elsevirium, 1678-79.
3 v. port. 20cm.
Engraved t.-p.
Vol. 2-3 have title: T. Livii Patavini Historiarum ab urbe condita ... 1678.
Book-plate: Edw. Hugh Boscawen.
I. Sigonio, Carlo, 1524?-1584, ed. II. Gronovius, Joannes Fredericus, 1611-671. III. Gronovius, Jacobus, 1645-1716.

ICU MB MdBP PU WU NN CtY MiD
NL 0421663 MiU NIC FU PPL IU CSt MA ViLxW RPB MH MiD

LIVIUS,TITUS.
Titi Livii...Historiarum quod extat,cum perpetuis Car.Sigonii & J.Fr.Gronovii notis. Jac. Gronovius probavit,suasque & aliorum notas adjecit. Editio nova... Basileae,apud E.& J.R. Thurnisios,1740.
3 v. 19½cm.
Added t.-p.,engr.;title vignette.
Vol.2-3 have title:T.Livii Patavini Historiarum ab urbe condita...
Pirated from the edition of 1679.

NL 0421664 ICU MB InU NjP NcD MiD IU PBm PU TxDaM-P

Livius, Titus
... Historiarum Quod Extat, cum perpetuis Car. Sigoni et J. F. Gronovii Notis. Jac Gronovius probavit, suasque et aliorum Notis adjecit.
Amstelodamj, Apud Danielem Elsevirium, Anº 1769.
3 vols: 22 p.*l.*, 922 p., 35 *l.*(indices), 62 p.; 973, [1] p., 30 *l.* (indices), 58 p.; 1080 p., 42 *l.* (indices), (last *l.* blank), port. 20 cm.

Engraved title-page in vol. I; second and third vols dated 1678.
Dibdin: Greek and Latin Classics, II, p. 167.

NL 0421665 MWiW-C

878.4 Livius, Titus.
L788HG
Historiarum Romanarum libri qui **supersunt.** Ex recensione Jo. Nic. Madvigii. Ediderunt **Jo.** Nic. Madvigius et Jo. L. Ussingius. **Hauniae,** Sumptibus Librariae Gyldendalianae, **1861-66.**
4 v. 21 cm.

Each vol. originally issued in 2 pts.; each pt. has special t. p. only.
Contents.-v. 1. pars 1. Libros quinque

primos continens. pars 2. Libros a sexto ad decimum continens.-v. 2. pars 1. Libros a vicesimo primo ad vicesimum quintum continens. pars 2. Libros a vicesimo sexto ad tricesimum continens.-v. 3. pars 1. Libros a tricesimo primo ad tricesimum quintum continens. pars 2. Libros a tricesimo sexto ad quadragesimum continens.-v. 4. pars 1. Libros a quadrage-

simo primo ad quadragesimum quintum continens. pars 2. Fragmenta librorum amissorum et periochas continens.

ViU NIC CtW
NL 0421668 NcD NcU ICU MiU CU PU KU InU CtY RPB MH

Livius, Titus
Historiarum Romanarum libri qui supersunt; ex recensione Io. Nic. Madvigii...Hauniae, 1863-75.
4 v. 8°

NL 0421669 NN ViU

Livius, Titus.
Historiarum romanarum libri qui supersunt; ex recensione I.N. Madvigii... ediderunt I.N. Madvigius & L.L. Ussingius.. Haunie, 1864-80.
4v.

NL 0421670 PBm OCU

LIVIUS.
Historiarum romanarum libri qui supersunt. Ex recensione I.N.Madvigii. Ediderunt I.N. Madvicius et I.L.Ussingius.Hauniae.1873-84,'65.

Vol. I. [ ] 3 vol.
Vol. I.,II. pars 2, III.1 are 2d ed.;
II.1 is 3d ed.

NL 0421671 MH

LIVIUS, Titus.
Historiarum Romanarum libri qui supersunt. Recognovit R.Folli. Lib.I-II. Mediolani,Valentiner et Mues,1870.

17 cm.

NL 0421672 MH

PA6452 Livius, Titus.
.A2
1872 Titi Livii Historiarum romanarum libri qui supersunt. Ex recensione Io. Nic. **Madvigii. Iterum** ediderunt Io. Nic. Madvigius et Io. L. Ussingius ... Hauniae, Sumptibus librariae **Gyldendalianae** (Hegel) 1872-
4 v. in 8. 20½cm.

1. Rome—Hist. I. Madvig, Johan Nikolai, 1804-1886, ed. II. Ussing, Johan Louis, 1820-1905, joint ed.

NL 0421673 ViU PU

PA Livius, Titus.
6452 T. Livii Patavini Historiarum **libri superstites,** cum deperditorum voluminum **compendiis,**
A2 ab antiquo scriptore confectis. **Ex editione**
1819 Arnoldi Drakenborch ... Londini: **Rodwell et**
Tucker Martin, **1819.**
5 v. **13cm.**

1. Rome - Hist. I. Drakenborch, **Arnoldus,** 1684-1748.

NL 0421674 ViW MdBP MA PU CtY NN MH ViLxW NNG

PA6452 **Livius, Titus.**
f.A2 T. Livii Patavini ... Libri omnes, qvotqvot ad nos perve-
1588 nere; nove editi, et recogniti ... a Francisco Modio ... In evndem Livivm observationes, emendationes ... Henrici Loriti Glareani, Beati Rhenani, M. Antonii Sabellici ... [et al.] Ipsivs demvm Modii in Livivm prope vniversvm notae, partim ab eo scripta, partim ex Brissonii, Lipsii Cviacii, aliorumq; ... editu ... Qvibvs accessere ... Chronologia noua Caroli Sigonii, & eiusdem in eandem obseruationes,

Tabula Concionum atq; orationum omnium T. Liuii ... Francofurti, impensis S. Feyrabendii & sociorum, 1588.
3 v. in 1. 38cm.
Title in red and black, with vignette; head and tail pieces; initials.
Vol. 2 has title: Chronologia in Titi Livii Historiam, accommodata ad tabvlas capitolinas Verrii Flacci.
Vol. 2-3 have imprint: Francofvrdi ad Moenvm, apud I. Wechelum impensis Sigismundi Feyrabendii, Henrici Thack, & Petri Vischeri sociorum.
Dedication of v. 2 by Ioachim Grellius.

1. Rome—Hist.

NL 0421676 ICU CtY MH InU RPB

---

q871 Livius, Titus.
L5 Titi Livii Patavini, Romanæ historiæ principis,
1568 [libri omnes, qvotqvot ad nostram ætatem pervenervnt: vna cvm doctissimorvm virorvm in eos lvcvbrationibvs, post omnes aliorum editiones, summa fide ac diligentia ... recogniti, & artificiosis picturis ... exornati, inq; duos tomos distributi ... Francofvrti ad Moenvm, 1568.
2v. in 1. illus. 39½cm.

Colophon (at end of [v.1]): Impressvm Francofvrti ad Moenvm, apvd Georgivm Corvinvm, Sigismvndvm

Feierabend, et hæredes Wigandi Galli. M.D.LXVIII.
Title within historiated border; initials.
Woodcuts by Jost Ammon.
Device of printer on special title-pages and on last leaf of vols.1 and 2 accompanying colophons.
Epitomes by L. Florus.
[Vol.1] includes Chronologia in Titi Livii Historiam, accommodata ad tabvlas Capitolinas Verrii

Flacci ... with special t.-p.
"Francisci Robortelli Vtinensis de convenientia svppvtationis Liuianæ ann. cum marmoribus Romanis, quæ in Capitolio sunt": Chronologia, p.51-56.
[Vol.2] includes: In Titi Livii Patavini Romanæ historiæ principis libros omnes qvi extant, doctissimorvm ... virorvm annotationes, castigationes & scholia ... with special t.-p.; Caroli Sigonii Scholia ... with special t.-p.; Dvo Tarqvinii Lvcivs ac

Arvns, Prisci Tarqvinii filii ne an nepotes fverint, adversvs Livivm Lavrentii Vallae ... disputatio ...; In Titi Livii Patavini Historiarvm ab vrbe condita libros, qvi qvidem extant, omnes, observationes, ex variis avtorvm scriptis collectae, per Vilhelmvm Godelevævm, with special t.-p.

NL 0421680 IU MiU IaU NNC MB ICU OrU

VOLUME 336

Livius, Titus.

Titi Livii Patavini, Romanae historiae principis libri omnes, qvotqvot ad nostram aetatem peruenerunt: vna cvm doctissimorvm virorvm in eos lucubrationibus, post omnes aliorum editiones, summa fide ac diligentia, & veterum & recentiorum exemplarium collatione nunc denuo recogniti ... Cum indice copiosissimo. Cum gratia & priuilegio Caes. Maiest. Francoforti ad Moenvm, Apvd Iohannem & Sigismundum Feyerabendt, 1578.
17 p.l., 805 [i.e.905], [23]* 47 p., 6 p.l., 119 p., 2-82 numb. l., 104, 3-93 p., 1 l. illus. 37cm.

*pages wanting: Collation from Dfu from NIC. Colophon and chronology wanting.
Signatures)(4, B6, C-D4, A-Z6, a-z6, Aa-Zz6, Aaa-Eee6, 2 unsigned l., Fff8, Ggg-Hhh6.
Title in red and black, within ornamental border. Initials; marginal notes.
Annotations and observations of various authors on Livius compiled by Wilhelmus Godelevaeus.
Edited, with a chronology, by Joachimus Grellius.
1. Rome—Hist. I. Grellius, Joachim, ed. II. Godelevaeus, Wilhelm

NL 0421682 ViU DCU InU NIC MH

Livius, Titus
Titi Liuij Patauini ... Libri omnes qvotqvot ad nostram aetatem pervenervnt ad publicam vtilitatem denuo editi. Qvibvs adivncta est chronologia noua, accommodata ad tabulas Capitolinas Verii Flacci ... Impressum Londini, Per Edmvndvm Bollifantvm, 1589.
6 pts. in 1 v. 18 cm.
From colophon: Impensis I. Harison
S.T.C. 16612b.
Dedication signed: Sigismvndvs Feyrabendivs.
Includes epitomes by L. Florus.
Special title-pages for [pt. 5] "Chronologia" and [pt. 6] "In Titi Livii Patavini Historiarvm ab erbe condita libros, qvi qvidem extant, omnes, observationes, ex varijs autorum scriptis collectæ per Vuilhelmum Godeleuaeum."
Printer's device on each title-page.

NL 0421684 NNC CtY CSmH IU DFo ICU MH

FILM
Livius,Titus.
Titi Liuij Patauini Romanae historiae principis,libri omnes,qvotqvot ad nostram aetatem pervenervnt,post varias doctorum virorum emendationes,& veterum & recentium exemplarium collatione summa fide ac diligentia recogniti,& ad publicam vtilitatem denuò editi. Qvibvs adivncta est chronologia noua,accommodata ad tabulas Capitolinas Verii Flacci,annotationibus vtilissimis,varietatem seu dissensionem auctorum circa consulum Romanorum nomina demonstrata illustrata ... Impressum Londini, per Edmvndvm Bollifantvm. 1589.

Colophon: Londini impensis G.Bishop.
Dedication signed: Sigismvndvs Feyrabendivs.
Epitomes by L.Florus.
"Chronologia" has special t.p.
"Francisci Robortelli vtinensis de convenientia svppvtationis Liuianae annotat.cum marmoribus Rom. quae in Capitolio sunt": Chronologia,p.91-99.
Includes (with special t.p.): In Titi Livii Patavini Historiarvm ab vrbe condita libros,qvi qvidem extant, omnes,observationes,ex varijs autorum scriptis collectae per Vuilhelmum Godeleuaeum.
University microfilms no.15920 (case 68,carton 405)
Short-title catalogue no.16612.
1.Rome—Hist. I. Florus,Lucius Annaeus. II. Godelevaeus,Wilhelmus.

NL 0421686 MiU ViU

Gn&40 b589b
Livius, Titus
Titi Livii ... Historiae principis libri omnes, quotquot ad nostram aetatem peruenerunt. Post varias doctorvm virorum emendationes & veterum & recentium exemplarium collatione summa fide ac diligentia recogniti, & ad publicam utilitatem denuo editi. Qvibvs adivncta est chronologia noua accommodata ad tabulas capitolinas, Verii Flacci, annotationibus vtilissimis varietatem seu dissensionem auctorum circa consulum Romanorum nomina demonstrata, illustrata. Cum indice calci libri annexo. Francofvrti,E

Continued in next column

Continued from preceding column

collegio Paltheniano,cura & sumtibus heredum P.Fischeri,1599.
8,1259,124,[30],229[i.e.228]p. illus. 19cm.
Pages 227-228 misnumbered 229-229.
"Chronologia in Titi Livii Historiam accommodata ad tabvlas capitolinas Verrii Flacci ...", and "In Titi Livii ... Historivm ab vrbe condita libros ... Obseruationes ... collectæ per VVilhelmvm Godelevævm" have special t.-p.s.

NL 0421688 CtY

Livius,Titus
Historiae Romanae principis libri omnes superstites;post aliorum omnium emendationes nunc praeterea castigati ad fidem vetustiss,manu exaratorum codicum Bibliothecae Palatinae,à J.Grutero. Accessit index rerum & verborum copiosissimus. Frankfurt, N.Hoffmann,1609. 4v.

NL 0421689 InU

Livius,Titus
Historicorum Romanorum principis, libri omnes superstites,recongiti pridem et emendati...a Iano Grutero...Frankfort on Main,Ioannis Saurii,1612.

NL 0421690 InU CU MeB MB PU

PA6452 A2 1619
Livius, Titus.

Libri omnes svperstites: post aliorvm omnivm emendationes nunc praeterea castigati ad fidem vetvstiss. manv exaratorum codicum Bibliothecae Palatinae à Iano Grutero... Editio secunda, & melior. Francofurti, E typographeo Nicolai Hoffmanni, sumptibus haeredum Iacobi Fischeri, 1619.
2 v.in 1. 21cm.
Title in red and black; printer's device on t.p.; headpieces; initials.

Paged continuously; numerous errors in pagination.
Vol.2 has title: Historiarvm ab vrbe condita decadis III. liber trigesimus.
Imperfect copy: t.p. mutilated.
Bound with Godelevaeus, Wilhelmus. In Titi Livii Patavini, historiarvm ab vrbe condita libros ... observationes. Francofvrti, 1619.
I.Gruterus, Janus, 1560-1627, ed.
878.4.JG89

NL 0421692 CSt

Case Y 672 .L 506
LIVIUS, TITUS.
T.Livii...libri omnes svperstites recogniti... et emendati...a Iano Grvtero. Accedunt in eundem Liuium obseruationes, emendationes, annotationes... Lavrentii Vallæ, M.Antonii Sabellici [et aliorum]... Cum indice rerum ac verborum locupletissimo huic nouissimæ editioni adaptato. Præter appendices ac supplementa... Paris,Apud Societatem miniman, 1625.
2v.in 1. 39cm.

Bookplate of Skene library.
Title in red and black, with vignette.
Vol.[2] has title: In T.Livii...opera observationes, emendationes, animaduersiones, annotationes, &c. Lavrentii Vallæ, M. Antonii Sabellici [et aliorum]...

NL 0421694 ICN MiU MH

Gn&40 +b628
Livius, Titus.
Titi Livii Patavini ... Libri omnes superstites, recogniti et emendati ad manvscriptorum codicum fuldensium, moguntinensium & coloniensium fidem, à Francisco Modio; nvnc etiam comparati cvm membranis bibliothecæ palatinæ electoralis, melioresq; facti curâ tertiâ Iani Grvteri: cvivs accedvnt notæ criticæ et politicæ, nec non qvinqvaginta aliqvot in Corn. Tacitvm Discvrsvs, aut auctiores longè prioribus, aut nouè vulgati ...

Francofvrti ad Moenvm, Excusi typis Guolphgangi Hofmanni,impensis hæredum I.Fischeri, 1628.
10p.ℓ.,39,[8],656,[58],175,69,116[i.e.167]p. port. 37½cm.

NL 0421696 CtY MB CSt InU MShM PPAmP PU ViU CU

2877 .1696
Livius, Titus.
...Libri omnes superstites, tertia Jani Gruteri cura recogniti et emendati, nunc vero recusi novisque additionibus...meliores facti accurante Jo.Gerhardo Arnoldo... Francofurti, Sumtibus F.Knochii, 1696.
11 ℓ.,43,6,1275(i.e.1279),152,304 p. front.(port.) 19 cm.
Book 30 has special t.-p.
"In Titi Livii...Historiarum...libros...observationes ex variis auctorum lucubrationibus collectae per Wilhelmum Godelevaeum aliosque": 152 p.following main pagination, with special t.-p.

I.Gruterus,Janus,1560-1627,ed. II. Arnold,Johann Gerhard,1637-1717,ed. III. Godelevaeus,Wilhelm,16th cent.,ed. IV.

NL 0421698 NjP NcD NN InU

---

870 L788 tA.1
Livius, Titus.
Titi Livii Patavini Historiae romanae principis libri omnes superstites, optimorum exemplarium collatione recogniti, et novis additamentis illustrati. Frorentiae [!], Typis Regiae Celsitudinis, Apud. P.A.Brigonci, M.DCCI [i.e.1701]
4v. 15x8cm.

Imprint on vols.2-4 reads: Florentiae.

NL 0421699 CLSU

Livius, Titus.
In Titi Livii Patavini Romanae historiae principis libros omnes qui extant ... annotationes, castigationes & scholia ... 1568
see under title

Y 672 .L 5082
Livius, Titus.

Titi Livii Patavini [opera qvae exstant omnia ex recensione G.A.Rvperti, cvm svpplementis Freinshemii... Avgvstae Tavrinorvm,1825-26. 14v.O.

"Procemivm G.A.Rvperti de Livii vita et scriptis": v.1, 3d p.l., p.[i]-lvii.
Vol.14 includes: Dispvtatio de ponderibvs, pecvnia, mensvris a Livio identidem memoratis, avctore Creverio, p.154-170. De aere gravi [avctore Creverio] p.171-179. Tabvlae octo, nvmmorvm, pondervm, mensvrarvm, apvd Romanos et Graecos, avctore A.Letronne, p.[181]-197. Notitia literaria de T.Livio, ex Io. Alb. Fabricii Bibliotheca latina a Io. Avg. Ernesti avctivs edita, t.I, cap.II, p.201-296.

NL 0421702 ICN ViU DCU OCU

VOLUME 336

Livius, Titus
Opera, quae supersunt...Editio postrema Patavina. Cui accedunt Capita XVII, quae hactenus desiderabantur, adnotations variorum. Excerptae ex editione Oxoniensi a.1708...Patavium, Typis Seminarii, 1740. v.1-5.

NL 0421703 InU

Livius, Titus
Opera quae supersunt, obscuriorum locorum interpretationibus, & selectis adnotationibus illustrata. Cum supplementis in postremos libros ex recensione Arn. Drakenborkii. Editio postrema... Patavium, Joannem Manfre, 1766. v.1-6.

NL 0421704 InU

PA6452 .A2 1777 LIVIUS, TITUS.
... Opera, quae supersunt, obscuriorum locorum interpretationibus, & selectis adnotationibus illustrata. Cum supplementis in postremos libros ex recensione Arn. Drakenborkii. Editio postrema ... Cui nunc primum in calce accedit novum T. Livii fragmentum a clariss. viris Vito M. Giovenazzio, Paulo Jacobo Bruns in Vaticana Bibliotheca recens repertum, accurateque descriptum ... Venetiis, sumptib. heredis N. Pezzana, 1777.
6 v.
Vol.6 has title: Exercitationes rhetoricae in orationes T. Livii quibus accedunt Joannis Clerici animadversiones.

NL 0421705 ICU

PA6452 .A2 1799 Livius, Titus.
T. Livii Opera, qvae svpersunt, obscuriorum locorum interpretationibus & selectis adnotationibus illustrata ab J. B. L. Crevier, cum ejusdem supplementis in postremos libros, ex recensione Arn. Drakenborch. Accedit, praeter ea omnia quae sequenti pagina & epistola indicantur, fragmentvm libri XCI nuper inventum in Bibliotheca Vaticana, & scholiis illustratum a Vito M. Giovenazzio. Editio prima conimbricensis ad Drakenborch Amstelaed. MDCCXXXVIII castigata ... v. 2-6. Conimbricae, typis academicis, 1799-1813.

5 v. 16 cm.
Title from v. 2.
"Titi Livii Historiarum lib. XCI fragmentum descriptum, et recognitum a clariss. viris Vito M. Giovenazzio, Paulo Jacobo Bruns: v. 6, p. [643]-678.

NL 0421707 DLC

Gnl40 b791b Livius, Titus.
T.Livii Opera quae supersunt obscuriorum locorum interpretationibus et selectis adnotationibus illustrata ab J.B.L.Crevier. Cum ejusdem supplementis in postremos libros ex recensione Arn. Drakenborkii ... Cui ... accedit fragmentum libri XCI. Nuper inventum ... & scholiis illustratum a Vito M.Giovenazzio ... Bassani, Suis typis Remondini edidit, 1821.
7v. 17cm.
"L.Flori Decadum XIV. Titi Livii Patavini Historiarum ... epitome": v.6, p.[3]-8?.

NL 0421708 CtY NcU

Livius, Titus.
Opera quae supersunt...interpretationibus ...illustrata ab J. B. L. Crevier, ex recensione Arn. Drakenborkii, ed... a Giovenazzio Romae, ex typ. Ven. hospitii apostolici, 1884-86. 7v.

NL 0421709 MA

PA6452 .A2 1780 LIVIUS, TITUS.
Titi Livii Opervm omnivm volvmen I-III. Animadversionibvs illvstravit Fridericvs Andreas Stroth. Gothae, apvd C.G.Ettingervm, 1780-84.
3 v. 18cm.

NL 0421710 ICU

Livius, Titus Patavinus.
Operum omnium...animadversionibus illustravit F.A.Stroth. Recensuit et suas observationes adspersit F.G.Doering. ...Gothae, C.G.Ettingerum, 1796-1813. v.1-4,6-7.

NL 0421711 InU MH

---

ar V 11244 Livius, Titus.
Operum omnium; animadversionibus illustravit Fridericus Andreas Stroth. Recensuit et suas observationes adspersit Fridericus Guilielmus Doering. Accedit Index historicus. Ed. auctior et emendatior. Gothae, Sumtibus Librariae Ettingeriae, 1801-19
[v.1, 1816]
7 v. 18cm.
"Index historicus," planned as v.8, was not published.

NL 0421712 NIC

Livius, Titus
Operum omnium...recensuit et observationibus, instruxit F.G.Doering. Gotha, Apud Ettingerum, 1808. v.5.

NL 0421713 InU

Livius, Titus.
Titi Liuii Patauini Historici clarissimi que extant Decades cum Epitome. L. Flori in omnes libros. Cum Annotationib⁹ M. Antonii Sabellici in eos qui extant. Cum indice alphabetico recentius ab Ascensio collecto. Et cum explanatione praefationis et praenotamentis eiusdem Ascensii in lectionem Liuianam. [Parrhisiis] Uendantur ab Joanne paruo et Ascensio ipso. [1511]
26 p.l., CCLXXX numb. l. 34 cm.
Colophon: Diligentiore cura: in aedibus Ascensianis: in illustri Parrhisiorum Academia: Impesis Ioannis Parui: & ipsius Ascensii. Anno

salutis Christiane. M. D. X. ad Idus Martias.
Verso of numb. l. 280 blank.
Roman letter. Headlines in Gothic letter.
Signatures: $aa^4(aa^2$ signed $Aa^2)$ $bb\text{-}cc^8dd^6a\text{-}z^8$ $A\text{-}M^8$
A few errors in foliation and signatures.
54 lines on a page.
Woodcut initials. Badius' device on t.p.
Ms. notes in margins.
1st (t.p.) and 4th p.l. (c. sig. $aa^{1.4}$) wanting.
Slightly water-stained.
Stamped pigskin over card-board.
Title taken from Renouard, Bibliographie de ... Josse Badius

NL 0421715 CtY MH

Rare Book Room Gnl40 +b491h Livius, Titus.
T. Liuij Patauini historici clarissimi, quae extant Decades ad decem diuersa exempla acri iudicio repositae ... Cũ annotationibus. M. Antonii Sabellici ... [In Parrisiorum academia] Venundantur ab Joanne Paruo et Iodoco Badio Ascensio. [Anno redẽptionis humanę 1513. Ad Nonas Decẽbres]
40p.l., CCLXXXnumb.l. 32½cm.
Described in Ph. Renouard, Bibliographie des impressions et des oeuvres de Josse Badius, Paris, 1908, vol.3, p.11-12.

NL 0421716 CtY MH InU NNUT

---

q871 L5 1516 Livius, Titus.
T. Liuij Patauini historici clarissimi quae extant Decades ad decem diuersa exempla acri iudicio repositae. Cum indice literaria serie etiam in Epitomem L. Flori: adiectis compluribus prius intermissis: rursus ab Ascensio collecto. Cum praenotamentis, regulis & omnium vocularum, con structionum, sententiarumqȝ subdifficilium quae inter legendum occurrerunt, eiusdem explicatione. Cũ. L. Flori in omneis libros Epitome recognita & literis vt indice explicari possit ab eodem Ascen sio distincta. Cũ annotationibus M. Antonii Sa

bellici diligenter recognitis. Cũqȝ primae praefationis familiari Ascensii p̃fati explanatione. [Parisiis] vęnundantur ab Joanne Paruo [1516]
40 l., cclxxx numb.l. 30cm.

Colophon: Ex aedibus Ascensianis longe accurati ore q̃ pridem vigilantia ... in illustri Parrhisior Academia: rursus opera & accuratione Ascẽsiana: anno redẽptionis humanae M.D.XVI. ad nonas iunias.

Signatures: 8 l. unsigned, $aa\text{-}dd^8$, $a\text{-}z^8$, $A\text{-}M^8$.
Title and printer's mark framed within historiated border. Initials.

I. Badius Jodocus, Ascensius, 1462-1535. II. Sabellico, Marco Antonio Coccio, called, 1436-1506.

NL 0421719 IU InU DFo CSt

PA 6452 A2 1530 Cage Livius, Titus.
... Quae manifesto extant, librorum decades, cum nuper in Germania inuẽtis quibusdam fragmentis, rursus... repositae... Cum Epitome L. Flori in omnes etiam non extantes libros. Cum M. Antonii Sabellici ad Liuianae historiae veriorem lectionem adnotatis. Comq; Iodoci Badii Ascensii de historico decoro regulis... Vaenundantur ipsi Ascensio, 1530.
Colophon: Sub prelo Ascensiano, 1531.

[22] 323 [1] xl [16] l. Fo.
Smedley copy.

NL 0421720 DFo MH

PA6452 .A2 1824 Livius, Titus.
T.Livii Patavini Qvae svpersvnt omnia et deperditorvm epitomae edidit fragmenta et indicem historicvm ex Bipontina editione adiecit Carolvs Fridericvs Boehmert. Editio stereotypa. Lipsiae, svmtibvs et typis C.Tavchnitii, 1824.
4 v. 19cm.

1.Rome--Hist.

NL 0421721 ICU

Beinecke Library Gnl40 B679 Livius, Titus. 1679.
Titi Livii Qui extant Historiarum libri. In duobus tomis correctis & emendatis. Cantabrigiae, Ex Officina Joan. Hayes, impensis Joan. Creed & Henr. Dickinson, 1679.
2 v. 18 cm.
Paged continuously; v. 1: 1 p.ℓ., 728 p.; v. 2: 1 p.ℓ., 731-1428, [36] p.

NL 0421722 CtY ViW MWA PPAmP PMA NN

Livius, Titus.
En amice lector apportamvs tibi, svmma diligentia excvsvm, post germanam editionem. T. Livii Patavini latinae historiae principis, qvicquid hactenus editum fuit, sed aliquanto quàm antea emaculatius. Accesserunt autem decadis quintae libri quinq;, nunq̃ antehac editi, cum Chronologia Henrici Glareani, temporum supputationem, & personarum nomina, in quibus hactenus ingens fuit confusio, dilucide commonstrante. Adiunctus est insuper index omnium quae notatu digna uisa sunt, copiosissimus ... Venetiis mense febrvario, 1532.
4 p. l., 312, 16 numb. l., [80] p. 32cm.

Continued in next column

VOLUME 336

Continued from preceding column

Giunti's device on t.-p. and at end; initials.
Colophon (p. 312): Venetiis in ædibus Lucæantonii Iuntæ Florentini anno Domini .M.DXXXII. die decima Ianuarii ...
Reprint of the edition, Basel, 1531, in which Grynaeus for the first time published books 41–45, discovered by him in a manuscript of the abbey of Lorsch (now cod. vindobon. no. 15)

I. Grynaeus, Simon, 1493–1541. II. Glareanus *i. e.* Heinrich Loriti, of Glarus, 1488–1563.

18-7480

NL 0421725 DLC CSt NNC PBa

Livius, Titus.
En magnis impendiis, svmmisqve laboribvs damvs amice lector T. Livii Patavini ... qvicqvid hactenvs fuit aeditum, sed aliquanto quàm antea, tum magnificentius, tum emaculatius. Accesserunt autem Quintae decadis libri quinq, nunquam antehac aediti ... Addita est Chronologia Henrici Glareani, temporum supputationem, & personarum nomina ... commonstrans. Adiunctus est & index copiosissimus ... Basileae, In officina

Frobeniana, 1531.
[8], 244, 243, 210, 91, [74], 45, [1] p. 39cm.

Edited by Erasmus.

NL 0421727 NNC IU ICN DFo NcD CtY

Rare Book Room Gnℓ40 +B525S

Livius, Titus.
T. Livii Patavini ... Rervm gestarvm popvli Romani ex centvm qvadraginta, libri triginta, qvi soli svpersvnt, castigatiores ... avtore Iacobo Sobio. L. Flori Epitome in libros C.XL. [Coloniae Apvd Io.Soterem, impensis ... Petri Quentel]An.1525.Men. [Avgvsto-]Septemb.
30p.ℓ.,XXXV,[1],DCLVII,[1]p. 30cm.
Signatures: a-b⁴c-d⁶e⁴f⁶aaa-ccc⁶a-z⁶ A-Ii6(Ii6 blank)

NL 0421728 CtY ScU InU CSt

Rare Book Room Gnℓ40 +b528

Livius, Titus. 1528.
T. Livii Patavini ... Rerum gestarum populi Romani ... ex centum quadraginta, libri triginta, multo quàm antehac unquam emaculatius excusi. L. Flori epitome ... [Cologne]Eucharius Ceruicornus excudebat,Anno 1528.
50p.ℓ.,702p. 30cm.
Signatures: a-d⁶e⁸A-C⁶a-z⁶aa-zz⁶aaa-kkk⁶ ℓℓℓ-mmm⁸(mmm8 [blank?] wanting)

NL 0421729 CtY CSt DFo InU PPL

Livius, Titus.
T. Livii Patavini historici clarissimi rerum gestarum populi Romani libri triginta. Lucij Flori epitome in CXL. T. Livij libros. Parisiis, F. Regnault, 1529.

[61] cclxxxvii ℓ. 34cm.
The text has added t.-p.: T. Livii ... Rerum gestarum populi Romani... Cum annotationibus m. Antonij Sabellici diligenter recognitis.
I.Sabellico Marco Antonio Coccio, called, 1436-1506,ed.

NL 0421730 MnU

PA6452 .A2 1841

Livius, Titus.
Titi Livi Rerum romanarum ab urbe condita libri ad codicum manu scriptorum fidem emendati ab Car. Frid. Sig. Alschefski ... Berolini, Sumptibus F. Dümmleri, 1841-46.
3 v. 21½cm.
Vol.3 has added t.-ps.: Titi Livi Ab urbe condita decas tertia . Berolini, 1846, and Titi Livi Ab urbe condita liber tricesimus ... Berolini, 1839.
v.3, copy 2, has not 1839 t.-p.
CONTENTS.—v.1. Primae decadis partem priorem contines. 1841.—v.2. Primae decadis partem alteram continens. 1843. —v.3. Libros Livianos XXI., XXII., XXIII. continens. Titi Livi Ab urbe condita decas tertia, pars I, libros I., II., III. 1846.
I. Rome—Hist. I. Alschefski, Karl Friedrich Siegmund, 1805-1852, ed.

NL 0421731 ViU CU ICU InU NjP RPB MH PBm PU NN

PA6452 .A2 1843

Livius, Titus.
Titi Livi Rerum romanarum ab urbe condita libri ex emendatione Car. Frid. Sigism. Alschefski ... Berolini, Sumptibus F. Dümmleri, 1843-44.
4 v. 21cm.
CONTENTS.—pars I. Liber I-V. 1843.—pars II. Liber VI-X. 1843.—pars III. Liber XXI-XXV. 1843.—pars IV. Liber XXVI-XXX. 1844.

1. Rome—Hist. I. Alschefski, Karl Friedrich Sigismund, 1805-1852, ed.

NL 0421732 ViU NN NIC ICU

Lℓ 16 120*

Livius. 1621.
Titi Livii Romanae historiae qvi exstant qvinqve et triginta libri, vna cvm omnivm eivsdem librorum, qui aliàs exstiterunt, epitomis, triplici opera insigniter hac editione illustrati: primùm digestis ad singula rerum capita sectionum notis: deinde adscriptis ad singvlarvm pagellarum frontem, & ad anniuersaria magistratuum comitia, vrbis Romae conditae annis: adiectis deniqve dvobvs indicibvs, altero concionum, selectae latinitatis altero. Hac porro editione accesservnt libri tricesimi

tertij, hactenus desideratae, septuaginta duae sectiones, In collegio lugdunensi societatis Iesv.
Lvgdvni, svmtibvs Thomae Sovbron,CIↃ IↃC XX. [1621] Ex auctoritate Christianiss. Francorum regis.
8p.ℓ.,1186,[73]p. 24.5cm.

Colophon: Lvgdvni ex typographia Petri Marniolles. CIↃ IↃC XXI.
Publisher's mark on t.-p.
Numerous errors in paging, including repetition of 215-216 and omission of 514-515 in numbering.

NL 0421735 MH CU OGC

Livius, Titus
Latinae historiae facilé principis tres, cum dimidia quae solae extant, Decades, longe omnium, quae hactenus exierint emendatissimae. Lugduni, Apud Johannem Frellonium, 1553.

Grässe 4:228

NL 0421736 NcU CU

Livius, Titus. 1554.
T. Livii Patavini Latinae historiae facilè principis tres, cum dimidia, quae solae extan Decades, longe omnium, quae hactenus exierint emendatissimae. Accessere marginales aliquot annotatiunculae, quibus priscorum Romanorum pecuniae, ad nostri temporis rationem aestimantur. Adiectae svnt praeterea doctorvm quorundam virorum, in Tit. Liuium lucubration quarum catalogum sequens pagina indicabit. Lvgdvni,Apud A.Vincentium,1554.

Continued in next column

Continued from preceding column

17p.ℓ.,580,[12],[250]p. 36cm.
Henrichi Loriti Glareani ... In omneis quae quidem extant, T. Liuii Patauini clarissimi historici Decadas, annotationes cum eiusdem Chronologia in totam romanam historiam nunc primum non sine foenore recognita ... Lvgdvni, Apvd A.Vincentivm,1553, [250]p. at end, has special t.-p.

NL 0421738 CtY

Latin and English

Livius, Titus.
Livy, with an English translation by B. O. Foster. London, Heinemann; New York, Putnam, 1919–59.
14 v. fold. col. maps. 17 cm. (The Loeb classical library. [Latin authors])
Latin and English.
Vols. 6–8, 12–14 have imprint: Cambridge, Harvard University Press; v. 9–11: London, Heinemann; Cambridge, Harvard University Press.
Vols. 6–8 translated by F. G. Moore; v. 9–11 by E. T. Sage; v. 12 by E. T. Sage and A. C. Schlesinger; v. 13 by A. C. Schlesinger; v. 14 by A. C. Schlesinger, with a general index to Livy by R. M. Geer.
(Series)
PA6156.L5 1919 937 20-2836 rev2
PA6452.A2 1919

TU OOxM CtY MiU CU PBm MB OC1W PU PSC PHC PPT
NL 0421740 DLC NN InU ODW TxU NIC OC1 OCU MH MB Vi

Gnℓ40 b919c

Livius, Titus.
Livy, with an English translation by B.O.Foster ... London,W.Heinemann,ltd.; Cambridge,Mass.,Harvard university press, 1922-
v. fold.maps. 17cm. (The Loeb classical library)
Latin and English on opposite pages.
Vols.1,11- have imprint: London,W. Heinemann,ltd.;Cambridge,Mass.,Harvard university press;v.2-5 have imprint: London, W.Heinemann;New York,G.P.Putnam's sons;

v.9-10: Cambridge,Mass.,Harvard university press;London,W.Heinemann,ltd.
Vol.9- tr. by E.T.Sage. v.12- tr. by E.T.Sage and A.C.Schlesinger.
Vol.1, 1939; v.2, 1922; v.3,1924; v.4, 1926; v.5, 1929; v.9-10,1935; v.11,1936; v.12,1938.

NL 0421742 CtY OU

Livius, Titus.
Livy. With an English translation by B.O.Foster. [Rev.ed.] Cambridge, Harvard UP, 1939-
(The Loeb classical library)

NL 0421743 MH

Livius, Titus.
Livy, with an English translation by B. O. Foster. London, Heinemann; New York, Putnam, 1950-

NL 0421744 FU

VOLUME 336

Latin and French

Livius, Titus.
Histoire romaine de Tite-Live. Traduction nouvelle par mm. Dureau de Lamalle et Noël. 2 ed., rev., corr. et augm. de suppléments de Freinshémius ... Paris, L.G. Michaud, 1824.
17 v. 22 cm.
Latin and French on oppostie pages.
Contents.- t. 1. Livre 1-2.-t. 2. Livre 3-4.-t. 3. Livre 5-7.-t. 4. Livre 8-10.-t. 5. Suppléments de Freinshémius, livre 11-16.-t. 6. Suppléments de Freinshémius, livre 17-20.-t. 7. Livre 21-23:27.-t. 8. Livre 23:28-25.-t. 9. Livre 26-28:18.-t. 10. Livre 28:19-30.-t.

11. Livre 31-34:42.-t. 12. Livre 34:43-37.-t. 13. Livre 38-40.-t. 14. Livre 41-44.-t. 15. Livre 45. Suppléments de Freinshémius, livre 49-52.-t. 17. Suppléments de Freinshémius, livre 53-54. Fragment du livre XCI, CXXX. Table méthodique et analytique des hommes et des choses.

NL 0421747 CU

871 .L5 1830 Livius, Titus.
Histoire romaine de Tite Live. Traduction nouv. par MM. A. A. J. Liez ... N. A. Dubois ... V. Verger ... Paris, 1830-35.
17v. (Half-title: Bibliothèque latine-française pub. par C. L. F. Panckoucke)
Text and translation on opposite pages.
"Supplémens de Freinshemius": v.6-7.

NL 0421748 IU MdBP NN ICarbS OU

PA6169 .G3L6 1934 Livius, Titus.
... Histoire romaine. Traduction nouvelle avec une introduction et des notes par Eugène Lassere ... Paris, Garnier frères ͺ1934-38ͺ
4 v. fold.maps. 18½cm. (On cover: Classiques Garnier. ͺAuteurs latinsͺ)
At head of title: Tite-Live.
Latin and French on opposite pages.
I. Lasserre, Eugène, ed. and tr.

NL 0421749 OCU

Livius, Titus.
Histoire romaine. Texte établi par Jean Bayet et traduit par Gaston Baillet. Paris, Belles Lettres, 1940- ͺv. 1, 1944ͺ
v. fold. maps. 20 cm. (Collection des universités de France)
French and Latin text on opposite pages, numbered in duplicate.
1. Rome—Hist. I. Bayet, Jean, 1892- ed. II. Baillet, Gaston, tr.
PA6454.B3 A 48-8425 rev*
ͺr56b2ͺ†

MH OCU CaBVaU
NL 0421750 CtY DLC TxU KyU CoU OU NcU WU CU PBm

4DG-89 Livius, Titus.
Histoire romaine [par] Tite-Live. Traduction nouv., avec une introd. et des ses notes, par Eugène Lasserre. Paris, Garnier frères [1941-
v. 1-7 (Classiques Garnier)

NL 0421751 DLC-P4

Livius, Titus.
...Histoire romaine; traduction nouvelle avec une introduction et des notes, par Eugène Lasserre... Paris, Garnier ͺ1944-1948ͺ
7 v. maps. 18½ cm. (Classiques Garnier)
Latin and French on opposite pages.
"Bibliographie": v.1,p.i.

NL 0421752 NjP

PA6452 .A2 1946 Livius, Titus.
Histoire romaine. Texte établi par Jean Bayet et traduit par Gaston Baillet. Paris, Société d'édition "Les Belles Lettres", 1946- ͺv.1, 1947ͺ
v. map. (Collection des universités de France)
1. Rome--Hist.

NL 0421753 ICU

878.4 Kf 1954 Livius, Titus
Histoire romaine. Texte établi par Jean Bayet et traduit par Gaston Baillet. Paris, Les Belles Lettres, 1954-65. ͺv.4, 1954ͺ
5v. 20cm. (Collection des Universités de France)
French and Latin on opposite pages.
Vol. 1 is 8th ed., rev. and corrected.
I. Bayet, Jean, 1892- ed. II. Title. (Series)

NL 0421754 KU NIC CLSU NNC

878 L5 tN72 Livius, Titus
Oeuvres de Tite-Live (Histoire romaine) avec la traduction en français, pub. sous la direction de M.Nisard...Paris, J.J.Dubochet et compagnie, 1838-39.
2 v. 26½ cm. (Collection des auteurs latins)
Latin text at foot of page.

NL 0421755 MiU

*PA6169 .N6L5 1839 Livius, Titus.
Oeuvres de Tite-Live (Historie romaine); avec la traduction en français, publiées sous la direction de m.Nisard... Paris, J.-J.Dubochet, ͺ1839,1844ͺ
2 v. 27 cm. (Half-title: Collection des auteurs latins...pub.sous la direction de m.Nisard)
Title vignettes.
Latin text at foot of page. Notes in French.

"La traduction...est de mm.LeBas... Charles Nisard, Kermoisan(?) Théophile Baudement, Bouteville; de mm.Boistel, Magin, Paret, Le Prévost, Leudière, Capelle... et de m.Bellaguet..."
Contain book-plates of D.H.Holmes.
I.Nisard, Désiré, 1806-1888, ed. II. LeBas, Philippe, 1794-1860, tr. III. Nisard, Charles, 1808-1889, tr. IV.Ker-

moysan, Jean, tr. V. Baudement, Théophile Charles Étienne, 1808-1874, tr. VI. Bouteville, professeur, tr. VII. Boistel, professeur, tr. VIII.Magin-Marrens, Alfred, 1806-1870, tr. IX. Paret, A.,tr. X. Le Prévost, C., tr. XI. Leudière, professeur, tr. XII. Capelle, professeur, tr. XIII. Bellaguet. Louis François, 1807-, tr.

NL 0421758 OCU MB

LIVIUS, Titus.
Oeuvres de Tite-Live (Histoire romaine) avec la traduction en français, publiées sous la direction de M.Nisard. Paris, J.J.Dubochet, Le Chevalier, etc., 1850.
2 vol.
Half-title: Collection des auteurs latins avec la traduction en francais.

NL 0421759 MH

Livius, Titus.
Oeuvres de Tite-Live (Histoire romaine) Avec la traduction en français, publiées sous la direction de Nisard. Paris, F. Didot, 1857.
2 v. 27 cm.
French and Latin.
Various translators.
I. Nisard, Desiré. 1806-1888, ed.

NL 0421760 CU-S OCU

Livius, Titus.
Œuvres de Tite-Live (Histoire romaine) avec la traduction en français, publiées sous la direction de m. Nisard ... Paris, Chez Firmin Didot frères, fils et c^ie^, 1860.
2 v. 28^cm^. (*Half-title:* Collection des auteurs latins avec la traduction en français, pub. sous la direction de m. Nisard)
The work of several translators.
1. Rome—Hist.
Library of Congress PA6169.A32 33-35125
(870.82) 878.4

NL 0421761 DLC ODW

PA6452 A2 1864 Livius, Titus.
Oeuvres de Tite-Live (Histoire romaine) avec la traduction en français, publiées sous la direction de m. Nisard ... Paris, F. Didot frères, fils et cie, 1864.
2 v. 27cm. (Half-title: Collection des auteurs latins avec la traduction en français, pub. sous la direction de m. Nisard)
French translation above, Latin text below.
The work of several translators; cf. p.(vii) v.1.
Contents. - v.1. Books I-XXVI. - v.2. Books XXVII-XLV.

NL 0421762 CU

PA 6169 A4 v.27-28 Livius, Titus.
Oeuvres (Histoire romaine) avec la traduction en français, publiées sous la direction de m. Nisard. Paris, Firmin-Didot, 1882.
2 v. 27cm. (Collection des auteurs latins avec la traduction en français)
1. Rome--Hist. I. Livius, Titus. Works. Latin & French II. Nisard, Désiré, 1806-1888, ed.

NL 0421763 OU

Livius, Titus
Oeuvres completes de Tite-Live, avec la traduction française de la collection Panckoucke, par MM. Liez, Dubois, Verger et Corpet. Nouv. éd. très-soigneusement revue par M.E.Pessonneaux...M.Blanchet... et M.Charpentier...et precédée d'une étude sur Tite-Live, par M.Charpentier. Paris, Garnier, 1860. v.

NL 0421764 InU CU MH

VOLUME 336

Latin and Italian

PA6452 A2 1928 Livius, Titus. Latin and Italian.
Le deche della storia romana; versione di Emilio Bodrero. [La Santa (Milano) Istituto editoriale italiano, 1928]
v. (Collezione romana)

Added title pages in Latin.
Latin and Italian on opposite pages.

I. Bodrero, Emilio, 1874- tr.

NL 0421766 CU

PA6452 .A2 1952 Livius, Titus.
Storia di Roma; testo latino e versione di Guido Vitali. Bologna, N. Zanichelli, 1952-
v. (Prosatori di Roma)
Latin and Italian on opposite pages.

I. Vitali, Guido, 1881- ed. and tr.

NL 0421767 ICU CU OCU

K-10 1816
LIVY.
Storia di Roma. Testo latino e versione di Guido Vitali. Bologna, N. Zanichelli, 1955-58. 5 v. 20cm. (Prosatori di Roma)

[Vols.] 1-5
Latin and Italian on opposite pages.
CONTENTS.--1. Dalle origini al decemvirato.--2-5. La seconda guerra punica.
I. Vitali, Guido, ed. and tr.

NL 0421768 NN

Danish

Livius, Titus.
Forsøg til en oversættelse af T. Livius's Romerske historie, med de allernødvendigste anmærkninger, især for ustuderede, ved mag. Rasmus Møller ... Kiøbenhavn, Trykt paa D. Liunges forlag, hos S. Popp, 1801.
2 v. 18cm.
Translation of: Ab urbe condita libri.
1. Rome—Hist. I. Møller, Rasmus, 1763-1842, tr.

NL 0421770 ViU

Dutch

LIVIUS, TITUS.
Titus Liuius, dat is, De Roemsche historie... doer...Titum Liuiu bescreuen...nu eerstmael in onser Nederlantscher spraken ghedruckt. Tantwerpen [Ghedruckt by J.Grapheus] 1541.
[14], ccccclxvij ℓ. woodcuts. 32cm.

Title within illustrated woodcut border; initials, tail-pieces.
Armorial bookplate: Ex libris Raimond van Marle.

NL 0421772 ICN MiU

English

Special Coll. Livius, Titus

The history of Rome. Translated from the original, with notes and illustrations, by George Baker, M. A. London, Printed for A. Strahan, and T. Cadell jun., and W. Davies, 1797.
6 v. 23 cm.

I. Baker, George, M. A., tr.

NL 0421774 MeB

Livius, Titus.
The history of Titus Livius, with the entire supplement of John Freinsheim; tr. into English, and illustrated with geographical and chronological notes ... London, J. Davis, 1814-15.
3 v. 24cm.
Imprint varies slightly.

1. Rome—Hist. I. Freinsheim, Johann, 1608-1660.

Library of Congress DG207.L76 1814 a 15-9744

NL 0421775 DLC NcU ODW

DG207 .L5B3 1797 Livius, Titus.

The history of Rome, by Titus Livius. Tr. from the original, with notes and illustrations, by George Baker ... London, Printed for A. Strahan, [etc.], 1797.
6 v. 23cm.
Tr. of: Ab urbe condita libri.

1. Rome—Hist. I. Baker, George, M. A., tr.

NL 0421776 ViU PMA MeB CtY NBuG MB MH PPL IU NjP

Livius, Titus.
The history of Rome, by Titus Livius. Tr. from the original, with notes and illustrations, by George Baker ... 2d ed., cor. London, T. Cadell and W. Davies, 1814.
6 v. 21cm.

1. Rome—Hist. I. Baker, George, M. A., tr.

Library of Congress DG207.L76 1814 15-8478

NL 0421777 DLC MHi NN PPFr

Y 672 .L 5182 LIVIUS, TITUS.
The history of Rome... Translated from the original, with notes and illustrations, by George Baker... The 3d edition... London, T.Cadell, 1822.
6v.

NL 0421778 ICN NN CtY

DG 207 .L 78 1823 Livius, Titus.
The history of Rome, by Titus Livius. Translated from the original, with notes and illustrations, by George Baker, A.M. ... First American, from the last London edition... Baltimore, F. Lucas, jr. [etc.] 1823.
6 v. 22cm.

NL 0421779 MdBJ Vi Nh RPB

Livius, Titus.
The history of Rome, by Titus Livius. Translated from the original, with notes and illustrations, by George Baker, A. M. ... First American, from the last London edition ... Boston, Wells & Lilly [etc.] 1823.
6 v. 21½cm.
Imprint varies slightly.
Translation of: Ab urbe condita libri.

NL 0421780 ViU

Livius, Titus.
The history of Rome, by Titus Livius. Translated from the original, with notes and illustrations, by George Baker, A.M. 1st American, from the last London edition. Lexington, Ky., W.W. Worseley, 1823.
6 v. 22 cm.

NL 0421781 KyU

Livius, Titus,
The history of Rome, by Titus Livius. Tr. from the original, with notes and illustrations, by George Baker...Amer. from the last Lond. ed. Georgetown, Thomas and Gideon, 1823.

1. Rome-Hist. I.Baker, George, M. A., tr.

Library of Congress DG207.L76 1814 15-8478

NL 0421782 DNW CtY

Livius, Titus.
The history of Rome, by Titus Livius. Translated from the original, with notes and illustrations, by George Baker ... First American, from the last London ed. ... New York, Published by Peter A. Meiser [etc.] 1823.
6 v. 24 cm.

NL 0421783 CtY

DG207 .L5B3 1823b Livius, Titus.
The history of Rome. Translated from the original, with notes and illustrations by George Baker. 1st American, from the last London ed. Philadelphia: H. C. Carey [etc.] 1823.
6 v. 22cm.
Translation of Ab urbe condita libri.

1. Rome—Hist. I. Baker, George, M. A., tr.

NL 0421784 ViU MH Nh MiU NIC PU ViW NNC OCl OCX OO OO

Livius, Titus.
The history of Rome, by Titus Livius. Translated from the original, with notes and illustrations, by George Baker, A. M. ... First American, from the last London edition ... Washington, Davis & Force, 1823.
6 v. 21½cm.

1. Rome—Hist. I. Baker, George, M. A., tr.

Library of Congress DG207.L5B3 1823 a 30-30156

[937] 878.4

NL 0421785 DLC PPG

Livius, Titus.
The history of Rome, by Titus Livius. Tr. from the original, with notes and illustrations, by George Baker ... A new ed., carefully cor. and rev. ... London, Jones & co., 1830.
2 v. front. (port.) 21½cm.

1. Rome—Hist. I. Baker, George, M. A., tr.

CA 15-896 Unrev'd

Library of Congress DG207.L76 1830

NL 0421786 DLC NjNbT PU PPDrop MdBP NIC MB InU ViU IRA

VOLUME 336

Livius, Titus.
The history of Rome ... tr. from the original with notes and illustrations by George Baker. A new edition carefully corrected and revised. Phila., Wardle, 1836.
2 v. port. 23 cm.

NL 0421787 ViLxW AU OC1JC OCU OO NN

PA 6452 A3S36 Livius, Titus.
The history of Rome, with English notes, marginal references, and various readings by Charles William Stocker. Oxford, J. H. Parker, 1838-44 [v. 1, 1844]
v. in 23cm.

Contents.--v. 1, pt.1. The first decade. [Bk.1-4]--v. 2. The third decade.

I. Stocker, Charles William, ed.

NL 0421788 NIC MdBP PU MA CtY

Livius, Titus.
The history of Rome, by Titus Livius. Tr. from the original, with notes and illustrations, by George Baker ... A new ed., carefully cor. and rev. ... Philadelphia, T. Wardle, 1839.
2 v. front. (port.) 24cm.

Translation of: Ab urbe condita libri.

NL 0421789 ViU AU

Livius, Titus.
The history of Rome. By Titus Livius. Tr. from the original, with notes and illustrations, by George Baker ... New ed., carefully cor. and rev. ... Philadelphia, T. Wardle, 1840.
2 v. front. (port.) 21½cm.

1. Rome—Hist. I. Baker, George, M. A., tr.

17-5294

Library of Congress DG207.L76 1840

NL 0421790 DLC

DG207 L5B3 1844 Livius, Titus
The history of Rome. Translated from the original, with notes and illustrations, by George Baker. New ed. carefully corr. and rev. Philadelphia, McCarty & Davis, 1844.
2 v. port. 23 cm.

1. Rome - History. I. Baker, George, M. A., tr.

NL 0421791 MeB

DG207 .L5S6 1849 Livius, Titus. Historiae. English.
The history of Rome; literally translated, with notes and illus. London, Bohn, 1849-50.
4 v. front. (v. 2) 18cm. (Bohn's standard library)
CONTENTS.—v. 1. The first 8 books, translated by D. Spillan.—v. 2. Books 9-26, translated by D. Spillan and Cyrus Edmonds.—v. 3. Books 27-36, translated by Cyrus Edmonds.—v. 4. Books 37 to the end, with the epitomes and fragments of the lost books, translated by William A. M'Devitte.

1. Rome—Hist. I. Spillan, Daniel, d. 1854, tr. II. Edmonds, Cyrus, R., joint tr. III. McDevitte, William Alexander, joint tr.

NL 0421793 MB OCU MH ODW MiU NN ICN ViU

---

ar V 8673 Livius, Titus.
The history of Rome. London, Bell, 1849-78. [v.4, 1849]
4 v. 19cm. (Bohn's classical library)

Contents.--v.1. The first eight books literally translated with notes and illus. by D. Spillan.--v.2. Books nine to twenty-six, literally translated with notes and illus. by D. Spillan and Cyrus Edmonds --v.3. Books twenty-seven to thirty-six, literally translated with notes and illus. by Cyrus Edmonds.--v.4. Books thirty-seven to the end, with the epitomes and fragments of the lost books, literally translated by William A. M'Devitte.

Vol. 4 has imprint London, Bohn, 1849.

NL 0421795 NIC NcU

Livius, Titus.
The history of Rome. London, H. G. Bohn, 1850-54.
4 v. (2278 p.) 19 cm. (Bohn's classical library, v. 44-47)
CONTENTS.—v. 1. The first eight books, literally translated, with notes and illustrations, by D. Spillan. 1854.—v. 2. Books nine to twenty-six, literally translated, with notes and illustrations, by D. Spillan and C. Edmonds. 1854.—v. 3. Books twenty-seven to thirty-six, literally translated, with notes and illustrations, by C. Edmonds. 1850.—v. 4. Books thirty-seven to the end, with the epitomes and fragments of the lost books, literally translated by W. A. M'Devitte. 1850.
1. Rome—Hist. I. Spillan, Daniel, 1797?-1854, tr. II. Edmonds, Cyrus R., tr. III. McDevitte, William Alexander, tr. (Series)

PA3606.B6 vol. 44-47 54-20696

NL 0421796 DLC MH MsU MB ViU NN OC1W

Livius, Titus.
The history of Rome. by Titus Livius ... London, Henry G. Bohn, 1850-1856.
4 v. front. (v. 2: port.) 19cm. (On cover: Bohn's classical library)
CONTENTS.—[I] The first eight books, literally translated, with notes and illustrations by D. Spillan. 1854.—[II] Books nine to twenty-six, literally translated, with notes and illustrations, by D. Spillan and Cyrus Edmonds. 1856.—[III] Books twenty-seven to thirty-six, literally translated, with notes and illustrations, by Cyrus Edmonds. 1850.—[IV] Books thirty-seven to the end, with the epitomes and fragments of the lost books, literally translated by William A. M'Devitte. 1850.
1. Rome—History. I. Spillan, Daniel. 1797?-1854, tr. II. Edmonds, Cyrus R., joint tr. III. McDevitte, William Alexander, joint tr.

H. E. Huntington library for Library of Congress [DG207.L A31-1047

NL 0421797 CSmH PPGi PPL PBa

Livius, Titus.
The history of Rome, ... Translated ... by George Baker... A new ed. ... N. Y., Bangs, 1852.
2 vols.

NL 0421798 OO PU CtY

Livius, Titus.
The history of Rome, by Titus Livius ... London, Henry G. Bohn, 1853.
4 v. front. (v. 2: port.) 19cm. (On cover: Bohn's classical library)
CONTENTS.—[I] The first eight books, literally translated, with notes and illustrations by D. Spillan. 1853—[II] Books nine to twenty-six, literally translated, with notes and illustrations, by D. Spillan and Cyrus Edmonds. 1855—[III] Books twenty-seven to thirty-six, literally translated, with notes and illustrations, by Cyrus Edmonds. 18 .—[IV] Books thirty-seven to the end, with the epitomes and fragments of the lost books, literally translated by William A. M'Devitte. 18 .

NL 0421799 ViU CU

Livius, Titus.
The history of Rome, by Titus Livius ... London, Henry G. Bohn, 1854.
4 v. front. (v. 2: port.) 19cm. (On cover: Bohn's classical library)
CONTENTS.—[I] The first eight books, literally translated, with notes and illustrations by D. Spillan. 1854.—[II] Books nine to twenty-six, literally translated, with notes and illustrations, by D. Spillan and Cyrus Edmonds. 185 —[III] Books twenty-seven to thirty-six, literally translated, with notes and illustrations, by Cyrus Edmonds. 185 .—[IV] Books thirty-seven to the end, with the epitomes and fragments of the lost books, literally translated by William A. M'Devitte. 18 .
Imperfect: p.1-4 wanting; v.1.
1. Rome—History. I. Spillan, Daniel, 1797?-1854, tr. II. Edmonds, Cyrus R., joint tr. III. McDevitte, William Alexander, joint tr. IV. Ser.

NL 0421800 ViU

Livius, Titus.
The history of Rome, by Titus Livius. Tr. from the original, with notes and illustrations, by George Baker ... A new ed., carefully corr. and rev. ... New York, Bangs, brother, & co., 1855-59.
2 v. 23 cm.
Vol. 2 has imprint: New York, Derby & Jackson
Contents. - v. 1. Book I-XXVII.-v. 2. Book XXVIII-XLV. Contents of the lost books.
I. Baker, George, M.A., tr.

NL 0421801 CU ViU

Livius, Titus.
—— History of Rome. Literally tr. by D. Spillan, Cyrus Edmonds, and William A. McDevitte. London, 1856-62. 4 v. p. 8°. (Bohn. H. G., Class. Libr.) 2757

NL 0421802 MdBP

Livius, Titus
The History of Rome, by Titus Livius. Translated from the original, with notes and illustrations, by George Baker. New ed., carefully corrected and revised. New York, Derby & Jackson, 1858.

2 v. 24 cm.
Library has vol. 2.

1. Rome - History. I. Baker, George, tr.

NL 0421803 PLatS MiU

Livius, Titus.
History of Rome, ... Tr. fr. the original with notes and illustrations. New ed. corrected and revised. N.Y., Derby, 1859.
2 v.

NL 0421804 OO

---

878 L5 tS76 M1 Livius, Titus.
The history of Rome. By Titus Livius... Literally trans. with notes...by D. Spillan & Cyrus Edmonds. London, H.G. Bohn, 1861.
4 v. front. (v.2) 19cm. (Bohn's classical library)

NL 0421805 MiU

Livius, Titus.
History of Rome, literally translated, with notes, by D. Spillan and Cyrus Edmonds. London. Bell, 1865.
4 v. ports. D.
v. 4 translated by William A. M'Devitte
1. Rome-History. Latin historians. I. Spillan, Daniel, tr. II. Edmonds, Cyrus R., tr. III. M'Devitte, William A., tr.

NL 0421806 NcU

DG207 .L5S6 1867 Livius, Titus.
The history of Rome. By Titus Livius ... London, Bell & Daldy, 1867.
4 v. fronts. (v.2: port.) 18cm.
T.-p. for v.1 lacking.
CONTENTS.—v.1. The first eight books, literally translated, with notes and illustrations, by D. Spillan.—v.2. Books nine to twenty-six, literally translated, with notes and illustrations, by D. Spillan and Cyrus Edmonds.—v.3. Books twenty-seven to thirty-six, literally translated, with notes and illustrations, by Cyrus Edmonds.—v.4. Books thirty-seven to the end, with the epitomes and fragments of the lost books, literally translated by William A. M'Devitte.
1. Rome—Hist. I. Spillan, Daniel, d. 1854, tr. II. Edmonds, Cyrus R., joint tr. III. M'Devitte, William A., joint tr.

NL 0421807 ViU

VOLUME 336

871
L5.Es
1868
Livius, Titus.
The history of Rome ... literally translated, with notes and illustrations ... London, 1868.
4v.

No general t.-p.
Contents: v.1 Books 1-8, tr. by D. Spillan.- v.2 Books 9-26, tr. by D. Spillan and Cyrus Edmonds.- v.3 Books 27-36, tr. by Cyrus Edmonds.- v.4. Books 37 to the end, tr. by W. A. M'Devitte.

NL 0421808 IU NjP

Livius, Titus.
The history of Rome, by Titus Livius ... Literally tr., with notes and illustrations ... New York, Harper & brothers, 1871.
2 v. 19 cm.

NL 0421809 ViU ODW PU OU MH

LIVIUS, Titus.
The history of Rome. Literally translated, with notes and illustrations by D.Spillan. New York,Harper & Brothers,1880,'71.

2 vol. 19 cm.
Cover: Harper's classical library.
Vol.II translated by D.Spillan and Cyrus Edmonds.
Contents:1.Books I-XX.-ii.Books XXI-XXX.
Ll 16.421.5

NL 0421810 MH

Livius, Titus,
History of Rome by Titus Livius...Liberally translated, with notes and illustrations...
Lond., Bell, 1873-73.
4 v. 18cm.

NL 0421811 DNW

Livius, Titus.
The history of Rome, ... New York, Harper & brothers, 1875-1883.
2 v.

NL 0421812 OCl MiU

Livius, Titus.
The history of Rome. London, Bell, 1878-1881 [v. 1, 1880]
4 v. (2278 p.) port. 18 cm. (Classical library)

Contents.—v. 1. The first eight books, translated by D. Spillan.—v. 2. Books nine to twenty-six, translated by D. Spillan and C. Edmonds.—v. 3. Books twenty-seven to thirty-six, translated by C. Edmonds.—v. 4. Books thirty-seven to the end, with epitomes and fragments of the lost books, translated by W. A. M'Devitte.

1. Rome—Hist. (Series: Bohn's classical library)

DG207.L5S48 62-55121

NL 0421813 DLC

LIVIUS, Titus.
The history of Rome. Literally translated, with notes and illustrations by D.Spillan. New York,Harper & Brothers,1879-82.

2 vol.
"Harper's new classical library."
Vol.II translated by D.Spillan and Cyrus Edmonds.

NL 0421814 MH OFH

Livius, Titus.
The history of Rome, by Titus Livius; literally translated, with notes and illustrations, by D. Spillan and Cyrus Edmonds. New York: American Book Co. [1880?] 2 v. 12°.

1. Rome.—History. 2. Spillan, Daniel, translator. 3. Edmonds, Cyrus R., translator.

CENTRAL CIRCULATION.
March 15, 1911.

NL 0421815 NN

Livius, Titus.
The history of Rome, by Titus Livius ... Literally translated, with notes and illustrations ... New York, Harper & brothers, 1881.
2 v. 19½cm. (Lettered on cover: Harper's classical library)
Vol. I translated by D. Spillan; vol. II, by D. Spillan and Cyrus Edmonds.
Cover wanting.

1. Rome—Hist. I. Spillan, Daniel, d. 1854, tr. II. Edmonds, Cyrus R., joint tr. III. Ser.

NL 0421816 ViU

Livius, Titus.
The history of Rome, by Titus Livius ... Literally translated, with notes and illustrations ... New York, Harper & brothers, 1883.
2 v. 19½cm. (Lettered on cover: Harper's classical library)
Vol. I translated by D. Spillan; vol. II, by D. Spillan and Cyrus Edmonds.

NL 0421817 ViU

Livius, Titus.
History of Rome,literally tr. by D. Spillan.
London, Bell, 1885.
4 v.

NL 0421818 OO

871
L5.Es
1890
Livius, Titus.
The history of Rome. Literally translated, with notes and illustrations, by D. Spillan.
New York, Harper, 1890-
v. 20cm. (Harper's classical library)

NL 0421819 IU CU PSC NjP MH

Livius, Titus.
The history of Rome, by Titus Livius ... Literally translated, with notes and illustrations ... New York, Harper & brothers, 1892.
2 v. 19½cm. (Lettered on cover: Harper's classical library)
Vol. I translated by D. Spillan; vol. II, by D. Spillan and Cyrus Edmonds.

1. Rome—Hist. I. Spillan, Daniel, d. 1854, tr. II. Edmonds, Cyrus R., joint tr.

22-6921

Library of Congress DG207.L5S5

NL 0421820 DLC PV OClJC

DG
207
L78
1892
Livius, Titus.

Livy's History of Rome, translated by J. H. Freese. London, New York, G. Bell, 1892-93 [Book 5, 1892]
5 v. in 1. maps. 19cm. (Bell's classical translations)

Books 1-4 translated by John Henry Freese, Book 5 translated by Edward Sprague Weymouth.

NL 0421821 NIC

DG207
.L5S6
1893
Livius, Titus.

The history of Rome, by Titus Livius ... Literally translated, with notes and illustrations ... New York, Harper & brothers, 1893-1895.
2 v. 19½cm. (Lettered on cover: Harper's classical library)
Vol. I translated by D. Spillan; vol.II, by D. Spillan and Cyrus Edmonds.

1. Rome—Hist. I. Spillan, Daniel, d. 1854, tr. II. Edmonds, Cyrus R., joint tr. III. Ser.

NL 0421822 ViU

Livius, Titus.
The history of Rome, by Titus Livius ... Literally translated, with notes and illustrations ... New York, Harper & brothers, 1896.
2 v. 19½cm. (Lettered on cover: Harper's classical library)
Vol. I translated by D. Spillan; vol. II, by D. Spillan and Cyrus Edmonds.

NL 0421823 ViU

Livius, Titus.
The history of Rome, by Titus Livius ... Literally tr., with notes and illustrations ... New York, Cincinnati [etc.] American book company [190-?]
2 v. 19 cm. (On cover: Harper's classical library)
Vol. I translated by D. Spillan; vol. II, by D. Spillan and Cyrus Edmonds.

1. Rome—Hist. I. Spillan, Daniel, d. 1854, tr. II. Edmonds, Cyrus R., joint tr.

DG207.L5S52 [937] -878.4 4-14056

NL 0421824 DLC OOxM NjP CLSU

Livius, Titus.
The history of Rome. Literally translated by D. Spillan [and others].
— London. Bell. 1900-03. 4 v. Portrait. [Bohn's Classical library.] Sm. 8°. 2929.88
Vol. 1 was translated by D. Spillan, vol. 2 by Spillan and Cyrus Edmonds, vol. 3 by Edmonds, vol. 4 by William A. M'Devitte.
Same. Vol. 2-4. Bohn. 1850, 67. 2929.62
Two copies of vol. 2, one of which lacks the title-page.

F1528 — S.r. — Rome. Hist. — Spillan, Daniel, tr. — Edmonds, Cyrus R., tr. — MacDevitte [M'Devitte], William Alexander, tr.

NL 0421825 MB

878
L764hYe
Livius, Titus.
The history of Rome... London, George Bell & sons, 1906-09.
4v. 19cm. (On cover: Bohn's Libraries)

1. Rome--Hist. I. Spillan, Daniel, 1797?-1854, tr. II. Edmonds, Cyrus R., jt. tr. III. McDevitte, William Alexander, jt. tr.

NL 0421826 LU OCl OCU

VOLUME 336

PA6453 A2 1911 Livius, Titus. English.
The history of Rome; literally translated. London, G. Bell, 1909-12 [v.1, 1911]
4 v. front.(v.1) (Bohn's classical library)

Translated by D. Spillan, Cyrus Edmonds and William A. M'Devitte.

1. Rome - Hist. I. Spillan, Daniel, d. 1854, tr.

NL 0421827 CU

Livius, Titus.
History of Rome... Lond., 1909-15.
4v.

NL 0421828 PBm

Livius, Titus.
History of Rome... London, Bell, 1909-21.
5 v.

NL 0421829 OClW

Livius, Titus.
The history of Rome, by Titus Livius ... London & Toronto, J. M. Dent & sons, ltd.; New York, E. P. Dutton & co. [1912-24]
6 v. 17 cm. (*Half-title:* Everyman's library, ed. by Ernest Rhys. Classical. [no. 603, 669, 670, 749, 755, 756])
Translated with introduction by Canon Roberts.
Summary and notes in each volume.
Bibliography: v. 1, p. xvii.
Index: v. 6, p. 307-315.

1. Rome—Hist. I. Roberts, William Masfen, d. 1927, tr.
[DG207.L5R] [937] 878.4 A 25—366
Enoch Pratt Free Libr. for Library of Congress [a60j½]

NL 0421830 MdBE WaU OCU PRosC OCl OO IEG NjP PP InU

DG207 .L5S6 1915 Livius, Titus.
The history of Rome. Literally translated. London, G. Bell, 1915.
4 v. 19cm. (Bohn's libraries)

CONTENTS.—v.3. Books XXVII-XXXVI, translated by Cyrus Edmonds.—v.4. Books thirty-seven to the end, with the epitomes and fragments of the lost books, translated by William A. M'Devitte.

1. Rome—Hist.

NL 0421831 ViU OWorP

Livius, Titus.
The history of Rome [by] Livy. London, J. M. Dent & sons, ltd.; New York, E. P. Dutton & co., inc. [1921?-37]
6 v. 17½cm. (*Half-title:* Everyman's library, ed. by Ernest Rhys. [603, 669-670, 749, 755-756])
Title within ornamental border (v. 2, 6)
First published 1912-24.
Vol. 1 (reprint) 1937; v. 2, undated; v. 3 (reprint) 1931; v. 4, [1921?]; v. 5, [1924?]; v. 6 undated.
Vol. VI has imprint: London & Toronto, J. M. Dent & sons, ltd; New York, E. P. Dutton & co.
"Translated, with introduction, by Rev. Canon Roberts."
Bibliography: v. 1, p. xvii.
1. Rome—Hist. I. Roberts, William Masfen, d. 1927, tr. 40-6729
Library of Congress DG207.L5R6
[937] 878.4

NL 0421832 DLC TxU

Livius, Titus.
The history of Rome, by Titus Livius ... London & Toronto, J. M. Dent & sons; New York, E. P. Dutton & co. [1926-31]
6 v. 17½cm. (*Half-title:* Everyman's library, ed. by E. Rhys. Classical. [603, 669-670, 749, 755-756])
First published 1912-24; v. 1 reprinted 1926, v. 3, 1931; v. 2, 4-6 undated.
Title within ornamental border.
Vol. 2 has imprint: London, J. M. Dent & sons; New York, E. P. Dutton & co.
"Translated, with introduction, by Rev. Canon Roberts."
Bibliography: v. 1, p. xvii.
1. Rome—Hist. I. Roberts, William Masfen, d. 1927, tr. 37-5631
Library of Congress AC1.E8 no. 603, 669-670, 749, 755-756
[937] 878.4

NL 0421833 DLC OU NBuU

Livius, Titus.
Livy. Translated by George Baker ... London, A. J. Valpy, 1833-34.
7 v. front. (port.) 15cm.

1. Rome—Hist. I. Baker, George, M. A., tr.
22-6920
Library of Congress DG207.L5B3 1833

NL 0421834 DLC MiD ViW MH PPDrop PP PU ICU

---

871 L5.Eb
Livius, Titus.
Livy. Translated by George Baker. New York, Harper, 1836.
5 v. 16cm.

1. Rome - Hist. I. Baker, George, M. A., tr.

NL 0421835 FU CU MdBP

PA6453 A2 1842 Livius, Titus.
Livy. Translated by George Baker ... New York, Harper & brothers [1842-47.
5 v. front.(port.) 16cm.

Contents. - v.1. Book I-VI [n.d.] - v.2. Book VII-X. Contents of lost books. Book XXI-XXIII. 1847. - v.3. Book XXIV-XXX. 1842. - v.4. Book XXXI-XXXVIII. 1847. - v.5. Book XXXIX-XLV. Contents of lost books. 1844.

I. Baker. George, tr.

NL 0421836 CU

Livius, Titus.
Livy. Tr. by George Baker ... New-York, Harper & brothers [1844]
5 v. front. 16cm. (*Lettered on cover:* [Harper's] classical library. no. 24-28)

1. Rome—Hist. I. Baker, George, M. A., tr.
28-19712
Library of Congress PA3606.H4 no. 24-28

NL 0421837 DLC NN ViU PV InU

Livius, Titus.
Livy, translated by George Baker. N.Y., 1855.
5 v.

NL 0421838 ODW

878.4 Ke 1864 Livius, Titus
Livy. Tr. by George Baker. New York, Harper [1864-1870]
5v. front. 16cm. (Harper's classical library)

Vol.5 dated 1864.

1. Rome. History.

NL 0421839 KU

Livius, Titus.
The Roman history. Tr. by P. Holland. London, for A. Churchill 1686. fol.

NL 0421840 MWiW-C

DG207 L5 1744 Livius, Titus.
The Roman history by Titus Livius; with the entire supplement of John Freinsheim; translated into English, and illustrated with geographical and chronological notes. London, Printed by James Bettenham, and sold by J. Clarke; C. Hitch; G. Hawkins; A. Millar, and W. Millar, 1744-45.
6 v. illus., maps. 21 cm.

RARE BOOK COLLECTION

1. Rome- Hist. I. Freinsheim, Johann, 1608-1660.

NL 0421841 CU-A NjN InU ViU PPL OCU PU

Livius, Titus.
Titus Livius's Roman history, tr. into English, and illustrated with notes, critical, historical, and geographical... By William Gordon... Glasgow: W. Smith [etc., etc.] 1783. 2 v. in 1. 18cm.

210048B. 1. No subject. I. Gordon, William, of the Academy, Glasgow.
May 6, 1943

NL 0421842 NN PPL MH NjP

Livius, Titus
Roman history. Translated into English, and illustrated with notes, critical, historical and geological, for the use of students in humanity, by William Gordon. Edinburgh, Bell & Bradfute, 1813.
496 p. 18 cm.
Our copy lacks p. 495-6.

1. Rome - History. I. Gordon, William, tr. II. Title.

NL 0421843 KAS MB MH PHi

Livius, Titus.
Roman history, by Titus Livius; tr. by John Henry Freese, Alfred John Church, and William Jackson Brodribb; with a critical and biographical introduction and notes by Duffield Osborne ... New York, D. Appleton and company, 1898.
2 p. l., iii-xvii, 486 p. 4 pl. (1 col.) 2 port. (incl. front.) 3 maps. 28½ cm. (*Half-title:* The World's great books ... R. Johnson, editor. Aldine edition)
Plates accompanied by guard sheets with descriptive letterpress.
1. Rome—Hist. I. *Osborne, Duffield, 1858-1917, ed. II. Freese, John Henry, tr. III. Church, Alfred John, 1829-1912, joint tr. IV. Brodribb, William Jackson, 1829-1905, joint tr.
DG207.L5F7 1898 98—2188

NL 0421844 DLC IU AkU OClND PRosC PPLas OClW

VOLUME 336

DG
207
L5
F85
1899

Livius, Titus.
Roman history. Translated by John Henry Freese, Alfred John Church, and William Jackson Brodribb. With a critical and biographical introd. and notes by Duffield Osborne. New York, D. Appleton, 1899 [c1898]
xvii, 486 p. illus., maps. 24cm.

1. Rome--Hist. I. Osborne, Duffield, 1858-1917, ed.

NL 0421845 NIC

DG
207
L58
F7213

Livius, Titus.
Roman history. Trans. by John Henry Freese, Alfred John Church, and William Jackson Brodribb; with a critical and biographical introduction and notes by Duffield Osborne. New York, D. Appleton, 1904[c1898]
xvi,486p. illus. 22cm.
1. Rome--Hist. I. Freese, John Henry, tr. II. Church, Alfred John, 1820-1912, joint tr. III. Brodribb, William Jackson, 1829-1905, joint tr. IV. Title.
12/68 dsr-mk

NL 0421846 UU

Livius, Titus.
Titus Livius's Roman history from the building of the city, / With the supplement of John Freinsheim. Translated into English, and illustrated with notes historical and geographical ... Edinburgh, Printed by A. Donaldson and J. Reid, for A. Donaldson, 1761.
8 v. 17cm.
Autograph signed by Thomas M. Randolph, jun. (Feb. 24 1809)

1. Rome—Hist. I. Freinsheim, Johann, 1608-1660.

NL 0421847 ViU MdBP MB

Livius, Titus.

The Roman history written in Latine by Titus Livius. With the supplements of the learned John Freinshemius, and John Dujatius. From the foundation of Rome to the middle of the reign of Augustus. Faithfully done into English. London, Printed for Awnsham Churchill ... 1686.
5 p.l.,3-281,lxxx,283-346,351-481,501-940, [18] p. 15 ports. on 1 l.,fold.plate,2 maps. 33½cm.

Signatures: 1 leaf unsigned, A^4, A^2, $B-Z^4$, Z^4, $Aa-Mm^4$, Nn^2, $B-L^4$, $Oo-Xx^4$, $Aaa-Qqq^4$, Rrr^2, $Aaaa-Zzzz^4$, $Aaaaa-Zzzzz^4$, $Aaaaaa-Dddddd^4$, $Eeeeee-Ssssss^2$, $Tttttt1$.
Title within double line border: title vignette(portrait)
Armorial book-plate of Agnew of Lochnaw.
Bound in old sprinkled calf.

NL 0421849 CLU-C CtY MWA MH CU MnU CU-S MiU NNU ViU

Livius, Titus.
The Romane historie written by T. Livivs of Padva. Also the Breviaries of L. Florus: with a chronologie to the whole historie: and the topographie of Rome in old time. Tr. out of Latin into English, by Philemon Holland ... London, Printed by A. Islip, 1600.
5 p. l., 1408, [41] p. 2 illus. (ports.) 32 cm.
Printer's mark on t.-p.
"A svmmarie collected by Iohn Batholomew Marlinavs ... tovching the topographie of Rome in ancient time": p. 1347-1408.
1. Rome—Hist.—Republic, 510-30 B. C. 2. Rome (City)—Antiq. I. Florus, Lucius Annaeus. II. Holland, Philemon, 1552-1637, tr. III. Marliani, Giovanni Bartolommeo, d. ca. 1560.

DG207.L5H6 20—11881

NNC OCU ICN NjP MWiW-C MNS PU-F
NL 0421850 DLC CSmH MB NN ViU NcD CtY MH OU CU CSt

FILM

Livius,Titus.
The Romane historie written by T.Livivs ... Also,the Breviaries of L.Florus: with a chronologie to the whole historie: and the topographie of Rome in old time. Translated out of Latine into English,by Philemon Holland ... London, Printed by Adam Islip. 1600.
"The topographie of Rome" was written by Giovanni Bartolommeo Marliani.
University microfilms no.15921 (case 56,carton 336)
Short-title catalogue no.16613.
1.Rome--Hist. I.Florus,Lucius Annaeus. II.Holland, Philemon,1552-1637,tr. III.Marliani,Giovanni Bartolommeo,d.ca.1560.

NL 0421851 MiU

Livius, Titus.
The Romane historie written by T. Livius of Padua. Also the Breviaries of L. Florus: with a chronology to the whole historie; and the topography of Rome in the old time. Translated out of Latine into English, by Philemon Holland. To which is now added, A supplement of the second Decad of Livy (which was lost) lately written in Latine by I. Freinshemivs and now newly translated into English. London, Printed by W. Hunt for Gabriel Bedell, 1659.
5 p.l., 1122 p., [31] l., 95, [1] p. port., printer's devices. 34 cm.

"A summary collected by John Bartholmew [sic] Marlianus ... touching the topography of Rome in ancient time": p.1074-1122.
"A supplement of the second Decad of Livie's Roman history" has special t. p. with imprint: London, Printed for Joshua Kirton, Abel Roper, Gabriel Bedell, and George Sawbridge, 1659. NjR

1. Rome - Hist. - Republic, 510-30 B.C. 2. Rome (City) - Antiq. I. Florus, Lucius Annaeus. II. Holland, Philemon, 1552-1637, tr. III. Freinsheim, Johann, 1608-1660. IV. Marliani, Giovanni Bartolommeo, d. ca. 1560.

NL 0421853 NjR MWA RPB MiU MShM NRU DCU DFo TxU NNC

French

---

fPA6454
A2
1653

Livius, Titus. French.
Les decades de Tite-Live avec les suplemens de I. Freinshemius sur les mesme autheur. De la traduction de P. Du-Ryer ... A Paris, A. de Sommaville, 1653.
2 v. 33cm.

I. Freinsheim, Johann, 1608-1660. II. Du Ryer, Pierre, 1606-1658, tr.

NL 0421855 CU

Livius, Titus.
Les decades de Tite-Live, avec les supplemens de I. Freinshemius; nouvellement augmentées d'un abregé chronologique: mises en françois par P. Du-Ryer ... [Ornament] Suivant la copie imprimée. A Lyon, M. DC. XCIV-VI.
8 v. front. (port.) 16½cm.
Title in red and black.
Added t.-p. engr.
Head and tail pieces; initials.
Bookplate of William Short.
1. Rome—Hist. I. Du Ryer, Pierre, d. 1658, tr. II. Freinsheim, Johann, 1608-1660. III. Title. Translation of Ab urbe condita.

NL 0421856 ViU

Livius, Titus

Les decades de Tite-Live. De la traduction de P. Du-Ryer... Nouvelle edition, revue & corrigée de quantité de fautes & d'obmissions qui s'étoient glissées dans les précedentes. A Amsterdam: Chez A. de Hoogenhuysen, 1722. 8 v. front. (port.) 16cm.
Vol. 1 has added illustrated engraved t.-p.
Vol. 3 has title: Les suplémens de J. Freinshemius, sur la seconde decade de Tite-Live...
Vols. 3–8 each have added t.-p. with imprint: A Rouen, chez Jore, imprimeur-libraire, 1720–21.

120692–9B. 1. No subject. I. Freinsheim, Johann, 1608–1660. II. Du Ryer, Pierre, 1606–1658, tr.
September 12, 1941

NL 0421857 NN MH

Livius, Titus
Les décades qvi se trovvent, de Tite Live, mises en langve francoise: la premiere, par Blaise de Vigenere Bourbonnois: auec des annotations & figures pour l'intelligence de l'antiquité romaine: plus vne description particulière des lieux: & vne chronologie générale des principaux potentats de la terre. La tierce, tournée autrefois par Iean Hamelin de Sarlac: & récentement recourüe & amendée presque tout de neuf. Le reste, de la traduction d'Anthoine de la Fay Paris, Chez

Iacques du Puys, 1583, '80.
2 v. illus., fold. pl., maps. 38½cm.
Title vignettes engr.; engraved head and tail-pieces and initials.
Vol. 2 has title: La troisiesme décade de Tite-Live, contenant La seconde gverre pvniqve, sovbs la consvite d'Annibal: mise cy devant en françoise par Iehan Hamelin de Sarlat; & depuis resuyvie presque tout à neuf, par V.D.V.

NL 0421859 MdBJ PU

Livius, Titus.

Les decades qvi se trovvent... Avec des annotations et figures pour l'intellizence de l'anticuite romaine...par B. de Vigenere... Paris, Chez A.Langelier, 1606.
2 v. illus.,maps. 41 cm.

Engravings on the t.-p. and on pp. 960,1033,1057,1328,1409,1462 are by Thomas de Leu. The other illustrations are probably by him also.

NL 0421860 NjP

Gn&40
Bh5044B

Livius, Titus.
Les gestes rommaines. Nouuellement imprimees a Paris. [Colophon: Cy finist les gestes rommaines et Les statuz et ordonnances des heraulx darmes / trãslatez de latin en frãcoys par Maistre Robert Guaguin ... Imprime a Paris le .vii. iour du moys de septembre mil cinq cens et .xv. [1515] par Michel Le Noir libraire iure en Luniuersite de Paris demourant en la grant rue Sainct Jacques a lẽseigne de la Rose Blanche Couronnee]

6p.ℓ.,CCxii numb.ℓ. illus. 25cm.
Signatures: $ã^6a\text{-}z^6\&^6A\text{-}K^6L^8$.
The 3d decade of Livy.

NL 0421862 CtY ICN

VOLUME 336

SPECIAL COLLECTIONS
GONZALEZ LODGE

Livius, Titus.
Histoire romaine de Tite Live ... Nouuellement traduite de latin en françois par Antoine de la Faye. Auec vne table ... A Geneve, Par Iacob Stoer, 1582.
[14], 625 (i. e. 625), [29] l. port. 40cm.

Printer's device on title-page.
Initials.
Two unnumbered leaves between l. 597-598.

NL 0421863 NNC CSt

Livius, Titus
Histoire romaine de Tite-Live; traduite en françois, avec les supplements de Freinshemius. Nouv. éd. rev. & corr. ... Paris, De Lormel [etc.] 1769–72 (v. 5–7, '69)
10 v. 17cm.
Translated by François Guérin; revised by P. C. Cosson.
CONTENTS.—[v. 1–3] La premiere decade.—[v. 4] Seconde décade, ou Les suppléments de J. Freinshemius.—[v. 5–7] Troisieme decade.—[v. 8–10] Quatrieme décade.
1. Rome—Hist. I. Freinsheim, Johann, 1608–1660. II. Guérin, François, 1681–1751, tr. III. Cosson, Pierre Charles, 1737–1801, ed.
44-28481
Library of Congress PA6454.G8

NL 0421864 DLC CtY CU MB

Livius, Titus.
Histoire romaine de Tite-Live, traduction nouvelle par Dureau de Lamalle ... rev. par M. Noël ... Paris, Michaud frères [etc.] 1810–12.
15 v. 19½cm.
Imprint varies: v. 2–4, Giguet et Michaud.
Title-page, v. 8–15, reads: "... traduction nouvelle par Dureau de Lamalle ... et par M. Noël ..."
Vols. 5–6: Histoire romaine de Tite-Live, ou Les suppléments de J. Freinshémius, tr. en français par Guérin ...
"Table méthodique et analytique [par M. Gallais]": v. 15, p. [197]–419.
I. Dureau de la Malle, Adolphe Jules César Auguste, 1777–1857, tr. II. Noël, François Joseph Michel, 1755–1841, ed. III. Freinsheim, Johann, 1608–1660. IV. Guérin, François, 1681–1751, tr. V. Gallais, Jean Pierre, 1756–1820.
18-17885

NL 0421865 DLC ViU MoU InU

LIVIUS, Titus.
Histoire romaine de Tite Live; traduction nouvelle par M. Gaucher. Paris, L.Hachette et cie, 1867.
4 vol.

NL 0421866 MH

Livius, Titus.
Historiae Romanae decades. [French] Paris [Jean de Prê] I) 27 Nov. 1486; II) 24 June 1487; III) [n.d.]
Hain-Copinger 10143; Coff L-250.

NL 0421867 CSmH CtY

Typ 515 30.526F
Livius, Titus.
Le premier[-tiers] volume des grãs decades de Tyt9 Liuius translatees de latin en francoys nouuellement corrigees & amendees. Et en ensuyuãt les faictz dudit Tytus Liuius aucunes addicions de plusieurs grans historiographes, si comme Orose Saluste Suetone & Lucain.
Imprime pour Jehan Petit libraire iure de luniuersite de Paris.[1530]
3v. illus. 34cm.
Colophon in each volume; full colophon in v.3: ... Imprimme [!] a Paris le

Continued in next column

Continued from preceding column

vingtseptiesme iour de juing mil cinq cens et trente par Nicolas Sauetier imprimeur demourãt en la rue des Carmes a lenseigne de lhomme sauluaige. MH57-3465
Title within ornamental border including publisher's device. Volumes 2 and 3 have secondary signatures, separate foliation, and special t.-p. dated 1530, with publisher's device and border containing printer's initials.
Translated by Petrus Berchorius.

Volume 1 includes " ... traicte de la pmiere guerre punicque que cõpilla en latin ... Leonard de Arecio ..." (verso of leaf clxxi to leaf cxcvi), an anonymous translation.
Petit issue of an edition divided among Petit, A. Girault, and P. Le Noir; also issued with Girault or Le Noir named in the colophon.

NL 0421870 MH

German

Livius,Titus
Römische geschichte...mit anmerkungen versehen von G.Grosse. Vienna, F.Haas,1798-9. v.1-10.

NL 0421872 InU

PA6455 .A2H4
Livius, Titus.
Titus Livius Römische geschichte, übersetzt mit kritischen und erklärenden anmerkungen von Konrad Heusinger ... Braunschweig, F. Vieweg, 1821.
5 v. 20½cm.
Translation of Ab urbe condita libri.

1. Rome—Hist. I. Heusinger, Konrad. ed. and tr.

NL 0421873 ViU ICU CtY CU NIC InU MH RPB IU

---

871 L5.Gk
Livius, Titus.
Römische geschichte, übers. von C. F. Klaiber ... Stuttgart, 1826-34.
26v. in 6. (Added t.-p.: Römische prosaiker in neuen uebersetzungen ...)

Paged continuously.

NL 0421874 IU InU PLatS MH PPG MB CtY ICU CU

Livius, Titus.
Römische geschichte, uebersetzt von Dr. Oertel, bd. 1-7. Stuttgart, L.F. Rieger, 1840-1841.
7 v. Plates. (Die klassiker der Römer und Griechen, bd. 1-7)

NL 0421875 InU

Livius, Titus
... Römische Geschichte, uebersetzt von Dr. Oertel. 3 durchgesehene aufl. Stuttgart, Scheible, Rieger & Sattler, 1844.

8 v. in 4, fronts., 16 cm.
Added title page engraved.

1. Rome - History. I. Oertel, Eucharius Ferdinand Christian, 1765-1842, tr.

NL 0421876 PLatS IU ODW CtY InU RPB

PA6455 A2 1853
Livius, Titus. German.
Titus [Livius. Römische geschichte, übers. von C.F. Klaiber ... Stuttgart, verlag der J.B. Metzler'schen buchhandlung, 1853-61.
3 v. 16cm.
Bound irregularly.
Contents. - v.1. bd.1. Buch I-VI. 1853. bd.2. Buch VI-XXI. 1854 [p.1-96] bd.6. Buch XL bis CXL. 1855 [p.1-128] p.97-224 of bd.2. - v.2. bd.4. Buch XXVIII bis XXXIV. 1859. p.49-230 of bd.3. bd.3:2. Buch XXV, XXVI, XXVII. 1861. - v.3. p.129-416 of bd.6. bd.5. Buch XXXV bis XXXIX. 1856. p.225-430 of bd.2. dup.t.-p. for bd.2. bd.3. Buch XXII bis XXVII. 1859 [p.1-48]

NL 0421877 CU

Livius, Titus. G878-L
Römische Geschichte; übersetzt von C. F. Klaiber. Stuttgart: J. B. Metzler, 1855–59. [ ] v. 16°.
v. 3. Buch XXII bis XXVII.
v. 4. Buch XXVIII bis XXXIV.
v. 5. Buch XXXV bis XXXIX.
v. 6. Buch XL bis CXL.

1. Rome—Hist. February 20, 1933

NL 0421878 NN

Livius, Titus.
...Römische Geschichte. Deutsch von Fr. Dor. Gerlach... Stuttgart, Hoffmann, 1856–58. 2 v. in 1. 17cm.
At head of title: Titus Livius.
Imperfect: t.-p. of v. 2 wanting; t.-p. for v. 1 incorrectly bound.

710027B. 1. No subject. I. Gerlach, Franz Dorotheus, 1793–1876, tr.
October 9, 1945

NL 0421879 NN

PA6455 .G37
LIVIUS,TITUS.
...Römische geschichte. Deutsch von Fr.Dor. Gerlach... Stuttgart,Hoffmann,1858-67.
4 v.in 3. 17cm. [Neueste sammlung ausgewählter griechischer und römischer classiker]
Vol.1 has special t.-p.,dated 1856.

NL 0421880 ICU MdBP

PA6455 .H61
Livius,Titus.
...Römische geschichte. Uebersetzt von professor Konrad Heusinger. Neu hrsg.von dr.Otto Güthling. Leipzig,P.Reclam jun.[pref.1884]
4 v. 15cm. (On cover:Universal-bibliothek,nr. 2031-35,2076-80,2111-15,2146-50)
At head of title:Titus Livius.

1.Rome--Hist.

NL 0421881 ICU IU PLatS DLC-P4

PA 6455 .G4 1914
Livius, Titus.
Römische Geschichte. Deutsch von Fr. Dor. Gerlach. Berlin, Langenscheidtsche [1914-19, v. 1, 1917]
5 v. (Langenscheidtsche Bibliothek sämtlicher griechischen und römischen Klassiker in neueren deutschen Musterübersetzungen, Bd. 97-101)
Each volume has special t.p.
This set is made up of various editions.
#Rome--History.
(A)Gerlach, Franz Dorotheus, 1793-1876, tr.

NL 0421882 MoU

VOLUME 336

RARE PA 6455 .G7

Livius, Titus.
Römische Geschichte, von Erbauung der Stadt an (so viel wir noch davon haben) nach Drakenborchscher Ausg. aus dem Lateinischen übersetzt und mit Anmerkungen versehen von Gottfried Grosse. Halle, J. J. Gebauer, 1789-95.
7 v.
*Rome--History.
(A) Drakenborch, Arnoldus, ed.
(A) Grosse, Gottfried, tr.

NL 0421883 MoU

DG207 .L783 1790

Livius, Titus.
Römische Geschichte, was davon auf unsere Zeiten gekommen ist, übersezt und mit erläuternden Anmerkungen begleitet von J. P. Ostertag. Frankfurt am Main, J. C. Hermann, 1790-
v.

1. Rome--Hist.

NL 0421884 ICU

Livius, Titus,
Titi Liuii dess aller redtsprechsten unnd hochberumptsten geschicht schreibers: Römische historien mit eclichen newen translation auss dem Latein... durch Nicolaum Carbachium... durch Jacobum Micvllum... Gedruckt zû Menntz durch Juonem Schoeffer... Im jar M.D.XXXiii.

Folio. 14 p.l., 545 numbered leaves. Wdcts. in text, wdct. initials and printer's device on leaf 546. 29.6 cm. 11 5/8 in.

Brunet III, 1113

NL 0421885 MdBJ-G MWiW-C

SPECIAL COLLECTIONS B87LJ KS2

Livius, Titus.
Titi Liuij ... Römische Historien, jetzundt mit gantzem fleiss besichtigt, gebessert vnd gemehret ... Gedruckt in Meyntz, durch Juonem Scheffer, 1541.
[14], ccccl (i.e. 448), xciii, [1] l. illus. 32cm.

Translation by Bernhard Schöferlin, continued by Ivo Wittig, Nicolaus Carbach, and Jakob Moltzer.
Printer's device on t.-p. and at end.

"Das vierdt theil ... auss fünff büchern Titi Liuij in latein newlich erfunden, vnnd verteütschet" has separate pagination. Each part has illustrated half-title.
Numerous errors in pagination.

NL 0421887 NNC

Livius, Titus.
Römsche history. Strassburg, J. Grüninger 1507. fol.

NL 0421888 MWiW-C MH

Livius, Titus.
Römische geschichte von erbauung der stadt an, nach drakenborchscher ausgabe aus dem lateinischen uebersetzt und mit anmerkungen versehen von Gottfried Grosse. Vienna, Haas, 1789-99.
10 v.

NL 0421889 OClW

144090 [1505]

Livius, Titus.

Romiſche Hiſtorie vſz Tito liuio gezogen. colophon: ... Mentz durch vleiſz Johan Schoffers ... am ſechſtē tagk des Monedts Marcij ... Tauſent funffhunderth vnd jm funffte Jare. [6 Mar. 1505]

12 p.l., LXXXIX numb. l., 1 l., XC-CCXXI, 1 l., CCXXII-CCCCX numb l., illus. 31 cm. Old vellum boards.
Title-page loose.
Illuminated initial, folio II.
In Library, July 20, 1929.
38-1513-5

NL 0421890 CSmH DLC NjP

---

*PA 6455 S36 1514

Livius, Titus.
[Romische historie Titi Livii, meniglich, kürtzweilich und dienstlich zu lesen. Mentz, Durch Johann Schöffers, 1514]
ccccx l. illus.(woodcuts)

Imperfect copy: approximately 87 leaves wanting, including t.p. and final leaf, the prefaces, dedication and other scattered leaves. Title supplied from Bibliothèque National. Cat. général des livres, v.190, 241-242.

Bernhard Schöferlin's translation, continued by Ivo Wittig.

I. Schöferlin, Bernhard. II. Wittig, Ivo, d.1507.

NL 0421892 CLU CoMC

Livius, Titus.
Romische Historien, mit etlichen newē Translation̄, so kurtz uerschienen Jaren im hohē Thum Styfft zu Mentz jm Latein erfunden, vnd vorhyn nit mer gesehen. [Mentz, Getruckt durch I. Schoeffer, 1523]
ccccx, ccxxxii-ccxlvii, ccccxi-ccccxx l. illus. 33 cm.
Bernhard Schöferlin's translation, continued by Ivo Wittig and Nicolaus Carbach.
Contemporary blind stamped half pigskin over wooden boards.
1. Rome—Hist. I. Schöferlin, Bernhard, tr. II. Wittig, Ivo, d. 1507, tr. III. Carbach, Nicolaus, 16th cent., tr. IV. Title.
PA6455.S4 Rosenwald Coll. 48-37314 rev*
—— ——— Copy 2. Rosenwald Coll. Blind stamped vellum over boards, with initials RVNH and date 1600 on front cover.

NL 0421893 DLC RPB

Case fY 672 .L 5235

LIVIUS, TITUS.
[Romische historien ... mit etliche newe translation auss dem Latein ... Mainz, J. Schöffer, 1530]
3pt.in 1v.([10], 447 l.) illus. 30cm.

Imperfect: t.-p. wanting; supplied by Xerox copy.
Printer's device on verso of last leaf; initials.

Colophon: Getruckt zu Meyntz durch Johan Schöffer, im September des jars ... Taussent fünffhundert vnnd dreissigsten.
Woodcuts are reprinted from the 1505 ed.
"Der Römischen historien. Nicolaus Carbacchius dem leser": l. 447 (recto)
Bound in pigskin over wooden boards; clasps.

NL 0421895 ICN OrU MH

Livius Patavinus, Titus, 59 B.C.-17 A.D.
Titus Livius Ankunfft und Ursprung dess Römischen Reichs ... Zetzund auffs neuw auss dem Latein verteutscht ... durch Zachariam Müntzer. Mit schönen Figuren geziert, dessgleichen vorhin im Druck nie aussgangen. Franckfurt am Mayn [Bey G. Raben, S. Feyrabend und W. Hanen Erben] 1568.
1 v. (unpaged) illus. 35 cm.
1. Early printed books, 1500-1650, in the University of Oregon library. I. Florus, Lucius Annaeus, 2 cent. II. Müntzer, Zachariam, tr.

NL 0421896 OrU

Livius, Titus
Titus Livius und Lucius Florus. Von ankunfft und ursprung des Römischen Reichs, der alten Römer herkommen... aus dem Latein verteutscht...durch Z. Müntzer...Frankfort on the Main, 1571.

NL 0421897 InU MWiW-C KAS

---

xfPA6455 M8 1574

Livius, Titus
Livius Titus und Lucius Florus. Von Ankunfft unnd Ursprung des Römischen Reichs, der alten Römer Herkommen, Sitten, Weissheyt, Ehrbarkeyt, löblichem Regiment, Victori unnd Sig... Auch von allerley Händeln un̄ Geschichten so sich...zu Rom, in Italia und bei andern Nationen, damit die Römer...zu thuen gehabt... von Erbawung der Statt an...biss auff der ersten Römischen Keyser Regierung...zugetragen. Jetzund auff dass newe auss dem Latein verteutscht

und mit ordentlicher Verzeychniss der fürnemsten Historien, Jarrechnung kurtzer Livischen Chronica, Register und schönen Figuren geziert, dessgleichen vorhin im Truck nie aussgangen. [Strassburg, Getruckt durch Theodosium Rihel, 1574]
[28], 887, [22] p. col.illus. 35cm.

"Lucij Flori Innhalt der ubrigen Bücher Titi Livij, so nicht vorhanden seind": p.886-887.
"Vorrede", signed: Theodosius Rihel.
Translation by Zacharias Münster and Bernhard Schöfferlin. cf. Bibl.nat. Cat.gén. (Tite Live, no.218); Brit.Mus. Gen.cat., v.140, col.195.

NL 0421900 IaU NNC ICU

Rare PA 6455 M94++ 1598

Livius, Titus.

Titus Liuius, vnd Lucius Florus, von Ankunfft vnd vrsprung des Römischen Reichs, der alten Römer herkommen, Sitten, Weissheyt ... löblichem Regiment, Ritterlichen Thaten, Victori vnd Sig, gegen ihren Feinden: Auch von allerley Händeln vn̄ Geschichten, so sich ... von erbawung der Statt an, erstlich vnter der Könige, vnd volgends ... biss auff der ersten Römischen Keyser Regierung, verloffen vnd zugetragen. Jetzund auff dass newe auss

dem Latein verteutscht ... [Strassburg, Getruckt durch Theodosium Rihel, 1598]
[28], 878 (i.e. 887), [22] p. illus. 34cm.

Title within woodcut ornamental border.
Imprint, with device of t. Rihel on verso of last leaf.
Translated by Zacharias Muentzer.
Page 887 erroneously numbered 878.

NL 0421902 NIC NNC MH

Rare book coll. Folio PA6452 .A2

Livius, Titus.
Titus Liuius und Lucius Florus, von Ankunfft und Vrsprung desz Römischen Reichs der alten Römer herkommen Sitten, Weiszhent, Ehrbarkent, löblichem Regiment, Ritterlichen Thaten, Victori und Sig gegen jhren seinden ... Jetzund auss das newe ausz dem Latein verteutscht ... [Strassburg, T. Rikel, 1603]
887p. illus. 34cm.

I. Florus, Lucius Annaeus.

NL 0421903 NcU NNC

VOLUME 336

Livius, Titus.
Titus Liuius vnd Lucius Florus, von Ankunfft vnd Ursprung dess Römischen Reichs, der alten Romer herkommen, Sitten, Weissheyt, Ehrbarkeyt, löblichem Regiment, Ritterlichen Thaten, Victori vnd Sig, gegen ihren Feinden: Auch von allerley Händeln vñ Geschichten ... fast innerhalb achthundert jaren, von erbawung der Statt an ... biss auff der ersten Römischen Keyser Regierung, verloffen vnd zugetragen. Jetzund auff das newe auss dem Latein verteutscht, vnd mit orden licher verzeychniss der ... Historien, Jarrechnung, kurtzer Liuische Chronica, Register, vnd schönen Figuren gezieret, dessgleichen vorhin im Truck nie aussgangen ... [Strassburg, Getruckt durch T. Rihel, 1605]
[28], 887, [22] p. illus. 34 cm.
Title in red and black within historiated border; initials.
Printer's device on last page.
Translation by Zacharias Müntzer.
"Lucii Flori Inhalt der vbrigen Bücher Titi Liuii so nicht vorhanden seind": p. 866-887.
I. Florus, Lucius Annaeus. II. Müntzer, Zacharias.

NL 0421905 OU MH

---

*PA6455 Livius, Titus.
A2R5 Titus Livius unnd Lucius Florus. Von Ankunfft unnd Ursprung des Romischen Reichs. Jetzund auff dass newe auss dem Lateinverteutsch. [Strassbourg, T. Rihel, 1613]
887, [22] p. illus. 35cm.
I. Florus, Lucius Annaeus.

NL 0421906 NBuG

Ex
2877 Livius, Titus
.2619q Titus Livius vnnd Lucius Florus. Von Ankunfft vnd Vrsprung des Römischen Reichs, der alten Römer herkommen... Jetzund auss dem newe auss dem Latein verteutscht... [Strassburg, T. Rihel, 1619]
[35], 887, [22] p. illus. 37 cm.
Translated by Zacharias Müntzer.

NL 0421907 NjP CtY InU

Italian

Livius, Titus.
2239.9
Z3L5 Deche di Tito Liuio vlugare [sic]
1502 historiate. [Venetia, Per Bartholamio
f de Zani de Portes, 1502]
iii, [379] l. illus. 31cm.
429 woodcut illus., including some repetitions; the first page of each Decade with large woodcut and decorative border; initials
"Libro ... de la guerra punica ... composto dal ... meser Leonardo Aretino": leaf 362 verso -379.
Printed in double columns.

NL 0421909 CSt MH

Case
fY LIVIUS, TITUS.
672 Deche di Tito Liuio vulgare hystoriate.
.L 524 [Venetia, Stāpate p B.de Zāni, 1511]
iiii, [378] l. illus. (woodcuts) 32cm.
Woodcut and Giunta Press device on t.-p.; title and Giunta device in red. Initials.
Signatures: 4 l. unsigned, a-o[8] (a 1 wanting), p[10]; aa[6], bb-pp[8], qq[10]; A[6], B-Q[8] (Q 8 wanting)
Imperfect: t.-p. mutilated, first leaf of text (sig. a 1) and last leaf (sig. Q 8) wanting; wormholes.

NL 0421910 ICN MWiW-C MiDA

Livius, Titus.
Le deche di Tito Livio volgari, delle storie romane, cõ somma diligenza corrette, & d'infiniti errori emēdate, & nuouamente etiādio in molti luoghi ritradotte ... [In Venegia, Impresso per Vettor di Rauani, & Compagni, 1535]
[19], 528, 72 l. port. 21cm.
Imprint from colophon.
Printer's device at end.
"La quinta deca" has separate foliation.
Title within ornamental border.

NL 0421911 NNC CtY InU

Livius, Titus.
Le Deche delle historie romane di Tito Livio Padovano, tradotte nuouamente nella lingua toscana, da Iacopo Nardi ... In Venetia [nella stamparia degli heredi di Luc Antonio Giunti] 1540.
[4], 484, [1] l. 32cm.
Printer from colophon.
Giunta device on title-page and on verso of l. 484.

NL 0421912 NNC PPL

Livius, Titus.
KB [Ab urbe condita. Italian. Nardi. 1547]
1547 Le deche ... delle historie romane, tradotte
L5 nella lingua toscana, da Iacopo Nardi ... &
f nuouamente dal medesimo riuedute & emendate... In Venetia, Nella stamperia degli heredi di Luc'Antonio Giunti, 1547.
[22 (last blank)], 485 l. 31cm.
Printer's device on t.p. and verso of last leaf; initials.
I. Nardi, Jacopo, 1476-1563, tr.

NL 0421913 CSt PU CtY NN ICN CU

PA Livius, Titus.
6456 Le deche di T. Livio Padovano delle his-
A2 torie romane, tradotte nella lingua toscana,
1554 da M. Iacopo Nardi...& nuouamente dal medesimo gia la terza volta riuedute, & emendate; con le postille parimente ampliate nelle margini del libro, che dichiarano molti vocaboli delle cose vecchie, piu degne di cognitione... In Venetia, nella Stamperia de Givnti, 1554.
4 p.l., 38, 485 numb. l. 30 cm.
1.Rome - History. I.Nardi, Jacopo, 1476-ca. 1563, tr.

NL 0421914 IMunS MnCS CU MH

PA6456 Livius, Titus.
.N22 Le deche di T. Livio padovano delle historie romane, tr. nella lingua toscana, da M. Iacopo Nardi ... & nuouamēte dal medesimo gia la terza volta riuedute, & emendate ... Et appresso, la valuta delle monete romane, ridotta al pregio di quelle de tempi nostri ... la dichiaratione di tutte le misure ... Con la tauola de re, consoli, tribuni militari con la podesta consolare, & dittatori ... Aggiuntiui li nomi de pretori ... & interregi ... Venetia, Stamperia de Givnti, 1562.
[8] p., 34, 485 numb. l. 33½cm.
Printer's mark on t.-p. and at end; initials.
Errors in numbering of leaves.
Imperfect: leaves 8 and 11 of first group wanting; leaves 258 and 263 duplicated.
1. Rome—Hist.

NL 0421915 ICU OOC WU NcD CtY DLC

PA Livius, Titus.
6456 Le deche di T. Livio Padovano dell'istor-
N2 ie romane, divise in due parti. Tradotte in
1574 lingva toscana da M.Iacopo Nardi...Con le postille, che dichiarano secondo i nomi moderni, i paesi, le città, i fiumi, i luoghi, le monete e molte altre cose, degne d'esser notate, per intelligenza del lettore.... In Vinegia, al segno del seminante, 1574.
2 v. 21 cm. Paged continuously.
1.Rome - History. I.Nardi, Jacopo, 1476-ca.1563, tr. II.Sixteenth century books, 1574

NL 0421916 IMunS

Rare
PA
6456 Livius, Titus.
N3 Deche di Tito Livio Padovano delle historie romane, già tradotte da M. Iacopo Nardi, cittadino Florentino: & hora, oltra quello, che è nella seguente faccia notato, riuedute, corrette, accresciute de' sommarij a ciascun libro, & de gli anni della città, nelle margini d'esso, & del svpplimento della seconda deca, da M. Francesco Tvrchi, Treuigiano. Venetia, Givnti, 1575.
[4], 18, 537 l. 32 cm.
Translation of Ab urbe condita.
1. Rome--Hist. I. Nardi, Jacopo, 1476-ca. 1563, tr. II. Turchi, Francesco, ed. III. Title.

NL 0421917 LU WU

SPECIAL COLLECTIONS GONZALEZ LODGE
1586 Livius, Titus.
L76 Deche di T. Livio Padovano dell'istorie romane ... Tradotte da M. Iacopo Nardi ... Oue sono aggiunti li sommarij a ciascun libro, & molte confrontationi fatte con altri istorici del suo tempo, per M. Curtio Marinelli ... In Vinegia, Presso Bernardo Giunti, 1586.
2 v. ([67], 829 l.) 21cm.
From colophon: Appresso Camillo Franceschini, 1581.
Title-vignettes.

NL 0421918 NNC

PA Livius, Titus.
6456 Le deche di Tito Livio Padovano delle
A2 historie romane, tradotte in lingua tosca-
1734 na da M. Jacopo Nardi...E nuovamente rivedu-
Folio te, corrette ed accresciute da M. Francesco Turchi... Col supplimento della seconda deca, che manca all'historie medeme. Venezia, nella Stamperia Baglioni, 1734.
4 p.l., 679 p. 34 1/2 cm.
1.Rome - History. I.Nardi, Jacopo, 1476-ca.1563, tr. II.Turchi, Francesco, 16th cent., ed.

NL 0421919 IMunS

---

ar V Livius, Titus.
11242
Le deche di Tito Livio Padovano, delle Istorie Romane, tradotte nella lingua Toscana da Jacopo Nardi, e rivedute, corr., ed accresciute da Francesco Turchi. ... Napoli, A spese di A. Cervone, 1774-
v. 19cm.
Contents.--tomo 1. Libros 1-6.

NL 0421920 NIC CU

---

871 Livius, Titus.
L5.In Le deche delle istorie romane, tr. nella lingua toscana da Jacopo Nardi ... e riv., cor., ed accresciute da Francesco Turchi ... col supplemento della seconda deca ... Milano, 1799-1800.
10v. in 9.

NL 0421921 IU NN

Livius, Titus
Le deche di Tito Livio volgari, delle storie Roman... [Vinegia, Vettor di Rauani & compagni, 1805.

NL 0421922 InU

VOLUME 336

PA 6456 A2 1842 Livius, Titus.
Le deche di T. Livio, volgarizzamento del buon secolo, corretto e ridotto a miglior lezione dal P. Francesco Pizzorno... Savona, presso Luigi Sambolino, 1842-1849.
6 v. in 3. 19 cm.
Vol.5 has added t.-p.:La quarta deca di Tito Livio volgarizzata da Gioanni Boccaccio...(cf.Pref. of vol.5).
1.Rome - History. I.Pizzorno, Francesco,ed. II.Boccaccio, Giovanni, 1313-1375, tr.

NL 0421923 IMunS NjP

Livius, Titus.
... Delle deche di T. Livio Padovano, Dell' istorie romane, tradotte da M. Iacomo Nardi ... ove sono aggivnti li sommarii à ciascun libro, & i tempi particolari delle cose auuenute, & le confrontationi fatte con altri istorici del suo tempo per M. Curtio Marinello ... 2 parts Vinegia, 1581.
1 v. 21 cm.
Water-stained.

NL 0421924 CtY

Livius, Titus.
Historiae Romanae decades [Italian] Venice, Antonio de Bartolommeo da Bologna (Miscomini) I) [n.d.]; II) 1478; III) 11 Apr. 1478.
Hain-Copinger 10145; Goff L-252.

NL 0421925 CtY

Livius, Titus.
Historiae Romanae decades. [Italian] Venice, Octavianus Scotus, II) 28 June 1481.
Hain-Reichling 10146; Goff L-253.

NL 0421926 NNC ICN

Livius, Titus.
Historiae Romanae decades. [Italian] Venice, Andreas Torresanus, de Asula, et Socii, 13 Aug. 1485.
Hain-Copinger (+Add.) 10147; Goff L-254.

NL 0421927 MH IU NcD

Livius, Titus.
Historiae Romanae decades. [Italian] Rome, Apud Sanctum (Vitus Puecher) I) [n.d.] II) 20 July 1476; III) 30 Max 1476.
Hain-Reichling 10144; Goff L-251.

NL 0421928 MH CSmH

Livius, Titus.
Historiae Romanae decades. Italian. Venice, Joannes (Rubeus) Vercellensis, for Lucantonio Giunta, 11 Feb. 1493.
[382] l.; leaf [18] blank. woodcuts: illus., borders, publisher's device (in red) f°. 32.8 cm.
Leaf [1a] (t. p.): Deche di Tito Liuio vulgare historiate.
Some of illus. signed F or b.
"El libro chiamato De la guerra punica ... composto da ... Leonardo Aretino. prima in latino: poi in lingua materna": leaves [365b]-[381b]
Hain. Repertorium (with Copinger's Supplement) *10149. Brit. Mus. Cat. (xv cent.) v, p. 417 (IB.23157) Sander. Livre à fig. ital., 3997; Goff L-255.

Continued in next column

Continued from preceding column

1. Rome—Hist. I. Bruni, Leonardo Aretino, 1361-1444. De la guerra punica.
Incun. 1493.L55 Rosenwald Coll. 49-30819
—— —— Copy 2. 31.8 cm. Bookplate of L. S. Olschki.
—— —— Copy 3. 33.6 cm. L. C. copy imperfect: leaves [9], [18], [232], [233] and [382] wanting; a number of leaves, incl. t.-p., damaged and repaired. In old blind stamped pigskin binding, originally belonging to another book, with label on spine lettered: Specvlvm Ivris Ioan de Stina, and bookplate of Franciscus Hartman ab Hartmanstain, dated 1637.

NL 0421930 DLC CSmH MH ICN NcU NcD

Livius, Titus.
Historiae romanae decades. Venice, Iohannes Rubeus, second press, 10 Feb. 1493.
Microfilm copy, made in 1960 of the original in Vatican. Biblioteca vaticana. Positive.
Negative in Vatican. Biblioteca vaticana.
Collation of the original as determined from the film: [381] *l*.
Hain. Repertorium 10149; Proctor. Index 5133.
Sig.: 17 un- signed leaves, a^8-p^{10}, aa^8-pp^{10}, AA^8-P^7.

1. Rome--History. (Series: [Manuscripta, microfilms of rare and out-of-print books. List 17, no. 33])

NL 0421932 MoSU NcD NcU

PA6456 .M2 LIVIUS,TITUS.
...I libri della storia romana di Tito Livio tr.dal C.Luigi Mabil... Milano,D.Briola,1889-
v. 18cm. (Scrittori classici greci e latini nelle migliori traduzioni italiane)

1.Rome--Hist.

NL 0421933 ICU

PA 6456 .N3 1824 Livius, Titus.
La storia romana, recata in italiano da Jacopo Nardi, aggiunti i supplimenti del Freinshemio nuovamente tradotti da Francesco Ambrosoli. Milano, N. Bettoni, 1824-25.
7 v. (Biblioteca storica di tutte le nazioni. Classe prima: Storici latini)
#Rome--History.
(A)Nardi, Jacopo, 1476-ca. 1563.

NL 0421934 MoU

Livius, Titus.
Storia romana di Tito Livio. Milano, E. Sonzogno, 1886.
149 p. 16°. (Biblioteca Universale. No. 150)

NL 0421935 NN

---

xI378 L788s Livius, Titus.
Storia romana. Tradotta da Iacopo Nardi. Firenze, A. Salani [1925]
5 v. fronts. (Collezione Salani: I classici)

1. Rome--Hist. I. Title.

NL 0421936 RP

Livius, Titus.
... Storia romana, con cenni sull' autore ... Milano, Sonzogno [1933-
v. 18cm. (*On cover:* Biblioteca classica economica. [146-
At head of title: Tito Livio.

Translation of Ab urbe condita.
PA6456.S6 878.4 46-44396

NL 0421937 DLC

Norwegian

PC 1457 .S11 T5 1905 Livius, Titus.
... Rom's historie; udvalgte stykker oversatte af Valdemar Thoresen ... København, Kristiania, Gyldendalske boghandel, Nordisk forlag, 1905.
2 v. in 1. 20cm.

Contents.-I. Rom i kongetiden. -II. Republikkens aeldste tid.

1. Rome - Hist. I. Thoresen, Valdemar tr.

NL 0421939 MdBJ

Rumanian

PA6457 .R7 Livius, Titus.
Istoria romana de Titus Livins ... Publicata de Academia romănă ... București, Instit. de arte grafice "Carol Göbl" s-sor I. S. Rasidescu, -1915.
v. in 26cm.

I. Barbu, Nicolae, tr. II. Locusteanu, Nd., tr. III. Petrescu, I. S., tr. IV. Academia romănă, Bucharest. V. Title.

NL 0421941 DLC ICN MH

Spanish

Livius, Titus.
Las decadas de tito liujo [1-4]. Translated by Pedro Lopez de Ayala] Burgos, Andres de Burgos, May 24 1505.

NL 0421943 NNH

DG 207 L77 N3 1888 Livius, Titus.
Décadas de la historia romana, por Tito Livio. Traducidas del latín al castellano, por Francisco Navarro y Calvo. Madrid, Viuda de Hernando, 1888-89.
7 v. 18 cm. (Biblioteca clásica, 111-12, 115-16, 118, 121-122)

1. Rome - Hist. I. Navarro y Calvo, Francisco, tr.

NL 0421944 CU-S CU NIC

VOLUME 336

Livius, Titus.
Historiae Romanae decades [Spanish]
Salamanca [Printer of Nebrissensis 'Gramatica'] 15 Aug. 1497.
Hain-Copinger 10150; Goff L-249.

NL 0421945 NNC CSmH

Livius, Titus.
Las quatorze decadas de Tito Liuio, trasladadas agora nueuamente de latin en nuestra lēgua castellana. La primera, tercera y quarta enteras segun en latin se halla, y las otras onze segū la abreuiaciō de Lucio Floro. [Translacion q̄ dellas hizo Pedro dela Vega. Çaragoça, Imprimidas por G. Coci, 1520]
ccccxxxiii l. illus. 31 cm.
Engr. t. p. with large col. coat of arms of Charles I, King of Spain (Charles V, Emperor of Germany)
Red morocco binding; in gilt on both covers: Biblioteca Salvá.
Provenance: Ricardo Heredia (label with his monogram)
I. Rome—Hist. I. Florus, Lucius Annaeus. II. Vega, Pedro de la, 16th cent., tr. III. Title.

PA6457.S6V4 Rosenwald Coll. 65-59188

NL 0421946 DLC CtY LU NNH MB

*XfD .241 .1
Livius, Titus. Works. Spanish.
Todas las decadas de Tito Livio padvano, qve hasta al presente se hallaron y fveron impressas en latin, traduzidas en romançe castellano, agora nueuamente reconosçidas y emendadas, y añadidas de mas libros sobre la vieja traslaçion.
Vendese la presente obra en Anuers en casa de Arnaldo Byrcman, a la enseña de la Gallina gorda. Con privilegio. [1552]

3 p.ℓ., ccvii, lxxxv-ciii numb.ℓ., [2] p. 31cm. (fol.)

Title vignette: coat-of-arms.
Colophon: Acabose de imprimir ... en la ciudad ... de Argentina en case de Augustin Frisio, à costas de Arnoldo Birckmanno librero en el año ... de M. D. LII.
Bookseller's device on final page.
Translated by Pedro de la Vega, corrected and augmented by Francisco de Enzinas.

As with other copies, the present is bound in 2 volumes.
Ex libris: Debruyeres (signature); James Walker, M.D. (armorial bookplates)

NL 0421949 MB

*PA 6457 S7 1553
Livius, Titus
Todas las decadas de Tito Livio padvano, qve hasta al presente se hallaron y fueron impressas en latin, traduçidas en romançe castellano, agora nueuamente reconosçidas y emendadas, sobre la viejà translaçion, y añadidas de mas libros. [Colonia Agrippina, A. Byrckmann] 1553.
dcvii,lxxv-ciii ℓ.

Translated by Pedro de la Vega; revised by Francisco de Enzinas.

NL 0421950 CLU NNH

FILM 4296 AC Roll 83
Livius, Titus.
[Type II:] Todas las decadas de Tito Livio Padvano, qve hasta al presente se hallaron y fveron impressas en Latin, traduzidas en Romance Castellano, agora nueuamente reconoscidas y emendadas, y anadidas de mas libros sobre la vieja traslacion. Fendese la presente obra en Anuers en casa de Arnaldo Byrcman, a la enseña de la Gallina gorda. Con privilegio. 1553.
Microfilm.

NL 0421951 CU

3. Ab urbe condita-one or more books

Latin

PA6452 .B01M88
LIVIUS,TITUS.
Titi Livi Ab urbe condita liber I. Für den schulgebrauch erklärt von dr.Moritz Müller... Leipzig,B.G.Teubner,1875.
iv,164 p. 21½cm.

NL 0422003 ICU MA ViU MoU

PA6452 .B01H6
LIVIUS,TITUS.
Titi Livii Ab urbe condita liber I. Für den schulgebrauch erklärt von dr.Max Heynacher... Gotha,F.A.Perthes,1885.
[3],101 p. 21cm.

NL 0422004 ICU MoU

PA6452 .B01H61
LIVIUS,TITUS.
Titi Livii Ab urbe condita liber I. Nach text und kommentar getrennte ausgabe für den schulgebrauch von dr.Max Heynacher... Gotha,F.A.Perthes, 1885.
2 v. in 1. 21cm.
Contents.--1.abt. Text.--2.abt.Kommentar.

NL 0422005 ICU

Livius,Titus.
Titi Livi Ab urbe condita liber I. Livy book I. Text with indicated quantities by John C.Rolfe ... Revised ed. Boston, Allyn and Bacon, 1896.
iv,74 p. 18cm.

I.Rolfe,John Carew,1859- ed.

NL 0422006 MiU

PA 6452 .B1 1899
Livius, Titus.
Ab urbe condita, liber I, für den Schulgebrauch erklärt von Max Heynacher. 3., verb. Aufl. Gotha, F. A. Perthes, 1899.
98 p. (Bibliotheca Gothana, 32A)

#Rome--Hist.--Kings, 753-510 B. C.
Heynacher, Max, 1848-

NL 0422007 MoU

PA6452 .B1 1917
Livius, Titus.
Titi Livi Ab vrbe condita liber I. Edited with introduction, notes and vocabulary, by C. E. Freeman. Oxford, The Clarendon press, 1917.
198 p., 1 ℓ. incl. front.(map) 17cm.

I. Freeman, Charles Earle, d. 1921, ed.

NL 0422008 OCU PV PHC MiU

Livius, Titus.
...Ab vrbe condita, liber I; ed. with introduction, notes and vocabulary by C.E. Freeman... Oxford, Clarendon press [1939]
198 p.

NL 0422009 PHC

PA6452 .B2 1878
Livius, Titus.
Titi Livi Ab urbe condita liber II. Für den schulgebrauch erklärt von dr. Moritz Müller ... Leipzig, B. G. Teubner, 1878.
2 p.l., 160 p. 21cm.
Text in Latin.

1. Rome—Hist. I. Müller, Moritz, ed.

NL 0422010 ViU PU

PA 6452 .B2 1897
Livius, Titus.
Ab urbe condita, liber II, mit ausgewählte Abschnitten aus Liber III-VI, für den Schulgebrauch erklärt von Theodor Klett. 2., verb. und verm. Aufl. Gotha, F. A. Perthes, 1897.
128 p. (Bibliotheca Gothana, 29A)

#Rome--Hist.--Republic, 510-265 B. C.
Klett, Theodor, 1851-1905.

NL 0422012 MoU

PA6452 .B02M9
LIVIUS,TITUS.
Titi Livi Ab urbe condita liber II,für den schulgebrauch erklärt von dr.Moritz Müller... 2.,verb.aufl.von dr.Wilhelm Heraeus... Leipzig,B.G.Teubner,1909.
[3],160 p. 21½cm.

NL 0422013 ICU

PA 6452 .B3 1876
Livius, Titus.
Ab urbe condita, liber III, erklärt von Carl Tücking. Paderborn, F. Schöningh, 1876.
117 p.

#Rome--Hist.--Republic, 510-265 B. C.
Tücking, Karl, 1827-1912.

NL 0422014 MoU

Livius, Titus.
T. Livi ab urbe condita, liber III, ed. with introduction and notes by P. T. Jones ... Oxford, Clarendon press, 1914.
281 p.

NL 0422015 InU PHC PV

PA6452 B3B4 1948
Livius, Titus. Latin.
Ab urbe condita liber III; introduzione e commento di Giorgio Berzero. [1. ed.] Torino, G.B. Paravia [1948]
xxxi,220 p. (Scrittori latini commentati)

Bibliography: p.[xxx]-xxxi.

I. Berzero, Giorgio, ed.

NL 0422016 CU

Livius, Titus.
Ab urbe condita liber VI; für den schulgebrauch erklärt von Franz Luterbacher. Lpz., 1888.
101 p.

NL 0422017 PBm OCU

VOLUME 336

PA 6452 .B8 1889 Livius, Titus.
Ab urbe condita, liber VIII, für den Schulgebrauch erklärt von Ernst Ziegeler. Gotha, F. A. Perthes, 1889.
84 p. (Bibliotheca Gothana, 82A)

#Rome--Hist.--Republic, 510-265 B. C. Ziegeler, Ernst, 1849-

NL 0422018 MoU InU CU

PA 6452 .B9 1891 Livius, Titus.
Ab urbe condita, liber IX, für den Schulgebrauch erklärt von Ernst Ziegeler. Gotha, F. A. Perthes, 1891.
91 p. (Bibliotheca Gothana, 99A)

#Rome--Hist.--Republic, 510-265 B. C. Ziegeler, Ernst, 1849-

NL 0422019 MoU

Livius, Titus.
T. Livi ab vrbe condita liber IX; ed. with introduction and notes, by T. Nicklin ... Oxford, Clarendon press, 1910.
169, [1] p. 19cm.

I. Nicklin, T., ed.

A 11-526

Title from Leland Stanford Jr. Univ. Printed by L. C.

NL 0422020 CSt InU ODW PU

Livius, Titus
Ab urbe condita, liber IX. Edited, with introduction and notes, by T. Nicklin ... Oxford, Clarendon press, 1930
170p. 19cm.
"Impression of 1930. First edition, 1910"

NL 0422021 PV

Livius, Titus.
Ab urbe condita liber IX; by T. Nicklin... Oxford, Clarendon press [1910] Repr. 1935.
169 p.

NL 0422022 OCU

Livius, Titus.
Ab urbe condita liber XXI. ... Gotha, Perthes, 1862.
148 p.

NL 0422023 OCU

PA6452 .321 1873 Livius, Titus.
Titi Livii Ab urbe condita liber XXI. Für den schulgebrauch erklärt von Eduard Wölfflin. Leipzig, B. G. Teubner, 1873.
xxiv, 127, [1] p. $20\frac{1}{2}$cm.
Text in Latin.

1. Rome—Hist. I. Wölfflin, Eduard von, 1831-1908, ed.

NL 0422024 ViU AU GU MiU ODW NjP PLatS

PA6452 .B21 1880 Livius, Titus.
Titi Livii Ab urbe condita liber XXI. Für den schulgebrauch erklärt von Eduard Wölfflin. 2. aufl. Leipzig, B. G. Teubner, 1880.
2 p.l., 135, [1] p. $20\frac{1}{2}$cm.
Text in Latin.

1. Rome—Hist. I. Wölfflin, Eduard von, 1831-1908, ed.

NL 0422025 ViU MH

Livius, Titus.
Ab urbe condita liber XXI, für den schulgebrauch erklärt von F. Luterbacher. Gotha, A. Perthes, 1882.
[4] + 149 p.

NL 0422026 InU CtY

Livius, Titus.
Ab urbe condita liber XXI. ... Leipzig, Teubner, 1884.
126 p.

NL 0422027 OO InU CtY OU

PA6452 .B21T9 LIVIUS, TITUS.
Titi Livii [Ab urbe condita liber XXI. Für den schulgebrauch erklärt von dr. Karl Tücking... 3. verb. aufl. Paderborn, F. Schöningh, 1884.
118 p. 20cm.

NL 0422028 ICU

Livius, Titus.
Ab urbe condita liber XXI. ... 4. verb. aufl. Paderborn, F. Schoeningh, 1892.
116 p.

NL 0422029 OCU

Livius, Titus.
Ab urbe condita liber XXI. ... 5. verb. aufl. Gotha, Perthes, 1897.
146 p.

NL 0422030 OCU OCl

878.4 S 942 Livius, Titus.
Ab urbe condita, liber XXI. Leipzig, B. G. Teubneri, 1900.
iv, 130 p. map 22 cm.
(Griechische Und Lateinische Klassiker)

NL 0422031 MWAC OO

PA 6452 .C1 1907 Livius, Titus.
Ab urbe condita, liber XXI, für den Schulgebrauch erklärt von Franz Luterbacher. 8., verb. Aufl. Gotha, F. A. Perthes, 1907.
156 p. (Bibliotheca Gothana, 3A)

#Rome--Hist.--Republic, 265-30 B. C.
#Punic War, 2d, 218-201 B. C.
Luterbacher, Franz.

NL 0422032 MoU

PA6452 .B21L9 LIVIUS, TITUS.
Titi Livii Ab urbe condita liber XXI. Nach text und kommentar getrennte ausgabe für den schulgebrauch von Franz Luterbacher... 9. verb. aufl. Gotha, F. A. Perthes, 1910.
2 v. 21cm. (On cover: Bibliotheca gothana... 3b)
Contents.--1. abt. Text.--2. abt. Kommentar.

NL 0422033 ICU

PA 6452 B21 1914 Livius, Titus.
Ab urbe condita liber XXI; für den Schulgebrauch erklärt von Eduard Wölfflin. 6. Aufl. besorgt von Franz Luterbacher, mit einem Anhang über Hannibals Alpenübergang und einer Karte. Berlin, B. G. Teubner, 1914.
iv, 122 p. 21cm. (Griechische und lateinische Klassiker-Schulausgaben mit Anmerkungen)

NL 0422034 NIC

Livius, Titus.
Titi Livi Ab vrbe condita liber XXI. Ed. with introduction, notes, and vocabulary, by John Pyper. Oxford, The Clarendon press, 1921.
191, [1] p. incl. front., maps. 17cm. (*On cover:* Junior Latin series)

I. Pyper, John, ed.

21—10630

Library of Congress PA6452.C21 1921

NL 0422035 DLC OClJC

Livius, Titus.
Ab urbe condita liber XXI. Ed. with notes by John Pyper. Oxford, Clarendon press [1921. Repr. 1936].
191 p.

NL 0422036 OCU

Livius, Titus.
Ab urbe condita, liber XXI. Introd. e note di Lorenzo d'Amore. Torino, Editrice libraria italiana [1940]
xvi, 138 p. 20 cm. (Collezione di classici greci e latini)

1. Rome—Hist.

PA6452.C1 1940 [937] 878.4 49-31467*‡

NL 0422037 DLC

PA6452 .C1 1953 Livius, Titus.
Ab urbe condita liber XXI. Edited with introd., notes, and vocabulary, by John Pyper. Oxford, Clarendon Press [1953]
191 p. illus., maps. 17cm.

I. Pyper, John, ed.

NL 0422038 ViU

Livius Titius
Titi Livii Ab urbe condita liber xxii. Für den Schulgebrauch erklärt von Eduard Wölfflin. Mit einem kärtchen. Leipzig, B.G. Teubner, 1875.
vi, 99 p. 21 cm.

I. Wölfflin, Eduard, ed.

NL 0422039 PLatS InU CU ICU ViU MH RPB

VOLUME 336

Livius, Titus.
Ab urbe condita liber XXII, für den schulgebrauch erklärt C. Tücking. 2. verbesserte aufl. Paderborn, F. Schöningh, 1879.
121 p.

NL 0422040 InU

PA6452 .B22F9
LIVIUS, TITUS.
Titi Livii Ab urbe condita liber XXII. Med förklaringar af A.Frigell. Stockholm, P.A.Norstedt & söner, 1879.
[1], 104 p. 20½cm.

NL 0422041 ICU InU

PA6452 .B22T9
LIVIUS, TITUS.
Titi Livii [Ab urbe condita liber XXII. Für den schulgebrauch erklärt von dr. Karl Tücking... 3., verb. aufl. Paderborn [etc.] F. Schöningh, 1889.
121 p. 21cm.

NL 0422042 ICU CU InU

PA 6452 .C2 1891
Livius, Titus.
Ab urbe condita liber XXII, für den Schulgebrauch erklärt von Eduard Wölfflin. 3. Aufl. Leipzig, Teubner, 1891.
108 p.

#Punic War, 2d, 218-201 B. C.
#Cannae, Battle of, 216 B. C.
Wölfflin, Eduard von, 1831-1908.

NL 0422043 MoU

Livius, Titus.
... Ab urbe condita liber XXII, für den schulgebrauch erklärt von F. Luterbacher. 4. verbesserte aufl. Gotha, F. A. Perthes, 1897.
4+124 p.

NL 0422044 InU OCU

PA 6452 .C2 1904
Livius, Titus.
Ab urbe condita, liber XXII, für den Schulgebrauch erklärt von Franz Luterbacher. 6., verb. Aufl. Gotha, F. A. Perthes, 1904.
123 p. illus. (Bibliotheca Gothana, 17A)

#Rome--Hist.--Republic, 265-30 B. C.
#Punic War, 2d, 218-201 B. C.
Luterbacher, Franz.

NL 0422045 MoU

Livius, Titus.
Ab urbe condita liber XXII; ... Leipzig und Berlin, B. G. Teubner, 1905. Vierte auflage.
114 p.

NL 0422046 OCU

Livius, Titus.
Titi Livi [Ab vrbe condita liber XXII. Ed. with introduction, notes and vocabulary, by John Pyper. Oxford, The Clarendon press, 1919.
196 p. incl. front. (map) diagr. 16½cm. (Lettered on cover: junior Latin series)

I. Pyper, John, ed.

NL 0422047 MiU PHC OCU OO OC1JC NIC

PA6452 .B23 1883
Livius, Titus.
Titi Livi Ab urbe condita liber XXIII. Für den schulgebrauch erklärt von E. Wölfflin und F. Luterbacher. Leipzig, B. G. Teubner, 1883.
2 p.l., 99, [1] p. 21½cm.
Text in Latin.

1. Rome—Hist. I. Wölfflin, Eduard von, 1831-1908, ed. II. Luterbacher, Franz, ed.

NL 0422048 ViU NjP PBm

PA 6452 .C3 1894
Livius, Titus.
Ab urbe condita, liber XXIII, für den Schulgebrauch erklärt von G. Egelhaaf. 2., neu bearb. Aufl. von J. Miller. Gotha, F. A. Perthes, 1894.
84 p. (Bibliotheca Gothana, 23A)

#Rome--Hist.--Republic, 265-30 B. C.
#Punic War, 2d, 218-201 B. C.
Egelhaaf, Gottlob, 1848-1934.

NL 0422049 MoU

Livius, Titus.
Ab urbe condita, liber XXIII, für schulgebrauch erklärt von F. Luterbacher. 2. verbesserte aufl. Leipzig, B.G. Teubner, 1906.
4+103 p.

NL 0422050 InU OCU

PA 6452 B24 1901
Livius, Titus.
Ab urbe condita liber XXIIII; für den Schulgebrauch erklärt von H. J. Müller. 2. Aufl. Leipzig, B. G. Teubner, 1901.
121 p. map. 21cm.

I. Müller, Hermann Johannes, 1844-1912.

NL 0422051 NIC InU

PA6452 .B25 1879
Livius, Titus.
Titi Livi Ab urbe condita liber XXV. Für den schulgebrauch erklärt von dr. Hermann J. Müller ... Mit einem kärtchen. Leipzig, B. G. Teubner, 1879.
2 p.l., 104 p. map. 21½cm.
Text in Latin.

1. Rome—Hist. I. Müller, Hermann Johann, 1844-1912, ed.

NL 0422052 ViU InU

878 L5.V 1929 Classics Lib'y
Livius, Titus.
Titi Livi Ab vrbe condita liber XXV. Edited with introd., notes and vocabulary by W.D. Monro. Oxford, At the Clarendon Press, 1929.
viii, 183p. front., plates. 18cm.

I. Monro, W.D., ed. II. Title.

NL 0422053 TxU OCU CU

PA 6452 C5 1939
Livius, Titus
Ab urbe condita liber XXV. Ed. with introd., notes, and vocabulary by W. D. Monro. Oxford, Clarendon Press [1939]
vii, 183 p. illus.

Text in Latin.

I. Monro, William Douglas.

NL 0422054 WaU

Livius, Titus.
Ab urbe condita; liber XXV. Edited, with introd., notes and vocabulary by W. D. Monro. Oxford, Clarendon Press [1946]

183 p. illus. 17 cm.

First published 1929.

I. Monro, W D ed.

NL 0422055 CaBVaU

Livius, Titus.
...Titi Livi Ab urbe condita liber XXV, a cura di Francesco E.Martorelli. Torino, Paravia [1948]
178 p. 20½cm. (Scrittori latini commentati)

I. Martorelli, Francesco E ed.

NL 0422056 NjP

PA6452 .B26 1880
Livius, Titus.
Titi Livi Ab urbe condita liber XXVI. Für den schulgebrauch erklärt von dr. F. Friedersdorff ... Leipzig, B. G. Teubner, 1880.
3 p.l., 116 p. 21cm.
Text in Latin.

1. Rome—Hist. I. Friedersdorff, Franz, 1846- ed.

NL 0422057 ViU

ar W 29610
Livius, Titus.
Ab urbe condita liber XXVI. Hrsg. von Anton Stitz. Leipzig, G. Freytag, 1895.
viii, 89 p. illus., maps. 23cm. (Sammlung griechischer und römischer Klassiker. Ausgabe mit erklärenden Anmerkungen, 1)

NL 0422057-1 NIC OCU

PA6452 .B27C4
LIVIUS, TITUS.
...Ab urbe condita liber XXVII con introduzione e commento di Emanuele Cesareo. Torino[etc.]G.B.Paravia & c., 1929.
viii, 262 p. 20cm. (Half-title: Biblioteca scolastica di scrittori latini e greci con note)
Latin text.

NL 0422058 ICU CU

Livius, Titus.
... Ab urbe condita liber XXIX, für den schulgebrauch erklärt von F. Luterbacher. Leipzig. B.G. Teubner, 1893.
84 p.

NL 0422059 InU OCU

PA 6452 .C9 1896
Livius, Titus.
Ab urbe condita, liber XXIX, für den Schulgebrauch erklärt von Wilhelm Wegehaupt. Gotha, F. A. Perthes, 1896.
91 p. (Bibliotheca Gothana, A, 111A)

#Rome--Hist.--Republic, 265-30 B. C.
#Punic War, 2d, 218-201 B. C.
Wegehaupt, Conrad Wilhelm Gustav, 1845-

NL 0422060 MoU InU

VOLUME 336

PA6452 Livius, Titus. Latin.
B29P4 Ab urbe condita liber XXIX; a cura di
1948 Giuseppe Antonio Pelosi. [1. ed.] Torino,
G.B. Paravia [1948]
xi,132 p. (Scrittori latini commentati)

I. Pelosi, Giuseppe Antonio, ed.

NL 0422061 CU

PA6452 Livius, Titus.
.B30
1839 Titi Livi Ab urbe condita liber tricesimus
ad codicum manu scriptorum fidem emendatus ab
C. F. S. Alschefski. Berolini, F. Dümmler,
1839.
cvii, [1], 100 p. 21cm.

1. Rome—Hist. I. Alschefski, Karl Friedrich Siegmund, 1805–1852, ed.

NL 0422062 ViU CU InU ICU PU

Livius, Titus.
... Ab urbe condita liber XXX, für den
schulgebrauch erklärt von F. Luterbacher.
Leipzig, B.G. Teubner, 1892.
87 p.

NL 0422063 InU PBm

PA Livius, Titus.
6452 Ab urbe condita, liber XXX, für den
.C95 Schulgebrauch erklärt von Wilhelm Wegehaupt.
1895 Gotha, F. A. Perthes, 1895.
95 p. (Bibliotheca Gothana, 107A)

#Rome--Hist.--Republic, 265-30 B. C.
#Punic War, 2d, 218-201 B. C.
Wegehaupt, Conrad Wilhelm Gustav, 1845-

Spillan, Daniel, d. 1854.
Edmonds, Cyrus R.

NL 0422065 MoU MH

PA6452 Livius, Titus.
.B33
1839 T. Livii Ab urbe condita liber tricesimus tertius. Ad codicis Bambergensis et editionum antiquarum fidem denuo edidit et adnotationem criticam adiecit Ioannes Theophilus Kreyssig. Accessit varietas lectionum in libris XXX-XXXII et XXXIV-XXXVIII ex codice Bambergensi diligenter enotata. Misenae, Sumptibus et typis C. E. Klinkichtii et fil., CIƆIƆCCCXXXIX (1839).
cxxiv p., 2 l., [3]-400 p. 21½cm.
1. Rome—Hist. I. Kreyssig, Johann Gottlieb 1779–1854, ed.

NL 0422066 ViU PU InU ICU

PA6452 LIVIUS,TITUS.
.B01M9 Titi Livi Ab urbe condita liber I[-II] Für
den schulgebrauch erklärt von dr.Moritz Müller...
Leipzig,B.G.Teubner,1888.-
2 v. in 1. 21½cm.
Vol.1,2.aufl.

NL 0422067 ICU CLSU CtY PBm NIC OO NjP PPiPT

PA6452 LIVIUS,TITUS.
.B01N9 Titi Livi Ab urbe condita libri I et II. Scholarum in usum recensuit Robertus Novák. Pragae,
sumptus fecit I.Otto,1890.
[2],124 p. 21cm.

NL 0422068 ICU OOxM

---

ar W Livius, Titus.
29608
Ab urbe condita libri I-II.
Mit inleiding en aanteekeningen voorzien
door J. W. van Rooijen. Zutphen, W. J.
Thieme [Pref. 1917]
viii, 186 p. 23cm.

I. Rooijen, J P van, ed.

NL 0422069 NIC

2877 Livius, Titus.
.311
.444 Ab urbe condita. Libri I et II...
edidit Gustavus Meyer. Turici, Aedibus
O.Füssli [1944]
186 p. 19 cm. (Editiones helveticae.
Series latina,8)

I.Meyer, Gustav, 1850-1900, ed.

NL 0422070 NjP CU ICU

---

871 Livius, Titus.
L5.X Titi Livi Ab urbe condita libri I et II, prae-
1946 missis eorvndem librorvm Periochis, edidit Gustavvs Meyer. Turici, O. Füssli [1946]
186p. (Editiones helveticae, hrsg. von der
Konferenz der kantonalen erziehungsdirektoren ...
Series latina. 8)

I. Meyer, Gustav, ed.

NL 0422071 IU

Hum
PA Livius, Titus
6452
A3 Ab urbe condita libri I, II, XXI, XXII.
A7 With notes by Charles Anthon and Hugh Craig.
New York, Harper [c1877]
592p.

I. Anthon, Charles, 1792-1867, ed.

NL 0422072 FTaSU MH

Livius, Titus.
Titi Livi Ab urbe condita, libri I, II, XXI
et XXII. With notes by Charles Anthon and by
Hugh Craig. New York, Harper & brothers, 1879.

NL 0422073 MH

Livius, Titus.
Titi Livi Ab urbe condita, libri I, II,
XXI et XXII, with notes by Charles Anthon,
and by Hugh Craig. New York, Harper & brothers.
1882.
xxiii,592 p. 20 cm.

1.Rome - Hist. I.Anthon, Charles, 1797-1867, ed. II.Title: Ab urbe condita.

NL 0422074 KAS OCU ICU ViU MH

LIVIUS, Titus.
Ab urbe condita libri I,II,XXI,XXII. Adiunctae sunt partes selectae ex libris III,IV,VI.
Scholarum in usum edidit Antonius Zingerle. Ed.
altera,correctior. Vindobonae et Pragae,sumptus
fecit F.Tempsky,etc.,etc.,1887.

19 cm. Maps.
"Bibliotheca scriptorum Graecorum et Romanorum."

NL 0422075 MH OCU

Livius, Titus.
Titi Livi Ab urbe condita libri I, II, XXI.
et XXII; with notes by Charles Anthon and by
Hugh Craig. N.Y., Harper, 1890.
xxiii [25]-592p. 18cm.

NL 0422076 PLatS OCU

Livius, Titus.
Ab urbe condita libri I. II. XXI. XXII. Wien
und Prag, Verlag von F. Tempsky, 1892.
356 p.

NL 0422077 OCU InU

PA6452
.A327 Livius, Titus.
1896 T. Livii Ab urbe condita libri I. II.
XXI. XXII. Adiunctae sunt partes selectae ex libris III. IV. V. VI. VIII. XXVI.
XXXIX. Unter mitwirkung von A. Scheindler für den schulgebrauch hrsg. von Anton
Zingerle. 4. verb. aufl. Mit 3. karten
und 1 abbildung ... Leipzig, Verlag von
G. Freytag, 1896.
viii, 352 p, illus., 3 fold. col.
maps. 19cm.

Maps hinged at outer edge of back
cover.
Accompanied by commentary by A. M. A.
Schmidt (1903)

I. Zingerle, Anton, 1842-1910, ed.
II. Scheindler, Augustin, 1851- ed.

NL 0422079 OCU

---

ar W Livius, Titus.
29600
Ab urbe condita libri I. II. XXI.
XXII. Adiunctae sunt partes selectae ex
libris III, IV, V, VI, VIII, XXVI, XXXIX.
Unter Mitwirkung von A. Scheindler für
den Schulgebrauch hrsg. von Anton Zingerle.
6. Aufl. Leipzig, G. Freytag, 1903 .
vi, 352 p. illus., maps. 19cm.

NL 0422080 NIC

Livius, Titus.
Ab urbe condita libri I, II, XXI, XXII,
adiunctae sunt partes selectae ex libris III, IV, V,
VI, VIII, XXVI, XXXIX, unter mitwirkung von
A. Scheindler für den schulgebrauch hrsg. von
A. Zingerle. 7. durchgesehene aufl. ... Vienna,
F. Tempsky, 1906.
[8]+352 p.

NL 0422081 InU CU

Livius, Titus.
Ab urbe condita libri 1-4, 21-22, fur
den Schulgebrauch erklart von Dr. Karl
Tucking. Paderborn 1870-87.
6 books bd. in 1 vol.

NL 0422082 MA

Livius, Titus.
Ab urbe condita libri I–X. Textauswahl und Einleitung
von Erich Burck. [2. Aufl.] Heidelberg, F. H. Kerle, 1949.

235 p. fold. map. 21 cm. (Heidelberger Texte. Lateinische
Reihe, Bd. 7)

"Wissenschaftliche Literatur zu Livius": p. 22–23.

I. Burck, Erich, 1901- ed. (Series)

PA6452.A5 1949 59–27808

NL 0422083 DLC OCU

VOLUME 336

PA6452 .A4B9 1949 Livius, Titus.
Ab urbe condita libri I-X; Textauswahl, Einleitung und erklärendes Namenverzeichnis von Erich Burck. [3. Aufl.] Heidelberg, F. H. Kerle, 1949.
287 p. fold. maps. (Heidelberger Texte. Lateinische Reihe, Bd.7)

I. Burck, Erich, 1901- ed. Series.

NL 0422084 ICU CtY IEN CU MH

Livius, Titus.
... Titi Livi ab vrbe condita libri I, XXI, XXII; ed., with introduction, commentary and index, by Emory B. Lease ... New York, Boston [etc.] University publishing company, 1905.
lxxii, 438 p. maps, plans. 19cm. (Gildersleeve-Lodge Latin series)

I. Lease, Emory Bair, 1863-1931, ed.
5-13181
Library of Congress PA6111.G5L5 1905

NL 0422085 DLC TNJ PPLas MiU PU OCIND NNC OO ViU

PA6452 A3L35 1907 Livius, Titus. Latin.
Ab urbe condita, libri I, XXI, XXII; edited with introd., commentary and index by Emory B. Lease. 2d ed., rev. Boston, D.C. Heath, 1907.
lxxii,438 p. (Gildersleeve-Lodge Latin series)

I. Lease, Emory Bair, 1863- ed.

NL 0422086 CU NNC

Livius, Titus.
T. Livii Ab urbe condita lib. III–VI qvae svpersvnt in codice rescripto veronensi, descripsit et edidit Th. Mommsen ... Berolini, formis academicis, in commissis librariae F. Duemmleri, 1868.
2 p. l., 33-215, [1] p. 27½ x 22cm.
Cancels for p. 209-210, [213]-214 inserted (loose)
"Ex commentationibvs Regiae academiae scientiarvm berolinensis, a. MDCCCLXVIII."
"T. Livii Ab urbe condita lib. XCI qvae svpersvnt in codice vaticano palatino": p. [207]-215.
Issued also in Philologische und historische abhandlungen der K. Akademie der wissenschaften zu Berlin. Aus dem jahre 1868. Berlin, 1869, p. [31]-215.
I. Verona. Biblioteca capitolare. Mss. 40 (38) II. Vatican. Biblioteca Vaticana. Mss. (Cod. vat. palatinus 24) III. Mommsen, Theodor, 1817-1903, ed.
32-8851
Library of Congress PA6452.A5 1868 [937] 878.4

NL 0422087 DLC ViU MH CU NIC

PA 6452 B21 1837 Livius, Titus.
Ab urbe condita libri XXI et XXII. Mit Anmerkungen von Ernst Wilhelm Fabri, neu bearb. von Heinrich Wilhelm Heerwagen. Leipzig, J. L. Schrag [pref. 1837]
xvi, 428, xxxv p. 22cm.

I. Fabri, Ernst Wilhelm, ed. II. Heerwagen, Heinrich Wilhelm, ed.

NL 0422088 NIC

PA6452 .B21 1851 Livius, Titus.
Titi Livii Ab urbe condita libri XXI et XXII. Mit anmerkungen von dr. Ernst Wilhelm Fabri ... Neu bearb. von dr. Heinrich Wilhelm Heerwagen ... Leipzig, J. L. Schrag [pref. 1851]
xvi, 428, XXXV, [1] p. 22cm.
Text in Latin.

1. Rome—Hist. I. Fabri, Ernst Wilhelm, 1796-1845, ed. II. Heerwagen, Heinrich Wilhelm, ed.

NL 0422089 ViU ICU MH

PA6452 .B21 1852 Livius, Titus.
Titi Livii Ab urbe condita libri XXI et XXII. Mit anmerkungen von dr. Ernst Wilhelm Fabri ... Neu bearb. von dr. Heinrich Wilhelm Heerwagen ... Nürnberg, J. L. Schrag, 1852.
xvi, 428, xxxv, [1] p. 21½cm.
Text in Latin.

1. Rome—Hist. I. Fabri, Ernst Wilhelm, 1796-1845, ed. II. Heerwagen, Heinrich Wilhelm, ed.

NL 0422090 ViU CU PU PBm InU MH

PA6452 .B21T88 LIVIUS,TITUS.
Titi Livii Ab urbe condita libri XXI et XXII. Für den schulgebrauch erklärt von dr.Carl Tücking ... Paderborn,F.Schoningh,1870.
2 v. 21cm.
Contents.--hft.I. Buch XXI.--hft.II. Buch XXII.

NL 0422091 ICU MH

Livius, Titus.
Ab urbe condita, libri 21, 22... ed. by O. Riemann & E. Benoist. Ed. 4. Par., 1887.
379 p.

NL 0422092 OCU

Livius, Titus.
Ab urbe condita libri 21-22, ed. by M. S. Dimsdale. Camb., 1888-9. 2v. (Pitt. Press Series).

NL 0422093 MA CtY

Livius, Titus.
Ab urbe condita libri XXI et XXII. ... Pragae sumptus fecit I. Otto, 1891.
116 p.

NL 0422094 OCU

Livius, Titus.
Ab urbe condita libri xxi-xxiii. Textausgabe für den schulgebrauch von M. Müller. Leipzig, B.G. Teubner, 1898.
31+268 p. Plan. (Bibliotheca schultexte Teubneriana)

NL 0422095 InU

ar V 11249 Livius, Titus.
Ab urbe condita libri XXI, XXII texte latin publié avec une notice sur la vie et les ouvrages de Tite-Live, des notes critiques et explicatives des remarques sur la langue, un index des noms propres, historiques, et géographiques et des antiquités, d'après trois cartes et des illustrations d'après les monuments par O. Reimann et E. Benoist. 10. éd. rev. Paris, Hachette, 1904.
xxiv,379 p. illus., maps. 16cm.

NL 0422096 NIC PBm

Livius, Titus.
Titi Livii libri XXI et XXII, edited with introduction, notes, vocabulary, and supplementary themes, by Leo W. Keeler ... Chicago, Ill., Loyola university press, 1924.
2 p. l., 3-325 p. fold. map. 19½cm.

1. Rome—Hist. I. Keeler, Leo W., ed.
25-5200
Library of Congress PA6452.B21 1924

NL 0422097 DLC OCX OClUr

871 L5.X 1946[3] Livius, Titus.
Ab urbe condita libri XXI-XXII, praemissis eorundem librorum Periochis. Edidit Gustavus Meyer. Turici, O. Füssli [1946]
304p. 20cm. (Editiones Helveticae. Series Latina [no.]13)

Errata slip inserted.

I. Meyer, Gustav, ed. (Series)

NL 0422098 IU MH

PA6452 A706 1908 Livius, Titus.
Ab urbe condita, libri XXI-XXIII; met aanteekeningen en met opmerkingen over taal en stijl van T. Livius, door J.M.A. van Oppen. 3. druk. Kerkrade, N. Alberts, 1908.
vi,293 p.

I. Oppen, J.M.A. van, ed.

NL 0422099 CU

PA6452 B3 1926 Livius, Titus.
...Ab urbe condita libri. Libri XXI-XXIII. Belgrad, G.Koh, 1926.
1 p.l., 124p. 15cm. (Bibliotheca scriptorum graecorum et romanorum)

NL 0422100 PPiU

PA6452 .B21M6 Livius, Titus.
Ab urbe condita libri XXI-XXIII, praemissis eorundem librorum Periochis. Edidit Gustavus Meyer. Turici, in aedibus Orell Füssli [194-]
304 p. (Editiones Helveticae. Ser. Latina. 13)

NL 0422101 ICU

Livius, Titus.
Ab urbe condita libri XXI, XXII, XXIII, XXIV, XXX edidit A. Zingerle, für den schulgebrauch bearb. von P. Albrecht 2. aufl. Leipzig, G. Freytag, 1904.
[8]+336 p. Maps. Plan.

NL 0422102 InU CU

Livius, Titus
Titi Livi Ab urbe condita libri XXI-XXX. La troisième decade de Tite-Live. Nouvelle éd. a l'usage des classes publiée d'après les meilleurs et les plus récents travaux de la critique avec des notes explicatives ... par Henri Goelzer ... Paris, Garnier, 1910.
xi,828p. fold.maps.18cm.

NL 0422103 PV

Livius, Titus.
Ab urbe condita libri XXI-XXX; Textauswahl, Einleitung und erklärendes Namenverzeichnis von Erich Burck. Heidelberg, F.H. Kerle, 1949.
230 p. charts, fold. maps. (Heidelberger Texte. Lateinische Reihe, Bd. 11)
I. Burck, Erich, 1901- ed.

NL 0422104 ICU CU

VOLUME 336

PA 6452 B23 1840 Livius, Titus.
Ab urbe condita libri XXIII et XXIV; mit Anmerkungen von Ernst Wilhelm Fabri. Leipzig, J. L. Schrag ⌐Pref. 1840⌐
iv, 378 p. 22cm.
I. Fabri, Ernst Wilhelm, ed.

NL 0422105 NIC

Livius, Titus.
Ab urbe condita, libri XXIII, XXIV, XXV. Texte Latin. Publié avec une notice sur la vie et les ouvrages de Tite-Live, des notes critiques et explicatives ... par O.Riemann et E.Benoist. 6.éd. Paris, Hachette et cie., 1897.

NL 0422106 MH

PA6452 .B24M9 Livius, Titus.
Titi Livi Ab urbe condita liber XXIII⌐-XXV⌐ Für den schulgebrauch erklärt von dr. Herm. Johannes Müller ... Leipzig, B. G. Teubner, 1878-79.
2 v. map. 20cm.
1. Rome—Hist.

NL 0422107 ICU MWAC NIC

PA 6452 A7 1879 Livius, Titus.
Ab urbe condita libri a vicesimo sexto ad tricesimum. Recensuit Augustus Luchs. Berolini, Weidmann, 1879.
cl, 393 p. 23cm.
I. Luchs, August, ed.

NL 0422108 NIC ViU ICU OU InU CtY PBm MH

PA6452 .A7R5 LIVIUS,TITUS.
Titi Livii Ab urbe condita libri XXVI-XXX. Texte latin pub.avec une notice sur la vie et les ouvrages de Tite-Live,des notes critiques et explicatives,des remarques sur la languo,un index, des noms propres historiques et géographiques,un commentaire historique,des cartes et des plans, par O.Riemann...et T.Homolle... Paris,Hachette et c[ie],1889.
xvi,719,⌐1⌐ p. illus.(plans) 5 fold.maps. 15½cm.
1.Punic war,2d,B. C.218-201.

NL 0422109 ICU NcD

PA6452 A7 1893 Livius, Titus. (1893. Riemann; Homolle)
Ab urbe condita libri XXVI-XXX; texte latin, publié avec une notice sur la vie et les ouvrages de Tite-Live, des notes critiques et explicatives, des remarques sur la langue, un index, des noms propres historiques et géographiques, un commentaire historique, des cartes et des plans, par O. Riemann et T. Homolle. 3. éd. Paris, Hachette, 1893.
xvi,719 p. maps(4 fol.,part col.),plans. 16cm.
I. Riemann, Othorn, 1853-1901, ed. 8+1

NL 0422110 CSt

PA6452 B27F8 1947 Livius, Titus. Latin.
Ab urbe condita libri XXVII-XXVIII; door J.W. Fuchs en C. Zijderveld. Haarlem, J.H. Gottmer ⌐1947⌐
2 v. in 1. illus. (Roma; latijnse cursus voor gymnasia en lycea, 13)
Contents.- ⌐deel⌐ A. Tekst.- ⌐deel⌐ B. Hulpboekje.

NL 0422111 CU

PA6452 .B31 1855 Livius, Titus.
Titi Livi Ab urbe condita libri XXXI-XXXII. Til skolebrug bearbeidede af Eduard Flemmer ... Kjöbenhavn, O. Schwartz, 1855.
2 p.l., 123, ⌐1⌐ p. 20cm.
Text in Latin.
1. Rome—Hist. I. Flemmer, Eduard, ed.

NL 0422112 ViU

Livius,Titus.
... Titi Livi Ab vrbe condita libri XLI-XLV Caesar Giarratano recensvit. Romae, typis Regiae officinae polygraphicae, 1933.
1 p.l.,7-370 p. 25cm. (Scriptores graeci et latini ivssv Beniti Mvssolini consilio R.Academiae lynceorvm editi)
I.Giarratano,Cesare,1880- ed.

NL 0422113 MiU CU CtY ICU

---

871 L5.X 1937 Livius, Titus.
... Titi Livi Ab vrbe condita libri XLI-XLV. Caesar Giarratano recensvit. Impressio altera. Romae, typis Regiae officinae polygraphicae, 1937.
370p. (Scriptores graeci et latini, ivssv Beniti Mvssolini, consilio R. Academiae Lynceorvm editi)
Text-critical edition.
I. Giarratano, Cesare, 1880- ed.

NL 0422114 IU MH InU NBuU TNJ NcD DCU TxU OU NIC

PA6452 .B01S4 LIVIUS,TITUS.
...Livy,book I,with introduction,historical examination and notes by J.R.Seeley... 3d ed. Oxford,The Clarendon press,1881.
vii,199 p. 22cm. (Clarendon press series)

NL 0422115 MWelC PSC PU PBm PHC ICU MH MdBP NIC OCl OOxM OO ODW InU OCU

Livius, Titus.
Livy, book I with notes by J. Prendeville... Re-ed. and partly re-written by J. H. Freese... Cambridge, Deighton, 1892.
131 p.

NL 0422116 OU

Livius, Titus.
... Livy: book I. Edited by A. H. Allcroft ... and W. F. Masom ... 3d ed. London, W. B. Clive, University correspondence college press ⌐1896?⌐
144 p. 18cm. (On cover: The university tutorial series)
At head of title: Univ. corr. coll. tutorial series.
Text in Latin.
I. Allcroft, Arthur Hadrian, 1865-1929, ed. II. Masom, William Frederick, , joint ed. III. Ser.

NL 0422117 ViU OO

Livius, Titus.
... Livy, book I, by John K. Lord ... Boston, New York ⌐etc.⌐ Leach, Shewell, and Sanborn, 1897.
v, ⌐1⌐, 100 p. 18cm. (The students' series of Latin classics)
I. Lord, John King, 1848- ed.
12-36253

NL 0422118 DLC OCU ViU

Livius, Titus.
Livy, book I, by John K. Lord... Boston, New York, Leach, Shewell, and Sanborn, 1900.
100 p.

NL 0422119 OCU

PA6452 .B01L8 LIVIUS,TITUS.
...Livy,book I,by John K.Lord... Boston,B.H. Sanborn & co.,1902.
v,⌐1⌐,100 p. 18cm. (The students' series of Latin classics)

NL 0422120 ICU

PA6111 .C7L5 1903 Livius, Titus.
... Livy, Book I. Edited, with introduction and notes, by J. B. Greenough. Boston and London, Ginn & company, 1903.
xvii, 147 p. 19cm. (College series of Latin authors)
With this is bound HIS: Books XXI and XXII. Boston and London, 1903.
I. Greenough, James Bradstreet, 1833-1901, ed. II. Ser.

NL 0422121 ViU

Livius, Titus.
Livy, book 1; by J. K. Lord... Boston, Sanborn & co., 1921, c1896.
388 p.

NL 0422122 OClJC

PA6452 B1G56 1952 Livius, Titus. Latin.
Titus Livius, Book one; edited by H.E. Gould and J.L. Whiteley. London, Macmillan, 1952.
xxi,271 p. map. (Modern school classics)
I. Gould, H.E., ed.

NL 0422123 CU OCU

Livius, Titus.
Livy; book I and selections from books II-X, by Walter Dennison ... New York, The Macmillan company, 1908.
xxvii, ⌐3⌐, 344 p. front., maps. 18 cm. (*Half-title:* Macmillan's Latin classics; ed. by J. C. Egbert ...)
"Books of reference": p. xxv-xxvii.
I. Dennison, Walter, 1869-1917, ed.
PA6111.M3L45 1908 8—3145

NL 0422124 MH WaS DLC ViU PPLas PV MiU OO OCl PU MWAC

VOLUME 336

PA 6452 A5 1908 Livius, Titus.
Livy; book I and selections from books II-X, by Walter Dennison. New York, Macmillan, 1909 [c1908]
xxvii,344p. maps. 18cm. (Macmillan's Latin classics)

Bibliography: p.xxv-xxvii.

I.Dennison, Walter, 1869- ed.

NL 0422125 CLSU

Livius, Titus.
... Livy, book I, complete; books XXI and XXII, with omissions; and selections from books XXVI, XXVII, and XXX; introduction and notes by J. H. Westcott ... Boston, New York [etc.] Allyn and Bacon [1924]
3 p. l., v-xxxiii, 431 p. front., maps. 19½cm. (Allyn and Bacon's college Latin series)
Bibliography: p. xxxii-xxxiii.

I. Westcott, John Howell, 1858- ed.

Library of Congress PA6111.A7L5 1924 24-29962

NL 0422126 DLC MH PRosC OCl OClND PV PU

Livius, Titus.
Liby, book II with notes by J. Prendeville... Cambridge, Deighton, 1892.
154 p.

NL 0422127 OU

PA6111 .P5L5 bk 2 1901 Livius, Titus.
... Livy book II. Edited with introduction and notes by R. S. Conway ... Cambridge, The University press, 1901.
xxiii,[1],208 p., incl.maps(incl.front) 17cm. (Pitt press series. [Latin authors])
I.Conway, Robert Seymour, 1864-1933, ed.

NL 0422128 OCU OU

Livius, Titus.
Livy, book II; ed. with introduction and notes by R. S. Conway. Stereotyped ed. Cambridge, University press, 1902.
xxiii, 208 p. front., map. (Pitt press series)

I. Conway, Robert Seymour, 1864-1933, ed.

NL 0422129 NNC NcD OrU CU

Livius, Titus
Livy, book II. Edited by R. S. Conway ... Cambridge, University press, 1910.

xxii, 208p. 17cm. (Pitt press series)

NL 0422130 PV

Barnard D87L76 I21
Livius, Titus
Livy, Book II. Edited by R. S. Conway. [1st ed.] Cambridge [Eng.] University Press, 1912.
xxiii, 208 p. maps. (Pitt Press series)

"First edition 1901. Reprinted 1902 ... 1912."

NL 0422131 NNC IU

Livius, Titus
Livy, book II. Edited by Margaret Alford ... London, Macmillan and co., ltd., 1933.

xix,247p. 15cm. (Elementary classics)

NL 0422132 PV

874 OrU L76xxmas Livius, Titus.
Livy: book III. Ed. by W.F.Masom. London, W.B. Clive, University Correspondence College Press [1895]
160, 93p. illus. 18cm. (The University tutorial series)

I. Masom, W. F, ed. II. Series.

NL 0422133 OrU CaBVaU

Barnard D87L76 I212
Livius, Titus
Livy, Book IV. Edited for the syndics of the University Press by H. M. Stephenson. Cambridge [Eng.] University Press, 1890.
xvi, 142 p. (Pitt Press series)

I. Stephenson, Henry Major ed.

NL 0422134 NNC InU

PA6452 .B4 1925 Livius, Titus.
Livy Book IV. Edited by H. M. Stephenson. Cambridge [Eng.] University Press, 1925.
xvi,142 p. 17cm. (Pitt Press series)
"First edition 1890, reprinted 1925."
Text in Latin, introduction and notes in English.

I. Stephenson, H M ed. II. Ser.

NL 0422135 MiDW MoU NcU PSC OCU

PA6452 .B05W5 LIVIUS,TITUS.
...Livy,book V. Ed.for the syndics of the university press by L.Whibley... Cambridge[Eng.] The University press,1890.
xxxii,200 p. front.(fold.map) 17cm. (Pitt press series)

NL 0422136 ICU

874 L76xxal Livius, Titus.
Livy, book V. With notes and vocabulary, by M.Alford. London, Macmillan, 1892.
195p. illus. 15cm. (Elementary classics)

I. Alford, Margaret, ed. II. Series.

NL 0422137 OrU

Livius, Titus
Livy, book V. Edited for the syndics of the University press by L. Whibley ... Cambridge, University press, 1894.

xxxii,200p. 17cm. (Pitt press series)

NL 0422138 PV OCU

Livius, Titus.
...Livy, book V; ed., with introduction and notes, by L.Whibley... Stereotyped ed. Cambridge [Eng.] University press, 1898.
32,200 p. front.(fold.map) 16½ cm. (Pitt press series)

With this is bound his Livy, book VI... 1903.

I.Whibley,Leonard,ed. II.Main cd.(SC) III.Same entry(set)

NL 0422139 NjP CtY

Barnard D87L76 I26
Livius, Titus
Livy, Book V. Edited by Leonard Whibley. Cambridge [Eng.] University Press, 1910.
xxxii, 200 p. fold. map. (Pitt Press series)

I. Whibley, Leonard ed.

NL 0422140 NNC ODW InU

Livius, Titus.
Livy, book v; edited by J. E. Pickstone ... London, G. Bell & sons, ltd., 1938.
viii, 196 p. illus. (maps) 12 pl. on 6 l. 17cm. (*Half-title:* The Alpha classics; ed. by R. C. Carrington. [Latin authors])

1. Latin language—Chrestomathies and readers. I. Pickstone, J. E., ed.
A 40-2575

Cincinnati. Univ. Libr. for Library of Congress PA6112.A6L5 bk. 5 1938 [2]

NL 0422141 OCU IaU

PA6452 .B6 1892 Livius, Titus.
... Livy, book VI. With introduction and notes by H. M. Stephenson ... edited for the syndics of the University press. Cambridge [Eng.] At the University press, 1892.
xiv, 132 p. 17cm. (Pitt press series)
Text in Latin.

1. Rome—Hist. I. Stephenson, H. M., ed. II. Ser.

NL 0422142 ViU PV NNC

874 L76xxst2 Livius, Titus.
Livy, book VI. With introd. and notes by H.M.Stephenson. Stereotyped ed. Cambridge, University Press, 1897.
132p. 18cm. (Pitt press series)

I. Stephenson, Henry Major, ed. II. Series.

NL 0422143 OrU

Livius, Titus.
Livy, Book VI. With introduction, notes, and exercises by W. Cecil Laming. London, [etc.] Blackie & son, ltd., 1900.
210 p. illus. 19 cm.

NL 0422144 PV

VOLUME 336

Livius, Titus.
Livy, book VI; ed.by F.H.Marshall.. Cambridge [Eng.] University press, 1903.
34,171 p. front.,fold.maps. 16½ cm. (Pitt press series)
With his Livy, book V... 1898.
I.Marshall,Frederick Henry,1878-

NL 0422145 NjP OrU OCU OO ODW

Livius, Titus.
Livy, book VI: ed. by F.H. Marshall. Cambridge Univ. press, 1908
34+171 p. Map. (Pitt press series)

NL 0422146 InU

PA6452 .B6 1934
Livius, Titus.
Livy Book VI. Edited by F. H. Marshall. Cambridge [Eng.] University Press, 1934.
xxxiv,171 p. fold.maps. 17cm. (Pitt Press series)
"First edition 1903, reprinted...1934."
Text in Latin, introduction and notes in English.
I. Marshall, Frederick Henry, ed.

NL 0422147 MiDW MoU NcU

PA6452 .B9 1894
Livius, Titus.
... Livy, book IX. With introduction and notes by H. M. Stephenson ... edited for the syndics of the University press. Cambridge [Eng., At the University press, 1894.
3 p.l., [v]-xxvi, 152 p. 17cm. (Pitt press series)
Text in Latin.
1. Rome—Hist. I. Stephenson, H. M., ed. II. Ser.

NL 0422148 ViU OCU ODW

Livius, Titus.
..Livy, book IX; with introduction and notes by H.M.Stephenson.. Stereotyped ed. Cambridge [Eng.] University press, 1901.
26,152 p. 16½ cm. (Pitt press series)
I.Stephenson,Henry Major,ed. II. Main cd.(SC)

NL 0422149 NjP

PA 6452 B9 1906
Livius, Titus.
Livy; Book IX, edited by H. M. Stephenson. Cambridge, University Press, 1906.
xxvi, 152 p. 18cm. (Pitt Press series)
I. Stephenson, Henry Major, ed.

NL 0422150 NIC OO

Livius, Titus.
Livy, book IX; ed. with introduction, notes, etc. by W. B. Anderson ... Cambridge, University press, 1909.
xxiv, 276 p. incl. front. (map) 17½cm. (Half-title: Pitt press series)
I. Anderson, W. B., ed.
A 11-540
Title from Leland Stanford Jr. Univ. Printed by L. C.

NL 0422151 CSt NIC InU

PA 6452 B9 1934
Livius, Titus.
Livy, book IX; edited by W. B. Anderson. 3d ed., rev. Cambridge, University Press, 1934.
xxiv, 276 p. map. 18cm. (Pitt press series)
I. Anderson, W. B., ed.

NL 0422152 NIC

Livius, Titus, 59 B.C.-17 A.D.
Livy, book IX. Edited by W. B. Anderson. Third edition. Cambridge, at the University Press, 1953.
276p. map. 17cm. (Pitt Press Service)
Reprinted from 1928 edition.
I. Anderson, William Blair, 1877- ed.

NL 0422153 NcU

Livius, Titus.
Livy, book XXI. With introduction, notes, &c., by A. H. Allcroft and W. F. Masom. London, Clive [1889]
150 p. double map. (Univ. corr. coll. tutorial series)
I. Allcroft, Arthur Hadrian, 1865-1929. ed. II. Masom, William Frederick, ed.

NL 0422154 NNC

PA6452 .B21D58
LIVIUS,TITUS.
...Livy,book XXI. Ed.for the syndics of the University press by Marcus S.Dimsdale... Cambridge[Eng.]The University press,1890.
xv,[1],192 p. front.,fold.map. 17cm. (Pitt press series)
Latin text.
1.Punic war,2d.,B.C.218-201.

NL 0422155 ICU

Livius, Titus.
...Livy, book XXI. Adapted from Mr. Capes's edition, with notes and vocabulary by J. E. Melhuish ... London and New York, Macmillan and co., 1890.
2 p.l., vii-viii, 182 p. 15cm. (Elementary classics)
Series title also on cover.
Text in Latin.
"Notes": p.80-130.
1. Rome—Hist. I. Capes, William Wolfe, 1834-1914. II. Melhuish, J. E., ed. III. Ser.

NL 0422156 ViU NcD CtY OO

Livius, Titus
Livy, book XXI. Edited for the syndics of the University press by Marcus S. Dimsdale ... Cambridge, University press, 1894.
xv,192p. maps,17cm. (Pitt press series)

NL 0422157 PV

PA 6452 .B21 1896
Livius, Titus.
Book XXI. Adapted from Cape's edition; with notes and vocabulary by J.E. Melhuish. London, New York, MacMillan, 1896.
viii, 197 p. maps. 16 cm. (Elementary classics)

NL 0422158 OrU OO

DG7L76 I5
Livius, Titus.
... Livy, book XXI. Edited with introduction and notes by Marcus S. Dimsdale ... Stereotyped edition. Cambridge [Eng.] University press, 1899.
xvi, 224 p. incl. front. (map) 17½cm. (Pitt press series)
I. Dimsdale, Marcus Southwell, ed.

NL 0422159 NNC OO

PA 6452 .C1 1900
Livius, Titus.
Livy, book XXI, edited by A. H. Allcroft and B. J. Hayes. London, University Tutorial Press [190-?]
152 p.
#Rome--Hist.--Republic, 265-30 B. C. Allcroft, Arthur Hadrian, 1865-1929.

NL 0422160 MoU MiDW

Livius, Titus.
Livy: Book XXI. Edited with introd. and notes by F.E.A.Trayes. London, Bell, 1901.

NL 0422161 MH MB

Livius, Titus.
Book XXI, ed. by Dimsdale. Camb. Univ. Pr., 1902.
192p.

NL 0422163 OO

Livius, Titus.
Book XXI, adapted from Mr. Capes's edition, ... London, 1902.

NL 0422164 ODW

Livius, Titus
Livy, book XXI. Adpated from Mr. Capes's edition, with notes and vocabulary, by J. E. Melhuish ... London, Macmillan and co., ltd., 1907.
viii,191p. 15cm. (Elementary classics)

NL 0422165 PV

VOLUME 336

PA6452 .B21D6 LIVIUS,TITUS.
Livy. Book XXI,ed.by Marcus S.Dimsdale... Cambridge[Eng.]The University press,1914.
xv,[1],192 p. front.,fold.map. 17½cm. (Half-title:Pitt press series)
Latin text.

1.Punic war,2d,B.C.218-201.

NL 0422166 ICU OC1JC

878.4 T 218 Livius, Titus.
Livy, book XXI. With introduction and notes by M. T. Tatham. Oxford, At the Clarendon Press, 1916.
98,63 p. map 18 cm.

NL 0422167 MWAC

Livius, Titus.
Book XXI, Edited by Dimsdale. Cambridge University Press, 1921.
192 p.

NL 0422168 OCX

Livius, Titus.
Livy, book XXI; adapted from Mr. Capes's edition with notes and vocabulary by J. E. Melhuish. London, Macmillan and co., ltd., 1921.
197 p.

NL 0422169 OC1

PA6452 B21 1927 Livius, Titus
Livy: book XXI. Adapted from Mr. Cape's edition, with notes and vocabulary, by J. E. Melhuish. London, Macmillan, 1927.
xviii, 197 p. illus., maps (1 fold.) 15 cm. (Elementary classics)

NL 0422170 MeB

PA6111 .P5L5 bk. 21 1912 Livius, Titus.
Livy, book XXI; edited by Marcus S. Dimsdale ... Cambridge [Eng.] The University press [1912] Repr. 1928.
xv,[1],192 p. front., fold map. 17½cm. (Half-Title: Pitt press series. [Latin authors])
"First edition, 1888 ... revised edition, 1912; reprinted ... 1928."
I. Dimsdale, Marcus S., ed.

NL 0422171 OCU

Livius, Titus.
Livy, Book XXII, adapted from Mr. Capes's ed. with notes and vocabulary, by Melhuish. Lond., Macmillan, 1857.
215 p.

NL 0422172 OO

PA 6452 B22 1888 Livius, Titus.
Livy Book XXII. Edited with introd., notes, and maps by Launcelot Downing Dowdall. Cambridge, Deighton, Bell, 1888.
xi, 266 p. maps. 19cm.
I. Dowdall, Lancelot John George Downing, ed.

NL 0422173 NIC InU MH MA MeB OU

Livius, Titus
Livy, book XXII. Edited with introduction and notes by Marcus S. Dimsdale, M.A. ... Stereotyped ed. Cambridge, University press, 1896.
xvi,224p. 17cm. (Pitt press series)

NL 0422174 PV

PA 6452 .C2 1902 Livius, Titus.
Livy, book XXII, adapted from Capes's edition, with notes and vocabulary by J. E. Melhuish. London, New York, Macmillan, 1902.
213 p. illus. (Elementary classics)
"First edition, 1890 ... Re-issue with illustrations, 1902."
Text in Latin.
#Rome--History--Republic, 265-30 B. C.
#Punic War, 2d, 218-201 B. C.
(A) Capes, William Wolfe, 1834-1914, ed.
(A) Melhuish, John Edmund, ed.

NL 0422176 MoU

PA6452 .C2 1905 Livius, Titus.
Livy: Book XXII. Edited by John Thompson and F. G. Plaistowe. London, University Tutorial Press [1905?]
xii,136 p. 18cm.

I. Thompson, John ed.

NL 0422177 MiDW

PA6111 .P5L5 bk. 22 1889 Livius, Titus.
Livy, book XXII; edited by Marcus S. Dimsdale ... Cambridge [Eng.] The University press [1889] Repr. 1930.
xvi,260 p. front.(map) 17½cm. (Half-title: Pitt press series. [Latin authors])
"First edition, 1889. Reprinted ... 1930."
Half-title on back of frontispiece.
I. Dimsdale, Marcus S., ed.

NL 0422178 OCU

PA6452 B22 1933 Livius, Titus
Livy: book XXII. Adapted from Mr. Cape's edition, with notes and vocabulary, by J. E. Melhuish. London, Macmillan, 1933.
xxiii, 213 p. illus., maps (1 fold.) plan. 15 cm. (Elementary classics)

I. Capes, William Wolfe, 1834-1914.
II. Melhuish, J. E. ed.

NL 0422179 MeB PV

ar V 11251 Livius, Titus.
Livy; Book XXIII; edited by A. G. Peskett. Cambridge, University Press, 1917.
xxiv, 159 p. map. 18cm. (Pitt Press series)
I. Peskett, Arthur George, ed.

NL 0422180 NIC PV PHC MdBJ InU

PA6111 .P5L5 bk.23 1917 Livius, Titus.
Livy, book XXIII; edited by A. G. Peskett ... Cambridge [Eng.] The University press [1917] Repr.1937.
xxiv,159 p. fold.map. 17½cm. (Half-title: Pitt press series. [Latin authors])
"First edition 1917; reprinted 1937."
I. Peskett, Arthur George, ed.

NL 0422181 OCU

Livius, Titus.
Livy: book XXVI. Ed., with notes and vocabulary, by James Tierney. Dublin, Browne and Nolan, 1945.
xlviii, 246 p. 17 cm. (Browne & Nolan's Latin classics)

I. Tierney, James, ed.

A 48-5248*

Harvard Univ. Library for Library of Congress [1]

NL 0422182 MH OrU CU IaU LU

PA6452 .B27S8 LIVIUS,TITUS.
...Livy,book XXVII. With introduction and notes by H.M.Stephenson... Ed.for the syndics of the University press. Cambridge[Eng.]The University press,1890.
xxiii,140 p. plan. 17cm. (Pitt press series)

NL 0422183 ICU PV OO OCU ICU ViU IU NjP

PA6452 .B27 1896 Livius, Titus.
... Livy, book XXVII. Edited with introduction and notes by H. M. Stephenson ... Stereotyped ed. Cambridge [Eng.] At the University press, 1896.
xxiii, 140 p. map. 17cm. (Pitt press series)
Text in Latin.
1. Rome—Hist. I. Stephenson, H. M., ed. II. Ser.

NL 0422184 ViU PV OO MH NjP

PA6452 .B27 Livius, Titus.
Livy, book XXVII. Edited with introduction and notes by H.M. Stephenson. Cambridge [Eng.] University Press, 1909.
140p. 18cm. (Pitt press series)

I. Stephenson, Henry Major.

67-10-4AAvg 4

NL 0422185 NcU

Livius, Titus.
Livy, book xxvii; ed. by S. G. Campbell ... Cambridge [Eng.] 1913.
xxviii, 218p. fold. diagr., fold. map.

NL 0422186 IU PU InU

VOLUME 336

PA6111
.P5L5
bk.27
1913

Livius, Titus.
Livy, book XXVII; edited by S. G. Campbell ... Cambridge ⌊Eng.⌋ The U University press ⌊1913⌋ Repr. 1926.
xxviii, 218 p. fold. map, fold. diagr. 17½cm. (Half-title: Pitt press series. ⌊Latin authors⌋)
"First edition 1913; reprinted... 1926."
I. Campbell, Sidney George, 1875- ed.

NL 0422187 OCU PV

Barnard
D87L76
I63

Livius, Titus
Livy, Book XXVIII. By G. Middleton and A. Souter. Edinburgh, W. Blackwood, 1902.
xvii, 143 p. plates (1 col.) (Blackwoods' classical texts)
I. Middleton, George ed.

NL 0422188 NNC

Livius, Titus.
Livy, book xxx; edited by H. E. Butler ... and H. H. Scullard ... With a map and 3 plans. London, Methuen & co. ltd. ⌊1939⌋
ix, ⌊1⌋, 176 p. incl. map. pl. (3 plans) 17½cm. ⌊Methuen's classical texts⌋
"This edition first published in 1932."
I. Butler, Harold Edgeworth, 1878- ed. II. Scullard, Howard Hayes, 1903- ed.
Wisconsin. Univ. Libr. for Library of Congress ⌊2⌋ A40-2199

NL 0422189 WU PBm ICU OCU

Barnard
D87L76
I62

Livius, Titus
Livy, Book XXX. Edited by H. E. Butler and H. H. Scullard. 2d ed. London, Methuen ⌊1941⌋
vii, 144 p. map, plans. (Methuen's classical texts)
I. Butler, Harold Edgeworth, 1878- ed.

NL 0422190 NNC OC1W

Livius, Titus.
... Livy, books I. and II. Ed., with introduction and notes, by J. B. Greenough. Boston and London, Ginn & company, 1891.
xvii, 270 p. 19cm. (College series of Latin authors)
I. Greenough, James Bradstreet, 1833-1901, ed.
Library of Congress 12-36250

NL 0422191 DLC CtY OCU OC1 OC1W MH MiU PSC MiU OO

EducT 1035.433.893.5

Livius, Titus.
Livy. Books I. and II. Edited with introduction and notes, by J.B.Greenough. Boston, etc., Ginn & co., 1893.
"College series of Latin authors."

NL 0422192 MH

Livius, Titus.
Livy, Books 1 and 2, edited by Greenough. Boston, Ginn and co., 1895, c1891.
270 p.

NL 0422193 OC1ND MH

PA
6452
.B1
1896

Livius, Titus.
Livy, books I. and II. Edited, with introduction and notes, by J. B. Greenough. Boston and London, Ginn & company, 1896.
232 p. (College series of Latin authors)
(A)Greenough, James Bradstreet, 1833-1901.

NL 0422194 MoU OCU

PA6452
B1
1897

Livius, Titus
Livy: books I. and II. Edited, with introduction and notes, by J. B. Greenough. Boston, Ginn, 1897.
xvii, 270 p. 19 cm. (College series of Latin authors)
I. Greenough, James Bradstreet, 1833-1901, ed.

NL 0422195 MeB OCU

Livius, Titus.
Livy, Books I. and II. Edited, with introduction and notes, by J. B. Greenough. Boston, Ginn & Co., 1902.
xvii, 232p. 19cm.
At head of title: College series of Latin authors
I. Greenough, James Bradsteet, 1833-1901., ed.

NL 0422196 NcU InU

PA6452
.A3G7
1903

Livius, Titus.
... Livy, books I. and II. Edited, with introduction and notes, by J. B. Greenough. Boston and London, Ginn & company, 1903.
xvii, 270 p. 19cm. (College series of Latin authors)
I. Greenough, James Bradstreet, 1833-1901, ed.

NL 0422197 MB MH

PA
6452
A3G81

Livius, Titus.
Livy, books I, II, XXI and XXII. Edited, with introd. and notes, by J. B. Greenough. Boston, Ginn, 1902 ⌊c1891-93⌋
2 v. in 1. 19cm. (College series of Latin authors)
Half title; each vol. has separate t.p. Books XXI and XXII edited by J. B. Greenough and Tracy Peck.

NL 0422198 NIC RPB

Livius, Titus.
Books I-V, with notes by J. Prendeville, ... London, 1892-1903.
5 v.

NL 0422199 ODW

Livius, Titus
Livy, books 1-10; with introduction...Oxford, 1871.
8°

NL 0422200 NN NcU CtY ViLxW OO MiU MB CU

PA
6452
.B1
1874

Livius, Titus.
Livy, books I-X. With introd., historical examination, and notes by J. R. Seeley. Book I. 2d ed. Oxford, Clarendon Press, 1874.
vii, 199 p. 23 cm. (Clarendon Press series)
No more published.
I. Seeley, Sir John Robert, 1834-1895.

NL 0422201 DCU OCH CtY CU OU NcU MiU MH OCU NcD

878.4
W 524

Livius, Titus.
Livy, books I, XXI, and XXII. With introduction and notes by J.H. Westcott. Boston, Allyn and Bacon ⌊c1890⌋
xxxiv, 429 p. 19 cm. (College Latin Series)
I. Title.

NL 0422202 MWAC MH OCU MiU NjP OC1

PA6452
A3W38
1891

Livius, Titus. Latin.
Livy, books I., XXI., and XXII; with introd. and notes by John Howell Westcott. Boston, Allyn and Bacon, 1891.
xxvii, 399 p. map.
Bibliography: p.xxvi-xxvii.
I. Westcott, John Howell, 1858- ed.

NL 0422203 CU TNJ NjP ViU MH OCX NN OO OCU

PA6452
B1
1890

Livius, Titus
⌊Ab urbe condita liber I⌋
Livy: books I., XXI., and XXII. With introduction and notes, by John Howell Westcott. Boston, Allyn and Bacon, 1895 ⌊c1890⌋
xxviii, 399 p. maps, plans. 19 cm. (Allyn and Bacon's college Latin series)
At head of title: Libri I., XXI., XXII.
I. Westcott, John Howell, 1858-1942, ed. II. Livius, Titus. Ab urbe condita libri XXI-XXII.

NL 0422204 MeB

Livius, Titus.
Livy. Books I, XXI, XXII edited, with introduction and notes, by J. B. Greenough. Boston, Ginn & Company, Publishers, 1900.
232 p. O.

NL 0422205 NcD

PA6111
.A7L5
1904

Livius, Titus.
... Livy. Books I, XXI, and XXII; with introduction and notes by J. H. Westcott ... Rev. ed. Boston and Chicago, Allyn and Bacon ⌊°1904⌋
xxxiv, 429 p. incl. front. maps, plan. 19 cm. (Allyn and Bacon's college Latin series)
Bibliography: p. xxxii-xxxiv.
I. Westcott, John Howell, 1858- ed.
PA6111.A7L5 1904 4-22259

NL 0422206 DLC OC1W OC1ND ODW OO

VOLUME 336

LT PA6452 1904 .W4 **Livius, Titus.**
... Livy. Books I, XXI, and XXII; with introduction and notes by J. H. Westcott ... Rev. ed. Boston and Chicago, Allyn and Bacon [c1904]
1p.l.,211p. maps, plan. 19cm. (Allyn and Bacon's college Latin series)

NL 0422207 NNU-W NcD

Livius, Titus.
... Livy, books I, XXI and XXII; with explanatory notes and a vocabulary by Thomas Chase ... Rev. by Benjamin W. Mitchell ... New York, Hinds, Noble & Eldredge [c1905]
xi, 13-496 p. 19 cm. (Chase & Stuart's new classical series)

I. Chase, Thomas, 1827-1892. II. Mitchell, Benjamin Wiestling, 1861-

PA6111.C5L5 1905 5—28167

NL 0422208 DLC PV

Livius, Titus.
... Livy, books I, XXI, and XXII, with brief introduction and commentary and numerous illustrations, by Emory B. Lease ... Boston, New York [etc.] D. C. Heath & company [c1914]
xxxviii, 352 p. illus., plates, maps, plans. 19cm. (Gildersleeve-Lodge Latin series)
"A briefer edition of my 'Livy'."—Pref.

I. Lease, Emory Bair, 1863-1931, ed.

14—10635

Library of Congress

NL 0422209 DLC TNJ LU PROSC ODW OCl OClND PHC MB

PA6111 .C5L5 1925 Livius, Titus.
... Livy, books I, XXI, and XXII; with explanatory notes and vocabulary by Thomas Chase ... Rev. by Benjamin W. Mitchell ... New York, Noble & Noble, [c1925]
xi, 13-496 p. 19cm. (Chase & Stuart's new classical series)
Text in Latin.

I. Chase, Thomas, 1827-1892. II. Mitchell, Benjamin Wiestling, 1861- III. Ser.

NL 0422210 ViU CU OCl

Livius, Titus.
Livy. Books 2, 3. Edited with introductions and notes by H.M. Stephenson. London,1882.

NL 0422211 MWelC NIC OO MH ODW

Barnard D87L96 I33 **Livius, Titus**
Livy, Books II. and III. Edited with introduction and notes by Rev. H. M. Stephenson. London, New York, Macmillan, 1886.
xxviii, 299 p. (Macmillan's school class books)

I. Stephenson, Henry Major ed.

NL 0422212 NNC OU PV ICU

Livius, Titus.
Books II and III; ed. with introd. and notes by H. M. Stephenson. London, Macmillan and co., 1897.
26+299 p. (Classical series)

NL 0422213 InU

PA6452 .B2 1882 **Livius, Titus.**
Livy, books II. and III. Edited with introduction and notes, by the Rev. H. M. Stephenson ... London, Macmillan and co. [1882] Repr. 1911.
xxviii, 299 p. 17cm. (On cover: Macmillan's school class books)
"First edition 1882; reprinted ... 1911."

I. Stephenson, H. M., ed.

NL 0422214 OCU

PA6452 .A5C6 LIVIUS,TITUS.
...Livy,books V,VI,and VII from the war against Veii to the beginning of the Samnite wars,ed.with notes by A.R.Cluer... Oxford, The Clarendon press,1881.
xi,285 p. 17cm. (Half-title:Clarendon press series)

NL 0422215 ICU MH MA

Livius, Titus.
Livy, books V, VI, and VII; with introduction and notes by A.R. Cluer ... New ed., revised by P.E. Matheson ... Oxford, At the Clarendon press, 1889.
228, 147 p. (Clarendon press series)

1. Rome - Hist.

NL 0422216 TxHU PV NjP

---

878 L5.V 1904 LIVIUS, TITUS
... Livy; books V, VI, and VII, with introduction and notes, by A.R. Cluer ... New ed., rev. by P.E. Matheson ... Oxford, The Clarendon press, 1904.
2v. in 1. fold. map. 17cm. (Clarendon press series)

Contents.- pt.I.- Introduction and text.- pt. II. Notes.

I. Cluer, A R ed.
II. Matheson, Percy Ewing, 1859- ed.

NL 0422217 TxU NIC ODW OCl OO InU PV PU PSC

PA6452 B21 1878 Livius, Titus.
Books XXI and XXII. Hannibal's first campaign in Italy, ed. with introductions, notes, appendices, and maps, by W.W. Capes. London and New York, Macmillan [1878]
1v, 327 p. maps. 17cm.
Text in Latin.

I. Capes, William Wolfe, 1834-1914, ed.

NL 0422218 CoU

Livius, Titus.
Books 21 and 22. Hannibal's first campaign in Italy. Ed. with introductions, ... W. W. Capes. London, Macmillan, 1879.
327 p.

NL 0422219 OClW MH OCU

PA6452 B21 1880 **Livius, Titus**
Livy: Books XXI. and XXII. Hannibal's first campaign in Italy. Edited, with introduction, notes, appendices, and maps, by W. W. Capes. London, Macmillan, 1880.
lv, 327 p. 17 cm. (Macmillan's school class books)

I. Capes, William Wolfe, 1834-1914, ed.

NL 0422220 MeB MH MWelC MB

PA2099 .L8C2 Livius,Titus.
Livy,books XXI.and XXII. Hannibal's first campaign in Italy. Ed.with introductions,notes, appendices,and maps,by the Rev.W.W.Capes... London,1881.
lv,[1],327p. front.,2 double maps. 17cm. (On cover:Macmillan's school class books)

NL 0422221 ICU

Livius, Titus.
Livy, books XXI. and XXII. Hannibal's first campaign in Italy. Edited with introductions, notes, appendices, and maps, by the Rev. W. W. Capes ... London, Macmillan and co., 1883.
lv, [1], 327 p. 3 maps, incl. front. 17cm. [Classical series]
Text in Latin.
On cover: Macmillan's school class books.
I. Capes, William Wolfe, 1834-1914, ed. II. Title: Hannibal's first campaign in Italy. III. Ser. IV. Ser.

NL 0422222 ViU RPB PSC

Livius, Titus.
Livy, books XXI. and XXII. Hannibal's first campaign in Italy. Edited with introductions, notes, appendices, and maps, by the Rev. W. W. Capes ... London and New York, Macmillan and co., 1887.
lv, [1], 327 p. 3 maps (incl. front.) 17cm. [Classical series]
On cover: Macmillan's school class books.
Text in Latin.
I. Capes, William Wolfe, 1834-1914, ed. II. Title: Hannibal's first campaign in Italy. III. Ser. IV. Ser.

NL 0422223 ViU NNC RPB

Livius, Titus.
Livy, books21 [&] 22; ed. by M.S.Dimsdale. Cambridge,[England] 1889-90. [2v.] (Pitt press series)

NL 0422224 MWelC

Gn240 e878d Livius, Titus.
Livy, books XXI.and XXII. Hannibal's first campaign in Italy. Ed.with introductions,notes, appendices,and maps, by the Rev. W.W.Capes ... London,and New York,Macmillan and co.,1889.
lv,[1],327p. front.,2 double maps. 17cm. (On cover: Macmillan's school class books)

I.Capes, William Wolfe, 1834-1914, ed. (stamp) x.ser.

NL 0422225 CtY CU OO OCl MH

Livius, Titus.
... Livy, books XXI and XXII; edited on the basis of Wölfflin's edition with introduction and maps, by John K. Lord ... Text edition. Boston and New York, Leach, Shewell, & Sanborn [c1890]
1 p. l., xxii-xxv, 145 p. 17½cm. (The students' series of Latin classics)

I. Lord, John King, 1848-1926, ed.

12-36255

Library of Congress PA6111.S8L5 1890 a

NL 0422226 DLC CU MiU OO NIC

Livius, Titus.
... Livy, books XXI and XXII: edited on the basis of Wolfflin's edition with introduction and maps, by John K. Lord ... Text edition. New York, Shewell and Sanborn [c1890]
1 p.l., xxii, xxv, 145 p. 17.5 cm (The students' series of Latin classics)
I. Lord, John King, 1848-1926, editor.

NL 0422227 PV

VOLUME 336

Livius, Titus.
... Livy, books xxi and xxii; ed. on the basis of Wölfflin's edition with introduction and maps, by John K. Lord ... Boston and New York, Leach, Shewell, & Sanborn, 1891.
xxv, 388 p. 3 fold. maps (incl. front.) plan. 18cm. (The students' series of Latin classics)

I. Lord, John King, 1848– ed.
Library of Congress 12—36254

NL 0422228 DLC MH ViU OClW OCU

PA6111 .S8L45 1892 Livius, Titus.
... Livy, books XXI and XXII; ed. on the basis of Wölfflin's edition with introduction and maps, by John K. Lord ... Boston and New York, Leach, Shewell & Sanborn, 1892.
xxv,388 p. 17½cm. (The students' series of Latin classics)
Text in Latin.

I. Lord, John King, 1848– ed. II. Ser.

NL 0422229 ViU OO MH

Livius, Titus.
... Livy, books xxi. and xxii. Edited, with introduction and notes, by J. B. Greenough ... and Tracy Peck ... Boston and London, Ginn & company, 1893.
xiv, 232 p. 19cm. (College series of Latin authors)

I. Greenough, James Bradstreet, 1833-1901, ed. II. Peck, Tracy, 1838-1921, joint ed.
Library of Congress PA6111.C7L6 1893 12-36251
Copyright 1893: 38176 (a26g1)

NL 0422230 DLC PPD PV MiU OCU OO PSC ViU

Livius, Titus.
Livy, books XXI and XXII. Hannibal's first campaign in Italy; ed. with introd., notes, appendices and maps, by W.W. Capes. London, 1894.
327 p.

NL 0422231 PBm

Livius, Titus.
Books 21 and 22, ed. on basis of Woelfflin's edition ... Bost., Leach, 1895.
388 p.

NL 0422232 OO

Livius, Titus.
Livy, books XXI and XXII. Edited ... by J. B. Greenough... and Tracy Peck... Boston, and London Ginn and co., c1893, Repr. 1896.
149 p.

NL 0422233 OCU

Livius, Titus.
... Livy, books XXI and XXII: edited on the basis of Wölfflin's edition with introduction and maps, by John K. Lord ... Boston and New York, Leach, Shewell, & Sanborn, 1897.
xxv, 388 p. 3 fold. maps (incl. front.) plan. 18 cm. (The students' series of Latin classics)

NL 0422234 PV

Livius, Titus.
Livy, books XXI and XXII, edited on the basis of Woelfflin's edition... Text edition... Boston, Sanborn & co., 1900.
388 p.

NL 0422235 OCU

Livius, Titus.
Livy, books xxi and xxii, edited with introduction and notes by J. B. Greenough and Tracy Peck. Boston, Ginn, 1902.
232 p. 19 cm. (College series of Latin authors)

NL 0422236 ViLxW InU

Livius, Titus.
Books XXI and XXII: Hannibal's first campaign in Italy; ed. with introd. notes, appendices and maps, by W.W. Capes. London, Macmillan, 1902.
55+1+327 p. Maps. (Classical series)

NL 0422237 InU

PA6111 .C7L5 1903 Livius, Titus.
... Livy, books XXI. and XXII. Edited, with introduction and notes, by J. B. Greenough ... and Tracy Peck ... Boston and London, Ginn & company, 1903.
1 p. l., [v]-xiv, 232 p. 19cm. (College series of Latin authors)
With his Book I. Boston and London, 1903.

I. Greenough, James Bradstreet, 1833-1901, ed. II. Peck, Tracy, 1838-1921, joint ed. III. Ser.

NL 0422238 ViU MWAC

Livius, Titus.
Books XXI and XXII; ed. on the basis of Wölfflin's edition with introduction and maps by J.K. Lord. Boston, 1905.
25+388. Maps. (Students' series of Latin classics)

NL 0422239 InU MB NN OCl

Livius, Titus.
Books 21 and 22. ... London, Macmillan, 1914.
237 p.

NL 0422240 OClJC

Livius, Titus.
Livy, books XXi and XXii; edited on the basis of Wölfflin's edition with introduction and maps by J. K. Lord. Boston, Benj. H. Sanborn, 1921, c1890.
388 p.

NL 0422241 OClUr

Livius, Titus.
Titi Livii libri xxi et xxii, edited with introduction, notes, vocabulary, and supplementary themes, by Leo W. Keeler ... Rev. ed. Chicago, Ill., Loyola university press, 1925.
2 p. l., 3-326 p. fold. map. 19½ cm.

1. Rome—Hist. I. Keeler, Leo William, 1890-1937, ed.
PA6452.C1 1925 25—21794

NL 0422242 DLC

Livius, Titus.
Livy; books 21, 22, and 23. with notes by M.T. Tatham... Oxford, Clarendon press, 1886.
375 p.

NL 0422243 OU CtY MWelC

Livius, Titus.
Livy, books XXI, XXII, and XXIII; with introduction and notes by M.T. Tatham ... 2d ed. Oxford, At the Clarendon press, 1889.
251, 167 p. maps (part fold.) (Clarendon press series)

1. Rome - Hist.

NL 0422244 TxHU MeB

PA6452 .A7T2 1895 LIVIUS,TITUS.
...Livy,books XXI,XXII,and XXIII with introduction and notes by M.T.Tatham... 2d ed. Oxford,The Clarendon press,1895.
2 v.in 1. fold.map. 17½cm. (Clarendon press series)
Latin text.
Contents.--pt.I.Introduction and text.--pt.II. Notes,appendix,etc.

NL 0422245 ICU NjP NIC OCU CtMW InU

LIVIUS, Titus,
Livy, books XXI - XXIV. With short English notes for the use of schools. Oxf.,etc. 1877.
32°.
(The OXFORD pocket classics.- Texts with short notes.)

NL 0422246 MH ViU

Livius, Titus.
Livy, books xxiii and xxiv; edited with introduction and notes by G. C. Macaulay ... London, Macmillan and co., 1885.
xxxv, 215 p. front., double map. 17cm. (Macmillan's classical series for colleges and schools)
On cover: Macmillan's school class books.

I. Macaulay, George Campbell, 1852-1915, ed.
12-36423 Revised
Library of Congress PA6112.M3L5 1885

NL 0422247 DLC OU ODW

PA 6452 .B23 1888 Livius, Titus.
Livy, books XXIII and XXIV; edited with introduction and notes by G. C. Macaulay. London, Macmillan and New York, 1888.
xxxv, 215 p. front., double map. (Macmillan's classical series for colleges and schools)
On cover: Macmillan's school class books.

I. Macaulay, George Campbell, 1852-1915, ed.

NL 0422248 INS FTasU NIC

Livius, Titus.
Books XXIII and XXIV; ed. with introd. and notes by G.C. Macaulay. London, Macmillan and co., 1900.
35+215 p. Maps. (Classical series)

NL 0422249 InU

VOLUME 336

Livius, Titus.
Livy, books xxiii and xxiv; ed. with introd. by Macaulay... London, Macmilland and company [1885]. Repr. 1920.

NL 0422250 OO PV OCU

Livius, Titus.
Books 37 to the end ... tr. by M'Devitte. London, 1862.
2278 p.

NL 0422251 OCU

Livius, Titus.
Titi Livii Patavini Decadis qvintae libri qvinqve. [*Colophon:* Venetiis in aedibvs haeredvm Aldi Manvtii Romani, et Andreae Asvlani soceri, mense maio. M.D.XXXIII]
3 p. l., 3 (*i. e.* 4)–131 numb. l., [10] p. 15½cm.
Signatures: A–R⁸.
Leaf 4 erroneously numbered 3.
Italic type; spaces with guide letters left blank for initials.
Printer's mark on t.-p., and on verso of last leaf.
Edited by Francesco Torresani.
Forms the fifth volume of "Ex XIIII T. Livii Decadibus prima, tertia, quarta" ... issued in 5 vols., 1518–33.
I. Torresani, Francesco, d. 1546, ed.
36-24903
Library of Congress PA6452.A9T6 1533
[2] 878.4

NL 0422252 DLC InU NcD MH

Livius, Titus.
The first five books of T. Livy. With English explanatory notes and examina tion questions. By D. B. Hickie. For the use of schools and colleges. [London], Sold by Longman; Whittaker; Baldwin; and all other booksellers [1832].
xvii, 444 p. 20 cm.

NL 0422253 PLatS

LIVIUS, Titus.
Historiae libri quinque priores, cum annotationibus ex omnibus prioribus commentatoribus selectis et anglice redditis A.Jacobo Prendeville. Ed. nova. Dublin, 1842.

NL 0422254 MH

PA 6452 A5 1845 Livius, Titus.
Titi Livii Historiae libri quinque priores, cum annotationibus probatissimis et utilissimis, ex omnibus prioribus commentatoribus accurate selectis et anglice redditis; quibus et nonnullae suae sunt adjectae a Jacobo Prendeville...Editio nova. Dublinii, G. Curry, 1845.
xi, 575 p. 18 cm.
1.Rome - History. I.Prendeville, James, ed.

NL 0422255 IMunS

Livius, Titus.
Titi Livii Patavini historiarum ab urbe condita decadis III, liber trigesimus. Francofurti [Frankfort],apud Joh. Beyerum, Ammonium & serlinum, 1659.
2 v. in 1 (v.2 & 3)

NL 0422256 ViLxW InU IU MWelC

LIVIUS,TITUS
Historiarvm ab urbe condita decadis qvartae. [Francofvrti ad Moenum, Apud Georgium Coruinum, Sigismundum Feierabend, etc., 1568]
436, [16] p., 1 l., 230, [7] p. 8vo
Caption-title.
Bound with Grellius, J. Chronologia in Titi Livii historiam ...

NL 0422257 InU NN

---

*fNC5 Er153 531l Livius, Titus.
T. Livii patavini Historiarvm ab vrbe condita decadis qvintae libri qvinqve, nvnc primvm excvsi.
[Basileae]In officina Frobeniana,anno MDXXXI. Cum gratia & priuilegio caesareo ad annos sex.
f°. 91,[1]p. 37.5cm. (In his Historia, 1531)
Colophon: Basileae, in officina Frobeniana per Hieronymum Frob., Io. Heruagium, & Nicolaum Episcopium, MDXXXI.
Printers' mark on t.-p. & p.[92].

NL 0422258 MH

Livius, Titus.
T. Livii Patavini Historiarvm ab vrbe condita decadis qvintae libri qvinqve. Index praeterea appositus. Lvgdvni, Apvd haeredes Simonis Vincentii, 1537.
235 p. 17 cm.

NL 0422259 OU

Livius, Titus.
Historiarum ab urbe condita. Decas quinta. Rotomagi, apud R. & N. Lallemant, 1732.
335 p. 13 cm.
1. Rome - Hist.

NL 0422260 MdBP

---

* PA6452 .A6 1554 Livius, Titus.
T. Livii Patavini Historiarum ab urbe condita, Decas tertia. Basileae, apud Nicolaum Episcopium Iuniorem, 1554.
668 p. 18cm.
Publisher's device on title page.

NL 0422261 ViU InU PU

Titus, Livius.
Titi Livii Patavini Historiarum ab urbe condita decas tertia. Rotomagi: Apud J.J.Le Boullenger, 1761. 355 p. 12 x 6cm.

NL 0422262 NN

Gnl40 c579 Livius, Titus.
T.Livii Historiarvm ab vrbe condita liber primvs. Recensuit I.Lipsivs. Antverpiae,Ex officina C.Plantini,1579.
79p. 15½cm
I.Lipsius, Justus, 1547-1606, ed.

NL 0422263 CtY

Gnl40 c579 Livius, Titus.
T.Livii Historiarvm ab v. c. liber XXXIII. Praecipva parte, quae desiderabatur, expletus ex codice manuscripto ... Romae,Apud B. Zannettum,1616.
79p. 15½cm [Bound with Livius, Titus. ed. Lipsius. ... Historiarvm ab vrbe condita liber primvs ... Antverpiae,1579]
Running-title, p.16-79: T.Liuij hist. liber XLIII [!]
Edited by Gaspar Lusignanus.

NL 0422264 CtY

PA6452 .B23 1840 Livius, Titus.
Titi Livii Historiarum ab urbe condita liber XXIII et XXIV. Recognovit et commentariis scholarum in usum instruxit Ernestus Guilielmus Fabri ... Norimbergae, J. L. Schrag, 1840.
iv, 378 p. 20½cm.
1. Rome—Hist. I. Fabri, Ernst Wilhelm, 1796–1845, ed.

NL 0422265 ViU CU MH PBm ICU NjP PU MoU

PA6452 .B1 1856 Livius, Titus.
T. Livii Patavini Historiarum ab urbe condita libri I. II. Livy's History of Rome. (Part I.) Books I. II. With notes by Henry Young. London, J. Weale, 1856.
2 p.l., 144 p. 17½cm.
Text in Latin.
"Of most school editions ... the text of Drakenborch forms the basis ... I have generally adopted the text of Crevier; pointing out however in the Notes most of the various readings of Drakenborch and Alschefski."—pref.
1. Rome—Hist. I. Young, Henry, ed.

NL 0422266 ViU

Livius, Titus.
... Historiarum ab urbe condita, libri I, II. Livy's history of Rome, books I, II ... With English notes by Henry Young ... London, 1882-
1 v. 18 cm. (Weale's rudimentary scientific and educational series)

NL 0422267 CtY

Livius, Titus.
Historiarum ab urbe condita libri quinque priores ad optimas editiones castigati. Bostoniae, T. et J. Fleet, 1788.
298 p. 19 cm.
PA6452.A5 1788 55-54182

NL 0422268 DLC NN CtY InU Nh MB MiU-C RPJCB MH MWA

---

871 L5 1788 v Tayloe **Livius, Titus.**
Titi Livii Patavini Historiarum ab urbe condita libri quinque priores; ad optimam T. Ruddimanni editionem fideliter expressi. Usui scholarum. Edinburgi, Veneunt apud C. Elliot; Londini, et apud C. Elliot & socios, 1788.
299 p. 18cm.

NL 0422269 ViW

Livius, Titus.
Titi Livii Patavini. Historiarum ab urbe condita libri quinque priores. Ad optimas editiones castigati. Cantabrigiæ, excudebant Hilliard et Metcalf, 1810.
1 p. l., 293 p. 17½cm.
1. Rome—Hist.
24-16684
Library of Congress PA6452.A5 1810

NL 0422270 DLC MiU ViU

VOLUME 336

Gn 40 c751k Livius, Titus.
Titi Livii ... Historiarum ab urbe condita libri quinque priores, ad optimam Ruddimanni editionem fideliter expressi. Cura Joannis Dymock. Edinburgi, Veneunt apud Bell & Bradfute [etc.]: Glasguae, A.et J.M.Duncan, 1818.
1p.l.,ii,293p. 16½cm.

NL 0422271 CtY

Livius, Titus.
... Historiarum ab urbe condita libri quinque priores ... recensuit G.M. Gunn. Edinburgi, 1843.
17 cm.

NL 0422272 RPB

Livius, Titus.
... Historiarum belli Punici secundi libri quinque priores, ad optimas editiones castigati, cura J. Hunter. 8 ed., Edinburgi, 1845.
18 cm.

NL 0422273 RPB

---

*Yx 840 H8l Livius, Titus.
Titi Livii Patavini Historiarum liber primus et selecta quaedam capita. Curavit notulisque instruxit Carolus Folsom ... Cantabrigiae, Hilliard et Brown, 1829.
ix,287,[1]p. 18½cm.
Copyright Sept.2, 1829. Cancel t.-p., copyright Dec.30, 1829, inserted.
Bookplate of James Mason Hoppin, with his autograph on p.[iii]
Interleaved, with some ms. notes and illustrations.
Lettered on cover: Carrington Hoppin.

NL 0422274 CtY OCU IU PV MH

Livius, Titus.
Titi Livii Patavini Historiarum liber primus et selecta quædam capita. Curavit notulisque instruxit Carolus Folsom ... Ed. stereotypa. Cantabrigiæ, Hilliard et Brown, 1831.
ix, 287, [1] p. 18½cm.

I. Folsom, Charles, 1794-1872, ed.

1-21817

Library of Congress PA6452.B1 1831

NL 0422275 DLC NjP MH NcD OClJC OO OFH MB

PA6452 .A3F68 LIVIUS,TITUS.
Titi Livii Patavini Historiarum liber primus et selecta quædam capita. Curavit notulisque instruxit Carolus Folsom ... Ed.stereotypa. Cantabrigiæ, sumptibus Hilliard,Gray,et soc.,1833.
ix,[1],286,[1]p. 19cm.
Half-title:Excerpta Liviana.

NL 0422276 ICU MH

Livius, Titus.
Titi Livii Patavini. Historiarum liber primus et selecta quaedam capita. Curavit notulisque instruxit Carolus Folsom ... Editio stereotypa. Bostoniae, sumptibus Hilliard, Gray, et soc., 1835.
ix p., 1 l., 286 p., 1 l. 19cm.
Title vignette.
"The text of Drakenborch has been adopted."-cf. Pref.

NL 0422277 NNC NjP CtY MH CtHT-W

Livius, Titus.
Historiarum. liber primus, et selecta quaedam capita. Curavit notulisque instruxit Carolus Folsom. Ed. stereotypa. Bostoniae, sumptibus Hilliard, Gray, et soc., 1837.

Half-title: Excerpta Liviana.

NL 0422278 MH OCl

Livius, Titus.
Historiarum liber primus, et selecta quaedam capita. Curavit notulisque instruxit Carolus Folsom, Editio stereotypa. Bostoniae, Hilliard, Gray, et soc., 1838.

NL 0422279 MH

---

878 L5 1839 LIVIUS, TITUS
Titi Livii Patavini Historiarum liber primus et selecta quaedam capita. Curavit notulisque instruxit Carolus Folsom ... Ed. stereotypa. Bostoniae, Hilliard, Gray, et soc., 1839.
ix,[1],287,[1]p. 18cm.

I. Folsom, Charles, 1794-1872, ed.

NL 0422280 TxU NNC MH PU

Y 672 .L 5083 LIVIUS, TITUS.
Titi Livii Patavini Historiarum liber primus et selecta quædam capita. Curavit notulisque instruxit Carolus Folsom. Ed. stereotypa. Bostoniæ,S.G.Simpkins,1841.
286p. 19cm.

NL 0422281 ICN MiU MH

PA6452 .A3F6 1842 Livius, Titus.
Historiarum liber primus et selecta quædam capita. Curavit notulisque instruxit Carolus Folsom. Editio stereotypa. Bosteniae, Sumptibus S.G. Simpkins, 1842.
ix, 286 p. 19cm.
Half title: Excerpta Liviana.

I. Folsom, Charles, 1794-1872, ed.

NL 0422282 ViU PLatS PU PPTU OClUr IU

Livius, Titus.
Titi Livii Patavini historiarum liber primus et selecta quædam capita. Curavit notulisque instruxit Carolus Folsom. 13th stereotype edition. Bostoniæ [Boston] sumptibus S. G. Simpkins, 1843.
286 p. 19 cm.

NL 0422283 ViLxW MH

---

871 L5 1844 Livius, Titus.
Titi Livii Patavini Historiarum liber primus et selecta quædam capita. Curavit notulisque instruxit Carolus Folsom ... 14th stereotype ed. Bostoniæ, sumptibus S. G. Simpkins, 1844.
ix p., 1 l., 286, [1]p. 19½cm.

Half-title: Excerpta Liviana.
Title vignette (author's portrait)

I. Folsom, Charles, 1794-1872, ed.

NL 0422284 IU NjP OClWHi

Livius, Titus
Historiarum liber primus et selecta quaedam capita; curavit Carolus Folsom. Boston, Published by Phillips and Sampson; and S. G. Simpkins, 1846.
286 [1] p.

NL 0422285 MiD MH CU ViU

Livius, Titus.
Historiarum liber primus et selecta quaedem capita. Curavit notulisque instruxit Carolus Folsom. 19th sterotype ed. Boston, Phillips and Sampson, 1849.
ix, 286 p. 19 cm.
Interleaved.
I. Folsom, Charles, 1794-1872, ed.

NL 0422286 MdBP

Livius, Titus.
Titi Livii Patavini Historiarum liber primus et selecta quædam capita. Curavit notulisque instruxit Carolus Folsom ... 30th stereotype edition. Boston, Phillips and Sampson, and S. G. Simpkins, 1851.
ix p., 1 l., 286 p., 1 l. 19½cm.
Half-title: Excerpta Liviana.
Title vignette: portrait.

I. Folsom, Charles, 1794-1872, ed.

NL 0422287 ViU

PA6452 .A3F6 1852 Livius, Titus.
Historiarum liber primus et selecta quædam capita. Curavit notulisque instruxit Carolus Folsom. 13th stereotype ed. Boston, Phillips and Sampson, 1852.
ix, 286 p. 19cm.

I. Folsom, Charles, 1794-1872, ed.

NL 0422288 ViU OClUr MH NcD

PA6452 .B21F2 LIVIUS,TITUS.
Titi Livii...Historiarum liber XXI et XXII. Mit anmerkungen von dr.Ernst Wilhelm Fabri... Nürnberg,J.L.Schrag,1837.
x,356,xxx,[2] p. 21cm.

1.Punic war,2d,B.C.218-201.

NL 0422289 ICU RPB PU

Livius, Titus.
Historiarum liber 23 ed. by John T. White. Lond. Longmans, Green, 1873.

NL 0422290 MA

Livius, Titus.
...T. Livii Patavini historiarum libri I, II, XXII. Edinburgh, William and Robert Chambers, 1850.
364 p.

NL 0422291 PPAN

VOLUME 336

PA6452 Livius, Titus.
.A2
1860 ... T. Livii Patavini Historiarum libri I, II, XXI, XXII. Philadelphia, Blanchard and Lea, 1860.
xii, 13-343 p. front., maps. 17½cm. (Classical series. Edited by Drs. Schmitz and Zumpt)
Series note also on cover.
Text in Latin.
Occasional tail-pieces.

1. Rome—Hist. I. Schmitz, Leonhard, 1807-1890, ed. II. Zumpt, Karl Gottlob, 1792-1849, joint ed. III. Ser.

NL 0422292 ViU NjP PHi NN OC1JC PLatS OO KAS PL

Livius, Titus.
... Historiarum, libri I, II, XXI, XXII. New York, 1872.
16 cm. (Classical series)

NL 0422293 RPB

Livius, Titus Patavinus.
Historiarum. Libri I-X. Mit erklärenden anmerkungen von G.C.Crusius ...Hanover, Hahn, 1846-7. 2v.

NL 0422294 InU PLatS IU InU CtY MH

Livius, Titus
Historiarum. Libri IX-X., mit erklärenden anmerkungen von Gottl. Christ. Crusius...Fortgesetzt von G.Mühlmann ...Hanover, Hahn, 1852.

NL 0422295 NjP

Livius. 1813.
Ll 16 T. Livii patavini Historiarum libri priores
275* quinque: in usum juventutis academicae. Uticae: excudebant Seward et Williams. MDCCCXIII.
1p.l., [5]-285p. 18cm.
Page 40 misnumbered 26.

NL 0422296 MH CU MWA CtY MeB ViU NjP N NIC I'Ut

PA6452 Livius, Titus.
.A5
1818 Titi Livii Patavini Historiarum libri priores quinque: in usum juventutis academicae. Editio secunda Uticae. Uticae: Excudebat W. William, 1818.
272 p. 18cm.

1. Rome—Hist.

NL 0422297 ViU NNU NN NIC OU MH NNUT MWA

PA6452
.A5
1821 Livius, Titus.
Historiarum libri priores quinque: in usum Juventutis academicæ. Editio tertia uticensis. Uticæ, Excudebat Guilielmus Williams, 1821.
267 p. 18cm.

NL 0422298 ViU NN CU CtY OCU MiU MH CSmH MB PPL

Livius, Titus.
Titi Livii Patavini. Historiarum libri quinque priores; ad optimas editiones castigati, paucis notis adjectis ... Hallowell (Me.) excudebant Goodale, Glazier & soc., 1823.
4, 296 p. 18.5cm.

NL 0422299 NNC MB MWA OOxM MH ViU

Livius, Titus.
Titi Livii Patavini Historiarum libri quinque priores; ad optimas editiones castigati, paucis notis adjectis ... Hallowell (Me.) sumptibus et typis C. Spaulding, 1827.
300 p. 18cm.

1. Rome—Hist.

41-33180

Library of Congress PA6452.A5 1827

NL 0422300 DLC IU

LIVIUS, Titus.
Histories, books I, XXI and XXII, with extracts from books IX, XXVI, XXXV, XXXVIII, XXXIX, XLV. Edited and annotated by Thomas Chase. Philadelphia, Eldredge & Brother, 1872.

17 cm.
"Chase and Stuart's classical series."

NL 0422301 MH RPB OC1W NN DLC CtY

Livius, Titus.
The histories of Livy. Books I, XXI, and XXII. With extracts from books IX, XXVI, XXXV, XXXVIII, XXXIX, XLV. Edited and annotated by Thomas Chase. Philadelphia, Eldredge & brother, 1874.

"Chase and Stuart's classical series."

NL 0422302 MH NcD MiU

LIVIUS, Titus.
The Histories, books i, xxi, and xxii, with extracts from books ix, xxvi, xxxv, xxxviii, xxxix, xlv. Edited and annotated by Thomas Chase. Philadelphia, 1876. [cop. 1872].

(Chase and Stuart's classical series.)

NL 0422303 MH

Livius, Titus. 2929a.113
The histories of Livy, books I, XXI, and XXII, with extracts from books IX, XXVI, XXXV, XXXVIII, XXXIX, XLV. Edited and annotated by Thomas Chase.
Philadelphia. Eldredge. 1878. 364 pp. [Chase & Stuart's Classical series.] 16½ cm., in 8s.

H8536 — Chase, Thomas, President of Haverford College, editor. 1827-1892.— S.r.

NL 0422304 MB ODW

Livius, Titus.
... The histories of Livy, books I, XXI, and XXII. With extracts from books IX, XXVI, XXXV, XXXVIII, XXXIX, XLV. Edited and annotated, by Thomas Chase ... Philadelphia, Eldredge & brother, 1882.
xii, [13]-364 p. 17cm. (Chase and Stuart's classical series)

1. Rome—Hist. I. Chase, Thomas, 1827-1892.

32-17870

Library of Congress PA6452.A3C5 [937] 878.4

NL 0422305 DLC

PA6452
B1
1872 Livius, Titus
The histories of Livy, books I, XXI, and XXII. With extracts from books IX, XXVI, XXXVIII, XXXIX, XLV. Edited and annotated by Thomas Chase. Philadelphia, Eldredge, 1883 [c1872]
xii, 364 p. 17 cm. (Chase and Stuart's classical series)

NL 0422306 MeB

Livius, Titus.
... The histories of Livy, books I, XXI, and XXII, with extracts from books IX, XXVI, XXXV, XXXVIII, XXXIX, XLV. Edited and annotated by Thomas Chase ... Philadelphia, Eldredge & brother, 1884.
xii, 13-364 p. 17cm. (Chase and Stuart's classical series)

I. Chase, Thomas, 1827-1892, ed.

41-30926

Library of Congress PA6111.C4L51 1884

NL 0422307 DLC MoU NjP KAS OC1ND OCU MH

Livius, Titus.
... The histories of Livy, books I, XXI, and XXII. With extracts from books IX, XXVI, XXXV, XXXVIII, XXXIX, XLV. Edited and annotated, by Thomas Chase ... Rev. ed. Philadelphia, Eldredge & brother, 1885.
xii, 13-364 p. 17cm. (Chase and Stuart's classical series)

1. Rome—Hist. I. Chase, Thomas, 1827-1892, ed.

32-30590

Library of Congress PA6452.A3C5 1885 [937] 878.4

NL 0422307-1 DLC IU OC1 PV ViU OO

Livius, Titus.
Livy's History of Rome, books I, II, from the building of the city, B.C.735, to the taking of Antium, B.C.468. With English notes, by Henry Young. For the use of colleges and schools. London, C.Lockwood and co., 1882.

Cover: Weale's classical series, 16.

NL 0422308 MH

Livius, Titus.
Livy's history of Rome, books, III, IV, V, from the consulship of Quintus Fabius, B.C. 467 to the defeat of the Gauls by Camillus, B.C. 388; with English notes, by Henry Young: for the use of colleges and schools. London, Lockwood, 1876.
171 p. S. (Titi Livii Patavini historiarum ab urbe condita, libri III, IV, V.)

NL 0422309 NcD

Livius, Titus
Titi Livi liber I. Edited ... for the use of schools, by Rev. H. M. Stephenson ... London, Macmillan and co., ltd., 1927.
xxviii, 177p. illus. 15cm. (Elementary classics)

NL 0422310 PV

PA6452 Livius, Titus.
.B10A6 ... Titi Livii liber x Ab urbe condita, a cura di Edmondo d'Arbela. 2. ed. Milano, A. Mondadori, 1928.
[iii]-xxxi, [1], 127, [1] p. 20½cm. (Edizioni Mondadori per le scuole medie)
"Supplemento bibliografico": p. [xxxii]

1. Rome—Hist.—Republic, B.C. 510-265.

NL 0422311 ICU

Livius Patavinus, Titus. 2929a.123
Titi Livi Libri I., XXI., XXII. Livy. Books I., XXI., and XXII. With introduction and notes by John Howell Westcott.
= Boston. Allyn & Bacon. 1895. xxviii, 399 pp. Maps. 12°.
Bibliography, pp. xxvi-xxviii.

G5004 — Westcott, John Howell, ed.

NL 0422312 MB MH OC1

VOLUME 336

Livius, Titus. 2929a.123
[Titi Livi Libri I, XXI, XXII.] Livy. Books I, XXI, and XXII. With introduction and notes by J. H. Westcott. Revised edition.
Boston. Allyn & Bacon. [1904.] xxxiv, (1), 429 pp. Maps. [Allyn and Bacon's College Latin series.] 18½ cm.

M4323 — S.r. Westcott, John Howell, ed., 1858–

NL 0422313 MB PV PU PPT

PA6452 B1C6 1922 Livius, Titus.
Il libro I delle storie di Tito Livio, commentato da Enrico Cocchia, con introduzione storica intorno alla vita e all'opera di Tito Livio. 3.ed. accuratamente riveduta (ristampa). Torino, G. Chiantore, 1922.
xxxix,218 p. 20cm. (On cover: Collezione di classici greci e latini con note italiane)

I. Cocchia, Enrico, 1859-1930, ed.

584438

NL 0422314 CU

PA6452 B1C6 1922 Livius, Titus.
Il libro II delle storie di Tito Livio, commentato da Enrico Cocchia. 2.ed. accuratamente riveduta ed emendata (ristampa) Torino, G. Chiantore, 1923.
viii,207,[1] p. 20cm. [With Livius, Titus. Selected works. Latin. Il libro I delle storie di Tito Livio, commentato da Enrico Cocchia. Torino, 1922]

On cover: Collezione di classici greci e latini con note italiane.

NL 0422315 CU

Livius, Titus.
Il libro XXI delle storie di Tito Livio, commentato da Enrico Cocchia. 2. ed. accuratamente riveduta ed emendata (ristampa) Torino, E. Loescher, 1912.
vii, 148 p. 21 cm.
I. Cocchia, Enrico, 1859-1930, ed.

NL 0422316 CU

871 L5.X 1946[2] Livius, Titus.
... Tito Livio libro XXI; edición, estudio preliminar y comentario por José Vallejo, con un índice de las notas gramaticales, mapas y otros grabados. Madrid, Instituto "Antonio de Nebrija," 1946.
cxx, 156p. illus., plates, maps(1 fold.) (Clásicos "Emerita")
At head of title: Consejo superior de investigaciones científicas. Patronato Menéndez y Pelayo.
"Selección bibliográfica": p.cxviii-cxix.

NL 0422317 IU MiU CU OCU ViU IaU MdBJ

PA6452 B22C6 1892 Livius, Titus.
Il libro XXII delle storie di Tito Livio, commentato da Enrico Cocchia con una introduzione storico-critica alla terza deca di T. Livio ... Torino, Roma [etc.] Ermanno Loescher, 1892.
lxxix,162 p. fold.map. 21cm.

I. Cocchia, Enrico, 1859-1930, ed.

NL 0422318 CU

PA6452 B22C6 1925 Livius, Titus.
Il libro XXII delle storie di Tito Livio, commentato da Enrico Cocchia, con una introduzione storico-critica alla terza deca di T. Livio ... 2.ed. accuratamente riveduta (ristampa) Torino, G. Chiantore, 1925.
lxxx,160 p. map. 21cm. (On cover: Collezione di classici greci e latini con note italiane)

I. Cocchia, Enrico, 1859-1930, ed.

NL 0422319 CU

PA6452 B23M6 1923 Livius, Titus.
Il libro XXIII delle storie di Tito Livio, commentato da Umberto Moricca ... (ristampa) Torino, G. Chiantore, 1923.
xxii p.,1 l.,176 p. fold.col.map. 21cm. (On cover: Collezione di classici greci e latini con note italiane)

I. Moricca, Umberto, 1888- ed.

ser

600929

NL 0422320 CU

PA6452 .B23M47 Livius, Titus.
Il libro XXIII, commento da Gino Mazzoni. [Firenze] Vallecchi [1949]
168 p. (Biblioteca di classici greci e latini)

NL 0422321 ICU

Livius, Titus.
Il libro XXIV delle storie di Tito Livio, commentato da G.B.Bonino. 2ª edizione notevolmente modificata ed accresciuta da Umberto Moricca. Torino, Casa editrice G.Chiantore, successore E.Loescher [1932]
xii, 194 p. 21cm. (On cover: Collezione di classici greci e latini con note italiane)
I.Bonino,G B II.Moricca, Umberto.

NL 0422322 CSt

PA6452 .B40R7 Livius, Titus.
Il libro XL delle storie, con introduzione e commento di Alessandro Ronconi. [Firenze] Vallecchi [1948]
120 p. (Biblioteca di classici greci e latini. Nuov. ser.)

NL 0422323 ICU

Livius, Titus.
Tito Livio, libros XXI y XXII, edición de José Vallejo. 2. ed., rev. (con mapas y otros grabados) Madrid, Instituto "Antonio de Nebrija," 1947.
165 p. illus., maps (1 fold.) 21 cm. (Clásicos "Emérita," griegos y latinos, sin notas, 1)

1. Rome—Hist. I. Vallejo, José, ed. (Series)

PA6452.C1 1947 878.4 48-20588*

NL 0422324 DLC

Livius, Titus.
...La prima deca. A cura di Luciano Perelli. [Torino] Unione tipograficoeditrice torinese [1953]
773 p. illus. 23½ cm. (Classici latini. v.8)

"Nota bibliografica": p.29-31.

I.Perelli, Luciano, ed.& tr.

NL 0422325 NjP CU NNC

PA6452 .A2W7 1858 LIVIUS,TITUS.
Titi Livii Rerum romanarum ab urbe condita libri I-III. Med anmärkningar af A.F.Wimmercranz... 2. öfversedda och förbättrade upplagan. Hernösand[J.A. Johansson & komp.]1858.
[4],316 p. 21½cm.

NL 0422326 ICU

Livius, Titus.
Livy, the second Punic war, book XXI and selections from books XXII–XXX, by James C. Egbert ... New York, The Macmillan company, 1913.
xvii, 306 p. front., maps. 17½cm. (Half-title: Macmillan's Latin classics, ed. by J. C. Egbert ...)

1. Punic war, 2d, B. C. 218–201. I. Egbert, James Chidester, 1859– ed.

13-15537

Library of Congress PA6111.M3L8 1913

NL 0422327 DLC NjP MWAC ViU NcD PPLas PHC OCl OO

LIVIUS, Titus.
The second Punic war. Book XXI and selections from books XXII-XXX. By James C.Egbert. New York,Macmillan Co.,1914.
18 cm. Maps and plans.
Half-title:Macmillan's Latin classics.
"Published July 1913;reprinted April 1914."
L1 16.327.10

NL 0422328 MH MiU

Livius, Titus.
The second Punic war, Livy XXI & XXII. London, Dent, 1928.
vii, 168 p. maps (Dent's Latin texts)

NL 0422329 MH

Livius, Titus.
Livy, the second Punic war, book XXI and selections from books XXII–XXX, by James C. Egbert ... New York, The Macmillan company, 1922
xvii, 306 p. front., maps. 17½cm. (Half-title: Macmillan's Latin classics, ed. by J. C. Egbert ...)

NL 0422330 ViU DCU

PA6452 .B01P4 Livius, Titus.
Le storie. Libro primo [e secondo] a cura di Luciano Perelli. [Verona] Mondadori [1949-50]
2 v. maps. (Collana di testi latini e greci)
Vol.1, 2.ed; v.2, 1.ed.

NL 0422331 ICU

VOLUME 336

PA6452 B21F7 1950 Livius, Titus. Latin.
Le storie, libro XXI; a cura di Bruno Franchi. Roma, Gismondi [1950]
xiii,191 p. (Convivium; collana di autori greci e latini, 13)

I. Franchi, Bruno, ed.

NL 0422332 CU OCU MH

Livius, Titus.
... Livy, xxx-xxxiii, edited, with introduction and notes, by Clarence W. Mendell ... New York & London, The Century co. [°1928]
xx p., 2 l., 3-293 p. 21cm. (The Century college Latin series) $2.25

I. Mendell, Clarence Whittlesey, 1883- ed.

Library of Congress PA6452.A9M4 28-16473

NL 0422333 DLC TNJ PPLas PSC PV OC1W OO PHC

Livius, Titus.
The twenty-first book of Livy. With explanatory and grammatical notes and a vocabulary of proper names. Edited by Thomas Nash, M.A. ... 4th ed. London, Longmans, Green, and co., 1882.
vi, 141 p. 17½cm.
Caption title: Ab urbe condita historiarum liber XXI.
Text in Latin.

I. Nash, Thomas, 1845-1885, ed.

NL 0422334 ViU

---

ar V 11248 Livius, Titus.
The twenty-first book of Livy; with explanatory and grammatical notes and a vocabulary of proper names. Edited by Thomas Nash. 6th ed. London, Longmans, Green, 1887.
vi, 141 p. 18cm.

NL 0422335 NIC MH MiU

PA6452 .B21 1889 Livius, Titus.
The twenty-first book of Livy. With explanatory and grammatical notes and a vocabulary of proper names. Edited by Thomas Nash. 7th ed. London, New York, Longmans, Green, 1889.
vi, 141 p. 18cm.
Caption title: Ab urbe condita historiarum liber XXI.
Latin text.
I. Nash, Thomas, 1845-1885, ed.

NL 0422336 ViU OCU

---

ar V 11245 Livius, Titus.
The twenty second book of Livy; with explanatory and grammatical notes and a vocabulary of proper names. By John T. White. New ed. London, Longmans, Green, [pref. 1875]
151 p. 19cm.

I. White, John Tahourdin, 1809-1893, ed.

NL 0422337 NIC ViU OCU

Livius, Titus.
The twenty-third book of Livy. With explanatory and grammatical notes and a vocabulary of proper names. Edited by John T. White ... 5th ed. London, Longmans, Green, and co., 1880.
viii, 110 p. 18½cm. [White's grammar-school texts]
Caption title: Titi Livii Historiarum liber XXIII.
Text in Latin.
Advertising matter: p.[1-11].
I White, Tahourdin, 1809-1893, ed. II. Ser.

NL 0422338 ViU

Latin and English

Livius, Titus.
Livy, book V. Edited by W.F.Masom and A.H. Allcroft. London, W.B.Clive [1907?]

130, 24, 72 p. 18 cm.
"The university tutorial series."
"Test papers" and "Vocabulary," 24 p., interleaved.
"A translation," 72 p.

NL 0422340 MH

Livius, Titus.
Livy, book VI. Edited by W.F.Masom. London, W.B.Clive [1907?]

130, 23, 61 p. map. 18 cm.
"The university tutorial series."
"Test papers" and "Vocabulary," 23 p., interleaved.
"A translation," 61 p.

NL 0422341 MH

PA2099 .L8A35 Livius, Titus.
... Livy, book xxi. With introduction, notes, vocabularies, & translation, by A. H. Allcroft ... and W. F. Masom ... London, W. B. Clive & co. [1890?]
150, (24), 70 p. front. (double map) 18cm. (Univ. corr. coll. tutorial series)

1. Punic war, 2d, B. C. 218-201.

NL 0422342 ICU

Livius, Titus
Books XXVI and XXVII of Livy, with English notes and literal translation by Philomerus. Dublin, Printed by P. Dixon Hardty for J.J. Ekens, 1836.

4-222 p. 18 cm.
Latin and English on opposite pages.

I. Philomerus, tr. and ed.

NL 0422343 PLatS

Livius, Titus.
The close of the second Punic war, being Livy, books XXIX, XXX; partly in original and partly in translation. Edited by H. E. Butler. Oxford, Clarendon press, 1925.
182 p. maps.

I. Butler, Harold Edgeworth, 1878- ed.

NL 0422344 NNC PU

PA6452 B29 1937 Livius, Titus
The close of the second punic war; being Livy, books XXIX and XXX, partly in the original and partly in translation. Ed. by H.E. Butler. Oxford, Clarendon Press [1937]
182p. maps. 19cm.

"First published 1925; Reprinted 1937."

NL 0422345 RPB NN OCU CU

---

871 L5.X 1954 Livius, Titus.
The close of the second Punic War; being Livy, books XXIX, XXX, partly in the original and partly in translation. Edited by H. E. Butler. Oxford [Eng.] Clarendon Press [1954]
182p. maps. 19cm.

"First published 1925."

1. Punic War, 2d, B.C.218-201. I. Butler, Harold Edgeworth, 1878- ed. II. Title.

NL 0422346 IU NRU IaU

Livius, Titus.
Hannibal's invasion of Italy, being Livy, books XXI, XXII, partly in the original and partly in translation, ed. by John Jackson. Oxf., Clarendon press. 1924.
180 p.

NL 0422347 PHC MWAC

878.4 Mh.j Livy, Titus,
Hannibal's invasion of Italy, being Livy, Books XXI, XXII, partly in the original and partly in translation, edited by John Jackson. Oxford, Clarendon Press, 1926.

180p. illus. maps 19cm.

I.Jackson, John, 1881- , editor
II.Title.

NL 0422348 OWorP

---

878 L5.j Class. Livius, Titus
Hannibal's invasion of Italy; being Livy, books XXI, XXII, partly in the original and partly in translation; ed. by John Jackson. Oxford, Clarendon [1946]
180p. illus. D.

1.Hannibal. Crossing of the Alps, B.C.218. I.Jackson, John ed.

NL 0422349 IaU

Livius, Titus.
... The history of Rome by Titus Livius, books xxi. and xxii. The original text reduced to the natural English order, with a literal, interlinear translation ... New York city, A. Hinds and company, °1893.
1 p. l., 380 p. 18½cm. (Classic interlinear translations)

Library of Congress 12—36248

NL 0422350 DLC

VOLUME 336

Latin and Italian

PA6452
.B21
1925
Livius, Titus.
La storia di Roma dalle sue origini. Testo, costruzione, versione letterale, argomenti e note. Libro XXI. 4. ed. migliorata. Milano, Società Editrice Dante Alighieri de Albrighi, Segati, 1925.
356 p. 20cm. (Raccolta di autori latini)
Text in Latin and Italian.

NL 0422352 ViU

Latin and Spanish

878
L5.V.8m Livius, Titus.
Desde la fundacion de Roma, I-II. Versión española y notas por Agustín Millares Carlo. [México] Univ. Nacional Autónoma de México, 1955.
438p. 20cm. (His Obras completas)

Bibliotheca scriptorum Graecorum et Romanorum Mexicana.
Latin and Spanish on opposite pages.

NL 0422354 TxU

Danish

Livius, Titus.
Rom og Hannibal. Oversat af Gustav Hermansen. København, Gyldendal, 1944-
v. 20cm. (Selskabet til historiske kildeskrifters oversaettelse. [Skrifter. 12. raekke. 7])

Contents.- I. Romerske historie, bog 21-23.

I. Hermansen, Gustav, tr.

NL 0422356 MnU

Dutch

Livius, Titus.
Romeinsche geschiedenis Boeken I-III. Uittreksels. In het Nederlandsch vertaald door J. Verdyck. Antwerpen, Standaard-Boekhandel, 1946.
100 p. 18 cm. (Onze reeks klassieke vertalingen)

1. Rome—Hist.

PA6457.D7V4 55-58227

NL 0422358 DLC

English

Livius, Titus.
Livy, book I. A literal translation, by H.M. Grindon. London, W.B.Clive [1907?]

79 p. 18 cm.
"The university tutorial series."

NL 0422360 MH

Livius, Titus.

PA6155.K4
L5B7.21
... Livy. Book XXI. Literally translated by T. J. Arnold. London, James Cornish & sons [1865?]

67p. 18cm. (Kelly's keys to the classics)

I. Arnold, Thomas James, tr.

NL 0422361 NBuG

Livius, Titus.
Book XXI; translated into English by A. J. Church and W. J. Brodribb, 1894.
66 p.

NL 0422362 OClUr

Livius, Titus.
Livy, book XXI. A translation by A.H.Allcroft and W.F.Mason. London, W.B.Clive [1907?]

70 p. 18 cm.
"The university tutorial series."

NL 0422363 MH

PA6155.K4
L5B7.22
Livius, Titus.
... Livy. Book XXII. Literally translated, by T. J. Arnold. London, James Cornish & sons [1865?]

72p. 18cm. (Kelly's keys to the classics)

I. Arnold, Thomas James, tr.

NL 0422364 NBuG

PA6155.K4
L5B7.23
Livius, Titus.
... Livy. Book XXIII. Literally translated, by T. J. Arnold. London, James Cornish & sons [1865?]

58p. 18cm. (Kelly's keys to the classics)

I. Arnold, Thomas James, tr.

NL 0422365 NBuG

Livius, Titus.

PA6155.K4
L5B7.24
... Livy. Book XXIV. Literally translated by T. J. Arnold. London, James Cornish & sons [1865?]

61p. 18cm. (Kelly's keys to the classics)

I. Arnold, Thomas James, tr.

NL 0422366 NBuG

PA6155.K4
L5B7.4
Livius, Titus.
... Livy: Books IV. & V. Translated literally, by William Lewers ... and William A. M'Devitte ... Dublin, William B. Kelly, 1862.

143p. 16½cm. (Kelly's keys to the classics)

I. Lewers, William, tr. II. M'Devitte, William Alexander, tr.

NL 0422367 NBuG

Livius, Titus.
Livy, books xxi-xxv, The second Punic war, translated into English with notes, by Alfred J. Church and W. J. Brodribb, with maps. London, Macmillan, 1883.
xxxi, 335 p. front. maps. 19 cm.

NL 0422368 ViLxW MH OO ViU PBm

DG
207
L5
C5
Livius, Titus
Livy, Books XXI-XXV: The Second Punic War. Translated into English with notes by Alfred John Church and William Jackson Brodribb. London and New York, Macmillan, 1890.
xxxi [i] 347p. maps (1 fold.) 20cm.

1. Punic war, 2d, B.C. 218-201. I. Church, Alfred John, 1829-1912, ed. II. Brodribb, William Jackson, 1824-1905, ed.

NL 0422369 IMunS CU NRU ICU NNF

PA6453
A7
1901
Livius, Titus.
Livy, books XXI.-XXV, the second Punic war, translated into English with notes, by Alfred John Church and William Jackson Brodribb. London, Macmillan, 1901.
xxxi, 335 p. maps (1 fold.)

"First edition, 1883. Reprinted ... 1901."
Photocopy (positive)

1. Punic war, 2d., B.C. 218-201. I. Church, Alfred John, 1829-1912, tr. II. Brodribb, William Jackson, 1829-1905, joint tr.

NL 0422370 CU MB RPB OClJC OCU

Bon.
Coll.
No.12088
LIVIUS, TITUS.
The first five books of the Roman history: translated from the Latin...by John Bellenden. Edinburgh, W. and C. Tait, 1822.
xii, viii, 479, [1]p. 25cm.

NL 0422371 ICN NcGU ICU MiD MdBP OCU MH IU MB

Livius, Titus.
The history of Rome, by Titus Livius. Books I. and II. Literally tr., with notes, by D. Spillan ... With an introduction by Edward Brooks, jr. Philadelphia, D. McKay [c1896]
viii, 9-208 p. 16cm. [Pocket literal translations of the classics]

I. Spillan, Daniel, d. 1854, tr.

Library of Congress 12-36256

NL 0422372 DLC ViU OrStbM NcD OCl MH

Livius, Titus.
... The history of Rome, by Titus Livius, books I and II, literally translated, with notes, by D. Spillan ... with a brief introduction by James Kendrick, A. B. New York, Translation publishing company, inc. [c1924]
1 p. l., 157 p. 15½cm. (The students' literal translations)

1. Rome—Hist. I. Spillan, Daniel, d. 1854, tr.
Library of Congress PA6157.S8L4 1924 25-4059

NL 0422373 DLC NNUT

VOLUME 336

Livius, Titus.
History of Rome, books I, II, III, literally translated into English with progegomena und original notes, by Henry Owgan... Dublin, Kelly, 1855.
234 p.

NL 0422374 PU OCl

Livius Patavinus, Titus. 6250d.83,84
The history of Rome, by Titus Livius. Books I.–V. A treatise on Germany, and The life of Agricola, by C. Cornelius Tacitus. London. George Routledge & Sons, Ltd. [189–?] (4), 497, (1) pp. [Sir John Lubbock's Hundred books. 83, 84.] 18 cm., in 8s.
Translated by Daniel Spillan.
Tacitus's Germany and Agricola are catalogued separately.

L4975 — S.r. — Spillan, Daniel, tr., –1854. — Subject ref. made.

NL 0422375 MB

Livius, Titus.
The history of Rome. Bks. 1.-XX Tr. by D. Spillan. New York, 1871.

NL 0422376 DSI

878 L5 tS76 N8 Livius, Titus
The history of Rome by Titus Livius. Books i-xxx. Literally trans. with notes & illustrations by D. Spillan...New York, Harper & brothers, 1878.
2 v. 19½ cm. (Harper's new classical library.)
v.2 ed. by D. Spillan & Cyrus Edmonds.

NL 0422377 MiU

878 L78hxS Livius, Titus
The history of Rome. Books nine to twenty-six literally translated, with notes and illustrations by D. Spillan and Cyrus Edmonds. London, George Bell & Sons, 1884.
4 v. 19 cm.

I. Spillan, Daniel, 1797-1854, ed. & tr. II. Edmonds, Cyrus R joint ed.
aa:5

NL 0422378 NcU

PA6453 .A2S7 LIVIUS, TITUS.
...The history of Rome, by Titus Livius, books XXI and XXII, literally translated, by D. Spillan and Cyrus Edmonds. New York, Hinds & Noble [1889]
[5]-148 p. 15½cm. (Handy literal translations)

1. Rome--Hist.

NL 0422379 ICU NNUT OCl MiU MH

PA6155 .H3L5 1902 Livius, Titus.
... The history of Rome, by Titus Livius, books XXI and XXII. Literally translated by D. Spillan and Cyrus Edmonds. New York city, A. Hinds & co. [1902?]
1 p.l., [7]-148 p. 15½cm. (Handy literal translations)
Series note also on cover.
Translation of Ab urbe condita libri.

1. Rome—Hist. I. Spillan, Daniel, d. 1854, tr. II. Edmunds, Cyrus R., joint tr. III. Ser.

NL 0422380 ViU

Livius, Titus.
... The history of Rome, by Titus Livius, books XXI and XXII, literally tr., with notes, by D. Spillan ... and Cyrus Edmonds, with a brief introduction by James Kendrick, A. B. New York, Translation publishing company, inc. [©1922]
iv, [1], [7]-148 p. 15½cm. (The students' literal translations)

1. Rome—Hist. I. Spillan, Daniel, d. 1854, tr. II. Edmonds, Cyrus R., joint tr.
22—21579
Library of Congress DG207.L5S64

NL 0422381 DLC OO PPT

Livius, Titus.
Livy's history of Rome, the first five books, translated into Scots by John Bellenden, 1533; ed., with introduction, notes, and glossary by W. A. Craigie ... Edinburgh and London, Printed for the Society by W. Blackwood and sons, 1901–03.
2 v. 3 fold. facsim. (incl. fronts.) 23cm. (*Half-title:* The Scottish text society. [Publications. 47, 51])

I. Bellenden, John, ca. 1495–1550, tr. II. Craigie, William Alexander, 1867– ed.
9-14624

NL 0422382 DLC MH NN NjP PU PP OU MiU OClW ViU

Livius, Titus.
The history of Rome by Titus Livius: the first eight books literally translated, with notes and illustrations, by D. Spillan. London. Bohn, 1857.
558 p. D.

NL 0422383 NcD

KD 24373
Livius, Titus.
The history of Rome. The first eight books, literally translated, with notes and illustrations, by D.Spillan. London, H.G.Bohn, 1859.

NL 0422384 MH

Livius, Titus.
The history of Rome, by Titus Livius. Books XXI. and XXII. Literally tr., with notes, by D. Spillan and Cyrus Edmonds. With an introduction by Edward Brooks, jr. Philadelphia, D. McKay [1896]
viii, 9–181 p. 16cm. (Pocket literal translations of the classics)

I. Spillan, Daniel, d. 1854, tr. II. Edmonds, Cyrus R., joint tr.
12—36249
Library of Congress

NL 0422385 DLC CtY MoU OO

Livius, Titus.
The legendary history of Rome. (From the founding of the city by Romulus 753 B. C., to the burning of the city by the Gauls, B. C. 390) Tr. from the original text of Titus Livius by George Baker ... New York, R. Worthington, 1883 [1882]
2 p. l., 173 p. front., illus., plates, maps, plans. 38cm.

1. Rome—Hist.—Kings, B. C. 753–510. 2. Rome—Hist.—Republic, B. C. 510–265. I. Baker, George, M. A., tr. II. Title.
5—8476
Library of Congress DG207.L76

NL 0422386 DLC OKentU PU OCl PPL

PA6453 A5 1830 Livius, Titus.
A literal translation of the first three books of Prendeville's Livy, by a graduate-scholar of the university. Dublin, J. Cumming, 1830.
1 p.l., iv, [iii]-vi, 266 p. 19cm.

I. Graduate-scholar of the university

NL 0422387 CU

KD 31299
Livius. Titus.
Roman history, translated into English containing the first five books of the Second Punic war... Edinburgh, Printed for W.M.'Willam, 1812.

NL 0422388 MH

French

Livius, Titus.
Le premier livre de la premiere Decede de Tite Live de Padoue, des histoires depuis la ville fondée, tr. de latin en françois, par Jaques Gohori Parisien. Paris, Arnoul l'Angelier, 1548.
[4], 65 (i.e. 66), [4] leaves. illus. 22cm.

I. Gohory, Jacques, d. 1576, tr.

NL 0422390 MnU

*FC6 M2946 621l Livius, Titus.
Le xxxiii. livre de Tite Live novvellement treuvé à Bamberg en Allemagne. Traduit par le s^r de Malherbe ...
A Paris, Chez Tovssainct dv Bray, ruë Sainct Iacques aux Epics-meurs. Et en sa boutique au Palais en la galerie des prisonniers. M.DC.XXI. Auec priuilege du roy.
8p.l., 242p. 19.5cm.
Printer's mark on t.-p.
Errors in paging.

NL 0422391 MH

German

Livius, Titus.
Römische Geschichte, I. und II. Buch. Übers. von Ernst Bednara. Limburg-Lahn, Steffen-Verlag, 1951.
199 p. (Griechisch-römische Schriftenreihe in deutscher Sprache)

NL 0422393 ICU ICRL

*fSC5 V8375 En544b Livius, Titus.
Das vierdt theil der Römischen historien, auss fünff büchern Titi Liuij im latein newlich erfunden, vnd verteütschet, zwey durch Nicolaum Carbachium, die ander drey durch Jacobum Micyllum.
[Mainz, J. Schöffer, 1551]
xciii numb. l. 32.5cm. (In Titi Livii ... Römische Historien, 1551)
Title within ornamental border.
No. 5 in a volume lettered on spine: Caii Plinij Secūdi ...

NL 0422394 MH

VOLUME 336

Italian

PA6456 A4 1846 FONTANA LIBRARY Livius, Titus.
La prima deca di Tito Livio, volgarizzamento del buon secolo publicato dal manoscritto Torinese, riveduto sul latino e corretto co'frammenti del codice Adriani del 1326 col testo Riccardiano del 1352 e con altre varielezioni per cura del prof. Claudio Dalmazzo ... Torino, Stamperia reale, 1845-46.
2 v. 23cm.
Contents. - v.1. Books 1-4. - v.2. Books 5-10.

NL 0422396 CU

Livius, Titus.
I primi quattro [i. e., due] libri del volgarizzamento della terza deca di Tito Livio padovano attribuito a Giovanni Boccaccio, pubblicati per cura del conte Carlo Baudi di Vesme. Bologna, G. Romagnoli, 1875–76.
2 v. 20 cm. (Scelta di curiosità letterarie inedite o rare dal secolo XIII al XVII. Dispensa 143, 153)
"Edizione di soli 202 esemplari per ordine numerati." Vol. 1, "N. 140"; v. 2, "N. 190."
Vols. 3–4 not published.
I. Boccaccio, Giovanni, 1313–1375, supposed author. II. Baudi di Vesme, Carlo, conte, 1809–1877, ed. (Series)
PQ4204.A3C6 vol. 143, 153 A 53–4641
Cincinnati. Univ. Libr. for Library of Congress [3]†

NL 0422397 OCU MdBP RPB CU MB MH DLC

Portuguese

4PA Latin 288 Livius, Titus
Historia romana. Traducção dos 5 primeiros livros por Manoel Bernardes Branco. Porto, A. J. da Silva Teixeira, 1861.
514 p.

NL 0422399 DLC-P4

---

4. Periochae

Latin

PA6452 .P4 1853 Livius, Titus.
T. Livi Ab vrbe condita librorvm CXLII periochae. Ivlii obseqventis ab anno vrbis conditae dv prodigiorvm liber. Recensvit et emendavit Otto Iahn. Lipsiae, Typis et svmptibvs Breitkopfii et Haertelii, 1853.
xxvi, 154 p. $22\frac{1}{2}$cm.
1. Rome—Hist. I. Jahn, Otto, 1813-1869, ed.

NL 0422402 ViU PBm PU MiU ICU IU MoU InU MH CU

Livius, Titus.
Titi Livii Patavini Decadvm XIIII epitome. Lvgdvni, Apvd haeredes Simonis Vincentii, 1537.
75 [i. e. 95] p. 17 cm.

NL 0422403 OU PV MB

---

881 P7.Lp 1542 cop.2 Livius, Titus.
Titi Livii Patavini [Decadvm XIIII Epitome. Lvgdvni, apvd Seb. Gryphivm, 1542.
94p. 18cm. [With Polybius. Polybii historiographi Historiarvm libri quinqve. Lvgdvni, 1542. cop.2]
Signatures: Aaa-Fff[8].
Device of printer on t.-p.; initial.

NL 0422404 IU MB NjP InU

Livius, Titus.
Titi Livii Patavini Librorvm Epitomae. Lvcivs Florvs. Colophon: Venetiis In Aedibvs Aldi, et Andreae Soceri, Mense Martio. M. D. XXI. [March, 1521]
56, 310, [2] numb. l. 16 1|2 cm. Panelled calf.
"Polybii Historiarvm Libri Qvinqve in Latiam ... Nicolao Perotto interprete": leaves 69-310.
Printer's device on t.-p. and verso of last leaf.
Constable-Binns-Baker copy, with ex-libris of the first two.
I. Florus, Lucius Annaeus. II. Polybius. III. Title: Librorvm Epitomae...

NL 0422405 CSmH NcU MiD IU

Livius, Titus.
Die neue Livius-epitome aus Oxyrhynchus; text und untersuchungen von Ernst Kornemann ... Mit einer tafel. Leipzig, Dieterich'sche verlagsbuchhandlung, T. Weicher, 1904.
5 p. l., 131, [1] p. pl. $28\frac{1}{2}$cm. (*Added t.-p.:* Beiträge zur alten geschichte ... hrsg. von C. F. Lehmann und E. Kornemann. 2. beiheft)
I. Kornemann, Ernst, 1868–
5—26522

NL 0422406 DLC MH NjP OCU OU MiU MB NcU PBm ViU DSI

Livius, Titus.
T. Livi [Periochae omnivm librorvm, Fragmenta Oxyrhynchi reperta, Ivlii Obseqventis Prodigiorvm liber; edidit Otto Rossbach. Adiecta est tabvla phototypica. Lipsiae, in aedibvs B. G. Tevbneri, 1910.
xli, [1], 201, [1] p. front. (fold. facsim.) 17cm. (*Lettered on cover:* Bibliotheca scriptorum graecorum et romanorum Teubneriana. [S. r.])
Facsimile: Papyr. oxyrhynch. Mus. britann. 668 col. VII lib. 53, 54.
1. Rome—Hist. 2. Manuscripts, Latin (Papyri) I. Rossbach, Otto, 1858– ed. II. Obsequens, Julius.
Library of Congress PA6104.L51 1910 10–22141

NL 0422407 DLC InU NjP NcU PHC PU PSC OO MiU OCU NIC PBm

---

5. Selections

Latin

Livius, Titus.
Ab urbe condita, eine Auswahl; bearb. von Otto Leggewie. Berlin, Weidmann-Greven-Verlag [1953]
2 v. 18 cm. (Sammlung griechischer und lateinischer Texte mit Kommentar. Lateinische Reihe, Heft 2)
Bibliography: v. 1, p. v.
CONTENTS.—[1] Text.—[2] Kommentar.
I. Leggewie, Otto, 1910– ed. II. Title. (Series)
PA6105.S3 Heft 2 878.4 54–16197

NL 0422410 DLC LU

Livius, Titus.
Ab urbe condita libri, eine Auswahl des Bedeutsamsten aus der ersten und dritten Dekade. Ausg. B. für den Schulgebrauch in verkürzter und sprachlich erleichterter Form bearb. und hrsg. von Joseph Werra und Julius Uppenkamp. Mit Titelbild, 2 Karten und 21 Abbildungen von Julius Uppenkamp. Münster (Westf.) 1946.
v. illus., maps (part fold.) 19 cm. (Aschendorffs Sammlung lateinischer und griechischer Klassiker)
CONTENTS.—[1] Text. 3. bis 7. Aufl.
I. Werra, Joseph, ed. II. Uppenkamp, Julius, ed.
PA6452.A3W37 52–17857

NL 0422411 DLC MH

Livius, Titus.
Ab urbe condita librorum partes selectae; is usum scholarum iterum edidit J. C. Grysar. Vindobonae, Caroli Gerold filii, 1874.
373 p.

NL 0422412 OCIND

PA2099 .L8G9 LIVIUS,TITUS.
T.Livii Ab urbe condita librorum partes selectae. In usum scholarum edidit C.J.Grysar. Recognovit et in unum volumen contraxit addito indice locorum et IV tabulis geographicis Rudolphus Bitschofsky... Vindobonae,sumptibus et typis Gerold filii,1889.
xv,397 p. 4 maps(3 fold.) 17cm.

NL 0422413 ICU

LIVIUS, Titus.
L'assedio di Siracusa, [selections from books xxiv and xxv]; con introduzione e commento [by Gaetano Gigli]. Roma, 1900.
pp. 96. Map and wdcts.

NL 0422414 MH

Livius, Titus.
Ausgewählte stücke aus der dritten dekade des Livius mit anmerkungen für den schulgebrauch von W. Jordan. 3. aufl. Stuttgart, Paul Neff, 1883.
[16]+187 p.

NL 0422415 InU

Livius, Titus.
Ausgewählte Stücke aus der dritten Dekade des Livius. Mit Anmerkungen für den Schulgebrauch von W. Jordan. 4., durchgesehene Aufl. Stuttgart, P. Neff, 1891.
xvi, 187 p. 18 cm.
I. Jordan, Wilhelm, ed.

NL 0422416 InU PLatS

---

ar W 29607 Livius, Titus.
W. Jordans ausgewählte Stücke aus der dritten Dekade des Livius; mit Anmerkungen für den Schulgebrauch. 5. Aufl. Neu bearb. von C. Minner und [Hermann] Planck. Stuttgart, A. Bonz, 1904.
xii, 199 p. 21cm.

NL 0422417 NIC

4PA Latin 292 Livius, Titus
Auswahl aus der ersten und dritten Dekade. Verkürzte Neubearbeitung nach Fügners Auswahl von Wilhelm Heraeus. 4. Aufl. Leipzig, B. G. Teubner, 1937.
94, 115 p.
(Teubners Schülerausgaben)

NL 0422418 DLC-P4

VOLUME 336

DE71 .A63 v.16 Livius, Titus.
Bloemlezing uit de vierde en vijfde decade van T. Livius, met inleiding en aantekeningen door Dr. R. J. Dam en Dr. K. Sprey. 3. druk. Groningen, J. B. Wolters, 1945.
205 p. (Antieke cultuur ꞓv.16ꞓ)

NL 0422419 ICU OCU

PA2099 .L8E19 LIVIUS,TITUS.
Camillus and other stories from Livy,ed.,with introduction,maps,notes and vocabulary by G.M. Edwards... Cambridge,Eng.,The University press, 1911.
xv,124 p. front.(map)plan. 17cm. (Half-title: Pitt press series)
"This selection...from the fifth,sixth,and eighth books...has been made for students in their third year of Latin reading."--Pref.
1.Latin language--Chrestomathies and readers.

NL 0422420 ICU MH OCU

878 L788c Livius, Titus.
Camillus and other stories from Livy. Edited, with intro., maps, notes and vocabulary by G.M. Edwards. Cambridge, at the University Press 1939 [i. e. 1911]
124 p. map. plan. (Cambridge elementary classics)

Contents.--Camillus. Manlius. Great Latin war. Appendix to text.

1. Camillus, Marcus Furius d. 365 B.C. 2. Manlius, Marcus d. 384 B.C. I. Edwards, Gerald Maclean, 1857- ed.

NL 0422421 PrU

Livius, Titus.
Chrestomathie aus Livius für den schulgebrauch hrsg. von J. Golling. 2. verbesserte aufl. Vienna, A. Hölder, 1900.
[4]+12+340 p. Maps.

NL 0422422 InU

Beinecke Library Gnl40 B532P Livius, Titus.
T. Livii Patavini Conciones, cvm argvmentis et annotationibus Ioachimi Perionij ... Parisiis Apud Simonem Colinæum Anno Domini 1532.Mense Ianuario,ad calculum Romanum.
21p.l.,544p. 17cm.
Signatures: aa-bb^{8}cc^6(cc6 blank)a-z^{8}A-L^8.
Imperfect: prelim. leaves 19-20 (sig. cc$_{3-4}$) wanting.

NL 0422423 CtY CtS NNC

878 L5 L48 Livius,Titus.
...Extracts from Livy,with English notes ...by H.Lee-Warner...Oxford, Clarendon press,
v. map,plans. 16½ cm. (Clarendon press series)
Contents:-v.1. The Caudine disaster.-v.2. Hannibal's campaign in Italy.

NL 0422424 MiU MWiW-C CtY NcD MH

Livius, Titus.
Extracts from Livy, with English notes and a map by H. Lee-Warner Oxford, 1880.
16 cm. (Clarendon press series)

NL 0422425 RPB

PA6452 .A3L5 Livius, Titus.
Extracts from Livy, by H. Lee-Warner ... New illus. ed., rev. by E. Norman Gardiner ... Oxford, The Clarendon press, 1927.
viii, 247 p. incl. front., illus., maps, plans, diagrs. 17½cm.
Contents.—The Caudine disaster, 321-320 B. C.—Hannibal's campaign in Italy, 218-216 B. C.—The Macedonian war, 170-168 B. C.

NL 0422426 ICU MWAC OCU

Livius, Titus.
Hannibal at bay ...
see his Selections. Latin.

PA6452 A3N3 1950 Livius, Titus.
Hannibal at bay; selections from Livy XXIII-XXVI, edited with introd., notes and vocabulary by A.H. Nash-Williams. London, Macmillan, 1950.
xxv,113 p. illus. (Modern school classics)

I. Nash-Williams, A.H., ed. II. Title.

NL 0422428 CU

PA6114 .A85 v.3 LIVIUS, TITUS.
Hannibal, Auswahl aus der dritten und vierten Dekade, von Julius Baer. 2. Aufl., durchgesehen von Max Leitschuh. Bamberg, C. C. Buchner, 1954.
80, 15p. (Aus dem Schatze des Altertums; ausgewählte griechische u. lateinische Texte. B: Lateinische Reihe, 3)

I. Baer, Julius, ed. II. Leitschuh, Max, ed.

NL 0422429 ICU

Livius, Titus.
Hannibal in defeat. Selections from Livy XXV-XXX. Edited with introduction, notes and vocabulary by A. H. Nash-Williams. London, Macmillan, 1953.

xxvi, 137 p. illus., map. 18cm. (Modern school classics)

NL 0422430 OCU MdU

Livius, Titus.
The Hannibalian or second Punic war, extracted from the third decade of Livy, with notes by the Rev. E. D. Stone ... 2d ed., with a map and plans. Eton, Williams and son; London, Simpkin, Marshall, & co., 1881.
viii, 170 p. fold. map, plan. 18cm.
"Notes": p.ꞓ129ꞓ-170.
Text in Latin.

1. Punic war, 2d, B.C. 218-201. I. Stone, Edward Daniel, ed.

NL 0422431 ViU NIC

PA6452 B21 1880a Livius, Titus
The Hannibalian war ꞓofꞓ Livy. Being part of the twenty-first and twenty second books of Livy, adapted for the use of beginners, by G. C. Macaulay. London, Macmillan, 1880.
xvii, 124 p. map. 15 cm. (Elementary classics)

I. Macaulay, George Campbell, 1852-1915, ed.

NL 0422432 MeB OO

Livius, Titus.
Livy; The Hannibalian war;being part of the twenty-first and twenty second books of Livy; adapted for the use of beginners, by G.C. Macaulay. ... London, Macmillan co., 1882.
124 p.

NL 0422433 PPLas RPB

878 L5 M12 Livius,Titus.
...Livy.The Hannibalian war...by G.C.Macaulay...London, Macmillan & co., 1886.
177 p. 1 double.map. 15½ cm. (Elementary classics)

NL 0422434 MiU

LIVIUS, Titus.
The Hannibalian war; being part of the twenty-first and twenty-second books of Livy, adapted by G.C.Macaulay. London,Macmillan and co., limited,1910.

Plates and maps.
"Elementary classics."
Verso of title-page: 1st ed.1880; 2d ed. 1903. reprinted 1910.
Text in Latin.

NL 0422435 MH

PA2099 .L8M2 Livius, Titus.
... The Hannibalian war, being part of the twenty-first and twenty-second books of Livy. Adapted for the use of beginners by G. C. Macaulay ... London, Macmillan and co., 1924.
[4], xx, 159 p. plates, 2 fold. maps (incl. front.) 15cm. (Elementary classics)

1. Punic war, 2d, B. C. 218-201.

NL 0422436 ICU

878.4 M 117 Livius, Titus.
The Hannibalian War. London, Macmillan abd Co., 1951.
xx,159 p. maps 16 cm.
(Elementary Classics)

NL 0422437 MWAC

PA 6452 A9 1886 Livius, Titus.
The last two kings of Macedon. Extracts from the fourth and fifth decades of Livy, selected and edited by F. H. Rawlins. London, Macmillan, 1886.
xxix, 215 p. map. 17cm. (Classical series)

NL 0422438 NIC PV CtY PPGi

Livius, Titus.
... The last two kings of Macedon. Extracts from the fourth and fifth decades of Livy. Selected and ed. by F. H. Rawlins ... London, Macmillan and co., ltd; New York, The Macmillan company, 1897.
xxix, [3], 215 p. front. (fold. map) 17cm. (At head of title: Classical series)

I. Rawlins, Francis Hay, ed.

NL 0422439 MiU InU

VOLUME 336

Livius, Titus.
... The last two kings of Macedon. Extracts from the fourth and fifth decades of Livy. Selected and ed. by F. H. Rawlins ... new and rev. ed. London, Macmillan and co., ltd., 1926.
xxix, [3], 215 p. front. (fold. map) 17 cm. (Classical series)

NL 0422440 CU

Livius, Titus.

Wilkinson, Herbert.
Legends of ancient Rome from Livy, adapted and edited with notes, exercises, and vocabularies, by Herbert Wilkinson ... with an introduction by Mary L. Breene ... New York, The Macmillan company, 1926.

PA6452 .A3B3 1813 Livius, Titus.
Liviana excerpta; vel Chrestomathia Liviana; in usum scholarum castigatius repetita Car.Lud. Bauero. Ed. tertia emendatior. Lipsiae, In Bibliopolio Hahniano, 1813.
3 v.in 1. 18cm.

I. Bauer, Karl Ludwig, 1730-1790, ed. II. Title. III. Title: Chrestomathia Liviana.

NL 0422442 OCU PPDrop

Livius, Titus
Liviana excerpta vel Chrestomathia Liviana in usum scholarum castigatius repetita a Car. Lud. Bauero, denuo edidit et annotationes adjecit Fridericus Büttner. Ed. 4 emendatior. Lipsaie, in bibliopolio Hahniano, 1824.

xciv, 230, 108 p. 21 cm.

I. Bauer, Karl Ludwig, ed. II. Büttner, Friedrich, ed.

NL 0422443 FLatS MoU InU

Livius, Titus.

Livius pro prima classe gymnasiorum scholarumque latinarum... A m.Martino Frider.Soergel... Lemgoviae, Ex officina Meyeriana, 1771.
296 p. 17½ cm.

I.Soergel, Martin Friedrich, d.1787, ed.

NL 0422444 NjP

878.4 V S8 1827 Livius, Titus
Narrationes ex Tito Livio excerptae, ad usum scholarum accommodatae. Nova editio accuratissimè recognita ... Avenione, Stephanum Chailot, 1827.
2 pts. in 1. 18cm.

NL 0422445 TNJ

Livius, Titus
Narrationes e Tito Livio excerptae, ad usum scholarum accommadatae. Editio accurate emendata. Lyon & Paris, Librairie classique de Perisse Freres, 1839.

383 p. 14 cm.

NL 0422446 PLatS

Livius, Titus.
Narrationes e Tito Livio excerptae. Lugduni, 1843.
383 p.

NL 0422447 OO

PA 6452 A3R57 Livius, Titus.

T. Livio Padovano; Narrazioni scelte e dichiarate; con note italiane da Giuseppe Rigutini. 7. ed., nuov. corretta. Prato, F. Alberghetti, 1881.
xxiii,312 p. 19cm.

I. Rigutini, Giuseppe, 1829-1903, ed.

NL 0422448 NIC

PA 6452 B5 1537 Cage Livius, Titus
... Orationes omnes, ex libris de II. Bello Punico, artificio dialectico & rhetorico illustratae. Ex iisdem libris miscellanea, obseruationes, et apophthegmata ... excerpta per Reinhardum Lorichium ... Francoforti, Christianus Egenolphus excudebat
Colophon: 1537.

[12] 202 [2] l. $2a^8$, $2b^4$, A-Z^8, a-b^8, c^4. 8vo.

NL 0422449 DFo InU

Rare Book Room Gn140 b537b Livius, Titus.
T. Livii Patavini ... Orationes, separatim cum argumentis æditæ ... Quibus accesserunt orationes omnes, quæ iam extant apud C.Crispum Salustium. Q.Curtium. C. Cæsarem. P.Cornelium Tacitum. et Herodianum ... Marpurgi Excusum in officina Christiani Egenolphi.[Anno 1541.Pridie Kalend.Aprilis]
8p.ℓ.,404numb.ℓ.,4ℓ. 15cm.
Signatures: §.^{8}A-Z^8a-ee^8.
Edited by Reinhardus Lorichius.

NL 0422450 CtY

Livius, Titus.
Origines Romanae... 4th ed. London, 1867.
147 p.

NL 0422451 OO

Livius, Titus.
Prisca virtus romana, Auswahl aus der ersten Dekade des Livius von Julius Baer. 7. Aufl. Bamberg, C. C. Buchner, 1944.
54, 26 p. 19 cm. (Aus dem Schatze des Altertums, ausgewählte griechische u. lateinische Texte. B: Lateinische Reihe, 2)

I. Baer, Julius, ed. I. Title. (Series)
PA6452.A3B3 1944 A F 49-167*

Chicago. Univ. Libr. for Library of Congress [1]†

NL 0422452 ICU MH DLC

PA2099 .L8D2 Livius, Titus.
... Rēgēs cōnsulēsque rōmānī. Fābellae ex T. Līvī historia, by F. R. Dale ... Oxford, The Clarendon press, 1915.
84 p. 19cm. (Lingua latina)

1. Latin language—Chrestomathies and readers.

NL 0422453 ICU CU PBm MA NNC OO OCU

PA6452 .A7W3 LIVIUS,TITUS.
... The revolt and fall of Capua, being selections from Livy XXIII-XXVI,ed.by T.C.Weatherhead... Cambridge[Eng.]The University press,1914.
xli,[1],166 p. illus.(maps) 17½cm. (Half-title: Cambridge elementary classics)

1.Punic war,2d,B.C.218-201.

NL 0422454 ICU

Livius, Titus.
Roman history. Selections from the first five books, w. twenty first & twenty-second books entire. N.Y., Am. book co., [c1882].
372 p.

NL 0422455 OO RPB

Gn140 c847x Livius, Titus.
Livy's Roman history. Selections from the first five books, with the twenty-first and twenty-second books entire. By John L. Lincoln ... Revised edition, with references to Harkness's New standard Latin grammar. New York,D.Appleton and company,1884.
viii,372p. 2 fold.maps. 19cm.

I.Lincoln, John Larkin, 1817-1891, ed. II.Alschefski, Karl Friedrich Siegmund, 1805-1852, ed. Stamp both.

NL 0422456 CtY RPB

PA6452 .A3L5 1883 Livius, Titus.

Livy's Roman history. Selections from the first five books, with the twenty-first and twenty-second books entire. By John L. Lincoln ... Rev. ed., with references to Harkness's New standard Latin grammar. New York, D. Appleton and company, 1883.
viii, 372 p. fold. map, fold. plan. 18½cm.
Text in Latin.

1. Rome—Hist. I. Lincoln, John Larkin, 1817-1891.

NL 0422457 ViU MeB MH

Livius, Titus.
Livy's Roman history; selections from the first five books, ... Rev. ed. ... New York, Appleton, 1886.
372 p.

NL 0422458 OCl

PA6452 .A3L5 1888 Livius, Titus.

Livy's Roman history. Selections from the first five books, with the twenty-first and twenty-second books entire. By John L. Lincoln ... Rev. ed., with references to Harkness's New standard Latin grammar. New York, D. Appleton and company, 1888.
viii, 372 p. fold. map, fold. plan. 18½cm
Text in Latin.

1. Rome—Hist. I. Lincoln, John Larkin, 1817-1891, ed.

NL 0422459 ViU

EducT 1035.520.890
Livius, Titus.
Roman history; selections from the first five books, with the twenty-first and twenty-second books entire, by John L.Lincoln. Revised ed., with references to Harkness's New standard Latin grammar. New York, etc., American book co. [1890?, c.1882]

NL 0422460 MH

VOLUME 336

Livius, Titus.
Roms Anfänge und Aufstieg zur Weltherrschaft, ausgewählt und erläutert von Ernst Habenstein. 2. Aufl. Leipzig, B. G. Teubner, 1941.
60 p. plates, maps (part fold.) diagr. 21 cm. (Teubners altsprachliche Texte)
I. Habenstein, Ernst, 1900- ed. II. Title.
PA6452.A3H3 1941 878.4 49-36327*
NL 0422461 DLC MH

Livius, Titus.
Scenes from the life of Hannibal; selections from Livy; ed., with historical introduction, notes, maps, vocabularies and English exercises by W. D. Lowe ... Oxford, Clarendon press, 1908.
127, [1] p. maps, plans. 17cm.
I. Lowe, William Douglas, ed.
NL 0422462 NNC MiD MA OCU

Livius, Titus. 2929.31
Selections from Livy, edited, with notes and introduction; by Harry Edwin Burton.
— New York. American Book Company. [1904.] 375 pp. Maps. [Morris and Morgan's Latin series.] 18½ cm., in 8s.
—S.r. — Burton, Harry Edwin, ed.
NL 0422463 MB

Livius, Titus.
Selections from Livy; edited, with notes and introduction, by Harry Edwin Burton ... New York, Cincinnati [etc.] American book company [c1905]
375 p. front., maps (1 double) 19 cm. (Half-title: Morris and Morgan's Latin series)
I. Burton, Harry Edwin, 1868- ed.
PA6111.M7L5 1905 5-30576
NL 0422464 DLC OCl OO MiU PU PV MWAC ViU

Livius, Titus.
... Selections from Livy; edited by Harry Edwin Burton ... Text ed. New York, Cincinnati [etc.] American book company [c1905]
165 p. 18½ cm. (Morris and Morgan's Latin series)
I. Burton, Harry Edwin, 1868- ed.
PA6111.M7L5 1905a 5-30255
NL 0422465 DLC LNHT

Livius, Titus.
T. Livius Narrator; selections from Livy, edited by Hubert McNeill Poteat ... New York, Prentice-Hall, inc., 1938.
xii, 276 p. 21cm. [Prentice-Hall classics series; C. J. Kraemer, jr. ... editor]
"It is high time Livy had a cognomen: Narrator is suggested."—Pref.
"Notes": p. [91]-276.
I. Poteat, Hubert McNeill, 1886- ed.
Library of Congress PA6452.A3P6 38-17941
——— Copy 2.
Copyright A 119325 [2] 878.4
NL 0422466 DLC PV TxU OClW OCU PHC

Livius, Titus.
... Selections from the first five books, together with the twenty-first and twenty-second books entire. Chiefly from the text of Alschefski. With English notes for schools and colleges. By J. L. Lincoln ... With an accompanying plan of Rome, and a map of the passage of Hannibal. New York, D. Appleton & company; Philadelphia, G. S. Appleton, 1847.
vi p., 1 l., 329 p. fold. map, fold. plan. 20cm.
I. Lincoln, John Larkin, 1817-1891. II. Alschefski, Karl Friedrich Siegmund, 1805-1852.
Library of Congress PA6452.A3L5 1847 19-3899
NL 0422467 DLC OClND PPT PP PU PV OCU MB NN ViU

878
L5
L74
E8
Livius, Titus.
...Selections from the first five books, together with the twenty-first & twenty-second books entire. Chiefly from the text of Alschefski. With English notes ...by J.L.Lincoln...4th ed.rev. New York, D.Appleton & co., Philadelphia, G.S.Appleton, 1848.
vi, 329 p. fold.maps 19½cm.
NL 0422468 MiU OO MH PPL PU

EducT 1035.520.850
Livius, Titus.
Selections from the first five books, together with the twenty-first and twenty-second books entire, chiefly from the text of Alschefski. With English notes for schools and colleges. By J.L.Lincoln. 6th ed., revised. New York, D. Appleton & co., etc., etc., 1850.
NL 0422469 MH

Livius, Titus.
Selections from the first five books, together with the twenty-first and twenty-second books entire, chiefly from the text of Alschefski. With English notes for schools and colleges by J.L.Lincoln. 6th ed., revised. New-York, D. Appleton & co., 1851.
NL 0422470 MH

Livius, Titus.
Selections from the first five books, together with the twenty-first and twenty-second books entire. Chiefly from the text of Alschefski. With English notes for schools and colleges. By J. L. Lincoln. New York, D. Appleton, & Co., 1852.
vi p.l., il., 329 p. 2 map. 12°.
6th ed.
NL 0422471 NN MH

Livius, Titus.
Selections from the first five books together with the twenty-first and twenty-second books entire, chiefly from the text of Alschefski, with English notes for schools and colleges, by J. L. Lincoln ... 6ed. rev. New York, 1853.
map. (fold.) 19 cm.
NL 0422472 RPB MH

PA6452
.A3L5
1854
Livius, Titus.
... Selections from the first five books, together with the twenty-first and twenty-second books entire. Chiefly from the text of Alschefski. With English notes for schools and colleges. By J. L. Lincoln ... With an accompanying plan of Rome, and a map of the passage of Hannibal. New York, D. Appleton & company; 1854.
vi p., 1 l., 329 p. fold. map, fold. plan. 20cm.
Text in Latin
NL 0422473 ViU MH

EducT 1035.520.855
Livius, Titus.
Selections from the first five books, together with the twenty-first and twenty-second books entire, chiefly from the text of Alschefski. With English notes for schools and colleges by J.L.Lincoln. 8th ed., revised. New York, D. Appleton & co., 1855.
NL 0422474 MH MiU

Livius, Titus.
Selections from the first five books; with the twenty-first and twenty-second books entire, chiefly from the text of Alschefski; with English notes for schools and colleges by J. L. Lincoln. 10th ed., rev. N. Y., D. Appleton and co., 1856.
6+[2]+329 p. Map.
NL 0422475 InU PPeSchw OO MH

Y
672
.L 50849
LIVIUS, TITUS.
...Selections from the first five books, together with the twenty-first and twenty-second books entire. Chiefly from the text of Alschefski. With English notes for schools and colleges. By J.L.Lincoln... With an accompanying plan of Rome, and a map of the passage of Hannibal. 10th edition, revised. New York, D.Appleton & co., 1857.
329p.
NL 0422476 ICN MH MB

LIVIUS, Titus.
Selections from the first Five Books. With the Twenty-first and Twenty-Second Books. Chiefly from the Text of Alschefski. With English Notes for School and Colleges, by J.L. Lincoln 11th Ed., [revi]sed. N.Y. 1858.
NL 0422477 MH ICN

Livius, Titus.
... Selections from the first five books, together with the twenty-first and twenty-second books entire. Chiefly from the text of Alschefski. With English notes for schools and colleges. By J. L. Lincoln ... With an accompanying plan of Rome, and a map of the passage of Hannibal. *New York, D. Appleton & co., 1859.
vi p., 1 l., 329 p. fold. map, fold. plan. 19.
*12th ed., rev.
NL 0422478 ViU OCl OO

Livius, Titus.
... Selections from the first five books, together with the twenty-first and twenty-second books entire. Chiefly from the text of Alschefski. With English notes for schools and colleges. By J. L. Lincoln ... With an accompanying plan of Rome, and a map of the passage of Hannibal. *New York, D. Appleton & co., 1860.
vi p., 1 l., 329 p. fold. map, fold. plan. 18½cm.
*14th ed., rev.
NL 0422479 ViU OCl MH

Livius, Titus.
... Selections from the first five books, together with the twenty-first and twenty-second books entire. Chiefly from the text of Alschefski. With English notes for schools and colleges, by J. L. Lincoln ... 15th ed., rev. New York, D. Appleton & co., 1861.
vi p., 1 l., 329 p. fold. map, fold. plan. 19 cm.
I. Lincoln, John Larkin, 1817-1891, ed. II. Alschefski, Karl Friedrich Siegmund, 1805-1852.
NL 0422480 CU

VOLUME 336

Livius, Titus.
... Selections from the first five books: together with the twenty-first and twenty-second books entire. Chiefly from the text of Alschefski. With English notes for schools and colleges. By J.L.Lincoln ... With an accompanying plan of Rome, and a map of the passage of Hannibal. 15th ed., revised. New York, D.Appleton & co., 1863.
vi p., 1 ℓ., 329 p. fold.map., fold.plan. 19cm.

I. Lincoln, John Larkin, 1817-1891, ed.

NL 0422481 MiU WaU MH

Livius, Titus.
Selections from the first five books, together with the twenty-first and twenty-second books entire, chiefly from the text of Alschefski. With English notes for schools and colleges. By J.L.Lincoln. 18th ed., revised. New York, D. Appleton & co., 1864.

NL 0422482 MH PU

PA 6452 .A3L5 1866 Livius, Titus.
Selections from the first five books, together with the twenty-first and twenty-second books entire. Chiefly from the text of Alschefski. With English notes for schools and colleges. By J.L.Lincoln. With an accompanying plan of Rome, and a map of the passage of Hannibal. 18th ed., rev. New York, D.Appleton, 1866 [c1847]
vi, 329p. fold.map, fold.plan. 19cm.

Text in Latin, commentary in English.

NL 0422483 CLSU MH PPL

Livius, Titus.
Selections from the first five books... 20th ed. New York, Appleton, 1867.
329p. illus.

NL 0422484 ICRL NcD IaU

Livius, Titus.
... Selections from the first five books, together with the twenty-first and twenty-second books entire. Chiefly from the text of Alschefski. With English notes for schools and colleges. By J. L. Lincoln ... With an accompanying plan of Rome, and a map of the passage of Hannibal. New York, D. Appleton & co., 1869.
vi p., 1 l., 329 p. fold. map., fold. plan. 19 cm.

1. Lincoln, John Larkin, 1817-1891, ed. I. Alschefski, Karl Friedrich Siegmund, 1805-1852, ed.

NL 0422485 CtY

KD 30906

Livius, Titus.
Selections from the first five books, together with the twenty-first and twenty-second books entire. Chiefly from the text of Alschefski. With English notes for schools and colleges, by J.L.Lincoln. With an accompanying plan of Rome, and a map of the Passage of Hannibal. 21st ed. New York, D.Appleton & co., 1870.

NL 0422486 MH ViU

Livius, Titus.
Selections from the first five books of Livy's Roman history, with the twenty-first and twenty-second books entire; with explanatory notes, a plan of Rome, and a map of the passage of Hannibal. By John L.Lincoln ... New ed. New York, D.Appleton and company, 1871.
viii, 370 p. fold.map. 19cm.

I. Lincoln, John Larkin, 1817-1891, ed.

NL 0422487 MiU OU MH ViU NN MB

Livius, Titus
Selections from the first five books, together with the twenty-first and twenty-second books entire. With an interlineal translation as nearly literal as the idiomatic differences of the Latin and English languages will allow. For the use of schools and private learners, by I. W. Bieber. Philadelphia, D. McKay [1872]
601 p. (Hamilton, Locke and Clark series)

I. Bieber, I W

NL 0422488 ViU WaU PU PP PV NN NBuG OCU CtY OClW MH

Livius, Titus.
Selections from the first five books of Livy's Roman history, ... New edition. New York, Appleton, [c1871]. Repr. 1873.
370 p.

NL 0422489 OCU MH

Livius, Titus.
Selections from the first five books of Livy's Roman history, with the twenty-first and twenty-second books entire; with explanatory notes, a plan of Rome, and a map of the passage of Hannibal, by John L.Lincoln. New ed. New York, D.Appleton and co., 1875.

NL 0422490 MH

PA6452 .A3L5 1876 Livius, Titus.
Selections from the first five books of Livy's Roman history, with the twenty-first and twenty-second books entire; with explanatory notes, a plan of Rome, and a map of the passage of Hannibal. By John L. Lincoln ... New ed. New York, D. Appleton and company, 1876.
viii, 370 p. fold. map., fold. plan.

Imperfect: plan missing.

I. Lincoln, John Larkin, 1817-1891. II. Alschefski, Karl Friedrich Siegmund, 1805-1852.

NL 0422492 MB

EducT 1035.520.879

Livius, Titus.
Selections from the first five books of Livy's Roman history, with the twenty-first and twenty-second books entire. With explanatory notes, a plan of Rome, and a map of the passage of Hannibal, by John L.Lincoln. New ed. New York, D. Appleton and co., 1879.

NL 0422493 MH

Livius, Titus.
Selections from the first five books of Livy's Roman history, with the twenty-first and twenty-second books entire; with explanatory notes...by J. L. Lincoln. New York: D. Appleton and Company, 1880. viii, 370 p., 1 map, 1 plan. new ed. 12°.

1. No subject. 2. Lincoln, John L., editor.
N. Y. P. L. September 13, 1911.

NL 0422494 NN

LIVIUS, Titus.
The seven kings of Rome; being portions of the first book of Livy, selected and simplified with introduction, etc., by G.H.Nall. Macmillan and co., limited, 1910. London.

[Elementary classics."
Text in Latin.

NL 0422495 MH

PA2099 .L8N2 Livius, Titus.
... The seven kings of Rome, being portions of the first book of Livy selected and simplified for the use of beginners. With introduction, notes, exercises, and vocabularies by G. H. Nall ... London, Macmillan and co., 1921.
ix, [1], 146 p. 15cm. (Elementary classics)

1. Rome—Hist.—Kings, B. C. 753-510. 2. Latin language—Composition and exercises.

NL 0422496 ICU

PA2099 .L8N22 LIVIUS, TITUS.
The seven kings of Rome; selections from Livy Book I, simplified. With preface, notes, exercises, and vocabulary by G.H.Nall...and an introduction by F.Winifred Given... New York, The Macmillan company, 1927.
xiv, [1], 184 p. illus. 17cm. (On cover: Elementary Latin classics)

1. Rome--Hist.--Kings, B.C.753-510. 2. Latin language --Composition and exercises.

NL 0422497 ICU CU PP CLSU

LIVIUS, Titus.
The siege of Syracuse; being part of books XXIV. and XXV of Livy, with notes, etc., exercises and vocabulary, adapted by G.Richards and A.S. Walpole. London, Macmillan and co., limited, etc. etc., 1905.

Plates and map.
"Elementary classics."
Verso of title-page: 1st printed 1886; reprinted 1905.

NL 0422498 MH

Latin and English

Livius, Titus.
Latin prose exercises based upon Livy
see his Selections. Latin and English.

VOLUME 336

Livius, Titus.
Latin prose exercises based upon Livy, book XXI, and selections for translation into Latin, with parallel passages from Livy. By A. Judson Eaton ... Boston and London, Ginn & company, 1892.
iv, 64 p. 18½cm.

1. Latin language—Composition and exercises. I. Eaton, Adoniram Judson, 1850–
A 35-34

NL 0422501 ViU CtY OO

Livius, Titus.
Latin prose exercises, based upon Livy, book XXI., and selections for translation into Latin, with parallel passages from Livy. By A. Judson Eaton ... Boston and London, Ginn & co., 1898.
iv, 64 p. 18½cm.

1. Latin language—Composition and exercises. I. Eaton, Adoniram Judson, 1850–

NL 0422502 MiU

English

Livius, Titus.
Synopsis of Livy's History of the second Punic war, books XXI.-XXIV. With appendices, notes, maps, and plans by J. B. Worcester ... 2d ed. Oxford, J. Thornton, 1877.
4 p.l., 111 p. maps (1 fold.) plans. 17cm.
Translation of: Ab urbe condita libri.

1. Rome—Hist. I. Worcester, J B ed.

NL 0422504 ViU

[Livius, Titus]
... Hannibal in Italy. London, Glasgow [etc.] Blackie & son, limited [19 –]
123 p. 16½cm. (Blackie's English texts, ed. by W. H. D. Rouse)
On cover: Blackie's English school texts ...
"The translation from which these selections are made is by Philemon Holland."—Introd.

1. Punic war, 2d, B. C. 218-201. I. Holland, Philemon, 1552-1637, tr. II. Title. III. Ser.

NL 0422505 ViU

French

871 Livius, Titus.
L5.X.Fa Les concions et harengves de Tite Live, nouuellement traduictes en françois par I. de Amelin.
1567 Á Paris, par Vascosan, imprimeur du roy, 1567.
5 p.l., 314 numb.l., 16 l. 17cm.

Bookplate of Richard Bolger Kerrin.

NL 0422507 IU CtY

German

PA Livius, Titus.
6455 Scipio Africanus Maior, der Bezwinger
F67 Hannibals und Begründer der römischen
1955 Weltherrschaft; Auswahl aus der 3. und 4. Dekade. Neubearb. von Michael Forstner. Paderborn, F. Schöningh [1955]
2 v. (Schöninghs lateinische Klassiker)

Text in German.
Contents.- [v.1] Text.- [v.2] Erläuterungen.

NL 0422509 WaU

Italian

Livius, Titus.
... Roma contro Cartagine; prefazione di Manlio Lupinacci. Torino, G. Einaudi, 1942 [i. e. 1943]
2 p. l., vii-xvi, 411 p., 1 l. 18cm. (Half-title: Universale Einaudi. 2)
At head of title: Tito Livio.
Colophon dated 1943.
Translated by Jacopo Nardi. cf. p. xvi.

1. Rome—Hist. I. Nardi, Jacopo, 1476-ca. 1563, tr. II. Lupinacci, Manlio, ed.

PA6456.N33 A F 47-2394
Columbia univ. Libraries for Library of Congress [2]†

NL 0422511 NNC ICRL DLC

Polish

Livius, Titus.
Dzieje od założenia miasta Rzymu; wybór. Przeł. i opracował Władysław Strzelecki. Wyd. 2., poszerzone. Wrocław, Zakład im. Ossolińskich [1955]
424 p. illus., facsims., fold. map (in pocket) 17 cm. (Biblioteka narodowa. Seria II, nr. 77)
At head of title: Tytus Liwiusz.
Translation of Ab urbe condita.
Includes bibliographies.

1. Rome—Hist. I. Title.

PA6457.P6S7 1955 68-52699

NL 0422513 DLC MB

6. Selective index

Livius, Titus.
Ab urbe condita, eine Auswahl ...
see his Selections. Latin.

Livius, Titus.
L'assedio de Siracusa
see his Selections. Latin.

Livius, Titus.
Ausgewählte Stücke aus der dritten Dekade
see his Selections. Latin.

Livius, Titus.
Auswahl aus der ersten und dritten Dekade
see his Selections. Latin.

Livius, Titus.
Bloemlezing uit de vierde en vijfde decade
see his Selections. Latin.

Livius, Titus.
Camillus ...
see his Selections. Latin.

Livius, Titus.
Chrestomathie aus Livius
see his Selections. Latin.

Livius, Titus.
The close of the second Punic War ...
see his Ab urbe condita-one or more books. Latin and English.

Livius, Titus.
Conciones
see his Selections. Latin.

Livius, Titus.
Les concions et harengves ...
see his Selections. French.

Livius, Titus.
Decadas ...
see his Ab urbe condita-Collections of all extant books. Spanish.

Livius, Titus.
Decades ...
see his Ab urbe condita- Collections of all extant books. Latin.

Livius, Titus.
Les decades ...
see his Ab urbe condita-Collections of all books extant. French.

Livius, Titus.
Decadis ...
see his Ab urbe condita-Collections of all extant Books. Latin.

Livius, Titus.
Decadvm XIIII epitome
see his Periochae. Latin.

VOLUME 336

Livius, Titus.
Decas ...
see his Ab urbe condita-Collections of all extant books. Latin.

Livius, Titus.
Dechades ...
see his Ab urbe condita-Collections of all extant books. Latin.

Livius, Titus.
Le deche ...
see his
Ab urbe condita-Collections of alle extant books. Latin and Italian;
Ab urbe condita-one or more books. Italian.

Livius, Titus.
Desde la fundacio de Roma
see his Ab urbe condita-one or more books. Latin and Spanish.

Livius, Titus.
Duobus libris auctvs
see his Ab urbe condita-Collections of all extant books. Latin.

Livius, Titus.
Dzieje od zalozenia miasta Rzymu
see his Selections. Polish.

Livius, Titus.
En amice lector apportamvs tibi svmma diligentia exvsvm ...
see his ... qvicquid hactenus editum fuit ...

Livius, Titus
En magnis impendis, svmmisqve laboribvs damvs amice lector ...
see his ... qvicqvid hactenvs fuit aeditum ...

Livius, Titus.
Ex XIIII T. Livii decadibvs
see his Ab urbe condita-Collections of all extant Books. Latin.

Livius, Titus.
Exercitationes rhetoricae in orationes T. Livii
see under title

Livius, Titus.
Extracts from Livy
see his Selections. Latin.

Livius, Titus.
Forsøg til en oversaettelse af T. Livius's Romerske historie ...
see his Ab urbe condita. Collections of all extant books. Danish.

Livius, Titus.
Les gestes rommaines
see his Ab urbe condita-Collections of all extant books. French.

Livius, Titus.
Hannibal at bay
see his Selections. Latin.

Livius, Titus.
Hannibal, Auswahl aus der dritten und Vierten Decade
see his Selections. Latin.

Livius, Titus.
Hannibal in defeat
see his Selections. Latin.

Livius, Titus.
Hannibal in Italy
see his Selections. English.

Livius, Titus.
The Hannibalian or second Punic war
see his Selections. Latin.

Livius, Titus.
The Hannibalian war
see his Selections. Latin.

Livius, Titus.
Hannibal's invasion of Italy.
see his Ab urbe condita-one or more books. Latin and English.

Livius, Titus.
Histoire romaine ...
see his
Ab urbe condita-Collections of all extant books. Latin;
Ab urbe condita- one or more books. Latin and French.

Livius, Titus.
Historia romana
see his Ab urbe condita-one or more books. Portuguese.

Livius, Titus.
Historiae Romanae ...
see his Ab urbe condita-Collections of all extant books. Latin.

Livius, Titus.
Historiae romanae decades ...
see his
Ab urbe condita-Collections of all extant books. Latin;
Ab urbe condita-Collections of all extant books. French;
Ab urbe condita-Collections of all extant books. Italian.

Livius Titus.
Historiarum ...
see his
Ab urbe condita-Collections of all extant books. Latin.
Ab urbe condita-one or more books. Latin.

Livius, Titus.
The history ...
see his Ab urbe condita-Collections of all book extant. English.

Livius, Titus.
The Irish Blasters: or, The votaries of Bacchus ... 1738
see under title

Livius, Titus.
Istoria romana
see his Ab urbe condita-Collections of all extant books. Rumanian.

Livius, Titus.
The last two Kings of Macedon ...
see his Selections. Latin.

Livius, Titus.
Latin prose; based on first book of Livy
see under Gray, Louis Herbert.

Livius, Titus.
The legendary history of Rome
see his Ab urbe condita-one or more books. English.

Livius, Titus.
Librorum Epitomae
see his Periochae. Latin.

VOLUME 336

Livius, Titus.
Liviana excerpta ...
see his Selections. Latin.

Livius, Titus.
Livius pro prima classe gymnasiorum ...
see his Selections. Latin.

Livius, Titus.
Narrationes ...
see his Selections. Latin.

Livius, Titus.
Narrazioni scelte e diachiarate
see his Selections. Latin.

Livius, Titus.
Die neue Livius-epitome aus Oxyrhynchus
see his Periochae. Latin.

Livius, Titus.
Niet-Alphabetische woordenlijst op Livius
see under Fuchs, Johan Wilhelmus.

Livius, Titus.
Oeuvres ...
see his Ab urbe condita-Collections of all extant books. Latin and French.

Livius, Titus.
Orationes ...
see his Selections. Latin.

Livius, Titus.
Origines Romanae
see his Selections. Latin.

Livius, Titus.
Prisca virtus romana
see his Selections. Latin.

Livius, Titus.
La quatorze decadas
see his Ab urbe condita-Collections of all extant books. Spanish.

Livius, Titus.
Que extant decades ...
see his Ab urbe condita-Collections of all extant books. Latin.

Livius, Titus.
Reges consulesque romani
see his Selections. Latin.

Livius, Titus.
Rervm gestarvm popvli Romani
see his Ab urbe condita-Collections of all book extant. Latin.

Livius, Titus.
Rerum romanarum ...
see his Ab urbe condita-Collections of all extant books. Latin; Ab urbe condita-one or more books. Latin.

Livius, Titus.
The revolt and fall of Capua
see his Selections. Latin.

Livius, Titus.
Römische Geschichte ...
see his
Ab urbe condita-Collections of all extant books. Latin;
Ab urbe condita-one or more books. German.

Livius, Titus.
Römische Historien
see his Ab urbe condita-Collections of all extant books. German.

Livius, Titus.
Rom og Hannibal
see his Ab urbe condita-one or more books. Danish.

Livius, Titus.
Roma contro Cartagine
see his Selections. Italian.

Livius, Titus.
Romane historie
see his Ab urbe condita-Collections of all extant books. English.

Livius, Titus.
Romeinsche geschiedenis. Boeken I-III.
see his Ab urbe condita-one or more books. Dutch.

Livius, Titus.
Roms Anfänge und Aufstieg zur Weltherrschaft
see his Selections. Latin.

Livius, Titus.
Rom's historie
see his Ab urbe condita-Collections of all extant books. Norvegian.

Livius, Titus.
Scenes from the life of Hannibal
see his Selections. Latin.

Livius, Titus.
Scipio Africanus Maior, der Bezwinger Hannibals ...
see his Selections. German.

Livius, Titus.
The second Punic war
see his Ab urbe condita-one or more books. Latin.

Livius, Titus.
The seven kings of Rome
see his Selections. Latin.

Livius, Titus.
The siege of Syracuse
see his Selections. Latin.

Livius, Titus.
Storia di Roma
see his
Ab urbe condita-Collections of all books extant. Latin and Italian.
Ab urbe condita-one or more books. Latin and Italian.

Livius, Titus.
La Storia romana
see his Ab urbe condita-Collections of all extant books. Italian.

Livius, Titus.
Le storie ...
see his Ab urbe condita-one or more books. Latin.

Livius, Titus.
Synopsis of Livy's History ...
see his Selections. English.

VOLUME 336

Livius, Titus.
Titus, Livius, dat is, De Roemische historie
see his Ab urbe condita-Collections of all extant books. Dutch.

Livius, Titus.
Todas las decadas
see his Ab urbe condita-Collections of all extant books. Spanish.

Livius, Titus.
Vetus romana historia, sive, Supplementorum Livianorum libri sexaginta
see under Freinsheim, Johann, 1608-1660.

Livius, Titus.
Von Ankunft und Ursprung des Römischen Reichs ...
see his Ab urbe condita-Collections of all extant books. German.

****

Livius, Titus, *Foro-Juliensis*
see
Frulovisi, Tito Livio dei, *fl.* 1429-1456.

Livius Patavinus, Titus
see Livius, Titus.

Livizzani, Giovanni Battista, *fl. 17th cent.*
Il zimbello, overo La Italia schernita ... In San Marine, Presso Fillo Etimagoro, 1641.
183, ⌐1┐ p. 12½ x 7cm.
Fictitious imprint. *cf.* Melzi.
"Pubblico ... in occasione delle guerre, che allor travagliavan l'Italia pel ducato del Monferrato."—Tiraboschi. Biblioteca modenese.

1. Italy—Hist.—1559-1789. I. Title.

NL 0422602 MiU

Livlaender, Robert
Determination of the longitude of the Tartu observatory by the wireless. ...Tartu, 1928.
29 p.

NL 0422603 OU

Livländer, Robert
Determination of the longitude of the Tartu observatory by wireless, second paper: Observations in 1929-1930 in Tartu and in Pulkovo. Final results, by R. Livländer. Tartu (K. Mattiesen) 1931.
76 p. incl. tables, diagrs. front. 24 cm. (Publications de l'Observatoire astronomique de l'Université de Tartu (Dorpat) t. XXVII, no. 3)
Bibliographical foot-notes.

NL 0422604 DN-Ob OU

Livländer, Robert
Die kontinentalen verschiebungen von Amerika und Madagaskar, von R. Livländer. Braunschweig (F. Vieweg & shon akt.-ges.) 1930.
cover-title, p. (134)-140 incl. tables. 22 cm.
(Sonderdruck aus der "Zeitschrift für geophysik", jahrg. 6, heft 3)

NL 0422605 DN-Ob

Livländer, Robert.
... Longitude and latitude determinations in Estonia from 1935 to 1937, by R. Livländer. Tallinn, 1940.
30, ⌐1┐ p. incl. tables, map. 24cm. (Tallinna tehnikaülikooli toimetused. Publications from the Technical university of Estonia at Tallinn. Series A, no. 13, July 1940)

1. Longitude. 2. Latitude. A 41-2258
Northwestern univ. Libr. for Library of Congress ⌐2┐

NL 0422606 IEN

Livländer, Robert
On the colour of Mars, by R. Livländer. Tartu ⌐Printed by C. Mattiesen incorp.┐ 1933.
29 p. incl. tables, diagrs. 24cm. (Tartu. Ülikool. Acta et commentationes Universitatis tartuensis (dorpatensis) A: Mathematica, physica, medica. xxv⁶)

1. Mars (Planet) I. Title: The colour of Mars. A C 36-1963
Title from Stanford Univ. Library of Congress [AS262.D62 A, vol. 25, no. 6]

NL 0422607 CSt NIC DN-Ob OU

Livländer, Robert.
... Recomputation of the Estonian latitude determinations, by R. Livländer. Tallinn, 1940.
19 p. incl. tables. 24cm. (Tallinna tehnikaülikooli toimetused. Publications from the Technical university of Estonia at Tallinn. Series A, no. 12, July 1940)

1. Latitude. I. Title. A 41-2257
Northwestern univ. Libr. for Library of Congress ⌐2┐

NL 0422608 IEN

DK 511 .L 3 L 68 LIVLÄNDISCHDEUTSCHE HEFTE, 1.- Jan. 1876-. Lübeck, W. Gläser, 1876-
v. in
Binder's title.
On cover 1. Heft: Der Dörptschen Zeitung, achtundachtzigster Jahrgang.
The following Hefte have special titles:
3. Drei Weihnachtabinde ...
4. Deutschlivland, Nebukadnezar und das Russische Zartum.

NL 0422609 InU

LIVLÄNDISCHE beiträge. [Edited by Woldemar von Bock. 2 bd. Berl., 1868 [1'67]-69.
Portrs. Balt. 2021.1
The same. Neue folge. Bd.I. Leipz., 1869-71. Balt. 2021.1.2
Alphabetisches namen-und sach register zu bd. I. und II. [1er folg] Bon W.v.Bock. Leipz., 1870.
pp.(4), 63, Balt 2021.1

NL 0422610 MH

Livländische gemeinnützige und ökonomische sozietät.
Baltisches stammbuch edlen rindviehs. ⌐1.┐- jahrg.; 1885-
⌐Dorpat, H. Laakmann's buch- und steindruckerei┐ 1886-⌐19
v. tables, diagrs. 23cm.

1. Cattle—Baltic provinces. 2. Cattle—Herd-books. I. Title.
SF192.R9L5 12-13978 rev

NL 0422611 DLC NN

Livlaendische Gemeinnuetzige und Oekonomische Sozietaet,
Bericht.
1
Berlin, 1 4°.
v. tables.
18 1 contain: Liv-Estlaendisches Bureau für Landeskultur. Bericht,

1. Economic history, Livonia. 2. Agriculture, Livonia.
N. Y. P. L. April 26, 1923.

NL 0422612 NN DLC

Livländische gemeinnützige und ökonomische Sozietät.
Sresnevskii, Boris Izmailovich, 1857-
Bericht an die Kaiserliche livländische gemeinnützige und ökonomische sozietät. Erstattet am 20. november 1908 von dem leiter des Liv-kur-estländischen meteorologischen netzes, professor dr. B. Sresnewsky. Dorpat, Druck von H. Laakmann, 1909.

Livländische gemeinnützige und ökonomische sozietät.
Bericht über die ergebnisse der beobachtungen an den regenstationen des liv-est-kurländischen netzes. 1885-
⌐Dorpat┐ 1886-⌐19
v. tables. 26-29½cm. annual.
Title varies slightly.
QC925.4.R95
—— —— 15-jährige mittelwerte der niederschlagsmenge, anzahl der niederschlagstage und temperatur für den zeitraum 1886-1900, zusammengestellt von prof. dr. B. Sresnewsky ... ⌐Jurjew (Dorpat)┐ 1904.
47 p. incl. tables. 2 charts (1 fold.) 26cm.
1. Rain and rainfall—Livonia. I. Sreznevskii, Boris Izmailovich, 1857-
Library of Congress QC925.4.R952 46-41556

NL 0422614 DLC NN DAS

Livlaendische gemeinnuetzige und oekonomische Sozietaet.
Ergebnisse der Gewitterbeobachtungen in den Ostseeprovinzen...
1
Dorpat ⌐etc.┐, 1 8°.
nos. illus.
1 at head of title: Veröffentlichungen des baltischen meteorologischen Netzes...

1. Storms, Russia: Baltic provinces.
N. Y. P. L. September 13, 1922.

NL 0422615 NN

VOLUME 336

4GA 80 Livländische Gemeinnützige und Ökonomische Sozietät.
General-Nivellement von Livland der kaiserlichen, livländischen gemeinnützigen und ökonomischen Societät. Dorpat, Druck von H. Laakmann's Buch- und Steindruckerei, 1887.
128, 447 p.

NL 0422616 DLC-P4 InU

Livländische gemeinnützige und ökonomische sozietät.
Mittheilungen.
Jurjew (Dorpat) 1893–
v. tables, di[illegible]rs. (part fold.) 29[illegible].

1. Agriculture—Societies. 2. Agriculture—Livonia.

46-41153

Library of Congress S16.R9L5

NL 0422617 DLC

HD 719 .L 7 A3 1902 LIVLÄNDISCHE GEMEINNÜTZIGE UND ÖKONOMISCHE Sozietät
Die Programmpunkte der Besonderen Konferens über die Nothlage der Landwirtschaft, welche den örtlichen Komitees zur Beschlussfassung überwiesen sind. Юрьевъ, 1902.
93 p.

Title and text also in Russian.

1. Land tenure--Livonia. 2. Livonia--Econ. cond. 3. Russia--Osoboe soveshchanie o nuzhdakh sel'skokhoziaistven nnoi promyshlennosti, 1902-1905.

NL 0422618 InU

Livländische genealogische gesellschaft, Riga.

Müller, Max.
Beitrag zur baltischen wappenkunde. Die wappen der bürgerlichen und im lande nicht immatrikulierten adligen familien der früheren russischen ostseeprovinzen Liv-, Est- und Kurland (jetzt Lettland und Estland) mit einer kurzen einführung; unter mitwirkung der Livländischen genealogischen gesellschaft zu Riga gesammelt und nach den originalsiegeln gezeichnet von Max Müller ... Riga, Aktien-gesellschaft Ernst Plates, 1931–

Livländische geschichtsliteratur ...

Riga, N. Kymmel, 18
v. 16½–22cm.
Editors: 18 –1901, Arthur Poelchau.—1908-07, Arnold Feuereisen.—1908, Paul baron Osten-Sacken.—1909, Woldemar Wulffius.—1910, Leonid Arbusow, jun.—1911– Woldemar Wulffius.
1902– "In verbindung mit den baltischen geschichtsforschenden gesellschaften, hrsg. von der Gesellschaft für geschichte und altertumskunde der Ostseeprovinzen Russlands."
1. Livonia—Hist.—Bibl. I. Poelchau, Arthur H. Petrovich, 1845– ed. II. Feuereisen, Arnold, 1868– ed. III. Osten-Sacken, Paul, baron, ed. IV. Wulffius, Woldemar, ed. V. Arbusow, Leonid, 1882– ed. VI. Gesellschaft für geschichte und altertumskunde der Ostseeprovinzen Russlands, Riga.

CA 15-278 Unrev'd

Library of Congress Z2514.L4|L

NL 0422620 DLC NN

Uzl0 L76 Livländische Jahrbücher der Landwirtschaft.
1.-10. Bd., Jan. 1825 - Apr. 1827; Neue Reihenfolge 1.- Bd.; Okt, 1837- Dorpat, Krakow.
illus. 17-23 cm.

1. Agriculture - Periodicals, etc.
2. Agriculture - Livonia - Periodicals, etc.

NL 0422621 CtY

Livländische ökonomische sozietät
see
Livländische gemeinnützige und ökonomische sozietät.

Livländische Reimchronik.
Atskaņu chronika; Ditleba Alnpeķes "Rīmju chronika". Atdzējojis Jēkabs Saiva [pseud.], R. Klaustiņa ievads un piezīmes. Rīgā: Valters un Rapa a./s., 1936. xix, 298 p. 22½cm.

Attributed to Ditleb von Alnpeke.

975024A. 1. Livonia—Hist. 2. Church history—Livonia. I. Ditleb von Alnpeke, 13th cent. II. Jansons, Jēkabs, 1890– , tr. III. Klaustiņš, Roberts, 1875– IV. Title.
N. Y. P. L. December 30, 1938

NL 0422623 NN

Livländische reimchronik.
Ditleb's von Alnpeke Livländische reimchronik, enthaltend Der riterlichen meister vnd bruder zu Nieflant geschicht; nach dem Bergmannschen drucke mit den ergänzungen und den abweichenden lesearten der Heidelberger handschrift neu bearb. und hrsg.
(*In* Scriptores rerum livonicarum ... Riga und Leipzig, 1853, '48. 26cm. 1. bd. (1853) p. [489]-827)
Attributed to Ditleb von Alnpeke.
"Einleitung, paraphrase, glossar und erläuterungen von C. E. Napiersky, text, orts- und personenregister von Th. Kallmeyer."—Winkelmann, Bibl. Livoniae historica.
1. Livonia—Hist. I. Ditleb von Alnpeke, 13th cent. II. Napiersky, Karl Eduard, 1799–1864, ed. III. Kallmeyer, Theodor *i. e.* Johann August Theodor, 1809–1859.

15-4249

Library of Congress DK511.L3S4

NL 0422624 DLC

Livländische Reimchronik.
Ditleb's von Alnpeke Livländische Reimchronik, enthaltend, Der riterlichen Meister und Bruder zu Nieflant geschicht; nach dem Bergmannschen Drucke, mit den Ergänzungen und den abweichenden Lesearten der Heidelberger Handschrift, neu bearbeitet und herausgegeben. Riga: N. Kymmel's Buchhandlung, 1857. 339 p. 26cm.

Attributed to Ditleb von Alnpeke.
"Einleitung, Paraphrase und Erläuterungen von C. E. Napiersky, Orts- und Personen-Register, von Th. Kallmeyer."—*Winkelmann, E. A. Bibliotheca Livoniæ historica. 1870. p. 70.*

258932. 1. Livonia—Hist. 2. Poetry, German, Middle High. I. Ditleb von Alnpeke, 13th cent. II. Napiersky, Karl Eduard, 1799–1864, editor. III. Kallmeyer, Theodor, 1809–1859. *Revised*
N. Y. P. L. August 11, 1933

NL 0422626 NN

Livländische reimchronik.
...Ergänzung des von Dr. Liborius Bergmann herausgegebenen Fragments einer Urkunde der ältesten livländischen Geschichte in Versen, nach der Heidelberger Handschrift jener Reimchronik, mit einem Facsimile derselben und einigen Erläuterungen zum Drucke besorgt, und als Gratulationsschrift zur dritten Secularfeier der Universität Königsberg hrsg. von Carl Eduard Napiersky... Riga: E. Frantzen, 1844. 63 p. facsim. 4°.

Bibliographical footnotes.

1. Livonia—Hist 2. Koenigsberg. Universitaet. 3. Napiersky, Karl Eduard, 1799–1864, ed.
N. Y. P. L. September 10, 1926

NL 0422627 NN

Livländische reimchronik.
Fragment einer urkunde der ältesten Livländischen geschichte in versen, aus der original-handschrift zum druck befördert, mit einigen erläuterungen und einem glossar, versehen von dr. Liborius Bergmann...Riga, W. F. Häcker, 1817.
3 p. l., [3]—220 p. 25½x20½cm.
"Geschrieben [i.e. probably transcribed, but according to some, composed] ... durch den D. von A." British museum catalog.

1. Livonia—History—Sources I. Bergmann, Liborius von, 1754-1823

NL 0422628 MiU

Livländische reimchronik, hrsg. von **Franz Pfeiffer.** Stuttgart, Literarischer verein, 1844.
viii, 332 p. 21½cm. (Bibliothek des Literarischen vereins in Stuttgart. [bd. VII, 2])
Vol. VII of the series is wrongly numbered I.

1. Livonia—Hist.—Sources. I. Pfeiffer, Franz, 1815–1868, ed.

2-9098

Library of Congress PT1101.L5 vol.7

NN MB MdBP OCl
NL 0422629 DLC AU CU PU NcD PBm OCU MiU OU NjP

PT 1566 .L 7 M64 LIVLÄNDISCHE REIMCHRONIK
Die Livländische Reimchronik von Dittlieb von Alnpeke, in das Hochdeutsche übertragen und mit Anmerkungen versehen von E. Meyer. Reval, F. Kluge, 1848.
374 p.

Attributed to Ditleb von Alnpeke. Cf. Library of Congress entry under Livländische Reimchronik.

I. Livonia--Hist. I. Alnpeke, Ditleb von, 13th cent. II. Meyer, Eduard, Oberlehrer am Gymnasio zu Reval, ed.

NL 0422630 InU OCl PU

947.4 L765l **Livländische Reimchronik.**
Livländische Reimchronik; mit Anmerkungen, Namensverzeichnissen und Glosser, hrsg. von Leo Meyer. Paderborn, F. Schöningh, 1876.
416 p. 21cm.

1. Livonia - Hist. - Sources. I. Meyer, Leo, 1830-1910, ed.

NL 0422631 MiDW CU InU PU NN CtY OCl NIC

Livlaendische Reimchronik.
Varianten zur Bergmannschen Ausgabe der Reimchronik Ditleb's von Alnpeke
see under Frantzen, Eduard.

Livlaendische Rückblicke... Dorpat: C. Mattiesen, 1878. 129 p. 8°.

1. Livonia—Hist.
N. Y. P. L. February 24, 1925

NL 0422633 NN

DK651 .R5A23 Livlaendischer kalender ... Riga, W. F. Häcker [1897–]
v. 18 cm.

NL 0422634 DLC

Livländischer Verein zur Beförderung der Landwirthschaft und des Gewerbfleisses.
Baltische Verkehrs-Studien
see under Guleke, Reinhold, ed.

Livlaendisches Koch- und Wirthschaftsbuch für grosse und kleine Haushaltungen
see under [Fehre, Catharina (Krohss)] b.1788.

VOLUME 336

Livland
see
Livonia.

4DK
645 Livland und Irland; ein Briefwechsel. Leipzig, Duncker & Humblot, 1883.
160 p.

NL 0422638 DLC-P4 MH NN

DK 611
.L3 L73 LIVLAND'S LANDRÄTE UND LANDMARSCHÄLLE
Tartu ₍K₎ Mattiesens Buchdr., 1932.
76 p. illus.

Vorwort by Nicolas Wolff.

I. Wolff, Nicolas

NL 0422639 InU

Livland's lebendiges recht ...
see under [Sivers, Jegor von] 1823-1879.

Livne, D 1902–
(Ḥolmim u-magshimim no'azim)
חולמים ומגשימים נועזים; ספור לנוער ולבוגר (ממראות חזון תקומת הארץ) ₍מאת₎ ד. עמיאב. ₍עין חרוד₎ הוצאת "יחוד," 702 ₍1941 or 2₎

287 p. 18 cm.

I. Title.

PJ5053.L535H6 53-55049
rev

NL 0422641 DLC

Livne, Zvi, 1891–
עלילות פוטי, מאת צבי ליברמן. ציר: סני. ₍תל־אביב₎ מ. ניומן, תשי"ב ₍1951/52₎

128 p. illus. 23 cm. (חרם)
Vocalized.

I. Title.
Title transliterated: 'Alilot Puti.

PZ90.H3L472 57-50072 rev

NL 0422642 DLC

Livne, Zvi, 1891–
ארבעה מלחים; ספוריים לנער ₍מאת₎ צבי לבנה (ליברמן) תל־אביב, החבל הימי לישראל, תשט"ו ₍1955₎

106 p. 21 cm.
Vocalized.

I. Title.
Title transliterated: Arba'ah malaḥim.

PZ90.H3L4725 57-53076 rev

NL 0422643 DLC

Livne, Zvi, 1891–
אביטל וזלזל; ספורים לילדים, מאת צבי ליברמן. ירושלים, קרית־ספר, תשי"א ₍1951₎

30 p. illus. 20 x 23 cm.
Vocalized.

I. Title.
Title transliterated: Avital ve-Zalzal.

PZ90.H3L473 56-49979 rev

NL 0422644 DLC

Livne, Zvi, 1891–
בהרי ירושלים, מאת צבי ליברמן. הציר: ד. שיפרין. תל־אביב, עמיחי ₍1953₎

100 p. illus. 21 cm.
Vocalized.

1. Israel-Arab War, 1948-1949—Juvenile literature. I. Title.
Title transliterated: Be-hare Yerushalayim.

PZ90.H3L474 57-53143 rev

NL 0422645 DLC

Livne, Zvi, 1891–
דוד ויהונתן; ספור לבני הנעורים ₍מאת₎ צבי ליבנה (ליברמן) תל־אביב, עמיחי ₍1953/54₎

144 p. 22 cm.
Vocalized.

I. Title.
Title transliterated: David vi-Yehonatan.

PZ90.H3L4744 57-53753 rev

NL 0422646 DLC

Livne, Zvi, 1891–
גדעון וחבריו, ספורים לילדים, מאת צבי ליברמן. ירושלים, קרית־ספר, תשי"א ₍1951₎

29 p. illus. 20 x 23 cm.
Vocalized.

I. Title.
Title transliterated: Gid'on va-ḥaverav.

PZ90.H3L475 56-49978 rev

NL 0422647 DLC

Livne, Zvi, 1891–
חלום השלשה; ספור לבני הנעורים ₍מאת₎ צבי ליברמן. תל־אביב, מצפה ₍1937₎

144 p. 20 cm.
Vocalized.

I. Title.
Title transliterated: Ḥalom ha-sheloshah.

PZ90.H3L48 54-48480 rev

NL 0422648 DLC

Livne, Zvi, 1891–
חלום השלשה; ספור לבני הנעורים ₍מאת₎ צבי ליברמן. תל־אביב, י. צ'צ'יק ₍1950₎

104 p. 20 cm.
Vocalized.

I. Title.
Title transliterated: Ḥalom ha-sheloshah.

PZ90.H3L48 1950 54-48479 rev

NL 0422649 DLC

Livne, Zvi, 1891-
התישבות חיילים ונוטרים. ₍תל־אביב₎ הסתדרות הפועלים החקלאים, הועדה להתישבות חיילים ונוטרים ₍1944/45₎

19 p. 17 cm.
Cover title.

1. Veterans—Israel. 2. Agricultural colonies—Israel. 3. Land settlement—Israel. I. Title.
Title transliterated: Hityashvut ḥayalim ve-notrim.

UB359.I 7L5 HE 68-292

NL 0422651 DLC

PZ90
H3L5
Hebr Livne, Zvi, 1891–
מסעי זיזי הגמד, מאת צבי ליברמן. הציורים: ד. גלבוע. ₍תל־אביב, 1942/43₎

110 columns. col. illus. 20 x 28 cm.
Cover title.
Vocalized.

I. Title.
Title transliterated: Mas'e Zizi ha-gamad.

PZ90.H3L5 44-13160 rev

NL 0422652 DLC

Livne, Zvi, 1891–
מעל ההרבות, ספור, מאת צבי ליברמן. תל־אביב, מצפה ₍1938₎

181 p. illus. 20 cm.
Vocalized.

I. Title.
Title transliterated: Me-'al he-ḥoravot.

PZ90.H3L512 57-57215 rev

NL 0422653 DLC

Livne, Zvi, 1891–
מבבל לירושלים; ספור היסטורי ₍מאת₎ צבי ליברמן. תל־אביב, נ. טברסקי, תש"ז ₍1946/47₎

267 p. 18 cm.

I. Title.
Title transliterated: Mi-Bavel li-Yerushalayim.

PJ5053.L54M5 57-57183

NL 0422654 DLC

Livne, Zvi, 1891–
נחמיה; סיפור היסטורי. תל־אביב, עם עובד, תש"י. ₍1950₎

398 p. 17 cm.

1. Nehemiah—Fiction. I. Title.
Title transliterated: Neḥemyah.

A 52-6319 rev

New York. Public Libr.
for Library of Congress ₍r64b½₎

NL 0422655 NN

Livne, Zvi, 1891–
נחמיה; סיפור היסטורי ₍מאת₎ צבי ליברמן. מהד. ב. ₍ערוך בידי א. ל. פאיאנס₎ תל־אביב, עם עובד, תשט"ו ₍1954/55₎

397 p. 19 cm.

1. Nehemiah—Fiction.
Title transliterated: Neḥemyah.

PJ5053.L54N4 1954 57-53131

NL 0422656 DLC

VOLUME 336

Livne, Zvi, 1891–
הנוטע הקטן [ספור לילדים. מאת] צבי ליברמן. ירושלים, קרית
ספר, תרצ"ז [1936/37]
30 p. 21 cm.
Cover title.
Vocalized.

I. Title. *Title transliterated:* ha-Note'a ha-katan.
PZ90.H3L513 55-55188 rev
NL 0422657 DLC

Livne, Zvi, 1891–
תבל בתחיתה [מאת] צבי לבנה (ליברמן) תל-אביב, עמיחי
[1955]
378 p. 21 cm.

I. Title. *Title transliterated:* Tevel bi-teḥiyatah.
PJ5053.L54T4 57-53771
NL 0422659 DLC

Livne, Zvi, 1891–
ילדי העמק [מאת] צבי לברמן. ירושלים, קרית-ספר, תש"ה
[1944/45]
[100] p. illus. 21 cm.
Vocalized.

I. Title. *Title transliterated:* Yalde ha-'Emek.
PZ90.H3L52 47-42560 rev
NL 0422660 DLC

Livneh, David
see
Livne, D 1902-

Livneh, Eliezer, 1902–
בשער התקופה, מסות ומאמרים [מאת] אליעזר ליבנה. [תל-
אביב] מפלגת פועלי ארץ-ישראל, 1952.
351 p. 21 cm.

I. Title. *Title romanized:* Be-sha'ar ha-tekufah.
PJ5005.L54 57-51949
NL 0422662 DLC

Livneh, Eliezer, 1902–
עם הויכוח הציוני [מאת] אליעזר ליבנשטין. תל-אביב, עם
עובד, 704 [1944]
67 p. 15 cm. (ספרית "דעות")

1. Palestine—Pol. & govt. 2. Zionism. I. Title.
Title romanized: 'Im ha-vikuaḥ ha-tsiyoni.
DS126.L538 HE 68-991 rev
NL 0422663 DLC

Livneh, Eliezer, 1902–
מדינה וגולה; עיון בעתידה של התנועה הציונית [מאת] אליעזר
ליבנה. ירושלים, המחלקה לענייני הנוער והחלוץ של ההסתדרות
הציונית בהוצאת ר. מס, 713 [1952 or 3]
59 p. 19 cm. (ערכים, 21)

1. Zionism. I. Title. (Series: 'Arakhim, 21)
Title romanized: Medinah ve-golah.
DS149.L575 A 55-7785 rev
New York. Public Libr.
for Library of Congress [r68b2]†
NL 0422664 NN DLC

Livneh, Eliezer, 1902–
מבחנה של עצמאות [מאת] אליעזר ליבנה. תל-אביב, מסדה,
715 [1954 or 5]
231 p. 22 cm.

1. Israel—Social conditions. 2. Israel—Economic conditions.
I. Title. *Title romanized:* Mivḥanah shel 'atsma'ut.
HN761.P32L5 56-55609
NL 0422665 DLC

Livneh, Eliezer, 1902-
Le nouveau territorialisme juif. Version française de Hans Löwensohn. Jérusalem, Publications du Département de la jeunesse de l'Organisation sioniste mondiale, R.Mass, 1945.
48 p. (Les Dossiers sionistes)
NL 0422666 MH

Livneh, Eliezer, 1902-
State and Diaspora. Jerusalem, Youth and Hechalutz Dept. of the Zionist Organization, 1953.
92 p. 17 cm. (Modern Israel library, 1)

1. Zionism. I. Title. (Series)
DS149.L485 55-42697
PPDrop
NL 0422667 DLC OrPS CSt NN UU AAP OCH MB NNJ CU

Livneh, Eliezer, 1902–
הטריטוריאליזם החדש. מאת א. ליבנשטין. ירושלים, המחלקה
לעניני הנוער של הנהלת ההסתדרות הציונית ובהשתתפות קרן
היסוד בהוצאת ר. מס, 704 [1943 or 4]
29 p. 19 cm. (ערכים; ספרית המכון למדריכים, 9)

1. Jews—Colonization. I. World Zionist Organization. Youth and Hechalutz Dept. II. Palestine Foundation Fund. III. Title. (Series: Arakhim, 9)
Title romanized: ha-Teritoryalizm he-ḥadash.
DS126.L539 HE 68-992 rev
NL 0422668 DLC

Livneh, Eliezer, 1902-
...Toward unity of youth and the Kibutz movement. [New York] Young Poale Zion alliance [1939] 21 p. 28cm.
Cover-title.
Reproduced from typewritten copy.
"Bibliography on the Kibutz and youth movements," p. [3] of cover.

1. Youth movement, Jewish. 2. Zionism. I. Young Poale Zion alliance.
N. Y. P. L. December 9, 1940
NL 0422669 NN

DS
150
R4
P3
v.1
Livneh, Eliezer, 1902-
The truth about Revisionism. New York, 1935.
54 p. 15cm.
(In Revisionist Zionism pamphlets , v.l.)
NL 0422670 NNJ

Livneh, Eliezer, 1902-
The truth about Revisionism... New York, Zionist socialist party, 1935.
54 p.

1.Jews in Palestine. 2.Jews-Pol.& govt. I.Title: Revisionism.
NL 0422671 NjP

Livneh, Eliezer, 1902–
הציונות ואנגליה, מאת אליעזר ליבנשטיין. תל-אביב, הועד
הארצי למען החייל היהודי, 706 [1945 or 6]
128 p. 16 cm. (ספרית החייל)

1. Zionism. I. Title. *Title romanized:* ha-Tsiyonut ve-Angliyah.
DS149.L578 A 47-2095 rev*
Zionist Archives and Library
for Library of Congress [r68c2]†
NL 0422672 NNZI DLC

Livneh, Eliezer, 1902-
Wo steht der Revisionismus? [Von] Elieser Liebenstein. [Berlin, Zionistische Vereinigung für Deutschland in Gemeinschaft mit dem Hechaluz, Deutscher Landesverband] 1934
31 p.
1. Revisionist Zionism - Germany
NL 0422673 MH OCH OCl NNJ

Livneh, Tsevi
see
Livne, Zvi, 1891–

Livneh, Yitsḥak.
מי ראה את האפרוח? שירים לילדים. ירושלים, הוצאת "קרית-
ספר." [Jerusalem, 1950]
30 p. col. illus. 25 cm.
Vocalized text.

I. Title. *Title transliterated:* Mi ra'ah et ha-efroaḥ?
PZ90.H3L56 56-49262
NL 0422675 DLC

PJ5053
.L55M5
Hebr
Livneh, Yitsḥak, 1920–1948.
מלים פשוטות, שירים מן העזבון. תל-אביב, הוצאת תנועת
המושבים והברת "מסדה," תש"י. [Tel-Aviv, 1949/50]
77 p. port. 18 cm. (ספרית "אלה הבנים")
Vocalized text.

I. Title. *Title transliterated:* Milim peshutot.
Name originally: Yitshak Belinky.
PJ5053.L55M5 57-50771
NL 0422676 DLC

VOLUME 336

Livneh, Ze'ev.
מִפִּלְאֵי הַחַי; ספורים על בעלי־חיים משנים בעולם ומלואו. מאת זאב לבנה (לרמן) ירושלים, ר. מס. [Jerusalem, 1952]
138 p. illus. 22 cm. (תבל)
Vocalized text.

1. Zoology—Juvenile literature. (Series: Tevel)
Title transliterated: Mi-pil'e he-ḥai.
Name originally: Ze'ev Lerman.
QL49.L774 56-52537

NL 0422677 DLC

LIVNET ou guide à l'usage des voyageurs de Bayonne en Espagne. Bayonne, [18–].
pp. 30. Span 1701.1

NL 0422678 MH

Livney, Eliezer
see
Livneh, Eliezer, 1902–

Livni, Zvi, illus.
Alef-bet
Ephraim, *pseud.?*
אלף־בית. מציר על ידי צבי מלבנציק. תל־אביב, מצפה. [Tel-Aviv, 1943/44?]

I4563 **Livni, Zvi, illus.**
28A8 Alef, bet, gimal
ebr Kaspi, Rachel, *ed.*
אלף בית גימל. ספר לילד. ערוך ומציר בידי רחל כספי וצבי מלבנציק. תל־אביב, הוצאת "אל המעין." [Tel-Aviv, 194–]

?Z90 **Livni, Zvi, illus.**
H3K34
Hebr Kaspi, Rachel, *ed.* (Zer peraḥim)
זר פרחים; ספורים, שירים, משחקים. ציר, צבי מלבנציק. תל־אביב, הוצאת יבנה." [Tel-Aviv, 1945]

Livny, David.
... ירושלים דליטא ... תל־אביב, תר"ץ. [Tel-Aviv, 1929]
2 v. in 1. plates, ports., facsim. 17½cm.
At head of title: דוד לבני (ויסבורד)
CONTENTS.—חלק א׳. ווילנא לפני ארבעים שנה.—חלק ב׳. א) צער גידול בנות (ספור) ב) הגאון מווילנא ע"פ פרופ. ש. שכטר (תרגם ש. ארנסט)
Schechter's essay was first published in his Studies in Judaism (New York, 1896)
1. Jews in Vilna. 2. Elijah ben Solomon, gaon of Vilna, 1720–1797. I. Schechter, Solomon, 1847–1915. II. Ernst, Simon, 1898– tr.
Title transliterated: Yerushalayim de-Lita.
[*Name originally:* David Weissbord]
46-32692
Library of Congress DS135.R93V555

NL 0422683 DLC

Livny, Isaac Jonah, 1890– 1965.
דקדוק הלשון העברית החדשה והישנה. אזן וקדם יצחק אפשטין. ירושלים, הוצאת "דרור." תש"ב־
[Jerusalem, 1941–
v. 25 cm.
CONTENTS.— ספר א. מלתא.

1. Hebrew language—Grammar.
Title transliterated: Dikduk ha-lashon ha-'ivrit.
Name originally: Isaac Jonah Ziegel.
PJ4556.L5 43-50216 rev*

NL 0422684 DLC

Livny, Yitzhak
see
Livny, Isaac Jonah, 1890–1965.

Livo, Marius, *pseud.*
see
Urai, Vilmos.

Livois (Eugène). *Recherches sur les échinocoques chez l'homme et chez les animaux. 128 pp., 1 pl. 4°. *Paris,* 1843, No. 185, v. 406.

NL 0422687 DNLM PPAN

Livok
see
De Kayville, Victor.

Livolsi, Luigi Balsamo
see Balsamo Livolsi, Luigi.

KD 55468
Li Volsi, Saverio.
Gli astri e la mano. [Milano] Zibetti [1954]

NL 0422690 MH

4BL Li Volsi, Saverio
479 Astromanzia e tarocco astrologico.
[Milano, G. Zibetti [1955]
189 p.
(Le Forze occulte, 4)

NL 0422691 DLC-P4

LI VOLSI, SAVERIO.
Evoluzione dell'occultismo. [Milano] G. Zibetti [1952] 183 p. 20cm. (Le Forza occulte. 2)
Bibliography, p. [10]

1. Occult sciences--Hist. I. Le Forza occulte.

NL 0422692 NN MH

Livon, Charles, d. 1917.
——. Choléra de 1884. 78 pp. 8°. Marseille, *Barlatier-Feissat père & fils,* 1884.

NL 0422693 DNLM

Livon, Charles
——. De l'action physiologique de l'acide salicylique et du salicylate de soude sur la respiration. 13 pp. 8°. *Marseille, Barlatier-Feissat père & fils,* 1880.

NL 0422694 DNLM

Livon, Charles
——. De l'évolution générale de la physiologie. 20 pp. 8°. *Marseille, Barlatier-Feissat père & fils,* 1883.

NL 0422695 DNLM

Livon, Charles
——. Du croton-chloral, ou chloral crotonique. 32 pp. 8°. *Paris, Vve. A. Delahaye & Cie.,* 1877.

NL 0422696 DNLM

Livon, Charles
——. Du progrès dans les sciences biologiques par l'expérimentation. 30 pp. 8°. *Aix, J. Remondet-Aubin,* 1881.

NL 0422697 DNLM

Livon, Charles. 616.22
Du traitement des polypes laryngiens, par le Dr Charles Livon N301
... Paris, A. Delahaye, 1873.
76, [2] p. 24cm.

NL 0422698 ICJ DNLM

WO LIVON, Charles
100 Manuel de vivisections. Paris,
L788m Baillière, 1882.
1882 vii, 343 p. illus.

NL 0422699 DNLM NRU MiU RPB PU DLC

Livon, Charles, d.1917, joint author.
Bertulus, Evariste.
Notice historique sur la Société de médecine de Marseille. Par MM. les docteurs E. Bertulus [et] Ch. Livon ... Marseille, Typ. et lith. Barlatier-Feissat père et fils, 1878.

Livon, Charles
——. Rapport sur une mission à Paris pour étudier auprès de M. Pasteur les inoculations préventives de la rage. 30 pp. 8°. *Marseille. Barlatier-Feissat,* 1886.

NL 0422701 DNLM

Livon, Charles
——. Recherches sur le choléra. 16 pp. 8°. *Marseille, Barlatier-Feissat père & fils.* 1884.

NL 0422702 DNLM

Livon (Charles) d. 1917. Travaux de physiologie expérimentale. 2 p. l., 125 pp. roy. 8°. Paris, J.-B. Baillière et fils, 1910.
For biography see Marseille méd., 1916-17, liii, 753-754, port.

NL 0422703 DNLM

Livon (Jean) [1877–]. *Grossesses et accouchements consécutifs aux ruptures utérines. 111 pp. 8°. Paris, 1903. No. 72.

NL 0422704 DNLM

MISSISSIPPI

MsG William Alexander Percy Memorial Library, Greenville.
MsSC* Mississippi State University, State College.
MsSM Mississippi State University, State College.
MsU University of Mississippi, University.

MONTANA

MtBC Montana State University, Bozeman.
MtBozC* Montana State University at Bozeman.
MtU University of Montana, Missoula.

NEW YORK

N New York State Library, Albany.
NAlU State University of New York at Albany.
NAurW Wells College, Aurora.
NB Brooklyn Public Library, Brooklyn.
NBB Brooklyn Museum Libraries, Brooklyn.
NBC Brooklyn College, Brooklyn.
NBM Medical Research Library of Brooklyn.
NBPol Polytechnic Institute of Brooklyn, Brooklyn.
NBSU-M State University of New York, Downstate Medical Center Library, Brooklyn.
NBiSU-H State University of New York, Harpur College, Binghamton.
NBronSL Sarah Lawrence College, Bronxville.
NBu Buffalo and Erie County Public Library, Buffalo.
NBuC State University of New York, College at Buffalo.
NBuG Grosvenor Reference Division, Buffalo and Erie County Public Library, Buffalo.
NBuU State University of New York at Buffalo.
NCH Hamilton College, Clinton.
NCaS St. Lawrence University, Canton.
NCorniC Corning Glass Works Library, Corning. (Includes Corning Museum of Glass Library)
NCoxHi Greene County Historical Society, Inc., Coxsackie.
NFQC Queens College Library, Flushing.
NGrnUN* United Nations Library.
NHC Colgate University, Hamilton.
NHi New York Historical Society, New York.
NIC Cornell University, Ithaca.
NJQ Queens Borough Public Library, Jamaica.
NL* Newberry Library, Chicago.
NLC Not a library symbol.
NN New York Public Library.
NNAB American Bible Society, New York.
NNAHI Augustinian Historical Institute, New York.
NNAJHi American Jewish Historical Society, New York.
NNB Association of the Bar of the City of New York, New York.
NNBG New York Botanical Garden, Bronx Park, New York.
NNC Columbia University, New York.
NNC-T — Teachers College Library.
NNCFR Council on Foreign Relations, New York.
NNCoCi City College of New York, New York.
NNE Engineering Societies Library, New York.
NNF Fordham University, New York.
NNFI French Institute in the United States, New York.
NNG General Theological Seminary of the Protestant Episcopal Church. New York.
NNGr Grolier Club Library, New York.
NNH Hispanic Society of America, New York.
NNHeb Hebrew Union College, Jewish Institute of Religion Library, New York.
NNHi New York Historical Society.
NNJ Jewish Theological Seminary of America, New York.
NNJIR* Jewish Institute of Religion, New York.
NNJef Jefferson School of Social Science, New York. (Library no longer in existence)
NNM American Museum of Natural History, New York.
NNMM Metropolitan Museum of Art Library, New York.
NNMor* Pierpont Morgan Library.
NNNAM New York Academy of Medicine, New York.
NNNM New York Medical College, Flower & Fifth Avenue Hospitals, New York.
NNNPsan New York Psychoanalytic Institute, New York.
NNPM Pierpont Morgan Library, New York.
NNQ* Queens Borough Public Library, New York.
NNQC* Queens College Library, Flushing.
NNRI Rockefeller Institute for Medical Research, New York.
NNSU-M* State University of New York College of Medicine at New York City.

NEW YORK *continued*

NNU New York University Libraries, New York.
NNU-W — Washington Square Library.
NNUN United Nations Library, New York.
NNUN-W — Woodrow Wilson Memorial Library.
NNUT Union Theological Seminary, New York.
NNUT-Mc — McAlpin Collection.
NNWML Wagner College Library, Staten Island.
NNYI Yivo Institute for Jewish Research, New York.
NNZI Zionist Archives and Library of Palestine Foundation, New York.
NNerC College of New Rochelle, New Rochelle.
NNiaU Niagara University, Niagara University.
NPV Vassar College, Poughkeepsie,
NRAB Samuel Colgate Baptist Historical Library of the American Baptist Historical Society, Rochester.
NRU University of Rochester, Rochester.
NSchU Union College, Schenectady.
NSyU Syracuse University, Syracuse.
NUt Utica Public Library.
NWM U.S. Military Academy, West Point.
NYPL* New York Public Library.
NYhI International Business Machines Corporation, Thomas J. Watson Research Center, Yorktown Heights.

NEBRASKA

NbOC Creighton University, Omaha.
NbU University of Nebraska, Lincoln.

NORTH CAROLINA

Nc North Carolina State Library, Raleigh.
Nc-Ar North Carolina State Department of Archives and History, Raleigh.
NcA Pack Memorial Public Library, Asheville.
NcA-S — Sondley Reference Library.
NcAS* Sondley Reference Library, Asheville.
NcC Public Library of Charlotte & Mecklenburg County, Charlotte.
NcCC Charlotte College Library, Charlotte.
NcCJ Johnson C. Smith University, Charlotte.
NcCU University of North Carolina at Charlotte.
NcD Duke University, Durham.
NcDurC North Carolina College at Durham, Durham.
NcGU* University of North Carolina at Greensboro.
NcGW University of North Carolina at Greensboro.
NcGuG Guilford College, Guilford.
NcR Olivia Raney Public Library, Raleigh.
NcRR Richard B. Harrison Public Library, Raleigh.
NcRS North Carolina State University at Raleigh.
NcU University of North Carolina, Chapel Hill.
NcWfC* Wake Forest College, Winston-Salem.
NcWfSB Southeastern Baptist Theological Seminary Library, Wake Forest.
NcWilA Atlantic Christian College, Wilson.
NcWilC Carolina Disciplinian a Library, Wilson.
NcWsW Wake Forest College, Winston-Salem.

NORTH DAKOTA

NdFA North Dakota State University, Fargo. (Formerly North Dakota Agricultural College)
NdHi State Historical Society of North Dakota, Bismarck.
NdU University of North Dakota Library, Grand Forks.

NEW HAMPSHIRE

Nh New Hampshire State Library, Concord.
NhD Dartmouth College, Hanover.
NhU University of New Hampshire, Durham.

NEW JERSEY

NjGbS Glassboro State College, Glassboro.
NjHi New Jersey Historical Society, Newark.
NjMD Drew University, Madison.
NjN Newark Public Library.
NjNBR* Rutgers–The State University, New Brunswick.
NjNbS New Brunswick Theological Seminary, New Brunswick.
NjNbT* New Brunswick Theological Seminary.
NjP Princeton University, Princeton.
NjPT Princeton Theological Seminary, Princeton.
NjR Rutgers–The State University, New Brunswick.
NjT Trenton Free Library, Trenton.

NEW MEXICO

NmA Albuquerque Public Library, New Mexico.
NmU University of New Mexico, Albuquerque.
NmUpU New Mexico State University, University Park.

NEVADA

NvU University of Nevada, Reno.

OHIO

O Ohio State Library, Columbus.
OAU Ohio University, Athens.
OAkU University of Akron, Akron.
OBerB Baldwin-Wallace College, Berea.
OBlC Bluffton College, Bluffton.
OC Public Library of Cincinnati and Hamilton County, Cincinnati.
OCH Hebrew Union College, Cincinnati.
OCHP Historical and Philosophical Society of Ohio, Cincinnati.
OCLloyd Lloyd Library and Museum, Cincinnati.
OCU University of Cincinnati, Cincinnati.
OCX Xavier University, Cincinnati.
OCl Cleveland Public Library.
OClCS Case Institute of Technology, Cleveland.
OClFC Cleveland State University, Cleveland. (Formerly Fenn College)
OClJC John Carroll University, Cleveland.
OClMA Cleveland Museum of Art, Cleveland.
OClSA Cleveland Institute of Art, Cleveland.
OClW Case Western Reserve University, Cleveland.
OClWHi Western Reserve Historical Society, Cleveland.
ODW Ohio Wesleyan University, Delaware.
ODa Dayton and Montgomery County Library, Dayton.
ODaStL St. Leonard College Library, Dayton.
ODaU University of Dayton, Dayton.
OEac East Cleveland Public Library.
OFH Rutherford B. Hayes Library, Fremont.
OGK Kenyon College, Gambier.
OHi Ohio State Historical Society, Columbus.
OKentC Kent State University, Kent.
OO Oberlin College, Oberlin.
OOxM Miami University, Oxford.
OSW Wittenberg University, Springfield.
OTU University of Toledo, Toledo.
OU Ohio State University, Columbus.
OWibfU Wilberforce University, Carnegie Library, Wilberforce.
OWicB Borromeo Seminary, Wickliffe.
OWoC College of Wooster, Wooster.
OWorP Pontifical College Josephinum, Worthington.
OYesA Antioch College, Yellow Springs.

OKLAHOMA

Ok Oklahoma State Library, Oklahoma City.
OkEG Graduate Seminary Library, Enid.
OkS Oklahoma State University, Stillwater.
OkT Tulsa Public Library.
OkU University of Oklahoma, Norman.

OREGON

Or Oregon State Library, Salem.
OrCS Oregon State University Library, Corvallis.
OrHi Oregon Historical Society, Portland.
OrP Library Association of Portland, Portland.
OrPR Reed College, Portland.
OrPS Portland State College, Portland.
OrSaW Willamette University, Salem.
OrStbM Mount Angel College, Mount Angel Abbey, Saint Benedict.
OrU University of Oregon, Eugene.

PENNSYLVANIA

PBL Lehigh University, Bethlehem.
PBa Academy of the New Church, Bryn Athyn.
PBm Bryn Mawr College, Bryn Mawr.
PCA* Samuel Colgate Baptist Historical Library of the American Baptist Historical Society, Rochester, N. Y.
PCC Crozer Theological Seminary, Chester.
PCamA Alliance College, Cambridge Springs.
PCarlD Dickinson College, Carlisle.
PHC Haverford College, Haverford.
PHi Historical Society of Pennsylvania, Philadelphia.
PJA Abington Library Society, Jenkintown.
PJAlG Alverthorpe Gallery, Rosenwald Collection, Jenkintown.
PJB Beaver College, Jenkintown.